A Subject Index of the Modern Works Added to the Library of the British Museum

In the years 1891-1895

G. K. Fortescue

Alpha Editions

This edition published in 2020

ISBN : 9789354035319

Design and Setting By
Alpha Editions
email - alphaedis@gmail.com

This Subject Index to modern books recently added to the Library of the British Museum comprises, like its predecessors, the acquisitions of five years, extending from January 1891 to December 1895. Novels, poetry and tracts of small importance have, as on previous occasions, been omitted; but it will be found to comprise almost everything that can substantially aid literary research, and its value is sufficiently attested by the continual demand for the preceding parts among the frequenters of the Reading Room. Like them, it has been compiled by Mr. G. K. Fortescue, Assistant-Keeper of Printed Books, and until lately Superintendent of the Reading Room, to whom the warmest acknowledgments of the Keeper of Printed Books and the public are due for the ability he has displayed and the time and industry he has devoted to so laborious an undertaking, chiefly performed in non-official hours. The number of entries in the present volume is about 47,760, while the total number of entries in the three volumes covering the period between 1880 and 1895 is about 124,700.

R. Garnett,
Keeper of Printed Books.

February 6th, 1897.

PREFACE.

THE first Subject Index of Modern Works added to the Library of the British Museum was published in 1886. It contained an Index of the books published in and after the year 1880 which had been acquired between January 1880 and August 1885. The second volume, issued in 1891, continued the work from September 1885 to the end of December 1890, while the present volume carries on the Index from January 1891 to the end of December 1895. The system of arrangement adopted in this volume follows as closely as possible that of the second Index, but as the latter will not necessarily be in the hands of those who may use the present work, it may be desirable to repeat here, almost verbatim, the explanations previously given.

The primary object of the Index is to assist readers in their researches in the Library of the British Museum; it has not therefore been considered necessary to reproduce such portions of the General Catalogue of Printed Books as are of the nature of a Class Catalogue. Thus, the heading 'Bible' will not be found in the present Index, although a considerable proportion of the Biblical literature of the last five years has been included, under such headings as Christianity, Church History, Jews, etc. For the same reason no personal names have been taken as subject headings, and the heading 'Biography' has been used only for collected biographies, although such individual biographies as serve to illustrate History, Art or Science have been frequently included, and will be found throughout the work under various subject headings. Novels, poems, plays, and miscellaneous essays are also omitted, and only critical or historical works and selections will be found under such headings as Drama, Fiction, Hymns and Poetry. It should also be noted that when several editions of a book have been published during the period included in the present series, reference has been made to the most recent edition only.

Works in Slavonic, Hungarian, Celtic and Oriental languages are not included.

In arranging the entries under each heading a chronological order has been followed whenever it has been possible, as under the history of each country, province or town; but when no such arrangement has been practicable the books have been arranged alphabetically, irrespective of the languages in which they are written. It should, however, be clearly understood that the alphabetical order has been departed from whenever it has been thought useful to group together books commenting upon each other or directly bearing upon the same branch of each subject.

The Compiler has again to express his sincere gratitude to many of his colleagues and friends who have given him valuable assistance and advice.

G. K. F.

NOTE.

UNDER each country subheadings will be found for works on the Antiquities, Army, Colonies, Constitution and Government, History, Law (general systems and codes), Navy, Politics, Social Life, Topography, Trade and Finance.

Separate headings have been made for works on the following subjects, which will consequently be found under such headings and not under the names of the various countries: Agriculture, Architecture, Art, Ballads, Biography, Birds, Botany, Capital and Labour, Drama, Education, Local Fauna (under Zoology), and Flora (under Botany), Folk Lore, Forestry, Geology, Heraldry and Genealogy, Land Tenures, Law (Criminal, Commercial, Ecclesiastical, Maritime, Military and Naval), Law Reports, Numismatics, Painting, Police, Railways, Sport, Succession and Probate, and Typography.

Art Galleries, Exhibitions and Libraries have been grouped together under the headings "Exhibitions" and "Libraries," and have not been placed under the countries or towns in which they are situated. Private Collections of objects of Art will be found under the heading "Collections and Collectors."

Many abbreviations have been used throughout the work. Most of these are sufficiently intelligible, but the following may require explanation:

Ac.	for	Academies.
Ephem.	„	Ephemerides.
G. B. and I.	„	Great Britain and Ireland.
P.P.	„	Periodical Publications.
U.S.	„	United States of America.

B

SUBJECT INDEX, 1891-1895.

AACHEN

AACHEN. *See* Aix-la-Chapelle.

AARGAU: AARAU. Blattner (H.) Ueber die Mundarten des Kantons Aargau. pp. 80. *Brugg*, 1890. 8°.   12901. d. 20. (6.)

Merz (W.) Der Rechtsquellen des Kantons Argau. Herausgegeben von W. Merz. *Arau*, 1894, *etc.* 8°.   10195. e.

—— Die Rechtsquellen der Stadt Arau. 1894, *etc.* 8°. Argovia. Bd. 25.   Ac. 6922.

Schumann (A.) Die Litteratur des Kantons Aargau, 1888, 1889. 1890. 8°. Argovia. Bd. 21.   Ac. 6922.

—— Aargauische Litteratur, 1890.   1891. 8°. Argovia. Bd. 22.   Ac. 6922.

ABANO. Le terme d' Abano. pp. 19. 1889. 8°.   7462. g. 2. (13.)

Capretti Guidi (V.) Abano. 130. *Padova*, 1884. 16°.   7462. de. 27.

ABATTOIRS. Dembo (J. A.) Jewish Method of Slaughter. pp. 111. *Lond.* 1894. 8°.   7291. i. 17.

Haug (H.) Auch ein Kulturbild. pp. 35. *Gotha*, 1894. 8°.   Pam. 31.

Lancia (G.) Manuale del Macellais. pp. 690. *Torino*, 1892. 8°.   7942. l. 42.

Oldfield (J.) A Groaning Creation. pp. 77. *Lond.* 1895. 8°.   8425. bbb. 44.

ABBEVILLE. Lefranc (E.) L'authenticité des reliques de Saint Wulfran possédées à Abbeville. pp. 51. *Paris*, 1890. 8°. Pam. 10.

ABBREVIATIONS. Martin (C. T.) The Record Interpreter. pp. 341. *Lond.* 1892. 8°.   2050. d.

Volta (Z.) Delle Abbreviature nella Paleografia Latina. pp. 328. *Milano*, 1892. 8°. 7709. aa. 29.

ABDOMEN. Cripps (H.) Abdominal Sections in the women's ward, St. Bartholomew's Hospital. pp. 70. *Lond.* 1894. 8°. 07581. e. 27.

Jenner (*Sir* W.) Lectures and Essays on abdominal tumours, *etc.* pp. 329. *Lond.* 1895. 8°.   7616. h. 23.

Keith (S.) Text Book of Abdominal Surgery pp. 508. 1894. 8°. Pentland's Medical Series. Vol. 4.   7641. ee.

Malcolm (J. D.) Physiology of death from Traumatic Fever. pp. 129. *Lond.* 1893. 8°.   7561. k. 19.

Martin (C.) After-treatment of cases of Abdominal Section. pp. 48. *Lond.* 1894. 8°.   07482. ee. 11.

ABERDEEN

ABDOMEN—*continued*.

Oliver (J.) Abdominal Tumours in Women. pp. 289. *Lond.* 1895. 8°.   7630. bbb. 17.

Smith (J. G.) Abdominal Surgery. pp. 806. *Lond.* 1891. 8°.   7620. df. 26.

Tait (R. L.) Diseases of Women and Abdominal Surgery. *Leicester*, 1889, *etc.* 8°. 2255. e. 16.

Wells (*Sir* T. S.) Modern Abdominal Surgery. pp. 51. *Lond.* 1891. 8°.   07305. h. 8. (10.)

See also Digestion : Genito-Urinary Organs : Hernia : Liver : Stomach, *etc.*

ABERDEEN, City of. Members of Parliament for Aberdeen, 1357–1886. pp. 55. *Aberd.* 1889. 16°.   Pam. 68.

—— Inventories of Records illustrating the History of Aberdeen. pp. 60. *Aberd.* 1890. 4°.   11900. h. 19.

Anderson (P. J.) Charters illustrating the History of Aberdeen, 1171–1804. pp. 466. *Aberd.* 1890. 4°.   10370. h. 20.

Jeffrey (J. T.) House Proprietors' Manual of Police Law of Aberdeen. pp. 49. *Aberd.* 1894. 8°.   6583. b. 25.

Robbie (W.) Aberdeen, its traditions and history. pp. 517. *Aberd.* 1893. 8°.   010370. f. 29.

Rodger (E. H. B.) Aberdeen Doctors. pp. 355. *Edinb.* 1893. 8°.   7679. df. 37.

University.

Bulloch (J. M.) History of the University of Aberdeen. pp. 220. *Lond.* 1895. 8°.   8367. aa. 18.

—— Lord Rectors of the University. pp. 55. *Aberd.* 1890. 8°.   8306. de. 19. (7.)

Rait (R. S.) The Universities of Aberdeen. pp. 382. *Aberd.* 1895. 8°.   8366. de. 44.

Ac. Aberdeen. *University.* Lists of Officers. 1495–1860. pp. 94. *Aberd.* 1893. 4°.   8364. h. 11.

—— *New Spalding Club.* Officers and Graduates of University and King's College, mvd–mdccclx. pp. 399. *Aberd.* 1893. 4°.   Ac. 8245/9.

—— *University.* Records of the Arts Class, 1868–72. pp. 250. *Aberd.* 1892. 4°. 8365. f. 37.

Macpherson (N.) Notes on the Chapel and other Buildings of King's College. pp. 39. *Aberd.* 1890. 4°.   7814. e. 23.

Anderson (P. J.) Historical Notes on the Libraries of the Universities. pp. 27. *Aberd.* 1893. 8°.   Pam. 6.

ABERDEENSHIRE : DIOCESE OF ABERDEEN. Ac. Aberdeen. *New Spalding Club.* ROBERTSON (A. W.) Bibliography of the shire of Aberdeen. pp. 133. *Aberd.* 1893. 8°.
011903. l. 16.

MACCONNOCHIE (A. J.) Bennachie. pp. 174. *Aberd.* 1890. 8°. 010370. f. 15.

DEESIDE. The Deeside Guide. pp. 115. *Aberd.* 1893. 8°. 10369. aaa. 46.

TEMPLE (W.) The Thanage of Fermartyn. pp. 710. *Aberd.* 1894. 4°. 10369. k. 1.

Ac. Aberdeen. *New Spalding Club.* BOETHIUS (H.) Hectoris Boetii Aberdonensium episcoporum vitae. pp. 210. *Aberd.* 1894. 4°.
Ac. 8245/12.

See also ABOYNE STRATHBOGIE.

ABINGDON. Ac. London. *Camden Society.* N.S. LI. Accounts of the Obedientiars of Abingdon Abbey. pp. 195. *Lond.* 1892. 4°.
Ac. 8113/136.

P.P. *Abingdon.* The Abingdonian. *Abingdon,* 1890, *etc.* 4°. P.P. 6152. n. & 2089.

R., W. H. Olim Alumni. *Abingdon,* 1891, *etc.* 8°. 8366. aa. 19.

ABLON-SUR-SEINE. BONNIN (P.) Ablon-sur-Seine. pp. 170. *Paris,* 1890. 8°.
10172. f. 13.

—— Ablon-sur-Seine pendant la Fronde. pp. 112. *Paris,* 1892. 8°. 10169. cc. 15.

ÅBO. Ac. Åbo. *Finska Universitet.* Åbo Universitets lärdomshistoria. 1890, *etc.* 8°. Ac. Helsingfors. *Svenska Literatursällskapet.* Skrifter. Vol. 16, *etc.* Ac. 9082.

SCHYBERGSON (M. G.) Historiens studium vid Åbo Universitet. pp. 166. 1891. 8°. Ac. Helsingfors. *Svenska Literatursällskapet.* Skrifter. No. 19. Ac. 9082.

ABORTION. THOMAS (T. G.) Abortion and its Treatment. pp. 112. *N. Y.* 1890. 12°.
7581. bbb. 31.

See also MEDICINE, *Legal :* OBSTETRICS.

ABOYNE. Ac. Aberdeen. *New Spalding Club.* GORDON (C.) *Marquis of Huntly.* Records of Aboyne. pp. 589. *Aberd.* 1894. 4°. Ac. 8245/11.

ABRUZZO. BELLINI (G. M.) L'Arte in Abruzzo. pp. 38. *Lanciano,* 1889. 8°.
7704. e. 18 (6.)

FARAGLIA (N. F.) Saggio di corografia abruzzese medioevale. 1891. 8°. Archivio storico per le Province Napoletane. anno 16. Ac. 6534.

FINAMORE (G.) Tradizioni Abruzzesi. pp. 241. 1894. 8°. PITRÉ (G.) Curiosità tradizionali. Vol. 13. 12450. f. 16.

—— Vocabolario dell' uso abruzzese. pp. 321. *Città di C.* 1893. 8°. 12942. cc. 24.

GINALDI (U.) La Proprietà negli statuti degli Abruzzi. pp. 143. *Bologna,* 1890. 8°.
5359. ee. 23.

PANNELLA (G.) Usi nuziali dell' Abruzzo. pp. 24. *Teramo,* 1894. 8°. Pam. 37.

ROMANI (F.) Abruzzesismi. pp. 82. *Teramo,* 1890. 8°. 12901. ccc. 13. (8.)
See also MOLISE.

ABSCESSES. CHEYNE (W. W.) Treatment of abscesses. pp. 197. *Edinb.* 1894. 8°.
7481. aaa. 36.

MAYDL (C.) Über subphrenische Abscesse. pp. 357. *Wien,* 1894. 8°. 07482. l. 1.

ABSIE, *Abbey.* Cartulaires de l'Abbaye. pp. 234. 1895. 8°. Archives du Poitou. 25.
Ac. 6887.

ABYSSINIA. FUMAGALLI (G.) Bibliografia Etiopica. pp. 288. *Milano,* 1893. 8°.
011900. h. 12.

NOELDEKE (T.) Sketches from Eastern History. pp. 288. *Lond.* 1892. 8°. 9055. d. 9.

'AMDA ṢĔYON, *King of Ethiopia.* Histoire des guerres d''Amda Syôn. pp. 205. *Paris,* 1890. 8°. 754. b. 14.

ṢAINEANŬ (M.) L'Abyssinie dans la seconde moitié du XVIᵉ siècle. pp. 54. *Leipz.* 1892. 8°.
9008. g. 10. (8.)

ABYSSINIA. Corpus Juris Abessinorum. *Berolini,* 1889, *etc.* 4°. 754. c. 7.

BENT (J. T.) The Sacred City of the Ethiopians. pp. 309. *Lond.* 1893. 8°. 010096. ee. 40.

BORELLI (J.) Éthiopie Méridionale. pp. 520. *Paris,* 1890. fol. 10095. i. 9.

CONSTANTIN (de) L'Archimandrite Païsi et l'Ataman Achinoff. pp. 344. *Paris,* 1891. 18°.
8027. bb. 13.

MUENZENBERGER (E. F. A.) Abessinien und seine Bedeutung für unsere Zeit. pp. 160. *Freiburg,* 1892. 8°. 010096. i. 17.

NERAZZINI (C.) Itinerario in Etiopia. 1885. pp. 78. *Roma,* 1890. 8°. 10095. dd. 8.

PARONI (L.) Da Napoli a Sabarguma. pp. 152. *Roma,* 1893. 8°. 010096. m. 25.

PORTAL (G. H.) My mission to Abyssinia. pp. 261. *Lond.* 1892. 8°. 010096. f. 24.

SCHWEINFURTH (G.) Abyssinische Pflanzennamen. pp. 84. 1893. 4°. Ac. Berlin. *Societas Regia.* Abhandlungen. 1893. Ac. 855/6.
See also AFRICA, *Central and East :* ERITREA.

Languages.
See AMHARIC, GALLA AND TIGRÉ LANGUAGES.

ACANTHOCEPHALA. *See* PARASITES.

ACARINA. GROULT (P.) Acariens. pp. 248. 1887. 8°. Histoire naturelle de la France. pt. 15.
7207. cc.

MÉGNIN (P.) Les Acariens parasites. pp. 182. 1892. 8°. Encyclopédie des aide-mémoire.
8709. g.

See also ARACHNIDAE : PARASITES.

ACCIDENTS. DULLES (C. W.) Accidents and Emergencies. pp. 154. *Lond.* 1893. 8°.
7481. bb. 14.

GIBON (A.) Les Accidents du Travail. pp. 250. *Paris,* 1890. 4°. 8277. i. 8.

HAMILTON (W. M.) Common Accidents. pp. 23. 1893. 8°. Health Lectures. 1893. No. 2.
7404. bbb.

PAGE (H. W.) Railway Injuries. pp. 148. *Lond.* 1891. 8°. 6095. f. 24.

Law of : Prevention, etc.
BUSWELL (H. F.) Civil Liability for personal Injuries. pp. 463. *Bost.,* 1893. 8°. 06616 k. 12.

COËNE (de) Congrès des Accidents du Travail, Berne, 1891. pp. 63. *Rouen,* 1891. 8°.
08276. k. 18.

KRAFT (M.) Maschinelle Einrichtungen gegen Unfälle. 2 pt. 1894. 8°. WEYL (T.) Handbuch der Hygiene. Vol. 8. 7391. dd.

MEETEREN (F. W. W. van) Mededeelingen omtrent Ongelukken bij den Arbeid, *etc.* pp. 157. *Amsterd.* 1890. 8°. 8275. k. 6.

PARIS. *Congrès des Accidents du Travail.* Rapports. 2 tom. *Paris,* 1889-90. 8°. 8276. h. 21.

ROTERING (F.) Fahrlässigkeit und Unfallsgefahr. pp. 106. *Berl.* 1892. 8°. 05604. h. 22.
See also AMBULANCE : SURGERY.

ACCOUNTANTS. DICKSEE (L. R.) Auditing. pp. 305. *Lond.* 1892. 8°. 8531. df. 10.

FOX (W. H.) Accountants' Accounts. pp. 82. *Lond.* 1888. fol. 8534. f. 24.

ACCOUNTANTS—*continued.*

GUIDE. Guide to the Accountancy Profession. pp. 56. *Lond.* 1892. 8°.   8535. df. 35.

LISLE (G.) Examination Papers of the Chartered Accountants of Scotland. pp. 84. *Edinb.* 1894. 8°.   8535. df. 36.

LYNCH (H. F.) Revise work for Accountant Students. pp. 100. *Lond.* 1891. 8°. 6376. bb. 19.

MILLAR (R. C.) Accountant's Handbook. 2 pt. *Edinb.* 1891. 8°.   8535. d. 7.

PIXLEY (F. W.) Chartered Accountants' charges. pp. 197. *Lond.* 1894. 8°.   6376. f. 20.

VAN DE LINDE (G.) A Chartered Accountants' Office. pp. 55. *Lond.* 1893. 8°. 08227. g. 49. (16.)

VERSLUYS (J.) Toegepast Rekenen. pp. 104. *Amsterd.* 1890. 8°.   8435. ccc. 30.

See also BOOK-KEEPING.

ACERRA. CAPORALE (G.) Ricerche della Diocesi di Acerra. *Napoli,* 1892, *etc.* 8°. 4605. ee.

ACHAEAN LEAGUE.
See GREECE, *History.*

ACHEEN. BOOMS (P. G.) De eerste Atjehsche Expeditie en hare enquête. pp. 139. *Amsterd.* 1880. 8°.   9055. g. 6.

HEUTSZ (J. B. v.) De onderwerping Atjeh. pp. 117. *'s-Gravenh.* 1893. 8°.   8023. f. 30.

HURGRONJE (C. S.) De Atje'hers. 2 Deel. *Batavia,* 1893, 94. 8°.   010055. i. 3.

LEENDERTZ (C. J.) Van Atjeh's stranden tot de koraalrotsen van Nieuw-Guinea. pp. 309. *Arnhem,* 1890. 8°.   10055. ee. 14.

MELANTJONG. Atjeh à vol d'oiseau. pp. 254. *Leiden,* 1880. 8°.   010055. e. 6.

PETIT (W. L. de) La conquête de la vallée d'Atchin. pp. 371. *Paris,* 1891. 8°. 9056. g. 2.

SCHERER (G. A.) Hoe moet Atjeh gepacificeerd worden? pp. 46. *'s-Gravenh.* 1891. 8°.
          8028. f. 32. (5.)

See also INDIES, *Dutch* : SUMATRA.

ACHMIN, *El. See* EGYPT, *Antiquities.*

ACIDS. JURISCH (C. W.) Handbuch der Schwefelsäurefabrikation. pp. 368. *Stuttgart,* 1893. 8°.   8909. ccc. 4.

KOEHLER (H.) Carbolsäure und Carbolsäure-Präparate. pp. 192. *Berl.* 1891. 8°. 8909. cc. 17.

RANDALL (W. W.) Ortho-sulpho-paratoluic Acid. pp. 18. *Baltimore,* 1891. 8°.   Pam. 13.

LUNGE (G.) Treatise on the Manufacture of Sulphuric Acid and Alkali. *Lond.* 1891, *etc.* 8°.
          8909. cc. 19.

ACKWORTH SCHOOL. Superintendents and Teachers of Ackworth School from 1779 to 1894. pp. 108. *Leominster,* 1895. 8°. 8365. d. 42.

ACOUSTICS. BARNES (C. F.) Sound. pp. 79. 1893. 8°. Nisbet's Science Manuals. 8708. ee.

BASSET (A. B.) Elementary Treatise on Sound. pp. 187. *Camb.* 1890. 8°.   8768. d. 32.

BROADHOUSE (J.) Student's Helmholtz. Musical Acoustics. pp. 440. *Lond.* 1892. 8°.
          8716. bb. 45.

GARDINER (A.) Sound. 1893, *etc.* 8°.
MAJOR (H.) Science Manuals.   8708. a.

GRAF (E.) Die Theorie der Akustik im griechischen Altertum. pp. 16. *Gumbinnen,* 1894. 4°.
          8709. c. 13. (9.)

GREAT BRITAIN. *Department of Science and Art.* Outline of experiments for illustrating instruction in sound. pp. 93. *Lond.* 1893. 8°. Pam. 18.

HUGHES (M. W.) Voice Figures. pp. 48. *Lond.* 1891. 8°.   8715. f. 43.

ACOUSTICS—*continued.*

LEES (W.) Acoustics. pp. 95. 1893. 8°. Collins' Advanced Science Series.   8708. aa.

LYNCH (G.) Advanced Sound. pp. 193. *Lond.* 1895. 8°.   8716. b. 50.

P.P. *London.* The Phonogram. *Lond.* 1893, *etc.* 8°.   2199.

ROBEL (E.) Die Sirenen. Ein Beitrag zur Entwickelungsgeschichte der Akustik. *Berl.* 1891, *etc.* 4°.   8755 dd.

SPENCER (J.) Sound. pp. 223. *Lond.* 1890. 8°.   8716. aaa. 32.

STRUTT (J. W.) *Baron Rayleigh.* Theory of Sound. *Lond.* 1894, *etc.* 8°.   2244. f. 11.

TAYLOR (S.) Sound and Music. pp 223. *Lond.* 1895. 8°.   2244. e. 13.

THOMPSON (S. P.) Physical Foundation of Music. pp. 31. *Lond.* 1890. 8°.   Pam. 24.

TYNDALL (J.) Sound. pp. 464. *Lond.* 1893. 8°.   2244. e. 14.

ZELLNER (L. A.) Vorträge über Akustik. 2 Bde. *Wien,* 1892. 8°.   8704. e. 27.

See also EAR : MUSIC : PHYSICS.

ACQUI. ALESSANDRI (D. de) Acqui. pp. 294. *Acqui,* 1880. 8°.   7462. ee. 40.

ACRE. SAREPTA (J. de) Diocèse de Saint Jean d'Acre. pp. 56. *Paris,* 1890. 8°. Pam. 93.

ACRIDIDAE. *See* ORTHOPTERA.

ACROCEPHALUS PALUSTRIS.
See MARSH WARBLER.

ACROMEGALY. Ac. London. *New Sydenham Society.* MARIE (P.) Essays on Acromegaly. pp. 182. *Lond.* 1891. 8°. Ac. 3838/55.

ACTINOMYCOSIS. BÉCUE (G.) De l'Actinomycose. pp. 153. *Lille,* 1892. 8°.
          7641. dd. 19.

ILLICH (A.) Beitrag zur Klinik der Aktinomykose. pp. 201. *Wien,* 1892. 8°. 7641. dd. 12.

ACTINOZOA. KENT (W. S.) The Great Barrier Reef of Australia. pp. 387. *Lond.* 1893. fol.   K.T.C. 9. b. 3.

ACTUARIES. GLEN (N.) Actuarial Science. pp. 95. *Glasgow,* 1893. 8°.   8531. d. 40.
See also INSURANCE.

ADDISCOMBE. VIBART (H. M.) Addiscombe. pp. 779. *Westminster,* 1894. 8°.
          8364. d. 47.

ADÉ. FOURCADE (J. F.) Adé. pp. 468. *Tarbes,* 1891. 8°.   010171. f. 31.

ADEL. Registers. pp. 231. 1895. 8°. Publications of the Thoresby Society. Vol. v.
          Ac. 8092.

ADELAIDE. WORSNOP (T.) Adelaide and its environs. pp. 96. *Adelaide,* 1880. 8°.
          10492. aa. 23.

See also AUSTRALIA, *South.*

ADEN. Three hours in Aden. pp. 58. *Bombay,* 1891. 8°.   10077 de. 17.

G. B. & I. *Hydrographic Office.* Red Sea Pilot. pp. 564. *Lond.* 1892. 8°.   10496. gg. 35.

ADIRONDACK MOUNTAINS. STODDARD (S. R.) The Adirondacks. pp. 218. *Glens Falls,* 1891. 8°.   10410. aaa. 47.

ADLER-KOSTELETZ. LANGER (E.) Aus dem Adlergebirge. *Prag,* 1891, *etc.* 8°.
          12350. dd.

ADMIRALTY ISLANDS. RAY (S. H.) Note on the Admiralty Islands. pp. 12. *Lond.* 1891. 8°.   12901. d. 36 (9.)
See also PACIFIC OCEAN.

ADOPTION, Law of. *See* SUCCESSION.

ADRIATIC SEA. HAMARD (P. J.) Par delà l'Adriatique. pp. 402. *Paris*, 1890. 8°.
10125. ee. 29.

ADULTERATION. CRIPPS DAY (F. H.) Adulteration. Agricultural Fertilisers and Feeding Stuffs. pp. 140. *Lond.* 1894. 8°.
07076. i. 17.

DESCLOZEAUX (J.) Code des Falsifications. pp. 498. *Paris*, 1893. 12°. 5403. cc. 6.
See also FOOD : PHARMACY.

ADVENT. ADVENT LIGHT. Daily Life in Advent Light. pp. 63. *Lond.* 1892. 8°
3457. dd. 31.

BATHE (A.) An Advent with Jesus. pp. 152. *Lond.* 1892. 32°. 3456. a. 65.

CLARKE (R. F.) Meditations for Advent. pp. 30. *Lond.* 1891. 16°. Pam. 77.

GRANGER (M. E.) Advent Readings. pp. 221. *Lond.* 1891. 8°. 3457. ddd. 5.

LIDDON (H. P.) Advent in St. Paul's. Sermons. pp. 613. *Lond.* 1891. 8°. 4465. f. 17.
See also SEASONS, *Ecclesiastical.*

ADVERTISEMENTS. BLACKWOOD (J.) How to reply to Advertisements. pp. 32. *Liverp.* 1895. 24°. Pam. 23.

BOLTON (C. K.) Catalogue of posters, chiefly American. *Brookline*, 1895. 8°. 011901. e. 28.

CATALOGUES. Catalogue d'affiches illustrées. pp. 112. *Paris*, 1891. 8°. 7857. dd. 16.

DATZ (P.) Histoire de la publicité. *Paris*, 1894, *etc.* 8°. 11852. ff.

EVANS (R.) The Age of Disfigurement. pp. 112. *Lond.* 1893. 8°. 7807. e. 31.

FOWLER (N. C.) About Advertising. pp. 160. *Bost.* 1889. 8°. 11899. f. 40.

HADDON (W.) Advertiser's Vade Mecum, *etc.* pp. 32. *Lond.* 1890. 8°. 08227. i. 45.

HIATT (C.) Picture Posters. pp. 367. *Lond.* 1895. 8°. 7858. gg. 37.

LONDON. List of leading London & Provincial Advertisement Contractors. *Lond.* 1890. 8°.
08226. h. 14. (10.)

—— *Half-Price Closed Letter Co.* Successful Advertising. pp. 15. *Lond.* 1892. 8°.
08226. h. 14. (12.)

P.P. London. Advertising. *Lond.* 1891, *etc.* 8°.
N.R.

TEELE (A. L.) Ideal Advertising. pp. 75. *Lond.* 1892. 8°. 8228. aa. 52.

THATCHER (T.) Power of Advertisement. pp. 16. *Lond.* 1893. 8°. 8228. aaaa. 17. (21.)

TURNER (C.) Advertising. pp. 7. *Lond.* 1894. 8°. 08275. ee. 21. (16.)

AERONAUTICS. *See* BALLOONS.

AESTHETICS. ABEL (L.) Der gute Geschmack. pp. 368. *Wien*, 1895. 8°.
11825. p. 22.

BAIN (F. W.) Body and Soul. pp. 466. *Lond.* 1894. 8°. 8468. k. 24.

BERGER (C.) Die Entwicklung von Schillers Ästhetik. pp. 325. *Weimar*, 1894. 8°.
11825. dd. 54.

BIESE (C. J. A.) Die Philosophie des Metaphorischen. pp. 229. *Hamburg*, 1893. 8°.
8462. g. 35.

BOSANQUET (B.) History of Æsthetic. pp. 502. 1892. 8°. MUIRHEAD (J. H.) Library of Philosophy. 8486. h.

AESTHETICS—*continued.*

CARRIERE (M.) Materialismus und Aesthetik. pp. 44. 1892. 8°. SCHMIDKUNZ (H.) Gegen den Materialismus, *etc.* No. 1. 4016. h. 13.

CHILD (T.) The Desire of Beauty. pp. 177. *Lond.* 1892. 8°. 7808. a. 44.

DIEZ (M.) Theorie des Gefühls. pp. 172. *Stuttgart*, 1892. 8°. 11805. f. 46.

FISCHER (H.) Lessings Laokoon und die Gesetze der bildenden Kunst. pp. 200. *Berl.* 1887. 8°.
012357. k. 22.

FRÉSON (J. G.) L'Esthétique de R. Wagner. 2 vol. 1893. 8°. Essais de philosophie de l'art. no. 1. 7808 df.

GERMAIN (A.) Pour le Beau. pp. 128. *Paris*, 1893. 8°. 7808. df. 9.

—— Du beau moral et du beau formel. pp. 54. *Paris*, 1895. 12°. 8410. bbb. 41.

GROOS (C.) Einleitung in die Aesthetik. pp. 409. *Giessen*, 1892. 8°. 011824. f. 47.

HARNACK (O.) Die klassische Ästhetik der deutschen. pp. 243. *Leipz.* 1892 8°.
011824. i. 33.

HEINE (G.) Das Verhältnis der Ästhetik zur Ethik bei Schiller. pp. 56. *Göthen*, 1894. 8°.
Pam. 85.

HILDEBRAND (A.) Das Problem der Form in der bildenden Kunst. pp. 125. *Strassb.* 1893. 8°.
7856. aa. 48.

HOSTINSKÝ (O.) Herbarts Ästhetik. pp. 135. *Hamb.* 1891. 8°. 011824. h. 5.

JUNGMANN (J.) Aesthetik. 2 Bde. *Freiburg i. B.* 1886. 8°. 011824. i. 16.

KNIGHT (W.) Philosophy of the Beautiful. pp. 288. 1891. 8°. University Extension Manuals. vol. 1. 12204. f.

KUEHNEMANN (E.) Kants und Schillers Begründung der Ästhetik. pp. 185. *München*, 1895. 8°. 11825. p. 18.

LARSEN (A. C.) Æstetiken og Livet. pp. 213. *Kjøbenh.* 1891. 8°. 011824. de. 24.

LE HÉRICHER (É.) Esthétique et Critique littéraire. 1892. 8°. Ac. Avranches. *Société Archéologique.* Mémoires. tom. 10. Ac. 5287.

LIPPS (T.) Beiträge zur Ästhetik. *Hamb.* 1890, *etc.* 8°. 012357. l.

MARSHALL (H. R.) Pain, Pleasure and Æsthetics. pp. 364. *Lond.* 1894. 8°. 8462. e. 27.

—— Æsthetic Principles. pp. 201. *N.Y.* 1895. 8°. 8406. bbb. 36.

OVERLOOP (E. v.) Essai d'une théorie du sentiment esthétique. *Brux.* 1889, *etc.* 8°. 011824. k.

PICHTOS (N. M.) Die Aesthetik A. W. v. Schlegels. pp. 108. *Berl.* 1894. 8°. 011824. h. 85.

PILO (M.) L'Estetica psicologica e la Fisiologia del Bello di P. Mantegazza. pp. 323. *Milano*, 1892. 8°. 011850. f. 6.

—— Estetica. pp. 260. *Milano*, 1894. 8°. 012200. h. 109.

RAYMOND (G. L.) Art in Theory. pp. 266. pp. 266. *N.Y.* 1894. 8°. 7808. df. 12.

VALENTIN (V.) Ästhetische Schriften. *Berl.* 1892, *etc.* 8°. 011824. f.

VOLKELT (J.) Ästhetische Zeitfragen. pp. 258. *München*, 1895. 8°. 11825. l. 13.

WALTER (J.) Geschichte der Ästhetic im Altertum. pp. 891. *Leipz.* 1893. 8°. 8460. dd. 27.
See also ART.

AFGHANISTAN. FORBES (A.) The Afghan Wars 1839–42 and 1878–80. pp. 337.
Lond, 1892. 8°.   9057. c. 6.

EVATT (G. J. H.) Recollections of the Afghan Campaigns 1878–79–80. pp. 74.
Calcutta, 1891. 8°.   9007. ff. 4. (8.)

MALE (A.) Scenes through the Battle Smoke. pp. 484. *Lond.* 1891. 8°.   9009. cc. 1.

WHEELER (S.) The Ameer Abdur Rahman. pp. 251. 1895. 8°. Public men. Vol. 1.
                                            10600. e.

AFGHAN POLITICS. Afghan Politics. pp. 42.
Lond. 1890. 8°.   8022. bb. 27. (5.)

GORE (F. ST. J.) Hill Life in the Afghan Highlands. pp. 269. *Lond.* 1895. 8°. 010057. i. 4.

GRAY (J. A.) At the Court of the Ameer.
pp. 523. *Lond.* 1895. 8°.   010057. ee. 38.

MUTCHMORE (S. A.) Moghul, Mongol, Mikado and Missionary. 2 vol. *N.Y.* 1891. 8°.
                                            10058. de. 4.

THORBURN (S. S.) Asiatic Neighbours. pp. 315.
Edinb. 1894. 8°.   8023. d. 2.

WEIR (T. S.) From India to the Caspian.
pp. 111. *Bombay,* 1893. 8°.   10076. e. 5.
See also ASIA, *Central:* INDIA : PUSHTO LANGUAGE.

AFRICA.—Bibliography.

KELTIE (J. C.) Partition of Africa. Bibliographical appendix. pp. 498. *Lond.* 1895. 8°.
                                            2386. d. 1.

LUZAC AND Co. Bibliographical List of Books on Africa. 1889–92. pp. 79. *Lond.* 1892. 12°.
                                            011900. de. 2.

General Works.

Ac. *Weimar. Geographisches Institut.* Kettlers Afrikanische Nachrichten.
Weimar, 1892, *etc.* 4°.   592.

AFRICA. Great Explorers of Africa. 2 vol.
Lond. 1894. 8°.   010096. m. 27.

—— L'Esclavage en Afrique. pp. 518.
Paris, 1890. 12°.   8156. de. 6.

BADIA Y LEYBLICH (D.) Viatjes per África y Assia. 1803–07. 3 tom.
Barcelona, 1888–89. 8°.   10026. k. 7.

BETTANY (G. T.) Dark Peoples of the Land of Sunshine. pp. 221. *Lond.* 1890. 8°.
                                            10007. f. 21.

BROWN (R.) Story of Africa and its Explorers.
Lond. 1892, *etc.* 8°.   964.

CHAPMAN (E. F.) Paper on the mapping of Africa. pp. 6. *Lond.* 1895. fol.   Pam. 89.

COLVILLE (Z.) Round the Black Man's Garden.
pp. 344. *Edinb.* 1893. 8°.   010096. f. 32.

DU BOURGET (C. C. M. J.) Campagnes et géographie politique de l'Afrique. pp. 262.
Paris, 1892. 8°.   9009. d. 14.

FALKENHORST (C.) Schwarze Fürsten. 2 pt.
Leip. 1891, 92. 8°.   9061. dd. 6.

FREITAG (O.) Zehn Jahre im dunklen Afrika.
8 Bde. *Dresd.* 1892. 8°.   10097. cc. 24.

FULTERER (C.) Afrika in seiner Bedeutung für die Goldproduktion. pp. 191. *Berl.* 1895. 8°.
                                            7107. e. 14.

GARNIER (N.) L'Afrique. Anthologie géographique. pp. 566. *Paris,* 1894. 12°.
                                            10097. ccc. 22.

KEANE (A. H.) Africa. 1895, *etc* 8°. Stanford's Compendium of Geography. 2060. a.

KINGSTON (W. H. G.) Great African Travellers.
pp. 509. *Lond.* 1890. 8°.   010096. ee. 9.

LANIER (L.) L'Afrique. pp. 917.
Paris, 1895. 18°.   10097. ccc. 21.

LAWSON (W.) Geography of Africa. 4 pt.
Edinb. 1891. 12°.   10003. aaaa. 40.

AFRICA.—General Works—*continued.*

LIVINGSTONE (D.) Livingstone and Stanley.
pp. 151. *Lond.* 1895. 8°.   10097. c. 41.

STANLEY (H. M.) Stanley and Africa. pp. 433.
Lond. 1890. 8°.   010096. e. 20.

DESGRAND (L.) Les Missions de Stanley.
1891, *etc.* 8°. Ac. Lyons. *Soc. de Géographie.*
Bulletin. Tom. 10.   Ac. 6028.

NOYANT ( ) Les Horreurs de l'Esclavage, de la sorcellerie, et du cannibalisme en Afrique.
pp. 95. *Paris,* 1891. 8°.   8156. df. 15.

P.P. Lond n. Kindell's African Market Manual. *Lond.* 1890, *etc.* 24°.   P.P. 2490. nxa.

PIMBLETT (W. M.) Stories from African History. pp. 316. *Lond.* 1891. 8°. 9061. ccc. 10.

—— In Africa with the Union Jack. pp. 248.
Lond. 1894. 8°.   9061. ccc. 16.

PRÉVILLE (A. de) Les Sociétés Africaines.
pp. 345. *Paris,* 1894. 8°.   10096. e. 1.

RICCHIERI (G.) Sulle difficoltà dell' esplorazione africana. pp. 94. *Milano,* 1890. 8°. Pam. 89.

SCHNEIDER (W.) Die Religion der afrikanischen Natur-Völker. pp. 283, 1891. 8°. Darstellungen aus dem Gebiete der nichtchristlichen Religionsgeschichte. Bd. 5, 6.   4506. f.

SPECHT (C. A.) Afrikanische Sitten und Gebräuche. pp. 48. *Leipz.* 1890. 8°. Pam. 41.

SEVIN DESPLACES (L.) Afrique et Africains.
pp. 352. *Paris,* 1892. 8°.   10097. ccc. 7.

SIEVERS (W.) Afrika. *Leipz.* 1891, *etc.* 8°.
                                            10096. i. 3.

STUART (J. M.) Ancient Gold Fields of Africa.
pp. 312. *Lond.* 1891. 8°.   07109. l. 3.

VINCENT (F.) Actual Africa. pp. 541.
Lond. 1895. 8°.   010096. m. 26.

WALLER (H.) 'Ivory, Apes, and Peacocks;'
pp. 90. *Lond.* 1891. 8°.   10096. bb. 10.
See also infra: Colonisation: NEGROES.

Central and East.

ARLAY P. d') Choses d'Afrique. pp. 398.
Paris, 1892. 8°.   010096. ff. 13.

ARNOT (F. S.) Bihé and Garenganze. pp. 150.
Lond. 1893. 8°.   10097. d. 5.

B., H. v. Ostafrikanische Erinnerungen. pp. 78.
Berl. 1891. 8°.   Pam. 89.

BAUMANN (O.) Durch Massailand zur Nilquelle.
pp. 385. *Berl.* 1894. 8°.   10097. l. 14.

BAUMGARTEN (J.) Ostafrika. pp. 563.
Gotha, 1890. 8°.   010096. e. 15.

BELLINGHAM (W.) Diary of a Working Man in Central Africa. pp. 141. *Lond.* 1890. 8°.
                                            4429. aaa. 3.

BOTTEGO (V.) Il Giuba esplorato. pp. 537.
Roma, 1895. 8°.   010096. m. 29.

BURDO (A.) Les Belges dans l'Afrique centrale. 6 tom. *Brux.* 1891. 4°.   10095. i. 12.

DESCAMPS (É.) Les Stations civilisatrices au Tanganika. pp. 15. *Brux.* 1894. 8°. Pam. 81.

DEVIC (L. M.) Le Pays des Zendjs au Moyen-Age. pp. 280. *Paris,* 1883. 8°. 010096. f. 21.

DRUMMOND (H.) Tropical Africa. pp. 228.
Lond. 1891. 8°.   010096. e. 28.

DU CHAILLU (P. B.) Adventures in Equatorial Africa. pp. 476. *Lond.* 1890. 8°. 010096. e. 16.

FOTHERINGHAM (L. M.) Adventures in Nyassaland. pp. 304. *Lond.* 1891. 8°. 010096. e. 27.

FRANZOJ (A.) Aure Africane. pp. 149.
Milano, 1892. 8°.   010096. e. 47.

HOEHNEL (L. v.) Ostäquatorial-Afrika. pp. 44. 1890. 8°. Mittheilungen aus Perthes' Geographischer Anstalt. (Ergänzungsheft Nr. 99.)
                                            P.P. 3946.

AFRICA.—Central and East—*continued.*

HOEHNEL (L. v.) Zum Rudolph-See und Stephanie-See. *Wien, 1891, etc.* 8°.   010096. i.

—— Discovery of Lakes Rudolf and Stefanie. 2 vol. *Lond.* 1894. 8°.   010096. i. 20.

—— Beiträge zur geologischen Kenntniss des östlichen Afrika. 1891. fol.   Ac. Vienna. *Akademie der Wissenschaften.* Denkschriften. Math. Classe. Bd. 58.   Ac. 810/13.

HORE (E. C.) Tanganyika. pp. 306. *Lond.* 1892. 8°.   010096. ff. 17.

JAMES (F. L.) The Unknown Horn of Africa. pp. 273. *Lond.* 1890. 8°.   010096. e. 23.

JOHNSTON (H. H.) Livingstone and the exploration of Central Africa. pp. 372. 1891. 8°. World's Great Explorers.   10024. cc.

JUNKER (W.) Travels in Africa 1875–1878. pp. 582. *Lond.* 1890. 8°.   010096. i. 9.

—— Travels in Africa 1882–1886. pp. 586. *Lond.* 1892. 8°   010096. f. 27.

LE ROY (A.) *Bp. of Alinda.* Au Kilima Ndjaro. *Paris,* 1893. 8°.   10097. i. 18.

LORIOT (C. F.) Explorations dans l'Afrique équatoriale. pp. 375. *Paris,* 1890. 12°.   10097. cc. 17.

MAISTRE (C.) A travers l'Afrique centrale. pp. 307. *Paris,* 1895. 8°.   10095. g. 13.

MANDAT-GRANCEY (E. de) Souvenirs de la Côte d'Afrique. pp. 308. *Paris,* 1892. 12°.   10097. ccc. 4.

MEYER (H.) Across East African Glaciers; ascent of Kilimanjaro. pp. 404. *Lond.* 1891. 8°.   10097. m. 21.

MOIR (J. F.) Lady's Letters from Central Africa. pp. 91. *Glasgow,* 1891. 12°.   010096. e. 25.

MOLONEY (J. A.) With Captain Stairs to Katanga. pp. 280. *Lond.* 1893. 8°.   010096. e. 59.

PAULITSCHKE (P.) Ethnographie Nordost-Afrikas. pp. 338. *Berl.* 1893. 8°.   10095. g. 9.

PRUEN (S. T.) The Arab and the African. pp. 338. *Lond.* 1891. 8°.   10095. c. 1.

SCHLICHTER (H.) Ptolemy's Topography of Eastern Equatorial Africa. pp. 41. 1891. 8°.   010096. f. 11. (1.)

SCHMIDT (R.) Geschichte des Araberaufstandes in Ost-Africa. pp. 360. *Frankfurt a. O.* 1892. 8°.   9061. dd. 9.

STANLEY (H. M.) The Great Forest of Central Africa. pp. 40. *Lond.* 1890. fol.   10097. m. 20.

TRIVIER (E.) Mon Voyage au Continent Noir. pp. 386. *Paris,* 1891. 8°.   010096. e. 33.

TUVACHE (L.) Trois Mois chez les Nègres. pp. 134. *Baugé,* 1893 8°.   10097. dd. 25.

VIGNERON (L.) Sang noir. Scènes de la vie esclavagiste. pp. 293. *Paris,* 1893. 12°.   010096. bb. 11.

WISSMANN (H. v.) Meine zweite Durchquerung Äquatorial-Afrikas. pp. 261. *Frankfurt a. O.* 1890. 8°.   010096. ff. 9.

—— My Second Journey. pp. 326. *Lond.* 1891. 8°.   010096. ee. 31.

—— Im Innern Afrikas. pp. 461. *Leipz.* 1891. 8°.   010096. ff. 16.

See also infra: Colonisation, etc.: Emin Pasha: MASAI LAND: MISSIONS: SLAVERY: SOMALILAND: SOUDAN: SPORT: ZAMBESI.

Colonisation: Possessions of European Nations.

HERTSLET (*Sir* E.) The Map of Africa by Treaty. 2 vol. *Lond.* 1894. 8°.   8028. f. 37.

KELTIE (J. S.) The Partition of Africa. pp. 564. *Lond.* 1895. 8°.   2386. d. 1.

WHITE (A. S.) The Development of Africa. pp. 307. *Lond.* 1892. 8°.   010096. e. 44.

AFRICA.—Colonisation, etc.—*continued.*

FAURE (C.) La Conférence africaine de Berlin. pp. 40. *Genève,* 1885. 8°.   Pam. 66.

ITALY.—*Army.* Possedimenti Europei in Africa, 1889. pp. 179. *Roma,* 1889. 8°.   10096. g. 11.

MALAVIALLE (L.) Le Partage Politique de l'Afrique. 1891. 8°. Ac.—Montpellier.—*Société de Géographie.* Bulletin. Tom. 14. Ac. 6033.

MILLINGEN (F.) [OSMAN BEY]. Partage de l'Afrique selon la fable d'Ésope. pp. 23. *Nice,* 1894. 8°.   Pam. 67.

NOBLE (F. P.) The Congress on Africa. 1892. fol.   1865. c. 3. (24.)

SÉBILLOT (A.) Le Transafricain. [Railway across Africa.] pp. 67. *Paris,* 1893. 8°.   Pam. 76.

British Possessions.

BRUCE (A. L.) The Cape to Cairo; Britain's sphere of influence. pp. 48. *Edinb.* 1892. 8°.   010096. h. 6.

G. B. & I.—*War Office.* Handbook of British East Africa. pp. 176. *Lond.* 1893. 8°.   10097. dd. 26.

LUGARD (F. J. D.) British East Africa and Uganda. pp. 67. *Lond.* 1892. 8°   8028. e. 31.

—— Rise of our East African Empire. 2 vol. *Edinb.* 1893. 8°.   010096. h. 4.

MACDERMOTT (P. L.) British East Africa. pp. 632. *Lond.* 1895. 8°.   8154. dd. 17.

P.P. *Zomba.* British Central Africa Gazette. *Zomba,* 1894, *etc.* fol.   P.P. 9637.

PIMBLETT (W. M.) In Africa with the Union Jack. pp. 248. *Lond.* 1894. 8°.   9061. ccc. 16.

See also supra: General: Central and East; infra: South: West: CAPE OF GOOD HOPE: ENGLAND, *Colonies:* MISSIONS: MASHONALAND: NYASSALAND: UGANDA.

French Possessions.

Ac. Paris. *Société Africaine.* Bulletins de mémoires. *Paris,* 1891, *etc.* 8°.   Ac. 460.

ALIS (H.) Nos Africains. pp. 568. *Paris,* 1894. 8°.   010095. i. 4.

DAGLAN (P.) La délimitation franco-allemande dans la région du lac Tchad. pp. 8. *Paris,* 1894. 4°.   Pam. 67.

DESCAMPS-DAVID (E.) Discours sur l'Avenir de la Civilisation en Afrique. pp. 16. *Louvain,* 1891. 8°.   Pam. 66.

DUPONCHEL (A.) La Colonisation africaine. pp. 52. *Paris,* 1890. 8°.   Pam. 66.

ESTAMPES (L. d') La France au Pays noir. pp. 368. *Paris,* 1893. 8°.   9061. e. 3.

MIZON (L. A. A.) Une Question africaine. pp. 63. *Paris,* 1895. 8°.   8028. ff. 21.

P.P. *Paris.* France Noire. *Paris,* 1894, *etc.* fol.   234.

PHILEBERT (C.) La France en Afrique. pp. 96. *Paris,* 1890. 8°.   Pam. 67.

SALLÈS (A.) Cardinal Lavigerie et l'influence française en Afrique. pp. 58. *Lyon,* 1893. 12°.   Pam. 40.

VERDIER (A.) Questions coloniales. Côte d'Ivoire. pp. 14. *Paris,* 1895. 8°.   Pam. 89.

See also FRANCE, *Colonies:* GABOON: OBOK: SOUDAN.

German Possessions.

BAUMANN (O.) Usambara und seine Nachbargebiete. pp. 375. *Berl.* 1891. 8°.   010090. ff. 1.

BEHR (H. F. v.) Kriegsbilder aus dem Araberaufstand in Deutsch-Ostafrika. pp. 343. *Leipz.* 1891. 8°.   9061. ccc. 23.

BLEY (F.) Deutsche Pionierarbeit in Ostafrika. pp. 140. *Berl.* 1891. 8°.   010096. ee. 23.

BLUEMCKE (K.) Der Aufstand in Deutsch-Ostafrika. pp. 96. *Berl.* 1890. 8°.   8028. c. 22.

AFRICA.—Colonisation, etc.—*continued.*

GUERICH (G.) Deutsch Südwest-Afrika. pp. 216.
1891. 8°. Ac. Hamburg. *Geographische Gesellschaft.* Mittheilungen. 1891. Heft 1. Ac. 6054.

KAERGER (C.) Tangaland. pp. 177.
Berl. 1892. 8°.   010096. ff. 18.

KALLENBERG (F.) Auf dem Kriegspfad gegen
die Massai. pp. 200. *München*, 1892. 8°.
010096. ff. 27.

KLUGER. Dr. Hertzka's Ostafrikanaan. pp. 30.
Leipz. 1891. 8°.   Pam. 82.

MAERCKER (G.) Unsere Schutztruppe in Ostafrika. pp. 216. *Berl.* 1893. 8°. 010096. ee. 43.

MERENSKY (A.) Deutsche Arbeit am Njassa.
pp. 368. *Berl.* 1894. 8°.   010097. g. 4.

REICHARD (P.) Deutsch-Ostafrika. pp. 524.
Leipz. 1892. 8°.   010096. ee. 32.

SCHINZ (H.) Deutsch-Südwest-Afrika. pp. 568.
Oldenburg, 1891. 8°.   010096. i. 13.

WEIDMANN (C.) Deutsche Männer in Afrika.
pp. 194. *Lübeck*, 1894. 8°.   010707. ff. 8.

See also CAMEROON : DAMARALAND : GERMANY,
Colonies.

Italian Possessions.

BOMPIANI (S.) Italian Explorers in Africa.
pp. 202. *Lond.* 1891. 8°.   10097. de. 16.

BORROMEO (A.) Progretto sulla colonizzazione
Africana. pp. 34. *Firenze*, 1890. 8°.
08227. ee. 45. (8.)

C., V. Colonie italiane. pp. 46.
Massa, 1890. 8°.   Pam. 66.

GRANDI (T.) L'Italia in Africa. pp. 27.
Alessandria, 1890. 8°.   08276. f. 22. (5.)

MARTINI (F.) Nell' Africa italiana. pp. 291.
Milano, 1891. 8°.   10097. ccc. 1.

See also ERITREA.

Portuguese Possessions.

ANDRADE CORVO (J. de) Estudos sobre as
Provincias Ultramarinas. 4 vol.
Lisboa, 1883–87. 8°.   8155. ee. 14.

BRANDÃO CRÓ DE CASTRO FERRERI (A.) De
Lisboa a Moçambique. pp. 156.
Lisboa, 1884. 8°.   10097. de. 22.

EPHEM. Almanach Luso-Africano.
Lisboa, 1894. 8°.   P.P. 2387. g.

MACKAY (W.) The Prisoner of Chiloane.
pp. 184. *Lond.* 1890. 4°.   010096. ee. 16.

MONTEIRO (R.) Delagoa Bay. pp. 274.
Lond. 1891. 8°.   010096. e. 39.

MOZAMBIQUE COMPANY. Handbook of the
Mozambique Company. pp. 186.
Lond. 1893. 8°.   010096. ee. 33.

OLIVEIRA (J. P.) Portugal em Africa. pp. 240.
Porto, 1891. 8°.   8022. aaa. 3.

PERRY DA CAMARA ( ) Africa Oriental.
pp. 32. *Lisboa*, 1893. 8°.   Pam. 89.

SARMENTO (A.) Estudos coloniaes. pp. 134.
Lisboa, 1891. 8°.   8154. e. 24.

WEALE (J. P. M.) Truth about the Portuguese
in Africa. pp. 196. *Lond.* 1891. 8°. 8027. bb. 12.

See also PORTUGAL, *Colonies and Politics,
Foreign.*

Spanish Possessions.

PÉREZ DEL TORO (F.) España en el Noroeste
de África. pp. 288. *Madrid*, 1892. 8°.
8027. aa. 9.

REPARÁZ (G.) España en África. pp. 218.
Madrid, 1891. 8°.   8027. aa. 8.

See also SPAIN, *Colonies.*

Diseases, Hygiene.

See DISEASES : HYGIENE.

AFRICA—*continued.*

Emin Pasha Expedition, etc.

CASATI (G.) Dieci anni in Equatoria e ritorno
con Emin Pascia. 2 vol. *Milano*, 1891. 8°.
010096. h. 1.

DESGRAND (L.) Les Missions de Stanley dans
l Afrique Équatoriale. 1891, *etc.* 8°. Ac.
Lyons. *Société de Géographie.* Bulletin. Tom.
10, livr. 4, *etc.*   Ac. 6028.

HASSAN (V.) Die Wahrheit über Emin Pascha.
2 Tle. *Berl.* 1893. 8°.   10097. dd.

LIVINGSTONE (D.) Livingstone and Stanley.
pp. 151. *Lond.* 1895. 8°.   10097. c. 41.

PARKE (T. H.) My experiences in Equatorial
Africa. pp. 526. *Lond.* 1891. 8°. 010096. ff. 8.

PETERS (C.) Die deutsche Emin-Pascha-Expedition. pp. 560. *München*, 1891. 8°.
10096. dd. 4.

—— New Light on Dark Africa. German Emin
Pasha Expedition. pp. 597. *Lond.* 1891. 8°.
010096. m. 6.

REDDALL (H. F.) H. M. Stanley. pp. 411.
N.Y. 1890. 8°.   10827. aaa. 35.

REICHARD (P.) Dr. Emin Pascha. pp. 313.
Leipz. 1891. 8°.   010096. ee. 27.

REINHARDT (F.) Die englische Emin-Entsatz-Expedition. pp. 46. 1890. 8°. Sammlung
wissenschaftlicher Vorträge. N. F. No. 107.
12249. m.

SCHYNSE (A. W.) Mit Stanley und Emin Pascha.
pp. 88. 1890. 8°. Görres-Gesellschaft. Vereinsschrift.   Ac. 2026/2.

—— À travers l'Afrique avec Stanley et Emin-Pacha. pp. 298. *Paris*, 1890. 8°. 010096. e. 19.

SMITH (R. M.) Stanley in Tropical Africa.
pp. 196. *Lond.* 1890. 8°.   10096. aa. 8.

STABY (L.) Emin-Pascha.
Stuttgart, 1890, *etc.* 8°.   010707. f. 3.

STANLEY (H. M.) Across Africa. pp. 35.
Lond. 1890. fol.   10097. m. 18.

—— The Rescue of Emin Pasha. pp. 41.
Lond. 1890. fol.   10097. m. 19.

—— Stanley and Africa. pp. 433.
Lond. 1890. 8°.   010096. e. 20.

STUHLMANN (F.) Mit Emin Pascha ins Herz
von Afrika. pp. 901. *Berl.* 1894. 8°. 10097. l. 2.

TIEDEMANN (A. v.) Mit Karl Peters zu Emin
Pascha. pp. 332. *Berl.* 1892. 8°. 010096. ff. 21.

UHL (G.) Emin Pascha und die deutschen Besitzungen in Ostafrica. pp. 39.
Leipz. 1894. 8°.   9007. g. 20. (7.)

VOLZ (B.) Emin Paschas Entsatz. pp. 324.
Leipz. 1891. 8°.   010096. ee. 26.

See also supra : Central and East.

Ethnology.

*See supra : General : Central and East ; infra :
South West :* ETHNOLOGY : NEGROES.

Missions. *See* MISSIONS.

Mohammedanism, *in Africa.*

See MOHAMMEDANISM.

North : Roman Province, etc.

Ac. Paris. *Comité des travaux historiques.* L'épigraphie chrétienne dans l'Afrique romaine.
pp. 140. *Paris*, 1890. 8°.   07708. f. 24.

AFRICA. Géographie de l'Afrique chrétienne.
pp. 417. *Rennes*, 1894. 8°.   4534 c. 31.

AUDOLLENT (A.) Mission épigraphique en Algérie. 1890. 8°. Ac. Rome. *École Française.*
Mélanges. Année 10.   Ac. 5233.

BALLU (A.) Monuments antiques de l'Algérie.
Paris, 1894. 8°.   07708. f. 44.

BŒSWILLWALD (E.) Timgad sous l'Empire
romain. *Paris*, 1891, *etc.* 4°.   7703. b.

AFRICA.—North, etc.—continued.

CAGNAT (R.) L'armée romaine d'Afrique. pp. 809. *Paris,* 1892. 4°. 9039. i. 10.

CAT (É.) Documents espagnols sur l'Afrique du Nord. pp. 148. 1891. 8°. Ac. Algiers. *École Supérieure.* Publications. pt. 8. Ac. 5350/2.

FRANCE. *Ministère de l'Instruction.* Atlas archéologique de la Tunisie. *Paris,* 1893. fol. 144.

GSELL (S.) Chronique africaine. 1894. 8°. Revue Africaine. Année 38. Ac. 6915.

—— Recherches archéologiques en Algérie. pp. 434. *Paris,* 1893. 8°. 7708. d. 37.

HOUDARD (L.) Étude à propos d'Antiquités recueillies en Tunisie. pp. 51. *Paris,* 1891. 8°. Pam. 3.

HOUDAS (D.) Épigraphie Tunisienne. pp. 40. *Alger,* 1882. 4°. 7707. aaa. 49.

MONCEAUX (P.) Étude sur la littérature latine d'Afrique. pp. 500. *Paris,* 1894. 12°. 11312. e. 37.

NEUMANN (R.) Nordafrika, nach Herodot. pp. 165. *Leipz.* 1892. 8°. 9061. dd. 10.

PALLU DE LESSERT (C.) Vicaires et Comtes d'Afrique. pp. 183. 1892. 8°. Ac. Constantine. *Société Archéologique.* Recueils, *etc.* série 3. vol. 5. Ac. 5349.

PARIS. *Association de l'Afrique du Nord.* Bulletin, *etc.* Année I., II. *Paris,* 1889, 90. 8°. 010096. f.

SCHWARZE (A.) Untersuchungen über die äussere Entwicklung der afrikanischen Kirche. pp. 194. *Göttingen,* 1892. 8°. 4534. f. 18.

SIMAIKA ('A. A.) Essai sur la province romaine d'Égypte. pp. 234. *Paris,* 1892. 8°. 9061. d. 4.

WHITEHOUSE (F. C.) Note sur trois cartes ptolémaiques de l'Afrique. pp. 6. *Le Caire,* 1892. 8°. 07703 h. 1. (11.)

See also ALGERIA : CARTHAGE : EGYPT : MAROCCO : MEDITERRANEAN : SAHARA : VANDALS.

South.

See also BASUTOLAND : BECHUANALAND : CAPE OF GOOD HOPE : DAMARALAND : ENGLAND, *Colonies :* GRIQUALAND, *West :* MASHONALAND : MISSIONS : NATAL : ORANGE FREE STATE : SWAZILAND : TRANSVAAL : ZAMBEZI : ZULULAND.

Dutch Language in.

See DUTCH LANGUAGE.

Geography : Guide Books, etc.

Ac. Cape Town. *Royal Observatory.* Geodetic Survey of S. Africa. pp. 11. *Cape Town,* 1892. 8°. Pam. 89.

AFRICA, *South.* Emigrants' Guide. pp. 139. *Lond.* 1891. 8°. 10097. ccc. 16.

—— Health : voyage to S. Africa. pp. 80. *Lond.* 1891. 8°. 7686. aaa. 4.

—— Sailing Directions for the Southern Coast of Africa. pp. 128. *Lond.* 1893. 8°. 10496. a. 11.

BLINK (H.) Aardrijkskunde van Zuid-Afrika. 2 deel. *Amsterd.* 1889. 8°. 010096. e. 53.

BROWN (A. S.) South Africa ; guide. pp. 245. *Lond.* 1893. 8°. 010096. e. 56.

CASTLE LINE. Handbook of information for passengers. pp. 65. *Lond.* 1893. 8°. 10498. a. 25.

AFRICA, *South.* Castle Line Atlas of South Africa. pp. 47. *Lond.* 1895. 8°. 10095. g. 12.

GLANVILLE (E.) Union Steamship Co.'s Guide to S. Africa. pp. 107. *Lond.* 1890. 8°. 10097. ccc. 17.

GRESWELL (W. H. P.) Geography of Africa south of the Zambesi. pp. 400. *Oxf.* 1892. 8°. 010096. e. 42.

LYDE (L. W.) Elementary Geography of British S. Africa. pp. 84. *Lond.* 1893. 8°. 10005. aa. 21.

AFRICA.—South—continued.

SILVER (S. W.) Handbook to S. Africa. pp. 793. *Lond.* 1891. 8°. 10097. bb. 38.

WHITESIDE (J.) Geography of S. Africa. pp. 73. *Cape Town,* 1893. 8°. 10097. ccc. 15.

WHITTON (J. R.) Geographical Reader for S. Africa. pp. 239. *Lond.* 1894. 8°. 10005. b. 1.

WILMOT (A.) Outlines of Geography of S. Africa. pp. 48. *Cape Town,* 1891. 8°. Pam. 89.

Gold and Diamond Fields.

See DIAMONDS : GOLD AND SILVER.

History : Politics.

BESWICK (F.) Outlines of the History of S. Africa. pp. 62. *Cape Town,* 1893. 8°. 9061. bb. 5.

MOODIE (D. C. F.) History of the Battles and Adventures of the British, Boers and Zulus. 2 vol. *Cape Town,* 1888. 8°. 9061. de. 35.

MURRAY (R. W.) S. Africa from Arab domination to British rule. pp. 223. *Lond.* 1891. 8°. 9061. ee. 26.

SIDWELL (H. B.) The Story of S. Africa. pp. 136. *Cape Town,* 1891. 8°. 9061. a. 8.

THEAL (G. M. C.) History of S. Africa from 1486. *Lond.* 1888, *etc.* 8°. 9061. eec. 20.

—— Primer of S. African History. pp. 139. *Lond.* 1895. 8°. 9061. aaa. 7.

—— Short history of S. Africa, 1486-1826. pp. 252. *Cape Town,* 1890. 8°. 9061. ccc. 6.

—— South Africa. pp. 397. 1894. 8°. Story of the Nations. 9004. ccc. 13.

WILMOT (A.) Story of the Expansion of S. Africa. pp. 290. *Lond.* 1894. 8°. 9061. cc. 37.

AFRICA, *South.* Letters. By the Times Correspondent. pp. 116. *Lond.* 1893. 8°. 010096. e. 52.

—— Lettres au "Times" sur l'Afrique du Sud. pp. 286. *Paris,* 1893. 8°. 9061. aaa. 3.

CLOTTEN (F. E.) England and S. Africa. pp. 83. *Lond.* 1891. 8°. Pam. 66.

CURRIE (*Sir* D.) South Africa. An Address. pp. 44. *Lond.* 1888. 8°. Pam. 66.

MELLO (C. de) Os Inglezes na Africa austral. pp. 239. *Lisboa,* 1890. 8°. 8154. aa. 12.

SMITH (A.) Short Papers on S. African subjects. pp. 222. *Lovedale,* 1893. 8°. 012330. h. 11.

WORSFOLD (W. B.) S. Africa. Study in colonial administration. pp. 266. *Lond.* 1895. 8°. 9061. b. 44.

Industries. *See infra : Trade.*

Reformed Church, Dutch.

AFRICA, *South.* Handelingen der 17de Vergadering van de Synode der Gereformeerde Kerk, *etc.* pp. 85. *Kaapstad,* 1890. 4°. 5017. b. 1.

—— Verzameling van de Bepalingen der Synoden der Gereformeerde Kerk, 1876. pp. 93. *Paarl,* 1891. 8°. 4182. aa. 41.

—— Wetten en Bepalingen voor het bestuur der Gereformeerde Kerk. pp. 191. *Kaapstad,* 1890. 8°. 5125. aa. 3.

—— Handelingen van de twaalfde algem. synodale Kerkvergadering. pp. 83. *De Paarl,* 1894. 8°. 4183. c. 59.

EPHEM. Almanak voor de Gereformeerde Kerk, 1891. *Kaapstad,* 1891, *etc.* 8°. P.P. 2579. ua.

CACHET (J. L.) Opmerkingen over het boekje : "Mijne Overkomst tot de Gereformeerde Kerk." pp. 92. *Paarl,* 1894. 8°. 4183. c. 58.

Trade : Industries.

AFRICA, *South.* The Immigrant's Prospects in S. Africa. pp. 20. *Lond.* 1890. 8°. Pam. 89.

COCORDA (G. D.) Sud-Africa commerciale ed industriale. *Milano,* 1890. 8°. 8227. k. 38. (3.)

AFRICA.—Trade, etc.—_continued._

MULLER (H. P. N.) Industrie des Cafres de Sud-Est de l'Afrique. pp. 49. _Leyde,_ 1893. fol.
1788. a. 28.

P.P. _Cape Town._ S. African Trade Journal. _Cape Town,_ 1891, _etc._ fol.   476.

WILMOT (A.) Book of South African Industries. _Cape Town,_ 1892, _etc._ 8°.   08227. g.

See also DIAMONDS: GOLD: MINERALOGY AND MINING.

Travel, Sport, etc.

BALDWIN (W. C.) African Hunting and Adventure. pp. 428. _Lond._ 1894. 8°. 010096. h. 5.

BALFOUR (A. B.) Twelve Hundred Miles in a Waggon. pp. 265. _Lond._ 1895. 8°. 010097. g. 8.

BOYLE (R.) Sanitary Crusade through S. Africa. pp. 34. _Lond._ 1891. 8°.   Pam. 79.

BRYDEN (H. A.) Gun and Camera in S. Africa. pp. 544. _Lond._ 1893. 8°.   010096. ff. 26.

CAMPBELL (J. K.) Rambles in S. Africa. pp. 300. _Lond._ 1891. 8°.   010096. ee. 29.

CHURCHILL (_Lord_ R. H. S.) Men, Mines and Minerals in S. Africa. pp. 337. _Lond._ 1892. 8°.
010096. f. 28.

CUMMING (R. G.) Hunting Adventures in S. Africa. pp. 349. _Lond._ 1892. 8°. 7903. c. 40.

GROSER (A.) S. African Experiences. pp. 66. _Devonport,_ 1891. 8°.   010096. i. 14.

HOLUB (E.) Von der Capstadt ins Land der Maschukulumbe. _Wien,_ 1890, _etc._ 8°. 010096. f. 19.

INGRAM (J. F.) The Land of Gold. pp. 233. _Lond._ 1891. 8°.   010096. e. 67.

JOHNSTON (J.) Reality versus Romance in S. Central Africa. pp. 353. _Lond._ 1893. 8°.
10097. dd. 27.

KNOX (T. W.) Hunters Three. pp. 248. _Lond._ 1895. 4°.   7905. cc. 28.

KROPF (A.) Das Volk der Xosa-Kaffern im östlichen Südafrika. pp. 209. _Berl._ 1889. 8°.
010096. ee. 20.

LECLERCQ (J.) A travers l'Afrique australe. pp. 312. _Paris,_ 1895. 8°.   010097. e. 4.

MARTIN (A.) Home Life on an Ostrich Farm. pp. 288. _Lond._ 1890. 8°.   010096. e. 24.

MEUGENS, afterwards BELL (N.) Heroes of S. African Discovery. pp. 400. _Lond._ 1893. 8°.
10097. de. 26.

MULLER (H. P. N.) Z. Afrika. Reisherinneringen. pp. 396. _Leiden,_ 1890. 8°.   010096. ee. 10.

RITCHIE (J. E.) Brighter S. Africa. pp. 232. _Lond._ 1892. 8°.   10097. de. 18.

SELOUS (F. C.) Travel in S.-East Africa. pp. 503. _Lond._ 1893. 8°.   10096. ff. 12.

WHITER (J. S.) Trip to S. Africa. pp. 247. _Sutton,_ 1892. 8°.   10097. ccc. 13.

West.

BASTIAN (A.) Zur Mythologie und Psychologie der Nigritier in Guinea. pp. 162. _Berl._ 1894. 8°.   12430. l. 13.

BINGER (G.) Du Niger au Golfe de Guinée. 2 tom. _Paris,_ 1892. 8°.   10096. i. 8.

BOUTEILLER (J.) De Saint-Louis à Sierra-Leone. pp. 332. _Paris,_ 1891. 18°.   10097. cc. 21.

DIEDERICHS (H.) Herzog Jacobs von Kurland Kolonien an der Westküste. pp. 71. _Mitau,_ 1890. 4°.   9061. f. 21.

DYBOWSKI (JEAN) Du Loango au Chari. pp. 381. _Paris,_ 1893. 8°.   10097. i. 36.

ELLIS (A. B.) Ewé-speaking Peoples of West Africa. pp. 331. _Lond._ 1890. 8°. 010096. i. 8.

AFRICA.—West—_continued._

ELLIS (A. B.) Yoruba-speaking Peoples of West Africa. pp. 402. _Lond._ 1894. 8°. 10006. e. 11.

GOLDIE (_Sir_ G. T.) The Hausa Association. pp. 9. _Woking,_ 1895. 8°.   Pam. 47.

—— West African Liquor Trade. pp. 8. _Lond._ 1895. 8°.   Pam. 85.

HODGES (F. E.) Consular Jurisdiction in the Niger Coast. pp. 201. _Lond._ 1895. 8°.
06955. ee. 14.

LAUMANN (E. M.) A la Côte occidentale d'Afrique. pp. 266. _Paris,_ 1894. 8°. 10097. c. 43.

LUCAS (C. P.) Historical Geography of the British Colonies. Vol. III. _Oxf._ 1894. 8°.
10004. dd. 2.

MANN (A.) Die Yoruba-Küste. pp. 8. _Stuttgart,_ 1886. 8°.   Pam. 47.

MONNIER (M.) France noire. Côte d'Ivoire et Soudan. pp. 298. _Paris,_ 1894. 8°. 010096. e. 68.

MARQUES (A. S.) Expedição Portugueza ao Muata-Ianvo. _Lisboa,_ 1889, _etc._ 8°.
010096. ff. 12.

PAYNE (J. A. O.) Table of events in Yoruba history. pp. 111. _Lagos,_ 1893. 8°. 9061. ee. 31.

SALMON ( ) Le massacre de la mission Mizon par les Anglais. pp. 159. _Paris,_ 1895. 12°.
8027. a. 14.

SAVORGNAN DE BRAZZA (P. P. F. C.) Conférences et lettres sur ses explorations dans l'Ouest africain. pp. 463. _Paris,_ 1887. 8°. 10096. gg. 6.

SCHLICHTER (H.) Geography of South-West Africa. pp. 26. 1891. 8°. 010096. ff. 11. (2.)

See also supra: Central: ANGOLA: ASHANTI: CAMEROON: CONGO: ENGLAND, _Colonies:_ GABOON: GOLD COAST: HYGIENE: LIBERIA: LUNDA: MISSIONS: NIGER: SIERRA LEONE: TIMBUKTO.

AFRICAN LANGUAGES. CHRISTALLER

(J. G.) Die sprachen Africas. pp. 59. _Stuttgart,_ 1892. 8°.   12910. dd. 23.

—— Die Töne der Neger-Sprachen. pp. 19. _Basel,_ 1893. 8°.   12910. bb. 47. (9.)

CUST (R. N.) Essay on the progress of African philology to 1893. pp. 48. _Lond._ 1893. 8°.
12903. e. 26. (9.)

ELLIS (A. B.) Yoruba-Speaking Peoples. Appendix containing comparison of the Tshi, Gã, Ewe, and Yoruba languages. pp. 402. _Lond._ 1894. 8°.   10006. e. 11.

P.P. _Berlin._ Zeitschrift für afrikanische Sprachen. _Berl._ 1895, _etc._ 8°.   P.P. 4991. ha.

SCHLEICHER (A. W.) Afrikanische Petrefakten. pp. 93. _Berl._ 1891. 8°.   12902. dd. 30.

SEIDEL (A.) Grammatiken der Hauptsprachen Deutsch-Südwestafrikas. pp. 180. 1891. 8°. Kunst der Polyglottie. Tl. 37.   12902. c.

TEGNÉR (E. H. W.) Nordiska författares arbeten om afrikanska språk. pp. 22. _Lund,_ 1884. 8°.
Pam. 47.

CHRISTALLER (J. G.) Übungen in der Akra- oder Ga-Sprache. pp. 103. _Basel,_ 1890. 8°.
12910. b. 32.

ZIMMERMANN (J.) Akra songs for children. pp. 61. _Basel,_ 1880. 8°.   884. e. 1.

TORRENDS (J.) Grammar of the Bantu languages. pp. 336. _Lond._ 1891. 8°.   12910. i. 32.

ALMKVIST (H.) Bischari-deutsches und deutsch-bischarisches Wörterbuch. pp. 113. _Upsala,_ 1885. 4°.   12910. i. 28.

WOODWARD (H. W.) Stories in the Bondei language. pp. 59. _Lond._ 1894. 8°. 4429. a. 83.

JUANOLA (J.) Primer paso á la lengua Bubí. pp. 189. _Madrid,_ 1890. 8°.   12910. dd. 19.

AFRICAN LANGUAGES—*continued.*

HENRY (G.) Grammar of Chinyanja. pp. 232.
Aberd. 1891. 8°.   12910. aa. 48.

W., M. E. Vocabulary of English-Chinyanja and
Chinyanja-English. pp. 88. *Lond.* 1895. 8°.
                12910. aa. 70.

BENTLEY (W. H.) Appendix to the Dictionary
of the Kongo language. *Lond.* 1895. 8°.
                12910. d. 29.

CAMBIER (E.) Essai sur la Langue congolaise.
pp. 124. *Brux.* 1891. 8°.   12910. cc. 6.

CONGO LANGUAGE. Éléments de la langue congolaise. Suivis d'un choix de phrases graduées et
de deux vocabulaires. pp. 95. *Lille*, 1895. 8°.
                12910. a. 54.

GUINNESS (H. G.) Mosaic and Gospel Story,
epitomised in Congo. pp. 87. *Lond.* 1882. 8°.
                3068. f. 6.

LEJEUNE (L.) Dictionnaire Français-Fang.
pp. 347. *Paris*, 1892. 8°.   12910. aa. 51.

BONNAVENTURE (A. A.) Éléments de grammaire
de la langue Fon ou Dahoméenne, suivis d'un
vocabulaire, *etc.* pp. 72. *Paris*, 1895. 8°.
                12910. bb. 49.

DELAFOSSE (M.) Manuel dahoméen. pp. 435.
Paris, 1894. 12°.   12910. c. 8.

COURDIOUX (P. E.) Dictionnaire de la langue
dahoméenne. 1880. 8°. Ac. Paris. *Société
Philologique.* Actes. tom. 9.   Ac. 9808.

CHRISTALLER (T.) Handbuch der Duala-Sprache.
pp. 214. *Basel*, 1892. 8°.   12907. b. 40.

SEIDEL (A.) Leitfaden zur Erlernung der Dualla-
Sprache. pp. 83. *Berl.* 1892. 8°. 12910. ccc. 1.

EWÉ READING-BOOK. Ewé Xextĕ-Agbalĕ.
pp. 64. *Bremen*, 1892. 8°.   12910. c. 5.

KNUESLI (J.) Ewé-German-English Vocabulary.
pp. 1084. *Keta*, 1891. 4°.   12910. cc. 17.

HENRICI (E.) Lehrbuch der Ephe-Sprache, Ewé,
Anlo-, Anecho- und Dahome-Mundart. pp. 270.
1891. 8°. SACHAU (C. E.) Lehrbücher, *etc.*
Bd. 6.   12906. h.

GUIRAUDON (T. G. de) Manuel de la langue
Foule. pp. 144. *Lond.* 1894. 8°. 12910. b. 41.

TAUTAIN ( ) Contribution à l'étude de la langue
Foule. pp. 81. *Orléans*, 1882. 8°.
                12901. d. 30. (3.)

FAIDHERBE (L. L C.) Grammaire et vocabulaire
de la langue poul. pp. 164. *Paris*, 1882. 12°.
                12910. aa. 33.

TAYLOR (W. E.) Giryama Vocabulary. pp. 140.
Lond. 1891. 8°.   12910. aaa. 67.

CRAWSHAW (C. J.) First Kafir Course. pp. 133.
Cape Town, 1894. 8°.   12910. d. 27.

LOVEDALE KAFFIR READERS. Kaffir Readers.
Lovedale, 1890, etc. 8°.   12910. aa.

AMBROSIUS (P.) Grammatik der Zulu-Kaffri-
schen Sprache. pp. 210.
Mariannhill, 1890. 8°.   12910. b. 35.

ELMSLIE (W. A.) Introductory Grammar of the
Ngoni, Zulu, Language. pp. 51.
Aberd. 1891. 8°.   12910. aa. 47.

ROBERTS (C.) English-Zulu Dictionary.
pp. 267. *Lond.* 1895. 8°.   12910. a. 50.
—— Zulu-Kafir Language. pp. 177.
Lond. 1895. 8°.   12910. b. 46.

INCWADI. Incwadi Yamaculo : Zulu Hymnbook.
pp. 283. *Lovedale*, 1890. 16°.   3434. ccc. 29.

TORREND (J.) Outline of a Xosa-Kafir grammar.
pp. 95. *Grahamstown*, 1887. 8°.   12910. aa. 41.

EDDIE (J. B.) Kilolo-English Vocabulary.
pp. 159. *Lond.* 1891. 8°.   12910. aa. 36.

LUGANDA GRAMMAR. Essai de Grammaire ru-
ganda. pp. 98. *Paris*, 1885. 8°. 12910. aa. 34.

LUGANDA PRIMER. Luganda Primer. pp. 12.
Lond. 1890. 12°.   Pam. 47.

AFRICAN LANGUAGES—*continued.*

LITURGIES. England, *Church of.* The Collects
translated into Luganda. pp. 32.
Lond. 1893. 8°.   Pam. 75.

O'FLAHERTY (P.) Collections for a Lexicon in
Luganda and English. pp. 41.
Lond. 1892. 8°.   12910. aa. 65.

PILKINGTON (G. L.) Hand-book of Luganda.
pp. 93. *Lond.* 1892. 8°.   4429. aa. 59.

P., G. L. Hymns in the Luganda Language.
pp. 16. *Lond.* 1892. 8°.   4429. a. 79.

MAC KITTRICK (J.) and (F. T.) Guide to the
Lunkundu Language. pp. 230. *Lond.* 1893. 8°.
                12910. a. 32.

DIAS DE CARVALHO (H. A.) Methodo pratico
para fallar a lingua da Lunda. pp. 391.
Lisboa, 1890. 8°.   12910. dd. 20.

HARTMANN (A. M.) English-Mashona Diction-
ary. pp. 78. *Cape Town*, 1894. 16°.
                12910. a. 38.
—— Outline of a Grammar of the Mashona
Language. pp. 69. *Cape Town*, 1893. 8°.
                12910. aaa. 74.

WEALE (M. E.) Matabele and Makalaka vocabulary. pp. 32. *Cape Town*, 1893. 8°.
                12910. aaa. 68.

ELMSLIE (W. A.) Table of Concords of the Ngoni
Language. *Aberd.* 1891. fol.   12910. aa. 46.

SCHILS (G. H.) Grammaire de la langue des
Namas. pp. 94. *Louvain*, 1891. fol.
                12910. k. 14.

SAGALLA READING BOOK. Kisagalla. pp. 16.
Lond. 1892. 8°.   4422. ddd. 55. (6.)

DELACOUR (E. W. S.) Shironga Vocabulary.
pp. 31. *Lond.* 1893. 8°.   12901. d. 36. (16.)

SCHLEICHER (A. W.) Die Somali-Sprache.
Berl. 1892, etc. 8°.   12910. dd. 22.

MADAN (A. C.) English-Swahili Dictionary, *etc.*
pp. 415. *Oxf.* 1894. 8°.   12910. aaa. 70.

SACLEUX (C.) Dictionnaire français-swahili.
pp. 989. *Zanzibar*, 1891. 8°.   12910. aa. 42.

BUETTNER (C. G.) Wörterbuch der Suaheli-
Sprache. pp. 269. 1890. 8°. SACHAU (C. E.)
Lehrbücher, *etc.* Bd. 3.   12906. h.

A B CH. Syllabaire swahili. pp. 60.
Zanzibar, 1887. 12°.   12910. a. 31.

ALĪDĪNĀ SOMAJĪ LĪLĀṆĪ. Guide to the Swahili
language. pp. 204. *Bombay*, 1890. 8°.
                14150. b. 24.

BUETTNER (C. G.) Suaheli-Schriftstücke in arabischer Schrift. pp. 206. 1892. 8°. SACHAU
(C. E.) Lehrbücher, *etc.* Bd. 10. 12906. h.

M., A. C. Swahili Historical Reader. pp. 146.
Lond. 1894. 8°.   4429. a. 72.

NETTELBLADT (F. v.) Suaheli-Dragoman.
pp. 256. *Leip.* 1891. 8°.   12910. aa. 45.

RADDATZ (H.) Die Suahili-Sprache. pp. 176.
Leip. 1892. 8°.   12906. bbb. 36.

SAINT PAUL ILLAIRE (W. v.) Suaheli Handbuch.
pp. 202. 1890. 8°. SACHAU (C. E.) Lehrbücher, *etc.* Bd. 2.   12906. h.

SEIDEL (A.) Praktische Grammatik der Suaheli-
Sprache. pp. 182. 1890. 8°. Die Kunst der
Polyglottie, *etc.* Th. 32.   12902. c.

SLACK (C.) Introduction to Swahili. pp. 16.
Lond. 1891. 8°.   12910. a. 24.

BUETTNER (C. G.) Anthologie aus der Suaheli-
Litteratur. 2 Th. *Berl.* 1894. 8°. 12411. g. 25.
—— Lieder und Geschichten der Suaheli.
pp. 202. 1894. 8°. Beiträge zur Volks- und
Völkerkunde. Bd. 3.   10007. f.

TAYLOR (W. E.) African Aphorisms ; Saws
from Swahili-land. pp. 182. *Lond.* 1891. 8°.
                4429. aa. 7.

AFRICAN LANGUAGES—*continued.*

LITURGIES. Rome, *Church of.* Vicariat apostolique de Zanzibar. pp. 443. *Zanzibar*, 1893. 12°.   3365. a. 39.

WRAY (J. A.) Introduction to the Taita language. pp. 128. *Lond.* 1894. 8°. 12910. aa. 69.

VIVINO. Hymns in the language of Taveta. pp. 30. *Lond.* 1894. 8°.   4429. a. 121.

OTYI READING-BOOK. Reading Book in the Tshi language. pp. 200. *Basel*, 1892. 8°.
12910. a. 39.

ELMSLIE (W. A.) Table of Concords of the Tumbuka Language, *etc. Aberd.* 1891. 8°.
12910. aa. 44.

—— Notes on the Tumbuka Language. pp. 32. *Aberd.* 1891. 8°.   12910. aa. 43.

PEREIRA DO NASCIMENTO (J.) Grammatica do Umbundu. pp. 105. 1894. 8°. Ac. Lisbon. *Sociedade de Geographia.* Boletim. 13ª serie. no. 1 & 2.   Ac. 6020.

WOHLRAB ( ) and JOHANSEN ( ) Shambaa-Lesefibel, (Usambara). pp. 48. *Berl.* 1892. 8°.
Pam. 47.

HYNDE (R. S.) Second Yao-English Primer. pp. 104. *Lond.* 1894. 8°.   12910. a. 37.
See also AMHARIC, GALLA AND TIGRE LANGUAGES.

AGEN. Agen. Inventaire-Sommaire des archives. 1884. 4°. Collection des Inventaires-sommaires.   1814–15. b., *etc.*

ANDRIEU (J.) Une Province à travers les siècles. 2 tom. *Paris*, 1893. 8°.   10171. dd. 3.

—— Excentriques et Grotesques littéraires de l'Agenais. pp. 50. *Paris*, 1895. 8°.
011824. k. 32.

CLAUDIN (A.) Le premier livre imprimé à Agen. pp. 21. *Paris*, 1894. 8°.   Pam. 6.

DUCOM (A.) La commune d'Agen. pp. 330. *Paris*, 1892. 8°.   10171. e. 7.

DURENGUES ( ) L'Église d'Agen. pp. 750. *Agen*, 1894. 8°.   4629. ee. 2.

AGENCY, Law of. EVANS (W.) Law relating to the Remuneration of Commission Agents. pp. 298. *Lond.* 1891. 8°.   6376. d. 20.

PEARSON-GEE (A. B.) The new Factors Act annotated. pp. 100. *Lond.* 1890. 8°. 6376. d. 9.

PEARSON (T. A.) Law of Agency in British India. pp. 500. 1890. 8°. Tagore Law Lectures.   5318. aaa.

WRIGHT (E. B.) Law of Principal and Agent. pp. 428. *Lond.* 1894. 8°.   6325. df. 25.

AGNOSTICISM: SCEPTICISM.

ABBOT (F. E.) The Way out of Agnosticism. pp. 75. *Bost.* 1890. 8°.   4018. e. 36.

AGNOSCO. Outlines of Rationalistic Philosophy. pp. 64. *Lond.* 1894. 8°.   8469. aaa. 48.

AGNOSTIC FAITH. Agnostic Faith. pp. 59. *Lond.* 1894. 8°.   4018. aa. 6.

DARBY (J. N.) Irrationalism of Infidelity. pp. 354. *Lond.* 1890. 8°.   4017. f. 13.

DVĀRAKĀDĀSA. Atheism and Agnosticism. pp. 29. *Lahore*, 1888. 8°.   4371. ee. 3. (2.)

FIGGIS (J. B.) Agnosticism and related subjects. pp. 94. *Lond.* 1891. 8°.   4018. bbb. 27.

FITZGERALD (P. F.) Protest against Agnosticism. pp. 155. *Lond.* 1890. 8°.   4016. h. 12.

KOSMOS. Religion of Agnostic Philosophy in relation to Christianism. pp. 84. *Calcutta*, 1892. 8°.   4372. cc. 22. (8.)

AGNOSTICISM, etc.—*continued.*

MORDEN (J. W.) Agnosticism found Wanting. pp. 180. *Lond.* 1891. 8°.   4018. g. 32.

ROBERTY (E. de) Agnosticisme. pp. 164. *Paris*, 1892. 8°.   4017. e. 18.

STEPHEN (L.) An Agnostic's Apology. pp. 380. *Lond.* 1893. 8°.   4018. c. 22.

WACE (H.) Christianity and Agnosticism. pp. 339. *Edinb.* 1895. 8°.   4018. ff. 17.
See also ATHEISM: CHRISTIANITY.

AGRA. MIRZA AMIR BEG. Handbook of Agra, *etc. Lucknow*, 1891. 8°.   Pam. 88.

SATYACHANDRA MUKHOPĀDHYAYA. Traveller's Guide to Agra. pp. 176. *Delhi*, 1892. 8°.
10057. aa. 17.

AGRICULTURE.—General: Farm Management, etc.

Ac. *Congrès d'Agriculture.* Compte-rendu. *Paris, etc.*, 1889, *etc.* 8°.   Ac. 3382.

—— Ithaca. *Cornell University. College of Agriculture.* Annual Report. *Ithaca*, 1889, *etc.* 8°.
Ac. 2692. h.

—— London. *R. Agricultural Society of England.* Elements of Agriculture. pp. 486. *Lond.* 1892. 8°.   07076. e. 41.

ALLEN (R. L.) New American Farm Book. pp. 526. *N.Y.* 1879. 8°.   07076. e. 54.

ARRHENIUS (J.) Jordbrukslärans hufvudgrunder. pp. 352. *Norrköping*, 1889. 8°.   07076. e. 28.

BARNARD (C.) Talks about the Soil in its relation to plants. pp. 127. *N.Y.* 1894. 8°.
7006. aaa. 20.

BARNARD (E. A.) Manuel d'Agriculture pp. 534. *Montréal*, 1895. 8°.   07077. g. 6.

BELEZE (G.) Dictionnaire universel de la vie pratique, *etc. Paris*, 1890, *etc.* 8°.   012216. i.

BERGSTRAND (C. E.) Handbok för Jordbrukare. 3 del. *Stockholm*, 1894. 8°.   07076. e. 57.

BERTHAULT (F.) Les Prairies. pp. 223. 1894. 8°. Encyclopédie scientifique.   8709. g.

BOITEL (A.) Agriculture générale. pp. 607. *Paris*, 1891. 8°.   7077. ee. 8.

Bos (J. R.) Zoologie für Landwirte. pp. 182. 1892. 8°. Thaer-Bibliothek. Bd. 78. 7078. d.

—— Agricultural Zoology. pp. 256. *Lond.* 1894. 8°.   7204. a. 30.

BRIGHT (T.) Agricultural Valuer's Assistant. pp. 186. *Lond.* 1892. 8°.   7075. a. 4.

BUCHENBERGER (A.) Agrarwesen und Agrarpolitik. 1892, *etc.* 8°. WAGNER (A.) Handbuch der politischen Oekonomie. Hptabth. 3. Tl. 3.   08207. h.

BURGESS (A. T.) First stage Agriculture. pp. 124. *Lond.* 1893. 8°.   7077. de. 38.

BUSSARD (L.) L'Agriculture. pp. 508. *Paris*, 1895. 8°.   07077. g. 4.

CASSELL (J.) Agricultural Readers. "Downton" Series. *Lond.* 1891, *etc.* 8°.   7077. de.

CHRISTENSEN (C.) Landbrugets Kulturplanter. pp. 128. *Kjøbenh.* 1891. 8°.   07076. k. 12.

CICCONE (A.) Protezione e Agricoltura. 1892. 4°. Ac. Naples. *R. Accademia di Scienze.* Atti. Vol. 25.   Ac. 96/2.

COMES (O.) Crittogamia agraria. pp. 600. *Napoli*, 1891. 8°.   07076. m. 10.

CONVERT (F.) Les Enterprises agricoles. pp. 480. *Montpellier*, 1890. 8°.   8277. aa. 63.

COTTON (*Sir* A. T.) Lecture on Agriculture. pp. 24. *Dorking*, 1893. 8°.   7074. c. 10. (9.)

AGRICULTURE.—General: Farm Management, etc.—*continued.*

FAWCETT (W.) Agriculture. pp. 114. 1893. 8°. Ac. Kingston. *Institute of Jamaica.* Special Publications. No. 3.   Ac. 1958/2.

FRANCIS (S.) Tables and calculated Results for Farmers. pp. 256. *Lond.* 1894. 32°. 8548. a. 31.

FREAM (W.) Soils and their Properties. pp. 176. 1890. 8°. Bell's Agricultural Series. 7075. de.

GUDE (J.) Lærebok i Landkunna. pp. 228. *Bergen,* 1889. 8°.   10004. aa. 5.

HEUZÉ (G.) La Petite Culture. pp. 401. *Paris,* 1891. 8°.   07076. e. 23.

HOUDAILLE (F.) Météorologie agricole. pp. 542. *Montpellier,* 1893. 8°.   8756. dd. 14.

GAYE (S.) The Great World's Farm. pp. 365. *Lond.* 1893. 8°.   07023. k. 5.

GOLTZ (T. A. G. L. v. der) Agricoltura. 1886, 87. 8°. Biblioteca dell' economista. Ser. 3. Vol. 12.   8205. l.

GOMIS (C.) Meteorología y agricultura populars. pp. 176. 1888. 8°. Ac. Barcelona. *Associació d'Excursions.* Biblioteca popular. Vol. 5.   Ac. 8883.

G. B. & I. *Board of Agriculture.* Journal of the Board of Agriculture. *Lond.* 1894, *etc.* 8°. N.R.

—— Leaflets. *Lond.* 1894, *etc.* 8°. 07076. l.

ITALY. *Ministero di Agricoltura.* Coltivazioni sperimentali promosse dal Ministero. *Roma,* 1889, *etc.* 8°.   07076. m. 8.

—— Risultati delle coltivazioni sperimentali. 1885–88. pp. 328. *Roma,* 1889. 8°. 07076. m. 9.

LAURIE (A. P.) The Food of Plants. pp. 77. *Lond.* 1893. 8°.   7054. de. 3.

LAWES (*Sir* J. B.) Memoranda of the experiments on the farm at Rothamsted. pp. 87. *Lond.* 1893. 8°.   7078. i. 31.

ROTHAMSTED. Rothamsted Jubilee Fund. Report of the Executive Committee. pp. 40. *Lond.* 1893. 8°.   07076. k. 13.

LAWRENCE (W. T.) Agriculture. pp. 184. *Lond.* 1891. 8°.   07076. e. 30.

LECOUTEUX (É.) L'Agriculture à grands rendements. pp. 363. *Paris,* 1892. 12°. 7707. de. 37.

LE FEUVRE (R. F.) La Quinta Normal de Agricultura. pp. 424. *Paris,* 1889. 8°. 7077. i. 3.

LONG (J.) Handbook for Farmers. pp. 227. *Lond.* 1892. 8°.   7074. e. 7.

MALDEN (W. J.) Tillage. pp. 156. 1891. 8°. Bell's Agricultural Series.   7075. de.

MARTIN (J. M.) Tabular Chart of Agricultural Prices. *Exeter,* 1894. 8°.   8229. de. 39.

MEITZEN (P. A.) Agricoltura. 1886, 87. 8°. Biblioteca dell' Economista. Ser. 3. Vol. 12.   8205. l.

MUIR (J.) Agriculture. pp. 343. *Lond.* 1895. 8°.   07076. e. 59.

NOWACKI (A. J.) Praktische Bodenkunde. pp. 180. 1892. 8°. Thaer-Bibliothek. 7078. d.

PABST (C.) Électricité agricole. pp. 376. *Paris,* 1894. 8°.   8758. ccc. 2.

P.P. *Berlin.* Journal für Landwirtschaft. *Berl.* 1894, *etc.* 8°.   P.P. 2350. d.

—— London. *Mark Lane Express.* Agricultural Annual. *Lond.* 1892, *etc.* 8°. P.P. 2487. ta.

PETRI (L.) Computisteria Agraria. pp. 211. *Milano,* 1892. 8°.   012200. h. 97.

POHL (J.) Landwirtschaftliche Betriebslehre. *Leipz.* 1885, *etc.* 8°.   7077. h. 4.

POTT (E.) Die landwirtschaftlichen Futtermittel. pp. 730. *Berl.* 1889. 8°.   07293. l. 4.

AGRICULTURE.—General: Farm Management, etc.—*continued.*

POTTER (M. C.) Text-book of Agricultural Botany. pp. 250. 1893. 8°. University Extension Series.   012202. g.

SARTORI (F.) Grande e piccola coltivazione. pp. 144. *Milano,* 1891. 8°.   07076. l. 4.

SCOTT (J.) Agricultural Surveying. pp. 128. *Lond.* 1884. 8°.   8703. ccc. 50.

SMYTHE (W. E.) Greatest Irrigated Farm in the World. Kern County Land Co. pp. 24. *San Francisco,* 1893. 8°.   Pam. 1.

SOWERBY (W.) Thorough Cultivation. pp. 250. *Lond.* 1895. 8°.   07076. e. 58.

STEPHENS (H.) Catechism of practical Agriculture. pp. 85. *Edinb.* 1895. 8°. 7077. c. 2.

TRESCA (A.) Le matériel agricole moderne. *Paris,* 1893, *etc.* 8°.   07076. f.

U.S. *Dept. of Agriculture.* Experiment Station Bulletin. *Wash.* 1889, *etc.* 8°.   7053. e. 17.

—— Experiment Station Record. *Wash.* 1889, *etc.* 8°.   7053. e. 19.

VALLIS (S.) The Cottage Farmer. pp. 74. *Lond.* 1893. 8°.   7078. bbb. 48.

VIENNA. *Internationaler land- und forstwirthschaftlicher Congress.* Bericht über die Verhandlungen des Congresses 1890. *Wien,* 1890. 8°.   07076. i. 1.

VILLE (G.) La Production Agricole définie par la science. pp. 43. *Paris,* 1892. 12°.   7074. e. 8. (10.)

—— La conquête du soleil. pp. 39. *Paris,* 1892. 12°.   7074. e. 8. (9.)

WAHNSCHAFFE (F.) Guide to the examination of Soils. pp. 177. *Philad.* 1892. 8°. 7106. ff. 14.

WALLACE (R. H.) Agriculture. pp. 352. *Lond.* 1895. 8°.   7077. bbb. 1.

WARINGTON (R.) Notes on the properties of Soils, etc. pp. 24. *Lond.* 1894. 8°.   Pam. 1.

—— On the relations of Agricultural Art and Natural Science. pp. 36. *Lond.* 1895. 8°. Pam. 1.

WEBB (H. J.) Elementary Agriculture. pp. 196. *Lond.* 1891. 8°.   07076. e. 32.

—— Advanced Agriculture. pp. 672. 1894. 8°. Longmans' Advanced Science Manuals.   8709. h.

WHITNEY (M.) Physical properties of Soils in relation to Moisture and Crop Distribution. pp. 90. 1892. 8°. U.S. *Depart. of Agriculture.* Bulletin. No. 4.   7053. e. 40.

WOLFF (E. T.) Farm Foods. pp. 365. *Lond.* 1895. 8°.   07293. g. 22.

WOOD (T.) Animal and Plant Life with reference to Agriculture. 1891. 8°. Blackie's Science Readers. Nos. IV., V.   8703. aa.

WRIGHT (R. P.) Principles of Agriculture. pp. 206. 1891. 8°. Blackie's Science Text-Books.   8703. bb.

YOUATT (W.) The complete Grazier. pp. 1086. *Lond.* 1893. 8°.   7291. d. 13.

See also infra: Various Countries: LAND.

Banks. *See* BANKING.

Chemistry. *See* CHEMISTRY, *Applied.*

Crops and Diseases of Plants.

See supra: General : BOTANY, *Economic:* CORN : ENSILAGE : GRASSES.

Dairy Farming.

See DAIRY MANAGEMENT.

Education.

BUISSON (B.) Agricultural Teaching in Foreign Countries. pp. 40. *Lond.* 1891. 8°.   7074. c. 10. (4.)

AGRICULTURE.—Education—continued.

INNES (T.) Technical Instruction in Agriculture. pp. 23. *Edinb.* 1891. 8°.   7074. e. 10. (6.)

KELLER (A.) Sulla istruzione agraria nelle Università. 1894. 8°. Ac. Venice. *Istituto di Scienze.* Atti. Ser. 7, Tom. 5.   Ac. 110.

PECILE (G. L.) L' Insegnamento agrario in Italia. pp. 67. *Torino,* 1894. 8°.   7076. g. 2.

P.P. *Cirencester.* Agricultural Students' Gazette. *Cirencester,* 1889, etc. 8°.   P.P. 2295. c.

SAUNDERS (W.) Agricultural Colleges. pp. 111. *Ottawa,* 1886. 8°.   07076. i. 21.

Farm Buildings : Machinery, etc.

CHICAGO. *Columbian Exposition.* Official Catalogue. Pt. I. Agriculture Building, *etc.* pp. 327. *Chicago,* 1893. 8°.   7958. bb. 18.

CLARKE (A. D.) Modern Farm Buildings. pp. 147. *Lond.* 1895. 8°.   7817. bb. 5.

KLEIN (A.) Danske Landbrugs Bygninger. pp. 55. *Kjøbenh.* 1893. 8°.   7815. cc.

KUTSCHER (H.) Plan- und Situationszeichnen. pp. 50. 1892. 8°. Thaer-Bibliothek. 7078. d.

SCOTT (J.) Farm Buildings. pp. 167. *Lond.* 1884. 8°.   8703. ccc. 47.

—— Barn Implements and Machines. pp. 199. *Lond.* 1884. 8°.   8703. ccc. 48.

—— Farm Roads, Fences and Gates. pp. 123. *Lond.* 1883. 8°.   8703. ccc. 46.

SEELHORST (C. von) Die Belastung der Grundrente durch das Gebäudekapital in der Landwirtschaft. pp. 78. *Jena,* 1890. 8°.   8226. ff. 33. (3.)

WEIGH-BRIDGE. The Weigh-Bridge for the Farmer. pp. 32. *Stirling,* 1892. 8°. 7293. d. 27.

Insurance. *See* INSURANCE.

Irrigation. *See* IRRIGATION.

Live Stock.

See ANIMALS, *Domestic* : CATTLE : HORSE : PIG : POULTRY : SHEEP, *etc.*

Market, Vegetable and Fruit Farming.
See GARDENING.

Manures. *See* MANURES.

Tenures and Rent.

See infra : *Various Countries* : LAND, *Tenures.*

Tropical.

NICHOLLS (H. A. A.) Elementary Text-book of Tropical Agriculture. pp. 221. *Kingston, Jam.* 1891. 8°.   7054. df. 4.

—— Text-book of Tropical Agriculture. pp. 312. *Lond.* 1892. 8°.   7074. e. 6.

SEMLER (H.) Die tropische Agrikultur. 4 Bde. *Wismar,* 1886–93. 8°.   07077. i. 3.

WOHLTMANN (F.) Handbuch der tropischen Agrikultur. *Leipz.* 1892, *etc.* 8°.   07076. k.

See also infra : *India.*

Agriculture and Agricultural Classes in various Countries.

Algeria.

BRIEZ (J. L.) Calendrier agricole. Guide du cultivateur algérien. pp. 260. *Alger,* 1880. 8°.   07076. i. 18.

LESCARE (J.) L'Agriculture algérienne. pp. 360. *Paris,* 1892. 12°.   07076. e. 47.

SAUVAIGO (E.) Les cultures sur le littoral de la Méditerranee. pp. 318. *Paris,* 1894. 12°.   7078. e. 5.

AGRICULTURE.—Australasia.

Australasia.

WALLACE (R.) Rural economy of Australia and New Zealand. pp. 541. *Lond.* 1891. 8°.   07076. i. 3.

NEW SOUTH WALES. *Department of Agriculture.* Agricultural Gazette. *Sydney,* 1890, etc. 8°.   P.P. 2304. b.

—— Miscellaneous Publications. *Sydney,* 1892, etc. 8°.   07076. k.

—— *Commissioners for the Columbian Exposition, Chicago.* Agriculture in New South Wales. pp. 50. *Sydney,* 1893. 8°.   7958. g. 22.

PERCEVAL (W. B.) Farming and Labour in New Zealand. pp. 59. *Lond.* 1892. 8°.   Pam. 1.

See also LAND, *Tenures.*

Austria-Hungary.

COMMENDA (H.) Materialen zur landeskundlichen Bibliographie Oberösterreichs. pp. 790. *Linz,* 1891. 8°.   011901. e. 4.

CSERHÁTI (S.) Die Ergebnisse der Tiefcultur in Ungarn. pp. 86. *Wien,* 1892. 8°.   Pam. 1.

GRABMAYR (C. v.) Schuldnoth und Agrar-Reform. pp. 211. *Meran,* 1894. 8°. 8276. g. 29.

SCHAMBERGER (G.) Die Geschichte des Bauernstandes. pp. 172. *Pram,* 1891. 8°. 08276. i. 27.

Belgium.

SOIGNIE (J. de) La crise agricole. pp. 30. *Gand,* 1890. 8°.   08276. i. 2. (12.)

Canada.

CANADA. *Department of Agriculture.* Report on Canada and its agricultural resources. pp. 30. *Ottawa,* 1885. 8°.   Pam. 86.

—— Visit of tenant-farmer delegates to Canada, 1890. pp. 262. *Lond.* 1891. 8°.   07076. i. 13.

—— Free Farms. Manitoba, Alberta, Assiniboia, Saskatchewan. *Lond.* 1890. *s. sh.* fol. Pam. 86.

—— What farmers say. Letters from Farmers in Western Canada. pp. 16. *Winnipeg,* 1892. 8°.   10470. dd. 30. (7.)

—— Farming and Ranching in Western Canada. pp. 40. *Ottawa,* 1893. 8°.   Pam. 1.

QUEBEC, *Province of.* Concours provincial de Merite Agricole. *Québec,* 1891, *etc.* 8°. 07076. g.

RITCHIE (P. R.) Manitoba and N.W. Territories. Report of a tour. pp. 52. *Ottawa,* 1892. 8°.   Pam. 86.

SAUNDERS (W.) Agricultural Colleges and Experimental Farm Stations. pp. 111. *Ottawa,* 1886. 8°.   07076. i. 21.

See also CANADA, *Topography.*

Chili.

LE FEUVRE (R. F.) L'Agriculture au Chili. pp. 48. *Paris,* 1890. 8°.   7074. k. 12. (5.)

Denmark.

RIEGELS (F.) Forslag til Landbrugets Organisation. pp. 75. *Kjøbenh.* 1891. 8°.   7074. e. 11. (5.)

WINKEL (J.) Landbrugets Benyttelse, 1872–90. pp. 48. *Kjøbenh.* 1892. 4°.   8245. ff. 36.

See also LAND, *Tenures.*

Egypt.

WALLACE (R.) University of Edinburgh.—Agricultural Department. Address on Egyptian Agriculture. pp. 26. *Edinb.* 1891. 8°.   7074. i. 8. (10.)

England.

AG. London. *R. Agricultural Society.* Charter, Bye-laws and Privileges of Members. pp. 32. *Lond.* 1892. 8°.   7074. i. 8. (12.)

AGRICULTURE.—England—*continued.*

ANDREW (P. H.) Is the present Low Price of Produce beneficial to Prosperity. pp. 9. *Barnstaple*, 1892. 8°.   8228. aaaa. 17. (12.)

CALLIE (J. W. S.) Criticisms on the pamphlet " Is the present Low Price of Agricultural Produce beneficial." pp. 9. *Barnstaple*, 1892. 8°.
8228. aaaa. 17. (14.)

BRAMAH (E.) Farming and why I turned it up. pp. 181. *Lond.* 1894. 8°.   7074. e. 13.

CONNELL (I.) Farmer's Legal Hand-Book. pp. 192. 1894. 8°. Scottish Chamber of Agriculture Series.   7074. e.

DAY (J.) Agriculture. Way to overcome the crisis. *Ashford*, 1892, *etc.* 8°.   8285. aa.

DIXON (H. H.) Law of the Farm. pp. 712. *Lond*, 1892. 8°.   2230. a. 2.

FARMER. A Remedy for Bad Times. pp. 28. *Lond.* 1893. 8°.   Pam. 1.

GARNIER (R. M.) History of the English Landed Interest. pp. 406. *Lond.* 1892. 8°. 2238. cc. 14.

GILLESPIE (A.) New Testament of Agriculture. pp. 241. *Newcastle*, 1892. 4°.   6325. i. 1.

HOBSON (J. A.) Co-operative Labour upon the Land. pp. 140. *Lond.* 1895. 8°. 08276. ee. 5.

JOINT STOCK FARMING. Joint Stock Farming. pp. 13. *Lond.* 1893. 8°.   7074. e. 10. (11.)

LALANDE (F. L. M. A.) L'agriculture anglaise et le libre-échange. pp. 38. *Paris*, 1885. 8°.
7032. h. 7. (7.)

LEFEVRE (*Right Hon.* G. J. S.) Agrarian Tenures. pp. 313. *Lond.* 1893. 8°.   6306. bb. 16.

MORLEY (*Right Hon.* J.) Rural Reforms. Two speeches. pp. 27. *Westminster*, 1891. 8°.
Pam. 68.

PELL (A.) The making of the Land in England. pp. 22. *Lond.* 1887. 8°. 7074. i. 8. (3.)

RICHARDS (W.) Agricultural Distress. pp. 130. *Lond.* 1893. 8°.   08227. i. 13.

ROBINSON (T.) The Next Revolution : agricultural remedy for the present distress. pp. 11. *Lond.* 1894. 8°.   Pam. 82.

ROGERS (J. E. T.) Six Centuries of Work and Wages. pp. 591. *Lond.* 1890. 8°. 08277. g. 19.

SHELDON (J. P.) Future of British Agriculture. pp. 158. *Lond.* 1893. 8°.   7077. de. 36.

VILLE (G.) The Perplexed Farmer : how is he to meet alien competition ? pp. 208. *Lond.* 1891. 8°.   07076. e. 26.

WINEARLS (W. G.) Proposals for two Bills. pp. 18. *Swaffham*, 1887. fol.   8228. l. 17. (3.)

BURNE (J. B.) Parson and Peasant. pp. 260. *Lond.* 1891. 8°.   012357. e. 4.

GARNIER (R. M.) Annals of the British Peasantry. pp. 460. *Lond.* 1895. 8°.   08277. g. 20.

G. B. & I. *National Liberal Federation.* Condition of the Rural Population. pp. 27. *Westminster*, 1891. 8°.   8282. ff. 12. (4.)

HASBACH (W.) Die englischen Landarbeiter in dem letzten hundert Jahren. pp. 410. 1894. 8°. *Ac. Leipsic. Verein für Socialpolitik.* Schriften. Th. 59.   Ac. 2322.

HEATH (R.) The English Peasant. pp. 382. *Lond.* 1893. 8°.   8277. ee. 27.

KEBBEL (T. E.) The Agricultural Labourer. pp. 271. *Lond.* 1893. 8°.   08276. e. 51.

LIFE. Life in our Villages. pp. 192. *Lond.* 1891. 8°.   8139. aa. 46.

LONDON. *Land Restoration League.* Special Report, 1891. *Lond.* 1891. 8°.   Pam. 82.

AGRICULTURE.—England—*continued.*

LONDON. *Land Restoration League.* Special Report, 1892. pp. 22. *Lond.* 1893. 8°.
8282. ff. 11. (9.)

STUBBS (C. W.) The Land and the Labourers. pp. 228. *Lond.* 1891. 8°.   08276. e. 6.
See also LAND, *Tenures.*

France.

AMESTOY (C.) Le bail à métairie. pp. 55. *Bayonne*, 1891. 12°.   8228. aaaa. 19. (4.)

BAUDRILLART (H. J. L.) Les populations agricoles de la France. 1° 2° série. pp. 643. *Paris*, 1888. 8°.   08276. h. 27.

—— Les populations agricoles de la France. 3° série. pp. 654. *Paris*, 1893. 8°. 08276. h. 52.

BOUZERAND (L.) Réflexions d'un paysan sur la culture. pp. 152. *Paris*, 1890. 8°. 07076. e. 20.

BRUTAILS (J. A.) Étude sur les populations rurales du Roussillon au moyen âge. pp. 314. *Paris*, 1891. 8°.   08276. k. 5.

BERNIER (P. D.) Essai sur le Tiers-État rural de Basse-Normandie au XVIII° siécle. pp. 315. *Paris*, 1892. 8°.   08276. g. 27.

CORÉ (F.) Esquisse de l'historique agricole de la France. pp. 211. *Paris*, 1890. 18°. 07076. e. 14.

DUBOIS DE LHERMONT (L.) L'Organisation agricole et la Sécheresse, 1893. pp. 192. *Orthez*, 1893. 8°.   07076. i. 16.

LAVOISIER (A. L.) Statistique agricole et projets de réformes. pp. 186. *Paris*, 1895. 8°.
7077. aa. 3.

MAURICE (F.) L'Agriculture et la Question sociale. pp. 380. *Paris*, 1892. 12°. 08276. f. 38.

NOTTELLE (L.) The French Peasantry since the Revolution. pp. 64. *Birmingham*, 1892. 8°.
8275. aa. 57.

PRUDHOMME (A.) Agriculture du département de la Meuse. pp. 374. *Bar-le-Duc*, 1893. 8°.
07028. l. 25.

REROLLE (L.) Du Colonage partiaire et du Métayage. pp. 674. *Paris*, 1888. 8°. 8282. f. 28.

ROCQUIGNY DU FAYEL (H. M. R. de) Les Syndicats agricoles et le socialisme agraire. pp. 344. *Paris*, 1893. 8°.   08275. e. 6.

SAUVAIGO (É.) Les cultures sur le littoral de la Méditerranée. pp. 318. *Paris*, 1894. 12°.
7078. e. 5.

TIXIER AUBERGIER (E.) Considérations sur la crise agricole. pp. 107. *Paris*, 1895. 8°.
08226. f. 26.

ZOLLA (D.) Code manuel du propriétaire-agriculteur. pp. 308. *Paris*, 1894. 12°. 7078. e. 9.
See also LAND, *Tenures.*

Germany.

BARRE (E.) Der ländliche Wucher. pp. 56. *Berl.* 1890. 8°.   Pam. 23.

BERGER (P.) Doppelwährung und Landwirthschaft. pp. 32. 1891. 8°. Deutsche Zeit- und Streit-Fragen. Neue Folge. Heft 78. 12209. f.

FRANKENSTEIN (K.) Die Arbeiterfrage in der deutschen Landwirthschaft. pp. 326. *Berl.* 1893. 8°.   08276. k. 22.

GOLTZ (T. A. G. L. v. der) Die ländliche Arbeiterklasse. pp. 300. *Jena*, 1893. 8°.
8277. h. 27.

GRABMAYR (C. v.) Landwirthschaft und Realexekution. pp. 117. *Meran*, 1894. 8°.
5549. de. 10.

JUVAN (F.) Bericht über eine durch Deutschland landwirthschaftliche Studienreise. pp. 100. *Klagenfurt*, 1890. 8°.   7074. k. 12. (4.)

AGRICULTURE.—Germany—continued.

KNAPP (G. F.) Die Landarbeiter in Knechtschaft und Freiheit. pp. 92. *Leipz.* 1891. 8°.
8277. ee. 28. (4.)

MANCKE (W.) Ein Kompromiss des Agrarstaats mit dem Industriestaat. pp. 134.
Berl. 1894. 8°. 08276. g. 74.

SKAŔŻYŃSKI (W. v.) Die Agrarkrisis und die Mittel zu ihrer Abhilfe. pp. 127.
Berl. 1894. 8°. 08276. i. 39.

MEYER (G.) Über die Schwankungen in dem Bedarf an Handarbeit in der deutschen Landwirtschaft. pp. 100. 1893. 8°. Staatswissenschaftliche Studien. Bd. 5. 8207. h.

MORRE (C.) Die Arbeiter-Partei und der Bauernstand. pp. 75. *Graz,* 1890. 8°. Pam. 83.

SEIFARTH (F.) Die Berufsstatistik des deutschen Reiches. *Heidelberg,* 1892, etc. 8°. 8206. bb. 30.

SOHNREY (H.) Der Zug vom Lande und die soziale Revolution. pp. 138. *Leipz.* 1894. 8°.
08276. i. 35.

See also LAND, *Tenures.*

India.

BENSON (C.) Records of the Saidápet Experimental Farm. pp. 251. *Madras,* 1885. 8°.
7073. dd. 15.

BHUPĀLACHANDRA VASU. Notes on Indian Agriculture. pp. 251. *Calcutta,* 1893. 8°. 07077. f. 1.

FRASER (A. T.) Land improvement in India. pp. 22. *Bombay,* 1892. 8°. 07076. g. 6.

MOTILĀLA KASHALCHAND SHĀH. Principles of Agriculture for India. pp. 286.
Ahmedabad, 1888. 8°. 07076. e. 16.

WILSON (H. M.) Irrigation in India. 1891. 4°. U.S. *Geological Survey.* Annual Report. No. 12. 1828. aa.

POELCHER (J. A.) Report on the Improvement of Indian Agriculture. pp. 460. *Lond.* 1893. 8°.
07076. l. 6.

See also LAND, *Tenures.*

Indies, Dutch.

MOREU (H. H.) Leerboekje der aardrijkskunde van Nederlandsch Oost-Indië. pp. 48.
Batavia, 1885. 8°. Pam. 88.

Italy.

WEBER (M.) Die römische Agrargeschichte. pp. 281. *Stuttgart,* 1891. 8°. 5254. bbb. 29.

CAREGA DI MURICCE (F.) Estimo rurale. pp. 161. *Milano,* 1890. 8°. 12206. b. 66.

GUFFANTI (A.) La crisi e la questione sociale agraria. pp. 287. *Stradella,* 1891. 8°.
08276. k. 11.

LEVI (E.) Le Condizioni dell' Agricoltura. pp. 249. *Torino,* 1887. 8°. 08227. de. 25.

PANIZZA (M.) Risultati dell' inchiesta sulle condizioni sanitarie dei lavoratori della terra. pp. 398. *Roma,* 1890. 8°. 8776. ff. 36.

PECILE (G. L.) L' Insegnamento agrario in Italia. pp. 67. *Torino,* 1894. 8°. 7076. g. 2.

RABBENO (A.) Manuale della mezzeria. pp. 196. *Milano,* 1895. 16°. 012200. h. 76.

SANTANGELO SPOTO (I.) L' Homestead e le condizioni della Proprietà in Italia. pp. 30.
Palermo, 1890. 8°. 08267. k. 4. (14.)

—— Paysan agriculteur de Torremaggiore. 1891. 8°. Ac. Paris. *Société des études pratiques.* Les ouvriers des deux mondes. Série 2. Fasc. 23. 8282. f. 18.

SAUVAIGO (É.) Les cultures sur le littoral de la Méditerranée. pp. 318. *Paris,* 1894. 12°.
7078. e. 5.

AGRICULTURE.—Italy—continued.

VITERBI (A.) Gli Infortunii agricoli. pp. 20. *Mantova,* 1891. 8°. 8277. h. 20. (9.)
See also LAND, *Tenures.*

Japan.

FESCA (M.) Beiträge zur Kenntniss der japanischen Landwirthschaft. *Berl.* 1890, etc. 8°.
7076. ee. 3.

—— Atlas. 1890. fol. 1827. c. 8.

Netherlands.

NETHERLANDS. Uitkomsten van het onderzoek naar du toestand van den Landbouw in Nederland. 4 Dl. *'s-Gravenh.* 1890. 8°. 08225. l. 10.

New South Wales and New Zealand.

See supra : AUSTALASIA.

Palestine.

NEIL (J.) Land Tenure in ancient times as preserved in Palestine. pp. 49. *Lond.* 1891. 8°.
08276. g. 6.

VOGELSTEIN (H.) Die Landwirthschaft in Palästina zur Zeit der Misnâh. *Berl.* 1894, etc. 8°.
4034. m.

Rome. *See supra :* ITALY.

Roumania.

ARION (C. C.) La Situation du paysan en Roumanie. pp. 127. *Paris,* 1895. 8°. 08277. h. 2.

Russia.

MIKLASHEVSKY (I.) Die Entwicklung des landwirthschaftlichen Bildungswesens in Russland. pp. 48. *Wien,* 1892. 8°. 8226. g. 40. (12.)

Scotland.

JOHNSTON (C. N.) Agricultural Holdings (Scotland) Acts 1883 & 1889. pp. 124.
Edinb. 1891. 8°. 6583. b. 22.

MACKENZIE (W. J.) Hope for the Farm Servant. pp. 79. *Elgin,* 1887. 8°. 8277. a. 59. (1.)

RANKINE (J.) Lecture on the Agricultural Holdings, Scotland, Act, 1883. pp. 72.
Edinb. 1894. 8°. 6583. a. 6.

See also supra : England : LAND, *Tenures.*

Spain.

MARTÍN CONTRERAS (E.) *Count de la Oliva.* La revolución agraria. pp. 149. *Madrid,* 1893. 8°.
08275. e. 5.

MARTÍNEZ Y GONZÁLEZ (S.) La crisis de la agricultura. pp. 457. *Salamanca,* 1893. 8°.
08227. de. 37.

See also LAND, *Tenures.*

Switzerland.

Ac. Berne. *Centralkommission für Landeskunde.* Bibliographie der schweizerischen Landeskunde. *Bern,* 1893, etc. 8°. Ac. 3417.

SCHWENDIMANN (J.) Der Bauernstand des Kantons Luzern. pp. 206. *Luzern,* 1893. 8°.
8275. dd. 23.

United States.

ALDRICH (W.) Farming Corporations. pp. 255. *N.Y.,* 1892. 8°. 08227. de. 21.

CONNER (J. B.) Indiana Agriculture. pp. 24. *Indianap.* 1893. 8°. Pam. 1.

FORT COLLINS. *State Agricultural College.* Register of the Officers and Students.
Fort Collins, 1890, etc. 8°. 07076. f.

HYDE (J.) Geographical Concentration, a feature of American Agriculture. pp. 19.
Wash. 1893. 8°. Pam. 1.

LEVASSEUR (É.) L'Agriculture aux États-Unis. 1895. 8°. Ac. Paris. *Société d'Agriculture.* Mémoires. Tom. 136. Ac. 3408.

AGRICULTURE.—United States—cont.

MILLS (C. A.) Competition and the Farmer. pp. 22. *Camb., Mass.*, 1892. 8°. 8229. a. 17.

OETKEN (F.) Die Landwirthschaft in den Vereinigten Staaten. pp. 848. *Berl.* 1893. 8°. 08227. i. 28.

PEFFER (W. A.) The Farmer's Side. pp. 275. *N.Y.* 1891. 8°. 08276. f. 32.

STRANGE (D.) Farmers' Tariff Manual. pp. 363. *N.Y.* 1892. 8°. 08225. ee. 6.

U.S. *Dept. of Agriculture.* Report. New Series. *Wash.* 1883, *etc.* 8°. 7053. e. 27.

—— Index to the Reports of the Bureau of Statistics. *Wash.* 1889, *etc.* 8°. 7053. e. 28.

WOHLTMANN (F.) Landwirthschaftliche Reisestudien über Chicago und Nord-Amerika. pp. 440. *Breslau*, 1894. 8°. 10412. dd. 21.

Uruguay.

SAINT-FOIX (de) *Count.* Étude agricole sur l'Uruguay. pp. 51. *Montevideo*, 1887. 8°. 7075. f. 1. (4.)

AIGUEVIVES. DAVID (P.) Aiguevives et son Pèlerinage. pp. 46. *Bordeaux*, 1890. 8°. 10106. ff. 6. (5.)

AIGUILLON. ALIS (R. L.) Histoire de la ville d'Aiguillon. pp. 564. *Agen*, 1895. 8°. 010171. m. 41.

AILSA CRAIG. LAWSON (R.) Ailsa Craig. pp. 80. *Paisley*, 1888. 8°. 10369. ccc. 15.

AINOS. BATCHELOR (J.) The Ainu of Japan. pp. 336. *Lond.* 1892. 8°. 4429. df. 6.

HOWARD (B. D.) Life with Trans-Siberian Savages. pp. 209. *Lond.* 1893. 8°. 10075. bbb. 7.

LANDOR (A. H. S.) Alone with the Hairy Ainu. pp. 325. *Lond.* 1893. 8°. 010057. f. 23.

MACRITCHIE (D.) The Aïnos. pp. 69. 1888. 4°. P.P. *Leyden.* Internationales Archiv. Vol. 4. Supplement. P.P. 3863. h.

MORSE (E. S.) A Curious Aino Toy. pp. 7. *Salem*, 1893. 8°. 07703. i. 2. (15.)

AIR: ATMOSPHERE: ETHER.

ÅNGSTRÖM (K.) Beiträge zur Kenntniss der Absorption der Wärmestrahlen durch die verschiedenen Bestandtheile der Atmosphäre. pp. 29. 1889. 8°. Ac. Stockholm. *K. S. Vetenskaps Academi.* Bihang. Bd. 15. Ac. 1070/7.

ARCHBUTT ( ) Dust. pp. 20. *Derby*, 1891. 8°. 8708. i. 25. (9.)

BECQUEREL (A. E.) and (H.) Mémoire sur la température de l'air à la surface du sol et de la terre. 1888. 4°. Ac. Paris. *Acad. des Sciences.* Mémoires. Ser. 2, tom. 44. 2099. b.

BUELNA (E.) Constitución de la Atmósfera. pp. 114. *México*, 1889. 8°. 8756. c. 48.

DRUDE (P.) Physik des Aethers auf elektromagnetischer Grundlage. pp. 592. *Stuttgart*, 1894. 8°. 8757. h. 28.

GREELY (A. W.) Geography of the Air. 1892. 8°. National Geographic Magazine. Vol. 4. Ac. 6192.

HAASE (F. H.) Die atmosphärische Elektrizität. pp. 46. *Berl.* 1892. 8°. 8755. dd. 7. (8.)

HAWKINS (A. E.) A Term's Lessons on Air. pp. 188. *Lond.* 1893. 8°. 8756. dd. 11.

LEWES (V. B.) Air and Water. pp. 183. 1890. 8°. University Extension Series. 012202. g.

MENDENHALL (T. C.) Report of studies of Atmospheric Electricity. *Washington*, 1889. 4°. 8756. f. 40.

MERRY (A. S.) Interstellar Æther. pp. 30. *Lond.* 1891. 8°. Pam. 4.

PETERMANN (A.) and GRAFTIAU (J.) Recherches sur la composition de l'atmosphère. 1892, *etc.* 8°. Ac. Brussels. *Académie.* Mémoires couronnés. Tom. 47, *etc.* Ac. 985/4.

AIR: ATMOSPHERE: ETHER.—cont.

PICKERING (E. C.) Atmospheric Refraction. pp. 25. *Camb., Mass.*, 1886. 8°. Pam. 79.

SCHEELE (C. W.) Chemische Abhandlung von der Luft. pp. 112. 1894. 8°. Ostwald's Klassiker. Nr. 58. 8706. de.

TEISSERENC DE BORT (L.) Report of the present state of our Knowledge respecting the circulation of the Atmosphere. pp. 20. *Lond.* 1893. 4°. 8706. f. 23. (11.)

See also OXYGEN.

Hygiene, etc.

AIKMAN (C. M.) Air. pp. 128. 1895. 12°. Manuals of Health. 7404. a.

GRÉHANT (N.) Les Poisons de l'Air. pp. 320. *Paris*, 1890. 8°. 8908. aa. 43.

KEY (W.) Paper on the purification of Air supply. pp. 18. *Glasgow*, 1893. 8°. 8777. bbb. 28. (8.)

KORSCHELT (O.) Die Nutzbarmachung der lebendigen Kraft des Aethers in der Heilkunst, *etc.* pp. 182. *Berl.* 1892. 8°. 07509. e. 18.

POWNALL (A. E.) Considerations of the effects of Air Pollution. pp. 14. 1892. 8°. MANCHESTER. *Noxious Vapours Abatement Association.* Air Pollution. Ser. 4, no. 4. 8755. bbb. 31.

WANKLYN (J. A.) Air-Analysis. pp. 82. *Lond.* 1890. 8°. 8756. dd. 6.

See also VENTILATION.

AIR, Compressed. POPP (V.) L'Air comprimé à Paris. pp. 53. *Paris*, 1894. 8°. 8767. m. 9.

RAND (A. C.) Uses of Compressed Air. pp. 134. *N.Y.* 1894. *obl.* 8°. 8767. ee. 6.

AIRE AND CALDER NAVIGATION.

PATERSON (M. McC.) Pollution of the Aire and Calder. pp. 32. *Lond.* 1893. 8°. Pam. 79.

AIREDALE. GRAY (J.) Through Airedale. pp. 302. *Leeds*, 1891. 8°. 10360. e. 20.

AISNE, Department. VAUVILLÉ ( ) Mémoire sur plusieurs enceintes antiques du Département de l'Aisne. 1890. 8°. Ac. Paris. *Société des Antiquaires.* Mémoires. Sér. 5, tom. 10. Ac. 5331.

See also CHAMPAGNE.

AIX, Bouches du Rhone. CONSTANTIN (M.) Les Paroisses du diocèse d'Aix. *Aix*, 1890, *etc.* 8°. 4629. de. 6.

BELIN (F.) Histoire de l'ancienne université de Provence. 1893, *etc.* 8°. Ac. Aix. *Société des Amis des Sciences.* Mémoires. Tom. 15, *etc.* Ac. 233.

MÉCHIN (É.) Annales du Collège Royal Bourbon d'Aix. *Marseille*, 1890, *etc.* 8°. 8356. f.

DURANTI LA CALADE (M. de) Notice sur un temple antique aux environs d'Aix. pp. 47. 1890. 8°. Documents sur l'histoire de Provence. Fasc. 5, 6. 010174. h. 24.

SAINT-EUTROPE (É. de) Observations sur les écrits relatifs à la défaite des Ambrons et des Teutons aux environs d'Aix. pp. 22. *Aix*, 1892. 8°. Pam. 28.

AIX-LA-CHAPELLE. FROMM (E.) Die Literatur über die Thermen von Aachen. pp. 31. *Aachen*, 1890. 8°. 011900. ee. 6. (7.)

ALEXANDER (L.) Aix-la-Chapelle. pp. 348. *Aix-la-Ch.* 1891. 8°. 7470. dd. 11.

—— Aix-la-Chapelle as a Health Resort. pp. 323. *Lond.* 1892. 8°. 07686. k. 4.

CHARLES I., called *Charlemagne.* Das falsche Diplom Karls des Grossen. 1890. 8°. Ac. Cologne. *Gesellschaft für Rheinische Geschichtskunde.* Publicationen. No. 7. Ac. 7028.

AIX-LA-CHAPELLE—*continued.*

FUERTH (H. A. v.) Beiträge zur Geschichte der
Aachener Patrizier-Familien. 3 Bde.
Aachen, 1890. 8°.   9916. bb. 18.

GROSS (H. J.) Beiträge zur Geschichte des
Aachener Reichs. pp. 237. *Aachen,* 1894. 8°.
                                    09325. h. 15.

KESSEL (J. H.) and RHOEN (C.) Beschreibung
der karolingischen Pfalz zu Aachen. pp. 96.
1881. 8°. Ac. Aix-la-Chapelle. *Aachener Geschichtsverein.* Zeitschrift. Bd. 3. Ac. 2008.

LULVÈS (J.) Die gegenwärtigen Geschichtsbe-
strebungen in Aachen. pp. 104. 1892. 8°.
Moderne Geschichtsforscher. 1.   9009. l.

RHOEN (C.) Die römischen Thermen zu Aachen.
pp. 68. *Aachen,* 1890. 8°.   7706. g. 4. (14.)

—— Die ältere Topographie der Stadt Aachen.
pp. 138. *Aachen,* 1891. 8°.   10255. ee. 5.

—— Geschichte der St. Foilanskirche. pp. 80.
Aachen, 1892. 8°.   Pam. 29.

—— Die Befestigungswerke der Reichsstadt
Aachen. pp. 217. *Aachen,* 1894. 8°. 8827. c. 67.

SCHJERNING (W.) Aachen und seine Umgebung.
pp. 80. *Aachen,* 1895. 8°.   10255. ccc. 14.

WACKER (C.) Die Aachener Geschichtsforschung.
pp. 95. *Aachen,* 1893. 8°.   10235. i. 12.

JARDON (A.) Grammatik der Aachener Mundart.
Aachen, 1891, *etc.* 8°.   12962. q.

Peace of, 1748.

BROGLIE (A. L. V. C. de) *Duke.* La Paix d'Aix-
la-Chapelle. pp. 346. *Paris,* 1895. 12°.
                                    9078. ee. 39.

AIX-LES-BAINS. AIX-LES-BAINS, *Collegiate
Church of.* La Collégiale d'Aix. 1891. 8°. Ac.
Chambéry. *Société d'histoire.* Mémoires.
Série 2, tom. 5.   Ac. 5240.

—— Établissement thermal d'Aix-les-Bains.
pp. 14. *Melun,* 1890. 8°.   7461. i. 9. (11.)

BRACHET (L.) Aix-Les-Bains; medical treatment. pp. 125. *Lond.* 1891. 8°.   7462. aaa. 41.

GRAVILLON (A. de) Lettre pour la restauration
du temple de Diane. pp. 7. *Lyon,* 1890. 8°.
                                   7704. e. 19. (4.)

LEGRAND (M.) Aix-les-Bains. Guide Joanne.
pp. 146. *Paris,* 1893. 16°.   10171. a. 19.

VIDAL (F.) Du traitement thermal de l'arthritis
à l'Hospice d'Aix. pp. 30. *Bourg,* 1880. 8°.
                                   7462. e. 10. (9.)

—— Du degré de thermalité des eaux d'Aix dans
le traitement de la goutte. pp. 48.
Chambéry, 1886. 8°.   7462. e. 10. (17.)

AJACCIO. WISE (A. T. T.) The Climate of
Ajaccio. pp. 12. *Lond.* 1891. 8°. 7306. df. 19. (8.)

STEIN (H.) Le Musée d'Ajaccio. pp. 16.
Paris, 1894. 8°.   Pam. 24.
See also CORSICA.

AKHMIN. *See* EGYPT, *Antiquities.*

AKRA LANGUAGE.
See AFRICAN LANGUAGES.

ALABAMA, *State.* ALABAMA. *Geological
Survey.* Bulletin. *Montgomery,* 1892, *etc.* 8°.
                                    07108. g.

ALAGNA. Ac. Turin. *Club Alpino Italiano.*
GIORDANI (G.) La colonia tedesca di Alagna-
Valsesia. pp. 201. *Torino,* 1891. 8°. 12963. k. 32.
See also VALSESIA.

ALAIS. BARDON (A.) Histoire de la ville
d'Alais, 1250–1340. pp. 236. *Nimes,* 1894. 8°.
                                    10173. ee. 7.

ALASKA. BROKE (G.) With Sack and Stock
in Alaska. pp. 158. *Lond.* 1891. 8°.
                                    10460. bb. 24.

ALASKA—*continued.*

KARR (H. W. S.) Bear-Hunting in the White
Mountains. pp. 156. *Lond.* 1891. 8°.
                                    7908. eee. 3.

RUTGERS (L.) On and Off the Saddle. pp. 201.
N.Y. 1894. 8°.   10408. aa. 31.

SCIDMORE (E. R.) Appletons' Guide-Book to
Alaska. pp. 156. *N.Y.* 1893. 8°. 10413. aaa. 16.

TANNER (Z. L.) Explorations of the Fishing
Grounds of Alaska. 1890. 8°. U.S. *Commission of Fisheries.* Bulletin. vol. 8. 7290. dd.

U.S. *Census.* Eleventh Census. Report on
Population and Resources of Alaska. pp. 282.
Wash. 1893. 4°.   1882. c.

—— *Coast Survey.* Alaska. *Wash.* 1891, *etc.* 4°.
                                    10497. ff. 15.

WEBB (W. S.) California and Alaska. pp. 268.
N.Y. 1891. 8°.   10409. d. 20.

WILEY (W. H.) and (S. K.) The Yosemite,
Alaska and the Yellowstone. pp. 230.
Lond. 1893. 4°.   10410. g. 21.

ALASSIO. GALLO (I. R.) *Marquis.* Storia
della città di Alassio. 3 pt. *Chiavari,* 1888. 8°.
                                    10130. bbb. 19.
See also RIVIERA.

ALBANIA. GLUECK (L.) Albanien und
Macedonien. pp. 71. *Würzburg,* 1892. 8°.
                                    10125. aa. 20.

PISKO (J.) Skanderbeg. pp. 162.
Wien, 1894. 8°.   10606. h. 21.

JUNGG (G.) Elementi della lingua albanese.
pp. 112 *Scutari,* 1881. 8°.   12976. dd. 29.

ROSSI (F.) Vocabolario italiano-epirotico.
pp. 953. *Roma,* 1886. 8°.   12975. n. 8.

DOZON (L. A. H.) Contes albanais. pp. 264.
1881. 12°. Collection de Chansons, *etc.* vol. 3.
                                    2348. a.

ALBANO. SALVAGNINI (U.) Terme d'Albano.
3 pt. *Padova,* 1888, 89. 8°.   7461. i. 7.

SMILARI (A.) Gli Albanesi d'Italia. pp. 79.
Napoli, 1891. 8°.   10131. cc. 8.

ALBERTA. CALGARY. — *Board of Trade.*
Advantages of Alberta. pp. 4. *Calgary,* 1892. 8°.
                                   10470. dd. 30. (4.)

MANITOBA. The North-West farmer in Alberta,
etc. 1891. pp. 55. *Liverp.* 1891. 8°. Pam. 1.

—— What Farmers say of Alberta, *etc.* pp. 16.
Lond. 1892. 8°.   Pam. 86.

—— Proceedings of a Delegation from the Mari-
time Provinces to Alberta, *etc.* pp. 24.
Lond. 1892. 8°.   Pam. 86.
See also CANADA, *North West Provinces.*

ALBI, *Tarn.* SALABERT (H.) Les saints du
diocèse. pp. 824. *Toulouse,* 1892, *etc.* 8°.
                                    4825. g. 3.

MAFFRE (J.) Histoire des prêtres du diocèse
d'Alby qui furent mis à mort pendant la Révolution. pp. 316. *Alby,* 1891. 8°. 4866. ee. 9.

ALBIGENSES. CANET (V.) Simon de
Montford et la Croisade contre les Albigeois.
pp. 294. *Lille,* 1891. 8°.   4629. i. 22.

DOUAIS (C.) L'Albigéisme et les Frères prêcheurs
à Narbonne. pp. 149. *Paris,* 1894. 8°.
                                    4629. ee. 6.

LITURGIES. Albigenses. *Ritual and Ceremonial
Books.* Rituel provençal. Manuscrit de la
Bibliothèque à Lyon. pp. 13. 1890. 8°. CLÉDAT
(L.) Collection de reproductions, *etc.* Vieux
provençal. 1.   12205. k.
See also FRANCE, *History, Ecclesiastical.*

ALCALÁ DE HENARES. CATALINA GAR-
CIA (J.) Ensayo de una Tipografía Complutense. pp. 673. *Madrid,* 1889. 8   11899. h. 34.

ALCALÁ DE LOS GAZULES. Sánchez del Arco (E.) Monografía de Alcalá. pp. 112. *Cádiz*, 1893. 8°.   10106. ff. 6. (10.)

ALCHEMY. Berthelot (M. P. E.) La chimie au Moyen Âge, *etc.* 3 tom. *Paris*, 1893. 4°.   8906. g. 14.

Bombast von Hohenheim (P. A. T.) Hermetic and Alchemical Writings of Paracelsus. 2 vol. *Lond.* 1894. 4°.   8905. g. 2.

Schubert (E.) Bibliography of the Paracelsus Library of E. Schubert. pp. 46. *Lond.* 1893. 8°.   Pam. 6.

Collectanea. Collectanea Chemica. pp. 160. *Lond.* 1893. 8°.   8631. eee. 32.

Kelly (E.) Alchemical Writings of E. Kelly. pp. 153. *Lond.* 1893. 8°.   8905. de. 35.

Muir (M. M. P.) Alchemical Essence and Chemical Element. pp. 94. *Lond.* 1894. 8°.   8906. cc. 28.

Poisson (A.) Cinq traités d'alchimie. pp. 134. *Paris*, 1890. 4°.   8906. a. 1.

—— Théories et symboles des alchimistes. pp. 184. *Paris*, 1891. 16°.   8905. de. 18.

Ruland (M.) Lexicon of Alchemy. pp. 466. *Lond.* 1892. 4°.   C. 54. c. 11.

Tiffereau (C. T.) L'Art de faire de l'or. pp. 108. *Paris*, 1892. 8°.   8906. aaa. 2. *See also* Occult Science.

ALCOHOL. Bauer (E.) Gährungstechnische Untersuchungs-methoden. pp. 408. *Braunschweig*, 1891. 8°.   8908. i. 26.

Birch (G.) Handbook of Gauging. pp. 133. *Wolverhampton*, 1894. 8°.   7942. a. 76.

Brevans (J. de) Manufacture of Liquors. pp. 200. *N.Y.* 1893. 8°.   7942. de. 24.

Maclean (J. O.) New spirit reducing table. pp. 17. *Edinb.* 1895. 8°.   07944. g. 14.

Mac Neill (A. A.) Table of the weights of Spirits. pp. 65. *Lond.* 1894. 4°.   8548. df. 41.

Maercker (M.) Das Flusssäureverfahren in der Spiritusfabrikation. pp. 150. *Berl.* 1891. 8°.   8908. l. 8.

Martin (É.) L'Alcool en Suisse. Le monopole. pp. 94. *Paris*, 1891. 8°.   8435. e. 20.

Nettleton (J. A.) Manufacture of Spirit. pp. 431. *Lond.* 1893. 8°.   7942. dd. 10.

Sand (H.) Das Deutsche Spiritus-Monopol. pp. 16. *Berl.* 1893. 8°.   8227. k. 38. (4.)

Scarisbrick (J.) Spirit Manual. pp. 152. 1891. 8°. Revenue Series. No. 2.   8226. cc.

—— Hydrometry, and Spirit Values. pp. 177. 1893. 8°. Revenue Series. No. 3.   8226. cc.

Sorel (E.) La Rectification de l'Alcool. pp. 168. 1894. 8°. Encyclopédie scientifique.   8709. g.

—— La Distillation. pp. 244. 1894. 8°. Encyclopédie scientifique.   8709. g.

Warren (A.) Methylated Spirit. pp. 14. *Bristol*, 1894. 8°.   Pam. 13.

Bird (W. V.) Action of Alcohol on the Body. pp. 19. *Lond.* 1893. 8°.   8435. e. 24. (26.)

Clark (*Sir* A.) Action of Alcohol upon Health. pp. 12. *Lond.* 1893. 12°.   8436. f. 3. (6.)

Coleg (F. C.) Alcohol as a Medicine. pp. 15. *Lond.* 1894. 8°.   8436. f. 3. (15.)

Erdmann (A. L.) Die Alkoholfrage. pp. 166. *Bamberg*, 1895. 8°.   8436. ccc. 3.

Forshaw (C. F.) Alcohol: its influence, *etc.* pp. 16. *Stanningley*, 1887. 8°. 8436. f. 1. (2.)

Horsley (J. W.) What Doctors say about Alcohol. pp. 24. *Lond.* 1891. 8°.   8436. f. 1. (18.)

ALCOHOL—*continued.*

Larbalétrier (A.) L'Alcool. pp. 312. *Paris*, 1888. 8°.   7944. d. 15.

Ridge (J. J.) Alcohol and Public Health. pp. 91. *Lond.* 1893. 8°.   8436. c. 11.

—— Facts about Alcohol. pp. 16. *Lond.* 1895. 8°.   Pam. 85.

Salomon (L.) L'Alcool et la dépopulation de la France. pp. 101. *Paris*, 1895. 12°. 8436. aa. 45.

Steele (J. D.) Alcohol: its effects on body and mind. pp. 23. *Lond.* 1893. 8°.   8436. f. 3. (5.)

Taylor (W.) Easy Lessons on Alcohol. *Westminster*, 1892, *etc.* 8°.   8436. c.

Wakely (C.) Alcohol and the human Body. *Lond.* 1894. fol.   Tab. 11747. a. (84.)

See also Brandy: Distillation: Licensing Laws: Temperance.

ALCOHOLISM: INEBRIETY. Basset (N.) Étude physiologique sur l'Ivresse. pp. 533. *Paris*, 1892. 12°.   8436. cc. 2.

Bolton (H. C.) Notes on the Gold-Cure. pp. 6. *N.Y.* 1892. 8°.   Pam. 13.

Cauderlier (É.) L'alcoolisme en Belgique. pp. 163. *Brux.* 1893. 8°.   8435. ee. 10.

Cadéac (C.) and Meunier (A.) Contribution à l'étude de l'alcoolisme. 1892. 8°. Ac. Lyons. *Société d'Agriculture.* Annales. Sér. 6, tom. 4.   Ac. 362/3.

Clark (C. S.) The Keeley Cure. pp. 147. *Milwaukee*, 1892. 8°.   8436. aaa. 56.

Gerényi (F.) Die Trinkerasyle Englands. pp. 82. *Wien*, 1893. 8°.   8435. ee. 9.

Hicks (E. L.) Legislation on the control of habitual Drunkards. pp. 12. 1892. 8°. Manchester. *Sanitary Association.* Health Lectures. Pamph. Series. No. 2.   7404. bbb.

Kerr (N. S.) Inebriety. pp. 780. *Lond.* 1894. 8°.   8436. ccc. 1.

New York. *Association for the Cure of Inebriety.* Disease of Inebriety. pp. 394. *Bristol*, 1893. 8°.   8435. de. 17.

Pierrot (A.) Essai d'étude sur l'atténuation de l'alcoolisme par le modification de la loi du 17 juin 1880 sur les cafés. pp. 29. *Montmédy*, 1895. 8°.   Pam. 85.

Tuckey (C. L.) Hypnotism in chronic Alcoholism. pp. 57. *Lond.* 1892. 8°. 7410. cc. 39

Usher (J. E.) Alcoholism and its treatment. pp. 151. *Lond.* 1892. 8°.   8436. c. 6. *See also* Temperance.

ALDENHAM GRAMMAR SCHOOL. The Aldenhamian. Vol. vi., *etc.* *Estree*, 1892, *etc.* 4°.   P.P. 6142. c. & 2253.

ALDERLEY EDGE. Keyworth (W. W.) Sketches of Alderley Edge. *Manch.* 1890. fol.   10360. k. 10.

ALDERNEY. *See* Channel Islands.

ALDRIDGE, Staffordshire. Smith (J. F.) Notes relating to Aldridge. 2 pt. *Leicester*, 1884, 89. 8°.   9904. f. 6.

ALENÇON. Duval (L.) La Généralité d'Alençon sous Louis xiv. pp. 429. *Paris*, 1890. 4°.   010171. h. 38.

ALESSANDRIA. Borromeo (C.) Origine e libertà dei comuni Borgoglio-Gamondio-Marengo. 2 pt. *Alessandria*, 1892, 93. 8°. 10132. bbb. 31.

Guasco (C.) Cronaca Alessandrina. pp. 42. *Torino*, 1894. 4°.   10135. i. 10.

Bobbio (G.) Alessandria e i moti del 1821. pp. 112. *Alessandria*, 1894. 8°.   9167. f. 6.

ALET. Aleth. Notice sur l'eau d'Alet. pp. 14. *Vichy*, 1889. 8°.   7462. e. 10. (21.)

ALEXANDRIA. Thomsen (L. W.) Blandt Arabere. pp. 151. *Kjøbenh.* 1893. 8°.
10095. aa. 13.

See also EGYPT.

ALFRISTON. Pagden (F. A.) History of Alfriston. pp. 44. *Brighton,* 1895. 4°. Pam. 90.

ALGAE. Agardh (J. G.) Species Sargassorum Australiæ descriptæ. pp. 133. 1889. 4°. Ac. Stockholm. *K. Svenska Academien.* Handlingar. Ny Földj. Bd. 23.   Ac. 1070.

Bornet (É.) Los Algues de P. K. A. Schousboe. 1892. 8°. Ac. Cherbourg. *Société des Sciences.* Mémoires. Tom. 28.   Ac. 2844.

O., J. Collecting fresh-water Algæ. pp. 8. *Birmingham,* 1893. 8°.   Pam. 1.

Foslie (M.) Contribution to knowledge of marine Algæ of Norway. 1890. 8°. Ac. Tromsœ. *Museum.* Aarshefter. Vol. xiii.   Ac. 2980.

—— Norwegian Forms of Ceramium. pp. 21. *Trondhjem,* 1893. 8°.   Pam. 1.

Hansen (A.) Über Stoffbildung bei den Meeresalgen. 1893. 8°. Ac. Naples. *Zoologische Station.* Mittheilungen. Bd. 11. Ac. 3552/2.

Hariot (P.) Atlas des algues marines des côtes de France. *Paris,* 1892. 8°.   7029. dd. 4.

Holmes (E. M.) Revised List of British marine Algae. *Lond.* 1892. 8°.   7029. dd. 8.

Kjellman (F. R.) Handbok i Skandinavians hafsalg flora. *Stockholm,* 1890, *etc.* 8°.
07028. m. 9.

—— Om Beringhafvets Algflora. pp. 58. 1889. 4°. Ac. Stockholm. *K. Svenska Academien.* Handlingar. Ny Földj. Bd. 23.   Ac. 1070.

Klebs (G.) Über die Organisation der Gallerte bei einigen Algen. 1886. 8°. Ac. Tubingen. *Botanisches Institut.* Untersuchungen. Bd. 2.
Ac. 3260.

Lewin (M.) Über spanische Süsswasseralgen. pp. 24. 1888. 8°. Ac. Stockholm. *K. Svenska Academien.* Bihang. Bd. 14. Afd. 3. Ac. 1070/7.

Murray (G. R. M.) Introduction to the study of Seaweeds. pp. 271. *Lond.* 1895. 8°.
07028. e. 57.

—— Catalogue of marine Algæ of the West Indian Region. pp. 46. *Lond.* 1889. 8°.
07028. f. 22.

Nordstedt (O.) Fresh-water Algæ in New Zealand and Australia. pp. 98. 1888. 8°. Ac. Stockholm. *K. Svenska Academien.* Handlingar. Bd. 22.   Ac. 1070.

Sequeira (E.) Á beira mar. pp. 182. *Porto,* 1889. *obl.* 8°.   K.T.C. 22. a. 1.

See also AQUARIUM : BOTANY : DIATOMACEAE : LICHENS : PALAEONTOLOGY.

ALGEBRA. Algebra. Imperial Algebra. 2 pt. *Lond.* 1888. 8°.   8533. d. 11.

Appell (P.) Théorie des fonctions algébriques. pp. 530. *Paris,* 1895. 8°.   8535. i. 9.

Bachmann (P.) Vorlesungen über die Natur der Irrationalzahlen. pp. 151. *Leipz.* 1892. 8°.
8535. dd. 17.

Ball (W. W. R.) Elementary Algebra. pp. 486. 1890. 8°. Pitt Press Mathematical Series.
8535. aaa.

Bayliss (R. W.) Preliminary Algebra. pp. 183. *Lond.* 1893. 8°.   8532. aa. 39.

Bettazzi (R.) Teoria delle Grandezze. pp. 180. *Pisa,* 1890. 4°.   8532. g. 27.

Björling (C. F. E.) Lärobok i algebraisk analys. pp. 366. *Lund,* 1893. 8°. 8534. d. 37.

Blackie (W. G.) Algebra for Beginners. pp. 79. *Lond.* 1892. 8°.   8532. aa. 29.

Browne (W. J.) Junior Algebra. pp. 147. 1895. 8°. Elementary Science Manuals. 8708. ee.

Catalan (E. C.) Nouvelles Notes d'Algèbre. pp. 98. 1892. 4°. Ac. Brussels. *Académie.* Nouveaux Mémoires. Tom. 48.   Ac. 985/7.

Cusack (J.) Cusack's Algebra. *Lond.* 1895, *etc.* 8°.   8533. ee. 1.

Davis (E. W.) Introduction to the Logic of Algebra. pp. 136. *N.Y.* 1894. 8°. 08533. h. 1.

Dupuis (N. F.) Principles of elementary Algebra. pp. 336. *Lond.* 1892. 8°.   8535. aa. 35.

Easton (J. G.) First Book of Algebra. pp. 190. *Lond.* 1893. 8°.   8532. aa. 35.

Elliott (E. B.) Introduction to the Algebra of Quantics. pp. 423. *Oxf.* 1895. 8°. 8535. d. 27.

Fine (H. B.) Number-System in Algebra. pp. 131. *Boston,* 1890. 8°.   8535. df. 17.

Glaser (S.) Über einige nach Binomial Koeffizienten fortschreitende Reichen. pp. 28. *Berl.* 1895. 4°.   Pam. 38.

Graham (R.) Elementary Algebra. pp. 312. *Lond.* 1893. 8°.   8533. c. 34.

Hall (H. S.) Algebra for Beginners. pp. 216. *Lond.* 1892. 8°.   8532. aa. 25.

—— Solutions of Examples. pp. 331. *Lond.* 1891. 8°.   8535. bb. 55.

—— Higher Algebra. pp. 557. *Lond.* 1894. 8°.
8533. de. 32.

Hathornthwaite (J. T.) Manual of Elementary Algebra. pp. 298. *Lond.* 1894. 8°.
8507. bb. 14.

Hayward (R. B.) Algebra of Coplanar Vectors and Trigonometry. pp. 343. *Lond.* 1892. 8°.
8534. aa. 45.

Holbrook (G. W.) Forward Examination Algebra. pp. 100. *Birmingham,* 1894. 8°.
8533. de. 29.

Jarman (J. A.) Algebraic Factors. pp. 141. *Lond.* 1892. 8°.   8535. aa. 28.

Klein (F.) On Riemann's Theory of Algebraic Functions. pp. 76. *Camb.,* 1893. 8°.
8530. cc. 43.

Lobatto (R.) Lobatto's Lessen over de hoogere algebra. pp. 445. *Sneek,* 1892. 8°. 8533. dd. 6.

Macfarlane (A.) Imaginary of Algebra. pp. 22. *Salem,* 1892. 8°.   8535. gg. 6. (6.)

Mitcheson (T.) Examples in Algebra. pp. 80. *Lond.* 1895. 8°.   8530. aaa. 52.

Netto (E.) Die vier Gauss'schen Beweise für die Zerlegung ganzer algebraischer Functionen. 1890. 8°. Ostwald's Klassiker. Nr. 14.
8706. de.

Orio y Rubio (M.) Libro de problemas algebraicos, *etc. Palencia,* 1894. 4°.   8531. df.

Paul (J. D.) Detached Coefficients in elementary Algebra. pp. 50. *Camb.* 1894. 8°.
8531. dd. 28. (12.)

Pincherle (S.) Algebra Complementare. pp. 169. *Milano,* 1893. 8°.   012200. h. 104.

Potts (W. A.) Elementary Algebra. pp. 138. *Lond.* 1890. 8°.   8533. d. 7.

Scheffler (H.) Die quadratische Zerfällung der Primzahlen. pp. 169. *Leipz.* 1892. 8°.
8535. d. 18.

Scott (R. P.) Elementary Algebra. pp. 86. *Lond.* 1892. 8°.   8503. de. 31.

Smith (C.) Treatise on Algebra. pp. 646. *Lond.* 1893. 8°.   8533. de. 33.

Cracknell (A. G.) Solutions of Examples in C. Smith's elementary Algebra. pp. 254. *Lond.* 1891. 8°.   8535. aaa 49.

ALGEBRA—*continued.*

SMITH (J. H.) Elementary Algebra. pp. 471.
1894. 8°. Hamblin Smith's Mathematical
Series. 8533. de.

—— Key to Elementary Algebra. pp. 415.
1894. 8°. Hamblin Smith's Mathematical Series.
8533. de.

SPENCER (J.) Algebra. *Lond.* 1892, *etc.* 8°.
8534. a.

STAUDACHER (H.) Lehrbuch der Grundrech-
nungsarten, *etc.* pp. 252. 1891. 8°. Kleyer's
Encyclopädie. 8705. g.

—— Lehrbuch der Kombinatorik, *etc.* pp. 298.
1893. 8°. Kleyer's Encyklopädie. 8705. g.

TANNERY (J.) Introduction à l'étude de l'algèbre supérieure. pp. 350. *Paris,* 1895. 8°.
8534. dd. 11.

THOMAS (P. A.) Enunciations in Algebra.
pp. 84. *Lond.* 1893. 8°. 8532. aa. 38.

THOMPSON (W. T.) Scholarship Algebra. pp. 280.
Lond. 1895. 8°. 8533. e. 43.

TIBBETS (G. P.) College Requirements in Algebra.
pp. 46. *Bost.* 1892. 8°. 8534. b. 36.

WEBER (H.) Lehrbuch der Algebra.
Braunschweig, 1895, *etc.* 8°. 08533. h.

WELSFORD (J. W. W.) Elementary Algebra.
pp. 407. *Lond.* 1895. 8°. 8534. df. 13.

WENTWORTH (G. A.) Algebraic Analysis. Pt. I.
pp. 418. *Bost.* 1889. 8°. 8534. bbb. 41.

—— Higher Algebra. pp. 521. *Bost.* 1891. 8°.
8533. de. 17.

WILLS (H.) Handbook of Algebra. pp. 264.
1893. 8°. Jarrold's Pupil Teachers' Series.
12200. dd.

See also DETERMINANTS: EQUATIONS: MATHE-
MATICS.

Examination Questions, etc.

Ac. Oxford. *University.* Oxford Questions in
Algebra, Pass Moderations, 1881–91. pp. 59.
Oxf. 1892. 8°. 8535. aa. 33.

—— Answers to Exercises in Algebra in the
Student's Guide. pp. 31. *Oxf.* 1884. 8°.
8530. bb. 42.

Ac. London. *College of Preceptors.* Answers to
Examination Papers in Algebra. 1876–91. 2 pt.
Lond. 1892, 93. 8°. 8535. df. 29.

AMBLER (W. B.) Algebraical Test Cards. Stage 1.
Lond. 1887. 8°. 12210. bbb.

EVANS (T.) Government Examinations in Algebra. *Lond.* 1891. 8°. 12210. cc. 3.

LANGLEY (E. M.) Graduated Examination Papers
in Algebra. *Lond.* 1893. 8°. 8533. d. 21.

ROBSON (J. H.) Solutions of Examination Papers
in algebra, set for entrance to the R. M. C.,
Sandhurst, 1880–88. 2 pt. *Lond.* 1890. 8°.
8533. e. 17.

ALGERIA : ALGIERS. [*See note on
page* 1.]

Administration : Politics.

DESSOLIERS (F.) Organisation politique de l'Algérie. pp. 217. *Paris,* 1894. 8°. 8155. ee. 21.

ALGERIA. Alger du 28 juin au 5 juillet 1884.
pp. 253. *Alger,* 1884. 8°. 9061. ccc. 27.

—— Le Mal de l'Algérie. pp. 63.
Paris, 1894. 8°. Pam. 66.

ANTON (G. K.) Französische Agrarpolitik in Algerien. pp. 127. *Leipz.* 1893. 8°. 8028. ec. 27.

BENOIST (C.) Enquête algérienne. pp. 330.
Paris, 1892. 12°. 8155. de. 11.

BONYOM (E.) La France algérienne. pp. 106.
Alger, 1889. 8°. 8155. f. 3.

ALGERIA.—**Administration, etc.**—*cont.*

BURDEAU (A.) L'Algérie en 1891. pp. 406.
Paris, 1892. 8°. 10097. ccc. 10.

CHATRIEUX (É.) Études algériennes. pp. 351.
Paris, 1893. 12°. 9061. aaa. 1.

FERRY (J.) Le gouvernement de l'Algérie.
pp. 116. *Paris,* 1892. 8°. 8027. a. 12.

GOURGEOT (F.) Les Sept Plaies d'Algérie.
pp. 340. *Alger,* 1891. 8°. 8154. ee. 32.

GUY (A.) Des Famines périodiques en Algérie.
pp. 19. *Paris,* 1893. 8°. 8282. g. 25. (6.)

JACQUES ( ) La Question algérienne devant le
Sénat. pp. 54. *Bordeaux,* 1891. 16°. Pam. 66.

MUḤAMMAD IBN BARAKAH. Choses d'Algérie.
pp. 329. *Évreux,* 1891. 8°. 10097. c. 35.

PAOLI (L.) La Sécurité en Algérie. pp. 23.
Paris, 1894. 12°. Pam. 66.

PENSA (H.) Voyage de la délégation de la Commission sénatoriale. pp. 464. *Paris,* 1894. 8°.
010096. ee. 45.

PRAX (V.) Étude sur la question algérienne.
pp. 120. *Bône,* 1892. 8°. 8154. cc. 13.

RÉVEILLAUD (E.) L'établissement d'une colonie
de Vaudois français en Algérie. pp. 118.
Paris, 1893. 12°. 10096. bb. 12.

SARRAUTON (H. de) La Question algérienne.
pp. 27. *Oran,* 1891. 8°. Pam. 66.

X. Simples Réflexions d'un Colon algérien.
pp. 117. *Paris,* 1891. 8°. 8154. aaa. 40.

See also infra : Topography. AFRICA, *Colonisation :* FRANCE, *Colonies.*

Antiquities.

AFRICA. Géographie de l'Afrique chrétienne.
Numidie. pp. 417. *Rennes,* 1894. 8°.
4534. c. 31.

AUDOLLENT (A.) Mission épigraphique en Algérie.
1890. 8°. Ac. Rome. *École Française.* Mélanges. An 10. Ac. 5233.

BALLU (A.) Monuments antiques de l'Algérie.
pp. 39. *Paris,* 1894. 8°. 07708. f. 44.

CAISE (A.) Monuments historiques. Le tombeau
de Juba II. pp. 7. *Blida,* 1892. 8°.
07703. f. 2. (4.)

GSELL (S.) Recherches archéologiques en Algérie.
pp. 434. *Paris,* 1893. 8°. 7708. d. 37.

LA BLANCHÈRE (R. de) Musées de l'Algérie.
Paris, 1890, *etc.* 4°. 7703. b.

See also AFRICA, *North.*

Forestry. *See* FORESTRY.

History.

CAT (É.) Petite histoire de l'Algérie. 2 tom.
Alger, 1888, 91. 8°. 9061. de. 33.

BOUTROUE (A.) L'Algérie à travers les âges.
pp. 62. *Paris,* 1893. 8°. 9061. dd. 11.

TURBA (G.) Über den Zug Kaiser Karls V. gegen
Algier, *etc.* 1890. 8°. Archiv für österreichische
Geschichte. Bd. 76. Ac. 810/8.

BASSET (R.) Documents musulmans sur le siège
d'Alger en 1541. pp. 48. *Paris,* 1890. 8°.
14555. e.

PLANTET (E.) Correspondance des Deys d'Alger
avec la Cour de France 1579–1833. 2 tom.
Paris, 1889. 8°. 9061. h. 2.

CONESTAGGIO (G.) Relation des préparatifs faits
pour surprendre Alger, 1602. pp. 28.
Alger, 1882. 8°. Pam. 28.

DELMAS DE GRAMMONT (H.) Correspondance des
Consuls d'Alger, 1690–1742. pp. 293.
Alger, 1890. 8°. 9061. ee. 27.

IRISSON D'HÉRISSON (M. d') *Count.* Guerres
d'Algérie. pp. 364. *Paris,* 1891. 18°. 9061. ccc. 8.

BOURNAND (F.) Le Maréchal Bugeaud. pp. 364.
Paris, 1895. 8°. 10661. k. 30.

ALGERIA.—History—*continued.*

CORNULIER-LUCINIÈRE (H. R. R. de) *Count.* La Prise de Bone et Bougie, 1832–1833. pp. 377. *Paris*, 1895. 8°. 9061. aaa. 6.

GRANDIN (L.) Le dernier Maréchal de France. Canrobert. pp. 343. *Paris*, 1895. 8°. 010662. i. 35.

BOSQUET (P. J. F.) Lettres du Maréchal Bosquet. pp. 400. *Paris*, 1894. 8°. 010920. f. 43.

DUCROT (A. A.) La Vie du Général Ducrot. 2 tom. *Paris*, 1895. 8°. 010663. i. 13.

CADART (C. R.) Souvenirs de Constantine, 1838–39. pp. 385. *Paris*, 1894. 12°. 10095. aaa. 7.

BOURJADE (É. J. E. G.) Notes pour servir à l'histoire de l'occupation française dans la région d'Aumale, 1846–87. pp. 222. *Alger*, 1891. 8°. 9061. h. 8.

GALENS (G.) Marche de la Colonisation algérienne. pp. 47. *Alger*, 1892. 8°. 9004. gg. 31. (7.)

LE CHATELIER (A.) Les Medaganat. pp. 180. *Alger*, 1888. 8°. 9061. h. 6.

RINN (L.) Histoire de l'insurrection de 1871 en Algérie. pp. 671. *Alger*, 1891. 8°. 9061. dd. 3.

TRUMELET (C.) Histoire de l'Insurrection dans le sud d'Alger. 2 pt. *Alger*, 1879, 84. 8°. 9061. ff. 26.

INNOCENTI (J. C. A. A.) Insurrection du Sud-Oranais en 1881. pp. 134. *Paris*, 1893. 12°. 9061. aaa. 2.

See also FRANCE, *Colonies.*

Law.

BACHMANN (P.) Étude sur la condition des personnes en Algérie. pp. 228. *Nancy*, 1894. 8°. 5206. ee. 25.

BARIAT (E.) L'Anarchie judiciaire en Algérie. pp. 104. *Oran*, 1894. 8°. 05319. k. 10.

BESSON (E.) La Législation civile de l'Algérie. pp. 364. *Paris*, 1894. 8°. 05319. i. 13.

DRAPIER (H.) La Justice française en Algérie. pp. 35. *Constantine*, 1891. 8°. Pam. 34.

Native Races.

ALGERIA. Vocabulaire destiné à fixer la transcription en français des noms des indigènes. pp. 393. *Alger*, 1891. 4°. 12904. f. 22.

CAIX DE SAINT-AYMOUR (A. de) Arabes et Kabyles. pp. 287. *Paris*, 1891. 12°. 8027. bb. 14.

CŒUR (P.) L'Assimilation des indigènes musulmans. pp. 85. *Paris*, 1890. 8°. Pam. 66.

KLEIN (F.) Les Villages d'Arabes chrétiens. pp. 71. *Fontainebleau*, 1890. 16°. Pam. 89.

MERCIER (E.) La Propriété foncière chez les Musulmans d'Algérie. pp. 48. *Paris*, 1891. 8°. 5423. g. 1. (4.)

VIVAREZ (M.) Transmutations ethniques. pp. 22. *Alger*, 1891. 8°. Pam. 66.

See also ARABS : BERBERS.

Sheep in. *See* SHEEP.

Topography.

FRANCE. *Dépôt des Cartes et Plans de la Marine.* Instructions nautiques sur la côte d'Algérie. pp. 196. *Paris*, 1893. 8°. 10497. bb. 36.

GINDRE DE MANCY (J. B.) Dictionnaire des Communes de l'Algérie. pp. 783. *Paris*, 1890. 32°. 10171. aa. 22.

MEYRAT (J.) Dictionnaire des communes d'Algérie. pp. 721. *Tours*, 1895. 8°. 10174. c. 18.

POMEL (A.) Carte géologique de l'Algérie. 2 pt. *Alger*, 1890. 4°. 7105. g. 12.

BARAUDON (A.) Algérie et Tunisie. pp. 327. *Paris*, 1893. 12°. 10097. de. 25.

BERGOT (R.) L'Algérie telle qu'elle est. pp. 316. *Paris*, 1890. 18°. 10097. cc. 18.

ALGERIA.—Topography—*continued.*

BLACKBURN (H.) Artistic Travels. pp. 320. *Lond.* 1892. 8°. 10108. f. 1.

CONSTANS (H.) Quelques mois en Algérie. pp. 210. *Bar-le-Duc*, 1892. 8°. 010096. ee. 39.

DELAUNEY DU DÉZEN ( ) Manuel du colon en Algérie. pp. 200. *Paris*, 1895. 8°. 10095. aa. 14.

FOCK (A.) Algérie, Sahara, Tchad. pp. 75. *Paris*, 1891. 8°. 8155. ee. 11.

FRISCH (R. J.) Guide en pays arabe. pp. 377. *Paris*, 1892. 12°. 10096. aa. 9.

GRÉPON (E.) Neuf ans en Algérie, *etc.* pp. 186. *Paris*, 1893. 8°. 10026. ccc. 6.

GUILLAUMET (G.) Tableaux algériens. pp. 274. *Paris*, 1891. 12°. 10097. cc. 22.

HARRIS (G. W.) Practical Guide to Algiers. pp. 176. *Lond.* 1895. 8°. 010097. de. 1.

LALLEMAND (C.) L'Ouest de l'Algérie. pp. 215. *Paris*, 1891. 8°. 010096. g. 12.

LAVERRENZ (C.) Zwei Wanderungen durch das nördliche Afrika. pp. 172. *Berl.* 1891. 8°. 010096. f. 23.

LEFORT (A.) Voyage en Algérie. pp. 141. *Fontenay*, 1893. 8°. 010096. e. 54.

LOMBAY (G. de) En Algérie. pp. 392. *Paris*, 1893. 12°. 10097. c. 42.

MASQUÉRAY (É.) Souvenirs d'Afrique. pp. 444. *Paris*, 1894. 12°. 10097. c. 40.

MIGEON (G.) Sac au Dos. pp. 157. *Paris*, 1892. 8°. 10171. dd. 4.

NUGENT (*Hon.* E. G.) Land of Mosques and Marabouts. pp. 190. *Lond.* 1894. 8°. 010096. i. 22.

PEASE (A. E.) Biskra and the oases and deserts of the Zibans. pp. 112. *Lond.* 1893. 8°. 10097. aaa. 47.

PIESSE (L.) Algérie. Guide Joanne. pp. 429. *Paris*, 1893. 8°. 10097. cc. 28.

PLAYFAIR (*Sir* R. L.) Murray's Handbook for travellers in Algeria. pp. 363. *Lond.* 1895. 8°. 2364. a. 1.

ROBERT (G.) Voyage à Travers l'Algérie. pp. 404. *Paris*, 1891. 4°. 10096. i. 9.

ROSIER (J.) Souvenirs d'Algérie. pp. 323. *Paris*, 1892. 8°. 010096. ee. 38.

SESSIONS (F. C.) In Western Levant. pp. 252. *N.Y.* 1890. 8°. 10024. cc. 15.

STAEHELIN (A.) In Algerien. pp. 461. *Basel*, 1891. 8°. 10024. cc. 16.

THOLIN (G.) Impressions, études et souvenirs. pp. 391. *Lyon*, 1890. 8°. 12355. i. 32.

VIGNON (L.) La France en Algérie. pp. 552. *Paris*, 1893. 8°. 010096. f. 31.

VIVAREZ (M.) Alger. pp. 85. *Alger*, 1891. 8°. 010096. m. 10.

VUILLOT (P.) Des Zibans au Djerid. pp. 168. *Rennes*, 1893. 8°. 10096. h. 4.

WORKMAN (F. B.) and (W. H.) Algerian Memories. pp. 216. *Lond.* 1895. 8°. 10097. bb. 39.

DRIEU (L.) Walks around Algiers. pp. 118. *Algiers*, 1891–92. 16°. 10097. a. 35.

WAHL (M.) Alger. 1892. 4°. Les Capitales du Monde. No. 14. 10025. g.

See also FRANCE, *Colonies.*

ALGOMA. ALGOMA. Algoma! The New Ontario !! pp. 64. *Sault S. Marie*, 1892. 8°. Pam. 86.

B., H. N. Life in Algoma. pp. 167. *Lond.* 1894. 8°. 4429. c. 36.

See also CANADA, *North-west Provinces.*

ALGONQUIN LANGUAGES.

See INDIAN LANGUAGES.

ALHAMBRA. Valladar (F. de P.) El incendio de la Alhambra. 1890. pp. 88.
Granada, 1890. 8°.   10151. aa. 6.
See also Granada.

ALKALI. Herty (C. H.) The Double Halides of Lead and the Alkali Metals. pp. 25.
Baltimore, 1890. 8°.   Pam. 13.
Hurter (F.) Alkali-Makers' Handbook. 1891. 8°. The Specialists' Series.   8708. k.
Lunge (G.) Treatise on the Manufacture of Alkali. *Lond.* 1891, *etc.* 8°.   8909. cc. 19.
Stadelmann (E.) Über den Einfluss der Alkalien auf den menschlichen Stoffwechsel. pp. 176.
Stuttgart, 1890. 8°.   8906. f. 11.

ALKALOIDS. Farquharson (A. C.) Ptomaines and other animal alkaloids. pp. 152.
Bristol, 1892. 8°.   7442. a. 30.
Sohn (C. E.) Dictionary of the active Principles of Plants. pp. 194. *Lond.* 1894. *obl. fol.*
     8909. a. 25.

ALLAHABAD. Mīrzā Amīr Beg. Hand book of Allahabad, *etc.* pp. 46.
Lucknow, 1891. 8°.   Pam. 88.

ALLOTMENTS. Leadam (I. S.) Allotments and Small Holdings. pp. 8.
Altrincham, 1890. 8°.   Pam. 82.
Little (J. B.) Law of Allotments. pp. 477.
Lond. 1895. 8°.   6426. aaaa. 36.
Wright (W. P.) Plan of Allotment for Fruit and Vegetables. *Lond.* 1894.   1882. c. 2. (182.)

ALPHABET. Berger (P.) Histoire de l'écriture dans l'Antiquité. pp. 389.
Paris, 1891. 8°.   2268. f. 21.
Maury (A.) La Invencion de la Escritura.
pp. 146. *Madrid*, 1891. 8°.   7706. a. 44.
English Alphabet. Numerical value of the English Alphabet.
Wolverhampton, 1893. *s. sh.* 8°. 1865. c. 1. (21.)
Hake (T. G.) Powers of the Alphabet: tonic scale of alphabetic sounds. pp. 23.
Lond. 1883. 8°.   12982. ccc. 3.
Terrien de Lacouperie (A. É. J. B.) Beginnings of Writing in Central and Eastern Asia.
pp. 208. *Lond.* 1894. 8°.   7704. d. 14.
S., E. J. De l'alphabet universel. pp. 24.
Paris, 1893. 12°.   Pam. 48.
Sheldon (E. S.) Origin of English names of letters of the Alphabet. 1890. 8°.
     12903. e. 29. (1.)

———

Bry (J. T. de) Initials. An Alphabet from the year 1596. *Lond.* 1894. 4°.   7709. aa. 32.
Favaloro (M.) Spicilegio storico paleografico di alfabeti. Tav. 77. *Palermo*, 1893. 4°.
     K.T.C. 19. a. 8.
Strange (E. F.) Alphabets. Handbook of lettering. pp. 294. 1895. 8°. Ex-Libris Series.
     K.T.C. 42. a. 1.
Vorlagen. Vorlagen zum Schriften-Zeichnen.
Borna, 1891. 8°.   11899. i. 45.
See also Illuminations.

ALPS.—General : Western Alps (Switzerland : France : Savoy).

Ac. *Congrès géologique.* Livret-guide géologique dans les Alpes de la Suisse. pp. 306.
Paris, 1894. 8°.   07109. g. 45.
Allais (G.) Le Alpi occidentali nell' antichità.
pp. 207. *Torino*, 1891. 8°.   07708. g. 13.
Boehm (A.) Steiner Alpen. pp. 91.
Wien, 1893. 8°.   7106. i. 18.

ALPS.—General, etc.—*continued.*

Burnaby, afterwards Main (E. A. F.) Hints on Snow Photography. pp. 14. *Lond.* 1895. 8°.
     8909. cc. 11.
Conway (*Sir* W. M.) The Alps from end to end.
pp. 403. *Lond.* 1895. 8°.   10195. ee. 11.
—— and Coolidge (W. A. B.) Climbers' Guides.
Lond. 1892, *etc.* 16°.   10108. b.
Dent (C. T.) Mountaineering. pp. 481.
1892. 4°. Badminton Library.   7905. f.
Diener (C.) Der Gebirgsbau der Westalpen.
pp. 243. *Wien*, 1891. 8°.   7105. cc. 2.
Fraas (E.) Scenerie der Alpen. pp. 325.
Leipz. 1892. 8°.   7105. cc. 3.
Hoermann (L. v.) Haussprüche aus den Alpen.
pp. 201. *Leipz.* 1890. 32°.   12304. a. 57.
Hugo (V. M.) Alpes et Pyrénées. pp. 316.
Paris, 1891. 12°.   10106. ccc. 27.
Lioy (P.) Alpinismo. pp. 395.
Milano, 1890. 8°.   10196. e. 9.
Mummery (A. F.) My Climbs in the Alps.
pp. 360. *Lond.* 1895. 8°.   K.T.C. 35. b. 2.
Meurer (J.) Der Bergsteiger im Hochgebirge.
pp. 264. *Wien*, 1893. 8°.   10196. ee. 4.
Switzerland. *Alpen-Club.* Alpina.
Zürich, 1893, *etc.* fol.   10195. g.
—— Die ersten 25 Jahre des Schweizer Alpenclub. pp. 240. *Glarus*, 1889. 8°. 10196. b. 7.
Stephen (L.) The Playground of Europe.
pp. 339. *Lond.* 1894. 8°.   2362. b. 4.
Uzielli (G.) Leonardo da Vinci e le Alpi.
pp. 76. *Torino*, 1890. 8°.   7806. de. 22. (6.)
Whymper (E.) Scrambles amongst the Alps, 1860–69. pp. 468. *Lond.* 1893. 8°.
     K.T.C. 11. a. 4.

———

Muller (A.) A Travers l'Oberland Bernois.
pp. 355. *Mulhouse*, 1891. 12°.   10195. aa. 3.
Spiez. Ein Wanderbild. Von Spiez durchs Kanderthal. *Zürich*, 1890, *etc.* 8°. 10195. aa.
Conway (W. M.) Climbers' Guide to the Eastern Pennine Alps. pp. 152. *Lond.* 1891. 8°.
     10196. aa. 17.
Miles (E. J.) Byeways in the Southern Alps.
pp. 120. *Zürich*, 1893. 8°.   10132. c. 4.
Yung (É.) Zermatt et la vallée de la Viège.
pp. 102. *Genève*, 1894. 4°.   K.T.C. 26. b. 6.
Guszfeldt (P.) Der Montblanc. pp. 280.
Berl. 1894. 8°.   10195. ee. 10.
Kurz (L.) The Chain of Mont Blanc. pp. 143. 1892. 16°. Conway and Coolidge's Climbers Guides.   10108. b.
Tutt (J. W.) Rambles in Alpine Valleys (Italian side of Mt. Blanc). pp. 208.
Lond. 1895. 8°.   10196. b. 8.
Bignami - Sormani (E.) Dizionario Alpino Italiano. pp. 309. *Milano*, 1892. 8°.
     10135. aa. 18.
Brusoni (E.) Guida alle Alpi italiane.
Domodossola, 1892. 8°.   10136. bb. 3.
Carloni (A.) Le Alpi dal Monte Rosa alle sorgenti dell' Adige. pp. 316. *Como*, 1891. 8°.
     10196. aa. 20.
Ac. Grenoble. *Société des Touristes.* Conférences sur les Alpes françaises. pp. 56.
Paris, 1893. 8°.   Ac. 6025/2.
Bertrand (M.) Études dans les Alpes françaises.
1894. 8°. Ac. Paris. *Société géologique.* Bulletin. Sér. 3, tom. 22.   Ac. 3115.
Coolidge (W. A. B.) Central Alps of Dauphiny.
pp. 248. 1892. 16°. Conway and Coolidge's Climbers' Guides.   10108. b.

ALPS.—General, etc.—_continued._

DERENNES (G.) À travers les Alpes françaises.
pp. 223. _Paris_, 1890. 8°.   10172. i. 5.

FALSAN (A.) Les Alpes français. pp. 286.
Paris, 1893. 8°.   10170. ccc. 2.

FIORIO (C.) and RATTI (C.) I Pericoli dell' Alpinismo e norme per evitarli. pp. 210.
Torino, 1889. 8°.   7906. ee. 31.

HAUG (É.) Les chaines subalpines entre Gap et Digne. pp. 197. 1891. 8°. FRANCE. _Ministère des Travaux Publics._ Bulletin. Tom. 3. No. 21.
     07109. k.

JOANNE (P.) Alpes Dauphinoises. Guide Joanne.
Paris, 1890, etc. 8°.   2362. a.

JUGE (S.) Guide bleu des Alpes françaises.
Paris, 1894, etc. 8°.   10174. aa.

PEZAY (de) _Marquis._ Noms et détails des vallées de la France le long des Grandes Alpes dans le Dauphiné et la Provence. pp. 104.
Grenoble, 1894. 8°.   010171. g. 15.

See also APENNINES : DAUPHINÉ : ENGADINE : SAVOY : SWITZERLAND.

Eastern Alps (Austria: Bavaria: Tyrol).

Ac. Germany. _Deutscher Alpenverein._ Die Erschliessung der Ostalpen. _Berl._ 1893, etc. 8°.
     Ac. 6048/3.

BAEDEKER (C.) The Eastern Alps. pp. 518.
Leipz. 1895. 8°.   2352. a. 1.

MEURER (J.) Führen durch die Ostalpen.
Wien, 1892, etc. 8°.   10205. bb. 24.

ROTHPLETZ (A.) Ein geologischer Querschnitt durch die Ost-Alpen. pp. 268.
Stuttgart, 1894. 8°.   07109. h. 41.

WEINSCHENK (E.) Beiträge zur Petrographie der östlichen Centralalpen. 1895. 4°. Ac. Munich. _K. Akademie._ Abhandlungen der math. physikal. Classe. Bd. 18.   Ac. 713/4.

Ac. Vienna. _Oesterreichischer Touristen Club._ GROEGER (G.) Die Entwicklung der Hochtouristik in den österreichischen Alpen.
pp. 258. _Wien_, 1890. 8°.   Ac. 6069.

HAUSHOFER (M.) Alpenlandschaft in den bayerischen Bergen. pp. 89. 1890. 8°. REINHARDSTOETTNER (C. v.) Bayerische Bibliothek.
Bd. 21.   12253. g,

Ac. Germany. _Deutscher Alpenverein._ WUNDT (T.) Wanderungen in den Ampezzaner Dolomiten. pp. 136. _Berl._ 1893. 4°.   10201. g. 4,

DAVIES (J. S.) Dolomite Strongholds. pp. 176,
Lond. 1894. 4°.   10201. e. 1.

MEURER (J.) Führer durch die Dolomiten.
pp. 321. _Wien_, 1890. 8°.   10215. aa. 12.

Ac. Berlin. _Geodätisches Institut._ HELMERT (F. R.) Die Schwerkraft im Hochgebirge.
pp. 52. _Berl._ 1890. 4°.   Ac. 4301/25.

RIVIÈRE (L.) Entre l'Inn et le lac de Constance.
pp. 330. _Paris_, 1891. 12°.   10215. aaa. 35.

See also AUSTRIA : BAVARIA : TYROL.

Fauna. _See_ ZOOLOGY.

Flora. _See_ BOTANY.

Glaciers. _See_ GLACIERS.

Medical Works.

HARDWICKE (H. J.) Alpine Climates for Consumption. pp. 65. _Lond._ 1894. 8°. 7616. a. 47.

WISE (A. T. T.) Alpine Winter in its medical Aspects. pp. 114. _Lond._ 1892. 8°.
     7686. aa. 4.

See also WATERING PLACES AND HEALTH RESORTS.

Military History; Alpine Defence, etc.
See MOUNTAINS.

ALSACE-LORRAINE.
     Dialects, etc.

KAHL (W.) Mundart im Elsass. pp. 62.
Zabern, 1893. 8°.   12962. o. 2.

PFISTER (C.) La limite de la langue française et de la langue allemande en Alsace-Lorraine.
pp. 44. _Paris_, 1890. 8°.   12901. d. 20. (8.)

WITTE (H.) Das deutsche Sprachgebiet Lothringens. pp. 129. 1894. 8°. LEHMANN (R.) Forschungen zur deutschen Volkskunde. Bd. 8.
     10235. i. 10.

     History, etc.

KAEPPELIN (R.) L'Alsace à travers les ages.
pp. 367. _Paris_, 1890. 18°.   9325. aaa. 20.

BERNHARDT (C.) Les Peuples préhistoriques en Lorraine. pp. 162. _Nancy_, 1890. 8°.
     07708. f. 22.

Ac. Strasburg. _Société pour la Conservation des Monuments._ Fragments des anciennes chroniques d'Alsace. _Strasb._ 1887, etc. 8°. Ac. 5284/2.

GERMAIN (D.) Documents sur l'histoire de la Lorraine. 1890. 8°. Ac. Nancy. _Société d'Archéologie._ Mémoires. Sér. 3, vol. 18.   Ac. 5314.

PFISTER (C.) Le Duché Mérovingien d'Alsace et la Légende de Sainte Odile. pp. 270.
Paris, 1892. 8°.   9340. g. 11.

SCHIBER (A.) Die fränkischen und alemannischen Siedlungen in Gallien. pp. 109.
Strasb. 1894. 8°.   9225. b. 39.

MEISTER (A.) Die Hohenstaufen im Elsass.
pp. 159. _Strassb._ 1890. 8°.   9327. cc. 7.

PANGE (M. de) _Count._ Le Patriotisme français en Lorraine antérieurement à Jeanne d'Arc.
pp. 107. _Paris_, 1889. 16°.   9210. c. 8.

NERLINGER (C.) Pierre de Hagenbach et la domination bourguignonne en Alsace. pp. 172.
Nancy, 1890. 8°.   9335. k. 5.

GOYON (M. de R. de) _Countess._ Quelques pages sur l'ancienne Lorraine. pp. 74.
Mesnil, 1893. 8°.   9902. f. 38.

BAUMONT (H.) Études sur le règne de Léopold, duc de Lorraine, 1697–1729. pp. 638.
Paris, 1894. 8°.   9077. dd. 22.

RITTNER (C. H.) Erinnerungen eines Reichsbeamten aus Elsass-Lothringen. 1871–73.
pp. 143. _Saarbrücken_, 1894. 8°.   9327. c. 15.

WITTE (H.) Lothringen und Burgund. pp. 100.
1890. 8°. Ac. Metz. _Gesellschaft für Lothringische Geschichte._ Jahr-Buch. Jahrg. 2.
     Ac. 7112.

WITTE (H.) Zur Geschichte des Deutschtums in Lothringen. 1890. 8°. Ac. Metz. _Gesellschaft für Lothringische Geschichte._ Jahr-Buch.
Jahrg. 2.   Ac. 7112.

FITTE (S.) Das Verhältnis des Herzogtums Lothringen zum deutschen Reich, seit dem Jahre 1542. pp. 102. 1891. 8°. ALSACE. Beiträge zur Volkskunde. Heft. 14.   10240. c.

REUSS (R.) L'Alsace pendant la Révolution française. 2 vol. _Paris_, 1880–94. 8°. 9231 l. 7.

ALSATIAN CHURCH HISTORY. Quellenschriften der elsässischen Kirchengeschichte.
Strassb. 1894, etc. 8°.   4662. f.

BRUCKER (P. P.) L'Alsace et l'Église au temps du Pape Léon IX. 2 tom. _Strassb._ 1889. 8°.
     4856. f. 9,

SCHNEIDER (I.) Die elsässische Kirche in der Zeit der Revolution. pp. 42. 1889. 8°.
ALSACE-LORRAINE. _Protestantischer Verein._
Schriften. No. 31.   3910. aaa,

SCHNEIDER (J.) Geschichte der evangelischen Kirche des Elsass in der Zeit der Revolution.
pp. 212. _Strassb._ 1890. 8°.   4661. dd. 22.

ALSACE-LORRAINE—continued.

Law.

BONVALOT (É.) Histoire du droit de la Lorraine, 843–1789. pp. 386. *Paris*, 1895. 8°.
9327. dd. 14.

LEONI (A.) Das öffentliche Recht des Reichslandes. *Freiburg*, 1892, *etc.* 8°. 05604. k. 2.

HOLLERITH (A.) Die Gesetze über das Enregistrement in Elsass-Lothringen. pp. 386. *Strassburg*, 1891. 8°. 5606. d. 9.

Politics.

ECKEL (A.) La Réunion de l'Alsace à la France. pp. 57. *Vesoul*, 1894. 8°. 9078. c. 25. (6.)

HEIMWEH (J.) Triple Alliance et Alsace-Lorraine. pp. 138. *Paris*, 1892. 8°. 8026. b. 22.

—— Le Régime des Passeports en Alsace-Lorraine. pp. 76. *Paris*, 1890. 8°. 8026. bb. 25.

LAVISSE (E.) La question d'Alsace dans une âme d'Alsacien. pp. 52. *Paris*, 1891. 8°.
8026. aa. 22.

MOCH (G.) Alsace-Lorraine. Réponse à un pamphlet allemand. pp. 272. *Paris*, 1895. 12°.
8026. aa. 39.

PASSOT (L.) Comment on peut reprendre l'Alsace. pp. 76. *Paris*, 1894. 4°. 12330. dd. 34.

PATIENS. L'Alsace-Lorraine devant l'Europe. pp. 584. *Paris*, 1894. 12°. 8026. aa. 31.

ROHDEWALD (W.) Die Abtretung des Elsass an Frankreich. pp. 76. *Halle*, 1893. 8°. 9327. ccc.

ROSENBOURG (B. de) Solution de la question de l'Alsace-Lorraine par le partage de la Turquie. pp. 23. *Lausanne*, 1890. 8°. 8026. aaa. 40. (5.)

WALDTEUFEL (É.) Mémoire pour la rétrocession de l'Alsace Lorraine. pp. 287. *Paris*, 1893. 8°.
8026. aa. 27.

Topography : Social Life.

AUERBACH (B.) Le Plateau Lorrain. pp. 358. *Paris*, 1893. 8°. 10170. b. 2.

FRISCH (R. J.) Topographie militaire de la haute Alsace. pp. 92. *Paris*, 1893. 8°. 10169. d. 5.

GERLAND (G.) Geographische Abhandlungen aus den Reichslanden. *Stuttgart*, 1892, *etc.* 8°.
10195. ee.

MATTHIS (C. E.) L'Alsace à travers les siècles. pp. 374. *Paris*, 1891. 4°. 10250. h. 5.

POGNON (P.) Le Paysan Lorrain. pp. 166. *Neufchateau*, 1891. 8°. 9902. ccc. 9.

STOEBER (A.) Die Sagen des Elsasses. *Strassburg*, 1892, *etc.* 8°. 12430. k.

ALSTON, Cumberland. PAGE (I. E.) Walks round Alston. pp. 94. *Carlisle*, 1894. 8°. 10350. aaa. 47.

ALTAI. GRUNZEL (J.) Entwurf einer vergleichenden Grammatik der altaischen Sprachen. pp. 90. *Leip.* 1895. 8°. 12910. d. 34.

ALTENBURG. BESSER (G.) Beiträge zur Geschichte des Magdalenen-Stifts zu Altenburg. pp. 160. *Altenburg*, 1892. 8°. 4662. c. 23.

ALTMARK. ZAHN (W.) Geschichte der Altmark. pp. 92. *Stendal*, 1891. 8°.
9008. g. 12. (6.)

ALTONA. ALTONA. Bericht über die Gemeinde-Verwaltung der Stadt Altona 1863–88. *Altona*, 1889, *etc.* fol. 8228. k.

—— Altona unter Schauenburgischer Herrschaft. *Altona*, 1891, *etc.* 8°. 10250. g. 2.

EHRENBERG (R.) Altona's topographische Entwickelung. pp. 36. *Altona*, 1894. 4°. 1781. a. 5.

See also SCHLESWIG-HOLSTEIN.

ALUMINIUM. LEJEAL (A.) L'Aluminium. pp. 357. *Paris*, 1894. 12°. 7105. aa. 5.

LE VERRIER (U.) Études sur l'Aluminium. 1892, *etc.* 8°. Ac. Paris. *Conservatoire des Arts.* Annales. Sér. 2, tom. 4. Ac. 4415.

LUDWIG ( ) Ueber Aluminium. pp. 30. 1892. 8°. HUTH (E.) Sammlung naturwissenschaftlicher Vorträge. 8705. ff.

MINET (A.) L'Aluminium. pp. 312. *Paris*, 1893. 8°. 7106. b. 48.

NEUHAUSEN. *Société pour l'Industrie de l'Aluminium.* L'Établissement de la Société. pp. 149. *Schaffhouse*, 1890. 8°. 7106. c. 13.

PROPERTIES. The Properties of Aluminium. pp. 14. *Lond.* 1892. 16°. 7106. de. 2.

STEAD (J. E.) Report on Aluminium in Steel. pp. 33. *Lond.* 1890. 8°. 7942. i. 43. (11.)

See also MINERALOGY.

ALWINGTON. HINGESTON-RANDOLPH (F. C.) Rectors and Patrons of Alwington. ff. 14. *Exeter*, 1894. 4°. Pam. 29.

AMAZON, *River.* ACUÑA (C. de) Nuevo descubrimiento del gran Rio de las Amazonas. pp. 235. 1891. 8°. AMERICA. Collección de libros. tom. 2. 9551. bbb.

BATES (H. W.) The Naturalist on the River Amazons. pp. 389. *London*, 1892. 8°. 2374. f. 1.

CARVAJAL (G. de) Descubrimiento del Río de las Amazonas. pp. 278. *Sevilla*, 1894. 8°.
9771. eee. 18.

LEAL (O.) O Amazonas. pp. 66. *Lisboa*, 1894. 8°. 10480. bbb. 40.

ORDINAIRE (O.) Du Pacifique à l'Atlantique. pp. 291. *Paris*, 1892. 12°. 10481. aa. 37.

SCHICHTEL (C.) Der Amazonen-Strom. pp. 117. *Strassburg*, 1893. 8°. 10481. ff. 39.

AMAZULA LANGUAGE.

See AFRICAN LANGUAGES.

AMBALA. UMBALLA. Gazetteer. 1892–93. pp. 156. *Lahore*, 1893. 8°. 10056. k. 36.

AMBASSADORS. *See* DIPLOMACY : LAW, *International.*

AMBER. HADDOW (J. G.) Amber. pp. 59. 1892. 8°. Cope's Smoke Room Booklets. no. 7.
012314. i. 3.

AMBLAINVILLE. MANNEVILLE (C. A. A. de) De l'état d'Amblainville, du XIIᵉ au XVᵉ siècle. pp. 389. *Beauvais*, 1890. 8°. 10174. g. 27.

AMBOISE, Indre et Loire. CROY (J. de) Documents pour l'histoire de la création des Résidences royales du bord de la Loire. pp. 218. *Paris*, 1894. 8°. 10171. g. 3.

AMBULANCE. BEATSON (G. T.) Ambulance Handbook. pp. 383. *Glasgow*, 1891. 8°.
7688. a. 35.

BRODIE (J. E.) Manual of Stretcher Drill. pp. 67. *Glasgow*, 1894. 16°. 7688. a. 54.

CAMERON (A.) Practical Hints on Ambulance. pp. 32. *Manch.* 1895. 16°. 07686. de. 5.

CLARK (A.) First Aid to the Injured. pp. 79. *Lond.* 1888. 8°. 7481. aa. 28.

DAMICO (F.) Secours aux noyés, asphyxiés et blessés. pp. 186. *Paris*, 1895. 8°. 7615. d. 13.

DARWIN (G. H.) Ambulance Lectures. pp. 95. *Manch.* 1892. 8°. 7688. a. 38.

DULLES (C. W.) Accidents and Emergencies. pp. 154. *Lond.* 1893. 8°. 7481. bb. 14.

ESMARCH (F.) First Aid to the Injured. pp. 115. *Lond.* 1893. 8°. 7688. a. 42.

AMBULANCE—*continued.*

GELL (H. W.) Aids to the Injured and Sick.
pp. 32. 1892. 8°. London. *National Health
Society.* Pamphlets. 7404. df.

HUSSEY (E. L.) In Accidents. pp. 56.
Oxf. 1889. 8°. 7481. aaa. 31.

LAWLESS (E. J.) First Aid to the Injured.
pp. 262. *Edinb.* 1894. 8°. 7688. aa. 52.

MARTIN (J. M. H.) Illustrated Ambulance Lectures. pp. 148. *Lond.* 1895. 8°. 7688. aa. 58.

MARTIN (J. W.) Ambulance Work. pp. 70.
Lond. 1895. 16°. 7688. a. 61.

MORGAN (L.) Ambulance Card.
Liverp. 1893. 12°. 1830. c. 1. (88.)

OSBORN (S.) Ambulance Lectures. pp. 148.
Lond. 1894. 8°. 7688. a. 53.

—— Premiers secours à donner aux malades.
pp. 150. *Paris*, 1894. 12°. 7688. aa. 50.

—— Conferenze sull' ambulanza. pp. 109.
Firenze, 1894. 8°. 7688. a. 50.

PARTRIDGE (S.) Practical Ambulance Tablets.
pp. 59. *Lond.* 1895. 16°. 7688. a. 64.

PILCHER (J. E.) First Aid in Illness and Injury.
pp. 304. *Lond.* 1892. 8°. 7481. aaa. 33.

RIDDELL (J. S.) Manual of Ambulance.
pp. 214. *Lond.* 1894. 8°. 7688. aa. 53.

ROBERTS (R. L.) Lectures on Ambulance Work.
pp. 206. *Lond.* 1895. 8°. 7688. aa. 55.

SHEPHERD (P.) First Aid to the Injured.
pp. 95. *Lond.* 1893. 16°. 7688. a. 44.

SUTHERLAND (J. F.) The Ambulance Pupil's
Vade-Mecum. *Glasg.* 1894. 32°. 7688. a. 57.

THOMPSON (C. J. S.) "The Best Thing to do."
pp. 53. *Lond.* 1893. 8°. 7688. aa. 48.

ZIFFEL (G. L.) Manuel de l'Ambulancière.
pp. 169. *Paris*, 1891. 8°. 7688. aaa. 43.

See also ACCIDENTS : BANDAGING.

Red Cross Society : Military Ambulance.

BAUER (M.) Unter rothgekreuzten Standarten
im Felde und Daheim. pp. 133.
Berl. 1895. 8°. 9080. f. 7.

BEYER (H. G.) First Aid to the Injured. 1892. 8°.
Ac. Annapolis. *Naval Institute.* Papers.
vol. 18. Ac. 4398.

BUNGARTZ (J.) Der Hund im Dienste des rothen
Kreuzes. pp. 63. *Leipz.* 1892. 8°. 7291. aaa. 31.

COLLEVILLE (M. de) La croix-rouge à Reims.
pp. 55. *Reims*, 1890. 8°. 8830. c. 43. (9.)

FRANCE. *Ministère de la Guerre.* École de l'Infirmier militaire. 2 vol. *Paris*, 1894. 12°. 8823. f. 5.

FROELICH (L.) Du Transport des blessés sur voies
ferrées. pp. 27. *Frauenfeld*, 1892. 8°.
07305. h. 18. (8.)

G. B. & I. *Army. Medical Services.* Manual of
Ambulance Transport. pp. 453. *Lond.* 1893. 8°.
8828. ff. 22.

—— Manual of drills and exercises for Volunteer
Bearer Companies. pp. 60. *Lond.* 1893. 16°.
8831. a. 88. (6.)

U.S. *Association of the Red Cross.* History of the
Red Cross. pp. 227. *Wash.* 1883. 8°. 7687. g. 14.

See also MEDICINE, *Military.*

AMERICA.—Bibliography.

AMERICA. Colección de libros que tratan de América. *Madrid*, 1891, *etc.* 8°. 9551. bbb.

HUNNEWELL (J. F.) Illustrated Americana, 1493-
1889. pp. 37. 1890. 4°. 11899. f. 42.

Antiquities.

Ac. Boston, *Mass. Archæological Institute.*
Papers. American Series.
Boston, 1883, *etc.* 8°. Ac. 5790/8.

AMERICA.—Antiquities - *continued.*

Ac. Washington. *Smithsonian Institution.* The
Earthworks of Ohio. pp. 33. *Wash.* 1889. 8°.
7706. g. 6. (5.)

—— THOMAS (C.) Problem of the Ohio Mounds.
pp. 54. *Wash.* 1889. 8°. 7706. g. 8. (12.)

MOOREHEAD (W. K.) Primitive Man in Ohio.
pp. 246. *N.Y.* 1892. 8°. 7709. e. 6.

DELORME SALTO (R.) Los Aborígenes de América. pp. 230. *Madrid*, 1894. 8°. 10408. cc. 35.

DOUAY (L.) Études étymologiques sur l'Antiquité
américaine. pp. 158. *Paris*, 1891. 8°.
12910. e. 35.

KABELL (S. K.) America før Columbus.
Rønne, 1892, *etc.* 8°. 9551. i. 15.

KEDĀRANĀTHA VASU. Hindu Civilization in
ancient America. pp. 30. *Calcutta*, 1888. 4°.
07708. f. 19.

P.P. Boston. Journal of American Ethnology
and Archæology. *Boston*, 1891, *etc.* 4°.
P.P. 3862. c.

PEET (S. A.) Prehistoric America.
Chicago, 1890, *etc.* 8°. 7706. e. 35.

RIAÑO (J. F.) El arte monumental americano.
pp. 20. *Madrid*, 1892. 8°. 7704. i. 12. (7.)

SHALER (N. S.) Nature and Man in America.
pp. 290. *Lond.* 1892. 8°. 7001. b. 9.

TOWNSEND (M. I.) Prehistoric Structures of
Central America. Who erected them?
pp. 31. *Troy, N.Y.* 1895. 8°. 9551. f. 14.

SMITH (H. I.) American Antiquities at the Columbian Exposition. *Saginaw*, 1892. 8°. Pam. 3.

STUEBEL (A.) Die Ruinenstaette von Tiahuanaco.
pp. 67. *Breslau*, 1892. fol. 1706. c. 15.

UHLE (F. M.) Ausgewählte Stücke des Museums
für Völkerkunde zur Archäologie Amerikas.
1889. 8°. BERLIN. *K. Museen.* Veröffentlichungen. Bd. 1, Heft 1. 7708. g. 24.

VILANOVA Y PIERA (J.) Protohistoria americana.
pp. 45. *Madrid*, 1892. 8°. Pam. 27.

See also INDIANS, *American* : MEXICO : PERU.

Central. *See infra : South, etc.*

Discovery & Early Voyages.

Ac. Berlin. *Gesellschaft für Erdkunde.* Die
Entdeckung Amerika's. pp. 471.
Berl. 1892. 4°. 1854. a. 3.

—— Atlas. fol. 1854. b. 1.

Ac. Madrid. *Ateneo Científico.* Conferencias.
Madrid, 1892. 8°. 9551. l. 7. (1–23.)

Ac. Paris. *Bibliothèque Nationale.* Quatrième
centenaire de la découverte de l'Amérique. Catalogue des documents géographiques. pp. 77.
Paris, 1892. 8°. 11903. d. 31. (10.)

CASTELAR Y RIPOLL (E.) Historia del Descubrimiento de América. pp. 594.
Madrid, 1892. 8°. 9551. k. 5.

CRONAU (R.) Amerika. Die Geschichte seiner
Entdeckung. *Leipz.* 1892, *etc.* 4°. 9551. l. 6.

FISKE (J.) The Discovery of America. 2 vol.
Lond. 1892. 8°. 2398. b. 9.

GAFFAREL (P.) Histoire de la Découverte de
l'Amérique. 2 tom. *Paris*, 1892. 8°. 9551. i. 16.

HAMBURG. Hamburgische Festschrift zur Erinnerung an die Entdeckung Amerika's. 2 Bde.
Hamb. 1892. 8°. 9551. k. 6.

HARRISSE (H.) Discovery of North America.
Lond. 1892, *etc.* 4°. 9551. l.

—— Nouvelles recherches sur l'histoire de l'Amérique. pp. 11. *Paris*, 1890. 8°. 9004. m. 7. (13.)

AMERICA.—Discovery, etc.—*continued.*

HEYWOOD (J. C.) Documenta selecta e tabulario secreto Vaticano. ff. 45. *Romae*, 1893. fol.
K.T.C. 3. b. 20.

KRETSCHMER (K.) Die Entdeckung Amerika's. pp. 471. *Berl.* 1892. fol.
S. 228. (17.) & S. 237. (4.)

MEUGENS, afterwards BELL (N.) Heroes of American Discovery. pp. 370. *Lond.* 1893. 8°.
9551. b. 3.

PANDO Y VALLE (J.) El Centenario del Descubrimiento de América. *Madrid*, 1892, etc. 8°.
9551. bb.

ROME. Raccolta di Documenti e Studi. *Roma*, 1892, etc. 4°. 1856. c.

SALIS Y FERRÉ (M.) El Descubrimiento de América. pp. 255. *Sevilla*, 1893. 8°. 9551. b. 5.

SCHUSTER (G.) Die Entdeckung Amerika's. pp. 195. *Basel*, 1892. 8°. 9551. c. 12.

HOWELL (G. R.) Pre-Columbian Discoveries of America, etc. pp. 25. *Albany*, 1893. 8°. Pam. 28.

VALLE (M. M. del) Precedentes del descubrimiento de América. pp. 80. *Madrid*, 1892. 8°.
9551. dd. 2.

VÉLEZ (B.) Descubrimiento precolombino de la America. pp. 116. *Paris*, 1894. 12°. 9551. b. 4.

FLATEY-CODEX. The "Flatey-Book." — Flatö Bogen. *Copenh.* 1893. fol. 1857. c. 12.

BAXTER (J. P.) Present status of pre-Columbian discovery of America by Norsemen. pp. 7. *Wash.* 1894. 8°. 9007. g. 20. (3.)

GELCICH (E.) Zur Geschichte der Entdeckung Amerikas durch die Skandinavier. 1892. 8°. Ac. Berlin. *Gesellschaft für Erdkunde.* Zeitschrift. Bd. 27. Ac. 6075/2.

HORN (F. W.) Nordboernes Rejser til Amerika. pp. 23. *Kjøbenh.* 1890. 12°. Pam. 86.

SLAFTER (E. F.) Discovery of America by the Northmen. 985–1015. pp. 24. *Concord*, 1891. 8°. 9555. f. 4. (4.)

HORSFORD (E. N.) Discovery of the ancient city of Norumbega. *Camb. Mass.* 1889. 4°.
7709. k. 13.

—— The Defences of Norumbega. pp. 84. *Bost.* 1891. 4°. 9551. m. 1.

—— The Landfall of Leif Erikson, A.D. 1000. pp. 148. *Bost.* 1892. 4°. 10411. k. 11.

—— Leif's House in Vineland. pp. 40. *Bost.* 1893. 4°. 9551. l. 8.

BROWN, afterwards SHIPLEY (M. A.) Roman Catholic evidence confirming Leif Erikson's discovery of America. pp. 27. *N.Y.* 1890. 12°.
9004. g. 21. (6.)

OLSON (J. E.) Review of the Problem of the Northmen and the Site of Norumbega. pp. 22. 1891. 4°. 9551. k. 3.

SHEPARD (E. G.) Guide-Book to Norumbega & Vineland. pp. 48. *Bost.* 1893. 8°. 9551. bb. 22.

TORFÆUS (T.) History of ancient Vinland by Thormod Torfason. pp. 83. *N.Y.* 1891. 8°.
9551. i. 17.

DE COSTA (B. F.) Pre-Columbian voyages of the Welsh to America. pp. 12. *Albany*, 1891. 8°.
Pam. 28.

STEPHENS (T.) Discovery of America by Madoc ap Owen Gwynedd in the 12th century. pp. 249. *Lond.* 1893. 8°. 9551. i. 20.

UZIELLI (G.) Paolo dal Pozzo Toscanelli, iniziatore della scoperta d'America. pp. 247. *Firenze*, 1892. 8°. 9551. b. 6.

FUMAGALLI (G.) Bibliografia degli scritti italiani sopra C. Colombo. pp. 217. 1893. 4°. ROME. *R. Commission Colombianae.* Raccolta di documenti. pt. 6. 1856. c.

AMERICA.—Discovery, etc.—*continued.*

Ac. London. *Hakluyt Society.* COLOMBO (C.) Journal of Columbus, 1492–93. pp. 259. *Lond.* 1893. 8°. Ac. 6172/68.

COLOMBO (C.) Epistola C. Colom. de Insulis Indie. 1894. 4°. 9551. c. 15.

—— Epistola de insulis nouiter repertis. Photolithograph. *Lond.* 1893. 8°. 9551. c. 9.

—— The Letter of Columbus on the Discovery of America. pp. 61. *N.Y.* 1892. 8°.
9551. bb. 18.

—— The Spanish Letter of Columbus to Luis de Sant' Angel. *Lond.* 1893. 4°. 9551. f. 7.

—— Christopher Columbus. His Book of Privileges. 1502. *Lond.* 1893. fol. K.T.C 24. b. 4.

HARRISSE (H.) Autographes de C. Colomb récemment découverts. pp. 23. *Paris*, 1893. 8°.
Pam. 6.

ABAJO FERNANDEZ (J.) Colón ante el comercio del mundo. pp. 180. *Madrid*, 1892. 8°.
9551. b. 2.

ADAMS (C. K.) C. Columbus; his life and work. pp. 261. *N.Y.* 1892. 8°. 10630. bb. 43.

ADAMS (H. B.) Columbus and his Discovery of America. pp. 88. 1892. 8°. Johns Hopkins University Studies. Ac. 2689.

ANGLERIUS (P. M.) Fuentes históricas sobre Colón y América. 4 tom. *Madrid*, 1892. 8°.
9551. aaa. 1.

ASENSIO Y TOLEDO (J. M.) Colón, su vida, sus viajes. 2 tom. *Barcelona*, 1892. 4°.
10632. h. 14.

BALAGUÈR (V.) C. Colón. Essays. pp. 247. *Madrid*, 1892. 8°. 10630. c. 45.

BELLIO (V.) Cristoforo Colombo. pp. 159. *Milano*, 1892. 8°. 012200. h. 48.

BRUNET Y BELLET (J.) Colón. Fué el verdadero descabridor de América? pp. 99. *Barcelona*, 1892. 8°. 9004. gg. 30. (4.)

CARDELL (A. J.) Columbus and the Discovery of America. pp. 76. *Lond.* 1892. 8°.
9004. gg. 23. (5.)

CAUSA (C.) Vita e viaggi di Cristoforo Colombo. pp. 524. *Firenze*, 1892. 8°. 10630. cc. 32.

COLOMBO (C.) Columbus and Cook. pp. 152. *Lond.* 1895. 8°. 10602. aaaa. 27.

—— Columbus and his times. pp. 128. *Lond.* 1892. 8°. 4429. de. 30.

—— Photographs of the first Forts, Towns, Churches, built by Columbus. pp. 32. *N.Y.* 1893. obl. 8°. 10481. a. 17.

CROCE (E.) Christophe Colomb. Études. pp. 78. *Paris*, 1885. 8°. Pam. 8.

ELTON (C. I.) The Career of Columbus. pp. 307. *Lond.* 1892. 8°. 10631. f. 44.

FASTENRATH (J.) C. Columbus. Studien. pp. 636. *Dresd.* 1895. 8°. 10630. c. 51.

FEUILLETTE ( ) C. Colomb. Discours. pp. 54. *Paris*, 1892. 8°. 9551. i. 18.

FOURNIER (A.) Histoire de la Vie de C. Colomb. pp. 739. *Paris*, 1894. 12°. 10630. b. 52.

FRANCISCANS. C. Colombo e il quarto centenario dalla scoperta dell' America. pp. 542. *Firenze*, 1893. fol. 9551. l. 9.

GENOA. Cronache della Commemorazione del IV. Centenario Colombiano. pp. 435. *Genova*, 1892. fol. 1850. a. 7.

GIAMBERINI (A.) C. Colombo e il IV. centenario della scoperta dell' America. pp. 217. *Bologna*, 1894. 8°. 9551. bb. 26.

HARRISSE (H.) C. Colomb devant l'histoire. pp. 121. *Paris*, 1892. 8°. 10630. g. 26.

—— Colomb, les Corses, et le Gouvernement français. pp. 32. *Paris*, 1890. 8°. 10630. ff. 37.

AMERICA.—Discovery, etc.—_continued._

HAUTREUX (A.) Le Voyage de Découverte de Colomb. 1892. 8°. Ac. Bordeaux. _Académie de Sciences._ Actes; année 54. Ac. 297.

INNES (A.) Life of Columbus. pp. 147. _Glasgow_, 1892. 8°. 9551. a. 2.

IRVING (W.) Life of Columbus. pp. 412. _N.Y._ 1893. 8°. 10630. c. 46.

LAZZARONI (M. A.) C. Colombo. Osservazioni critiche. 2 vol. _Milano_, 1892. 4°. 10630. g. 27.

LUCCI-MARCHI (G.) C. Colombo e la Scoperta del Nuovo Mondo. pp. 163. _Milano_, 1892. 8°. 9551. i. 19.

MAC KIE (C. P.) With the Admiral of the Ocean Sea. pp. 338. _Lond._ 1892. 8°. 9551. bb. 15.

MARKHAM (C. R.) Life of Columbus. pp. 375. 1892. 8°. KELTIE (J. S.) The World's Explorers. 10024. cc.

MARTINEZ (M.) C. Colón. Biografía. 2 pt. _Granada_, 1892. 8°. 9551. f. 8.

MONTEIRO (M.) C. Columbus. pp. 176. 1893. 8°. Heroes of the Cross. 4804. cc.

MUNDELL (F.) Into the unknown West. pp. 253. _Lond._ 1892. 8°. 9551. bb. 16.

N., F. C. Colon. pp. 64. _Barcelona_, 1892. 8°. 10601. a. 38. (5.)

OBERZINER (L. A.) C. Colombo. pp. 29. _Chiavari_, 1892. 8°. 9551. k. 8. (4.)

PERAGALLO (P.) Disquisizioni Colombine. _Lisboa_, 1895, _etc._ 8°. 10631. g.

POOLE (W. F.) Columbus and the finding of the New World. pp. 19. _Chicago_, 1892. 16°. 9004. bbb. 15. (6.)

RASTOUL (A.) C. Colomb. pp. 382. _Paris_, 1893. 8°. 10630. g. 25.

REIN (J.) Columbus und seine vier Reisen nach dem Westen. pp. 244. 1892. 8°. _Geographische Abhandlungen._ No. 1. 10002. dd.

RICARD (A.) C. Colomb. pp. 391. _Tours_, 1892. 4°. 10631. i. 19.

RISSO (G.) Vita e viaggi di Colombo. pp. 117. _Genova_, 1892. 8°. 9551. bb. 23.

SABAZIO (S.) Intorno alla patria di Colombo. pp. 80. _Savona_, 1893. 8°. Pam. 8.

SALTER (W.) The voyage of Columbus. 1492. pp. 78. _Burlington_, 1892. 8°. 9551. c. 11.

SAUNDERS (F.) Story of the Discovery of the New World by Columbus. pp. 145. _N.Y._ 1892. 8°. 9551. bb. 17.

SCHMELZER (A.) Columbus und die Entdeckung Amerikas. pp. 34. _Merseburg_, 1892. 8°. 9008. l. 1. (9.)

SEELYE (E. E.) The Story of Columbus. pp. 303. _N.Y._ 1892. 8°. 9551. bb. 19.

SERRATO (F.) C. Colón. Historia del descubrimiento de América. pp. 422. _Madrid_, 1893. 8°. 9551. d. 1.

TORRE Y VÉLEZ (A. de la) Estudios acerca de un período de la vida de Colón, 1449-1491. pp. 304. _Madrid_, 1892. 8°. 10630. e. 39.

V., B. A. Colomb et ses historiens espagnols. pp. 19. _Paris_, 1892. 8°. Pam. 8.

VIDAL GORMÁZ (F.) Las primeras tierras que vió Colon al descubrir el Nuevo Mundo. pp. 34. _Santiago de C._ 1892. 8°. Pam. 28.

VIDART (L.) Colon y la ingratitud de España. pp. 35. _Madrid_, 1892. 8°. 9009. m. 8. (7.)

WINSOR (J.) Columbus, how he received and imparted the spirit of discovery. pp. 674. _Lond._ 1891. 8°. 2402. e. 14.

Ac. Barcelona. _Ateneo._ Centenario del descubrimiento de América. Conferencias. pp. 450. _Barcelona_, 1893. 8°. 9180. g. 26.

AMERICA.—Discovery, etc.—_continued._

Ac. Europe. _Congrès des Américanistes._ Memorias presentadas en Congresos Internacionales. pp. 91. _Chartres_, 1893. 8°. Ac. 6220/2.

FERNÁNDEZ DURO (C.) Pinzón en el Descubrimiento de las Indias. pp. 363. _Madrid_, 1892. 8°. 9551. b. 1.

GAFFAREL (P.) Découvertes des Portugais en Amérique au temps de Colomb. pp. 38. _Paris_, 1892. 8°. 9551. k. 8. (2.)

IBARRA Y RODRIGUEZ (E.) D. Fernando el Católico y el descubrimiento de America. pp. 203. _Madrid_, 1892. 8°. 9551. bb. 20.

MIR (M.) Influencia de los Aragoneses en el descubrimiento de América. pp. 93. _Palma de Mallorca_, 1892. 8°. 9551. bb. 25.

MANDONNET (P. F.) Les dominicains et la découverte de l'Amérique. pp. 255. _Paris_, 1893. 12°. 9551. bb. 24.

Ac. Venice. _Deputazione Veneta di Storia Patria._ Di Giovanni e Sebastiano Caboto, memorie raccolte da F. Tarducci. pp. 429. _Venezia_, 1892. 8°. Ac. 6580/5.

HARRISSE (H.) John Cabot, the discoverer of North America, and Sebastian, his son. pp. 503. _Lond._ 1895. 8°. K.T.C. 37. a. 1.

TARDUCCI (F.) J. and S. Cabot. pp. 409. _Detroit_, 1893. 8°. 9551. i. 23.

V., B. A. Sébastien Cabot, 1497-1557. pp. 43. _Paris_, 1895. 8°. Pam. 8.

Ac. London. _Hakluyt Society._ VESPUCCI (A.) Letters of Amerigo Vespucci. pp. 121. _Lond._ 1894. 8°. Ac. 6172/71.

HARRISSE (H.) Americus Vespuccius. Review of two recent English books concerning that Navigator. pp. 67. _Lond._ 1895. 8°. 9551. c. 14.

HUGUES (L.) Amerigo Vespucci. 1894. fol. ROME. _Reale Commissione Colombiana._ Raccolta di documenti. Vol. 2. 1856. c.

VESPUCCI (A.) First Four Voyages of A. Vespucci. _Lond._ 1893. 4°. 9551. f. 4.

MARCEL (G.) Reproductions de cartes relatifs à la découverte de l'Amérique du XVIᵉ au XVIIIᵉ siècle. 2 pt. 1893. 8°. SCHEFER (C.) Recueil de Voyages, _etc._ 10024. i. & 14000. i. 21.

WINSOR (J.) Geographical Discovery in the Interior of North America, 1537-1700. pp. 379. _Lond._ 1894. 8°. 9551. f. 11.

SHIPLEY (J. B.) English Rediscovery and Colonization of America. pp. 151. _Lond._ 1891. 8°. 9551. bb. 11.

HAKLUYT (R.) Voyages of the Elizabethan Seamen to America. _Oxf._ 1893, _etc._ 8°. 10408. de.

DE COSTA (B. F.) Voyage of Pierre Angibaut to the Coast of Maine, 1608. pp. 7. _Albany_, 1891. 8°. 9004. m. 6. (14.)

See also VOYAGES AND TRAVELS.

History.

MABIE (H. W.) and BRIGHT (M. H.) Memorial Story of America, 1492 to 1892. pp. 851. _Phila._ 1892. 8°. 9555. f. 6.

PAYNE (E. J.) History of the New World. _Oxf._ 1892, _etc._ 8°. 2398. d. 9.

PERRY (W. S.) _Bishop of Iowa._ Four Centuries of Conflict for the Continent of N. America. 1497-1897. pp. 36. 1895. 12°. Pam. 29.

SCHMIDT (E.) Vorgeschichte Nordamerikas im Gebiet der Vereinigten Staaten. pp. 216. _Braunschweig_, 1894. 8°. 9551. d. 2.

WINSOR (J.) Rival Claimants for N. America. 1497-1755. pp. 21. _Worcester, Mass._, 1895. 8°. 9551. k.

AMERICA.—History—*continued.*

ZIMMERMAN (G. A.) Vierhundert Jahre Amerikanischer Geschichte. pp. 736.
Milwaukee, 1893. 8°. 9551. f. 9.

Indians. *See* INDIAN LANGUAGES: INDIANS.

Topography.

AMERICA, *North.* Geography of North America. pp. 38. *Lond.* 1894. 8°. Pam. 86.

GAMBINO BAGNASCO (G.) Americæ Retectio. Atlas by J. van der Straet and F. H. Brueghel. pp. 27. *Palermo,* 1892. 8°. 9551. k. 4.

OBERLAENDER (C.) Ein Ausflug nach Amerika. pp. 212. *Hamb.* 1893. 8°. 10409. aa. 37.

PAASCHE (H.) Kultur- und Reiseskizzen aus Nord- und Mittel-Amerika. pp. 553.
Magdeburg, 1894. 8°. 10408. dd. 13.

SCAIFE (W. B.) America: its geographical history, 1492–1892. pp. 176. 1892. 8°. Johns Hopkins University Studies. Ac. 2689.

SHALER (N. S.) Reader in Geography of N. America. pp. 290. *Bost.* 1892. 8°. 10409. c. 36.

See also under each country in the continent of America.

North. *See supra: General: General:* CANADA: MEXICO: UNITED STATES, *etc.*

South and Central (Spanish and Portuguese).

Antiquities. See supra: AMERICA, *Antiquities:* MEXICO: PERU.

ENCYCLOPAEDIAS. Diccionario enciclopedico Hispano-Americano, *etc. Barcelona,* 1887, *etc.* 4°. 1878. c.

LARRABURE Y UNANUE (E.) Monografías histórico-Americanas. pp. 426. *Lima,* 1893. 8°. 9551. f. 10.

LLORENTE VÁZQUEZ (M.) Cuadros Americanos— Venezuela, Brasil, California, Guatemala, Montevideo y Ecuador. pp. 432. *Madrid,* 1891. 8°. 9771. aaa. 1.

ZABÁLBURU (F. de) Nueva colección de documentos para la historia de España y de sus Indias. *Madrid,* 1892, *etc.* 8°. 9180. ff.

LUMMIS (C. F.) The Spanish Pioneers. pp. 292. *Chicago,* 1893. 8°. 9551. b. 7.

FERNÁNDEZ ARIAS (E.) Paralelo entre la conquista de América y el descubrimiento de Filipinas. pp. 62. *Madrid,* 1893. 8°. 9551. bb. 28.

SPAIN. CHARLES V. *Emperor of Germany.* The New Laws of the Indies. 1542–43. pp. 13. *Lond.* 1893. fol. K.T.C. 1. b. 8.

QUESADA (V. G.) Crónicas Potosinas. 2 tom. *Paris,* 1890. 18°. 9772. aaa. 27.

—— La Sociedad bajo la dominación española. pp. 53. *Madrid,* 1893. 8°. 9771. e. 2.

MADRID.—*Exposición Americana.* Catálogo de los documentos de Indias. pp. 134.
Madrid, 1892. 8°. 7959. f. 36.

SPAIN. Isagoge historico de todas las Indias. pp. 445. *Madrid,* 1892. 4°. 9772. g. 8.

SCHMIDEL (U.) U. Schmidels Reise nach Südamerika in den Jahren 1534–54. pp. 60. *Straubing,* 1893. 8°. Pam. 86.

CASTAÑOS Y MONTIJANO (M.) Narración de algunos hechos de armas de la guerra separatista de América. pp. 144. *Toledo,* 1892. 8°. 9772. b. 15.

LAMAS (A.) El génesis de la revolucion de la América Española. pp. 67. 1891. fol. Ac. La Plata. *Museo.* Anales. Pt. 1. Tab. 1227. a.

MITRE (B.) Historia de San Martín y de la emancipación sudamericana. 3 tom. *Buenos A.* 1887–88. 8°. 010882. k. 1.

AMERICA.—South and Central—*cont.*

MITRE (B.) Emancipation of South America. pp. 499. *Lond.* 1893. 8°. 9771. eee. 17.
See also under each country of CENTRAL & SOUTH AMERICA.

Indians. See INDIAN LANGUAGES: INDIANS.

Politics, etc.

ANGULO GURIDI (A.) Examen de las constituciones de Hispano-América, el Brasil, y Haití. 2 tom. *Santiago de C.* 1891. 8°. 8180. k. 7.

RIVA-AGUERO (E. de la) El Principio de Conquista en América. pp. 60. *Lima,* 1893. 12°. Pam. 65.

SORELA (L.) Los Estados ibero-americanos y la Liga Internacional Antiesclavista. pp. 55. *Madrid,* 1893. fol. 8156. f. 8.

Topography.

ENCYCLOPAEDIAS. Diccionario enciclopedico Hispano-Americano, *etc. Barcelona,* 1887, *etc.* 4°. 1878. c.

AMERICA, *South.* Pacific Line Guide. pp. 151. *Lond.* 1895. 8°. 10492. ee. 27.

AVENEL (H.) L'Amérique latine. pp. 319. *Paris,* 1892. 8°. 10480. e. 30.

BALLOU (M. M.) Equatorial America. pp. 371. *Bost.* 1892. 8°. 10480. bbb. 38.

CHILD (T.) Spanish-American Republics. pp. 444. *Lond.* 1892. 4°. 10481. i. 22.

DICKINS (M.) Along Shore with a Man-of-War. pp. 212. *Bost.* 1893. 8°. 10481. de. 7.

FORD (I. R.) Tropical America. pp. 409. *Lond.* 1893. 8°. 10481. de. 5.

G. B. & I. *Hydrographic Office.* South America Pilot. *Lond.* 1893, *etc.* 8°. 10496. h. 25.

IONIN (A.) Durch Süd-Amerika.
Berl. 1895, *etc.* 8°. 10481. de.

KENNEDY (W. R.) Sporting sketches in South America. pp. 269. *Lond.* 1892. 8°. 7908. df. 14.

MANTEGAZZA (P.) Ricordi dell' America Spagnuola. pp. 216. *Milano,* 1894. 8°. 10160. b. 4.

MARIN (A.) Souvenirs de l'Amerique de sud. pp. 384. *Paris,* 1891. 8°. 10492. ff. 12.

MATKOWSKY (A.) Exotisches. pp. 106. *Berl.* 1895. 8°. 10027. cc. 4.

ORDINAIRE (O.) Du Pacifique à l'Atlantique par les Andes et l'Amazone. pp. 291.
Paris, 1892. 12°. 10481. aa. 37.

OSTANI (L.) Note di viaggio. pp. 51. *Venezia,* 1887. 8°. 10481. de. 8.

P.P. *Montevideo.* La Ilustración Sud-Americana. *Montevideo,* 1894, *etc.* fol. P.P. 9349. ab.

SCHANZ (M.) Quer durch Süd-America. pp. 154. *Hamb.* 1891. 8°. 10481. aaa. 48.

STUART (H. W. V.) Adventures amidst the Forests and Rivers of S. America. pp. 268. *Lond.* 1891. 8°. 10481. i. 23.

THOUAR (A.) Explorations dans l'Amérique du Sud. pp. 421. *Paris,* 1891. 8°. 10481. cc. 28.

VINCENT (F.) In and out of Central America. pp. 246. *N.Y.* 1890. 8°. 10480. b. 35.

VINCENT (E. G.) China to Peru, over the Andes. pp. 333. *Lond.* 1894. 8°. 10027. ee. 2.

VIAULT (F.) Sensations d'Amérique, *etc.* pp. 347. *Paris,* 1895. 8°. 10480. b. 39.

WATERTON (C.) Wanderings in South America. Review by Sydney Smith. pp. 367. *Lond.* 1891. 8°. 10481. ee. 30.

See also under each country of Central and South America.

AMERICA, South and Central—*cont.*
Trade : Finance.

Loques (P.) Le commerce extérieur de la France. pp. 31. *Paris*, 1886. 8°. Pam. 23.

P.P. *Lima.* Le Courrier de l'Amérique du Sud. *Lima*, 1891, *etc.* fol. P.P. 9893. b.

—— *Paris.* Revue franco-sud-américaine. *Paris*, 1891, *etc.* fol. P.P. 1423. de.

Perojo (J. del) Comercio de España con las repúblicas americanas. pp. 38. *Madrid*, 1892. 8°. 08227. i. 30. (10.)

Saenz Peña (R.) El Zollverein americano. 2 pt. *Wash.* 1890. 8°. 8180. h. 32.

Savage (T.) Manual of Intercourse between the United States and Spanish America. pp. 629. *San Fran.* 1890. 8°. 08227. e. 22.

Seminario (M. E.) La cuestion monetaria en la America. pp. 264. *Paris*, 1893. 8°. 08225. h. 8.

U.S. *Bureau of American Republics.* Annual Report. *Wash.* 1892, *etc.* 8°. 08227. g. 56.

American Republics. Handbook of American Republics. 1891, *etc.* 8°. U.S. *Bureau of the American Republics.* Bulletin. No. 1. *etc.* 08225. k. 1.

See also under each country of Central and South America.

United States of America.
See United States.

AMERICAN DIALECTS. — English :
German. Ac. Cambridge, *Mass. American Dialect Society.* Dialect Notes. *Bost.* 1890, *etc.* 8°. Ac. 9962.

Maitland (J.) The American Slang Dictionary. pp. 303. *Chicago*, 1891. 4°. 12982. f. 14.

Molec (E.) Pure Saxon English. Americans to the Front. 2 pt. *Chicago*, 1890. 8°. 12981. c. 33.

Hoffman (W. J.) Grammatic notes and vocabulary of Pennsylvania German Dialect. 1889. 8°. Ac. Philadelphia. *American Philosophical Society.* Proceedings. Vol. 26, no. 129. Ac. 1830.

For Spanish American Dialects : *See* Spanish Language.

AMERICAN INDIANS.
See Indian Languages : Indians.

AMERICAN LITERATURE.—English.
Barr (J.) The Humour of America. pp. 462. 1893. 8°. Dircks (W. H.) International Humour. 012314. g.

Boyesen (H. H.) Literary and social Silhouettes. pp. 218. *N.Y.* 1894. 8°. 12355. a. 40.

Garland (H.) Crumbling Idols. pp. 192. *Chicago*, 1894. 8°. 011824. de. 56.

Knortz (C.) Geschichte der Nordamerikanischen Literatur. 2 Bde. *Berl.* 1891. 8°. 011824. f. 6.

Sladen (D. B. W.) Younger American Poets. pp. 666. *Lond.* 1891. 8°. 11687. e. 42.

Smith (G. J.) Synopsis of American Literature. pp. 125. *Bost.* 1890. 8°. 011840. h. 59.

Stedman (E. C.) Library of American Literature. *N.Y.* 1892, *etc.* 8°. 011824. k. 8.

Underwood (F. H.) Builders of American Literature. *Lond.* 1893, *etc.* 8°. 10883. c.

Vedder (H. C.) American Writers of To-Day. pp. 326. *N.Y.* 1894. 8°. 10883. bb. 34.

Wagner (L.) New Readings from American Authors. pp. 144. *Lond.* 1889. 8°. 12295. c. 31.

Whitcomb (S. L.) Chronological Outlines of American Literature. pp. 285. *N.Y.* 1894. 8°. 011850. g. 52.

White (G.) Sketch of Philosophy of American Literature. pp. 66. *Bost.* 1891. 8°. 011824. e. 24. *See also* English Literature : Poetry.

AMERICAN LITERATURE—*continued.*
Spanish and Portuguese.

Delheye (P.) Literatura americana. pp. 88. *Rioja*, 1890. 8°. 011824. de. 21.

Figueroa (P. P.) Pensadores americanos. pp. 137. *Santiago de C.* 1890. 8°. 010882. h. 23.

Vaca-Guzman (S.) La literatura boliviana. pp. 206. *Buenos A.* 1883. 8°. 011824. f. 56.

Figueroa (P. P.) Galeria de Escritores chilenos. pp. 272. *Santiago*, 1885. 8°. 10883. aa. 21.

—— La literatura chilena. pp. 50. *Santiago de C.* 1891. 8°. 011824. de. 23. (3.)

Anrique R. (N.) Noticia de algunas publicaciones ecuatorianas anteriores á 1792. pp. 23. *Santiago de C.* 1891. 8°. 011902. e. 22. (4.)

—— La Libreria en Chile. pp. 57. *Santiago de C.* 1894. 8°. 11904. l. 14. (9.)

Verissimo (J.) Estudos brazileiros. 2 ser. *Pará*, 1889–94. 8°. 011824. k. 33.

See also Poetry, *Spanish.*

AMHARIC LANGUAGE. Abbadie (A. T. d') Dictionnaire de la Langue Amariñña. coll. 1336. 1881. 8°. Ac. Paris. *Société philologique.* Actes. Tom. 10. Ac. 9808.

Mondon-Vidailhet (C.) Manuel de langue abyssine. pp. 201. *Paris*, 1891. 12°. 12903. aaa. 27.

AMHERST COLLEGE. Tyler (W. S.) History of Amherst College. pp. 312. *N.Y.* 1895. 8°. 8364. aa. 55.

AMIENS. Durand (G.) Inventaire sommaire des Archives communales. 1891, *etc.* 4°. Collection des Inventaires. 1815. b, *etc.*

Janvier (A.) Livre d'Or de la municipalité amiénoise. pp. 458. *Amiens*, 1892. 8°. 9902. d. 9.

AMMUNITION. *See* Gunpowder.

AMOY. Pitcher (P. W.) Fifty Years in Amoy. pp. 207. *N.Y.* 1893. 8°. 4767. d. 16.

AMPHIBIA : BATRACHIA. Ac. Frankfurt. *Senckenbergische Naturforschende Gesellschaft.* Katalog der Batrachier-Sammlung. pp. 73. *Frankfurt*, 1892. 8°. Ac. 2878/4.

Ammon (L. v.) Die permischen Amphibien der Rheinpfalz. pp. 119. *München*, 1889. fol. 7204. g. 7.

Bedriaga (J. v.) Amphibiens recueillis en Portugal. pp. 87. *Coimbra*, 1889. 8°. 7290. e. 23.

Duerigen (B.) Deutschlands Amphibien. *Magdeburg*, 1890, *etc.* 8°. 7290. f. 19.

Field (H. H.) Development of the pronephros and segmental duct in Amphibia. 1891. 8°. Ac. Cambridge. *Harvard University. Museum of Zoology.* Bulletin. Vol. 21, no. 5. Ac. 1736/2.

Knauer (F. C.) Amphibiologie. pp. 340. *Wien*, 1883. 8°. 7290. e. 27.

Lachmann (H.) Die Reptilien und Amphibien Deutschlands. pp. 229. *Berl.* 1890. 8°. 7290. e. 22.

Ac. Calcutta. *Indian Museum.* List of Batrachia in the Indian Museum. pp. 43. *Lond.* 1892. 8°. 7290. b. 11.

Colombo. *Museum.* Report on the collection of Batrachia. pp. 39. *Colombo*, 1891. 8°. 7290. aaa. 12.

Cooke (M. C.) Our Reptiles and Batrachians. pp. 200. *Lond.* 1893. 8°. 7290. a. 22.

Cope (E. D.) Catalogue of Batrachians of Central America and Mexico. pp. 98. 1887. 8°. Bulletin of the U.S. National Museum. Separate Issue. No. 32. Ac. 1875/13.

AMPHIBIA—*continued.*

Cope (E. D.) Batrachia of North America. pp. 525. 1889. 8°. Bulletin of the U.S. National Museum. Separate Issue. No. 34. Ac. 1875/13.

Granger (A.) Batrachiens. pp. 186. 1888. 8°. Histoire naturelle de la France. Pt. 4. 7207. cc.

Perrin (A.) Contributions à l'Étude de la Myologie comparée. pp. 181. *Paris*, 1893. 8°.
7290. e. 29.

Schulze (F. E.) Über die inneren Kiemen der Batrachierlarven. 1889. 4°. Ac. Berlin. *Societas Scientiarum.* Abhandlungen. Ac. 855/6.

Bergendal (D.) Über eine dritte vordere Extremität eines braunen Frosches. pp. 35. 1889. 8°. Ac. Stockholm. *K. Svenska Academien.* Bihang till Handlingar. Bd. 14. Afd. 4.
Ac. 1070/7.

Marshall (A. M.) The Frog. pp. 163. *Manch.* 1894. 8°. 7290. aa. 25.

Schuberg (A.) Über den Bau der Haft-Apparate des Laubfrosches. 1891. 8°. Ac. Wurzburg. *Zoologisches Institut.* Arbeiten. Bd. 10. Heft 1.
Ac. 3567.

Wightman (A. C.) On the Ventricular Epithelium of the Frog's Brain. pp. 16. *Baltimore*, 1889. 4°. 07305. h. 7. (4.)

Plessen (J. v.) Die Kopfnerven von Salamandra Maculata im vorgerückten Embryonalstadium. pp. 20. *München*, 1891. 4°. 7290. k. 7.

AMPHIOXUS. Hatschek (B.) Amphioxus and its development. pp. 181. *Lond.* 1893. 8°.
7298. aaa. 21.

Willey (A.) Amphioxus. pp. 316. 1894. 8°. Ac. *N.Y.* Columbia University Biological Series. No. 2. 7002. e.

AMRITSAR. Amritsar. Gazetteer of Amritsar District. pp. 171. *Lahore*, 1894. 8°.
10056. k. 40.

AMSTERDAM. Amsterdam. Ervaringen van een Middernachtzendeling te Amsterdam. pp. 296. *Amsterd.* 1890. 8°. 8282. df. 45.

Frederiks (J. G.) De historische namen gegeven aan de nieuwe straten van Amsterdam. pp. 108. *Amsterd.* 1892. 8°. 10760. bb. 26.

Havard (H.) Amsterdam. [1892.] Capitales du Monde. No. 18. 1892, *etc.* 4°. 10025. g.

Swaving (J. C.) De Aanwending van Lichte Pantsers bij de bevestiging der stelling van Amsterdam. pp. 125. *'s Gravenh.* 1893. 8°.
8823. n. 28.

AMULETS. *See* Charms.

AMUR, River. Vend (V.) L'amiral Nevelskoy et la conquête du fleuve Amour. pp. 232. *Paris*, 1894. 8°. 010790. de. 1.
See also Siberia.

AMWÂS. *See* Emmaus.

ANAESTHETICS. Ac. Glasgow. *Medico-Chirurgical Society.* Discussion on Anæsthetics. pp. 136. *Glasgow*, 1891. 8°. Ac. 3853. b.

Auvard (A.) Anesthésie chirurgicale et obstétricale. pp. 268. *Paris*, 1892. 8°. 7482. aa. 6.

Buxton (D. W.) Anæsthetics. pp. 222. 1892. 8°. Lewis's Practical Series. 7482. a.

Chaigneau (J.) Étude des agents anésthesiques employés dans des accouchements. pp. 174. *Paris*, 1890. 8°. 07581. df. 10.

Davis (H.) Guide to the Administration of Anæsthetics. pp. 92. *Lond.* 1892. 8°. 07482. e. 8.

Hewitt (F. W.) Anæsthetics and their administration. pp. 357. *Lond.* 1893. 8°. 07482. e. 13.

—— Inquiry concerning Chloroform in dental Surgery, *etc.* pp. 32. *Lond.* 1895. 8°. Pam. 39.

ANÆSTHETICS—*continued.*

Hillischer (H. T.) Sammlung von Vorträgen über Schlafgas. pp. 62. *Wien*, 1891. 8°.
Pam. 39.

Hyderabad. *Chloroform Commission.* Report. pp. 339. *Bombay*, 1891. 4°. 7460. dd. 2.

Julliard (G.) L'éther est-il préférable au chloroforme? pp. 59. *Genève*, 1894. 8°. 07482. g. 24.

Kirk (R.) New Theory of Chloroform Syncope. pp. 58. *Glasgow*, 1890. 8°. 7481. aa. 25.

Reclus (P.) La cocaïne en chirurgie. pp. 192. 1894. 8°. Encyclopédie scientifique. 8709. g.

Rydygier (L.) Wie soll man chloroformiren? pp. 14. 1893. 8°. Sammlung klinischer Vorträge. N. F. Nr. 69. 7441. g.

Terrier (F.) Petit Manuel d'Anesthésie. pp. 220. *Paris*, 1894. 8°. 07482. e. 17.

Underwood (A. S.) Notes on Anaesthetics in dental Surgery. pp. 166. *Lond.* 1893. 8°.
7442. aa. 16.

See also Coca.

ANALYSIS, Chemical. *See* Chemistry.

ANALYSIS, Mathematical. Catalan (E. C.) Nouvelles Notes d'Analyse. pp. 98. 1892. 4°. Ac. Brussels. *Académie.* Nouvéaux Mémoires. Tom. 48. Ac. 985/7.

Gravelius (H.) Lehrbuch der höheren Analysis. *Berl.* 1893, *etc.* 8°. 8535. d.

MacFarlane (A.) Fundamental Theorems of Analysis generalised for space. pp. 31. *Bost.* 1893. 8°. 8535. gg. 6. (8.)

—— Principles of Analysis. pp. 47. *Bost.* 1894. 8°. 8535. gg. 6. (9.)

Picard (É.) Traité d'Analyse. *Paris*, 1891, *etc.* 8°. 8535. dd.

See also Mathematics.

ANAM. *See* Annam.

ANARCHISM: NIHILISM. Armstrong (W. J.) Siberia and the Nihilists. pp. 160. *Oakland*, 1890. 8°. 8094. aa. 14.

Anarchia. L'Anarchia. pp. 59. *Lond.* 1891. 16°. 8277. a. 58. (6.)

Anarchism. Anarchism and Outrage. pp. 8. *Lond.* 1893. 8°. Pam. 82.

Anarchists. A collection of newspapers, etc., issued by Anarchists in Europe. 1884–94. 8° & fol. 1851. c. 23.

—— A collection of Anarchist placards in French. *Paris*, 1890–93. fol. 1850. d. 17.

Anarchy. Anarchy. *Smithfield, N.S.W.* 1891. 8°. 1879. c. 5. (6.)

Bakunin (M. A.) God and the State. pp. 54. *Lond.* 1894. 8°. 08276. i. 21.

Biblioteca. Biblioteca Anarhista. 2 no. *Bucuresci*, 1891. 16°. 8275. aa. 63.

Bourdeau (J.) Le socialisme allemand et le nihilisme russe. pp. 318. *Paris*, 1892. 12°.
8277. de. 35.

Brochure. La Brochure. No. 1–10 *Saint-Josse-ten-Noode*, 1894. 8°. 8275. aa. 68.

Cafiero (C.) Anarchia e comunismo. pp. 11. *Ancona*, 1891. 8°. 8277. de. 29. (10.)

—— Anarchie et communisme. pp. 20. *Foix*, 1890. 8°. 8277. ee. 2. (10.)

Carvajal y Hue (J. de) Los Anarquistas en Madrid. pp. 133. *Madrid*, 1894. 8°.
8275. bbb. 58.

Chicago. The Chicago Martyrs: speeches in Court. pp. 152. *Glasgow*, 1893. 8°. 8282. df. 50.

Cyon (E. v.) Nihilisme et anarchisme. pp. 315. *Paris*, 1892. 12°. 08276. f. 77.

ANARCHISM—*continued.*

DALLEMAGNE (J.) Anarchie et responsabilité.
pp. 20. *Brux.* 1895. 8°. Pam. 82.

DARNAUD (É.) Qu'est-ce que l'Anarchie?
Foix, 1892. *s. sh.* 4°. 1882. c. 2. (41.)

DUBOIS (F.) The Anarchist Peril. pp. 284.
Lond. 1894. 8°. 08275. ee. 14.

DUNCAN (H. H.) A Plea for Anarchist Communism. pp. 15. *Aberd.* 1893. 8°.
08275. ee. 23. (2.)

FABREGUETTES (M. P.) De la complicité intellectuelle de la propagande anarchiste. pp. 102.
Paris, 1894–95. 8°. 5423. g. 3.

FRANCE. *Société nouvelle des Femmes.* La Société nouvelle des Femmes de France. pp. 13.
Paris, 1894. 16°. 08275. e. 30. (7.)

GARBAUD (R.) L'Anarchie et la répression.
pp. 118. *Paris,* 1895. 8°. 08277. g. 17.

GRAVE (J.) La Société mourante et l'Anarchie.
pp. 298. *Paris,* 1893. 12°. 08276. g. 62.

—— La Société au lendemain de la Révolution.
pp. 113. *Paris,* 1893. 8°. 08275. ee. 7.

HAMM (A. F.) Les Hommes et les théories de l'anarchie. pp. 31. *Paris,* 1893. 4°.
08275. ee. 23. (4.)

HAMON (A. F.) Psychologie de l'anarchiste-socialiste. pp. 322. *Paris,* 1895. 18°. 08277. f. 4.

JEHAN-PRÉVAL ( ) Anarchie et nihilisme.
pp. 240. *Paris,* 1892. 12°. 08276. f. 69.

KROPOTKIN (P. A.) Aux Jeunes Gens. pp. 32.
Paris, 1889. 8°. 08275. ee. 23. (7.)

—— Place of Anarchism in Socialistic Evolution.
pp. 16. *Lond.* 1890. 8°. 08275. ee. 22. (8.)

—— Les Prisons. pp. 59. *Paris,* 1890. 16°.
8282. aa. 59. (2.)

—— La Morale anarchiste. pp. 74.
Paris, 1891. 8°. 8277. a. 59. (3.)

—— La Conquête du Pain. pp. 297.
Paris, 1892. 12°. 08276. f. 79.

—— Esprit de Révolte. pp. 32.
Paris, 1892. 16°. 8282. aa. 59. (8.)

—— La Loi, l'Autorité. pp. 37.
Paris, 1892. 8°. 08276. df. 8. (6.)

—— Le Salariat. *Paris,* 1892. 8°.
8282. aa. 59. (9.)

—— L'Agriculture. pp. 32. *Paris,* 1893. 4°.
08275. ee. 23. (5.)

—— La grande Révolution. pp. 39.
Paris, 1893. 8°. 08275. ee. 23. (6.)

—— Un siècle d'attente, 1789–1889. pp. 32.
Paris, 1893. 4°. 08275. ee. 23. (8.)

—— Les temps nouveaux. pp. 63.
Paris, 1894. 8°. 08275. ee. 23. (9.)

—— L'anarchie dans l'évolution socialiste.
pp. 35. *Brux.* 1895. 8°. Pam. 82.

LABORI (F.) Attentat du Palais-Bourbon. Affaire Vaillant. Plaidoirie. pp. 39.
Paris, 1894. 8°. Pam. 34.

LOEWENTHAL (E.) Der Anarchismus und das Recht der Schwachen. pp. 22. *Berl.* 1894. 8°.
8282. cc. 47. (15.)

LOMBROSO (C.) Gli Anarchici. pp. 146.
Torino, 1895. 8°. 08276. k. 30.

MACKAY (J. H.) The Anarchists. A picture of civilization at the close of the 19th century.
pp. 305. *Bost.* 1891. 8°. 012706. g. 21.

MAJETTI (R.) L'Anarchia e le leggi che la reprimono in Italia. pp. 142. *Caserta,* 1894. 8°.
08276. k. 27.

MELONI (P.) Anarchici e socialisti. pp. 16.
Sassari, 1894. 4°. Pam. 82.

MERLINO (S.) Nécessité et bases d'une entente.
pp. 32. *Brux,* 1892. 16°. 8282. a. 85. (4.)

ANARCHISM—*continued.*

MIRAMONT (J.) Compte rendu des conférences au théâtre Chave, février, 1892. pp. 57.
Marseille, 1892. 8°. 8277. ee. 28. (14.)

NIHILISM. Le Nihilisme scientifique.
Leide, 1891, *etc.* 8°. 8470. f.

ORSAT ( ) Les précurseurs de l'anarchie.
pp. 37. *Chambéry,* 1894. 8°. Pam. 45.

O'SQUARR (F.) Les Coulisses de l'Anarchie.
pp. 351. *Paris,* 1892. 8°. 8277. de. 34.

PAPUS. Anarchie, Indolence et Synarchie. pp. 28.
Paris, 1894. 8°. 8282. g. 28. (5.)

PAYSANS. Entre Paysans. pp. 68.
Paris, 1893. 8°. 8282. aa. 59. (11.)

P.P. *Smithfield, N.S.W.* Anarchy.
Smithfield, 1891, *etc.* 4°. 1865. c. 3. (34.)

PINI (V.) Un brano della difesa del nostro compagno Vittorio Pini. pp. 15.
Milano, 1894. 8°. 08275. e. 30. (8.)

PRÉCIS. Précis du mouvement 1866–91. pp. 31.
Foix, 1892. 16°. 8282. aaa. 56. (5.)

RECLUS (J. J. É.) A mon Frère le Paysan.
pp. 16. *Genève,* 1890. 16°. 8282. aa. 60. (2.)

—— Evolution and revolution. pp. 16.
Lond. 1885. 8°. 08275. ee. 22. (2.)

—— L'Idéal et la jeunesse. pp. 13.
Brux. 1894. 8°. 8282. g. 27. (15.)

REICHESBERG (N.) Sozialismus und anarchismus.
pp. 40. *Bern,* 1895. 8°. Pam. 82.

RICHESSE. Richesse et Misère. pp. 72.
Paris, 1890. 12°. 8282. aa. 59. (3.)

SARNO (G.) L'Anarchia. pp. 64.
Naples, 1890. 8°. 08276. f. 22. (6.)

SAURIN (D.) L'Ordre par l'anarchie. pp. 72.
Paris, 1893. 12°. 08275. ee. 20. (8.)

SCHAACK (M. J.) Anarchy and anarchists. Chicago Haymarket Conspiracy. pp. 698.
Chicago, 1889. 8°. 8277. h. 17.

SEYMOUR (H.) The Two Anarchisms.
Lond. 1894. *s. sh.* fol. 1879. c. 4. (24.)

SHAW (G. B.) Anarchism versus state socialism.
pp. 8. *Lond.* 1889. 8°. Pam. 82.

SHAW (G. B.) Impossibilities of Anarchism.
pp. 27. 1893. 8°. Fabian Tracts. No. 45.
8275. dd. 7.

SIVIERI (E.) Un Anarchico ed un repubblicano.
pp. 22. *Lond.* 1891. 16°. 8277. a. 58. (7.)

STEPNIAK. Nihilism as it is. pp. 122.
Lond. 1895. 8°. 8093. b. 32.

TRAVAILLEURS. Les Travailleurs des villes aux travailleurs des compagnes. pp. 23.
Lyon, 1893. 12°. Pam. 82.

TROCCHI (L.) Anarchia e bancarotta? pp. 8.
Ascoli, 1890. 8°. Pam. 70.

TUCKER (B. R.) State Socialism and anarchism.
pp. 16. *Lond.* 1895. 8°. Pam. 82.

YARROS (V.) Anarchism: its aims and methods.
pp. 30. *Bost.* 1887. 16°. 8277. a. 56. (2.)

ANATOMY.

See also BIOLOGY : BONES : HISTOLOGY.

Artistic.

BRUECKE (E. W.) The Human Figure.
pp. 188. *Lond.* 1891. 8°. 7858. f. 5.

ROCHET (C.) La Figure humaine scientifiquement étudiée. pp. 157. *Paris,* 1892. 12°.
7856. a. 50.

ROTH (C.) Student's Atlas of artistic Anatomy.
pp. 50. *Lond.* 1891. fol. 7421. k. 6.

WINDLE (B. C. A.) Proportions of the human Body. pp. 82. *Lond.* 1892. 8°. 7858. gg. 7.

ANATOMY.—General.

General: Comparative.

GRAFF (L. v.) Bibliothek des Professors der vergl. Anatomie. pp. 337. *Graz*, 1891. 8°.
011902. m. 15.

Ac. Manchester. *Owens College.* Studies in Anatomy. *Manch.* 1891, etc. 8°.   Ac. 2672/5.

CHAUVEAU (A. P.) Comparative Anatomy of the domesticated animals. pp. 1084.
Lond. 1891. 8°.   2254. f. 2.

COOKE (T.) Plea for practical Work in Anatomy. pp. 32. *Lond.* 1893. 8°.   7419. bb. 2.

GIROD (P.) Manipulations de Zoologie. 2 pt. *Paris*, 1889, 92. 8°.   7206. k. 26.

LESSHAFT (P.) Grundlagen der theoretischen Anatomie. *Leipz.* 1892, etc. 8°.   7419. g.

LANG (A.) Text-book of comparative Anatomy. *Lond.* 1891, etc. 8°.   7419. i. 18.

MACALISTER (A.) The History of the study of Anatomy in Cambridge. pp. 28.
Camb. 1891. 8°.   07305. e. 23. (12.)

MARXOW (E. F. v.) Gesammelte Abhandlungen. pp. 548. *Leipz.* 1893. 8°.   7305. ee. 20.

MERKEL (F.) Anatomische Hefte. *Wiesbaden*, 1891, etc. 8°.   7419. g.

OPPEL (A.) Vergleichung des Entwicklungsgrades der Organe zu Entwicklungszeiten bei Wirbeltieren. pp. 181. *Jena*, 1891. 8°.
7206. k. 24.

P.P. Jena. Anatomischer Anzeiger. *Jena*, 1886, etc. 8°.   P.P. 3200. o.

RETZIUS (G.) Biologische Untersuchungen. *Stockholm*, 1890, etc. fol.   1819. a. 25.

VOGT (C.) Traité d'anatomie comparée. *Paris*, 1883, etc. 8°.   7421. dd. 14.

VESQUE (J.) Epharmosis, sive materiæ ad instruendam anatomiam systematis naturalis. *Vincennes*, 1889, etc. 8°.   7419. g.

WEDERSHEIM (R.) Das Gliedmassenskelet der Wirbelthiere. 2 pt. *Jena*, 1892. 8°.   7296. cc. 2.

WIRÉN (A.) Beiträge zur Anatomie der limivoren Anneliden. pp. 52.   1887. 4°.   Ac. Stockholm. *Svenska Academien.* Handlingar. Bd. 22.   Ac. 1070.

WYLDE (J.) Pocket Glossary of terms employed in Anatomy. pp. 192. *Lond.* 1890. 16°.
7321. a. 8.

———

CARAZZI (D.) Tecnica di anatomia microscopica. pp. 211. *Milano*, 1894. 16°.   012200. i. 3.

HIS (W.) Der mikrophotographische Apparat der Leipziger Anatomie. pp. 22.
Leipz. 1892. 8°.   8906. h. 9.

LAUNOIS (P. E.) Manuel d'anatomie microscopique. pp. 513. *Paris*, 1892. 12°.
7419. a. 2.

SCHUMANN (K.) Morphologische Studien. *Leipz.* 1892, etc. 8°.   7029. dd.

SCHWALBE (G.) Morphologische Arbeiten. *Jena*, 1891, etc. 8°.   7419. i. 21.

Human.

BARNETT (H. O.) The Making of the Body. pp. 288. *Lond.* 1894. 8°.   7419. aa. 7.

BOENNING (H. C.) Treatise on practical Anatomy. pp. 481. *Phila.* 1891. 8°.   7419. i. 19.

BROESIKE (G.) Cursus der normalen Anatomie des menschlichen Körpers. pp. 759.
Berl. 1892. 8°.   7419. i. 27.

COOKE (T.) Aphorisms in applied Anatomy. pp. 173. *Lond.* 1891, 8°.   7481. aaa. 30.

—— Dissection Guides. pp. 118.
Lond. 1891. 8°.   7419. f. 5.

ANATOMY.—Human—*continued.*

COOKE (T.) Tablets of Anatomy. pp. 328. *Lond.* 1894. 4°.   7419. i. 32.

CUNNINGHAM (D. J.) Manual of practical Anatomy. 1893, etc. 8°. Pentland's Students' Manuals.   7383. d.

DARLING (W.) Essentials of Anatomy. pp. 629. *Lond.* 1880. 8°.   7419. bb. 1.

DEBIERRE (C.) Traité d'Anatomie de l'Homme. 2 tom. *Paris*, 1890. 8°.   7419. bb. 4.

ELLIS (G. V.) Demonstrations of Anatomy. pp. 782. *Lond.* 1890. 8°.   2024. c.

FORT (A. J. A.) Anatomie descriptive et dissection. 3 tom. *Paris*, 1892. 8°.   7419. aa. 3.

GERLACH (J.) Handbuch der speciellen Anatomie des Menschen. pp. 918. *München*, 1891. 8°.
7419. i. 22.

GRAY (H.) Anatomy, descriptive and surgical. pp. 1112. *Lond.* 1893. 8°.   7419. g. 1.

COTTERELL (E.) The Pocket Gray. pp. 263. *Lond.* 1893. 8°.   7419. a. 5.

HEATH (C.) Practical Anatomy. pp. 744. *Lond.* 1893. 8°.   2254. b. 8.

KIMBER (D. C.) Text-book of Anatomy for Nurses. pp. 268. *N.Y.* 1895. 8°.   7419. c. 1.

MACALISTER (A.) Morphological lessons taught by Human Variations. pp. 31. *Lond.* 1894. 8°.
Pam. 29.

MACCLELLAN (G.) Regional Anatomy. *Edinb.* 1891, etc. 4°.   7420. gg. 24.

MORRIS (H.) Treatise on Human Anatomy. pp. 1310. *Lond.* 1893. 8°.   7419. l. 10.

POIRIER (P.) Traité d'Anatomie humaine. *Paris*, 1892, etc. 8°.   7420. dd.

POTTER (S. O. L.) Compend of Human Anatomy. pp. 289. *Edinb.* 1892. 8°.   7419. aa. 4.

PRODHOMME (A.) Atlas-manuel d'Anatomie descriptive du corps humain. pp. 284.
Paris, 1890. 12°.   7419. aa. 1.

QUAIN (J.) Elements of Anatomy. *Lond.* 1890, etc. 8°.   2024. e.

SCHMIDT (E. O.) Philips' Anatomical Model. pp. 16. *Lond.* 1893. 8°.   7419. l. 11.

TESTUT (L.) Traité d'Anatomie humaine. *Paris*, 1889–94. 8°.   7419. dd. 4.

TOURTAREL (L.) De l'Identité établie par l'étude du Squelette. pp. 90. *Lyon*, 1892. 8°.
7419. i. 24.

WILSON (*Sir* W. J. E.) Anatomist's Vade Mecum. pp. 840. *Lond.* 1892. 8°.   2254. b. 21.

Pathological: Surgical.

BAUMGARTEN (P.) Arbeiten auf dem Gebiete der pathologischen Anatomie.
Braunschweig, 1891, etc. 8°.   7441. d.

BOWLBY (A. A.) Surgical Pathology. pp. 640. *Lond.* 1895. 8°.   7481. b. 18.

GERDES (E.) Grundriss der pathologischen Anatomie. pp. 340. *Stuttg.* 1893. 8°.   7421. ee. 22.

GREEN (T. H.) Introduction to Pathology. pp. 579. *Lond.* 1895. 8°.   7442. ee. 3.

HALL (H. N.) Compend of general Pathology. pp. 204. *Edinb.* 1894. 8°.   7442. aa. 17.

KAST (A.) Illustrations of pathological Anatomy. *Lond.* 1892, etc. fol.   1563.

P.P. Jena. Centralblatt für pathologische Anatomie. *Jena*, 1890, etc. 8°.   1079.

RIBBERT (H.) Die pathologische Anatomie. pp. 128. *Bonn*, 1891. 8°.   7419. i 20.

SCHMAUS (H.) Grundriss der pathologischen Anatomie. 2 Thle. *Wiesbaden*, 1893. 8°.
7441. f. 10

ANATOMY. — Pathological, Surgical—
continued.

SHEILD (A. M.) Surgical Anatomy. pp. 226.
Edinb. 1891. 8°.   07482. e. 6.

THOMA (R.) Lehrbuch der pathologischen
Anatomie. *Stuttgart*, 1894, *etc.* 8°.   7441. d.

TILLAUX (P. J.) Traité d'anatomie topographique avec applications à la chirurgie.
pp. 1113. *Paris*, 1890. 8°.   7419. i. 12.

YONGE (E. S.) Aids to Surgical Anatomy.
pp. 158. *Lond.* 1895. 8°.   7481. a. 11.

ANCIENT LIGHTS, Law of.
See LIGHTING.

ANCONA. BUONCOMPAGNO ( ) Un secondo
testo dell' Assedio d'Ancona. 1895. 8°. Ac.
Rome. Instituto Storico. Bullettino. No. 15.
                                             Ac. 6543/2.

TENCKHOFF (F.) Der Kampf der Hohenstaufen
um die Mark Ancona. pp. 108.
Paderborn, 1893. 8°.   9073. bbb. 20.

STELLUTI SCALA (I.) Le Istituzioni di beneficienza di Ancona. pp. 241.
Firenze, 1893. 8°.   08276. i. 32.

ANCYRA, Council of. ANCYRA, *Council of.*
Text of the Canons of Ancyra. 1891. 8°. DRIVER
(S. R.) Studia Biblica. Vol. 3.   3127. l.

ANDABRE. DURAND-FARDELL (C. L. M.)
Étude sur les eaux minérales d'Andabre.
pp. 12. *Paris*, 1890. 12°.   7462. e. 10. (22.)

ANDALUSIA. *See* SEVILLE.

ANDECY, Abbey. MILLARD (A.) Histoire
de l'abbaye d'Andecy. pp. 279.
Châlons, 1890. 8°.   4629. d. 4.

ANDERNACH. ANDERNACH. Stadtarchiv
zu Andernach. pp. 170. 1894. 8°. Ac. Cologne.
Historischer Verein. Annalen. Heft. 59.
                                             Ac. 7335.

ANDERSONVILLE. *See* UNITED STATES
OF AMERICA, *History, Civil War.*

ANDES. BEHRENDSEN (O.) Zur Geologie des
Ostabhanges der argentinischen Cordillere.
1891. 8°. Ac. Berlin. *Deutsche geologische Gesellschaft.* Zeitschrift. Bd. 43.   Ac. 3137.

BRACKEBUSCH (L.) Die Kordillerenpässe. 1892. 8°.
Ac. Berlin. *Gesellschaft für Erdkunde.* Zeitschrift. Bd. 27.   Ac. 6075/2.

HETTNER (A.) Die Kordillere von Bogotá.
pp. 131. 1892. 4°. Mitteilungen aus Perthes'
geograph. Anstalt. Ergänzungsheft. Nr. 104.
                                             P.P. 3946.

ORDINAIRE (O.) Du Pacifique à l'Atlantique par
les Andes. pp. 291. *Paris*, 1892. 12°.
                                             10481. aa. 37.

WHYMPER (E.) Travels amongst the great
Andes of the Equator. pp. 456. *Lond.* 1892. 8°.

—— Supplementary Appendix. pp. 147.
Lond. 1891. 8°.   10481. ce. 33.
See also MOUNTAINS: VOLCANOES.

ANDORRA. AVILÈS ARNAU (J.) El Pallás
y Andorra. pp. 224. *Barcelona*, 1893. 8°.
                                             10161. a. 4.

GRATIOT (M.) Deux Parisiens dans le Val
d'Andorre. pp. 151. *Paris*, 1890. 12°.
                                             10161. aa. 10.
See also PYRENEES.

ANECDOTES. BOMBAUGH (C. C.) Gleanings
for the Curious. pp. 864. *Lond.* 1890. 8°.
                                             12331. . 25.

HARRISON (W.) Social circle of Anecdote.
pp. 192. *Lond.* 1891. 8°.   012314. cc. 2.

MILES (A. A.) One thousand and one Anecdotes. pp. 388. *Lond.* 1894. 8°. 012330. g. 67.

ANECDOTES—*continued.*

STANDING (B.) Anecdotes, Aphorisms and Proverbs. pp. 183. *Lond.* 1891. 8°. 12305. c. 47.
See also QUOTATIONS.

ANELLETTO, Game. RULES. Rules for playing the game of "Anelletto," *etc.* pp. 11.
Horbury, 1891. 8°.   7915. de. 15. (5.)

ANGELS. Fallen Angels A disquisition
upon human Existence. pp. 230.
Lond. 1894. 8°.   4376. gg. 16.

HITCHCOCK (H. W.) The Angels' Ministry.
pp. 93. *Lond.* 1895. 8°.   4371. cc. 5.

KELLER (J. A.) Angeli Dei. pp. 182.
Lond. 1893. 8°.   4399. i. 10.

LANZONI (L.) Gli Angeli nelle Divine Scritture.
pp. 414. *Torino*, 1891. 8°.   3127. h. 11.

LATHAM (H.) A Service of Angels. pp. 223.
Camb. 1894. 8°.   4371. b. 35.

RICHARDS (J. F.) Ministering Spirits. pp. 48.
Lond. 1893. 16°.   4372. a. 20.

S., L. A. H. Angels. pp. 96.
Lond. 1895. 8°.   4372. a. 28.

ANGERMÜNDE. LOESENER ( ) Chronik
der Stadt Angermünde. pp. 78.
Angermünde, 1893. 8°.   10105. e. 4. (7.)

ANGERS. GONTARD DE LAUNAY ( ) Recherches sur les familles des maires d'Angers.
Angers, 1893, *etc.* 8°.   9904. g.

GRANDET (J.) Histoire du Séminaire d'Angers.
2 tom. *Angers*, 1893. 8°.   8357. f. 20.

URSEAU (C.) L'Instruction Primaire avant 1789
dans Angers. pp. 344. *Angers*, 1890. 12°.
                                             8355. df. 9.

ANGINA PECTORIS. *See* HEART.

ANGKOV. *See* CAMBODIA.

ANGLES, Race. ERDMANN (A.) Über die
Heimat und den Namen der Angeln. pp. 118.
1890. 8°. Ac. Upsal. *Humanistiska Vetenskapssamfundet.* Skrifter. Bd. 1.   Ac. 1078.

ANGLICAN CHURCH. *See* ENGLAND,
Church of and History, Ecclesiastical : IRE-
LAND, *Church of:* SCOTLAND, *Episcopal Church:*
UNITED STATES OF AMERICA, *Protestant Epis-
copal Church :* WALES, *Church of England in,*
etc., etc.

ANGLO - ISRAELISM. DIXON (J. W.)
"Are we Israel of the Ten Tribes?"
Caistor, 1890. 8°.   1897. c. 8. (116.)

DOUGLAS (R.) Darkest Britain's Epiphany.
pp. 346. *Lond.* 1891. 8°.   4034. de. 40.

HENDLEY (J. E.) England Heir of the World.
pp. 180. *Lond.* 1894. 8°.   4034. k. 33.

HOWLETT (T. R.) Anglo-Israel. pp. 103.
Phila. 1894. 8°.   4034. k. 36.

LAGRANGE (C.) The Great Pyramid, a witness
to the British-Israel identity. pp. 278.
Lond. 1894. 8°.   07703. e. 1.

MARTIN (L.) L'Anglais est-il un Juif?
pp. 399. *Paris*, 1895. 12°.   4034. de. 48.

SINCLAIR (M.) *Countess of Caithness.* Les vrais
Israélites. pp. 149. *Paris*, 1888. 8°.
                                             4033. g. 42.

TOTTEN (C. A. L.) Romance of History. Lost
Israel found. pp. 260.
New Haven, Conn. 1890. 8°.   4034. dc. 27.

—— Our Race; its origin and destiny.
New Haven, Conn. 1890, *etc.* 8°.   4033. de.

ANGOLA. CHATELAIN (H.) Folk-tales of
Angola. pp. 315. 1894. 8°. Ac. Boston. *American Folk-Lore Society.* Memoirs. Vol. 1.
                                             Ac. 9959/2.

ANGOLA—*continued.*

DELANNOY (C.) L'Angola et la colonisation portugaise. 1895. 8°. Ac. Brussels. *Société de Géographie.* Bulletin. Ann. 19. Ac. 6098.
See also AFRICA, *Colonisation: West.*

ANGOULÊME: ANGOUMOIS.

BOISSONNADE (P.) Essai sur la géographie historique d'Angoumois. pp. 180.
Angoulême, 1890. 8°. 10172. f. 12.

—— Quomodo Comites Engolismenses erga reges Angliæ et Franciæ se gesserint. pp. 132.
Engolismæ, 1893. 8°. 9225. i. 18.

—— and BERNARD (J.) Histoire du collège d'Angou.ême. pp. 472. *Angoulême,* 1895. 8°.
8356. d. 16.

BOISSONNADE (G.) Angoumois au XVIII°. siècle. pp. 180. 1890. 8°. Ac. Angoulême. *Société Archéologique.* Bulletin. Ser. 5. Tom. 11.
Ac. 5286.

FLEURY (P. de) *Marquis.* Les anciens orgues de la Cathédrale d'Angoulême. 1890. 8°. Ac. Angoulême. *Société Archéologique.* Bulletin. Ser. 5. Tom. 11. Ac. 5286.

LIÈVRE (A. F.) Angoulême. pp. 150.
Angoulême, 1885. 8°. 10171. e. 8.

NANGLARD (J.) Pouillé historique du diocèse d'Angoulême. pp. 324. 1893. 8°. Ac. Angoulême. *Société Archéologique.* Bulletin. Série 6. Tom. 2. Ac. 5286.

ANHALT. DUNCKER (H.) Anhalts Bekenntnisstand, 1570–1606. pp. 256.
Dessau, 1892. 8°. 4661. ee. 31.

BUETTNER PFAENNER ZU THAL ( ) Anhalts Bau- und Kunst-Denkmäler.
Dessau, 1892, *etc.* 4°. 10260. f. 3.

ANHOLT, Denmark. KRISTENSEN (E. T.) Øen Anholt. pp. 128. *Kjøbenh.* 1891. 8°.
10280. e. 14.

ANIMALS, Domestic. BOS (J. R.) Zoologie für Landwirte. pp. 128. 1892. 8°. Thaer-Bibliothek. Bd. 78. 7078. d.

BOUCHER (H.) Hygiène des animaux domestiques. pp. 504. *Paris,* 1894. 12°. 7291. aa. 31.

BREVANS (J. de) Le Pain et la Viande. pp. 364. *Paris,* 1892. 12°. 7942. de. 23.

CHICAGO.—*Columbian Exposition.* Official Catalogue. Part III. Live Stock Exhibits. pp. 86. *Chicago,* 1893. 8°. 7958. bb. 16.

CORNEVIN (A. M. C. I.) Des Résidus dans l'Alimentation du Bétail. pp. 544.
Paris, 1892. 8°. 07076. f. 12.

MAC JANNET (J. D.) Live Stock Ready Reckoner. *Glasg.* 1894. fol. 1802. c. 4.

MEIRE (G. H.) Valuation of Live Stock from the live weight. *Lond.* 1891, *etc.* 16°.
7293. aa. 19.

PETIT (P.) Nutrition et production des animaux. pp. 331. *Paris,* 1892. 8°. 07076. e. 49.

PION (E.) Vente et achat du bétail vivant. pp. 300. *Paris,* 1893. 12°. 08227. de. 44.

SINCLAIR (J.) Live Stock Handbooks.
Lond. 1893, *etc.* 8°. 7291. c.

U.S. *Animal Industry, Bureau of.* Bulletin.
Wash. 1893, *etc.* 8°. 7053. e. 41.

—— Miscellaneous publications.
Wash. 1889, *etc.* 8°. 7053. e. 6.

—— Circular. No. 11, *etc.*
Wash. 1889, *etc.* 8°. 7053. e. 12.

WALLACE (R.) Farm Live Stock of Great Britain. pp. 350. *Lond.* 1893. 8°.
07293. i. 8.

ANIMALS.—Domestic—*continued.*

WRIGHTSON (J.) Live Stock. pp. 200. 1892. 8°. Cassell's Agricultural Readers. 7077. de.

YOUATT (W.) The Complete Grazier. pp. 1086.
Lond. 1893. 8°. 7291. d. 13.

CORNEVIN (A. M. C. I.) Traité de l'âge des animaux domestiques. pp. 462.
Paris, 1894. 8°. 07293. m. 12.

DUPONT (M.) L'âge du cheval et des principaux animaux domestiques. pp. 187.
Paris, 1893. 8°. 07293. g. 14.

HUIDEKOPER (R. S.) Age of the domestic animals. pp. 217. *Phila.* 1891. 8°.
07293. m. 5.

BONNET (R.) Grundriss der Entwickelungsgeschichte der Haussäugethiere. pp. 282.
Berl. 1891. 8°. 07293. i. 7.

BRUENING ( ) Westfalens Haus-Säugetiere. pp. 199. *Hagen i. W.* 1892. 8°. 07293. i. 17.

PRIDHAM (C.) Domestic Pets. pp. 112.
Lond. 1893. 4°. 07293. i. 23.

See also ANATOMY: ASS: CAT: CATTLE: DAIRY MANAGEMENT: DOG: DUCKS: GOAT: GOOSE: HORSE: PIG: PIGEONS: POULTRY: SHEEP: TURKEY: ZOOLOGY, *General and Miscellaneous, etc.*
For Diseases of Domestic Animals, *see* VETERINARY MEDICINE.

ANIMALS, Kindness and Cruelty towards. CARRINGTON (E.) Appeals on behalf of the Speechless. 6 pt. *Lond.* 1892. 8°.
8425. aaa. 32.

—— Creatures delivered into our Hands.
Lond. 1893, *etc.* 8°. 8425. c.

COBBE (F. P.) Jesuit Doctrines concerning the Rights of Animals. pp. 16. *Lond.* 1895. 8°.
Pam. 85.

COLLINS (H. H.) Kindness to Animals. pp. 8.
Montreal, 1890. 8°. Pam. 85.

FLORENCE. *Soc. protettrice degli Animale.* Report. *Florence,* 1892. 8°. 8425. c. 69. (6.)

HIPPEL (R. VON) Die Tierquälerei in der Strafgesetzgebung. pp. 198. *Berl.* 1891. 8°.
6006. k. 1.

HAMBURG. *Hamburger Thierschutz - Verein.* Jahres-Bericht. *Hamb.* 1892, *etc.* 8°. 8425. e.

LOEW (A.) Thierschutz im Judenthume. pp. 36.
Brünn, 1890. 8°. Pam. 31.

P.P. *London.* The Animals' Friend.
Lond. 1894, *etc.* 8°. P.P. 1080. c. & 894.

SALT (H. S.) Animals' Rights considered. pp. 176. *N.Y.* 1894. 8°. 8425. aaa. 37.

WHAT. What is it? Read it. pp. 122.
Lond. 1893. 8°. 8425. a. 64.

See also VIVISECTION.

ANKLAM. TAEGLICHSBECK (F.) Die Belagerung der Stadt Anklam, 1676. 1893. 8°. Baltische Studien. Jahrg. 43. Ac. 7380/2.

ANNAM.

ANAM. L'empire d'Annam. pp. 380.
Paris, 1889. 8°. 10055. aaaa. 27.

BAILLE ( ) Souvenirs d'Annam. pp. 266.
Paris, 1890. 18°. 10058. de. 3.

CASTONNET DES FOSSES (H.) Les relations de la Chine et de l'Annam. 1890. 8°. Ac. Paris. *Société indo-chinoise.* Bulletin. Sér. 2. Tom. 6.
Ac. 8812/3.

DENJOY (P.) Indo-Chine française. pp. 271.
Paris, 1894. 8°. 5319. bb. 11.

DESTELAN (P.) Annam et Tonkin. pp. 322.
Paris, 1892. 12°. 9055. aaa. 24.

ANNAM—*continued.*

DUMONTIER (G.) Les symboles et les accessoires du culte chez les Annamites. pp. 172. *Paris*, 1891. 12°.　　　　　4503. bb. 28.

LEMIRE (C.) Le Laos Annamite. pp. 86. *Angers*, 1894. 8°.　　　　　10057. df. 17.

ORY (P.) La Commune Annamite au Tonkin. pp. 147. *Paris*, 1894. 8°.　　　010057. f. 30.

See also COCHIN CHINA: FRANCE, *Colonies*: INDO-CHINA: MISSIONS: TUNG-KING.

Language.

DIGUET (É.) Éléments de grammaire annamite. pp. 132. *Paris*, 1892. 8°.　　12910. c. 38.

DIRR (A.) Grammatik der annamitischen Sprache. pp. 164. 1894. 8°. Die Kunst der Polyglottie. Thl. 42.　　　　12902. c.

FREY (H.) L'Annamite, mère des langues. pp. 248. *Paris*, 1892. 8°.　　12902. cc. 49.

—— Annamites. Recherches sur l'origine des langues. pp. 272. *Paris*, 1894. 8°. 12901. g. 23.

LAUNE (H.) Notions de langue annamite. pp. 250. *Paris*, 1890. 8°.　　12907. ff. 17.

ANNELIDAE. *See* VERMES.

ANNUITIES. OWENS (S. H.) New Method of solving problems in Annuities. pp. 64. *Richmond, Va.* 1894. 8°.　　　8548. cc. 8.

WERKER (W. M. J.) Die zusammengesetzte Zinsen- und Zeitrenten- oder Annuitätenrechnung. 2 Bde. *Utrecht*, 1893. 8°.　　8548. df. 45.

See also INSURANCE.

ANTARCTIC OCEAN. FRICKER (C.) Die Entstehung des antarktischen Treibeises. pp. 208. *Leipz.* 1893. 8°.　10481. e. 37.

MURDOCH (W. G. B.) From Edinburgh to the Antarctic. pp. 364. *Lond.* 1894. 8°. 10460. f. 29.

NORDENSKIOLD (N. A. E.) Projet d'une exploration antarctique. 1892. 8°. Ac. Paris. *Société de Géographie.* Bulletin. 1891.　Ac. 6035.

TISSOT (V.) Le Pôle Nord et le Pôle Sud. pp. 230. *Paris*, 1889. 8°.　10460. ee. 40.

ANTELOPES. SCLATER (P. L.) The Book of Antelopes. *Lond.* 1894, *etc.* 4°.　7206. l.

ANTHEMS. *See* HYMNS.

ANTHRAX. BOUGAN (A.) L'Anthrax. pp. 92. *Paris*, 1892. 8°.　　7560. i. 12.

See also VETERINARY MEDICINE.

ANTHROPOLOGY AND PREHISTORIC ARCHÆOLOGY.—General.

Ac. Europe. *Congrès d'Anthropologie.* 10ème session tenue à Paris. 1889. pp. 48. *Paris*, 1890. 8°.　　　　　Ac. 5600.

—— 11ème Session, à Moscou. *Moscou*, 1892. 8°.　　　　Ac. 5600.

—— G. B. & I. *British Association.* Notes and Queries on Anthropology. pp. 242. *Lond.* 1892. 8°.　　　10007. a. 3.

—— Paris. *Association pour l'Enseignement des Sciences Anthropologiques.* Revue mensuelle. *Paris*, 1891, *etc.* 8°.　　　Ac. 6228.

—— Rome. *Società di Antropologia.* Atti. *Roma*, 1893, *etc.* 8°.　　　Ac. 6222.

—— Vienna. *Anthropologische Gesellschaft.* Festschrift. pp. 108. *Wien*, 1894. 4°.
　　　　　　　　　　7705. ee. 37.

BALKWILL (F. H.) The Testimony of the Teeth to Man's Place in Nature. pp. 240. *Lond.* 1893. 8°.　　　7006. e. 17.

BIAZZI (F.) Sull' unità della specie umana. pp 264. *Torino*, 1889. 12°.　10007. c. 40.

BRINTON (D. G.) Nomenclature and teaching of Anthropology. 1892. 8°.　　Pam. 49.

BUCKLAND (A. W.) Anthropological Studies. pp. 295. *Lond.* 1891. 8°.　10007. aaa. 1.

CALDERWOOD (H.) Evolution and Man's place in Nature. pp. 349. *Lond.* 1893. 8°. 7006. b. 48.

CAUCASIAN. Anthropology for the People. pp. 334. *Richmond, Va.* 1891. 8°.　10007. bb. 15.

CHICAGO. *Columbian Exposition.* Memoirs of the International Congress of Anthropology. pp. 375. *Chicago*, 1894. 8°.　10007. h. 46.

DARVILLE (L.) Hommes et Singes. pp. 315. *Paris*, 1893. 12°.　　　7006. aaa. 23.

DRUMMOND (H.) Lectures on the Ascent of Man. pp. 444. *Lond.* 1894. 8°.　2236. cc. 20.

JAKOB (A.) Der Mensch, die Krone der irdischen Schöpfung. pp. 159. *Freiburg i. B.* 1890. 8°.
　　　　　　　　　　10007. h. 42.

JESSOP (C. M.) Past and Future. pp. 307. *Lond.* 1892. 8°.　　　　7003. aa. 8.

KINMONT (A.) Natural History of Man. pp. 335. *Phila.* 1891. 12°.　　　8703. de. 42.

LANGKAVEL (B.) Der Mensch und seine Rassen. pp. 644. *Stuttgart*, 1892. 8°.　10007. g. 46.

PARIS.—*Exposition Universelle*, 1889. Histoire du Travail et des Sciences anthropologiques. *Paris*, 1889. fol.　　　7958. k. 2.

RATZEL (F.) History of Mankind. *Lond.* 1895, *etc.* 8°.　　　　7002. h.

SCIENCES. Les Sciences biologiques, *etc.* pp. 800. *Paris*, 1893. 8°.　7001. g. 7.

SMITH (H. J.) Work in Anthropology at the University of Michigan. pp. 14. *Ann Arbor*, 1894. 8°.　　　Pam. 3.

STARR (F.) Anthropological Series. *N.Y.* 1894, *etc.* 8°.　　　10007. aaa.

TOPINARD (P.) L'Homme dans la Nature. pp. 352. *Paris*, 1891. 8°.　　8708. cc.

VOGT (J. G.) Die Menschwerdung. pp. 392. *Leipz.* 1892. 8°.　　　7006. cc. 21.

WIEDERSHEIM (R.) The Structure of Man, an Index to his past history. pp. 227. *Lond.* 1895. 8°.　　　　7419. c. 2.

See also ANTHROPOMETRY: ARYANS: CANNIBALISM: ETHNOLOGY: EVOLUTION: FAMILY: GIANTS AND DWARFS: RELIGION: SKULL.

Prehistoric Man: Origin of Man.

Ac. Nuremberg. *Germanisches Nationalmuseum.* Katalog der vorgeschichtlichen Denkmäler, *etc.* pp. 147. 1887. 4°. Anzeiger für Kunde des deutschen Mittelalters, *etc.*　　P.P. 3542. aa.

ALLEVI (G.) Offida preistorica. pp. 146. *Ascoli*, 1889. 8°.　　　7706. g. 2.

ANDERSON (E. L.) Universality of Man's appearance, *etc.* pp. 28. *Edinb.* 1891. 8°.
　　　　　　　　7002. e. 11. (12.)

CAPRON (F. H.) The Antiquity of Man. pp. 98. *Lond.* 1892. 8°.　　　8466. f. 30.

CATTELL (C. C.) The Man of the Past. pp. 50. *Lond.* 1891. 8°.　　7004. de. 23. (4.)

CLODD (E.) The Story of "Primitive" Man. pp. 206. *Lond.* 1895. 8°.　012208. df. 2.

BUECHNER (F. C. C. L.) Das goldene Zeitalter. pp. 352. *Berlin*, 1891. 8°.　12249. cc. 35.

COLBERT (E.) Humanity in its origin and growth. pp. 409. *Chicago*, 1892. 8°.　7006. e. 15.

COTTEAU (G.) Le préhistorique en Europe. pp. 313. *Paris*, 1889. 8°.　7706. a. 48.

DESSAILLY (　) L'antiquité de la race humaine. *Paris*, 1893. 12°.　　3900. aa. 24.

**ANTHROPOLOGY.—Prehistoric Man :
Origin of Man**—*continued.*

Du POUGET (J. F. A.) *Marquis de Cadaillac.*
Manners and Monuments of Prehistoric Peoples.
N.Y. 1892. 8°.   7707. aaa. 48.

FORRER (R.) Præhistorische Varia aus dem
Unterhaltungsblatt "Antiqua." pp. 6, 52.
Zürich, 1889. 8°.   7708. c. 42.

—— Beiträge zur prähistorischen Archäologie. pp. 65. *Strassb.* 1892. 8°.
     7706. d. 2.

HALNA DU FRETAY ( ) L'homme avant notre
ère. pp. 162. *Saint-Brieuc,* 1892. 8°.
     07708. g. 19.

HAMARD (P. J.) L'âge de la pierre. pp. 503.
Paris, 1883. 8°.   7708. a. 40.

HANSEN (A. M.) Menneskeslægtens Ælde.
Kristiania, 1894, etc. 8°.   07708. i.

HECHLER (W. H.) Die älteste Geschichte der
Menschen im Lichte der neuesten Forschungen.
pp. 11. *Wien,* 1892. 8°.   7705. h. 34. (8.)

—— The oldest History of Man.
Vienna, 1892. 8°.   07703. i. 1. (10.)

HEWITT (J. F.) The ruling Races of prehistoric
times in India, *etc.* pp. 627.
Westminster, 1894. 8°.   9056. ee. 19.

HOERNES (M.) Die Urgeschichte des Menschen.
Wien, 1891, *etc.* 8°.   07708. g.

HOSTMANN (C.) Studien zur vorgeschichtlichen
Archäologie. pp. 221.
Braunschweig, 1890. 8°.   7708. cc. 49.

HUNTER-DUVAR (J.) The Stone, Bronze and
Iron Ages. pp. 285. *Lond.* 1892. 8°.
     7707. df. 10.

KRAUSE (E.) Tuisko-Land der arischen Stämme
und Götter Urheimat. pp. 624.
Glogau, 1891. 8°.   10007. h. 44.

KURZ (H.) Adam und die menschliche Urhei-
math. pp. 45. *Hannover,* 1895. 8°.
     10007. bb. 18.

LAING (S.) The Antiquity of Man. pp. 19.
Brighton, 1890. 8°.   7002. e. 11. (9.)

—— Human Origins. pp. 422.
Lond. 1892. 8°.   7704. e. 20.

MAQUIN (P. DE) Adam, est-il le premier homme ?
pp. 20. *Nimes,* 1890. 8°.   3103. df. 2. (4.)

MASON (O. T.) The Origins of Invention.
pp. 419. 1895. 8°. Contemporary Science Series.
No. 28.   8709. i.

MÉGRET (A.) Étude de mensurations sur l'homme
préhistorique. pp. 16. *Nice,* 1894. 8°.
     07703. i. 2. (18.)

MEUNIER (Mme. S.) Misère et Grandeur de
l'Humanité primitive. pp. 292.
Paris, 1893. 8°.   7707. e. 51.

MUELLER (J.) Über Ursprung und Heimat des
Urmenschen. pp. 62. *Stuttgart,* 1894. 8°.
     7006. cc. 22.

PALAZZI (G.) L'Origine de l'Homme. pp. 63.
Paris, 1895. 8°.   7006. h. 3.

P.P. *London.* Archæological Review. Vol. 1–4.
Lond. 1888–90. 8°.   P.P. 1925. df.

—— *Munich.* Prähistorische Blätter.
München, 1889, *etc.* 8°.   P.P. 1898. bc. & 1017.

PFAFF (A. B. I. F.) The age and origin of Man.
1883. 8°. Present Day Tracts. No. 13. 4018. aa.

RAHON (J.) Recherches sur les ossements hu-
mains anciens et préhistoriques en vue de la
reconstitution de la taille. pp. 56.
Paris, 1892. 4°.   7383. ddd. 1. (8.)

RECLUS (É.) Primitive Folk. pp. 339.
1891. 8°. Contemporary Science Series. 8709. i.

ROCK INSCRIPTIONS. Archaic Rock Inscriptions ;
Cup and Ring Markings. pp. 99.
Lond. 1891. 8°.   7707. aa. 42.

**ANTHROPOLOGY.—Prehistoric Man :
Origin of Man**—*continued.*

SALMON (P.) L'Age de la Pierre à l'Exposition
de 1889. pp. 66. *Paris,* 1889. 8°. 07708. f. 18.

SCHWARTZ (W.) Nachklänge prähistorischen
Volksglaubens in Homer. pp. 52.
Berlin, 1894. 8°.   Pam. 14.

SEEBOHM (H. E.) On the Structure of Greek
Tribal Society. pp. 147. *Lond.* 1895. 8°.
     9026. ff. 41.

SIMCOX (E. J.) Primitive Civilizations. 2 vol.
Lond. 1894. 8°.   2238. d. 17.

STARCKE (C. N.) La Famille primitive. pp. 287.
Paris, 1891. 8°.   8708. cc.

TYLOR (E. B.) Primitive Culture. 2 vol. *Lond.*
1891. 8°.   2024. b.

VIÇWÃ-MITRA. Les Chamites. Indes préaryennes.
Berceau. pp. 786. *Paris,* 1892. 8°. 10007. k. 7.

WERNER (O. J.) Die Stellung des Menschen in
der beseelten Schöpfung. pp. 95.
Leipz. 1895. 8°.   8465. bb. 39.

WRIGHT (G. F.) Man and the Glacial Period.
pp. 385. 1892. 8°. International Scientific
Series. vol. 72.   2324. bb. 9.

See also ARYANS : CAVES : EARTH.

Local Discoveries, etc.

America.

Ac. Washington. *Smithonian. Institution.*
Thomas (C.) Prehistoric Works, East of the
Rocky Mountains. pp. 246. *Wash.* 1891. 8°.
     07708. f. 34.

—— Earthworks of Ohio. pp. 33.
Wash. 1889. 8°.   Pam. 3.

—— Problem of the Ohio Mounds. pp. 54.
Wash. 1889. 8°.   Pam. 3.

MOOREHEAD (W. K.) Primitive Man in Ohio.
pp. 246. *N.Y.* 1892. 8°.   7709. e. 6.

BANDELIER (A. F.) Visit to the Aboriginal Ruins
in the Valley of the Rio Pecos. 1883. 8°. Ac.
Bost. Mass. *Archæological Institute.* Papers.
American series. I.   Ac. 5790/8

Belgium and France.

HARROY (E.) Notes de préhistoire. Cromlechs et
Dolmens de Belgique. pp. 181.
Namur, 1890. 8°.   7708. aa. 51.

Ac. Bourges. *Société des Antiquaires.* Objets
du dernier âge du bronze et du premier âge du
fer découverts en Berry. pp 14.
Bourges, 1891. 8°.   07703. g. 1. (5.)

SAINT-VENANT (J. de) Stations de l'époque de
la pierre polie à la bastide d'Engras. pp. 40.
Nimes, 1894. 8°.   07703. g. 1. (21.)

BERCHON (E.) Études sur l'âge du bronze,
spécialement en Gironde. 1889. 8°. Ac.
Bordeaux. *Société Archéologique.* Tom. 14.
Fasc. 3.   Ac. 5297.

GIROD (P.) and GAUTIER (P.) L'Homme préhistorique de Gravenoire. pp. 22.
Paris, 1894. 8°.   07305. l. 13. (5.)

SAINT-VENANT (J. de) Station néolithique à
Jussy-Champagne. pp. 12. *Bourges,* 1888. 8°.
     07703. f. 3. (9.)

PERRIER DU CARNE ( ) Armes de l'époque du
bronze, recueillis dans les environs de Mantes.
pp. 24. *Versailles,* 1892. 8°.   Pam. 3.

PETITOT (É.) La sépulture dolménique de
Mareuil-les-Meaux. pp. 202. *Paris,* 1892. 12°.
     7708. aa. 62.

PILLOY (J.) La Picardie Souterraine.
Saint-Quentin, 1891. 4°.   7707. g. 37.

DEBOUT (H.) Tardingen et les sépultures sous
dalles. pp. 63. *Arras,* 1894. 8°. 7705. cc. 33.

ANTHROPOLOGY—Local Discoveries, etc.—*Belgium and France—continued.*

BRUNG (F.) L'âge de pierre en Touraine. pp. 64.
Tours, 1892. 8°.　　　　　07708. g. 20.

Central and Eastern Europe.

Ac. Vienna. *Gesellschaft zur Verbreitung wissenschaftlicher Kenntnisse.* Calliano (G.) Prähistorische Funde in Baden. pp. 145.
Wien, 1891. 8°.　　　　　7709. g. 35.

NAUE (J.) Die Bronzezeit in Oberbayern. 2 pt.
München, 1894. 4°.　　　　　7709. l. 19.

RICHLY (H.) Die Bronzezeit in Böhmen. pp. 213.
Wien, 1894. 4°.　　　　　7705. g. 45.

DORR (R.) Uebersicht über die prähistorischen Funde in Elbing. pp. 42. *Elbing*, 1893. 4°.
　　　　　Pam. 3.

BERNHARDT (C.) Les Peuples préhistoriques en Lorraine. pp. 162. *Nancy*, 1890. 8°.
　　　　　07708. f. 22.

MUELLER (G. A.) Vorgeschichtliche Kulturbilder aus der Höhlen und älteren Pfahlbautenzeit.
pp. 142. *Bühl*, 1892. 8°.　　　07708. f. 33.

STUDER (T.) and BANNWARTH (E.) Crania Helvetica antiqua. pp. 55. *Leipz.* 1894. fol.
　　　　　7420. h. 3.

Ac. Lausanne. *Musée Archéologique.* Antiquités lacustres, *etc. Lausanne*, 1894, *etc.* fol.　289.

RADIMSKY (V.) Die prähistorischen Fundstätten mit Rücksicht auf Bosnien und die Hercegovina.
pp. 184. *Sarajevo*, 1891. 8°.　　07708. c. 44.

Ac. etc. Sarajevo, *Zemaljski Muzej u Bosni i Hercegovini.* Die neolithische Station von Butmir bei Sarajevo. Ausgrabungen im Jahre 1893. pp. 54. *Wien*, 1895. fol.　1700. b. 8.

Great Britain and Ireland.

Ac. London. *Society of Antiquaries.* Prehistoric Stone Monuments, Cornwall, by W. C. Lukis.
pp. 31. *Lond.* 1885. fol.　　　7703. b. 31.

EVANS (A. J.) On a Late-Celtic Urn-Field at Aylesford. 1890. 4°. Archæologia, vol. 52, pt. 2.
　　　　　Cat. Desk I.

SMITH (W. G.) Man, the primeval savage. His haunts from Bedfordshire to Blackwall. pp. 349.
Lond. 1894. 8°.　　　　07708. g. 23.

SMITH (J.) Prehistoric Man in Ayrshire. pp. 248.
Lond. 1895. 8°.　　　　07708. g. 43.

See also under the subheading ANTIQUITIES *of each country.*

ANTHROPOMETRY. AMMON (O.) Die natürliche Auslese beim Menschen. pp. 326.
Jena, 1893. 8°.　　　　7407. f. 30.

See also ANTHROPOLOGY : CRIME : HAND.

ANTICOSTI. ANTICOSTI. Anticosti. pp. 38.
Lond. 1887. 8°.　　　　10409. aa. 38.

GREGORY (J. U.) Anticosti, its shipwrecks.
pp. 33. *Quebec*, 1881. 8°.　　　Pam. 43.

ANTIGUA. OLIVER (V. L.) History of Antigua. *Lond.* 1894, *etc.* fol.　1855. c. 5.
See also WEST INDIES.

ANTIMONY. VALENTINUS (B.) Triumphal Chariot of Antimony, 1685. pp. 204.
Lond. 1893. 8°.　　　　8905. dc. 36.

ANTIOCH. TREPPNER (M.) Das Patriarchat von Antiochien. pp. 252. *Würzburg*, 1891. 8°.
　　　　　4534 ee. 7.

ANTIOQUIA. MUÑOZ (F. de P.) Tratado de la legislación de Minas de Antioquia.
pp. 155. *Medellin*, 1886. 8°.　　6785. b. 12.

ANTIPYRIN. RONDOT (É.) L'Antipyrine.
pp. 61. *Bordeaux*, 1892. 8°.　07305. k. 13. (11.)

ANTISEPTIC AND ASEPTIC MEDICINE AND SURGERY. ANDERSON (A. M.) Antiseptic treatment of Typhoid Fever. pp. 23. *Dundee*, 1892. 4°.
　　　　　7560. i. 11.

BAUDOUIN (M.) L'asepsie et l'antisepsie à l'Hôpital Bichat. pp. 214. *Paris*, 1890. 8°.
　　　　　7509. dd. 7.

BOXALL (R.) Use of Antiseptics in Midwifery.
Lond. 1894. 8°.　　　7306. e. 22. (11.)

BRAATZ (E.) Die Grundlagen des Aseptik.
pp. 159. *Stuttgart*, 1893. 8°.　07482. ee. 13.

BURLUREAUX (C.) La Pratique de l'Antisepsie dans les maladies contagieuses. pp. 274.
Paris, 1892. 12°.　　　　7460. aa. 4.

HACKER (V. R. von) Introduction to the Antiseptic Treatment of Wounds. pp. 66.
Lond. 1891. 8°.　　　　07482. e. 7.

KAHLE (J. F. E.) Über Antiseptik im Alterthum und Mittelalter. pp. 28.
Hannover, 1895. 8°.　　　　Pam. 39.

ROBB (H.) Aseptic Surgical Technique.
pp. 264. *Phila.* 1894. 8°.　　07482. e. 16.

SCHIMMELBUSCH (C.) Aseptic Treatment of Wounds. pp. 250. *Lond.* 1894. 8°.
　　　　　7481. b. 17.

SCHWARTZ (C. É.) La pratique de l'asepsie et de l'antisepsie en chirurgie. pp. 380.
Paris, 1894. 8°.　　　　07482. e. 15.

TROUESSART (É. L.) La Thérapeutique antiseptique. pp. 280. *Paris*, 1892. 8°.
　　　　　7482. e. 17.

WESSLER (J.) Våra antiseptica. pp. 78.
Stockholm, 1889. 8°.　　　　Pam. 39.

WILSON (E. T.) Disinfectants and Antiseptics.
Lond. 1893. 12°.　　　1830. c. 1. (88.)

See also MEDICINE : SURGERY.

ANTRIM. BOYD (J.) Pictorial Guide to Larne and the Antrim Coast. pp. 98.
Larne, 1891. 8°.　　　　10390. aaaa. 19.

ANTS. BATH (W. H.) Young Collector's Handbook of Ants. pp. 108. 1888. 8°. Young Collector Series.　　　　　7001. aaa.

EMERY (C.) Revision des Fourmis de la Tunisie.
pp. 21. 1891. 8°. Exploration scientifique de la Tunisie.　　　　　10105. ff.

JANET (C.) Études sur les fourmis. 8° note.
Paris, 1895. 8°.　　　　Pam. 42.

—— Sur le système glandulaire des fourmis.
pp. 4. *Paris*, 1894. 4°.　　1810. d. 1. (64.)

—— Sur les Nerfs de l'antenne chez les fourmis.
pp. 4. *Paris*, 1894. 4°.　　1810. d. 1. (64.)

SAUSSURE (H. F. de) Histoire Naturelle des Hyménoptères. 2 pt. 1890, 91. 4°.

GRANDIDIER (A.) Histoire de Madagascar.
Vol. 20.　　　　　10105. i.

WALSH (J. H. T.) Habits of certain "Harvesting" Ants. 1891. 4°. P.P. *Calcutta.* Scientific Memoirs. Pt. 6.　　　7305. h.

WHITE (W. F.) Ants and their Ways. pp. 255.
Lond. 1895. 8°.　　　　7298. aaaa. 24.

See also HYMENOPTERA.

ANTWERP. CAUWENBERGHS (C. van) La corporation des Quatre Couronnés d'Anvers, 1324-1542. pp. 53. *Anvers*, 1889. 8°. Pam. 23.

GOOVAERTS (A. J. M. A.) Antverpiana.
Brux. 1886, *etc.* 8°.　　　10271. ee. 6.

ANTWERP—*continued.*

GOOVAERTS (A. J. M. A.) Le "Dilf" ou chantier d'Anvers du XIII° au XIV° siècle. pp. 16
Anvers, 1889. 8°.   Pam. 91.

—— La Flotte de Louis de Male devant Anvers, 1356. pp. 30. *Brux.* 1886. 8°.   9007. ff. 4. (4.)

—— Construction de l'église Saint-Jacques à Anvers. 1518–35. pp. 22. *Anvers*, 1891. 8°.
     4535. cc. 2. (5.)

ROOSES (M.) Oud-Antwerpen. pp. 105.
Brussel, 1894. *obl.* 4°.   K.T.C. 27. a. 7.

SCHAFFERS (V. F.) Un mot sur le port d'Anvers.
1889. *s. sh.* fol.   1298. m. 11. (113.)

ANUS. *See* RECTUM.

AORTA. *See* HEART.

APACHE INDIANS.
See INDIANS, *American.*

APENNINES. MORIS (H.) Opérations militaires dans les Alpes et les Apennins, 1742–48. pp. 360. *Paris*, 1886. 8°.   9079. k. 4.

SACCO (F.) L'Appennino settentrionale. 1891. 8°. Ac. Rome. *Società Geologica.* Bollettino. Vol. 10.   Ac. 3104.

—— L'Appennino dell' Emilia. Studio geologico sommario. 1893. 8°. Ac. Rome. *Società Geologica.* Bollettino. Vol. 11.   Ac. 3104.

STOKES (M. M.) Six months in the Apennines: Pilgrimage in search of vestiges of Irish Saints in Italy. pp. 313. *Lond.* 1892. 8°. 10136. f. 12.

APHASIA. *See* VOICE, *Diseases, etc.*

APOPLEXY. BOWLES (R. L.) On Stertor, Apoplexy. pp. 125. *Lond.* 1891. 8°. 7616. f. 2.

APOSTOLIC SUCCESSION. *See* CLERGY: ENGLAND, *Church of.*

APOTHECARIES.
See CHEMISTS AND DRUGGISTS.

APPALACHIAN MOUNTAINS.
See GREEN MOUNTAINS.

APPARITIONS. *See* GHOSTS.

APPENDIX, Vermiform: APPENDICITIS. *See* INTESTINES.

APPENZELL. RICHMAN (I. B.) Appenzell. pp. 206. *Lond.* 1895. 8°.   10196. cc. 13.

APPLES. IMPEY (C.) What shall we do with our Apples? pp. 4. *Lond.* 1892. 8°.
     8435. bb. 62. (7.)

TRUELLE (A.) L'art de reconnaître les Fruits de Pressoir. pp. 520. *Paris*, 1893. 12°.
     07076. e. 48.

See also GARDENING, *Fruit.*

APULIA. APULIA. L'Arte in Puglia nel Medioevo e nel Rinascimento.
Bari, 1895, *etc.* fol.   K.T.C. 31. a.

APURE, River. CARVAJAL (J. DE) Relación del descubrimiento del río Apure hasta su ingreso en el Orinoco. pp. 444. *Leon*, 1892. 8°.
     9771. dd. 6.

AQUARIUM. BATEMAN (G. C.) Fresh-Water Aquaria. pp. 316. *Lond.* 1890. 8°.
     7298. aaa. 18.

COUPIN (H.) L'Aquarium d'eau douce. pp. 347.
Paris, 1893. 12°.   7001. c. 6.

SCHERREN (H.) Ponds and Rock Pools. pp. 208.
Lond. 1894. 8°.   4429. ece. 17.

See also ALGAE : FISH : ZOOLOGY, *Marine.*

AQUILONIA. GRASSO (G.) Studi di storia antica. *Ariano*, 1893, *etc.* 8°.   7706. cc.

AQUINCUM. KUZSINSZKY (B.) Die Ausgrabungen zu Aquincum. pp. 125.
Budapest, 1892. 8°.   7708. de. 40.

AQUITAINE: GUIENNE. BARKER (E. H.) Wanderings by Southern Waters. pp. 403.
Lond. 1893. 8°.   010171. f. 39.

—— Two Summers in Guyenne. pp. 411.
Lond. 1894. 8°.   010171. f. 45.

BLADÉ (J. F.) L'Aquitaine et la Vasconie cispyrénéenne. 1891, *etc.* 8°. Ac. Bordeaux. *Faculté des Lettres.* Annales.   Ac. 8917.

MOISANT (J.) Le Prince Noir en Aquitaine 1355–76. pp. 294. *Paris*, 1894. 8°. 9072. dd. 1.

See also GIRONDE : LOT, *Departments.*

ARABIA. COWPER (H. S.) Through Turkish Arabia. pp. 490. *Lond.* 1894. 8°. 10076. ee. 10.

HAIG (F. T.) Report of a Journey to the Red Sea Ports. pp. 40. *Lond.* 1887. 8°. Pam. 40.

HAYNES (A. E.) Man-Hunting in the Desert, Palmer Search-Expedition, 1882–83. pp. 305.
Lond. 1894. 8°.   9055. ece. 30.

HUBER (C.) Journal d'un voyage en Arabie, 1883–84. pp. 778. *Paris*, 1891. 8°. 10075. i. 3.

NOLDE (E. F. VON) *Baron.* Reise nach Innerarabien. pp. 272. *Braunschweig*, 1895. 8°.
     10077. b. 18.

TWEEDIE (W.) The Arabian Horse. His country and people. pp. 411. *Edinb.* 1894. 4°.
     7294. h. 5.

See also ARABS : SINAI : YEMEN.

ARABIC LANGUAGE.—Dictionaries.

CAMERON (D. A.) Arabic-English Vocabulary pp. 322. *Lond.* 1892. 8°.   12904. df. 50.

MARRIOTT (R. A.) Arabic Glossary of Military Words. pp. 31. *Lond.* 1887. 8°. 12904. de. 4.

MEAKIN (J. E. B.) English-Arabic Vocabulary, Grammar, Notes. pp. 256. *Lond.* 1891. 8°.
     12903. aaa. 24.

STACE (E. V.) English-Arabic Vocabulary. pp. 218. *Lond.* 1893. 8°.   012904. g. 1.

WORTABET (J.) English-Arabic Dictionary. 2 pt.
Cairo, 1894. 8°.   012904. f. 2

YÚSUF YA'ḰÚB ḤUBAISH. Dictionnaire françaisarabe. *Le Caire*, 1890, *etc.* 4°.   012904. k. 1

IBRÁHÍM JÁD. Dictionnaire français-arabe de termes judiciaires et commerciaux. pp. 1589.
Alexandrie, 1894. 8°.   12903. f. 29

MARCEL (J. J.) Dictionnaire français-arabe de dialectes d'Algérie, de Tunisie, du Maroc et d'Égypte. pp. 572. *Paris*, 1885. 8°.
     012904. g. 6.

REINISCH (S. L.) Wörterbuch der BedauyeSprache. pp. 365. *Wien*, 1895. 8°. 012904. g. 7.

LERCHUNDI (J.) Vocabulario Español-Arábigo del dialecto de Marruecos. pp. 863.
Tánger, 1892. 8°.   012904. h. 11.

DUVAL (R.) Notes de lexicographie syriaque et arabe. 1893. 8°. Journal Asiatique. Sér. 9, tom. 2.   2098. d.

DICTIONARIES. Ein türkisch-arabisches Glossar. 2 pt. *Leiden*, 1894. 8°.   758. g. 44.

Grammars, Handbooks, etc.

'ABBÁS ('A. A. ibn H.) Guide-gendarme au milieu de la population arabe. pp. 103.
Paris, 1894. 8°.   012904. de. 2.

ABÚ AL-ḰÁSIM. Cours pratique de langue arabe. pp. 290. *Alger*, 1891. 8°.   12904. bbb. 40.

ARABIC GRAMMAR. Éléments de grammaire arabe. 2 pt. *Beyrouth*, 1886. 8°. 12904. e. 33.

ARABIC LANGUAGE. — Grammars, Handbooks, etc.—*continued.*

FREUND (S.) Die Zeitsätze im Arabischen. pp. 107. *Breslau,* 1893. 8°.   012904. b. 14.

FRISCH (R. J.) Guide en pays arabe. pp. 377. *Paris,* 1892. 12°.   10096. aa. 9.

GOURLIAU (E.) Méthode pour l'étude de l'arabe ecrit. pp. 370. *Miliana,* 1888. 8°. 012904. g. 5.

GREEN (A. O.) Arabic grammar. *Oxf.* 1893, *etc.* 8°.   2270. aa. 3.

HOMMEL (F.) Aufsätze arabistisch-semitologischen Inhalts. *München,* 1892, *etc.* 8°.   012904. h.

ḰUR'ĀN. Elementary Arabic text and glossary. pp. 78. *Lond.* 1893. 8°.   14514. a. 7.

LAMMENS (H.) Remarques sur les mots français dérivés de l'arabe. pp. 314. *Beyrouth,* 1890. 8°.   012904. ee. 1.

MANASEVICH (B.) Die Kunst die arabische Sprache zu erlernen. pp. 184. 1890. 8°. Die Kunst der Polyglottie. Theil 23.   12902. c.

MARION (L.) Nouvelle méthode de langue arabe. pp. 263. *Sétif,* 1890. 8°. 12903. h. 24.

PRENDERGAST (W. J.) Collection of Arabic sentences. pp. 39. *Madras,* 1890. 8°.   14586. e.

SOCIN (A.) Arabic Grammar. pp. 170. 160. 1895. 8°. Porta linguarum orientalium.   012904. df. 1.

TIEN (A.) Manual of colloquial Arabic. pp. 419. *Lond.* 1891. 8°.   12904. de. 2.

VERNIER (D.) Grammaire arabe. *Beyrouth,* 1891, *etc.* 8°.   012904. k.

WAHRMUND (A.) Praktisches Handbuch der neu-arabischen Sprache. 3 Thle. *Giessen,* 1886. 8°.   2268. c. 18.

WIED (C.) Arabischer Sprachführer. pp. 93. *Leipz.* 1887. 8°.   12904. b. 44.

'ALLĀWAH IBN YAḤYĀ. Recueil de thèmes et versions. Arabe parlé. pp. 111. *Mostaganem,* 1890. 8°.   14586. d. 33.

HABIL ḰLARIN M'TA EL CHOTT. Vocabulaire de la Langue parlée dans les Pays barbaresques. pp. 527. *Paris,* 1890. 8°.   012904. e. 1.

SEIDEL (A.) Praktisches Handbuch der arabischen Umgangssprache ägyptischen Dialekts. pp. 310. *Berlin,* 1894. 8°.   012904. h. 22.

PROBST (F.) Arabischer Sprachführer in ägyptischem Dialect. pp. 280. *Giessen,* 1892. 8°.   12904. bbb. 42.

VOLLERS (C.) Lehrbuch der aegypto-arabischen Umgangssprache. pp. 231. *Kairo,* 1890. 8°.   012904. cc. 4.

—— Modern Egyptian dialect of Arabic. Grammar. pp. 276. *Camb.* 1895. 8°. 012904. ee. 8.

MEAKIN (J. E. B.) Introduction to the Arabic of Morocco. pp. 256. *Lond.* 1891. 8°.   12903. aaa. 24.

HARFOUCH (J.) Le drogman arabe, guide de l'arabe parlé. pp. 354. *Beyroutt,* 1894. 12°.   012904. de. 1.

MARIE-BERNARD, *Frère.* Méthode d'arabe parlé. Idiome du Sénégal. 2 pt. *Paris,* 1893. 8°.   12904. cc. 26.

MORITZ (B.) Sammlung arabischer Schriftstücke aus Zanzibar. pp. 111, 136. 1892. 8°. SACHAU (C. E.) Lehrbücher des Seminars, *etc* Bd. 9.   12906. h.

REINHARDT (C.) Ein arabischer Dialekt gesprochen in Zanzibar. pp. 428. 1894. 8°. SACHAU (C. E.) Lehrbücher des Seminars, *etc.* Bd. 13.   12906. h.

See also SEMITIC LANGUAGES.

ARABIC LITERATURE. Ac. London. *British Museum. Department of Oriental Books and MSS.* Catalogue of Arabic Books. By A. G. Ellis. *Lond.* 1894, *etc.* 4°. Cat. Desk B.

—— Supplement to the Catalogue of Arabic Manuscripts. By C. Rieu. pp. 935. *Lond.* 1894. 4°.   Cat. Desk A.

CHAUVIN (V.) Bibliographie des ouvrages arabes ou relatifs aux Arabes publiés dans l'Europe 1810-85. *Liège,* 1892, *etc.* 8°   011900. f.

BRUENNOW (R. E.) Chrestomathy of Arabic prose-pieces. pp. 311. 1895. 8°. Porta linguarum orientalium, *etc.*   12904. de.

DERENBOURG (H.) Chrestomathie de l'arabe littéral. pp. 220. *Paris,* 1892. 8°. 14586. b. 32.

HIRSCHFELD (H.) Arabic Chrestomathy. pp. 174. *Lond.* 1892. 8°.   754. e. 16.

HOUDAS (O.) Chrestomathie maghrébine. 2 pt. *Paris,* 1891. 12°.   12904. bbb. 41.

JEWETT (J. R.) Arabic Proverbs. 1891. 8°. Ac. Boston. *American Oriental Society.* Journal. Vol. 15. No. 1.   Ac. 8824.

LIPPERT (J.) Studien auf dem Gebiete der griechisch-arabischen Übersetzungslitteratur. *Braunschweig,* 1894, *etc.* 8°.   11825. k.

MERX (E. O. A.) Documents de paléographie hébraïque et arabe. pp. 59. *Leyde,* 1894. fol.   1984. ff. 1.

P. P. *Woking.* Arabic Quarterly Review. *Woking,* 1889, *etc.* 8°.   14599. d.

STEINSCHNEIDER (M.) Die arabischen Uebersetzungen aus dem Griechischen. pp. 111. 1893. 8°. Centralblatt für Bibliothekswesen. Beiheft. No. 12.   P.P. 4649. e.

—— Schriften der Araber in hebräischen Handschriften. 1893. 8°. Ac. Germany. *Morgenländische Gesellschaft.* Zeitschrift. Bd. 47.   Ac. 8815/2.

STUMME (H.) Tunisische Märchen und Gedichte. 2 Bde. *Leipz.* 1893. 8°.   14583. c. 10.

ARABS. CHAUVIN (V.) Bibliographie des ouvrages relatifs aux Arabes publiés dans l'Europe 1810-85. *Liège,* 1892, *etc.* 8°.   011900. f.

ARABS. Manners, customs and religions of Pre-Islamic Arabs. pp. 28. *Lahore,* 1891. 8°.   Pam. 41.

DRAPER (J. W.) Arabs and their intellectual progress. pp. 26. *Lahore,* 1893. 8°. Pam. 41.

BOURNICHON (J.) L'Invasion Musulmane en Afrique. pp. 351. *Tours,* 1890. fol.   9061. h. 5.

ESTOURNELLES DE CONSTANT (P. D') Les Congrégations religieuses chez les Arabes. pp. 72. *Paris,* 1887. 12°.   4503. a. 42.

FRISCH (R. J.) Guide pratique en pays arabe. pp. 377. *Paris,* 1892. 12°.   10096. aa. 9.

JACOB (G.) Welche Handelsartikel bezogen die Araber des Mittelalters aus den nordischbaltischen Ländern? pp. 83. *Berl.* 1891. 8°.   08227. f. 28.

KLEIN (F.) Les Villages d'Arabes chrétiens. pp. 71. *Fontainebleau,* 1890. 16°.   Pam. 89.

MUIR (*Sir* W.) The Caliphate. pp. 612. *Lond.* 1892. 8°.   2386. f. 1.

POOLE (S. L.) The Mohammedan Dynasties. pp. 361. *Westm.* 1894. 8°.   9055. aaa. 38.

BROOKS (E. W.) Chronology of the Conquest of Egypt by the Saracens. *Leipz.* 1895. 8°.   Pam. 28.

ARABS—*continued.*

See also AFRICA, *North, Central and East:* ARABIA: ART: GRANADA: MOHAMMEDANISM: TUNIS. For the History of the Arabs in Spain, *see* SPAIN, *History.*

ARACHNIDAE. BERTEAUX (L.) Le poumon des arachnides. 1889. 8°. CARNOY (J. B.) La Cellule. Tom. 5. 7421. i.

LANCELEVÉE (T.) Arachnides recueillis aux environs d'Elbeuf. 1885. 8°. Ac. Elbeuf. *Societe d'Enseignement Mutuel.* Bulletin. Année 3. Ac. 2844. c.

THORELL (T.) Aracnidi di Nias, *etc.* 1890. 8°. Annali del Museo Civico di Genova. Ser. 2. Vol. 10. Ac. 2809.

—— On an apparently new Arachnid belonging to the Family Cryptostemmoidæ. pp. 18. 1892. 8°. Ac. Stockholm. *K. Svenska Akademi.* Bihang till handlingar. Bd. 17. Ac. 1070/7. *See also* ACARINA: SPIDERS.

ARAGON. ARAGON. Recopilacion de los fueros en el reino de Aragon. pp. 267. *Zaragoza,* 1880. 8°. 5383. e. 6.

FUENTE (V. de la) Estudios sobre la historia y el derecho de Aragón. 3 ser. *Madrid,* 1884–86. 12°. 9181. aaa. 1.

SWIFT (F. D.) The Life of James the First. pp. 311. *Oxf.* 1894. 8°. 10632. e. 33.

DESDEVISES DU DEZERT (G.) Don Carlos d'Aragon, Prince de Viane. pp. 455. *Paris,* 1889. 8°. 10631. ee. 46.

MIR (M.) Influencia de los Aragoneses en el descubrimiento de América. pp. 93. *Palma de M.* 1892. 8°. 9551. bb. 25. *See also* SPAIN.

ARAKAN. HAY (J. O.) Arakan. pp. 216. *Edinb.* 1892. 8°. 010057. f. 2. *See also* BURMA.

ARAMAIC LANGUAGE. LEVY (J.) *Rabbi, of Breslau.* Neuhebräisches und Chaldäisches Wörterbuch über die Talmudim. 4 Bde. *Leipz.* 1889. 4°. 12903. h. 25.

DALMAN (G. H.) Grammatik des jüdisch-palästinischen Aramäisch. pp. 348. *Leipz.* 1894. 8°. 012904. h. 24.

SCHWALLY (F.) Idioticon des christlich palästinischen Arameisch. pp. 134. *Giessen,* 1893. 8°. 012904. h. 16. *See also* SEMITIC LANGUAGES.

ARANJUEZ. VIÑAS Y REY (S.) Aranjuez. pp. 97. 1890. 8°. Biblioteca de la Provincia de Madrid. Tom. 5. 10160. bbb.

ARARAT. LECLERCQ (J.) Voyage au Mont Ararat. pp. 328. *Paris,* 1892. 12°. 10077. aa. 15.

ARAUCANIA. LARA (H.) Crónica de la Araucanía. 2 tom. *Santiago de C.* 1889. 8°. 9771. eee. 16.

PRENDEZ (P. N.) La Araucanía. pp. 98. *Valparaiso,* 1884. 8°. 10480. bbb. 41.

ARBITRATION. BENTWICH (H.) Chambers of Arbitration. pp. 15. *Lond.* 1893. 8°. 6146. bbb. 26. (3.)

FLETCHER (B.) Arbitrations. pp. 119. *Lond.* 1893. 8°. 6376. a. 55.

LONDON. *Chamber of Arbitration.* Rules, *etc.* pp. 57. *Lond.* 1892. 8°. 6190. cc. 3. (13.)

ARBITRATION—*continued.*

LYNCH (H. F.) Redress by Arbitration. pp. 83. *Lond.* 1892. 8°. 6325. cc. 22.

PRASCHKAUER (M.) Ein Abriss ueber das englische Arbitrations Wesen. pp. 86. *Lond.* 1894. 8°. 6376. e. 33.

RUGGIERO (E. de) L'Arbitrato pubblico in relazione col privato presso i Romani. pp. 395. *Roma,* 1893. 8°. 5206. e. 31.

RUSSELL (F.) Power and Duty of an Arbitrator. pp. 958. *Lond.* 1891. 8°. 2017. b.

SALAMAN (J. S.) Arbitrator's Manual under the London Chamber of Arbitration. pp. 212. *Lond.* 1893. 8°. 6282. aa. 24.

SHEARMAN (M.) London Chamber of Arbitration. Law and practice. pp. 138. *Lond.* 1893. 8°. 6376. aa. 50.

See also LAW, *Commercial.*

For works on Industrial Arbitration: *See* CAPITAL AND LABOUR, *Boards of Conciliation, etc.*

International.

ANTWERP. *Conférence du Jeune Barreau.* Arbitrage International. pp. 51. *Brux.* 1891. 8°. 12315. i. 63.

APPLETON (L.) Fifty Years of Foreign Policy. *Lond.* 1889–92. 8°. 8026. c. 8.

CATCHPOOL (W.) International Arbitration. pp. 17. *Lond.* 1894. 16°. Pam. 85.

CORSI (A.) Arbitrati internazionali. pp. 310. *Pisa,* 1893. 8°. 8010. ee. 7.

DREYFUS (F. C.) L'arbitrage international. pp. 395. *Paris,* 1892. 12°. 6916. aa. 15.

REVON (M.) L'Arbitrage international. pp. 541. *Paris,* 1892. 8°. 06955. df. 12.

ROUARD DE CARD (E.) Les Destinées de l'arbitrage international. pp. 264. *Paris,* 1892. 8°. 8010. ee. 11.

See also BEHRING SEA: LAW, *International.*

ARBROATH. MACBAIN (J. M.) Bibliography of Arbroath. Periodical Literature, *etc.* pp. 126. *Arbroath,* 1889. 8°. 11899. ee. 36.

ARCADIA. IMMERWAHR (W.) Die Kulte und Mythen Arkadiens. *Leipz.* 1891, *etc.* 8°. 4503. cc. 10.

ARCHÆOLOGY. For the Antiquities of each country, see under the country.

General.

MARSY (A. de) *Count.* Les Congrès archéologiques d'Abbeville et de Londres, 1893. pp. 90. *Caen,* 1893. 8°. Pam. 3.

P.P. *London.* The Archæological Review. Vol. 1–4. *Lond.,* 1888 90. 8°. P.P. 1925. df.

Biblical.

See ASSYRIA: EGYPT: JEWS: PALESTINE: THEOLOGY, *Biblical Dictionaries.*

Christian. *See* ART, *Christian.*

Prehistoric. *See* ANTHROPOLOGY.

ARCHERY. GRAND WESTERN ARCHERY SOCIETY. Rules and shooting regulations. pp. 106. *Exeter,* 1892. 8°. 7912. aa. 16.

LONGMAN (C. J.) and WALROND (H.) Archery. pp. 589. 1894. 4°. Badminton Library. 7905. f. *See also* SPORT.

ARCHITECTURE. *See also* ART: BUILDING.

Bibliography.

BOSTON. *Public Library.* Catalogue of books relating to Architecture. pp. 150. *Bost.* 1894. 8°. 11900. i. 39.

ARCHITECTURE.—General.

Pt. I. General.

Ac. London. *Architectural Association.* Architectural Association, Session 1892-93. *Lond.* 1892, *etc.* 8°. Ac. 4882.

—— London. *Society of Architects.* Journal of the Society. *Lond.* 1893, *etc.* 4°. Ac. 4876.

—— List of Members; Rules: Report. *Lond.* 1892, *etc.* 8°. 7814. b.

ARCHITECT. Valuator and Directory of Architects, *etc. Manch.* 1890. 8°. 7815. cc. 8.

BURN (R. S.) Illustrated Architectural Drawing-Book. pp. 155. *Lond.* 1893. 8°. 7855. c. 53.

CATTIER (E.) Idées sur l'architecture. pp. 242. *Brux.* 1891. 8°. 7817. g. 20.

CHADWICK (J. W.) Evolution of Architecture. 1891. 8°. Ac. Brooklyn. *Ethical Association.* Evolution series. No. 12. 7006. bbb.

DU BOIS (A.) Les Architectes par leurs œuvres. 3 tom. *Paris,* 1893. 8°. 7814. h. 9.

FULLERTON (W.) Architectural Examples. pp. 220. *Lond.* 1890. 4°. 7814. f. 14.

LETHABY (W. R.) Architecture, Mysticism and Myth. pp. 272. *Lond.* 1892. 8°. 7820. cc. 13.

MASSELIN (O.) Dictionnaire des connaissances utiles aux architectes. pp. 612. *Paris,* 1891. 8°. 8767. l. 23.

P.P. *N.Y.* Architecture. *N.Y.* 1890, *etc.* fol. P.P. 1669.

—— *Paris.* Moniteur des Architectes. *Paris,* 1887, *etc.* 4°. P.P. 1662. ad.

ROGERS (F.) Architect's Guide. pp. 351. *Lond.* 1894. 8°. 2260. a. 3.

RUSKIN (J.) Lectures on Architecture. pp. 256. *Orpington,* 1891. 8°. 7808. bbb. 20.

—— Poetry of Architecture. pp. 261. *Orpington,* 1893. 4°. Tab. 648. b.

SACHERI (G.) Esposizione italiana di Architettura in Torino. pp. 250. *Torino,* 1891. 8°. 7817. i. 2.

SCHLIEPMANN (H.) Betrachtungen über Baukunst. pp. 110. *Berl.* 1891. 8°. 7816. a. 7.

SCHULTZ (W.) Die Harmonie in der Baukunst. *Hannover,* 1891, *etc.* 4°. 7816. c. 1.

SEDDING (J. D.) Art and Handicraft. pp. 179. *Lond.* 1893. 8°. 7808. e. 13.

SHAW (R. N.) Architecture, a profession or an art? pp. 244. *Lond.* 1892. 8°. 7817. g. 23.

STATHAM (H. H.) Architecture for general readers. pp. 332. *Lond.* 1895. 8°. 7817. bbb. 2.

VAN NOSTRAND (J. J.) Study in Architectonic. 1894. 8°. & fol. 1810. d. 1. (50.)

WHITE (W. H.) The Architect and his Artists. pp. 64. *Lond.* 1892. 8°. 7807. c. 30 (11.)

WOODLEY (W. F.) The Design of Buildings. pp. 108. *Lond.* 1894. 8°. 7814. de. 21.

Details.

CHURCH CARVINGS. On Church Carvings. pp. 11. *Lond.* 1891. 8°. 4429. aa. 60 (2.)

COMPER (J. N.) Considerations on the Gothic or English Altar. 1890. 8°. Ac. London. *Saint Paul's Ecclesiological Society.* Transactions. Vol. III. pt. 4. Ac. 5670.

DAMIANI ALMEYDA (G.) Istituzioni ornamentali. *Torino,* 1890. fol. 1711. c.

INDIA. *Archæological Survey.* Illustrations of Indian Architectural Decorative Work. *Calcutta,* 1886, *etc.* fol. 266.

ARCHITECTURE.—Details—*continued.*

JACOB (S. S.) Jeypore Portfolio of Architectural Details. 6 pt. *Lond.* 1890. fol. 1736. c. 1.

MUENZENBERGER (E. F. A.) Zur Kenntniss der mittelalterlichen Altäre Deutschlands. *Frankfurt,* 1885, *etc.* fol. 192.

PALEY (F. A.) Manual of Gothic Moldings. pp. 100. *Lond.* 1891. 8°. 7817. f. 21.

SYMPSON (E. M.) On Lincolnshire Rood-Screens and Rood-Lofts. pp. 29. *Linc.* 1891. 8°. 7820. cc. 12.

Domestic and Secular.

BIRCH (J.) Examples of Labourers' Cottages. pp. 65. *Edinb.* 1892. 8°. 7817. k. 10.

—— Examples of Stables, Hunting-boxes, Kennels, *etc.* pp. 64. *Edinb.* 1892. 8°. 7817. k. 9.

BOGUE (J. W.) Cottages and Villas. pp. 42. *Edinb* 1888. 4°. 7820. h. 14.

BRIGGS (R.A.) Bungalows and Country Residences. *Lond.* 1895. 4°. 7814. k. 15.

CORFIELD (W. H.) Dwelling Houses. pp. 125. *Lond.* 1894. 8°. 8777. aaa. 37.

FRANCE. *Ministère de l'Instruction.* Enquête sur les conditions de l'habitation en France. Les maison-types. pp. 381. *Paris,* 1894. 8°. 7817. i. 8.

FROST (H.) House-building Illustrations. pp. 19. *Lond.* 1891. 8°. Pam. 24.

FULLER (A. W.) Artistic Homes. ff. 70. *Boston,* 1891. *obl.* fol. 1730. a. 5.

GOETZ (W.) Das nordische Wohnhaus während des 16. Jahrhunderts. pp. 31. 1891. 8°. Sammlung wissenschaftlicher Vorträge. Heft 131. 12249. m.

HIRTH (G.) Das deutsche Zimmer. pp. 448. *München,* 1886. 4°. 7814. f. 16.

WILLIAMS (J.) Sketches of Village Buildings. pp. 34. *Lond.* 1891. *obl.* 4°. 7817. e. 11. *See also* ART, *Decorative:* BUILDING: CAPITAL AND LABOUR, *Housing of the Working Classes:* FURNITURE, *etc.* For the Domestic Architecture of each country, *see infra:* Pt. II.

Ecclesiastical.

BARGÈS (J. J. L.) Notice sur quelques Autels du moyen âge. pp. 118. *Paris,* 1890. 8°. 3475. g. 1.

BERLIN. *Vereinigung Architekten.* Der Kirchenbau des Protestantismus. pp. 559. *Berl.* 1893. 8°. 7814. i. 1.

CUBITT (J.) Handbook of Nonconformist Church Building. pp. 121. *Lond.* 1892. 8°. 7820. aaa. 36.

HECKNER (G.) Praktisches Handbuch der kirchlichen Baukunst. pp. 411. *Freiburg,* 1891. 8°. 7817. f. 24.

SAVERY (C. E.) Designs for Village Churches. *Lond.* 1892. 4°. 7814. h. 5.

—— Wooden Churches. *Lond.* 1893. fol. 7815. g. 14.

WIMMER (F.) Anleitung zur Erforschung und Beschreibung der kirchlichen Kunstdenkmäler. pp. 152. *Linz,* 1892. 8°. 7817. i. 5. *See also supra: Details:* ART, *Christian.* For the Ecclesiastical Architecture of each country, *see infra:* Pt. II.

Formulae: Specifications: Terms.

BARTHOLOMEW (A.) Specifications for practical Architecture. pp. 416. *Lond.* 1893. 8°. 7817. g. 25.

BOUFFIER (H.) Grundriss der architektonischen Formenlehre. pp. 54. 1891. 8°. Bossong's kunsttechnische Bibliothek, *etc.* Bd. 3. 7858. f.

ARCHITECTURE.—Formulæ: Specifications: Terms—*continued.*

BURNS (G. J.) Glossary of technical terms in Architecture. pp. 136. *Lond.* 1895. 8°. 7817. b. 6.

DICTIONARIES. Dictionary of technical terms of architectural design. pp. 296.
Lond. 1891–93. 8°.   7817. e. 27.

LEANING (J.) Specifications for the use of Architects. pp. 140. *Lond.* 1894. 8°.   7817. b. 5.

TARN (E. W.) Mechanics of Architecture.
pp. 374. *Lond.* 1894. 8°.   7820. aaa. 39.
See also BUILDING.

Gothic. *See supra: Details; infra: Styles.*

History.

BILDER-ATLAS. Bilder-Atlas zur Geschichte der Baukunst. pp. 40. *Leipz.* 1890. 4°. 7816. g. 22.

FERGUSSON (J.) History of Architecture.
Lond. 1893, etc. 8°.   7817. ee. 2.

PERRY (J. T.) Chronology of mediæval and renaissance Architecture. pp. 290.
Lond. 1893. 8°.   07816. h. 1.
See also ART. For the Architectural History of each country, *see infra:* Pt. II.

Perspective. *See* PERSPECTIVE.

Renaissance Architecture. *See infra: Styles: and Pt. II.*

Styles.

BARBEROT (E.) Histoire des styles d'architecture. 2 tom. *Paris*, 1891. 8°.   7814. h. 3.

FERGUSSON (J.) History of the modern styles of Architecture. 2 vol. *Lond.* 1891. 8°. 2260. e. 2.

SPIERS (R. P.) Orders of Architecture.
Lond. 1893. fol.   7815. d. 6.

VAN BRUNT (H.) Greek Lines, and other essays. pp. 274. *Bost.* 1893. 8°.   7814. b. 2.

GOSSET (A.) Les coupoles d'Orient et d'Occident. pp. 35. *Reims*, 1891. 8°. 7806. de. 22. (12.)

CORROYER (É.) L'Architecture gothique.
pp. 382. *Paris*, 1891. 8°.   2261. c.
—— Gothic Architecture. pp. 388.
Lond. 1893. 8°.   7817. c. 21.

DEHIO (G.) Untersuchungen über das gleichseitige Dreieck als Norm gotischer Bauproportionen. pp. 24. *Stuttgart*, 1894. 8°. 7814. c. 24.

GONSE (L.) L'Art Gothique. pp. 476.
Paris, 1891. fol.   7805. g. 7.

MORRIS (W.) Gothic Architecture. pp. 68.
Lond. 1893. 8°.   7814. a. 5.

RUSKIN (J.) The Nature of Gothic. pp. 127.
Lond. 1892. 8°.   K.T.C. 6. a. 2.

PALUSTRE (L.) L'Architecture de la Renaissance. pp. 352. *Paris*, 1892. 8°.   2261. c.
See also supra: History. For the national styles of each country, *see infra:* Pt. II.

Pt. II. National Architecture.

Belgium.

CAUWENBERGHS (C. van) La corporation des Quatre Couronnés d'Anvers, 1324–1542. pp. 53. *Anvers*, 1889. 8°.   Pam. 23.

Denmark.

HEALES (A. C.) Architecture of the Churches of Denmark. pp. 138. *Lond.* 1892. 8°. 7817. g. 21.

HELMS (J.) Danske Tufstens-Kirker. Bd. 1.
Kjøbenh. 1894. fol.   1736. c. 6.

MEJBORG (R.) Om Bygningsskikke i Slesvig.
pp. 32. *Kjøbenh.* 1891. 4°.   7820. i. 9.

ARCHITECTURE.—National Architecture—*continued.*

England.

AXON (W. E. A.) Rambling Sketches by T. R. Davison. 12 pt. *Lond.* 1890, 91. 8°. 7814. h. 12.

G. B. & I. Historic Houses. pp. 328.
Lond. 1891, 92. 4°.   7814. h. 10.

HARRIS (T.) Three periods of English Architecture. pp. 185. *Lond.* 1894. 8°. 07816. i. 1.

HARROW SCHOOL. Catalogue of a series of photographs illustrating the development of Gothic Architecture in England. pp. 60.
Harrow, 1894. 8°.   7808. bbb. 27. (7.)

SAVERY (C. E.) History of Church Architecture in England. pp. 88. *Lond.* 1893. 8°.
       7820. aa. 30.

HARRISON (J. P.) English Architecture before the Conquest. 1893. 8°. Archæologia Oxoniensis. Part 2.   P.P. 1925. em.

FILES (G. T.) The Anglo-Saxon House. With plates. pp. 65. *Leipz.* 1893. 8°. 7709. c. 8.

NEILSON (G.) Peel: its meaning. pp. 33.
Glasgow, 1893. 4°.   7709. e. 7.

GOTCH (J. A.) Architecture of the Renaissance in England, 1560–1630. *Lond.* 1891, etc. fol.
       1733. c. 10.

LOFTIE (W. J.) Inigo Jones and Wren. pp. 284.
Lond. 1893. 4°.   7814. g. 3.

SÉDILLE (P.) L'Architecture moderne en Angleterre. pp. 131. *Paris*, 1890. 4°. 7814. ee. 16.

P.P. LONDON. *The Builder.* Builder Album of R. Academy Architecture, 1891. pl. lxxvi.
Lond. 1891. fol.   1731. c. 6.

WASMUTH (E.) Neubauten in Grossbritannien.
Berl. 1892, etc. fol.   1733. d.

BAYLY (J.) Churches in the Deanery of Buckrose, restored or built by G. F. Street. pp. 5.
Lond. 1894. fol.   7815. d. 8.

PHILIPS (N. G.) Views of the Old Halls in Lancashire and Cheshire. pp. 121.
Lond. 1893. fol.   1788. c. 28.

BRADBURY (E.) Architectural sketches in and around Northampton. *Northampton*, 1894. 4°.
       7816. f. 28.

P.P. *Northampton.* Architectural Notes, relating to Churches of Northamptonshire.
Northampton, 1890–92. 8°.   P.P. 1818. b.

CRANAGE (D. H. S.) Architectural account of the Churches of Shropshire.
Wellington, 1894, etc. 4°.   7814. h.

NEVILL (R.) Old Cottage and Domestic Architecture in Surrey. pp. 142. *Guildford*, 1891. 8°.
       7817. k. 8.

ELYARD (S. J.) Some Old Wiltshire Homes.
pp. 88. *Lond.* 1894. fol.   10348. l. 9.
See also supra, Pt. I.: *Details:* ENGLAND, *Churches.*

France.

AC. PARIS. *Société de l'Art Français.* La France monumentale. *Paris*, 1892, etc. 4°.   1755. g.

BISHOP (H. H.) Pictorial Architecture of France.
pp. 175. *Lond.* 1893. *obl.* 8°.   1732. a 5.

PETIT (J. L.) Architectural Studies in France.
pp. 402. *Lond.* 1890. 8°.   2260. c. 1.

ROSIÈRES (R.) L'Évolution de l'Architecture en France. pp. 290. *Paris*, 1894. 12°. 7820. a. 26.

SABINE (H.) Table du Dictionnaire raisonné de l'Architecture française par Viollet-Le-Duc.
pp. 387. *Paris*, 1889. 8°.   2031. c.

CHAMPEAUX (A. de) Les Travaux d'Art exécutés pour Jean de France. *Paris*, 1894. 4°.
       7808. g. 19.

PENANRUN (D. de) 1819 94. Les Architectes élèves de l'École des Beaux-Arts. pp. 317.
Paris. 1895. 8°.   7814. g. 5.

ARCHITECTURE.—National Architecture.—_continued._

MAGNE (L.) L'Architecture française du siècle. pp. 42. _Paris_, 1890. 8°.   7820. g. 17.

FRANCE. _Ministère de l'Instruction._ Enquête sur les conditions de l'Habitation. Les maisons-types. _Paris_, 1894. 8°.   7817. i. 8.

BONPAIX (A.) Répertoire de jurisprudence à l'usage des architectes. 2 tom. _Paris_, 1892. 8°.   5406. de. 13.

PENANRUN (D. DE) Les Architectes et leurs rapports avec les Propriétaires. pp. 829. _Paris_, 1892. 8°.   5424. dd. 9.

BRUNE (P.) Les Églises romanes et l'architecture religieuse dans le Jura. pp. 46. _Caen_, 1894. 8°.   Pam. 24.

VIREY (J.) L'architecture romane de Mâcon. 1889, _etc._ 8°. Ac. Autun. _Société Éduenne._ Mémoires. Nouvelle série. Tom. 17. Ac. 5288/2.

LEFÈVRE-PONTALIS (E.) L'Architecture religieuse dans l'ancien diocèse de Soissons. _Paris_, 1894, _etc._ 4°.   695.

Germany.

Ac. Dresden. _Verein für Erforschung der väterlandischen Alterthümer._ STECHE (R.) Darstellung der Bau- und Kunstdenkmäler Sachsen's. _Dresd._ 1882, _etc._ 8°.   Ac. 7042/3.

LUDORFF (A.) Die Bau- und Kunstdenkmäler von Westfalen. _Münster_, 1893, _etc._ 4°. 7808. g.

MOELLINGER (C.) Die deutsch-romanische Architektur. _Leipz._ 1886-91. 4°.   7814. e. 14.

OTTE (H.) Handbuch der kirchlichen Kunst-Archäologie des deutschen Mittelalters. 2 Bde. _Leipz._ 1883-85. 8°.   7707. bb. 54.

GERMAN RENAISSANCE. Tafeln zum Studium des deutschen Renaissance- und Barockstils. _Leipz._ 1890. 8°.   7808. f. 1.

PERRY (J. T.) Influence of the Hanseatic League on the Architecture of Northern Europe. _Lond._ 1894. 4°.   7817. d. 1.

See also supra Pt. I.: _Details._

Greece.

FALKENER (E.) The Grecian House as described by Vitruvius. pp. 21. _Lond._ 1893. 4°.   7706. ee. 40.

See also ART, _Ancient:_ GREECE, _Antiquities._

India.

INDIA. _Archæological Survey._ Illustrations of Indian Architectural Decorative Work. _Calc._ 1886, _etc._ fol.   266.

NAPIER (F.) _Baron Napier and Ettrick._ Arts in India. Architecture. pp. 29. _Madras_, 1894. 8°.   7808. b. 17.

TIKĀRĀMA. Modern Indian Architecture. pp. 52. _Bombay_, 1892. fol.   7814. d. 5.

SIMPSON (W.) Origin and Mutation in Indian and Eastern Architecture. 1891. 8°. Ac. London. _Institute of British Architects._ Transactions. N. S. Vol. 7.   Ac. 4880/3

See also supra, Pt. I.: _Details._

Ireland.

FALLOW (T. M.) Cathedral Churches of Ireland. pp. 99. _Lond._ 1894. 8°.   10390. f. 13.

WESTROPP (T. J.) Churches with Round Towers in Clare. _Dublin_, 1894, _etc._ 8°.   07708. f. 41.

See also supra: England.

Italy.

ENLART (C.) Origines françaises de l'architecture gothique en Italie. pp. 335. 1894. Ac. Athens. _École Française._ Bibliothèque. Fasc. 66.   Ac. 5206/2.

ARCHITECTURE.—National Architecture.—_continued._

CLAUSSE (G.) Basiliques chrétiennes. Italie-Sicile. 2 tom. _Paris_, 1893. 8°.   7808. f. 11.

GIARRIZZO (M.) L'Architettura in Italia. pp. 88. _Palermo_, 1892. 8°.   7814. de. 20.

ROTTA (P.) Sullo Stile delle Chiese Milanesi. pp. 37. _Milano_, 1892. 8°.   Pam. 24.

Norway.

BRUUN (J.) Norges Stavkyrkor. pp. 117. _Stockholm_, 1891. 8°.   7817. k. 11.

DIETRICHSON (L. H. S.) De norske Stavkirker. _Christiania_, 1891, _etc._ 8°.   7817. k.

Schleswig. See supra: Denmark.

Scotland.

MAC GIBBON (D.) Ecclesiastical Architecture of Scotland. _Edinb._ 1895, _etc._ 8°.   7814. g.

MUIR (T. S.) Ecclesiological Notes on the Islands of Scotland. pp. 315. _Edinb._ 1885. 8°.   7708. b. 48.

MYLNE (R. S.) Master Masons to the Crown of Scotland and their works. pp. 304. _Edinburgh_, 1893. fol.   1732. c. 6.

NEILSON (G.) Peel, its meaning, _etc._ pp. 33. _Glasgow_, 1893. 4°.   7709. e. 7.

See also supra: England.

Spain.

GURLITT (C.) Die Baukunst Spaniens. 2 Bde. _Dresd._ 1889-93. fol.   1711. e.

PRENTICE (A. N.) Renaissance Architecture in Spain. pp. 16. _Lond._ 1894. fol.   1733. d. 20.

Sweden.

PERRY (J. T.) Mediæval Architecture in Sweden. _Lond._ 1891. 4°.   7817. d. 2.

Switzerland.

NAEHER (J.) Die Schlösser, Burgen und Klöster der romanischen Schweiz. _Karlsruhe_, 1886. 4°.   Pam. 91.

ARCOS DE LA FRONTERA. MANCHEÑO Y OLIVARES (M.) Galería de Arcobricenses. pp. 592. _Arcos de la F._ 1892. 8°.   10631. f. 49.

ARCTIC REGIONS. Ac. London. _Hakluyt Society._ Foxe (L.) Voyages of Captain L. Foxe and Captain T. James in search of a N.W. Passage, 1631-32. 2 vol. _Lond._ 1894. 8°.   Ac. 6172/70.

SMITH (G. B.) Sir John Franklin and the romance of the N.W. Passage. pp. 160. _Lond._ 1895. 8°.   10460. aaa. 30.

NORDENSKIÖLD (N. A. E.) Vegas Reise omkring Asia og Europa. 2 Del. _Kristiania_, 1881. 8°.   10460. ff. 17.

HOVGAARD (A.) Nordenskiöld's Voyage round Asia and Europe. pp. 293. _Lond._ 1882. 8°.   2352. d.

STUXBERG (A. J.) Minnen från Vegas färd. pp. 358. _Stockholm_, 1890. 8°.   10460. e. 30.

TSCHERSKI (J. D.) Wissenschaftliche Resultate der zur Erforschung des Janalandes und der Neusibirischen Inseln ausgesandten Expedition. pp. 511. 1892. 4°. Ac. Saint Petersburg. _Academia Scientiarum._ Mémoires. Tom. 40.   Ac. 1125/3.

KLINCKOWSTRÖM (A.) Tre Månaders Dag Minnen från Svenska Spetsbergs-Expeditionen. pp. 176. _Stockholm_, 1891. 8°.   10460. b. 37.

JEANNETTE, _Ship._ Le naufrage de la Jeannette dans l'océan glacial arctique. pp. 306. _Paris_, 1891. 8°.   10460. f. 26.

PEARY (J. D.) My Arctic Journal. pp. 240. _N.Y._ 1893. 8°.   10460. e. 34.

ARCTIC REGIONS—continued.

HEILPRIN (A.) The Arctic Problem and Narrative of the Peary Relief Expedition. pp. 165. *Phila.* 1893. 8°.   10460. e. 33.

KEELY (R. N.) Voyage of the "Kite" with the Peary expedition. pp. 524. *Lond.* 1893. 8°.   10470. h. 27.

BARRY (R. von) Zwei Fahrten in das nördliche Eismeer unternommen von Prinz Heinrich von Bourbon. pp. 169. *Pola*, 1894. 8°. 10470. h. 34.

JACKSON (F. G.) Narrative of a journey across the Tundras and a sojourn among the Samoyads. pp. 297. *Lond.* 1895. 8°.   10460. f. 30.

TREVOR-BATTYE (A.) Ice-bound on Kolguev. pp. 458. *West*, 1895. 8°.   10470. f. 39.

PEEL (A. H.) Polar Gleams. Voyage on the yacht 'Blencathra.' pp. 211. *Lond.* 1894. 8°.   10460. f. 28.

GELCICH (E.) Uebersicht der Entdeckungsreisen, *etc.* 1892. 8°. Ac. Vienna. *Geographische Gesellschaft.* Mittheilungen. Bd. 35. No. 5.   Ac. 6068.

TILLOTSON (J.) Adventures in the Ice. pp. 284. *Lond.* 1890. 8°.   10460. aa. 22.

TISSOT (V.) Le Pôle Nord et le Pôle Sud. pp. 230. *Paris*, 1889. 8°.   10460. ee. 40. *See also* SPITZBERGEN.

ARDÈCHE, *Department*. RANCUS, *Le Docteur*. Voyage à travers l'Ardèche.

Le Puy, 1894, *etc.* 8°.   10174. bb.

VASCHALDE (H.) L'Ardèche à la Convention. pp. 300. *Paris*, 1893. 8°.   9225. d. 4. *See also* CEVENNES: LANGUEDOC: VIVARAIS.

ARDEN, *Forest*. *See* WARWICKSHIRE.

ARDENNES, *Department and Forest*. ARDENNES, *Department*. Inventaire des archives antérieures à 1790. 1890, *etc.* 4°. FRANCE. *Ministère de l'Intérieur.* Collection des inventaires, *etc.*   1815. b. *etc.*

HANNEDOUCHE (A.) Les illustrations Ardennaises. pp. 199. *Sedan*, 1890. 18°. 010661. h. 22.

HEINS (M.) En Ardennes. pp. 218. *Gand*, 1890. 8°.   10271. bb. 20.

LAURENT (P.) Variétés historiques ardennaises. *Paris*, 1890, *etc.* 8°.   010171. g.

—— Centuries du pays des Essuens. pp. 620. 1894. 8°. GANNERON (F.) Annales.   4629. dd. 16.

P.P. *Paris*. Revue historique Ardennaise. *Paris*, 1894, *etc.* 8°.   P.P. 3554. vb.

RAYEUR (J. A.) La Trouée des Ardennes. pp. 280. *Charleville*, 1894. 8°.   9226. c. 27. *See also* CHAMPAGNE.

ARDRES. RANSON (E.) Histoire d'Ardres. pp. 719. *Saint-Omer*, 1891. 8°.   01074. i. 9.

ARGENTEUIL. ARGENTEUIL. Manuel du Pèlerin à la Sainte Tunique. pp. 44. *Lille*, 1894. 8°.   Pam. 75.

FAIVRE (H.) Ostension de la tunique de N. S. Jésus-Christ. pp. 187. *Versailles*, 1894. 12°.   4807. b. 4.

JACQUEMONT (A.) La tunique sans couture. pp. 299. *Lille*, 1894. 8°.   44807. bbb. 15.

WYARD (R.) Histoire de la sainte tunique d'Argenteuil. pp. 296. *Paris*, 1894. 12°.   4807. c. 6.

ARGENTINE REPUBLIC.—Army.

DINGSKIRCHEN (J.) Observaciones sobre la disciplina del Ejército Argentino. pp. 215. *Buenos A.* 1892. 8°.   8823. h. 31.

History and Politics.

POWER (J.) "The Land we Live in." pp. 132. *Buenos A.* 1891. 8°.   9771. b. 3.

ARGENTINE REPUBLIC.—continued.

CERBONI (C.) Cenni storici sulla Repubblica Argentina, 1515-1860. pp. 247. *Buenos A.* 1891. 8°.   9781. e. 11.

DIAZ DE GUSMAN (R.) Argentina. Historia. pp. 240. *Buenos A.* 1882. 8°.   9772. de. 3.

BERNARD ( ) *Marquis de Sassenay*. Napoléon 1er et la fondation de la République Argentine. pp. 285. *Paris*, 1892. 12°.   9772. aa. 19.

MITRE (B.) Historia de San Martin y de la emancipación Sud-Americana. 4 tom. *Paris*, 1890. 8°.   010882. m. 18.

ARGENTINE REPUBLIC. Registro oficial de la República Argentina, 1810-73. 6 tom. *Buenos A.* 1879-84. 8°.   9772. g. 5.

PELLIZA (M. A.) La Dictadura de Rosas. pp. 478. *Buenos A.* 1894. 8°.   9772. b. 19.

SALDÍAS (A.) Rozas y su época. 5 tom. *Buenos A.* 1892. 8°.   9772. dd. 6.

SOPRANO (P. P.) La Virgen del Valle y la conquista del antiguo Tucuman. pp. 429. *Buenos A.* 1889. 8°.   9772. c. 1.

ZUVIRÍA (J. M.) Los Constituyentes de 1853. pp. 400. *Buenos A.* 1889. 8°.   9772. e. 6.

ARGENTINE REPUBLIC. Campaña de los Andes al sur de la Patagonia por la 2a division del ejercito. pp. 664. *Buenos A.* 1883. 8°.   9772. ccc. 5.

CALVO (A.) Política americana. pp. 155. *Buenos A.* 1886. 8°.   8180. i. 10.

QUESADA (E.) La Política americana y las tendencias yankees. pp. 34. *Buenos A.* 1887. 8°.   Pam. 65.

ARGENTINE REPUBLIC. Die Revolution in Buenos Aires, Juli 1890. pp. 74. *Buenos A.* 1890. 8°.   9004. l. 34. (8.)

AUZON (E.) Historia de la Revolucion de Julio de 1890. pp. 110. *Buenos A.* 1890. 8°. Pam. 28.

BUENOS AYRES. The July Revolution, 1890. pp. 22. *Buenos A.* 1890. fol.   Pam. 28.

CASTIGLIONI (A.) Recuerdo de la revolucion, Julio de 1890. pp. 152. *Buenos A.* 1890. 8°.   9772. aa. 15.

GUTIERREZ (A. M. de) La Revolucion, 1890. pp. 91. *Buenos A.* 1890. 8°. 9004. gg. 20. (7.)

ESCALPELO. El Senado de 1890. pp. 252. *Buenos A.* 1891. 8°.   012314. f. 11.

MARIANI (M.) L'ultima rivoluzione, Luglio 1890. pp. 127. *Milano*, 1890. 8°. 9771. aa. 9.

MENDIA (J. M.) La Revolucion. Tom. 1. *Buenos A.* 1890. 8°.   9772. aaa. 28.

MITRE (B.) Despedida del General Mitre. pp. 16. *Buenos A.* 1890. 8°.   Pam. 46.

GRAHAM (W.) English Influence in the Argentine Republic. pp. 45. *Buenos A.* 1890. 8°.   Pam. 65.

LAMAS (P. S.) Objetivos de mis trabajos en Europa en favor de la República Argentina, 1882-90. *Paris*, 1890, *etc.* 8°.   8180. i.

MARTINEZ (A. B.) El Presupuesto nacional. pp. 363. *Buenos A.* 1890. 8°.   8179. c. 1.

GUTIERREZ (V. F.) Crisis y solucion. pp. 46. *Buenos A.* 1891. 8°.   Pam. 65.

MARTINEZ (J. A.) Sistema político Argentino. pp. 151. *La Plata*, 1891. 8°.   8179. a. 12.

ARGENTINE REPUBLIC. *Ministerio de Relaciones Exteriores.* Cuestiones de límites entre las repúblicas Argentina, el Brasil y Chile. pp. 342. *Buenos A.* 1892. 12°.   8180. aa. 17.

SERRANO MONTANER (R.) Límites con la República Arjentina. pp. 50. *Santiago*, 1895. 8°.   Pam. 65.

ARGENTINE REPUBLIC—*continued.*

VALDERRAMA (M.) La Cuestion de limites entre Chile i la República Arjentina. pp. 99.
Santiago, 1895. 8°. 8180. aa. 24.

BRAZIL. Statement submitted by Brazil to the President of the U.S. as Arbitrator between Brazil and the Argentine Republic. 6 vol.
N.Y. 1894. 4°. 8180. k. 8.

BELIN SARMIENTO (A.) Una república muerta. pp. 232. *Buenos A.* 1892. 8°. 8180. f. 37.

BROWN ARNOLD (J.) La muerte de la Republica. pp. 317. *Buenos A.* 1892. 8°. 9772. bb. 5.

See also AMERICA, *Central and South.*

Immigration to.

DAIREAUX (É.) La vie sociale et la vie légale des étrangers. pp. 95. *Paris,* 1889. 8°.
8180. h. 33.

JANNONE (G.) L'Emigrazione italiana nell' Argentina. pp. 215. *Napoli,* 1891. 8°.
7462. de. 28.

LEHMANN (B.) Die Rechtsverhä.tnisse der Fremden in Argentinien. pp. 148.
Buenos A. 1889. 8°. 6784. g. 7.

VACA-GUZMÁN (S.) La naturalización de los extranjeros. pp. 142. *Buenos A.* 1891. 8°.
6955. e. 15.

Indians. *See* INDIANS, *South American.*

Law. *See infra : Trade.*

Topography.

AKERS (C. E.) Argentine Sketches. pp. 190.
Lond. 1893. 8°. 10481. bbb. 46.

AURIGNAC (R. d') Trois ans chez les Argentins. pp. 483. *Paris,* 1890. 4°. 10481. i. 18.

DAVIS (G. G.) Ligeros apuntes sobre el clima de la República Argentina. pp. 254.
Buenos A. 1889. 4°. 8756. eee. 27.

GALVEZ (V.) Memorias de un viejo. 3 tom.
Buenos A. 1889. 8°. 10481. dd. 27.

GUILAINE (L.) La République Argentine. pp. 348. *Paris,* 1889. 8°. 10481. d. 32.

ICELY (R. H.) Argentine Republic. Railway Guide. pp. 58. *Buenos A.* 1892. 8°. 8235. cc. 47.

KÖNIG (A.) A través de la República Arjentina. pp. 422. *Santiago,* 1890. 8°. 10481. d. 30.

LANDIN (J.) Från Argentina. pp. 150.
Stockholm, 1890. 8°. 10481. bbb. 43.

LATZINA (F.) Diccionario geográfico argentino. pp. 619. *Buenos A.* 1891. 8°. 10481. i. 20.

—— Géographie de la République Argentine. pp. 488. *Buenos A.* 1890. 8°. 10481. ff. 36.

MODRICH (G.) Repubblica Argentina. Note di viaggio. pp. 447. *Milano,* 1890. 8°.
10481. cc. 27.

PEYRET (A.) Una visita á la colonias de la Republica Argentina. 2 tom.
Buenos A. 1889. 8°. 10481. dd. 20.

RIGUERA MONTERO (M.) Bosquejo geografico, *etc.* pp. 127. *Montevideo,* 1882. 8°. 10481. c. 33.

SANCHEZ NUÑEZ (M.) Ojeada sobre la parte Argentina de la region del Rio de la Plata. pp. 289. *Madrid,* 1879. 8°. 10481. e 40.

SOBONDO (A.) Nociones de geografía argentina. pp. 288. *Buenos A.* 1890. 8°. 10481. cc. 31.

TURNER (T. A.) Argentina and the Argentines. pp. 370. *Lond.* 1892. 8°. 10481. ee. 32.

X. Quinze Jours au Pays des Cédules. pp. 225. *Gand,* 1893. 4°. 10481. bbb. 48.

See also AMERICA, *Central and South;* GRAN CHACO ; LA PLATA ; MISIONES.

Trade, Finance, *etc.*

ARGENTINE REPUBLIC. Code de Commerce Argentin. pp. 451. *Paris,* 1893. 8°. 6784. b. 6.

ARGENTINE REPUBLIC.—*continued.*

ARGENTINE REPUBLIC. Exposicion sobre el estado económico de la República Argentina. pp. 246.
Buenos A. 1893. 8°. 08229. g. 48.

—— Les fonds argentins. pp. 16.
Paris, 1890. 8°. 8226. f. 60. (4.)

—— *Ministerio de relaciones exteriores.* Negociaciones entre Estados Unidos y la República Argentina. pp. 57. *Buenos A.* 1892. 8°.
Pam. 65.

BORAIN (J.) La République argentine et ses créanciers européens. pp. 80.
Brux. 1891. fol. 8226. g. 40. (8.)

BUENOS AYRES. *Banco Hipotecario.* Memoria del Banco Hipotecario, 1891. pp. 180.
Buenos A. 1892. 8°. 8245. ff. 35.

HOLMES (W. W.) Plan for the collection of the Customs Duties of the Republic. pp. 8.
Lond. 1891. 8°. 08227. ee. 45. (14.)

MADRID. *Exposición Americana.* Catálogo de la República Argentina. pp. 24.
Madrid, 1892. 8°. Pam. 18.

MORRIS (J.) Forced Currency Law of 1885 and Gold Contracts. pp. 80. *Lond.* 1891. 8°.
8226. cc. 50.

QUESADA (S. J.) Las finanzas de la República. pp. 434. *Buenos A.* 1892. 8°. 8226. h. 40.

SCHMITZ (O.) Die Finanzen Argentiniens. pp. 267. 1895. 8°. Exotische Werte. Bd. 2.
08226. l.

SCOTT (A. de C.) Review of the economic position of the Republic. pp. 60. *Lond.* 1892. 8°.
08227. g. 47. (12.)

SEEBER (F.) Finanzas y administracion. pp. 514. *Buenos A.* 1892. 8°. 08226. g. 1.

ARGENTINE LITERATURE.
See AMERICAN LITERATURE, *Spanish.*

ARGOS. WALDSTEIN (C.) Excavations at the Heraion of Argos, 1892. *Lond.* 1892, *etc.* 4°.
7705. h. 31.

See also GREECE.

ARGYLESHIRE. CAMPBELL (*Lord* A.) Waifs and Strays of Celtic Tradition.
Lond. 1889, *etc.* 8°. 12341. k.

See also SCOTLAND, *Highlands.*

ARIANO, Avellino. GRASSO (G.) Studi di storia antica. *Ariano,* 1893, *etc.* 8°. 7706. cc.

ARITHMETIC—General.

ALBERT ARITHMETIC. Albert Arithmetic. (Answers.) *Lond.* 1890, *etc.* 8°. 8534. aaa. 46.

ARITHMETIC. Self-testing Arithmetic. pp. 48.
Aberd. 1893. 16°. 8533. a. 7.

—— Typical Arithmetic. *Lond.* 1891. 8°.
8535. b. 42.

BEETZ (K. O.) Beiträge zu den Tagesströmungen im elementaren Rechenunterricht. pp. 50. 1891. 8°. Pädagogische Zeit- und Streitfragen. No. 18. 8310. c.

BLACKIE (W. G.) Combined Standard Arithmetics for Course "S." 3 pt. *Lond.* 1893. 8°.
8533. aa. 24.

—— Comprehensive Arithmetics. 7 pt.
Lond. 1893. 8°. 8532. aa. 44.

BLAIR (W.) School Arithmetic. Pt. 3.
Colombo, 1889. 8°. 8503. c. 33.

BROOK-SMITH (J.) Arithmetic in theory and practice. pp. 424. *Lond.* 1891. 8°. 2242. aa. 15.

—— Key. pp. 789. *Lond.* 1890. 8°. 8507. cc. 1.

CHAMBERS (W.) Graduated Arithmetic.
Lond. 1894, *etc.* 8°. 8534. a.

CHUO. Petite arithmétique swahilie. pp. 105.
Zanzibar, 1887. 12°. 8533. aa. 18.

ARITHMETIC.—General—continued.

CLASS-TEACHER. Class-Teacher's Arithmetic.
Lond. 1894, etc. 8°. 8534. df. 10.

COLES (J.) Arithmetic for the Third Standard.
pp. 26. Leeds, 1891. 8°. 8530. bbb. 27. (6.)

—— Geography and Arithmetic for candidates.
3 pt. Lond. 1891. 8°. 12200. ee. 5.

COX (H.) Principles of Arithmetic. pp. 172.
Lond. 1895. 8°. 8507. b. 61.

DAVIDSON (W.) Arithmetic. pp. 432. 32.
Lond. 1890. 8°. 8533. e. 31.

DAVIES (C.) Demonstrations of Arithmetic.
pp. 119. Lond. 1890. 8°. 8506. c. 48.

DIOPHANTUS, Alexandrinus. Die Arithmetik
des Diophantus. pp. 346. Leipz. 1890. 8°.
8535. g. 37.

DIXON (A. C.) Girls' Arithmetic. pp. 314.
Lond. 1891. 8°. 8535. ccc. 26.

ELLERY (T. B.) Course of Arithmetic. (Answers.)
3 pt. Lond. 1891. 8°. 8507. c. 37.

ENGLISH ARITHMETICS. Royal English Arithmetics.
Lond. 1893, etc. 8°. 8532. aa. 41.

EVANS (T.) Examination Arithmetic. pp. 224.
Lond. 1890. 8°. 8533. d. 10.

—— Midland 'Course S.' Arithmetic. 3 pt.
Lond. 1892. 8°. 8506. c. 51.

—— Problematic Arithmetic. Standard v.
pp. 32. Lond. 1892. 8°. 8535. aa. 34.

FEMMER (N.) N. Femmers Hovedregningsopgaver.
Kjøbenh. 1893, etc. 8°. 8533. e.

FIELDEN (S. J.) Arithmetic for infant schools.
pp. 36. Manch. 1891. 8°. 8503. bbb. 52.

FREGE (G.) Grundgesetze der Arithmetik.
Jena, 1893, etc. 8°. 8533. k.

GOYEN (P.) Key and Companion to higher
Arithmetic. pp. 416. Lond. 1893. 8°.
8533. de. 25.

GRASSMANN (R.) Die Zahlenlehre. pp. 242.
Stettin, 1891. 8°. 8535. ccc. 37.

GUNN (E. S.) Business Arithmetic. pp. 61.
Lond. 1893. 8°. 8535. df. 34.

HAND-AND-EYE ARITHMETIC. Arithmetic for
Infants. pp. 128. Lond. 1894. 8°. 8533. de. 31.

HANDBOOK. Handbook of the principles of
Arithmetic. pp. 51. Blackburn, 1893. 8°.
8530. bbb. 27. (14.)

HARTLEY (J. A.) Teachers' Manual of elementary
Arithmetic. Pt. 1. Adelaide, 1887. 8°.
8506. bb. 49.

HAUGH (J. J.) Higher Arithmetic. pp. 288.
Dublin, 1894. 8°. 8534. aa. 49.

HOWARD (C. F.) Art of Reckoning. pp. 192.
Lond. 1891. 8°. 8535. g. 36.

HULL ARITHMETIC. The Hull Arithmetic. 13 pts.
1890. 8°. Brown's School Series. 12210. c.

HUSSERL (E. G.) Philosophie der Arithmetik.
Halle, 1891, etc. 8°. 8535. ccc. 38.

INGRAM (A.) Principles of Arithmetic. pp. 154.
Edinb. 1894. 12°. 8533. aa. 28.

JACKSON (S.) Commercial Arithmetic. pp. 371.
1893. 8°. Macmillan's Commercial Class Books.
012202. h.

JONES (L. D.) Welsh Bi-Lingual Arithmetic.
Manch. 1893, etc. 8°. 8533. aa.

JUNIOR LOCAL ARITHMETIC. "Junior Local"
Arithmetic. pp. 192. Lond. 1893. 8°.
8530. aa. 46.

KEEFE (J.) Civil Service Arithmetic. pp. 89.
Lond. 1891. 8°. 8532. aa. 21.

LANDGRAF (E. R.) Afrikaansch Rekenboekje.
Kaapstad, 1890, etc. 8°. 8535. aa.

LANGLEY (E. M.) Treatise on Computation.
pp. 184. Lond. 1895. 8°. 8533. de. 35.

ARITHMETIC.—General—continued.

LAYNG (A. E. F.) Arithmetic.
Lond. 1895, etc. 8°. 8534. df. 11.

LISHMAN (R.) Concrete Arithmetic.
Lond. 1890, etc. 8°. 8530. aaa. 48.

LOCK (J. B.) Arithmetic for Schools. pp. 448.
Lond. 1894. 8°. 8531. aa. 50.

—— Arithmetic. Edited for use in India by
T. C. Lewis. pp. 357. Lond. 1891. 8°.
8534. aa. 43.

—— Arithmetic for the Standards. 14 pt.
Lond. 1892. 8°. 8535. aa. 37.

—— Shilling book of Arithmetic. pp. 216.
Lond. 1890. 8°. 8506. aa. 61.

CARR (H.) Key to J. B. Lock's Shilling
Arithmetic. pp. 288. Lond. 1893. 8°. 8506. c. 52.

LUNDIE (D.) Aritmética práctica. pp. 68. 8.
Huelva, 1886. 8°. 8506. bb. 52. (1.)

MACLEAN (H. S.) Hints on teaching Arithmetic.
pp. 108. Toronto, 1895. 8°. 8534. b. 39.

MAGUIRE (I. G.) Arnold's Arithmetic. 8 pt.
Leeds, 1890. 8°. 8534. aaa. 48.

MARSHALL (F. E.) Longmans' School Arithmetic.
pp. 449. Lond. 1892. 8°. 8535. b. 48.

NÚÑEZ DE COUTO (A.) Tratado de aritmética.
pp. 435. Madrid, 1893. 8°. 8529. e. 34.

ORME (T. A.) Concrete Arithmetic. pp. 114.
1892. 8°. Newmann's Science Manuals. 8708. ce.

PAGE (E.) Arithmetic for Standards I. and II.
pp. 21. Lond. 1891. 8°. 8506. bb. 52. (3.)

PALIN (E. F.) Best Methods of teaching Arithmetic.
pp. 53. Ripon, 1890. 8°. 8534. aa. 29.

PARRY (T.) New Code Arithmetic. 7 pt.
Lond. 1890, 91. 8°. 8507. c. 35.

PICKERING (E. T.) Mercantile Arithmetic.
pp. 280. Lond. 1893. 8°. 8534. aa. 48.

PRESTON. Grammar School. Arithmetical notes
& formulæ. Preston, 1892. 8°. 8531. c. 47. (4.)

PRINCE (J. J.) Graphic Arithmetic. pp. 48.
Lond. 1893. 8°. 8533. aa. 20.

RICHARD (L.) Sténarithmie-Richard. pp. 86.
Paris, 1887. 8°. 8534. a. 23.

ROYAL ENGLISH ARITHMETICS. Royal English
Arithmetics. Lond. 1893, etc. 8°. 8532. aaa. 24.

SEELEY (L.) The Grube method of teaching
arithmetic. pp. 64. N.Y. 1890. 8°. 8534. cc. 32.

BADANES (S.) Falsity of the Grube method.
pp. 47. N.Y. 1895. 8°. 8533. dd. 11. (8.)

SMITH (B.) Arithmetic for Schools. pp. 458.
Lond. 1892. 8°. 2242. aa. 13.

SMITH (C.) Arithmetic for Schools. pp. 320.
1894. 8°. Pitt Press Mathematical Series.
2322. cc. 53.

—— Solutions of Examples. By George Hale.
pp. 443. Camb. 1894. 8°. 8535. de. 15.

SOLUTION. Solution of Difficulties in Arithmetic.
pp. 326. Lond. 1891. 8°. 8535. aa. 25.

SPENCER (J.) Commercial Arithmetic. pp. 299.
Lond. 1890. 8°. 8534. aa. 27.

SPICKERNELL (G. E.) Explanatory Arithmetic.
pp. 258. Portsmouth, 1891. 8°. 8531. aa. 37.

STONE (S.) Shortcut Arithmetic. pp. 64.
Lond. 1890. 8°. 8530. bbb. 27. (3.)

TAYLOR (F. G.) Short commercial Arithmetic.
pp. 94. 1894. 8°. Methuen's Commercial Series
No. 10. 08227. de.

THOMAS (P. A.) Enunciations in Arithmetic.
pp. 84. Lond. 1893. 8°. 8532. aa. 38.

THOMSON (W. S.) Civil Service Arithmetic.
Aberd. 1893. 8°. 8535. df. 30.

THORNEYCROFT (W.) Century supplementary
Arithmetic. pp. 96. Lond. 1892. 8°. 8533. aa. 16.

ARITHMETIC.—General—*continued.*

TORRECILLA (G.) Aritmética de Niños. pp. 120.
Madrid, 1891. 16°. 8532. aa. 36.

UP TO DATE ARITHMETIC. "Up to Date" Arithmetic. 6 pt. *Lond.* 1891. 8°. 8531. de. 5.

WATSON (W.) The Quarterly Arithmetic.
Preston, 1891, *etc.* 8°. 8507. cc. 3.

—— Watson's Practical Rules and Exercises.
pp. 47. *Lond.* 1886. 8°. 12981. aa. 51.

WOLLMAN (J.) Daily working Arithmetics.
Lond. 1892, *etc.* 8°. 8535. b. 41.

—— Teachers' Arithmetic. pp. 254.
Lond. 1892. 8°. 8535. aaa. 52.

—— Some Wrinkles in Arithmetic. pp. 51.
Rotherham, 1893. 8°. 8533. aa. 19.

WORMELL (R.) Mercantile Arithmetic. pp. 352·
Lond. 1892. 8°. 8533. d. 15·

DITTMAR (W.) Chemical Arithmetic.
Glasgow, 1890, *etc.* 8°. 8908. h. 32.

SLOANE (T. O'C.) Arithmetic of Electricity.
pp. 138. *Lond.* 1891. 16°. 8757. aa. 36.

Examination Papers : Exercises : Test-Cards.

Ac. Oxford. *University.* Oxford Questions in Arithmetic : papers set in Responsions, 1880-90. pp. 188. *Oxford*, 1890. 8°. 8535. b. 37.

—— Oxford. *University.* "Junior Local" Arithmetic examination papers in full. pp. 208. 1894. 8°. Concise Series of School-Books.
012200. k.

ARNOLD (E. J.) Official Examination Tests in Arithmetic. *Leeds*, 1893, *etc.* 8°. 8533. de.

BAXENDALE (P.) "Times" Inspectors' Arithmetical Questions. 8 pt. *Manch.* 1887. 8°. 8531. aa. 38.

BLACKWOOD (W.) Arithmetical Exercises.
Lond. 1890, *etc.* 8°. 8534. aaa. 47.

CLARKE (A. D.) Army and Civil Service Examination Papers in Arithmetic. pp. 312. *Lond.* 1893. 8°. 2242. a. 3.

ELLERY (T. B.) Problems in Arithmetic. 2 pt. *Lond.* 1892. 8°. 8534. aa. 42.

EVANS (T.) Systematic Problems.
Lond. 1891, *etc.* 8°. 8535. aa.

—— 'Unique' Examinations in Arithmetic.
Lond. 1893, *etc.* 8°. 8530. aa.

EXERCISES. Exercises in the higher Rules. pp. 128. 4. 1893. 8°. Collins's School Series.
12205. c.

—— Arithmetical exercises for senior pupils. pp. 357. 73. *Edinb.* 1892. 8°. 8534. aa. 39.

GOVERNMENT PROBLEMS. Typical Government Problems. *Lond.* 1893, *etc.* 8°. 8533. aa. 25.

HALL (J.) Civil Service examples in Arithmetic. pp. 244. *Lond.* 1893. 8°. 8535. aa. 36.

HILEY (A.) Recapitulatory examples in Arithmetic. pp. 202. *Lond.* 1891. 8°. 8533. d. 14.

LANGLEY (E. M.) Exam. papers in Arithmetic, *etc. Lond.* 1893. 8°. 8533. d. 21.

MAC CRONE (R.) General Arithmetical examples for elementary examinations. pp. 35.
Cape Town, 1893. 8°. 8506. bb. 52. (5.)

MITCHESON (T.) Modern Side Arithmetic. Examples only. *Lond.* 1892, *etc.* 8°. 8548. cc.

NEWELL (A.) Problems in Arithmetic. pp. 187. *Lond.* 1892. 8°. 8506. c. 50.

NORTH STAR MECHANICAL EXERCISES. "North Star" mechanical exercises.
Burnley, 1893. 12°. 12210. aaa. 5.

ORIO Y RUBIO (M.) Libro de problemas aritméticos. *Palencia*, 1894, *etc.* 4°. 8531. df.

ARITHMETIC—Examination—*continued.*

SKERRY (G. E.) Papers in preliminary Arithmetic. pp. 92. *Lond.* 1890. 8°. 8504. aaaa. 42.

—— Papers in higher Arithmetic, *etc.*
pp. 150. *Lond.* 1893. 8°. 8533. de. 26.

WORKMAN (W. P.) Arithmetic Prize Papers. pp. 60. *Lond.* 1895. 8°. 12204. aaa. 18.

A. L. A. L. "Perfect" Test Cards.
Leeds, 1893. 32°. 12210. aaa. 3.

ARITHMETIC TEST CARDS. "Forward" Arithmetic Test Cards. *Birmingham*, 1893. 8°.
8532. aa. 37.

—— The "Safety" Test Cards.
Lond. 1891, *etc.* 8°. 12210. bbb.

ARNOLD (E. J.) "Practical" examination tests.
Leeds, 1889, *etc.* 12°. 12204. bbbb.

BLACKIE (W. G.) Vivid concrete and abstract Arithmetic Sheets. *Lond.* 1894. fol.
Tab. 11747. b. (64.)

CASSELL (J.) "Modern School" Test Cards.
Lond. 1894. 16°. 12210. aaa. 7.

EVANS (T.) "Champion" Test Cards.
Lond. 1893. 8°. 8532. aaa. 23.

—— "Climax" Test Cards.
Lond. 1894, *etc.* 8°. 12210. aaa. 9.

—— "Daily" Test Cards. 6 pt. *Lond.* 1889. 8°.
12210. bb. 4.

—— Economic Test Cards. *Lond.* 1888, *etc.* 16°.
12210. b. 13.

—— "Genuine" Test Cards.
Lond. 1893. *etc.* 16°. 12210. d. 5.

—— "New" Paper Tests, in Arithmetic.
Lond. 1891, *etc.* 8°. 8507. c. 36.

—— Scholarship Arithmetic Cards. 16 nos.
Lond. 1892. 8°. 8530. aa. 45.

EXAMINER. New Examiner's Test Cards. 6 pt.
Lond. 1892. 8°. 12210. cc. 5.

EXAMINATION TESTS. New Examination Tests in arithmetic. *Lond.* 1894. 8°. 12210. d. 3.

EXAMINATION CARDS. Typical Examination Cards on arithmetic. 5 pt. *Lond.* 1889. 8°.
12210. bbb.

HEYWOOD (D.) Hull Test Cards. 7 pt.
1889. 12°. Brown's School Series. 12210. c.

IDEAL ARITHMETIC TEST CARDS. "Ideal" Test Cards. *Birmingham*, 1893. 8°. 12210. d. 4.

LEDSHAM (J. B.) Arithmetic Test Cards.
1891, *etc.* 8°. World School Series. 12200 aa.

—— 1891 Arithmetical Test Cards.
Manch. 1891, *etc.* 16°. 12210. cc.

MERCHANT (G.) Primary arithmetical Test Cards. *Lond.* 1893. 12°. 12210. aaa. 6.

OLDEN (J. E.) Adaptable arithmetical Test Cards. *Leeds*, 1888. 8°. 12210. bbb.

PREMIER TEST CARDS. "New" Premier Test Cards. 5 pt. *Lond.* 1888. 8°. 12210. bb. 8.

READE (H. E.) Lindum Test Cards in Arithmetic. 7 pt. 1892. 8°. Brown's School Series.
12210. cc.

RELIANCE. Reliance Test Cards in Arithmetic.
5 pt. *Birmingham*, 1892. 8°. 12210. cc. 6.

STONEY (R. W.) Automatic arithmetical Cards.
Leeds, 1890, *etc.* 8°. 12210. bbb.

TEST CARDS. "Progressive" Test Cards.
Lond. 1893. 16°. 12210. d. 2.

TRAINER (P. E.) "Practical" Series of Test Cards. *Gorton*, 1891, *etc.* 8°. 12210. bbb.

WADDINGTON (R.) "Monthly Progress" arithmetical Tests. *Bolton*, 1894, *etc.* 8°. 12210. d.

WATSON (W.) New Series Inspectors' Tests.
Preston, 1893, *etc. obl.* 16°. 12210. b. 12.

ARITHMETIC.—Mental.

Mental Arithmetic.

ARITHMETIC. Mental Arithmetic. pp. 168.
Lond. 1891. 8°.   8535. b. 39.

BAILEY (M. A.) American mental Arithmetic.
pp. 160. *N.Y.* 1892. 8°.   8531. aa. 46.

BARRACLOUGH (T.) 1892 "Eclipse" mental
Standards. pp. 48. *Lond.* 1893. 8°. Pam. 38.

BLACKIE (W. G.) The Vivid mental Calculator.
Lond. 1894. *s. sh.* fol.   Tab. 11747. b. (66.)

EVANS (T.) "Premier" mental Arithmetic.
Lond. 1893, *etc.* 8°.   8506. cc.

EXERCISES. Exercises in mental Arithmetic.
pp. 94. *Lond.* 1892. 8°.   8531. aa 40.

HANDBOOK. Handbook of mental Arithmetic.
pp. 259. *Lond.* 1894. 8°.   8533. c. 35.

Separate Rules.

BLACKIE (W. G.) Tot-Cards. *Lond.* 1890. 8°.
           8507. dc. 1.

EVANS (T.) Examination Tots. *Lond.* 1891. 8°.
           8507. aa. 37.

HULL TOT BOOK. Hull Tot Book. pp. 16.
1890. 8°. Brown's School Series.   12210. cc.

KEEFE (J.) Civil Service Tot Book.
Lond. 1893. *obl.* 8°.   8533. de. 22.

MERCHANT (G.) Tot Arithmetic. pp. 40.
Lond. 1891. 8°.   8506. aaa. 73. (4.)

—— Tot Test Cards. *Lond.* 1891. 16°.
           12210. bbb. 1.

TOWN (C. E.) Long and cross Civil Service
Tots. 2 pt. *Lond.* 1892. 4°. & 8°.   8507. e. 8.

WATSON (W.) Graduated Tots. pp. 32.
Lond. 1890. 8°.   8506. aaa. 73. (3.)

BIRCH (W. T.) Bills of Parcels. pp. 34.
Cape Town, 1892. 8°.   Pam 38.

COWHAM (J. H.) Fractions at a Glance.
Lond. 1890. *s. sh.* fol.   1865. c. 1. (1.)

WILLIAMS (E. A.) First Book of Fractions.
pp. 39. *Lon'l.* 1894. 8°.   8533. e. 38.

CALVERT (J.) Treatise on Decimal Arithmetic.
pp. 56. *Manch.* 1895. 8°.   8531. b. 52.

HUNTER (H. S. J. A.) Decimal Approximations.
pp. 55. *Lond.* 1892. 8°.   8533. aa. 15.

MILNER (H. S.) Notes on proportion in Arithmetic. pp. 20. *Camb.* 1893. 8°. 8532. aa. 32.

CASAMAJOR (L. DE) Takirithmie. pp. 72.
Paris, 1890. 12°.   8506. cc. 40. (5.)

ARIZONA. BOURKE (J. G.) On the Border
with Crook. pp. 491. *Lond.* 1892. 8°.
           10412. cc. 29.

ARKANSAS. HARRELL (J. M.) Brooks and
Baxter War. History of Reconstruction in
Arkansas. pp. 276. *St. Louis*, 1893. 4°.
           9605. ff. 10.

ARKANSAS. Arkansas. Description of the State.
pp. 31. 1893. 8°.   Pam. 86.

CUTTER (C.) Guide to the Hot Springs of
Arkansas. pp. 66. *St. Louis*, 1893. 8°. Pam. 86.

ARLES. DUCHESNE ( ) La Primatie d'Arles.
1892. 8°. Ac. *Paris. Société des Antiquaires.*
Mémoires, etc. Série 6. Tom. 2.   Ac. 5331.

FOURNIER (P.) Le Royaume d'Arles 1138–1378.
pp. 554. *Paris*, 1891. 8°.   9225. k. 25.

RANCE (A. J.) L'Académie d'Arles au xviime
siècle. 3 tom. *Paris*, 1886–90. 8°. 8355. eee. 14.

ARMAGNAC. TIERNY (P.) La Sénéchaus-
see d'Armagnac. pp. 15. *Auch*, 1894. 8°.
           5423. g. 1. (12.)

See also GASCONY: GERS, *Department.*

ARMENIA. ISAVERDENTZ (H.) Histoire de
l'Arménie. pp. 259. *Venise*, 1888. fol.
           1851. a. 10.

M. L'Armeno-Veneto. Compendio storica.
Venezia, 1893, *etc.* 8°.   9055. g.

ARMENIAN ATROCITIES. "Atrocities," Armenian
and others. pp. 23. *Lond.* 1895. 4°. Pam. 67.

ARMENIAN QUESTION. La Question arménienne.
pp. 18. *Constantinople*, 1880. 8°.
        8028. de. 31. (3.)

DES COURSONS (R. de) *Viscount.* La Rébellion
arménienne. pp. 102. *Paris*, 1895. 8°.
         8027. bbb. 22.

GLADSTONE (*Right Hon.* W. E.) The Armenian
Question. pp. 15. *Lond.* 1895. 8°.   Pam. 67.

GREENE (F. D.) The Armenian Crisis. pp. 180.
Lond. 1895. 8°.   8005. bbb. 29.

LONDON. *Anglo - Armenian Association.* The
Case for the Armenians. pp. 54.
Lond. 1893. 8°.   8028. de. 30. (17.)

MACCOLL (M.) England's Responsibility towards
Armenia. pp, 72. *Lond.* 1895. 8°. Pam. 67.

NAZARBEK (A.) Armenian Revolutionists upon
the Armenian Problem. pp. 16.
Lond. 1895. 8°.   Pam. 67.

P. P. *Dacca.* Ara: journal of Armenian Politics. *Dacca*, 1894, *etc.* 8°.   P. P. 3800. k.

—— *New York.* Haik. Armenian political
fortnightly. *New York*, 1891, *etc.* fol. Arm. 68.

WORCESTER, *Mass.* Garden of Eden Defiled!
pp. 12. *Worcester, Mass.* 1894. 8°.   Pam. 67.

ARARAT. The Land of Ararat. pp. 348.
Lond. 1893. 8°.   10077. bbb. 21.

BARKLEY (H. C.) Ride through Asia Minor and
Armenia. pp. 350. *Lond.* 1891. 8°.
         10076. ccc. 18.

CHANTRE (B.) À travers L'Arménie russe.
pp. 368. *Paris*, 1893. 8°.   10077. l. 16.

CHOLET (A. P. de) Voyage en Turquie d'Asie.
pp. 394. *Paris*, 1892. 12°.   10077. aa. 14.

LANIN (E. B.) Armenia and the Armenians.
pp. 16. 1890. 8°.   Pam. 88.

NOLDE (E. F. von) *Baron.* Reise nach Armenien,
etc. Braunschweig, 1895. 8°.   10077. h. 18.

MUELLER - SIMONIS (P.) Relation des missions
scientifiques de H. Hyvernat et P. Müller-
Simonis, 1888–89. pp. 628.   *Wash.* 1892. 8°.
           10075. k. 7.

TCHERAZ (M.) Armenia. pp. 3. 1891. 8°.
           Pam. 88.

TELFER (J. B.) Armenia and its People.
Lond. 1891. 8°.   10076. ff. 13.

YERGNAVOR (A.) The Armenian at Home.
pp. 60. 1895. 8°.   10076. aa. 9.

ARMENIAN CHURCH. GELZER (H.)
Die Anfänge der armenischen Kirche. 1895. 8°.
Ac. Leipsic. *Gesellschaft der Wissenschaften.*
Berichte. Philol. historische Classe. 1895.
           Ac. 700/2.

DER-MIKELIAN (A.) Die armenische Kirche.
pp. 121. *Leipz.* 1892. 8°.   4695. eee. 8.

KATERJIAN (J.) De fidei symbolo, quo Armenii
utuntur, observationes. pp. 52.
Viennae, 1893. 8°.   3506. h. 7.

VERNIER (D.) Histoire du Patriarcat arménien
catholique. pp. 347. *Lyon*, 1891. 8°. 4534. f. 17.

ARMENIAN LANGUAGE, LITERA-
TURE, etc. MISKJIAN (H.) Lexicon armeno-
latinum. pp. 483. *Romae*, 1887. 8°.
         12901. d. 32.

KAINZ (C.) Grammatik der armenischen
Sprache. pp. 196. 1891. 8°. Die Kunst der
Polyglottie. Th. 35.   12902. c.

ARMENIAN LANGUAGE—*continued.*

BUGGE (E. S.) Etruskisch und Armenisch. Sprachvergleichende Forschungen. *Christiania*, 1890, *etc.* 8°.   12933. dd.

BAYAN (G.) Armenian Proverbs and Sayings. pp. 58. *Venice*, 1889. 12°.   889. g. 15.

P. P. *Dacca.* Ara : journal of literature. *Dacca*, 1894, *etc.* 8°.   P. P. 3800. k.

—— *Vienna.* "Monthly Magazine" of literature, in Armenian. *Vienna*, 1887 *etc.* 4°. 890. m.

STRZYGOWSKI (J.) Das Etschmiadzin-Evangeliar. pp. 127. 1891. 8°. Byzantischer Denkmäler, *etc.* No. 1.   7705. f.

VIENNA. *Mechitarist Congregation.* Haupt Catalog der armenischen Handschriften. *Wien*, 1891, *etc.* 4°.   761. l. 1.

ARMINIANISM. *See* CALVINISM.

ARMS AND ARMOUR. *See* WEAPONS.

ARONA. PERUCCHETTI (P.) Arona. pp. 211. *Arona*, 1894. 8°.   10131. f. 2.

ARRAH. HALLS (J. J.) Arrah in 1857. pp. 137. *Dover*, 1893. 8°.   9057. aa. 19.

ARRAN. MILNER (G.) Studies of Nature on the Coast of Arran. pp. 189. *Lond.* 1894. 8°.   010370. ff. 2.

ARRANCY. GERMAIN (L.) L'église d'Arrancy. 1891. 8°. Ac. Bar-le-Duc. *Société des Lettres.* Mémoires. Sér. 2. Tom. 9.   Ac. 271.

ARRAS. ADVIELLE (V.) Les Places d'Arras à la fin du 18ème siècle. pp. 4. *Paris*, 1893. 4°.   10172. i. 8.

DEPOTTER (   ) Les Brigittines à Arras. 1892. 8°. Ac. Arras. *Société des Sciences.* Mémoires. Sér. 2. Tom. 23.   Ac. 255.

RICHARD (J. M.) Cartulaire de l'hôpital Saint-Jean-en-l'Estrée d'Arras. pp. 154. *Paris*, 1888. 8°.   4629. c. 6.

ARSENIC. SANGER (C. R.) Quantitative determination of Arsenic. pp. 21. 1891. 8°.   Pam. 13.

—— Formation of volatile compounds of Arsenic from arsenical Wall Papers. pp. 65. 1894. 8°.   Pam. 13.

ART.

Bibliography.

DESTAILLEUR (H. A. G. W.) Catalogue de livres et estampes relatifs aux beaux-arts. pp. 420. *Paris*, 1895. 8°   11902. h. 39.

Pt. I. General.

ADELINE (J.) Adeline's Art Dictionary. pp. 422. *Lond.* 1891. 8°.   7808. c. 20.

ALBERTI (C.) Natur und Kunst. pp. 320. *Leipz.* 1890. 8°.   012357. c. 42.

ARTI. Le Belle Arti e le vessazioni della burocrazia. pp. 31. *Roma*, 1894. 8°.   Pam. 24.

BARKAS (H. D.)   Art Student's pocket manual. *Reading*, 1892, *etc.* 12°.   7854. b. 24.

BICHET (P.) L'Art et le Bien-être chez soi. pp. 330. *Paris*, 1890. 8°.   7807. aa. 2.

BOUFFIER (H.) Kleines Handbuch der Liebhaberkünste. pp. 82. 1892. 8°. Bossong's Kunsttechnische Bibliothek. Bd. 6.   7858. f.

CARTERON (C.) and (E.) Introduction à l'étude des beaux-arts. pp. 287. *Paris*, 1891. 12°.   7808. aa. 40.

CHERBULIEZ (C. V.) L'Art et la Nature. pp. 322. *Paris*, 1892. 8°.   7808. a. 45.

DIDEROT (D.) Thoughts on Art and Style. pp. 291. *Lond.* 1893. 8°.   011850. g. 11.

DU BOIS REYMOND (E.) Naturwissenschaft und bildende Kunst. pp. 64. *Leipz.* 1891. 8°.   7807. i. 14. (11.)

ART.—General—*continued.*

FRÉSON (J. G.) Essais de philosophie de l'art. *Paris*, 1893, *etc.* 8°.   7808. df.

GAEDERTZ (T.) Kunststreifzüge. pp. 239. *Lübeck*, 1889. 8°.   7807. b. 10.

GEFFROY (G.) La vie artistique. *Paris*, 1892, *etc.* 12°.   7808. de.

GILLE (P. H.) Causeries sur l'art. pp. 358. *Paris*, 1894. 8°.   7808. df. 18.

HILDEBRAND (A.)   Das Problem der Form in der bildenden Kunst. pp. 125. *Strassb.* 1893. 8°.   7856. aa. 48.

HIRTH (G.) Aufgaben der Kunstphysiologie. pp. 611. *München*, 1891. 8°.   7807. k. 16.

HOLZ (A.) Die Kunst. pp. 156. *Berl.* 1891. 8°.   7808. a. 34.

HUNT (W. H.)   Obligations of the Universities towards Art, *etc.* pp. 46. *Lond.* 1895. 8°.   7807. aaaa. 17.

KESSLER (R.) Zeitgemässe Betrachtungen über schöne Kunst. pp. 85. *Berl.* 1890. 8°.   7807. k. 17. (7.)

LA GRASSERIE (R. de) De la Classification des arts. pp. 304. *Paris*, 1893. 8°.   8464. eec. 30.

MORRIS (W.) The Aims of Art. pp. 39. *Lond.* 1887. 16°.   7808. de. 5.

—— Art and Socialism. pp. 72. 1884. 8°. Leek Bijou Freethought Reprints. No. 7.   4017. a. 8.

NISBET (H.) Where Art begins. pp. 232. *Lond.* 1892. 8°.   7807. i. 5.

P.P. *London.* The Art Interchange. *Lond.* 1890, *etc.* fol.   1552.

—— The Studio. *Lond.* 1893, *etc.* 8°.   1532.

PHIPSON (E. A.) Art under Socialism. pp. 16. *Lond.* 1895. 8°.   Pam. 82.

POLLINARI (B.) Scritti d'Arte. pp. 302. *Piacenza*, 1894. 8°.   7807. aaa. 44.

QUILTER (H.) Preferences in Art. pp. 404. *Lond.* 1892. 4°.   K.T.C. 18. b. 3.

REYNOLDS (*Sir* J.) Sir J. Reynolds's Discourses. *Chicago*, 1891. 8°.   7855. c. 51.

RUSKIN (J.) Letters on Art. pp. 98. *Lond.* 1894. 8°.   7806. aaa. 16.

COLLINGWOOD (W. G.)   Art Teaching of Ruskin. pp. 376. *Lond.* 1891. 8°.   7808. aaa. 48.

WALDSTEIN (C.)   Work of J. Ruskin. pp. 189. *Lond.* 1894. 8°.   011850. f. 74.

STERNE (C.) Natur und Kunst. pp. 395. *Berl.* 1891. 8°.   12249. cc. 38.

SOURIAU (P.) La Suggestion dans l'Art. pp. 348. *Paris*, 1893. 8°.   7808. e. 22.

STORY (W. W.) Excursions in Arts. pp. 295. *Bost.* 1891. 8°.   012357. e. 38.

TAINE (H. A.) Lectures on Art. 2 ser. *N.Y.* 1889. 12°.   7808. df. 1.

TAYLOR (J. A.) The Evolution of Art. 1891. 8°. Evolution Series. No. 11.   7006. bbb.

TOLSTOI (L. N.)   Die Bedeutung der Wissenschaft und der Kunst. pp. 117. *Dresd.* 1890. 8°.   011824. h. 26.

TRINQUIER (L.) Les Petits Arts d'amateur. pp. 272. *Paris*, 1891. 12°.   7942. a. 58.

VALETTE (M.) Les Révolutions de l'Art. pp. 482. *Bordeaux*, 1890. 8°.   7806. de. 20.

VAN DYKE (J. C.) Art for Art's Sake. pp. 249. *Lond.* 1893. 8°.   7857. e. 28.

—— Principles of art. pp. 291. *N.Y.* 1887. 8°.   7808. df. 11.

VEIT (P.) Zehn Vorträge über Kunst. pp. 120. 1891. 8°. Görres - Gesellschaft Vereinschrift 1891.   Ac. 2026/2.

ART.—General—_continued._

WHITE (W.) The Principles of Art. pp. 634.
Lond. 1895. 8°.   7807. f. 33.

WHITE (W. H.) Arts and Artists. pp. 27.
Lond. 1891. 8°.   7808. aa. 44. (7.)

BELL (N.) Tourist's Art Guide to Europe.
pp. 328. _Lond._ 1893. 8°.   10107. aa. 9.

CHEFS-D'ŒUVRE. Les chefs-d'œuvre de l'Art
au xixᵉ siècle. 5 tom. _Paris_, 1892. 4°.
                                   K.T.C. 9. b. 2.

HAMERTON (P. G.) Man in Art. pp. 344.
Lond. 1892. 4°.   K.T.C. 3. b. 17.

PELLISSIER (P. A.) Les chefs-d'œuvre de l'Art
moderne. pp. 264. _Paris_, 1893. 8°. 7807. c. 9.

VACHON (M.) La Femme dans l'Art. pp. 616.
Paris, 1893. 4°.   7808. g. 14.

CHARCOT (J. M.) Les difformes et les malades
dans l'Art. pp. 162. _Paris_, 1889. 4°.
                                    7808. g. 9.

See also ÆSTHETICS : ANATOMY, _Artistic_ : AR-
CHITECTURE : DRAWING : EXHIBITIONS : MUSIC :
PAINTING : SCULPTURE.

Ancient.

CONWAY (_Sir_ W. M.) Dawn of Art in the ancient
world. pp. 189. _Lond._ 1891. 8°.
                                   7704. aaa. 49.

COUGNY (G.) L'Art antique. pp. 344.
Paris, 1892. 8°.   7702. b. 41.

EBE (G.) Abriss der Kunstgeschichte des Alterthums. pp. 675. _Düsseldorf_, 1895. 8°.
                                    7808. cc. 6.

EMERSON (E. R.) Masks, Heads and Faces ; rise
and development of Art. pp. 312.
Bost. 1891. 8°.   07708. e. 1.

GROSSE (E.) Die Anfänge der Kunst. pp. 301.
Freiburg i. B. 1894. 8°.   7808. e. 30.

HEUZEY (L.) Les Origines orientales de l'Art,
etc. _Paris_, 1891, _etc._ 4°.   7806. ee. 34.

GAYET (A.) L'Art Persan. pp. 319.
Paris, 1895. 8°.   2261. cc. 8.

PETRIE (W. M. F.) Egyptian Art. pp. 128.
Lond. 1895. 8°.   7704. aa. 45.

RYAN (C.) Egyptian Art. pp. 115.
Lond. 1894. 8°.   7704. aa. 38.

PERROT (G.) and CHIPIEZ (C.) History of Art in
Persia. pp. 508. _Lond._ 1892. 8°. 2259. f. 14.

—— History of Art in Primitive Greece. 2 vol.
Lond. 1894. 8°.   2259. g. 2.

—— History of Art in Phrygia, Lydia, Caria,
and Lycia. pp. 405. _Lond._ 1892. 8°. 2259. f. 20.

BRUNN (H. von) Griechische Kunstgeschichte.
München, 1893, _etc._ 8°.   7808. cc.

DUMON (K.) Études d'Art grec. pp. 32.
Paris, 1894. 4°.   7808. h. 4.

GENTILE (I.) Arte greca. _Milano_, 1892. 8°.
                                   012200. h. 76.

MICHAELIS (A. T. F.) Altattische Kunst.
pp. 39. _Strassb._ 1893. 8°.   Pam. 3.

SYBEL (L. von) Wie die Griechen ihre Kunst
erwarben. pp. 22. _Marburg_, 1892. 8°. Pam. 22.

BULLE (H.) Die Silene in der archaischen
Kunst der Griechen. pp. 77.
Muenchen, 1893. 8°.   Pam. 3.

SEEMANN (T.) Die Kunst der Etrusker. pp. 72.
Dresd. 1890. 8°.   7708. cc. 48.

GENTILE (I.) Storia dell' Arte Romana. 2 pt.
Milano, 1892. 8°.   012200. h. 75.

DIEHL (C.) L'Art byzantin dans l'Italie méridionale. pp. 267. _Paris_, 1894. 8°.
                                   7808. bbb. 33.

ART.—Ancient—_continued._

FORRER (R.) Die Zeugdrucke der byzantinischen, romanischen, und spätern Kunstepochen. pp. 39. _Strassb._ 1894. 4°.
                                   K.T.C. 26. b. 8.

P.P. Leipsic. Byzantinische Zeitschrift.
Leipz. 1892, _etc._ 8°.   P.P. 4748. p.

STRZYGOWSKI (J.) Byzantische Denkmäler.
Wien, 1891, _etc._ fol.   7705. f.

See also ASSYRIA : EGYPT : GREECE : ROME
VASES.

Biographies of Artists. _See_ BIOGRAPHY.

Christian Art and Archæology : Symbolism.

AC. Amiens. _Société d'Archéologie._ Album
Archéologique. _Amiens_, 1886, _etc._ fol. 7704. l.

ALLEN (J. R.) Christian Symbolism in Great
Britain and Ireland. pp. 408. _Lond._ 1887. 8°.
                                    2260. b. 2.

BOURNAND (F.) Histoire de l'Art chrétien.
2 tom. _Paris_, 1891. 8°.   7808. e. 5.

CONTI (A.) Religione ed Arte. pp. 433.
Firenze, 1891. 8°.   7808. a. 43.

CUTTS (E. L.) History of early Christian Art.
pp. 368. _Lond._ 1893. 8°.   4429. bbb. 12.

DETZEL (H.) Christliche Ikonographie. pp. 583.
Freiburg, 1894, _etc._ 8°.   7807. k. 27.

EBERS (G.) Die koptische Kunst, ein neues
Gebiet der altchristlichen Sculptur. pp. 61.
Leipz. 1892. 8°.   7706. ee. 38.

GATTY (C. T.) Christian Art. pp. 12.
Lond. 1890. 8°.   3939. ccc. 2. (8.)

HULME (F. E.) History of Symbolism in
Christian Art. pp. 234. _Lond._ 1891. 8°.
                                   7808. bbb. 22.

PÉRATÉ (A.) L'Archéologie chrétienne.
pp. 368. _Paris_, 1892. 8°.   2261. c.

P.P. _Rome._ Nuovo Bullettino di Archeologia
cristiana. _Roma_, 1895, _etc._ 8°. P.P. 1931. dia.

SALMON (F. R.) Histoire de l'Art chrétien au
dix premiers siècles. pp. 609. _Lille_, 1891. 8°.
                                   7806. de. 21.

SCHMIDT (H.) Handbuch der Symbolik.
pp. 491. _Berl._ 1890. 8°.   3504. f. 28.

SCHULTZE (V.) Archäologie der altchristlichen
Kunst. pp. 382. _München_, 1895. 8°.
                                   7807. h. 36.

ENGELS (M.) Die Darstellung der Gestalten
Gottes des Vaters, in der Malerei. pp. 118.
Luxemburg, 1894. 4°.   7857. f. 56.

FARRAR (F. W.) Life of Christ as represented in
Art. pp. 507. _Lond._ 1894. 8°.   2261. d. 1.

NOACK (F.) Die Geburt Christi in der bildenden
Kunst. pp. 72. _Darmstadt_, 1894. 8°.
                                   7875. e. 28.

VAN DYKE (H. J.) The Christ-Child in Art.
pp. 236. _N.Y._ 1894. 8°.   7808. e. 34.

FORRER (R.) Kreuz und Kreuzigung Christi in
ihrer Kunstentwicklung. pp. 33.
Strassb. 1894. 4°.   K.T.C. 26. b. 10.

WEAL (A. de) Das Kleid des Herrn auf den
frühchristlichen Denkmälern. pp. 51.
Freiburg, 1891. 8°.   7704. i. 12. (3.)

BREYMANN (A.) Adam und Eva in der Kunst
des christlichen Alterthums. pp. 162.
Wolfenbüttel, 1893. 8°.   7808. bbb. 26.

ROHAULT DE FLEURY (C.) Les Saints de la
Messe et leurs Monuments. _Paris_, 1893, _etc._ 4°.
                                   K.T.C. 20. b. 3.

BARGÈS (J. J. L.) Notice sur quelques Autels
du moyen âge. pp. 118. _Paris_, 1890. 8°.
                                   3475. g. 1.

ART.—Christian—*continued.*

ARMELLINI (M,)   Gli antichi cimiteri cristiani di Roma e d'Italia.   pp. 779.   *Roma*, 1893. 8°.
                         7706. d. 3.

DAVIN (V.)   Les Antiquités chrétiennes rapportées à la Cappella Greca du cimetière de Priscille.   pp. 867.   *Paris*, 1892. 8°.
                         7706. cc. 13.

WAAL (A. de)   Archäologische Ehrengabe der römischen Quartalschrift zu De Rossi's LXX. Geburtstage.   pp. 424.   *Roma*, 1892. 4°.
                         7705. ee. 31.

FORRER (R.)   Die frühchristlichen Alterthümer aus dem Gräberfelde von Achmin-Panopolis. pp. 29.   *Strassb.* 1893. 4°.   7709. k. 24.

BROCKHAUS (H.)   Die Kunst in den Athos-Klöstern.   pp. 305.   *Leipz.* 1891. 4°.   7807. m. 4.

CLAUSSE (G.)   Les Monuments du Christianisme au moyen âge.   2 tom.   *Paris*, 1893. 8°.
                         7808. f. 11.

MUENZENBERGER (E. F. A.)   Zur Kenntniss der mittelalterlichen Altäre Deutschlands. *Frankfurt.* 1885, *etc.* fol.   192.

OTTE (H.)   Handbuch der kirchlichen Kunst-Archäologie des deutschen Mittelalters.   2 Bde. *Leipz.* 1883–85. 8°.   7707. bb. 54.

See also ARCHITECTURE, *Ecclesiastical and Styles : infra,* History : CROSS.

Education.

BUSHEY.   *Herkomer School.*   Annual Report. *Bushey*, 1891, *etc.* 8°.   7808. c.

HATTON (R. G.)   Guide to the establishment of Art Classes.   pp. 114.   *Lond.* 1895. 8°.
                         7856. aaa. 33.

LONDON.   *National Art Training School.*   Prospectus.   1887.   *Lond.* 1887, *etc.* 8°.   7958. b.

P.P.   *London.*   Art Schools of London. *Lond.* 1895, *etc.* 8°.   P.P. 2495. bc.

TAYLOR (E. R.)   Elementary Art Teaching. pp. 166.   *Lond.* 1890. 8°.   7807. i. 3.

WALDSTEIN (C.)   The Study of Art in Universities.   pp. 129.   *Lond.* 1895. 8°.   7808. de. 6.

History.

BELL (N.)   The Students' Hand-Book of Art. pp. 323.   *Lond.* 1895. 8°.   07807. b. 1.

BUCHER (B.)   Katechismus der Kunstgeschichte pp. 323.   *Leipz.* 1890. 8°.   7808. a. 32.

CAVALLUCCI (C. J.)   Manuale di Storia dell' Arte.   *Firenzi*, 1895, *etc.* 8°.   7814. aa.

FORRER (R.)   Die Zeugdrucke der byzantinischen, gothischen und spätern Kunstepochen. pp. 39.   *Strassb.* 1894. 4°.   K.T.C. 26. b. 8.

GOELER VON RAVENSBURG (F.) *Baron.*   Grundriss der Kunstgeschichte.   pp. 478.   *Berl.* 1894. 8°.
                         7808. e. 37.

HADDON (A. C.)   Evolution in Art.   pp. 364. 1895. 8°.   ELLIS (H. H.)   Contemporary Science Series.   Vol. 30.   8709. i.

LEITHAEUSER (G.)   Bilder aus der Kunstgeschichte.   pp. 226.   *Hamb.* 1894. 8°. 7808. aaa. 30.

OVERBECK (J.)   Kunstgeschichtliche Miscellen. 1892, *etc.* 8°.   Ac. Leipzic.   *K. Sächsische Gesellschaft der Wissenschaften.*   Berichte.   Phil.-hist. Classe.   1892, *etc.*   Ac. 700/2.

PEYRE (R.)   Histoire des Beaux-Arts.   pp. 786. *Paris*, 1894. 12°.   7806. aaa. 14.

SCHMARSOW (A.)   Studien und Forschungen zur Kunstgeschichte.   *Leipz.* 1894, *etc.* 8°.   7808. c.

SCHULTZ (A.)   Allgemeine Geschichte der bildenden Künste.   *Berl.* 1895, *etc.* 8°.   7807. m.

VAN DYKE (J. C.)   College Histories of Art. *N.Y.* 1894, *etc.* 8°.   7805. b.

ART.—History—*continued.*

COUGNY (G.)   L'Art au moyen âge.   pp. 308. *Paris*, 1894. 8°.   7808. c. 27.

FALKE (J. von)   Geschichte des Geschmacks im Mittelalter.   pp. 374.   *Berl.* 1892. 8°.   12249. cc. 5.

SCHLOSSER (J. von)   Beiträge zur Kunstgeschichte aus den Schriftquellen des frühen Mittelalters, *etc.*   pp. 186.   1891. 8°.   Ac. Vienna.   *K. Akademie.*   Sitzungsberichte.   Phil.-hist. Classe. Bd. 123.   Ac. 810/6.

REBER (F. v.)   History of Mediæval Art. pp. 743.   *N.Y.* 1887. 8°.   7808. e. 8.

GONSE (L.)   L'Art Gothique.   pp. 476. *Paris*, 1891. fol.   7805. g. 7.

Ac.   Paris.   *École du Louvre.*   COURAJOD (L.) Les Origines de l'Art goth.que.   pp. 62. *Paris*, 1892. 8°.   Pam. 24.

HOPPIN (J. M.)   The early Renaissance. pp. 306.   *Bost.* 1895. 8°.   7858. e. 10.

ASHBEE (C. R.)   Table of arts and crafts of the Renaissance.   *Lond.* 1893. 8°.   7808. bbb. 24.

MENTION (F.)   Les lettres et les arts, au XVI°. siècle.   pp. 235.   *Paris*, 1892. 8°.   011824. k. 5.

ROGER-MILÈS (L.)   Beaux Arts.   La Renaissance. pp. 144.   *Paris*, 1894. 8°.   7856. e. 40.

REYMOND (M.)   De l'influence néfaste de la Renaissance.   pp. 16.   *Paris*, 1890. 8°.
                         7807. m. 6. (9.)

GOODYEAR (W. H.)   Renaissance and modern Art.   pp. 310.   *Meadville*, 1894. 8°.   7808. df. 19.

LEHFELDT (P.)   Luthers Verhältniss zu Kunst. pp. 130.   *Berl.* 1892. 8°.   7808. e. 24.

See also supra, Ancient : Christian : *infra,* Pt. II. National Art.

Pt. II. National Art.

Arabs.

GAYET (A.)   L'Art arabe.   pp. 316. *Paris*, 1893. 8°.   2261. cc. 3.

BOURGOIN (J.)   Précis de l'art arabe. *Paris*, 1889, *etc.* 4°.   7806. f.

Austria-Hungary : Bohemia.

ILG (A.)   Kunstgeschichtliche Charakterbilder aus Österreich-Ungarn.   pp. 406. *Wien*, 1893. 8°.   7807. l. 42.

NEUWIRTH (J.)   Geschichte der bildenden Kunst in Böhmen.   *Prag*, 1893, *etc.* 8°.   7858. c. 21.

PRIESTER (C. A.)   Kunstgeschichte von Tirol. pp. 410.   *Bozen*, 1885. fol.   7808. f. 13.

Belgium.

TAEYE (E. L. de)   Les Artistes belges contemporains.   *Brux.* 1894, *etc.* 4°.   7858. d.

Bohemia. See supra, Austria.

Borneo. See infra, India.

Byzantine Empire. See supra, Pt. I. Ancient.

Chili.

GREZ (V.)   Les Beaux-Arts au Chili.   pp. 76. *Paris*, 1889. 8°.   7806. dd. 6.

Denmark.

FRIIS (F. R.)   Bidrag til dansk Kunsthistorie. *Kjobenh.* 1890, *etc.* 8°.   7808. cc.

Egypt. See supra, Ancient : EGYPT, *Antiquities.*

England.

GRAVES (A.)   Dictionary of Artists who have exhibited in the London Exhibitions, 1760–1893. pp. 314.   *Lond.* 1895. 4°.   7808. g. 21.

P.P.   *Lond.*   The Art Schools of London. *Lond.* 1895, *etc.* 8°.   P.P. 2495. bc.

France.

BOURNAND (F.)   Histoire de l'Art en France. pp. 368.   *Paris*, 1891. 4°.   7808. g. 4.

ART.—National.—*France—continued.*

HORSIN-DÉON (L.) Histoire de l'Art en France.
pp. 331. *Paris*, 1891. 8°.   7808. c. 22.

JOUIN (H.) L'Art et la Province.
Paris, 1893, *etc.* 8°.   7808. e. 23.

LARROUMET (G.) Études de Littérature et d'Art.
pp. 376. *Paris*, 1893. 8°.   011850. f. 36.

LECHEVALLIER - CHEVIGNARD (E.) Les Styles
français. pp. 375. *Paris*, 1892. 8°.   2261. c.

PROUST (A.) L'Art français. pp. 184.
Paris, 1891. 4°.   K.T.C. 4. b. 11.

CHAMPEAUX (A. de) and GAUCHERY (P.) Les
Travaux d'Art exécutés pour Jean de France.
pp. 230. *Paris*, 1894. 4°.   7808. g. 19.

LEMONNIER (H.) L'art français au temps de
Richelieu et de Mazarin. pp. 420.
Paris, 1893. 8°.   7808. df. 10.

DUCHALET (V.) Les Arts sous Louis XIV. pp. 20.
Paris, 1890. 8°.   Pam. 24.

Ac. Paris. *Société de l'Histoire de l'Art français.*
GRANGES DE SURGÈRES (de). Artistes français
des XVIIe et XVIIIe siècles. pp. 246.
Paris, 1893. 8°.   Ac. 4550/16.

DELABORDE (H.) L'Académie des Beaux-Arts.
pp. 396. *Paris*, 1891. 8°.   7808. c. 23.

HAMERTON (P. G.) Present state of the Fine
Arts in France. pp. 90. *Lond.* 1892. fol.
K.T.C. 3. b. 11.

MARTIN (J.) Nos Artistes. Portraits et biographies. pp. 448. *Paris*, 1895. 8°. 010663. de 4.

PROUST (A.) L'Art sous la République.
pp. 276. *Paris*, 1892. 12°.   7806. aaa. 12.

PERRAULT-DABOT (A.) L'Art en Bourgogne.
pp. 284. *Paris*, 1894. 8°.   7008. f. 19.

PARROCEL (É.) Les Beaux-Arts en Provence.
pp. 102. *Paris*, 1889. 8°.   7807. m. 1.

Germany.

GERMAN ART HISTORY. Studien zur deutschen
Kunstgeschichte. *Strassb.* 1894, *etc.* 8°. 7808. e.

MERLO (J. J.) Kölnische Künstler in alter und
neuer Zeit. pp. 1206. 1893–95. 4°. Ac. Cologne.
Gesellschaft für Rheinische Geschichtskunde.
Publikationen. Bd. 9.   Ac. 7028.

LUDORFF (A.) Die Bau- und Kunstdenkmäler
von Westfalen, *etc. Münster*, 1893, *etc.* 4°.
7808. g.

RIEHL (B.) Deutsche Kunstcharaktere. pp. 254.
Frankfurt, 1893. 8°.   7805. d. 1.

Greece. See supra : Pt. I. Ancient.

Egypt. See supra : Pt. I. Ancient.

India ; Malaysia, etc.

VARADĀCHĀRIYAR, S. Indian Arts. pp. 24.
Madras, 1894. 8°.   Pam. 94.

POUVOURVILLE (A. de) L'Art indo-chinois.
pp. 291. *Paris*, 1894. 8°.   2261. cc. 5.

HEIN (A. R.) Die bildenden Künste bei den
Dayaks auf Borneo. pp. 228. *Wien*, 1890. 8°.
7805. e. 6.

Italy.

RIEHL (B.) Deutsche und italienische Kunstcharaktere. pp. 254. *Frankfurt*, 1893. 8°.
7805. d. 1.

DIEHL (C.) L'Art byzantin dans l'Italie méridionale. pp. 267. *Paris*, 1894. 8°. 7808. bbb. 33.

FRIZZONI (G.) Arte italiana del Rinascimento.
pp. 393. *Milano*, 1891. 8°.   7805. de. 18.

ITALY. Le Gallerie Nazionali italiane.
Roma, 1894, *etc.* 4°.   7808. h.

ITALIAN LIFE. La Vita Italiana nel Rinascimento. pp. 519. *Milano*, 1893. 8°.   9167. c.

BUONARROTI (M. A.) Les correspondants de
Michel-Ange. *Paris*, 1890, *etc.* 4°. 7808. g. 10.

ART.—National.—*Italy—continued.*

HEUSLER (A.) Goethe und die italienische Kunst.
pp. 41. *Basel*, 1891. 8°.   7807. k. 19. (6.)

PUDOR (H.) Ketzerische Kunstbriefe aus Italien.
pp. 160. *Dresd.* 1893. 8°.   7858. f. 18.

See also supra : Pt. I. Ancient.

Japan.

Ac. London. *Japan Society.* Transactions and
Proceedings. *Lond.* 1893, *etc.* 8°.   Ac. 8821.

—— London. *South Kensington Museum.* Japanese
Art. *Lond.* 1893, *etc.* 8°.   7958. e.

ANDERSON (W.) Japanese Wood Engravings.
pp. 80. 1895. 8°. P.P. Lond. The Portfolio.
Monographs. No. 17.   P.P. 1931. pcd.

BARBOUTAU (P.) Catalogue d'une collection
d'objets d'art. pp. 102, 45. *Paris*, 1893. 8°.
7808. e. 27.

BOSTON. *Museum of Fine Arts.* Department of
Japanese Art. Exhibitions. *Bost.* 1893, *etc.* 8°.
7856. a.

—— An Exhibition of Japanese Paintings.
pp. 38. *Bost.* 1894. 8°.   7808. df. 15. (6.)

BUNTY (P.) Catalogue de peintures et estampes
japonaises. pp. 223. *Paris*, 1891. 8°. 7855. i. 20.

HUOT DE GONCOURT (E. L. A.) L'Art japonais
du XVIIIe siècle. *Paris*, 1891, *etc.* 12°.
10606. bbb. 6.

HUISH (M. B.) Japan and its Art. pp. 288.
Lond. 1895. 8°.   10058. cc. 38.

—— Catalogue of a collection of Japanese works
of art formed by Sir T. Lawrence. pp. 158.
Lond. 1895. 4°.   K.T.C. 22. c. 14.

LIVERPOOL. *Bowes Museum of Japanese Art.*
Handbook. pp. 48. *Liverp.* 1893. 8°.
7808. aaa. 20.

MULLER (F.) L'Art japonais. Collection du
docteur J. Titsingh. pp. 73. *Amsterd.* 1893. 8°.
7858. l. 12.

WARRINGTON. *Museum.* Catalogue of Japanese
Paintings. pp. 8. *Warrington*, 1890. 8°.
Pam. 24.

HEDIARD (G.) Deux maîtres japonais. pp. 8.
Le Mans, 1893. 8°.   Pam. 24.

BIRCH, aft. SALWEY (C. M.) Fans of Japan.
pp. 149. *Lond.* 1894. 4°.   7808. g. 17.

Netherlands.

GROOT (C. H. de) Quellenstudien zur holländ-
ischen Kunstgeschichte. pp. 530.
Haag, 1893. 8°.   7808. bbb. 25.

EWERBECK (F.) Die Renaissance in Belgien und
Holland. *Leipz.* 1883–89. fol.   1734. b. 24.

Persia.

GAYET (A.) L'Art Persan. pp. 319.
Paris, 1895. 8°.   2261. cc. 8.

See also supra : Pt. I. Ancient.

Spain.

FLAT (P.) L'Art en Espagne. pp. 242.
Paris, 1891. 18°.   7808. aa. 39.

PRENTICE (A. N.) Renaissance Architecture and
Ornament in Spain. pp. 16. *Lond.* 1894. fol.
1733. d. 20.

Portugal.

P.P. *Lisbon.* Arte Portugueza.
Lisboa, 1895, *etc.* fol.   15.

Sweden.

NORDENSVAN (G.) Svensk konst och svenska
konstnärer. *Stockholm*, 1891, *etc.* 8°. 7808. f. 5.

United States of America.

PARTRIDGE (W. O.) Art for America. pp. 192.
Bost. 1894. 8°.   07807. e. 1.

ART, Decorative.

Ac. Berlin. *Archaeologisches Institut.* Wand- und
Deckenschmuck eines roemischen Hauses. pp. 14.
Berl. 1891. fol.   557. h.

—— London. *South Kensington Museum.* Appendix to the list of photographs of works of
decorative art. pp. 49. *Lond.* 1891. 8°. Pam. 18.

—— Switzerland. *Vereinigte Schweizerische Museen. Völkerschau.* Kunst und Gewerbe aller
Zonen und Zeiten. *Aarau,* 1888, *etc.* fol.
                                                7708. g. 29.

ALEXANDRE (A.) Histoire de l'Art décoratif du
xvi° siècle. pp. 336. *Paris,* 1891. 4°.
                                          K.T.C. 3. b. 13.

ARTS AND CRAFTS ESSAYS. Arts and Crafts
Essays. pp. 420. *Lond.* 1893. 8°. 7808. df. 2.

ASHBEE (C. R.) Table of Arts of the Renaissance.
Lond. 1893. 8°.   7808. bbb. 24.

AUDSLEY (G. A.) La Décoration pratique. 10 liv.
Paris, 1892. fol.   7805. g. 8.

—— Practical Decorator and Ornamentist.
Glasgow, 1892, *etc.* fol.   1811. a. 9.

BALFOUR (H.) The Evolution of Decorative Art.
pp. 131. *Lond.* 1893. 8°.   7808. e. 14.

BAYE (J. de) *Baron.* Industrial Arts of the
Anglo-Saxons. pp. 135. *Lond.* 1893. 4°.
                                                7709. k. 20.

BENSON (W. A. S.) Elements of Handicraft.
pp. 151. *Lond.* 1893. 8°.   7808. df. 4.

BRIDGE (W.) Trainer's Aids to Design.
Manch. 1892, *etc.* 8°.   7855. d.

BRINCKMANN (J.) Ein Beitrag zur Kenntniss des
japanischen Kunstgewerbes. pp. 36. 1892. 8°.
Ac. Aarau. *Mittelschweizerische Gesellschaft.*
Fernschau Jahrbuch. Bd. 5.   Ac. 6047.

BURN (R. S.) Ornamental Draughtsman and
Designer. pp. 142. *Lond.* 1892. 8°. 7854. d. 40.

CARLETTI (R.) Le Leggi dell' Arte decorativa.
Torino, 1895, *etc.* 8°.   07816. de.

CELTIC ORNAMENT. Examples of Celtic Ornament, from the Book of Kells, *etc.* pp. 30.
Dublin, 1892. 4°.   7709. c. 10.

CHAMPEAUX (A. de) Histoire de la Peinture
décorative. pp. 360. *Paris,* 1890. 8°. 7854. e. 33.

CHURCH (A. H.) Some Minor Arts as practised
in England. pp. 82. *Lond.* 1894. fol.
                                          K.T.C. 24. b. 3.

CRANE (W.) Claims of Decorative Art. pp. 191.
Lond. 1892. 8°.   7808. e. 6.

DAMIANI ALMEYDA (G.) Istituzioni ornamentali.
Torino, 1890. fol.   1711. c.

DAY (L. F.) Some Principles of every-day Art.
pp. 148. *Lond.* 1894. 8°.   7807. aaaa. 14.

—— Nature in Ornament. pp. 247. 1894. 8°.
Text Books of Ornamental Design.   7808. b.

FOURNISS (W.) Colour Studies. pp. 29.
Manch. 1893. 4°.   7856. f. 9.

GOODYEAR (W. H.) Grammar of the Lotus.
pp. 408. *Lond.* 1891. 4°.   7808. g. 3.

HASLUCK (P. N.) House Decoration. pp. 160.
Lond. 1894. 8°.   7943. aa. 61.

HATTON (R. G.) Text-Book of elementary
Design. pp. 115. *Lond.* 1894. 8°. 7807. aaa. 10.

HAVARD (H.) Les Arts de l'ameublement. pp. 176.
Paris, 1892. 8°.   7942. f.

—— La Peinture décorative au xix° siècle.
pp. 224. *Paris,* 1895. 4°.   K.T.C. 18. b. 8.

HEALD (F. B.) Selection of suggestive Designs.
Nottingham, 1892, *etc.* fol.   1812. c. 32.

HEATON (A.) A Record of Work : illustrations
of printing, stained glass, embroidery, and other
decorative works. *Lond.* 1894. 4°. 7808. f. 14.

HULME (F. E.) Birth and development of Ornament. pp. 340. *Lond.* 1893. 8°. 7808. e. 18.

ART, Decorative—*continued.*

JACKSON (F. G.) Theory and practice of Design.
pp. 216. *Lond.* 1894. 8°.   7808. e. 29.

MARX (R.) La Décoration à l'Exposition Universelle de 1889. pp. 60. *Paris,* 1890. 4°.
                                                7805. eee. 27.

MAYEUX (H.) Manual of decorative Composition.
pp. 310. *Lond.* 1894. 8°.   7808. e. 32.

MEYER (F. S.) Handbook of Ornament. pp. 580.
Lond. 1893. 8°.   2262. b. 2.

MOSER (F.) Handbuch der Pflanzenornamentik.
pp. 68. 1893. 8°. Seemanns kunstgewerbliche
Handbücher. No. 10.   7805. de. 3.

NIMBEAU (F.) L'Entrepreneur de peinture en
bâtiment. pp. 372. *Paris,* 1894. 8°. 7858. gg. 30.

—— Métrage de la peinture en bâtiment. pp. 207.
Paris, 1895. 8°.   8535. df. 38.

RIEGL (A.) Stilfragen Grundlegungen zu einer
Geschichte der Ornamentik. pp. 346.
Berl. 1893. 8°.   7805. de. 24.

RIS-PAQUOT (O. E.) Le Mobilier et les objets
qui s'y rattachent. pp. 122. *Paris,* 1893. 8°.
                                                07944. e. 24.

—— Les petites Occupations d'amateur, *etc.*
pp. 160. *Paris,* 1894. 12°.   07944. e. 36.

ROGER-MILÈS (L.) La Peinture décorative.
pp. 144. *Paris,* 1892. 8°.   7857. f. 55.

SCHAUERMANN (F. L.) Theory and analysis of
Ornament. pp. 208. *Lond.* 1892. 8°. 7808. e. 11.

SHORROCK (M.) "Adaptable" Series of Designs.
1893. *obl.* fol.   1810. a. 29.

STANNUS (H.) The Theory of Storiation in
applied art. pp. 14. *Lond.* 1893. 8°.
                                          7807. cc. 4. (12.)

STURM (G.) Animals in Ornament.
Lond. 1894, *etc.* fol.   K.T.C. 8. b.

SUTHERLAND (W.) Art of Graining and Imitating
Woods. 2 pt. *Manch.* 1892. fol. 1811. b. 21.

TAYLOR (E. R.) Drawing and Design. pp. 114.
Lond. 1893. *obl.* 8°.   7854. aa. 15.

TOMLIN (I.) New Decorator's Handbook.
pp. 103. *Barnsley,* 1894. 8°.   7855. aa. 46.

VARADĀCHĀRIYAR. Indian Arts, *etc.* pp. 24.
Madras, 1894. 8°.   Pam. 94.

WARD (J.) Principles of Ornament. pp. 139.
Lond. 1892. 8°.   7808. e. 9.

WHITE (J. G.) Practical Designing. pp. 327.
Lond. 1893. 8°.   7807. e. 28.

WORNUM (R. N.) Analysis of Ornament.
pp. 190. *Lond.* 1893. 8°.   7808. f. 9.

YOUNG (F. C.) Decorative Work for house and
home. pp. 110. 1893. 8°. Ward and Lock's
Amateurs' Aid Series.   07944. ee.

See also ARCHITECTURE : BOOK BINDING : BRASS
WORK : CERAMICS : COLLECTIONS : FURNI-
TURE : GLASS : GOLD AND SILVER WORK : IN-
DUSTRIES : IRON WORK : METAL WORK : TAP-
ESTRY : WOODWORK.

ARTERIES. *See* BLOOD.

ART GALLERIES. *See* EXHIBITIONS, Pt. I.

ARTHONIA. *See* LICHENS.

ARTHRITIS. *See* JOINTS.

ARTHROPODA. FERNALD (H. T.) Re-
lationships of Arthropods. pp. 82.
Baltimore, 1890. 8°.   7298. ee. 20.

WASMANN (E.) Kritisches Verzeichniss der
myrmekophilen und termitophilen Arthropoden.
pp. 231. *Berl.* 1894. 8°.   7298. ee. 27.

WATASE (S.) Morphology of the compound
Eyes of Arthropods. pp. 47.
Baltimore, 1889. 8°.   7298. ee. 21.

For each Class, Order, *etc.,* of ARTHROPODA, *see*
under the name required.

ARYAN LANGUAGES.

FENNELL (C. A. M.) Indo-European Vowel-System. *Camb.* 1891. 8°. 12901. d. 30. (14.)

FICK (F. C. A.) Vergleichendes Wörterbuch der indogermanischen Sprachen.
Göttingen, 1890, *etc.* 12902. dd.

ABEL (C.) Offener Brief in Sachen der ägyptisch-indogermanischen Sprachverwandtschaft.
pp. 35. *Leipz.* 1891. 8°. Pam. 47.

BECHTEL (F.) Die Hauptprobleme der indogermanischen Lautlehre. pp. 414.
Göttingen, 1892. 8°. 12907. eee. 40.

BRUGMAN (C.) Grundriss der vergleichenden Grammatik der indogermanischen Sprachen.
Strassb. 1886, *etc.* 8°. 12901. i. 30.

—— Die Ausdrücke für den Begriff der Totalität in der indogermanischen Sprachen.
pp. 80. *Leipz.* 1894. 4°. 12902. i. 9.

P.P. *Strasburg.* Indogermanische Forschungen.
Strassb. 1891, *etc.* 8°. P.P. 5043. ad.

REGNAUD (P.) Études sur l'évolution morphologique dans les langues Indo-Européennes.
pp. 39. *Orléans,* 1891. 8°. 12901. d. 20. (12.)

SCHRADER (O.) Über den Gedanken einer Kulturgeschichte der Indogermanen, *etc.* pp. 22.
Jena, 1887. 8°. 12902. dd. 37.

STEYRER (J.) Der Ursprung der Sprache der Arier. pp. 175. *Wien,* 1891. 8°. 12901. f. 40.

See also LANGUAGE.

ARYANS.

BRUNNHOFER (H.) Vom Aral bis zur Gangâ. pp. 245. 1892. 8°. Einzelbeiträge zur Sprachwissenschaft. Heft 12. 12902. g.

KRAUSE (E.) Tuisko-Land der arischen Stämme und Götter Urheimat. pp. 624.
Glogau, 1891. 8°. 10007. h. 44.

JHERING (R. von) Vorgeschichte der Indoeuropäer. pp. 486. *Leipz.* 1894. 8°.
 9008. cc. 16.

LEIST (B. W.) Alt-arisches Jus Civile.
Jena, 1892, *etc.* 8°. 5254. cc.

P.P. *Strasburg.* Indogermanische Forschungen.
Strassb. 1891, *etc.* 8°. P.P. 5043. ad.

REGNAUD (P.) Le Rig-Véda et les origines de la mythologie indo-européenne.
1892, *etc.* 4°. Annales du Musée Guimet.
 7704. h. 21.

REINACH (S.) L'Origine des Aryens. pp. 124.
Paris, 1892. 12°. 10007. aa. 7.

SEILER (F.) Die Heimath der Indogermanen.
1894, *etc.* 8°. Sammlung wissenschaftlicher Vorträge. Heft 210, *etc.* 12249. m.

WOLFF (C. J. F.) Recherches sur les Aryas.
pp. 192. *Mâcon,* 1893. 12°. 10007. i. 7.

See also ANTHROPOLOGY : ETHNOLOGY.

ASBESTOS.

JONES (R. H.) Asbestos.
pp. 236. *Lond.* 1890. 8°. 7106. a. 38.

See also MINERALOGY.

ASBY.

ASBY. Asby Church Register, 1657–1798. pp. 144. *Lond.* 1894. 8°. 9904. f. 14.

ASCENSION, THE.

See CHRISTIANITY, *Person and Teaching of Christ.*

ASCIDIA.

KOVALEVSKY (A.) Beiträge zur Bildung des Mantels der Ascidien. pp. 20.
1892. 4°. Ac. Saint Petersburg. *Academia Scientiarum.* Mémoires. Tom. 38. No. 10.
 Ac. 1125/3.

RITTER (W. E.) Tunicata of the Pacific Coast.
1894, *etc.* 8°. Ac. San Francisco. *Academy of Natural Sciences.* Proceedings. Ser. 2. Vol. 4.
Pt. 1, *etc.* Ac. 3037.

ASCOLI PICENO.

LUZI (E.) Cenno storico della cattedrale. pp. 199.
Ascoli, 1894. 8°. 4605. aa. 8.

ASEPTIC MEDICINE AND SURGERY.

See ANTISEPTIC MEDICINE, *etc.*

ASHANTEE.

REINDORF (C. C.) History of the Gold Coast and Asante. pp. 356.
Basel, 1895. 8°. 9061. d. 27.

RAMSEYER (F. A.) Vier Jahre gefangen in Asante. pp. 79. *Basel,* 1892. 8°. Pam. 40.

MILUM (J.) Freeman, Missionary to Ashanti.
pp. 160. *Lond.* 1893. 8°. 4905. de. 43.

STANLEY (H. M.) Coomassie. Story of the campaign 1873–4. pp. 212. *Lond.* 1895. 8°.
 9061. aaa. 8.

See also AFRICA, *West.*

ASHBOURNE.

JOURDAIN (F.) Guide to Ashburne. pp. 31. *Ashburne,* 1891. 8°.
 10360. d. 20.

ASHMORE, *Dorset.*

WATSON (E. W.) History of the parish. pp. 136. *Gloucester,* 1890. 4°.
 010358. g. 12.

ASIA.

Ac. London. *Royal Asiatic Society.* Catalogue of the Library. pp 537.
Lond. 1893. 8°. BB.I. a. 12.

ASIA. The Geography of Asia. pp. 38.
Lond. 1893. 8°. Pam. 88.

FAR OFF. Asia described. 2 pt.
Lond. 1890–93. 8°. 10058. aa. 31.

JOHNSTON (A. K.) Short Geography of Asia.
pp. 99. *Lond.* 1891. 8°. 10055. aaaa. 28.

LANIER (L.) L'Asie. Lectures de géographie.
2 pt. *Paris,* 1889–92. 12°. 10055. aaaa. 31.

LAWSON (W.) Geography of Asia. 4 pt.
Edinb. 1891. 12°. 10003. aaaa. 40.

HEWITT (J. F.) Ruling Races of Prehistoric Times in India, South-Western Asia, *etc.*
pp. 627. *Westminster,* 1894. 8°. 9056. ee. 19.

ODORICUS. Voyages en Asie au XIVᵉ siècle.
pp. 602. 1891. 8°. Recueil de Voyages. No. 10.
 10024. i.

ALLEN (T. G.) and SACHTLEBEN (W. L.) Across Asia on a Bicycle. pp. 234. *N.Y.* 1894. 8°.
 10055. df. 23.

BADIA Y LEYBLICH (D.) Viatjes per Africa y Assia, 1803. 3 Tom. *Barcelona,* 1888–89. 8°.
 10026. k. 7.

KONOW (H.) I Asiens Farvande.
Kjøbenhavn, 1892–94. 8°. 010057. f.

See also ARYANS : ETHNOLOGY : ORIENTAL CONGRESS, and under each country of Asia.

Central.

BIDDULPH (C. E.) Four months in Persia and Trans-Caspia. pp. 137. *Lond.* 1892. 8°.
 10076. ff. 15.

CAPUS (G.) À travers le royaume de Tamerlan.
pp. 434. *Paris,* 1892. 8°. 10077. h. 14.

COCHARD (L.) Paris, Boukara, Samarcande.
pp. 146. *Paris,* 1891. 8°. 10076. ff. 14.

CUMBERLAND (C. S.) Sport on the Pamirs.
pp. 278. *Lond.* 1895. 8°. 07905. h. 25.

KAARSBERG (H. S.) Gjennem Stepperne og blandt Kalmukkerne tilhest og med Trespand.
Kjøbenhavn, 1891, *etc.* 8°. 10024. f.

LANDSDELL (H.) Chinese Central Asia. 2 vol.
Lond. 1893. 8°. 10075. f. 16.

MARVIN (C.) Letters to the "Morning Post."
pp. 427. *Allahabad,* 1891. 8°. 8023. cc. 23.

MURRAY (C. A.) *Earl of Dunmore.* The Pamirs.
2 vol. *Lond.* 1893. 8°. 10076. e. 4.

NEY (J. N.) En Asie centrale à la vapeur.
pp. 466. *Paris,* 1890. 8°. 10076. eee. 17.

PAQUIER (J. B.) L'Asie centrale à vol d'oiseau.
pp. 175. *Paris,* 1881. 12°. 10076. a. 5.

ASIA.—Central—continued.

PONTEVÈS-SABRAN (J. B. E. M. C. de) *Count.* Un raid en Asie. pp. 445. *Paris*, 1890. 12°.
10075. aa. 9.

SPECHT (É.) Études sur l'Asie centrale. *Paris*, 189°, *etc.* 8°. 9055. bb.

STERN (B.) Vom Kaukasus zum Hindukusch. pp. 322. *Berlin*, 1893. 8°. 10075. aaa. 26.

THORBURN (S. S.) Asiatic Neighbours. pp. 315. *Edinburgh*, 1894. 8°. 8023. d. 2.

ASIA. Antagonismus der englischen und russischen Interessen in Asien. pp. 187. *Wien*, 1890. 8°. 8028. e. 21.

LEE (F.) Suppressed Truth. Revelations regarding Russian conquests in Asia. pp. 70. *Lahore*, 1893. 8°. 9055. a. 25.

POPOWSKI (J.) The Rival Powers in Central Asia. pp. 235. *Westminster*, 1893. 8°. 8028. dc. 29.

RUSSIA. Russia's march towards India. 2 vol. *Lond.* 1894. 8°. 8023. ce. 42.

See also AFGHANISTAN : BOKHARA : KHIVA : KIRGHIZ : MERV : SIBERIA : RUSSIA : TIBET : TURKESTAN.

ASIA MINOR.

Antiquities, etc.

GARDNER (P.) Historical results of recent excavations in Asia Minor. pp. 459. *Lond.* 1892. 8°.
9026. f. 9.

JUDEICH (W.) Kleinasiatische Studien. pp. 370. *Marburg*, 1892. 8°. 9026. ff. 29.

LANCKOROŃSKI (C.) *Count.* Städte Pamphyliens und Pisidiens. *Wien*, 1890, *etc.* fol. 1705. a. 10.

—— Les villes de la Pamphylie et de la Lydie. *Paris*, 1890, *etc.* 4°. 7703. d.

PERROT (G.) und CHIPIEZ (C.) History of Art in Phrygia, Lydia, Caria, and Lycia. pp. 405. *Lond.* 1892. 8°. 2259. f. 20.

REINACH (S.) Documents sur les fouilles et découvertes dans l'Orient hellénique, 1883–90. pp. 786. *Paris*, 1891. 8°. 7704. cc. 22.

AC. Boston. *School of Classical Studies at Athens.* STERRETT (J. R. S.) Report of an archæological Journey in Asia Minor. pp. 45. *Bost.* 1885. 8°. Ac. 5790/10.

STERRETT (J. R. S.) The Wolfe Expedition to Asia Minor. pp. 448. 1888. 8°. Ac. Boston. *School of Classical Studies.* Papers. Vol. 3. Ac. 5790/9.

WILSON (*Sir* C. W.) Murray's Handbook for Asia Minor. *Lond.* 1895. 8°. 2364. b. 32.

See also INSCRIPTIONS : LYCIA and LYDIA : TROY.

Topography, etc.

CUINET (V.) La Turquie d'Asie. *Paris*, 1890, *etc.* 8°. 10077. k. 18.

HIRSCHFELD (G.) Historical Geography of Asia Minor. pp. 39. 1891. 8°. Pam. 88.

RAMSAY (W. M.) Historical Geography of Asia Minor. pp. 495. 1890. 8°. Ac. London. *R. Geographical Society.* Supplementary Papers. Vol. IV. 2058. a.

TOMASCHEK (W.) Zur historischen Topographie von Kleinasien im Mittelalter. pp. 106. 1891. 8°. Ac. Vienna. *K. Akademie der Wissenschaften.* Sitzungsberichte. Philosoph.-hist. Classe. Bd. 124. Ac. 810/6.

BARKLEY (H. C.) Ride through Asia Minor. pp. 350. *Lond.* 1891. 8°. 10076. ccc. 18.

CALLAN (H.) From the Clyde to the Jordan. pp. 312. *Lond.* 1895. 8°. 10026. ccc. 7.

CHOLET (A. P. de) *Count.* Voyage en Turquie d'Asie. pp. 394. *Paris*, 1892. 12°. 10077. aa. 14.

ASIA MINOR.—Topography—continued.

DESCHAMPS (G.) Sur les Routes d'Asie. pp. 364. *Paris*, 1894. 8°. 10077. aa. 16.

MUELLER-SIMONIS (P.) Relation des missions scientifiques, *etc.* pp. 628. *Wash.* 1892. 8°.
10075. k. 7.

PATERSON (J. G.) From Bombay through Babylonia. pp. 204. *Glasg.* 1895. 8°. 4767. bbb. 16.

WOODS (H. F.) *Pasha.* Truth about Asia Minor. pp. 16. *Lond.* 1890. 8°. 8028. de. 30. (8.)

See also ARMENIA : BRUSA : KURDISTAN : TURKEY.

ASKRIGG.

WHALEY (C.) The Parish of Askrigg. pp. 100. *Lond.* 1891. 8°.
010358. e. 10.

ASNIÈRES.

PÉRIER (E.) Notes sur la ville d'Asnières. pp. 64. *Asnières*, 189°. 8°.
10172. g. 4.

ASPHALTE.

JACCARD (A.) Le pétrole et l'asphalte au point de vue géologique. pp. 292. *Paris*, 1895. 8°. 8708. cc.

ASS.

SCHLIEBEN (A.) Der Esel und der Mensch. pp. 140. *Wiesbaden*, 1894. 8°.
07293. i. 29.

TEGETMEIER (W. B.) Horses, Asses, *etc.* pp. 166. *Lond.* 1895. 8°. 07293. i. 27.

See also ANIMALS, *Domestic.*

ASSAB.

AMEZAGA (C. de) Assab. pp. 57. *Roma*, 1880. 8°. 10095. dd. 7.

See also ERITREA.

ASSAM.

ASSAM. Notes on the Marriage Systems of Assam. pp. 56. *Calcutta*, 1892. 12°.
Pam. 37.

YOGEṢACHANDRA DATTA. Old Relics in Kamrup. pp. 27. *Calcutta*, 1892. 12°. 14058. a. 9.

BROWN (N.) Grammatical Notes on the Assamese language. pp. 95. *Nowgong, Assam*, 1893. 8°.
12910. aaa. 71.

See also CACHAR : NAGAS.

ASSAYING.

See GOLD AND SILVER : METALLURGY.

ASSINIBOIA.

MANITOBA. North - West farmer in Assiniboia. pp. 55. *Liverp.* 1891. 8°.
Pam. 1.

—— What farmers say of Assiniboia, *etc.* *Lond.* 1892. 8°. Pam. 86.

—— Proceedings of a Delegation to report upon Assiniboia, *etc.* pp. 24. *Lond.* 1892. 8°.
Pam. 86.

See also CANADA, *North West.*

ASSOS.

AC. Boston, *Mass. Archæological Institute.* CLARKE (J. T.) Doric Shaft and Base found at Assos. pp. 21. *Baltimore*, 1886. 8°. Ac. 5790/12.

STERRETT (J. R. S.) Inscriptions of Assos. 1885. 8°. Ac. Boston. *School of Classical Studies.* Papers, *etc.* Vol. 1. Ac. 5790/9.

ASSURANCE. *See* INSURANCE.

ASSYRIA AND BABYLONIA. *See also* CHALDEA : MEDIA : MESOPOTAMIA : SUSA.

Antiquities.

AC. Boston. *Archæological Institute.* WARD (W. H.) Notes on Oriental Antiquities. pp. 19. *Baltimore*, 1887. 8°. Ac. 5790/14.

—— Report on the Wolfe Expedition to Babylonia. pp. 83. *Bost.* 1886. 8°. Ac. 5790/13.

BUZANTIOS (D. C. S.) Ἡ Βαβυλωνία, *etc.* pp. 99. ἐν Ἀθήναις, 1890. 16°. Pam. 54.

BONAVIA (E.) Flora of the Assyrian Monuments. pp. 215. *Westminster*, 1894. 8°. 7704. e. 27.

DELATTRE (A. J.) L'Assyriologie depuis onze ans. pp. 119. *Paris*, 1891. 8°. 7704. c. 44.

FRADENBURGH (J. W.) Fire from Strange Altars. pp. 324. *Cincinnati*, 1891. 8°. 4503. bb. 27.

ASSYRIA.—Antiquities—*continued*.

HOMMEL (F.) Der babylonische Ursprung der ägyptischen Kultur. pp. 68.
München, 1892. 8°.   7702. aaa. 41.

LAURENT (A.) La Magie et la divination chez les Chaldéo-Assyriens. pp. 89.
Paris, 1894. 8°.   8632. d. 29.

LAYARD (*Sir* A. H.) Early Adventures in Persia, Susiana and Babylonia. pp. 436.
Lond. 1894. 8°.   10075. bb. 20.

LEPSIUS (C. R.) Ueber den Apiskreis. pp. 22.
Leipz. 1853. 8°.   7704. e. 26. (3.)

LINCKE (A. A.) Bericht über die Fortschritte der Assyriologie, 1886–1893. pp. 124.
Leipz. 1894. 8°.   7704. bb. 49.

MAC CALLESTER (S. H.) Babylon and Nineveh. pp. 184. *Bost.* 1892. 8°.   7702. de. 13.

MASPERO (G.) Life in ancient Assyria. pp. 376. *Lond.* 1892. 8°.   7702. a. 39.

MEISSNER (B.) and ROST (P.) Noch einmal das bît-hillâni und die assyrische Säule. pp. 16.
Leipz. 1893. 8°.   07703. h. 1. 16.

MONACO (A.) Orientalia. pp. 189.
Roma, 1891. 8°.   4506. bb. 30.

MUELLER-SIMONIS (P.) Relation des missions scientifiques, *etc.* pp. 628. *Wash.* 1892. 8°.
     10075. k. 7.

PATERSON (J. G.) From Bombay through Babylonia. pp. 204. *Glasg.* 1895. 8°. 4767. bbb. 16.

P.P. *Paris.* Revue d'Assyriologie.
Paris, 1884, *etc.* 4°.   P.P. 4993. c.

PINCHES (T. C.) Babylonian and Assyrian Cylinder-seals and Signets in possession of Sir H. Peek. pp. 17. *Lond.* 1890. 4°. 7703. e. 25.

—— Notes on the private life of the Babylonians. pp. 62. *Lond.* 1892. 8°.   7704. e. 22.

—— Religious Ideas of the Babylonians. pp. 26. *Lond.* 1893. 8°.   4503. c. 16.

SAYCE (A. H.) Social Life among the Assyrians. pp. 126. 1893. 8°. Bye-Paths of Bible Knowledge. No. 18.   2202. a.

—— Primer of Assyriology. pp. 127. 1894. 8°. *See* PRESENT DAY PRIMERS. Present Day Primers.   4429. eee.

TERRIEN DE LACOUPERIE (A. E. J. B.) Western origin of early Chinese civilisation. pp. 418. *Lond.* 1894. 8°.   9055. g. 5.

WINCKLER (H.) Altorientalische Forschungen. *Leipz.* 1893, *etc.* 8°.   7704. bb.

See also ART, *Ancient*.

Assyria, Babylonia, and Biblical Criticism.

BOSCAWEN (W. S. C.) The Bible and the Monuments. pp. 177. *Lond.* 1895. 8°. 7704. aaa. 55.

BUXTON (C. M.) Side Lights upon Bible History. pp. 299. *Lond.* 1892. 8°.   3149. d. 6.

EDWARDS (C.) The Witness of Assyria. pp. 183. *Lond.* 1893. 8°.   3149. c. 6.

EIK (G. D. K.) De Schriftuur bewezen uit de Archaeologie van Assyrië, *etc.* pp. 401.
Alkmaar, 1891. 8°.   3149. dd. 5.

EVETTS (B. T. A.) New Light on the Bible and the Holy Land. pp. 469. *Lond.* 1892. 8°.
     7702. c. 36.

KITCHIN (J. G.) Bible Student in the British Museum. pp. 88. *Lond.* 1892. 8°. 7702. aa. 43.

MAC CURDY (J. F.) History, Prophecy and the Monuments. *N.Y.* 1894, *etc.* 8°. 4516. d.

SAYCE (A. H.) The "Higher Criticism" and the verdict of the monuments. pp. 575.
Lond. 1894. 8°.   4429. d. 1.

WINCKLER (H.) Keilinschriftliches Textbuch zum Alten Testament. *Leipz.* 1892, *etc.* 8°.
     3149. ddd.

ASSYRIA.—Biblical Criticism—*continued*.

PIETRINI (O.) Il Nembrot Biblico. pp. 97.
Viareggio, 1892. 8°.   3155. k. 44.

BERTIN (G.) Populations of the Fatherland of Abraham. pp. 103. *Lond.* 1893. 8°. 7704. aa. 41.

MARTIN (G.) La Campagne de Sennakhérib en Palestine et les propheties. pp. 122.
Montauban, 1892. 8°.   3166. ee. 48.

See also JEWS, *History*.

History, Geography and Law.

HOMMEL (F.) Geschichte Babyloniens und Assyriens. pp. 802. 1885. 8°. ONCKEN (W.) Allg. Geschichte.   2068. (2.)

LINCKE (A. A.) Assyrien und Ninive in Geschichte und Sage der Mittelmeervölker, nach 607/6. pp. 56. *Berl.* 1894. 8°.   Pam. 14.

MASPERO (G.) Histoire ancienne des peuples de l'Orient. pp. 811. *Paris*, 1893. 8°.
     9055. bb. 34.

MUERDTER (F.) Geschichte Babyloniens und Assyriens. pp. 263. 1891. 8°. Reiche der alten Welt. Bd. 2.   9008. aaa. 5.

RAGOZIN (Z. A.) Assyria. pp. 450. 1891. 8°. Story of the Nations.   9004. ccc. 4.

SMITH (G.) History of Babylonia. Edited by A. H. Sayce. pp. 183. *Lond.* 1895. 8°. 2378. a.

WINCKLER (H.) Geschichte Babyloniens und Assyriens. pp. 354. 1892. 8°. Völker des alten Orients. No. 1.   9056. cc.

—— Ein Beitrag zur Geschichte der Assyriologie in Deutschland. pp. 44. *Leipz.* 1894. 8°.
     Pam. 3.

BERTIN (G.) Babylonian Chronology and History. pp. 52. *Lond.* 1892. 8°.   07703. g. 1. (12.)

OPPERT (J.) La Fixation de la chronologie des derniers rois de Babylone. 1893. 8°.
     07703. f. 3. (16.)

BERTIN (G.) Populations of the Fatherland of Abraham. pp. 103. *Lond.* 1893. 8°. 7704. aa. 41.

RABOISSON ( ) Description géographique des anciens empires d'Assyrie. *Paris*, 1890, *etc.* 8°.
     7702. bb. 41.

TIELE (C. P.) Western Asia according to the most recent discoveries. pp. 36. *Lond.* 1894. 8°.
     7704. aa. 42.

BILLERBECK (A.) Susa. pp. 184.
Leipz. 1893. 8°.   7702. c. 37.

KOHLER (J.) and PEISER (F. E.) Aus dem babylonischen Rechtsleben. *Leipz.* 1890, *etc.* 8°.
     7704. b. 51.

MEISSNER (H.) Beiträge zum altbabylonischen Privatrecht. pp. 160. 58. 1893. 8°. Assyriologische Bibliothek. No. 11.   12903. h. 19.

PEISER (F. E.) Jurisprudentiæ Babylonicæ quæ supersunt. pp. 41. *Cöthen*, 1890. 8°.
     7706. g. 7. (9.)

See also infra: Language and Inscriptions: CHALDEA: HISTORY, *Ancient*: MEDIA: PERSIA.

Language: Inscriptions: Tablets.

DELITZSCH (F.) Assyrisches Handwörterbuch. *Leipz.* 1894, *etc.* 4°.   12903. g. 29.

MUSS-ARNOLT (W.) Concise Dictionary, Assyrian—English—German. *Berl.* 1894, *etc.* 8°.
     012904. k. 3.

LYON (D. G.) Assyrian Manual. pp. 138.
Chicago, 1886. 8°.   7704. bb. 46.

MEISSNER (B.) Assyrisch-Babylonische Chrestomathie. pp. 68. *Lieden*, 1895. 4°. 7705. ee. 19.

Ac. London. *British Museum*. Selection from the Inscriptions of Assyria. pp. 63. 12.
Lond. 1891. fol.   1705. c. 12.

ASSYRIA.—Language, etc.—*continued.*

ABEL (L.) and WINCKLER (H.) Keilschrifttexte. pp. 100. *Berl.* 1890. fol.   7704. l. 23.

FRIEDRICH (T.) Kabiren und Keilinschriften. pp. 94. *Leipz.* 1894. 8°.   4503. ee. 30.

HILPRECHT (H. V.) Babylonian Inscriptions. 1893, *etc.* 4°. Ac. Philadelphia. *American Philosophical Soc.* Transactions. N.S. Vol. 18, *etc.*   Ac. 1830/3.

PEISER (F. E.) Babylonische Verträge des Berliner Museums. pp. 351. 56. *Berl.* 1890. 8°.   7703. e. 27.

WINCKLER (H.) Liste ausgewählter Keilschriftzeichen. pp. 24. *Leipz.* 1893. 4°. 7705. f. 52. (8.)

—— Sammlung von Keilschrifttexten. *Leipz.* 1893, *etc.* 4°.   7702. i.

—— Keilinschriftliches Textbuch zum Alten Testament. *Leipz.* 1892, *etc.* 8°.   3149. ddd.

Ac. London. *British Museum.* Tell el-Amarna Tablets in the British Museum. pp. 157. *Lond.* 1892. 4°.   7703. aa. 30.

BEZOLD (C.) Oriental Diplomacy : transliterated text of the Cuneiform Despatches discovered at Tell el-Amarna. pp. 124. *Lond.* 1893. 8°.   7704. aaa. 54.

SCHEIL (F. V.) Tablettes d'El-Amarna. 1893. 4°. Mémoires publiés par les membres de la Mission Archéologique. Tom 6.   7703. k.

BOISSIER (A.) Recherches sur quelques contrats babyloniens, *etc.* pp. 65. *Paris,* 1890. 8°.   7706. f. 20. (1.)

—— Documents assyriens relatifs aux présages. *Paris,* 1894, *etc.* 4°.   7702. k.

HARPER (R. F.) Assyrian and Babylonian Letters in the British Museum. *Lond.* 1892, *etc.* 8°.   7704. b. 52.

JASTROW (M.) Fragment of the Babylonian "Dibbarra" Epic. 1891. 8°. Ac. Philadelphia. *University.* Publications. Series in Philology. Vol. 1. No. 2.   Ac. 2692. p. /2.

JOHNSTON (C.) Two Assyrian letters, and the Sumero-Akkadian Question. *Baltimore,* 1893. 8°.   07703. h. 1. (15.)

KNUDTZON (J. A.) Assyrische Gebete an den Sonnengott. 2 Bde. *Leipz.* 1893. fol. & 8°.   7704. l. 29. and i. 9.

OPPERT (J.) Annuaire astronomique babylonien traduit en partie en grec par Ptolémée. pp. 24. *Paris,* 1890. 8°.   7706. g. 6. (9.)

—— La plus ancienne inscription sémitique. pp. 7. *Paris,* 1894. 8°.   Pam. 3.

PINCHES (T. G.) Zwei assyrische Briefe. *Leipz* 1887. 8°.   7704. d. 10. (18.)

—— Inscribed Babylonian Tablets in possession of Sir H. Peck. 2 pt. *Lond.* 1888–90. 4°.   7703. e. 26.

SENNACHERIB. *King.* Die Bauinschriften Sanheribs. pp. 119. *Leipz.* 1893. 8°. 7702. bb. 45.

TALLQVIST (K. L.) Babylonische Schenkungsbriefe. pp. 24. 1891. 4°. Ac. Helsingfors. *Finska Universitet.* Commentationes. Tom 3, 4.   Ac. 1095.

—— Die Sprache der Contracte Nabû-Nâ'ids. pp. 148. *Helsingfors,* 1890. 8°. 7702. aaa. 39. *See also supra :* ANTIQUITIES.

ASTHMA. THOROWGOOD (J. C.) Asthma and chronic Bronchitis. pp. 136. *Lond.* 1894. 8°.   7616. a. 46. *See also* LUNGS.

ASTI. CIPOLLA (C.) Appunti sulla storia di Asti. 1890, *etc.* 8°. Ac. Venice. *Istituto di Scienze, etc.* Atti. Ser. VII. Tom 1. Ac. 110.

ASTROLOGY. ACKROYD ( ) Astro-Phrenology. pp. 56. *Rochdale,* 1885. 8°. Pam. 36.

ASTROLOGY. Astrology. From the Marathi. pp. 40. *Bombay,* 1890. 12°.   14139. a.

BARKER (C. J.) Astrologer's Ready Reckoner. pp. 33. *Halifax,* 1895. 8°.   8610. f. 19.

BROUGHTON (L. D.) Planetary Influence. pp. 61. *N.Y.* 1893. 8°.   Pam. 36.

COLLINGWOOD (W. G.) Astrology in the Apocalypse. pp. 150. *Orpington,* 1886. 8°.   8610. aaa. 46.

DALTON (J. G.) Spherical Basis of Astrology. pp. 67. *Bost.* 1893. 4°.   8610. f. 18.

GABOTTO (F.) Bartolomeo Manfredi e l' Astrologia alla Corte di Mantova. pp. 41. *Torino,* 1891. 8°.   Pam. 36.

—— Nuove ricerche sull' astrologia alla corte degli Estensi. pp. 30. *Torino,* 1891. 4°. Pam. 36.

HERZ (N.) Keplers Astrologie. pp. 147. *Wien,* 1895. 8°.   8610. g. 1.

KIRK (E.) Influence of the Zodiac upon human Life. pp. 179. *Brooklyn,* 1894. 8°. 8610. aaa. 54.

LIZERAY (H.) Horoscopes des poètes. pp. 16. *Paris,* 1892. 8°.   Pam. 36.

MAYER (E.) Handbuch der Astrologie. pp. 87. *Berl.* 1891. 8°.   8610. de. 1.

NĀRĀYAṆA BHAṬṬA. Chamatkar Chintamani, or the Gem of Astrology. pp. 47. *Bombay,* 1894. 12°.   14053. b.

NĀRĀYAṆASVĀMI AIYAR. Guide to Hindu Astrology. pp. 150. *Madras,* 1889. 8°.   759. c. 16.

P.P. *London.* Future: journal of predictive science. *Lond.* 1892, *etc.* 4°.   P.P. 1557. b.

RAPHAEL. Private Instructions in genethliacal Astrology. ff. 110. *Lond.* 1881. 4°. 8610. e. 5.

—— Pythoness of the East. pp. 212. *Lond.* 1894. 8°.   8632. aa. 25.

SIMMONITE (W. J.) Complete Arcana of Astral Philosophy. pp. 414. *Lond.* 1890. 8°.   8610. ee. 14.

STAR (É.) Cours d'Astrologie. pp. 160. *Paris,* 1892. 8°.   8610. aa. 56.

STORY (J.) The Daily Guide on revolutions or Solar Figures. pp. 56. *Lond.* 1891. 8°.   8610. ee. 15.

SŪRYANĀRĀYAṆA RĀVU. Astrological Primer. pp. 73. *Bellary,* 1892. 8°.   8610. aa. 59.

—— Astrological Self Instructor. pp. 208. *Bellary,* 1893. 8°.   8610. aaa. 48.

—— Revival of Astrology, *etc.* pp. 11. *Bellary,* 1893. 8°.   Pam. 36.

UPENDRĀCHĀRYA. Jinendramala of Upendracharia, horary Astrology. pp. 161. *Madras,* 1890. 8°.   14053. b. 26.

WILDE (G.) Treatise on natal Astrology. pp. 216. *Halifax,* 1894. 8°.   8610. bb. 58.

ZARIEL. Horoscope revised. pp. 65. *Lond.* 1895. 8°.   8610. aaa. 56.

ASTRONOMY.

Bibliography.

Ac. Berkeley, *California.* *Lick Observatory.* Catalogue of the Library. *Sacramento,* 1891, *etc.* 8°.   011901. ee.

—— Edinburgh. *Royal Observatory.* Catalogue of the Crawford Library. pp. 497. *Edinb.* 1890. 4°.   11902. l. 19.

—— Madison. *Washburn Observatory.* Catalogue of the Woodman Astronomical Library. Pt. 1. *Madison,* 1884. 8°.   11903. f. 35. (3.)

LANCASTER (A.) Liste des Observatories et des Revues astronomiques. pp. 147. *Brux.* 1890. 8°.   8562. aaa. 39.

ASTRONOMY—*continued.*

General.

AC. London. *British Astronomical Association.* Journal. *Lond.* 1890, *etc.* 8°.   Ac. 4176.

—— Memoirs. *Lond.* 1892, *etc.* 8°. Ac. 4176/2.

—— Paris. *Société Astronomique.* Bulletin mensuel. *Paris,* 1895, *etc.* 8°.   Ac. 4130.

AIRY (*Sir* G. B.) Popular Astronomy. pp. 302. *Lond.* 1891. 8°.   2320. a. 9.

ALDIS (*Mrs.* W. S.) Consider the Heavens. pp. 224. *Lond.* 1895. 8°.   4429. ee. 36.

BACKHOUSE (T. W.) Structure of the Sidereal Universe. 1891. 4°. SUNDERLAND. *West Hendon House Observatory.* Publications. No. 1.   8563. g.

BAILLAUD (B.) Cours d'Astronomie. *Paris,* 1893, *etc.* 8°.   8561. i. 24.

BALL (*Sir* R. S.) In the High Heavens. pp. 383. *Lond.* 1893. 8°.   8561. cc. 37.

—— The Story of the Heavens. pp. 556. *Lond.* 1891–93 8°.   2022. e.

BULLINGER (E. W.) Witness of the Stars. pp. 204. *Lond.* 1893. 8°.   8610. ee. 16.

C., A. J. Lois de Kepler. Simplicité des mouvements des corps célestes. pp. 108. *Voiron,* 1892. 8°.   8561. aaaa. 46.

CHAMBERS (G. F.) Pictorial Astronomy. pp. 268. 1891. 8°. Whittaker's Library of Science.   8709. aa.

—— Story of the Stars. pp. 192. *Lond.* 1895. 8°.   8563. a. 26.

CLERKE (A. M.) System of the Stars. pp. 424. *Lond.* 1890. 8°.   2022. e.

COMSTOCK (G. C.) Studies in Practical Astronomy. 1895. 8°. Ac. Madison. *University of Wisconsin.* Bulletin. Science Series. Vol. 1. No. 3.   Ac. 1792.

CROSLAND (N.) The New Principia. pp. 87. *Lond.* 1885. 8°.   8563. a. 20.

DADE (A. Z.) Travels with a Sunbeam. *Birmingham,* 1893, *etc.* 8°.   8563. b. 45.

DALLET (G.) Astronomie pratique. pp. 362. *Paris,* 1890. 8°.   8560. h. 41.

DELESTRE (P. F. P.) Exploration du Ciel théocentrique. pp. 492. *Paris,* 1890. 8°.   8561. cc. 35.

DENNING (W. F.) Telescopic work for starlight Evenings. pp. 361. *Lond.* 1891. 8°. 8562. d. 34.

DURHAM (W.) Astronomy. pp. 133. 1890. 8°. Science in Plain Language.   8709. aaa.

EASTON (C.) La Voie lactée dans l'Hémisphère Boréal. pp. 71. *Paris,* 1893. fol.   8560. k. 11.

FLAMMARION (C.) Popular Astronomy. pp. 686. *Lond.* 1894. 8°.   8561. h. 43.

GIBERNE (A.) The Starry Skies. pp. 242. 1894. 8°. Seeley's First Lesson Books. 012202. ff.

—— Radiant Suns. pp. 328. *Lond.* 1895. 8°. 8562. b. 51.

GORE (J. E.) Astronomical Lessons. pp. 136. *Lond.* 1890. 8°.   8563. aa. 40.

—— Astronomical Glossary. pp. 139. *Lond.* 1893. 8°.   8563. aa. 32.

—— Scenery of the Heavens. pp. 320. *Lond.* 1892. 8°.   8563. aa. 28.

—— The Visible Universe. pp. 346. *Lond.* 1893. 8°.   8562. cc. 35.

—— The Worlds of Space. pp. 338. *Lond.* 1894. 8°.   8561. b. 48.

ASTRONOMY.—**General**—*continued.*

GREGORY (R. A.) The Vault of Heaven. pp. 188. 1890, *etc.* 8°. University Extension Series.   012202. g.

GRUSON (H.) Im Reiche des Lichtes. pp. 263. *Braunschweig,* 1895. 8°.   8563. bb. 28.

GUILLEMIN (A.) Esquisses astronomiques. pp. 267. *Paris,* 1892. 8°.   8562. aaa. 44.

GUYOU (É.) Cours élémentaire d'astronomie. pp. 570. *Paris,* 1893. 8°.   8561. cc. 38.

HOPKINS (B. J.) Astronomy for every-day Readers. pp. 102. *Lond.* 1893. 8°.   8562. aaa. 41.

JOHNSTON (S. P.) Notes on Astronomy. pp. 86. *Manch.* 1892. 8°.   8563. aaa. 27.

KENNEDY (C.) Chapters on Astronomy. pp. 150. *Lond.* 1894. 8°.   8561. aaaa. 51.

LARKIN (H.) Elliptical Orbits. pp. 16. *Lond.* 1895. 8°.   Pam. 4.

LYNN (W. T.) Brief Lessons in Astronomy. pp. 36. *Lond.* 1892. 16°.   8563. a. 14.

—— Celestial Motions. pp. 128. *Lond.* 1894. 8°.   8563. a. 19.

MEE (A.) Observational Astronomy. pp. 79. *Cardiff,* 1893. 8°.   8562. ee. 23.

MEYER (M. W.) Mussestunden eines Naturfreundes. pp. 376. *Berl.* 1891. 8°. 12249. cc. 36.

MITCHELL (O. M. K.) The Orbs of Heaven. pp. 304. *Lond.* 1892. 8°.   8563. aa. 27.

—— Popular Astronomy. pp. 304. *Lond.* 1892. 8°.   8563. aa. 26.

PARKER (G. W.) Elements of Astronomy, *etc.* pp. 236. *Lond.* 1894. 8°.   8562. d. 39.

PECK (W.) Popular Handbook of Astronomy. pp. 176. *Lond.* 1890. 4°.   8560. h. 39.

P.P. *Leipsic.* Jahrbuch der Astronomie. *Leipz.* 1891, *etc.* 8°.   P.P. 1548.

—— *Northfield.* Popular Astronomy. *Northfield,* 1893, *etc.* 8°.   P.P. 1565. ea.

—— *Northfield.* The Astrophysical Journal. *Chicago,* 1895, *etc.* 8°.   P.P. 1565. e.

—— *Paris.* Les Sciences populaires. *Paris,* 1895, *etc.* 8°.   P.P. 1551. ab.

PRATT (H.) Principia Nova Astronomica. pp. 194. *Lond.* 1894. 4°.   8561. k. 7.

ROMANES (J.) Some Thoughts on subjects astronomical. pp. 61. *Edinb.* 1891. 8°.   Pam. 4.

SCHNEIDERS (G.) Die Naturphilosophie des Himmels. pp. 45. *Aachen,* 1893. 8°. Pam. 4.

STANLEY (W. F.) Notes on the Nebular Theory. pp. 259. *Lond.* 1895. 8°.   8560. ce. 28.

STARS. The Stars and the Earth. pp. 60. *Lond.* 1895. 16°.   8562. aa. 33.

TITUS (C.) Das Sternenzelt. pp. 379. *Berl.* 1893. 8°.   8561. aaaa. 49.

WALKER (J. E.) The Voices of the Stars. pp. 215. *Lond.* 1894. 8°.   8562. b. 50.

WARREN (H. W.) Recreations in Astronomy. pp. 284. *N.Y.* 1895. 8°.   8560. c. 32.

WEBB (T. W.) Celestial Objects for common Telescopes. *Lond.* 1893, *etc.* 8°. 8560. aaa. 25.

WILLIAMS (J. W.) The Telescope. pp. 128. 1888. 8°. Young Collector Series.   7001. aaa.

WOLF (C.) Astronomie et géodésie. pp. 414. *Paris,* 1891. 8°.   8561. i. 23.

WOLF (R.) Astronomische Mittheilungen. 1893. 8°. Ac. Zurich *Naturforschende Gesellschaft.* Vierteljahrschrift. Jahrg. 38.   Ac. 2869.

WOODWARD (R. S.) Report on Astronomical Work, 1889–90. pp. 79. 1890. 8°. U.S. *Geological Survey.* Bulletin. No. 70. 1829. a. 7.

ASTRONOMY.—General—_continued._

BARLOW (C. W. C.) Elementary Mathematical Astronomy. pp. 442. 1893. 8°. Tutorial Series. 12205. c. 100.

G. B. _Committee on Education._ Demonstrations in Astronomical Physics. pp. 59. _Lond._ 1891. 8°. Pam. 18.

POINCARÉ (H.) Les Méthodes nouvelles de la mécanique céleste. _Paris,_ 1892, _etc._ 8°. 8561. h. 41.

SOUCHON (A. A.) Traité d'Astronomie théorique. pp. 504. _Paris,_ 1891. 8°. 8561. i. 22.

See also COMETS : EARTH : JUPITER : METEORS : MOON : PHYSICS : PHYSIOGRAPHY : SPECTRUM ANALYSIS : STARS : SUN and SOLAR SYSTEM.

Geodetical. _See_ GEODESY.

History.

MUELLER (F.) Zeittafeln zur Geschichte der Mathematik und Astronomie, bis zur Jahre 1500. pp. 103. _Leipz._ 1892. 8°. 8704. e. 29.

BALL (_Sir_ R. S.) Great Astronomers pp. 372. _Lond._ 1895. 8°. 10000. ee. 1.

PROCTOR (R. A.) Old and New Astronomy. pp. 816. _Lond._ 1892. 8°. 2022. f.

TAYLOR (L.) Astronomers and their observations. pp. 160. _Lond._ 1895. 8°. 8561. aaaa. 52.

WOLF (R.) Handbuch der Astronomie. Geschichte. _Zürich,_ 1890, _etc._ 8°. 8561. i. 19.

TANNERY (P.) Recherches sur l'histoire de l'Astronomie ancienne. pp. 370. _Paris,_ 1893. 8°. 8561. i. 25.

LOCKYER (J. N.) The Dawn of Astronomy. pp. 432. _Lond._ 1894. 8°. 2258. d. 14.

MIERLO (J. van) De Sterrenkunde der Chaldeërs. pp. 31. _Gent._ 1891. 8°. Pam. 4.

ARATUS. Translation of the Astronomy of Aratus. pp. 82. _Lewes,_ 1895. 8°. 8563. b. 47.

CLEOMEDES, _the Astronomer._ Cleomedis de motu circulari corporum caelestium libri duo. _Gr. and Lat._ pp. 257. _Lipsiæ,_ 1891. 8°. 2278. c. 19.

ELLIS (R.) Dissertationes in Astronomica Manilii. pp. 255. _Oxonii,_ 1891. 8°. 11312. f. 47.

CARRA DE VAUX (A.) _Baron._ Les Sphères célestes selon Nasîr-Eddîn Attûsî. pp. 27. _Bordeaux,_ 1893. 8°. Pam. 4.

DREYER (J. L. E.) Tycho Brahe. pp. 405. _Edinb._ 1890. 8°. 10761. g. 27.

MONCHAMP (G.) Galilée et la Belgique. pp. 346. 76. _Saint-Trond,_ 1892. 8°. 8562. c. 51.

CLERKE (A. M.) The Herschels. pp. 224. 1895. 8°. Century Science Series. 8709. f.

—— History of Astronomy during the 19th century. pp. 573. _Lond._ 1893. 8°. 2022. e.

Nautical. _See_ NAVIGATION.

Observatories, _etc._

LANCASTER (A.) Liste des Observatoires. pp 147. _Brux._ 1890. 8°. 8562. aaa. 39.

ANDRÉ (C.) Comparaison des effets des petits et grands instruments d'astronomie. 1889. 8°. Ac. Lyons. _Académie des Sciences._ Mémoires. Classe des Sciences. Vol. 30. Ac. 364/2.

Ac. Bombay. _Observatory._ Report on the Observatory, _etc. Bombay,_ 1889, _etc._ fol. 8756. g. 27.

Ac. Cape Town. _Royal Observatory._ Annals. _Cape Town,_ 1886, _etc._ 4°. 8567. f. 16.

—— Heliometer Observations for determination of stellar parallax. pp. 167. _Lond._ 1893. 8°. 8563. bb. 27.

GILL (D.) The Cape Astronomers. pp. 42. _Cape Town,_ 1892. 12°. Pam. 4.

ASTRONOMY.—Observatories—_cont._

Ac. Cambridge, _Mass. Harvard University._ The Observatory of Harvard College. pp. 4. _Camb._ 1893. 8°. Pam. 4.

BAKER (D. W.) History of Harvard College Observatory. pp. 32. _Camb._ 1890. 8°. Pam. 4.

PICKERING (W. H.) The Harvard Observatory in Peru. pp. 7. _Camb._ 1894. 8°. Pam. 4.

FAUTH (P.) Astronomische Beobachtungen erhalten auf seiner Privatsternwarte zu Kaiserslautern von P. Fauth. _Kaiserslautern,_ 1893, _etc._ 4°. 8563. g.

Ac. Berkeley. _Lick Observatory._ Account of the Lick Observatory. pp. 29. _Sacramento,_ 1895. 8°. Pam. 4.

SHINN (M. W.) Lick Astronomical Department of the University of California. pp. 22. _San Francisco,_ 1892. 8°. Pam. 4.

Ac. Potsdam. _Astrophysikalisches Observatorium._ Die königlichen Observatorien. pp. 159. _Berl._ 1890. 8°. 8752. i. 15.

SUNDERLAND. _West Hendon House Observatory._ Publications. _Sunderland,_ 1891, _etc._ 4°. 8563. g.

Ac. Washington. _Naval Observatory._ Report of the Superintendent. _Wash._ 1890, _etc._ 8°. 8807. f.

Photography. _See_ PHOTOGRAPHY.

Plans, Atlases, _etc._

Ac. Williamstown, _Victoria. Observatory._ Planisphere of the Southern Sky. _Melb._ 1889. fol. 8564. k. 7.

BILFINGER (G.) Die Sterntafeln in den ägyptischen Königsgräbern von Bibân el Molûk. pp. 80. _Stuttgart,_ 1891. 4°. 8560. f. 39.

KETTLER (J. I.) Grimm's Atlas der Astrophysik. _Lahr._ 1881, _etc._ fol. 8564. k. 3.

PECK (W.) Handbook and Atlas of Astronomy. pp. 176. _Lond._ 1890. 4°. 8560. h. 39.

RUSSELL (H. C.) Preparations in Sydney Observatory for the photographic chart of the heavens. pp. 10. _Sydney,_ 1891. 8°. Pam. 4.

VALENTINER (C. W. F. J.) Astronomische Bilder pp. 450. _Leipz._ 1881. 8°. 8561. h. 16.

ASTURIAS. ACEVEDO Y HUELVES (B.) Los vaqueiros de alzada en Asturias. pp. 283. _Oviedo,_ 1893. 8°. 10161. dd. 10.

FORONDA Y AGUILERA (M. de) De Llanes á Covadonga. pp. 241. _Madrid,_ 1893. 8°. 10161. de 3.

RATO Y HÉVIA (A. de) Vocabulario de las palabras que se hablaron antiguamente en el principado de Asturias. pp. 149. _Madrid,_ 1891. 8°. 12942. d. 8.

ATACAMA. FIGUEROA (P. P.) Atacama en la guerra del Pacífico. pp. 142. _Santiago de C._ 1888. 8°. 12354. dd. 2. (5.) _See also_ CHILI.

ATHABASCA. MAC CONNELL (R. G.) Report on a portion of Athabasca. pp. 67. 1893. 8°. CANADA. _Geological Survey._ Report. New Series. Vol. 5. Pt. 1. 7202. d.

SOMERSET (H. S.) The Land of the Muskeg. pp. 248. _Lond._ 1895. 8°. 10413. k. 27. _See also_ CANADA, _North West Provinces._

ATHEISM: FREETHOUGHT: SECULARISM. BONHAM (J. M.) Secularism. pp. 396. _N.Y._ 1894. 8°. 4018. ff. 7.

CLARKE (J.) Why I left Atheism. pp 8 _Lond._ 1891. 8°. 4018. df. 13. (5.)

DVĀRAKĀDĀSA. Atheism and Agnosticism. pp. 29. _Lahore,_ 1888. 8°. 4371. ee. 3. (2.)

FREETHOUGHT. Freethought, is it destructive or constructive? pp. 82. _N.Y._ 1890. 8°. Pam. 77.

ATHEISM—*continued.*

GEM (S. H.) Christianity and Secularism.
pp. 12. *Lond.* 1890. 8°.   Pam. 95.

HARRIS (W. H.) The Secularist Programme.
pp. 64. *Lond.* 1891. 8°.   4103. b. 8.

HASTINGS (H. L.) Atheism and arithmetic.
pp. 63. *Bost.* 1889. 8°.   4018. df. 15.

P.P. Calcutta. The Cosmopolitan. Freethought journal. *Calcutta,* 1890, *etc.* 8°.
     P.P. 656. c.

POTTER (R.) Examination of Secularism.
pp. 16. *Melbourne,* 1883. 8°.   4371. e. 5. (8.)

PUCCINI (R.) La scienza e l'ateismo. pp. 264
Siena, 1890. 8°.   4016. df. 13.

WHEELER (J. M.) Freethought Readings and
Secular Songs. pp. 238. *Lond.* 1892. 8°.
     4016. e. 7.

See also AGNOSTICISM : CHRISTIANITY.

ATHENÆUM CLUB. *See* CLUBS.

ATHENS : ATTICA.

Antiquities.

Ac. Boston. *Archæological Institute. School of
Classical Studies at Athens.* Bulletin.
Bost. 1883, *etc.* 8°.   Ac. 5790/5.

—— Papers. *Bost.* 1885, *etc.* 8°.   Ac. 5790/9.

BAND (O.) Das Attische Demeter-Kore-Fest
der Epikleidia. *Berl.* 1887, *etc.* 4°.   4503. g.

BOSMANS (J.) Athènes et ses monuments.
Brux. 1893. fol.   1700. c. 5.

CHERBULIEZ (C. V.) A Phidian Horse. pp. 330.
Camden, N.J. 1893. 8°.   7875. a. 43.

LANGE (E.) Athen im Spiegel der aristopha-
nischen Komödie. pp. 50. 1894. 8°. Sammlung wissenschaftlicher Vorträge. Heft. 206.
     12249. m.

VLIET (J. v. d.) Athenae et Hierosolyma.
pp. 32. *Trajecti ad R.* 1891. 8°.   4534. c. 30. (7.)
See also GREECE.

History : Government, *etc.*

CURTIUS (E.) Die Stadtgeschichte von Athen.
pp. 339. *Berl.* 1891. 8°.   7705. c. 39.

GILBERT (G.) Constitutional Antiquities of
Athens. pp. 463. *Lond.* 1895. 8°. 9026. c. 17.

FRANCOTTE (H.) L'Organisation de la Cité
Athénienne et la Réforme de Clisthènes.
pp. 127. 1892. 8°. Ac. Brussels. *Académie.*
Mémoires couronnés. Tom. 47.   Ac. 985/4.

HEADLAM (J. W.) Election by Lot at Athens.
pp. 195. 1891. 8°. Cambridge Historical
Essays. No. 4.   9009. c.

ABBOTT (E.) Pericles and the Golden Age of
Athens. pp. 379. 1891. 8°. Heroes of the
Nations.   10601. f.

MICHELI (H.) La Révolution oligarchique des
Quatre-Cents à Athènes. pp. 132.
Genève, 1893. 8°.   9026. cc. 15.

Ac. London. *British Museum.* Aristotle on
the Constitution of Athens. Facsimile.
Lond. 1891. fol.   Tab. 437. b.

—— Aristotle on the Constitution of Athens.
Edited by F. G. Kenyon. pp. 229.
Lond. 1892. 8°.   2238. c. 24.

ARISTOTLE. Aristotelis Πολιτεία 'Αθηναίων. Edidit F. Blass. pp. 123. *Lipsiæ,* 1895. 8°.
     2278. 1. 13.

—— De Republica Atheniensium. Post Keny-
onem ediderunt H. van Herwerden et J. van
Leeuwen. pp. 241. *Lugd. Bat.* 1891. 8°.
     8005. dd. 3.

—— Aristotelis Πολιτεία 'Αθηναίων ediderunt
G. Kaibel et U. de Wilamowitz-Moellendorff.
pp. 100. *Berolini,* 1891. 8°.   8005. d. 2.

ARISTOTLE. Aristotle's Constitution of Athens.
Revised text, by J. E. Sandys. pp. 302.
Lond. 1893. 8°.   2238. d. 16.

—— Der Staat der Athener für den Schulge-
brauch erklärt von K. Hude. pp. 62.
Leipz. 1892. 8°.   Pam. 64.

—— Aristotle on the Athenian Constitution.
Translated by F. G. Kenyon. pp. 126.
Lond. 1891. 12°.   8005. aaa. 7.

—— Aristotle's Constitution of Athens. Translated by T. J. Dymes. pp. 147. *Lond.* 1891. 8°.
     8005. ccc. 13.

—— Aristotle on the Constitution of Athens.
Translated by E. Poste. pp. 101.
Lond. 1891. 8°.   8005. cc. 26.

—— Aristote, Constitution d'Athènes : traduite
par B. Haussoullier. pp. 112. 1891. 8°. Ac.
Paris. *École des Hautes Études.* Bibliothèque.
Sciences philologiques et historiques. Fasc. 89.
     Ac. 8929.

—— La République athénienne. Traduite par
T. Reinach. pp. 124. *Paris,* 1891. 8°.
     8008. aa. 14.

—— Aristoteles Schrift vom Staatswesen der
Athener verdeutscht von G. Kaibel und A.
Kiessling. pp. 108. *Strassb.* 1891. 8°.
     8005. cc. 25.

—— Aristoteles Staat der Athener. Übersetzt
von F. Poland. pp. 114. *Berl.* 1891. 8°.
     8005. bb. 11.

BAUER (A.) Forschungen zu Aristoteles 'Αθηναίων Πολιτεία. pp. 190. *München,* 1891. 8°.
     11312. l. 46.

CASSEL (S. P.) Vom neuen Aristoteles. pp. 39.
Berl. 1891. 8°.   11312. q. 6. (6.)

CAUER (F.) Hat Aristoteles die Schrift von
Staate der Athener geschrieben? pp. 78.
Stuttg. 1891. 8°.   11312. bbbb. 18.

CAVAZZA (P.) Aristotele e la Costituzione
di Atene. pp. 30. *Firenze,* 1891. 8°.
     8009. i. 32.

COSTANZI (V.) Quaestiuncula Aristotelea.
pp. 5. *Torino,* 1893. 8°.   8465. ee. 25. (9.)

DARESTE (R.) Aristote. 'Αθηναίων Πολιτεία.
Critique. pp. 17. *Paris,* 1891. 4°.
     11312. ee. 4. (4.)

DE-SANCTIS (G.) Studi sulla Costituzione
d'Atene attribuita ad Aristotele. pp. 19.
Torino, 1891. 8°.   Pam. 64.

GOMPERZ (T.) Die Schrift vom Staatswesen der
Athener und ihr neuester Beurtheiler, F.
Rühl. pp. 48. *Wien,* 1891. 8°.   8005. dd. 4.

HERZOG (E.) Zur Litteratur über den Staat der
Athener. pp. 33. *Tübingen,* 1892. 4°.
     11312. ee. 1. (11.)

DROYSEN (H.) Zu Aristoteles 'Αθηναίων πολιτεία.
pp. 23. *Berl.* 1891. 4°.   11312. ee. 1. (8.)

KAIBEL (G.) Stil und Text der Πολιτεία
'Αθηναίων des Aristoteles. pp. 277.
Berl. 1893. 8°.   11312. o. 8.

KEIL (B.) Aristotle on the Constitution of
Athens. Besprochen von B. Keil. pp. 56.
Berl. 1891. 8°.   8005. ccc. 12.

—— Die solonische Verfassung in Aristoteles
Verfassungsgeschichte Athens. pp. 218.
Berl. 1892. 8°.   8009. e. 15.

LECOUTÈRE (C.) L'Archontat Athénien; histoire
d'après la Πολιτεία 'Αθηναίων. pp. 124.
Louvain, 1893. 8°.   8009. k. 25.

MEYER (P.) Des Aristoteles Politik und die
'Αθηναίων Πολιτεία. pp. 72. *Bonn,* 1891. 8°.
     8005. ccc. 11.

ATHENS.—History, etc.—*continued.*

MULLER (H. C.) Kann Aristoteles' Schrift vom Staate der Athener eine Fälschung sein? pp. 36. *Amsterd.* 1893. 8°.   Pam. 14.

SCHJÖTT (P. O.) Aristoteles om Athens Statsforfatning. pp. 16. 1891. 8°. Ac. Christiania. *Videnskabs-Selskab.* Forhandlinger. aar 1891. No. 2.   Ac. 1054.

SCHVARCZ (G.) Aristoteles und die 'Αθηναίων πολιτεία auf dem Papyrus des British Museums. pp. 27. *Leipz.* 1891. 8°.   11312. q. 5. (6.)

—— Kritik der Staatsformen des Aristoteles. pp. 138. *Eisenach,* 1890. 8°.   8008. h. 10.

TREMENHEERE (H. S.) Summary of Aristotle's work on the Constitution of Athens. pp. 33. *Lond.* 1891. 8°.   8139. bb. 48. (14.)

VANDERKINDERE (L.) Le Manuscrit d'Aristote récemment découvert. pp. 16. *Brux.* 1891. 8°.   11312. q. 3. (6.)

WILAMOWITZ - MOELLENDORFF (U. von) Aristoteles und Athen. 2 Bde. *Berl.* 1893. 8°.   8009. h. 23.

See also GREECE.

Topography.

MOÜY (C. de) *Count.* Athènes. 1892. 4°. Les Capitales du Monde. No. 6.   10025. g.

TÉLFY (I.) Meine Erlebnisse in Athen. pp. 143. *Budapest,* 1890. 8°.   10125. aa. 15.

WRIGHT (F.) A Few Days in Athens. pp. 86. *Lond.* 1893. 8°.   012330. h. 25.

See also GREECE.

ATHERTON. HOPE (T. H.) Errors about Atherton in Mr. Croston's "History of Lancashire." pp. 15. *Manchester,* 1891. 8°.   10348. ccc. 57. (5.)

ATHLONE. STOKES (G. T.) Athlone in the Seventeenth Century. *Dublin,* 1890. 8°.   10347. g. 5. (6.)

ATHOS, *Mount.* BROCKHAUS (H.) Die Kunst in den Athos-Klöstern. pp. 305. *Leipz.* 1891. 4°.   7807. m. 4.

MÉYER (P.) Die Hauptturkunden für die Geschichte der Athosklöster. pp. 303. *Leipz.* 1894. 8°.   4534. d. 3.

ATLANTIC OCEAN. BECHER (A. B.) Navigation of the Atlantic Ocean. pp. 192. *Lond.* 1892. 8°.   10496. a. 19.

IMRAY (J. F.) and JENKINS (H. D.) Atlantic Ocean Pilot. pp. 1008. *Lond.* 1884. 8°.   10496. d. 12.

MAGINNIS (A. J.) The Atlantic Ferry, its ships, men and working. pp. 208. *Lond.* 1893. 8°.   8806. b. 43.

ATLANTIS. KNOETEL (A. F. R.) Atlantis und das Volk der Atlanten. pp. 418. *Leipz.* 1893. 8°.   10007. b. 27.

ATLAS, *Mount.* HALIBURTON (R. G.) The Dwarfs of Mount Atlas. pp. 41. *Lond.* 1891. 8°.   Pam. 89.

ATOMIC THEORY. BISCHOFF (C. A. G.) Handbuch der Stereochemie. *Frankf,* 1894, *etc.* 8°.   8909. m.

DEBUS (H.) Fundamental Sätze der Chemie, insbesondere das Dalton Avogadro'sche Gesetz, *etc.* pp. 99. *Cassel,* 1894. 8°.   8908. bb. 36.

DÉLANO (M. A.) Conferencias sobre la Teoría Atómica. pp. 70. *Londres,* 1892. 8°.   8708. i. 22.

DILLMANN (E.) Eine neue Verstellung der Leibnizischen Monadenlehre. pp. 525. *Leipz.* 1891. 8°.   8462. e. 11.

FRÉBAULT (A.) Système atomique. pp. 422. *Paris,* 1889. 8°.   8908. b. 15.

ATOMIC THEORY—*continued.*

HOFF (J. H. van 't) Chemistry in Space. pp. 128. 1891. 8°. Clarendon Press Series.   2319. a. 25.

MAJOR (F.) Spacial and Atomic Energy. Part I. pp. 62. *Lond.* 1889. 8°.   8708. c. 16.

MEUSEL (E.) Der Monismus der chemischen Elemente. pp. 58. *Liegnitz,* 1893. 8°.   8907. bb. 34.

—— Das Atomvolumen in chemischen Verbindungen. pp. 127. *Liegnitz,* 1894. 8°.   8908. k. 18.

STUDLER (A.) La Structure des molécules chimiques. pp. 275. *Paris,* 1893. 8°.   8909. k. 2.

WILDE (H.) On Elementary Substances, and on some relations of their atomic weights. 2 pt. *Lond.* 1892. 4°.   8906. h. 7.

See also CHEMISTRY : PHYSICS.

ATONEMENT. *See* CHRISTIANITY.

ATRI. CRUGNOLA (G.) Pregio della Porta S. Domenico in Atri, *etc.* pp. 8. *Teramo,* 1890. 8°.   Pam. 24.

ATTERCLIFFE. HESTER (G.) Attercliffe as a seat of learning. pp. 60. *Lond.* 1893. 8°.   8365. dd. 17. (19.)

ATTICA. *See* ATHENS.

AUCAMVILLE. GALABERT (F.) Monographie d'Aucamville. pp. 193. *Montauban,* 1890. 8°.   010171. m. 34.

AUCH. BÉNÉTRIX (P.) Lazare Carnot à Auch. pp. 15. *Auch,* 1891. 8°.   9004. c. 16. (5.)

CLAUDIN (A.) Les origines de l'imprimerie à Auch. pp. 32. *Paris,* 1894. 8°.   11904. l. 16. (14.)

DELLAS (É.) La Noblesse de la Sénéchaussée d'Auch, 1789. pp. 23. *Auch,* 1894. 8°.   9916. b. 29. (13.)

CAZAURAN ( ) Diocèse d'Auch—Histoire paroissiale. pp. 403. *Paris,* 1890. 8°.   010171. h. 40.

See also GERS, *Department.*

AUCKLAND, N.Z. AUCKLAND. Memories of the Past. *Auckland,* 1890. 8°.   9781. a. 2.

Ac. Auckland. *University College.* Calendar, 1895. pp. 59. *Auckland,* 1895. 8°. P.P. 2677. c.

See also NEW ZEALAND.

AUCTIONS. BATEMAN (J.) Law of Auctions. pp. 595. *Lond.* 1895. 8°.   2232. b. 3.

DANIELS (G. St. L.) Compendium of Commission Cases. pp. 313. *Lond.* 1893. 8°.   6305. a. 52.

G. B. & I. *Auctioneers' Institute of the United Kingdom.* Year Book. *Lond.* 1892, *etc.* 8°.   08227. e.

GRESSWELL (H. W.) How to buy and sell at Auction Rooms. pp. 124. *Lond.* 1891. 8°.   8228. bb. 26.

P.P. London. The Auctioneer. Nos. 1–12. *Lond.* 1892. 8°.   N.R.

SQUIBBS (R.) Auctioneers, their Duties and Liabilities. pp. 320. *Lond.* 1891. 8°. 6376. c. 29.

See also SALE, *Law of.*

AUDITING. *See* ACCOUNTANTS.

AUGHTON. NEWSTEAD (G. C.) Gleanings towards the Annals of Aughton. pp. 174. *Liverp.* 1893. 4°.   10358. d. 48.

AUGSBURG. BUFF (A.) Augsburg in der Renaissancezeit. pp. 139. *Bamberg,* 1893. 8°.   10256. c. 14.

JOACHIMSOHN (P.) Zur städtischen Geschichtschreibung Augsburgs im 15ten Jahrhundert. pp. 69. *Bonn,* 1894. 8°.   10256. d. 3.

MEYER (C.) Eine deutsche Stadt im Zeitalter des Humanismus. pp. 36. 1891. 8°. Sammlung Vorträge. N. F. No. 122.   12249. m.

AUGSBURG—*continued.*

WOLF (G.) Der Augsburger Religionsfriede. pp. 171. *Stuttgart*, 1890. 8°.   4661. dd. 21.

GRASSMANN (J.) Die Entwickelung der Augsburger Industrie im 19ᵗᵉⁿ. Jahrhundert. pp. 272. *Augsburg*, 1894. 8°.   08227. ee. 59.

HOPP (J.) Pfründe-Statistik der Diözese Augsburg. *Augsburg*, 1893, *etc.* 8°.   4662. g.

AUGSBURG CONFESSION.
See LUTHERAN CHURCH.

AUK. PARKER (W. K.) On the Morphology of the Auk Tribes. pp. 132. 1890. 4°. Ac. Dublin. *Royal Irish Academy.* Cunningham Memoirs. No. 6.   Ac. 1540/6.

AULDHAME. WADDELL (P. H.) An Old Kirk Chronicle. pp. 166. *Edinb.* 1893. 8°.   4735. eee. 13.

AULPS, *Abbey.* AULPS. Trente-deux chartes inédites relatives à l'abbaye d'Aulps. 1891. 8°. Ac. Chambéry. *Société d'histoire.* Mémoires. Sér. 2. Tom 5.   Ac. 5240.

AUMESSAS. FLORIS (U.) La Réforme à Aumessas. pp. 91. *Nimes*, 1893. 8°. 4629. a. 49.

AUNEAU. LEFEBVRE (A.) Notice historique sur la Chatellenie d'Auneau. pp. 187. *Paris*, 1890. 8°.   10174. h. 18.

AUNIS. DELAVAUD (L.) Troubles en Poitou et Aunis, 1643 et 1644. 1891. 8°. Ac. Saintes. *Société des Archives.* Archives. Vol. 19.   Ac. 6892.

AURORA BOREALIS. ANGOT (A.) Les Aurores polaires, *etc.* pp. 318. *Paris*, 1895. 8°.   8708. cc.

TIBERI (E.) Nuova teoria del fenomeno celeste l'Aurora polare. pp. 40. *Arezzo*, 1890. 8°.   8709. bb. 2. (4.)

See also METEOROLOGY.

AUSTRALIA : AUSTRALASIA.

Bibliography.

COWAN (F.) Australasiana. Catalogue of books, periodicals, maps. pp. 24. *Greensburgh*, 1894. 8°.   Pam. 6.

SYDNEY. *Free Public Library.* Australian Bibliography. 3 pt. *Sydney*, 1893. 4°.   2060. e.

Aborigines.

ETHERIDGE (R.) Contributions to a catalogue of works on the Australian and Tasmanian Aborigines. 1890, *etc.* 4°. NEW SOUTH WALES. *Geological Survey.* Memoirs. Palæontology, No. 8.   7203. h.

BETTANY (G. T.) The Red Brown and Black Men of Australia. pp. 289. *Lond.* 1890. 8°.   10007. f. 20.

CALVERT (A. F.) The Aborigines of Western Australia. pp. 55. *Lond.* 1894. 8°. 10491. b. 41.

CUNOW (H.) Die Verwandtschafts-Organisationen der Australneger. pp. 190. *Stuttgart*, 1894. 8°.   10007. l. 1.

FROGGATT (W. W.) Notes on Natives of West Kimberly. *Sydney*, 1888. 8°.   Pam. 87.

HOWITT (A. W.) On the Organization of Australian Tribes. 1889. 4°. Ac. Melbourne. *Royal Society.* Transactions. New edition. Vol. 1. Pt. 2.   Ac. 1980/8.

NEW SOUTH WALES. *Commissioners for the Exposition, Chicago.* Aborigines of New South Wales. By J. Fraser. pp. 102. *Sydney*, 1892. 8°.   7958. g. 21.

—— Notes on the Aborigines of New South Wales. By R. Hill and G. Thornton. pp. 8. *Sydney*, 1892. 8°.   7958. g. 30.

ROTH (H. L.) Aborigines of Tasmania. pp. 224. *Lond.* 1890. 8°.   10492. f. 32.

AUSTRALIA.—**Aborigines**—*continued.*

THRELKELD (L. E.) An Australian Language as spoken by the Awabakal, N.S.W. 4 pt. pp. 227. 148. *Sydney*, 1892. 8°.   12910. b. 43.

See also NEW ZEALAND : TASMANIA.

     Constitution. *See infra :* POLITICS.

     Crime. *See* CRIME.

     Federation. *See infra :* POLITICS.

     Gold Production. *See* GOLD AND SILVER.

History.

AUSTRALIAN HEROES. Australian Heroes. pp. 151. *Lond.* 1889. 8°.   10803. aaa. 29.

BLAIR (D.) Cyclopædia of Australasia. pp. 780. *Melbourne*, 1881. 8°.   10491. h. 9.

FAVENC (E.) The Story of Our Continent. *Sydney*, 1891, *etc.* 4°.   53.

GRIMM (G.) Concise History of Australia. pp. 126. *Sydney*, 1891. 8°.   9781. c. 3.

JENKS (E.) The History of the Australasian Colonies. pp. 352. 1895. 8°. PROTHERO (G. W.) Cambridge Historical Series.   2378. b. 28.

LEVEY (G. C.) Australasian Encyclopædia. pp. 437. *Lond.* 1892. 8°.   10492. cc. 24.

MARTIN (A. P.) Stories from Australasian History. pp. 320. *Lond.* 1893. 8°.   9781. aaa. 6.

GIBB (E.) Thrilling Incidents of the Convict System in Australasia. pp. 155. *Lond.* 1895. 8°.   6056. aaa. 30.

SUTHERLAND (A.) History of Australia. pp. 248. *Lond.* 1894. 8°.   9781. bb. 2.

PARKES (*Sir* H.) Fifty years in the making of Australian history. 2 vol. *Lond.* 1892. 8°.   2398. d. 10.

TREGARTHEN (G.) Australian Commonwealth. pp. 444. 1893. 8°. Story of the Nations.   9004. ccc. 10.

Politics.

AUSTRALIA. *Australasian Convention.* Official Record. pp. 455. *Sydney*, 1891. fol. 8154. k. 1.

—— Official Report of the National Australasian Convention Debates. pp. 964. *Sydney*, 1891. 8°.   8155. ee. 15.

—— Draft Bill to constitute the Commonwealth of Australia. pp. 68. *Sydney*, 1891. 8°. Pam. 66.

AUSTRALIA. Australia and the New Hebrides. pp. 7. *Sydney*, 1893. 8°.   Pam. 87.

BAKER (R. C.) Manual of reference for the use of the members of the National Australasian Convention. pp. 300. *Adelaide*, 1891. 8°.   8155. df. 8.

PARKES (*Sir* H.) Federal Government of Australasia. pp. 189. *Sydney*, 1890. 8°. 8154. c. 4.

WILLOUGHBY (H.) Australian Federation. pp. 154. *Melbourne*, 1891. 8°.   8154. aa. 20.

FAIRFIELD (C.) State Socialism in the Antipodes. 1891. 8°. MACKAY (T.) A Plea for Liberty, *etc.*   8276. g. 44.

FORTESCUE (*Hon.* J. W.) State Socialism and the collapse in Australia. 1894. 8°.

MACKAY (T.) A Policy of Free Exchange, *etc.*   08225. k. 5.

VINCENT (J. E. M.) Problems of Australian Colonization. pp. 29. *Lond.* 1892. 8°. Pam. 66.

Topography.

Ac. Sydney. *R. Geographical Society.* Transactions and proceedings. *Sydney*, 1888, *etc.* 8°. Ac. 6214.

BARTON (C. H.) Outlines of Australian Physiography. pp. 180. *Maryborough*, 1895. 8°.   10491. bb. 38.

BORTHWICK (T.) Contribution to the Demography of South Australia. pp. 67. *Lond.* 1891. 8°.   8223. dh. 7.

AUSTRALIA.—Topography—*continued.*

CALVERT (A. F.) Discovery of Australia. pp. 91.
Lond. 1893. 4°.   9781. e. 12.

—— Exploration of Australia. pp. 236.
Lond. 1895. 4°.   9781. g. 10.

CHISHOLM (G. G.) Longmans' Geography for
Australasia. pp. 330. Lond. 1891. 8°.
                                         10004. h. 6.

COGHLAN (T. A.) Statistical Account of the
Seven Colonies. Sydney, 1891, etc. 8°. 8223. dh.

GARRAN (A.) Picturesque Atlas of Australasia.
3 vol. Sydney, 1886-89. fol.   1790. b. 3.

—— Australasia Illustrated. Pt. 1.
Sydney, 1891. fol.   1788. a. 27.

GRIMM (G.) The Australian Explorers. pp. 247.
Melbourne, 1888. 8°.   9781. aaa. 4.

HOGAN (J. F.) The Sister Dominions. pp. 234.
Lond. 1895. 8°.   10026. ccc. 8.

KENT (W. S.) The Great Barrier Reef of Australia. pp. 387. Lond. 1893. fol.
                                         K.T.C. 9. b. 3.

LEVEY (G. C.) Australasian Encyclopædia.
pp. 437. Lond. 1892. 8°.   10492. cc. 21.

—— Handy Guide to Australasia. pp. 392.
Lond. 1891. 8°.   10492. aaa. 49.

LYDE (L. W.) Elementary Geography of Australia. pp. 168. Lond. 1893. 8°. 10005. aa. 20.

MORRIS (E. E.) Cassell's Picturesque Australasia. 4 vol. Lond. 1889, 92. 8°. 10491. h. 10.

NANDALĀLA DĀSA. Reminiscences, English and
Australasian. pp. 242. Calcutta, 1893. 8°.
                                         10492. ee. 29.

NEW SOUTH WALES. *Commissioners for the Exposition, Chicago.* Australia and America in
1892. pp. 172. Sydney, 1893. 8°. 7958. g. 23.

RANKEN (G.) Federal Geography of British
Australasia. pp. 506. Sydney, 1891. 8°.
                                         10492. cc. 20.

SILVER (S. W.) Handbook for Australia.
pp. 449. Lond. 1888. 8°.   10492. aaa. 5'.

WALLACE (A. R.) Australia. pp. 505. 1893. 8°.
Stanford's Compendium of Geography. 2060. a.

ARTHUR (J. K.) Kangaroo and Kauri. pp. 132.
Lond. 1894. 8°.   10492. e. 17.

BOOTHBY (G.) On the Wallaby. pp. 344.
Lond. 1894. 8°.   10491. ff. 16.

BUTTERWORTH (H.) Zigzag Journeys in Australia. pp. 319. Bost. 1891. 4°. 10492. ee. 20.

CANNEY (E. H.) Land of the Dawning. pp. 180.
Lond. 1894. 8°.   10491. aaa. 47.

CHIPS. Chips by an Old Chum. pp. 94.
Lond. 1893. 8°.   10492. a. 43.

CLERGYMAN. Australia as it is. pp. 257.
Lond. 1894. 8°.   10492. d. 24.

COMETTANT (J. P. O.) Au Pays des Kangourous.
pp. 386. Paris, 1890. 12°.   10491. aaa. 42.

DEMARR (J.) Adventures in Australia fifty years
ago. pp. 368. Lond. 1893. 8°. 10492. ee. 23.

FERGUSON (D.) Vicissitudes of Bush Life.
pp. 327. Lond. 1891. 8°.   012631. i. 23.

GOULD (N.) On and off the Turf in Australia.
pp. 214. Lond. 1895. 8°.   07905. ee. 1.

GRENVILLE (A. A.) *Duchess of Buckingham.*
Glimpses of Four Continents. pp. 291.
Lond. 1894. 8°.   10024. ccc. 6.

HACKENBERGER (C.) Trois ans en Australie.
1891. 8°. Ac. Nancy. *Société de Géographie.*
Bulletin.   Ac. 6034.

HOLMES (T. W.) My Experiences during a trip
to Australia. pp. 8. Lond. 1892. 8°. Pam. 91.

HUGHES (J.) Australia revisited in 1890.
pp. 499. Lond 1891. 8°.   10492. cc. 18.

AUSTRALIA.—Topography—*continued.*

JAMES (G. L.) Shall I try Australia? pp. 290.
Liverp. 1892. 8°.   10492. b. 47.

KINGLAKE (E.) The Australian at home. pp. 159.
Lond. 1891. 8°.   10492. cc. 17.

LEMIRE (A.) D'Irlande en Australie. pp. 177.
Lille, 1890. 8°.   10026. i. 14.

LENDENFELD (R. von) Australische Reise.
pp. 325. Innsbruck, 1892. 8°.   10491. g. 20.

MUSKETT (P. E.) Art of Living in Australia.
pp. 431. Lond. 1894. 8°.   07944. e. 23.

NISBET (H.) A Colonial Tramp. 2 vol.
Lond. 1891. 8°.   10491. ee. 24.

PARKER (G.) Round the Compass in Australia.
pp. 447. Lond. 1892. 8°.   10491. ee. 26.

PHYSICIAN. Seventy Years of Life in the Victorian Era. pp. 283. Lond. 1893. 8°.
                                         10491. de. 15.

PIONEER. Reminiscences of Australian Early
Life. pp. 245. Lond. 1893. 8°. 10491. aaa. 45.

POWELL (B. F. S. B.) In Savage Isles and
Settled Lands. pp. 438. Lond. 1892. 8°.
                                         10026. g. 4.

RAINAUD (A.) Le Continent austral. pp. 490.
Paris, 1893. 8°.   10460. ff. 19.

TOWERS (E.) Land of Sunshine and Gold. pp. 112.
Lond. 1892. 8°.   10491. de. 14.

VERSCHUUR (G.) At the Antipodes. pp. 330.
Lond. 1891. 8°.   10491. cc. 9.

Trade.

ANSON (L.) English Manufactures and Australasian Trade. pp. 99. Lond. 1893. 8°. 08227. e. 46.

Dialect.

LENTZNER (C.) Wörterbuch der englischen
Volkssprache in Australien. pp. 237.
Halle, 1892. 8°.   12982. f. 15.
See also AUSTRALIA, *South and Western* : FIJI :
NEW GUINEA : NEW SOUTH WALES : NEW ZEA-
LAND : QUEENSLAND : TASMANIA.

AUSTRALIA, South. AUSTRALIA, *South.*
South Australia: its development and financial
position. pp. 7. Adelaide, 1892. 8°.
                                         8227. i. 40. (7.)

NOWELL (E. C.) History of the Relations
between the two Houses of Parliament in
S. Australia. pp. 158. Hobart, 1890. 8°.
                                         8153. c. 24.

AUSTRALIA, *South. Parliament.* Index to Parliamentary Papers, 1857-81. pp. 116.
Adelaide, 1882. fol.   8155. h. 4.

SMITH (J. W.) Index of Public Statutes in
force in South Australia. pp. 48.
Adelaide, 1885. 8°.   6606. aaa. 7.

BROWN (H. Y. L.) South Australia.
Adelaide, 1892. fol.   Pam. 87.

—— South Australia. Report on journey.
pp. 6. Adelaide, 1890. fol.   Pam. 87.

HODDER (E.) History of South Australia. 2 vol.
Lond. 1893. 8°.   9781. df. 8.

P.P. Adelaide. Year-Book of South Australia.
Adelaide, 1889, etc. 8°.   P.P. 2623. h.

PARSONS (J. L.) Products of the Northern Territory. pp. 16. Adelaide, 1891. 8°.   Pam. 1.

SCOTT (H. J.) South Australia in 1887-8.
pp. 187. Adelaide, 1888. 8°.   10492. b. 49.

SOUTH AUSTRALIA. Some particulars of development and financial position. pp 7.
Adelaide, 1892. 8°.   8227. i. 40. (7.)

STOW (J. P.) South Australia : history, productions and natural resources. pp. 307.
Adelaide, 1884. 8°.   10492. cc. 28.

AUSTRALIA, South—continued.

Woods (J. D.)　Province of South Australia.
pp. 446.　*Adelaide*, 1894. 8°.　　10491. f. 35.
See also Australia : England, *Colonies.*

AUSTRALIA, Western. Haynes (T. H.)
Legislation in Western Australia.　pp. 11.
Lond. 1889. 8°.　　　　　　　　Pam. 66.

New South Wales.　New Constitution for
Western Australia.　pp. 33.　*Sydney*, 1889. 8°.
　　　　　　　　　　　　　　　Pam. 66.

Australia, *Western*.　Album of Western Australia.　1892. 4°.　　　　　　10492. aaa. 53.

Calvert (A. F.)　Western Australia.　pp. 61.
Lond. 1893. 8°.　　　　　　　10491. cc. 10.

—— Western Australia and its welfare.
pp. 168.　*Lond.* 1895. 8°.　　10491. aaa. 48.

Favenc (E.)　Western Australia.　pp. 84.
Sydney, 1887. 4°.　　　　　　10492. ff. 13.

Hart (F.)　Western Australia.
Perth, 1892, *etc.* 8°.　　　　10492. ee. 25.

Mennell (P.)　The Coming Colony.　pp. 144.
Lond. 1894. 8°.　　　　　　　10492. d. 27.

Nicolay (C. G.)　Handbook of Western Australia.　pp. 186.　*Perth*, 1880. 8°. 10492. c. 33.

Parsons (H. G.)　Handbook to Western Australia.　pp. 134.　*Lond.* 1894. 8°.
　　　　　　　　　　　　　10492. aaa. 54.

P.P.　Perth, *Western Australia*.　Western Australian Year Book.　*Perth*, 1891, *etc.* 8°.
　　　　　　　　　　　　　　　P.P. 2645. b.

—— *London.*　Stoneham's Westralian Market
Manual.　*Lond.* 1895, *etc.* 8°.　P.P. 2490. pe.
See also Australia : England, *Colonies.*　For
Gold and other Mines and Minerals, *see* Gold
and Silver : Mines and Mineralogy.

AUSTRIA - HUNGARY.　[*See note on*
p. 1.]　*See also* Bohemia : Bosnia : Bukowina :
Carinthia : Carniola : Croatia : Dalmatia :
Hungary : Istria : Moravia : Silesia : Transylvania : Tyrol, *etc.*

Army.

Dupain (L.)　L'Administration militaire austro-
hongroise.　pp. 368.　*Paris*, 1894. 8°.
　　　　　　　　　　　　　8826. ccc. 39.

Foedransperg (H. v.)　Vierzig Jahre in der
österreichischen Armee.　*Dresden*, 1894, *etc.* 8°.
　　　　　　　　　　　　　8830. bbb.

G. B. & I.　*War Office.*　Handbook of the Military Forces of Austria-Hungary.　pp. 198.
Lond. 1891. 8°.　　　　　　　8823. g. 19.

Kaulbars (A. V.)　L'Armée Austro-Hongroise.
pp. 269.　*Paris*, 1893. 8°.　　8828. ff. 26.

Kuhn (F. v.)　The Austro-Hungarian Army.
189 . 8°.　Armies of to-day, *etc.*　8829. i. 9.

Lachapelle Aguilar (C. de)　El Ejército austro-
húngaro.　pp. 316.　*Madrid*, 1893. 8°.
　　　　　　　　　　　　　8823. h. 46.

Majláth (K. J.)　*Count.*　Heldenthaten der
oesterreich-ungarischen Armee.
Wien, 1891, *etc.* 8°.　　　　09315. e.

Purschka (F. v.)　Rückblicke auf die Entwickelung des österreichischen Heeres.　pp. 302.
Lemberg, 1892. 8°.　　　　　8823. ddd. 26.

Treuenfest (G. A. v.)　Armee-Album.　pp. 148.
Wien, 1889. fol.　　　　　　1765. b. 25.

Austria.　*Army.*　Die grossen Manöver 1894 in
Böhmen und Ungarn.　pp. 206.　*Wien*, 1895. 8°.
　　　　　　　　　　　　　8830. bb. 50.

David (G.)　Ceterum censeo.　Unser militärisches
Deficit.　pp. 85.　*Wien*, 1891. 8°.　8072. eee. 9.

Czerlien (M. v.)　Die Friedens-Arbeit der
Cavallerie.　pp. 606. *Wien*, 1894. 8°. 8829. i. 21.

Strobl (F.)　Geschichte des 12. Dragoner-Regiments.　pp. 452.　*Wien*, 1890. 8°. 8823. dd. ; 6.

AUSTRIA-HUNGARY.—Army—cont.

Fischer von Wellenborn (C.)　Ein Beitrag zur
Geschichte des Uhlanen-Regimentes Nr. 1.
pp. 247.　*Wien*, 1894. 8°.　　9080. d. 41.

Regenspursky (C.)　Studien über den taktischen
Inhalt des Exercier-Reglements für die Fusstruppen.　pp. 144.　*Wien*, 1892. 8°. 8830. k. 27.

Treuenfest (G. A. v.)　Geschichte des kärnth-
nerischen Infanterie-Regimentes Nr. 7.
pp. 1005.　*Wien*, 1891. 8°.　　8828. k. 17.

Branko (F. v.)　Geschichte des Infanterie-
Regimentes Nr. 44.　pp. 734.　*Wien*, 1880. 8°.
　　　　　　　　　　　　　8824. k. 12.

Scherach (C.)　Die Geschichte des Corps-Ar-
tillerie-Regimentes Nr. 3.　pp. 175.
Graz, 1894. 8°.　　　　　　　8828. cc. 47.

Sann (H. v. d.)　Lorbeerblätter aus der
Ruhmesgeschichte steirischer Truppenkörper,
etc.　pp. 331.　*Graz*, 1893. 8°.　9080. i. 18.

Austria.　Schematismus der Militär-Erziehungs-
und Bildungs-Anstalten für 1885.　pp. 53.
Wien, 1885. 8°.　　　　　　　8830. f. 33.

Kirchenberger (S.)　Kaiser Josef II. als Reformator des Militär-Sanitäts-Wesens.　pp. 108.
Wien, 1890. 8°.　　　　　　　8824. ff. 40.

Constitution and Government.

Burckhard ( )　Leitfaden der Verfassungs-
kunde der Monarchie.　pp. 139.　*Wien*, 1893. 8°.
　　　　　　　　　　　　　8074. f. 35.

Coldstream (J. P.)　Institutions of Austria.
pp. 127.　*Westminster*, 1895. 8°.　8073. d. 20.

Gumplowicz (L.)　Das oesterreichische Staatsrecht.　pp. 655.　*Wien*, 1891. 8°.　5549. e. 24.

Huber (A.)　Geschichte der Staatsbildung und
des öffentlichen Rechts.　pp. 280.
Prag, 1895. 8°.　　　　　　　05549. k. 1.

Kiesler (H.)　Die Staatsverfassung Oesterreichs
dargestellt.　pp. 64.　*Czernowitz*, 1892. 8°.
　　　　　　　　　　　8074. b. 2. (19.)

Lucz (A.)　Ministerverantwortlichkeit und Staatsgerichtshöfe.　pp. 51.　*Wien*, 1893. 8°.
　　　　　　　　　　　5551. g. 20. (11.)

Luschin von Ebengreuth (A.)　Osterreichische
Reichsgeschichte.　*Bamberg*, 1895, *etc.* 8°.
　　　　　　　　　　　　　05549. k.

Seidler (G.)　Studien zur Geschichte des österreichischen Staatsrechtes.　pp. 188.
Wien, 1894. 8°.　　　　　　　05549. h. 7.

Werunsky (E.)　Osterreichisches Rechtsge-
schichte.　Ein Lehr- und Handbuch.
Wien, 1894, *etc.* 8°.　　　　05551. k.
See also infra : Politics.

History.

Jireček (H.)　Unser Reich vor zweitausend
Jahren.　pp. 67.　*Wien*, 1893. 8°. 9315. g. 15.

Leger (L.)　Histoire de l'Autriche-Hongrie.
pp. 687.　1895. 8°.　Duruy (V.)　Histoire
universelle, *etc.*　　　　　　9006. d. 9.

Mayer (F. M.)　Geschichte der österreichisch-
ungarischen Monarchie.　pp. 320.
Wien, 1894. 8°.　　　　　　　9315. g. 20.

Strakosch-Grassmann (G.)　Geschichte der
Deutschen in Oesterreich.　*Wien*, 1895, *etc.* 8°.
　　　　　　　　　　　　　09315. g.

Teuber (O.)　Ehrentage Oesterreichs.　pp. 408.
Wien, 1892. 8°.　　　　　　　9079. h. 17.

Zoehrer (F.)　Oberösterreichs Chronik.
Linz, 1894, *etc.* 8°.　　　　　9314. aa.

Seemueller (J.)　Ottokars Reimchronik.
1890, *etc.* fol.　Monumenta Germaniae Historica.　tom. 5, *etc.*　　　　Ac. 7003/2.

Juritsch (G.)　Geschichte der Babenberger und
ihrer Länder, 976-1046.　pp. 724.
Innsbruck, 1894. 8°.　　　　9906. e. 12.

AUSTRIA.—History—*continued.*

SCHEICHL (F.) Bilder aus der Zeit des Gegen-reformation, 1564–1618. pp. 51.
Gotha, 1890. 8°. 4662. c. 25. (5.)

STIEVE (F.) Der oberösterreichische Bauernauf-stand des Jahres 1626. 2 Bde.
München, 1891. 8°. 09315. e. 2.

BACHMANN (A.) Nachträge zur österreichisch-deutschen Geschichte im Zeitalter Kaiser Fried-rich III. pp. 503. 1892. 8°. Fontes Rerum Austriacarum. Abth. 2. Bd. 46. Ac. 810/9.

VILLERMONT (de) *Count.* Marie - Thérèse. 2 tom. *Paris*, 1895. 8°. 10704. k. 8.

BRUNNER (S.) Joseph II. a's absoluter Beherrscher. 1892. 8°. Frankfurter zeitgemässe Broschüren. N. F. Bd. 14. 12209. g.

UNZER (A.) Hertzbergs Anteil an den preuss-isch-österreichischen Verhandlungen, 1778, 79. pp. 182. *Frankf. a. M.* 1890. 8°. 9079. h. 10.

KRONES VON MARCHLAND (F. X.) Zur Geschichte Oesterreichs, 1792–1816. pp. 396.
Gotha, 1886. 8°. 9315. bbb. 3.

ZEISSBERG (H. v.) Erzherzog Carl.
Wien, 1895, etc. 8°. 10704. k.

WAECHTLER (W.) Der alte treue Radetzky. pp. 159. *Podersam*, 1893. 8°. 010707. g. 43.

TROLARD (E.) Pèlerinage aux champs de bataille français d'Italie. pp. 410. *Paris*, 1893. 8°. 10136. bbb. 29.

ZWIEDINECK-SUEDENHORST (H. v.) Erzherzog Johann von Österreich im Feldzuge von 1809. pp. 260. *Graz*, 1892. 8°. 10704. f. 33.

JOHN, *Archduke of Austria.* Aus dem Tagebuch Erzherzog Johanns 1810–15. pp. 251.
Innsbruck, 1891. 8°. 9314. cc. 9.

KRONES VON MARCHLAND (F. X.) Aus Oester-reichs stillen Jahren, 1810–12 und 1813–15. pp. 417. *Innsbruck*, 1892. 8° 09315. e. 10.

WOYNAR (C.) Österreichs Beziehungen zu Schweden und Dänemark, 1813–14. 1891. 8°. Archiv für österreichische Geschichte. Bd. 77. Ac. 810/8.

HUEBNER (J. A. v.) Une année de ma vie. 1848–49. pp. 574. *Paris*, 1891. 8°. 010707. ee. 1.

BERTHA (A. de) François Joseph I. et son règne. pp. 155. *Paris*, 1888. 8°. 9315. dd. 20.

RAUTER (D.) Geschichte Österreichs, 1818–90. pp. 103. *Wien*, 1891. 8°. 09315. ee. 3.

AUSTRIA. *Army.* Der Krieg im Jahre 1859. pp. 272. *Bamberg*, 1894. 8°. 9080. l. 7.

RATHLEF (G.) Bismarck und Oesterreich bis 1866. pp. 92. *Reval*, 1893. 8°. 8072. f. 4.

KANNGIESSER (O.) Geschichte des Kreiges von 1866. *Basel*, 1892, etc. 8°. 9080. f.

SCUDIER (A. v.) Betrachtungen über den Feldzug 1866 in Italien. *Wien*, 1894, etc. 8°. 9167. i.

WAGNER (A. L.) Campaign of Königgrätz. pp. 121. *Fort Leavenworth*, 1889. 8°. 9080. bbb 21.

KOENIGGRAETZ. Führer über das Schlachtfeld bei Königgrätz. pp. 83. *Königgrätz*, 1892. 8°. 10215. aa. 20.

SCHMITT (R.) Die Gefechte bei Trautenau, 1866. pp. 271. *Gotha*, 1892. 8°. 9314. cc. 10.

MOLTKE (H. C. B. v.) *Count.* Moltkes Feldzugs-Entwurfs 1866 und die Lage Benedeks am Juni und Juli 1866. pp. 41. *Berl.* 1892. 8°. Pam. 2.

See also EUROPE: FRANCE, *Revolutionary Wars*: GERMANY: HOLY ROMAN EMPIRE: THIRTY YEARS' WAR.

Law.

KRAINZ (J.) System des österreichischen Privat-rechts. 3 Thle. *Wien*, 1885–89. 8°. 5549. d. 13.

AUSTRIA.—Law—*continued.*

PFERSCHE (E.) Die Irrthumslehre des oester-reichischen Privatrechts. pp. 342. *Graz*, 1891. 8°. 5549. e. 28.

DEMELIUS (E.) Kritische Studien zu den Gesetz-entwurfen. *Wien*, 1894, etc. 8°. 05549. k.

ECKSTEIN (J.) Die Intervention nach öster-reichischem Rechte. pp. 295. *Leipz*, 1893. 8°. 05549. h. 2.

HASENOEHRL (V) Das oesterreichische Obliga-tionenrecht. *Wien*, 1892, etc. 8°. 05549. k.

SCHEY (J. v.) Die Obligationsverhältnisse des österreichischen Privatrechts.
Wien, 1890, etc. 8°. 5549. dd.

PFERSCHE (E.) Österreichisches Sachenrecht. *Wien*, 1893, etc. 8°. 05549. h.

WERUNSKY (E.) Österreichisches Rechtsge-schichte. *Wien*, 1894, etc. 8°. 05551. k.

See also LAW, *Commercial : Criminal : Ecclesi-astical.*

Navy.

LEHNERT (J. v.) Geschichte der österreich-isch-venetianischen Kriegs-Marine, 1797–1802. pp. 464. 1891. 8°. AUSTRIA. Geschichte der Kriegs-Marine. Thl. 2. 8807. i. 5.

Politics.

AUSTRIA. Die deutsch-liberale Partei und die Zukunft des Liberalismus in Oesterreich. pp. 36. *Wien*, 1892. 8°. 8074. ff. 31. (8.)

—— Ziele einer wahren conservativen Volks-Partie in Oesterreich. pp. 49. *Wien*, 1892. 8° 8074. h. 2. (8.)

BRENTANO (F.) Meine letzten Wünsche für Oesterreich. pp. 80. *Stuttgart*, 1895. 8°. 8074. c. 30.

DUMREICHER (A. v.) Südostdeutsche Betrach-tungen. pp. 143. *Leipz*. 1893. 8°. 8072. f. 5.

HAINISCH (M.) Die Zukunft der Deutsch-Österreicher. pp. 162. *Wien*, 1892. 8°. 08227. f. 40.

HERKNER (H.) Die Zukunft der Deutsch Oesterreicher. pp. 24. *Wien*, 1893. 8°. 8074. ff. 31. (10)

PATRIOT. Der Konservatismus und Österreichs Zukunft. pp. 106. *Wien*, 1891. 8°. 8074. f. 27.

PATTAI (R.) Die neuesten politischen Ereig-nisse. pp. 33. *Wien*, 1893. 8°. Pam. 72.

SCHWINGENSCHLOEGL (R.) Der erste Beamten-Verein der österreichisch-ungarischen Mon-archie. pp. 537. *Wien*, 1890. 8°. 8006. f. 3.

Roman Catholic Church.

See ROMAN CATHOLIC CHURCH.

Topography.

CHÉLARD (R.) L'Autriche contemporaine. pp. 470. *Paris*, 1894. 8°. 10210. e. 3.

JAQUES (H.) Reden über Österreich. pp. 69. *Leipz*. 1891. 8°. 10107. ff. 27. (8.)

MISCHLER (E.) Oesterreichisches Städtebuch. *Wien*, 1887. etc. 8°. 8223. df. 22.

NEELMEYER-VUKASSOWITSCH (H.) Oesterreich-Ungarn. pp. 1099. *Leipz*. 1885. 8°. 10026. k. 9.

LOEWENTHAL (H.) Aquarelle aus Oesterreich. pp. 225. *Dresd.* 1893. 8°. 012554. i. 23.

STOKES (H. P.) Holiday Tour in Austria. pp. 43. *Lond.* 1890. 16°. 10215. aa. 17.

WHITMAN (S.) Realm of the Habsburgs. pp. 3 0. *Lond.* 1893. 8°. 10215. b. 6.

Trade and Finance.

MENSI (F. v.) Die Finanzen Oesterreichs 1701–40. pp. 775. *Wien*, 1890. 8°. 08227. f. 25.

AUSTRIA.—Trade, etc.—*continued.*

BEER (A.) Die Finanzverwaltung Oesterreichs 1749-1816. 1894. 8°. Mittheilungen des Instituts für oesterreich. Geschichtsforschung. Bd. 15.   Ac. 803.

—— Geschichte der österreichischen Volkswirthschaft unter Maria Theresia. pp. 133. 1894. 8°. Archiv für österreich. Geschichte. Bd. 81.   Ac. 810/8.

—— Die österreichische Handelspolitik. pp. 618. *Wien,* 1891. 8°.   8074. ff. 27.

BAZANT (J. v.) Die Handelspolitik Österreich-Ungarns 1875-92. pp. 193. *Leipz.* 1894. 8°.   08227. ee. 58.

MISCHLER (E.) Oesterreichisches Städtebuch. *Wien,* 1887, *etc.* 8°.   8223. df. 22.

AUSTRIAN STATISTICAL POCKETBOOK. Oesterreichisches statistiches Taschenbuch. pp. 257. *Wien,* 1890. 8°.   08225. ee. 3.

ADLER (C.) Das österreichisches Lagerhausrecht. pp. 234. *Berl.* 1892. 8°.   5549. df. 9.

BORUSSEN. Ablehnen oder Annehmen. pp. 108. *Gotha,* 1891. 8°.   8072. df. 10.

BUERNER (R.) Zollhandbuch für die Hauptindustrien Oesterreich-Ungarns. *Zittau,* 1895, *etc.* 8°.   08226. i.

DECRAIS (P. L. A.) Les Conditions du Travail en Autriche-Hongrie. pp. 104. 1890. 8°. Recueil de rapports, *etc.*   08276. k.

CHICAGO. *Columbian Exposition.* Special-Katalog der österreichischen Abtheilung auf der Weltaustellung. pp. 122. *Wien,* 1893. 8°.   7959. bb. 23.

GRUNZEL (J.) Die Handelsbeziehungen Oesterreich-Ungarns zu den Balkanländern. pp. 142. *Wien,* 1892. 8°.   08227. ee. 56.

HAINISCH (M.) Die Zukunft der Deutsch-Österreicher. pp. 162. *Wien,* 1892. 8°. 08227. f. 40.

MATLEKOVITS (S.) Die Zollpolitik der Monarchie. pp. 963. *Leipz.* 1891. 8°.   08227. h. 7.

MAYER (S.) Die Aufhebung des Befähigungsnachweises in Österreich. pp. 359. *Leipz.* 1894. 8°.   08227. h. 44.

OCKHARDT (G.) Zur Frage des neueren österreichischen Papiergeldes. pp. 99. *Leipz.* 1890. 8°.   08227. f. 10.

PACHER (P.) Die österreich.-ungarische Währung. pp. 104. *Leipz.* 1890. 8°. 08229. f. 49.

PEEZ (A.) Die österreichische Handelspolitik. 1892. 8°. Ac. Leipsic. *Verein für Socialpolitik.* Schriften. vol. 49.   Ac. 2322.

SCHILLERWEIN (I.) Die österreichisch-ungarischen Zollgesetze. pp. 797. *Wien,* 1893. 8°.   5549. dd. 15.

VAUTIER (G.) La Hongrie économique. pp. 486. *Paris,* 1893. 8°.   08225. k. 4.

WESTPHAL (P.) Die Aufnahme der Baarzahlungen in Oesterreich-Ungarn. pp. 123. *Wien,* 1892. 8°.   08227. h. 35.

AUTHORSHIP. *See* COPYRIGHT : BOOKSELLING, *etc.*

AUTOGRAPHS. Ac. Great Britain. *Society of Archivists.* Journal of the Society. *Lond.* 1895, *etc.* 4°.   Ac. 9116.

—— London. *British Museum.* Guide to the Manuscripts and Autographs exhibited. pp. 140. *Lond.* 1895. 8°.   11903. b. 42.

—— Fac-similes of Autographs in the British Museum. *Lond.* 1895. fol.   1565.

BOLOGNA. *Accadémia Filarmonica.* Catalogo della collezione d'autografi. *Bologna,* 1881, *etc.* 8°.   792.

AUTOGRAPHS—*continued.*

CHAMPFLEURY. Catalogue des Autographes composant la Collection Champfleury. 2 pt. *Paris,* 1891. 8°.   7709. . 19.

DREER (F. J.) Catalogue of the collection of Autographs of F. J. Dreer. *Philad.* 1890, *etc.* 4°.   11901. d. 22.

FACSIMILES. Facsimiles of Autographs of Artists. 1888. *s. sh. obl.* fol.   1240. k. (4.)

H., J. Diversions of an Autograph-Hunter. pp. 106. *Lond.* 1894. 8°.   12331. e. 44.

HABASQUE (F.) Autographes de personnages dans l'histoire de Bordeaux et de la Guyenne. 2 pt. 1895. 4°. Ac. Bordeaux. *Société des Archives.* Archives de la Gironde. Tom 30.   Ac. 6775.

HARDY (W. J.) Handwriting of the Kings and Queens of England. pp. 176. *Lond.* 1893. 8°.   7709. k. 21.

HENKELS (S. v.) Collection of Autographs belonging to J. H. Dubbs. pp. 208. *Philad.* 1893. 8°.   011903. m. 20.

—— Catalogue of Autograph collection of J. H. Rogers. pp. 199. *Philad.* 1895. 8°.   11900. ee. 34.

JONES (C. C.) Catalogue of the Autograph collection of C. C. Jones. pp. 148. *Philad.* 1894. 8°.   11902. g. 42.

MIRACLE Y CARBONELL (F.) Napoléon I. y su escritura. pp. 258. *Barcel.* 1892. 8°.   7942. h. 32.

P. P. *Leipz.* Mittheilungen für Autographensammler. Jahrg. 1-10. *Leipz.* 1884-93. 8°.   P.P. 6534.

SCOTT (H T.) and DAVY (S.) Guide to the collector of historical documents and autograph letters. pp. 218. ff. 95. 23. *Lond.* 1891. 8°.   11899. h. 36.

WISE (T. J.) Reference Catalogue of British and foreign Autographs. *Lond.* 1893, *etc.* fol.   1889. e.

See also MANUSCRIPTS : PALAEOGRAPHY.

AUTUN. THEVRAS (G.) Autun vers le XVe siècle. pp. 368. *Autun,* 1891. 8°. 10168. cc. 33.

MONTARLOT (P.) Le Bailliage d' Autun en 1789. 1892. 8°. Ac. Autun. *Société Éduenne.* Mémoires. tom. 20.   Ac. 5288/2.

AUVERGNE. BIÉLAWSKI (J. B. M.) L'Auvergne dans les temps anciens. pp. 276. *Paris,* 1890. 8°.   7708. aa. 52.

CARBONNAT (C. de) L'Auvergne sous les Romains. pp. 35. *Toulouse,* 1889. 8°.   10107. e. 11. (6.)

BONNEFOY (G.) Histoire de l'administration civile dans la province d'Auvergne. *Paris,* 1895. *etc.* 8°.   10174. f.

SERRES (J. B.) Histoire de la Révolution en Auvergne. *St Amand,* 1895. *etc.* 8°. 9231. aaa.

JOANNE (P.) Auvergne. pp. 374. *Paris,* 1892. 8°.   2362. a.

—— Le Mont-Dore et les Eaux Minérales d'Auvergne. pp. 191. 19. *Paris,* 1893. 8°.   10171. a 20.

MACQUARIE (J. L.) Les Bains du Centre, Auvergne. pp. 363. *Paris,* 1891. 8°. 10169. de. 18.

BRUNET (H.) Les difficultés de l'orthographe résolues par la traduction en l'idiome d'Auvergne. pp. 15. *Fontainebleau,* 1890. 8°.   12901. ccc. 12. (4.)

See also PUY DE DÔME, *Department.*

AUXERRE. MOLARD (F.) Histoire de l'ancien trésor de la Cathédrale d'Auxerre. 1892. 8°. Ac. Auxerre. *Société des Sciences.* Bulletin. vol. 46.   Ac. 2860.

AVERBODE. GOFFAERTS (C.) Les Stalles de l'Abbaye d'Averbode. 1892. 8°. Ac. Brussels. *Société d'Archéologie.* Annales. tom 6.
Ac. 5519.

AVIGNON. DUHAMEL (L.) Les Exécutions capitales à Avignon au XVIII° siècle. pp. 71. *Avignon,* 1890. 8°. 5423. g. 2. (3.)
—— Documents sur la réunion d'Avignon à la France, 1790-91. pp. 129. *Paris,* 1891. 8°.
9226. c. 24.
SAINT-JUST (C.) Esquisse de la Révolution d'Avignon. pp. 157. *Paris,* 1890. 8°.
9226. bbb. 20.
CLÉMENT (E.) Le Monastère-Collège de Saint-Martial. pp. 354. *Avignon,* 1893. 8°. 4630. de. 1.
DUHAMEL (L.) Les origines de l'imprimerie à Avignon. pp. 15. *Avignon,* 1890. 8°.
011900. ee. 6. (6.)
REQUIN ( ) Origines de l'imprimerie en France. Avignon 1444. pp. 15. *Paris,* 1891. 8°.
011902. m. 19. (9.)
See also CHURCH HISTORY, *Papacy :* COMTAT VENAISSIN.

AVIOTH. SCHANDEL (L.) Histoire d'Avioth. pp. 240. 1891. 8°. Ac. etc. Bar-le-Duc. *Société des Lettres.* Sér. 2. tom. 10. Ac. 271.

AVON, *Seine et Marne.* GROUCHY (E. H. de) *Viscount.* Extraits des Registres d'Avon, etc. pp. 14. *Fontainebleau,* 1890. 8°. Pam. 26.

AVON, *River, Warwickshire.*
QUILLER-COUCH (A. T.) The Warwickshire Avon. pp. 144. *Lond.* 1892. 8°. 10351. d. 38.

AVRANCHES. PIGEON (E. A.) Le Diocèse d'Avranches. pp. 714. 1887-88. 8°. Ac. Coutances. *Société Académique.* Mémoires. Ac. 313.
—— Texte des vies des Saints du diocèse de Coutances et Avranches.
Avranches, 1892, *etc.* 8°. 4829. b.
MENARD ( ) Un Chapitre de l'histoire de la Terreur à Avranches. pp. 44.
Avranches, 1894. 8°. Pam. 28.

AYLESBURY. CRANAGE (D. H. S.) St. Mary's, Aylesbury. pp. 20. *Aylesbury,* 1893. 8°.
7807. e. 30. (13.)
FOWLER (J. K.) Echoes of old Country Life. *Lond.* 1892. 4°. 12352. g. 31.

AYRSHIRE. SMITH (J.) Prehistoric Man in Ayrshire. pp. 248. *Lond.* 1895. 8°.
07708. g. 43.
ROBERTSON (W.) Historic Ayrshire. *Edinb.* 1891, *etc.* 8°. 010370. g. 1.
LAWSON (R.) The Covenanters of Ayrshire. pp. 76. *Paisley,* 1887. 8°. 9509. e. 21.
AINSLIE (H.) Pilgrimage to the land of Burns. pp. 367. *Paisley,* 1892. 8°. 12272. f. 15.
MACINTOSH (J.) Ayrshire Nights' Entertainments. pp. 400. *Kilmarnock,* 1894. 8°.
10369. ccc. 28.

AZORES. ALMEIDA (G.) Os Açores e a industria piscatoria. pp. 28. *S. Miguel,* 1893. 8°.
08226. k. 5. (4.)
PEREIRA (J. M.) Recordações dos Açores. 1893. 8°. Ac. Lisbon. *Sociedade de Geographia.* Boletim, *etc.* ser. 12. no. 7, 8. Ac. 6020.

AZTEC RACE. *See* MEXICO, *Antiquities.*

BAALBEC. FRAUBERGER (H.) Die Akropolis von Baalbek. pp. 14. *Frankf.* 1892. fol.
1706. c. 14. *See also* PALESTINE AND SYRIA.

BABENBERG, Counts of. JURITSCH (G.) Geschichte der Babenberger, 976-1246. pp. 724. *Innsbruck,* 1894. 8°. 9906. c. 12.

BABL. *See* PERSIA, *History.*

BABYLONIA. *See* ASSYRIA.

BACCARAT, Game. DISQUE, *pseud.* Baccarat. pp. 23. *Lond.* 1891. 16°. 7915. de. 2.
HOFFMANN (L.) Baccarat, Fair and Foul. pp. 119. *Lond.* 1891. 8°. 7913. ccc. 12.
LAUN ( ) Traité du Baccarat. pp. 64. *Paris,* 1892. 8°. 7913. e. 16.
See also CARDS.

BACCARAT, Meurthe et Moselle.
Deneuvre et Baccarat. pp. 296. *Nancy,* 1895. 8°.
10174. f. 24.

BACHARACH. THEILE (C.) Bilder aus der Chronik Bacharachs. pp. 152.
Gotha, 1891. 8°. 10255. f. 18.

BACON - SHAKSPERE CONTRO- VERSY. BACON (F.) *Viscount St. Albans.* Did Bacon write "Shakespeare"? By Mrs. H. Pott. *Lond.* 1893. 8°. 11764. c. 16.
BORMANN (E.) Das Shakespeare-Geheimniss. pp. 343. *Leipz.* 1894. 8°. 11766. l. 13.
—— The Shakespeare-Secret. pp. 278. *Lond.* 1895. 8°. 11766. i. 43.
—— Der Anekdotenschatz Bacon-Shakespeare's. pp. 121. *Leipz.* 1895. 8°. 11764. h. 22.
—— Der Fischer. Auch ein Beitrag zur Bacon-Shakespeare-Frage. *Leipz.* 1895. 8°. Pam. 80.
DIXON (T. S. E.) F. Bacon and his Shakespeare. pp. 461. *Lond.* 1895. 8°. 11764. cc. 25.
HALL (R.) Who wrote Shakespeare? pp. 17. *Manch.* 1892. 8°. Pam. 80.
JAMES (G.) F. Bacon the Author of Shakespeare. pp. 105. *Birmingham,* 1893. 8°.
011765. f. 2.
LENTZNER (C.) Zur Shakespeare-Bacon-Theorie. pp. 48. *Halle,* 1890. 8°. Pam. 80.
LONDON. *Bacon Society.* Baconiana. N. S. *Lond.* 1893, *etc.* 8°. P.P. 5942.
LOOSEN (O.) Shakespeare-Bacon. pp. 41. *Gent.* 1893. 8°. Pam. 80.
OWEN (O. W.) Sir F. Bacon's Cipher Story. *Lond.* 1894, *etc.* 8°. 011652. m. 1.
P.P. *London.* Baconiana. *Lond.* 1893, *etc.* 8°.
P.P. 5942.
POTT (*Mrs.* H.) F. Bacon and his Secret Society. pp. 421. *Lond.* 1891. 8°. 11763. df. 39.
RAYNAL (L. de) Shakspeare et Bacon. pp. 30. *Paris,* 1888. 8°. 11766. cc. 14. (7.)
REED (E.) Brief for Plaintiff. Bacon vs. Shakespeare. pp. 76.
Chicago, 1891. 8°. 11763. df. 33.
ROE (J. E.) The Mortal Moon, or, Bacon and his masks. pp. 605. *N.Y.* 1891. 8°.
11763. df. 43.
SCHAIBLE (C. H.) Shakespeare der Autor seiner Dramen. pp. 92. *Heidelberg,* 1889. 8°.
11765. bbb. 47. (9.)
SCHIPPER (L.) Shakespeare und dessen Gegner. pp. 64. *Münster i. W.,* 1895. 8°. 011765. h. 4.
THORPE (W. G.) Middle-Temple table-talk. pp. 336. *Lond.* 1894. 8°. 12354. i. 37.
WIGSTON (W. F. C.) The Columbus of Literature. pp. 217. *Chicago,* 1892. 8°. 011850. k. 4.
—— Discoveries in the Bacon Problem. pp. 14. *Edinb.* 1890. 8°. Pam. 80.

BACTERIOLOGY. General.
ABBOTT (A. C.) Principles of Bacteriology. pp. 263. *Lond.* 1892. 12°. 7561. d. 5.
ALTMANN (R.) Die Elementarorganismen und ihre Beziehungen zu den Zellen. pp. 145. *Leipz.* 1890. 8°. 7407. g. 10.

BACTERIOLOGY.—General—_continued._

ARLOING (S.) Les Virus. pp. 380.
Paris, 1891. 8°.   8708. cc.

BABES (V.) Address on the position of the State
in respect to Bacteriological Research. pp. 15.
Lond. 1894. 8°.   7306. e. 22. (10.)

BASTIN (A.) Contribution à l'étude du pouvoir
bactéricide du sang. pp. 34. _Lierre,_ 1892. 4°.
         7306. k. 20. (4.)

BAUMGARTEN (P.) Arbeiten auf dem Gebiete
der Anatomie und Bacteriologie.
Braunschweig, 1891. _etc._ 8°.   7441. d.

BERGONZINI (C.) I Micrococchi. 1889. 4°.
Ac. Modena. _R. Accademia._ Memorie. Ser. 2.
vol. 8.   Ac. 92.

BEYERINCK (W.) La biologie d'une bactérie pig-
mentaire. 1891. 8°. Ac. Haarlem. _Maat-
schappij der Wetenschappen._ Archives néerlandaises, tom. 25. livr. 3 & 4.   Ac. 2953.

BLACK (D. C.) Address on the germ-theory of
disease. _Glasg._ 1891. 8°.   07305. e. 23. (9.)

BOUCHARD (C.) Les Microbes pathogènes.
pp. 304. _Paris,_ 1892. 8°.   7560. de. 19.

BOYCE (R.) Methods employed in bacteriological
research, _etc._ 1893. 8°. KENWOOD (H. R.)
Public Laboratory Work.   7482. a.

CORNIL (A. V.) and BABES (V.) Les Bactéries.
2 tom. _Paris,_ 1890. 8°.   7561. i. 33.

CROOKSHANK (E. M.) Manual of Bacteriology.
pp. 460. _Lond._ 1890. 8°.   2255. e. 5.

DE BARY (A.) Comparative morphology and
biology of the Bacteria. pp. 525. _Oxf._ 1887. 8°.
         2252. f. 2.

EBERTH (C. J.) Bacteriologische Wandtafeln.
Berl. 1891, _etc._ fol.   Tab. 11747. b. (28.)

EISENBERG (J.) Bakteriologische Diagnostik.
pp. 508. _Hamb._ 1891. 8°.   7561. i. 36.

—— Bacteriological Diagnosis. pp. 184.
Philad. 1892. 8°.   7560. dd. 7.

FERMI (C.) and MONTESANO (G.) Sull' inversione
del saccarosio da parte dei microbii. 1894. 8°.
Annali dell' Istituto d'igiene sperimentale. N.S.
vol. 4.   Ac. 104. b.

FISCHER (B.) and BREBECK (C.) Zur Morphologie
der Kahmpilze. pp. 52. _Jena,_ 1894. 4°.
         7620. e. 25.

FRAENKEL (C.) Grundriss der Bakterienkunde.
pp. 515. _Berl._ 1890. 8°.   7561. i. 35.

FRAENKEL (C.) and PFEIFFER (R.) Mikrophotographischer Atlas der Bakterienkunde.
Berl. 1889–92. 8°.   7560. i. 2.

FRANKLAND (P. F.) Our secret Friends and
Foes. pp. 167. 1893. 8°. Romance of Science
Series.   4121. de.

GRIFFITHS (A. B.) Manual of Bacteriology.
pp. 348. 1893. 8°. Heinemann's Scientific
Handbooks.   8708. f.

—— Researches on Micro-Organisms. pp. 360.
Lond. 1891. 8°.   7561. de. 16.

GUENTHER (C.) Einführung in das Studium der
Bakteriologie. pp. 274. _Leipz._ 1891. 8°.
         7560. dd. 8.

HEIM (L.) Lehrbuch der bakteriologischen Untersuchung. pp. 528. _Stuttgart,_ 1894. 8°.
         7561. i. 41.

ITZEROTT (G.) and NIEMANN (F.) Mikrophotographischer Atlas der Bakterienkunde. pp. 115.
Leipz. 1895. 8°.   7560. i. 19.

KAIKHUSRAU NASARVÂNJÎ BAHÂDURJÎ. The Shib-
boleth of Germ Theory. pp. 36.
Bombay, 1893. 8°.   Pam. 39.

KANTHACK (A. A.) and DRYSDALE (J. H.) Course
of elementary practical Bacteriology. pp. 181.
Lond. 1895. 8°.   7561. aa. 17.

BACTERIOLOGY.—General—_continued._

KITT (T.) Bacterienkunde und pathologische
Mikroskopie. pp. 450. _Wien,_ 1893. 8°.
         7560. d. 3.

KLEIN (L.) and MIGULA (W.) Arbeiten aus dem
Bacteriologischen Institut der Technischen
Hochschule zu Karlsruhe.
Karlsruhe, 1894, _etc._ 8°.   7560. dd.

KLEMPERER (F.) and LEVY (E.) Grundriss der
klinischen Bakteriologie. pp. 340.
Berl. 1894. 8°.   7560. aa. 20.

KRAMER (E.) Die Bakteriologie in ihren Beziehungen zur Landwirtschaft.
Wien, 1890, _etc._ 8°.   7299. h. 7.

LOIR (A.) La Microbiologie en Australie.
pp. 86. _Paris,_ 1892. 4°.   7383. ddd. 1. (6.)

MACÉ (E.) Traité de Bactériologie. pp. 740.
Paris, 1891. 8°.   7561. k. 7.

MIGULA (W.) Die Bakterien. pp. 216.
Leipz. 1891. 8°.   7561. de. 18.

—— Bacteriologisches Practicum. pp. 200.
Karlsruhe, 1892. 8°.   7298. b. 14.

—— Introduction to practical Bacteriology.
pp. 247. _Lond._ 1893. 8°.   7298. b. 15.

MAGNIN (A.) Les Bactéries. _Paris,_ 1878. 8°.
         7561. k. 2.

NIELSEN (H. A.) Om Bakterierne i Drikkevand.
pp. 143. _Kjøbenhavn,_ 1890. 8°.   8777. g. 2.

NOLEN (W.) Bacteriologie en geneeskunde.
pp. 40. _Rotterdam,_ 1891. 8°.   07305. h. 9. (8.)

NOVY (F. G.) Directions for Laboratory Work
in Bacteriology. pp. 209. _Ann Arbor,_ 1894. 8°.
         7561. c. 1.

P.P. _Edinburgh._ Journal of Pathology and Bacteriology. _Edinb._ 1892, _etc._ 8°.   P.P. 3295. b.

PFEFFER (W.) Über chemotaktische Bewegungen
von Bacterien. 1888. 8°. Ac. Tubingen.
Botanishes Institut. Untersuchungen. Bd. 2.
         Ac. 3260.

PITTION (C. P.) La Photographie appliquée à
l'étude des microbes. pp. 47. _Lyon,_ 1890. 8°.
         8909. cc. 12.

RODET (A.) De la variabilité dans les microbes.
1895. 8°. Ac. Lyons. _Académie des Sciences._
Mémoires. Sér. 3. Tom. 3.   Ac. 364/5.

RUSSELL (H. L.) Bacteria in their relation to
vegetable tissue. pp. 41. _Baltimore,_ 1892. 8°.
         7054. h. 22.

SARLES (E.) Contribution à l'étude des Pto-
maïnes. pp. 47. _Montpellier,_ 1891. 8°.
         07305. k. 11. (5.)

SATTERTHWAITE (T. E.) Introduction to Bacteriology, _etc._ pp. 85. _Detroit,_ 1887. 16°.
         7561. bb. 14.

SCHENK (S. L.) Gundriss der Bakteriologie.
pp. 204. _Wein,_ 1893. 8°.   7560. d. 1.

—— Manual of Bacteriology. pp. 310.
Lond. 1893. 8°.   7560. aaa. 5.

SO. So kann es nicht weiter gehen. pp. 52.
Berl. 1891. 8°.   07305. h. 10. (5.)

SQUIRE (P. W.) Methods used in the preparation
of animal and vegetable Tissues for Microscopical Examination, _etc._ pp. 93.
Lond. 1892. 8°.   8706. aa. 32.

STERNBERG (G. M.) Manual of Bacteriology.
pp. 886. _New York,_ 1893. 8°.   7561. dd. 28.

VINOGRADSKY (S.) Beiträge zur Morphologie
der Bacterien. _Leipz._ 1888, _etc._ 8°.   7561. i. 21.

WHEELER (A.) Our Unseen Foes. pp. 84.
Bristol, 1891. 8°.   7561. de. 17.

WINDRATH (A.) Die Medicin unter der Herrschaft des bacteriologischen Systems. pp. 231.
Bonn, 1895. 8°.   07561. k. 1.

BACTERIOLOGY.—General—continued.

WOODHEAD (G. S.) Bacteria and their products. pp. 459. 1891. 8°. Contemporary Science Series.   8709. i.

WURTZ (R.) Technique bactériologique. pp. 192. 1892. 8°. Encyclopédie des aide-mémoire.   7560. de. 17.

—— Précis de Bactériologie clinique. pp. 492. *Paris*, 1895. 8°.   7561. a. 33.

FREUDENREICH (E. de) Les Microbes et leur Rôle dans la Laiterie. pp. 118. *Paris*, 1894. 8°.   7560. de. 22.

—— Dairy Bacteriology. pp. 115. *Lond.* 1895. 8°.   7560. de. 23.

JÖRGENSEN (A.) Die Mikro-organismen der Gärungsindustrie. pp. 230. *Berl.* 1892. 8°.   7298. ee. 25.

—— Micro-Organisms and Fermentation. pp. 257. *Lond.* 1893. 8°.   7299. e. 6.

KOCH (A.) Jahresbericht über die Fortschritte in der Lehre von den Gährungs-Organismen. *Braunschweig*, 1891, *etc.* 8°.   7299. f.

DESPEIGNES (V.) Étude sur les microbes des eaux. pp. 126. *Paris*, 1891. 8°. 07305. k. 10. (2.)

FISCHER (B.) Die Bakterien des Meeres. pp. 82. 1894. 4°. HENSEN (V.) Ergebnisse der Plankton-Expedition. Bd. 4.   1826. b.

FRANKLAND (P. F.) Micro-organisms in Water. pp. 532. *Lond.* 1894. 8°.   8777. g. 10.

LUSTIG (A.) Diagnostica dei batteri delle acque. pp. 121. *Torino*, 1890. 8°.   7299. f. 14.

MIQUEL (P.) Manuel d'analyse bactériologique des eaux. pp. 194. *Paris*, 1891. 12°.   8777. aaa. 25.

SALAZAR (A. E.) Examen bacteriológico de las aguas potables. pp. 513. *Londres*, 1890. 8°.   8777. cc. 28.

Various Diseases and Organs.

CUNNINGHAM (D. D.) Some species of Choleraic Comma Bacilli. 1891. 4°. P.P.   *Calcutta*. Scientific memoirs. pt. 6.   7306. h.

KOCH (R.) Professor Koch on the bacteriological Diagnosis of Cholera. pp. 150. *Edinb.* 1894. 8°.   7561. k. 22.

WALL (A. J.) Koch's Komma-Bacillus ist nicht Ursache der Cholera. pp. 32. *Hamb.* 1894. 8°.   Pam. 39.

PETRI (R. J.) Der Cholerakurs im K. Gesundheitsamte. pp. 259. *Berl.* 1893. 8°. 7560. g. 23.

—— Untersuchungen über die durch das Wachsthum der Cholerabakterien enstehenden chemischen Umsetzungen. 1890. 8°. GERMANY. *Kaiserliches Gesundheitsamt.* Arbeiten. Bd. 6.   7440. h.

EBERTH (C. J.) Die Untersuchung des Auswurfs auf Tuberkelbacillen. pp. 32. *Berl.* 1891. 8°.   Pam. 39.

STRAUS (I.) La Tuberculose et son bacille. pp. 884. *Paris*, 1895. 8°.   7615. g. 5.

BOURGES (H.) Les Angines de la scarlatine. pp. 111. *Paris*, 1891. 8°.   7561. f. 5.

SENN (N.) Bactériologie chirurgicale. pp. 318. *Paris*, 1890. 8°.   7560. i. 4.

DAVID (T.) Les Microbes de la bouche. pp. 302. *Paris*, 1890. 8°.   7560. i. 5.

VIGNAL (W.) Recherches sur les micro-organismes de la bouche. 1887. 8°. Ac. Paris. *École des hautes études.* Laboratoire d'histologie. Travaux, *etc.*   Ac. 8929/3.

MILLER (W. D.) Einleitung zum Studium der Bacterio-Pathologie der Zahnpulpa. 1894. 8°. Ac. Berlin. *Odontologische Gesellschaft.* Verhandlungen. Bd. 6.   Ac. 3774.

BACTERIOLOGY. — Various Diseases and Organs—continued.

IDE (M.) Anaérobiose du bacille commun de l'intestin. 1891. 8°. CARNOY (J. B.) La Cellule. tom. 7. fasc. 2.   7421. i.

SCRUEL (V) Contribution à l'étude de la fermentation du bacile de l'intestin. 1891. 8°. CARNOY (J. B.) La Cellule. tom. 7. fasc. 1.   7421. i.

SCHMIDT (M. B.) Die Pyelonephritis in anatomischer und bakteriologischer Beziehung. pp. 101. *Jena*, 1893. 8°.   7560. i. 17.

BADEN, *Grand Duchy.* ECK (H.) Verzeichniss der Literatur von Baden. 2 pt. 1890. 8°. Ac. Heidelberg. *Badische Geologische Landesanstalt.* Mitteilungen. Bd. 1.   Ac. 3141.

Ac. Carlsruhe. *Historische Commission.* Regesten der Markgrafen von Baden 1050–1515. *Innsbruck*, 1892, *etc.* 4°.   Ac. 7066/6.

NEFF (W.) Ludwig Wilhelm, Markgraf von Baden. pp. 48. *Berl.* 1892. 8°.   Pam. 8.

GUNTERMANN (A.) Mit Badens Wehr für deutsche Ehr. *Freiburg*, 1895, *etc.* 8°. 9335. bb.

MAAS (H.) Geschichte der katholischen Kirche in Baden. pp. 692. *Freiburg*, 1891. 8°.   4662. e. **12.**

BASSERMANN (H.) Geschichte der evangelischen Gottesdienstordnung in badischen Landen. pp. 259. *Stuttg.* 1891. 8°.   3476. f. 10.

BEHAGHEL (W.) Das badische bürgerliche Recht und der Code Napoléon. *Tauberbischofsheim*, 1891, *etc.* 8°. 05604. h. 20.

BARAZETTI (C.) Das Personenrecht mit Ausschluss des Familienrechts. pp. 432. *Karlsruhe*, 1893. 8°.   5604. aa. **1.**

Ac. Carlsruhe. *Historische Kommission.* KRIEGER (A.) Topographisches Wörterbuch des Grossherzogtums Baden. *Heidelberg*, 1893, *etc.* 8°.   Ac. 7066/7.

BADEN. Baden in geographischer, geschichtlicher und staatlicher Hinsicht dargestellt. 2 pt. *Karlsruhe*, 1885. 8°.   10261. h. 16.

See also BLACK FOREST : BREISGAU : CARLSRUHE : GERMANY.

BADEN-BADEN. LOESER (J.) Geschichte der Stadt Baden. pp. 571. *Baden*, 1891. 8°.   10230. ee. 10.

BAHAMAS. AGASSIZ (A.) Reconnaissance off the Bahamas. pp. 203. 1894. 8°. Ac. Cambridge. *Harvard University. Museum of Comparative Zoology.* Bulletin, vol. 26. no. 1.   Ac. 1736/2.

MANRIQUE (A. M.) Investigaciones sobre el derrotero de Cristóbal Colón por los Bahamas. pp. 228. *Arrecife*, 1890. 8°.   9551. i. 11.

See also WEST INDIES.

BAKARGANJ.

SAURĪNDRAMOHANA THĀKURA. History of Bakarganj. pp. 12. *Calcutta*, 1892. 8°.   Pam. 88.

BALBRONN. KIEFER (L. A.) Geschichte der Gemeinde Balbronn. pp. 360. *Strassb.* 1894. 8°.   10255. h. 8.

BALEARIC ISLES. CARTAILHAC (É.) Monuments des Iles Baléares. 2 pt. *Toulouse*, 1892. 4°.   7708. f. 37.

LECOY DE LA MARCHE (A.) Les relations de la France avec le royaume de Majorque. 2 tom. *Paris*, 1892. 8°.   9072. g. 10.

PEÑA (P. de A.) Guía de las Islas Baleares. pp. 480. *Palma*. 1891. 8°.   10161. a. 2.

PIFERRER (P.) Islas Baleares. pp. 1423. 1888–91. 8°. SPAIN. España.   2060. c.

VUILLIER (G.) Les Iles Oubliées. pp. 503. *Paris*, 1893. 4°.   K.T.C. 1. b. 11.

BALKAN MOUNTAINS AND PEN-INSULA. CAMBON (V.) Autour des Balkans. pp. 345.
Paris, 1890. 8°.   10126. aa. 20.
FRESNEAUX (M.) L'Orient. Chrétiens des Balkans. pp. 306.
Paris, 1892. 12°.   10125. aa. 19.
G * * * Le Raid du général Gourko dans les Balkans. pp. 23. *Paris,* 1890. 8°.
                                       9072. cc. 4. (17.)
HAMARD (P. J.) Par delà l'Adriatique et les Balkans. pp. 402. *Paris,* 1890. 8°.
                                       10125. ee. 29.
KALBERMATTEN (L. v.) Sumpfleben und Jagden. pp. 180. *Wien,* 1891. 8°.   10105. ee. 9.
MILLET (R.) Souvenirs des Balkans. pp. 401.
Paris, 1891. 8°.   10125. aa. 16.
SCARFOGLIO (E.) In Levante e a traverso i Balkani. pp. 245. *Milano,* 1890. 8°.
                                       10126. aa. 21.
TOULA (F.) Geologische Untersuchungen in östlichen Balkan. 189°. fol. Ac. Vienna. *Akademie der Wissenschaften.* Denkschriften. Mathemat. naturwissenschaftl. Classe. Bd. 57.
                                       Ac. 810/13.

BALKAN STATES.
See BOSNIA : BULGARIA : HERZEGOVINA : MONTENEGRO : ROUMANIA : SERVIA.

BALLADS AND SONGS. *See also* POETRY.

General.
MARTINENGO - CESARESCO (E.) *Countess.* La Poésie populaire. pp. 81. 1893. 8°. BLÉMONT (E.) Collection de la Tradition. vol 11.
                                       12430. aaa. 47.
STRETTELL, afterwards HARRISON (A.) Lullabies of Many Lands. pp. 127. *Lond.* 1894. 4°.
                                       11601. g. 25.
WILLIAMS (A. M.) Studies in Folk-Song.
pp. 329. *Bost.* 1894. 8°.   011850. eee. 32.

Albania.
GRAZIA (D. de) I Canti Popolari Albanesi.
pp. 20. *Noto,* 1889. 8°.   011824. f. 30. (6.)

Arabs. *See infra :* ORIENTAL.

Austria-Hungary.
HUNGARIAN POPULAR SONGS. Ungarische Volkslieder. pp. 39.
Wien, 1892. 8°.   011586. de. 103.
PANHOLZER (J.) Österreich über alles, oder Erklärung der österreichischen Volkshymme. pp. 228. *Wien,* 1890. 8°.   011824. h. 9.
SCHOSSER (A.) Bilder aus dem Natur—und Volksleben der oberösterreichischen Alpen von A. Schosser. pp. 103. *Linz,* 1889. 8°.
                                       M. C. 601.

Brazil.
BRAZILIAN TROUBADOUR. Album do Trovador Brazileiro. pp. 107. *Rio de J.* 1891. 8°.
                                       11452. aaaa. 42.
ROMÉRO (S.) Estudios sobre a poesia popular do Brazil. pp. 368. *Rio de J.* 1888. 8°.
                                       11851. c. 43.

Brittany.
LUZEL (F. M.) Chansons populaires de la Basse-Bretagne. 2 tom.
Paris, 1890. 8°.   11498. dd. 23.
QUELLIEN (N.) Chansons des Bretons. pp. 300
Paris, 1889. 8°.   11595. k. 5.

Bulgaria.
BULGARIAN POPULAR SONGS. Bulgarische Volksdichtungen. pp. 518. *Wien,* 1895. 8°.
                                       011586. g. 59.

BALLADS.—Bulgaria—*continued.*
MILLIEN (A.) Ballades tchèques et bulgares.
pp. 117. *Paris,* 1894. 8°.   11586. cc. 33.

Canada.
CANADIAN SONGS. Raise the flag, and other patriotic songs. pp. 63. *Toronto,* 1891. 8°.
                                       11687. ccc. 41.

Denmark and Sweden.
STEENSTRUP (J. C. H. R.) Vore Folkeviser fra Middelalderen. pp. 329. *Kjøbenhavn,* 1891. 8°.
                                       011824. f. 33.
VISEBOG. Den nyeste Visebog for Hvermand.
pp. 320. *Kristiania,* 1889. 16°. 11565. de. 32.

England.
STAINER (*Sir* J.) Catalogue of English Song Books. pp. 107. *Lond.* 1891. 8°. 11899. h. 42.
ASHTON (J.) Real Sailor-Songs. ff. 97.
Lond. 1891. fol.   11602. i. 9.
BALLADS. Favourite Ballads. *Lond.* 1891. 4.
                                       11601. g. 23.
BOOK. Book of Old Ballads. *Lond.* 1892. fol.
                                       1869 c. 39.
BULLEN (A. H.) Lyrics from the Song books of the Elizabethan age. pp. 233. *Lond.* 1891. 8°.
                                       11601. d. 17.
CHAPPELL (W.) Old English Popular Music. 2 vol. *Lond.* 1893. 8°.   2031. f.
FARMER (J.) Gaudeamus : a selection of songs. *Lond.* 1891. 16°.   11601. a. 42.
GUMMERE (F. R.) Old English Ballads. pp. 380.
Bost. 1894. 8°.   11601. d. 30.
HOLROYD (A.) Collection of Yorkshire Ballads. pp. 318. *Lond.* 1892. 8°.   11603. bbb. 36.
LAING (D.) Popular poetry of Scotland and the Northern Border. 2 vol. *Lond.* 1895. 8°.
                                       2292. h. 2.
LANG (A.) Border Ballads. pp. 87.
Lond. 1895 4°.   K. T. C. 30. b. 2.
MAIDMENT (J.) New Book of old Ballads.
pp. 57. 1885. 8°. GOLDSMID (E. M.) Bibliotheca Curiosa.   012202. de. 14.
MORICE (W. J.) Selected English Ballads.
pp. 64. *Lond.* 1891. 8°.   11603. ccc. 14.
MORLEY (H.) A Bundle of Ballads. pp. 196.
1891. 8°. Companion Poets. no. 2. 11622. e.
NORTHALL (G. F.) English Folk-Rhymes.
pp. 565. *Lond.* 1892. 8°.   12431. ee. 14.
PERCY (T.) *Bishop of Dromore.* Reliques. Edited by H. B. Wheatley. 3 vol. *Lond.* 1891. 8°.
                                       11621. f. 37.
—— Reliques. Edited by R. A. Willmott.
pp. 610. *Lond.* 1893. 8°.   11621. f. 38.
RITSON (J.) Northern Garlands. 4 pt.
Edinb. 1887, 88. 8°.   11602. f. 29.
SALT (H. S.) Songs of Freedom. pp. 345.
1893, etc. 8°. The Canterbury Poets, *etc.*
                                       11604. aaaa.
SMITH (G. B.) Illustrated British Ballads : old and new. *Lond.* 1895, etc. 8°. 11602. gg. 33.
WITHERS (H. L.) Selected English Ballads.
2 pt. 1891. 8°. GLAZEBROOK (M. G.) English Classics for Schools. Grade 1.   12204. aaa.
WRIGHT (T.) Political Songs of England, from the reign of John to Edward II. 4 vol.
1884. 8°. GOLDSMID (E. M.) Bibliotheca Curiosa.   012202. de. 7.

COLE (E. W.) Thousand Best Songs in the World. pp. 381. *Lond.* 1892. 8°. 11601. dd. 4.
—— Second Series. pp. 381. *Lond.* 1892, 93. 8°.
                                       11601. dd. 4.

BALLADS.—England—*continued.*

DEENAH DINAH DO SONGSTER. Deenah Dinah Do Songster. *Lond.* 1895. 8°.　　Pam. 58.

LABOUR CHURCH HYMN BOOK. Labour Church Hymn Book. pp. 32. *Lond.* 1895. 8°.
　　11601. bb. 23.

LYRIC SONGSTER. The Lyric Songster. *Lond.* 1892. 8°.　　11601. dd. 13. (2.)

MISTLETOE SONGSTER. The Mistletoe Songster. *Lond.* 1891. 8°.　　11601. dd. 13. (1.)

MOGUL SONGSTER. The Mogul Songster. *Lond.* 1892. 8°.　　11601. dd. 13. (3.)

MOHAWK MINSTRELS. Mohawk Minstrels' Songs. pp. 170. *Lond.* 1891. 8°.　　11686. e. 47.

MUSIC HALL SONGSTER. Music Hall Songster. *Lond.* 1893. 8°.　　11601. dd. 13. (5.)

OXFORD SONGSTER. The Oxford Songster. *Lond.* 1893. 8°.　　11601. dd. 13. (6.)

PARAGON SONGSTER. The Paragon Songster. *Lond.* 1893. 8°.　　11601. dd. 13. (7.)

SOCIALISTS. Songs for Socialists. pp. 40. *Aberd.* 1890. 16°.　　08276. de. 8. (5.)

SONG BOOK. Songbook for Socialists. pp. 34. *Lond.* 1893. 16°.　　Pam. 82.

STANDARD SONGSTER. Standard Songster. *Lond.* 1894. 8°.　　11601. d. 27. (8.)

TA-RA-RA-BOOM-DE-E SONGSTER. Ta-Ra-Ra-Boom-de-E Songster. *Lond.* 1893. 8°.
　　11601. dd. 13. (8.)

WAGNER (L.) Diprose's Modern Song Book. pp. 128. *Lond.* 1894. 8°.　　11601. dd. 22.

See also POETRY.

France.

AC. PARIS. *Société des anciens Textes.* Le Chansonnier de Saint-Germain-des-Prés. *Paris,* 1892, etc. 8°.　　Ac. 9811/33.

BEAUQUIER (C.) Chansons populaires recueillies en Franche-Comté. pp. 388. *Paris,* 1894. 8°.
　　M.D. 350.

FOURIER DE BACOURT (E.) *Count.* Anciens chants du Barrois. 1894. 8°. Ac. Nancy. *Société d'Archéologie.* Mémoires. tom. 44.　Ac. 5314.

HAUSER (H.) La Poésie populaire au XVI° siècle. pp. 26. *Clermont-Ferrand,* 1894. 8°.
　　11840. i. 47. (3.)

LEYMARIE (C.) Quelques mots sur les chansons du Limousin. pp. 31. *Limoges,* 1890. 8°.
　　011850. g. 8. (1.)

PATARD (V.) La vérité dans la question à propos du Vau-de-Vire. pp. 136. *Paris,* 1891. 12°.
　　011824. e. 20.

REIBER (F.) Le Centenaire de la Marseillaise. pp. 22. *Strasbourg,* 1892. 8°.　011850. f. 9. (9.)

BLONDIN (J. A.) Nouveau recueil de chansons comiques. pp. 200. *Montréal,* 1890. 8°.
　　11483. b. 58.

MARION DUMERSAN (T.) Chants populaires de la France. 4 vol. *Paris,* 1890. 8°.　11481. m. 1.

SARREPONT (H. de) Chants militaires de la France. pp. 228. *Paris,* 1893. 12°. 011850. f. 11.

See also supra : BRITTANY: POETRY.

Germany.

BOEHME (F. M.) Volksthümliche Lieder im 18. und 19. Jahrhundert. *Leipz.* 1895, etc. 8°.
　　M.E. 815.

BRUEMMER (F.) Deutschlands Helden in der deutschen Dichtung. pp. 428. *Stuttgart,* 1891. 8°.　　11521. g. 16.

BUCHHEIM (C. A.) Balladen und Romanzen. pp. 318. *Lond.* 1891. 8°.　11527. ccc. 51.

BALLADS.—Germany—*continued.*

CRAIGMYLE (B.) German Ballads. pp. 287. 1892. 8°. Canterbury Poets.　　11604. aaa.

ERK (L.) Deutscher Liederhort. 3 Bde. *Leipzig,* 1893, 94. 8°.　　M.F. 592. a.

FREYTAG (E. R.) Historische Volkslieder des sächsischen Heeres. pp. 172. *Dresden,* 1892. 8°.
　　11527. ccc. 75.

FRISCHBIER (H.) Hundert ostpreussische Volkslieder. pp. 152. *Leipz.* 1893. 8°. 11527. f. 42.

GOLDSCHMIDT (J.) Die deutsche Ballad. pp. 44. *Leipz.* 1893. 4°.　　11825. k. 7. (6.)

HONEGGER (J. J.) Das deutsche Lied der Neuzeit. pp. 299. *Leipz.* 1891. 8°. 011824. e. 27.

HONSEL (F.) Studenten-Poesie im Mittelalter. pp. 67. *Bielefeld,* 1894. 8°. 011850. eee. 57. (4.)

KONT (J.) Balladenbuch. pp. 243. *Paris,* 1891. 12°.　　11517. cc. 35.

LEIMBACH (C. L.) Zur Einführung in das deutsche Volkslied. pp. 277. *Bremen,* 1890. 8°.
　　011824. de. 14.

NEUMANN (L.) Die Volksdichte in Baden. pp. 172. 1892. 8°. LEHMANN (R.) Forschungen zur deutschen Landes- und Volkskunde. Bd. 7.
　　10235. i. 10.

TILLE (A.) Die deutschen Volkslieder vom Doktor Faust. pp. 207. *Halle,* 1890. 8°.
　　011840. h. 61.

TREICHEL (A.) Volkslieder aus Westpreussen. pp. 174. *Danzig,* 1895. 8°.　11528. k. 60.

VENDEL (A.) Étude sur quelques chants populaires allemands. pp. 75. *Bar-le-Duc,* 1892. 8°.
　　11525. f. 45.

WACKERNELL (J. E.) Das deutsche Volkslied. pp. 45. 1890. 8°. Sammlung wissenschaftlicher Vorträge, etc. N. F. no. 106.　12249. m.

WHITE (H. S.) Deutsche Volkslieder. pp. 324. *N. Y.* 1892. 24°.　　012202. eeee. 13.

ZIEGLER (H.) Deutsche Soldaten- und Kriegs-Lieder, 1386–1871. pp. 424. *Leipz.* 1884. 8°.
　　11528. c. 14.

Gipsies.

AXON (W. E. A.) Romany Songs Englished. pp. 3. 1890. 8°.　　Pam. 58.

WLISLOCKI (H. v.) Volksdichtungen der siebenbürgischen und südungarischen Zigeuner. pp. 431. *Wien,* 1890. 8°.　　11527. dd. 24.

Hungary. *See supra :* AUSTRIA.

Ireland.

IRELAND. Poems and Ballads of Young Ireland. pp. 80. *Dubl.* 1890. 8°.　11601. ccc. 28. (6.)

SPARLING (H. H.) Irish Minstrelsy. pp. 368. 1887. 8°. Canterbury Poets.　　11604. aa.

See also POETRY.

Italy.

CIAN (V.) Saggio di Canti popolari Logudoresi. pp. 16. *Palermo,* 1890. 8°.　　Pam. 60.

LOMBARD SONG BOOK. Il canzoniere popolare lombardo. 2 pt. *Milano.* 1891. 8°.
　　11429. ee. 25.

MARSÒN (L.) Canti politici raccolti a Vittorio. pp. 31. *Vittorio,* 1891. 8°.　　Pam. 60.

SCARPETTA (E.) Canzoni Napolitane. *Napoli,* 1890. 8°.　　11429. e. 32. (6.)

NIGRA (C.) Canti popolari del Piemonte. pp. 596. *Torino,* 1888. 8°.　　11436. i. 15.

NURRA (P.) La Poesia popolare in Sardegna. pp. 65. *Sassari,* 1893. 8°.　　Pam. 15.

BALLADS.—Italy—*continued.*

PITRÈ (G.) Canti Popolari Siciliani. 2 vo¹. *Palermo*, 1891. 8°.   11431. cc. 32.

CAPUANA (L.) La Sicilia nei canti popolari. pp. 53. *Bologna*, 1894. 12°.   011850. eee. 59.

RUGARLI (V.) Canti popolari raccolti in Fornovo di Taro. pp. 31. *Bologna*, 1893. 8°.
                                11429. h. 6. (6.)

SALANI (A.) Scelta delle canzonette amorose. pp. 128. *Firenze*, 1890. 8°.   11436. aaa. 35.

VANNI (M.) Canti del popolo Senese, 1554–1555. pp. 16. *Bagnolo*, 1890. 8°.   11429. h. 6. (3.)
See also POETRY.

Marathas. *See infra:* ORIENTAL.

Negroes. *See infra:* UNITED STATES.

Oriental.

ACWORTH (H. A.) Ballads of the Marathas. pp. 129. *Lond.* 1894. 8°.   14140. b. 25.

GARCIN DE TASSY (J. H.) Allegories et chants populaires traduits de l'arabe, du persan, de l'hindoustani et du turc. pp. 639.
† *Paris*, 1880. 8°.   752. k. 13.

STUMME (H.) Tripolitanisch-tunisische Beduinenlieder. pp. 153. *Leipz.* 1894. 8°.
                                14583. c. 11.
See also POETRY, *Arabs.*

Roumania.

VACARESCŬ (H.) Bard of the Dimbovitza. pp. 130. *Lond.* 1892. 8°.   011586. g. 47.

Scotland.

FORD (R.) The Harp of Perthshire. pp. 519. *Paisley*, 1893. 8°.   11621. f. 39.

LAING (D.) Early popular Poetry of Scotland. 2 vol. *Lond.* 1895. 8°.   2292. h. 2.

LANG (A.) Border Ballads. pp. 87. *Lond.* 1895. 8°.   K.T.C. 30. b. 2.

MACFARLANE (J.) Harp of the Scottish Covenant. pp. 341. *Lond.* 1895. 8°.   11622. ee. 12.

MAC LAREN (J. W.) Scots' Poems and Ballants. pp. 114. *Edinb.* 1892. 8°.   011653. h. 35.

MACLEAN (H.) Ultonian Hero-ballads, from 1516 till 1870. pp. 184. *Glasg.* 1892. 8°.
                                11595. c. 34.

MACQUOID (G. S.) Jacobite Songs and Ballads. pp. 534. *Lond.* 1888. 8°.   11603. ee. 21.

SCOTLAND. Ballad Minstrelsy of Scotland. pp. 656. *Paisley*, 1893. 8°.   11622. ee. 10.

SHARPE (C. K.) A Ballad Book. 2 pt. 1883. 8°. GOLDSMID (E. M.) Bibliotheca Curiosa.
                                012202. de. 5.

VEITCH (J.) History and Poetry of the Scottish Border. 2 vol. *Edinb.* 1893. 8°.   2308. c. 20.
See also POETRY.

Sicily. *See supra:* ITALY.

Slavonic.

D., A. Légendes Slaves. Recueil de chants. pp. 94. *Paris*, 1889. 8°.   011586. g. 10.

Sweden. *See supra:* DENMARK.

Ticino.

BARAGIOLA (A.) Il canto popolare a Bosco o Gurin. pp. 175. *Cividale*, 1891. 8°.
                                11528. l. 21.

United States of America.

CHAMBERLAIN (C. H.) Republican Campaign Songs. pp. 32. *Chicago*, 1892. 8°.   Pam. 58.

EGGLESTON (G. C.) American War Ballads and Lyrics. 2 pt. *N.Y.* 1895. 8°.   11687. aa. 46.

FAGAN (W. L.) Southern War Songs. pp. 389. *N.Y.* 1890. 8°.   11686. i. 9.

BALLADS.—United States—*continued.*

HARRIS (J. C.) Uncle Remus and his Friends. pp. 357. *Bost.* 1892. 8°.   12431. ee. 20.

STONE (W. L.) Ballads and Poems relating to the Burgoyne Campaign. *Albany*, 1893. 4°.
                                11687. h. 34.

Wales.

HUMPHREYS (J.) Old Welsh Knee Songs. pp. 38. *Carnarvon*, 1894. 4°.   Pam. 12.

BALLARAT. MEEK (J. M.) Past and present of Ballarat. *Ballarat*, 1893. *s. sh.* fol.
                             Tab. 11747. a. 24.

BALLINGRY. JAMIE (D.) Old Church life in Ballingry. pp. 104. *Kinross*, 1890. 8°.
                                4735. e. 23.

BALLISTICS. BASHFORTH (F.) Supplement to the experiments made with the Bashforth Chronograph. pp. 56. *Camb.* 1895. 8°.
                                8830. c. 19.

INDRA (A.) Neue ballistische Theorien. *Pola*, 1893, *etc.* 8°.   8828. ff.

OLLERO (D.) Balistica. 2 pt. *Madrid*, 1890. 8°.   8824. k. 24.

SPARRE (M. de) *Count.* Sur le mouvement des projectiles dans l'air. pp. 146. 1891. 8°. Ac. Brussels. *Société Scientifique.* Annales. Année 15.   Ac. 2958/2.

VALLIER (F. M. E.) Balistique des nouvelles poudres. pp. 180. 1894. 8°. Encyclopédie des aide-memoire.   8709. g.

—— Balistique extérieure. pp. 208. 1895. 8° Encyclopédie des aide-memoire.   8709. g.
See also GUNNERY.

BALLOONS: AERONAUTICS.

KUEHL (W. H.) Aëronautische Bibliographie. pp. 51. *Berl.* 1895. 8°.   011904. e. 1. (5.)

BERRUBÉ (É.) Plano-Aérostat, le véritable ballon dirigeable. pp. 32. *Paris*, 1894. 8°.
                                Pam. 79.

BREWER (G.) Aeronautics. pp. 160. *Lond.* 1893. 8°.   8756. cc. 39.

DELPRAT (A.) Navigation aérienne. pp. 64. *Paris*, 1892. 8°.   8756. ccc. 31. (2.)

DRONIER (P.) La Navigation aérienne. pp. 64. *Paris*, 1894. 8°.   Pam. 79.

EROS (L.) "Die Höhen der Lüfte." pp. 20. *Budapest*, 1892. 8°.   8756. ccc. 31. (3.)

FIJNJE VAN SALVERDA (J. G. W.) Aërial Navigation. pp. 209. *N.Y.* 1894. 8°. 8755. aaa. 44.

FONVIELLE (W. de) Manuel de l'aéronaute. pp. 246. *Paris*, 1894. 8°.   8758. b. 4.

GRAFFIGNY (H. de) Traité d'Aérostation. pp. 267. *Paris*, 1891. 12°.   8756. dd. 10.

LAFFAILLE (J.) Navigation aérienne. pp. 54. *Paris*, 1891. 8°.   8755. h. 46. (6.)

LYONS (E. E.) Aerial Navigation. pp. 8. *Lond.* 1893. 8°.   8756. cc. 44. (9.)

MOORE (C. J.) Keely and his discoveries. pp. 372. *Lond.* 1893. 8°.   8756. ccc. 27.

MOUILLARD (L. P.) L'Empire de l'air. pp. 284. *Paris*, 1881. 8°.   8756. c. 47.

P.P. *Boston.* The Aeronautical Annual. *Bost.* 1895, *etc.* 8°.   P.P. 1563. af.

—— *New York.* Aeronautics. *N.Y.* 1893, *etc.* 4°.
                                465.

—— *Paris.* L'Aéronaute. Anné XVIII, *etc.* *Paris*, 1885, *etc.* 8°.   P.P. 1563. ab.

—— *Paris.* L'Aérophile. *Paris*, 1893, *etc.* 8°.
                             P.P. 1563. aba.

PYNCHON (E.) High Explosives as a means of propulsion in Aerial Navigation. *N.Y.* 1894. fol.
                                Pam. 79.

BALLOONS—*continued.*

SOHNCKE (L.) Gewitterstudien auf Grund von Ballonfahrten. 1895. 4°. Ac. Munich.— *Akademie der Wissenschaften.* Abhandlungen der math.-physikal. Classe. Bd. 18. Ac. 713/4.

SOREAU (R.) Le Problème de la direction des ballons. 1893. 8°. Ac. Paris. *Société des Ingénieurs.* Mémoires. sér. 5. Ac. 4305.

STAGOPOULOS (P. J.) Météoropore. pp. 31. *Marseille,* 1891. 8°. 8756. ccc. 26. (12.)

STEIGER (C.) Vogelflug und Flugmaschine. pp. 101. *München,* 1891. 8°. 8755. f. 32.

STONAWSKI (G.) Beschreibung der Erfindung eines lenkbaren Luftschiffes. *Bielitz,* 1893. 8°. 8756. cc. 43. (12.)

—— Die Entwicklung der Luftschifffahrt. pp. 40. *Teschen,* 1893. 8°. 8756. ccc. 31. (6.)

Military.

A–Z. Die Thatsache der lenkbaren Luftschifffahrt und ihre Verwendung für Militärzwecke. pp. 15. *Leipz.* 1890. 8°. 8831. l. 10. (7.)

BÉTHUYS (G.) Les Aérostiers militaires. pp. 319. *Paris,* 1889. 8°. 8756. f. 36.

DIBOS (M.) Les Aérostats dans leur utilisation militaire. pp. 31. *Paris,* 1893. 8°. 8756. ccc. 31. (5.)

HOERNES (H.) Ueber Fesselballon-Stationen. pp. 115. *Wien,* 1892. 8°. 8824. cc, 41.

KEUCKER (A.) L'Aérostation et les pigeonniers militaires. pp. 105. *Paris,* 1884. 8°. Pam. 79.

MOEDEBECK (H.) Die Luftschifffahrt, *etc.* 2 Thle. *Leipz.* 1885, 86. 8°. 8755. i. 49.

BALMORAL. HUMPHREY (F. P.) The Queen at Balmoral. pp. 216. *Lond.* 1893. 8°. 10806. aaa. 15.

BALTA. *See* VOLAPÜK.

BALTIC CANAL. *See* NORTH SEA AND BALTIC CANAL.

BALTIC PROVINCES, of Russia.

P.P. *Reval.* Rossica und Baltica. Jahrg. 1–3. *Reval,* 1885–87. 8°. P.P. 6527. f.

BUNGE (T. v.) Der baltische Civilprocess. 2 Bde. *Reval,* 1890, 91. 8°. 5756. bbb. 23.

—— Aus dem baltischen Rechtsleben. pp. 63. *Mitau,* 1894. 8°. 5756. bbb. 27. (5.)

ENGELMANN (J.) Dorpater juristische Studien. *Dorpat,* 1893, *etc.* 8°. 5756. b.

ECK (S.) Die kirchliche Lage in den baltischen Provinzen. pp. 47. *Darmstadt,* 1891. 8° 3926. g. 37. (11.)

HANSEN (G. v.) Aus baltischer Vergangenheit. pp. 160. *Reval,* 1894. 8°. 9454. c. 24.

LÖÖRALT (W.) Baltenhetze. pp. 154. *Leipz.* 1890. 8°. 8093. c. 4.

RUSSIA. *Baltic Provinces.* Das Zerstörungswerk in den russischen Ostseeprovinzen. pp. 87. *Berl.* 1890. 8°. Pam. 74.

UHLENBECK (C. C.) Die lexicalische Urverwandtschaft des Baltoslavischen und Germanischen. pp. 51. *Leiden,* 1890. 8°. 12901. d. 33. (4.)

See also COURLAND; ESTHONIA: LETTS: LIVONIA.

BALTIC SEA. FRANCE. *Dépôt des Cartes et Plans.* Instructions nautiques sur les entrées de la Mer Baltique. pp. 505. *Paris,* 1890. 8°. 10497. f. 19.

G.B. & I. *Hydrographic Office.* The Baltic Pilot 2 pt. *Lond.* 1888, 93. 8°. 10496. f. 3.

MANTON (J. A.) Scandinavian and Russ, or by way of the Baltic. *Lond.* 1895. 8°. 10290. aaa. 17.

PHILO JUNIUS. Sul Baltico. pp. 190. *Milano,* 1892. 8°. 10107. bbb. 17.

BALTIMORE. BROWN (F. J.) Streets and Slums. Study in local municipal geography. pp. 21. *Baltimore,* 1891. 8°. 8277. ee. 28. (2.)

WILLIAMS (G. H.) Guide to Baltimore. pp. 139. *Baltimore,* 1892. 8°. 10409. aaa. 50.

BRIGHAM (W. T.) Baltimore Hats. pp. 142. *Baltimore,* 1890. 8°. 7942. e. 37.

See also JOHNS HOPKINS UNIVERSITY.

BALUCHI LANGUAGE. *See* PUSHTU.

BALUCHISTAN. THORNTON (T. H.) Sir R. Sandeman: his work on the Indian frontier. pp. 392. *Lond.* 1895. 8°. 10817. ee. 17.

See also ASIA, *Central:* ZHOB VALLEY.

BAMBERG. WEBER (H.) Der Name "Bamberg." pp. 68. *Bamberg,* 1891. 8°. 10107. ff. 27. (11.)

HUEBSCH (G.) Das Hochstift Bamberg und seine Politik, 1631, *etc.* pp. 154. *Bamberg,* 1895. 8°. 4662. dd. 7.

BAMBOROUGH. BATESON (E.) The Parish of Bamburgh. pp. 442. 1893. 4°. History of Northumberland. 10360. k. 19.

BANBURY. LOVELL (W.) Banbury Cross. pp. 8. 1892. 8°. 07703. g. 3. (11.)

DRAPER (E.) Notes on the Parish Church, Banbury. pp. 23. *Banbury,* 1892. 8°. 10360. ccc. 48.

BANDAGING. HEATH (C.) Manual of Minor Surgery and Bandaging. pp. 389. *Lond.* 1894. 8°. 2255. a. 4.

WHARTON (H. R.) Minor Surgery and Bandaging. pp. 497. *Edinb.* 1891. 8°. 07482. e. 10.

MARTIN (E.) Minor Surgery and Bandaging. pp. 166. *Lond.* 1891. 8°. 7482. bb. 25.

See also AMBULANCE: SURGERY.

BANFF AND BANFFSHIRE. Ac. Aberdeen. *New Spalding Club.* ROBERTSON (A. W.) Hand-list of Bibliography of Banff, *etc.* pp. 133. *Aberdeen,* 1893. 8°. 011903. l. 16.

Ac. Aberdeen. *New Spalding Club.* CRAMOND (W.) Annals of Banff. *Aberdeen.* 1891, *etc.* 4°. Ac. 8245/7.

CRAMOND (W.) The Making of a Banffshire Burgh. pp. 40. *Banff,* 1893. 12°. 10347. aa. 37. (9.)

—— Illegitimacy in Banffshire. pp. 74. *Banff,* 1888. 8°. 8277. de. 28. (6.)

—— Illegitimacy in Banffshire. Paper. pp. 24. *Banff,* 1892. 12°. 8277. de. 30. (5.)

See also MORAY.

BANGALORE. TAYLOR (G. W.) Guide to Bangalore. *Madras,* 1890. 8°. 10058. a. 21.

BANKING.—General.

ATTFIELD (J. B.) English and foreign Banks. pp. 123. *Lond.* 1893. 8°. 08227. h. 28.

BAIRD (H. C.) The Crisis and the Bank-Credit System. pp. 13. *Phila.* 1890. 8°. Pam. 82.

—— Money and Bank Credit in the United States, France and Great Britain. pp. 24. *Phila.* 1891. 8°. 08227. ee. 48. (3.)

BAGEHOT (W.) Lombard Street. pp. 361. *Lond.* 1892. 8°. 2240. aa. 2.

COBB (A. S.) Banks' Cash Reserves. A reply to "Lombard Street." pp. 179. *Lond.* 1891. 8°. 08227. e. 25.

BAKER (A. F.) Banks and Banking. pp. 29. *Lond.* 1892. 8°. 08227. g. 36. (13.)

BANK-MANAGER. The Banks and the Public. pp. 96. *Lond.* 1895. 8°. 08226. ee. 1.

BANKING.—General—*continued.*

BOSANQUET (B. T.) Our Banking System and the cash reserves. pp. 34. *Lond.* 1892. 8°.
08227. g. 47. (5.)

CARROLL (E.) Principles and practice of Finance. pp. 311. *Lond.* 1895. 8°. 08226. h. 28.

DURYEA (J. B.) Practical Treatise on the Business of Banking. pp. 432.
Des Moines, 1892. 8°. 08227. f. 43.

FRANÇOIS (G.) Clearing-Houses et Chambres de Compensation. pp. 175. *Lille*, 1887. 8°.
08227. k. 32.

GABET (G.) Les Banques d'Emission. pp. 38. *Paris*, 1892. 8°. 08227. k. 31. (7.)

GRILLON (E.) Le Chèque barré.
Paris, 1890, etc. 8°. 08227. g. 24.

—— Réponses aux critiques du Livre "Le Chèque barré." pp. 226. *Paris*, 1895. 8°.
08226. k. 7.

GAIRDNER (C.) Making of the Gold Reserves, etc. pp. 29. *Glasg.* 1891. 8°. 08227. g. 36. (7.)

HAUPT (O.) Arbitrages et Parités. pp. 922. *Paris*, 1894. 8°. 8227. i. 42.

HOWARTH (W.) Banking Statistics. 1885-90. pp. 68. *Lond.* 1891. 8°. 8228. aaa. 22.

KIDDY (J. G.) The Country Banker's Handbook. pp. 122. *Lond.* 1894. 8°. 08227. de. 43.

KUHLENBECK (L.) Der Check. pp. 220. *Leipz.* 1890. 8°. 08227. g. 29.

MACLEOD (H. D.) Theory and practice of Banking. *Lond.* 1892, etc. 8°. 2020. f.

MOXON (T. B.) English practical Banking. pp. 80. *Manch.* 1894. 8°. 08227. h. 43.

PALGRAVE (R. H. I.) Bank Acts and Bank Rate, 1845-91. pp. 68. *Lond.* 1892. 8°.
08227. g. 47. (11.)

SATTLER (H.) Die Effektenbanken. pp. 135. *Leipz.* 1890. 8°. 08227. g. 15.

SCHRAUT (M. v.) Currency and international Banking. pp. 42. *Lond.* 1894. 8°.
08226. k. 6. (15.)

STEELE (F. E.) On changes in the Bank Rate. pp. 25. *Lond.* 1891. 8°. 08227. g. 36. (12.)

WAGNER (A.) Del credito e delle banche. 1886, 87. 8°. Biblioteca dell' economista. Ser. 3. Vol. 11 & 12. 8205. l.

WHITE (H.) National and State Banks. pp. 30. 1893. 8°. Ac. Philadelphia. *American Academy.* Publications. No. 80. Ac. 2383/2.

See also infra: Banks of Various Countries: BILLS: MONEY : TRADE.

Banks of Various Countries.

GARROT (H.) La Banque de l'Algérie. pp. 310. *Paris*, 1892. 12°. 08227. de. 27.

LUMM (C. v.) Die Entwickelung des Bankwesens in Elsass-Löthringen. pp. 223. 1891. 8°. ELSTER (L.) Staatswissenschaftliche Studien. Bd. 3. 8207. h.

WIRTH (M.) Die Notenbank-Frage in Beziehung zur Währungs-Reform in Osterreich. pp. 116. *Frankfurt*, 1894. 8°. 08229. k. 9.

BUENOS AYRES, *Banco Hipotecario.* Memoria del Banco Hipotecario Nacional, 1891. pp. 180. *Buenos Aires*, 1892. 8°. 8245. ff. 35.

SANTELICES (R. E.) Los Bancos chilenos. pp. 467. *Santiago*, 1893. 8°. 8225. ee. 46.

ELLISEN (A.) Banking Questions asked by the Chancellor of the Exchequer with an attempted reply. pp. 15. *Lond.* 1891. 8°.
08227. g. 36. (6.)

G.B. & I. Outline of Alterations in the Bank Act of 1844. pp. 12. 14. *Lond.* 1892. 8°.
08227. g. 49. (6.)

BANKING.—Various Countries—*cont.*

GAIRDNER (C.) Mr. Goschen's Scheme for Reform of the Bank Acts. pp. 23.
Glasg. 1892. 8°. 08227. g. 36. (15.)

LECOFFRE (A.) Banques anglaises. pp. 197. *Londres*, 1892. 8°. 08229. g. 44.

PRICE (F. G. H.) Handbook of London Bankers. pp. 454. *Lond.* 1890. 8°. 8248. f. 20.

MARTINUZZI (P.) La Banca d'Inghilterra. pp. 152. *Livorno*, 1892. 8°. 08227. h. 29.

MARTIN (J. B.) "The Grasshopper" in Lombard Street. pp. 328. *Lond.* 1892. 8°. 8248. f. 25.

SMITH (T. J.) Banks and Bankers of Leek. pp. 38. *Leek*, 1891. 8°. 8248. d. 33.

PHILLIPS (M.) History of Banking in Northumberland, Durham and Yorkshire. pp. 432. *Lond.* 1894. 4°. 8245. g. 35.

BIZOUARNE (L.) La Haute Banque, son rôle dans la libération du territoire français en 1871-73. pp. 20. *Paris*, 1892. 8°. 8226. g. 40. (9.)

BOIS (G.) La Banque de France. pp. 164. *Paris*, 1891. 8°. 08227. g. 34.

DEFLY (J.) Le Privilège de la Banque de France. pp. 45. *Paris*, 1891. 8°.
8826. f. 60. (6.)

DUCHATEIL (P.) La Banque de France. pp. 168. *Paris*, 1890. 4°. 8207. l. 15.

GRILLON (E.) Critiques à propos du renouvellement du privilège de la Banque de France. pp. 24. *Paris*, 1891. 8°. 8226. ff. 33. (8.)

HOUDARD (A.) Essai sur le service des billets de banque. pp. 40. *Paris*, 1891. 4°.
8226. g. 39. (5.)

MERSCH (L.) L'Épargne nationale contre le renouvellement du privilège de la Banque de France. pp. 8. *Paris*, 1892. 8°.
08275. e. 30. (4.)

MOIREAU (A.) La Banque de France. Prorogation du privilège. pp. 233. *Paris*, 1891. 8°.
8228. aaa. 23.

ROTTEMBOURG (H.) Le haut personnel de la Banque de France. pp. 68. *Paris*, 1891. 8°.
8228. b. 56.

WERBROUCK (E. de) La Banque nationale de la France. pp. 69. *Paris*, 1891. 8°. Pam. 23.

ADLER (W.) Die Reichsbank als Hüterin der deutschen Goldwährung. pp. 39.
Breslau, 1895. 8°. Pam. 23.

KOCH (R.) Abrechnungsstellen in Deutschland. pp. 53. *Stuttgart*, 1883. 8°. Pam. 23.

DILLON (M.) History of Banking in Ireland. pp. 168. *Lond.* 1889. 8°. 08227. g. 23.

COLAJANNI (N.) Banche e Parlamento. pp. 391. *Milano*, 1893. 8°. 8032. c. 4.

ITALY. La Questione bancaria in Italia. pp. 190. *Firenze*, 1892. 8°. 08227. i. 7.

—— *Banca d'Italia.* La Banca e le finanze d'Italia. pp. 36. *Firenze*, 1894. 8°.
08226. k. 4. (12.)

COFFIN (G. M.) Hand-book for National Bank Shareholders. pp. 42. *Wash.* 1891. 8°.
08227. h. 22.

See also supra: General. Infra: Land Banks: Law of: Savings Banks.

Land and Agricultural Banks.

ANDRIMONT (L. d') Le Crédit agricole. pp. 84. *Liège*, 1888. 8°. 08229. g. 21.

DURAND (L.) Le Crédit agricole en France et à l'étranger. pp. 783. *Paris*, 1891. 8°. 08227. ee. 36.

FREDERIKSEN (D. M.) Mortgage Banking in America. pp. 32. *Paris*, 1894. 8°.
08226. k. 6. (12.)

BANKING.—Land Banks, etc.—cont.

FREDERIKSEN (D. M.) Mortgage Banking in Germany. pp. 32. *Bost.* 1894. 8°. 08226. k. 4. (10.)

—— Mortgage Banking in Russia. pp. 14. *Phila.* 1894. 8°.   08226. k. 4. (9.)

GUENIN (H.) Le Crédit agricole par l'Assurance. pp. 267. *Paris,* 1891. 12°.   08227. de. 7.

HECHT (F.) Die Organisation des Bodenkredits in Deutschland. *Leipz.* 1891, *etc.* 8°. 08227. g.

LE BARBIER (E.) Le Crédit agricole en Allemagne. pp. 463. *Paris,* 1890. 8°. 08227. k. 27.

LEIGH-SMITH (A.) Landbrugets Kreditinstituter i de Skandinaviske Lande. *Kjobenh.* 1892, *etc* 8°.   08227. h.

TORREJÓN Y BONETA (Á. de) El Crédito agrícola en Europa. pp. 39. *Madrid,* 1891. 8°. 08227. g. 47. (4.)

WOLFF (H. W.) Agricultural Banks. pp. 109. *Westminster,* 1894. 8°.   08227. de. 41.

—— Village Banks or Agricultural Credit Societies. pp. 43. *Lond.* 1894. 8°. 08226. f. 23. (7.)

Law of Banking.

BOONE (C. T.) Law of Banks and Banking. pp 642. *San Fran.* 1892. 8°.   6615. a. 15.

BIGELOW (M. M.) Elements of the Law of Bills, *etc.* pp. 325. *Lond.* 1893. 8°. 6375. aa. 55.

CORNWELL (W. C.) Currency and the Banking Law of Canada. pp. 86. *New York,* 1895. 4°. 6606. aaa. 8.

FORBES (U. A.) Statutory Law relating to Trustee Savings Banks. pp. 167. *Lond.* 1892. 12°. 6375. a. 55.

JACOBY (S.) Das Recht der Bankkommission nach dem deutschen Handelsgesetzbuche. pp. 202. *Erlangen,* 1891. 8°.   5606. de. 2.

NEW YORK. Banking Laws of New York. pp. 113. *New York,* 1892. 8°.   06616. k. 6.

SMITH (J. W.) Handy Book on the Law of Banker and Customer. pp. 180. *Lond.* 1894. 8°. 6376. ee. 7.

—— Handy Book on the Law of Bills, *etc.* pp. 193. 1894. Wilson's Legal Handy Books. 6426. aaa. 39.

TILLYARD (F.) Banking and Negotiable Instruments. pp. 303. *Lond.* 1891. 8°. 6376. e. 31.

VAN SCHAALK (H. C.) Law of Bank Checks in the U.S. pp. 290. *Denver,* 1892. 8°. 6617. aa. 12.

WALLACE (W.) and MACNEIL (A.) Banking Law. pp. 436. *Edinb.* 1894. 8°.   6376. ee. 4.
See also LAW, *Commercial.*

Savings Banks: "People's" Banks.

BONDÌ (F.) La Cassa postale di Risparmio. pp. 114. *Torino,* 1893. 8°.   08277. g. 3.

FENYVESSY (A.) Geschichte des Pester Sparcassa-Vereines. pp. 101. *Budapest,* 1890. 8°. 08227. k. 22.

FORBES (U. A.) Statutory Law relating to Trustee Savings Banks. pp. 167. *Lond.* 1892. 12°. 6375. a. 55.

FRANCE. *Congrès des Banques populaires.* Actes du Congrès. *Paris,* 1889, *etc.* 8°. 08225. h.

HEYDEN (W.) Die Hamburger Sparkasse von 1827. pp. 247. *Hamb.* 1893. 4°. 8225. ff. 37.

LAMBERT (A.) School Savings Banks. pp. 20. *Lond.* 1891. 8°.   3939. cc.

MICHAEL (B.) Sparkassen und Checkverkehr. pp. 84. *Berl.* 1892. 8°.   08227. h. 30.

U.S.A. *Post Office.* Postal Savings Banks. pp. 72. *Wash.* 1891. 8°.   08227. ee. 45. (16.)

WOLFF (H. W.) People's Banks. pp. 261. *Lond.* 1893. 8°.   08227. h. 24.

BANKING.— Savings' Banks, etc.—cont.

WOLFF (H. W.) People's Banks for England. pp. 20. *Lond.* 1893. 8°.   08227. g. 49. (19.)

—— Village Banks. pp. 43. *Lond.* 1894. 8°. 08226. f. 23. (7.)

—— People's Bank Manual. pp. 48. *Lond.* 1895. 8°.   08226. f. 23. (12.)

—— Les Banques populaires au point de vue coopératif. pp. 27. *Bordeaux,* 1894. 8°. 08226, h. 14. (18.)

ARNAUD (L.) Guide des Caisses d'Épargne. pp. 273. *Tours,* 1893. 8°.   08226. h. 1.

ARNOUX (J.) Conditions d'admission à tous les emplois dans l'administration. La Caisse nationale d'Épargne. pp. 81. *Lille,* 1895. 8°. 08247. ff. 29.

BAYARD (E.) La Caisse d'Épargne. pp. 402. *Paris,* 1892. 8°.   08227. e. 38.

LAURENT (H.) Les Caisses d'Épargne. 2 pt. *Pithiviers,* 1892. 8°.   08227. h. 19.

LA BOULAYE (J. T. de) Le krack des Caisses d'Épargne. pp. 60. *Paris,* 1892. 12°. 8228. aaaa. 19. (7.)

ROCHETIN (E.) La Caisse nationale de Prévoyance. pp. 244. *Paris,* 1894, 12°. 08275. f. 16.

ROSTAND (E.) La Réforme des Caisses d'Épargne. pp. 236. *Paris,* 1891.   08227. e. 24.

BANKRUPTCY. ALEXANDER (J.) Konkursgesetze aller Länder der Erde. pp. 530. *Berl.* 1892. 8°.   6005. de. 2.

DUNSCOMB (S. W) Bankruptcy. Study in comparative legislation. pp. 167. 1893. 8°. Ac. New York. *Columbia College.* Studies. Vol. 2. Ac. 2688/2.

REINHOLD (F.) Die Sequestration nach österreichischem Rechte. pp. 105. *Leipz.* 1894. 8°. 05549. i. 1.

SCHUBERT-SOLDERN (E. v.) Die Sequestration nach österreichischem Rechte. pp. 331. *Wien,* 1894. 8°.   5551. f. 15.

KUPFFER (V.) Kommentar zur baltischen Konkursordnung. 1893. 8°. Dorpater Juristische Studien. Bd. 2.   5756. b.

BRAZIL. Das brasilianische Falliments-Dekret vom 24 Oktober 1890. pp. 80. *Berl.* 1895. 8°. 6784. g. 20.

HEIN (A.) Tvangsakkord ifølge dans Konkurslov, 1872. pp. 212. *Kjøbenh.* 1891. 8°. 6005. h. 13.

BALDWIN (E. T.) Treatise upon the Law of Bankruptcy. pp. 1112. *Lond.* 1895. 8°. 2019. c.

CHALMERS (M. D. E. S.) and HOUGH (E. K.) Bankruptcy Acts, 1883-90. pp. 806. *Lond.* 1891. 8°.   6405. ee. 10.

G. B. & I. Bankruptcy Act, 1883. Order, 23rd August, 1893. *Lond.* 1893. 8°. 6190. cc. 4. (7.)

HEPBURN (E.) Summary of Bankruptcy Proceedings, 1883 & 1890. *Lond.* 1891. *s. sh.* fol. 1890. e. 3. (102.)

KERR (W. W.) Treatise on the Law as to Receivers. pp. 252. *Lond.* 1891. 8°. 2230. e. 9.

LANHAM (J.) Epitome of the Deeds of Arrangement Act, 1887. pp. 14. *Lond.* 1890. 8°. 6376. a. 52.

LAWRANCE (G. W.) Precedents of Deeds of Arrangement. pp. 160. *Lond.* 1892. 8°. 6405. ee. 13.

LEE (L. Y.) and WACE (H.) Bankruptcy Act, 1890. pp. 130. *Lond.* 1891. 8°. 6405. f. 4.

LEWIS (G. P.) Manual of the practice as to Winding-up. pp. 171. *Lond.* 1891, 8°. 2232. cc 16.

LYNCH (H. F.) Rights and duties of Liquidators, Trustees and Receivers. pp. 58. *Lond.* 1894. 8°. 6405. ee. 15.

BANKRUPTCY—*continued.*

MORRELL (C. F.) Bankruptcy. pp. 324.
Lond. 1891. 8°.   6405. de. 19.

MYERS (F.) New Bankruptcy Act to supplant the
Act of 1883. pp. 224. *Liverp.* 1893. 8°.
                6405. de. 22.

RINGWOOD (R.) Principles of Bankruptcy.
pp. 381. *Lond.* 1895. 8°.   2232. d. 17.

ROBSON (G. Y.) Treatise on the Law of Bankruptcy. pp. 1350. *Lond.* 1894. 8°. 2232. ccc. 10.

STEWART (C. E.) The Law of Bankruptcy.
pp. 199. 1892. 12°. Wilson's Legal Handy
Books.   6426. aaa. 39.

WILLIAMS (*Sir* R. L. V.) Law and Practice of
Bankruptcy. pp. 896. *Lond.* 1894. 8°. 2019. d.

WREFORD (H. F.) Rights and Duties of Trustees
in Bankruptcy. pp. 156. *Lond.* 1893. 8°.
                6355. aa. 21.

OETKER (F.) Konkursrechtliche Grundbegriffe.
Stuttgart, 1891, *etc.* 8°.   05604. k. 1.

SANGSTER (C. F. A.) Hongkong. Bankruptcy
Ordinance, 1891. pp. 10. *Hongkong,* 1892. 8°.
                Pam. 33.

CESAREO-CONSOLO (G.) Trattato della espro-
priazione contro il debitore. *Torino,* 1891, *etc.* 8°.
                5373. ee. 26.

LUCIANI (V.) Trattato del Fallimento.
Roma, 1893, *etc.* 8°.   6005. h.

PAGANO (G.) Teorica del fallimento.
Palermo, 1889, *etc.* 8°.   6005. f. 5.

GOUDY (H.) Treatise on the Law of Bankruptcy
in Scotland. pp. 900. *Edinb.* 1895. 8°. 6573. i. 6.

MARTORELL Y ROVIRA DE CASELLAS (L.) Quiebras
y suspensiones de pagos. 2 tom. *Madrid,* 1888. 8°.
                5385. dd. 3.

GRIVET (C.) Commentaire de la Loi Fédérale sur
la Faillite. pp. 238. *Lausanne,* 1891. 8°
                5551. b 6.

SWITZERLAND. Bundesgesetz über Schuldbetreibung und Konkurs. pp. 101. 72. *Zürich,* 1892. 8°.
                5511. aaa. 12.

WEBER (L.) and BRUESTLEIN (A.) Das Bundesgesetz über Schuldbetreibung. pp. 507.
Zürich, 1892. 8°.   5511. e. 1.

See also COMPANIES, *Law of:* COUNTY COURTS:
LAW, *Commerical.*

BANKURA. SAURĪNDRAMOHANA THĀKURA.
Brief History of Bankura. pp. 17.
Calcutta, 1892. 8°.   Pam. 88.

BANTAM. SANDICK (Q. A. v.) Leed en Lief
uit Bantam. pp. 240. *Zutphen,* 1892. 8°.
                10055. bb. 6.

See also JAVA.

BANTU LANGUAGE.
See AFRICAN LANGUAGES.

BAPTISM. A., E. J. Gospels of Water.
pp. 83. *Lond.* 1890. 8°.   Pam. 77.

BAKER (D.) Who should be Baptized? pp. 47.
Glasg. 1893. 8°.   4422. d. 16. (3.)

BARNES-LAWRENCE (A. E.) The Church View
of Baptism. 1895. 8°. Four Foundation
Truths.   4109. aa. 44.

—— Infant Baptism. pp. 39.
Blackheath, 1894. 16°.   4422. aa. 51. (3.)

BROWN (A.) Scripture Baptism. pp. 64.
Lond. 1892. 8°.   4324. aaa. 8.

BROWN (J.) Baptismal Regeneration tested by
Scripture. pp. 12. *Ampthill,* 1893. 8°.
                4109. aaaa. 20. (7.)

CRIPPEN (T. G.) Christian Baptism.
pp. 112. *Lond.* 1895. 16°.   4324. b. 26.

DELL (W.) Doctrine of Baptisms. pp. 24.
Brighton, 1891. 8°.   4323. c. 2.

BAPTISM—*continued.*

DIENEMANN (P.) Die heilige Taufe. 1894. 8°.

WEBER ( ) Sammlung theologischer Reden.
Ser. 5.   4224. ff. 25.

DUNN (J. C.) Lay Baptism impossible. pp. 89.
Lond. 1893. 8°.   4325. cc. 8.

FAIRFIELD (E. B.) Letters on Baptism. pp. 249.
Bost. 1893. 8°.   4323. aaa.

GLOAG (P. J.) The subjects and mode of
Baptism. pp. 26. *Paisley,* 1891. 8°.
                4374. df. 4. (5.)

HART (J. T.) The Maze and its clue. pp. 83.
Lond. 1891. 8°.   4371. e. 1. (10.)

HOPKINS (R. T.) Review of letters on Baptism.
pp. 79. *Lond.* 1895. 8°.   4324. c. 30.

JONES (J.) Baptism by Sprinkling. pp. 31.
Manch. 1885. 8°.   4324. cc. 18. (7.)

LITURGIES. England, *Church of.* Catechism on
the Baptismal Service. pp. 30. *Oxf.* 1892. 32°.
                Pam. 11.

MACLEANE (D.) Why then are Infants Baptized? pp. 48. *Lond.* 1892. 8°.
                4129. aa. 60. (8.)

MACLOY (W.) Infant Baptism. pp. 44.
Glasg. 1893. 8°.   4175. ff. 7. (6.)

MASON (A. J.) Relation of Confirmation to
Baptism. pp. 504. *Lond.* 1893. 8°. 4325. aaa. 7.

MOEREN (A. B. v. d.) Tractatus de sponsalibus
et matrimonio. pp. 196. *Gandavi,* 1889. 8°.
                5176. cc. 19.

PIRRET (D.) Facts and Fallacies anent Infant
Baptism. pp. 7. *Glasg.* 1895. 8°.
                4175. ff. 7. (8.)

RATE (J.) Letters on Baptismal Regeneration.
pp. 32. *Lond.* 1890. 8°.   4109. e. 39. (5.)

ROOKE (T. G.) Doctrine and history of Christian
Baptism. pp. 102. *Lond.* 1894. 8°. 4325. cc. 9.

SPENCER-SMITH (S. C.) Renewal and Conversion.
pp. 24. *Lond.* 1891. 8°.   4371. a. 3. (9.)

WATERLAND (D.) Letters on Lay-Baptism.
pp. 250. *Lond.* 1892. 8°.   4325. ee. 13.

WHITE (F. H.) Christian Baptism. pp. 134.
Lond. 1895. 16°.   4324. aa. 51.

See also BAPTISTS : SACRAMENTS.

BAPTISTS.—Doctrines.

CHRISTIAN (J. T.) Immersion, the act of
Christian Baptism. pp. 256.
Louisville, 1891. 8°.   4324. k. 8.

P.P. London. Light and Truth. Organ of the
old Baptist Union. Vol. 1. *Lond.* 1889–90. 4°.
                1865. a. 13.

—— Philadelphia. Baptist Quarterly Review.
N.Y. 1882–92. 8°.   P.P. 863. c.

PIRRET (D.) Baptist Positions untenable.
pp. 123. *Edinb.* 1889. 8°.   4323. df. 1.

See also BAPTISM.

History, etc.

VEDDER (H. C.) Short History of the Baptists.
pp. 245. *Phila.* 1891. 8°.   4715. aaa. 43.

BROHOLM (A.) 50 Aars Statistik for de danske
Baptistmenigheder. *Kjøbenh.* 1889. 8°.
                4532. g. 9. (3.)

EPHEM. Baptist Union Almanack.
Lond. 1891, *etc.* 8°.   P.P. 2485. cd.

WILLIAMS (J. de K.) Memories of Baptist
Ministers. pp. 20. *Lond.* 1891. 8°. Pam. 16.

NORTHAMPTON, *Association of Baptist Churches.*
Report of proceedings at the Annual Meetings.
pp. 43. *Northampton,* 1892. 8°.   4136. bb. 8.

WICKS (W. A.) History of the Baptist Church,
Walgrave. pp. 78. *Northampton,* 1892. 8°.
                4715. cc. 17.

BAPTISTS.—History, etc.,—*continued.*
DOEL (W.) Twenty Golden Candlesticks ! history of Baptists in Wiltshire. pp. 232.
Trowbridge, 1890. 8°.   4715. bb. 11.
NEWMAN (A. H.) History of Baptist Churches in the United States. pp. 513. 1894. 8°.
American Church History Series. vol. 2.
                                              4744. g.
CARROLL (H. K.) Report of Statistics of Churches in the U.S. pp. 812. 1894. 4°. U.S. Eleventh Census.   1882. c. 1.
LEICESTER, *Mass.* *Greenville Baptist Church.* Greenville Baptist Church. pp. 126.
Worcester, Mass. 1889. 8°.   4744. g. 12.
See also ENGLAND, *Nonconformists.*

Missions. *See* MISSIONS, *Foreign.*

BARBADOS. BARBADOES. Laws of Barbados.
Barbados, 1893, *etc.* 8°.   06606. h.
DAVIS (N. D.) The Cavaliers and Roundheads of Barbados, 1650–1652. pp. 261.
Georgetown, 1887. 8°.   9551. i 13.
EDGHILL (J. Y.) About Barbados. pp. 141.
Lond. 1890. 8°.   10470. cc. 37.
EPHEM. Barbados almanac.
Bridgetown, 1893. 12°.   P.P. 2586. gb.
P.P. *Bridgetown.* The West Indian Civil Rights Guardian. *Barbados*, 1891, *etc.* 8°.
                                              P.P. 3699.
WASHINGTON (G.) Journal of Major G. Washington in 1751–2, while on a tour to Barbadoes.
pp. 88. *Albany*, 1892. 8°.   10883. bb. 23.

See also ENGLAND, *Colonies :* WEST INDIES.

BARBEZIEUX. LIÈVRE (A. F.) Le Chateau de Barbezieux en 1496. pp. 31. *Paris*, 1890. 8°.
                                              10107. ff. 28. (1.)
BARBONNE. FAVATIER (L.) La Vie municipale à Barbonne au XVIIᵐᵉ siècle. pp. 192.
Narbonne, 1894. 8°.   10173. ee. 5.
BARCELONA. BARCELONA. *Societat Fotográfica.* Album de la Catedral de Barcelona.
Barcelona, 1888. 4°.   7814. ee. 18.
BARKSTONE-LE-VALE. GODFREY (J. T.) Note on Stone Coffins in the Churchyard at Barkstone-le-Vale. 1892. 8°.   Pam. .3
BARLEY, Herts. FRERE (A.) and (W. H.) Parochial History of Barley. pp. 32.
Stepney Green, 1890. 8°.   10348. d. 19. (7.)
BARNES. WINCH (A. W.) Bits about Barnes.
pp. 29. *Lond.* 1895. 16°.   Pam. 90.
See also LONDON, *Environs.*

BARNET, *East.* Ac. London. *Archæological Society.* CASS (F. C.) East Barnet. pp. 280.
Westminster, 1885–92. 4°.   10360. k. 6.
BARNSTAPLE. CHANTER (J. R.) Memorials of the Church of St. Peter, Barnstaple. pp. 188.
Barnstaple, 1882. 8°.   4705. aa. 45.
BAROMETER. *See* METEOROLOGY.

BARRISTERS-AT-LAW.
See LAW, *Profession of.*

BARROW-IN-FURNESS. FISHER (J.) History of Barrow-in-Furness, *etc.* pp. 176.
Bournemouth, 1891. 8°.   10360. d. 25.
BASEBALL. CRANE (N.) Baseball. pp. 103.
1891. 8°. All England Series.   7908. f.
See also GAMES.

BASEDOW'S DISEASE. BUSCHAN (G.) Die Basedow'sche Krankheit. pp. 184.
Leipz. 1894. 8°.   7615. dd. 1.
MANNHEIM (P.) Der Morbus Gravesii. pp. 156.
Berl. 1894. 8°.   7630. h. 33.

BASENTO. FITTIPALDI (E.) La Vallata del Basento. pp. 107. *Potenza*, 1893. 8°.
                                              07109. h. 40.
BASHAN. HEBER-PERCY (A.) Visit to Bashan and Argob. pp. 175. *Lond.* 1895. 8°.
                                              4429. k. 16.
See also PALESTINE AND SYRIA.

BASILICATA. GIANCASPRO (P.) La Insurrezione della Basilicata, 1860. pp. 149.
Trani, 1890. 8°.   9167. e. 2.
BASLE, City and Cantons.
Ac. Basle. *Historische Gesellschaft.* Urkundenbuch der Stadt Basel. *Basel*, 1890, *etc.* 4°.
                                              Ac. 6924/4.
BASLE. Sammlung der Gesetze des Kantons Basel-Stadt. pp. 432. *Basel*, 1892. 8°.
                                              5551. de. 13.
—— Historisches Festbuch zur Basler Vereinigungsfeier, 1892. pp. 335. *Basel*, 1892. 8°.
                                              10196. f. 17.
—— Festbuch zur Eröffnung des Historischen Museums. pp. 257. *Basel*, 1894. 4°. 7706. ee. 41.
BUECHER (C.) Die Bevölkerung des Kantons Basel-Stadt, 1888. pp. 96. *Basel*, 1890. 4°.
                                              8223, de. 45.
DANCE OF DEATH. La Danse des Morts dans la Ville de Basle. pp. 81. *Paris*, 1893. 8°.
                                              11483. aaa. 32.
FREIVOGEL (L.) Die Landschaft Basel in der zweiten Hälfte des 18ten Jahrhunderts, *etc.*
Basel, 1893, *etc.* 8°.   10196. d.
STOUFF (L.) Le Pouvoir temporel des évêques de Bâle jusqu'à la Réforme. 2 pt.
Paris, 1891. 8°   9304. e. 2.
HOFFMANN (E.) Der mundartliche Vokalismus von Basel-Stadt. pp. 94. *Basle.* 1890. 8°.
                                              12902. dd. 27. (7.)

BASQUE LANGUAGE AND LITERATURE.
VINSON (E. H. J.) Essai d'une bibliographie de la langue basque. pp. 471. *Paris*, 1891. 8°.
                                              011901. ee. 11.
DODGSON (E. S.) Supplément à la Bibliographie de la langue basque. pp. 16. *Paris*, 1892. 8°.
                                              11904. l. 17. (2.)
CHARENCEY (H. de) *Count.* De la parenté du basque avec divers idiomes. 1893. 8°. Ac. Caen. *Académie.* Mémoires. 1893. Ac. 305/2.
DODGSON (E. S.) Étude sur la langue Euskara.
pp. 11. 1895. 8°.   Pam. 47.
GABELENTZ (G. v. d.) Die Verwandtschaft des Baskischen mit den Berbersprachen.
pp. 286. *Braunschweig*, 1894. 8°. 12910. d. 33.
HUEBNER (E.) Monumenta Linguae Ibericae.
pp. 264. *Berolini*, 1893. 4°.   7705. h. 33.
STEMPF (V.) Besitzt die baskische Sprache ein transitives Zeitwort? pp. 16.
Bordeaux, 1890. 8°.   12903. dd. 37. (5.)
TOPOLOVSEK (J.) Die Basko-slavische Spracheinheit. *Wien*, 1894, *etc.* 8°.   12978. f.
POUVREAU (S.) Les Petites Œuvres Basques de S. Pouvreau. pp. 99. *Chalon*, 1892. 8°.
                                              886. h. 10.
DOYENHART (A.) A. D. et son Supplément des proverbes basques. pp. 24. *Bayonne*, 1892. 8°.
                                              012305. ee. 5. (3.)
BASQUE PASTORALS. Collection de pastorales basques. *Bordeaux*, 1891, *etc.* 8°. 11595. cc.
BASQUE RACE. AMESTOY (C.) Le bail à métairie. Usages du pays basque. pp. 55.
Bayonne, 1891. 12°.   8228. aaaa. 19. (4.)
ARANZADI Y UNAMUNO (T. de) El Pueblo Euskalduna. pp. 46. *S. Sebastian*, 1889. 8°.
                                              10007. k. 6.

BASQUE RACE—*continued.*

BASQUE LAWS. Los fueros vascongados y la unidad constitucional. pp. 45.
Valladolid, 1891. 8°.   Pam. 71.

BLANC SAINT-HILAIRE ( ) Les Euskariens ou Basques. pp. 446. *Paris*, 1888. 8°.
          10170. h. 12.

HENAO (G. de) Averiguaciones de las antigüedades de Cantabria. *Tolosa*, 1894, *etc*, 8°.
          07708. i.

INCHAUSPE ( ) Le peuple basque. pp. 38.
Pau, 1894. 8°.   Pam. 91.

SCHUCHARDT (H. E. M.) Baskische Studien. 1893, *etc.* fol. Ac. Vienna. *K. Akademie der Wissenschaften.* Denkschriften Philos. hist. Classe. Bd. 42.   Ac. 810/12.
See also BISCAY.

BASSES ALPES, Department. FERAUD (J. J. M.) Histoire des Basses-Alpes. pp. 520.
Digne, 1890. 8°.   10174. g. 25.
See also PROVENCE.

BASTIA. CAGNANI (A.) Documents sur les troubles de Bastia, 1791. pp. 117. 1894. 8°.
Ac. Bastia. *Société des sciences.* Bulletin
          Ac. 2861. (30.)
See also CORSICA.

BASTIDE DE CAZERES - SUR-L'ADOUR. MEYRANX (L. B.) Bastide de Cazères-sur-l'Adour, 1314–1887. pp. 185.
Dax, 1894. 8°.   010171. g. 16.

BASTILLE. *See* PARIS.

BASUTOLAND. WIDDICOMBE (J.) Fourteen Years in Basutoland. pp. 306.
Lond. 1892. 8°.   4767. bbb. 6.

BARKLY ( ) Among Boers and Basutos. pp. 270. *Lond.* 1894. 8°.   10095. de. 21.

JACOTTET (E.) Contes populaires des Bassoutos. pp. 292. 1895. 8°. Collection de Contes. 20.
          2348. aa. 30.
See also AFRICA, *South.*

BATALHA. CONDEIXA (de) O Mosteiro da Batalha em Portugal. pp. 205.
Lisboa, 1892. 4°.   7816. dd. 4.

BATAVIA. BUYS (M.) Batavia. pp. 158.
Batav. 1891. 8°.   10055. aaa. 9.
See also JAVA.

BATH. Ac. Somerset. *Record Society.* Two Chartularies of the Priory of St. Peter at Bath. pp. 262. *Lond.* 1893. 4°.   Ac. 8133/7.

HUNT (W.) Account of the Priory of St. Peter and St. Paul, Bath. pp. 70. *Lond.* 1893. 4°.
          4707. cc. 15.

Ac. *Somerset Record Society.* Church-Warden's Accounts of St. Michael's, Bath.
Lond. 1890. 4°.   Ac. 8133/4.

SISSMORE (T. L.) Annals of Holy Trinity Church, Bath, *etc.* pp. 91. *Bath*, 1893. 8°.
          4707. aa. 37.

FALCONER (R. W.) History of the Royal Hospital, Bath. pp. 158. *Bath*, 1888. 8°.
          7688. c. 30.

LOWE (T. P.) The Bath Thermal Waters. pp. 50. *Lond.* 1892. 8°.   7461. c. 16.

MURCH (J.) Biographical Sketches of Bath Celebrities. pp. 442. *Lond.* 1893. 8°.
          010358. f. 49.

PEACH (R. E. M.) Collections of Books belonging to the City. pp. 10. *Bath*, 1893. 8°.
          Pam. 6.

—— Life and Times of R. Allen of Prior Park, Bath. pp. 247. *Lond.* 1895. 4°. 10825. g. 17.

—— Street-Lore of Bath. pp. 154.
Lond. 1893. 8°.   10358. e. 27.

PENLEY (B. S.) The Bath Stage. pp. 180.
Lond. 1892. 8°.   11795. dg. 41.

BATH AND WELLS, Diocese. Ac. Somerset. *Somerset Record Society.* Calendar of the Register of John de Drokensford, Bishop of Bath and Wells A.D. 1309–29. pp. 351.
Lond. 1887. 4°.   Ac. 8133.

BATHS. ALLSOP (R. O.) Public Baths and Washhouses. pp. 98. *Lond.* 1894. 8°. 8777. b. 49.

BARTHOLOMEW (C.) Guide to Turkish, medicated and other Baths. pp. 42. *Lond.* 1887. 8°.
          Pam. 39.

KANE (J.) New System of Public Baths. pp. 14. *Lond.* 1895. 8°.   8777. e. 9.

SCHULTZE (R.) Volks- und Hausbäder, 1894. 8°.
WEYL (T.) Handbuch der Hygiene. Bd. 6.
          7391. dd.

STABLES (W. G.) Turkish and other baths. pp. 60. *Lond.* 1892. 8°.   07305. h. 16. (13.)
See also HYDROPATHY.

BATNA. BALLU (A.) Monuments antiques de l'Algérie. pp. 39. *Paris*, 1894. 8°. 07708. f. 44.

BATRACHIA. *See* AMPHIBIA.

BATUECAS, Las, Salamanca. BIDE (D. J. B.) Las Batuecas y las Jurdes. pp. 111.
Madrid, 1892. 8°.   10160. ee. 29.

BAUCO. ARCANGELI (M.) Memorie storiche di Bauco. pp. 376. *Frosinone*, 1891. 8°.
          10135. g. 13.

BAVARIA. [*See note on page 1.*] *See also* GERMANY.

Antiquities.

NAUE (J.) Die Bronzezeit in Oberbayern. 2 pt. *München*, 1894. 4°.   7709. l. 19.

Army.

Ac. Munich. *Bayerisches Kriegsarchiv.* Darstellungen aus der bayerischen Kriegs- und Heeresgeschichte. *München*, 1892, *etc.* 8°.
          8829. i.

For the Army since 1870. *See* GERMANY, *Army.*

Constitution and Government.

BAVARIA. Die Verfassungsurkunde Bayerns. pp. 300. *München*, 1895. 8°.   5604. de. 18.

STENGEL (C. v.) Die Verfassungsurkunde Bayerns. pp. 318. *Würzburg*, 1893. 8°.
          5604. de. 12.

BAVARIA. Bayerische Gemeindeordnung für die Landesteile diesseits des Rheins. pp. 234.
München, 1890. 8°.   05604. h. 7.

Emigration from. *See infra* Trade

History.

EBERL (F.) Geschichte der Karolinger in Bayern, *etc.* pp. 68. *Straubing*, 1891. 8°.
          9008. g. 11. (14.)

Ac. Munich. *Bayerisches Kriegsarchiv.* Darstellungen aus der bayerischen Kriegs- und Heeresgeschichte. *München*, 1892, *etc.* 8°.
          8829. i.

WITTELSBACH, *Family of.* Die Wittelsbachische Hausunion, 1724. 1891. 8°. Ac. Munich. *Akademie der Wissenschaften.* Sitzungsberichte der philosophisch-philologischen. Classe. 1891. Heft 2.   Ac. 713/8.

DU MOULIN ECKART (R.) *Count.* Bayern unter dem Ministerium Montgelas, 1799–1817. *München*, 1895, *etc.* 8°.   9340. h.

KOBELL (L. v.) Unter den vier ersten Königen Bayerns. 2 Bde. *München*, 1894. 8°. 9335. d. 1.

KURZ (F.) Der Antheil der Münchener Studentenschaft an den Unruhen, 1817–18. pp. 112. *München*, 1893. 8°.   8357. bb. 35.

MAXIMILIAN JOSEPH II., *King of Bavaria.* König Maximilian II. und Schelling. pp. 284. *Stuttgart*, 1890. 8°.   010920. f. 15.

BAVARIA.—History—*continued.*

TROST (L.) König Ludwig I. von Bayern in seinen Briefen an König Otto. pp. 202. *Bamberg*, 1891. 8°.   010707. f. 9.

HEIGEL (C. v.) König Ludwig II. von Bayern. pp. 387. *Stuttgart*, 1893. 8°   10703. de. 33.

KOBER (J. B.) Ludwig II. pp. 40. *Bamberg*, 1894. 8°.   Pam. 8.

LAMPERT (F.) Ludwig II. 15 Hft. *München*, 1890. 4°.   10703. i. 33.

FAZY (E.) Louis II. et Richard Wagner. pp. 216. *Paris*, 1893. 8°.   10703. de. 36.

REIDELBACH (H.) Luitpold Prinz-Regent. Festschrift zu Allerhöchstdessen siebzigster Geburtstagsfeier. pp. 283. *München*, 1891. fol.   10703. i. 34.

History, *Ecclesiastical.*

LECHNER (A.) Mittelalterliche Kirchenfeste in Bayern. pp. 286. *Freiburg i. B.* 1891. 8°.   3475. dd. 13.

Law.

MAYER (M.) Quellen zur Behörden-Geschichte Bayerns. pp. 464. *Bamberg*, 1890. 8°. 9340. f. 2.

ROCKINGER (L. v.) Denkmäler des baierischen Landesrechts. *München*, 1891, *etc.* 4°.   5605. h. 20.

SCHANZ (G.) Im Königreich Bayern zu Recht bestehende Gesetze. *Würzburg*, 1891, *etc.* 8°.   05604. h. 14.

Topography.

BAEDEKER (C.) The Eastern Alps. pp. 518. *Leipz.* 1895. 8°.   2352. a. 1.

BIRD (A. F. R.) Boating in Bavaria. pp. 160. *Hull*, 1893. 8°.   10108. f. 4.

KOESTLER (C.) Handbuch zur Gebiets- und Ortskunde des Königreiches. *München*, 1895, *etc.* 4°.   10256. i.

LAU (O. E.) Land und Leute im bayerischen Walde. 1890. 8°. REINHARDSTOETTNER (C. v.) Bayerische Bibliothek. Bd. 17.   12253. g.

SCHWANN (M.) Das neue Bayern. *Stuttgart*, 1892, *etc.* 8°.   10240. i.

RIVIÈRE (L.) Entre l'Inn et le lac de Constance. pp. 330. *Paris*, 1891. 12°.   10215. aaa. 35.

SEPP (J. N.) Denkwürdigkeiten aus dem Bayeroberland. pp. 275. *München*, 1892. 8°.   10255. f. 27.

TAPONIER (A.) Bavière et Tyrol. pp. 364. *Fribourg*, 1892. 8°.   10235. c. 8.

See also ALPS, *Eastern :* GERMANY.

Trade and Finance.

MAYER (M.) Bayerns Handel. Historische Skizze. pp. 100 *München.* 1893. 8°. 08225. h. 5.

KREIG (G.) Entwickelung und gegenwärtiger Zustand des Auswanderungswesens in Bayern. 1892. 8°. PHILIPPOVICH (E. v.) Auswanderung, *etc.*   Ac. 2322.

BAVARIAN DIALECT AND LITERATURE. Ac. Munich. *Akademie der Wissenschaften.* SCHMELLER (J. A.) Bayerisches Wörterbuch. 2 Bde. *München*, 1878–80. 4°.   12962. u. 1.

BRENNER (C.) Mundarten und Schriftsprache in Bayern. pp 83. 1890. 8°. REINHARDSTOETTNER (C. v.) Bayerische Bibliothek. Bd. 18.   12253. g.

—— Bayerns Mundarten. *München*, 1891, *etc.* 8°.   12963. k. 33.

DREYER (A.) Aus mein' Hoamatland. Gedichte. pp. 82. *Passau*, 1891. 8°.   Pam. 61.

BAVARIAN DIALECT, etc.—*continued.*

REINHARDSTOETTNER (C. v.) Forschungen zur Litteraturgeschichte Bayerns. *München*, 1893, *etc.* 8°.   011824. k.

BAYEUX. Ac. Rouen. *Société de l'Histoire.* BÉZIERS (M.) Mémoires pour servir à l'état du diocèse de Bayeux. *Rouen*, 1894. *etc.* 8°.   Ac. 6890/29.

DÉDOUIT (A.) Bayeux sous la Révolution et l'Empire. pp. 342. *Bellême*, 1892. 8°. 9226. aa. 13.

JOANNE (P.) Caen et Bayeux. pp. 60. *Paris*, 1895. 8°.   10174. a. 29.

BAYEUX TAPESTRY. *See* TAPESTRY.

BAYONNE. DUCÉRÉ (E.) Bayonne historique et pittoresque. pp. 114. *Bayonne*, 1893. 8°.   10172. g. 16.

LEON (H.) Histoire des Juifs de Bayonne. pp. 436. *Paris*, 1893. 8°.   4515. f. 2.

BAYREUTH. BENDINER (M.) Die Rechnungen über den Bau der Kirche St. Maria Magdalena zu Bayreuth. pp. 219. 1889. 8°. Ac. Bayreuth. *Historischer Verein.* Archiv. *etc.* Bd. 17.   Ac. 7015.

MEYER (C.) Quellen zur Geschichte der Stadt Baireuth. pp. 248. *Bayreuth*, 1891. 8°.   10255. h. 7.

—— Hardenberg und seine Verwaltung des Fürstenthums Bayreuth. pp. 159. *Breslau*, 1892. 8°.   10255. ccc. 13.

BOPP (W.) Die Bühnenfestspiele in Bayreuth. pp. 56. *Mannheim*, 1892. 8°.   Pam. 24.

FRÉSON (J. G.) Bayreuth. Un pèlerinage d'art. pp. 46. *Brux.* 1890. 8°.   7898. m. 14. (7.)

HECKEL (C.) Die Bühnenfestspiele in Bayreuth. pp. 88. *Leipz.* 1891. 8°.   Pam. 24.

NOVER (J.) Die Bühnenfestspiele in Baireuth. pp. 102. *Leipz.* 1891. 8°.   7896. de. 36.

BAZEILLES. *See* GERMAN-FRENCH WAR.

BEACHY HEAD. DAWSON (C.) Description of the Battle of Beachy Head. pp. 16. *Lewes*, 1895. 12°.   Pam. 28.

BEAR. CZYNK (E. v.) Der Bär. pp. 48. *Klagenfurt*, 1892. 16°.   07905. g. 8. (7.)

BEARCAMP RIVER. BOLLES (F.) At the North of Bearcamp Water. pp. 297. *Bost.* 1893. 8°.   10410. bbb. 26.

BEARN. BASCLE DE LAGRÈZE (G.) La société en Béarn. pp. 568. *Pau*, 1886. 8°. 10168. f. 23.

MARCA (P. de) *Archbishop of Paris.* Histoire de Béarn. *Pau*, 1894, *etc.* 4°.   10172. k.

LOCHARD (J.) Quelques pages d'un manuscrit sous la Terreur en Béarn. 1793–94. pp. 220. *Paris*, 1893. 8°.   9226. b. 30.

BLANCHET (J. A.) Numismatique du Béarn. 2 tom. *Paris*, 1893. 8°.   7757. e. 30.

CLAUDIN (A.) Notes pour servir à l'histoire de l'imprimerie en Béarn. pp. 3. *Auch*, 1893. 8°.   11904. l. 16. (5.)

LESPY (V.) Dictons et proverbs du Béarn. pp. 285. *Pau*, 1892. 8°.   12305. k. 11.

See also PAU.

BEAUCAIRE. EYSSETTE. Histoire de Beaucaire. 2 tom. *Beaucaire*, 1884–88. 8°.   010171. g. 3.

BEAUJEU. MARY, *the B. V., Church of, at Beaujeu.* Déclaration du Chapitre de Beaujeu, 1728. pp. 96. *Beaujeu*, 1890. 8°.   4629. i. 11.

BEAUMONT-LA-FERRIÈRE. GAUTHIER (G.) Monographie de la commune de Beaumont. pp. 240. *Nevers*, 1892. 8°.   010171 k. 5.

BEAUNE. BIGARNE (C.) Patois du Pays de Beaune. pp. 250. 21. *Beaune*, 1891. 8°.
12953. cc. 14.

BEAUVAIS. BEAUVAIS. Ville de Beauvais. Inventaire des archives. pp. 267. 1887. 4°. Collection des inventaires, *etc.* 1814-15. b. *etc.*

LABANDE (L. H.) Histoire de Beauvais jusqu'au commencement du xv° siècle. pp. 381.
Paris, 1892. 8°.   10172. f. 23.

LHUILLIER (V.) Beauvais en 1789. 1890. 8°. Ac. Beauvais. *Société Académique*. Mémoires. Tom. 14.   Ac. 278/2.

MARTIN (A.) Une Visite à Beauvais. pp. 94.
Paris, 1894. 8°.   10174. aaa. 50.

See also OISE, *Department.*

BEAVER. (H. T.) Castorologia. pp. 238.
Lond. 1892. 8°.   7206. h. 18.

BEC, *Abbey.* PORÉE ( ) L'Abbaye du Bec et ses écoles. pp. 106. *Évreux*, 1892. 8°.
4629. dd. 17.

BECHUANALAND. BRUCE (L. K.-) The Story of an African Chief, Khama. pp. 71.
Lond. 1893. 8°.   10606. aa. 19.

HEPBURN (J. D.) Twenty Years in Khama's Country. pp. 397. *Lond.* 1895. 8°. 4767. d. 21.

LLOYD (E.) Three African Chiefs. Khâmé, Sebelé, and Bathoeng. pp. 271.
Lond. 1895. 8°.   10606. bb. 41.

MACKENZIE (J.) Bechuanaland. pp. 13.
Cape Town, 1884. 8°.   Pam. 66.

—— Bechuanaland and our Progress Northward. pp. 12. *Cape Town*, 1884. 8°. Pam. 66.

—— The High Commissionership. pp. 16.
Lond. 1886. 8°.   Pam. 66.

See also AFRICA, *South.*

BECOISEAU, Château. Roz (F.) Les vieux châteaux de la Brie. pp. 27.
Coulommiers, 1894. 4°.   Pam. 91.

BEDFORD. BEDFORD. Bedford: town and schools. pp. 104. *Bedford*, 1890. 8°.
10368. aa. 43.

—— Municipal Handbook, 1892. pp. 89.
Bedford, 1891. 16°.   10360. a. 22.

—— Where to buy at Bedford. pp. 55.
Brighton, 1891. 4°.   10368. k. 20.

BEDFORDSHIRE. BEDFORD, *County.* Illustrated Bedfordshire. pp. 75.
Nottingham, 1895. 4°.   10351. k. 22.

BLAYDES (F. A.) Calendar of Bedfordshire Wills. pp. 43. *Bedford*, 1893. 8°. 9906. b. 2.

—— Genealogia Bedfordiensis. 1538-1700. pp. 507. *Lond.* 1890. 4°.   9916. c. 21.

HERTFORD, *County.* Murray's Handbook for Hertfordshire and Bedfordshire. pp. 19. 260.
Lond. 1895. 8°.   2364. b. 31.

BEECH TREE. *See* FORESTRY.

BEE-EATER. *See* MEROPIDAE.

BEER AND BREWING. A., B. H. The Cottage Brewer. pp. 16. *Bolton*, 1892. 8°.
7942. a. 59.

Ac. G.B. & I. *Federated Institutes of Brewing.* Journal. *Lond.* 1895, *etc.* 8°.   Ac. 3918.

BIRCH (G.) Handbook of Gauging at Breweries. pp. 133. *Wolverhampton*, 1894. 8°. 7942. a. 76.

BRISTOL. *Garton's Prize Medal Ale Brewery.* Description. pp. 41. *Lond.* 1891. 16°.
7942. a. 64. (3.).

HARRIS (W.) Lecture on Brewers' accounts. pp. 73. *Dublin*, 1893. 8°.   8535. df. 28.

HOOPER (E. G.) Manual of Brewing. pp. 366.
Lond. 1891. 8°.   07945. e. 58.

BEER AND BREWING—*continued.*

INSTRUCTIONS. Instructions on the handling of Pilsener or Lager Beer. pp. 18.
Lond. 1895. 8°.   Pam. 94.

JOHNSON (G. M.) Essais sur la science du Brassage. pp. 421. *Brux.* 1890. 8°. 7944. ee. 32.

JOHNSTRUP (H. C.) Meddelelser om Kongens Bryghus. pp. 40. *Kjøbenhavn*, 1891. 8°.
10280. eee. 17.

LINDET (L.) La Bière. pp. 206. 1892. 8°. Encyclopédie des aide-mémoire.   8709. g.

LINTNER (C. J.) Grundriss der Bierbrauerei. pp. 159. 1893. 8°. Thaer-Bibliothek. 7078. d.

LONDON. *Institute of Brewing.* List of Members. pp. 12. *Lond.* 1891. 8°.   08227. g. 26.

MORITZ (E. R.) Text-book of the Science of Brewing. pp. 534. *Lond.* 1891. 8°. 07945. f. 31.

P.P. *London.* Hop & Malt Trades' Journal. Nos. 1-5. *Lond.* 1891, 92. 4°.   1866. b. 6.

POCOCK (J.) Brewing of Non-excisable Beers. pp. 64. *Bangor*, 1895. 8°.   07914. e. 50.

S., H. Brewery Companies. pp. 88.
Lond. 1895. 8°.   8226. cc. 56.

SCARISBRICK (J.) Beer Manual. pp. 106. 1892. 8°. Revenue Series.   8226. cc.

STRUVE (E.) Die Entwicklung des bayerischen Braugewerbes. pp. 291. 1893. 8°. SCHMOLLER (G.) Staats- und socialwissenshaftliche Forschungen. Bd. 12.   8205. dd.

THURSTON (C. S.) Beer Gravity Tables.
Ipswich, 1891. 8°.   8548. de. 19.

WRIGHT (H. E.) Handy Book for Brewers. pp. 516. *Lond.* 1892. 8°.   07945. e. 83.

See also HOPS.

BEES. BELTRAMINI DE' CASATI (F.) Delle bibliographie di quella apistica. pp. 22.
Firenze, 1882. 8°.   Pam. 6.

Ac. PARIS. *Société Centrale d'Agriculture.* L'Apiculteur. Année 34, *etc.*
Paris, 1890, *etc.* 8°.   Ac. 3610/3.

BAELZ (C.) Das Recht an Bienen. pp. 135.
Stuttgart, 1891. 8°.   05604. h. 8.

BATH (W. H.) The Young Collector's Handbook of Bees. pp. 108. 1888. 8°. Young Collector Series.   7001. aaa.

BEE-KEEPING. Modern Bee-Keeping. pp. 95.
Lond. 1895. 8°.   7297. a. 62.

BELLEROSE (L. H.) Petit manuel d'apiculture. pp. 139. *Arthabaskaville*, 1883. 16°. 7297. a. 57.

BELTRAMINI DE' CASATI (F.) Vocabolario apistico Italiano. pp. 376. *Milano*, 1890. 8°.
7297. e. 28.

CANESTRINI (G.) Apicoltura. pp. 196.
Milano, 1894. 8°.   012200. h. 114.

COWAN (T. W.) The Honey Bee. pp. 220.
Lond. 1890. 8°.   7297. a. 40.

COWAN (T. W.) British Bee-Keeper's Guidebook. pp. 176. *Lond.* 1893. 8°. 7297. aaa. 37.

FRIESE (H.) Die Bienenfauna von Deutschland. pp. 80. *Berl.* 1893. 8°.   7297. c. 18. (14.)

HALLEUX (D.) Quelques mots sur la culture des Abeilles. pp. 92. *Huy*, 1891. 8°. 7297. e. 36.

HOVIND (H.) Bier og Honning. pp. 424.
Kristiania, 1894. 8°.   7298. c. 17.

JANET (CHARLES) Observations sur les Frelons. pp. 4. *Paris*, 1895. 4°.   Pam. 42.

KALTENEGGER (L.) Der Honig vor dem Richterstuhle der Geschichte, *etc.* pp. 165.
Linz, 1892. 8°.   7944. c. 33.

KELLEN (T.) Bilder und Skizzen aus dem Leben der Bienen. pp. 227. *Nördlingen*, 1890. 8°.
7297. bb. 22.

P.P. London. British Bee-Keepers' Adviser.
Lond. 1888-90. 4°.   P.P. 2043. ab

BEES—*continued.*

ROTHSCHUETZ (E.) Illustrierter Bienenzuchts-
betrieb. *Wien,* 1893, *etc.* 12°.   7297. a.

SAMSON (G. G.) Bees for Pleasure and Profit.
pp. 82. *Lond.* 1892. 8°.   7297. a. 50.

SIMMINS (S.) Modern Bee-Farm. pp. 274.
Lond. 1893. 8°.   7297. bb. 29.

THIRAUT (S.) Manuel d'Apiculture. pp. 104.
Liège, 1892. 8°.   7298. d. 3. (13.)

TOMBU (L.) Le Guide pratique de l'apiculteur.
pp. 53. *Liège,* 1895. 8°.   7297. b. 29.

WELLS (G.) Guide Book on the Two Queen
System of Bee Keeping. pp. 15.
Snodland, 1894. 8°.   7204. a. 31. (8.)

WHITE (C. N.) Pleasurable Bee-Keeping.
pp. 184. *Lond.* 1895. 8°.   7298. aaa. 25.

GLOCK (J. P.) Die Symbolik der Bienen in Sage,
Dichtung, Kultus, *etc.* pp. 411.
Hiedelberg, 1891. 8°.   011824. h. 41.

ROBERT-TORNOW (W.) De apium mellisque apud
veteres significatione. pp. 177.
Berolini, 1893. 8°.   11312. e. 34.

See also HYMENOPTERA.

BEETLES. *See* COLEOPTERA.

BEGBROKE. Ac. Oxford. *Historical Society.*
STAPLETON (M. H. A.) Three Oxfordshire
Parishes. pp. 400. *Oxford,* 1893. 8°. Ac. 8126/15.

BEGONIA. RYDER (S.) How to grow Tuber-
ous Begonias. pp. 46. *Manchester,* 1890. 8°.
7074. e. 10. (2.)

BEGUINES. LE GRAND (L.) Les Béguines
de Paris. 1895. 8°. Ac. Paris. *Société de
l'Histoire.* Mémoires. Tom. 20. Ac. 6883/2.

BEHAR. BEHAR. A Protest to the proposed
Cadastral Survey in Behar. 2 pt. 1892. 8°.
08227. i. 36.

See also BENGAL.

BEHARI LANGUAGE. HOERNLE (A. F. R.)
and GRIERSON (G. A.) Dictionary of the Bihārī
Language. *Calcutta,* 1889, *etc.* 4°.
12907. g. 23.

BEHRING SEA. DAWSON (G. M.) Geo-
gical notes on the coasts and islands of Behring
Sea. pp. 29. 1894. 8°. Ac. U.S. *Geological
Soc.* Bulletin. Vol. 5.   Ac. 3187.

U.S.A. *Coast Survey.* Early Expeditions to
Behring Sea and Strait. pp. 14. *Wash.* 1891. 4°.
10460. g. 11.

BEHRING SEA. *Tribunal of Arbitration.* Case
presented on the part of the Government of Her
Britannic Majesty. 5 vol, *Lond.* 1893. fol.
6915. h. 4.

—— Report of the Behring Sea Commission.
2 pt. *Lond.* 1893. fol.   6915. h. 7.

—— Argument of Her Majesty's Government.
pp. 162. *Lond.* 1893. fol.   6915. h. 6.

—— Counter-case presented on the part of the
Government of Her Britannic Majesty. 3 vol.
Lond. 1893. fol.   6915. h. 5.

—— Report on the Fur-Seal Fisheries of the
Pribylov Islands in 1890. By H. W. Elliott.
pp. 338. *Paris,* 1893. 8°.   6915. f. 3.

—— Indexes to the British Case, Counter-case,
and Argument. pp. 43. *Lond.* 1893. fol.
6915. h. 8.

—— The Case of the United States. 4 vol.
Wash. 1892. 8°.   6915. g. 8.

—— Mémoire des États-Unis, *etc.* pp. 230.
Paris, 1893. 8°.   6915. g. 10.

—— Argument of the United States, *etc.* 2 vol.
Wash 1893. 8°.   6915. g. 6.

BEHRING SEA.—*continued.*

—— Plaidoyer des États-Unis. pp. 398.
Paris, 1893. 8°.   6915. g. 11.

—— The Counter-Case of the United States.
2 vol. *Wash.* 1893. 8°.   6915. g. 7.

—— Contre-mémoire des États-Unis. pp. 154.
Paris, 1893. 8°.   6915. g. 9.

—— Report of the Proceedings of the Tribunal
of Arbitration. pp. 2336. *Paris,* 1893. fol.
6915. h. 9.

—— Sentence du Tribunal d'Arbitrage. *Fr & Eng.*
pp. 30. *Lond.* 1893. fol.   6915. h. 2.

—— Déclarations faites par le Tribunal d'Arbitrage. pp. 4. *Lond.* 1893. fol.   6915. h. 3.

—— Behring Sea Arbitration. Letters to The
Times. pp. 87. *Lond.* 1893. 8°.   Pam. 65.

DUANE (R.) The Case of the "Sayward," 1891.
pp. 14. *Phila.* 1891. 8°.   Pam. 33.

RAYNER (R.) An answer to the Hon. E. J.
Phelps' paper on the Bering Sea controversy.
pp. 22. *Salem,* 1891. 8°.   Pam. 65.

STANTON (S. B.) The Behring Sea Controversy.
pp. 102. *N.Y.* 1892. 8°.   8176. bbb. 18.

WISHART (A.) The Behring Sea Question.
pp. 54. *Edinb.* 1893. 8°.   8176. aaa. 49.

BELAD-EL-JERID. *See* SAHARA.

BELFAST. BELFAST. Town Book of the
Corporation of Belfast, 1613-1816. pp. 351.
Belf. 1892. 8°.   10390. h. 16.

—— Art Album of photographic Views of Belfast. 12 plates. *Belf.* 1895. 8°. 10390. bbb. 28.

ANDERSON (J.) Catalogue of early Belfast Printed
Books. pp. 85. *Belf.* 1890. fol. 11900. i. 32.

—— Catalogue of early Belfast Books. Supplementary. pp. 23. *Belf.* 1894. 4°. 11900. i. 37.

**BELGIAN DIALECT AND LITERA-
TURE, French.**

COLINGE (J.) Encore 1000 expressions vicieuses
belges. pp. 30. *Namur,* 1892. 8°.
12903. dd. 33. (8.)

GAUTIER (L.) La Littérature catholique et
nationale. pp. 376. *Bruges,* 1894. 8°.
011850. i. 53.

NÈVE (F.) La Renaissance des Lettres en
Belgique. pp. 439. *Louvain,* 1890. 8°.
011840. l. 48.

See also WALLOONS : For Flemish Language and
Literature, *see* DUTCH.

BELGIUM. — Antiquities.   *See* NETHER-
LANDS.

Army.

ARMÉE. L'armée de demain. pp. 30.
Brux. 1893. 8°.   8830. d. 11. (12.)

BRIALMONT (A. H.) Situation militaire de la
Belgique. pp. 117. *Brux.* 1894. 8°.
8831. k. 33.

GIRARD (C. H. E.) La Belgique et la guerre
prochaine. pp. 88. *Brux.* 1890. 8°.
8826. ff. 12.

LAROIÈRE (L. de) Panthéon militaire. pp. 587.
Bruges, 1880. 8°.   10759. k. 6.

P.P. *Brussels.* Annuaire de l'Armée belge, 1891.
pp. 530. *Brux.* 1891. 8°.   P.P. 2421. bb.

TIMMERMANS (J. J. T.) Historique de artillerie belge. pp. 112. *Gand,* 1886. 8°.
8824. ccc. 28.

WEIMERSKIRCH (T.) Étude de la défence nationale. pp. 149. *Brux.* 1890. 8°. 8823. dd. 40.

—— La question militaire. pp. 60.
Brux. 1894. 8°.   8081. g. 18.

Constitution and Government.

See infra : POLITICS.

BELGIUM—*continued.*

Emigration from. *See infra :* TRADE.

History, 1830, etc.

BALAU (L.) Soixante-dix ans d'histoire de Belgique. pp. 467. *Brux.* 1890. 8°. 9414. e. 2.

LALLEMAND (A.) Le Livre d'Or de la Dynastie belge. *Gand*, 1891, *etc.* 8°. 9415. k. 1.

JAUCKEN (L.) Aux héros de 1830. Grande scène historique. pp. 15. *Liége*, 1890. 8°.   Pam. 52.

BERTRAND (L.) Léopold II. et son règne, 1865–90. *Brux.* 1890, *etc.* 8°.   8079. b. 3.

For History before 1830 : *see* NETHERLANDS.

Politics : Revision of the Constitution.

VAUTHIER (M.) Das Staatsrecht des Königreichs Belgien. pp. 192. 1892. 8°.

MARQUARDSEN (H.) Handbuch des öffentlichen Rechts. Bd. 4.   6006. k.

NYSSENS (A.) Le Suffrage universel tempéré. pp. 12. *Brux.* 1890. 8°.   Pam. 73.

VERCAMER (C.) Nos prochaines Élections. pp. 48. *Brux.* 1890. 8°.   Pam. 73.

VOLDERS (J.) Le Peuple et le suffrage universel. pp. 16. *Gand*, 1890. 8°.   Pam. 73.

HOFFSCHMIDT (A. d') Effets de la représentation proportionnelle. pp. 70. *Brux.* 1891. 8°.   Pam. 64.

KEYSER (T.) Questions politiques et sociales. pp. 100. *Gand*, 1891. 8°.   Pam. 73.

PARTI. Le parti flottant et la revision. pp. 22. *Brux.* 1891. 8°.   Pam. 73.

VANDERKINDERE (L.) Fédération Libérale. La revision constitutionnelle. pp. 36. *Brux.* 1891. 8°.   Pam. 73.

BANNING (É.) La révision. pp. 58. *Brux.* 1892. 8°.   Pam. 73.

BELGIUM. Les elections à la Constituante, 1892. *Brux.* 1892. 8°.   Pam. 73.

BRUSSELS. La situation des partis à Bruxelles. pp. 24. *Brux.* 1892. 8°.   Pam. 73.

GREEF (G. de) La Constituante et le régime représentatif. pp. 338. *Brux.* 1892. 8°.   8010. de. 12.

ROLIN (É.) Note sur l'introduction du Veto royal suspensif dans la Constitution. pp. 20. *Brux.* 1892. 8°.   Pam. 73.

BELGIUM. Constitution revisée de la Belgique. pp. 39. *Brux.* 1893. 8°.   Pam. 73.

—— La Constituante et les Élections futures. pp. 31. *Brux.* 1893. 8°.   Pam. 73.

BREUX (F. de) Questions constitutionelles. pp. 292. *Louvain*, 1893. 8°.   8081. e. 7.

CHAMP. À travers le champ de bataille. pp. 379. *Gand*, 1893. 8°.   8051. de. 18.

QUÉKER (C. de) De la représentation des intérêts sociaux au parlement. pp. 31. *Brux.* 1893. 8°.   Pam. 73.

VERSPEYEN (G.) Le Parti catholique belge. pp. 153. *Gand*, 1893. 8°.   3925. b. 50.

ARNAUD (L.) La Revision Belge. pp. 238. *Paris*, 1894. 12°.   8081. aa. 17.

FRÈRE-ORBAN (H. J. W.) La Révision constitutionnelle en Belgique. pp. 155. *Brux.* 1894. 8°.   8081. g. 17.

GODDYN (A.) Les Listes électorales. Formation et revision. pp. 263. *Gand*, 1894. 12°.   8081. a. 3.

MOMMAERT (J.) La Sincérité du Régime représentatif. pp. 132. *Brux.* 1894. 8°. 8081. f. 8.

BELGIUM.—Politics, etc.—*continued.*

THIEBAULD (C.) Commentaire des articles revisés de la Constitution. pp. 208. *Brux.* 1894. 8°.   8081. h. 7.

WEIMERSKIRCH (T.) La Question militaire et la question congolaise. pp. 60. *Brux.* 1894. 8°.   8081. g. 18.

FRÈRE-ORBAN (H. J. W.) La Situation présente. pp. 46. *Brux.* 1895. 8°.   8081. aaa. 11.

PAQUAIJ (O.) Le Prolétaire urbain et rural. pp. 48. *Brux.* 1895. 8°.   Pam. 82.

PHILOPATOR. Libres propos d'un Belge. pp. 76. *Brux.* 1895. 8°.   8081. a. 2.

WASSENHOVE (A. v.) Le Parti catholique en face de la représentation proportionnelle. pp. 43. *Brux.* 1895. 8°.   8081. f. 9.

WOESTE (C.) À travers dix années, 1885–1894. 2 tom. *Brux.* 1895. 8°.   012357. k. 26. *See also* ELECTIONS.

Foreign.

FOUCAULT DE MONDION (A.) La Belgique livrée à l'Allemagne. 1886–91. pp. 301. *Paris*, 1891. 12°.   8026. aa. 23.

LANCKMAN (J. B.) Code des relations extérieures de la Belgique. pp. 770. *Braine-le-Comte*, 1892. 8°.   5695. a. 17.

MAZADE (C. de) L'Europe et les neutralités. pp. 117. *Paris*, 1893. 12°.   8026. bbb. 36.

WOESTE (C.) La Neutralité Belge. pp. 85. *Brux.* 1891. 8°.   8026. i. 2.

Roman Catholic Church.

See supra : Politics : ROMAN CATHOLIC CHURCH.

Topography.

BAEDEKER (C.) Belgium and Holland. pp. 423. *Leipsic*, 1894. 8°.   2352. a.

BLACK (C. B.) Belgium. pp. 224. 7. *Lond.* 1894. 8°,   10271. aa. 7.

BOSSUT (H.) Guide pratique du Vélocipédiste. pp. 127. *Brux.* 1891. 12°.   10271. aa. 4.

COOK (T.) Tourists' Handbook for Belgium, *etc.* pp. 376. *Lond.* 1895. 8°.   10271. aa. 10.

JOANNE (P.) Belgique. pp. 399. *Paris*, 1890. 8°.   10271. aa. 3.

JOURDAIN (A.) and STALLE (L. v.) Dictionnaire encyclopédique de géographie de Belgique. *Brux.* 1895, *etc.* 8°.   010271. i.

LAMI (E. O.) Voyages pittoresques et techniques. pp. 547. *Paris*, 1892. 8°   10172. g. 8.

LINDLEY (P.) Walks in Belgium. pp. 92. *Lond.* 1894. *obl.* 8°.   10271. a. 4.

WARD, LOCK AND Co. Illustrated guide to Belgium. pp. 266. *Lond.* 1892. 8°.   10271. aa. 6.

Trade and Finance.

ANSIAUX (M.) La question monétaire en Belgique. pp. 130. *Liége*, 1892. 8°. 08207. ee. 16.

FRÈRE-ORBAN (H. J. W.) La question monétaire en Belgique. pp. 116. *Brux.* 1890. 8°.   08229. g. 41.

ROCHUSSEN (J. J.) Supplément à " la Question Monétaire en Belgique de M. Frère-Orban. pp. 50. *La Haye*, 1890. 8°.   8226. g. 40. (7.)

MAHAIM (E.) La politique commerciale de la Belgique. 1892. 8°. Ac. Leipsic. *Verein für Socialpolitik.* Schriften. Vol. 49. Ac. 2322.

MARTEL (H.) Le Développement commercial de la Belgique. *Brux.* 1894, *etc.* 8°.   08227. i.

P.P. Brussels. Annuaire officiel du commerce. *Brux.* 1890. 4°.   P.P. 2421. ca.

BELGIUM.—Trade, etc.—*continued.*

RICHALD (L.) Les finances communales en Belgique. 2 tom. *Brux.* 1892. 12°. 08227. de. 14.

BOKEMEYER (H.) Das Auswanderungswesen in der Schweiz, in Belgien, *etc.* pp. 75.
Berl. 1892. 8°.　　　　　　　　Pam. 66.

BOURÉE (A.) Les Conditions du travail en Belgique. pp. 70. *Paris,* 1890. 8° 8276. f. 33.

DE CAMPS (G.) L'Évolution sociale en Belgique. L'enquête ouvrière, 1886. pp. 307.
Brux. 1890. 8°.　　　　　　　　08276. g. 2.

BELLS. ALLSOP (F. C.) Electric Bell Construction. pp. 131. *Lond.* 1890. 8°. 8757. bb. 27.

BOTTONE (S. R.) Electric-Bells and all about them. pp. 201. *Lond.* 1892. 8°. 8757. bb. 32.

CLARK (J. W.) History of the Bells of King's College, Camb. pp. 20. *Camb.* 1881. 8°. Pam. 3.

GERMAIN (L.) La Cloche de Bermont, Vosges. pp. 15. *Nancy,* 1890. 8°. 7706. g. 4. (10.)

—— Les anciennes cloches de Saugues. pp. 71. *Nancy,* 1890. 8°. 7706. g. 6. (7.)

MADGE (S.) Moulton Church and its Bells. pp. 95. *Lond.* 1895. 8°. 3477. ee. 3.

RAVEN (J. J.) Church Bells of Suffolk. pp. 266. *Lond* 1890. 8°. 3478. g. 13.

JONES (W.) Clavis Campanalogia. pp. 430. *Walthamstow,* 1887. 8°. 7944. d. 13.

PERMUTATION. Permutation; or, Mental Campanology. pp. 16. 1891. 16°. Pam. 24.

THOMPSON (W. H.) Diagram of a system of peals of Union Triples. pp. 47. *Camb.* 1893. 8°.
7898. b. 8.

BELLUNO. GUGGENHEIM (M.) Il Palazzo dei Rettori di Belluno. pp. 13.
Venezia, 1894. fol. K.T.C. 8. b. (2.)

BELPER. WILLOTT (C.) Historical Records of Belper. *Belper,* 1885. 8°. 10348. ccc. 58. (6.)

BENARES. MĪRZĀ AMĪR BEG. The Handbook of the sights of Lucknow and Benares. pp. 46. *Lucknow,* 1891. 8°. Pam. 88.

MURDOCH (J.) Kasi, or Benares. pp. 39. *Madras,* 1894. 8°. 10056. h. 9.

BENDIGO. Bendigo. pp. 54. *Bendigo,* 1893. *obl.* fol. 10491. de. 16.

MACKAY (G.) History of Bendigo. pp. 195. *Bendigo,* 1891. 8°. 10492. c. 36.

BENEDICTINES. BENEDICT, *Saint.* Regula Sancti Patris Benedicti. pp. 143. *Ratisbonae,* 1892. 8°. 4071. de. 27.

BERNARDUS, *Abbot.* Bernardi in Regulam S. Benedicti expositio. pp. 435.
Montis Casini. 1894. 8°. 4071. l. 14.

BENEDICTINES. Album Benedictinum. pp. 549. *Phila.* 1880. 8°. 4782. k. 12.

BESSE ( ) Le Moine Bénédictin. pp. 138. 1892. 8°. Biographies Monastiques. No. 1.
4855. aaa.

DOUAIS (C.) L'arrivée des Bénédictins à Saint-Savin de Lavedan, 1625. pp. 46.
Paris, 1891. 8°. 4629. ee. 7. (5.)

P.P. *Maredsous,* Revue Bénédictine. *Maredsous,* 1884, *etc.* 8°. P.P. 173. c.

VANEL (J. B.) Les Bénédictins de Saint-Germain-des-Prés. pp. 379. *Paris,* 1894. 8°.
4630. dd. 3.

See also BEC: EVESHAM: EYSSES: GLADBACH: GLASTONBURY: HAMBYE: MONTE CASSINO: RELIGIOUS ORDERS, *etc. etc.*

BENEVENTO. MEOMARTINI (A.) I Monumenti di Benevento. *Benevento,* 1889, *etc.* 8°.
924.

BENGAL. HUNTER (*Sir* W. W.) Bengal MS. Records. 4 vol. *Lond.* 1894. 8°.
8023. dd. 25.

MAHEṢACHANDRA DATTA. Folk-Lore in Bengal. *Calcutta,* 1893, *etc.* 8°. 12430. k.

NANDALĀLA SARKĀR. Extension of Local Government in Bengal. pp. 24.
Calcutta, 1892. 8°. Pam. 67.

RĀMAGOPĀLA SĀNYĀLA. Biography of Bengal Celebrities. *Calcutta,* 1889, *etc.* 8°. 10606. c. 20.

RAMFSACHANDRA DATTA. Brief History of Bengal. pp. 104. *Calcutta,* 1893. 8°. 9056. b. 33.

—— Separation of judicial and executive functions in Bengal. pp. 17. *Calcutta,* 1894. 8°.
Pam. 33.

RISLEY (H. H.) Tribes of Bengal. Anthropometic Data. 2 vol. *Calcutta,* 1891. 8°.
010057. k. 1.

—— Ethnographic glossary. 2 vol. *Calcutta,* 1891. 8°. 010057. k. 2.

See also BAKARGANG: BANKURA: BEHAR: BURDWAN: CHOTU NAGPORE: INDIA: LAW REPORTS: TIPPERAH.

Bay of.

G.B. & I. *Hydrographic Office.* The Bay of Bengal Pilot. pp. 476. *Lond.* 1892. 8°.
10496. f. 31.

BENGALI LANGUAGE AND LITERATURE. ADĀLAT KHAN. Vocabulary of one thousand words in Bengalī, *etc.* pp. 67.
Calcutta, 1890. 8°. 12907. b. 39.

CAREY (W.) Dictionary of the Bengalee Language. pp. 637. *Calcutta,* 1890. 8°. 12907. cc. 31.

DURGĀCHARANA VANDYOPĀDHYĀYA. Bengali-and-English Dictionary. pp. 1114.
Calcutta, 1889. 16°. 12906. bbb. 34.

RĀMACHANDRA GHOSHA. Student's Dictionary in English and Bengali. pp. 1080.
Calcutta, 1891. 8°. 12907. cc. 34.

BEAMES (J.) Grammar of the Bengali Language. pp. 178. *Oxford,* 1894. 8°. 12907. bbb. 43.

YATES (W.) Introduction to the Bengali Language. *Calcutta,* 1891. 12°. 12907. cc. 30.

MUKHOPĀDHYĀYA (F. X.) Differences in idiom between Bengali and English. pp. 95.
Calcutta, 1889. 8°. 14131. g. 27.

RAJANĪKĀNTA MUKHOPĀDHYĀYA. Idiomatic phrases in English and Bengali. pp. 169.
Calcutta, 1889. 12°. 14131. g. 25.

DHANAVALLABHA SET. How to translate from Bengalee into English. pp. 118.
Calcutta, 1889. 12°. 12901. ccc. 9. (3.)

KRISHNABANDHU MUKHOPĀDHYĀYA. Mode of translation. pp. 135. *Serajgunge,* 1891. 12°.
14131. e. 21. (1.)

VENĪMĀDHAVA GANGOPĀDAYĀYA. Manual of translation from Bengali into English. pp. 266.
Calcutta, 1891. 8°. 14131. g. 26.

HARAPRASĀDA SĀSTRĪ. Vernacular Literature of Bengal. pp. 16. *Calcutta,* 1891. 8°.
14131. d. 24.

BENI-HASAN. *See* EGYPT, *Antiquities.*

BENNACHIE. MAC CONNOCHIE (A. I.) Bennachie. pp. 174. *Aberd.* 1890. 8°.
010370. f. 15.

BEN NEVIS. BUCHAN (A.) Meteorology of Ben Nevis. pp. 406. 1890. 4°. Ac. Edinburgh. *Royal Society.* Transactions. Vol. 34.
2099. g.

BERBERIDAE. CITERNE (P. É.) Berbéridées. pp. 160. *Paris,* 1892. 8°. 07028. m. 12.

BERBERS: KABYLES.

HANOTEAU (L. A.) La Kabylie et les coutumes Kabyles. 3 tom. *Paris,* 1893. 8°. 010096. m. 2.

BERBERS—*continued.*

LIOREL (J.) Races Berbères. pp. 544.
Paris, 1893. 8°.　　　　　10095. de. 19.

SCHIRMER (H.) De Nomine populorum qui
Berberi vulgo dicuntur. pp. 80.
Parisiis, 1892. 8°.　　　　010096. ee. 41.

See also ALGERIA : SAHARA.

Languages.

BASSET (R.) Études sur les dialectes berbères.
pp. 164. 1894. 8°. Ac. Algiers. *École
Supérieure.* Publications. Tom. 14. Ac. 5380/2.

—— Le dialecte berbère de Taroudant. pp. 63.
1894. 8°. Ac. Florence. *Società Asiatica.*
Giornale. Vol. 8.　　　　　.Ac. 8804.

BRINTON (D. G.) Alphabets of the Berbers.
pp. 11. *Phila.* 1894. 8°.　12910. d. 31. (10.)

GABELENTZ (G. v. d.) Die Verwandtschaft
des Baskischen mit den Berbersprachen.
pp. 286. *Braunschweig*, 1894. 8°. 12910. d. 33.

GOURLIANT (E.) La conversation française-kabyle.
pp. 228. *Miliana*, 1893. 8°.　12910. a. 42.

BERCK - SUR - MER. PLANCOUARD (L.)
Monographie de l'Église de Berck-sur-mer.
pp. 68. *Montreuil*, 1891. 12°. 10105. e. 4. (5.)

BERG, Duchy of. HARLESS (W.) Beiträge
zur Kenntnis der Vergangenheit des Bergischen
Landes. pp. 262. *Düsseldorf*, 1890. 8°.
　　　　　　　　　　　　　10255. f. 17.

BERGA. VILARDAGA Y CAÑELLAS (J.) Historia de Berga. pp. 376. *Barcelona*, 1890. 8°.
　　　　　　　　　　　　　10161. de. 18.

BERGAMO, Town and Province. BERGAMO.
Un Giorno a Bergamo. *Bergamo*, 1892. 8°.
　　　　　　　　　　　　　10129. a. 6.

CARNAZZI (I.) Bergamo e sua provincia.
pp. 308. *Bergamo*, 1893. 8°.　10136. c. 26.

FORNONI (E.) Studii sulla antica città di Bergamo. pp. 100. *Bergamo*, 1891. 8°. 10136. h. 12.

FRIZZONI (G.) La Galleria Morelli in Bergamo.
pp. 89. *Bergamo*, 1892. 8°.　　7857. k. 32.

LOROK (J. E.) Altbergamaskische Sprachdenkmäler. pp. 226. 1893. 8°. FOERSTER (W.)
Romanische Bibliothek. No. 10.　12238. e.

MAZZOLENI (P.) I Bergamaschi in Polonia nel
1863. pp. 81. *Bergamo*, 1893. 8°. 9476. i. 16.

BERGEN. JÆGER (H.) Bergen og Bergen-
serne. pp. 112. *Bergen*, 1889. 4°. 10281. l. 4.

BERGERAC. CHARIER (G.) Les Jurades
de la ville de Bergerac. *Bergerac*, 1892, *etc.* 8°.
　　　　　　　　　　　　　10172. b. 4.

LABROUE (E.) Bergerac sous les Anglais.
pp. 231. *Bordeaux*, 1893. 4°.　10171. ff. 5.

BERGHEIM. KORTH (L.) Volksthümliches
aus dem Kreise Bergheim. pp. 60. 1891. 8°.
Ac. Cologne. *Historischer Verein*, Annalen.
Heft 52.　　　　　　　　　Ac. 7335.

BERIBERI. BENTLEY (A. J. M.) Bèri-Bèri.
pp. 245. *Edinb.* 1893. 8°.　　7561. d. 6.

BRADDON (W. L.) Dochmia and Beriberi. pp. 68.
Singapore, 1893. 8°.　　　　7560. f. 44.

GILES (G. M. J.) Report of an investigation into
the causes of Beri-beri. pp. 156. 2.
Shillong, 1890. 8°.　　　　　7561. i. 39.

LAMB (J. M.) Beriberi of British North Borneo.
pp. 31. *Lond.* 1889. 8°.　07305. h. 16. (4.)

MANSON (P.) Beriberi. 1893. 8°. DAVIDSON (A.)
Hygiene of Warm Climates.　,7686. dd. 2.

PEKELHARING (C. A.) Recherches sur la nature
et la cause du Béri-Béri. pp. 140.
Utrecht, 1888. 4°.　　　　　7620. g. 7.

BERKSHIRE. Ac. Oxford. *Historical Soc.*
Index to Wills in the Court of the Archdeacon of
Berks, 1508-1652. pp. 199, *Oxford*, 1893. 8°.
　　　　　　　　　　　　　Ac. 8126/14.

—— Reading. *Berks Archæological Soc.* Quarterly
Journal. April, 1889, *etc. Reading*, 1889, *etc.* 8°.
　　　　　　　　　　　　　Ac. 5695.

P.P. *Lond.* Berkshire Notes & Queries.
Lond. 1890, *etc.* 8°.　　　　P.P. 6019. id.

WALFORD (E.) Tourist's Guide to Berkshire.
pp. 131. *Lond.* 1892. 8°.　　10352. a. 62.

BERLIN. Ac. Berlin. *Verein für die Geschichte Berlin.* Mittheilungen.
Berl. 1884, *etc.* 4°.　　Ac. 7327/2. & 492.

—— Urkunden-Buch zur berlinischen Chronik.
1232-1550. pp. 514. *Berl.* 1880. fol. Ac. 7327.

—— Vermischte Schriften. 3 Bde.
Berl. 1888. fol.　　　　　Ac. 7327.

—— Die Stammbäume der Mitglieder der französischen Colonie in Berlin. pp. 220.
Berl. 1887. fol.　　　　　Ac. 7327.

AJALBERT (J.) Notes sur Berlin. pp. 115.
Paris, 1894. 8°.　　　　　10256. a. 22.

BERLIN. Die Bevölkerungs- und Wohnungs-
Aufnahme, 1885. *Berl.* 1890. *etc.* 4°.　8223. e.

—— BERLIN. Berlin. Typen und Bilder.
pp. 110. *Berl.* 1895. *obl.* 8°.　10256. de. 1.

BERLIN SOCIETY. Aus der Berliner Gesellschaft
unter Kaiser Wilhelm II. pp. 297.
Berl. 1892. 8°.　　　　　10256. c. 10.

BORRMANN (R.) Leitfaden der Entwickelungsgeschichte Berlins. pp. 24. *Berl.* 1893. 8°.
　　　　　　　　　　　10105. ee. 12. (9.)

CARELSEN (G.) Berlijn. pp. 332.
Amsterd. 1891. 8°.　　　　10255. f. 25.

CARSTENN-LICHTERFELDE (v.) Die zukünftige
Entwicklung Berlins. pp. 59. *Berl.* 1892. 8°.
　　　　　　　　　　　10107. ff. 28. (5.)

DIESTELKAMP (L.) Jetzt fort mit der Kirchennoth
Berlins. pp. 21. *Berl.* 1890. 8°. 3911. ee. 50. (5.)

DULLO (G.) Berliner Plakate des Jahres 1848.
pp. 90. *Zürich*, 1893. 8°.　9005. d. 26. (13.)

FISCHER (L. H.) Aus Berlins Vergangenheit.
pp. 205. *Berl.* 1891. 8°.　　10255. f. 24.

GEIGER (L.) Berlin, 1688-1840. *Berl.* 1892, *etc.* 8°.
　　　　　　　　　　　011824. k.

GERSAL (L.) L'Athènes de la Spree. pp. 395.
Paris, 1892. 12°.　　　　　10256. b. 44.

GILLET DE GRANDMONT ( ) Berlin au point de
vue de l'hygiène. pp. 152. *Paris*, 1891. 8°.
　　　　　　　　　　　7391. g. 14.

HELLMANN (G.) Das klima von Berlin.
1891, *etc.* fol. Ac. Berlin. *Meteorologisches
Institut.* Abhandlungen. Bd. 1. No. 4, *etc.* 696.

JOZE (V.) Babylone d'Allemagne. pp. 205.
Paris, 1894. 12°.　　　　　012330. g. 58.

LANO (P. de) La cour de Berlin. pp. 284.
Paris, 1894. 12°.　　　　　10256. bb. 4.

LEIXNER (O. v.) Soziale Briefe aus Berlin.
pp. 392. *Berl.* 1891. 8°.　　8277. d. 31.

LENTZNER (C.) Der berlinische Dialekt. pp. 15.
Lond. 1893. 8°.　　　　12903. dd. 34. (14.)

LINDAU (P.) Unter den Linden. 1892. 8°.
Great Streets, *etc.*　　　　10026. k. 16.

LINDENBERG (P.) Berlin in Wort und Bild.
Berl. 1894, *etc.* 8°.　　　　10261. h.

NEUKOMM (E.) Berlin tel qu'il est. pp. 292.
Paris, 1891. 12°.　　　　　10256. c. 6.

POLLARD (J.) The corporation of Berlin.
pp. 164. *Edinb.* 1893. 8°.　　8277. de. 20.

RAPSILBER (M.) Das Reichstagshaus in Berlin.
pp. 80. *Berl.* 1894. 8°.　　　8074. c. 29.

SCHWEBEL (O.) Aus Alt-Berlin. pp. 487.
Berl. 1891. 8°.　　　　　10235. k. 22.

BERLIN—*continued.*

University.

VIRCHOW (R. L. C.) Die Gründung der berliner Universität. pp. 32. *Berl.* 1893. 8°.
8357. cc. 50. (6.)

BERMONT. GERMAIN (L.) La Cloche de Bermont. pp. 15. *Nancy,* 1890. 8°.   Pam. 3.

BERMUDAS. Ac. London. *Hakluyt Society.* BERMUDAS. Historye of the Bermudaes. pp. 327. *Lond.* 1882. 8°.   Ac. 6172/57.

EPHEM. Bermuda Pocket Guide. *Hamilton,* 1881–89. 8°.   P.P. 2584. a.

BERNAY. BOIVIN-CHAMPEAUX (L.) Notices bernayennes. pp. 141. *Évreux,* 1893. 8°.
10174. bb. 24.

—— Bernay et la Ligue. pp. 78. *Bernay,* 1889. 8°.   10174. a. 21.

FOUCQUES DASNIÈRE (   ) Histoire de Bernay écrite en 1765. pp. 36. *Bernay,* 1890. 8°.
10106. i. 1. (7.)

LOTTIN (R. V.) Bernay et son arrondissement. pp. 280. *Bernay,* 1890. 8°.   10168. cc. 28.

VEUCLIN (E. V.) La Fontaine minérale de Bernay. pp. 4. *Bernay,* 1890. 8°.   10106. i. 1. (6.)

BERNE, City and Canton. BERNE. Die 700jährige Gründungsfeier der Stadt Bern. pp. 256. *Bern,* 1891. 8°.   9930. dd. 11.

STUERLES (M. v.) Der Laupenkrieg, 1339–40. pp. 89. *Bern,* 1890. 8°.   Pam. 28.

DUNANT (É.) Les Relations politiques de Genève avec Berne, 1536–1654. pp. 222. *Genève,* 1894. 8°.   9304. f. 16.

GOBAT (A.) Berne et la France pendant les guerres de religion. pp. 242. *Paris,* 1891. 8°.
9079. h. 15.

FAZY (H.) L'alliance de 1584 entre Berne, Zurich et Genève. pp. 127. *Genève,* 1891. 8°.
9305. b. 12.

ERLACH (R. v.) Zur bernischen Kriegsgeschichte, 1798. pp. 972. *Berlin,* 1881. 8°.
9304. c. 20.

MUELINEN (E. F. v.) Beiträge zur Heimathkunde des Kantons Bern. *Bern,* 1880, *etc.* 8°.
10196. cc. 8.

MULLER (A.) À travers l'Oberland Bernois. pp. 355. *Mulhouse,* 1891. 12°.   10195. aa. 3.
See also ALPS.

BERRI. Ac. Bourges. *Société des Antiquaires.* Objets du dernier âge du bronze et du premier âge du fer découverts en Berry. pp. 14. *Bourges,* 1891. 8°.   07703. g. 1. (5.)

JENY (L.) Jeanne d'Arc en Berry. pp. 145. *Paris,* 1892. 8°.   010662. g. 7.

LA LOJE (P. de) Glossaire du Bas Béri. *Paris,* 1891, *etc.* 8°.   12954. g.
See also INDRE.

BERSHEH. *See* EGYPT, *Antiquities.*

BERTHIER, Quebec. MOREAU (S. A.) Précis de l'Histoire de Berthier. pp. 118. 1889. 8°.   10460. c. 33.

BERWICK, North. NORTH BERWICK. Guide to North Berwick. pp. 61. *N. Berwick,* 1895. 8°.
10369. aaa. 51.

BERWICK - ON - TWEED. MILLS (   ) Penny Guide to Berwick. pp. 32. *Berwick-on-T.* 1893. 16°.   10348. aa. 9. (6.)

BERWICKSHIRE. BROWN (J. W.) Covenanters of the Merse. pp. 259. *Edinb.* 1893. 8°.
4735. bb. 31.

CROCKETT (W. S.) Minstrelsy of the Merse. pp. 343. *Paisley,* 1893. 8°.   11622. a. 19.

BESANÇON. ANTOINE (E.) Besançon fabrique d'ébauches. pp. 54. *Besançon,* 1890. 8°.
Pam. 79.

BESANÇON—*continued.*

BEAUSÉJOUR (G. de) La citadelle de Besançon. pp. 20. *Besançon,* 1892. 8°. ||10107. ff. 28. (2.)
See also FRANCHE-COMTE.

BESTIARIES. GOLDSTAUB (M.) Ein toscovenezianischer Bestiarius. pp. 526. *Halle,* 1892. 8°.   7206. h. 20.

GUILLAUME, *de Normandie.* Le Bestiaire. pp. 441. 1892. 8°. FOERSTER (W.) Altfranzösische Bibliothek. Bd. 14.   11498. ccc.

BETHUNE. CORNET (E.) Histoire de Béthune. 2 tom. *Bethune,* 1892. 8°. 010171. m. 35.

BETTERMENT. *See* TRADE AND FINANCE. *Taxation.*

BETTING. B.LL. Money Making on the Stock Exchange and Racecourse. pp. 14. *Blackb.* 1894. 8°.   08226. f. 23. (6)

CHURCHILL (S.) Betting and Gambling. pp. 212. *Lond.* 1894. 8°.   8425. aaa. 36.

HAWKE (J.) A Blot on the Queen's Reign. pp. 36. *Lond.* 1893. 12°.   8409. ccc. 27. (5.)

NORRIS (W. H.) A Hint to the Clergy and anti-gambling crusaders. pp. 16. *Lond.* 1894. 8°.
8425. bbb. 43. (16.)

ROWLAND (A.) A Talk with young men on Betting. pp. 15. *Lond.* 1890. 8°.
8425. b. 62. (9.)

STUDENT. Betting and Gambling. pp. 15. *Lond.* 1895. 8°.   4421. aa. 58. (10.)

BRANDON. Practicable System of Backing Horses. *Manch.* 1893. 24°.   7915. de. 14. (6.)

CHILTON (C.) New Turf System. *Manch.* 1893. 12°.   7907. df. 18. (7.)

—— Horses worth following. *Liverp.* 1890, *etc.* 8°.   7912. de.

JONATHAN. Jonathan's Calculator. *Liverp.* 1893. 32°.   8548. aa. 33.

PEDDIE (J.) Racing for Gold. pp. 308. *Lond.* 1891. 8°.   7912. a. 5.

SUTCLIFFE (R.) Instantaneous Starting Price Ready Reckoner. *Lond.* 1893. 8°.
1882. d. 2. (78.)

TURF COUPLING SYSTEM READY RECKONER. Turf Coupling System. *Lond.* 1891. 8°. 7906. aaa. 47.

WAY. Way to win money on Races. pp. 16. *Lond.* 1892. 16°.   7915. de. 19. (3.)

BEURON. ZINGELER (C. T.) Geschichte des Klosters Beuron. pp. 271. *Sigmaringen.* 1890. 8°.   4662. d. 15.

BEVERAGES. BREVANS (J. de) Manufacture of Liquors and Preserves. pp. 200. *N.Y.* 1893. 8°.   7942. de. 24.

BURCKER (E.) Traité des falsifications des boissons. pp. 474. *Paris,* 1892. 8°.   07945. g. 4.

DAVIES (F.) Temperance Drinks. pp. 121. *Lond.* 1892. 8°.   7942. de. 15.

DE SALIS (H. A.) Drinks à la mode. pp. 100. *Lond.* 1891. 8°.   07945. e. 62.

DUBELLE (G. H.) The "Non plus ultra" Soda Fountain Requisites. pp. 157. *N.Y.* 1893. 8°.
7942. e. 45.

HÉBERT (A.) Examen des boissons falsifiées, *etc.* pp. 176. 1893. 8°. Encyclopédie des aide mémoire.   8709. g.

MALEPEYRE (F.) Manuel de la fabrication des boissons économiques. pp. 352. 1892. 18°. Encyclopédie Roret.   12208. b.

MEW (J.) and ASHTON (J.) Drinks of the World. pp. 362. *Lond.* 1892. 8°.   07945. g. 5.

OXFORD NIGHT CAPS. Oxford Night Caps. pp. 56. *Oxf.* 1893. 12°.   Pam. 94.

BEVERAGES—*continued.*

PAUL (C.) American and other drinks. pp. 73.
Lond. 1887. 12°.   7942. a. 74.

STANDAGE (H. C.) Temperance and light drinks.
pp. 88. Lond. 1893. 8°.   7945. a. 51.

STEVENSON (W.) Manufacture of Aerated Beverages. pp. 92. Lond. 1891. 8°.   07945. f. 26.

See also ALCOHOL : BEER : WHISKEY.

BEVERLEY. Ac. Huddersfield. *Yorkshire Archæological Association.* Excursion to Beverley.
pp. 10. *Worksop,* 1892. 8°.   07703. h. 1. (5.)

BEWDLEY. RAMBLER. Historical Guide to
Bewdley. pp. 34. *Bewdley,* 1895. 8°.
                                     10368. c. 46.

BEX. EXCHAQUET (T.) Notice sur les bains
de Bex. pp. 53. *Lausanne,* 1881. 8°.
                                     7462. i. 2. (6.)

BEXHILL. BEXHILL. Views of Bexhill-on-Sea. *Bexhill,* 1895. 8°.   10360. h. 61.

BÉZIERS. SOUCAILLE (A.) Béziers pendant
la Révolution. pp. 360. *Béziers.* 1894. 8°.
                                     9231. k. 8.

—— Historique de la Société populaire de
Béziers, 1790–95. pp. 102. *Béziers,* 1892. 8°.
                                     9226. i. 15.

BÉZIQUE. BERKELEY. Bézique and Cribbage.
pp. 63. 1890. 8°. Club Series.   7908. ee.

CAMDEN. The standard rules of Bézique. pp. 11.
Lond. 1889. 16°.   7915. de. 16. (3.)

CAVENDISH. Pocket Guide to Rubicon Bézique.
pp. 21. *Lond.* 1893. 16°   7915. de. 17. (6.)

—— Laws of Rubicon Bézique. pp. 51.
Lond. 1895. 8°.   7913. df. 19.

BHUTAN. LOUIS (J. A. H.) The Gates of
Thibet. pp. 183. *Calcutta,* 1894. 8°.
                                     010057. k. 13.

BIARRITZ. GERMOND DE LAVIGNE (L. A. G.)
Biarritz. pp. 175. *Paris,* 1891. 8°. 10174. de. 1.

BIBLIOGRAPHY.

See also BLOCK BOOKS : BOOK PLATES : BOOK-SELLING : BOOKBINDING : LIBRARIES. For incunabula and early printed books and for books issued by various printing-presses, *see* TYPOGRAPHY, and for Bibliographies of each country or subject see under the name required.

General and Miscellaneous.

Ac. G.B. & I. *Library Association.* The
Library. *Lond.* 1889, *etc.* 8°.   Ac. 9115/5.

—— Edinburgh. *Scottish History Society.*
YOUNG (P.) The Library of James VI., 1573–1583. pp. 86. *Edinb.* 1893. 8°.   Ac. 8256/3.

—— London. *Bibliographical Society.* Transactions. *Lond.* 1893, *etc.* 4°.   Ac. 9670.

—— N.Y. *Grolier Club.* Catalogue of Early
Editions of some of the Works of English Writers
from Langland to Wither. *N.Y.* 1893. 8°.
                                     Ac. 4714/2.

—— Paris. *Société des Bibliophiles.* Annales
littéraires. *Paris,* 1890, *etc.* 8°.   Ac. 8932.

ANTWERP. *Conférence du Livre,* 1890. Compte-rendu. pp. 272. *Anvers,* 1891. 4°. 11900. k. 24.

ARLÍA (C.) Dizionario bibliografico. pp. 100.
Milano, 1892. 8°.   012200. h. 24.

BERALDI (H.) Estampes et Livres. pp. 277.
Paris, 1894. 4°.   11899. i. 44.

BLADES (W.) Books in Chains and other papers.
pp. 232. 1892. 8°. Book-Lover's Library.
                                     11900. aa.

BOLLIOUD-MERMET (L.) Crazy Book-Collecting.
pp. 60. *N.Y.* 1894. 8°.   11901. aa. 35.

BIBLIOGRAPHY.—General—*continued.*

BOUCHOT (H.) Des livres modernes qu'il convient d'acquérir. pp. 100. *Paris,* 1891. 18°.
                                     11899. bb. 45.

BRIDGES (R.) Suppressed Chapters and other
Bookishness. pp. 159. 1895. 8°. 012356. k. 4.

CAMPBELL (F. B. F.) The Battle of Bibliography.
pp. 11. *Lond.* 1893. 8°.   011900. ee. 20.

—— Bibliography of the Future. pp. 16.
Lond. 1895. 8°.   011900. h. 25.

—— Memorandum relative to the need for special
Bibliographical Societies. pp. 7.
Lond. 1894. fol.   11900. k. 3.

CUGIA PILO (G.) Bibliosofia. pp. 160.
Sassari, 1893, *etc.* 8°.   011900. ee.

CLAYE (A. de) La Bibliophilie en 1891–1892.
pp. 165. *Paris,* 1893. 4°.   011900. ee. 22.

DITCHFIELD (P. H.) Books fatal to their Authors.
pp. 244. 1895. 8°. Book-Lover's Library.
                                     11900. d.

DZIATZKO (C.) Bibliographische Miscellen.
pp. 9. *Leipz.* 1892. 8°.   Pam. 6.

ELTON (C. I.) and (M. A.) The Great Book-Collectors. 1893. 8°. POLLARD (A. W.) Books
about Books.   2312. d.

ENGLISH BOOK-COLLECTORS. Contributions towards a Dictionary of English Book-Collectors.
Lond. 1892, *etc.* 8°.   011901. f.

FARRER (J. A.) Books condemned to be burnt.
pp. 206. 1892. 8°. Book-Lover's Library, *etc.*
                                     11900. aa.

FISKE (W.) Bibliographical notices.
Florence, 1886, *etc.* 8°.   011902. f. 2.

GRAY (J. G.) Index to Hazlitt's Handbook and
his Bibliographical Collections. pp. 866.
Lond. 1893. 8°.   2048. b.

GUIGARD (J.) Nouvel Armorial du Bibliophile.
2 tom. *Paris,* 1890. 8°.   2400. g.

IRELAND (A.) The Book-Lover's Enchiridion.
pp. 511. *Lond.* 1890. 8°.   11899. aaa. 24.

LANG (A.) Books and Bookmen. pp. 177.
Lond. 1892. 8°.   11900. bb. 53.

LISTER (R. J.) Catalogue of a portion of the
Library of Edmund Gosse. *Lond.* 1893. 4°.
                                     11900. h. 20.

LORIMER (G. C.) What I know about Books.
pp. 110. *Bost.* 1892. 8°.   011824. de. 49.

LOVETT (R.) The Printed English Bible, 1525–1885. pp. 159. 1894. 8°. Present Day Primers.
                                     4429. eee.

MASSENA (A. P. V.) *Duke de Rivoli.* Les Missels
imprimés à Venese 1481–1600. 4 livr.
Paris, 1894, *etc.*   K.T.C. 25. b.

OTTINO (G.) Bibliografia. pp. 166.
Milano, 1892. 8°.   012200. h. 23.

PARIS. *Cercle de la librairie.* Le cercle de la
librairie de Paris à l'Exposition du livre.
Paris, 1892. 4°.   011900. f. 14.

P.P. Lond. Bibliographica. *Lond.* 1894, *etc.* 8°.
                                     P.P. 6484. eb.

—— The Bookman. *Lond.* 1891, *etc.* 8°.
                                     P.P. 6479. e.

—— The Bookbuyer. *Lond.* 1894, *etc.* 4°.   54.

—— International Book-Finder.
Lond. 1894, *etc.* 8°.   P.P. 6490. bb. p. 2024.

—— *N.Y.* Annual Literary Index.
N.Y. 1893, *etc.* 8°.   Cat. Desk. B.

—— *Paris.* Bibliographie instructive.
Paris, 1891, *etc.* 12°.   P.P. 6457.

—— Le Livre et l'Image. *Paris,* 1893, *etc.* 4°.
                                     P.P. 6475. bab.

POLLARD (A. W.) Books about Books. 6 vol.
Lond. 1893–94. 8°.   2312. d.

BIBLIOGRAPHY.—General—*continued.*

POLLARD (A. W.) Italian Book Illustrations. pp. 80. 1894. fol. P.P. *Lond.* Portfolio. Monographs. No. 12.   P.P. 1931. pcd.

—— Last Words on the History of the Title-page. pp. 39. *Lond.* 1891. 4°·   K.T.C. 4. b. 5.

—— Early Illustrated Books. pp. 256. 1893. 8°. Books about Books.   2312. d.

ROBERTS (W.) The Book-Hunter in London. pp. 333. *Lond.* 1895. 4°.   11902. i. 24.

—— Rare Books and their Prices. pp. 156. *Lond.* 1895. 8°.   011901. h. 3.

ROGERS (W. T.) Manual of Bibliography. pp. 213. *Lond.* 1891. 8°.   11899. e. 32.

SLATER (J. H.) Book Collecting. pp. 130. 1892. 8°. Young Collector Series.   7001. aaa.

—— Early Editions. pp. 339. *Lond.* 1894. 8°.   2049. bb.

—— Round and about the Book-Stalls. pp. 119. *Lond.* 1891. 8°.   011899. h. 1.

—— The Library Manual. pp. 424. *Lond.* 1892. 8°.   011902. i. 8.

STEIN (H.) Mélanges de Bibliographie. *Paris*, 1893, *etc.* 8°.   011902. m.

TREDWELL (D. M.) Monograph on Privately Illustrated Books. pp. 502. *Flatbush*, 1892. 8°.   11904. g. 33.

UZANNE (O.) Book-Hunter in Paris. pp. 232. *Lond.* 1893. 4°.   11903. m. 4.

VERAX (J.) Les Faussaires de Livres. pp. 12. *Châteaudun*, 1891. 8°.   011900. ce. 3. (8.)

VICAIRE (G.) Manuel de l'Amateur de Livres du XIX° siècle. *Paris*, 1894, *etc.* 8°.   011901. ee.

Catalogues of Selected Works.

ACLAND (A. H. D.) Guide to the Choice of Books. pp. 128. *Lond.* 1891. 4°. 011902. g. 37.

BUFFALO. *Young Men's Library.* Books for young readers. pp. 62. *Buffalo, N.Y.* 1881. 8°.   11903. aa. 3. (1.)

GROWOLL (A.) A Bookseller's Library. pp. 72. *N.Y.* 1891. 12°.   11899. b. 51.

RICHARDSON (C. F.) The Choice of Books. pp. 208. *N.Y.* 1890. 8°.   012357. f. 56.

SARGANT (E. B.) and WHISHAW (B.) Guide Book to Books. pp. 344. *Lond.* 1891. 8°.   Centre Desk R. R.

SONNENSCHEIN (W. S.) The Best Books, *etc.* pp. 1009. *Lond.* 1894. 4°.   Cat. Desk. C.

—— Reader's Guide to contemporary Literature. pp. 775. *Lond.* 1895. 4°.   Cat. Desk C.

BICYCLES AND TRICYCLES.

BAUDRY DE SAUNIER (L.) Histoire de la Vélocipédie. pp. 321. *Paris*, 1891. 8°. 7908. ee. 24.

BOURLET (C.) Traité des bicycles et bicyclettes. pp. 232. 1894. 8°. Encyclopédie des aide mémoire.   8709. g.

BOWDEN (F.) Points for Cyclists. pp. 49. *Leicester*, 1891. 8°.   7912. ee. 2. (5.)

BOWDEN (E. M.) Pocket Guide to Cycling. pp. 112. *Lond.* 1895. 8°.   7908. a. 107.

CORTIS (H. L.) Principles of training for amateur Athletes. pp. 46. *Lond.* 1887. 8°. Pam. 83.

CYCLE. The Cycle of to-day. pp. 52. *Lond.* 1894. 8°.   7912. de. 1. (7.)

DUNCAN (H. O.) and SUBERBIE (L.) L'Entraînement à l'usage des vélocipédistes. pp. 200. *Paris*, 1890. 8°.   7908. eee. 12.

GALANTE (A.) Manuale del ciclista. pp. 194. *Milano*, 1894. 8°.   012200. h. 117.

GENDRY (E.) Sport vélocipédique. pp. 210. *Angers*, 1891. 8°.   7908. eee. 16.

GIFFARD (P.) La Reine Bicyclette. pp. 79. *Paris*. 1891. 8°.   7912. f. 1. (6.)

BICYCLES, etc.—*continued.*

GIRLING (T. W.) Information respecting "Cycles." pp. 10. *Brighton*, 1891. 8°.   7912. ee. 2. (6.)

HARTUNG (C. W.) Cycles of 1892. pp. 80. *Lond.* 1892. 8°.   7908. c. 38.

HILLIER (G. L.) and BRAMSON (W. G. H.) Amateur Cycling. pp. 103. *Lond.* 1893. 8°.   07905. f. 12.

HILLIER (G. L.) Account of the One Mile Amateur Bicycle Path Record. *Lond.* 1890. 4°.   Pam. 83.

HINTS. Practical Hints on Cycling. pp. 54. *Lond.* 1893. 8°.   7907. df. 17. (6.)

INGEMAN-PETERSEN. Cycle-sport. pp. 140. *Kjøbenh.* 1891. 8°.   7912. df. 2. (7.)

IRIART D'ETCHEPARE (L. d') Historique de l'Union Vélocipédique de France. pp. 36. *Bordeaux*, 1893. 8°.   7907. df. 17. (7.)

JENNINGS (O.) La santé par le tricycle. pp. 193. *Paris*, 1889. 12°.   7912. aa. 11.

—— Cycling and Health. pp. 304. *Lond.* 1893. 8°.   07905. f. 10.

KEPPEL (W. C.) *Earl of Albemarle.* Cycling. pp. 400. 1895. 8°. Badminton Library.   2264. aa. 4.

LE BOULENGÉ (P.) Détermination des vitesses vélocipédiques. pp. 50. *Brux.* 1894. 8°.   7912. aa. 35.

LEECHMAN (G. D.) Safety Cycling. pp. 180. *Lond.* 1895. 8°.   7906. aaa. 48.

PENNELL (E. R.) Cycling. 1894. 8°. GREVILLE (B. V.) *Baroness Greville.* Ladies in the Field.   07905. f. 15.

P.P. Boston. The Wheelman. Vol. 1. No. 1–6. *Bost., Mass.* 1883. 8°.   P.P. 1873. l.

—— Hull. Yorkshire Cyclists' Annual. *Hull*, 1892, *etc.* 32°.   P.P. 2489. rb.

—— London. The Cyclist Annual. *Lond.* 1891, *etc.* 4°.   P.P. 2489. zf.

—— The Stanley Gazette. *Lond.* 1892, *etc.* 8°.   P.P. 1873. ga. and 2117.

P.P. The Cycle Magazine. *Lond.* 1895, *etc.* 8°.   P.P. 1873. gb.

—— Paris. Annuaire générale de la Vélocipédie. *Paris*, 1892, *etc.* 8°.   P.P. 2405. cb.

PORTER (L. H.) Cycling for Health and Pleasure. pp. 173. *Lond.* 1895. 8°.   7907. df. 20.

PREGALDINO (C.) Manuel du vélocipédiste. pp. 107. *Gand*, 1894. 16°.   7907. df. 19.

RANDOLPH (J. A.) Complete List of Bi- and Tricycle Championships, 1886. *Ryde*, 1886. 8°.   7912. f. 1. (4.)

REICHEL (L. P.) La vélocipédie dans le mouvement athlétique. pp. 56. *Paris*, 1892. 16°.   7908. de. 8.

VÉTÉRAN. La vélocipédie pour tous. pp. 271. *Paris*, 1892. 8°.   07905. h. 4.

WILLARD (F. E.) A Wheel within a Wheel. pp. 75. *Lond.* 1895. 8°.   7907. df. 16.

Military.

GERARD (H.) Le Problème de l'Infanterie montée resolu par l'emploi de la bicyclette. pp. 103. *Paris*, 1894. 8°.   8829. aa. 22.

G.B. & I. *Army.* Drill of a Cyclist-Infantry Section. pp. 46. *Lond.* 1893. 16°.   8831. a. 88. (2.)

SOLEIL (F.) Étude sur la vélocipédie militaire. pp. 158. *Brux.* 1892. 8°.   8823. bb. 33.

Road Books: Travels.

BARONCELLI (A. de) Guide routier du Velloce-man en France & en Europe. pp. 352. *Paris*, 1891. 8°.   10106. de. 3.

BICYCLES.—Road Books, etc.—continued.

BERTOT (J.) Guides du cycliste en France. De Paris à Bordeaux, etc. pp. 131.
Paris, 1895. 16°.   10174. a. 26.

—— De Paris à Grenoble et Marseille. pp. 185.
Paris, 1895. 12°.   10174. a. 25.

DELITTLE (F. R.) Cyclist's Pocket Road Book for England, Wales and Scotland. pp. 244.
Lond. 1893. 12°.   10347. aa. 35.

MILESTONE GUIDES. Milestone Guides. Books 1–12. *Lond.* 1894. 16°.   10347. a. 23.

LONDON. *Cyclists' Touring Club.* British Road Book. *Lond.* 1891. etc. 8°.   10347. c. 32.

OXFORD. *Oxford University Bicycle Club.* The Roads round Oxford. pp. 47.
Oxford, 1892. 8°.   10351. aa. 57.

ROWELL (H.) Cycling mileage Guide. Yorkshire, Durham, and Northumberland. pp. 48.
Lond. 1891. 16°.   7906. a. 69.

P.P. *Glasg.* Scottish Cyclist Road Book.
Glasg. 1894. etc. 8°.   P.P. 2510. t.

SPENCER (C.) Cyclist's Road Book. pp. 222.
Lond. 1891. 8°.   10347. cc. 19.

SPURRIER (W. J.) Cyclists' Route Book.
pp. 188. *Lond.* 1893. 8°.   10348. cc. 24.

ALLEN (T. G.) and SACHTLEBEN (W. L.) Across Asia on a Bicycle. pp. 234. *N.Y.* 1894. 8°.
     10055. df. 23.

BALLY (S. E.) Six semaines de Vacances en Vélocipède. pp. 124. *Lond.* 1891. 8°.
     10125. cc. 19.

JEFFERSON (R. L.) Awheel to Moscow and back.
pp. 172. *Lond.* 1895. 8°.   10107. b. 2.

PERRODIL (É de) À Vol de Vélo. De Paris à Vienne. pp. 330. *Paris,* 1895. 12°. 10105. cc. 5.

RUMNEY (A. W.) Cycling in the English Lake District. pp. 18. *Bradford,* 1894. 8°.
     10347. aa. 37. (5.)

THWAITES (R. G.) Our Cycling Tour in England.
pp. 315. *Chicago,* 1892. 8°.   10349. cc. 20.

WORKMAN (F. B.) and (W. H.) Algerian Memories : a bicycle tour. pp. 216.
Lond. 1895. 8°.   10097. bb. 39.

DOOLITTLE (P. E.) Wheel Outings in Canada.
Toronto, 1895. 8°.   10460. f. 32.

BIDEFORD. GRANVILLE (R.) History of Bideford. pp. 110. *Bideford,* 1883. 8°.
     10360. e. 32.

HINGESTON-RANDOLPH (F. C.) Rectors and Patrons of Bideford. ff. 16. *Exeter,* 1895. 8°.
     Pam. 29.

BIDSTON. BIDSTON. Registers of the parish of Bidston. pp. 100. *Birkenhead,* 1893. 8°.
     9906. e. 5.

IRVINE (W F.) Notes on the Parish of Bidston.
pp. 48. *Liverp.* 1894. 8°.   10348. d. 20. (11.)

BIGAMY. *See* MARRIAGE.

BIGORRE. COLOMEZ ( ) Histoire de la province et comté de Bigorre. pp. 285.
Paris, 1886. 8°.   010171. g. 6.

ROSAPELLY (N.) La Cité de Bigorre. pp. 216.
Tarbes, 1890. 8°.   010171. m. 3.

—— Au Pays de Bigorre. pp. 92.
Tarbes, 1891. 8°.   10171. h. 2.

DUPLAN (A. P.) Patois de Bigorre. pp. 129.
Tarbes, 1891. 4°.   12952. i. 9.

RICAUD (L.) La Bigorre pendant la Révolution.
pp. 302. *Paris,* 1894. 8°.   9231. l. 8.
See also GASCONY : HAUTES PYRÉNÉES.

BIHARI LANGUAGE. *See* BEHAR.

BIJAPUR. COUSENS (H.) Bijapur.
pp.145. *Poona,* 1889. 8°.   10056. bbb. 8.

INDIA. *Archæological Survey.* Notes on Buildings and other Remains at Bijapur. pp. 109.
Bombay, 1890. fol.   7706. h. 15.

BILE. COURVOISIER (L. G.) Beiträge zur Pathologie und Chirurgie der Gallenwege.
pp. 375. *Leipz.* 1890. 8°.   7460. ff. 20.

THOMSON (J.) Congenital Obliteration of the Bile-ducts. pp. 52. *Edinb.* 1892. 8°.
     7620. df. 27.

See also DIGESTION : LIVER.

BILHARZIA HAEMATOBIA.
See PARASITES.

BILLIARDS. ACHARD (C.) Die Kunst des Billard-Spiels. pp. 76. *Berl.* 1891. 8°.
     7912. df. 4. (1.)

ARNOUS DE RIVIÈRE (J.) Traité du jeu de Billard.
pp. 310. *Paris,* 1891. 8°.   7913. cc. 32.

BENNETT (J.) Billiards. pp. 475.
Lond. 1894. 8°.   2264. b. 3.

BUCHANAN (J. P.) Hints on Billiards. pp. 208.
Lond. 1895. 8°.   7912. c. 3.

LINDSAY (J. L.) *Earl of Crawford.* Tables for ascertaining the factor of a Billiard Player.
Wigan, 1890. 8°.   7913. d. 40.

P.P. *Lond.* The Billiard Review.
Lond. 1895, etc. 8°.   P.P. 1831. o.

VIGNAUX ( ) Le Billard. pp. 414.
Paris, 1895. 8°.   7913. e. 31.
See also GAMES.

BILLITON. LANGE (G. A. de) Mijnontginning van staatswege op Billiton. pp. 64.
's Gravenh. 1891. 8°.   8226. ff. 33. (9.)

VROLIK (W. K. M.) Billiton. pp. 44.
's Gravenh. 1892. 8°.   8023. f. 22. (12.)
See also INDIES, Dutch.

BILLS OF COSTS. MOIMEM. It is not Business. Party-and-Party Costs. pp. 36.
Lond. 1895. 8°.   Pam. 32.

PRIDMORE (T. W.) Guide to the preparation of Bills of Costs. pp. 923. *Lond.* 1891. 8°.
     2230. bb. 7.

SMITH (R. E. M.) Law of Expenses in the Courts of Scotland. pp. 442. *Edinb.* 1892. 8°.
     6583. g. 11.

See also LAW, *Profession of.*

BILLS OF EXCHANGE. BIGELOW (M. M.) Elements of the Law of Bills. pp. 325.
Lond. 1893. 8°.   6375. aa. 55.

BYLES (*Right Hon. Sir J. B.*) Treatise on the Law of Bills of Exchange. pp. 584.
Lond. 1891. 8°.   2018. c.

CHALMERS (M. D. E. S.) Digest of the Law of Bills of Exchange. pp. 431. *Lond.* 1891. 8°.
     6375. i. 21.

HERTZKA (T.) Wechselcurs und Agio. pp. 162.
Wien, 1894. 8°.   8074. f. 39.

KÖLKENBECK (A.) Rates of Stamp Duties on bills of exchange. pp. 49. *Lond.* 1895. 8°.
     8228. aa. 64.

LOYD (A. K.) Four Lectures on Bills of Exchange. pp. 174. *Lond.* 1895. 8°. 08226. h. 19.

SCHAPS (G.) Zur Geschichte des Wechselindossaments. pp. 187. *Stuttgart,* 1892. 8°.
     08227. f. 38.

SMITH (J. W.) Handy Book on the Law of Bills pp. 193. 1894. 12°. Wilson's Legal Handy Books.   6426. aaa. 39.

WENDT (O. H.) Das allgemeine Anweisungsrecht. pp. 299. *Jena,* 1895. 8°. 6005. cc. 4.

See also BANKING : LAW, *Commercial.*

BILLS OF LADING. CARVER (T. G.) On some defects in the Bills of Lading Act, 1855. pp. 18. *Lond.* 1890. 8°.   6146. k. 13. (1.)

LEGGETT (E.) Treatise on the Law of Bills of Lading. pp. 671. *Lond.* 1893. 8°. 6835. df. 15.

POLLOCK (H. E.) Bill of Lading Exceptions. pp. 104. *Hong-Kong,* 1895. 8°. 6835. df. 20.

SCRUTTON (T. E.) Contract of Affreightment. pp. 370. *Lond.* 1893. 8°.   6375. de. 9.
See also LAW, *Maritime.*

BILLS OF SALE. GREEN (W.) Bills of Sale, Ireland, Act, 1879, Amendment Act, 1883. pp. 68. *Dublin,* 1890. 8°.   Pam. 32.

HAYCRAFT (T. W.) Handy Book on the Bills of Sale Acts, 1878 & 1882. pp. 132.
Lond. 1890. 8°.   6405. bb. 31.

BILSTON. LAWLEY (G. T.) A History of Bilston. pp. 262. *Bilston,* 1893. 8°.
          010358. l. 37.

BINGLEY. FORSHAW (C. F.) Poets of Keighley, Bingley, and district. pp. 196. *Bradford,* 1891. 8°.   11601. ff. 20.

BIOGRAPHY.—General and Miscellaneous.

BIOGRAPHIA. Biographia: public men at home and abroad. *Lond.* 1894, *etc.* 4°. 10601. g. 8.

CASSELL (J.) New Biographical Dictionary. pp. 741. *Lond.* 1895. 8°.   10600. de. 2.

MEN. Men and Women of the Time. pp. 986. *Lond.* 1895. 8°.   2034. a.

MORRIS (D. K.) Notes of a thousand Men. *Lond.* 1891. 8°.   10601. cc. 17.

PERSONS. Eminent Persons. Biographies from the Times. *Lond.* 1892, *etc.* 8°.   10601. e.

P.P. *Berlin.* Biographische Blätter. *Berlin,* 1895, *etc.* 8°.   P.P. 3825. e.

P.P. *London.* The Biographer. *Lond.* 1894, *etc.* 4°.   P.P. 3848. d. & 1289.

P.P. *London.* Monthly record of eminent Men. *Lond.* 1890, *etc.* 8°. P.P. 3858. ad. & 837.

P.P. *London.* Weekly Gallery of Celebrities. *Lond.* 1891, *etc.* 4°.   P.P. 3848. e.

SMITH (B. E.) Cyclopædia of Names. A dictionary of names. pp. 1085. *Lond.* 1894. fol.
          2112. g.

VAPEREAU (L. G.) Dictionnaire des Contemporains. pp. 1629. *Paris,* 1893. 8°.   2037. c.

Miscellaneous.

BEGINNINGS. Small Beginnings ; or, the way to get on. pp. 284. *Lond.* 1891. 8°. 10601. aa. 30.

BIOGRAPHIES. Biographies du xixᵉ siècle. pp. 325. *Paris,* 1890. 8°.   10602. dd. 16.

BENOIST (C.) Souverains. Hommes d'état, *etc.* pp. 278. *Paris,* 1893. 12°.   10601. bb. 33.

BLATHWAYT (R.) Interviews. pp. 354. *Lond.* 1893. 8°.   12350. d. 34.

BROOKS (E. S.) Great Men's Sons. pp. 303. *New York,* 1895. 8°.   10600. ee. 3.

CHARLES (F.) Mirabeau, Robespierre, Napoléon, Metternich, Cavour, Bismark. *Paris,* 1893. *etc.* 8°.   010662. ff.

COCHRANE (R.) Beneficent and useful Lives. pp. 288. *Lond.* 1890. 8°.   10602. c. 30.

GODWIN (P.) Commemorative Addresses. pp. 239. *New York,* 1895. 8°.   10603. b. 27.

GRAAE (T.) Moderne Profiler. pp. 156. *Kjøbenhavn,* 1892. 8°.   10761. aa. 57.

GRAHAM (P. A.) Nature in Books. Studies in Biography. pp. 194. *Lond.* 1891. 8°.
          10601. ce. 8.

HARRISON (F.) New Calendar of Great Men, in the Positivist Calendar. pp. 644.
Lond. 1892. 8°.   10601. ee. 7.

BIOGRAPHY.—Miscellaneous—*cont.*

HITCHCOCK (T.) Unhappy Loves of Men of Genius. pp. 212. *New York,* 1891. 8°.
          10601. aa. 29.

HOGG (J.) Fortunes made in Business. pp. 406. *Lond.* 1891. 8°.   08229. de. 39.

HOPE (A. R.) Royal Youths. pp. 355. *Lond.* 1892. 8°.   10601. cc. 20.

HOW (H.) Illustrated Interviews. pp. 311. *Lond.* 1893. 8°.   10803. g. 13.

HUTTON, afterwards ALEXANDER (B.) " Fair Women and Brave Men." pp. 362. *Lond.* 1892. 8°.   10601. e. 16.

JAPP (A. H.) Successful Business-Men. pp. 232. *Lond.* 1892. 8°.   10601. ee. 10.

JORISSEN (T. T. H.) Historische Karakters. pp. 370. *Haarlem,* 1892. 8°. 10604. bbbb. 20.

LORD (J.) Modern European Statesmen. pp. 623. *N.Y.,* 1891. 8°.   9080. cc. 12.

MARDEN (O. S.) Pushing to the Front. pp.416. *Boston,* 1894. 8°.   8409. h. 26.

MEN. Men of Achievement. *Lond.* 1894, *etc.* 8°.   10601. df..

—— Men with a Mission. *Lond.* 1890, *etc.* 8°.   4804. a.

—— Some Men of To-Day. pp. 112. *Lond.* 1891. 8°.   10601. e. 8.

NĀRĀYANA HEMACHANDRA. Noble deeds of Men. pp. 112. *Ahmedabad,* 1895. 8°.
          10601. a. 48.

—— Noble deeds of Boys. pp. 120. *Ahmedabad,* 1895. 8°.   10601. a. 50.

O'CONNOR (T. P.) Some old Love Stories. pp. 337. *Lond.* 1895. 8°.   10601. e. 22.

PERCIVAL (A.) Heroes of Modern Days. pp. 124. *Lond.* 1892. 8°.   4920. de. 15.

SAGLIO (A.) Maisons d'Hommes célèbres. pp. 326. *Paris,* 1893. 8°.   10601. e. 17.

SCHLICHTEGROLL (C. F. v.) and ZOLLER (E. v.) Portrait Gallerie der regierenden Fürsten und Fürstinnen Europas. *Stuttgart,* 1890, *etc.* fol.
          1764. c.

SCOTT (C. W.) Stories of Valour and Adventure. pp. 239. *Lond.* 1893. 8°. 012807. ff. 45.

SMALLEY (G. W.) Studies of Men. pp. 396. *Lond.* 1895. 8°.   10825. eee. 18.

SMITH (G. B.) Leaders of modern Industry. pp. 477. *Lond.* 1894. 8°.   10604. bb. 25.

SMITH (H. G.) Romance of History, *etc.* pp. 335. *Lond.* 1891. 8°.   10601. ee. 9.

STEAD (W. T.) Character Sketches. pp. 189. *Lond.* 1892. 4°.   10804. ee. 16.

TILLOTSON (J.) Pioneers of Civilisation. pp. 320. *Lond.* 1891. 8°.   10601. e. 10.

TISSANDIER (G.) Les Héros du Travail. pp. 312. *Paris,* 1891. 8°.   10604. f. 17.

TOWLE (G. M.) Heroes of History. *Lond.* 1891, *etc.* 8°.   10603. dd.

Female.

ADAMS (W. H. D.) Some Historic Women. pp. 348. *Lond.* 1891. 8°.   10601. e. 9.

BARINE (A.) Princesses et grandes Dames. pp. 354. *Paris,* 1890. 8°.   10601. aaa. 33.

BLACK (H. C.) Notable Women Authors of the Day. pp. 312. *Glasg.* 1893. 8°. 10856. f. 7,

BOLTON (S. K.) Famous Types of Womanhood. pp. 350. *N.Y.* 1892. 8°.   10602. c. 33.

BONNEFONT (G.) Les Héroïnes du Travail. pp. 308. *Paris,* 1894. 8°.   10604. k. 11.

—— Nos grandes Françaises. pp. 238. *Paris,* 1893. 8°.   10659. h. 25.

BROOKS (E. S.) Historic Girls. pp. 225. *N.Y.* 1890. 8°.   10605. g. 26.

BIOGRAPHY.—Female—*continued.*

BUOY (C. W.) Representative Women of Methodism. pp. 476. *N.Y.* 1893. 8°. 4907. de. 10.

BUTLER (A.) Lives of Women Saints. pp. 256. *Lond.* 1887. 8°. 4829. cc. 4.

CHAPMAN (*Mrs.* E. F.) Sketches of some distinguished Indian Women. pp. 139. *Lond.* 1891. 8°. 10606. b. 43.

COURSON (R. de) Quatre portraits de femmes. Épisodes des persécutions d'Angleterre. pp. 455. *Paris,* 1895. 12°. 4906. de. 31.

EMINENT WOMEN SERIES. Eminent Women Series. *Lond.* 1895, etc. 8°. 10803. ccc.

FINNISH WOMEN. Finska Qvinnor på olika arbetsområden. pp. 257. *Helsingfors,* 1892. 8°. 10790. bbb. 39.

GIMENO DE FLAQUER (C.) Mujeres, vidas paralelas. pp. 260. *Madrid,* 1893. 8°. 10602. g. 10.

HALE (S. J.) Lessons from Women's Lives. pp. 220. *Edinb.* 1889. 8°. 10602. aaa. 26.

HAMILTON (C. J.) Women Writers. *Lond.* 1892, etc. 8°. 10601. ee.

HUTTON aft. ALEXANDER (B.) Fair Women and Brave Men. pp. 362. *Lond.* 1892. 8°. 10601. e. 16.

IMBERT DE SAINT AMAND (A. L.) *Baron.* Women of the Valois Court. pp. 356. *Lond.* 1894. 8°. 010661. ee. 48.

JOHNSTONE (G.) Leading Women of the Restoration. pp. 221. *Lond.* 1892. 8°. 10803. cc. 8.

KEELING (A. E.) Heroines of Faith and Charity. pp. 286. *Lond.* 1891. 8°. 4804. aaa. 13.

KOHUT (A.) Die grössten deutschen Soubretten des 19ten Jahrhunderts pp. 203. *Düsseldorf,* 1890. 8°. 010707. e. 10.

LEE (E.) Some noble Sisters. pp. 332. *Lond.* 1892. 8°. 10601. ee. 15.

LHOMME (F.) Les Femmes écrivains. pp. 546. *Paris,* 1892. 8°. 12237. k. 2.

MANUEL. Manuel de biographie des femmes célèbres. pp. 895. *Turin,* 1892. 8°. 10601. ee. 17.

MASON (A. G.) Women of the French Salons. pp. 286. *Lond.* 1891. 8°. K.T.C. 5. b. 1.

MAYER (G. T.) Women of Letters. 2 vol. *Lond.* 1894. 8°. 10855. c. 25.

MEN. Men and Women of the Time. pp. 986. *Lond.* 1895. 8°. 2034. a.

MILLER (F. F.) In Ladies' Company. pp. 210. *Lond.* 1892. 8°. 10601. g. 9.

NĀRĀYANA HEMACHANDRA. Noble Deeds of Women and Girls. pp. 116. *Ahmedabad,* 1895. 8°. 10601. a. 49.

NIGG (M.) Biographien der österreichischen Schriftstellerinnen. pp. 61. *Korneuberg,* 1893. 8°. 10601. g. 7. (6.)

PALÉOLOGUE (M.) Profils de Femmes. pp. 346. *Paris,* 1895. 8°. 10601. aaa. 35.

POOL (J. J.) Woman's Influence in the East: lives of Queens and Princesses of India. pp. 283. *Lond.* 1892. 8°. 10606. c. 19.

SMITH (G. B.) Noble Womanhood. pp. 361. *Lond.* 1894. 8°. 4430. b. 20.

—— Women of Renown. pp. 478. *Lond.* 1893. 8°. 10601. df. 3.

TYTLER (S.) Tudor Queens and Princesses. pp. 418. *Lond.* 1895. 8°. 10805. bb. 23.

WALFORD (L. B.) Twelve English Authoresses, etc. pp. 200. *Lond.* 1892. 8°. 10803. e. 9.

WILLARD (F. E.) Woman of the Century. Biographical sketches. pp. 812. *Buffalo,* 1892. 4°. 10880. i. 12.

WILMOT (S.) Queens of England. 2 vol. *Lond.* 1887–89. 10805. g. 3.

WOMEN. Excellent Women. 12 pt. *Lond.* 1894. 8°. 4429. k. 8.

BIOGRAPHY.—Female—*continued.*

ZIRNDORF (H.) Some Jewish Women. pp. 280. *Phila.* 1892. 8°. 10606. bbb. 10.

Collected Biographies of Various Nations.

For Biographies of Artists, Lawyers, Literary Persons, *etc. etc.* of each country, see *infra*: *Biographies of various classes.*
For Women of each country, see *supra*: *Female.*

America, South.

FIGUEROA (P. P.) Diccionario biográfico chileno. pp. 452. *Santiago,* 1887. 8°. 010882. h. 20.

—— Miscelánea biográfica americana. pp. 216. *Santiago,* 1888. 8°. 10883. aa. 22.

PEREZ (M.) Figuras americanas. pp. 182. *Paris,* 1891. 8°. 010882. f. 14.

SUAREZ (J. B.) Rasgos biográficos de hombres notables de Chile. pp. 254. *Valparaiso,* 1886. 8°. 10883. aaa. 30.

Australia.

AUSTRALIAN MEN. Australian Men of Mark. 2 vol. *Sydney,* 1889. 4°. 10804. f. 17.

MENNELL (P.) Dictionary of Australasian Biography. pp. 542. *Lond.* 1892. 8°. 2035. a.

Austria.

NIGG (M.) Biographien der österreichischen Schriftstellerinnen. pp. 61. *Korneuburg,* 1893. 8°. Pam. 8.

Belgium.

HAULLEVILLE (P. C. A. de) *Baron.* Portraits et silhouettes. pp. 359. *Bruxelles,* 1893. 12°. 10601 bb. 34.

Canada.

BIBAUD (M.) Le Panthéon canadien. pp. 320. *Montréal,* 1891. 8°. 010882. k. 9.

Chili. See *supra*: *America, South.*

France.

CORLIEU (A.) La mort des rois de France depuis François 1er. pp. 384. *Paris,* 1892. 8°. 010662. g. 20.

BONNEFONT (P.) Nos grandes Françaises. pp. 238. *Paris,* 1893. 8°. 10659. h. 25.

GAUTIER (L.) Portraits du XVIIe siècle. pp. 294. *Paris,* 1890. 8°. 10658. b. 36.

BETTELHEIM (A.) Deutsche und Franzosen. pp. 316. *Wien,* 1895. 8°. 10602. cc. 22.

BIRÉ (E.) Portraits historiques et littéraires. pp. 389. *Lyon,* 1892. 8°. 010662. h. 16.

BOYER D'AGEN (A. J.) Des Hommes. *Paris,* 1891, etc. 8°. 010661. g.

DEROSNE (L. B.) Sur le Vif. pp. 330. *Paris,* 1893. 12°. 010662. g. 22.

FAGUET (É.) Politiques et moralistes du 19me siècle. *Paris,* 1891, etc. 12°. 011824. c. 22.

GRENIER ( ) Nos Sénateurs. Biographies. pp. 452. *Paris,* 1895. 32°. 8052. a. 5.

MALLET (C.) Dictionnaire des notabilités contemporains, etc. *Paris,* 1894, etc. 8°. 10663. i.

MARX (A.) Silhouettes de mon temps. pp. 337. *Paris,* 1889. 12°. 012330. f. 20.

CHEVASSU (F.) Les Parisiens. pp. 276. *Paris,* 1892. 12°. 012330. f. 28.

ROUSSEAU (P.) Les héros de Paris. pp. 312. *Paris,* 1891. 4°. 10662. i. 33.

DICTIONARIES. Dictionnaire drôlatique des contemporains dauphinois. pp. 132. *Grenoble,* 1891. 8°. 010661. m. 50.

Germany.

BETTELHEIM (A.) Deutsche und Franzosen. pp. 316. *Wien,* 1895. 10602. cc. 22.

BIOGRAPHY.—Germany—continued.

HELDEN. Unsere Helden. *Salzburg*, 1885, *etc.* 8°.
10708. de.

NEUMANN-STRELA (C.) Deutschlands Helden in Krieg und Frieden. *Hannover*, 1892, *etc.* 8°.
10703. h 38.

ZOBELTITZ (H. v.) Lebensbilder deutscher Männer aus neuerer Zeit. pp. 441.
Bielefeld, 1892. 8°. 10703. ee. 29.

Great Britain and Ireland.

BAGEHOT (W.) Biographical Studies. pp. 398.
Lond. 1895. 8°. 2342. a. 1.

LE FÈVRE-DEUMIER (J.) Célébrités anglaises.
pp. 335. *Paris*, 1895. 8°. 10804. g. 4.

GUINEY (L. I.) A Little English Gallery.
pp. 291. *N.Y.* 1894. 16°. 10803. a. 15.

SECCOMBE (T.) Lives of Twelve Bad Men.
pp. 373. *Lond.* 1894. 8°. 10803. g. 14.

OLIPHANT (M. O.) Historical Characters of the Reign of Queen Anne. pp. 207. *N.Y.* 1894. 8°.
10803. f. 4.

STATESMEN. Statesmen Past and Future. pp. 211.
Lond. 1894. 8°. 10815. df. 7.

TILLOTSON (J.) Our untitled Nobility. pp. 278.
Lond. 1895. 8°. 10803. aa. 33.

BOLTON (S. K.) English Statesmen of Victoria's Reign. pp. 460. *N.Y.* 1891. 8°. 10803. de. 2.

BOASE (F.) Modern English Biography.
Truro, 1892, *etc.* 8°. 2036. f.

ALBERY (R. J.) Our Conservative Statesmen.
Lond. 1893, *etc.* fol. 1559.

LIGHTFOOT (L. F.) Some well-known English-men and Americans on the Continent. pp. 141.
Nice, 1894. 8°. 10803. bb. 31.

LONDON. Leading Men of London. pp. 444.
Lond. 1895. 4°. 10804. i. 1.

STRATFORD (J.) Gloucestershire Biographical Notes. pp. 360. *Gloucester*, 1887. 8°.
10803. g. 12.

HUTCHINSON (J.) Men of Kent and Kentishmen.
pp. 160. *Canterbury*, 1892. 8°. 10803. bb. 26.

WILLIAMS (R.) Montgomeryshire Worthies.
pp. 340. *Newtown*, 1894. 8°. 10803. d. 1.

NORTHAMPTONSHIRE BIOGRAPHICAL NOTICES.
Northamptonshire Biographical Notices.
Northampton, 1892, *etc.* 8°. 10803. c. 9.

PRESS (C. A. M.) Yorkshire Leaders.
Leeds, 1892, *etc.* 4°. 10804. g. 2.

FORSHAW (C. F.) Yorkshire Poets. 4 vol.
Bradford, 1888–91. 8°. 11602. ee. 39.

CRAVEN (J. B.) Scots Worthies : 1560–1688.
pp. 144. *Edinb.* 1894. 8°. 4955. dd. 12.

GOODFELLOW (J. C.) Border Biography. pp. 83.
Hawick, 1890. 8°. 10803. a. 14.

SOMERVILLE (T.) George Square, Glasgow ; the lives of those whom its statues commemorate.
pp. 304. *Glasgow*, 1891. 8°. 10370. d. 33.

COLLIER (W. F.) Central Figures of Irish History to 1603. pp. 244. *Lond.* 1891. 8°. 10803. bb. 21.

HOGAN (E.) Distinguished Irishmen of the 16th century. 1894, *etc.* 8°. Quarterly series.
Vol. 90, *etc.* 3605. de.

Greece and Rome.

PLUTARCH. Plutarch's Lives. pp. 736.
Lond. 1893. 8°. 10606. bbb. 9.

SMITH (*Sir* W.) Dictionary of Greek and Roman Biography, *etc.* pp. 1018. *Lond.* 1894. 8°.
2259. b. 16.

India and Oriental.

BEALE (T. W.) Oriental Biographical Dictionary.
pp. 431. *Lond.* 1894. 8°. 10606. h. 19.

GRIFFIN (*Sir* L. H.) The Panjab Chiefs. 2 vol.
Lahore, 1890. 8°. 9056. ff. 24.

BIOGRAPHY.—India, etc.—continued.

INDIANS. Noted Indians of modern times. pp. 160.
Madras, 1892. 8°. 10606. bbb. 13.

RĀMAGOPĀLA SĀNYĀLA. Biography of Bengal Celebrities. *Calcutta*, 1889, *etc.* 8°. 10606. c. 20.

STARK (H. A.) and MADGE (E. W.) East Indian Worthies. pp. 57. *Calcutta*, 1892. 8°.
10803. aaa. 32.

Italy.

CHIESI (G.) Italiani illustri. pp. 334.
Milano, 1890. fol. 10630. h. 21.

CORTESI (G.) The Silent Company of the Pincio.
pp. 241. *Rome*, 1893. 8°. 10631. b. 46.

GOLINELLI (A.) Glorie Liguri.
Genova, 1894, *etc.* 8°. 10630. dd. 31.

LEFÈVRE-DEUMIER (J.) Célébrités italiennes.
pp. 442. *Paris*, 1894. 8°. 10629. h. 33.

MAURI (A.) Scritti biografici. 2 vol.
Firenze, 1894. 8°. 10629. a. 45.

Oriental. *See supra* : INDIA.

Rome. *See supra* : GREECE.

Spain.

BURDO BAZAN (E.) Españoles ilustres. pp. 121.
Madrid, 1891. 8°. 10632. aa. 51

United States of America.

AMERICA. America's Celebrities. pp. 256.
Chicago, 1895. fol. 1763. c. 16.

ENCYCLOPÆDIAS. National Cyclopædia of American Biography. *N.Y.* 1892, *etc.* 8°.
10880. k. 9.

GIDDINGS (E. J.) American Christian Rulers.
pp. 590. *N.Y.* 1889. 8°. 4986. f. 60.

MARTYN (C.) American Reformers.
N.Y. 1890. *etc.* 8°. 10883. bbb. 1. *etc.*

RAND (J. C.) One of a Thousand. Biographical sketches of Massachusetts. pp. 707.
Bost. 1890. 8°. 10880. i. 7.

FISKE (S.) Offhand portraits of New Yorkers.
pp. 357. *N.Y.* 1884. 8°. 10883. bb. 33.

LIGHTFOOT (L. F.) Well-known Americans on the Continent. pp. 141. *Nice*, 1894. 8°.
10803. bb. 31.

Biographies of Various Classes, etc.
Artistic. (Painters, Sculptors, etc.)

BARAUD (A.) Artistes, Littérateurs et Savants au XIXᵉ siècle. pp. 350. *Paris*, 1892. 8°.
10663. i. 28.

BOLTON (S. K.) Famous Artists. pp. 348.
Lond. 1892. 8°. 10601. e. 11.

EWART (H. C.) Toilers in Art. pp. 378.
Lond. 1891. 8°. 10601. e. 7.

FRONTAURA (C.) Diccionario biográfico de artistas del siglo XIX. *Madrid*, 1890, *etc.* 10606. l.

GAUTHIER (J.) Dictionnaire des Artistes franc-comtois antérieurs au XIXᵉ siècle. pp. 24.
Besançon, 1892. 8°. Pam. 24.

REDGRAVE (R.) and (S.) A Century of Painters of the English School. pp. 479.
Lond. 1893. 8°. 7856. df. 40.

VIÑAZA (de la), *Count*. Adiciones al Diccio-nario de los profesores de las bellas artes en España. *Madrid*, 1889, *etc.* 8°. 10632. de.

Clerical and Religious.

AUBINEAU (L.) Gens d'Église. 2 tom.
Lyon, 1891. 8°. 4804. h. 1.

BAILEY (J. B.) From Sinner to Saint : or character transformations. pp. 344.
Lond. 1892. 8°. 10803. e. 7.

BIOGRAPHY.—Clerical, etc.—*continued.*

BENSON (A. C.) Men of Might. pp. 295.
Lond. 1892. 8°. 4804. c. 34.

BURGON (J. W.) Lives of Twelve Good Men.
pp. 484. *Lond.* 1891. 8°. 4902. g. 26.

CLAUS (W.) Württembergische Väter. 2 Bde.
Stuttgart, 1887, 88. 8°. 4888. a.

CUMMING (J. E.) Holy Men of God. pp. 314.
Lond. 1893. 8°. 4804. g. 4.

ELLIS (J. J.) Lives that speak.
Lond. 1891, *etc.* 8°. 4907. e.

FOTSCH (W.) Glaubenshelden. pp. 678.
Cincinnati, 1893. 8°. 4920. g. 36.

HEROES. Heroes of the Cross.
Lond. 1893, *etc.* 8°. 4804. cc.

JOGAND PAGÈS (G.) Les Conversions célèbres.
pp. 426. *Paris*, 1891. 8°. 4804. c. 31.

LESUR (É.) Nos grands Évêques au XIXᵉ siècle.
pp. 413. *Tours*, 1895. 8°. 4864. e. 26.

OEHNINGER (F.) Miniaturbilder aus persönlichem
Verkehr mit Vertreten verschiedener Kirchen.
pp. 256. *Basel*, 1893. 8°. 4371. b. 11.

SMITH (G. B.) Eminent Christian Workers of
the 19th Century. pp. 416. *Lond.* 1893. 8°.
4429. c. 4.

STEDMAN (A. M. M.) English Leaders of Religion. *Lond.* 1891, *etc.* 8°. 4907. d.

TURBERVILLE (A. C.) Types of the Saintly Life.
pp. 168. *Lond.* 1892. 8°. 4804. c. 32.

WHITE (*Mrs.* E. G.) Patriarchs and Prophets.
pp. 756. *Lond.* 1892. 8°. 3155. k. 40.
See also CHURCH HISTORY : SAINTS.

Dramatic. *See* DRAMA, *France: Germany:
Great Britain and Ireland: United States.*

Literary.

FRONTAURA (C.) Diccionario biográfico internacional de escritores del siglo XIX.
Madrid, 1890, *etc.* 8°. 10606. l.

GUBERNATIS (A. de) Dictionnaire international
des Écrivains du jour. *Florence*, 1888–91. 8°.
2036. d.

LACROIX (O.) Quelques maîtres étrangers et
français. pp. 394. *Paris*, 1891. 8°.
011824. f. 23.

BELL (C. D.) Some English Poets. pp. 280.
Lond. 1895. 8°. 10803. e. 19.

BOLTON (S. K.) Famous English Authors of the
19th Century. pp. 451. *N.Y.* 1890. 8°.
10803. e. 3.

FORSHAW (C. F.) Yorkshire Poets. 4 vol.
Bradford, 1888–91. 8°. 11602. ee. 39.

HOWITT (W.) Homes and haunts of British
Poets. pp. 642. *Lond.* 1894. 8°. 10803. e. 14.

MASSON (D.) In the Footsteps of the Poets.
pp. 381. *Lond.* 1893. 8°. 10803. aaa. 30.

O'DONOGHUE (D. J.) Poets of Ireland.
Lond. 1892, *etc.* 8°. 10803. c. 8.

WOLFE (T. F.) Literary Pilgrimage among the
haunts of British Authors. pp. 260.
Phila. 1895. 8°. 10348. bbb. 33.

BARAUD (A.) Artistes, Littérateurs, *etc.*, au XIXᵉ
siècle. pp. 350. *Paris*, 1892. 8° 10663. i. 28.

FORSTER (J.) Some French and Spanish Men of
Genius. pp. 330. *Lond.* 1891. 8°. 10601. cc. 18.

FOUQUIER (M.) Profils et Portraits. pp. 310.
Paris, 1891. 8°. 011824. e. 19.

GAUTIER (L.) Portraits du XIXᵉ siècle. 2 tom.
Paris, 1894. 8°. 010662. k. 1.

RIENZI (M. de) Panthéon des Lettres. pp. 572.
Paris, 1893. 8°. 10660. h. 21.

BIOGRAPHY.—Literary—*continued.*

SAINTE-BEUVE (C. A.) Galerie de portraits
littéraires. pp. 517. *Paris*, 1893. 8°.
10659. f. 16.

ERNST (A. W.) Litterarische Characterbilder.
pp. 319. *Hamb.* 1894, 95. 8°. 010707. ee. 38.

VEDDER (H. C.) American Writers of to-day.
pp. 326. *N.Y.* 1894. 8°. 10883. bb. 34.

Medical.

AC. London. *Royal College of Surgeons.* Catalogue of Portraits in the Royal College of
Surgeons. pp. 68. *Lond.* 1892. 8°. 7808. cc. 2.

ROGER (J.) Les Médecins normands. pp. 372.
Paris, 1890. 8°. 7680. e. 6.

SEMELAIGNE (R.) Les grands Aliénistes français.
Paris, 1894, *etc.* 8°. 010662. i.

RIOS (J. M. de los) Médicos venezolanos.
pp. 206. *Carácas*, 1893. 8°. 10881. f. 26.
See also MEDICINE, *History.*

Military and Naval.

KNOLLYS (W. W.) Our Soldiers and Sailors.
8 pt. *Lond.* 1892. 8°. 10602. b. 24.

MORRIS (W. O'C.) Great Commanders of Modern
Times. pp. 364. *Lond.* 1891. 8°. 10604. g. 13.

SOUTHEY (R.) English Seamen. pp. 403.
Lond. 1895. 8°. 10804. b. 22.

WILSON (J. G.) Great Commanders.
Lond. 1893, *etc.* 8°. 10883. d.

YONGE (C. D.) Our great Military Commanders.
pp. 413. *Lond.* 1892. 8°. 10803. bb. 22.

GRIFFITHS (A.) French Revolutionary Generals.
pp. 259. *Lond.* 1891. 8°. 010661. ee. 38.

BUSSLER (W.) Preussiche Feldherren und Helden. *Gotha*, 1890, *etc.* 8°. 010707. h.
See also VICTORIA CROSS.

Musical.

BENNASSI-DESPLANTES (F. J.) Les Musiciens
célèbres. pp. 282. *Limoges*, 1889. 8°.
10603. i. 23.

BIOGRAPHIES. Biographies of Musicians.
Lond. 1893, *etc.* 8°. 10602. c.

BRÉMONT (A. de) The World of Music. 3 pt.
Lond. 1892. 8°. 7898. aaaa. 22.

CROWEST (F. J.) Catechism of Musical Biography. pp. 168. *Lond.* 1883. 8°. 7896. a. 56.

CULVERHOUSE (E.) History of Music and Musicians from the Renaissance. pp. 124.
Lond. 1893. 8°. 7897. a. 76.

CUMMINGS (W. H.) Biographical Dictionary of
Musicians. pp. 73. 1892. 8°. Novello's Music
Primers. 7895. ff.

DICTIONARIES. A Dictionary of Musicians.
pp. 80. *Lond.* 1894. 8°. 7899. aaa. 22.

DOLE (N. H.) A Score of famous Composers.
N.Y. 1891. 8°. 10803. de. 1.

EYMIEN (H.) Études et biographies musicales.
pp. 180. *Paris*, 1892. 8°. 7899. aaa. 10.

HANNEDOUCHE (A.) Les Musiciens et Compositeurs français. pp. 238. *Paris*, 1890. 8°.
7895. ee. 27.

IMBERT (H.) Profils de Musiciens. pp. 150.
Paris, 1888. 8°. 7878. l. 20.

—— Nouveaux Profils. pp. 234.
Paris, 1892. 8°. 7898. k. 48.

JULLIEN (A.) Musiciens d'aujourd'hui.
pp. 459. *Paris*, 1892. 12°. 7897. l. 20.

LAWRENCE (J. T.) Dictionary of musical Biography. pp. 129. *Lond.* 1892. 8°. 10601. b. 37.

MASUTTO (G.) I maestri di Musica Italiani.
pp. 200. *Venezia*, 1882. 8°. 10629. h. 28.

BIOGRAPHY.—Musical—_continued._

MORRIS (L. T.) Famous musical Composers. pp. 264. _Lond._ 1891. 8°.   10601. b. 32.

MUSICIANS. Celebrated Musicians of all nations. pp. 40. _Dresd._ 1883. 4°.   10602. m. 7.

PAINE (J. K.) Famous Composers and their Works. _Bost._ 1892, _etc._ 8°.   7895. f. 34.

RABE (M.) Die Heroen der deutschen Tonkunst. pp. 208. _Leipz._ 1890. 8°.   010707. f. 11.

ROEDER (E.) Lexikon, enthaltend Biographien in Schlesien geborener Tonkünstler. pp. 58. _Bunzlau_, 1890. 8°.   Pam. 8.

ROWBOTHAM (J. F.) Private Life of great Composers. pp. 340. _Lond._ 1892. 8°. 10601. ee. 13.

STREATFIELD (R. A.) Masters of Italian Music. pp. 270. 1895. 8°. Masters of Contemporary Music.   10601. df.

WILLEBY (C.) Masters of Contemporary Music. _Lond._ 1893, _etc._ 8°.   10601. df.

CLARKE (A. M.) Biographical Dictionary of Fiddlers. pp. 360. _Lond._ 1895. 8°. 10601. a. 51.

EHRLICH (A.) Berühmte Geiger der Vergangenheit und Gegenwart. pp. 316. _Leipz._ 1893. 8°.   10601. df. 2.

See also MUSIC, _History, etc._

Scientific.

BOLTON (S. K.) Famous Men of Science. pp. 377. _Lond._ 1890. 8°.   10601. cc. 15.

BRITTEN (J.) Biographical Index of British Botanists. pp. 188. _Lond._ 1893. 8°.   10803. cc. 2.

LEADERS. Leaders in Science. _N.Y._ 1891, _etc._ 8°.   10601. df.

LODGE (O. J.) Pioneers of Science. pp. 404. _Lond._ 1893. 8°.   8562. c. 53.

MAC RAE (C.) Fathers of Biology. pp. 108. _Lond._ 1890. 8°.   10601. cc. 16.

SCHAEDLER (C.) Handwörterbuch der wissenschaftlich bedeutenden Chemiker. pp. 162. _Berl._ 1891. 8°.   10603. de. 8.

BIOLOGY. Ac. New York. _Columbia College._ Biological Series. _N.Y._ 1894, _etc._ 8°.   7002. e.

ADLER (H.) Alternating Generations. Study of oak galls and gall flies. pp. 198. _Oxf._ 1894. 8°.   7297. aa. 36.

ARNDT (R.) Biologische Studien. pp. 203. _Greifswald_, 1892, _etc._ 8°.   7406. dd.

BEALE (P. T. B.) Practical Lessons in Biology. pp. 136. _Lond._ 1894. 8°.   7203. aa. 6.

BIDGOOD (J.) Course of practical Biology. pp. 353. _Lond._ 1893. 8°.   7406. cc. 8.

BILLROTH (C. A. T.) On the Mutual Action of living Vegetable and Animal Cells. 1894. 8°. Ac. London. _New Sydenham Society._ Clinical Lectures. Series 3.   Ac. 3838/27.

CAMPBELL (H. J.) Text-Book of Biology. pp. 306. _Lond._ 1895. 8°.   7405. aaa. 30.

CHAUVEAU (A.) La Vie et l'Énergie chez l'Animal. pp. 104. _Paris_, 1894. 8°. 7405. de. 9.

CONN (H. W.) The Living World. pp. 195. _N.Y._ 1891. 8°.   7006. e. 11.

DAVIS (J. R. A.) Elementary Text-book of Biology. 2 pt. _Lond._ 1893. 8°.   7204. a. 27.

DREYER (F.) Ziele und Wege biologischer Forschung. pp. 103. _Jena_, 1892. 8°.   7407. f. 27.

DRIESCH (H.) Die mathematisch-mechanische Betrachtung morphologischer Probleme der Biologie, _etc._ pp. 59. _Jena_, 1891. 8°.   8533. dd. 12. (7.)

BIOLOGY—_continued._

GOULD (G. M.) Illustrated Dictionary of Biology. pp. 1633. _Lond._ 1894. 8°.   07305. h. 12.

GOWERS (W. R.) The Dynamics of Life. pp. 70. _Lond._ 1894. 8°.   7404. g. 2.

HAECKEL (E. H. P. A.) Systematische Phylogenie. _Berl._ 1894, _etc._ 8°.   07031. h.

HERTWIG (O.) Zeit- und Streitfragen der Biologie. _Jena_, 1894, _etc._ 8°.   7405. de.

MARSHALL (A. M.) Biological Lectures and Addresses. pp. 363. _Lond._ 1894. 8°.   7006. b. 49.

MITCHELL (P. C.) Outlines of Biology. pp. 297. _Lond._ 1894. 8°.   7404. g. 1.

NEVILL (J. H. N.) Biology of daily Life. pp. 136. _Lond._ 1890. 8°.   7406. cc. 7.

PARKER (T. J.) Lessons in Biology. pp. 408. _Lond._ 1893. 8°.   7407. de. 7.

SCIENCES. Les Sciences biologiques, _etc._ pp. 800. _Paris_, 1893. 8°.   7001. g. 7.

SHIPLEY (A. E.) Cambridge Natural Science Manuals. Biological Series. _Camb._ 1893, _etc._ 8°.   8709. h.

WELLS (H. G.) Text-book of Biology. 1894, _etc._ 8°. Tutorial Series.   12205. c. 207.

WIESNER (J.) Die Elementarstructur und das Wachsthum der lebenden Substanz. pp. 283. _Wien_, 1892. 8°.   7405. f. 14.

WILLIAMS (J. W.) Aids to Biology. _Lond._ 1895, _etc._ 8°.   7407. a. 10.

See also ANATOMY : BOTANY : CELLS : EMBRYOLOGY : PHYSIOLOGY : PROTOPLASM : ZOOLOGY, _etc._

BIRCHINGTON. BARRETT (J. P.) History of Birchington. pp. 227. _Margate_, 1893. 8°.   010358. f. 46.

BIRDS.—General.

Ac. Europe. _Ornithological Congress._

SCLATER (P. L.) Geographical distribution of Birds. pp. 45. _Budapest_, 1891. 8°. Ac. 3581/3.

—— SHARPE (R. B.) Review of recent attempts to classify Birds. pp. 90. _Budapest_, 1891. 8°.   Ac. 3581/2.

BARROWS (A.) Eggs. pp. 159. _Bost._ 1890. 8°.   7285. a. 46.

BOOTH (H. T.) Collecting and preserving Birds' Eggs and Nests. pp. 8. _Birmingham_, 1891. 8°.   7004. de. 23. (3.)

BOWDICH, afterwards LEE (S.) Anecdotes of Birds. pp. 323. _Lond._ 1891. 8°.   7204. a. 21.

COUES (E.) Handbook of field and general Ornithology. pp. 343. _Lond._ 1890. 8°.   7285. f. 6.

DIXON (C.) Jottings about Birds. pp. 239. _Lond._ 1893. 8°.   7285. de. 29.

—— The Migration of Birds. pp. 300. _Lond._ 1892. 8°.   7285. aaa. 7.

DRZEWIECKI (S.) Le Vol Plané. pp. 48. _Paris_, 1891. 8°.   Pam. 79.

GRANT (W. R O.) Hand-Book to the Game-Birds. 1895, _etc._ 8°. SHARPE (R. B.) Allen's Naturalist's Library.   7001. eee.

HEADLEY (F. W.) Structure and life of Birds. pp. 412. _Lond._ 1895. 8°.   7285. aaa. 8

KEYSER (L. S.) In Bird Land. pp. 269. _Chicago_, 1894. 8°.   7285. c. 1.

LACROIX-DANLIARD ( ) La plume des Oiseaux. pp. 368. _Paris_, 1891. 12°.   7285. b. 2.

LEROY (E.) Chez les Oiseaux, _etc._ _Paris_, 1893. 8°.   7284. g. 5.

LEVERKUEHN (P.) Fremde Eier im Nest. pp. 212. _Berl._ 1891. 8°.   7285. f. 13.

LYDEKKER (R.) The Royal Natural History. Vols. 3 and 4. _Lond._ 1893-95. 8°. 7206. m. 5.

BIRDS.—General—*continued*.

MARSHALL (W.) Der Bau der Vögel. pp. 462.
Leipz. 1895. 8°.   7285. c. 2.

MILLA (C.) Die Flugbewegung der Vögel.
pp. 93. *Leipz.* 1895. 8°.   7285. dd. 2.

MILLER (O. T.) Little Brothers of the Air.
pp. 271. *Bost.* 1892. 8°.   7284. de. 7.

MILLER-HAUENFELS (A. v.) Der mühelose Segel-
flug der Vögel. pp. 66. *Wien*, 1890. 8°.
     8708. l. 8. (4.)

MIVART (S. G.) Birds. pp. 329.
Lond. 1892. 8°.   7285. b. 3.

MOUILLARD (L. P.) L'Empire de l'Air.
pp. 284. *Paris*, 1881. 8°.   8756. c. 47.

NEWTON (A.) Dictionary of Birds.
Lond. 1893, etc. 8°.   7285. bb. 3.

OUSTALET (E.) Notice sur quelques espèces
d'oiseaux actuellement éteintes. 1893. 4°. Ac.
Paris. *Muséum National d'Histoire Naturelle.*
Centenaire, *etc.*   7003. f. 4.

PATON (F. N.) Bards and the Birds. pp. 514.
Lond. 1894. 8°.   11601. ee. 39.

PIDSLEY (W. E. H.) Collecting and Preserving
Birds. pp. 8. *Birmingham*, 1891. 2°.
     7004. de. 23. (8.)

SCHAECK (F. de) Vocabulaire ornithologique.
pp. 67. *Paris*, 1894. 8°.   7204. a. 31. (7.)

SHARPE (R. B.) Analytical Index to the works
of J. Gould. pp. 375. *Lond.* 1893. fol.
     1819. a. 27.

SKIZZEN. Gesammelte ornithologische und jagdliche Skizzen. pp. 167. *Wien*, 1884. 8°.
     7284. ee. 17.

SUCHETET (A.) Les Oiseaux hybrides rencontrés
à l'état sauvage. 1890, 91. 8°. Ac. Paris.
Société Zoologique. Mémoires. Tom, 3, 4.
     Ac. 3556/3.

VEILLARD ( ) Les Nids d'oiseaux. pp. 33.
Paris, 1891. 8°.   7285. de. 33. (6.)

W., M. M. Life in Feather-land. pp. 139.
Paisley, 1891. 4°.   7285. de. 31.

WICKMANN (H.) Die Entstehung der Färbung
der Vogeleier. pp. 64. *Münster*, 1893. 8°.
     Pam. 42.

WINTER (W.) Der Vogelflug. pp. 172.
München, 1895. 8°.   7285. aaa. 9.

CHENEY (S. P.) Wood Notes Wild : notations
of Bird Music. pp. 261. *Bost.* 1892. 8°.
     7285. de. 22.

HAYWARD (J. M.) Bird Notes. pp. 181.
Lond. 1895. 8°.   7284. aa. 7.

RAMBERT (E.) Chants d'Oiseaux. pp. 287.
Neuchâtel, 1894. 8°.   7285. aaaa. 2.

See also PALAEONTOLOGY : NATURAL HISTORY :
ZOOLOGY. For each order, genus, and species,
see under the name required.

Cage Birds.

BECHSTEIN (J. M.) Cage Birds. pp. 231.
Lond. 1892. 8°.   7293. bbb. 35.

BUTLER (A. G.) Foreign Finches in captivity.
Lond. 1894, etc. 4°.   K.T.C. 26. b. 13.

GREENE (W. T.) Favourite foreign Birds.
pp. 124. *Lond.* 1891. 8°.   7285. aa. 19.
See also CANARY : PARROT, *etc.*

Domestic Birds. See ANIMALS, *Domestic* :
DUCK : GOOSE : POULTRY : TURKEY, *etc.*

Game Birds. See *supra* : *General*; *infra* :
Local :—GROUSE : PHEASANT : SPORT, *etc.*

BIRDS.—Local Fauna.

See also ZOOLOGY, *Local Fauna.*

America.

ABBOTT (C. C.) The Birds about us. pp. 288.
Phila. 1895. 8°.   7285. b. 6.

BENDIRE (C.) Life Histories of North American
Birds. pp. 446. 1892. 8°. Smithsonian Contributions. Vol. 28.   Ac. 1875.

ELLIOT (D. G.) North American shore Birds.
pp. 268. *Lond.* 1895. 8°.   7285. de. 36.

GRANT (J. B.) Our common Birds. pp. 216.
N.Y. 1891. obl. 8°.   7285. a. 50.

KEELER (C. A.) Evolution of the Colors of
American Land Birds. pp. 361. 1893. 8°.
Ac. San Francisco. *Academy of Natural
Sciences.* Occasional Papers. No. III. Ac. 3037/4.

MILLER (O. T.) Bird-Lover in the West. pp. 278.
Bost. 1894. 8°.   012356. e. 15.

NEHRLING (H.) Die Nord-Amerikanische Vogel-
welt. *Leipz.* 1891, etc. 4°.   7284. i.

NUTTALL (T.) Popular Handbook of the Ornithology of the U.S. and Canada. 2 vol.
Bost. 1891. 8°.   7285. de. 25.

RIDGWAY (R.) Nomenclature of North American
Birds. pp. 94. 1881. 8°. Bulletin of the U.S.
National Museum. No. 21.   Ac. 1875/13.

U.S. *Dept. of Agriculture.* Circular. No. 11, *etc.*
Wash. 1889, etc. 8°.   7053. e. 12.

—— Report of the Ornithologist.
Wash. 1888, etc. 8°.   7053. e. 10.

WRIGHT (M. O.) Birdcraft. A field-book.
pp. 317. *N.Y.* 1895. 8°.   7285. aa. 20.

MAC ILWRAITH (T.) Birds of Ontario. pp. 426.
Lond. 1894. 8°.   7284. c. 13.

DIONNE (C. E.) Catalogue des Oiseaux de
Québec. pp. 110. *Québec*, 1889. 8°. 7285. aa. 18.

MINOT (H. D.) Land and Game Birds of New
England. pp. 492. *Bost.* 1895. 8°. 7284. ee. 18.

COUES (E.) Avifauna Columbiana. pp. 133.
1883. 8°. Bulletin of the U.S. National Museum.
No. 26.   Ac. 1875/13.

GOSS (N. S.) History of the Birds of Kansas.
pp. 692. *Topeka*, 1891. 8°.   7285. g. 12.

BELDING (L.) Land Birds of the Pacific District.
pp. 274. 1890. 8°. Ac. San Francisco. *Academy of Natural Sciences.* Occasional Papers.
No. 2.   Ac. 3037. 4.

OUSTALET (E.) Oiseaux. 1891. 4°. HORN, *Cape.*
Mission scientifique. Tom. 6.   8709. d.

Asia. *See infra : Siberia, etc.*

Australia and Polynesia.

Ac. Sydney. *Australian Museum.* Catalogue
of Australian Birds. *Sydney*, 1890, 91. 8°.
     7285. bb. 2.

—— Descriptive Catalogue of Nests & Eggs of
Birds found breeding in Australia and Tasmania.
pp. 416. *Sydney*, 1889. 8°.   7285. f. 8.

WIGLESWORTH (L. W.) Aves Polynesiae. pp. 92.
1892. 4°. Ac. Dresden. *K. Zoologisches Museum.*
Abhandlungen, *etc.* 1890, 91.   Ac. 3562.

Bavaria. *See infra : Germany.*

Biblical.

PRIESTMAN (J.) God's Birds. pp. 91.
Lond. 1893. 8°.   3127. i. 10.

Bosnia. *See infra : Hungary.*

Canary Islands.

CABRERA Y DÍAZ (A.) Catálogo de las aves del
Archipiélago Canario. 1893. 8°. Ac. Madrid.
Sociedad de Historia Natural. Anales. Tom. 22.
     Ac. 2826.

BIRDS.—Local Fauna—*continued.*

Carinthia. *See infra: Hungary.*

Ceylon. *See infra : India.*

China, Western. *See infra : Siberia.*

Denmark and Norway.

PETERSEN (S.) Vore Sangfugle. pp. 210.
Kjøbenh. 1890. 8°.   7285. a. 49.

BARFOD (K.) Iagttagelser over Sydsællands
Fugle. pp. 45. *Aalborg,* 1892. 8°. 7204. c. 16. (6.)

COLLET (R.) Bird Life in Arctic Norway.
pp. 42. *Lond.* 1894. 8°.   7285. de. 33. (9.)

France.

DEYROLLE (E.) Oiseaux. pp. 304. 1892. 8°.

FRANCE. Histoire naturelle. pt. 3.   7207. cc.

AIX - EN - PROVENCE. *Ligue Ornithophile.* Les
Oiseaux de Provence. pp. 83. *Aix,* 1894. 8°.
                                    7285. aaa. 10.

Germany.

FUERST (H.) Deutschlands nützliche und
schädliche Vögel. *Berl.* 189 ɟ, *etc.* 8°. & fol.
                                            7285. k.

MEYER (A. B.) Jahresbericht der ornitholo-
gischen Beobachtungstationen in Sachsen.
pp. 124. 1889. 4°. Ac. Dresden. *K. Zoologisches Museum.* Abhandlungen, *etc.* 1888–89.
                                    Ac. 3562.

JAECKEL (A. J.) Systematische Übersicht der
Vögel Bayerns. pp. 392. *München,* 1891. 8°.
                                    7285. bb. 1.

Gibraltar.

IRBY (L. H. L.) Ornithology of the Straits of
Gibraltar. pp. 326. *Lond.* 1895. 8°. 7284. g. 7.

Great Britain and Ireland.

BLACKBURN (J.) Birds drawn from nature.
pp. 191. *Edinb.* 1895. 8°.   7285. bb. 5.

DIXON (C.) Nests and Eggs of British Birds.
pp. 371. *Lond.* 1893. 8°.   7285. de. 27.
—— Nests and Eggs of Non-indigenous British
Birds. pp. 368. *Lond.* 1894. 8°. 7285. de. 34.
—— Migration of British Birds. pp. 320.
Lond. 1895. 8°.   7284. aaa. 33.
—— Birds of our Rambles. pp. 249.
Lond. 1891. 8°.   7285. aaa. 4
—— Game Birds and Wild Fowl of the British
islands. pp. 468. *Lond.* 1893. 8°. 7285. f. 16.

FOWLER (W. W.) Summer Studies of Birds.
pp. 288. *Lond.* 1895. 8°.   7285. aaaa. 1.

FROST (H.) Our Shells and Marine Birds.
pp. 10. *Lond.* 1891. 8°.   7004. de. 23. (6.)

GORDON (W. J.) Our Country's Birds. pp. 152.
Lond. 1892. 8°.   7285. b. 4.

GRAHAM (P. A.) Country Pastimes for Boys.
pp. 448. *Lond.* 1895. 8°.   07905. f. 32.

GRANT (W. R. O.) Handbook to the Game-
Birds. 1895, *etc.* 8°. Allen's Naturalist's Library.   7001. eee.

GREAT BRITAIN. Wild-Fowl and Sea-Fowl.
pp. 326. *Lond.* 1895. 8°.   7285. ee. 17.

HUDSON (W. H.) British Birds. pp. 363.
Lond. 1895. 8°   7285. de. 35.
—— Birds in a Village. pp. 232.
Lond. 1893. 8°.   7285. de. 30.

IRBY (L. H. L.) British Birds. pp. 69.
Lond. 1892. 8°.   7285. aaa. 5.

JESSOP (A.) Pity the Poor Birds. pp. 63.
Lond. 1893. 8°.   8425. a. 65.

KEARTON (R.) British Birds' Nests. pp. 368.
Lond. 1895. 8°.   7285. dd. 1.

LEFFINGWELL (W. B.) Wild Fowl Shooting.
pp. 373. *Lond.* 1890. 8°.   7908. ee. 10.

BIRDS.—Local Fauna—*continued.*

MACPHERSON (H. A.) Introduction to the study
of British Birds. pp. 120. 1890. 8°. Young
Collector Series.   7001. aaa.

MILLAIS (J. G.) Game Birds and Shooting
Sketches. pp. 72. *Lond.* 1892. 4°. 7285. k. 10.

MORRIS (F. R.) British Game Birds and Wild-
fowl. 2 vol. *Lond.* 1895. 8°.   7285. g. 21.

MORRIS (F. O.) History of British Birds.
6 vol. *Lond.* 1891. 8°.   2250. g.

PARKHURST (H. E.) The Birds' Calendar.
pp. 351. *Lond.* 1895, *etc.* 8°. 7284. aa. 8.

POYNTING (F.) Eggs of British Birds.
Lond. 1895, *etc.* 4°.   7284. g. 8.

ROBINSON (P.) Birds of the Wave and Woodland.
pp. 224. *Lond.* 1894. 8°.   7285. h. 3.

SAUNDERS (H.) List of British Birds. pp. 24.
Lond. 1892. 8°.   7285. de. 33. (7.)

SEEBOHM (H.) Geographical distribution of
British Birds. pp. 39. *Lond.* 1893. 8°.
                                    7285. f. 17.

SHARPE (R. B.) Chapter on Birds. Rare British
Visitors. pp. 124. *Lond.* 1895. 8°. 4430. b. 25.

SWAYSLAND (W.) Familiar Wild Birds.
Lond. 1894, *etc.* 8°.   7285. b.

WATSON (J.) Ornithology in relation to Agriculture and Horticulture. pp. 220. *Lond.* 1893. 8°.
                                    7285. de. 24.

WINTRINGHAM (W. H.) The Birds of Wordsworth.
pp. 426. *Lond.* 1892. 8°.   011824. h. 42.

WILLCOX (S. J. B.) Egg Collector's dictionary of
local names of British birds. pp. 48.
Portsmouth, 1894. 16°.   7285. a. 52.

WITHERBY (H. F.) Forest Birds. pp. 98.
Lond. 1894. 8°.   7285. b. 7.

WYATT (C. W.) British Birds. ff. 25.
Lond. 1894. 4°.   7284. i. 8.

CHRISTY (R. M.) Catalogue of Local Lists of
British Birds. pp. 42. *Lond.* 1891. 8°.
                              011902. m. 20. (11.)

WHITLOCK (F. B.) Birds of Derbyshire.
pp. 239. *Lond.* 1893. 8°.   7285. de. 26.

D'URBAN (W. S. M.) The Birds of Devon.
pp. 459. *Lond.* 1892. 8°.   7284. ee. 13.

PIDSLEY (W. E. H.) The Birds of Devonshire.
pp. 194. *Lond.* 1891. 8°.   7285. f. 10.

BARRETT-HAMILTON (G. E. H.) Harrow Birds.
pp. 50. 1892. 16°. Harrow School Scientific
Society's Memoirs.   8364. aa.

DUBLIN. *Science and Art Museum.* A List of
Irish Birds. pp. 38. *Dublin,* 1890. 8°. Pam. 18.

GRAHAM (H. D.) The Birds of Iona & Mull.
pp. 279. *Edinb.* 1890. 8°.   7285. aa. 16.

MITCHELL (F. S.) The Birds of Lancashire.
pp. 271. *Lond.* 1892. 8°.   7285. e. 28.

STONYHURST. The Birds of the Stonyhurst District.
pp. 14. *Market Weighton,* 1888. 8°.
                              7004. df. 22. (3.)

OWEN (J. A.) Within an Hour of London Town,
among Wild Birds. pp. 314. *Edinb.* 1892. 8°.
                                    7284. de. 4.

PIGOTT (T. D.) London Birds. pp. 168.
Lond. 1892. 8°.   7206. cc. 6.

SWANN (H. K.) The Birds of London. pp. 136.
Lond. 1893. 8°.   7285. b. 5.

VALENTINE (J. T. T.) London Birds. pp. 319.
Lond. 1895. 8°.   7206. bb. 20.

POWYS (T. L.) *Baron Lilford.* Notes on the Birds
of Northamptonshire. 2 vol. *Lond.* 1895. 4°.
                                    7284. i. 10.

MATHEW (M. A.) The Birds of Pembrokeshire.
pp. 131. *Lond.* 1894. 4°.   7284. g. 6.

BIRDS.—Local Fauna—*continued.*

PRENTIS (W.) Notes on the Birds of Rainham. pp. 92. *Lond.* 1894. 8°.   7284. de. 9.

BRUCE (G.) The Land Birds in and around St. Andrews. pp. 563. *Dundee*, 1895. 8°.   7285. aaaa. 3.

SAXBY (J. M. E.) Birds of Omen in Shetland. pp. 32. 1893. 8°.   12430. g. 39. (7.)

BORRER (W.) The Birds of Sussex. pp. 385. *Lond.* 1891. 8°.   7285. e. 26.

Ac., *etc.* Winchester. *Winchester College.* Macro-Lepidoptera and birds of Winchester. pp. 31. *Linc.* 1891. 8°.   7004. de. 23. (10.) *See also* SPORT.

Greece.

THOMPSON (D'A. W.) Glossary of Greek Birds. pp. 204. *Oxford*, 1895. 8°.   7284. c. 12.

Greenland.

HAGERUP (A. T.) The Birds of Greenland. pp. 62. *Bost.* 1891. 8°.   7004. df. 22. (6.)

Hawaiian Islands.

ROTHSCHILD (*Hon.* L. W.) The Avifauna of Laysan, *etc. Lond.* 1893, *etc.* fol. 7285. k. 11.

WILSON (S. B.) Aves Hawaiienses. *Lond.* 1890, *etc.* 4°.   7284. i. 9.

Heligoland.

GAETKE (H.) Die Vogelwarte Helgoland. pp. 600. *Braunschweig*, 1891. 8°. 7285. g. 15.

—— Heligoland as an ornithological Observatory. pp. 599. *Edinb.* 1895. 8°.   7285. g. 20.

Horn, Cape. *See supra : America.*

Norway. *See supra : Denmark.*

Hungary, Carinthia, Bosnia, etc.

FRIVALDSZKY (J.) Aves Hungariæ. pp. 197. *Budapestini*, 1891. 8°.   7285. g. 16.

KELLER (F. C.) Ornis Carinthiae. pp. 332. *Klagenfurt*, 1890. 8°.   7285. f. 9.

Ac. Europe. *International Ornithological Congress.* REISER (O.) Die Vogelsammlung des Landesmuseums in Sarajevo. pp. 148. *Budapest*, 1891. 8°.   Ac. 3581.

India and Ceylon.

BLANFORD (W. T.) Fauna of British India and Ceylon. *Lond.* 1888, *etc.* 8°.   7208. ee.

LUCKNOW. *Provincial Museum.* Catalogue of the Birds in the Provincial Museum, Lucknow. pp. 357 *Allahabad*, 1890. 8°.   7285. aa. 17.

MURRAY (J. A.) Edible and Game Birds of British India and Ceylon. pp. 237. *Lond.* 1889. 8°.   7285. f. 12.

—— Avifauna of Ceylon. pp. 382. *Lond.* 1890. 8°.   7285. g. 14.

Japan.

SEEBOHM (H.) Birds of the Japanese Empire. pp. 386. *Lond.* 1890. 8°.   7285. f. 5.

Netherlands.

HOYER (A. G. E.) Al onze inlandsche kamer- en volière-vogels. pp. 82. *En-chede*, 1891. 8°.   Pam. 42.

Norway.

COLLETT (R.) Fugleliv i det arctiske Norge. pp. 45. *Kristiania*, 1892. 8°.   Pam. 42.

Palestine. *See supra : Biblical.*

Saxony. *See supra : Germany.*

BIRDS.—Local Fauna—*continued.*

Siberia, Turkestan, etc.

TACZANOWSKI (W.) Faune ornithologique de la Sibérie orientale. 1891, *etc.* 4°. Ac. Saint Petersburg. *Academia Scientiarum.* Mémoires. Sér. vii. Tom. 39.   Ac. 1125/3.

OUSTALET (E.) Catalogue des oiseaux provenant du voyage de M. Bonvalot à travers le Turkestan, *etc.* 1893, *etc.* 4°. Ac. Paris. *Muséum National d'Histoire Naturelle.* Nouvelles Archives. Sér. 3.   Ac. 2855./4.

Sumatra.

VORDERMAN (A. G.) Les oiseaux de Sumatra. 1890. 8°. Ac. Batavia. *Natuurkundige Vereeniging.* Natuurkundig Tijdschrift. Ser. 8. Deel. 10.   Ac. 3096.

BIRKENHEAD. BIRKENHEAD. Views of Birkenhead. *Lond.* 1895. 8°.   10360. cc. 55.

BIRMINGHAM. BARCLAY (T.) Future Water Supply of Birmingham. pp. 30. *Birmingham*, 1891. 8°.   Pam. 79.

BETOCCHI (C.) Birmingham. Il comune modello. pp. 47. *Napoli*, 1893. 8°.   8248. e. 31.

BIRMINGHAM. *Trades Council.* Annual Report and Balance Sheet. *Birmingham*, 1894, *etc.* 8°.   8282. dd.

BIRMINGHAM SATURDAY HALF-HOLIDAY GUIDE. Birmingham Saturday Half-holiday Guide. pp. 92. *Birmingham*, 1892. 8°. 10358. ccc. 41.

DENT (R. K.) Making of Birmingham. pp. 583. *Birmingham*, 1894. 4°.   10352. l. 29.

DIRECTORIES. Streets and Inhabitants of Birmingham in 1770. pp. 114. *Birmingham*, 1886. 4°.   10352. d. 24.

THROKMORTON (C.) Survey of Birmingham, 1553. pp. 110. *Birmingham*, 1891. 4°. 010358. l. 35.

WARD, LOCK AND Co. Guide to Birmingham. pp. 160. *Lond.* 1895. 8°.   10360. aaa. 73.

KING EDWARD'S SCHOOL, *Birmingham.* King Edward's School Chronicle. N. S. Vol. 5, *etc. Birmingham*, 1887, *etc*, 8°. P.P. 6148. eb. & 199. *See also* EXHIBITIONS, Pt. 1.

BIRTHS, DEATHS, & MARRIAGES, Registration of. SCOTLAND. *Registrar-General.* List of Registrars of Births, Deaths and Marriages. pp. 75. *Edinb.* 1894. 8°.   Pam. 26.

BISCAY, Bay of. G.B. & I. *Hydrographic Office.* Sailing Directions for the West Coasts of France, Spain and Portugal. pp. 516. *Lond.* 1891. 8°.   10496. g. 7.

Province.

ADÁN DE YARZA (R.) Descripción de la provincia de Vizcaya. pp. 192. 1892. 8°. SPAIN. *Comisión del Mapa Geológico.* Memorias.   7108. gg.

SAGARMÍNAGA (F. de) El gobierno del señorío de Vizcaya. 8 tom. *Bilbao*, 1892. 8°. 8042. i. *See also* BASQUE PEOPLE.

BISHARI LANGUAGE. *See* AFRICAN LANGUAGES.

BISHOP HILL COLONY. MIKKELSEN (M. A.) The Bishop Hill Colony. pp. 80. 1892. 8°. Johns Hopkins University Studies, *etc.* Ser. 10. No. 1.   Ac. 2689.

BISHOPS. *See* CLERGY.

BISHOPS CANNINGS. PONTING (C. E.) Notes on the Church of St. Mary, Bishops Cannings. pp. 13. *Devizes*, 1880. 8°.   7808. bbb. 27. (2.)

BISKRA. PEASE (A. E.) Biskra and the oases and deserts of the Zibans. pp. 112. *Lond.* 1893. 8°.   10097. aaa. 47.

BISLEY. PEDDIE (J.) The New Wimbledon at Bisley. pp. 93. *Lond.* 1892. 8°.   Pam. 2.
CATER (J.) Bisley Bits. pp. 127.
Lond. 1892. 8°.   10360. c. 25.

BISMARCK ARCHIPELAGO. *See* NEW GUINEA.

BITSCH. IRLE (H.) Die Festung Bitsch. pp. 48. *Strassburg*, 1888. 8°.   10255. aaa. 17.
LEMPFRID (H.) Geschichte der Herrschaft Bitsch. pp. 53. 1892. 8°. Ac. Metz. *Gesellschaft für lothringische Geschichte.* Jahrbuch. Jahrg. 4.   Ac. 7112.

BIVALVES. *See* MOLLUSCA.

BIZERTA. GUEST (M. J.) The Tunisian question and Bizerta. pp. 30. *Lond.* 1881. 8°.   8027. bbb. 18.
See also TUNIS.

BJÖRNEBORG. BJÖRNEBORG RAILWAY QUESTION. Aktstycken till Björneborgska jernvägsfrågan. pp. 85. *Björneborg*, 1888. 8°.   Pam. 76.

BLACKBURN. ABRAM (W. A.) Blackburn Characters of a past generation. pp. 369. *Blackburn*, 1894. 8°.   10803. de. 5.

BLACK DEATH. *See* PLAGUE.

BLACK FOREST. COOK (T.) Tourists' Handbook for the Black Forest. pp. 376. *Lond.* 1895. 8°.   10271. aa. 10.
GOTHEIN (E.) Wirtschaftsgeschichte des Schwarzwaldes. *Strassb.* 1891, *etc.* 8°. 08225. l.
JENSEN (W.) Der Schwarzwald. 2 Th. *Berl.* 1890. 4°.   10260. f. 2.
STOCKER (F. A.) Vom Jura zum Schwarzwald. *Aarau*, 1884, *etc.* 8°.   12431. i.
See also BADEN, WURTEMBERG.

BLACKPOOL. BLACKPOOL. Illustrated Guide. pp. 39. *Blackpool*, 1891. 8°.   10348. d. 19. (10.)
SHARP (R.) and WORDEN (J.) Old Blackpool and New. pp. 27. *Blackpool*, 1894. 8°.   10348. ccc. 59. (11.)

BLACK SEA. G. B. & I. *Hydrographic Office.* Sailing directions for the Dardanelles, Sea of Marmara, and Bosporus. pp. 122. *Lond.* 1893. 8°.   10496. ff. 16.
KALBERMATTEN (L. v.) *Baron.* Sumpfleben und Jagden. pp. 180. *Wien*, 1891. 8°.   10105. cc. 9.

BLADDER. *See* GENITO-URINARY ORGANS.

BLANKENBURG. STEINHOFF (R.) Geschichte der Fürstentums Blankenburg. pp. 192. *Blankenburg*, 1891. 8°.   10255. g. 21.

BLANTYRE, Africa. *See* MISSIONS.

BLASTING. CINDERFORD. *Electric Blasting Apparatus Company.* Instructions re Electric Blasting. *Cinderford*, 1891. 8°.   8756. cc. 44. (7.)
GUTTMANN (O.) Blasting. pp. 179. *Lond.* 1892. 8°.   8768. l. 12.
See also ELECTRICITY; ENGINEERING: MINERALOGY.

BLATTIDAE. *See* ORTHOPTERA.

BLEACHING. BLEACHING. Modern Bleaching and finishing. pp. 70. *Manch.* 1893. 8°.   07944. e. 8.
See also TEXTILE FABRICS.

BLENCATHRA, Yacht. *See* ARCTIC REGIONS.

BLIND, The. ANNEVELLE (J.) Histoire d'un Aveugle. pp. 78. *Genève*, 1894. 8°.   10825. ccc. 17.

BLIND, The—*continued.*
BOSTON. *Perkins Institution.* Kindergarten and Primary School for the Blind. pp. 14. *Bost.* 1883. 8°.   8307. d. 57. (8.)
—— Proceedings of public meeting on behalf of the Printing Fund for the Blind. pp. 34. *Bost.* 1881. 8°.   8307. dd. 42. (11.)
BRAILLE (L.) Écriture à l'usage des Aveugles. 1890. *s. sh.* 8°.   1865. c. 1. (2.)
GUILLIE (S.) Essay on the Instruction and Amusements of the Blind. pp. 154. *Lond.* 1894. 8°.   7611. b. 49.
LA SIZERANNE (M. de) Dix ans d'études des Aveugles. pp. 418. *Tours*, 1890. 8°.   8277. aa. 68.
—— The Blind as seen through Blind Eyes. pp. 154. *N.Y.* 1893. 8°.   7611. aa. 29.

BLINDNESS. *See* EYE.

BLOCK BOOKS. HOCHEGGER (R.) Ueber die Entstehung und Bedeutung der Blockbücher. pp. 67. 1891. 8°, P.P. *Leipz.* Centralblatt für Bibliothekswesen. Beiheft 7. P.P. 4649. e.
ISRAEL, *Kings of.* Liber regum. pp. 6. *Leipz.* 1892. fol.   K.T.C. 24. b, 1.

BLOIS. CROY (J. de) Documents pour l'histoire des Résidences royales des bords de la Loire. pp. 218. *Paris*, 1894. 8°.   10171. g. 3.
SOYER (J.) Étude sur la communauté des habitants de Blois. pp. 141. *Paris*, 1894. 8°.   010171. k. 15.
PORCHER (R.) Notice sur les Imprimeurs et libraires blésois. pp. 292. *Blois*, 1895. 8°.   011900. de. 10.
THIBAULT (A.) Glossaire du Pays blaisois. pp. 355. *Blois*, 1892. 8°.   12954. ff. 29.

BLOOD AND BLOOD VESSELS.
BALLANCE (C. A.) Treatise on the Ligation of the Great Arteries. pp. 568. *Lond.* 1891. 8°.   07482. g. 13.
BASTIN (A.) Contribution à l'étude du pouvoir bactéricide du sang. pp. 34. *Lierre*, 1892. 8°.   7306. k. 20. (14.)
BENNETT (W. H.) On Varicocele. pp. 105. *Lond.* 1891. 8°.   07482. ee. 6.
BRUNTON (T. L.) Modern developments of Harvey's work. pp. 35. *Lond.* 1894. 8°.   7679. df. 41.
CLARKE (J. H.) Diseases of the Arteries. pp. 195. *Lond.* 1895. 8°.   7616. aaaa. 1.
COHEN (S. S.) Vasomotor Ataxia. pp. 18. *Phila.* 1894. 8°.   Pam. 39.
COUPLAND (S.) Notes on the clinical examination of the Blood. pp. 63. *Lond.* 1892. 8°.   7461. a. 15.
DROUIN (R.) Hémo-alcalimétrie. Hémo-acidimétrie. pp. 225. *Paris*, 1892. 8°. 7442. g. 24.
DUVAL (P. E. M.) Veines jugulaires superficielles. pp. 102. *Paris*, 1891. 8°.   7419. i. 25.
EHRLICH (P.) Farbenanalytische Untersuchungen zur Histologie und Klinik des Blutes. *Berl.* 1891, *etc.* 8°.   7419. f. 7.
FORSELLES (A. af) Die durch eitrige Mittelohrenentzündung verursachte Lateralsinus-Thrombose. pp. 125. *Kuopio*, 1893. 8°.   07482. k. 4.
GRASHEY (H.) Experimentelle Beiträge zur Lehre von der Blut-Circulation. pp. 75. *München*, 1892. fol.   1832. c. 20.
GRÉHANT (N.) Les gaz du sang. pp. 166. 1894. 8°. Encyclopédie des aide-mémoire.   8709. g.
GUERBER (A.) Die Salze des Blutes. pp. 21. 1894. 8°. Ac. Wurzburg. *Physikalisch-Medicinische Gesellschaft.* Verhandlungen. N. F. Bd. 28.   Ac. 3763/3.

BLOOD, etc.—*continued.*

Hénocque (A. W. L.) Spectroscopie du sang. pp. 199. 1895. 8°. Encyclopédie des aide-mémoire. 8709. g.

Jones (T. W.) Report on the state of the Blood in inflammation. pp. 67. *Lond.* 1891. 8°.
           7405. df. 16.

Kirchenberger (S.) Ätiologie und Histogenese der varicösen Venen-Erkrankungen. pp. 131. *Wien*, 1893. 8°. 7620. ee. 36.

Laennec (R. T. H.) De l'Auscultation médiate. pp. 126. *Paris*, 1893. 8°. 7679. a. 2.

Laveran (A.) and Blanchard (R.) Les Hématozoaires de l'homme et des animaux. 2 pt. *Paris*, 1894. 8°. 7405. a. 4.

Limbeck (R. R. v.) Grundriss einer klinischen Pathologie des Blutes. pp. 201. *Jena*, 1892. 8°.
           7441. f. 9.

Luk'yanov (S. M.) Grundzüge einer allgemeinen Pathologie des Gefäss-Systems. pp. 428. *Leipz.* 1894. 8°. 7442. i. 8.

Loewit (M.) Studien zur Physiologie und Pathologie des Blutes. pp. 141. *Jena*, 1892. 8°.
           7407. f. 29.

Oliver (G.) Pulse-gauging. pp. 174. *Lond.* 1895. 8°. 7442. de. 1.

Parkes (F. W.) On the Pathology of Arteriosclerosis. pp. 6. *Phila.* 1894. 8°. Pam. 39.

Poper (P.) Untersuchungen über die Elasticität der Arterienwand bei Insufficienz der Aortenklappen. pp. 56. *Dorpat*, 1890. 8°. Pam. 39.

Reinert (E.) Die Zählung der Blutkörperchen. pp. 248. *Leipz.* 1891. 8°. 7405. ee. 27.

Rieder (H.) Beiträge zur Kenntniss der Leukocytose. pp. 220. *Leipz.* 1892. 8°. 7620. e. 24.

Schiff (E.) Über das quantitative Verhalten der Blutkörperchen bei neugeborenen Kindern. 1890. 8°. Ac. Prague. *Medicinische Facultät. Zeitschrift.* Bd. 11. Ac. 3767.

Schmidt (A.) Weitere Beiträge zur Blutlehre. pp. 250. *Wiesbaden*, 1895. 8°. 7419. dd. 3.

Tigerstedt (R. A. A.) Blodomloppets fysiologi. 2 del. *Stockholm*, 1889, 90. 8°. 7405. ee. 26.

—— Lehrbuch der Physiologie des Kreislaufes. pp. 568. *Leipz.* 1893. 8°. 7405. de. 8.

Walsham (W. J.) Arteries, Veins and Lymphatics. 1893. 8°. Morris (H.) Treatise on Anatomy. 7419. l. 10.

Wernicki (J.) Supplément à l'étude de l'Hématologie. *Lemberg*, 1895, *etc.* 8°. 7420. gg.

Wooldridge (L. C.) On the Chemistry of the Blood. pp. 354. *Lond.* 1893. 8°.
           7420. aaa. 15.

Abrath (G. A.) Hæmatherapy. pp. 79. *Sunderland*, 1895. 8°. 7460. b. 8.

Héricourt (J.) De l'immunité conférée à des lapins par la transfusion péritoneale du sang de chien. 1890. 8°. Verneuil (A. A.) Études sur la tuberculose. Tom. 2. 7561. k. 1.

See also Heart : Septic Diseases.

BLOWPIPE. Landauer (J.) Blowpipe Analysis. pp. 173. *Lond.* 1892. 8°.
          8909. bb. 21.

See also Chemistry : Mineralogy.

BLUE MOUNTAINS. Woolcott (W. C.) Pocket Guide to the Blue Mountains, N.S. Wales. pp. 139. *Sydney*, 1890. 16°.
          10413. a. 15.

BLUNTISHAM. Dixon (R. W.) Century of Village Nonconformity at Bluntisham. pp. 311. *Lond.* 1887. 8°. 4715. bb. 32.

BLUSHING. Kendal (C.) Treatise on causes of Flushing and Blushing. pp. 16. *Lond.* 1895. 8°. 07305. f. 19. (8.)

BOATS AND BOATING. *See* Rowing : Yachts.

BOBBILI. Rañganaikulu Patrudu. Brief account of the Bobbili Zemindari. pp. 68. *Madras*, 1889. 8°. 10058. aa. 39.

BOBIGNY. Masson ( ) Bobigny. pp. 477. *Paris*, 1887. 8°. 10172. f. 14.

BOETIA. Roberts (W. R.) The Ancient Boeotians. pp. 92. *Camb.* 1895. 8°. 9026. g. 30. *See also* Greece.

BOGNOR. Bognor. Illustrated Guide to Bognor. pp. 181. *Bognor*, 1892. 8°.
          10368. aa. 44.

BOGOTA. Ibanez (P. M.) Las Crónicas de Bogotá. pp. 486. *Bogotá*, 1891. 8°. 9772. g. 11.

BOHEMIA. *See also* Austria.

Antiquities and History.

Richlý (H.) Die Bronzezeit in Böhmen. pp. 213. *Wien*, 1894. 4°. 7705. g. 45.

Jireček (H.) Antiquae Boemiae topographia historica. pp. 194. *Vindoboniæ*, 1893. 8°.
          10201. f. 10.

Bretholz (B.) Mähren und das Reich Herzog Boleslavs ii. 1895. 8°. Archiv für Kunde österreichischer Geschichts-Quellen. Bd. 82.
          Ac. 810/8.

Goerlitzer (M.) Die husitische Einfall, 1432. *Berl.* 1891, *etc.* 4°. 9325. ff.

Szalatnay (J. G. A.) Bilder aus der Toleranz-Zeit in Böhmen. pp. 98. *Barmen*, 1890. 8°.
         4535. b. 15. (7.)

Gindely (A.) Geschichte der Gegenreformation in Böhmen. pp. 532. *Leipz.* 1894. 8°. 4662. f. 8.

Gebauer (J.) Die Publicistik über den Böhmischen Aufstand von 1618. *Halle*, 1892. 8°.
         9327. ccc.

Denis (E.) Fin de l'indépendence bohême. 2 pt. *Paris*, 1890. 8°. 9314. k. 8.

Politics : Trade, etc.

Menger (M.) Der böhmische Ausgleich. pp. 298. *Stuttgart*, 1891. 8°. 8074. ee. 36.

Peisker (J.) Die Knechtschaft in Böhmen. pp. 82. *Prag*, 1890. 8°. 8277. ee. 29. (13.)

Skene (A. v.) Entstehen der Slavish-nationalen Bewegung in Böhmen und Mähren im xix. Jhrhdt. pp. 155. *Wien*, 1893. 8° 8074. ff. 29.

Ac. Prague. *Verein für Geschichte der Deutschen in Böhmen.* Geschichte der deutschen Industrie in Böhmen. *Prag*, 1893, *etc.* 8°. Ac. 7230/7.

Sitensky (F.) Über die Torfmoore Böhmens. 1891, *etc.* 8°. Ac. Prague. *Oba Komitéty pro Prirodovédécký Výskum země Ceské.* Archiv. Bd. 6. Ac. 2915.

Topography.

Baker (J.) Pictures from Bohemia. pp. 192. *Lond.* 1894. 8°. 10210. f. 7.

Cole (G. A. J.) The Gypsy Road. pp. 166. *Lond.* 1894. 8°. 10108. de. 12.

Jodl (J.) Orts-Lexikon des Königreiches Böhmen. *Prag*, 1894, *etc.* 8°. 10215. k.

Kisch (E. H.) Die Heilquellen und Curorte Böhmens. pp. 340. *Wien*, 1879. 8°. 7462. bb. 39.

Schimmelmann (I.) *Countess.* Auf Nebenwegen. pp. 108. *Hamb.* 1895. 8°. 10281. aaa. 21.

Bohemian Language and Literature.

Jonáš (K.) Bohemian made easy. pp. 234. *Racine*, 1890. 8°. 12976. bb. 30.

Ac. Prague. *Gesellschaft zur Förderung deutscher Literatur in Böhmen.* Übersicht über die Leistungen der deutschen Böhmens, 1891. pp. 150. *Prag*, 1893. 8°. Ac. 801. b.

BOHEMIA.—Language, etc.—continued.

WOLKAN (R.) Böhmens Antheil an der deutschen Litteratur des xvi. Jhrhdts. Prag, 1890, etc. 8°.
011902. f.

See also SLAVONIC LANGUAGES.

BÖHMERWALD. DANIEL (W.) Der südliche Böhmerwald. pp. 37. Prag, 1892. 4°.
8777. k. 14.

BOILERS. CLARK (D. K.) The Steam Engine. 2 vol. Lond. 1890. 8°.   8768. f. 2.

COLYER (F.) Treatise on Steam Boilers. pp. 108. Lond. 1892. 8°.   8767. f. 10.

DAY (C.) Indicator Diagrams and boiler testing. pp. 205. Manch. 1895. 8°.   8767. g. 27.

DUDEBOUT (A.) Appareils accessoires des chaudières à vapeur. pp. 176. 1894. 8°.
Encyclopédie des aide-mémoire.   8709. g.

FOLEY (N.) Mechanical Engineer's reference book. pp. 203. Lond. 1895. 4°.   8765. h. 27.

FOWLER (W. H.) History of the development of Green's Economiser. pp. 109. Manch. 1895. 8°.
8765. ff. 29.

HAEDER (H.) Bau und Betrieb der Dampfkessel. pp. 256. Düsseldorf, 1893. 8°.   8767. f. 39.
—— Atlas. obl. 4°.   8767. h. 23.

HUTTON (W. S.) Steam Boiler Construction. pp. 398. Lond. 1891. 8°.   8767. l. 20.

JONES (H. W.) Notes on Steam Engines & Boilers. pp. 23. Lond. 1891. 8°.   8631. l. 12. (6.)

KNIGHT (R.) The practical Boiler-Maker. pp. 158. Lond. 1890. 8°.   8807. aa. 39.

LEASK (A. R.) Triple and quadruple Expansion Engines and Boilers. pp. 246. Lond. 1892. 8°.
8767. g. 9.

LONDON. III. Perkins Engine Company. Three Official Reports of rigid trial tests. pp. 103. Lond. 1891. 8°.   8768. cc. 16.

MANCHESTER. Association for the prevention of Steam Boiler Explosions, etc. Report on experiments to ascertain the result of injecting the feed-water into a boiler when short of water, etc. pp. 55. Manch. 1889. 8°.   8767. h, 8.

MUNRO (R. D.) Steam Boilers. pp. 157. Lond. 1892. 8°.   8768. cc. 17.

PLATING. Plating and Boiler-making. pp. 364. Lond. 1895. 8°.   8767. g. 30.

SCHLIPPE (E.) Der Dampfkessel-Betreib. pp. 256. Dresd. 1890. 8°.   8768. c. 21.

SEXTON (M. J.) Pocket-book for Boiler Makers. pp. 287. Lond. 1895. obl. 8°.   8767. de. 5.

SINIGAGLIA (F.) Accidents de Chaudières. pp. 192. 1893. Encyclopédie des aide-mémoire.
3709. g.

STROMEYER (C. E.) Marine Boilers. pp. 343. Lond. 1893. 8°.   8806. ddd. 2.

TRIPLEX. Marine Boilers. pp. 105. Sunderland, 1891. 8°.   8807. dd. 27.

KITCHEN BOILER CONNECTIONS. Kitchen Boiler Connections. pp. 129. N.Y. 1894. 8°.
8777. cc. 34.

MUNRO (R. D.) Kitchen Boiler Explosions. pp. 51. Lond. 1895. 8°.   8777. b. 52.
See also MACHINERY : NAVAL SCIENCE : STEAM.

BOKHARA. COCHARD (L.) Paris, Boukara, Samarcande. pp. 146. Paris, 1891. 8°.
10076. ff. 14.
See also ASIA, Central.

Ship.

BOKHARA, Ship. The "Bokhara" Disaster. pp. 25. Hongkong, 1892. 8°.   Pam. 43.

BOLIVIA.

History and Topography.

ELIZALDE (R. de) Bolivia; orijen de su nacionalidad. pp. 79. Buenos A. 1892. 8°. 8180. h. 26.

BOLIVIA.—History, etc.—continued.

AHUMADA MORENO (P.) Guerra del Pacifico. 6 tom. Valparaiso, 1884–89. fol.   9781. i. 1.

CAMPUZANO (S.) Documentos relativos á la organizacion de la 5a division año 1879. pp. 291. La Paz, 1884. 8°.   8180. g. 18.

PAZ SOLDAN (M. F.) Narracion de la guerra de Chile contra el Perú y Bolivia. pp. 917. Buenos A. 1884. 8°.   9772. g. 9.

RIQUELME (D.) Recuerdos de la campaña al Perú i Bolivia, 1879–84. Santiago, 1890. 8°.
9772. b. 17.

RIVAS (E. A.) Episodios de la Guerra del Pacifico. pp. 153. Lima, 1891. 8°.   9772. aaa. 35.

CARDÚS (J.) Las misiones franciscanas entre los infieles de Bolivia, 1883 y 1884. pp. 429. Barcelona, 1886. 8°.   4767. dd. 9.

OLIVEIRA CEZAR (F. de) La Vida en los bosques sud-americanos. pp. 164. Buenos A. 1891. 8°.
10481. e. 32.

See also AMERICA, South.

Trade : Finance, etc.

BOLIVIA. Código mercantil de Bolivia. 2 tom. La Paz, 1891. 8°.   6784. b. 10.
—— Import Duties of Bolivia. pp. 255. 1891. 8°. U.S.A. Bureau of American Republics. Bulletin. No. 22.   08225. k. 1.

MADRID. Exposición Americana. Catálogo de los objetos que presenta la República de Bolivia. pp. 6. Madrid, 1892. 8°.   7959. f. 23.

VACA-GUZMAN (S.) Intereses comerciales entre Bolivia y el Plata. pp. 110. Buenos A. 1880. 8°.
8180. h. 27.

BOLIVIAN LITERATURE.
See AMERICAN LITÉRATURE, Spanish.

BOLOGNA. GAUDENZI (A.) Statuti delle società del popolo di Bologna. 1889, etc. 8°.
Fonti per la storia d'Italia. No. 3, etc. Ac. 6543.

RICCI (C.) Guida di Bologna. pp. 275. Bologna, 1893. 8°.   10136. a. 5.

SALVIONI (G. B.) La Popolazione di Bologna nel secolo XVII. 1890. 8°. Ac. Rome. R. Deputazione di Storia Patria. Atti. Ser. 3. Vol. 8.   Ac. 6495.

ZANNONI (A.) Arcaiche abitazioni di Bologna. 2 pt. Bologna, 1892. fol.   7705. i. 8.

Ac. Bologna. R. Deputazione di Storia Patria. I rotuli dei lettori dello Studio bolognese 1384–1799. Bologna, 1888, etc. 4°.   8356. k. 15.

BOLOGNA, Studio. Museo. Catalogo del Museo dell' ottavo centenario dello Studio bolognese. pp. 49. Bologna, 1892. 8°.   Pam. 3.

RISTELHUBER (P.) Strasbourg et Bologne. Étudiants alsaciens immatriculés à l'Université de Bologne, 1289–1562. pp. 153. Paris, 1891. 8°.
8356. h. 15.

GAUDENZI (A.) I suoni e le parole dell' dialetto della città di Bologna. pp. 292. Torino, 1889. 8°.
12942. bb. 37.

BOLSOVER. DOWNMAN (E. A.) History of Bolsover. pp. 72. Derby, 1895. 4°. 10350. cc. 42.

BOLTON ABBEY. WADDINGTON (T. A. J.) Guide to Bolton Abbey. pp. 40. York, 1895. 8°.
Pam. 90.

BOMBAY. City. BOMBAY. Bombay Riots August 1893. pp. 62. Bombay, 1893. 4°.
8022. f. 17.
—— Mahomedan and Hindu riots in Bombay, August, 1893. pp. 60. Bombay, 1893. 4°.
8022. f. 18.

R., K. Bombay Beggars and Criers. pp. 137. Bombay, 1892. 8°.   8277. ee. 39.

SCOTT (B.) City of Bombay Municipal Act, 1888. pp. 159. Bombay, 1890. 8°.   5318. d. 20.

BOMBAY. City—*continued.*

KESEVALĀLA MOTILĀLA. Bombay Municipal Code. pp. 198. *Ahmedabad*, 1890. 8°.
5318. b. 27.

See also PARSIS.

University.

ROBERTS (R. D.) Eighteen years of University Extension. pp. 114. *Bombay*, 1893. 8°.
8364. a. 50.

See also EXAMINATIONS.

BOMBAY. Presidency. BOMBAY. *Secretariat.* Selections from the letters and state papers. Marátha series. *Bombay*, 1885, *etc.* 4°. 8022. h.

—— Catalogue of the contents of the Bombay Records, 1630–1780. pp. 175. *Bombay*, 1887. 8°.
11899. dd. 6.

DOUGLAS (J.) Bombay and Western India. 2 vol. *Lond.* 1893. 8°.   010057. l. 11.

MARTINEAU (J.) Life of Sir B. Frere. 2 vol. *Lond.* 1895. 8°.   10816. cc. 27.

HUNTER (*Sir* W. W.) Bombay 1885–90. pp. 504. *Lond.* 1892. 8°.   8023. ee. 24.

ROGERS (A.) Land Revenue of Bombay. 2 vol. *Lond.* 1892. 8°.   8022. de. 23.

BOMBAY, *Presidency of.* Bombay Acts and Regulations. 2 vol. *Bombay*, 1894. 8°. 05319. k. 14.

JAM'ĪYATRĀM NĀNĀBHĀI and RUSTAM KHUR-SHEDJĪ R. KĀMĀ. Rules and Orders of the High Court of Judicature at Bombay. pp. 635. *Bombay*, 1893. 8°.   05319. k. 8.

See also INDIA.

BONA. BOUYAC (R.) Histoire de Bone. pp. 352. *Bone*, 1891. 8°.   10097. ccc. 5.

CORNULIER-LUCINIÈRE (H. R. R. de) La Prise de Bone. pp. 377. *Paris*, 1895. 8°. 9061. aaa. 6.

See also ALGERIA.

BONDEI LANGUAGE.   *See* AFRICAN LANGUAGES.

BONES. GELPKE (L.) Die Osteomalacie im Ergolzthale. pp. 86. *Liestal*, 1891. 8°.
07305. k. 13. (2.)

LOSSEN (H.) Die Resectionen der Knochen. pp. 338. 1894. 8°. BILLROTH (C. A. T.) Deutsche Chirurgie. Lief. 29 b.   7482. cc.

SAWTSCHENKO (J.) Zur Frage über die Veränderungen der Knochen beim Aussatze. 1890. 8°.

ZIEGLER (E.) Beiträge zur pathologischen Anatomie. Bd. 9.   7441. eee. 18.

SUTTON (J. B.) Osteology. 1893. 8°. MORRIS (H.) Treatise on Human Anatomy.   7419. l. 10.

See also ANATOMY : JOINTS : SURGERY.

BONN. P.P. *Bonn.* Bonner Archiv. *Bonn*, 1889, *etc.* fol.   P.P. 3533. c. and 1126.

BONNEVAL. MERLET (R.) Chronique de l'Abbaye de Bonneval de 857 à 1050. pp. 30. *Chartres*, 1890. 8°.   4629. ee. 7. (4.)

BONNEVILLE BASIN, U.S. GILBERT (G. K.) Lake Bonneville. pp. 438. 1890. 4°. U.S. *Geological Survey.* Monographs. Vol. 1.
7202. g.

BONVAUX, Priory. MARC (H.) Essai sur le Prieuré de Bonvaux. pp. 144. *Dijon*, 1890. 8°.   4629. dc. 8.

BOOKBINDING. Ac. Konigsberg. *Academia Albertina. Bibliothek.* Die Silberbibliothek Herzog Albrechts von Preussen. pp. 40. *Leipz.* 1894. 4°.   11905. d. 8.

—— London. *Burlington Fine Arts Club.* Exhibition of Bookbindings. pp. 132. *Lond.* 1891. 4°.   K.T.C. 3. b. 12.

—— Nuremberg. *Germanisches Nationalmuseum.* Katalog der vorhandenen interessanten Bucheinbände. pp. 102. 1889. 4°. P.P. *Munich.* Anzeiger für Kunde des deutschen Mittelalters, *etc.* Bd. 2.   P.P. 3542. aa.

BOOKBINDING—*continued.*

ADAM (P.) Die Kunst des Blinddrucks. pp. 60. *Leipz.* 1892. 4°.   7942. l. 43.

BERALDI (H.) Estampes et livres, 1872–1892. pp. 277. *Paris*, 1892. 4°.   11899. i. 44.

—— La Reliure du XIXᵉ siècle. *Paris*, 1895, *etc.* 8°.   K.T.C. 22. e. 10.

BICKELL (L.) Bucheinbände des XV. bis XVIII. Jahrhunderts aus hessischen Bibliotheken. *Leipz.* 1892. fol.   K.T.C. 21. b. 1.

BOOKBINDING. Photographs and cuttings relating to Bookbinding. fol.   Crach. I. Tab. 4. b.

BOSQUET (E.) Traité de l'Art du Relieur. pp. 323. *Paris*, 1890. 8°.   7943. e. 33.

BOSQUET (L.) La Reliure, études d'un practicien. pp. 188. *Paris*, 1894. 8°.   7943. ee. 32.

BOUCHOT (H.) De la Reliure. pp. 92. *Paris*, 1891. 12°.   K.T.C. 1. a. 1.

BRASSINGTON (W. S.) History of the Art of Bookbinding. pp. 277. *Lond.* 1894. 4°.
K.T.C. 22. c. 6.

—— Historic Bindings in the Bodleian Library. pp. 64. *Lond.* 1891. 4°.   K.T.C. 4. b. 24.

BRUNET (P. G.) Études sur la Reliure des livres. pp. 173. *Bordeaux*, 1891. 8°.   07945. h. 27.

BUCHHOLTZ (A.) Geschichte der Buchdruckerkunst in Riga. pp. 377. *Riga*, 1890. 8°.
11899. i. 36.

DAVENPORT (C. J.) Embroidered Books at the Burlington Fine Arts Club. 1891.
1810. b. 26. (3.)

—— Early London Bookbindings. *Lond.* 1891. fol.   1810. b. 26. (2.)

—— Notes on Book-binding. pp. 8. *Lond.* 1893. 8°.   Pam. 91.

DU BOIS (H. P.) Essay on the Art of Bookbinding. pp. 42. *N.Y.* 1883. 8°. 11899. bbb. 10.

FLETCHER (W. Y.) English Bookbindings in the British Museum. *Lond.* 1895. fol.
K.T.C. 31. b. 4.

—— English Bookbindings. 1894. fol.

CHURCH (A. H.) Some Minor Arts, *etc.*
K.T.C. 24. b. 3.

—— Bookbinding in France. pp. 80. 1894. fol. P.P. *London.* Portfolio. Monographs. No. 10.
P.P. 1931. pcd.

FOURNIER (É.) L'Art de la Reliure en France. pp. 268. *Paris*, 1888. 8°.   7944. dc. 46.

GAUTHIER (J.) Les Reliures des bibliothèques comtoises. 1894. 8°. Ac. Besançon. *Académie des Sciences.* ann. 1893.   Ac. 282/2.

GUIGARD (J.) Nouvel Armorial du Bibliophile. 2 tom. *Paris*, 1890. 8°.   2400. g.

HOLMES (R. R.) Specimens of Bookbinding from the Royal Library Windsor Castle. *Lond.* 1893. fol.   K.T.C. 29. b. 3.

HORNE (H. P.) Binding of Books. pp. 224. 1894. 8°. POLLARD (A. W.) Books about Books.
2312. d.

JACOBI (C. T.) On the Making and Issuing of Books. pp. 70. *Lond.* 1891. 4°. 11899. cc. 20.

LEDIEU (A.) Les Reliures artistiques de la Bibliothèque d'Abbeville. pp. 127. *Paris*, 1891. 8°.   11899. k. 22.

NOTTINGHAM. *Museum and Art Gallery.* Catalogue of the Exhibition of Art Bookbindings. pp. 53. *Nottingham*, 1891. 8°.   11899. c. 33.

P.P. *Stuttgard.* Allgemeiner Anzeiger für Buchbindereien. Jahrg. 6, *etc.* *Stuttgart*, 1892, *etc.* 4°.   140.

PRIDEAUX (S. T.) Historical Sketch of Bookbinding. pp. 303. *Lond.* 1893. 8°. 11899. cc. 35.

QUARITCH (B.) Collection of Facsimiles from historical or artistic Bookbinding. *Lond.* 1889. 4°.   7943. g. 20.

BOOKBINDING—*continued.*

THOINAN (E.) Les Relieurs français. 1500–1800. pp. 416. *Paris*, 1893. 8°.   7942. l. 47.

TREGASKIS (J.) International Bookbinding Exhibition at " The Caxton Head," High Holborn, London. pp. 25. *Lond.* 1894. 4°.
K.T.C. 28. a. 8.

ZAEHNSDORF (J. W.) Art of Bookbinding. pp. 190. 1890. 8°. WOOD (*Sir* H. T.) Technological Handbooks.   2266. a. 30.

BOOK-KEEPING.—General.

BARILLOT (H.) Deux monographies commerciales. pp. 41. *Paris*, 1891. 4°.   8548. g. 28.

BOOK-KEEPING. Book-keeping by double entry. pp. 52. *Auckland*, 1893. 16°.   8506. a. 54.

—— Book-keeping made easy. pp. 359. *Montreal*, 1895. 8°.   8535. e. 8.

BROCKLEHURST (G. R.) Practical Book-keeping. pp. 80. *Gainsborough*, 1894. 8°.
8531. dd. 28. (10.)

CAYLEY (A.) Principles of Book-keeping by double entry. pp. 20. *Camb.* 1894. 8°.
8533. d. 27. (11.)

CHAMBERS (W.) Chambers's Book-keeping. *Lond.* 1892, *etc.* 8°.   8535. aa.

CHILD (P.) Book-keeping and Accounts. pp. 95. *Lond.* 1891. 8°.   8535. f. 35.

CRELLIN (P.) Book-keeping. Key. 2 pt. *Lond.* 1892. 8°.   8532. bbb. 43.

DAVIDSON (A.) Introductory lessons in Book-keeping. 2 pt. *Lond.* 1892. 8°.   8535. dc. 9.

FLINT (G.) Short and easy Book-keeping. pp. 44. *Lond.* 1892. 8°.   8506. aaa. 73. (6.)

GITTI (V.) Trattato completo di ragioneria. 4 pt. *Milano*, 1893. 8°.   8535. i. 2.

HAMILTON (*Sir* R. G. C.) and BALL (J.) Book-keeping. pp. 146. 1893. 8°. Clarendon Press Series.   2320. c. 16.

HARDIE (W.) and ALLAN (A.) Book-keeping by double entry. pp. 41. *Edinb.* 1893. 8°.
8530. cc. 42.

HARLOW (E.) Book-keeping. Single entry. pp. 27. *Lond.* 1892. 8°.   8530. bbb. 27. (11.)

—— Book-keeping. Double entry. pp. 28. *Lond.* 1892. 8°.   8530. bbb. 27. (12.)

—— Examination questions in Book-keeping. pp. 96. *Lond.* 1894. 8°.   8506. ee. 24.

HYNDMAN (H.) Book-keeping. pp. 172. *Hongkong*, 1892. 8°.   8535. df. 32.

ISAAC (J.) The Science of Accounts: Indian method of double entry. pp. 208. *Bangalore*, 1892. 8°.   8535. gg. 3.

LASSEN (C.) Commercial Guide : Book-keeping by single and double entry. pp. 262. *Edinb.* 1891. 8°.   08227. ee. 25.

LISLE (G.) Elementary Book-keeping. pp. 168. *Lond.* 1894. 8°.   8534. cc. 35.

MACLEAN (J. D.) Introduction to Counting-house & Examination Book-keeping. pp. 138. *Lond.* 1892. 8°.   8535. de. 2.

—— Bookkeeping, Stages I. II. and III. *Lond.* 1892, *etc.* 8°.   8535. de. 13.

MADSEN (H. T.) Om status og det enkle bog-holderi. pp. 112. *Bergen*, 1889. 8°.
08227. g. 18.

MINCK (O. R. F.) Text Book of double entry Book-keeping. pp. 136. *Liverp.* 1893. 8°.
8533. de. 24.

MITCHELL (F. J.) Book-keeping simplified. pp. 232. *Lond.* 1895. 8°.   8535. de. 20.

NIXON (A.) Longman's Elementary Book-keeping. pp. 96. *Lond.* 1892. 8°.   8535. b. 49.

—— Longmans' Advanced Book-keeping. pp. 366. *Lond.* 1894. 8°.   8535. aa. 41.

BOOK-KEEPING.—General—*continued.*

NORTON (G. P.) Balancing for expert Book-keepers. pp. 61. *Lond.* 1894. 8°.   8533. cc. 43.

NOTLEY (A. F.) Test Cards for Book-keeping. *Lond.* 1887. 8°,   12210. bbb.

PHILLIPS (C.) Check-System of double entry Book-keeping. pp. 28. *Lond.* 1894. 8°.
8531. dd. 28. (13.)

PIXLEY (F. W.) and WILSON (J.) Book-keeping. pp. 112. *Lond.* 1892. 8°.   8535. de. 4.

SAWYER (J.) Practical Book-keeping, *etc.* pp. 35. *Lond.* 1895. 8°.   8530. h. 34.

SEEBOHM (B.) Theory of Book-keeping. pp. 62. *Lond.* 1892. 12°.   8535. aa. 29.

STEWART (J.) The Unique Cash-Book. *Liverp.* 1891. 8°.   8226. cc. 47.

THOMSON (A. W.) Text-Book of Book-keeping. pp. 153. *Lond.* 1895. 8°.   8535. de. 16.

THORNTON (J.) Manual of Book-keeping. pp. 527. 1895. 8°. Macmillan's Commercial Class Books.   012202. h.

—— Easy exercises in Book-keeping. pp. 133. *Lond.* 1892. 8°.   8534. a. 14.

TOLMIE (D.) Book-keeping. pp. 101. *Lond.* 1890. 8°.   8535. aa. 19.

VAN DE LINDE (G.) Book-keeping. pp. 150. *Lond.* 1891. 8°.   8535. df. 14.

VERNON (G. F. C.) Sets for practice in Book-keeping. pp. 36. *Lond.* 1893. 8°.
8530. bbb. 27. (16.)

—— Key to Book-keeping. *Lond.* 1890. 4°.
Pam. 38.

WHATLEY (G. E. S.) General Book-keeping for Traders. pp. 174. *Lond.* 1893. 8°.   8506. ee. 23.

ZANGHIERI (A.) La Scienza dei conti. pp. 294. *Roma*, 1890. 8°.   8533. i. 27.

Book-keeping for Special Professions, *etc.*

ACCOUNTS. How to keep the Accounts of a Parish Council. pp. 90. *Lond.* 1895. 4°.
8548. f. 25.

BRYNING (R.) Treatise on Asylum Account Keeping. pp. 91. *Lond.* 1890. 8°. 8535. df. 12.

BURDETT (H. C.) Uniform System of Accounts, for Hospitals and Institutions. pp. 76. *Lond.* 1893. 8°.   08227. e. 48.

BROCKLEHURST (G. R.) Treatise on Book-keeping for bakers, grocers, *etc.* pp. 51. *Gainsborough*, 1892. 8°.   8533. d. 27. (8.)

SAKER (S.) System of builders' Book-keeping. pp. 119. *Lond.* 1895. 8°.   8533. aaa. 45.

LEES (J. F.) Book-keeping for terminating Building Societies. pp. 125. *Oldham*, 1895. 8°.
8535. df. 37.

WEDDELL (G.) How do I stand? Hints in Book-keeping for chemists. pp. 117. *Newcastle*, 1891. 8°.   8535. aa. 21.

MANCHESTER. *Central Co-operative Board.* Outlines of Lessons on Co-operative Bookkeeping. pp. 36. *Manch.* 1889. 4°.   8535. h. 33. (4.)

WOODMAN (J. M.) Book-keeping for farmers and estate owners. pp. 165. *Lond.* 1893. 12°.
8532. aa. 42.

ALEXANDER (G.) "Simplex" system of hotel book-keeping, *etc.* pp. 8. *Lond.* 1895. 8°.
8531. cc. 28. (7.)

WHATLEY (G. E. S.) Hotel Book-keeping. pp. 76. *Lond.* 1893. 8°.   8506. ee. 22.

—— Companion to Hotel Book-Keeping. pp. 12. *Lond.* 1893. 8°.   8531. dd. 28. (9.)

HARDIE (W.) Manual of Book-keeping for law-agents. pp. 55. *Edinb.* 1893. 4°. 8530. f. 39.

KAIN (G. J.) Solicitors' Book-keeping by double entry. pp. 65. *Lond.* 1895. 8°.
8507. bb. 43.

BOOK-KEEPING.—Special—*continued.*

MARSDEN (N.) Joint Stock Company Book-keeping. pp. 8. *Des Moines*, 1892. 4°.
                      8228. i. 73.

CARR (E.) Investors' Book-keeping. pp. 15. 1892. 12°. Wilson's Legal Handy-books.
                6426. aaa. 39.

NORTON (G. P.) Textile manufacturers' Book-keeping. pp. 300. *Lond.* 1894. 8°. 8535. f. 41.

BOOK - PLATES. FINCHAM (H. W.) and BROWN (J. R.) Bibliography of Book-plates. pp. 24. *Plymouth*, 1892. 8°. 011902. m. 20. (15.)

Ac. Lond. *Ex-Libris Society.* Journal. *Lond.* 1891, *etc.* 4°.   Ac. 9672.

ALLEN (C. D.) American Book-plates. pp. 437. *Lond.* 1895. 8°.   K.T.C. 8. a. 17.

BOOKPLATES. A collection of Bookplates.
                C. 66. f. 3.

BOUCHOT (H.) Les Ex-libris. pp. 104. *Paris*, 1891. 8°.   11899. b. 49.

CASTLE (E.) English Book-plates. pp. 352. *Lond.* 1893. 8°.   K.T.C. 8. a. 13.

CONTADES (G. de) Les Ex-libris du canton de Carrouges. pp. 22. *Paris*, 1891. 8°.
         011900. cc. 6. (15.)

——— Ex-libris de J. C. A. Lallemant. pp. 12. *Alençon*, 1884. 8°.   011900. f. 10. (1.)

——— Ex-libris de Mr. Serais. pp. 11. *Alençon*, 1886. 8°.   011900. f. 10. (2.)

——— Ex-libris de D. B. Turgot. pp. 11. *Alençon*, 1886. 8°.   011900. f. 10. (3.)

EX-LIBRIS. "Ex-Libris" by Robert Day. pp. 7. *Birmingham*, 1885. 8°.   11899. cc. 13.

GAUTHIER (I.) Marques de bibliothèques et Ex-libris franc-comtois. pp. 75. *Besançon*, 1894. 8°.   9903. c. 23.

——— and LURION (R. de) Les Ex-libris des bibliothèques comtoises. 1894. 8°. Ac. Besançon. *Académie des Sciences.* Séance publique. Ann. 1893.   Ac. 282/2.

HAMILTON (W.) Dated Book-plates. *Lond.* 1894, *etc.* 4°.   9906. d. 1.

——— French Book-plates. pp. 175. *Lond.* 1892. 8°.   K.T.C. 8. a. 6.

HARDY (W. J.) Book-plates. pp. 175. 1893. 8°. POLLARD (A.) Books about Books. 2312. d.

HILDEBRANDT (A. M.) Heraldic Book-plates. *Berl.* 1892. 4°   9903. cc. 5.

INGOLD (A. M. P.) Les Ex-libris Oratoriens. pp. 15. *Paris*, 1892. 8°.   Pam. 26.

LABOUCHERE (N.) Ladies' Book-plates. pp. 358. 1895. 8°. WHITE (J. W. G.) Ex-libris Series.   K.T.C. 42. a. 1.

OTTO (G.) Zwanzig Bücherzeichen gezeichnet von G. Otto. *Berl.* 1894. 4°.   9906. cc. 12.

——— Score of Book-plates. *Lond.* 1894. 4°.
           9902. f. 46.

P.P. *Berlin.* Ex-libris. Zeitschrift. *Berl.* 1891, *etc.* 8°.   1002.

——— *London.* Book-plate Annual. *Lond.* 1894, *etc.* 4°.   P.P. 6479. c.

RYLANDS (J. P.) Notes on Book-plates, with special reference to Lancashire and Cheshire. 1890. 8°. Ac. Liverpool. *Historic Soc.* Proceedings. Vol. 40.   Ac. 8100.

SEYLER (G. A.) Illustriertes Handbuch der Ex-libris-Kunde. pp. 88. *Berl.* 1895. 8°.
           9905. c. 53.

VINYCOMB (J.) On the Processes for the Production of Ex-libris. pp. 96. *Lond.* 1894. 8°.
           9904. c. 6.

WARNECKE (F.) Die deutschen Bücherzeichen. pp. 255. *Berl.* 1890. 8°. 011902. I. 35.

BOOK-PLATES—*continued.*

WARNECKE (F.) Ex-libris des XV. u. XVI. Jahrhunderts. *Berl.* 1894. 8°.   9903. c. 21.

——— Rare Book-plates of the XVth and XVIth centuries. pp. 7. 20. *Lond.* 1893. 8°.
           9903. c. 16.

WHITE (J. W. G.) Ex-libris Series. *Lond.* 1895, *etc.* 8°.   K.T.C. 42. a. 1.

WOLFENBUTTEL. *Bibliotheca Augusta.* Die Ex-libris-Sammlung der Bibliothek. pp. 160. *Berl.* 1895. 4°.   9906. bb. 7.

BOOKSELLING AND PUBLISHING.
General.

BOOK. How to Print and Publish a Book. pp. 39. *Winchester*, 1890. 8°. 11899. aaa. 19.

CHICAGO. *Columbian Exposition.* Exposition de la Librairie Française. *Chicago*, 1893. 4°.
           7958. h. 29.

CLEGG (J.) Directory of second-hand Booksellers. pp. 308. *Rochdale*, 1891. 8°.   011902. e. 8.

GERMANY. *Börsen-Verein der Buchhändler.* Katalog der Ostermess-Ausstellung. pp. 584. *Leipz.* 1884. 4°.   11899. k. 19.

GROWOLL (A.) A Bookseller's Library. pp. 72. *N.Y.* 1891. 12°.   11899. b. 51.

HEINEMANN (W.) Bookselling. The system adopted in Germany. pp. 28. *Taunton*, 1895. 8°.   08227. de. 50.

JACOBI (C. T.) On the making and issuing of Books. pp. 70. *Lond.* 1891. 4°. 11899. cc. 20.

JOUAUST (D.) Aux Bibliophiles. Ultima. pp. 78. *Paris*, 1891. 8°.   11899. c. 39.

LICHT (W.) Die Entstehung des Nothstandes im Buchhandel. pp. 17. *Stolp*, 1891. 8°.
         011900. f. 8. (15.)

LONDON. *Society of Authors.* The Cost of Production. pp. 66. *Lond.* 1891. 8°. 11899. e. 37.

P.P. *Leipsic.* Buchgewerbeblatt. Monatsschrift. *Leipz.* 1892, *etc.* 4°.   P.P. 1623. f. and 1601.

P.P. *London.* New Book List for Booksellers. *Lond.* 1895, *etc.* 8°.   955.

——— The Bookman : monthly journal. *Lond.* 1891, *etc.* 8°.   P.P. 6479. c.

——— The International Book Finder. *Lond.* 1892, *etc.* 8°. P.P. 6490. bb. & 2024.

PRAKTIKUS. Der Autoren-Verkehr. Briefe von Verlegern an Autoren. pp. 77. *Leipz.* 1891. 8°.   Pam. 6.

PUTNAM (G. H.) Authors and their Public to the invention of printing. pp. 309. *N.Y.* 1894. 8°.   011850. h. 30.

UZANNE (O.) Bouquinistes et Bouquineurs. pp. 318. *Paris*, 1893. 8°. 10174. f. 23.

LAPORTE (A.) Les Bouquinistes et les quais de Paris. Réfutation d'O. Uzanne. *Paris*, 1893. 12°.   011900. de. 5.

History.

HUMPHREYS (A. L.) Piccadilly Bookmen : Memorials of the House of Hatchard. pp. 92. *Lond.* 1893. 8°.   11899. cc. 37.

MACMILLAN AND Co. Bibliographical Catalogue of Macmillan and Co.'s publications, 1843–89. pp. 715. *Lond.* 1891. 8°. 011902. g. 47.

RIVINGTON (S.) The House of Rivington. pp. 81. *Lond.* 1894. 8°. 011899. k. 1.

DREDGE (J. I.) Devon Booksellers, 17th and 18th centuries. ff. 133. *Plymouth*, 1885. 8°.!
         011900. cc. 28.

RYLANDS (W. H.) Booksellers in Warrington, 1639–57. 1888. 8°. Ac. Liverp. *Historic Soc.* Proceedings. Vol. 37.   Ac. 8100.

BROTHERHEAD (W.) Forty Years among the Booksellers of Philadelphia, *etc.* pp. 122. *Phila.* 1891. 8°.   11899. b. 50.

BOOKSELLING.—History—_continued._

LEA BROTHERS AND CO. One Hundred Years of Publishing, 1785–1885. pp. 20.
Phila. 1885. 8°.   10880. e. 57.

DELALAIN (P.) Étude sur le Libraire parisien du XIII° au XV° siècle. pp. 76. _Paris,_ 1891. 8°.   11902. g. 40.

COYECQUE (E.) Cinq librairies parisiennes sous François 1ᵉʳ. 1894. 8°. Ac. Paris. _Société de l'Histoire de Paris._ Mémoires. Tom. 21.
           Ac. 6883/2.

PARIS. _Cercle de la librairie._ Inventaire des marques d'imprimeurs et de libraires. pp. 355.
Paris, 1892. 8°.   11899. k. 23.

DELALAIN (P.) Notice sur Galliot du Pré, libraire, 1512–60. pp. 15. _Paris,_ 1890. 8°.
           Pam. 8.

GROUCHY (E. H. de) Vente de Livres à l'Imprimerie royale, 1684. pp. 12. _Paris,_ 1892. 8°.
           011900. ee. 6. 23.

DZIATKO (C.) Beiträge zur Kenntniss des antiken Buchwesens. pp. 18. _Göttingen,_ 1892. 8°.
           011902. m. 22. (4.)

FRIEDEL (E. A.) Zur Geschichte der Nicolaischen Buchhandlung, Berlin. pp. 55. _Berl._ 1891. 8°.
           011900. ee. 6. (12.)

OLTHOFF (F.) De Boekdrukkers, boekverkoopers en uitgevers in Antwerpen. pp. 134.
Antwerpen, 1891. 4°.   011900. f. 19.
See also BIBLIOGRAPHY.

BOOK WORMS. GREEN (S. A.) The ravages of Book-Worms. pp. 4.
Camb. Mass. 1893. 8°.   11903. d. 31. (15.)

BOOTMAKING. AUSTRIA. _Oesterreichischer Schuhmacher-Tag der Gehilfen._ Protokoll des IV. österr. Schuhmacher-Tages. pp. 64.
Wien, 1890. 8°.   Pam. 82.

FRANCKE (E.) Die Schuhmacherei in Bayern, _etc._ pp. 250. 1893. 8°. Münchener volkswirthschaftliche Studien.   08276. i.

GREEN (J. W.) How to Manage a Boot & Shoe Department. pp. 8. _Manch._ 1890. 8°.
           8276. aa. 59. (5.)

HASLUCK (P. N.) Boot Making. pp. 160. 1895. 8°. "Work" Handbooks.   07944. e.

HILL (H.) Manual of Boot and Shoe Manufacture. pp. 184. _Lond._ 1893. 8°. 7743. c. 24.

MOORE (A. J.) That uncomfortable Shoe.
pp. 138. _N.Y._ 1891. 8°.   7944. de. 45.

PAYGERT (C. v.) Die sociale Lage der galizischen Schuhmacher, _etc._ pp. 193. 1891. 8°. Staats- und socialwissenschaftl. Forschungen. Bd. 11.
           8205. dd.

SCHNEIDER (H. A.) Die moderne Schuhfabrikation. _Weimer,_ 1882. 8°.

—— Atlas. 4°.   7743. dd. 3.

TAIRE (A.) Traité de Cordonnerie. pp. 435.
Paris, 1893. 8°.   7743. c. 23.
See also FOOT.

BORAX. SPEARS (J. R.) Sketches of borax deserts of the Pacific Coast. pp. 226.
Chicago, 1892. 8°.   10412. bbb. 41.

BORDEAUX. GIRONDE. Inventaire des fonds de l'archevêché de Bordeaux. pp. 596. 1892. 4°. Collection des inventaires.   1814. b., _etc._

BORDEAUX. Inventaire des archives hospitalières. pp. 83. 27. 1885. 4°. Collection des inventaires.
           1814. b., _etc._

—— Bordeaux. Aperçu historique, _etc._ 4 pt.
Paris, 1892. 4°.   10172. f. 24.

CADÈNE (J.) L'Église Réformée de Bordeaux.
pp. 88. _Bordeaux,_ 1892. 8°.   4629. aa. 32.

JULLIAN (C.) Histoire de Bordeaux. pp. 804.
Bordeaux, 1895. 4°.   10172. i. 16.

BORDEAUX—_continued._

JULLIAN (C.) Ausone et Bordeaux. Les derniers temps de la Gaule romaine. pp. 174.
Paris, 1893. 4°.   10606. cc. 15.

LABAT (T.) Étude sur le port de Bordeaux. 1889. 8°. Ac. Bordeaux. _Académie des Sciences._ Recueil, 1889.   Ac. 297.

LABRAQUE-BORDENAVE (V.) Histoire des députés de Bordeaux au Conseil du commerce. 1700–93. 1889. 8°. Ac. Bordeaux. _Académie des Sciences._ Recueil, 1889.   Ac. 297.

LAROCHE (E.) À travers le vieux Bordeaux.
pp. 211. _Bordeaux,_ 1890. 8°.   10174. h. 17.

MARIONNEAU (C.) Les vieux souvenirs de la rue Neuve. 1890. 8°. Ac. Bordeaux. _Académie des Sciences._ Recueil, 1890.   Ac. 297.

SOMERVILLE (E. O.) In the Vine Country.
pp. 237. _Lond._ 1893. 8°.   010171. e. 14.

BORKEN. BRINKMANN (J.) Beiträge zur Geschichte Borken's. pp. 159. _Borken,_ 1890. 8°.
           10256. c. 9.

BORNEO. BORNEO. British North Borneo, the new tobacco country. pp. 16. _Lond._ 1892. 8°.
           Pam. 88.

BUYS (M.) Twee maanden op Borneo's Westkust.
pp. 230. _Leiden,_ 1892. 8°.   010057. e. 18.

G. B. & I. _Hydrographic Office._ Eastern Archipelago. 2 pt. _Lond._ 1890–93. 8°. 10496. ff. 20.

GUILLEMARD (F. H. H.) Stanford's Compend. of Geography. Australasia. Vol. 2. _Lond._ 1894. 8°.
           2060. a.

HEIN (A. R.) Die bildenden Künste bei den Dayaks auf Borneo. pp. 228. _Wien,_ 1890. 8°.
           7805. e. 6.

MARRAT (J.) The Land of the Dyaks. pp. 32.
Lond. 1891. 16°.   Pam. 88.

POSEWITZ (T.) Borneo; its geology, _etc._ pp. 495.
Lond. 1892. 8°.   010055. e. 9.

PRYER (_Mrs._ W. B.) A Decade in Borneo.
pp. 199. _Lond._ 1894. 8°.   10055. df. 22.

WHITEHEAD (J.) Exploration of Mount Kina Balu, North Borneo. pp. 317. _Lond._ 1893. 4°.
           10057. h. 9.
See also MALAY PENINSULA AND MALAYSIA.

BORNHOLM. JENSEN (J. P.) Bornholms Hesteavl. pp. 147. _Kjøbenh._ 1891. 8°.
           7293. l. 16.

KLOOS (J. H.) Die Insel Bornholm. pp. 34. 1890. 8°. Sammlung wissenschaftlicher Vorträge, _etc._ N. F. Ser. 5.   12249. m.

KOFVED ( ) Fortegnelse over Landejendommene paa Bornholm. pp. 86. _Rønne,_ 1892. 8°.
           10281. f. 11.

GORNITZKA (P. L.) Folke- og Skæmteviser i bornholmsk Mundart. pp. 22. _Nexø,_ 1892. 8°.
           Pam. 62.

BOSNIA AND HERZGOVINA. Ac., _etc._ Sarajevo. _Zemaljskij Muzej._ Wissenschaftliche Mittheilungen aus Bosnien und der Hercegovina. _Wien,_ 1893. _etc._ 8°.   10125. ff.

BALLIF (P.) Römische Strassen in Bosnien, _etc._ _Wien,_ 1893, _etc._ fol.   7707. h.

COQUELLE (P.) Histoire du Monténégro et de la Bosnie. pp. 490. _Paris,_ 1895. 8°. 9136. h. 9.

MUNRO (R.) Rambles in Bosnia-Herzegovina.
pp. 395. _Edinb._ 1895. 8°.   10126. eee. 1.

POSILOVIĆ (S.) Das Immobilar-Recht in Bosnien und Hercegovina. pp. 241. _Agram,_ 1894. 8°.
           5549. df. 13.

SCHNELLER (H.) Die staatsrechtliche Stellung von Bosnien und der Herzogowina. pp. 214.
Leipz. 1892. 8°.   8028. e. 32.

WAAL (A. d.) Reisebilder aus Bosnien. pp. 92.
Wien, 1895. 8°.   10125. eee. 8.

BOSNIA, etc.—continued.

WESSELY (V.) Die Catastral-Vermessung von Bosnien und der Hercegovina. pp. 260. *Pécs*, 1893. 8°. 08226. g. 9.

BOSTON, Lincolnshire. M., T. N. Sketch of the History of St. Botolph's Church, Boston. pp. 92. *Lond.* 1895. 8°. 4707. bb. 16.

BOSTON, Massachusetts. BOSTON. *Record Commissioners.* Report. pp. 302. *Bost.* 1886. 8°. 011903. k. 35.

BOSTON. *West Church.* The West Church, Boston. Commemorative Services, *etc.* pp. 124. *Bost.* 1887. 8°. 4745. ee. 12.

ERNST (C. W.) Constitutional History of Boston. pp. 173. *Bost.* 1894. 8°. 10411. f. 24.

GREEN (S. A.) Remarks on an early file of the Boston News Letter. pp. 7. *Bost.* 1890. 8°. 011900. f. 8. (7.)

HASSAM (J. T.) Confiscated Estates of Boston Loyalists. *Camb. Mass.* 1895. 8°. Pam. 28.

LODGE (H. C.) Boston. pp. 242. 1891. 8°. FREEMAN (E. A.) Historic Towns. 2368. a.

P.P. Boston. Commercial Bulletin. [An "Extra," illustrating the development of Boston.] *Bost.* 1892. fol. P.P. 9740.

SOISSONS (S. C. de) Boston Artists. pp. 96. *Bost.* 1894. 8°. 7854. c. 35.

SPRAGUE (H. H.) City Government in Boston. pp. 53. *Bost.* 1890. 8°. 8177. ee. 6.

TIFFANY (N. M.) From Colony to Commonwealth. pp. 180. *Bost.* 1891. 8°. 9605. aaa. 18. *See also* AMERICA, *Discovery, etc.:* MASSACHUSETTS.

BOTANY.

Pt. I. General.

AITKEN (E.) Elementary Text-book of Botany. pp. 248. *Lond.* 1893. 8°. 07028. k. 9.

ALLEN (G.) The Story of the Plants. pp. 232. *Lond.* 1895. 8°. 012208. df. 1.

AVELING (E. B.) Introduction to the Study of Botany. pp. 363. *Lond.* 1891. 8°. 07028. e. 27.

BOMMELI (R.) Die Pflanzenwelt. pp. 631. *Stuttgart*, 1894. 8°. 7054. d. 10.

BONAVIA (E.) Philosophical Notes on botanical Subjects. pp. 368. *Lond.* 1892. 8°. 07028. f. 41.

BOS (H.) Leerboek der Plantkunde. pp. 339. *Groningen*, 1892. 8°. 7054. d. 4.

BOWER (F. O.) Practical Botany. pp. 275. *Lond.* 1894. 8°. 7029. aa. 39.

BROOKE (A. E.) Botanical Charts and Definitions. pp. 34. *Lond.* 1894. 12°. 7054. c. 38.

BROWNE (W. J.) Botany for Schools. pp. 110. 1891. 8°. Elementary Science Manuals. 8708. ee.

BRUNCHORST (J.) Populære foredrag om udvikling i planteriget. pp. 199. *Bergen*, 1890. 8°. 07028. f. 36.

COSTERUS (J. C.) Beginselen der Plantkunde. pp. 304. *Amsterd.* 1892. 8°. 07028. k. 6.

DAMMER (U.) Handbuch für Pflanzensammler. pp. 342. *Stuttgart*, 1891. 8°. 07028. g. 24.

DARWIN (F.) Elements of Botany. pp. 235. 1895. 8°. Cambridge Natural Science Manuals. 8709. h.

DENDY (A.) Introduction to the study of Botany. pp. 271. *Melbourne*, 1892. 8°. 07028. e. 41.

DRUDE (O.) Handbuch der Pflanzengeographie. pp. 582. *Stuttgart*, 1890. 8°. 07028. g. 13.

FAIDEAU (F.) La Botanique amusante. pp. 379. *Paris*, 1894. 8°. 7028. bb. 1.

FRANK (A. B.) Lehrbuch der Botanik. *Leipz.* 1892, *etc.* 8°. 07028. g. 26.

BOTANY.—General—continued.

FRIES (T. M.) Lärobok i systematisk Botanik. *Stockholm*, 1891, *etc.* 8°. 07028. g.

GEDDES (P.) Chapters in modern Botany. pp. 201. 1893. 8°. University Extension Manuals. 12204. f.

GILBERT (A.) Remarks on Botany. pp. 61. *Lond.* 1894. 8°. 7054. df. 22.

GILCHRIST (A.) Collecting and Preserving Plants. pp. 8. *Birmingham*, 1891. 8°. 7004. de. 23. (7.)

GIRLING (H.) Light from Plant Life. pp. 178. *Lond.* 1895. 8°. 4371. cc. 6.

GREEN (J. R.) Manual of Botany. *Lond.* 1895, *etc.* 8°. 07028. e.

GRIERSON (G. A.) Lessons from Fields and Lanes. pp. 126. *York*, 1892. 8°. 07028. g. 19.

HULT (R.) Prof. M. Wilkomms Bildatlas öfver Växtriket. *Helsingfors*, 1893, *etc.* fol. 502.

JOHNSTONE (A.) Botany. pp. 260. *Edinb.* 1891. 8°. 07028. e. 28.

KERNER (A.) Natural History of Plants. *Lond.* 1894, *etc.* 8°. 7029. k.

KITCHENER (F. E.) Naked-eye Botany. pp. 180. 1894. 8°. Beginners' Text-books of Science. 8709. c.

KITCHENER (F. A.) A Year's Botany. pp. 264. *Lond.* 1894. 8°. 7033. aaa. 21.

KOEHLER (H.) Die Pflanzenwelt und das Klima Europas. *Berl.* 1892, *etc.* 8°. 07028. l.

LESAGE (P.) Influence du bord de la mer sur la structure des feuilles. pp. 112. *Rennes*, 1890. 8°. 07028. i. 28.

LONDON. *S.P.C.K.* [Lithographed sheets, illustrating Botanical Specimens.] *Lond.* 1894. fol. Tab. 11747. a. (44.)

LUBBOCK (*Right Hon. Sir* J.) Contribution to our knowledge of Seedlings. 2 vol. *Lond.* 1892. 8°. 7054. f. 26

MASSEE (G.) The Plant World. pp. 212. 1891. 8°. Whittaker's Library of Science. 8709. aa.

MOLISCH (H.) Die Pflanze in ihren Beziehungen zum Eisen. pp. 119. *Jena*, 1892. 8°. 07028. f. 46.

MOLL (J. W.) De invloed van Darwin's afstammingsleer op de Botanie. pp. 29. *Te Groningen*, 1890. 8°. Pam. 1.

MUHAMMAD 'ABD-AL-GHANĪ. Epitome of Botany. pp. 177. *Lahore*, 1890. 8°. 7054. aa. 27.

MURR (J.) Die Pflanzenwelt in der griechischen Mythologie. pp. 323. *Innsbruck*, 1890. 8°. 4503. e. 22.

OLIVER (J. W.) Elementary Botany. pp. 208. 1891. 8°. Blackie's Science Text-Books. 8703. bb.

—— Student's Handbook of systematic Botany. pp. 366. 1894. 8°. Blackie's Science Text-Books. 8703. bb.

PARKYN (E. A.) Movements of Plants. pp. 20. 1886. 8°. LONDON. *Sunday Lecture Society.* Selection. No. 4. 4018. o.

PEARCE (D.) Botany Lessons for children. pp. 41. *Lond.* 1895. 8°. 7030. de. 2.

PENZIG (O.) Pflanzen-Teratologie systematisch geordnet. *Genua*, 1890, *etc.* 8°. 07028. g. 11.

P.P. *Le Mans.* Le Monde des Plantes. *Le Mans*, 1891, *etc.* 8°. P.P. 2127. i.

POULSEN (V. A.) Lille Plantelære. pp. 48. *Kjøbenh.* 1892. 8°. 7029. b. 28.

SACCARDO (P. A.) Il Primato degli Italiani nella Botanica. *Padova*, 1893. 8°. 7209. dd. 7.

BOTANY.—General—continued.

SCHUMANN (C.) Lehrbuch der systematischen Botanik. pp. 705. *Stuttgart,* 1894. 8°.
7029. d. 11.

SNELGROVE (E.) Object Lessons in Botany. pp. 100. *Lond.* 1894. 8°. 7032. c. 1.

THOMSON (G. M.) Introductory Class-book of Botany. pp. 162. *Wellington,* 1891. 8°.
07028. f. 45.

TIEGHEM (P. v.) Traité de Botanique. 2 pt. *Paris,* 1891. 8°. 07028. i. 30.

TUCKWELL (W.) Tongues in Trees. pp. 151. *Lond.* 1891. 8°. 12355. f. 36.

VINES (S. H.) Students' Text-book of Botany. *Lond.* 1894, etc. 8°. 07028. l. 19.

WARMING (J. E. B.) Handbuch der systematischen Botanik. pp. 468. *Berl.* 1890. 8°.
07028. i. 26.

—— Handbook of systematic Botany. pp. 620. *Lond.* 1895. 8°. 07028. f. 58.

WITTE (H.) Plantkunde voor school en huis. 3 pt. *Groningen,* 1892. 8°. 07028. e. 42.

WULLING (F. J.) Evolution of Botany. 1891. 8°. Ac. Brooklyn. *Ethical Association.* Evolution Series. No. 7. 7006. bbb.

ZIEGLER (F.) Help for Students of Botany. pp. 21. *Mangalore,* 1890. 8°. 7073. df. 7. (4.)

For each Class, Order, Genus or Species, *see* under the name required.

Anatomy, Physiology, Microscopy, Chemistry.

BOULGER (G. S.) Physiological Unity of Plants and Animals. pp. 16. 1881. 8°. London. *Sunday Lecture Society.* Selection No. 4.
4018. c.

DARWIN (F.) and ACTON (E. H.) Practical Physiology of Plants. pp. 340. 1895. 8°. SHIPLEY (A. E.) Cambridge Natural Science Manuals. 8709. h.

FISCHER (H.) Beiträge zur vergleichenden Morphologie der Pollenkörner. pp. 72. *Breslau,* 1890. 8°. 07028. i. 27.

HENSLOW (G.) Origin of Plant Structures. pp. 256. 1895. 8°. International Scientific Series. Vol. LXXVII. 2324. bb. 14.

JOHANNSEN (W.) Lærebog i Plantefysiologi. pp. 360. *Kjobenhavn,* 1892. 8°. 07028. k. 12.

JOHNSTONE (A.) Elementary anatomical Botany. *Edinb.* 1893. fol. Tab. 11747. b. (58.)

KELLER (R.) Ueber Erscheinungen des normalen Haarverlustes an Vegetationsorganen der Gefässpflanzen. pp. 52. 1890. 4°. Ac. Germany. *Academia Naturæ Curiosum.* Nova acta. Bd. 55. Ac. 2871.

KLEBS (G.) Beiträge zur Physiologie der Pflanzenzelle. 1888. 8°. Ac. Tubingen. *Botanisches Institut.* Untersuchungen. Bd. 2.
Ac. 3260.

—— Beiträge zur Morphologie der Keimung. 1885. 8°. Ac. Tubingen. *Botanisches Institut.* Untersuchungen. Bd. 1. Ac. 3260.

LETELLIER (A.) Essai de Statique végétale. 1893. 4°. Ac. Caen. *Société Linnéene.* Mémoires. Vol. 17. Ac. 2842/3.

LOEW (E.) Einführung in die Blütenbiologie. pp. 432. *Berl.* 1895. 8°. 7406. f. 12.

LUDWIG (F.) Lehrbuch der Biologie der Pflanzen. pp. 604. *Stuttg.* 1895. 8°. 07028. i. 36.

MAC NAB (W. R.) Botany. Morphology and physiology. pp. 163. 1892. 8°. London Science class-books. 8709. a.

MARCHAL (E.) Physiologie végétale. pp. 28. *Brux.* 1893. 8°. 7306. c. 20. (10.)

BOTANY.—Anatomy, etc.—continued.

MEYER (A.) Untersuchungen über die Stärkekörner. pp. 318. *Jena,* 1895. 8°. 7029. k. 15.

NOLL (F.) Über heterogene Induktion. pp. 60. *Leipz.* 1892. 8°. Pam. 1.

PAX (F.) Allgemeine Morphologie der Pflanzen. pp. 404. *Stuttg.* 1890. 8°. 07028. g. 4.

P.P. *Padua.* Rivista di Patologia vegetale. *Padova,* 1892, etc. 8°. 939.

SACHS (J. v.) Gesammelte Abhandlungen über Pflanzen-Physiologie. *Leipz.* 1892, etc. 8°.
7029. d.

SCHUMANN (C.) Untersuchungen über den Blüthenanschluss. pp. 519. *Leipz.* 1890. 8°.
07028. i. 31.

SCOTT (D. H.) Introduction to structural Botany. pp. 288. *Lond.* 1894. 8°. 07028. e. 55.

SORAUER (P.) Popular Treatise on the Physiology of Plants. pp. 256. *Lond.* 1895. 8°.
7054. e. 15.

UGOLINI (U.) Morfologia vegetale. pp. 305. *Milano,* 1892. 8°. 7054. df. 15.

VOECHTING (H.) Über Transplantation am Pflanzenkörper. pp. 162. *Tübingen,* 1892. 4°.
7074. m. 6.

WIESNER (J.) Photometrische Untersuchungen auf pflanzenphysiologischem Gebiete. 1893, etc. 8°. Ac. Vienna. *Akademie der Wissenschaften.* Sitzungsberichte math.-naturwissenschaftl. Classe. Bd. 102. Ac. 810/6.

ZIMMERMANN (A.) Beiträge zur Morphologie der Pflanzenzelle. *Tübingen,* 1890, etc. 8°.
07028. g. 5.

BEHRENS (W. J.) Leitfaden der botanischen Mikroskopie. pp. 208. *Braunschweig,* 1890. 8°.
07028. h. 29.

DAVIS (F.) Practical histological Botany. pp. 66. *Lond.* 1894. 8°. 7033. b. 29.

POULSEN (V. A.) Botanisk Mikrokemi. pp. 87. *Kjøbenhavn,* 1891. 8°. 07028. f. 40.

ZIMMERMANN (A.) Die botanische Mikrotechnik. pp. 278. *Tübingen,* 1892. 8°. 7054. d. 2.

CROSS (C. F.) Chemistry of the structural elements of plants. pp. 320. *Lond.* 1895. 8°.
7028. aa. 3.

SOHN (C. E.) Analysis of Plants. pp. 8. 1892. 8°. 7074. i. 8. (13.)

—— Dict. of the active principles of Plants. pp. 194. *Lond.* 1894. fol. 8909. a. 25.

VOECHTING (H.) Über Transplantation am Pflanzenkörper. pp. 162. *Tübingen,* 1892. 4°.
7074. m. 6.

WIELER (A.) Chemische Untersuchungen über die Vegetation. 1890. 8°. Ostwald's Klassiker der Wissenschaften. Nos. 15, 16. 8706. de.

Botanical Gardens, Museums and Societies.

KRAUS (G.) Geschichte der Pflanzeneinführungen in die europäischen Botanischen Gärten. pp. 73. *Leipz.* 1894. 8°. 7054. h. 24.

Ac. Berlin. *Botanische Gesellschaft.* Berichte. *Berl.* 1883, etc. 8°. Ac. 3266.

PRANTL (K.) Arbeiten aus dem Botanischen Garten zu Breslau. pp. 166. *Breslau,* 1892, etc. 8°. 07028. m 11.

PERADENIYA. *Botanic Gardens.* Hand-guide. pp. 40. *Colombo,* 1894. 8°. Pam. 1.

Ac. Copenhagen. *Botanisk Forening.* Festskrift. pp. 296. *Kjøbenh.* 1890. 8°. Ac. 3353/2.

DUBLIN. *Science and Art Museum.* Herbarium and Botanical Collections. pp. 7. *Dubl.* 1891. 8° Pam. 18.

BOTANY.—Botanic Gardens, etc.—cont.

Ac. Geneva. *Laboratoire de Botanique.* Publications. *Genève,* 1893. 8°. Ac. 3254.

KEW GARDENS. Route Map and Index to the Royal Botanic Garden. *Kew,* 1886. *a card.*
1882. c. 2. (182.)

—— Guide to the North Gallery. pp. 161. *Lond.* 1892. 8°. 7054. df. 14.

—— Guide to the Museum of Economic Botany. *Lond.* 1886, *etc.* 8°. 7054. df.

BARBOSA RODRIGUES (J.) Plantas novas cultivadas no jardim botanico do Rio de Janeiro. 2 pt. *Rio de J.* 1891, 93. 4°. 7029. i. 14.

Ac. Stockholm. *Bergielunds Botaniska Trädgård.* Acta Horti Bergiani. *Stockholm,* 1891, *etc.* 4°. Ac. 3282.

TRINIDAD. *Botanic Gardens.* Bulletin of Miscellaneous Information. 1889, *etc.* 8°. 07076. h.

Ac. *etc.* Europe. *Congresso Botanico Internazionale.* Atti 1892. pp. 583. *Genova,* 1893. 8°. Ac. 3239.

—— Tubingen. *Botanisches Institut.* Untersuchungen aus dem botanischen Institut. 2 Bde. *Leipz.* 1881–88. 8°. Ac. 3260.

U.S. *Dept of Agriculture.* Contributions from the U.S. National Herbarium. *Wash.* 1890, *etc.* 8°. 7053. e. 8.

Chemistry. *See supra:* ANATOMY.

Classification and Nomenclature.

BONNIER (G.) Nouvelle Flore pour la determination facile des plantes. pp. 280. *Paris,* 1893. 12°. 7030. aa. 8.

FOTHERGILL (W. E.) Botanical Types. pp. 68. *Edinb.* 1889. 8°. 7054. aa. 30.

KEW GARDENS. Index Kewensis. *Oxf.* 1893, *etc.* 4°. 2028. f.

OLIVER (D.) Illustrations of the Natural Orders of the Vegetable Kingdom. pp. 120. *Lond.* 1893. 8°. 2252. f. 9.

Kuntze (O.) Revisio Generum Plantarum. 2 pt. *Leipz.* 1891. 8°. 07028. g. 23.

THONNER (F.) Anleitung zum Bestimmen der Phanerogamen. pp. 280. *Berl.* 1891. 8°. 07028. f. 39.

—— Key to the natural orders of Flowering-Plants. pp. 151. *Lond.* 1895. 8°. 07028. e. 48.

CROZIER (A. A.) Dictionary of Botanical Terms. pp. 202. *N.Y.* 1892. 8°. 07028. f. 49.

SAINT LAGER (J. B.) La priorité des noms de plantes. pp. 31. *Paris,* 1890. 8°. 7074. k. 12. (8.)

For Systematic Botany, *see supra:* GENERAL.

Cryptogamia.

COOKE (M. C.) Romance of low life amongst Plants. pp. 320. *Lond.* 1893. 8°. 7054. c. 36.

LUDWIG (F.) Lehrbuch der niederen Kryptogamen. pp. 672. *Stuttg.* 1892. 8°. 7054. d. 6.

MASSEE (G.) Evolution of Plant Life—Lower Forms. pp. 242. 1891. 8°. University Extension Series. 012202. g.

POIRAULT (G.) Développement des tissus dans les organes végétatifs des Cryptogames. pp. 26. 1890. 4°. Ac. Saint Petersburg. *Academia Scientiarum.* Mémoires. Sér VII. Tom. 37. Ac. 1125/3.

ROSS (C. M. W.) Manual of Crytogamic Botany. pp. 77. *Lond.* 1894. 8°. 7054. aa. 31.

SODIRO (L.) Cryptogamae Vasculares Quitenses. pp. 656. *Quiti,* 1893. 8°. 07028. h. 36.

See also supra: General and Anatomy; infra: Local Flora: ALGAE: FERNS: FUNGI: LICHENS: MOSSES.

BOTANY.—Economic.

Economic: Agricultural: Diseases of Plants.

BARNARD (C.) Talks about our Useful Plants. pp. 133. *N.Y.* 1894. 8°. 7006. aaa. 21.

FRANK (A. B.) Die Krankheiten der Pflanzen. *Breslau,* 1895, *etc.* 8°. 07028. f.

GRIFFITHS (A. B.) Diseases of Crops. pp. 174. 1890. 8°. Bell's Agricultural Series. 7075. de.

HEUZÉ (G.) Les Plantes industrielles. 4 tom. *Paris,* 1892–95. 12°. 07077. g. 2.

HOECK (F.) Nährpflanzen Mitteleuropas, *etc.* 1890. 8°. LEHMANN (R.) Forschungen zur deutschen Landes- und Volkskunde. Bd. 5. 10235. i. 10.

JACKSON (J. R.) Commercial Botany of the 19th Century. pp. 168. *Lond.* 1890. 8°. 07028. e. 26.

KEW GARDENS. Official Guide to the Museums of Economic Botany. *Lond.* 1886, *etc.* 8°. 7054. df.

LAURIE (A. P.) The Food of Plants. pp. 77. *Lond.* 1893. 8°. 7054. de. 3.

POTT (E.) Die landwirtschaftlichen Futtermittel. pp. 730. *Berl.* 1889. 8°. 07293. l. 4.

SVENDSEN (A.) Fodringslæren. pp. 284. *Kjøbenh.* 1890. 8°. 07076. k. 1.

TUBEUF (C. v.) Pflanzenkrankheiten durch kryptogame Parasiten verursacht. pp. 599. *Berl.* 1895. 8°. 7028. cc. 2.

VILMORIN-ANDRIEUX ET CIE. Les Légumes usuels. 2 tom. *Paris,* 1890. 8°. 07076. ee. 2.

WEED (C. M.) Manual concerning the fungous diseases of cultivated plants. pp. 228. *N.Y.* 1894. 8°. 7028. a. 4.

WOLFF (E. T.) Farm Foods. pp. 365. *Lond.* 1895. 8°. 07293. g. 22.

WRIGHTSON (J.) Farm Crops. pp. 224. 1891. 8°. Cassell's Agricultural Readers. 7077. de.

See also infra: Pt. II. Local Flora: AGRICULTURE: CORN: GARDENING: GRASSES.

Flowers. *See supra: General:* FLOWERS: GARDENING.

Folk Lore. *See* FOLK LORE.

Fossil Botany. *See* PALAEONTOLOGY.

Medical.

BROWN (O. P.) The complete Herbalist. pp. 504. *Lond.* 1890. 8°. 7321. cc. 6.

COSTER (D. J.) Inleiding tot de kennis van de plantaardige grondstoffen, vermeld in de Nederlandsche Pharmacopee. *Amsterd.* 1890, *etc.* 8°. 07509. f.

CROWET (A.) Plantes dont les vertus sont propres à soulager nos maux. pp. 320. *Namur,* 1892. 8°. 07028. k. 3.

DURAND-CAUBET (J. A.) Trésor médicinal des familles. pp. 594. *Paris,* 1890. 18°. 7321. c. 11.

FERNIE (W. T.) Herbal Simples. pp. 432. *Bristol,* 1895. 8°. 07509. de. 41.

HÉRAIL (J.) Manipulations de botanique médicale pp. 320. *Paris,* 1891. 8°. 07509. l. 6.

KNEIPP (S.) Plant-Atlas to "My Water-Cure." *Lond.* 1893. 8°. 7461. d. 4.

KOEHLER (E.) Medizinal-Pflanzen in naturgetreuen Abbildungen. 2 Bde. *Gera,* 1887. 8°. 7029. l. 3.

KOHL (F. G.) Die officinellen Pflanzen der Pharmacopoea Germanica. *Leipz.* 1891, *etc.* 4°. 7510. g. 7.

MURILLO (A.) Plantes médicinales du Chili. pp. 234. *Paris,* 1889. 8°. 7510. g. 6.

PLANCHON (F. G.) Les Drogues d'origine végétale. *Paris,* 1895, *etc.* 8°. 07509. l.

BOTANY.—Medical—*continued.*

SCHIMPFKY (R.) Unsere Heilpflanzen.
Gera, 1893, etc. 8°.　　　07028. k.

SLACK (G.) Slack's Herbal. pp. 125.
Lond. 1891. 8°.　　　7321. aaaa. 23.

TSCHIRCH (A.) Indische Heil- und Nutzpflanzen.
pp. 223. *Berl.* 1892. 8°.　　07076. k. 7.

WYLDE (J.) Pocket Glossary of terms employed
in Medical Botany, etc. pp. 192.
Lond. 1890. 16°.　　　7321. a. 8.

See also MATERIA MEDICA : PHARMACY.

Microscopy: Morphology.
See supra : Anatomy.

Nomenclature. *See supra : Classification.*

Physiology. *See supra : Anatomy.*

Pt. II. Local Flora.

Africa.

DURAND (T.) and SCHINZ (H.) Conspectus Floræ
Africæ. *Brux.* 1895, *etc.* 8°.　　7030. l.

DEWÈVRE (A.) Les Plantes utiles du Congo.
pp. 65. *Brux.* 1894. 8°.　　7028. c. 3.

JULIEN (A.) Flore de Constantine. pp. 332.
Constantine, 1894. 8°.　　7030. c. 7.

ENGLER (A.) Über die Hochgebirgsflora des
tropischen Afrika. pp. 461. 1892. 4°. Ac.
Berlin. *Societas Scientiarum.* Abhandlungen,
1891.　　　　Ac. 855/6.

LORET (V.) La Flore pharaonique. pp. 145.
Paris, 1892. 8°.　　　07076. m. 15.

JARDIN (E.) Aperçu sur la Flore du Gabon.
pp. 71. *Paris, 1891.* 8°.　　7030. g. 6. (8.)

SIM (T. R.) List of the Flora of Kaffraria.
pp. 92. *Cape Town, 1894.* 8°.　　7028. a. 5.

Alps : Switzerland : Tyrol, etc.

Ac. Switzerland. *Botanische Gesellschaft.* Bulletin de la Société. *Basel, 1891, etc.* 8°. Ac. 3256.

BEYER (R.) Beiträge zur Flora der Thäler
Grisanche und Rhêmes. pp. 30. *Berl.* 1891. 4°.
　　　　Pam. 1.

CORBOZ (F.) Flora Aclensis. pp. 24. 1887. 8°.
　　　　7074. i. 8. (2.)

CORREVON (H.) Flore de poche à l'usage du
touriste dans les montagnes. pp. 163.
Paris, 1894. 8°.　　　7030. de. 3.

—— Les Plantes alpines. pp. 237. *Paris. 1895.* 12°.
　　　　07077. e. 2.

COTTET (M.) Guide du botaniste dans le Canton
de Fribourg. pp. 358. *Fribourg, 1891.* 8°.
　　　　7054. f. 24.

DAFFNER (F.) Die Voralpenpflanzen. pp. 465.
Leipz. 1893. 8°.　　　07028. l. 17.

FALSAN (A.) Les Alpes françaises. La flore, *etc.*
pp. 356. *Paris, 1893.* 8°.　　7001. aa. 29.

FRANZONI (A.) Le piante fanerogame della
Svizzera. pp. 256. 1890. 4°. Ac. Switzerland. *Gesellschaft für die gesammten Naturwissenschaften. Neue Denkschriften.* Bd. 30.
　　　　Ac. 2866/7.

HEATHCOTE (E. D.) Flowers of the Engadine.
pp. 22. pl. 224. *Winchester, 1891.* 8°. 7054. g. 13.

JACCARD (H.) Catalogue de la flore valaisanne.
pp. 472. 1895. 8°. Ac. Switzerland. *Schweizerische Gesellschaft. Neue Denkschriften.*
Bd. 34.　　　　Ac. 2866/7.

SCHROETER (C.) Taschenflora des Alpen-
Wanderes. *Zürich, 1889.* 8°.　07028. f. 30.

PEYRITSCH (J.) Flora von Tirol und Vorarlberg.
1891, 8°. Ac. Innsbruck. *Naturwissenschaft-
lich-medizinischer Verein.* Berichte. Jahrg. 19.
　　　　Ac. 2907.

WUENSCHE (O.) Die Alpenpflanzen. pp. 244.
Zwickau, 1893. 8°.　　　7028. a. 2.

BOTANY.—Local Flora—*continued.*

Alsace. See infra : Germany.

America, North.

NEWHALL (C. S.) Shrubs of North-eastern
America. pp. 249. *N.Y.* 1893. 8°. 7054. e. 19.

GREENE (E. L.) Flora Franciscana. Vascular
plants of Middle California.
San Fran. 1891, *etc.* 8°.　　07028. h. 28.

COVILLE (F. V.) Botany of the Death Valley
Expedition. pp. 318. 1893. 8°. Contributions
from the U.S. Herbarium. Vol. iv. 7053. e. 8.

LESQUEREUX (L.) Flora of the Dakota Group.
pp. 400. 1891. 4°. UNITED STATES OF AMERICA.
Geological Survey. Monographs. Vol. 17.
　　　　1828. b.

RAND (E. L.) Flora of Mount Desert Island,
Maine. pp. 286. *Camb.* 1894. 8°. 07028. f. 59.

MINNESOTA. *Geological Survey.* Reports. Botanical Series. *Minneapolis, 1892, etc.* 8°. 7029. dd.

SESSÉ Y LACASTA (M.) and MOCIÑO (J. M.) Flora
Mexicana. pp. 240. *México, 1894.* 4°.
　　　　7028. h. 20.

See also infra : Greenland.

America, South.

NIEDERLEIN (G.) Resultados botánicos de exploraciones hechas en Misiones. pp. 79.
Buenos A. 1890. 8°.　　　Pam. 1.

PHILIPPI (R. A.) Verzeichniss der auf der
Hochebene der Provinzen Antofagasta und
Tarapacá gesammelten Pflanzen. pp. 96.
Leipz. 1891. 4°.　　　7028. g. 14.

SODIRO (L.) Cryptogamae Vasculares Quitenses.
pp. 656. *Quiti, 1893.* 8°.　　07028. h. 36.

MAURY (P.) Contributions à la Flore du Paraguay. 1889. 4°. Ac. Geneva. *Société de Physique.* Mémoires. Vol. 31.　　Ac. 2870.

SCHIMPER (A. F. W.) Botanische Mittheilungen
aus den Tropen. *Jena, 1888, etc.* 8°. 7029. k.

Asia Minor.

BARBEY (W.) Lydie, Lycie, Carie. Études botaniques. pp. 82. *Lausanne, 1890.* 4°. 7028. f. 1.

Australasia and Polynesia.

MOORE (C.) Handbook of the Flora of New
South Wales. pp. 582. *Sidney, 1893.* 8°.
　　　　07028. g. 33.

TATE (R.) Handbook of the Flora of South
Australia. pp. 303. *Adelaide, 1890.* 8°.
　　　　7030. b. 5.

TEPPER (J. G. O.) Flora of Roebuck Bay, W.
Australia. pp. 20. 1893. 8°.　　Pam. 1.

FEATON (E. H.) Art Album of New Zealand
Flora. *Wellington, 1889, etc.* 4°. 7054. i. 32.

HARRIS (E. C.) New Zealand Ferns, Flowers,
Berries. 3 pt. *Nelson, 1890.* fol. 7054. i. 31.

BAILEY (F. M.) Catalogue of the Plants of
Queensland. pp. 116. *Brisbane, 1890.* 8°.
　　　　07028. f. 28.

TWAMLEY, afterwards MEREDITH (L. A.) Bush
Friends in Tasmania : Native Flowers. pp. 76.
Lond. 1891. fol.　　　7028. h. 14.

DRAKE DEL CASTILLO (E.) Remarques sur la
Flore de la Polynésie. pp. 52. *Paris, 1890.* fol.
　　　　7054. i. 25.

See also infra : Malaysia.

Austria.

KERNER (A.) Schedae ad Floram exsiccatam
Austro-Hungaricam. *Vindobonae, 1881, etc.* 8°.
　　　　7032. c. 1. (6.)

BECK VON MANNAGETTA (G. v.) Flora von
Nieder-Österreich. *Wien, 1890, etc.* 8°.
　　　　07028. m. 10.

BOTANY.—Local Flora.—*Austria—cont.*

Ac. Brunn. *Naturforschender Verein.* OBORNY (A.) Flora von Mähren. 2 Bde.
Brünn, 1890. 8°. 07028. i. 29.

SAGORSKI (E.) and (SCHNEIDER (G.) Flora Carpatorum Centralium. 2 Hälfte. *Leipz.* 1891. 8°. 07028. e. 33.

See also supra: Alps.

Bosnia and Herzgovina.

MURBECK (S. S.) Beiträge zur Kenntniss der Flora von Südbosnien. pp. 182. 1891. 4°. Acta Universitatis Lundensis. Tom. 27. Ac. 1067.

Bourbon, Island.

JACOB DE CORDEMOY (E.) Flore de l'Ile de la Réunion. *Paris*, 1891, *etc.* 8°. 07028. l. 8.

Bulgaria.

VELENOVSKÝ (J.) Flora Bulgarica. pp. 676.
Pragae, 1891. 8°. 07028. f. 43.

Carparthians. See supra: Austria.

Caucasus.

RADDE (G.) On the Vertical Range of Alpine Plants in the Caucasus. 1890. 8°. 7074. i. 8. (7.)

Ceylon. See infra: India.

Denmark. See infra: Scandinavia.

Europe.

CARUEL (T.) Epitome florae Europae.
Florentiae, 1892, *etc.* 8°. 07028. l. 4.

RICHTER (C.) Plantae Europae.
Leipz. 1890, *etc.* 8°. 07028. g. 17.

LE JOLIS (A.) Notes à propos des "Plantæ Europæ" de M. Richter. 1891. 8°. Ac. Cherbourg. *Société des Sciences Naturelles.* Mémoires. Tom. 27. Ac. 2844.

HOECK (F.) Nährpflanzen Mitteleuropas.
1890. 8°. LEHMANN (R.) Forschungen, *etc.* Bd. 5. 10235. i. 10.

LOEW (E.) Blütenbiologische Floristik des mittleren Europa. pp. 424. *Stuttgart*, 1894. 8°. 07026. i. 38.

SCHULZ (A.) Grundzüge einer Entwicklungsgeschichte der Pflanzenwelt Mitteleuropas. pp. 206. *Jena*, 1894. 8°. 7054. h. 26.

See also supra: Alps; infra: Austria, Germany, France, etc.

France.

ACLOQUE (A.) Flore de France. pp. 816.
Paris, 1894. 12°. 07028. k. 21.

BONNIER (G.) and LAYENS (G. de) Tableaux des plantes vasculaires de la flore de la France. pp. 412. 1894. 8°. La végétation de la France. Pt. 1. 7030. f.

FRANCE. La végétation de la France.
Paris, 1894, *etc.* 8°. 7030. f.

MASCLEF (A.) Atlas das plantes de France. 3 tom. *Paris*, 1891. 8°. 07028. l. 1.

ROUY (G.) and FOUCAUD (J.) Flore de France.
Asnières, 1893, *etc.* 8°. 07028. l.

SIÉLAIN (R.) Atlas de poche des plantes des champs. ff. 162. *Paris*, 1894. 8°. 7054. aa. 34.

BLANCHET ( ) Catalogue des plantes du sudouest de la France. pp. 172. *Bayonne*, 1891. 8°. 7054. d. 1.

HUTEAU (H.) and SOMMIER (F.) Catalogue des plantes du département de l'Ain. pp. 212. *Bourg.* 1894. 8°. 07028. f. 56.

MIGOUT (A.) Flore du département de l'Allier. pp. 509. *Moulins*, 1890. 8°. 07028. g. 9.

AIX-LES-BAINS. Catalogue des plantes observées aux environs d'Aix-les-Bains, *etc.* pp. 193.
Aix-les-Bains, 1893. 8°. 07028. k. 15.

BOTANY.—Local Flora.—*France—cont.*

FLICHE (P.) Étude sur les flores de l'Aube et de l'Yonne. 1893. 8°. Ac. Troyes. *Société d'Agriculture.* Mémoires. Sér. 3. Tom. 30.
Ac. 260.

LEGUÉ (L.) Catalogue des plantes qui croissent dans le Canton de Mondoubleau. pp. 106.
Paris, 1891. 12°. 7029. aa. 35.

CORBIÈRE (L.) Nouvelle flore de Normandie.
pp. 716. *Caen*, 1893. 8°. 07028. k. 24.

BAILLON (H. E.) Les Herborisations parisiennes. pp. 482. *Paris*, 1890. 8°. 7054. aa. 22.

DUMONTEIL (F.) Les Fleurs à Paris. pp. 142.
Paris, 1890. 8°. 07028. h. 27.

MARTIN (E.) Catalogue des plantes de Romorantin. pp. 533. *Romorantin*, 1894. 8°. 7028. d. 4.

SOUCHÉ (B.) Flore du Haut-Poitou. pp. 332.
Niort, 1894. 8°. 07028. k. 27.

See also supra: Europe.

Germany.

FISCHER-BENZON (R. v.) Altdeutsche Gartenflora. pp. 254. *Kiel*, 1894. 8°. 7054. h. 28.

KARSCH (A.) Handbuch zum Bestimmen der in Deutschland wildwachsenden, *etc.* Pflanzen. pp. 1094. *Leipz.* 1894. 8°. 07028. l. 28.

MEDICUS (W.) Flora von Deutschland.
pp. 229. *Kaiserslautern*, 1893. 8° 07028. l. 15.

SCHLECHTENDAL (D. F. L. v.) Flora von Deutschland. 31 Bde. *Gera.* 1888. 8°
07031. g.

KALMUSS (F.) Die Flora des Elbinger Kreises. 1885. 8°. Ac. Dantzic. *Naturforschende Gesellschaft.* Schriften. N. F. Bd. 6.
Ac. 2935/4.

HIMPEL (J. St.) Flora von Elsass-Lothringen. pp. 325. *Strassb.* 1891. 8°. 7028. a. 3.

BARBER (E.) Die Flora der Görlitzer Heide. 1893. 8°. Ac. Görlitz. *Naturforschende Gesellschaft.* Abhandlungen. Bd. 20. Ac. 2938.

GUMPRECHT (O.) Die geographische Verbreitung einiger Charakterpflanzen der Flora von Leipzig, *etc.* pp. 46. *Leipz.* 1893. 4°. Pam. 2.

FUERNHOHR (H.) Excursions-Flora von Regensburg. pp. 170. *Regensburg*, 1892. 8°.
7029. aaa. 34.

KNUTH (P.) Geschichte der Botanik in Schleswig-Holstein. *Kiel*, 1890, *etc.* 8°. 07028. f. 31.

—— Blumen auf den Nordfriesischen Inseln. pp. 207. *Kiel*, 1894. 8°. 7002. gg. 17.

—— Botanische Wanderungen auf der Insel Sylt. pp. 116. *Tondern*, 1890. 8°. 7029. a. 12.

SCHUBE (T.) Zur Geschichte der schlesischen Floren. pp. 48. 1890. 4°. Ac. Breslau. *Schlesische Gesellschaft.* Jahresbericht 68.
Ac. 866/2.

LUTZE (G.) Flora von Nord-Thüringen. pp. 398.
Sondershausen, 1892. 8°. 7054. df. 10.

BECKHAUS (C.) Flora von Westfalen. pp. 1096.
Münster, 1893. 8°. 07028. k. 20.

KLINGGRAEFF (H. v.) Versuch einer Flora der Provinz Westpreussen. 1881. 8°. Ac. Dantzic. *Naturforschende Gesellschaft.* Schriften. N. F. Bd. 5. Ac. 2935/4.

WAGNER (H.) Flora des Regierungsbezirks Wiesbaden. *Bad-Ems*, 1890, *etc.* 8°.
07028. g. 16.

See also supra: Austria: Europe.

Great Britain and Ireland.

BENTHAM (G.) Illustrations of the British Flora. pp. 347. *Lond.* 1892. 8°. 07028. k. 26.

GORDON (W. J.) Our Country's Flowers. pp. 154.
Lond. 1891. 8°. 07028. g. 10.

BOTANY.—Local Flora.—_Great Britain and Ireland—continued._

HICK (T,) Synopsis of the natural orders of British flowering plants. _Manch._ 1891. 8°.
    07028. e. 31.

YOUNG (G. W.) Key-Table showing the characteristics of the natural orders of British Flora. _Lond._ 1893. 12°.   Pam. 1.

GRIFFITH (J. E.) Flora of Anglesey and Carnarvonshire. pp. 288. _Bangor_, 1895. 8°.
    07028. f. 63.

PLEYDELL (J. C. M.) Flora of Dorsetshire. pp. 345. _Dorchester_, 1895. 8°.   7030. f. 16.

WITCHELL (C. A.) Fauna and Flora of Gloucestershire. pp. 301. _Stroud_, 1892. 8°.
    7003. e. 3.

DAVY (J. B.) List of additions during 1891 to the Register of Phœnogams and Cryptogams of the Alford district. pp. 15. 1892. 8°. Pam. 1.

STONYHURST. Flora of Stonyhurst. pp. 45. _Clitheroe_, 1891. 8°.   7074. i. 8. (9.)

DUNN (S. T.) Flora of South-west Surrey. pp. 106. _Lond._ 1893. 8°.   7054. df. 13.

BAGNALL (J. E.) Flora of Warwickshire. pp. 519. _Lond._ 1891. 8°.   07028. g. 8.

SONNTAG (C. O.) Pocket Flora of Edinburgh. pp. 246. _Lond._ 1894. 8°.   7054. aa. 33.

See also supra : Europe.

Greece.

HALÁCSY (E. v.) Botanische Ergebnisse in Griechenland. 4 pt. 1894. 8°. Ac. Vienna. _Academie der Wissenschaften._ Denkschriften. Math.-naturwissenschaftl. Classe. Bd 61.
    Ac. 810/13.

See also supra : Europe.

Greenland.

LANGE (J. M. C.) Conspectus Florae Groenlandicae. 1880, _etc._ 8°. Meddelelser om Grønland. Heft 3.   10460. dd.

NATHORST (A. G.) Anmärkningar om den grönländska vegetationens historia. pp. 50. 1890. 8°. Ac. Stockholm. _Svenska Vetenskaps Academien._ Bihang till Handlingar. Bd. 16.
    Ac. 1070/7.

Herzgovina. See supra : Bosnia.

India and Ceylon.

NAIRNE (A. K.) Flowering Plants of Western India. pp. 401. _Lond._ 1894. 8°. 07028. k. 14.

GRAY (W.) Botany of Bombay. 1886. 8°.

BOMBAY, _Presidency._ Gazetteer. Vol. xxv.
    10055. g.

TALBOT (W. A.) Systematic List of the Trees, Shrubs and Woody-Climbers of Bombay. pp. 230. _Bombay_, 1894. 8°.   07076. g. 27.

TRIMEN (H.) Hand-Book to the Flora of Ceylon. _Lond._ 1893, _etc._ 8°.   7054. ee. 19.

Indies, Dutch. See infra : Malaysia.

Italy.

RICCIO (A. del) Descrizione dei fiori che fioriscono in Firenze. pp. 28. _Firenze_, 1890. 8°.
    Pam. 1.

PAOLUCCI (L.) Flora marchigiana. 2 pt. _Pesaro_, 1890, 91. 8°.   7054. g. 14.

TERRACCIANO (N.) Synopsis Plantarum Montis Pollini. pp. 191. 1891. 4°. Ac. Rome. _Istituto Botanico._ Annuario. An. 5.   Ac. 3241.

Japan.

CONDER (J.) Flowers of Japan. pp. 136. _Lond._ 1891. fol.   7028. g. 13.

MAKSIMOVICH (K. I.) Stirpes quaedam nuper in Japonia detectae, _etc._ pp. 41. _St. Petersburg_, 1893. 8°.   Pam. 1.

BOTANY.—Local Flora.—_Japan—cont._

PIGGOTT (F. T.) The Garden of Japan. pp. 60. _Lond._ 1892. 8°.   7054. h. 18.

YATABE RIŌKICHI. Iconographia floræ Japonicæ. _Tōkyō_, 1891, _etc._ 4°.   11099. d. 35.

Malaysia.

HAAK (J.) Plantenkunde voor Indie. _Semarang_, 1892. 8°.   07028. l. 23.
—— Plates. fol.   7028. h. 18.

HABERLANDT (G.) Indo-malayische Vegetationsbilder. pp. 300. _Leipz._ 1893. 8°. 7054. h. 23.

KING (G.) Materials for a Flora of the Malayan Peninsula. _Calcutta_, 1889, _etc._ 8°.   7054. h.

PHILIPPINE ISLANDS. Catálogo de las plantas del herbario. pp. 231. _Manila_, 1892. 8°. 7054. d. 3.

SCHIMPER (A. F. W.) Botanische Mittheilungen. Heft 3. Die Indo-malayische Strandflora. _Jena_, 1891. 8°.   7029. k.

See also supra : Australasia.

Mexico. See supra : America, North.

New South Wales and New Zealand. See supra : Australasia

North Frisian Islands. See supra : Germany.

Queensland. See supra : Australasia.

Scandinavia.

RAUNKIÆR (C.) Dansk Exkursions-Flora. pp. 287. _Kjøbenh._ 1890. 8°.   7029. aa. 33.

HOFFSTAD (O. A.) Norsk Flora. pp. 222. _Bergen_, 1891. 8°.   7029. aa. 36.

JORDAN (R. C. R.) Flora of Norway. 1891. 8°.

WILLSON (T. B.) The Handy Guide to Norway, _etc._   10281. aa. 11.

NORMAN (J. M.) Floræ Arcticæ Norvegiæ. pp. 59. 1893. 8°. Ac. Christiania. _Videnskabs-Selskab._ Forhandlinger. Aar 1893. No. 16.
    Ac. 1054.

SÖRENSEN (H. L.) Norsk flora. pp. 168. _Kristiania_, 1893. 8°.   7005. aaa. 24.

KROK (T. O. B. N.) Svenska Flora. _Stockholm_, 1893, _etc._ 8°.   7054. df.

SVENSSON (P.) Flora över Sveriges Kulturväxter. pp. 727. _Stockholm_, 1893. 8°. 07028. f. 60.

Schleswig-Holstein. See supra : Germany.

Scotland. See supra : Great Britain.

Sinai Peninsula.

PALESTINE. _Palestine Exploration Fund._ Account of the Flora of Sinai. pp. 255. _Lond._ 1891. 4°.
    2057. e.

Spain.

COINCY (A. de) Ecloga plantarum Hispanicarum. pp. 25. _Paris_, 1893. fol.   7028. h. 19.

PUERTA (G. de la) Botánica descriptiva y determinacion de las plantas en España. pp. 669. _Madrid_, 1891 8°.   07028. l. 7.

Sweden. See supra : Scandinavia.

Switzerland. See supra : Alps.

Tasmania. See supra : Australasia.

Tyrol. See supra : Alps.

BOTANY BAY. MYERS (F.) Botany Bay. pp. 96. _Sydney_, 1885. 4°.   10492. f. 33.

BOTHRIOCEPHALUS. See CESTODA.

BOULOGNE-LA-GRASSE. MARTIN-VAL ( ) Histoire de Boulogne-La-Grasse. pp. 284. _Compiègne_, 1891. 8°.   010171. g. 5.

BOULOGNE-SUR-MER. ROSNY (A. de) Album historique du Boulonnais. pp. 56. _Neuville_, 1892. fol.   1790. b. 6.

BOULOGNE-SUR-MER—*continued.*

VAILLANT (V. J.) Maistre Mahieu, satirique boulonnais du XIII° siècle. pp. 48. *Boulogne*, 1894. 8°. 10660. gg. 33.

GANNERON (F.) Les Comtes de Boulogne, MS. de 1640. pp. 269. *Boulogne*, 1891. 8°. 9916. c. 19.

PAYEN (G.) Ode sur le siège d'Ardres en Août 1657. pp. 46. *Boulogne*, 1891. 8°. Pam. 59.

FRANCE. *États-Généraux.* Assemblées du Boulonnais : Cahiers. pp. 628. *Boulogne*, 1889. 4°. 9231. m. 15.

MERRIDEW (H. M.) Guide to Boulogne-sur-Mer. pp. 182. *Lond.* 1894. 8°. 10174. aaa. 46.

HAIGNERÉ (D.) Notes sur les curés de Boulogne. pp. 25. 1888. 8°. Pam. 9.

LEFEBVRE (F. A.) Histoire de Notre-Dame de Boulogne. pp. 453. *Boulogne*, 1894. 8°. 4629. aaa. 39.

See also PAS DE CALAIS.

BOUNTY, H. M. S. YOUNG (R. A.) Mutiny of the Bounty. pp. 254. *Oakland*, 1894. 8°. 10491. b. 40.

BOURBON, Island. MAHY (F. de) Autour de l'Ile Bourbon. pp. 290. *Paris*, 1891. 8°. 010096. e. 45.

JACOB DE CORDEMOY (E.) Flore de d'Ile de la Réunion. *Paris*, 1891, *etc.* 8°. 07028. l. 8.

BOURBON L'ARCHAMBAULT.
RICHARD ( ) Histoire de l'insigne relique de la Vraie Croix de Bourbon l'Archambault. pp. 212. *Moulins*, 1891. 8°. 4807. aaaa. 6.

BOURBONNAIS. MONTEGUT (É.) En Bourbonnais et en Forez. pp. 336. *Paris*, 1888. 12°. 10171. de. 5.

SOULTRAIT (G. de) *Count.* Armorial du Bourbonnaise. 2 tom. *Moulins*, 1890. 4°. 9915. bb. 9.

BOURG-ACHARD. DUCHEMIN (P.) Histoire de Bourg-Achard. pp. 404. *Pont-Audemer*, 1890. 8°. 010171. f. 26.

BOURGES. FOURNIER (M.) L'Ancienne Université de Bourges, XV siècle. 1893. 8°. Ac. Bourges. *Commission Historique.* Mémoires. Sér. 4. Vol. 9. Ac. 6780.

MARGUERYE (R. de) Le grand incendie de la cathédrale de Bourges. 1890. 8°. Ac. Bourges. *Société des Antiquaires.* Mémoires. Vol. 17. Ac. 5291.

LAWRENCE, *Saint, Benedictine Monastery.* Les Benedictines de Saint-Laurent de Bourges. pp. 35. 483. *Bourges*, 1891. 8°. 4782. f. 8.

BRUNEAU (M.) L'Enseignement à Bourges, 1762-92. 1890. 8°. Ac. Bourges. *Commission Historique.* Mémoires. Sér. 4. Vol. 6. Ac. 6780.

GRELLET-DUMAZEAU (A.) Les exilés de Bourges, 1753-54. pp. 422. *Paris*, 1892. 8°. 9226. d. 2.

JONGLEUX (E.) Bourges et la Révolution, 1789-1804. pp. 338. *Bourges*, 1895. 8°. 9226. c. 28.

GUIDAULT (P.) La léproserie de Bourges. *Bourges*, 1892. 8°. 07305. h. 17. (8.)

BOURGTHEROULDE. BOUQUET ( ) Souvenirs de l'invasion allemande. pp. 64. *Lisieux*, 1890. 8°. 9080. aa. 8. (3.)

BOURNEMOUTH. ATKINSON (A.) Bright's Guide to Bournemouth. pp. 142. *Bournemouth*, 1894. obl. 8°. 1787. aa. 21.

BOURNEMOUTH. "Beautiful Bournemouth." pp. 32. *Bournemouth*, 1892. 8°. 10348. ccc. 57. (7.)

—— Hankinson's Guide to Bournemouth. pp. 112. *Bournemouth*, 1891. 8°. 10360. c. 22.

CURTIS (C. H. O.) Bright's Guide to Bournemouth. pp. 224. *Lond.* 1981. 8°. 10352. d. 22.

BOURNEMOUTH—*continued.*

GRANDPAPA. Three Weeks at Bournemouth. pp. 159. *Lond.* 1893. 8°. 10351. e. 45.

SHARWOOD (A.) Penny Guide to Bournemouth. pp. 48. *Bournemouth*, 1892. 16°. 10349. a. 33. (2.)

WARREN (W. J.) Picturesque Bournemouth and Neighbourhood. *Bournemouth*, 1891. fol. 1890. b. 1.

BOURNOIS. ROUSSEY (C.) Glossaire du Parler de Bournois. pp. 415. *Paris*, 1894. 8°. 12953. h. 22.

BOWDOIN COLLEGE. Ac. Brunswick, *Maine. Bowdoin College.* General Catalogue of Bowdoin College, 1794-1894. pp. 216. *Brunswick*, 1894. 8°. 8366. f. 33.

BOWLS. BROWN (J.) Manual of Bowling. pp. 124. *Edinburgh*, 1892. 8°. 7905. bb. 51.

WALKER (J. M.) Rounders, bowls, *etc.* pp. 71. 1892. 8°. All England Series. 7908. df.

See also GAMES.

BOXING. CORBETT (J. J.) Life and Battles of J. J. Corbett. pp. 96. *Lond.* 1894. 8°. 7912. df. 3. (8.)

DORAN (B. J.) Science of Self-Defence. pp. 108. *Toronto*, 1893. 8°. 7912. a. 24.

POLLOCK (W. H.) Fencing. Boxing. By E. B. Mitchell. pp. 304. 1893. 8°. Badminton Library. 2264. aa.

SULLIVAN (J. L.) Life and reminiscences. pp. 294. *Lond.* 1892. 8°. 7912. aa. 20.

VILLE (L.) La Lutte française. pp. 108. *Paris*, 1891. 8°. 7912. a. 15.

BOXLEY. BROWNE (J. C.) History of Boxley Parish. pp. 225. *Maidstone*, 1892. 8°. 010358. f. 40.

BRA. GABOTTO (F.) Ricerche sulla Storia di Bra. *Bra*, 1892, *etc.* 8°. 010171. e. 19.

BRABANT, North. BRABANT, *North.* Verzameling van reglementen betrekkelijk waterstaat, enz. voor de Provincie Noord-Brabant. pp. 152. *'s-Hertogenbosch*, 1890. 8°. 5686. a. 22.

BRACHIOPODA. BLOCHMANN (F.) Untersuchungen über den Bau der Brachiopoden. 2 pt. *Jena*, 1892. 4°. 7298. h. 4.

DALL (W. H.) Catalogue of Brachiopods of the S.E. Coast of the United States. pp. 221. 1889. 8°. Bulletin of the U.S National Museum. no. 37. Ac. 1875/13.

FISCHER (P.) Brachiopodes. pp. 139. 1891. 4°. FRANCE. *M. de l'Instruction.* Expéditions scientifiques. 1826. b.

—— Brachiopodes de l'Atlantique Nord. pp. 30. 1892. 8°. ALBERT, *Prince of Monaco.* Résultats des campagnes scientifiques. *etc.* Fasc. 3. 7299. l. 14.

SHIPLEY (A. E.) Brachiopods. 1895. 8°. Cambridge Natural history. Vol. 3. 7001. ee.

See also PALAEONTOLOGY.

BRADFORD, Yorkshire. CUDWORTH (W.) Histories of Bolton and Bowling, townships of Bradford. pp. 363. *Bradford*, 1891. 8°. 010358. f. 19.

BRADFORD-ON-AVON. JONES (W. H.) Stroll through Bradford-on-Avon. pp. 16.. *Devizes*, 1881. 8°. 10348. d. 18. (2.)

BRAHMANISM. *See* HINDUISM.

BRAHMA SAMAJ. BRĀHMA SAMĀJ. The Brahmo Somaj. pp. 53. *Calcutta*, 1885. 12°. 759. a. 9. (3.)

—— The New Dispensation. pp. 48. *Calcutta*, 1885. 8°. 4503. a. 52.

BRAHMA SAMAJ—*continued.*

BRĀHMA SAMĀJ. Order of Service in the Brahma Samaj. pp. 8. *Allahabad*, 1890. 8°.
14123. c. 15. (3.)

HARISCHANDRA MUKHOPĀDHYĀYA. Lectures on Religious Subjects. pp. 76.
Calcutta, 1887. 12°.   Pam. 41.

KESAVACHANDRA SENA. Prayers. Pt. 1. pp. 142.
Calcutta, 1884. 8°.   759. a. 11.

—— The New Dispensation. pp. 47.
Calcutta, 1884. 12°.   759. a. 9. (2.)

—— The New Samhita. pp. 107.
Calcutta, 1884. 8°.   759. a. 13.

—— Essays: Theological and Ethical. pp. 154.
Calcutta, 1885. 12°.   759. a. 12.

NĀRĀYANA GUNAJĪ VELANKAR. Bombay Brahmo Samaj. pp. 28. *Bombay*, 1888. 8°. Pam. 41.

NAVAKĀNTA CHATTOPĀDHYĀYA. Life and Character of Raja Ram Mohan Roy.
Dacca, 1890. 12°.   759. a. 6. (2.)

RĀJANĀRĀYANA VASU. Brahmo Catechism.
pp. 18. *Allahabad*, 1890. 16°. 14123. c. 25.

BRAIN. Anatomy: Physiology, etc.

BRISSAUD (E.) Anatomie du Cerveau de l'homme. 2 pt. *Paris*, 1893. 8°. & 4°. 7421. dd. 3.

BRUCE (A.) Illustrations of the Nerve Tracts in the mid and hind Brain. pp. 51.
Edinb. 1892. obl. 4°.   1832. a. 5.

CALDERWOOD (H.) Relations of Mind and Brain. pp. 551. *Lond.* 1892. 8°   2236. c. 6.

CAPPIE (J.) Intra-Cranial Circulation and its relation to the Physiology of the Brain. pp. 188.
Edinb. 1890. 8°.   7419. i. 9.

DONALDSON (H. H.) Growth of the Brain.
pp. 374. 1895. 8°. Contemporary Science Series. Vol. 29.   8709. i.

FERRIER (D.) Croonian Lectures on Cerebral Localisation. pp. 152. *Lond.* 1890. 8°.
7616. h. 11.

FLATAU (E.) Atlas of the Human Brain.
Berl. 1894. 4°.   7421. i. 18.

GOODALL (E.) Microscopical examination of the human Brain. pp. 186.   *Lond.* 1894. 8°.
7660. de. 17.

HEMISPHAERENMARK. Das Hemisphärenmark des menschlichen Grosshirns. 1892, *etc.* fol.
BRESLAU. Arbeiten aus der psychiatrischen Klinik.   7660. i.

HOLLANDER (B.) Demonstration of Centres of Ideation in the Brain. pp. 12. *Lond.* 1891. 8°.
07305. h. 8. (5.)

HORSLEY (V. A. H.) Contribution to Surface Anatomy of the Cerebral Hemispheres.
1892. 4°. Ac. Dublin. *Irish Academy.* Cunningham Memoirs. No. 7.   Ac. 1540/6.

—— Structure and Functions of the Brain.
pp. 223. *Lond.* 1892. 8°.   7630. ff. 31.

JOHNSTONE (J.) Action of Glycerine on the Brain. pp. 16. *Edinb.* 1891. 16°. Pam. 39.

KLINCKOWSTRÖM (A.) Recherches sur les artères du cerveau des vertébrés. pp. 26. 1890. 8°.
Ac. Stockholm. *K. Svenska Vetenskaps Academi.* Bihang. Bd. 15.   Ac. 107017.

KUEKENTHAL (W.) Untersuchungen über die Grosshirnfurchen der Primaten. pp. 122.
1894. 8°. Jenaische Zeitschrift für Medicin. Bd. 29.   Ac. 3760.

LUCIANI (L.) Il cervelletto. pp. 320.
Firenze, 1891. 8°.   7405. f. 16.

MACEWEN (W.) Atlas of Head Sections.
Glasg. 1893. 4°.   7440. i. 3.

MANOUVRIER (L.) Sur l'interprétation de la quantité dans le cerveau. 1888. 8°. Ac. Paris. *Société d'Anthropologie.* Mémoires. Sér. 2. Tom. 3.   Ac. 6227. 2.

BRAIN—*continued.*

MARCHI (V.) Sull' origine dei peduncoli cerebellari. pp. 38. *Frienze*, 1891. 8°.
07305. k. 11. (6.)

MEYNERT (T.) Sammlung von Vorträgen über den Bau des Gehirns. pp. 253. *Wien*, 1892. 8°.
7660. df. 32.

MOSSO (A.) La Temperatura del Cervello.
pp. 197. *Milano*, 1894. 8°.   7442. i. 10.

—— Die Temperatur des Gehirns. pp. 191.
Leipz. 1894. 8°.   7442. i. 4.

RAINALDI (R.) Le Localizzazioni cerebrali studiate in un caso d'Ipnotismo. pp. 332.
Foligno, 1891. 4°.   7407. i. 2.

SACHS (H.) Vorträge über Bau und Thätigkeit des Grosshirns. pp. 290. *Breslau*, 1893. 8°.
7660. g. 14.

SOURY (J.) Les Fonctions du Cerveau. pp. 470.
Paris, 1892. 8°.   7407. c. 7.

TAYLOR (J. W.) Functions of the Cerebellum. pp. 14. *Morecambe*, 1892. 8°. 7410. bb. 33. (10.)

TURNER (*Sir* W.) Convolutions of the Brain.
pp. 53. *Lond.* 1890. 8°.   Pam. 39.

See also ANATOMY: PSYCHOLOGY: SKULL.

Diseases: Medicine: Surgery.

ALTHAUS (J.) The Failure of Brain Power.
pp. 186. *Lond.* 1894. 8°.   7660. a. 16.

COTARD (J.) Études sur les Maladies cérébrales. pp. 443. *Paris*, 1891. 8°.   7660. e. 4.

DOWSE (T. S.) On Brain Exhaustion. pp. 140.
Lond. 1894. 8°.   7630. e. 20.

FRASER (A.) Guide to Operations on the Brain.
pp. 24. *Lond.* 1890. fol.   1833. b. 12.

HENSCHEN (S. E.) Beiträge zur Pathologie des Gehirns. *Upsala*, 1890. 4°.   7420. h.

IRELAND (W. W.) The Blot upon the Brain.
pp. 338. *Edinb.* 1893. 8°.   7660. g. 15.

KOERNER (O.) Die otitischen Erkrankungen des Hirns. pp. 163. *Frankfurt*, 1894. 8°.
7615. d. 11.

MAC EWEN (W.) Pyogenic infective Diseases of the Brain. pp. 354. *Glasg.* 1893. 8°. 7630. h. 28.

SAHLI (H.) Über hirnchirurgische Operationen. 1891. 8°. VOLKMANN (R. v.) Sammlung klinischer Vorträge. N. F. Nr. 28. 7441. g.

STARR (M. A.) Brain Surgery. pp. 295.
Lond. 1893. 8°.   07482. ee. 12.

TUKE (J. B.) The Insanity of Over-Exertion of the Brain. pp. 66. *Edinb.* 1894. 8°. 7660. g. 30.
See also INSANITY: MENINGITIS.

BRAMFIELD. HILL (T. S.) The Registrie Booke off Bramefeide. pp. 120.
Lond. 1894. 8°.   9906. g. 5.

BRANCOLI. MAZZAROSA (A.) *Marquis.* La Terra di Brancoli, *etc.* 1893. 8°. Ac. Lucca. *Accademia Napoleone.* Atti. Tom. 26. Ac. 58.

BRANDENBURG. DOHNA (F. S. zu) *Count.* Kurfürstliche Schlösser in der Mark Brandenburg. 3 Bde. *Berl.* 1889–93. 8°. 10240. k.

FONTANE (T.) Wanderungen durch die Mark Brandenburg. 4 Thl. *Berl.* 1892. 8°. 10235. cc.

For the history of Brandenburg, *see* PRUSSIA.

BRANDY. JACQUET (L.) La Fabrication des Eaux-de-vie. pp. 227. 1894. 8°. Encyclopédie des aide-mémoire.   8709. g.
See also ALCOHOL.

BRASS AND BRASS WORK. GAWTHORP (T. J.) Manual of Instruction in the Art of Brass Repoussé. pp. 55. *Lond.* 1891. 8°.
7807. aaa. 9. (5.)

LARKIN (J.) Practical Brass and Iron Founder's Guide. pp. 394. *Phila.* 1892. 8°. 7106. ff. 15.

BRASS AND BRASS WORK—*continued.*

LONDON. *Armourers and Braziers.* Exhibition of Art Brass Work. *Lond.* 1890, *etc.* 12°.
7958. aa.

See also ART, *Decorative* : METALS.

BRASSES, Monumental. BADGER (E. W.) Monumental Brasses of Warwickshire. pp. 66. *Birmingham,* 1895. 8°. 7709. bb. 85.

CREENY (W. F.) Illustrations of incised Slabs on the Continent. pp. 76. *Norwich,* 1891. fol. 1707. c. 10.

DAVIS (C. T.) Monumental Brass in the old church, Aberdeen. *Lond.* 1894. 8°.
07703. g. 3. (16.)

MACKLIN (H. W.) Monumental Brasses. pp. 144. *Lond.* 1890. 8°. 7709. b. 39.

OLIVER (A.) Notes on Flemish Brasses in England. pp. 8. *St. Albans,* 1889. 8°. 1701. b. 1. (98.)

—— Brass of R. Thornton: All Saints, Newcastle-on-Tyne. 1889. fol. 1701. b. 1. (98.)

THORNELY (J. L.) Monumental Brasses of Lancashire and Cheshire. pp. 322. *Hull,* 1893. 8°. 7709. bb. 62.

BRAZIL. [*See note on page* 1.]

History: Constitution of 1890: Politics.

REPARAZ (G.) El Brasil; descubrimiento, colonización é influencia. pp. 48. *Madrid.* 1892. 8°.
Pam. 86.

CUNHA (A. da) D. Pedro II. do Brazil. pp. 19. *Lisboa,* 1893. 4°. 10630. h. 28.

PEIXOTO DE LACERDA WERNECK (L.) Le Brésil, dangers de sa situation. pp. 133. *Rio de J.* 1889. 8°. 8180. aa. 12.

FIALHO (A.) Historia da fundação da Republica. pp. 188. *Rio de J.* 1891. 8°. 9772. bb. 10.

FULANO (T. H.) Der Sturz des Kaiserthrones in Brasilien. pp. 200. *Köln,* 1892. 8°. 8180. f. 36.

ARAUJO (O. d') L'idee républicaine au Brésil. pp. 153. *Paris,* 1893. 8°. 8180. aa. 18.

OTTONI (C. H. B.) O Advento da Republica no Brasil. pp. 136. *Rio de J.* 1890. 8°. 8179. d. 1.

P.P. *Rio de Janeiro.* A Collection of newspapers relating to the fall of the Empire. *Rio de J.* 1889. fol. P.P. 9880. d.

SILVEIRA (U. A. da) Galeria historica da Revolução de 1889. pp. 323. *Brazil,* 1890. 8°.
9781. e. 9.

S. (F. de) Fastos de dictadura militar no Brazil. 1890, *etc.* 8°. 8180. aa. 16.

OURO PRETO (de) Advento da dictadura militar no Brazil. pp. 232. *Paris,* 1891. 8°.
8180. e. 13.

SANTA BOAVENTURA (de) A Revolução no Brazil. pp. 64. *Lisboa,* 1894. 8°. 9772. c. 12.

VILLA-LOBOS (R.) A Republica Brasileira em 1890. pp. 344. *Rio de J.* 1890. 8°. 10480. dd. 37.

LEMOS (M.) Le Calendrier positiviste et M. le Ministre des Finances. pp. 7. *Rio de J.* 1890. 8°. Pam. 49.

BRAZIL. Constituição da Republica do Brazil. pp. 39. *Rio de J.* 1891. 8°. Pam. 65.

—— Constitution of the United States of Brazil. pp. 23. *Washington,* 1891. 8°. Pam. 65.

—— Constitution of Brazil. Project. pp. 36. *Rio de J.* 1890. 12°. Pam. 65.

ALENCASTRO AUTRAN (M. G. d') Constituição da Republica commentada, *etc.* pp. 91. *Rio de J.* 1892. 8°. 8180. aa. 21.

ANGULO GURIDI (A.) Examen comparativo de las constituciones de Hispano-América, el Brasil, y Haití. 2 tom. *Santiago de C.* 1891. 8°.
8180. k. 7.

DONNAT (L.) Critique de la constitution brésilienne. pp. 40. *Paris,* 1890. 8°. Pam. 65.

BRAZIL.—History, etc.—*continued.*

MILTON (A. A.) A Constituição do Brazil. pp. 156. *Rio de J.* 1895. 8°. 8179. cc. 8.

ARGENTINE REPUBLIC. *M. de Relaciones Exteriores.* Cuestiones de límites entre las repúblicas Argentina, el Brasil y Chile. pp. 342. *Buenos A.* 1892. 12°. 8180. aa. 17.

BRAZIL. Statement submitted by Brazil to the President of the United States as Arbitrator between Brazil and the Argentine Republic. 6 vol. *N.Y.* 1894. 4°. 8180. k. 8.

MELLO (C. J. de) Apontamentos para a historia da Revolução da 23 de Nov. 1891. pp. 90. *Rio de J.* 1895. 8°. 9772. aaa. 41.

GAMA E COSTA (F. A. da) Manifesto politico. pp. 144. *Paris,* 1891. 12°. 8180. aa. 14.

VILLALBA (E.) A Revolta da armada de 6de Set. de 1893. pp. 200. *Rio de J.* 1894. 8°. 9772. d. 6.

SALGADO (H.) A Insurreição de Janeiro. pp. 224. *Porto,* 1894. 8°. 9195. de. 5.

BRAZIL. *M. dos Negocios Estrangeiros.* Correspondence in regard to the surrender of the insurgent refugees on board the Portuguese corvettes. pp. 38. *Rio de J.* 1894. 8°. Pam. 65.

CARQUEJA (B.) Conflict diplomatique entre le Portugal et le Brésil. pp. 38. *Porto,* 1894. 8°.
Pam. 65.

MARTENS FERRÃO (J. B. de) La Question entre le Portugal et le Brésil. pp. 16. *Rome,* 1894. 8°.
Pam. 32.

PORTUGAL. Portugal e Brazil. Conflicto diplomatico. 5 vol. *Lisboa,* 1894, 95. 8°.
8180. h. 35.

BRAZIL. Peixoto (F.) *President.* Message to the National Congress 4th Oct. 1894. pp. 10. *Rio de J.* 1894. 8°. Pam. 65.

P.P. *Rio de Janeiro.* Revista Brazileira. *Rio de J.* 1895, *etc.* 8°. P.P. 4127. ca.

SILVA PRADO (E. da) A Illusão Americana. pp. 237. *Paris,* 1895. 8°. 8180. aa. 22.

See also AMERICA, *Central and South.*

Immigration.

FABRI (C.) Europäische Einwanderung in Brasilien. pp. 108. *Hamburg,* 1894. 8°. Pam. 65.

MACOLA (F.) L'Europa alla conquista dell' America latina. pp. 437. *Venezia,* 1894. 8°.
8180. f. 40.

Indians. *See* INDIAN LANGUAGES : INDIANS.

Law. *See* LAW, *Criminal.*

Topography : Social Life, etc.

ATCHISON (C. C.) A Winter Cruise in Summer Seas. pp. 369. *Lond.* 1891. 8°. 10026. i. 17.

BATES (H. W.) The Naturalist on the River Amazons. pp. 389. *Lond.* 1892. 8°. 2374. f. 1.

HETTNER (A.) Das südlichste Brasilien, 1891. 8°. Ac. Berlin. *Gesellschaft für Erdkunde.* Zeitschrift. Bd. 26. Ac. 6075/2.

LEVASSEUR (É.) Le Brésil. 2 pt. *Paris,* 1889. 4°. 10480. h. 15.

LECLERC (M.) Lettres du Brésil. pp. 268. *Paris,* 1890. 12°. 10481. aaa. 46.

MELLO-MORAES (A. J. de) Festas e Tradições populares do Brazil. pp. 480. *Rio de J.* 1895. 8°. 12430. i. 49.

MEYER (H.) Bogen und Pfeil in Central-Brasilien. pp. 54. *Leipz.* 1895. 8°. 8829. i. 26.

MORAES (E. J. de) Navegação interior do Brasil. pp. 600. *Rio de J.* 1894. 8°. 08235. i. 12.

RIJCKEVORSEL (— v.) Magnetic survey of the Eastern part of Brazil. pp. 166. 1890. 4°. Ac. Amsterdam. *Akademie van Wetenschappen.* Verhandelingen. Dl. 27. Ac. 944/2.

I

BRAZIL.—Topography, etc.—continued.

SANTA ANNA NERY (F. J. de) Aux États-Unis du Brésil. pp. 340. *Paris*, 1891. 8°. 10481. i. 21.

SCHANZ (M.) Brasilianische Reiseskizzen. pp. 121. *Leipz.* 1889. 8°. 10481. bb. 47.

—— Das heutige Brasilien. pp. 364. *Hamburg*, 1893. 8°. 10481. bb. 46.

STEINEN (C. v. den) Unter den Naturvölkern Zentral-Brasiliens. pp. 570. *Berl.* 1894. 8°. 10480. e. 32.

TOUSSAINT (A.) A Parisian in Brazil. pp. 166. *Bost.* 1891. 8°. 10481. aa. 33.

VOGEL (P.) Reisen in Mato Grosso, 1887/88. 1893. 8°. Ac. Berlin. *Gesellschaft für Erdkunde.* Zeitschrift. Bd. 28. Ac. 6075/2.

WRIGHT (W.) A few facts about Brazil. pp. 53. *Birmingham*, 1892. 8°. Pam. 86.

See also AMERICA, *Central and South.*

Trade and Finance.

BRAZIL. Les Finances en 1893. pp. 119. *Paris*, 1893. 8°. 08227. i. 8.

—— Brazil. 1891. 8°. U.S. *Bureau of American Republics.* Bulletin. No. 7. 08225. k. 1.

—— Import Duties of Brazil. pp. 139. 1891. 8°. U.S. *Bureau of American Republics.* Bulletin. No. 8. 08225. k. 1.

CHICAGO. *Columbian Exposition.* Catalogue of the Brazilian Section, etc. pp. 145. *Chicago*, 1893. 8°. 7958. bb. 37.

SILVEIRA (U. A. da) Fontes de Riqueza dos Estados Unidos do Brazil. pp. 593. 1890. 8°. 08227. e. 34.

BRAZILIAN LITERATURE. *See* AMERICAN LITERATURE.

BREAD : BAKING.

AUSTIN (G. W.) Bread, Baking & Bakers. pp. 31. *Lond.* 1891. 4°. Pam. 94.

BEBEL (A.) Zur Lage der Arbeiter in den Bäckereien. pp. 184. *Stuttgart*, 1890. 8°. 8277. d. 30.

BLANDY (J.) The Baker's Catechism. pp. 37. *Lond.* 1891. 8°. 07945. h. 29.

—— Bakery Economics. pp. 87. *Lond.* 1892. 8°. Pam. 94.

DAVIES (F.) Cakes and Biscuits. pp. 128. *Lond.* 1891. 8°. 7942. de. 10.

GALIPPE (V.) Le Pain. Aliment minéralisateur, etc. pp. 222. 1894. 8°. Encyclopédie des aidemémoire. 8709. g.

—— Le Pain. Technologie, pains divers, etc. pp. 215. 1895. Encyclopédie des aide mémoire. 8709. g.

GOODFELLOW (J.) Elementary Principles of Breadmaking. pp. 198. *Lond.* 1895. 8°. 07944. e. 52.

—— Dietetic Value of Bread. pp. 328. *Lond.* 1892. 8°. 7404. c. 36.

HIRSCHBERG (E.) Beiträge zur Statistik der Brodpreise im Deutschen Reich. pp. 51. *Berl.* 1893. 8°. 08226. k. 5. (5.)

JAGO (W.) Introduction to the study of Breadmaking. pp. 134. *Lond.* 1889. 8°. 07944. e. 49.

—— Cantor Lectures on Bread-making. 1889. pp. 53. *Lond.* 1890. 8°. Pam. 95.

—— Text-book of Bread-making. pp. 648. *Lond.* 1895. 8°. 07945. m. 24.

JÜRGENSEN (C.) Om. Brød. pp. 80. *Kjøbenh.* 1891. 8°. 07305. f. 16. (7.)

MERCIER (G.) Les Échanges de blé et de pain en Boulangerie. pp. 32. *Paris*, 1895. 8°. Pam. 94.

BREAD : BAKING—continued.

P.P. *London.* Bakers' Monthly Gazette. *Lond.* 1889, etc. 8°. & 4°. N.R.

ROWE (J. F.) The Bread Acts. pp. 49. *Lond.* 1894. 8°. 6145. aa. 37. (7.)

WALDO (F. J.) Bread, Bakehouses and Bacteria. pp. 65. *Lond.* 1895. 8°. 8777. b. 54.

WELLS (R.) Modern practical Bread Baker. pp. 139. *Manch.* 1892. 8°. 7942. c. 43.

—— Pastrycook and Confectioner's Guide. pp. 108. *Lond.* 1892. 8°. 07945. e. 76.

See also COOKERY : CORN.

BREAST. WILLIAMS (W. R.) Monograph on Diseases of the Breast. pp. 572. *Lond.* 1894. 8°. 7616. i. 14.

See also CANCER : WOMEN.

BRÉCEY. BRUNET (V.) A travers l'Avranchin. pp. 144. *Condé-sur-N.* 1890. 8°. 010171. f. 36.

BRECHIN. VATHEK. Brechin of to-day. pp. 120. *Brechin*, 1895. 8°. 10369. aaa. 50.

BRECKNOCK. KILNER (E. A.) Four Welsh Counties. pp. 266. *Lond.* 1891. 8°. 10369. cc. 44.

BREDA. BEZEMER (W.) Oude Rechtsbronnen der Stad Breda. pp. 184. 1892. 8°. Ac. Utrecht. *Vereeniging tot Uitgave der Bronnen van het Oude Recht.* Oude Werken. Reek 1. no. 14. 5685. e.

BREISGAU. KNOP (A.) Der Kaiserstuhl im Breisgau. pp. 538. *Leipz.* 1892. 8°. 7002. g. 19.

See also BADEN.

BREITENEGG. KAISER (M.) Geschichte der Herrschaft Breitenegg. pp. 104. *Regensburg*, 1893. 8°. 10256. cc. 17.

BREITENFELD. *See* THIRTY YEARS' WAR.

BREMEN. BIPPEN (W. v.) Geschichte der Stadt Bremen. *Bremen*, 1891, etc. 8°. 10235. h. 18.

BAHRFELDT (M.) Die Münzen der Herzogthümer Bremen und Verden, 1648–1719. pp. 156. 1892. 8°. Ac. Luneberg. *Historischer Verein.* Zeitschrift. Jahrg. 1892. Ac. 7085.

FOCKE (J.) Bremische Werkmeister aus älterer Zeit. pp. 268. *Bremen*, 1890. 8°. 08227. f. 20.

KUEHTMANN (A.) Die Romanisirung des Civilprocesses in der Stadt Bremen. pp. 102. 1891. 8°. GIERKE (O.) Untersuchungen zur deutschen Rechtsgeschichte no. 36. 6025. e. 9.

LUCE (F. L.) Fonds und Effecten der Bremer Börse. pp. 68. *Bremen*, 1891. 8°. 08227. e. 29.

See also HANSE TOWNS.

BRESCIA. BONARI (V.) I conventi ed i Cappuccini bresciani. pp. 667. *Milano*, 1891. 8°. 4866. g. 13.

RIZZINI (P.) Illustrazione dei civici musei di Brescia. pp. 99. *Brescia*, 1889. 8°. 07708. g. 4.

BRESLAU. GRUENHAGEN (C.) Das Bisthum Breslau, 1786–97. 1894. 8°. Ac. Breslau. *Verein für Geschichte Schlesiens.* Zeitschrift. Bd. 28. Ac. 7330.

HOLZ (A.) Die commerciellen Verhältnisse Breslau's. pp. 31. *Breslau*, 1892. 8°. 08227. ee. 46. (17.)

STADE (P.) Breslau, ein Schutzwall gegen das Slaventhum. pp. 36. 1895. 8°. Sammlung wissenschaftl. Vorträge. Heft. 213. 12249. m.

BRESSE. RABUT (F.) Liste des Châtelains de Bresse. 1893. 8°. Ac. Chambéry. *Société Savoisienne.* Mémoires. tom. 32. Ac. 5240.

BREST. KERNÉIS (A.) Trois anciens Plans de Brest. 1890. 8°. Ac. Brest. *Société Académique.* Bulletin. Sér. 2. Tom. 15. Ac. 300.
TRÉVÉDY (J.) Les anciennes Corporations brestoises. 1894. 8°. Ac. Quimper. *Société Archéologique.* Bulletin. Tom. 21. Ac. 5306.

BRETFORTON. SHAWCROSS (W. H.) The Story of our ancient Village. pp. 191. *Evesham,* 1890. 8°.   10360. aaa. 72.

BRETHREN, Moravian. BERGER (D.) History of the Church of the United Brethren. 1894. 8°. American Church History Series. vol. 12.   4744. g.
BURKHARDT (G.) Die Brüdergemeine. *Gnadau,* 1893, etc. 8°.   4662. b.
HUTTON (J. E.) Short history of the Moravian Church. pp. 280. *Lond.* 1895. 8°.   4685. aaa. 29.
MEUSEL (C.) Die Einwanderung böhmischer Brüder in Grosshennersdorf. 1885. 8°.
DIBELIUS (F.) Beiträge zur sächsischen Kirchengeschichte. Heft 3.   4662. c.
P.P. *London.* The Moravian Messenger. *Lond,* 1890, etc. 4°.   1379.
UNITED BRETHREN. Church Book of the Brethren's Unity of the British Province. pp. 225. *Lond.* 1892. 8°.   4136. aaa. 38.
WEAVER (J.) Comment on the Confession of Faith of the Church of the United Brethren. pp. 185. *Dayton, O.* 1892. 8°.   3504. b. 73.
WOLKAN (R.) Das Kirchenlied der Böhmischen Brüder im XVI. Jahrhunderte. pp. 178. *Prag,* 1891. 8°.   4999. b. 20.
SCHNEIDER (H. G.) Working and waiting for Tibet. Moravian Mission to the Western Himalayas. pp. 95. *Lond.* 1891. 8°. 4767. c. 27.
SENFT (E. A.) Les Missions moraves chez les peuples païens. pp. 424. *Neuchâtel,* 1890. 8°.   4767. c. 22.

BRETHREN, Plymouth. *See* PLYMOUTH BRETHREN.

BRETON LANGUAGE AND LITERATURE. LOTH (J.) Vocabulaire Vieux-Breton. pp. 249. 1884. 8°. Bibliothèque de l'École des Hautes Études. Sciences phil. Fasc. 57.   Ac. 8929.
DAGNET (A.) Le patois fougerais, dialecte haut-breton. pp. 90. *Laval,* 1890. 8°.   12901. d. 30. (11.)
DU RUSQUEC (H.) Dictionnaire du dialecte de Léon. pp. 320. *Paris,* 1895. 8°. 12978. k. 9.
CHARAUX (A.) Essai littéraire sur la Bretagne. Poètes et prosateurs. pp. 135. *Paris,* 1894. 12°.   011850. eee. 20.
KERVILER (R.) La Bretagne à l'Académie Française au XVIIIe siècle. pp. 658. *Paris,* 1889. 8°.   010661. f. 58.
LOTH (J.) Chrestomathie bretonne, *etc.* *Paris,* 1890, etc. 8°.   12978. h. 20.
LUZEL (F. M.) Chansons populaires de la Basse-Bretagne. 2 tom. *Paris,* 1890. 8°.   11498. dd. 23.
P.P. *Rennes.* L'Hermine. Revue littéraire. *Rennes,* 1889, etc. 8°.   P.P. 4356. b.
SAINT-JEAN, *Comte de.* Les Femmes poètes bretonnes. pp. 169. *Nantes,* 1892. 12°.   11850. cc. 42.
See also BRITTANY : CELTIC LANGUAGES.

BRIANÇON. ALBERT (A.) Biographie du Briançonnais. pp. 63. *Grenoble,* 1891. 8°.   011900. ee. 6. (10.)

BRICKS. DAVIS (C. T.) Treatise on the Manufacture of Bricks, *etc.* pp. 628. *Philad.* 1895. 8°.   07945. m. 25.

BRICKS—*continued.*
DOBSON (E.) Rudimentary Treatise on the Manufacture of Bricks. pp. 276. *Lond.* 1893. 8°.   8703. bbb. 12.
P.P. *London.* The British Clay Worker. *Lond.* 1892, etc. 4°.   N.R.
See also CERAMICS : TERRA COTTA.

BRIDES-LES-BAINS. DELASTRE (P.) Eaux minérales de Brides-les-Bains. pp. 86. *Moutiers,* 1892. 8°.   7462. e. 24.

BRIDGE, Game. BOAZ. The Laws of Bridge. pp. 39. *Lond.* 1895. 8°. 7913. df. 17.

BRIDGES. BARRÉ (L. A.) Ponts métalliques. pp. 106. 1894. 4°. VIGREUX (L.) Théorie et pratique de l'art de l'Ingénieur.   8529. dd.
CART (A.) Calcul des ponts métalliques. pp. 291. *Paris,* 1895. 8°.   8767. dd. 18.
CHICAGO. *Columbian Exposition.* Der Brückenbau in den Vereinigten Staaten. pp. 66. *Zürich,* 1895. 8°.   7957. b. 2.
DYKES (J. E.) Manual of the Roads and Bridges, Scotland, Act, 1878. pp. 238. *Edinb.* 1890. 8°.   6573. cc. 2.
FIDLER (T. C.) Practical Treatise on Bridge-Construction. pp. 444. *Lond.* 1893. 8°.   2249. i. 7.
FITZMAURICE (M.) Plate-Girder railway Bridges. pp. 104. *Lond.* 1895. 8°.   8767. h. 24.
HENRY (E.) Ponts sous rails et ponts-routes à travées métalliques. pp. 631. 1894. 8°. Encyclopédie des travaux publics, *etc.*   012216. i.
NEWMAN (J.) Notes on Cylinder Bridge Piers. pp. 136. *Lond.* 1893. 8°.   8768. cc. 25.
See also ENGINEERING : FORTH BRIDGE : LONDON, *Bridges.*

BRIDGNORTH. MORRALL (E. P.) Illustrated Guide to Bridgnorth. pp. 52. *Bridgnorth,* 1891. 8°.   10348. ccc. 60. (6.)

BRIDLINGTON. BRIDLINGTON QUAY. Guide to Bridlington Quay. pp. 131. *Lond.* 1893. 8°.   10347. aaa. 34.
COLLIER (C. V.) Some Notes on the Heraldry in the Priory Church of St. Mary, Bridlington. pp. 9. *Bridlington,* 1893. 8°.   Pam. 26.
FURBY (C.) Guide to Bridlington Quay. pp. 29. *Bridlington,* 1892. 8°   10348. ccc. 59. (5.)

BRIENZ. SCHILD (P.) Brienzer Mundart. *Basel,* 1891, etc. 8°.   12962. o. 1.

BRIGHTON. BISHOP (J. G.) Brighton in the Olden Time, *etc.* pp. 22. 434. *Brighton,* 1892. 8°.   10352. cc. 46.
——— Brighton in 1744–61. pp. 76. *Brighton,* 1895. 8°.   10352. bbb. 51.
BLEW (W. C. A.) Brighton and its Coaches. pp. 354. *Lond.* 1894 8°.   10349. h. 34.
BRIGHTON. Reports on the Sewerage of Brighton. pp. 82. *Brighton,* 1883. 8°.   7688. c. 26.
EYLES AND SON. Pocket Brighton Guide. pp. 95. *Brighton,* 1891. 16°. 10349. a. 31. (3.)
HALLET (W. H.) Brighton Waterworks. pp. 8. 1890. 8°.   8777. bbb. 24. (2.)
HARPER (C. G.) The Brighton Road. pp. 272. *Lond.* 1892. 8°.   010358. h 10.
PASCOE (C. E.) Brighton. pp. 80. *Lond.* 1891. 8°.   10360. a. 11.
PIKE (W. T.) Guide to Brighton. pp. 128. *Brighton,* 1888. 8°.   10358. cc. 48.
SALA (G. A.) Brighton as I have known it. pp. 79. *Lond.* 1895. 8°.   10352. e. 18.
SAWYER (J.) The Brighton Handy-Book. pp. 60. *Brighton,* 1890. 8°. 10348. ccc. 59. (1.)

BRIGHTON—*continued.*

SAWYER (F. E.) History of the Royal Pavilion at Brighton. pp. 16. *Brighton,* 1886. 4°·
010358. l. 12. (5.)

BISHOP (J. G.) The Brighton Pavilion. pp. 190. *Brighton,* 1894. 8°. 10352. f. 5.

BRIGHTON COLLEGE. Brighton College Register. *Brighton,* 1886, *etc.* 8°. 8364. f. 19.
See also SUSSEX.

BRIGITTINES. BINDER (G.) Die heilige Birgitta und ihr Klosterorden. pp. 205. *München,* 1891. 8°. 4829. c. 12.

BRINKBURN PRIORY. Ac. Durham. *Surtees Society.* vol. 90. Chartulary of Brinkburn Priory. pp. 224. *Durham,* 1893. 8°.
Ac. 8045/69.

BRISTOL. BRISTOL, *Cathedral Church of.* Sermons preached in Bristol Cathedral on the occasion of the restoration of the choir, *etc.* pp. 143. *Bristol,* 1895. 8°. 4478. de. 11.

BRISTOL. Where to buy at Bristol and Clifton. pp. 56. *Brighton,* 1890. 4°. 10368. k. 21.

GLOUCESTER. *County Council.* Report of the Bristol Boundaries Committee. pp. 6. *Gloucester,* 1892. 8°. Pam. 90.

LATIMER (J.) Annals of Bristol in the 18th century. pp. 550. *Frome,* 1893. 8°.
10358. k. 10.

PROUT (J. S.) Picturesque Antiquities of Bristol. *Bristol,* 1893. fol. 10368. k. 17.

WEARE (G. E.) Collectanea relating to the Bristol Friars Minors. pp. 111. *Bristol,* 1893. 8°. 4707. e. 24.

—— Burke's Connection with Bristol, 1774-80. pp. 174. *Bristol,* 1894. 8°. 10815 c. 17.

WARD, LOCK AND Co. Illustrated handbook to Bristol Cathedral. *Lond.* 1891. 8°.
010358. l. 19.

See also EXHIBITIONS. Pt. I.

BRISTOL CHANNEL. Ac. Hamburg. *Norddeutsche Seewarte.* Segelhandbuch des Bristol-Kanals. pp. 423. *Hamb.* 1895. 8°.
10497. a. 30.

BRISTOL CHANNEL. Bristol Channel illustrated. pp. 205. *Lond.* 1894. 8°. ·10368. c. 47.

COWPER (F.) Sailing Tours. Pt. IV. Bristol Channel. *Lond.* 1892, *etc.* 8°. 10360. c.

BRITISH COLUMBIA. BEGG (A.) History of British Columbia. pp. 568. *Toronto,* 1894. 8°. 9555. cc. 10.

CANADA. *Geological Survey.* Mineral wealth of British Columbia. pp. 163. *Montreal,* 1889. 8°.
7109. g. 39.

COLUMBIA, *British.* Guide map of the province. pp. 46. *Victoria,* 1891. 8°. Pam. 86.

—— British Columbia as a field for emigration and investment. *Victoria,* 1891. 8°. Pam. 86.

—— British Columbia. Its resources, commercial position and climate. pp. 48. *Victoria,* 1892. 8°. 10470. dd. 30. (11.)

—— The Pacific province. Its position, resources and climate, *etc.* pp. 31. *Ottawa,* 1893. 8°.
10470. dd. 30. (14.)

—— British Columbia; its resources and possibilities. pp. 109. *Victoria,* 1893. 8°.
10470. dd. 34

GOSNELL (R. E.) British Columbia. Digest of information. pp. 47. *Vancouver,* 1890. 8°.
Pam. 86.

KARR (H. W. S.) Bear-Hunting in the White Mountains. pp. 156. *Lond.* 1891. 8°.
7908. ccc. 3.

SOMERSET (H. S.) The Land of the Muskeg. pp. 248. *Lond.* 1895. 8°. 10113. k. 27.

BRITISH COLUMBIA—*continued.*

SAINT MAUR (S. M.) *Baroness Seymour.* Impressions of a Tenderfoot in the Far West. pp. 279. *Lond.* 1890. 8°. 10470. dd. 24.
See also CANADA : ENGLAND, *Colonies.*

BRITISH HONDURAS. see HONDURAS.

BRITISH MUSEUM. *See* EXHIBITIONS. Pt. I. : LIBRARIES, *etc.*

BRITTANY.

Bibliography.

SACHER (F.) Bibliographie de la Bretagne, *etc.* pp. 236. *Rennes,* 1881. 8°. 11904. dd. 31.

Antiquities : History, etc.

KERVILER (R.) Recueil d'études sur l'archéologie et l'histoire bretonne, 1873-92. 3 tom. *Paris,* 1892, 93. 8°. 010171. k. 8.

LOTH (J.) L'Émigration Bretonne en Armorique du IV° au VII° siècle. pp. 260. *Paris,* 1883. 8°. 9225. k. 15.

LE MOYNE DE LA BORDERIE (L. A.) Recueil de documents relatifs aux monuments de l'architecture militaire du moyen-âge en Bretagne. 1894. 8°. Ac. Brittany. *Association Bretonne.* Bulletin. Sér. 3. Tom. 12. Ac. 5292.

—— Le Bretagne aux grands siècles du moyen-âge. pp. 256. *Rennes,* 1892. 12°. 9220. ccc. 12.

COSNEAU (E.) Le Connétable de Richemont. 1393-1458. pp. 712. *Paris,* 1886. 8°.
010661. i. 21.

JOHN V., *Duke of Brittany.* Lettres et mandements de Jean V. 1402-42. 5 vol. 1889-95. 4°. Archives de Bretagne. tom. IV.-VIII.
Ac. 8926/10.

LE MOYNE DE LA BORDERIE (L. A.) La Bretagne aux temps modernes 1491- 1789. pp. 288. *Rennes,* 1894. 8°. 9210. bb. 36.

LA LANDE DE CALAN (C. de) La Défense de Bretagne aux XVI° et XVII° siècles. pp. 41. *Vannes,* 1892. 8°. 9007. g. 20. (2.)

HAUCOUR (T. X.) Les États de Bretagne. pp. 42. *Rennes,* 1892. 8°. 9007. g. 22. (4.)

CORRE (A.) Criminologie rétrospective. Bretagne, XVII° et XVIII° siècles. pp. 580. *Lyon,* 1895. 8°.
6057. e. 24.

DUPUY (A.) Études sur l'administration municipale en Bretagne au XVIII° siècle, *etc.* 2 pt. *Paris,* 1891. 8°. 8246. f. 36.

TRESVAUX DU FRAVAL (F. M.) Histoire de la persécution révolutionnaire en Bretagne. 2 tom. *Saint-Brieuc,* 1892. 12°. 4629. aaa. 27.

POTIER DE COURCY (P.) Nobiliaire de Bretagne. 3 tom. *Rennes,* 1890. 4°. 9915. dd. 5.

Language and Literature. *See* BRETON LANGUAGE.

Topography, Social Life, etc.

BESSIRE (E.) En Bretagne. pp. 217. *Genève,* 1894. 8°. 10174. aaa. 51.

BIRÉ (E.) Causerie littéraire. Paysages et monuments de la Bretagne. pp. 24. *Vannes,* 1892. 8°. 07703. i. 2. (6.)

BLACKBURN (H.) Artistic Travels in Brittany. pp. 320. *Lond.* 1892. 8°. 10108. f. 1.

BRITTANY. Paysages et Monuments de la Bretagne. *Paris,* 1892, *etc.* fol. K.T.C. 15. b.

CLOUARD (A.) Tour de Bretagne. pp. 497. *Paris,* 1892. 12°. 10174. b. 35.

COOK (T.) Cook's Handbook for Brittany. pp. 131. *Lond.* 1894. 8°. 10174. aaa. 49.

COWPER (F.) Sailing Tours. Pt. III. Coast of Brittany. *Lond.* 1892, *etc.* 8°. 10360. c.

DUBOUCHET (H.) Zig-Zags en Bretagne. *Paris,* 1894, *etc.* 8°. 10172. i.

BRUSSELS—*continued.*

MAHUTTE (F.) Bruxelles vivant. pp. 307.
Brux. 1891. 8°.   10271. aa. 5.

VERHAEGEN (P.) Le tribunal révolutionnaire de
Bruxelles, 1794–95. pp. 35. *Brux.* 1893. 8°.
                                 9007. g. 22. (8.)

BRUTON. STRONG (T. A.) Bruton Register
1826–90. pp. 145. *Lond.* 1894. 8°. 8366. b. 51.

BRYOZOA. *See* POLYZOA.

BUBASTIS. *See* EGYPT, *Antiquities.*

BUCCANEERS. *See* PIRACY.

BUCHAREST. BUCHAREST. Indicator alfabetic de tóte stradele capitalei.
Bucuresci, 1891, 92. 8°.   10126. aa. 24.

BUCHLAU. BERCHTOLD (L. A. v.) *Count.*
Vergangenheit und Gegenwart der Herrenburg
Buchlau. pp. 349. *Brunn,* 1893. 16°.
                                 10256. aa. 45.

BUCKINGHAMSHIRE. GIBBS (R.) Buckinghamshire Miscellany. *Aylesbury,* 1891. 4°.
                                 10358. k. 11.

ROSCOE (E. S.) Buckinghamshire Sketches.
pp. 70. *Lond.* 1891. 8°.   010358. f. 20.

BUCKLAND. BAZELEY (W.) Notes on
Buckland Manor A.D. 709–1546. pp. 22.
Gloucester, 1890. 8°.   10348. d. 19. (4.)

BUDAPEST. AMERIGHI (P.) Diario dell'
assedio di Buda, 1686. pp. 50. *Firenze,* 1894. 8°.
                                 9077. eee. 38.

CORNARO (F.) Avvisi del Cavaliere F. Cornaro,
ambasciatore veneto, circa l' assedio di Buda.
1686. pp. 415. *Budapest,* 1891. 4°. 9314. l. 1.

THIRRING (G.) Geschichte des statistischen
Bureaus der Stadt Budapest. pp. 41.
Berl. 1894. 8°.   Pam. 23.

KAHN (J.) Das heutige Budapest, *etc.* pp. 258.
Budapest, 1895. 8°.   10215. bb. 27.

—— Neuester Führer durch Budapest. pp. 53.
Budapest, 1895. 16°.   10215. aaa. 38.

—— Illustrated Guide of Budapest. pp. 120.
Budapest, 1891. 8°.   10215. cc. 3.

BUDDHISM. AC. Calcutta. *Buddhist
Text Society.* Journal. *Calcutta,* 1893, *etc.* 8°.
                                 14003. b. 19.

ARUNDALE (F.) The Idea of Re-birth. pp. 155.
Lond. 1890. 8°.   4503. a. 37.

ATKINSON (J. L.) Prince Siddartha: the
Japanese Buddha. pp. 309. *Bost.* 1893. 8°.
                                 4503. de. 9.

BARTHÉLEMY SAINT-HILAIRE (J.) The Buddha
and his Religion. pp. 384. 1895. 8°. Sir J.
Lubbock's Hundred Books. Vol. 94.
                                 012207. l. 94.

BASTIAN (A.) Der Buddhismus als religions-
philosophisches System. pp. 63. *Berl.* 1893. 8°.
                                 4503. f. 36.

—— Ideale Welten nach uranographischen
Provinzen. 3 Bde. *Berl.* 1892. 8°. 4503. h. 1.

BETTANY (G. T.) Great Indian Religions.
pp. 291. 1892. 8°. The World's Religions Series.
                                 4503. aaa.

BLONAY (G. de) Matériaux pour servir à l'histoire
de la déesse bouddhique Tārā. pp. 64. 1895. 8°.
AC. Paris *École des Hautes Études.* Bibliothèque. Sciences philologiques. fasc. 107.
                                 AC. 8929.

BOWDEN (E. M.) Imitation of Buddha: Quotations from Buddhist Literature. pp. 149.
Lond. 1891. 16°.   4503. a. 40.

BRITISH GOVERNMENT. History of the Connection
of the British Government with Buddhism.
pp. 150. *Colombo,* 1889. 8°.   8022. aaa. 2.

BUDDHISM—*continued.*

BUDDHA. The Higher Life. pp. 13.
Bombay, 1894. 12°.   Pam. 41.

—— Note on Buddha's Atheism. pp. 2.
Calcutta, 1890. 8°.   4503. b. 4. (2.)

—— Buddha on the Female Sex. pp. 21.
Calcutta, 1890. 8°.   4503. b. 4. (3.)

BUDDHARAKKHITA. Jinâlankâra, or "Embellish-
ments of Buddha." pp. 112. *Lond.* 1894. 8°.
                                 14098. c. 65.

BUDDHISM. How in 219 B.C. Buddhism entered
China. pp. 9. 1891. 8°.   Pam. 41.

BUDDHIST TRACT SERIES. Buddhist Tract Series.
Colombo, 1893, *etc.* 16°.   4504. de. 2.

CARUS (P.) The Gospel of Buddha. pp. 275.
Lond. 1894. 8°.   4503. b. 11.

CHABOSEAU (A.) Essai sur la philosophie bouddhique. pp. 251. *Paris,* 1891. 8°. 4504. cc. 2.

COBBOLD (G. A.) Religion in Japan. pp. 113.
Lond. 1894. 8°.   4429. c. 35.

CUNNINGHAM (*Sir* A.) Mahâbodhi or the Buddhist
Temple at Buddha-Gaya. pp. 87. *Lond.* 1892. 4°.
                                 759. k. 7.

DAVIDS (T. W. R.) Buddhism. pp. 252.
1894. 8°. Non-Christian Religious Systems.
                                 2212. a.

DHAMMACHETI. The Kalyāni Inscriptions at
Pegu, 1476 A.D. *Rangoon,* 1892. 8°. 14098. dd. 9.

E-TSING. Mémoire composé à l'époque de la
dynastie T'ang sur les Religieux qui allèrent
chercher la loi dans les pays d'Occident.
pp. 218. *Paris,* 1894. 8°.   11100. e. 25.

FEER (L.) Cent légendes bouddhiques.
1891. 8°. Annales du Musée Guimet. Tom. 18.
                                 7704. h. 21.

GERINI (G. E.) Retrospective View of the origin
of the Thet Maha Ch'at ceremony, Maha Jati
Desana. pp. 65. *Bangkok,* 1892. 8°. 4503. g. 7.

HARDY (E.) Der Buddhismus nach älteren Pâli-
Werken. pp. 168. 1890. 8°. Darstellungen aus
dem Gebiete der nichtchristlichen Religionsgeschichte. Bd 1.   4506. f.

HARLEZ (C. de) Le manuel du Bouddhisme.
pp. 36. *Louvain,* 1892. 8°.   Pam. 41.

INDIA. The Great Temples of Burma, *etc.*
pp. 96. *Madras,* 1894. 8°.   7814. e. 44.

JĀTAKAS. The Jātaka, or Stories of the Buddha's
former Births. *Camb.* 1895, *etc.* 8°. 14098. dd. 8.

KURODA (S.) Outlines of the Mahâyâna.
pp. 27. *Tokyo,* 1893. 8°.   4503. de. 11.

LAMAIRESSE (E.) La Vie du Bouddha. pp. 288.
Paris, 1893. 8°.   4503. de 4.

—— L'Inde après le Bouddha. pp. 464.
Paris, 1892. 12°.   4503. de. 5.

LILLIE (A.) Buddha and his Parables. pp. 102.
Lond. 1890. 8°.   4503. a. 35.

MAISEY (F. C.) Sánchi and its Remains.
pp. 142. *Lond.* 1892. 4°.   7705. h. 30.

MILLOUÉ (L. de) Religions de l'Inde. pp. 335.
1890. 8°. Annales du Musée Guimet. 7704. a. 37.

—— Le Bouddhisme dans le monde. pp. 253.
Paris, 1893. 8°.   4503. bb. 37.

MAHĀMANGALA. Buddhaghosuppati, or the historical romance of Buddhaghosa. 2 pt.
Lond. 1892. 8°.   14098. c. 59.

MINAEV (I. P.) Recherches sur le Bouddhisme.
pp. 315. 1894. 8°. Annales du Musée Guimet.
Tom. 4.   7704. i.

MUELLER (F. M.) Sacred Books of the Buddhists.
Lond. 1895, *etc.* 8°.   14003. ccc.

NANJIO (B.) Catalogue of the Chinese translation
of the Buddhist Tripitaka. pp. 480.
Oxford, 1883. 4°.   4505. g. 2.

BUDDHISM—continued.

NEUMANN (C. E.) Buddhistische Anthologie.
pp. 236. Leiden, 1892. 8°.   14098. c. 58.

PATNA. Patna, Gaya and Benares. pp. 135.
Calcutta, 1890. 8°.   4503. b. 4. (1.)

RIOTOR (L.) and LÉOFANTI ( ) Les Enfers
Bouddhiques—Le Bouddhisme Annamite.
pp. 84. Paris, 1895. 4°.   4504. h. 13.

ROCKHILL (W. W.) Life of the Buddha. pp. 273.
1884. 8°. Trübner's Oriental Series. 2318. g. 6.

ROSNY (L. L. de) La Morale du Bouddhisme.
pp. 24. Paris, 1891. 8°.   Pam. 41.

SAIZAU (M.) Le Bouddha et le Bouddhisme.
pp. 36. Paris, 1890. 8°.   Pam. 41.

SCHULTZE (T.) Vadenta und Buddhismus als
Fermente für eine Regeneration des religiösen
Bewusstseins. 2 pt. Leipz. 1893. 8°.
     4503. ee. 26.

SIDDHATTHA. Des Sarasaṅgaho, eines Kompen-
diums buddhistischer Anschauungen erstes Kapital. pp. 32. Leipz. 1891. 8°.   14098. c. 55.

SILBERNAGL (I.) Der Buddhismus nach seiner
Entstehung, etc. pp. 196. München, 1891. 8°.
     4503. ee. 5.

SPECHT (E.) Deux traductions chinoises du Mi-
lindapañho. pp. 25. Paris, 1893. 8°.
     11100. b. 28.

SUBHADRA. Buddhistik Katekes. pp. 103.
Stockholm, 1890. 12°.   4506. de. 6.

WADDELL (L. A.) The Buddhism of Tibet.
pp. 598. Lond. 1895. 8°.   4503. cc. 21.

—— Discovery of the site of Asoka's classic
capital of Pāṭaliputra. pp. 29.
Calcutta, 1892. 4°.   7706. f. 29.
See also RELIGION : History.

Buddhism and Christianity.

BERRY (T. S.) Christianity and Buddhism.
pp. 256. 1891. 8°. Non-Christian Religious
Systems.   2212. a.

DRYAS, pseud. Christus oder Buddha. pp. 49.
Bitterfeld, 1894. 8°.   Pam. 41.

LILLIE (A.) Influence of Buddhism on Primitive
Christianity. pp. 181. Lond. 1893. 8°.
     4503. aaa. 8.

LLOYD (A.) The Higher Buddhism in the light
of the Nicene Creed. pp. 39. Tokyo, 1893. 8°.
     Pam. 17.

NEUMANN (C. E.) Die innere Verwandtschaft
buddhistischer und christlicher Lehren. pp. 109.
Leipz. 1891. 8°.   759. d. 5.

VEINIÉ (C.) La morale du Bouddha et la morale
du Christ. pp. 121. Genève, 1892. 8°.
     4503. cc. 28.

Esoteric Buddhism. See THEOSOPHY.

Law.

JARDINE (J.) Notes on Buddhist Law. 8 pt.
Rangoon, 1882–83. 8°.   5319. c. 14 (3.)

MANUEL (R. A.) A digest of Buddhist Law.
pp. 188. Rangoon, 1885. 8°.   5319. c. 9.

SPARKS ( ) A Manual of Buddhist Law.
pp. 76. Mandalay, 1894. 8°.   5318. b. 30.

BUDNO. MENARINI (G.) Butrium. pp. 43.
Bologna, 1893. 8°.   10106. ff. 6. (9.)

BUENOS AIRES. ARATA (P. N.) El Clima
y las condiciones higiénicas de Buenos Aires.
pp. 133. Buenos A. 1889. 8°.   07686. l. 1.

BUENOS AYRES. A greeting from the River
Plate. pp. 16. Buenos A. 1890. 8°. 10481. b. 47.

LUDWIG (P.) Guia de la ciudad de Buenos Aires.
pp. 174. Buenos A. 1892. 8°.   10481. aa. 39.

BUENOS AIRES—continued.

MARTINEZ (A. B.) Finanzas comunales de Buenos
Aires. pp. 103. Buenos A. 1892. 8°.
     08227. g. 50.

MARTINEZ (C.) Buenos Aires. pp. 503.
México, 1890. 8°.   10481. a. 24.

MONNER SANS (R.) Los Catalanes en la defensa
y reconquista de Buenos-Aires. pp. 32.
Buenos A. 1893. 8°.   9004. bbb. 16. (7.)

NUÑEZ (J.) La Guardia Nacional de Buenos
Aires. pp. 138. Buenos A, 1892. 8°.
     8823. h. 30.

See also ARGENTINE REPUBLIC.

BUFFALO, New York. WELCH (S. M.) Recollections of Buffalo, 1830–40. pp. 423.
Buffalo, 1891. 8°.   10412. h. 25.

BUFFALOES, Order of. See FRIENDLY
SOCIETIES.

BUFFOONS. See JESTERS.

BUILDING. ABEL (L.) Allgemeiner Bau-
rathgeber. pp. 1035. Wien, 1893. 8°.
     7817. e. 24.

Ac. Chatham. R. Engineer Institute. Notes
on the chemistry of Building Materials.
pp. 155. Chatham, 1888. 8°.   8908. b. 48.

ALLEN (J. P.) Practical Building Construction.
pp. 446. Lond. 1893. 8°.   8768. k. 13.

ANGLIN (S.) The Design of Structures. pp. 497.
Lond. 1891. 8°.   8767. cc. 18.

BERG (L. de C.) Safe Buildings. 2 vol.
Bost. 1894. 8°.   7817. ee. 4.

BLACK (A.) First Principles of Building. pp. 329.
Lond. 1895. 8°.   7817. b. 3.

BLAGROVE (G. H.) Dangerous Structures.
pp. 84. Lond. 1892. 8°.   8768. cc. 24.

BOVEY (H. T.) Theory of Structures and strength
of materials. pp. 817. N.Y. 1893. 8°. 8767. k. l.

BUILDING CONSTRUCTION. Advanced Building
Construction. pp. 239. Lond. 1892. 8°.
     7820. aa. 28.

BUILDING DRAUGHTSMAN. The Building and
Machine Draughtsman. pp. 296.
     8768. c. 29.

BURNS (G. J.) Glossary of technical terms used
in the building trades. pp. 136.
Lond. 1895. 8°.   7817. b. 6.

CLARK (T. M.) Building Superintendence.
pp. 336. N.Y. 1894. 8°.   7817. ee. 5.

DICTIONARIES. Dictionary of technical terms of
building construction. pp. 296.
Lond. 1891–93. 8°.   7817. e. 27.

DOMESTIC HOUSE PLANNER. Domestic House
Planner and Sanitary Architect. pp. 263.
Lond. 1891. 8°.   7817. e. 12.

FERNANDEZ FRIAS (R.) Resistencia de Materiales.
pp. 511. Santiago de C. 1886. 8°. 8768. m. 5.

FROST (H.) House-building Illustrations. pp. 19.
Lond. 1891. 8°.   7808. aa. 44. (4.)

GUASTAVINO (R.) Essay on the theory and
history of Cohesive Construction. pp. 149
Lond. 1892. 8°.   8767. b. 48.

KECK (W.) Vorträge über Elasticitäts-Lehre
als Grundlage für die Festigkeits-Berechnung
der Bauwerke. 2 Th. Hannover, 1892 8°.
     8768. f. 10.

MITCHELL (C. F.) Building Construction.
pp. 506. Lond. 1894. 8°.   7817. b. 1.

NEWMAN (J.) Scamping Tricks practised upon
Public Works. pp. 129. Lond. 1891. 8°.
     7820. aa. 22.

NOTES. Notes on Building Construction.
Lond. 1891, etc. 8°.   2260. d. 2.

BUILDING—*continued.*

P.P.—*New York.* Architecture and Building. *N.Y.* 1890, etc. fol. P.P. 1669.

Purdy (C. T.) Steel Construction of Buildings. 1894. 8°. Ac. — Madison — *University of Wisconsin.* Bulletin. Engineering Series. Vol. 1. Ac. 1792.

Robertson (W. W.) A Missing Link in Economics of Construction. pp. 60. *Rangoon,* 1891. fol. 8766. g. 23.

Saker (S.) System of Builders' Book-keeping. pp. 119. *Lond.* 1895. 8°. 8533. aaa. 45.

Schmidt (O.) Die Hochbau-Constructionen. pp. 241. 1892. 8°. Durm (J.) Handbuch der Architektur. Th. 3. Bd. 3. Heft. 2. 7815. bb. 12.

Stephenson (G.) Estimating: a method of pricing builders' quantities. pp. 168. *Lond.* 1890. 8°. 8228. cc. 42.

—— Repairs: how to measure and value them. pp. 99. *Lond.* 1890. 8°. 8228. cc. 41.

Stock (C. H.) Treatise on Shoring and underpinning. pp. 54. *Lond.* 1893. 8°. 7817. c. 23.

Szerelmey (N. C.) Szerelmey and waterproof Walls. pp. 29. *Lond.* 1894. 8°. Pam. 79.

Tarn (E. W.) Elementary treatise on the Construction of Roofs. pp. 128. *Lond.* 1893. 8°. 8703. ccc. 47.

Viollet-Le-Duc (E. E.) Rational Building. pp. 367. *N.Y.* 1895. 8°. 7817. cc. 3.

Whiting (J.) The Cube Calculator. pp. 349. *Lond.* 1894. 8°. 8548. dc. 29.

Williams (H. J.) The Origin of Building. pp. 35. *Lond.* 1893. 8°. Pam. 24.

Wilson (J.) Elementary Building Construction. pp. 96. *Manch.* 1890. obl. 8°. 7817. e. 9.

—— Advanced Building Construction. pp. 176. *Manch.* 1890. obl. 8°. 7817. e. 7.

Young (F.) Every man his own Mechanic. pp. 924. *Lond.* 1890. 8°. 7817 g. 24.

See also Architecture: Bricks: Carpentry: Cements: Concrete: Elasticity: Houses: Levelling: Plastering: Stonework: Strains and Stresses. For Farm Buildings, *see* Agriculture, and for the Housing of the Working Classes, *see* Capital and Labour.

Law relating to Building.

Banks (G.) Treatise on the Law of Support for Buildings, etc pp. 177. *Lond.* 1894. 8°. 6306. h. 16.

Emden (A.) Law relating to Building. pp. 690. *Lond.* 1895. 8°. 6425. aaaa. 20.

Hudson (A. A.) Law of Building Contracts. pp. 880. *Lond.* 1891. 8°. 6375. k. 10.

Roscoe (E. S.) Digest of Cases relating to the Construction of Buildings. pp. 164. *Lond.* 1893. 8°. 6426. b. 59.

Craies (W. F.) The London Building Act, 1894. pp. 121. 28. *Lond.* 1894. 8°. 6426. f. 3.

David (A. J.) The London Building Act, 1894. pp. 144. *Lond.* 1894. 8°. 6425. dc. 25.

Dicksee (B.) The London Building Act, 1894. pp. 226. *Lond.* 1894. 8°. 6425. aaaa. 11.

Fletcher (B.) The London Building Act, 1894. pp. 267. *Lond.* 1895. 8°. 6426. aaaa. 26.

Glen (R. C.) The Law regulating Streets and Buildings in the Metropolis. pp. 682. *Lond.* 1895. 8°. 6425. aaaa. 19.

Griffiths (W. R.) Collection of Statutes regulating Building in London. pp. 360. *Lond.* 1893. 8°. 6426. cc. 30.

BUILDING.—Law, etc.—*continued.*

Griffiths (W. R.) London Building Act, 1894. pp. 480. *Lond.* 1895. 8°. 6425. aaaa. 16.

Statham (H. H.) The Changes in London Building Law. pp. 188. *Lond.* 1895. 8°. 6425. dc. 27.

Rozet (G.) Dictionnaire de la législation de la propriété. pp. 609. *Paris,* 1890. 8°. 5403. g. 8.

Rubenson (M.) Byggnadsstadgan för rikets städer och Stockholms byggnadsordning. pp. 135. *Stockholm,* 1890. 8°. 5725. a. 8.

Fryer (W. J.) Laws relating to Buildings, in New York. pp. 251. *N.Y.* 1892. 8°. 06616. k. 11.

BUILDING SOCIETIES. Bowen (I.) The Building Societies Act, 1894. pp. 87. *Lond.* 1894. 8°. 6376. d. 30.

Chester (E.) "Economic" Building Societies against "Provident." pp. 8. *Darwen,* 1892. 8°. 8228. aaaa. 17. (16.)

Lees (J. F.) Book-Keeping for terminating Building Societies. pp. 125. *Oldham,* 1895. 8°. 8535. df. 37.

Watts (J. S.) The Truth about the "Liberator" Building Society. pp. 19. *Lond.* 1893. 8°. 08221. g 47. (16.)

Wurtzburg (E. A.) Law relating to Building Societies. pp. 487. *Lond,* 1895. 8°. 6376. cc. 14.

Aberdeen. *Aberdeen "Economic" Building Society.* Rules. pp. 24. *Darwen,* 1895. 12°. Pam. 23.

Conner (A.) Prospectus and Rules for the use of "Guardian" Building Societies. pp. 22. *Manch.* 1895. 4°. 8245. c. 84.

"Economic" Building Society. Rules. pp. 24. *Darwen,* 1894. 8°. 08226. f. 20.

Foleshill. *Co-operative Land and Building Society.* Rules. pp. 33. *Coventry,* 1890. 8°. Pam. 23.

Sunderland. *Working Men's Permanent Building Society.* Rules. *Sunderland,* 1894. 12°. Pam. 23.

See also Friendly Societies.

BUITENZORG. Buys (M.) Batavia, Buitenzorg en de Preanger. pp. 158. *Batavia,* 1891. 8°. 10055. aaa. 9.

Treub (M.) 's Lands Plantentuin te Buitenzorg. pp. 512. *Batavia,* 1892. 8°. 7077. g. 7. *See also* Java.

BUKOWINA. Budinszky (J.) Die Bukowina zu Anfang des Jahres 1783. pp. 84. *Czernowitz,* 1894. 8°. 9315. aa. 37.

Bukowina. *Statistisches Landesamt.* Mittheilungen. *Czernowitz,* 1892, etc. 8°. 08225. l.

Dan (D.) Die Völkerschaften der Bukowina. *Czernowitz,* 1890, etc. 8°. 9456. dd.

Daszkiewicz (S.) Die Lage der Ruthenen in der Bukowinaer Erzdiöcese. pp. 171. *Czernowitz,* 1891. 8°. 3926. h. 23.

Kaindl (R. F.) Die Rutenen in der Bukowina. 2 Th. 1889, 90. 8°. Der Buchenwald. 10215. bb. 21.

Silvester, *Archbishop of Czernowitz.* Apologie der orthodoxen griechisch-orientalischen Kirche der Bukowina. pp. 60. *Czernowitz,* 1889. 8°. Pam. 93.

Splény von Miháldy (G.) Beschreibung der Bukowina. pp. 167. *Czernowitz,* 1893. 8°. 10215. aa. 22.

Werenka (D.) Bukowinas Entstehen und Aufblühen. 1892, etc. 8°. Archiv für österreichische Geschichte. Bd. 78. Ac. 810/8.

Wlislocki (H. v.) Märchen und Sagen der Bukowinaer. pp. 188. *Hamburg,* 1891. 8°. 12430. g. 38.

BUKOWINA—*continued.*

WOROBKIEWICZ (E.) Die Verhältnisse der Bukowina, *etc.* pp. 114. *Lemberg*, 1893. 8°.
       10292. h. 19.

ZIFFER (E. A.) Die Localbahnen in Galizien und der Bukowina. pp. 190. *Wien*, 1891. 4°.
       08235. m. 4.

See also AUSTRIA-HUNGARY.

BULGARIA. A., H. Die türkische Wehrmacht und die Armeen der Balkanstaaten. pp. 207. *Wien*, 1892. 8°.   8823. ddd. 23.

G. B. & I. *War Office.* Handbook of Armies of the Minor Balkan States. pp. 61. *Lond.* 1891. 8°.   8823. g. 20.

HUYSHE (W.) Liberation of Bulgaria. War notes in 1877. pp. 316. *Lond.* 1894. 8°.
       9136. g. 4.

GRABINSKI (G.) *Count.* Alexandre de Battenberg, prince de Bulgarie. pp. 39. *Paris*, 1893. 8°.
       Pam. 8.

ALESSIO (F.) A. di Battenberg. A criticism of Count G. Grabinski. pp. 12. *Firenze*, 1894. 8°.
       Pam. 8.

BEAMAN (A. H.) M. Stambuloff. pp. 240. 1895. 8°. Public Men of to-day.   10600. e.

CHOLET (A. P. de) *Count.* Étude sur la Guerre bulgaro-serbe. pp. 198. *Paris*, 1891. 8°.
       9077. f. 2.

REGENSPURSKY (C.) Die Kampfe bei Slivnica, Nov. 1885. pp. 179. *Wien*, 1895. 8°. 9136. g. 8.

DICEY (E.) The Peasant State. pp. 332. *Lond.* 1894. 8°.   10125. dd. 3.

JIREČEK (C. J.) Das Fürstenthum Bulgarien. pp. 573. *Wien*, 1891. 8°.   10125. ff. 8.

LAMOUCHE (L.) La Bulgarie dans le passé et le présent. pp. 519. *Paris*, 1892. 12°. 10126. c. 13.

MARIN (P.) Bulgares et Russes vis-à-vis la triple alliance. pp. 347. *Paris*, 1891. 12°.
       8028. aaaa. 17.

BALAKTSCHIEFF (I.) Die rechtliche Stellung des Fürstentums. pp. 83. *Würzburg*, 1893. 8°.
       8028. c. 2.

BULGARIA. Steht in Bulgarien eine Katastrophe bevor? pp. 40. *Berlin*, 1890. 8°.   Pam. 72.

BULGARIAN POLITICS. Bulgarische Politik. pp. 64. *Dresd.* 1891. 8°.   8028. ff. 16. (8.)

BATTENBERG (F. J. v.) *Prince.* Die volkswirthschaftliche Entwicklung Bulgariens. pp. 202. *Leipz.* 1891. 8°.   08225. l. 12.

HILLGER (H.) Die erste nationale Ausstellung Bulgariens. pp. 24. *Hamburg*, 1892. 8°.
       Pam. 18.

RAUSCH (C.) Bulgarien, seine wirtschaftliche und finanzielle Entwicklung. pp. 87. *Wien*, 1892. 8°.   8228. aaaa. 17. (17.)

STROELL (M.) Die Handelspolitik der Balkan Staaten. pp. 65. 1892. 8°. Ac. Leipsie. *Verein für Socialpolitik.* Schriften. No. 51.
       Ac. 2322.

BULGARIAN LANGUAGE. STRAUSZ (A.) and DUGOVICH (I.) Bulgarische Grammatik. pp. 170. *Wien*, 1895. 8°. 12975. i. 27.
See also SLAVONIC LANGUAGES.

BULL FIGHTS. DELGADO (J.) *called* HILLO. La Tauromaquia. pp. 100. *Madrid*, 1894. 16°.
       7908. a. 106.

HUOT (M.) Les Courses de Taureaux à Paris. pp. 24. *Paris*, 1890. 8°.   Pam. 69.

MÍNGUEZ (F.) Curiosidades Taurinas. pp. 268. *Madrid*, 1892, *etc.* 8°.   07905. f. 6.

NOVELI (N. R.) Reglas para Torear á Caballo. pp. 58. *Madrid*, 1894. 8°.   07905. h. 27.

SALANOBA (P.) Tauromaquia Hispana. Pintura poética, 1790. pp. 15. *Madrid*, 1894. 8°.
       Pam. 60.

BULL FIGHTS—*continued.*

SPANISH BULL FIGHTS. A collection of programmes of Spanish Bull-fights. fol.
       1818. d. 3.

VERAGUAS (de) *Duke.* La Fiesta Española en el Perú. pp. 118. *Lima*, 1892. 8°. 07905. g. 4.

BUNDABERG. WALKER (J Y.) The History of Bundaberg, Queensland. pp. 215. *Bundaberg*, 1890. 8°.   10492. bb. 43.

BURDWAN. OLDHAM (W. B.) Historical Aspects of the Burdwan District. pp. 33. *Calcutta*, 1894. 8°.   10057. bb. 6.

BURFORD. MONK (W. J.) History of Burford. pp. 197. *Burford*, 1891. 8°. 010358. e. 12.

BURGOS, *City and Province.* CANTÓN SALAZAR (L.) La Catedra, la Cartuja, el Real Monasterio de las Huelgas, *etc.* pp. 95. *Burgos*, 1888. 8°.   10106. de. 5. (2.)

OLIVER-COPONS (E. de) El castillo de Burgos. pp. 228. *Barcelona*, 1893. 8°.   10160. f. 7.

SALVÁ (A.) Cosas de la vieja Burgos. pp. 208. *Burgos*, 1892. 8°.   10160. cc. 9.

MARTÍNEZ AÑIBARRO Y RIVES (M.) Intento de un diccionario de autores de Burgos, *etc.* pp. 570. *Madrid*, 1889. 8°.   10632. f. 31.

BURGUNDY. PETIT (E.) Itinéraires de Philippe le hardi et Jean sans peur, 1363–1419. pp. 719. 1888. 4°. FRANCE. Collection de documents, *etc.*   9210. g.

MAAG (R.) Burgund und ihre Beziehungen zu der schweizerischen Eidgenossenschaft, 1477–1678. pp. 366. *Zürich*, 1891. 8°.   9305. c. 2.

WITTE (H.) Lothringen und Burgund. pp. 100. 1890. 8°. Ac. Metz. *Gesellschaft für Lothringische Geschichte.* Jahrbuch. Jhrg. 2.
       Ac. 7112.

See also FRANCHE-COMTÉ: CÔTE D'OR, and SAONE ET LOIRE, *Departments.*

BURIAL.

General.

ANUCHIN (D. G,) Use of Sledges, Boats and Horses at burials in Russia. pp. 8. *Lond.* 1892. 8°.   07703. f. 3. (4.)

BERNARD ( ) Nouveau mode de sépulture. pp. 31. *Alger*, 1894 8°.   7305. ee. 21. (7.)

COBB (A. G.) Earth-burial and Cremation. pp. 173. *N.Y.* 1892. 8°.   7391. df. 14.

ENGLAND. Earth to Earth Burial and Cremation. pp. 13. *Lond.* 1890. 8°. 4136. a. 42. (7.)

LITURGIES. Rome, *Ch. of.* Le Livre mortuaire. pp. 304. *Arras*, 1889. 16°.   3157. d. 43.

ROTELLA (G.) Cremazione o Inhumazione? pp. 182. *Spoleto*, 1891. 8°.   7404. cc. 18.

SMALL (E. M.) Sepulchral Pyramids. pp. 15. *Rochester*, 1894. 8°.   7404. aaa. 50.

WAHLTUCH (A.) Earth-burial one of the causes of high mortality. pp. 15. *Munch.* 1891. 8°.
       7306. df. 19. (7.)

WAKEFORD (W.) Modes of Burial. pp. 47. *Lond.* 1890. 8°.   Pam. 77.

WILDER (A.) Perils of premature Burial. pp. 27. *Lond.* 1895. 8°.   Pam. 39.

See also CREMATION: DEATH: EMBALMING.

Law of.

LITTLE (J. B.) The Law of Burial. pp. 912. *Lond.* 1894. 8°.   2230. a. 10.

Sepulchral Monuments.

CONZE (A. C. L.) Die attischen Grabreliefs. *Leipz.* 1890, *etc.* fol.   7704. l. 22.

CRULL (F.) Die Grabsteine der Wismarschen Kirchen. 1889–91. 8°. Ac. Schwerin. *Verein für Mecklenburgische Geschichte.* Jahrbücher. Jhrg. 54–56.   Ac. 7105.

BURIAL.—Sepulchral Monuments—*cont.*
CREENY (W. F.) Illustrations of Incised Slabs on the Continent. pp. 76. *Norwich,* 1891. fol.
1707. c. 10.
LÖFFLER (J. B.) Danske Gravestene fra Middelalderen. pp. 40. *Kjøbenh.* 1889. fol.
1702. d. 10.
MACKLIN (H. W.) Monumental Brasses. pp. 144. *Lond.* 1890. 8°. 7709. b. 39.
WALL (J. C.) Tombs of the Kings of England. pp. 485. *Lond.* 1891. 8°. 9503. ee. 16.
See also EPITAPHS : INSCRIPTIONS : SCULPTURE.

BURLESQUES. *See* PARODIES.

BURMA. GRAY (J.) The Alaung Pra Dynasty. pp. 182. *Rangoon,* 1885. 8°. 9055. aa. 9.
STAPLEY (L. A.) Catechism of the History of Burma. pp. 26. *Rangoon,* 1886. 12°.
9004. bbb. 14. (5.)
SANGERMANO (V.) The Burmese Empire a hundred years ago. pp. 311.
Westminster, 1893. 8°. 010057. f. 25.
MOYLE (J. C.) Almanac of English and Burmese Dates, 1822–96. pp. 296. *Rangoon,* 1895. 8°.
760. dd. 14.
CORDIER (H.) Historique des relations de la Grande-Bretagne avec la Birmanie. pp. 28. *Paris,* 1894. 8°. 9007. g. 20. (4.)
FORCHHAMMER (E.) Notes on the history and geography of British Burma. 2 pt.
Rangoon, 1884. 8°. 5319. c. 14. (1.)
COLBECK (J. A.) Letters from Mandalay. 1878–79 ; 1885–88. pp. 113. *Knaresborough,* 1892. 8°.
9056. aaa. 30.
MAUNG TET PYO. Customary Law of the Chin tribe. *Rangoon,* 1884. 8°. 11103. d.
CHAILLEY-BERT (J) Colonisation de l'Indo-Chine. L'expérience anglais. pp. 398.
Paris, 1892. 12°. 10058. cc. 32.
LEHAULT (P.) La France et l'Angleterre en Asie. *Paris,* 1892, *etc.* 8°. 9057. c. 9.

———

BARBERIS (T.) Cinque Anni in Birmania. pp. 201. *Milano,* 1890. 8°. 10056. h. 6.
BURMAH. Burma and the Burmese. pp. 50. *Madras,* 1892. 4°. Pam. 88.
CUMING (E. D.) In the Shadow of the Pagoda. pp. 362. *Lond.* 1893. 8°. 010055. de. 4.
EPHEM. Burma Pocket Almanac.
Rangoon, 1888–90. 8°. P.P. 2572. h.
HAY (J. O.) Arakan, past, present, future. pp. 216. *Edinb.* 1892. 8°. 010057. f. 2.
INDIA. Murray's Handbook for India and Burma. pp. 484. *Lond.* 1894. 8°. 2364. b. 24.
MACMAHON (A. R.) Far Cathay and Farther India. pp. 340. *Lond.* 1893. 8°. 010057. f. 6.
MILN (L. J.) When we were Strolling Players in the East. pp. 354. *Lond.* 1894. 8°.
010057. f. 29.
PARKER (E. H.) Burma, with reference to her relations with China. pp. 103.
Rangoon, 1893. 8°. 8023. aaa. 12.
PASKE (C. T.) Myamma. Retrospect of life in Lower Burmah. pp. 265. *Lond.* 1893. 8°.
010055. de. 2.
TAW SEIN-KO. Notes on an Archæological Tour through Ramannadesa. pp. 10.
Bombay, 1893. 4°. 7705. f. 52. (6.)
WINSTON (W. R.) Four years in Upper Burma. pp. 266. *Lond.* 1892. 8°. 10055. aaaa. 32.
See also ENGLAND, *Colonies :* INDO-CHINA.

BURMESE LANGUAGE. JUDSON (A.) English and Burmese Dictionary. pp. 930. *Rangoon,* 1894. 8°. 12907. cc. 49.

BURMESE LANGUAGE—*continued.*
JUDSON (A.) English and Burmese Dictionary. pp. 544. *Rangoon,* 1893. 8°. 12910. c. 9.
ANGLO-BURMESE GRAMMATICAL READER. Anglo-Burmese Reader. pp. 79.
Rangoon, 1889. 8°. 760. dd.
BENNETT (C.) Vocabulary and Phrase book, English-Burmese. pp. 155. *Rangoon,* 1886. 8°.
760. dd. 12.
FORCHHAMMER (E.) Notes on the languages and dialects of Burma. pp. 20. *Rangoon,* 1884. 8°.
5319. c. 14. (2)
GORDON (H. K.) Hand-book to colloquial Burmese in Roman character. pp. 63.
Rangoon, 1886. 4°. 760. dd. 10.
—— Companion to the Hand-book. Burmese character. pp. 108. *Rangoon,* 1886. 8°.
760. dd. 11.
HANCOCK (R. B.) Anglicized colloquial Assistant. pp. 128. *Rangoon,* 1883. 8°.
760. dd. 10.
JUDSON (A.) Grammar of the Burmese language. pp. 61. *Rangoon,* 1888. 8°. 12907. c. 30.
MACKERTICH (S. M.) Anglo-Burmese Ninety-nine Stories. pp. 191. *Rangoon,* 1887. 12°.
760. dd. 8.
SAINT JOHN (R. F. St. A.) Burmese Reader. pp. 256. *Oxf.* 1894. 8°. 12907. bb. 43.
WATSON (J.) Technical Dialogues in English and Burmese. pp. 76. *Rangoon,* 1885. 16°.
760. dd. 9.

BURNAGE. CORBETT (S. B.) Sketches of Burnage. *Manch.* 1891. fol. 10368. k. 12.

BURNSALL. BURNSALL. Parish Register of Burnsall-in-Craven. 2 vol. *Skipton,* 1893. 8°.
9903. ccc. 2.

BURY SAINT EDMUNDS. BARKER (H. R.) History of Bury St. Edmund's. pp. 104. *Bury,* 1885.-8°. 10351. dd. 12.
BARLOW (W. S.) The Good old Bury Simnell. pp. 80. *Bury,* 1892. 4°. 12431. a. 35.
EPHEM. Year Book of Information for the Town Council. *Bury,* 1891, *etc.* 8°. P.P. 2508. ar.
JAMES (M. R.) On the Abbey of S. Edmund at Bury. pp. 220. 1895. 8°. Ac. Cambridge. *Antiquarian Society.* Publications. Oct. Series. No. 28. Ac. 5624.
JESSOPP (A.) Studies by a Recluse in cloister, town and country. pp. 281. *Lond.* 1893. 8°.
012357. h. 2.
SPENCE (H. D. M.) Cloister Life in the days of Cœur de Lion. pp. 203. *Lond.* 1892. 4°.
4707. g. 12.
THOMPSON (J. R.) Records of Saint Edmund. pp. 170. *Lond.* 1890, 91. 4°. 4828. cc. 33.

BUTE. HEWISON (J. K.) Bute in the olden Time. *Edinb.* 1893. *etc.* 4°. 10370. dd. 19.

BUTTER AND BUTTERINE.
See DAIRY MANAGEMENT.

BUTTERFLIES. *See* LEPIDOPTERA.

BUTZBACH. OTTO (E.) Die Bevölkerung der Stadt Butzbach während des Mittelalters. pp. 103. *Darmstadt.* 1893. 8°. 10255. h. 6.

BUXTON. CROSTON (J.) Buxton. pp. 82. *Manch.* 1893. 8°. 10347. cc. 26. (3.)
GIFFORD-BENNET (R. O.) Buxton and its Waters. pp. 47. *Manch.* 1892. 8°. 7462. aaa. 43.
HYDE (S.) Buxton : its Baths and Climate. pp. 83. *Manch.* 1893. 8°. 7462. b. 48.

BYFIELD. LITTLE (W.) Contribution to the History of Byfield. pp. 12.
Newburyport, 1893. 8°. Pam. 86.

BYZANTINE ART. *See* ART.

BYZANTINE EMPIRE. Ac. St. Petersburg. *Academia Scientiarum.* Fontes Rerum
Byzantinarum. *Petrofroli,* 1892, *etc.* 8°. 9136. h.

GIBBON (E.) History of the Decline and Fall of
the Roman Empire. 2 vol. 1892. 8°. Sir
J. Lubbock's Hundred Books. No. 33.
012207. l. 33.

OMAN (C. W. C.) The Byzantine Empire.
pp. 364. 1892, 8°. Story of the Nations.
9004. ccc. 6.

P.P. *Leipsic.* Byzantinische Zeitschrift.
Leipz. 1892, *etc.* 8°. P.P. 4748. p.

NEUMANN (C.) Die Weltstellung des byzantinischen Reiches vor den Kreuzzügen. pp. 121.
Leipz. 1894. 8°. 9136. f. 23.

FLASCH (F. M.) Constantin der Grosse. pp. 159.
Würzburg, 1891. 8°. 10606. f. 13.

GARDNER (A.) Julian and the last struggle of
Paganism. pp. 364. 1895. 8°. Heroes of the
Nations. No. 13. 10601. f.

REINHARDT (G.) Der Perserkrieg des Kaisers
Julian. pp. 45. *Dessau,* 1892. 4°. 9055. ee. 14.

KRUEGER (G.) Monophysitische Streitigkeiten
im Zusammenhange mit der Reichspolitik.
pp. 104. *Jena,* 1884. 8°. Pam. 29.

ADAMEK (O.) Beiträge zur Geschichte des
Kaisers Mauricius, 582–602. 2 pt.
Graz, 1890–91. 8°. 8385. f. 4.

HOUSTON (J. D. C.) The Daughter of Leontius,
Eudocia. pp. 380. *Edinb.* 1894. 8°.
10603. bb. 40.

ROME, *Empire of.* BASIL I., *Emperor.* Parali-
pomena ad Basilica. pp. 31. *Lipsiae,* 1893. 8°.
Pam. 32.

MYSTAKIDIS (B. A.) Byzantinisch-Deutsche
Beziehungen zur Zeit der Ottonen. pp. 99.
Stuttgart, 1891. 8°. 9135. d. 1.

SCHLUMMBERGER (G.) Un Empereur byzantin,
Nicéphore Phocas. pp. 779. *Paris,* 1890. 8°.
K.T.C. 11. b. 14.

MANUEL II. [Palæologus], *Emperor.* Lettres de
l'empereur Manuel Paléologue.
Paris, 1893, *etc.* 8°. 10905. k.

MIYATOVIĆ (C.) Constantine, the last Emperor
of the Greeks. pp. 239. *Lond.* 1892. 8°.
9135. aaa. 18.

STUECKELBERG (E. A.) Der constantinische
Patriciat. pp. 131. *Basel,* 1891. 8°.
9041. cc. 32.

WIART (R.) Le régime des terres du fisc au Bas-
Empire. pp. 296. *Paris,* 1894. 8°. 5206. ee. 26.

KRUMBACHER (C.) Geschichte der byzantinischen
Litteratur. 527–1453. pp. 494. 1891. 8°.
MUELLER (I. E. P.) Handbuch der klassischen
Altertums-Wissenschaft. Bd. 9. 2259. g. 6.
See also CONSTANTINOPLE: CRUSADES: LAW,
Roman : ROME.

CABINET MAKING. *See* CARPENTRY.

CACHAR. WRIGHT (M. J.) Three Years in
Cachar. *Lond.* 1895. 8°. 10057. b. 9.

CACHY. LOGIE (T.) Phonology of the Patois
of Cachy. pp. 73. *Baltimore,* 1892. 8°.
12952. ee. 31.

CACTACEAE. HAAGE (F. A.) Haage's
Cacteen-Cultur. pp. 180. *Breslau,* 1892. 8°
07028. l. 11.

RUEMPLER (T.) Die Sukkulenten. pp. 263.
Berl. 1892. 8°. 07028. l. 12.

CADIOEOS INDIANS.
See INDIANS, *Central and South America.*

CADIZ. CASTRO Y ROSSI (A. de) Cadiz y la
primera expedicion de Colon. pp. 33.
Cadiz, 1891. 8°. Pam. 28.

CADMIUM. JONES (H. C.) Determination
of the Atomic Weight of Cadmium. pp. 37.
Baltimore, 1892. 8°. Pam. 13.
See also METALS.

CAEN. Ac. Caen. *Université.* Inventaire
des archives. 1892, *etc.* 4°. Collection des
Inventaires. 1814. b. *etc.*

BEAUREPAIRE (E. de) Journal des choses mé-
morables arrivées à Caen. Notes du XVIIe et
du XVIIIe siècles. 1890. 8°. Ac. Caen. *Association Normande.* Annuaire. An 56.
Ac. 412.

CAREL (P.) Étude sur le Barreau de Caen.
pp. 249. *Caen,* 1889. 12°. 6005. aa. 7.

JOANNE (P.) Caen. Guide Joanne. pp. 60.
Paris, 1895. 8°. 10174. a. 29.

CAERNARVONSHIRE. KILNER (E. A.)
Four Welsh Counties. pp. 266. *Lond.* 1891. 8°.
10369. cc. 44.

CAFFEINE. (PARISOT (E.) Étude physiologique de l'action de la caféine. pp. 112.
Paris, 1890. 8°. 07509. e. 10.

CAGLI. MAESTRINI (A.) La Chiesa Cattedrale
di Cagli, 1792. pp. 30. *Cagli,* 1892. 8°.
4532. g. 11. (5.)

CAILLI. SEALY (W.) Notes historiques sur
Cailli. pp. 38. *Torquay,* 1891. 4°. 9915. de. 25.

CAIRO. BARROIS (J.) Notice sur le climat
du Caire. 1890. 8°. Ac. Alexandria. *Institut
Égyptien.* Bulletin. Sér. 2. No. 10. Ac. 10/4.

FULLERTON (W. M.) In Cairo. pp. 70.
Lond. 1891. 8°. 010096. e. 41.

MINNAERT (E.) Le Caire. pp. 335.
Brux. 1891. 8°. 10095. bb. 8.

PELLETAN (C.) Le Caire. 1892. 4°. Les Capitales du Monde. No. 13. 10025. g.

POOLE (S. L.) Cairo. pp. 320. *Lond.* 1892. 8°.
10096. dd. 3.

CAITHNESS. EVANS (J. W.) Geology of
the North-east of Caithness. pp. 48.
Lond. 1891. 8°. Pam. 27.

SINCLAIR (T.) Caithness Events. pp. 180.
Wick, 1894. 4°. 10370. d. 35.

STEPHEN (D.) Gleanings in the North. pp. 219.
Haddington, 1891. 8°. 12316. l. 11.

CALABRIA. PAGANO (L.) Studii sulla
Calabria. *Napoli,* 1892, *etc.* 8°. 10132. c.

P.P. *Catanzaro.* Rivista calabrese di Storia e
Geografia. *Catanzaro,* 1893, *etc.* 8°.
P.P. 3556. l.

PASQUALE (L. de) Studio Calabro-comparativo
pp. 24. *Palermo,* 1892. 8°. 12902. de. 1. (6.)

CALAIS. DILLON (H. A.) *Viscount Dillon.*
Calais and the Pale. 1893. 4°. Archaeologia.
Vol. 53. 2096. g.

VOGUE (J.) Calais Harbour. pp. 156.
Havre, 1893. 8°. 10498. b. 15.

CALCAR. WOLFF (J. A.) Geschichte der
Stadt Calcar. pp. 154. *Frankf.* 1893. 4°.
10250. i. 7.

CALCULI. BURCKHARDT (E.) Atlas de
Cystoscopie. pp. 56. *Paris,* 1893. 8°.
7482. dd. 3.

EBSTEIN (W.) Über die experimentelle Erzeugung von Harnsteinen. pp. 137.
Wiesbaden, 1891. 8°. 7460. i. 5.

RIEDEL ( ) Erfahrungen über die Gallenstein-
krankheit. pp. 183. *Berl.* 1892. 8°. 7461. h. 23.

CALCULI—*continued.*

ROBERTS (*Sir* W.) Chemistry and Therapeutics of Uric Acid & Gravel. pp. 136. *Lond.* 1892. 8°.
7630. bbb. 16.

ROBSON (A. W. M.) Gall-stones and their treatment. pp. 285. 1892. 8°. Clinical Manuals.
2255. a. 35.

THOMPSON (*Sir* H.) Introduction to the Catalogue of the collection of Calculi removed by Sir H. Thompson. pp. 39. *Lond.* 1893, 8°.
7641. f. 27.

See also GENITO-URINARY ORGANS.

CALCULUS, Differential, Integral, etc.

BATTAGLINI (G.) Elementi di Calcolo infinitesimale. pp. 260. *Napoli,* 1889. 8°.
8535. dd. 8.

BEAUPAIN (J.) Sur quelques formules de calcul intégral. pp. 62. 1891. 8°. Ac. Brussels. *Académie.* Mémoires couronnés. Tom. 52.
Ac. 985/6.

BERGBOHM (J.) Neue Integrationsmethoden, *etc.* pp. 58. *Stuttg.* 1892. 8°.　　　　　Pam. 38.

—— Entwurf einer neuen Integralrechnung. pp. 66. *Leipz.* 1892. 8°.　　　　　Pam. 38.

BJÖRLING (C. F. E.) Lärobok i differential-kalkyl. pp. 366. *Lund,* 1893. 8°.　　8534. d. 37.

BÔCHER (M.) Ueber die Reihenentwickelungen der Potentialtheorie. pp. 258. *Leipz.* 1894. 8°.
8532. d. 34.

BYERLY (W. E.) Elements of the Differential Calculus. pp. 258. *Bost.* 1888. 8°. 8535. d. 14.

EDWARDS (J.) Differential Calculus. pp. 262. *Lond.* 1893. 8°.　　　　　　　8535. b. 51.

—— Integral Calculus. pp. 308. *Lond.* 1894. 8°.　　　　　　　　　　8534. df. 7.

GREENHILL (A. G.) Differential and Integral Calculus. pp. 455. *Lond.* 1891. 8°.
8533. de. 16.

GROTENDORST (N. C.) Beginselen der differentiaal- en integraalrekening. pp. 461. *Breda,* 1893. 8°.　　　　　　　8548. df. 47.

HAAG (P.) Cours de Calcul différentiel et intégral. pp. 612. *Paris,* 1893. 8°. 8535. dd. 16.

HARDY (A. S.) Elements of Differential and Integral Calculus. pp. 239. *Bost.* 1890. 8°.
8535. df. 13.

HARNACK (A.) Introduction to the study of Differential and Integral Calculus. pp. 404. *Lond.* 1891. 8°.　　　　　　8535. f. 37.

HOESCH (L.) Über die Koefficienten des Ausdrucks Δⁿ X, *etc.* pp. 22. *Berl.* 1888. 4°.
Pam. 38.

MILLER (T. H.) Introduction to Differential and Integral Calculus. pp. 88. *Lond.* 1891. 8°.
8535. aa. 22.

MUTH (P.) Grundlagen für die geometrische Anwendung der Invariantentheorie. pp. 131. *Leipz.* 1895. 8°.　　　　　　8535. i. 8.

RUCHONNET (C.) Éléments de calcul approximatif. pp. 79. *Lausanne,* 1887. 8°. 8535. df. 33.

STOLZ (O.) Grundzüge der Differential- und Integralrechnung. *Leipz.* 1893, *etc.* 8°.
8535. dd.

TAYLOR (J. M.) Elements of Differential and Integral Calculus. pp. 236. *Bost.* 1890. 8°.
8535. df. 23.

WILLIAMSON (B.) Elementary treatise on Differential Calculus. pp. 472. *Lond.* 1893. 8°.
2242. b. 31.

—— Elementary treatise on Integral Calculus. pp. 463. *Lond.* 1891. 8°.　2242. b. 32.

WYATT (M.) Introduction to Differential and Integral Calculus. pp. 98. *Rugby,* 1894. 8°.
8533 bb. 47.

See also MATHEMATICS.

CALCUTTA. DARMESTETER (J.) Calcutta. 1892. 4°. Les Capitales du Monde. No. 21.
10025. g.

KIPLING (R.) The City of Dreadful Night. pp. 108. *Allahabad,* 1891. 8°. 010057. cc. 18.

MITCHELL (E.) Thacker's guide book to Calcutta. pp. 247. *Calcutta,* 1890. 8°.　10058. a. 29.

CALDER, River. *See* AIRE AND CALDER.

CALDWELL, Idaho. CALDWELL. Caldwell, the Magic City. *Caldwell,* 1891. 8°. Pam. 86.

CALEDONIAN RAILWAY.
See RAILWAYS.

CALENDARS AND CHRONOLOGY.

BALCH (S. W.) History's misleading Chronology. pp. 8. 1893. 8°.　　　　　Pam. 4.

BERFRIED (E.) Alter und neuer immerwährender Kalender. *Mittelwalde-Schlesien,* 1892. 4°.
8563. aa. 30.

DAUMAX (V. A.) Révision et reconstitution de la chronologie. *Paris,* 1886, *etc.* 12°. 9008. aaa.

DIMBLEBY (J. B.) All Past Time by five lines of astronomical time. pp. 150. *Lond.* 1894. 8°.
8562. d. 38.

ENSOR (E. J.) A Chronological Chart. *Lond.* 1894. fol.　　　　　　　1850. d. 16.

EPHEM. The Era Calendar. *Birming.* 1884, *etc.* 32°.　　1881. a. 4. (67.)

—— Everybody's Almanac for 200 years. pp. 35. *Colombo,* 1891. 8°.　　　　P.P. 2575. r.

—— Perfect Calendar for every year of the Christian era. *N.Y.* 1891. 4°.　P.P. 2522. wb.

ESCYBI. Calendar for ten years from 1891 to 1900. pp. 40. *Lucknow,* 1892. 8°. 759. h. 13.

G., J. Weeks, Months and Years. pp. 13. 1895. 8°.　　　　　　　　Pam. 4.

GIRY (A.) Manuel de Diplomatique. pp. 944. *Paris,* 1894. 8°.　　　　　　2050. c.

GIRIŚACHANDRA TARKĀLANKĀRA and PRĀNANĀTHA SARASVATĪ. Chronological Tables, Christian, Bengalee, Moolkee, *etc.,* eras. 1764 to 1900. pp. 588. *Bhowanipore,* 1894. 8°.　759. h. 12.

GRANT (G. S.) Daily Record and Anniversary Calendar. pp. 416. *Lond.* 1895. 8°.
9009. aa. 26.

GRIFFITH (A.) The Cycle Calendar. *Lond.* 1892. 8°.　　　　　　　8562. e. 30.

JESUS CHRIST. Chronology of the World in its relation to the Advent of Christ. pp. 72. *Edinb.* 1894. 8°.　　　　　　8563. aaa. 42.

LACOINE (E.) Tables de concordance des dates des Calendriers arabe, copte, grégorien, israélite, julien, républicain, *etc.* pp. 64. *Paris,* 1891. 8°.
8562. ee. 14.

LECHNER (A.) Mittelalterliche Kalendarien in Bayern. pp. 286. *Freiburg,* 1891. 8°.
3475. dd. 13.

MACKENNA (J. T.) McKenna's Calendars. *N.Y.* 1891. 8°.　　　　　　8560. cc. 22.

MONTECATINUS (A.) Riforma del Calendario. 1582. pp. 12. *Argenta,* 1893. 8°.　Pam. 4.

PAGE (W. M.) New Light from old Eclipses; or, chronology corrected. pp. 590. *St. Louis,* 1890. 8°.　　　　　3226. de. 15.

PHILLIPS (D. H.) A perpetual English Calendar, 1800 to 2200. *Lond.* 1892. 8°.　Pam. 4.

RUSSOLOGUS. Le jour de l'an scientifique. pp. 8. *Paris,* 1889. 8°.　　　　Pam. 4.

TURCOLOGUS. La Turquie, le calendrier universel et le méridien initial de Jérusalem. pp. 7. *Paris,* 1888. 8°.　　　　　　Pam. 4.

TONDINI (C.) Sui vantaggi dell' adozione generale del Calendario Gregoriano. pp. 12. *Milano,* 1888. 8°.　　　　　　Pam. 4.

CAMBRAI—continued.

DIECKMEYER (A.) Die Stadt Cambrai. pp. 82.
Bielefeld, 1890. 8°.   10107. e. 12. (3.)

DURIEUX (A.) La défense nationale dans le
Cambresis. 1793–94. 1890. 8°. Ac. Cambray.
Société d'Émulation. Mémoires. Tom. 45.
                                                Ac. 307.

CAMBRIDGE, Town.

BOWES (R.) Catalogue of Books printed at or
relating to Cambridge. *Camb.* 1894. 8°.
                                    011900. ee. 34.

NEWTON (S.) Diary of S. Newton, Alderman of
Cambridge, 1662–1717. pp. 144.
Camb. 1890. 8°.   10826. g. 16.

SAINT MICHAEL, *Parish, Cambridge*. Register of
St. Michael's. pp. 213. 1891. 8°. Ac. Cam-
bridge. *Antiquarian Society*. Publications.
Octavo series. No. 25.   Ac. 5624.

WHITE (W.) Cambridge Visitor's Guide.
pp. 256. *Camb.* 1895. 8°.   10360. cc. 61.

University.

BOWES (R.) Catalogue of Books printed at or
relating to Cambridge. 2 pt. *Camb.* 1894. 8°.
                                    011900. ee. 34.

Ac. Cambridge. *University*. Graduati Cauta-
brigienses. 1800–84. pp. 682. *Camb.* 1884. 8°.
                                                2121. e.

—— Student's Guide to the University.
Camb. 1893. 8°.   8364. aaa.

CLARK (J. W.) Letters Patent of Elizabeth and
James the First addressed to the University of
Cambridge. pp. 70. *Camb.* 1892. 8°.
                                        8364. d. 44.

JONES (H. G.) Friends in Pencil. pp. 22.
Camb. 1893. obl. 4°.   1876. b. 22.

WILLIAMS (C. F. A.) Historical account of
Degrees in Music at Oxford and Cambridge.
pp. 167. *Lond.* 1894. 8°.   8367. bb. 8.

SATYANĀTHA (S.) Four years in an English
University. pp. 120. *Madras*, 1890. 8°.
                                        8366. aaa. 25.

SKENE (W. B.) Handbook of Acts affecting the
University of Cambridge in the sale and ad-
ministration of property. pp. 140.
Lond. 1894. 8°.   8367. e. 2.

MACKINDER (H. J.) University Extension, past,
present and future. pp. 144. *Lond.* 1891. 8°.
                                        8364. aa. 49.

ROBERTS (R. D.) Eighteen Years of University
Extension. pp. 129. *Camb.* 1891. 8°.
                                        8364. aaaa. 47.

P.P. *Cambridge*. Emmanuel College Magazine.
Camb. 1889–91. 8°.   P.P. 6119. ck.

—— The Caian. Magazine of Gonville and
Caius College. *Camb.* 1891, *etc.* 8°.
                                    P.P. 6119. cl.

SINKER (R.) Library of Trinity College, Cambridge. pp. 136. *Camb.* 1891. 8°. 11899. ee. 27.

See also EXAMINATIONS.

CAMBRIDGE, Massachusetts.

See HARVARD UNIVERSITY.

CAMBRIDGESHIRE. BOWES (R.) Cata-
logue of books printed at or relating to Cambridge. 2 pt. *Camb.* 1894. 8°.   11899. ff. 48.

CONYBEARE (J. W. E.) Guide to the County of
Cambridge. *Lond.* 1892. 8°.   10352. a. 67.

ESSEX. Murray's Handbook for Cambridgeshire,
etc. pp. 482. *Lond.* 1892. 8°.   2364. a. 13.

RYE (W.) Pedes Finium, Fines relating to the
County of Cambridge. pp. 196. 1891, 8°. Ac.
Cambridge. *Antiquarian Society*. Publications.
Octavo series. No. 26.   Ac. 5624.

CAMBRIDGESHIRE—continued.

CAMEL. LEONARD (A. G.) The Camel.
pp. 335. *Lond.* 1894. 8°.   07293. k. 14.

—— STEEL (J. H.) Manual of the Diseases
of the Camel. pp. 206. *Madras*, 1890. 8°.
                                        7294. ff. 8.

CAMEROON. JAEGER (H.) Kamerun und
Sudan. *Berl.* 1892, *etc.* 8°.   8027. c.

MORGEN (C.) Durch Kamerun von Süd nach
Nord. pp. 390. *Leipz.* 1893. 8°. 010096. f. 30.

ZINTGRAFF (E.) Nord-Kamerun. pp. 467.
Berl. 1895. 8°.   010096. i. 27.

See also AFRICA, *Colonisation* and *West:* GER-
MANY, *Colonies*.

CAMORRA. *See* NAPLES.

CAMPANOLOGY. *See* BELLS.

CAMPING OUT. MACDONELL (A. A.)
Camping out. pp. 153. 1893. 8°. BELL (E.)
Handbook of Athletic Sports.   2502. e.

CAMPOROSSO. ROSSI (F.) Il comune di
Camporosso. pp. 111. *Ventimiglia*, 1893. 8°.
                                    10132. b. 2.

CAMPSIE. CAMERON (J.) Parish of Campsie.
2 pt. *Kirkintilloch*, 1892. 8°.   4735. c. 31.

CAMPYLODISCUS. *See* DIATOMACEAE.

CANADA. [*See* note on page 1.]

See also AMERICA : BRITISH COLUMBIA : NEW
BRUNSWICK : NEWFOUNDLAND : NOVA SCOTIA :
ONTARIO : PRINCE EDWARD'S ISLAND : QUEBEC,
etc. etc.

Bibliography.

GAGNON (P.) Essai de bibliographie canadienne.
pp. 711. *Québec*, 1895. 8°.   11906. g. 1.

Army.

CANADA. *Militia*. Regulations and Orders for
the Militia. pp. 378. *Ottawa*, 1887. 16°.
                                        8831. e. 23.

—— Regulations for the Permanent Corps,
Active Militia. pp. 73. *Ottawa*, 1889. 8°.
                                    8831. e. 3. (I.)

—— Regulations for the Royal Schools of
Military Instruction. pp. 39.
Ottawa, 1887. 8°.   Pam. 2.

QUEBEC. *Royal Military College Club*. Reference Book, containing information respecting
the Royal Military College. pp. 64.
Quebec, 1892. 8°.   8831. e. 6.

SLATER (J.) Three Years under the Canadian
Flag as a cavalry soldier. pp. 240.
1893. 8°.   10803. e. 10.

BURNHAM (J. H.) Canadians in the Imperial
Naval and Military Service. pp. 240.
Toronto, 1891. 8°.   10883. b. 24.

Census 1891 and Statistics.

CANADA. Census of Canada, 1891.
Ottawa, 1891–93. 8°.   08225. g. 4.

—— Statistical Year Book of Canada.
Ottawa, 1890, *etc.* 8°.   8223. dg.

JOHNSON (G.) Graphic Statistics of Canada.
pp. 80. *Ottawa*, 1887. 8°.   8223. dh. 21.

Church of England in Canada.

LANGTRY (J.) History of the Church in Eastern
Canada. pp. 256. 1892. 8°. Colonial Church
Histories.   4421. dd.

Constitution and Government.

Ac. Toronto. *Canadian Institute*. Appeal on
the Rectification of Parliament. pp. 176.
Toronto, 1892. 8°.   8154. g. 26.

BOURINOT (J. G.) How Canada is governed.
pp. 344. *Boston*, 1895. 8°.   8154. bb. 27.

CANADA. Constitution, etc.—*continued.*

BOURINOT (J. G.) Parliamentary Government in Canada. 1892. 8°. Ac. United States. *Historical Association.* Annual Report, 1891.
Ac. 8504/2.

CHAPLEAU (J. A.) Constitution and Government of Canada. pp. 71. *Montreal,* 1894. 16°.
8154. a. 13.

COLBY (C. C.) Parliamentary Government in Canada. pp. 57. *Montreal,* 1886. 16°.
8154. aaa. 43.

HOUSTON (W.) Documents illustrative of the Canadian Constitution. pp. 338.
Toronto, 1891. 8°. 8154. e. 15.

HOWLAND (O. A.) The New Empire, *etc.* pp. 608. *Lond.* 1891. 8°. 9555. c. 2.

See also infra : Politics.

History.

For Early Voyages, *see also* AMERICA.

GAILLY DE TAURINES (C.) La Nation canadienne. Étude historique. pp. 338.
Paris, 1894. 12°. 10460. aa. 23.

KINGSFORD (W.) The History of Canada.
Lond. 1888, *etc.* 8°. 9555. ee. 7.

ROBERTSON (W. J.) Leading Facts of Canadian History. 1891. 8°. BUCKLEY, aft. FISHER (A. B.) High School History of England.
9503. c. 34.

TOUSSAINT (F. X.) Abrégé d'histoire du Canada. pp. 150. *Québec,* 1895. 12°. 9555. aa. 9.

Ac. Toronto. *Canadian Institute.* Transactions. *Toronto,* 1890, *etc.* 8°. Ac. 1885/3.

TORONTO. *Canadian Military Institute.* Selected Papers from the Transactions.
Toronto, 1891, *etc.* 8°. 8830. bbb.

BIBAUD (M.) Le Panthéon Canadien. Choix de biographies. pp. 320. *Montréal,* 1891. 8°.
010882. k. 9.

DAVIN (N. F.) The Irishman in Canada. pp. 692. *Lond.* 1887. 8°. 9555. eee. 14.

LE MOINE (J. M.) Maple Leaves. Canadian History. pp. 508. *Quebec,* 1894. 8°.
9555. eee. 18.

P.P. *Quebec.* La Canada-Français. Revue. 4 tom. *Quebec,* 1888–91. 8°. P.P. 6237. caa.

SULTE (B.) Pages d'histoire du Canada. pp. 471. *Montréal,* 1891. 8°. 9555. aaa. 30.

WINSOR (J.) Geographical Discovery in North America. 1537–1700. *Lond.* 1894. 8°.
9551. f. 11.

CARTIER (J.) Premier Voyage de J. Cartier au Canada. pp. 71. *Lévis,* 1890. 8°.
9004. gg. 24. (1.)

DIONNE (N. E.) La Nouvelle-France. 1540–1603. pp. 395. *Québec,* 1891. 8°. 9555. d. 3.

MACHAR (A. M.) Stories of New France. pp. 313. *Bost.* 1890. 8°. 9555. aaa. 22.

MYRAND (J. E.) 1690. Sir William Phips devant Québec. pp. 428. *Québec,* 1893. 8°.
9555. e. 11.

WINSOR (J.) The Struggle in America between England and France, 1697–1763. pp. 484. *Lond.* 1895. 8°. 9551. f. 12.

WILSON (J. G.) Lord Lovelace and the Second Canadian Campaign. pp. 28. *Wash.* 1892. 8°.
9551. k. 8. (3.)

CASGRAIN (H. R.) Lettres de la Cour de Versailles au Baron de Dieskau, *etc.* pp. 250. *Québec,* 1890. 8°. 9555. f. 3.

—— Extraits des archives des Ministères de la Marine et de la Guerre à Paris Canada. pp. 310. *Québec,* 1890. 8°. 9555. f. 2.

CANADA.—History – *continued.*

MONTCALM DE SAINT VÉRAN (L. J. de) *Marquis.* Journal du Marquis de Montcalm, 1756–59. pp. 626. *Québec,* 1895. 8°. 10661. i. 34.

—— Lettres du Marquis de Montcalm au Chevalier de Lévis. pp. 240. *Québec,* 1894. 8°.
10909. l. 12.

CASGRAIN (H. R.) Lettres et pièces militaires. 1756–60. pp. 367. *Québec,* 1891. 4°.
8824. k. 33.

LUCAS (F. W.) Appendiculæ Historicæ. pp. 216. *Lond.* 1891. 4°. 9555. h. 1.

MAURÈS DE MALARTIC (A. J. H. de) *Count.* Journal des campagnes au Canada, 1755–60. pp. 370. *Dijon,* 1890. 8°. 9555. eee. 15.

BRADLEY (A. G.) Wolfe. pp. 214. 1895. 8°. English Men of Action. 10803. bbb.

MICHAUX (A.) Portions of the Journal of A. Michaux, 1785–96. pp. 145. 1889. 8°. Ac. Philadelphia. *Philosophical Society.* Proceedings. Vol. 26. No. 129. Ac. 1830.

EDGAR (M.) Ten years of Upper Canada, 1805–15. pp. 389. *Lond,* 1891. 8°. 9555. e. 8.

GÉRIN-LAJOIE (A.) Dix Ans au Canada, 1840–50. pp. 619. *Québec,* 1888. 8°. 9555. f. 5.

DENT (J. C.) The Last Forty Years. 2 vol. *Toronto,* 1881. 4°. 9555. f. 7.

HINCKS (*Sir* F.) Reminiscences of Public Life. pp. 450. *Montreal,* 1884. 8°. 10825. bbb. 38.

HOWLAND (O. A.) The New Empire. pp. 608. *Lond.* 1891. 8°. 9555. c. 2.

DENT (J. C.) Story of the Upper Canadian Rebellion. 2 vol. *Toronto,* 1885. 4°.
9555. eee. 16.

RIEL (L. D.) La mort de Riel et la voix du sang. pp. 19. *Montréal,* 1885. 8°. Pam. 7.

COLLINS (J. E.) Life of Sir J. A. Macdonald. pp. 613. *Toronto,* 1891. 8°. 10815. eee. 14.

POPE (J.) Memoirs of Sir J. A. Macdonald. 2 vol. *Lond.* 1894. 8°. 10815. ee. 20.

History, *Ecclesiastical. See supra : Church of England :* ROMAN CATHOLIC CHURCH.

Immigration. *See infra : Topography.*

Indians. *See* INDIANS.

Law.

CRANKSHAW (J.) Practical guide to Police Magistrates and Justices. pp. 707.
Montreal, 1895. 8°. 06606. k. 3.

DANDURAND (R.) Manuel du juge de paix, *etc.* pp. 384. *Montréal,* 1891. 8°. 06606. f. 19.

PELISSIER (L. E.) Codes des Huissiers, Sherifs et Coroners. pp. 113. *Montréal,* 1891. 8°.
6606. a. 7.

See also LAW, *Criminal.*

North-west.

BEGG (A.) The Great Canadian North-west. pp. 135. *Montreal,* 1881. 8°. 10470. d. 32.

—— History of the North-west. 3 vol. *Toronto,* 1894, 95. 8°. 9555. ee. 11.

BOLTON (C. E.) Notes from letters written while lecturing in the North-west. pp. 15. *Camb., Mass.* 1892. Pam. 86.

CAMPBELL (J. G. E. H. D. S.) *Marquis of Lorne.* The Canadian North-west. pp. 20. *Ottawa,* 1881. 8°. Pam. 66.

CANADA. Pacific Railway and North-west Territories. pp. 32. *Ottawa,* 1886. 8°.
10408. cc. 34. (1.)

—— Emigration to North-western Canada. pp. 61. *Ottawa,* 1893. 8°. 10470. cc. 38.

—— Farming and Ranching in western Canada. pp. 40. *Ottawa,* 1893. 8°. Pam. 1.

CANADA.—North-West.—*continued.*

CANADA. Western Canada. How to get there, how to select lands. pp. 40. *Lond.* 1891. 8°.
Pam. 86.

—— Western Canada and its great resources. pp. 38. *Ottawa*, 1893. 8°.   Pam. 86.

DIONNE (N. E.) États-Unis, Manitoba et Nord-Ouest. pp. 184. *Québec*, 1882. 8°. 10409. a. 20.

DUGAS (G.) Un Voyageur des Pays d'en Haut. pp. 142. *Montréal*, 1890. 8°.   10470. f. 24.

PIKE (W.) The Barren Ground of Northern Canada. pp. 300. *Lond.* 1892. 8°. 10470. h. 25.

RITCHIE (P. R.) Manitoba and the North-west Territories. pp. 52. *Ottawa*, 1892. 8°. Pam. 86.

SOMERSET (H. S.) The Land of the Muskeg. pp. 248. *Lond.* 1895. 8°.   10413. k. 27.

See also infra: Topography: ALBERTA: ALGOMA: ASSINIBOIA: ATHABASCA: SASKATCHEWAN.

Politics.

BOURINOT (J. G.) Canada and the United States. 1891. 8°. Ac. United States. *Historical Association.* Papers. Vol. 5. Ac. 8504.

BOUTHILLIER-CHAVIGNY (C. de) *Viscount.* Justice aux Canadiens-français ! pp. 126. *Montréal*, 1890. 8°.   8154. d. 24.

CANADA. Under which Flag ? The great question for Canada. pp. 31. *Providence*, 1893. 8°.
8154. a. 12.

CHOUINARD (H. J. J. B.) Fête nationale des Canadiens-français. 1881-9. pp. 552. *Québec*, 1890. 8°.   9930. ccc. 20.

CONAN (L.) Si les Canadiennes le voulaient ! pp. 59. *Québec*, 1886. 8°.   Pam. 66.

DAVIN (N. F.) Dual Language and Federal Government. pp. 12. *Regina*, 1890. 8°.
Pam. 66.

—— Speech on the Redistribution Bill. pp. 15. *Regina*, 1892. 8°.   Pam. 66.

—— Speech on Charges against Sir A. Caron. pp. 7. *Ottawa*, 1892. 8°.   Pam. 66.

DESJARDINS (L. G.) Considérations sur l'Annexion. pp. 58. *Québec*, 1891. 8°.   Pam. 66.

DOUGLAS (J.) Canadian Independence, Annexation and Imperial Federation. pp. 114. *N.Y.* 1894. 8°.   8176. bbb.

FAUCHER DE SAINT-MAURICE (N. H. É.) Resterons-nous Français. pp. 136. *Québec*, 1890. 8°.
8051. df. 25.

LAURIER (W.) Wilfrid Laurier on the Platform. pp. 624. *Quebec*, 1890. 8°. 012301. f. 17.

MARMIER (X.) Les États-Unis et le Canada. pp. 236. *Tours*, 1886. 8°.   10408. i. 14.

MERCIER (H.) L'avenir du Canada. pp. 91. *Montréal*, 1893. 8°.   Pam. 66.

PRINCE (J. E.) La politique Cartier-Macdonald. pp. 29. *Québec*, 1894. 8°.   Pam. 66.

ROYAL (J.) Le Canada, république ou colonie. pp. 105. *Montréal*, 1894. 8°. 8154. aaa. 45.

SMITH (G.) Canada and the Canadian Question. pp. 325. *Lond.* 1891. 8°.   8154. d. 22.

—— Loyalty, Aristocracy and Jingoism. pp. 96. *Toronto*, 1891. 8°.   8154. aa. 16.

See also supra: Constitution: QUEBEC.

Roman Catholic Church in Canada.
See ROMAN CATHOLIC CHURCH.

Sport. *See* SPORT, *America.*

Statistics. *See supra: Census.*

Topography.

GRESWELL (W. P.) Geography of the Dominion of Canada. pp. 154. *Oxf.* 1891. 8°.
10470. dd. 25.

CANADA.—Topography—*continued.*

LYDE (L. W.) Elementary Geography of British North America. pp. 88. *Lond.* 1892. 8°.
10470. aa. 42.

BAEDEKER (C.) The Dominion of Canada. Handbook. pp. 254. *Leipsic*, 1894. 8°.
2352. a.

CANADA. Canada as a field for emigration. pp. 40. *Coventry*, 1891. 8°.   Pam. 86.

—— Official information relating to the Dominion of Canada. pp. 24. *Lond.* 1892. 8°.
Pam. 86.

—— Letters from Settlers in Canada, 1888-90. pp. 8. *Lond.* 1890. 8°.   Pam. 86.

—— Letters from Settlers in Canada, 1891-92. pp. 16. *Lond.* 1892. 8°.   10470. dd. 30. (8.)

—— Official handbook of information relating to the Dominion of Canada. pp. 88. *Ottawa*, 1893. 8°.   10470. d. 31.

—— Where to go to better yourself ! pp. 24. 1893. 8°.   Pam. 86.

—— Summer Resorts reached by the Grand Trunk Railway. pp. 40. *Toronto*, 1893. 4°.
Pam. 86.

—— The Maritime Provinces. pp. 122. *Lond.* 1892. 8°.   10470. dd. 30. (10.)

ROBERTS (C. G. D.) Canadian Guide-book. 2 vol. *Lond.* 1892. 8°.   10470. aa. 41.

BLACKWOOD (H. G.) *Marchioness of Dufferin and Ava.* My Canadian Journal 1872-8. pp. 417. *Lond.* 1891. 8°.   10470. dd. 28.

BOURGET (P. C. J.) Outre-Mer. 2 tom. *Paris*, 1895. 12°.   10409. aa. 41.

CHEVILLARD (V.) Paysages canadiens. pp. 225. *Paris*, 1891. 8°.   10470. bbb. 41.

CRAIB (A.) America and the Americans. pp. 325. *Paisley*, 1892. 8°.   10409. bb. 37.

CROONENBERGHS (C.) Trois Ans dans l'Amérique Septentrionale. pp. 371. *Paris*, 1892. 8°.
10470. h. 30.

DECKERT (E.) Die neue Welt. pp. 488. *Berl.* 1892. 8°.   10413. k. 20.

DEMANCHE (G.) Au Canada. pp. 192. *Paris*, 1890. 8°.   10460. ff. 16.

ELKINGTON (W. M.) Five Years in Canada. pp. 138. *Lond.* 1895. 8°.   10470. f. 36.

FRASER (J.) Canadian Pen and Ink Sketches. pp. 391. *Montreal*, 1890. 8°.   10470. dd. 36.

GORDON (I. M.) *Countess of Aberdeen.* Through Canada with a Kodak. pp. 249. *Edinb.* 1893. 8°.   10470. b. 34.

GUEST (*Lady* T.) A Round Trip in North America. pp. 270. *Lond.* 1895. 8°.
10408. dd. 15.

HOME (R.) Columbian Sketches. pp. 370. *Dublin*, 1895. 8°.   10408. bbb. 33.

HUGHES (T.) Vacation Rambles. pp. 405. *Lond.* 1895. 8°.   010026. h. 1.

JOHNSTONE (C. L.) Winter and summer Excursions in Canada. pp. 213. *Lond.* 1894. 8°.
10470. dd. 35.

MONCK (F. E. O.) My Canadian Leaves. pp. 367. *Lond.* 1891. 8°.   10470. f. 33.

MOORE (T.) Canada revisited. 1879-93. pp. 31. *Lond.* 1893. 8°.   Pam. 86.

PARKIN (G. R.) The Great Dominion. pp. 251. *Lond.* 1895. 8°.   10460. bb. 26.

RALPH (J.) On Canada's Frontier. pp. 325. *N.Y.* 1892. 8°.   10470. h. 29.

RICKMAN (T. M.) Notes of a visit to Canada and the States. pp. 54. *Lond.* 1886. 8°.
10470. c. 35.

CANADA.—Topography—continued.

ROUTHIER (A. B.) De Québec à Victoria.
pp. 392. *Québec,* 1893. 8°.   10470. dd. 31.

S., A. A summer trip to Canada. pp. 112.
Lond. 1885. 8°.   10409. aaa. 48.

SCRIVENER (S.) Off to Canada! pp. 8.
Lond. 1890. 8°.   8282. ff. 9. (11.)

SLADEN (D. B. W.) On the Cars and Off.
pp. 447. *Lond.* 1895. 8°.   10460. ff. 21.

VINCENT (E. G.) Newfoundland to Cochin China.
pp. 374. *Lond.* 1892. 8°.   10024. c. 23.

WEBB (W. S.) California and Alaska and over
the Canadian Pacific Railway. pp. 268.
N.Y. 1891. 8°.   10409. d. 20.

See also supra: North-West: SPORT.

Trade and Finance.

CORNWELL (W. C.) Currency and the Banking
Law of Canada. pp. 86. *N.Y.* 1895. 4°.
   6606. aaa. 8.

DAVIN (N. F.) The New Tariff: a speech.
pp. 12. *Ottawa,* 1894. 8°.   Pam. 45.

—— Speech on the Budget, July 1891.
Regina, 1891. 8°.   8139. bb. 51. (7.)

—— Speech on the Budget. 1892. pp. 8.
Regina, 1892. 8°.   Pam. 66.

AMYOT (G.) La Protection au Canada. pp. 58.
Lévis. 1895. 8°.   08226. h. 26.

MAC LEAN (S. J.) Tariff History of Canada.
pp. 53. 1895. 8°. ASHLEY (W. J.) Toronto
University Studies. No. 4.   8009. i. 24.

TRACT. Tract for the times on the situation.
pp. 14. *Toronto,* 1890. 8°.   Pam. 66.
See also supra : Census.

CANADIAN DIALECT, French. BUIES
(A.) Anglicismes et Canadianismes. pp. 106.
Québec, 1888. 12°.   12952. bb. 38.

CLAPIN (S.) Dictionnaire Canadien-Français.
pp. 388. *Montréal,* 1894. 8°.   12952. cc. 32.

LEGENDRE (N.) La langue française au Canada.
pp. 177. *Québec,* 1890. 8°.   12954. ccc. 2.

LUSIGNAN (A.) À la Presse française du Canada.
Fautes à corriger. pp. 179. *Québec,* 1890. 8°.
   12952. bbb. 42.

CANADIAN LITERATURE, English.
SLADEN (B. D. W.) Younger American Poets.
1830–1890. pp. 666. *Lond.* 1891. 8°.
   11687. e. 42.
*See also AMERICAN LITERATURE: ENGLISH
LITERATURE.*

CANADIAN PACIFIC RAILWAY.
See RAILWAYS.

CANALS. Ac. *Binnenschifffahrts-Congress.*
Berathungen und Beschlusse des Congresses.
1886. *Wien,* 1887. 8°.   Ac. 2206.

—— Referate über die dem Congresse zur Be-
rathung gestellten Fragen. *Frankf.* 1888. 8°.
   Ac. 2206.

—— Troisième Congrès, 1888. Rapports des
délégués français. pp. 371. *Paris,* 1890. 8°.
   08235. h. 16.

—— Quatrième Congrès, 1890. Rapports des
délégués français. pp. 403. *Paris,* 1892. 8°.
   08235. h. 29.

BOWES (I.) Railways and Waterways. Stephenson and De Lesseps. pp. 62. *Manch.* 1893. 8°.
   08235. f. 31.

BROWNE (J. H. B.) Railway and Canal Traffic
Act 1888. pp. 191. *Manch.* 1890. 8°. 08235. f. 15.

JEANS (J. S.) Waterways and Water Transport
in different countries. pp. 507.
Lond. 1890. 8°.   08235. f. 10.

LEHMAN (E.) Paris—portes de Saint-Ouen et de
Clichy—port de mer. pp. 22. *Paris,* 1890. 8°.
   8708. l. 7. (4.)

CANALS—continued.

FRÉMY (L.) Société pour l'éxécution d'une voie
navigable entre Nantes et Orléans. pp. 12.
Nantes, 1894. fol.   Pam. 76.

LIBAUDIÈRE (F.) Conférence sur le canal latéral
à la Loire de Nantes à Orléans. pp. 15.
Nantes, 1894. 8°.   Pam. 76.

PICARD (A.) Traité des eaux. Droit, *etc.* 4 tom.
Paris, 1890. 8°.   5403. g. 7.

TORONTO. *Deep Waterways Convention.* Pro-
ceedings of the Convention. pp. 108.
Toronto, 1894. 8°.   8235. h. 56.
*See also ENGINEERING: MANCHESTER SHIP CANAL:
NICARAGUA : NORTH SEA AND BALTIC CANAL :
PANAMA : SUEZ CANAL : TRANSPORTATION.*

CANARESE LANGUAGE. KITTEL (F.)
Kannada-English Dictionary. pp. 1752.
Mangalore, 1894. 4°.   12907. ff. 21.

RAJAGOPĀLA SETTI. Telugu, Canarees, Tamil,
English and Hindustani Vocabulary.
pt. 3. pp. 62. *Bellary,* 1887. 8°.   760. c. 9.

HANAMANTA GOVINDA JOSI. Samati-Sangraha,
collection of Canarese Proverbs. pp. 52.
Belgaum, 1894. 8°.   14176. d. 44.

AIMAN (S.) Popular Canarese Proverbs. pp. 22.
Mangalore, 1894. 12°.   14176. d. 43.

CANARY, Bird. BETTS (W. H.) The Pet
Canary. pp. 135. *Lond.* 1895. 8°. 7293. cc. 36.

COMMON SENSE. Common Sense of Canary Rearing. pp. 77. *Lond.* 1892. 16°.   Pam. 42.

GOULD (J. S.) My Canary Book. pp. 108.
Lond. 1894. 8°.   7293. bbb. 39.

RUSS (C.) Canary Birds. pp. 132. *Lond.* 1891. 8°.
   7285. a. 47.

SCHMID (J. C. v.) Il Canarin, jeu il Famiglia d'Er-
lau. pp. 52. *Malta,* 1894. 8°. 11599. b. 41. (5.)

WALLACE (R. L.) The Canary Book. pp. 429.
Lond. 1893. 8°.   07293. i. 16.
See also ANIMALS, Domestic : BIRDS, Cage Birds.

CANARY ISLANDS. ARCE MAZÓN (I. de)
El archipiélago Canario. pp. 53.
Madrid, 1886. 8°.   Pam. 89.

BROWN (A. S.) Madeira and the Canary Islands.
pp. 267. *Lond.* 1894. 8°.   10161. aaa. 19.

ELLERBECK (J. H. T.) Madeira and the Canary
Islands. pp. 31. *Liverp.* 1891. 8°.   Pam. 89.

—— A Guide to the Canary Islands. pp. 67.
Lond. 1892. 8°.   10095. a. 2.

LEE (H.) Madeira and the Canary Islands.
Liverp. 1888. 8°.   10095. bbb. 4.

LE MAIRE (J. J.) Voyage to the Canaries. pp. 76.
1887. 8°. Bibliotheca Curiosa. 012202. de. 40.

LOEHER (F. v.) Geschichte der Germanen auf
den Kanarischen Inseln. pp. 603.
München, 1895. 8°.   9061. d. 28.

MILLARES (A.) Historia de las Islas Canarias.
Las Palmas, 1893, *etc.* 8°.   9061. h.

OSSUNA Y VAN DEN HEEDE (M. de) La
Inscripción de Anaga, Tenerife. pp. 51.
Santa Cruz, 1889. 8°.   Pam. 3.

PEREZ (G. V.) Orotava as a health-resort. pp. 40.
Lond. 1893. 8°.   10096. bbb. 2.

PÉREZ DEL TORO (F.) España en el Noroeste de
África. pp. 288. *Madrid,* 1892. 8°. 8027. aa. 9.

QUINTANA Y LEON (J. de) La capital de la provincia de Canarias. pp. 320.
Gran-Canaria, 1882. 8°.   06606. f. 20.

ROTHPLETZ (A.) Die marinen Ablagerungen auf
Gran Canaria. 1891. 8°. Ac. Berlin. *Geolo-
gische Gesellschaft.* Zeitschrift. Bd. 42. Heft 4.
   Ac. 3137.

TAYLOR (J. C.) Health-Resorts of the Canary
Islands. pp. 94. *Lond.* 1893, 8°. 07686. k. 6.

CANARY ISLANDS—*continued.*

VERNEAU (R.) Cinq années de séjour aux Iles Canaries. pp. 412. *Paris*, 1891, 8°.
010096. i. 12.

WHITFORD (J.) The Canary Islands as a winter resort. pp. 150. *Lond.* 1890. 8°. 10097. cc. 16.

STUART (J. P. C.) *Marquis of Bute.* On the ancient Language of the natives of Teneriffe. pp. 54. *Lond.* 1891. 8°. Pam. 47.

See also LEPIDOPTERA: WATERING-PLACES, *etc.*

CANCALE. TREBUCHET (L.) La Baie de Cancale. pp. 160. *Paris*, 1888. 8°. 010171. c. 12.

CANCER. ALLINGHAM (H. W.) Colotomy for cancer. pp. 199. *Lond.* 1892. 8°. 07482. cc. 7.

BAMBER (H. K.) Cancer: its nature and treatment. pp. 31. *Lond.* 1894. 8°. 7620. a. 21.

BRUNON (R.) Enquête sur le cancer en Normandie. pp. 27. *Rouen*, 1893. 8°. 7305. f. 5. (5.)

BUTLIN (H. T.) On Cancer of the Scrotum in Chimney-Sweeps and others. pp. 56. *Lond.* 1892. 8°. 7641. bbb. 15.

BUCHER (R.) Beiträge zur Lehre vom Carcinom. 1893. 8°. ZIEGLER (E.) Beiträge zur pathologischen Anatomie. Bd. 14. 7441. ccc. 18.

CLARKE (J. J.) Cancer considered in relation to the Sporozoa. pp. 97. *Lond.* 1893. 8°. 7640. aa. 27.

CRITZMAN (D.) Le Cancer. pp. 167. 1894. 8°. Encyclopédie des aide-mémoire. 8709. g.

FAYARD (J.) Des Indications opératoires dans le Cancer du Rectum. pp. 62. *Lyon*, 1891. 8°. 07305. k. 13. (1.)

GOWAN (P.) Cancer: its nature and causes. pp. 83. *Lond.* 1895. 8°. 7630. b. 22.

—— Painless and successful Treatment of Cancer. pp. 15. *Lond.* 1894. 8°. 7306. c. 25. (8.)

HAUSER (G.) Das Cylinderepithel- Carcinom des Magens. pp. 268. *Jena*, 1890. 8°. 7620. f. 6.

HAVILAND (A.) Influence of Clays and Limestones on Medical Geography, illustrated by the geographical distribution of Cancer among females. pp. 16. *Lond.* 1891. 8°. Pam. 39.

JESSETT (F. B.) Cancer of the Mouth, tongue and œsophagus. pp. 183. *Lond.* 1892. 8°. 7616. f. 6.

—— Lectures on Cancer of the Uterus. pp. 80. *Lond.* 1894. 8°. 07581. df. 22.

KENNEDY (S.) Is Cancer Curable? Mattei v. the Knife. pp. 167. *Lond.* 1891. 8°. 7481. aaa. 32.

NEWMAN (D.) Malignant disease of the Throat and Nose. pp. 213. *Edinb.* 1892. 8°. 7616. f. 7.

RIEFFEL (H.) De quelques points relatifs aux Cancers du sein chez la femme. pp. 106. *Paris*, 1890. 8°. 7630. f. 17.

SNOW (H. L.) A Treatise, practical and theoretic on Cancers. pp. 384. *Lond.* 1893. 8°. 7630. c. 16.

—— Conditions of radical cure in Cancer. pp. 63 *Lond* 1895. 8°. 7616. a. 50.

—— Proclivity of Women to cancerous Diseases. pp. 58. *Lond.* 1891. 8°. 7581. c. 14.

SUTTON (J. B.) Tumours innocent and malignant. pp. 511. *Lond.* 1893. 8°. 7630. e. 18.

VOPELIUS ( ) Carcinosis, ein neues Krankheitsbild. pp. 37. *München*, 1895. 8°. Pam. 39.

WILLIAMS (W. R.) Monograph on Diseases of the Breast. pp. 572. *Lond.* 1894. 8°. 7616. i. 14.

CANDLES. CARPENTER (W. L.) Treatise on the manufacture of Soap and Candles. pp. 446. *Lond.* 1895. 8°. 07944. e. 53.

LEFEVRE (J.) Savons et Bougies. pp. 424. *Paris*, 1894. 12°. 07944. c. 45.

CANDLES—*continued.*

WATT (A.) Art of Soap-making. Appendix on candle-making. pp. 310. *Lond.* 1895, 8°. 07944. cc. 19.

See also LIGHTING.

CANDOLLEA. MUELLER (F. v.) Iconography of Candolleaceous Plants. *Melbourne*, 1892, etc. 4°. 7029. i.

CANNES. BLANC (H.) Advice to visitors to Cannes. pp. 42. *Lond.* 1893. 8°. 07686. e. 5.

PINATEL (P.) Quatre siècles de l'histoire de Cannes. pp. 245. *Cannes*, 1892. 12°. 10170. b. 3.

CANNIBALISM. BERGEMANN (P.) Die Verbreitung der Anthropophagie. pp. 53. *Bunzlau*, 1893. 8°. 10007. d. 8.

See also ANTHROPOLOGY: ETHNOLOGY.

CANNING INDUSTRY. *See* FOOD.

CANNON. *See* GUNNERY: MILITARY SCIENCE.

CANNSTATT. BECK (C. H.) Cannstatt und die neue Neckarbrücke. pp. 91. *Cannstatt*, 1893. 8°. 10255. h. 5.

CANOEING. *See* ROWING.

CANON, Biblical. *See* CHRISTIANITY.

CANON LAW. *See* LAW, *Ecclesiastical.*

CANONSLEIGH. ELWORTHY (F. T.) Canonsleigh. pp. 23. 1892. 4°. 10351. g. 32. (2.)

CANTABRIAN MOUNTAINS. CANTABRIA. De Cantabria. *Santander*, 1890. 4°. 10161. f. 11.

CANTERBURY, City and Cathedral. CARTWRIGHT, aft. ADY (J.) The Pilgrims' Way from Winchester to Canterbury. pp. 157. *Lond.* 1893. 8°. 10349. h. 32.

FOLKESTONE. Handbook to Canterbury, etc. *Folkestone*, 1894. 8°. 10350. aaa. 55.

HERNE BAY. Illustrated Guide to Canterbury, etc. pp. 108. *Herne Bay*, 1892. 8°. 10351. b. 69.

PLOMER (H. R.) Account of the Records of Canterbury. pp. 26. *Canterbury*, 1892. 8°. Pam. 6.

SMALL (E. M.) The Canterbury Cricket Week. pp. 151. *Canterbury*, 1891. 8°. 7912. a. 7.

CANTERBURY CATHEDRAL. Historical Records in Canterbury Cathedral. *Canterbury*, 1894. fol. 1865. c. 9. (14.)

AUGUSTINE, *Saint.* Account of the History of St. Augustine's Monastery. pp. 37. *Canterbury*, 1893. 8°. 4705. b. 46. (6.)

ROBINSON (C. H.) S. Augustine's, Canterbury. pp. 7. *Lond.* 1890. 8°. Pam. 29.

GEORGE, *Saint, Church of.* Register Booke of the Parish of St. George, Canterbury. pp. 304. *Canterbury*, 1891. 8°. 9916. cc. 3.

ROUTLEDGE (C. F.) History of St. Martin's Church, Canterbury. pp. 189. *Lond.* 1891. 8°. 4707. aaaa. 24.

PAUL. *Saint, Church of.* Register Book of St. Pauls, Canterbury. pp. 369. *Canterbury*, 1893. 8°. 9916. cc. 10.

CANTERBURY. *Wallon Church.* Registers of the Wallon Church, Canterbury. 1891, etc. 8°. Ac. London. *Huguenot Society.* Publications. Vol. 5, etc. Ac. 2073/4.

Diocese.

FOWLER (M.) Some Archbishops of Canterbury. pp. 222. *Lond.* 1895. 8°. 4429. dd. 9.

P.P. *Canterbury.* Canterbury Diocesan Gazette. *Canterbury*, 1892, etc. 8°. P.P. 344. b.

See also ENGLAND, *History, Ecclesiastical.*

CANTICLES. BLACKWOOD (*Sir* S. A.) Te Deum Laudamus. Addresses. pp. 127. *Lond.* 1892. 8°.   3475. aaa. 74.

LIDDON (H. P.) The Magnificat. Sermons. pp. 111. *Lond.* 1891. 8°.   4466. d. 13.

CANTON. HONGKONG. *Steamboat Company.* Information of general interest to travellers. Canton. pp. 21. *Hongkong,* 1893. 12°. Pam. 88.

HURLEY (R. C.) Tourists' Guide to Canton. pp. 87. *Hongkong,* 1895. 8°.   10057. aaa. 9.

KERR (J. G.) The Canton Guide. pp. 41. *Hongkong,* 1889. 8°.   010057. ee. 5. (7.)

For the Canton Dialect, *see* CHINESE LANGUAGE.

CAOUTCHOUC. *See* GUTTAPERCHA.

CAPE BRETON. BOURINOT (J. G.) Historical account of Cape Breton. pp. 183. *Montreal,* 1892. 4°.   10470. i. 16.

O'BRIEN (C.) *R.C. Archbishop of Halifax.* Mémoire sur les Missions du Cap-Breton, *etc.* pp. 269. *Québec,* 1895. 8°.   8765. cc. 30.

See also NOVA SCOTIA.

CAPE COD. THOREAU (H. D.) Cape Cod. pp. 252. *Boston,* 1892. 8°.   10408. de. 13.

See also MASSACHUSETTS.

CAPE OF GOOD HOPE: CAPE-TOWN.

Church of England.

WIRGMAN (A. T.) History of the English Church in S. Africa. pp. 276. *Lond.* 1895. 8°.   4744. bb. 11.

P.P. *Cape Town.* The Cape Church Monthly. *Cape Town,* 1892, *etc.* 8°.   P.P. 910. fh.

History, etc.

CAPE OF GOOD HOPE. Abstract of Debates and Resolutions of the Council of Policy, 1651–81. pp. 233. *Cape Town,* 1881. 8°.   8154. bbb. 31.

LEITH (G.) Metrical outline of Cape History. pp. 46. *Cape Town,* 1894. 8°.   Pam. 28.

REES (W. L.) Life of Sir G. Grey. 2 vol. *Lond.* 1892. 8°.   10817. dd. 9.

MARTINEAU (J.) Life of Sir B. Frere. 2 vol. *Lond.* 1895. 8°.   10816. cc. 27.

CAPE OF GOOD HOPE. *Parliament.* Debates, 1891, *etc.* *Cape Town,* 1891, *etc.* 8°.   8154. g.

—— *Afrikaner Bond.* Twaalfde Bestuurs Vergadering van den Afr. Bond. pp. 40. *Paarl,* 1894. 8°.   8154. b. 8.

See also AFRICA, *South :* ENGLAND, *Colonies.*

Law.

FOSTER (J.) Practice of the Deeds Registry Office of the Cape. pp. 120. *Johannesburg,* 1892. 8°.   06606. f. 11.

P.P. *Graham's Town.* Cape Law Journal. *Grahamstown,* 1887, *etc.* 8°.   P.P. 1351. g.

TENNANT (H.) Manual for the Guidance of Justices of the Peace. pp. 236. *Cape Town,* 1891. 8°.   06606. f. 9.

VAN ZYL (C. H.) Judicial Practice of the Colony. pp. 674. *Capetown,* 1893. 8°.   06606. f. 16.

See also LAW REPORTS.

Topography.

CAPE TOWN. Guide to Cape Town. pp. 131. *Cape Town,* 1891. 8°.   10097. a. 33.

—— Capetown Visitors' Guide. pp. 48. *Capetown,* 1891. 24°.   Pam. 89.

—— Cape Town Characteristics. pp. 31. *Cape Town,* 1892. 4°.   Pam. 89.

MARTIN (A.) Life on an Ostrich Farm. pp. 288. *Lond.* 1891. 8°.   010096. c. 40.

P.P. *Cape Town.* Cape Illustrated Magazine. *Cape Town,* 1890, *etc.* 8°.   P.P. 6231. bb.

CAPE OF GOOD HOPE.—Topography —*continued.*

P.P. *Cape Town.* Post Office Guide. *Cape Town,* 1892, *etc.* 8°.   P.P. 2579. o.

UITENHAGE. Guide to Uitenhage. pp. 24. *Uitenhage,* 1894. 8°.   Pam. 89.

See also AFRICA, *South :* GRAHAMSTOWN ; GRIQUA-LAND, *West.*

Trade, etc.

INNES (A. R.) Cape customs guide. pp. 79. *Cape Town,* 1890. 8°.   8244. de. 33.

CAPILLARITY. POINCARÉ (H.) Capillarité. pp. 189. *Paris,* 1895. 8°.   8535. g. 44.

CAPITAL AND LABOUR.

See also AGRICULTURE : CHARITIES : COOPERATION : FACTORIES : INDUSTRIES : MONEY : PAUPERISM : POLITICAL ECONOMY : PRICES : SOCIALISM : SOCIAL SCIENCE : TRADE.

Pt. I. General.

AVENEL (G. d') La Fortune privée à travers sept siècles. pp. 411. *Paris,* 1895. 12°.   08226. f. 27.

COPE (R.) The Distribution of Wealth. pp. 364. *Phila.* 1890. 8°.   08207. g. 10.

CUNNINGHAM (W.) Use and abuse of money. pp. 219. 1891. 8°. University Extension Manuals.   12204. f.

HOPKINS (A. A.) Wealth and Waste. pp. 274. *N.Y.* 1895. 8°.   08207. cc. 24.

HOBSON (J. A.) Evolution of modern Capitalism. pp. 388. 1894. 8°. Contemporary Science Series. Vol. 25.   8709. i.

HOGG (J.) Fortunes made in Business. pp. 406. *Lond.* 1891. 8°.   08229. de. 39.

JANNET (C.) Le Capital et la Spéculation. pp. 607. *Paris,* 1892. 8°.   8277. h. 38.

JOSEPH. Plan to revive the Patriarch Joseph's War on Capital. pp. 16. *Lond.* 1891. 8°.   08276. f. 20. (7.)

LEVASSEUR (É.) La Population et la Richesse. 1891. 8°. Ac. Paris. *Conservatoire des Arts.* Annales. Sér 2. Tom. 3. Fasc. 2. Ac. 4415.

LLOYD (H. D.) Wealth against Commonwealth. pp. 573. *Lond.* 1894. 8°.   8282. cc. 46.

LORIA (A.) Analisi della proprietà capitalista. 2 vol. *Torino,* 1889. 8°.   08227. f. 12.

MARX (C.) Das Kapital. *Hamb.* 1890, *etc.* 8°.   08207. g. 4.

AVELING (E. B.) The Students' Marx. pp. 180. *Lond.* 1892. 8°.   08276. c 25.

BRENTANO (L.) Meine Polemik mit Karl Marx. pp. 28. *Berl.* 1890. 8°.   08276. k. 4. (9.)

MEYER (R.) Der Capitalismus fin de siècle. pp. 487. *Wien,* 1894. 8°.   08276. h. 53.

MILLIONAIRES. Millionaires and how they became so. pp. 102. *Lond.* 1884. 8°.   8228. aaaa. 19. (1.)

NOVICOW (J.) Les Gaspillages des sociétés modernes. pp. 344. *Paris,* 1894. 8°.   08276. h. 62.

PASTOR (W.) Vom Kapitalismus zur Einzelarbeit. pp. 111. *Berlin,* 1892. 8°. 8277. b. 68.

PATTEN (S. N.) Consumption of Wealth. pp. 70. 1889. 8°. Ac. Philadelphia. *University* Publications. Pol. Econ. Series. No. 4.   Ac. 2692. p.

RANSOME (J. S.) Capital at Bay. pp. 24. *Lond.* 1892. 8°.   8277. de. 30. (14.)

ARBEITERFREUND. Die Arbeiterfrage. pp. 50. *Pilsen,* 1893. 8°.   8282. ff. 8. (14.)

CAPITAL, etc.—General—continued.

MOLINARI (G. de) Les Bourses du Travail.
pp. 335. *Paris*, 1893. 12°. 08276. g. 58.

MORRIS (A.) Discussions on Labour Questions.
pp. 64. *Lond.* 1893. 8°. 8277. de. 56.

NUNQUAM. Merrie England. pp. 101.
Lond. 1894. 4°. 8276. c. 86.

NEMO. Labour and Luxury. A reply to "Merrie England." pp. 191. *Lond.* 1895. 8°.
08275. f. 27.

O'BRIEN (J. B.) The Rise and progress of Human Slavery, etc. pp. 148. *Lond.* 1865. 8°.
08276. i. 22.

PARTHUM (F. v.) Unsere Zukunft. pp. 80.
Prag, 1893. 8°. 08276. i. 26.

PASTOR (P.) Obreros y burgueses. 3 pt.
Madrid, 1891, 92. 8°. 08276. f. 76.

P.P. *London.* The Economic Review.
Lond. 1891, etc. 8°. P.P. 1423. ad.

P.P. *Manchester.* The Labour Annual.
Manch. 1895, etc. 8°. P.P. 2502. n.

—— *New York.* The Social Economist.
N.Y. 1891, etc. 8°. P.P. 1423. ef.

PHILLIPS (W. A.) Labour, Land and Law.
pp. 471. *N.Y.* 1886. 12°. 8277. cc. 23.

PICOT (G.) Self-help for Labour. pp. 39.
Westminster, 1892. 8°. 8277. cc. 30 (15.)

PROCHOWNIK (B.) Das angebliche Recht auf Arbeit. pp. 123. *Berl.* 1891. 8°. 08276. f. 47.

RANSOME (J. S.) Modern Labour. pp. 159.
Lond. 1895. 8°. 08275. cc. 18.

REPUBLIC. The New Republic. pp. 62.
N.Y. 1893. 16°. Pam. 82.

SAMUELSON (J.) Labour-saving Machinery. Effect of mechanical appliances in the displacement of manual labour. pp. 94. *Lond.* 1893. 8°.
8277. de. 31.

SCHAEFFLE (A. E. F.) Theory and Policy of Labour Protection. pp. 252. *Lond.* 1893. 8°.
08276. c. 53.

SCHENCKENDORFF (E. v.) Zur Versöhnung des Besitzes und der Arbeit. 1891. 8°.

WOLFF (E.) Deutsche Schriften für nationales Leben. Reihe I. 12250. l.

SCHIKOWSKI (J.) Über Arbeitslosigkeit. pp. 88.
Leipz. 1894. 8°. 08276. i. 31.

—— Zur Methode der Arbeitslosenstatistik.
pp. 66. *Leipz.* 1895. 8°. Pam. 82.

SCHMIDT-WEISSENFELS (E.) Geschichte des modernen Reichtums. pp. 391. *Berl.* 1853. 8°.
09325. g. 8.

SCHWERIN (H.) Ein Vorschlag zur Lösung der handelspolitischen Wirren. pp. 22.
Berl. 1890. 8°. Pam. 23.

SHEPARD (E. F.) Labor and Capital are one.
pp. 38. *N.Y.* 1886. 8°. Pam. 82.

SINGER (R.) Das Recht auf Arbeit. pp. 84.
Jena, 1895. 8°. 8277. h. 32.

SKETCHLEY (J.) The Workman's Question.
pp. 24. *Birmingham*, 1882. 8°. Pam. 82.

SMITH (H. L.) Modern Changes in the Mobility of Labour. pp. 23. *Lond.* 1891. 8°.
8282. df. 44.

SNOW (A.) Christian Aspects of the Labour Question. pp. 32. *Lond.* 1894. 8°. Pam. 82.

SOHNREY (H.) Der Zug vom Lande und die soziale Revolution. pp. 138. *Leipz.* 1894. 8°.
08276. i. 35.

SULLIVAN (J. W.) Political Aspects of the Labor Problem. 1893. 8°. Ac. Brooklyn. *Ethical Association.* Evolution Series. No. 47.
7006. bbb.

CAPITAL, etc.—General—continued.

SWEENEY (E.) The Labour Question as it is.
pp. 8. *Liverp.* 1892. 8°. Pam. 82.

TOLSTOI (L. N.) L'Argent et le Travail. pp. 325.
Paris, 1892. 12°. 8277. de. 12.

LABOULAYE (R. de) L'Argent et le Travail, par le Comte L. Tolstoi. pp. 23. *Paris*, 1892. 8°.
8277. de. 13.

TREVOR (J.) Labour Church Tracts.
Manchester, 1892, etc. 8°. 8276. aa.

TRICHT (V. v.) De la condition des ouvriers dans la Société chrétienne. pp. 63.
Namur, 1892, 8°. 8282. cc. 48. (7.)

TRUSTIN (F.) The War between Capital and Labour, etc. pp. 8. *Lond.* 1890. 8°. Pam. 82.

UPWARD (A.) Trial by Jury and the Labour Movement. pp. 24. *Manchester*, 1891. 8°.
08276. f. 20. (20.)

VINCENT (E.) The Discontent of the Working-Classes. 1891. 8°. MACKAY (T.) A Plea for Liberty. 8276. g. 44.

VOLKMAR (G.) Die Währungs- und die Arbeiterfrage. pp. 86. *Wien*, 1893. 8°.
8282. cc. 48. (13.)

WHEELBARROW. Articles and discussions.
pp. 303. *Chicago*, 1894. 8°. 08275. ee. 32.

WILLIAMS (J. H.) Notes on Labour.
Lond. 1891, etc. 8°. 08276. g. 3.

WILSON (J. M.) Ethical Basis of the Labour Movement. pp. 29. *Lond.* 1894. 8°. Pam. 82.

Accidents. *See Infra : Laws, etc.* ACCIDENTS. INSURANCE.

Agricultural Labourers. *See* AGRICULTURE.

Boards of Conciliation and Arbitration.

DEPASSE (H.) Chambres et conseils du travail.
pp. 377. *Paris*, 1895. 18°. 08275. c. 40.

FRANCE. *M. du Commerce.* De la Conciliation et de l'arbitrage en France et à l'étranger. pp. 610.
Paris, 1893. 8°. 08276. k. 20.

GALET (D.) Les Conseils de Conciliation et d'arbitrage. pp. 16. *Paris*, 1892. 8°.
8277. cc. 28. (9.)

JEANS (J. S.) Conciliation and Arbitration.
pp. 194. *Lond.* 1894. 8°. 08276. f. 81.

LONDON. *Conciliation Board.* Annual Report.
Lond. 1892, etc. 8°. 08277. f.

LOWELL (J. S.) Industrial Arbitration and Conciliation. pp. 116. *N.Y.* 1893. 8°. 08276. g. 57.

MASSACHUSETTS. *Board of Conciliation.* Annual Reports. *Boston*, 1891, etc. 8°. 1591. 26.

PRASCHKAUER (M.) Ein Abriss ueber das englische Arbitrations-(Schiedsrichter) Wesen.
pp. 86. *Lond.* 1894. 8°. 6376. c. 33.

SAMUELSON (J.) Boards of Conciliation and Arbitration. pp. 32. *Lond.* 1891. 8°.
8277. ee. 1. (12.)

—— Boards of Conciliation. Address to the artizans of Liverpool. *Liverp.* 1892. 8°.
8277. cc. 28. (4.)

WHITCOMBE (C. D.) and TARANAKI (J. K.) Conciliation and Arbitration. pp. 23.
Sydney, 1890. 8° 8277. d. 39. (2.)
See also ARBITRATION.

Bureaus of Labour.

See infra : UNITED STATES OF AMERICA.

Clubs. *See* CLUBS.

Hours of Labour,

BRENTANO (L.) Hours in relation to Production.
pp. 143. *Lond.* 1894. 8°. 08276. c. 58.

CHAMPION (H. H.) Parliamentary Eight Hours Day. pp. 16. *Lond.* 1890. 16°.
8282. aaa. 56. (2.)

CAPITAL, etc.—Laws relating to Working Classes—*continued.*

MAURUS (H.) Die Lösung der Arbeiterfrage aus dem Rechtstandpunkte. pp. 103. *Berl.* 1890. 8°.
08276. h. 6.

GERMANY, *Empire.* Das Arbeiterschutzgesetz. pp. 48. *Leipz.* 1892. 8°.   5656. a. 5.

BRAUN (A.) Die Arbeiterschutzgesetze der europæischen Staaten. *Tübingen*, 1890, *etc.* 8°.
8276. g.

FEY (F.) Die Sonn- u. Festtagsruhe nach dem Arbeiterschutzgesetz. pp. 93. *Mainz*, 1892. 8°.
Pam. 34.

KAHL (A.) Die deutsche Arbeitergesetzgebung, 1883–92. pp. 128. *Freiburg*, 1893. 8°.
5605. dd. 2.

See also MASTER AND SERVANT.

Miners. *See* COAL : MINERALOGY.

Papal Encyclical of 15 May, 1891, etc.

ROME, *Ch. of.* Leo XIII., *Pope.* De conditione Opificum. Litteræ Encyclicae, 15 Maii, 1891. pp. 26. *Paris*, 1892. 8°.   5018. aaa. 5. (3.)

—— Lettre encyclique, 15 Mai, 1891. pp. 61. *Paris*, 1891. 8°.   5018. aaa. 5. (5.)

—— Ueber die Arbeiterfrage. Rundschreiben, *etc.* pp. 53. *Köln*, 1891. 8°. 4427. df. 8. (5.)

—— Encyclical Letter, May 15, 1891. *Dublin*, 1891. 8°.   5018. aaa. 5. (4.)

—— The Pope and the People. pp. 266. *Lond.* 1895. 8°.   5018. aaa. 4.

—— Leo XIII. on the Condition of the Working Classes. pp. 64. 1895. 16°. VAUGHAN (H.) *Cardinal.* Religious Books for the People. No. 16.   4401. aa. 42.

BLATCHFORD (R.) Socialism : reply to the Encyclical of the Pope. pp. 19. *Manch.* 1892. 8°.
Pam. 82.

CHARPILLET (C.) Erreurs de Léon XIII. dans l'Encyclique. pp. 272. *Paris*, 1894. 12°.
08275. f. 13.

GEORGE (H.) The Condition of Labour. Letter to Pope Leo XIII. pp. 195. *Lond.* 1891. 8°.
08276. e. 30.

GRÉGOIRE (L.) Le Pape et les Catholiques et la question sociale. pp. 323. *Paris*, 1895. 8°.
08275. f. 39.

LEMIUS (J. B.) Catéchisme de la question ouvrière d'après la lettre encyclique. pp. 83. *Paris*, 1892. 8°.   8277. ce. 32. (7.)

LEROY-BEAULIEU (A.) La Papauté, le Socialisme et la Démocratie. pp. 379. *Paris*, 1892. 12°.
08276. f. 62.

—— Papacy, Socialism and Democracy. pp. 311. *Lond.* 1892. 8°.   08276. f. 70.

MANNING (H. E.) *Cardinal.* La question ouvrière. pp. 157. *Paris*, 1892. 8°.   8275. aa. 67.

McCULLOG. Socialism and the Pope's Encyclical. pp. 56. *Manch.* 1892. 8°.   Pam. 82.

NICOTRA (S.) Le minimum de salaire et l'Encyclical. pp. 67. *Brux.* 1893. 8°. 8282. g. 25. (7.)

NOORT (G. v.) De Encycliek van Paus Leo XIII. populair besproken. pp. 119. *Amsterd.* 1893. 8°.
8277. c. 54.

PASCAL (G. de) L'Église et la Question sociale. pp. 128. *Brux.* 1891. 8°.   8275. aa. 65.

RICHARD (F. M. B.) *Cardinal.* Lettre pastorale de Son Éminence pour la publication de l'Encyclique de Leon XIII, pp. 156. *Paris*, 1892. 8°.
Pam. 96.

TACCONE-GALLUCCI (N.) Il Socialismo, il Cattolicismo e l'Enciclica. pp. 48. *Milano*, 1891. 8°.
8277. cc. 28. (7.)

VILLENEUVE (A.) La condition du Travail aux États Unis et l'Encyclique. pp. 32. *Paris*, 1892. 8°.   8277. cc. 32. (10.)

CAPITAL, etc.—*continued.*

Poor Laws. *See* PAUPERISM.

Profit Sharing. *See infra :* WAGES.

Savings Banks. *See* BANKING.

Strikes.

D. The General Strike, or, scaring the capitalists. pp. 14. *Aberd.* 1890. 16°. 08276. de. 8. (1.)

JOHNSTON (A. W.) Strikes and Labour Questions. pp. 128. *Lond.* 1895. 8°. 08275. f. 29.

KENNY (P. D.) How to prevent Strikes. pp. 76. *Manch.* 1894. 8°.   8282. ff. 12. (12.)

RENAULT (C.) Histoire des Grèves. pp. 288. *Paris*, 1887. 12°.   08275. c. 13.

U.S. *Bureau of Labor.* Strikes and Lockouts. pp. 1172. 1888. 8°. Annual Reports. Report III.
8275. k.

CHAMPION (H. H.) The great Dock Strike in London, 1889. pp. 30. *Lond.* 1890. 8°.
08276. f. 20. (7.)

MAVOR (J.) The Scottish Railway Strike, 1891. pp. 66. *Edinb.* 1891. 8°. 8282. aa. 51.

FRANCE. Statistique des Grèves en France, 1890 et 1891. pp. 121. *Paris*, 1892. 8°.
8282. dd. 16.

—— Statistique des Grèves en France, 1892. pp. 186. *Paris*, 1893. 8°. 8282. dd. 17.

DELORME (S.) Toute la vérité sur le drame de Fourmies. pp. 307. *Paris*, 1892. 12°.
08276. f. 63.

DRUMONT (É.) Le Secret de Fourmies. pp. 202. *Paris*, 1892. 8°.   8277. de. 11.

GIBON (A.) La Grève de Carmaux. pp. 87. *Paris*, 1893. 8°.   08275. k. 18.

HUBERT-VALLERONA (P.) Les Grèves d'Amiens. pp. 39. *Paris*, 1893. 8°. 8282. g. 25. (8.)

LOZÉ (É.) La Grève de 1891 dans les bassins houillers du Nord, *etc.* pp. 108. *Arras*, 1891. 16°.
8277. ee. 9.

LESPILETTE (C.) La vérité sur la Grève des mineurs du Nord, *etc.* pp. 179. *Paris*, 1894. 8°.
8277. g. 9.

MARON (A.) Le bilan et l'histoire de la Grève du Pas-de-Calais. pp. 35. *Paris*, 1894. 8°.
8282. g. 27. (14.)

CARWARDINE (W. H.) The Pullman Strike. pp. 135. *Chicago*, 1894. 8°. 08277. f. 3.

PULLMAN (G. M.) The Strike at Pullman. pp. 46. 1894. 8°.   Pam. 82.

WILHELMI (H.) Strike und öffentliche Meinung. pp. 106. *Güstrow*, 1895. 8°. 8277. cc. 23.

Trades Unions, etc.

WEBB (S.) and (B.) Bibliography of Trade Unionism. pp. 47. *Lond.* 1894. 011900. c. 2.

B., F. D. London and Suburban Trade Union Guide. pp. 66. *Lond.* 1891. 8°. 8276. aa. 55.

BAUER (A.) Haandværkerforeningen i Kjøbenhavn. pp. 181. *Kjøbenh.* 1890. 8°. 8275. i. 2.

BIRKS (J.) Trades' Unionism : criticism and a warning. pp. 50. *Hartlepool*, 1894. 8°.
08275. cc. 21. (12.)

BETOCCHI (C.) Le Coalizioni industriali. pp. 79. *Napoli*, 1891. 8°.   08276. h. 42.

CHARTERIS (F. W.) *Earl of Wemyss.* Trade-Unionism and Free Labour. pp. 11. *Lond.* 1891. 8°.   8277. h. 19. (5.)

CREE (T. S.) Criticism of the Theory of Trades' Unions. pp. 39. *Glasg.* 1891. 8°. 8282. ff. 12. (3.)

DUBOIS (E.) Les Trade-Unions en Belgique. pp. 223. *Gand.* 1894. 8°.   08275. cc. 30.

HANSTED (B.) Vort Aarhundredes Arbejdassociationer. *Kjøbenh.* 1890, *etc.* 8°. 6375. k.

CAPITAL, etc.—Trades Unions—*cont.*

HOWELL (G.) Liberty for Labour. 1891. 8°.

MACKAY (T.) Plea for Liberty. 8276. g. 44.

—— Trade Unionism. pp. 235. 1891. 8°.

GIBBINS (H. de B.) Social Questions. 08276. c.

LOUIS PHILIP ALBERT, *Count de Paris*. Le droit à l'association. pp. 49. *Paris*, 1894. 12°.
8050. bb. 21.

LYTTELTON (*Hon.* A.) Law of Trade Combinations. 1894. 8°. MACKAY (T.) Policy of Free Exchange. 08225. k. 5.

MACIVER (L.) Trades Unionism. *Beaufort*, 1891. 16°. 8277. d. 39. (1.)

MANN (T.) and TILLETT (B.) The new Trades Unionism. pp. 16. *Lond.* 1890. 8°. 8282. cc. 47. (3.)

MATHER (W.) Trade Unions and hours of labour. pp. 11. *Manch.* 1892. 8°. Pam. 82.

MOZZONI (A. M.) L'organizzazione del lavoratori. pp. 30. *Cremona*, 1891. 8°. 8277. cc. 31. (9.)

SCHULZE-GAEVERNITZ (G. v.) Social Peace. Study of the Trade Union movement in England. pp. 300. *Lond.* 1893. 8°. 08276. c. 55.

STERLING (J.) Trade Unionism. pp. 56. *Glasg.* 1889. 8°. Pam. 82.

WEBB (S.) and (B.) History of Trade Unionism. pp. 558. *Lond.* 1894. 8°. 08276. g. 68.

WEBB (B.) Relationship between Co-operation and Trade Unionism. Paper. pp. 16. *Manch.* 1892. 8°. 08275. cc. 22. (18.)

G. B. & I. *Trades Union Congress*. Report of the Trades Union Congress. *Manch.* 1890, etc. 8°. 8275. dd.

—— *Parliamentary Committee*. Report, etc. *Lond.* 1891, etc. 8°. 08276. i.

LONDON. *London Trades Council Labour Representation League*. Rules. pp. 11. *Lond.* 1892. 16°. Pam. 82.

LAVOLLÉE (R.) Le dernier Congrès des Trades Unions à Glasgow. pp. 23. *Paris*, 1893. 8°.
8282. g. 27. (13.)

AFRICA, *South*. *Knights of Labour*. Manifesto. pp. 102. 1892. 8°. 08276. g. 49.

BERLIN. *Centralverband deutscher Industridler*. Berichte der von industriellen Vereinen nach England entsendeten Kommissen. pp. 70. *Berl.* 1890. 8°. 08276. k. 26.

PARIS. *Congrès International de l'Industrie*. Rapports et résolutions. pp. 637. *Paris*, 1890. 8°. 08227. k. 29.

—— *Associations ouvrières*. Les Associations ouvrières et la Chambre Consultative. pp. 90. *Paris*, 1893. 4°. 8277. h. 28.

G. B. & I. *Society of Operative Painters*. Annual Report. *Manch.* 1887, etc. 8°. 8275. dd.

—— Quarterly Report. *Manch.* 1895, etc. 8°.
08277. g.

—— *Society of Locomotive Engineers and Firemen*. Monthly Journal. *Leeds*, 1894, etc. 8°.
P.P. 1111.

—— *Society of Railway Servants*. Report and financial statements. *Lond.* 1894, etc. 8275. dd.

—— *Federation of Butchers*. Annual Report, etc. *Lond.* 1894, etc. 8°. 8275. d.

—— *Union of Boot and Shoe Operatives*. Report. *Leicester*, 1894, etc. 8°. 08277. i.

GREENOCK. *United Trades' Council*. Annual Report. 1894. pp. 6. *Greenock*, 1894. 8°.
8277. bbb. 66.

BLACKBURN. *Power-loom Weavers' Association*. Annual Report. *Blackburn*, 1895, etc. 8°.
8276. a.

DUNDEE. *Plasterers' Federal Union*. Annual Report. *Dundee*, 1891, etc. 8°. 8275. dd.

CAPITAL, etc.—Trades Unions, etc.—cont.

DUNDEE. Monthly Report. *Dundee*, 1895, etc. 8°.
8275. d.

LEEDS. *Boot Manufacturers' Association*. Annual Report. *Leeds*, 1895, etc. 8°. 8275. d.

LEICESTER. *Trades' Council*. Annual Report. *Leicester*, 1893, etc. 8°. 08275. m.

LONDON.—*Society of Carpenters and Joiners*. Report and balance sheet. *Lond.* 1894, etc. 8°.
8282. c.

—— *Society of Compositors*. Annual Report. *Lond.* 1894, etc. 8°. 08275. m.

—— *Permanent Labourers' Association of the Docks*, etc. Rules. pp. 13. *Lond.* 1890. 8°.
Pam. 82.

—— *Society of Brush Makers*. Annual Balance Sheets and Report. *Lond.* 1893, etc. 8°.
08277. g.

—— Leaflets issued by the Society. *Lond.* 1892, etc. 8°. 8277. h.

BATTERSEA. *Labour League*. Objects and Rules. pp. 15. *Lond.* 1894. 8°. Pam. 82.

NEWCASTLE-UPON-TYNE. *Society of Boilermakers and Shipbuilders*. Annual Report. *Newcastle*, 1894, etc. 8°. 8248. c.

—— Annual Account of Moneys. *Newcastle*, 1894, etc. 8°. 8248. c.

—— Monthly report. *Newcastle*, 1893, etc. 8°.
8248. c.

WARRINGTON. *Trades and Labour Council*. Annual Report and Balance Sheet. *Warrington*, 1894, etc. 8°. 08275. c.

For Female Trades-Unions, see WOMEN.

Wages : Profit Sharing, etc.

ADLER (M. N.) Cheap Fares for the Working Classes. *Lond.* 1891. 4°. Pam. 82.

BATE (J.) Work, Workers and Wages. pp. 116. *Lond.* 1892. 8°. 8277. dc. 14.

BOEHMERT (C. V.) La Participation aux Bénéfices. pp. 752. *Paris*, 1888. 8°. 8276. h. 25.

BRENTANO (L.) Hours and Wages in relation to Production. pp. 143. *Lond.* 1894. 8°.
08276. c. 58.

BRICE (H.) Les Institutions patronales. pp. 340. *Paris*, 1895. 8°. 08276. h. 61.

BUSHILL (T. W.) Profit-Sharing and the Labour Question. pp. 262. *Lond.* 1893. 8°.
8277. dc. 22.

CONTENTO (A.) La Teoria del Salario. pp. 374. *Milano*, 1894. 8°. 08207. cc. 26.

ELEWYCK (E. v.) Les Salaires et la Protection. pp. 298. *Brux.* 1893. 8°. 08275. f. 22.

FLÜRSCHEIM (M.) Rent, Interest and Wages. pp. 238. *Lond.* 1895. 8°. 08275. f. 25.

FRANCE. *M. du Commerce*, etc. La Petite Industrie, salaires et durée du travail. *Paris*, 1893, etc. 8°. 8282. ff.

GILMAN (N. P.) Industrial Partnership. pp. 18. *Bost.* 1890. 16°. Pam. 23.

—— Die Teilung des Geschäftsgewinns zwischen Unternehmern und Angestellten. pp. 352. *Leipz.* 1891. 8°. 08276. g. 24.

LEVY (J. H.) Economics of Labour Remuneration. pp. 16. *Lond.* 1894. 8°. 08275. cc. 21. (14.)

MILLS (W. T.) Product-sharing Village. pp. 63. *Chicago*, 1894. 8°. 08277. f. 1.

NICHOLSON (J. S.) The Effects of Machinery on Wages. pp. 143. *Lond.* 1892. 8°. 08276. c. 39.

NICOTRA (S.) Le minimum de Salaire, et l'Encyclique. pp. 67. *Brux.* 1893. 8°.
8282. g. 25. (7.)

RAWSON (H. G.) Profit-sharing Precedents. pp. 192. *Lond.* 1891. 12°. 08276. g. 7.

CAPITAL, etc.—Wages.—*continued.*

SCHLOSS (D. F.) Methods of Industrial Remuneration. pp. 287. *Lond.* 1894. 8°.
                08276. g. 71.

SCHOENHOF (J.) Economy of high Wages. pp. 414. *N.Y.* 1892. 8°.   08276. f. 66.

SCHULZE (R.) Grundlagen für das Veranschlagen der Löhne bei der Bearbeitung der Maschinentheile. pp. 239. *Berl.* 1891. 8°.   8767. cc. 21.

SMITH (J. C.) The distribution of the Produce. pp. 77. *Lond.* 1892. 8°.   8282. de. 48.

TROMBERT (A.) La Participation aux Bénéfices. pp. 40. *Paris,* 1890. 8°.   8227. h. 37.

VOLTA (R. dalla) Le forme del Salario. pp. 202. *Firenze,* 1893. 8°.   08275. f. 18.

WARREN (G. O.) The true causes of Wageslavery discussed. pp. 15. *Lond.* 1894. 4°.
             08275. cc. 21. (17.)

See also supra : General : GUISE, *Familistère de.*

Pt. II.—Working Classes of Various Countries.

See also for each country under each previous sub-heading; for Agricultural Labourers of each country, *see* AGRICULTURE : for Miners, under COAL and MINERALOGY AND MINES.

Australia.

MITCHELL (E.) The Labour Question in Australia. pp. 29. *Melbourne,* 1892. 8°.
             08275. cc. 21. (4.)

ROYDHOUSE (T. R.) The Labour Party in New South Wales. pp. 127. *Lond.* 1892. 8°.
             8154. aa. 15.

Austria-Hungary.

AC. Vienna. *Museum für die Geschichte der österreichischen Arbeit.* Monographien. *Wien,* 1891, etc. 8°.   Ac. 4429. b.

DECRAIS (P. L. A.) Les conditions du Travail en Autriche-Hongrie. pp. 104. 1890. 8°. FRANCE. *M. des Affaires Étrangères.* Rapports, etc.   08276. k.

MAYER (S.) Die Aufhebung des Befähigungsnachweises in Österreich. pp. 359. *Leipz.* 1894. 8°.   08227. h. 44.

SCHWIEDLAND (E.) Kleingewerbe in Österreich. 2 Th. *Leipz.* 1894. 8°.   08276. i. 41.

TEIFEN (T. W.) Das soziale Elend in Oesterreich. pp. 180. *Wien,* 1894. 8°.   08277. i. 2.
See also INSURANCE.

Belgium.

BELGIUM. L'Impôt du sang en Belgique. pp. 31. *Brux.* 1894. 16°.   Pam. 2.

BOURÉE (A.) Les Conditions du travail en Belgique. pp. 70. 1890. 8°. FRANCE. *M. des Affaires Étrangères.* Rapports, etc.   08276. k.

BRUSSELS. *Assemblée des Patrons catholiques.* Mémoire sur la situation de l'industrie en Belgique. pp. 137. *Brux.* 1894. 8°. 08276. h. 64.

DE CAMPS (G.) L'Évolution sociale en Belgique. pp. 307. *Brux.* 1890. 8°.   08276. g. 2.

PAQUAIJ (O.) Le Prolétaire. pp. 48. *Brux.* 1895. 8°.   Pam. 82.

RAMAIX (de) La Question sociale en Belgique. pp. 269. *Brux.* 1891. 8°.   08276. h. 25.

REBEYROL (J.) Attentat aux libertés des prolétaires par le patronat. pp. 23. *Limoges,* 1895. 8°.   Pam. 82.

HEINS (M.) Les ouvriers gantois. pp. 98. *Gand,* 1893. 8°.   8282. ff. 10. (6.)
See also SOCIALISM : SOCIAL SCIENCE.

Canada.

SARTORIUS VON WALTERSHAUSEN (F. H. W. A. v.) Die Arbeits-Verfassung der englischen Kolonien in Nordamerika. pp. 232. *Strassb.* 1894. 8°.
             08276. i. 33.

CAPITAL, etc.—Various Countries, *cont.*

Denmark.

THOMSON (C.) Les conditions du Travail en Danemark. pp. 84. 1891. 8°. FRANCE. *M. des Affaires Étrangères.* Rapports, etc.   08276. k.
See also SOCIALISM : SOCIAL SCIENCE.

France

FRANCE. *M. du Commerce.* Le Placement des Employés en France. pp. 734. *Paris,* 1893. 8°.   8277. f. 53.

G., L. de. 1er Mai 1890, ou, la Question sociale. pp. 240. *Paris,* 1890. 8°.   8051. ccc. 16.

HUSSON (F.) La seconde Révolution française. pp. 207. *Paris,* 1892. 12°.   8277. de. 36.

LAUGIER (L.) La vérité sur les Docks. pp. 33. *Marseille,* 1891. 8°.   8277. cc. 30. (8.)
See also INSURANCE : SOCIALISM : SOCIAL SCIENCE.

Germany.

BAUER (F.) Kaiser und Arbeiter. pp. 158. *Bonn,* 1891. 8°.   08276. g. 8.

BRANTS (V. L. J. L.) Le Régime corporatif dans les États germaniques. pp. 159. *Louvain,* 1894. 8°.   08277. ff. 3.

BUECKER (F.) Unsere Arbeiter der Neuzeit. pp. 214. *Gotha,* 1890. 8°.   7942. f. 28.

HAENTSCHKE (H.) Die gewerblichen Produktivgenossenschaften in Deutschland. pp. 350. *Charlottenburg,* 1894. 8°.   08227. g. 54.

HERBETTE (J.) Les conditions du Travail en Allemagne. pp. 384. 1890. 8°. FRANCE. *M. des Affaires Étrangères.* Rapports, etc.   08276. k.

LASSALLE (F. J. G.) An die Arbeiter Berlins. pp. 36. *Berl.* 1892. 8°.   8282. cc. 47. (16.)

SCHEVEN (P.) Die Lehrwerkstätte. *Tübingen,* 1894, etc. 8°.   08277. h.

WOERISHOFFER (F.) Die sociale Lage der Fabrikarbeiter in Mannheim. pp. 383. *Karlsruhe,* 1891. 8°.   08276. k. 10.

ZACHER ( ) Arbeiterbewegung und Socialreform in Deutschland. pp. 26. *Berl.* 1893. 8°.
             8282. g. 25. (10.)

See also INSURANCE : SOCIALISM : SOCIAL SCIENCE.

Great Britain and Ireland.

BOOTH (C.) Labour and Life of the People. 4 vol. *Lond.* 1889–93. 8°.   2240. bb. 22.

—— The aged Poor in England and Wales. *Lond.* 1894, etc. 8°.   2020. c.

—— Dock and Wharf Labour, 1891-2. *Lond.* 1892. obl. fol.   14001. c. 23.

CAUBET (L.) Les conditions du Travail dans le Royaume-Uni. pp. 133. 1891. 8°. FRANCE. *M. des Affaires Étrangères.* Rapports. 08276. k.

ENGELS (F.) Condition of the Working Class in England in 1844. pp. 298. *Lond.* 1892. 8°.
             08276. c. 36.

FARRER (*Sir* T. H.) London County Council's Labour Bill. Memorandum. pp. 6. *Lond.* 1892. fol.   Pam. 82.

—— London County Council's Wages Bill. pp. 8. *Lond.* 1892. fol.   Pam. 82.

G. B. & I. *Royal Commission on Labour.* Collection of newspaper cuttings relative to Labour Questions. 48 vol. 1891-4. fol. 1877. a. etc.

HILL (W.) Labour and Liberalism. pp. 43. *Lond.* 1894. 8°.   8139. bb. 51. (18.)

P.P. *Lond.* The Labour Gazette. Journal of the Labour Department of the Board of Trade. *Lond.* 1893, etc. fol.   N.R.

ROGERS (J. E. T.) Six Centuries of Work and Wages. pp 591. *Lond.* 1890. 8°. 08277. g. 19.

CAPITAL, etc.—*Great Britain, etc.*—*cont.*

ROUSIERS (P. de) La Question ouvrière en Angleterre. pp. 532. *Paris,* 1895. 8°.
08275. cc. 40.

SPYERS (T. G.) The Labour Question. An Epitome of evidence and report of the R. Commission on Labour. pp. 248. *Lond.* 1894. 8°.
08276. e. 65.

TUCKLEY (H.) Masses and Classes. Industrial conditions in England. pp. 179.
Cincinnati, 1893. 8°.   08275. e. 15.

WILKINS (W. H.) The Alien Invasion. pp. 192. 1892. 8°. GIBBONS (H. de B.) Social Questions of to-day.   08276. e.

WILSON (J. M.) Religious aspect of the Labour Movement in England. pp. 23.
Lond. 1895. 8°.   Pam. 82.

See also ENGLAND, *Politics* : INSURANCE : LONDON, *Poor* : MASTER AND SERVANT : PAUPERISM : SOCIALISM : SOCIAL SCIENCE.
For the depopulation of Villages, *see* TOWNS.

Italy.

BILLOT (A.) Les conditions du Travail en Italie. pp. 51. 1891. 8°. FRANCE. *M. des Affaires Étrangères.* Rapports, *etc.*   08276. k.

SABBATINI (L.) Notizie sulle condizioni industriali di Milano. pp. 472. *Milano,* 1893. 8°.
08276. k. 24.

TYPALDO-BASSIA (A.) Des Classes ouvrières à Rome. pp. 150. *Paris,* 1892. 8°. 9041. g. 8.

Netherlands and Dutch Indies.

BYMHOLT (B.) Geschiedenis der Arbeidersbeweging in Nederland. *Amsterd.* 1893, *etc.* 8°.
08275. m.

LEGRAND (L.) Les conditions du Travail dans les Pays Bas. pp. 195. 1890. 8°. FRANCE. *M. des Affaires Étrangères.* Rapports, *etc.*
08276. k.

BERG (N. P. van den) Regeling der Verhouding tusschen Werkgevers en Arbeiders in Nederlandsch-Indië. *Amsterd.* 1890. 8°. Pam. 82.
See also SOCIALISM : SOCIAL SCIENCE.

New South Wales. See supra : *Australia.*

Norway. See infra : *Sweden.*

Portugal.

BHOURD (G.) Les conditions du Travail en Portugal. 1890. 8°. FRANCE. *M. des Affaires Étrangères.* Rapports, *etc.*   08276. k.

Spain.

BAZÁN (J. D.) Las manifestaciones de los Trabajadores. pp. 43. *Bilbao,* 1890. 8°.
8277. cc. 4. (2.)

BORREGO (A.) La situacion y el porvenir de las clases jornaleras. pp. 85. *Madrid,* 1890. 8°.
8042. f. 5.

CAMBON (P. P.) Les conditions du Travail en Espagne. 1890. 8°. FRANCE. *M. des Affaires Étrangères.* Rapports, *etc.*   08276. k.

SANTAMARÍA DE PAREDES (V.) El movimiento obrero. 1894. 8°. Ac. Madrid. *R. Academia de Ciencias.* Discursos de recepcion. Tom. 6.
Ac. 142/2.

See also SPAIN, *Politics.*

Sweden and Norway.

HULTGREN (E. O.) Untersuchung über die Ernährung schwedischer Arbeiter bei frei gewählter Kost. pp. 135. 1891. 8°. Ac. Stockholm. *Lorénska Stiftetse.* Skrifter. No. 4. Ac. 3475.

MILLET (R.) Les conditions du Travail en Suède et en Norvège. pp. 178. 1890. 8°. FRANCE. *M. des Affaires Étrangères.* Rapports, *etc.* 08276. k.

CAPITAL.—**Various Countries,** *cont.*

Switzerland.

ARAGO (E.) Les conditions du Travail en Suisse. pp. 84. 1890. 8°. FRANCE. *M. des Affaires Étrangères.* Rapports, *etc.* 08276. k.

BERGHOFF-ISING (F.) Die socialistische Arbeiterbewegung in der Schweiz. pp. 415.
Leipz. 1895. 8°.   08277. g. 10.

JAY (R.) Études sur la Question ouvrière en Suisse. pp. 308. *Paris,* 1893. 8°. 8277. de. 33.

United States of America.

CHAMBRUN (A. de) Les conditions du Travail aux États-Unis. pp. 111. 1891. 8°. FRANCE. *M. des Affaires Étrangères.* Rapports, *etc.* 08276. k.

CHICAGO. *Hull House.* Nationalities and wages in a congested district of Chicago. pp. 230.
N.Y. 1895. 8°.   08277. g. 18.

FAUCONNET (R.) L'employé aux États-Unis. Rapport au gouvernement français. pp. 54.
Rouen, 1891. 8°.   Pam. 82.

VILLENEUVE (A.) La condition du Travail aux États-Unis et l'Encylique. pp. 32.
Paris, 1892. 8°.   8277. cc. 32. (10.)

VINCENT (H.) The story of the Commonweal. pp. 247. *Chicago,* 1894. 8°. 9602. bb. 7.

U.S. *Bureau of Labour.* Special Report of the Commissioner of Labour. *Wash.* 1893, *etc.* 8°.
8275. k.

WRIGHT (C. D.) Growth and purposes of Bureaus of Statistics of Labour. pp. 17. *Bost.* 1888. 8°.
1591. 30.

CALIFORNIA. *Bureau of Labour.* Biennial Report. *Sacramento,* 1890, *etc.* 8°. 1591. 3.

COLORADO. *Bureau of Labour.* Laws of Colorado relating to Labour. pp. 116. *Denver,* 1893. 8°.
0646. de. 2.

CONNECTICUT. *Bureau of Labour.* Annual Report. *Hartford,* 1885, *etc.* 8°. 1591. 5.

ILLINOIS. *Bureau of Labour.* Biennial Report. *Chicago,* 1882, *etc.* 8°. 1591. 6.

MAINE. *Bureau of Labour.* Annual Report. *Augusta,* 1888. *etc.* 8°. 1591. 10.

MARYLAND. *Bureau of Industrial Statistics.* Annual Report. *Baltimore,* 1893, *etc.* 8°.
1591. 11.

MICHIGAN. *Bureau of Labour.* Annual Report. *Lansing,* 1884, *etc.* 8°. 1591. 12.

MINNESOTA. *Bureau of Labour.* Biennial Report. *Minneapolis,* 1890, *etc.* 8°. 1591. 13.

MISSOURI. *Bureau of Labour.* Annual Report. *Jefferson City,* 1889, *etc.* 8°. 1591. 14.

NEBRASKA. *Bureau of Labour.* Biennial Report. *Lincoln,* 1890, *etc.* 8°. 1591. 15.

NORTH DAKOTA. *Department of Agriculture and Labour.* Report. *Bismarck,* 1890, *etc.* 8°.
1591. 18.

OHIO. *Bureau of Labour.* Annual Report. *Columbus,* 1882, *etc.* 8°. 1591. 19.

RHODE ISLAND. *Bureau of Industrial Statistics.* Annual Report. *Providence,* 1888, *etc.* 8°.
1591. 21.

WISCONSIN. *Bureau of Labour.* Biennial Report. *Madison,* 1884, *etc.* 8°. 1591. 23.
See also SOCIALISM : SOCIAL SCIENCE.

CAPITAL PUNISHMENT.
See PUNISHMENT.

CAPRI. FEOLA (G.) Rapporto sullo stato attuale dei ruderi Augusto-Tiberiani nella isola di Capri. pp. 51. *Napoli,* 1894, 8°. 07708. k. 4.

MATTEUCCI (D.) Una gita alle isole d'Ischia e di Capri. pp. 30. *Jesi,* 1894. 8°. Pam. 91.

SCHOENER (R.) Capri. pp. 152. *Wien,* 1892. 8°.
10131. bbb. 37.

CAPRI—*continued.*

WALTERS (A.) Guide to Capri. pp. 26.
Naples, 1893. 16°.　　　　10136. aaa. 19.

—— A Lotos-Eater in Capri. pp. 377.
Lond. 1893. 8°.　　　　10136. f. 13.

CAPUA. B., D. L'Assedio di Capua nel 1734.
1893. 8°. Ac. Naples. *Società di Storia.*
Archivio. Anno 18.　　　　Ac. 6534.

CAPUCHIN ORDER. APOLLINAIRE, *de
Valence.* Bibliotheca Capuccinorum provin-
ciarum Occitaniae et Aquitaniae. pp. 171.
Romae, 1894. 4°.　　　　4999. k. 6.

BONARI (V.) I conventi ed i Cappuccini bresciani.
pp. 667. *Milano,* 1891. 8°.　　　　4866. g. 13.

FRANCE, *Capuchins.* Documents pour servir à
l'histoire des Capucins en France, 1568–85.
pp. 104. *Paris,* 1894. 8°.　　　　4629. aaa. 38.

LL., F. C. de. Biografía hispano-capuchina.
Barcelona, 1891, *etc.* 8°.　　　　4867. dd.

STEIDL (A.) Kurze Geschichte der Kapuziner
in Salzburg. pp. 114. *Salzburg,* 1893. 8°.
　　　　4661, aaaa. 39.

TRÉGUIER (F. de) Le Suffrage universel chrétien défendu par les moines. pp. 209.
Paris, 1890. 12°.　　　　4071. bbb. 27.

See also FRANCISCAN ORDER : RELIGIOUS ORDERS.

CARABOBO. *See* VENEZUELA.

CARBOHYDRATES. PAVY (F. W.) The
Physiology of the Carbohydrates. pp. 280.
Lond. 1894. 8°.　　　　7406. f. 10.

—— Die Physiologie der Kohlenhydrate.
pp. 257. *Leipz.* 1895. 8°.　　　　7406. g. 25.

—— Physiology of the Carbohydrates. An epi-
criticism. pp. 141. *Lond.* 1895. 8°.
　　　　7404. aaaa. 8.

CARBOLIC AND CARBONIC ACIDS.
See ACIDS.

CARCINOMA. *See* CANCER.

CARDIFF. JAMES (I.) Handbook for Cardiff.
pp. 244. *Cardiff,* 1891. 8°.　　　　10368. cc. 43.

JENKINS (J. A.) History of early Nonconformists
of Cardiff. pp. 99. *Cardiff,* 1891. 8°.
　　　　4715. aaa. 40.

JOHNSTONE (W. H. S.) History of the first
Cardiff Festival, 1892. pp. 204. *Lond.* 1894. 8°.
　　　　7895. aa. 61.

K., J. L. Cardiff. A guide book. pp. 123.
Lond. 1893. obl. 16°.　　　　10358. a. 50.

PARKER (E.) Commercial Handy sheet for
Cardiff. *Cardiff,* 1892. *s. sh.* fol.
　　　　1882. d. 2. (116.)

CARDINALS. *See* ROMAN CATHOLIC CHURCH,
Papacy.

CARDS. HORR (N. T.) Bibliography of Card-
games and of Playing-Cards. pp. 79.
Cleveland, 1892. 8°.　　　　011901. g. 15.

LENSI (A.) Bibliografia Italiana di Giuochi di
carte. pp. 46. *Firenze,* 1892. 12°.　　　Pam. 6.

Ac. *Chalcographical Society.* Playing Cards of
the Master E. S. of 1466. pp. 22.
Lond. 1892. fol.　　　　K.T.C. 4. b. 17.

Ac. Edinburgh. *Aungervyle Society.* GOLDSMID
(E. M.) Explanatory notes of a pack of Playing
Cards temp. Charles II. pp. 23.
Edinb. 1886. 8°.　　　　Ac. 9942/3.

—— Edinburgh. *Clarendon Society.* Facsimiles.
of a set of Playing Cards, satirizing the Commonwealth. *Edinb.* 1883–86. 8°.　　　1757. d. (12.)

—— Nuremberg. *Germanisches Nationalmuseum.*
Katalog der im germanischen Museum befind-
lichen Kartenspiele. pp. 35. 1886. 8°. P.P.
Munich. Anzeiger für Kunde des deutschen
Mittelalters. Bd. 1.　　　　P.P. 3512. aa.

CARDS—*continued.*

GUEST, afterwards SCHREIBER (*Lady* C. E.) Playing Cards of various ages. *Lond.* 1892, *etc.* fol.
　　　　1753. c. 4.

AQUARIUS. Italian and oriental Games at Cards.
pp. 61. *Lond.* 1890. 16°.　　　　7912. a. 1.

—— Spanish Games at Cards. pp. 76.
Lond. 1890. 16°.　　　　7912. a. 2.

BOUSSAC (J.) Encyclopédie des jeux de Cartes.
pp. 344. *Paris,* 1895. 18°.　　　　7915. df. 4.

GERVAIS ( ) Series of new Card Tricks. pp. 11.
Sunderland, 1894. 8°.　　　　Pam. 83.

MASKELYNE (J. N.) "Sharps and Flats." Revelation of the secrets of cheating. pp. 335.
Lond. 1894. 8°.　　　　7913. ee. 35.

QUINOLA (J.) Nouvelle Académie des Jeux.
pp. 448. *Paris,* 1893. 12°.　　　　7913. bbb. 47.

ROWLAND (T. B.) Card Tricks and puzzles.
1892. 8°. Club Series.　　　　7908. cc.

TRUMPS. The American Hoyle. pp. 514.
N.Y. 1892. 8°.　　　　7913. df. 11.

VAN RENSSELAER (M. K.) The Devil's Picture
Books. pp. 207. *Lond.* 1892. 8°.　7915. c. 23.

WRAY (B.) Round games with cards. pp. 112.
1891. 8°. Club Series.　　　　7908. cc.

See also BACCARAT : CRIBBAGE ; ÉCARTÉ : EU-
CHRE : GAMES : OMBRE : PATIENCE : PENCHANT :
PIQUET : POKER : WHIST.

CARIA. BARBEY (W.) Lydie, Carie. Études
botaniques. pp. 82. *Lausanne,* 1890. 4°.
　　　　7028. f. 1.

PERROT (G.) and CHIPIEZ (C.) History of Art in
Caria, *etc.* *Lond.* 1892. 8°.　2259. f. 20.

CARIBS. *See* INDIANS.

CARICATURE. ALEXANDRE (A.) L'art de
rire et de la Caricature. pp. 350.
Paris, 1893. 8°.　　　　7858. l. 15.

CHAMPFLEURY. Catalogue des Caricatures, *etc.*
pp. 127. *Paris,* 1891. 4°.　　　　7858. c. 17.

DERNJAC (J.) Die englischen Caricaturisten des
18. Jahrhunderts. pp. 46. *Wien,* 1895. 8°.
　　　　Pam. 24.

EVERITT (G.) English Caricaturists of the 19th
Century. pp. 427. *Lond.* 1893. 8°. 7857. dd. 17.

GRAND-CARTERET (J.) Napoléon en Images.
Estampes anglaises. pp. 190. *Paris,* 1895. 8°.
　　　　010662. k. 19.

—— Les Caricatures sur l'alliance Franco-
Russe. pp. 89. *Paris,* 1893. 8°. 012333. k. 5.

—— L'Année en Images. 1893, *etc.*
Paris, 1894, *etc.* 4°.　　　　12315. i.

LANGE (C.) Der Papstesel. pp. 118.
Göttingen, 1891. 8°.　　　　7807. h. 31.

LONDON. *R. Institute of Painters in Water-
Colours.* English Humourists in Art. pp. 96
Lond. 1889. 8°.　　　　7858. gg. 24.

SPIELMAN (M. H.) The History of "Punch."
pp. 592. *Lond.* 1895. 8°.　　11840. m. 40.

VEYRAT (G.) La Caricature à travers les siècles.
pp. 92. *Paris,* 1895. 4°.　　　　7857. f. 57.
See also PRINTS.

CARINTHIA. HAUSER (C.) *Baron.* Die
alte Geschichte Kärntens bis Karl dem Grossen.
pp. 147. *Klagenf.* 1893. 8°.　9365. bb. 5.

—— Kärntens Karolingerzeit, 788–918. pp. 65.
Klagenf. 1894. 8°.　　　　10215. bb. 26.

HAMBERGER (J.) Die französische Invasion in
Kärnten. pp. 58. *Klagenf.* 1889. 8°.
　　　　9008. g. 8. (3.)

Ac. Klagenfurt. *Katholisch-politischer Verein.*
Zur Ortsnamenforschung in Kärnten. pp. 32.
Klagenf. 1891. 8°.　　　　12901. d. 36. (6.)

CARINTHIA—*continued.*

Ac. Klagenfurt. *Katholisch-politischer Verein.* Schlusswort zur Ortsnamenforschung in Kärnten. pp. 28. *Klagenf.* 1891. 8°.   12901. d. 32. (8.)

JAKSCH (A. v.) Ueber Ortsnamen und Ortsnamenforschung, *etc.* pp. 44. *Klagenf.* 1891. 8°.   12902. g. 33. (6.)

See also AUSTRIA.

CARK-IN-CARTMEL. HINDLE (J.) Handbook to Cark-in-Cartmel. pp. 62. *Cark*, 1895. 8°.   Pam. 90.

CARLISLE, City and Diocese. Ac. Cumberland. *Antiquarian Society.* CARLISLE. Royal Charters of Carlisle. pp. 318. *Carlisle*, 1894. 8°.   Ac. 5630/11.

CARLISLE. Photographs of Carlisle. *Lond.* 1895. 8°.   10360. c. 36.

HEXHAM. Guide to Hexham, Carlisle, *etc.* pp. 224. *Lond.* 1895. 8°.   10347. aaa. 40.

JOPSON ( ) Guide to Carlisle. pp. 19. *Carlisle*, 1891. 8°.   10348. ccc. 60. (5.)

TODD (H.) Account of the City and Diocese of Carlisle. pp. 54. 1890. 8°. Ac. Cumberland. *Antiquarian Society.* Tract Series. No. 5.   Ac. 5630/6.

—— Notitia Ecclesiae Cathedralis Carliolensis. pp. 41. 1891. 8°. Ac. Cumberland. *Antiquarian Society.* Tract Series. No. 6.   Ac. 5630/6.

WARD, LOCK AND Co. Illustrated handbook to Carlisle Cathedral. *Lond.* 1890. 8°. 010358. l. 17.

Ac. Cumberland. *Antiquarian Society.* CARLISLE, *Diocese of.* Testamenta Karleolensia. Series of wills 1353–86. pp. 182. *Kendal*, 1893. 8°.   Ac. 5630/10.

CARTMEL. The Rural Deanery of Cartmel in the Diocese of Carlisle. pp. 125. *Ulverston*, 1892. 8°.   4705. cc. 12.

See also CUMBERLAND.

CARLSBAD. CARLSBAD. Guide to Carlsbad. pp. 32. *Lewes*, 1890. 8°.   10106. df. 17. (5.)

KLEEN (E.) Carlsbad. pp. 101. *N.Y.* 1893. 8°.   7462. aaa. 45.

KRAUS (J.) Carlsbad. pp. 138. *Lond.* 1891. 8°.   7462. bb. 31.

MERRYLEES (J.) Carlsbad and its environs. pp. 147. *Lond.* 1894. 8°.   10215. aa. 24.

CARLSRUHE. WEECH (F. v.) Karlsruhe. *Karlsruhe*, 1893, *etc.* 8°.   10255. h. *See also* BADEN.

CARLTON. CARLTON. Parish Registers of Carlton. pp. 92. 1886. 8°.   9916. f. 43.

CARMARTHENSHIRE. P.P. *Llanelly.* Carmarthenshire Miscellany and Notes. *Caermarthen*, 1889–92. 8°.   P.P. 6195. h.

CARMELITE ORDER. CURRIER (C. W.) Carmel in America. pp. 435. *Baltimore*, 1890. 8°.   4784. cc. 45. *See also* RELIGIOUS ORDERS.

CARNATION. G. B. & I. *National Carnation Society.* Carnation Manual. pp. 197. *Lond.* 1892. 8°.   07028. c. 40. *See also* FLOWERS.

CARNIOLA. MILKOWICZ (W.) Beiträge zur Rechts- und Verwaltungsgeschichte Krains. 1889, 90. 8°. Ac. Laybach. *Museal-Verein.* Mittheilungen. Jahrg. 2, 3.   Ac. 8978.

P.P. *Laibach.* Argo. Zeitschrift für krainische Landeskunde. *Laibach*, 1892, *etc.* 8°.   293.

SEIDL (F.) Das Klima von Krain. 1891–92. 8°. Ac. Laybach. *Museal-Verein.* Mittheilungen. Jahrg. 4, 5.   Ac. 8978.

CARNIOLA—*continued.*

WALLNER (J.) Krain zu Beginne des österreichischen Erbfolgekrieges. pp. 56. 1892. 8°. Ac. Laybach. *Museal-Verein.* Mittheilungen. Jahrg. 5. Abt. 1.   Ac. 8978. *See also* AUSTRIA.

CARNIVORA. LYDEKKER (R.) Hand-book to the Carnivora. 1895, *etc.* 8°. Allen's Naturalist's Library.   7001. ccc. See also under each GENUS: SPECIES, *etc.*, and ZOOLOGY.

CAROLINA, North. BASSETT (J. S.) Constitutional Beginnings of N. Carolina, 1663–1729. pp. 75. 1894. 8°. Johns Hopkins University Studies. Ser. 12. No. 3.   Ac. 2689.

WEEKS (S. B.) The Press of North Carolina in the 18th Century. pp. 80. *Brooklyn*, 1891. 8°.   11902. f. 43.

NORTH CAROLINA. *Board of Agriculture.* Handbook of North Carolina. pp. 333. *Raleigh*, 1893. 8°.   10412. c. 23.

—— Colonial Records of N. Carolina. 10 vol. *Raleigh*, 1886–1890. 8°.   9604. i. 1.

SHALER (N. S.) Account of the Fresh-water Morasses of the United States. 1890. 4°. U.S.A. *Geological Survey.* Report No. 10. Pt. 1.   1828. aa.

CAROLINA, South. CRUDEN (J.) Report on the management of Estates sequestered in S. Carolina in 1780–82 pp. 27. 1890. 8°. Winnowings in American History. Revolutionary. No. 1.   9551. aaa.

ALLEN (W.) Governor Chamberlain's administration in S. Carolina. pp. 544. *N.Y.* 1888. 8°.   8177. df. 23.

CAROLINE ISLANDS. COELLO Y QUESADA (F.) Les Iles Carolines. 1890. 8°. Ac. Paris. *Société indo-chinoise.* Bulletin. Sér. 2. Tom. 3.   Ac. 8812/3.

IBAÑEZ Y GARCÍA (L. de) Historia de las Islas Marianas. pp. 207. *Granada*, 1886. 8°. 9781. c. 2.

TAYLOR (A. W.) Les Iles Carolines. 1890. 8°. Ac. Paris, *Société indo-chinoise.* Bulletin. Sér. 2. Tom. 3.   Ac. 8812/3.

RAY (S. H.) Note on a Vocabulary of Ulia. pp. 3. *Lond.* 1890. 8°.   Pam. 47.

V., A. de. Ensayo de gramática de la lengua de Yap. pp. 142. *Manila*, 1888. 8°. 12910. aa. 53. *See also* SPAIN, Colonies.

CARP. *See* CYPRINIDAE.

CARPATHIAN MOUNTAINS. DOWIE, aft. NORMAN (M. M.) A Girl in the Carpathians. pp. 300. *Lond.* 1891. 8°.   10215. de. 9.

HADASZCZOK (J.) Führer durch die Beskiden. pp. 72. *Mähr-Ostrau*, 1891. 8°. 10205. aaa. 5.

KOLBENHEYER (K.) Die hohe Tatra. pp. 226. *Teschen*, 1891. 8°.   10215. aa. 15.

PAUL (C. M.) Das Südwest-Ende der Karpathen-Sandsteinzone. pp. 58. 1893. 8°. Ac. Vienna. *Geologische Reichsanstalt.* Jahrbuch. Bd. 43.   Ac. 3132.

TEMESVAR. Wegweiser des südungarischen Karpatenvereins. pp. 736. *Temesvár*, 1895. 8°.   10215. a. 8.

CARPENTRAS. LOUBET (M. A. L.) Carpentras avant et après l'annexion. pp. 139. *Carpentras*, 1891. 8°.   10169. de. 22.

CARPENTRY AND JOINERY. BAKHUYZEN (H. G. v. d. S.) Gronden der werktuigkunde. pp. 191. *Zaltbommel*, 1891. 8°.   8768. h. 20.

BENSON (W. A. S.) Elements of Handicraft and Design. pp. 151. *Lond.* 1893. 8°. 7808. df. 4.

BURN (R. S.) The Carpenter and Joiner. pp. 280. *Lond.* 1892. 8°.   7817. c. 22.

CARPENTRY, etc.—continued.

CABINET MAKER. The Cabinet Maker. pp. 178. Lond. 1892. 8°. 7817. c. 19.

COLLINGS (G.) Roof Carpentry. pp. 150. Lond. 1893. 12°. 8703. bbb. 11.

—— Practical Treatise on Handrailing. pp. 120. Lond. 1890. 8°. 8703. cc. 49.

DENNING (D.) Art and Craft of Cabinet-making. pp. 320. Lond. 1891. 8°. 7817. c. 14.

HASLUCK (P. N.) Cabinet Worker's Handy-book. pp. 140. Lond. 1890. 8°. 7945. cc.

K., M. le B. Carpentry for River and Garden. 1893. 8°. Ward & Lock's Amateurs' Aid Series. 07944. cc.

OSLET (G.) Traité de Charpente en bois. pp. 552. 1891. 8°. LACROIX (D.) Encyclopédie des connaissances civiles et militaires. 8708. n.

PANSEY (L.) Ornamental Carpentry. pp. 150. 1893. 8°. Ward & Lock's Amateurs' Aid Series. 07944. cc.

ROM (N. C.) Haandgerningsbog for Ungdommen. pp. 624. Kjøbenh. 1891. 8°. 07945. h. 30.

SIMMONDS (T. C.) Woodwork, Carpentry and Joinery. pp. 70. Lond. 1892. 8°. 7820. aa. 26.

WILSON (J.) Carpentry and Joinery. pp. 208. Manch. 1892. obl. 8°. 7817. c. 18.

YOUNG (F.) Every Man his own Mechanic. pp. 924. Lond. 1890. 8°. 7817. g. 24.

YOUNG (F. C.) Home-Carpentry. pp. 772. Lond. 1895. 8°. 7817. h. 2.

See also ARCHITECTURE : ART, Decorative : BUILDING : FURNITURE : STAIR - BUILDING : TURNING : WOODWORK.

CARPETS. ARARAT. Oriental Carpets and Rugs. Lond. 1891. obl. fol. 7943. k. 27.

FROEHLICH (W.) Orientalische Teppiche. Berlin, 1890. fol. 1809. b. 7.

JANITSCH (J.) Der orientalische Teppich als Vorbild. 1 p 34. Breslau, 1891. 8°. 7713. e. 1.

RIEGL (A.) Altorientalische Teppiche. pp. 214. Leipz. 1891. 8°.* 7708. aaa. 52.

STEBBING (E.) The Holy Carpet of the Mosque at Ardebil. pp. 25. Lond. 1892. 4°. 7945. f. 29.

See also TEXTILE FABRICS.

CARPI. SAMMARINI (A.) Il Duomo di Carpi. pp. 187. Modena, 1894. 8°. 4605. cc. 6.

CARRIAGES. CHICAGO. Columbian Exposition. Catalogue. Part VII. Transportation Exhibits. pp. 60. Chicago, 1893. 8°. 7958. bb. 29.

COACH-PAINTER. Coach-Painter's Handbook and Guide. pp. 131. Lond. 1895. 8°. 07944. ee. 17.

HOUGHTON (G. W. W.) Coaches of colonial New-York. pp. 31. N.Y. 1890. 8°. 7705. ee. 25. (5.)

LONDON. Institute of British Carriage Manufacturers. Fifth Autumnal Meeting. pp. 96. Apsley Guise, 1892. 8°. 7942. bbb. 50.

SALOMONS (Sir D. L.) The Horseless Carriage. pp. 27. Tunbridge Wells, 1895. 8°. Pam. 79.

SIMPSON (W.) Hand-Book for Coach-Painters. pp. 79. Lond. 1894. 8°. 07944. e. 31.

CARRICK-ON-SUIR. MEAGHER (J. F.) Annals of Carrick-on-Suir, etc. pt. 1 & 2. Dublin, 1881. 8°. 10348. d. 18. (13.)

CARRIERS. See TRANSPORTATION.

CARROUGES. CONTADES (G. de) Count. Canton de Carrouges. Bibliographie. pp. 127. Paris, 1891. 8°. 11901. a. 22.

DESPIERRES (Mme. G.) Le Château de Carrouges. pp. 30. Paris, 1893. 8°. 10105. ee. 11. (9.)

CARROW ABBEY. RYE (W.) Carrow Abbey. pp. 52. Norwich, 1889. 4°.
  4705. g. 24.

CARTAGENA, Colombia. CORRÁLES (M. E.) Documentos para la historia de Cartagena de Indias. 2 tom. Bogotá, 1883. 8°.
  9772. ccc. 10.

URUETA (J. P.) Cartagena y sus cercanías. pp. 200. Cartagena, 1886. 8°. 10481. i. 25.

—— Documentos para la Historia de Cartagena. Cartagena, 1887, etc. 8°. 9772. ccc. 9.

CARTHAGE. BOSSI (G.) La guerra annibalica in Italia. 1888–91. 4°. Ac. Rome. Accademia di Conferenze Storico-giuridiche. Studi, etc. An. 9–12. Ac. 6541.

DODGE (T. A.) Hannibal. pp. 682. Bost. 1891. 8°. 10606. c. 14.

FUCHS (J.) Der zweite punische Krieg und seine Quellen. pp. 120. Wiener-Neustadt, 1894. 8°. 9010. ff. 14.

LIVIUS (T.) Abstract of Livy's History of the Second Punic War. pp. 74. Oxf. 1891. 8°. 9041. aa. 10.

PERRIN (E.) Marche d'Annibal des Pyrénées au Pô. pp. 227. Metz, 1887. 8°. 9041. d. 22.

THIAUCOURT (C.) Les Causes et l'origine de la seconde Guerre punique. pp. 56. Paris, 1890. 8°. Pam. 28.

DELATTRE (A. L.) La Basilique de Damous el-Karita à Carthage. pp. 17. Constantine, 1892. 8°.. 07703. f. 3. (13.)

—— Les Tombeaux puniques de Carthage. pp. 104. Lyon, 1890. 8°. 7706. e. 33.

PRICOT DE SAINTE-MARIE (E.) Mission à Carthage. pp. 234. Paris, 1884. 8°. 7705. ee. 10.

THOMPSON (G. E.) Life in Tripoli, with a peep at Carthage. pp. 116. Liverp. 1894. 8°.
  010096. e. 63.

See also AFRICA, North : HISTORY, Ancient : TUNIS.

CARTHUSIAN ORDER. DOREAU (V. M.) Henri VIII. et les martyrs de la Chartreuse de Londres. pp. 435. Paris, 1890. 8°. 4829. cc. 6.

FABER (H.) Unter den Kathäusern. pp. 83. M. Gladbach, 1892. 8°. 4662. c. 22.

GANNERON (F.) Annales de Dom Ganneron. 2 pt. Paris, 1893. 8°. 4629. dd. 16.

LEFEBRE (F. A.) Saint Bruno et l'Ordre des Chartreux. 2 tom. Paris, 1883. 8°. 4829. f. 8.

LE VASSEUR (L.) Ephemerides Ordinis Cartusiensis. Monstrolii, 1890, etc. 4°. 4785. l.

THOMPSON (E. M.) History of the Somerset Carthusians. pp. 378. 1895. 8°. Catholic Standard Library. 3605. i.

See also DURBAN : GRAND CHARTREUSE : HAIN : MONT DIEU : RELIGIOUS ORDERS : SEILLON.

CARTMEL. CARTMEL. The Rural Deanery of Cartmel. pp. 125. Ulverston, 1892, 8°.
  4705. cc. 12.

CARTOGRAPHY. BELGIUM. M. de la Guerre. Institut cartographique militaire. pp. 28. Brux. 1894. 8°. 8829. i. 25.

FRANCE. Dépôt des Cartes et Plans. Catalogue des Cartes, etc. qui composent l'hydrographie française. pp. 423. Paris, 1892. 8°.
  011901 g. 5.

G. B. & I. War Office. Catalogue of Maps in the Intelligence Division, War Office. 4 vol. Lond. 1890, 91. fol. Map Room.

SPAIN. Almirantazgo. Catálogo de las Cartas, etc., existentes en el Depósito Hidrográfico. pp. 129. Madrid, 1893. 8°. 011900. h. 19.

FERNÁNDEZ DURO (C.) Noticia de las Cartas existentes en la biblioteca de S. M. el Rey. pp. 99. Madrid, 1889. 8°. 011900. f. 8. (3.)

CROOK (H. T.) Maps of the Ordnance Survey. pp. 42. Manch. 1892. 8°. 10349. g. 30.

CARTOGRAPHY—*continued.*

DERRÉCAGAIX (V. B.) Des Cartes topographiques européennes. pp. 103. *Paris*, 1891. 8°.
10105. ee. 8.

JURISCH (C. L. H. M.) Treatise on Map-Projections. pp. 88. *Cape Town*, 1890. 8°.
10002. c. 2.

LAGRANGE (J. L.) Ueber Kartenprojection, 1779. pp. 101. 1894. 8°. Ostwald's Klassiker der Wissenschaften. Nr. 55. 8706. de.

NORDENSKIÖLD (N. A. E.) *Baron.* Facsimile-Atlas till Kartografiens äldsta Historia. pp. 139. *Stockholm*, 1889. fol. 1853. c. 4.

THIERRY DE VILLE D'AVRAY (H. C.) Signes conventionnels des Cartes. pp. 125.
Paris, 1890. 18°. 10002. bb. 9.
See also MILITARY SCIENCE, *Topography, etc.*

CARVING, Wood. *See* WOODWORK.

CASERTA. FASOLO (F.) Carta della Provincia di Caserta. pp. 31. *Caserta*, 1891. 8°.
10106. ff. 6. (7.)

CASHMERE. *See* KASHMIR.

CASSEL, France. COUSSEMAKER (I. de) Fondation de l'insigne Collégiale du Saint-Pierre de Cassel. pp. 142. 1891. 8°. Ac. Dunkirk. *Comité Flamand.* Annales. Tom. 19.
Ac. 5298.

CASSEL, Prussia. Ac. Cassel. *Academia Cassellana.* Die Annalen und die Matrikel der Universtät. 1893. 8°. Ac. Cassel. *Verein für hessische Geschichte.* Zeitschrift. N. F. Bd. 18.
Ac. 7025.

CASTE. *See* HINDUISM : INDIA, *Native Races.*

CASTELLON. BALBÁS (J. A.) El libro de la provincia de Castellon. pp. 872.
Castellon, 1892. 8°. 10161. dd. 8.

CASTELNAU-DURBAN. CAU-DURBAN (D.) La Période révolutionnaire à Castelnau-Durban. pp. 56. *Foix*, 1892. 8°. 9008. g. 11. (7.)

CASTILLE. QUADRADO (J. M.) Castilla la Nueva. 3 tom. 1885-86. 8°. España. 2060. c.

CASTRES. CASTRES. Inventaire des archives communales de Castres. 1891. 4°. Collection des inventaires-sommaires. 1814, 15. b., *etc.*

CAT. ADELINE (J.) Le Chat d'après les Japonais. pp. 31. *Rouen*, 1893. 8°. 7293. b. 43.

BOSTON (F. J.) Cats and Kittens. *N.Y.* 1895. fol.
12809. w. 1.

GARDNER (J. G.) The Cat, with hints for feeding, breeding, *etc.* pp. 66. *St. Mary Cray*, 1892. 8°.
7293. k. 26.

G. B. & I. *National Cat Club.* Stud book and Register. *Bromley*, 1893. 8°. 7294. ccc.

HUIDEKOPER (R. S.) The Cat. Classification and varieties ; care and treatment. pp. 148.
N.Y. 1895. 8°. 7207. aa. 7.

JENNINGS (J.) Domestic or Fancy Cats. pp. 123. *Lond.* 1893. 8°. 7294. bbb. 15.

LANDRIN (A.) Le Chat. pp. 295. *Paris*, 1894. 8°.
07293. g. 17.

P.P. *Norwood.* The Fur Fanciers' Journal.
South Norwood, 1891, *etc.* 8°. P.P. 1859. cb.

SPIELMANN (M. H.) Henriette Ronner : the painter of cat life. pp. 47. *Lond.* 1891. 4°.
K.T.C. 3. b. 7.

VACHON (M.) Cats and Kittens by Henriette Ronner. pp. 39. *Lond.* 1894. fol.
K T.C. 31. b. 1.

TOMSON (G. R.) Concerning Cats : Poems by many authors. pp. 135. 1892. 8°. The Cameo Series. 11205. ee.
See also ANIMALS, *Domestic :* ZOOLOGY.

CATALAN LANGUAGE AND LITE-RATURE. P.P. *Barcelona.* Anuari Biblio-gráfich Catalá. *Barcelona*, 1889, *etc.* 8°.
P.P. 6477. b.

MARCET CARBONELL (M.) Vocabulario de Catalanismos. pp. 376. *Barcelona*, 1892. 8°.
12943. aaa. 32.

SAISSET (A.) Grammaire catalane. pp. 93.
Perpignan, 1894. 8°. 12942. bb. 41.

DENK (V. M. O.) Einführung in die Geschichte der altcatalanischen Litteratur. pp. 510.
München, 1893. 8°. 11825. i. 46.

FASTENRATH (J.) Catalanische Troubadoure der Gegenwart. pp. 502. *Leipz.* 1890. 8°.
11450. g. 12.

P.P. *Barcelona.* Revista Catalana.
Barcelona, 1889, *etc.* 8°. P.P. 4090, bc.

VERDAGUER (J.) Catalanische Lieder. pp. 54.
Münster, 1891. 8°. Pam. 60.
See also SPANISH LANGUAGE AND LITERATURE.

CATALOGUES of Art Collections, etc.
See COLLECTIONS : EXHIBITIONS.

CATALOGUES of Libraries, Books and Manuscripts. *See* BIBLIOGRAPHY : LIBRARIES : MANUSCRIPTS : PALAEOGRAPHY.

CATALONIA. COROLEU (J.) Documents historichs catalans del siglo XIV. pp. 155.
Barcelona, 1889. 8°. 9181. ee. 7.

FALGUERA (F. M.) Conferencias de derecho catalan pp. 209. *Barcelona*, 1889. 4°. 5383. f. 3.

MARIANO VIDAL (L.) Mas monumentos mega-líticos en Cataluña. pp. 24. *Barcelona*. 1894, 4°.
Pam. 3.

P.P. *Barcelona.* Revista Catalana.
Barcelona, 1889, *etc.* 8°. P.P. 4040. bc.

REIG Y VILARDELL (J.) Coleccio del monografías de Catalunya. *Barcelona*, 1890, *etc.* 8°.
10160. f. 4.

CATAMARCA. SORIA (M.) Curso de historia de Catamarca. pp. 128. *Catamarca*, 1891. 8°.
9772. c. 3.

CATARRH. DESSER (L. A.) Home Treatment for Catarrhs. pp. 118. *Lond.* 1894. 8°.
7616. c. 12.

See also BRONCHITIS : LUNGS.

CÂTEAU. FINOT (J.) Ville du Câteau. Inventaire des archives antérieures à 1790. 1887. 4°. Collection des inventaires sommaires.
1814. b, *etc.*

CATECHISMS, Theological.

Works on Catechising and Miscellaneous Catechisms.

CATHOLICS. A little Catechism for little catholics. pp. 35. *Lond.* 1893. 8°. Pam. 11.

CATÉCHISME. Catéchisme de la doctrine de l'église universelle chrétienne. pp. 559.
La Haye, 1889. 8°. 3504. c. 27.

CHAPMAN (D. F.) A plain Catechism on religion. pp. 24. *Preston*, 1892. 12°. Pam. 11.

DUPANLOUP (F. A. P.) *Bishop of Orleans.* The Ministry of catechising. pp. 612.
Lond. 1890. 8°. 3504. f. 25.

JONES (S. J.) The Clergy and the Catechism. An Attempt to adapt the "Méthode de St Sulpice," by Mgr. Dupanloup, to the English Church. pp. 159. *Lond.* 1895. 8°. 3504. c. 57.

GRUEBER (C. S.) Twenty cards containing questions and answers on "The Catholic Church." *Oxford*, 1895. 8°. 4109. de. 2.

HALL (H. E.) Manual of Christian Doctrine for confirmation classes. pp. 68.
Lond. 1894. 8°. 3505. c. 60.

JOHNSON (J. B.) Catechism on some great truths. pp. 41. *Lond.* 1893. 8°. Pam. 11.

CATTLE—*continued.*

SÖRENSEN (H.) Stambog over Tyre og Køer af rødt fyensk Malkekvæg. pp. 413. *Odense*, 1891, 8°.   7291. c. 11.

RICHARDS (W.) The Cattle Trade and farmers' accounts. pp. 56. *Lond.* 1893, 8°. 08227. i. 12.

SALMON (D. E.) Special Report on Cattle feeding. pp. 496. 1892. 8°. UNITED STATES. *Animal Industry, Bureau of.* Miscellaneous Publications.   7053. e. 6.

TWEED (I.) Cow-keeping in India. pp. 260. *Calcutta*, 1891. 8°   07293. i. 3.

WALLACE (R.) Lecture on American Cattle. pp. 28. *Edinb.* 1890. 8°.   7293. i. 12. (8.)

YOUATT (W.) The complete Grazier. pp. 1086. *Lond.* 1893. 8°.   7291. d. 13.

ROSCOE (W. C.) Sale by live weight of fat Cattle. *Liverp.* 1893. 16°.   8548. aa. 38. (4.)

TABLE. Table giving weight of Heifers and Bullocks. *Stirling*, 1891. s. sh. 8°.   1882. d. 2. (27.)

See also ANIMALS, *Domestic:* DAIRY MANAGEMENT: and for diseases of cattle, VETERINARY SCIENCE.

CAUCASUS: CAUCASIA, GULBENKIAN (C. S.) La Transcaucasie et la Péninsule d'Apchéron. pp. 336. *Paris*, 1891. 8°. 10075. bb. 19.

HAHN (C.) Aus dem Kaukasus. pp. 299. *Leipz.* 1892 8°   10126. f. 18.

KESSLER (W.) Aus Wald und Welt. *Neudamm*, 1890, *etc.* 8°.   10026. k. 14.

LANGE (O.) Karkasus. pp. 349. *Kjøbenh.* 1891. 8°   10125. c. 13.

LECLERCQ (J.) Du Caucase aux Monts Alaï. pp. 267. *Paris*, 1890. 18°.   10075. aa. 6.

MUELLER-SIMONIS (P.) Relation des missions scientifiques de H. Hyvernat et P. Müller-Simonis, 1888–89. pp. 628. *Wash.* 1892. 8°.   10075. k. 7.

MUMMERY (A. F.) My Climbs in the Alps and Caucasus. pp. 360. *Lond.* 1895. 8°.   K.T.C. 35. b. 2.

RUGARD (M.) Krim- und Kaukasus-Fahrt. pp. 240. *Breslau*, 1891. 8°.   10292. f. 5.

WILSON (*Sir* C. W.) Murray's Handbook for Travellers in Trans-Caucasia, *etc.* *Lond.* 1895. 8°.   2364. b. 32.

WOLYNSKI (H. A.) Popolazione del Caucaso. pp. 16. *Roma*, 1890. 8°.   Pam. 88.

KOVALEVSKY (M. M.) Droit coutumier ossétien. pp. 520. *Paris*, 1893. 8°.   5756. bbb. 26.

ERCKERT (R. v.) Die Sprachen des kaukasischen Stammes. 2 Th. *Wien*, 1895. 8°.   12907. cc. 50.

HÜBSCHMAN (H.) Etymologie der ossetischen Sprache. pp. 151. 1887. 8°. DICTIONARIES. Sammlung indogermanischer Wörterbücher. Vol. 1.   12902. dd.

CAUX. Ac. Rouen. *Société de l'Histoire de Normandie.* CAUX. Registre des Fiefs du bailliage de Caux en 1503. pp. 326. *Rouen*, 1891. 8°.   Ac. 6890/26.

CAVALRY. *See* MILITARY SCIENCE and under the subheading *Army* of each country.

CAVES. CHRISTY (R. M.) On Deneholes. pp. 17. *Derby*, 1895. 8°.   Pam. 3.

COUSENS (H.) Account of the Caves at Nadsur and Karsambla. pp. 11. 1891. 4°. INDIA, Western. *Archæological Survey.* Reports. No. 12.   7702. i.

MARTEL (E. A.) Les Abimes, les cavernes, *etc.* pp. 578. *Paris*, 1894. fol.   7105. g. 12.

CAVES—*continued.*

PEASE (A. P. L.) Discovery in a stone quarry in Tuscarawas County, Ohio. 1892. 8°. Pam. 3.

SMITH (J.) Monograph of the Stalactites and Stalagmites of the Cleaves Cove, Ayrshire. pp. 34. *Lond.* 1894. 4°.   7109. dd. 15.

See also ANTHROPOLOGY.

CAWNPORE. BROWNE (J.) Cawnpore and the Nana. pp. 27. *Cawnpore*, 1890. 8°.   Pam. 88.

MIRZA AMIR BEG. Handbook of Cawnpore, *etc.* *Lucknow*, 1891. 8°.   Pam. 88.

WESTCOTT (G. H.) Guide to Cawnpore. *Cawnpore*, 1892. 8°.   Pam. 88.

CAYENNE. *See* GUIANA, *French.*

CAYEUX. VULPIAN (P.) La Maison du Christ à Cayeux. pp. 306. *Paris*, 1895. 12°.   012550. i. 55.

CAYMAN ISLANDS. EDEN (W. T.) and MAC LAUGHLIN (E. N.) The Island of Grand Cayman. pp. 8. *Jamaica*, 1891. 8°. Pam. 86.

See also WEST INDIES.

CEARÁ, Brazil. STUDART (G.) Notas para a historia do Ceará. pp. 517. *Lisboa*, 1892. 8°.   10481. dd. 26.

CELEBES. G. B. & I. *Hydrographic Office.* The Eastern Archipelago. 2 pt. *Lond.* 1890–93. 8°.   10496. ff. 20.

See also MALAY PENINSULA AND MALAYSIA: NETHERLANDS, *Colonies.*

CELIBACY, *Clerical. See* CLERGY.

CELLE. *See* ZELL.

CELLS AND CELL THEORIES. BERGH (R. S.) Vorlesungen über die Zelle des thierischen Körpers. pp. 262. *Wiesbaden*, 1894. 8°.   7406. dd. 2.

CHATIN (J.) La Cellule animale. pp. 304. *Paris*, 1892. 8°.   7406. aaa. 5.

FRANCKE (C.) Die menschliche Zelle. pp. 746. *Leipz.* 1891. 8°.   7407. cc. 13.

GAUTIER (A.) La chimie de la cellule vivante. pp. 175. 1894. 8°. Encyclopédie des aide mémoire.   8709. g.

HANSEMANN (D.) Studien über die Spezificität der Zellen. pp. 96. *Berl.* 1893. 8°. 7407. f. 31.

HERTWIG (O.) Die Zelle und die Gewerbe. pp. 296. *Jena*, 1893. 8°.   7407. f. 28.

—— The Cell. pp. 368. *Lond.* 1895. 8°.   7407. bb. 9.

HODGE (C. F.) Effects of electrically stimulating Ganglion Cells. pp. 27. 1889. 8°.   Pam. 39.

KUNSTLER (J.) Fragments de biologie cellulaire. pp. 128. 1895. 8°. Ac. Bordeaux. *Société des Sciences.* Mémoires. Sér. 4. tom. 5.   Ac. 2840.

LUK'YANOV (S. M.) Grundzüge einer allgemeinen Pathologie der Zelle. pp. 325. *Leipz.* 1891. 8°.   7442. f. 22.

See also BIOLOGY: HISTOLOGY: PROTOPLASM.

CELTIC LANGUAGES. HOLDER (A.) Alt-celtischer Sprachschatz. *Leipz.* 1891, *etc.* 8°.   12978. i.

LOTH (J.) Chrestomathie bretonne, armoricain, gallois, cornique. *Paris*, 1890, *etc.* 8°.   12978. h. 20.

—— Les Mots latins dans les langues brittoniques. pp. 216. *Paris*, 1892. 8°. 12978. h. 21.

WILLIAMS (C. A.) Die französischen Ortsnamen keltischer Abkunft. pp. 87. *Strassb.* 1891. 8°.   12903. dd. 33. (7.)

See also BRETON, GAELIC, IRISH and WELSH LANGUAGES.

CELTIC RACES. ATKINS (T. de C.) The Kelt or Gael. pp. 96. *Lond.* 1892. 8°.
12978. f. 26.

BERTRAND (A.) Archéologie celtique et gauloise. *Paris,* 1889, *etc.* 8°.   07708. f.

BONWICK (J.) Irish Druids and old Irish religions. pp. 328. *Lond.* 1894. 8°.
4503. bb. 40.

FROMENT (A.) Le Monothéisme druidique. pp. 64. *Montauban,* 1893. 8°.   Pam. 41.

See also BRITTANY : CORNWALL : IRELAND : SCOTLAND, *Highlands :* WALES.

CEMAES. (MINTON E. J.) Cemaes as we saw it. ff. 36. *Manch.* 1890. 8°.   10369. f. 7.

CEMENTS. COLLINS (D. L.) A few Words on Portland Cement. *Lond.* 1888. 8°.
7942. i. 43. (6.)

FAIJA (H.) Portland Cement for users. pp. 108. *Lond.* 1890. 12°.   8703. cc. 50.

HEATH (A. H.) Manual of Lime and Cement. pp. 215. *Lond.* 1893. 8°.   7942. f. 37.

REDGRAVE (G. R.) Calcareous Cements. pp. 238. *Lond.* 1895. 8°.   7817. bbb. 1.

SPALDING (F. P.) Notes on the testing and use of Hydraulic Cement. pp. 108. *Ithaca,* 1893. 8°.
8767. b. 50.

STANDAGE (H. C.) Cements, pastes, glues and gums. pp. 164. *Lond.* 1893. 8°. 07944. e. 13.

See also BUILDING : CONCRETE : ENGINEERING.

CEMETERIES. *See* BURIAL.

CENTIPEDES. *See* MYRIOPODA.

CERAMICS.

Bibliography.

Ac. London. *S. K. Museum.* Classed catalogue of Printed Books. Ceramics. pp. 352. *Lond.* 1895. 8°.   2048. a.

General.

BILBAUT (T.) L'Art céramique au coin du feu. *Paris,* 1892, *etc.* 8°.   07945. m. 18.

DAVIS (C. T.) Treatise on the manufacture of Brick, Tiles and Terra-cotta. pp. 628. *Phila.* 1895. 8°.   07945. m. 25.

EARLE (A. M.) China collecting in America. pp. 429. *Lond.* 1892. 8°.   7808. c. 10.

GARBAN (E.) La Porcelaine. pp. 304. *Paris,* 1891. 8°.   7943. i. 36.

GUENEZ (E.) Décoration céramique au feu de moufle. pp. 199. 1893. 8°.. Encyclopédie des aide-mémoire.   8709. g.

HAINES (F. E.) A Keramic Study. pp. 127. *Bangor, U.S.A.,* 1895. 8°.   07944. e. 54.

HAVARD (H.) La Céramique. 2 tom. *Paris,* 1894. 8°.   07944. g. 9.

LIMOGES. *Cercle d'Études Commerciales.* Le Papier, la Porcelaine, *etc.* pp. 140. *Limoges,* 1892. 8°.   7942. dd. 8.

RIS-PAQUOT (O. E.) Faïences porcelaines et biscuits. pp. 243. *Paris,* 1894. 8°. 7808. df. 14.

ROBERT (K.) La Céramique. pp. 176. pp. 176. *Paris,* 1892. 8°.   7805. de. 21.

ROBERTS (W.) Rare Books. With chapters on Pottery, Porcelain, *etc.* pp. 155. *Lond.* 1895. 8°.
7757. aa.

UJFALVY-BOURDON (C. E. de). Les Biscuits de porcelaine. pp. 94. *Paris,* 1893. 4°.
7806. e. 20.

VOGT (G.) La Porcelaine. pp. 304. *Paris,* 1893. 8°.   2261. c. 26.

WYZEWA (T. de) Les Arts du Feu, céramique, *etc.* pp. 143. *Paris,* 1892. 8°.   7944. h. 32.

See also ARTS, *Decorative.*

Bricks. *See* BRICKS.

CERAMICS—*continued.*

Enamels. *See* ENAMELS.

Exhibitions and Collections.

HOUSMAN (H.) Notes on the Willet Collection of Pottery in the Brighton Museum. *Brighton,* 1893. 8°.   7808. e. 26.

LONDON. *Imperial Institute.* Catalogue of the Exhibition of decorative and artistic Pottery. pp. 128. *Lond.* 1894. 8°.   7958. aaa. 23.

See also infra: Ceramics of Various Countries : VASES.

Marks, etc.

HOOPER (W. H.) Manual of Marks on Pottery and Porcelain. pp. 240. *Lond.* 1894. 16°.
07944. de. 4.

RICHARD (A.) Marques de Potiers et inscriptions gallo-romaines. pp. 77. 1890. 8°. Ac. Poitiers. *Société des Antiquaires.* Mémoires. Sér. 2. Tom. 12.   Ac. 5326.

RIS-PAQUOT (O. E.) Dictionnaire des marques et monogrammes. 2 tom. *Paris,* 1893. 4°.

UJFALVY-BOURDON (C. E. de) Dictionnaire des Marques des biscuits de porcelaine. pp. 114. *Paris,* 1895. 8°.   07944. f. 16.

Painting : Encaustic.

BOUFFIER (H.) Anleitung zur Majolikamalerei. pp. 37. 1892. 8°. Bossong's Kunsttechnische Bibliothek. Bd. 7.   7858. f.

DONNER VON RICHTER (O.) Encaustic Painting of the Ancients. 1889. 8°. Catalogue of T. Graf's Gallery of Antique Portraits.   Pam. 24.

GOODYEAR (C.) Message to China Decorators. ff. 41. *N.Y.* 1890. *obl.* 4°.   7808. a. 39.

GREENFIELD (B. W.) Encaustic Tiles of the middle ages. pp. 25. 1892. 8°.
7808. bbb. 27. (4.)

JAENNICKE (F.) Handbuch der Porzellan Steingut- und Fayence-Malerei. pp. 316. *Stuttgart,* 1891. 8°.   7856. de. 22.

PICARD (M.) Traité de Peinture sur porcelaine et sur faïence. pp. 95. *Paris,* 1893. 12°.
7858. a. 33.

RENAUD (F.) Uses and teachings of ancient Encaustic Tiles. ff. 30. *Manch.* 1892. fol.
7803. i. 3.

Terra Cotta. *See* TERRA COTTA.

Ceramics of various Countries.

Austria.

Ac. Vienna. *Oesterreichisches Museum.* Die K.K. wiener Porzellanfabrik. pp. 90. *Wien,* 1887. 4°.   7943. k. 19.

Belgium. See infra : Netherlands.

China.

Ac. London. *Burlington Club.* Catalogue of blue and white Oriental Porcelain. pp. 55. *Lond.* 1895. 4°.   Ac. 4644/36.

BUSHELL (S. W.) Chinese Porcelain before the present dynasty. pp. 55. *Peking,* 1886. 8°.
7942. i. 43. (5.)

GRANDIDIER (E.) La Céramique chinoise. pp. 232. *Paris,* 1894. 4°.   K.T.C. 18. b. 6.

HIRTH (F.) Ancient Porcelain. Chinese mediæval industry. pp. 80. *Leipsic,* 1888. 8°.
7942. l. 46. (3.)

France.

DUPUY (E.) Bernard Palissy. pp. 334. *Paris,* 1894. 12°.   010663. f. 29.

PEYRUSSON (E.) L'Industrie de la porcelaine en Limousin. pp. 48. *Limoges,* 1892. 8°.
9008. g. 8. (12.)

CERAMICS.—France—*continued.*

RONDOT (N.) Les potiers de terre italiens à Lyon au 16me siècle. pp. 160. *Lyon*, 1892. 8°.
7808. f. 10.

FOUQUE (E.) Moustiers et ses Faïences. pp. 121. *Aix*, 1892, 8°. 7945. i. 46.

WIGNIER (C.) Carreaux vernissés du Ponthieu du XIIe au XVIIe siècle. pp. 20.
Abbeville, 1890. 8°. Pam. 3.

AUSCHER (E. S.) Étude sur la manufacture de Porcelaines de Sèvres. pp. 47. *Paris*, 1894. 8°.
7943. f. 31.

GERSPACH ( ) Documents sur les anciennes Faïenceries et la manufacture de Sèvres. pp. 246. *Paris*, 1891. 8°. 7945. i. 45.

LONDON. *Sette of Odd Volumes.* Old and Modern Sèvres China. pp. 22. *Lond.* 1890. 16°.
012202. cccc.

BILBAUT (T.) La Céramique des Colonies françaises. *Lond.* 1893, *etc.* 8°. 07945. g.

Germany.

SOLON (M. L.) Ancient Art stoneware of Germany. 2 vol. *Lond.* 1892. fol. 7808. i. 1.

STEGMANN (H.) Die braunschweigische Porzellanfabrik zu Fürstenberg. pp. 176.
Braunschweig, 1893. 8°. 07945. m. 21.

BERLING (K.) Die Fayence- und Steingutfabrik Hubertusburg. pp. 30. *Dresd.* 1891. 8°.
7942. l. 46. (7.)

Great Britain and Ireland.

Ac. London. *School of Mines.* Handbook to the Collection of British Pottery and Porcelain. pp. 178. *Lond.* 1893. 8°. 7957. d. 8.

CHURCH (A. H.) Old English Pottery. *Lond.* 1894. fol. K.T.C. 24. b. 3.

GRIFFINHOOFE (H. G.) Mediœval Tiles in St. Mary's, Monmouth. pp. 23.
Monmouth, 1894. 12°. Pam. 3.

HODGKIN (J. E.) Examples of early English Pottery. pp. 187. *Lond.* 1891. 4°. 7808. g. 1.

SMILES (S.) J. Wedgwood. pp. 304. *Lond.* 1894. 8°. 10825. bb. 39.

BIRMINGHAM. *Museum.* Old Wedgwood and Wedgwood Ware. pp. 104. *Lond.* 1885. 8°.
7807. g. 23.

P.P. London. The British Clay-Worker. *Lond.* 1892, *etc.* 4°. N.R.

—— London. British Clay-Worker Manuals. *Lond.* 1894, *etc.* 8°. 07944. c.

KIDSON (J. R.) Historical notices of the Leeds old Pottery. pp. 161. *Leeds*, 1892. 4°. 7808. g. 2.

ANDERSON (J. E.) Account of the Mortlake Potteries. pp. 14. *Richmond*, 1894. 8°. 07944. g. 7.

WORCESTER. *Royal China Manufactory.* Guide through the Porcelain Works. pp. 47.
Worcester, 1885. 8°. 7942. i. 43. (4.)

—— Royal Worcester. pp. 46. *Worcester*, 1893. obl. 8°. 7808. aa. 51.

Greece.

MILLIET (P.) Études sur les premières périodes de la Céramique grecque. pp. 169.
Lond. 1891. 8°. 7705. aaa. 37.

WILISCH (E.) Die altkorinthische Thonindustrie. pp. 176. *Leipz.* 1892. 8°. 7708. c. 40.

See also TERRA COTTA : VASES.

Italy.

ROME. *Museo Artistico-industriale.* Catalogo delle opere esposte sulla ceramica italiana. pp. 338. *Roma*, 1889. 8°. 07945. f. 22.

CATALOGUES. Catalogue d'une collection de Faïences italiennes. pp. 29. *Paris*, 1894. 8°.
7808. f. 17.

See also VASES.

CERAMICS.—Netherlands.

Netherlands.

SOLON (M. L.) Art Stoneware of the Low Countries. 2 vol. *Lond.* 1892. fol. 7808. i. 1.

LIÉGE ARMORIAL BEARINGS. Grès cérames à armoiries liégeoises. 1886. 8°. Ac. Liége. *Institut Archéologique.* Bulletin. Tom. 19. Livr. 1. Ac. 5527.

ANGENOT (F.) Documents sur la poterie de Raeren. 1885. 8°. Ac. Liége. *Institut Archéologique.* Bulletin. Tom. 18. Livr. 2. Ac. 5527.

Nicaragua.

BOVALLIUS (C.) Antiquités céramiques trouvées dans le Nicaragua. pp. 23.
Stockholm, 1891. 8°. 07763. g. 3. (8.)

Oriental. See supra : China ; *infra :* Persia.

Persia.

WALLIS (H.) Persian Ceramic Art in the collection of Mr. Godman. pp. 50. *Lond.* 1891. 4°.
K.T.C. 3. b. 8.

United States of America.

BARBER (E. A.) Pottery and Porcelain of the U.S. *Lond.* 1893. 8°. 7942. l. 49.

CERAMIUM. *See* ALGAE.

CEREBELLUM. *See* BRAIN.

CERIALE. MAINERI (B. E.) Le Conchiglie del Torsèro e i Turchi al Ceriale. pp. 177. *Roma*, 1890. 8°. 10132. g. 20.

CERNY. CLERCQ (H. de) Notice sur Cerny. 1890, *etc.* 8°. Ac. *Société Historique du Gatinais.* Annales. Tom. 8, *etc.* Ac. 6791. 2.

CESTODA. *See* PARASITES.

CETTE. BONNET (É.) Recherches sur l'Île de Cette. pp. 122. *Montpellier*, 1894. 8°.
10173. ec. 8.

CEUTA. BENTABÓL Y URETA (H.) Presente y porvenir de Ceuta. pp. 36. *Madrid*, 1894. 8°.
Pam. 67.

CEVENNES. JOANNE (P.) Les Cévennes. Guide-Joanne. pp. 471. *Paris*, 1893. 8°.
2362. a.

MALAVIALLE (L.) Les Cévennes, 1893. 8°. Ac. Montpellier. *Société Languedocienne.* Bulletin. Année 16. Ac. 6033.

MARTEL (E. A.) Les Cévennes. pp. 406. *Paris*, 1890. 8°. 10172. f. 7.

PORCHER (J.) Le pays des Camisards. pp. 320. *Paris*, 1894. 8°. 10174. bb. 26.

ROUVIÈRE ( ) La renaissance languedocienne dans les Cévennes. pp. 52. *Alais*, 1892. 8°.
011850. h. 16. (12.)

See also ARDÈCHE : FRANCE, *Protestants :* HÉRAULT, *Department.*

CEYLON. [*See note on page* 1.] *See also* BUDDHISM : COLOMBO : ENGLAND, *Colonies.*

History : Law : Politics : Trade : Finance.

CEYLON. The Tésawalamai ; laws and customs of the Malabars of Jaffna, 1707. pp. 30. *Colombo*, 1891. 8°. 05319. k. 3.

BRITISH GOVERNMENT. History of the connection of the British Government with Buddhism. pp. 150. *Colombo*, 1889. 8°. 8022. aaa. 2.

P.P. *Colombo.* The Ceylon Observer. *Colombo*, 1888, *etc.* fol. P.P. 9970. e.

—— Monthly Literary Register and Notes and Queries for Ceylon. *Colombo*, 1893, *etc.* 4°.
P.P. 3801. ai.

CEYLON.—History: Law, etc.—*continued.*

P.P. *Colombo.* The Ceylon Review.
Colombo, 1893, *etc.* 4°.   P.P. 3801. ah.

—— The Ceylon Law Journal.
Colombo, 1892, *etc.* 8°.   P.P. 1351. ak.

CEYLON. Rules of the Volunteer Forces in Ceylon.
pp. 24. *Colombo,* 1891. 16°.   Pam. 2.

VICTORIA, *Queen.* Monument of the Jubilee of
Her Majesty, 1887. pp. 31.
Kandy, 1891. 8°.   10601. f. 8. (14.)

———————

CEYLON PLANTER. The Ceylon Planter's " Vade
Mecum." pp. 41. *Colombo,* 1891. 8°.
               7075. f. 1. (8.)

CEYLON. Ceylon Government Railways. pp. 14.
Colombo, 1893. 8°.   08235. i. 11.

JAFFNA RAILWAY. Proposed Jaffna Railway.
pp. 105. *Colombo,* 1890. 8°.   8235. l. 46.

CHICAGO. *Columbian Exposition.* Handbook of
the Ceylon Courts. pp. 104.
Colombo, 1893. 8°.   7958. bb. 14.

FERGUSON (J.) Ceylon in 1893, *etc.*
Lond. 1893. 8°.   010057. e. 21.

CEYLON. *National Association.* Report of the
Committee on the Grain Tax. pp. 31.
Colombo, 1890. 8°.   Pam. 23.

FERGUSON (A. M.) Taxation in Ceylon : with
special reference to the grain taxes.
Colombo, 1890. 12°.   8228. aaa. 20.

STAREY (J. H.) The Paddy Tax in Ceylon.
pp. 19. *Colombo,* 1890. 8°.   Pam. 23.

WALL (G.) The Grain Tax in Ceylon. pp. 57.
Colombo, 1890. 8°.   Pam. 23.
See also TEA.

Language. *See* SINHALESE LANGUAGE.

Missions. *See* MISSIONS.

Topography.

ALBERT VICTOR, *Duke of Clarence.* Grand Tour
of the British Princes. pp. 38.
Colombo, 1882. 8°.   10056. f. 3.

CARPENTER (E.) From Adam's Peak to Elephanta. pp. 363. *Lond.* 1892. 8°. 010057. f. 10.

CAVE (H. W.) Picturesque Ceylon. pp. 69.
Lond. 1893. 8°.   10058. l. 12.

CHISHOLM (G. G.) Longman's Geography for
India and Ceylon. pp. 364. *Lond.* 1891. 8°.
               010057. e. 6.

CLUTTERBUCK (W. J.) About Ceylon. pp. 265.
Lond. 1891. 8°.   010055. de. 1.

COLOMBO. Colombo to Nuwara Eliya. pp. 241.
Colombo, 1891. 12°.   10058. a. 17.

CUMMING (C. F. G.) Two happy Years in Ceylon.
2 vol. *Edinb.* 1892. 8°.   010057. ee. 24.

DAALMANS (A.) Belgian Physician's Notes on
Ceylon, 1687–89. pp. 34. *Colombo,* 1888. 8°.
               Pam. 88.

DESCHAMPS (É.) Carnet d'un Voyageur.
pp. 480. *Paris,* 1892. 8°.   10095. e. 5.

GREGSON (F.) Letters from Ceylon. pp. 208.
Lond. 1893. 8°.   4767. c. 36.

HURST (J. F.) Country and People of India
and Ceylon. pp. 794. *N.Y.* 1891. 8°.
               010057. l. 9.

INDIA. Murray's Handbook for India and Ceylon.
pp. 484. *Lond.* 1894. 8°.   2364. b. 24.

—— Great Temples of India and Ceylon.
pp. 96. *Madras,* 1894. 8°.   7814. e. 44.

JANSZ (W.) Account of a travel from Galle to
the Northern and Eastern Provinces. pp. 16.
Colombo, 1891. 8°.   Pam. 88.

KESAVACHANDRA SENA. Diary in Ceylon.
pp. 67. *Calcutta,* 1888. 16°.   10058. a. 14.

CEYLON.—Topography—*continued.*

LE MESURIER (C. J. R.) Manual of the Nuwara
Eliya district. pp. 269. *Colombo,* 1893. 8°.
               010057. f. 27.

P., F. E. F. Fickle Fortune in Ceylon. pp. 69.
Madras, 1887. 8°.   010057. ee. 9.

SCOTT (C. W.) Cheery Ceylon. pp. 12.
Colombo, 1893. 12°.   Pam. 88.

TRUBRIDGE (H.) Home Notes on Ceylon. pp. 8.
1893. 8°.   Pam. 88.

WALTERS (A.) Palms and Pearls. pp. 317.
Lond. 1892. 8°.   010057. ee. 26.

WHITE (H.) Manual of the Province of Uva.
pp. 168. *Colombo,* 1893. 8°.   010057. e. 41.

ZALESKI (   ) Ceylon et les Indes. pp. 411.
Paris, 1891. 8°.   10058. aa. 35.

CHABONS. LAGIER (A.) La Révolution
dans les Terres-froides. pp. 147.
Valence, 1892. 8°.   9226. l. 22.

CHAD, Lake. *See* TCHAD.

CHAINTREAUX-LAGERVILLE. GUIL-
LOT (H.) Notice sur Chaintreaux-Lagerville.
pp. 240. *Troyes,* 1892. 8°.   10170. bb. 5.

CHALDAEA. JOHNSON (V. E.) Our Debt
to the past of Chaldean Science. pp. 118.
Lond. 1890. 8°.   7704. a. 40.

KROLL (G.) De oraculis Chaldaicis. pp. 76.
1894. 8°. Breslauer philologische Abhandlungen. Bd. 7.   12902. f. 25.

LAURENT (A.) La Magie chez les Chaldéo-Assyriens. pp. 89. *Paris,* 1894. 8°. 8632. d. 29.

MASPERO (G.) The Dawn of Civilisation.
pp. 800. *Lond.* 1894. 8°.   4430. dd. 1.

MIERLO (J. v.) De Sterrenkunde der Chaldeërs.
pp. 31. *Gent,* 1891. 8°.   Pam. 4.

OPPERT (J.) Un annuaire astronomique Chaldéen.
pp. 7. *Paris,* 1890. 4°.   Pam. 4.

WILLIAMSON (A.) Light from Eastern Lands on
the Lives of Abraham, Joseph and Moses.
pp. 242. *Edinb.* 1892. 8°.   3155. de. 24.
See also ASSYRIA : HISTORY, *Ancient:* SUSA.

CHALDEAN CHRISTIANS.
See NESTORIANS.

CHALDEE LANGUAGE. *See* ARAMAIC.

CHÂLONS-SUR-MARNE. LHOTE (A.)
Histoire de l'Imprimerie à Châlons-sur-Marne.
pp. 232. *Châlons,* 1894. 4°.   11901. h. 1.

CHAMBÉRY. BARBIER (V.) Monographie
de la Bibliothèque de Chambéry. pp. 170.
Chambéry, 1883. 8°.   11904. bbb. 34.

MORAND (L.) Les anciennes corporations de
Chambéry. pp. 338. *Chambéry,* 1892. 8°.
               8248. f. 27.

—— Personnel ecclésiastique du diocèse de
Chambéry, 1802–93. 1893. 8°. Ac. Chambéry.
Société Académique. Documents. Tom. 7.
               Ac. 34/2.

See also SAVOY.

CHAMBORD. CROY (J. de) Documents
pour l'histoire des Résidences royales des bords
de la Loire. pp. 218. *Paris,* 1894. 8°. 10171. g. 3.

CHAMPAGNE. CHALONS-SUR-MARNE, *Bibliothèque municipale.* Catalogue. Histoire de Champagne. pp. 252. *Châlons,* 1894. 8°. 011899. i. 2.

PETIT (M.) Les Prussiens en Champagne, 1792.
pp. 64. *Paris,* 1890. 12°.   9080. aaa. 33.
See also AISNE : ARDENNES : AUBE : HAUTE-
MARNE : MARNE : YONNE.

CHAMPLAIN, Lake. KEMP (J. F.) Trap
Dikes of the Lake Champlain Region. pp. 62.
1893. 8°. UNITED STATES. *Geological Survey.*
Bulletin. No. 107.   1829. a. 7.

CHAMPLAIN, Lake—*continued.*

MURRAY (W. H. H.) Lake Champlain. pp. 261. *Boston*, 1890. 8°.   10411. c. 41.

CHAÑABAL LANGUAGE. *See* INDIAN LANGUAGES.

CHANNEL ISLANDS. BARREAU (F. H.) ‡Documents relatifs aux Iles de la Manche, 1205–1327. 1891, *etc.* 4°. Ac. Saint Helier. *Société Jersiaise.* Publication 9.   . Ac. 8140.

DE GRAVE (J. W.) Notes on the Churches of the Channel Islands. 1890. 8°. Ac. London. *Huguenot Society.* Proceedings. Vol. 5.
                                                     Ac. 2073.

FAUCHER DE SAINT-MAURICE (N. H. É.) Les États de Jersey et la langue française. pp. 83. *Montréal*, 1893. 8°.   12954. d. 50.

GUERNSEY. Essai sur les institutions de l'île de Guernesey. pp. 232. *Guernesey*, 1889. 8°.
                                                     6605. aaa. 9.

POINGDESTRE (J.) Cæsarea, or a discourse of the Island of Jersey. 1889. 4°. Ac. Saint Helier. *Société Jersiaise.* Publication 10.   Ac. 8140.

ANSTED (D. T.) The Channel Islands. pp. 476. *Lond.* 1893. 8°.   2368. c. 1.

BEVAN (G. P.) Tourist's Guide to the Channel Islands. pp. 108. *Lond.* 1892. 8°. 10352. a. 65.

EPHEM. Godel's Jersey Almanac. *Jersey*, 1892, *etc.* 8°.   P.P. 2507. df.

—— Almanach de la Gazette de Guernesey. *Guernesey*, 1895, *etc.* 8°.   P.P. 2507. dg.

LOCH (J.) A Week in the Channel Islands. *Dublin*, 1894. 8°.   10368. bb. 63.

SIMS (G. R.) Dagonet on our Islands. pp. 172. *Lond.* 1894. 8°.   10368. aa. 50.

THOMPSON (E. S.) and BARLOW (W. S. L.) Climate of the Channel Islands. 1895. 8°. Ac. London. *Medical and Chirurgical Society.* Climates of Great Britain. Vol. 1.   7462. g.

WARD, LOCK AND CO. Guide to the Channel Islands. *Lond.* 1892. 8°.   10368. cc. 47.

CHANTELLE. BENNETOT (S.) Chantelle et son monastère. pp. 63. *Roanne*, 1892. 8°.
                                                     4629. h. 18.

CHANTELOUP. CHAUMEIL (A.) Le château de Chanteloup. pp. 114. *Bruges*, 1893. 8°.
                                                     010171. k. 13.

CHANTILLY. NOEL (C.) Chantilly, 1870–91. pp. 174. *Senlis*, 1891. 8°. 10169. e. 3.

CHAPELLE-BICHE. SURVILLE (A.) Un coin du bocage normand. pp. 396. *Le Mans*, 1893. 8°.   010171. m. 36.

CHAPELTOWN. HABERSHON (M. H.) Chapeltown Researches. pp. 218. *Lond.* 1893. 8°.
                                                     010358. f. 50.

CHARACEAE. HOLTZ (L.) Die Characeen Neuvorpommerns. 1892. 8°. Ac. Griefswald. *Naturwissenschaftlicher Verein.* Mittheilungen. Jahrg. 23.   Ac. 2940.

NORDSTEDT (O.) Australasian Characeæ. *Lund*, 1891, *etc.* 8°.   7074. m,

CHARACTER. BENZONI (R.) Meccanismo e dinamismo nella formazione del Carattere. pp. 53. *Genova*, 1893, 8°.   Pam. 49.

FOUILLÉE (A.) Tempérament et Caractère. pp. 378. *Paris*, 1895. 8°.   8463. g. 3.

LA SCOLA (F.) Osservazioni sulla origine e su talune manifestazioni del Carattere. pp. 232. *Palermo*, 1895. 8°.   8409. g. 44.

PAULHAN (F.) Les Caractères. pp. 237.‡ *Paris*, 1894. 8°.   8409. l. 21.

See also ETHICS : PSYCHOLOGY.

CHARADES. *See* THEATRICALS.

CHARENTE. BOISSONNADE (P.) Histoire des Volontaires de la Charente, 1791–94. pp. 364. *Angoulême*, 1890. 8°.   9231. dd. 1.

See also ANGOULÊME : ANGOUMOIS.

CHARGES, PASTORAL ADDRESSES, etc.

Episcopal.

WESTCOTT (B. F.) *Bp. of Durham.* The Incarnation. A Charge. pp. 53. *Lond.* 1892. 8°.
                                                     4429. b. 36.

ELLICOTT (C. J.) *Bp. of Gloucester and Bristol.* Diocesan Progress. pp. 19. *Gloucester*, 1891. 8°.
                                                     4446. e. 22. (7.)

MACLAGAN (W. D.) *Archbp. of York.* Pastoral Letters and Charges addressed to the diocese of Lichfield. pp. 311. *Lond.* 1892. 8°. 4446. e. 20.

LEGGE (*Hon.* A.) *Bp. of Lichfield.* A Charge. 1895. pp. 67. *Lond.* 1895. 8°.   Pam. 95.

RYLE (J. C.) *Bp. of Liverpool.* Stand Firm! A charge. pp. 44. *Lond.* 1893, 8°.   Pam. 95.

DAVIDSON (R. T.) *Bp. of Winchester.* A Charge to the diocese of Rochester, 1894. pp. 90. *Lond.* 1894. 8°.   4446. e. 23.

FESTING (J. W.) *Bp. of St. Alban's.* A Charge. pp. 54. *St. Albans.* 1892, 8°. 4446. e. 24. (6.)

JONES (W. B. T.) *Bp. of St. David's.* Charge. pp. 60. *Lond.* 1892. 8°.   4446. e. 22. (8.)

SANDFORD (C. W.) *Bp. of Gibraltar.* Pastoral Letter. 1892. pp. 44.   *Lond.* 1892. 8°.
                                                     4446. e. 22. (9.)

—— Pastoral Letter. 1893. pp. 82. *Lond.* 1893. 8°.   4446. e. 22 (11.)

BLYTH (G. F. P.) *Bp. of Jerusalem.* Primary Charge. pp. 79. *Lond.* 1891. 8°.
                                                     4446. e. 22. (6.)

CHURTON (É. T.) *Bp. of Nassau.* The last Seven Years. A Charge. 1893. pp. 20. *Lond.* 1893. 12°.
                                                     4446. e. 22. (10.)

PERRY (W. S.) *Bp. of Iowa.* Episcopal Address. 1890. pp. 13. *Davenport*, 1890. 8°. Pam. 95.

—— Episcopal Address. 1891. pp. 24. *Davenport*, 1891. 8°.   Pam. 95.

—— The Episcopal Address. 1892. pp. 21. *Des Moines*, 1892. 8°.   Pam. 95.

—— Episcopal Address. 1893. pp. 11. *Davenport*, 1893. 8°.   Pam. 95.

LEONARD (J.) *R.C. Bp. of Charedro.* Lenten Pastoral. pp. 9. *Cape Town*, 1895. 8°. Pam. 95.

BERNARD (A. X.) Mandements des Évêques de St Hyacinthe. 4 vol. *Montréal*, 1888–90. 8°.
                                                     4446. f. 5.

Archidiaconal.

PALMER (E.) *Archd. of Oxford.* Charge. 1891. pp. 19. *Oxf.* 1891. 8°.   Pam. 95.

—— Charge. 1892. pp. 19. *Oxf.* 1892. 8°.
                                                     Pam. 95.

SINCLAIR (W. M.) *Archd. of London.* The Church. Charge. pp. 74. *Lond.* 1892. 8°. 4446. e. 21.

—— Sacred Studies. Charge. pp. 47. *Lond.* 1893. 8°.   Pam. 95.

CHARITIES.

Bibliography.

GRANIER (C.) Essai de bibliographie charitable. pp. 449. *Paris*, 1891. 8°.   11899. f. 43.

General.

ACTION. Les œuvres nationales de la prévoyance. pp. 105. *Bordeaux*, 1894. 8°.   08276. k. 29.

BENEVOLENCE. Broadcast Benevolence. pp. 8. *Brighton*, 1894. 8°.   08275. ee. 21. (11.)

CHARITIES.—General—*continued*.

BOSANQUET (B.) Principles and dangers of the Administration of Charity. 1893. 8°. ADDAMS (J.) Philanthropy.   08276. g. 55.

DONATI (G.) Guida di Amministrazione e di contabilità per le Opere pie del Regno. pp. 488. *Perugia*, 1891. 8°.   8229. f. 42.

FERRY (J. B.) Organized Almsgiving. 2 pt. *Lond.* 1894. 8°.   Pam. 92.

GAUTIER (L.) Études, *etc.* pp. 403. *Lille*, 1890. 8°.   4534. c. 27.

GIGLIOLI (G. C.) L'Assistenza pubblica. pp. 148. *Roma*, 1891. 8°.   8277. g. 47.

LOCH (C. S.) Charity Organisation. pp. 106. *Lond.* 1890. 8°.   08276. e. 20.

—— How to Help in Cases of Distress. pp. 208. *Lond.* 1895. 8°.   8285. bbb. 74.

—— Necessary Reforms in Charitable Work. pp. 10. 1882. 8°. LONDON. *Society for Organising Charitable Relief.* Papers.   8277. dd.

LONDON. *Society for Organising Charitable Relief.* Charity Organisation Series. *Lond.* 1892, *etc.* 8°.   08276. f.

QUÉKER (C. de) Le Bienfaisance publique et privée. pp. 89. *Brux.* 1894. 8°.   Pam. 82.

RENTOUL (R. R.) The Reform of our Medical Charities. pp. 139. *Lond.* 1891. 8°.   7687. d. 17.

TRICHT (V. v.) La Charité personnelle. pp. 53. *Namur*, 1893. 8°.   4400. c. 4.

WARNER (A. G.) American Charities. pp. 430. *N.Y.* 1894. 8°.   8282. c. 87.

—— Charities. Relation of the State and the Individual to Philanthropic Work. pp. 12. 1889. 8°. Johns Hopkins University Studies. Notes. 1889. No. 7.   Ac. 2689.

WITT (H. de) La Charité en France. pp. 430. *Paris*, 1892. 8°.   4193. l. 1.

CHIGNELL (R.) London Charities. pp. 64. *Lond.* 1892. 8°.   08276. f. 43.

G. B. Handbook of Catholic Charities in Great Britain. pp. 103. *Lond.* 1894. 8°. 4192. b. 42.

LONDON. *Society for Organising Charitable Relief.* Charities Register. Convalescent section. pp. 78. *Lond.* 1890. 8°.   8277. d. 26.

—— Register of Charity Organisation Societies. 1892. pp. 56. *Lond.* 1893. 8°. 8282. g. 27. (4.)

PÉAN DE SAINT GILLES (A. M.) La Maison Philanthropique de Paris. 1780–1890. pp. 282. *Paris*, 1892. 12°.   8277. b. 67.

MANDON (L.) Histoire du Prêt-Gratuit de Montpellier, 1684–1891. pp. 272. *Montpellier*, 1891. 8°.   8282. ff. 3.

STELLUTI SCALA (I.) Le Istituzioni di beneficienza di Ancona. pp. 241. *Firenze*, 1893. 8°.   08276. i. 32.

SIMONS (E.) Die evangelische Gemeindearmenpflege am Niederrhein. pp. 166. *Bonn*, 1894. 8°.   4662. e. 22.

JENNESS (C. K.) The Charities of San Francisco. pp. 93. *San Francisco*, 1894. 8°. 8285. ee. 45. *See also* CHILDREN: DISTRICT VISITING: HOSPITALS: LONDON, *Poor, etc.*

Law of Charities.

DODD (J T.) Law of Parochial Charities. pp. 99. *Lond.* 1895. 8°.   6426. aaaa. 33.

BRISTOWE (L. S.) Treatise on the Mortmain and Charitable Uses Act, 1891. pp. 120. *Lond.* 1891. 8°.   6355. c. 32.

TYSSEN (A. D.) New Law of Charitable Bequests. pp. 26. *Lond.* 1891. 8°.   6190. ee. 3. (10.)

CHARITIES.—Law of.—*continued*.

HAMILTON (F. A. P.) Law relating to Charities in Ireland. pp. xiii. *Dublin*, 1881. 8°.   6503. aaa. 12.

PERSICO (G.) Il Diritto Italiano sulle istituzioni di beneficenza, *etc.* pp. 165. *Napoli*, 1893. 8°.   5359. ee. 35.

CHARKHARI. JAGESVARAPRASĀDA TRIPĀTHI. Juvenile History of Charkhari. pp. 121. *Benares*, 1886. 8°.   0100.57. ee. 14.

CHARLESTON. *See* UNITED STATES, *Civil War*.

CHARMS, AMULETS, etc. BLACK (G. F.) Scottish Charms and Amulets. 1893. 8°. Ac. Edinburgh. *Society of Antiquaries.* Proceedings. 1892–93.   Ac. 5770/2.

JĪVANJĪ JAMSHEDJĪ MODĪ. Charms for diseases of the eye. pp. 24. *Bombay*, 1894. 8°. 761. c.

MACKENZIE (W.) Gaelic Incantations of the Hebrides. pp. 86. *Inverness*, 1895. 8°.   8631. f. 48.

RQDKINSSOHN (M. L.) History of Amulets, charms, and talismans. pp. 93. *N.Y.* 1893. 8°.   8632. d. 23.

See also FOLK-LORE: OCCULT SCIENCE.

CHARTERHOUSE SCHOOL. WILMOT (E. P. E.) Charterhouse, Old and New. pp. 295. *Lond.* 1895. 8°.   8364. g. 7.

CHARTERHOUSE. Record of all Cricket and Football matches and Rifle contests between Charterhouse and other public schools p.p. 103. *Lond.* 1891. 8°.   7908. c. 36.

CHARTERS AND DEEDS. AC. G.B.&I. *Society of Archivists.* Journal of the Society. *Lond.* 1895, *etc.* 4°.   Ac. 9116.

BERKELEY (F. W. F.) *Baron FitzHardinge.* Catalogue of the Charters and Muniments in the possession of Lord FitzHardinge. pp. 443. *Bristol*, 1892. 8°.   011900. h. 6.

BIRD (S. R. S.) Guide to documents in the Public Record Office. pp. 355. *Lond.* 1891. 8°.   Cat. Desk. B.

ENGLAND AND WALES. *Record Office.* Calendar of the Patent Rolls. *Lond.* 1891, *etc.* 8°.   2076. g.

FRANCE. *M. de l'Instruction Publique.* Rapport sur la situation des archives. *Lille*, 1890, *etc.* 8°.   011901. ee.

HELFERT (J. A. v.) *Baron.* Staatliches Archivwesen. pp. 48. *Wien*, 1893. 8°.   Pam. 6.

LOEHER (F. v.) Archivlehre. pp. 490. *Paderborn*, 1890. 8°.   11899. g. 41.

MARTIN (C. T.) The Record Interpreter. pp. 341. *Lond.* 1892. 8°.   2050. d.

P.P. *Paris.* L'Archiviste. *Paris*, 1893, *etc.* 8°.   P.P. 3554. va.

ROUND (J. H.) Ancient Charters prior to A.D. 1200. 1888, *etc.* 8°. Ac. London. *Pipe Roll Society.* Publications. Vol. x., *etc.* Ac. 8115.

STUBBS (W.) *Bp. of Oxford.* Select Charters. pp. 554. 1895. 8°. Clarendon Press Series.   2319. aa. 7.

THOYTS (E. E.) Key to the Family Deed Chest. pp. 143. *Lond.* 1893. 8°.   7709. b. 47.

See also ÉCOLE DES CHARTES: MANUSCRIPTS: PALAEOGRAPHY: PARISH REGISTERS. For separate Chartularies. *see* ARRAS: BRINKBURN PRIORY: CONVERSANO: CYSOING: DURBON: GUISBOROUGH: LIÈGE: LILLE: LYONS: MARMOUTIER: PERTH: ROMORANTIN: VENDÔME: WORCESTER.

CHARTERS TOWERS GOLD MINES. *See* GOLD.

CHARTRES. Ac. Chartres. *Société Archéo-logique.* BUISSON (P.) Tableau de la ville de Chartres en 1750. *Chartres,* 1891, *etc.* 8°.
Ac. 5293/9.

—— Un Manuscrit Chartrain du 11ᵐᵉ siècle. *Chartres,* 1893. *etc.* 4°.   Ac. 5293/8.

BEAUHAIRE (J.) Chronologie des Évêques, des Curés, des Vicaires de Chartres. pp. 710. *Chateaudun,* 1892. 8°.   4629. k. 21.

JOANNE (P.) Chartres. Guide-Joanne. pp. 18. *Paris,* 1893. 8°.   10168. aa. 9.

MERLET (L.) Inventaire des archives de Chartres. 1888. 4°. Collection des inventaires-sommaires.   1814, 15. b., *etc.*

—— Inventaire des Hospices de Chartres. pp. 224. 1890. 4°. Collection des Inventaires-sommaires.   1814-15. b., *etc.*

CHÂTEAU-DE-MONTROND. MALLARD (C. N. V.) Histoire des deux villes de Saint-Amand et du Château de Montrond. pp. 508. *Saint-Amand,* 1895. 8°.   10171. dd. 6.

CHÂTEAUFORT. COSSONNET (F.) Re_cherches sur Châteaufort. *Versailles,* 1892. 8°.   10106. df. 17. (8.)

CHÂTEAUNEUF. CAIS DI PIERLAS (E.) Le Fief de Châteauneuf du xiᵉ au xvᵉ siècle 1892. 8°. Ac. Turin, *Deputazione di Storia. Patria.* Miscellanea. Tom. 29.   Ac. 6550.

CHATELLIERS. BARBIER DE MONTAULT (X.) L'Architecture à l'abbaye cistercienne de Chatelliers. 1892. 8°. Ac. Poitiers. *Société des Antiquaires.* Mémoires. Sér. 2. Tom. 14.
Ac. 5326.

See also CISTERCIAN ORDER.

CHATELOT. BEURLIN ( ) Les Villages de la Seigneurie du Chatelot. pp. 127. 1889. 8°. Ac. Montbéliard *Société Scientifique.* Mémoires. Vol. 20.   Ac. 375.

CHATHAM. SCAMMELL (S. D.) Chatham. pp. 57. *Chatham,* 1893, 8°. 10348. ccc. 59. (9.)

CHAUMONT. FORESTIER (L.) Société populaire de Chaumont. 1790-94. pp. 67. *Chaumont,* 1892. 8°   9004. c. 16. (7.)

CHAUX-DE-FONDS. CHAUX-DE-FONDS. 1894. La Chaux-de-Fonds, son passé et son présent. pp. 514. *La Chaux-de-Fonds,* 1894. 8°.   10196. cc. 9.

CHEATING. *See* FRAUD.

CHECKERS, Game. HILL (J.) The Game of Checkers. pp. 64. *Lond.* 1894. 8°.
7913. df. 14. (2.)

CHEDDAR. CHEDDAR CLIFFS. Tourist's Guide to Cheddar Cliffs. pp. 51. *Wells.* 1880. 8°.   10352. e. 15. (6.)

CHEESE. *See* DAIRY MANAGEMENT.

CHELLES, Abbey. BERTHAULT ( ) L'Abbaye de Chelles. 2 vol. *Meaux,* 1889-90. 8°.   4629. bb. 5.

CHELTENHAM. CHELTENHAM. Cheltenham illustrated. pp. 52. *Cheltenham,* 1893. 4°.
10352. l. 28.

—— Where to buy at Cheltenham. pp. 88. *Brighton,* 1890. 4°.   10368. k. 22.

——Photographic Views. *Lond.* 1895. 8°.
10360. cc. 62.

HUNTER (A. A.) Cheltenham College Register 1841-89. pp. 469. *Lond.* 1890, 4°. 8365. ff. 22.

CHEMISTRY.

Bibliography.

BOLTON (H. C.) Bibliography of Chemistry, 1492-1892. pp. 1212. 1893. 8°. Smithsonian Miscellaneous Collections. Vol. 36. Ac. 1875/2.

CHEMISTRY.—Bibliography—*continued.*
BOLTON (H. C.) Short list of books on Chemistry. pp. 18. 1895. 16°.   Pam. 6.

—— Titles of Chemical Periodicals, 1887. pp. 4, 1887. 8°.   011900. f. 8. (2.)

—— Bibliography of Analytical Chemistry. 1886, *etc.* 1887, *etc.* 8°.   011903. k.

General and Inorganic.

Practical and Theoretical.

Ac. Edinburgh. *Alembic Club.* Alembic Club Reprints. *Edinb.* 1893. *etc.* 8°.   8909. g.

—— London. *University.* Matriculation Chemistry Papers. 1891. 8°. Tutorial Series.
12205. c. 220.

BARLOW (C. W. C.) and STEWART (R. W.) Matriculation model answers: Chemistry. 1891. 8°. Tutorial Series.   12205. c. 58.

—— Manchester. *Owens College.* Studies from the chemical laboratories of Owens College. *Manch.* 1893, *etc.* 8°.   Ac. 2672/7.

Ac. Rome. *Regia Università.* Istituto Chimico. pp. 503. *Roma,* 1891. 8°.   Ac. 104.

ANDERSON (J. H.) Public School Chemistry. pp. 320. *Lond.* 1895. 8°.   8908. aa. 56.

ATTFIELD (J.) Chemistry. pp. 886. *Lond.* 1893. 8°.   2246. b. 1.

BARFF (F. S.) Introduction to scientific Chemistry. pp. 200. *Lond.* 1893. 8°. 2246. a. 1.

BENDER (A.) and ERDMANN (H.) Chemische Präparatenkunde. *Stuttgart,* 1893, *etc.* 8°.
8908. d.

BISCHOFF (C. A. G.) Handbuch der Stereochemie. *Frankfurt,* 1894, *etc.* 8°. 8909. m.

BLACKIE (W. G.) and SON. Chemistry Demonstration Sheets. *Lond.* 1894. fol.
Tab. 11747. b. (62.)

BLOXAM (C. L.) Chemistry, inorganic and organic. pp. 848. *Lond.* 1895. 8°. 2027. c.

—— Laboratory Teaching. pp. 324. *Lond.* 1893. 8°.   8909. g. 1.

BRANFORD (V. V.) Atlas of Chemistry. *Edinb.* 1885. *etc.* obl. 8°.   8909. bb. 13.

BRIGGS (W.) Synopsis of non-metallic Chemistry. pp. 90. 1892. 8°. Tutorial Series.
12205. c. 79.

CARNEGIE (D.) Law and theory in Chemistry. pp. 222. *Lond.* 1894. 8°.   8909. g. 9.

CARNELLEY (T.) Lecture on the place of Chemical Science. pp. 16. *Aberd.* 1888. 8°.
Pam. 13.

CLOWES (F.) Treatise on practical Chemistry. pp. 469. *Lond.* 1895. 8°.   2246. c. 2.

COOKE (S.) First Principles of Chemistry. pp. 260. *Lond.* 1895. 8°.   8908. g. 15

COOKE (J. P.) Laboratory Practice. pp. 192. *Lond.* 1892. 8°.   8909. bb. 15.

CORNISH (V.) Practical Proofs of Chemical Laws. pp. 52. *Lond.* 1895. 8°.   8909. b. 28.

COX (E. J.) Revision or Examination Sheets. *Lond.* 1891., *etc.* fol.   8530. g. 41.

—— Practical Inorganic Chemistry. pp. 51. *Lond.* 1890. 8°.   8909. cc. 47.

—— Standard Course of elementary chemistry. pp. 348. *Lond.* 1892. 8°.   8909. aaa. 42.

CUTLER (C. W.) Essentials of Chemistry. pp. 296. *N.Y.* 1889. 8°.   8909. bb. 32.

DAMMER (O.) Handbuch der anorganischen Chemie. *Stuttgart,* 1892, *etc.* 8°. 8909. d. 7.

DEBUS (H.) Ueber einige Fundamental-Sätze der Chemie. pp. 99. *Cassel,* 1894. 8°.
8908. bb. 36.

DOBBIN (L.) and WALKER (J.) Chemical Theory for Beginners. pp. 240. *Lond.* 1892. 8°.
8909. aa. 19.

CHEMISTRY.—Analysis—continued.

COOKE (S.) Student's practical Chemistry. Test Tables. pp. 24. Lond. 1895. 8°. Pam. 13.

COX (E. J.) Practical Inorganic Chemistry. pp. 57. Lond. 1894. 8°. 8908. aa. 58.

CROOKES (W.) Select methods in Chemical Analysis. pp. 718. Lond. 1894. 8°. 2246. c. 4.

CLOWES (F.) and COLEMAN (J. B.) Qualitative Chemical Analysis. pp. 180. Lond. 1894. 8°. 8908. ee. 41.

DAVIS (F.) Qualitative Analytical Tables. pp. 22. Lond. 1894. obl. 8°. 8909. de. 2.

FRANCIS (E.) Laboratory Exercise Book for Chemical Students. Lond. 1894. obl. 8°. 8909. a. 26.

GRANT (J.) Laboratory Guide and Analytical Tables. pp. 49. Manch. 1894. 8°. 8908. b. 53.

GUÉRIN (G.) Traité pratique d'Analyse chimique. pp. 492. Paris, 1893. 8°. 8908. h. 37.

HORWILL (E. E.) Course of qualitative Chemical Analysis. pp. 187. 1894. 8°. Blackie's Science Textbooks. 8703. bb.

JURITZ (C. F.) Systematic course of qualitative Chemical Analysis. pp. 71. Cape Town, 1890. 8°. Pam. 13.

KONINCK (L. L. de) Traité de Chimie analytique minérale. 2 tom. Liège, 1894. 8°. 8909. m. 1.

KRAUCH (C.) Die Prüfung der chemischen Reagentien auf Reinheit. pp. 254. Berl. 1891. 8°. 8909. cc. 18.

LETTS (E. A.) Qualitative Analysis Tables. pp. 91. Lond. 1893. 8°. 8908. h. 40.

LEWIS (J.) Practical Chemistry. Analytical tables. Brighton, 1891. fol. 8908. f. 40.

MENSCHUTKIN (N.) Analytical Chemistry. pp. 512. Lond. 1895. 8°. 8909. i. 2.

MILLER (J. A.) Outline of Qualitative Analysis. pp. 58. N.Y. 1895. 8°. 8908. d. 7.

MUTER (J.) Short Manual of Analytical Chemistry. pp. 211. Lond. 1895. 8°. 8908. m. 3.

OSTWALD (W.) Scientific foundations of Analytical Chemistry. pp. 207. Lond. 1895. 8°. 8909. g. 16.

RICHARDSON (A. T.) Tables for Chemical Analysis. Lond. 1890. 8°. 8908. h. 31.

SILVA (R. D.) Traité d'Analyse chimique. pp. 624. Paris, 1891. 8°. 8909. bb. 1.

TAYLOR (R .L.) Practical Chemistry. pp. 13. Manch. 1893. 8°. Pam. 13.

THORPE (T. E.) and MUIR (M. M. P.) Qualitative Chemical Analysis. pp. 246. 1894. 8°. GOODEVE (T. M.) Text-Books of Science. 2244. a. 22.

VALENTIN (W. G.) Course of practical Chemistry. pp. 330. Lond. 1893. 8°. 8908. f. 44.

WHITTAKER (T.) Practical Inorganic Chemistry. pp. 23. Lond. 1893. 8°. Pam. 13.

—— Organic Analysis. pp. 23. Lond. 1893. 8°. Pam. 13.

WHITTAM (W. G.) First Book of Chemical Analysis. Eastbourne, 1891, etc. 8°. 8909. b. 51.

WILLS (G. S. V.) Manual of Practical Analysis. pp. 121. Lond. 1894. 8°. 8909. f. 14.

Analysis, Quantitative.

ADDYMAN (F. T.) Agricultural Analysis. Manual of quantitative analysis. pp. 200. Lond. 1893. 8°. 7078. de. 26.

CLOWES (F.) and COLEMAN (J. B.) Quantitative Chemical Analysis. pp. 533. Lond. 1895. 8°. 8909. g. 17.

KONINCK (L. L. de) Traité de Chimie analytique minérale. 2 tom. Liège, 1894. 8°. 8909. m. 1.

SPRAUL (A.) Anleitung zum massanalytischen Arbeiten im Fabrik-Laboratorium. pp. 67. Stuttgart, 1893. 8°. Pam. 13.

CHEMISTRY—continued.

Analysis, Volumetric. See GAS.

Applied.

ARENDS (G.) Synonymen-Lexikon. Eine Sammlung der Benennungen aus dem Gebiete der technischen Chemie. Leipz. 1891. etc. 8°. 8908. k. 15.

GUICHARD (P.) Précis de la Chimie industrielle. pp. 422. Paris, 1894. 12°. 8909. f. 13.

HALPHEN (G. H.) La Pratique des Essais industriels. Matières minérales. pp. 342. Paris, 1892. 8°. 7942. aa. 71.

—— Matières organiques. pp. 351. Paris, 1893. 12°. 8909. bb. 34.

HOLMES (F. M.) Chemists and their Wonders. Application of chemistry to arts and manufactures. pp. 160. Lond. 1895. 8°. 8909. f. 23.

RENARD (A.) Traité de chimie appliquée à l'industrie. pp. 846. Paris, 1890. 8°. 8908. i. 23.

WAGNER (J. R. v.) Handbuch der chemischen Technologie. pp. 1164. Leipz. 1893. 8°. 2246. e. 13.

—— Manual of Chemical Technology. pp. 968. Lond. 1892. 8°. 2246. d. 7.

WITT (O. N.) Die chemische Industrie in ihren Beziehungen zum Patentwesen. pp. 143. Berl. 1893. 8°. 8908. d. 13.

ACLAND (Right Hon. Sir T. D.) Introduction to the Chemistry of Farming. pp. 222. Lond. 1891. 8°. 07076. e. 29.

ADDYMAN (F. T.) Agricultural Analysis. pp. 200. Lond. 1893. 8°. 7078. de. 26.

ADUCCO (A.) Chimica agraria. pp. 325. Milano, 1893. 8°. 012200. h. 47.

CHURCH (A. H.) Laboratory Guide. pp. 292. Lond. 1894. 8°. 2246. c. 1.

COLEMAN (J. B.) and ADDYMAN (F. T.) Practical Agricultural Chemistry. pp. 88. Lond. 1893. 8°. 8909. aa. 28.

DAVIS (G. W.) Hand-book on the Chemistry of Hops, Plants and manures. pp. 118. Lond. 1895. 8°. 7073. aa. 2.

DEHÉRAIN (P. P.) Traité de Chimie agricole. pp. 904. Paris, 1892. 8°. 07076. l. 5.

JOHNSTON (J. F. W.) Elements of Agricultural Chemistry. pp. 482. Edinb. 1894. 8°. 07076. o. 53.

MAYER (A.) Lehrbuch der Agrikulturchemie. Heidelberg, 1895, etc. 8°. 07077. i.

POSSANNER (B. v.) Chemische Technologie der landwirtschaftlichen Gewerbe. pp. 786. Wien, 1893. 4°. 8906. g. 18.

SIBSON (A.) Agricultural Chemistry. pp. 348. Lond. 1892. 8°. 7075. c. 2.

U.S. Department of Agriculture. Chemical Division. Circular. Wash. 1894, etc. 8°. 7053. e. 50.

WARINGTON (R.) Chemistry of the Farm. pp. 160. 1894. 8°. Handbook of the Farm Series. No. 1. 7078. bb.

WILEY (H. W.) Proceedings of the convention of the Association of Official Agricultural Chemists. pp. 403. 1894. 8°. See UNITED STATES. Department of Agriculture. Chemical Division. Bulletin. No. 43. 7053. c. 9.

KOENIG (J.) Chemie der menschlichen Nahrungsund Genussmittel. Berl. 1889, etc. 8°. 7942. l.

MOLISCH (H.) Grundriss einer Histochemie der pflanzlichen Genussmittel. pp. 65. Jena, 1891. 8°. Pam. 13.

Ac. Chatham. Engineer Institute. Notes on the Chemistry of Building Materials. pp. 155. Chatham, 1888. 8°. 8908. b. 48.

CHEMISTRY.—Applied—*continued*.

PHILLIPS (H. J.) Engineering Chemistry.
pp. 398. *Lond.* 1894. 8°.   8909. g. 10.

WILLIAMS (W. M.) Chemistry of Iron and Steel.
pp. 420. *Lond.* 1890. 8°.   7106. a. 31.

GRIFFIN (R. B.) and LITTLE (A. D.) Chemistry
of Paper-making. pp. 517. *N.Y.* 1894, 8°.
   07944. i. 1.

GEORGIEVICS (G. v.) Lehrbuch der chemischen
Technologie der Gespinstfasern.
Leipz. 1895, etc. 8°.   8908. l.

See also infra: Medical: PHOTOGRAPHY.

Atomic Theory. *See* ATOMIC THEORY.

Chemical Calculation.

COX (E. J.) Problems in chemical Arithmetic,
etc. pp. 76. *Lond.* 1891. 8°.   8909. a. 22

DITTMAR (W.) Chemical Arithmetic.
Glasg. 1890, etc. 8°.   8908. h. 32.

FRANK (C. E.) Arithmetical problems in elementary Chemistry. pp. 62. *Clifton,* 1892. 8°.
   8909. aaa. 22.

HELM (G.) Grundzüge der mathematischen
Chemie. pp. 138. *Leipz.* 1894. 8°. 8908. k. 20.

THORPE (T. E.) A series of chemical Problems.
pp. 88. *Lond.* 1890. 8°.   8909. aa. 11.

WHITELEY (R. L.) Chemical Calculations.
pp. 100. *Lond.* 1892. 8°.   8908. e. 60.

WOODWARD (C. J.) Arithmetical Chemistry.
Lond. 1890, etc. 8°.   8909. aaa.

WOOTTON (H.) Problems in chemical Physics.
pp. 67. *Lond.* 1893. 8°.   8909. bb. 39.

Electro-Chemistry.

DAVY (*Sir* H.) Electrochemische Untersuchungen. pp. 92. 1893. 8°. Ostwald's Klassiker
der exacten Wissenschaften. Nr. 45. 8706. de.

GORE (G.) Electro-Chemistry. pp. 134.
Lond. 1888. 8°.   8757. cc. 27.

OSTWALD (W.) Elektrochemie.
Leipz. 1894, etc. 8°.   8757. k.

SMITH (E. F.) Electro-chemical Analysis.
pp. 116. *Phila.* 1890. 8°.   8757. aa. 33.

TOMMASI (D.) Traité d'Électrochimie. pp. 1102.
Paris, 1889. 8°.   8757. i. 14.

VOGEL (F.) and ROESSING (A.) Handbuch der
Elektrochemie. pp. 280. *Stuttgart,* 1891. 8°.
   8757. i. 17.

History.

BERTHELOT (M. P. E.) Histoire des sciences. La
Chimie au moyen âge. 3 tom. *Paris,* 1893. 4°.
   8906. g. 14.

BOLTON (H. C.) Progress of Chemistry. 1893. 8°.
   Pam. 13.

ECCLES (R. G.) The Evolution of Chemistry.
1891. 8°. Ac. Brooklyn. *Ethical Association.*
Evolution Series. No. 5.   7006. bbb.

JAGNAUX (R.) Histoire de la Chimie. 2 tom.
Paris, 1891. 8°.   8908. l. 9.

MEYER (E. v.) A History of Chemistry.
pp. 556. *Lond.* 1891. 8°.   8909. cc. 15.

THORPE (T. E.) Essays in historical Chemistry.
pp. 381. *Lond.* 1894. 8°.   8908. d. 6.
See also ALCHEMY.

Medical, Physiological.

ARTHUS (M.) Éléments de Chimie physiologique.
pp. 347. *Paris,* 1895. 8°.   8909. aa. 37.

HALLIBURTON (W. D.) Text-book of chemical
Physiology and Pathology. pp. 874.
Lond. 1891. 8°.   7419. i. 7.

—— Essentials of chemical Physiology. pp. 166.
Lond. 1893. 8°.   8908. b. 47.

CHEMISTRY.—Medical—*continued*.

HAMMARSTEN (O.) Lehrbuch der physiologischen
Chemie. pp. 425. *Wiesbaden,* 1891. 8°.
   7407. f. 23.

—— Text-book of physiological Chemistry.
pp. 511. *N.Y.* 1893. 8°.   7407. e. 5.

HUGUET (R.) Traité de Chimie médicale et
pharmaceutique. pp. 1010. *Paris,* 1894. 8°.
   8908. d. 8.

KIMMINS (C. W.) Chemistry of Life and Health.
pp. 167. 1892. 8°. University Extension Series.
   012202.

LARKIN (F. C.) and LEIGH (R.) Outlines of physiological Chemistry. pp. 86. *Lond.* 1891. 8°.
   8909. aaa. 37.

LEA (A. S.) Chemical Basis of the Body.
pp. 290. *Lond.* 1892. 8°.   2024. bb.

NEUMEISTER (R.) Lehrbuch der physiologischen
Chemie. *Jena,* 1893, etc. 8°.   7406. dd.

ROEHMANN (F.) Anleitung zum chemischen Arbeiten für Studirende der Medecin. pp. 108.
Berl. 1890. 8°.   8908. i. 22.

SALKOWSKI (E.) Practicum der physiologischen
und pathologischen Chemie. pp. 314.
Berl. 1893. 8°.   8907. c. 16.

WESENER (F.) Lehrbuch der chemischen Unter-
suchungsmethoden zur Diagnostik innerer
Krankheiten. pp. 280. 1890. 8°. Wreden's
Sammlung medizinischer Lehrbücher. Bd. 15.
   7321. h.

Organic.

AUWERS (K.) Die Entwicklung des Stereochemie.
pp. 157. *Heidelberg,* 1890. 8°.   8908. h. 33.

BERNTHSEN (A.) Text-book of Organic Chemistry.
pp. 596. *Lond.* 1894. 8°.   8909. f. 16.

BUNSEN (R. W. E.) Untersuchungen über die
Kakodylreihe. pp. 148. 1891. 8°. Ostwald's
Klassiker der Wissenschaften. No. 27. 8706. de.

FISCHER (E.) Exercises in preparation of Organic
Compounds. pp. 80. *Glasg.* 1895. 8°.
   8909. b. 27.

GATTERMANN (L.) Die Praxis des organischen
Chemikers. pp. 303. *Leipz.* 1894. 8°.
   8908. k. 21.

HOFF (J. H. van 't) Chemistry in Space.
pp. 128. 1891. 8°. Clarendon Press Series.
   2319. a. 25.

PASTEUR (L.) Ueber die Asymmetrie bei natür-
lich vorkommenden organischen Verbindungen.
1891. 8°. Ostwald's Klassiker der Wissenschaften. No. 28.   8706. de.

LEAPER (C. J.) Outlines of Organic Chemistry.
pp. 118. *Lond.* 1892. 8°.   8908. c. 62.

LIEBIG (J. v.) Abhandlung über die Constitution der organischen Säuren. pp. 86. 1891. 8°.
Ostwald's Klassiker der Wissenschaften. No. 26.
   8706. ee.

KRAFFT (F.) Organische Chemie. pp. 725.
Leipz. 1893. 8°.   8908. d. 3.

KUEHLING (O.) Handbuch der stickstoffhaltigen
Orthocondensations-Producte. pp. 628.
Berl. 1893. 8°.   8908. d. 10.

LASSAR-COHN ( ) Laboratory Manual of Organic
Chemistry. pp. 403. *Lond.* 1895. 8°.
   8909. f. 24.

MEIER (V.) and JACOBSON (P.) Lehrbuch der
organischen Chemie. *Leipz.* 1891, etc. 8°.
   8908. d.

PERKIN (W. H.) and KIPPING (F. S.) Organic
Chemistry. *Lond.* 1894, etc.. 8°. 8909. f. 9.

—— Progress of Organic Chemistry. pp. 20.
Manch. 1893. 8°.   Pam. 13.

PINNER (A.) Die Imidoäther und ihre Derivate.
pp. 303. *Berl.* 1892. 8°.   8907. cc. 6.

CHEMISTRY.—Organic—*continued.*

PREYER (W.) Die organischen Elemente und ihre Stellung im System. pp. 47.
Wiesbaden, 1891. 8°.   8909. cc. 7.

REMSEN (I.) Introduction to the study of the Compounds of Carbon. pp. 362. *Bost.* 1893. 8°.
    8909. f. 1.

RICHTER (V. v.) Chemie der Kohlenstoff.
pp. 1132. *Bonn*, 1891. 8°.   8909. bb. 8.

—— Chemistry of the Carbon Compounds.
pp. 1040. *Phila.* 1892. 8°.   8908. b. 49.

SCHORLEMMER (C.) Rise and development of Organic Chemistry. pp. 280. *Lond.* 1894. 8°.
    8909. g. 13.

SOHN (C. E.) Dictionary of the active principles of Plants. pp. 194. *Lond.* 1894. fol. 8909. a. 25.

STREATFEILD (F. W.) Practical work in Organic Chemistry. pp. 156. 1894. 8°. Finsbury Technical Manuals.   7245. cc.

TURNER (C.) Manual of Organic Chemistry.
Manch. 1893, *etc.* 8°.   8908. b. 17.

TURPIN (G. S.) Lessons in Organic Chemistry.
Lond. 1894, *etc.* 8°.   8909. f. 10.

WHITELEY (R. L.) Organic Chemistry. pp. 291.
Lond. 1895. 8°.   8909. g. 14.

See also supra : Analysis.

    Pharmaceutical. *See* CHEMISTS AND DRUGGISTS : PHARMACY.

    Photographic. *See* PHOTOGRAPHY.

    Technical. *See supra : Applied.*

    Thermodynamics of. *See* HEAT.

CHEMISTS AND DRUGGISTS. BEASLEY (H.) Druggists' general Receipt Book. pp. 538.
Lond. 1895. 8°.   7509. aa. 13.

CHANCEREL (R.) Les Apothicaires de Paris. 1312–1780. pp. 121. *Dijon*, 1892. 8°. 7680. e. 8.

ELLIOTT (D.) Druggists' Price Book.
Lond. 1891. 12°.   7509. a. 9.

FLOOD (J. W.) Norges Apothekere, 1588–1889.
pp. 216. *Kristiania*, 1889. 8°. 10761. f. 1.

LONDON. *Livery Companies. Apothecaries.* Calendar of the Society of Apothecaries.
Lond. 1894, *etc.* 8°.   7680. de.

PETERSEN (E. P. F.) De gjældende Love for Apothekervæsenet i Danmark. pp. 132.
Kjøbenh. 1893. 8°.   5725. b. 19.

SLEMAN (R. R.) Papers set for the Examinations for Licentiate, Society of Apothecaries, London. pp. 18. *Lond.* 1890. 8°.   Pam. 39.

See also BOTANY, *Medical :* CHEMISTRY, *Medical :* PHARMACY.

CHENÔVE. MARCO (H.) Histoire de Chenôve.
pp. 351. *Dijon*, 1893. 8°. 010171. k. 9.

CHEPSTOW. Views in and around Chepstow. *Lond.* 1895. 8°.   10360. cc. 56.

MARSH (J. F.) Annals of Chepstow Castle.
pp. 287. *Exeter*, 1883. 4°.   9914. d. 4.

CHEROKEE INDIANS. *See* INDIANS.

CHESHIRE. AXON (E.) Bibliography of Cheshire Antiquities, 1890. pp. 12.
Manch. 1891. 8°.   011900. ee. 6. (16.)

—— Bibliography of Cheshire Antiquities, 1891. pp. 13. *Manch.* 1892. 8°. 011902. m. 22. (1.)

Ac. Manchester. *Chetham Society.* Remains. N.S. Vol 32. Notes on Churches of Cheshire. pp. 152. *Manch.* 1894. 4°.   Ac. 8120.

ANDREWS (W.) Bygone Cheshire. pp. 253.
Chester, 1895. 8°.   010358. i. 15.

MALBON (T.) Memorials of the Civil War in Cheshire. pp. 275. 1889. 8°. Ac. Manchester. *Record Society.* Publications. Vol. 19. Ac. 8121.

PHILIPS (N. G.) Views of Old Halls in Cheshire, 1822–24. pp. 121. *Lond.* 1893. fol. 1788. c. 28.

CHESHIRE—*continued.*

SULLEY (P.) The Hundred of Wirral. pp. 400.
Birkenhead, 1889. 8°.   10358. dd. 22.

THORNELY (J. L.) Monumental Brasses of Cheshire. *Hull*, 1893. 8°.   7709. bb. 62.

See also CHESTER.

CHESNOY. ROY (M.) Un épisode de la Fronde. Rencontre du 9 Janvier 1652 au Chesnoy. pp. 46. *Sens*, 1893. 8°.   Pam. 28.

CHESS. ARNOUS DE RIVIÈRE (J.) Traité-manuel du jeu des Échecs. *Corbeil*, 1892, *etc.* 8°.
    7913. f.

ASCHARIN (A.) Schach-Humoresken. pp. 198.
Riga, 1894. 8°.   7912. aa. 37.

BACHMANN (L.) Geistreiche Schachpartien.
Ansbach, 1893, *etc.* 16°.   7913. df.

BARDELEBEN (C. v.) and MIESES (J.) Lehrbuch des Schachspiels. pp. 480.
Leipz. 1894. 8°.   7913. f. 45.

—— Die Wiener Partie. pp. 80.
Leipz. 1893. 8°.   7912. ee. 1. (12.)

BERLIN. *Schachgesellschaft.* Fest Zeitung zur 62. Stiftungsfeier der Schachgesellschaft. pp. 8. *Berl.* 1889. 8°.   7912. f. 1. (5.)

—— Einladung zur Feier des 62-jährigen Stiftungsfestes der Schachgesellschaft.
Berl. 1889. 8°.   7912. f. 2. (4.)

BILGUER (P. R. v.) Handbuch des Schachspiels. pp. 852. *Leipz.* 1891. 8°. 7915. g. 1.

BINET (A.) Psychologie des grands joueurs d'Échecs. pp. 364. *Paris*, 1894. 8°.
    8462. bb. 44.

BIRD (H. E.) Chess History. pp. 136.
Lond. 1893. 8°.   7913. dd. 11.

—— Chess Novelties. pp. 304. *Lond.* 1895. 8°.
    7912. b. 1.

BLAND (J.) Grandchess. pp. 5. *Lond.* 1892. 16°.
    Pam. 83.

BLÂTHY (O. T.) Vielzügige Schachaufgaben.
pp. 82. *Leipz.* 1890. 8°. 7912. ee. 2. (2.)

BRUNET Y BELLET (J.) El Ajedrez. pp. 424.
Barcelona, 1890. 8°.   7915. e. 24.

BURT (J.) The Bristol Chess Club. pp. 202.
Bristol. 1883. 8°.   7913. cc. 33.

CHESS. Manual for beginners. pp. 63.
Lond. 1894. 8°.   7913. bbb. 49.

CUMMING (G. A. W.) Caissa's Ghost. One hundred chess problems. pp. 80.
Kirksville, 1890. 8°. 7913. de. 17. (1.)

DUFRESNE (J.) Das Buch der Schachmeister-partien. pp. 203. *Leipz.* 1893. 16°.
    7913. de. 15.

—— Examples of Chess Master-Play.
New Barnet, 1893, *etc.* 16°.   7913. df. 12.

ELLIS (J. H.) Chess Sparks. pp. 160.
Lond. 1895. 8°.   7913. e. 30.

FREEBOROUGH (E.) Chess Openings. pp. 292.
Lond. 1893. 8°.   7913. e. 23.

—— Chess Endings. pp. 240. *Lond.* 1891. 8°.
    7913. e. 18.

—— Select Chess End-Games. pp. 86.
Lond. 1895. 8°.   7913. e. 57.

GOSSIP (G. H. D.) The Chess-Player's Manual.
pp. 884. 122. *N.Y.* 1891. 8°.   2264. c. 5.

—— Theory of Chess openings. pp. 336.
Lond. 1891. 8°.   7913. e. 11.

—— Chess-player's Vade Mecum. pp. 83.
Lond. 1891. *obl.* 8°.   7915. de. 3.

—— Modern Chess Brilliancies. pp. 75.
Lond. 1892. 8°.   7913. ccc. 37.

—— Chess Player's Guide to Games at Odds.
pp. 64. *Lond.* 1893. *obl.* 8°.   7913. de. 12.

CHICAGO—*continued.*

Ac. Chicago. *University.* Annual Register. *Chicago*, 1894, etc. 4°.　　　Ac. 2691. d.

For the Chicago Exposition, 1893, *see* EXHIBITIONS, Pt. I. and II.

CHICHESTER. CAVIS-BROWN (J.) An old English Hospital. S. Mary's, Chichester. pp. 12. *Lond.* 1894. 8°.　　4705. e. 34. (5.)

WARD, LOCK AND Co. Historical handbook to Chichester Cathedral. *Lond.* 1890. 8°. 010358. l. 22.

CHIGWELL. CHIGWELL SCHOOL. The Chigwell Kalender. pp. 104. *Lond.* 1886. 8°. 8364. aaa. 45.

CHILDREN.

General.

ALDRICH (A. R.) Children, their models and critics. pp. 158. *N.Y.* 1893. 8°.　8311. a. 3.

AMICIS (G. de) L' Infanzia nella classe popolare. pp. 139. *Genova*, 1890. 8°.　8285. bb. 43.

BALDWIN (J. M.) Mental Development in the Child. pp. 496. *N.Y.* 1895. 8°.　8462. b. 41.

BARRY (C. A.) What shall we do with our Children? pp. 35. *Bost.* 1891. 8°. 8310. a. 30.

COMPAYRÉ (G.) L'Évolution intellectuelle et morale de l'enfant. pp. 371. *Paris*, 1893. 8°. 8462. g. 6.

DURAND (H.) Le Règne de l'Enfant. pp. 374. *Paris*, 1889. 18°.　011840. g. 80.

HARRISON (E.) Study of Child-nature. pp. 207. *Chicago*, 1891. 8°.　8309. cc. 47.

LUARD (J.) Royal Children. pp. 570. *Lond.* 1893. 8°.　10805. aaa. 38.

LOMBROSO (P.) Saggi di Psicologia del Bambino. pp. 284. *Torino*, 1894. 8°.　8462. h. 16.

MACRAE (D.) Quaint Sayings of Children. pp. 164. *Glasg.* 1895. 8°.　12316. cc. 52.

MEYER (B.) The Child physically and mentally. pp. 155. *N.Y.* 1893. 8°.　7581. aaa. 28.

NORTHCOTE (C.) Talks with Mothers. pp. 119. *Lond.* 1894. 8°.　8409. d. 3.

PEREZ (B.) Le Caractère de l'enfant à l'homme. pp. 308. *Paris*, 1892. 8°.　8462. f. 12.

PREYER (W.) The Mind of the Child. 2 pt. *N.Y.* 1893. 8°.　8311. aa. 34.

—— Mental development in the Child. pp. 170. *Lond.* 1894. 8°.　8311. aa. 33.

QUEYRAT (F.) L'Imagination chez l Enfant. pp. 162. *Paris*, 1893. 12°.　8463. b. 44.

SMITH (T. O.) Essay on the Care of Children. pp. 31. *Glasg.* 1894. 8°.　8409. ccc. 27. (9.)

SPENGLER (C.) L'avenir de nos Enfants. pp. 116. *Lausanne*, 1890. 8°.　Pam. 17.

SULLY (J.) Studies of Childhood. pp. 527. *Lond.* 1895. 8°.　8465. cc. 45.

THOROLD (A. W.) *Bp. of Winchester.* On Children. pp. 75. *Lond.* 1895. 8°.　8409. ccc. 29.

WIGGIN (K. D.) Children's Rights. pp. 235. *Lond.* 1892. 8°.　8308. aaa. 26.

BATAILLE (F.) Anthologie de l'enfance. pp. 342. *Paris*, 1893. 12°.　11483. dc. 19.

FIELD (L. F.) The Child and his Book. pp. 358. *Lond.* 1895. 8°.　011850. g. 63.

FORD (R.) Ballads of Bairnhood. pp. 348. *Paisley*, 1894. 8°.　11601. dd. 15.

NEWELL (W. W.) Games of American Children. pp. 242. *N.Y.* 1884. 4°.　7908. dc. 35.

SCUDDER (H. E.) Childhood in Literature and Art. pp. 253. *Bost.* 1894. 8°.　11850. cc. 43.

CHILDREN—*continued.*

Charities: Protection and Employment of Children.

BLACHE (R.) La protection de l'Enfance dans le département de la Seine. pp. 8. *Paris*, 1895. 8°.　　Pam. 34.

CRY. The Cry of the Children. pp. 123. *Lond.* 1892. 8°.　8277. de 17.

DETH (G. v.) De Weesinrichting te Neerbosch. 2 pt. *Amst.* 1893. 8°.　8282. e. 40.

FISCHER (A.) Die Waisenpflege der Stadt Berlin. pp. 310. *Berl.* 1892. 8°.　08276. h. 32.

GUERS (É.) L'Orphelinat d'Auteuil et l'abbé Roussel. pp. 326. *Paris*, 1891. 8°. 08276. f. 5.

HARLEZ (C. de) L'infanticide en Chine. pp. 46. *Louvain*, 1893. 8°.　8277. e. 45.

LAMMERS (A.) Die Verpflanzung armer Kinder ins Freie. pp. 31. 1890. 8°. Deutsche Zeit- und Streit- Fragen. N.F. Jahrg. 5. 12209. f.

LONDON. *National Refuges for Children* Our Work on behalf of the homeless. *Lond.* 1888. 8°.　8277. ee. 2. (5.)

P.P. *London.* Brothers and Sisters. Quarterly paper for children. *Lond.* 1890, etc. 8°. P.P. 1103. ccb. & 2239.

RIIS (J. A.) Children of the Poor. pp. 300. *Lond.* 1892. 8°.　4192. ee. 26.

TUCKWELL (G. M.) The State and its Children. pp. 164. 1894. 8°. GIBBINS (H. de B.) Social Questions.　08276. e.

SAINT JOHN, *Washington, Parish of.* Report of the Church Orphanage, Washington. *Wash.* 1895. 8°.　8282. e. 42.

SALLARÉS Y PLA (J.) El Trabajo de las Mujeres y de los Niños. pp. 211. *Sabadell*, 1892. 8°. 08276. i. 15.

SMITH (G.) Gypsy Children. 2 pt. *Rugby*, 1893. 8°.　10007. aaa. 4.

THULIÉ (J. B. H.) Colonisation par les enfants assistés. pp. 108. *Paris*, 1891. 8°.　Pam. 66.

U.S. *National Conference of Charities.* History of Child Saving in the United States. pp. 261, 59. *Bost.* 1893. 8°.　8282. ff. 4.

ZÜRICH. *Internationaler Kongress für Ferienkolonien.* Verhandlungen. pp. 115. *Hamb.* 1889. 8°.　7404. d. 9.

See also infra : Criminal : Laws.

Criminal Children, etc.

BERGASSE (P.) Comité de défense des Enfants. Rapport sur les devoirs de l'avocat dans la défense des enfants. pp. 24. *Marseille*, 1894. 12°. 5405. dc. 6. (6.)

FERRIANI (L.) Minorenni delinquenti. pp. 571. *Milano*, 1895. 8°.　6057. dd. 1.

FLANDIN (P.) Comité de la défense des Enfants. Exposé de la procédure suivie dans le département de la Seine. pp. 56. *Paris*, 1891. 8°. 5405. dc. 6. (3.)

GUILLOT (A) Observations au sujet des Enfants traduits en justice. pp. 70. *Paris*, 1890. 8°. 5408. e. 9.

HARTMANN (C. C.) Der jugendliche Verbrecher im Strafhause. pp. 55. 1892. 8°. Deutsche Zeit- und Streit-Fragen. N. F. Heft 99. 12209. f.

NICOLAY (F.) Les Enfants mal élevés. pp. 530. *Paris*, 1890. 8°.　8309. ee. 33.

RAUX ( ) Nos Jeunes Détenus. pp. 268. *Lyon*, 1890. 8°.　6057. e. 19.

ROGER-MILÈS (L.) Nos Femmes et nos Enfants. Choses sanglantes et criminalité. pp. 358. *Paris*, 1893. 12°.　8115. dc. 28.

TOMEL (G.) and ROLLET (H.) Les Enfants en Prison. pp. 299. *Paris*, 1892. 12°. 6057. aa. 35.

CHILDREN.—Criminal, etc.—*continued.*

WINSLOW (L. S. F.) On Eccentricity of Youth leading to crime. pp. 54. *Lond.* 1895. 8°.
07305. f. 19. (10.)
See also infra : PROTECTION, *etc.* : CRIME. For Reformatories, *see* PRISONS.

Laws relating to Children and Minors.

BONZON (J.) La législation de l'Enfance, 1789–1894. pp. 268. *Paris*, 1894. 8°. 5406. ccc. 2.
HALL (W. C.) The Law relating to Children. pp. 184. *Lond.* 1894. 8°. 6485. df. 11.
HOCHHEIMER (L.) Treatise on the Law relating to the Custody of Infants. pp. 249.
Baltimore, 1887. 8°. 6614. f. 10.
LEWIS (G. C.) and BARROWS (H. M.) Prevention of Cruelty to Children Act, 1894. pp. 17.
Lond. 1894. 8°. 6485. aa. 28.
MATTHEWS (J. B.) Law relating to Children. pp. 400. *Lond.* 1895. 8°. 6325. cc. 26.
DRUCLER (G.) La Protection des Enfants maltraités. pp. 415. *Paris*, 1894. 8°. 5403. dd. 5.
BARAZETTI (C.) Die Vormundschaft (la Tutelle), die Pflegschaft, *etc.* pp. 662.
Hannover, 1894. 8°. 05604. k. 7.
See also supra : Charities : Criminal Children.

Medicine, Hygiene, Diseases.

BABY. How to feed and clothe the Baby.
Leicester, 1893. fol. 1830. c. 1. (25.)
BRAIDWOOD (P. M.) Mother's Help to the management of her children. pp. 134. *Lond.* 1894. 8°.
07581. de. 41.
BRUECKE (E. W.) Wie behütet man Leben und Gesundheit seiner Kinder? pp. 230.
Wien, 1892. 8°. 07581. c. 22.
BUCK (H.) Infant Life. pp. 144.
Lond. 1889. 12°. 7581. a. 8.
BULL (W.) How shall I feed my Infant? pp. 18.
Lond. 1890. 8°. Pam. 39.
BURNETT (J. C.) Delicate, backward, and stunted children. pp. 164. *Lond.* 1895. 8°. 07581. de. 43.
CAMERER (W.) Der Stoffwechsel des Kindes von der Geburt bis zur Beendigung des Wachstums. pp. 150. *Tübingen*, 1894. 8°. 07581. h. 2.
CHAVASSE (P. H.) Counsel to a Mother. pp. 256.
Lond. 1890. 8°. 2256. a. 5.
CHEADLE (W. B.) On the principles to be observed in Artificial Feeding of Infants. pp. 248.
Lond. 1894. 8°. 07581. de. 42.
CLOTTEN (F. E.) Necessity of a Sanitary Reform in Infant Rearing. pp. 45. *Liverp.* 1888. 12°.
Pam. 39.
COLOMBO (V.) Il libro delle Mamme. 2 pt.
Bergamo, 1893. 8°. 7581. ccc. 4.
DAVIS (E. P.) and KEATING (J. M.) Mother and Child. pp. 472. *Phila.* 1893. 8°. 07581. e. 15.
DEWER (A. L.) Our Baby. pp. 136.
Bristol, 1891. 8°. 07581. de. 18.
HELLIER (J. B.) Infancy and Infant-rearing. pp. 121. *Lond.* 1895. 8°. 7581. df. 37.
HIDALGO U. (W.) Medicina doméstica de la infancia. pp. 440. *Santiago*, 1885. 8°. 07581. ee. 1.
KINGSCOTE (G.) The English Baby in India. pp. 184. *Lond.* 1893. 8°. 7581. ccc. 1.
KÖRÖSI (J.) Ueber den Einfluss des elterlichen Alters auf die Lebenskraft der Kinder.
Jena, 1892. 8°. Pam. 39.
MARSH (J. J.) Nursery Hand-book. pp. 48.
Lond. 1891. 8°. 7321. aaa. 22. (4.)
MEYER (B.) The Child physically and mentally. pp. 155. *N.Y.* 1893. 8°. 7581. aaa. 28.
PARKS (M. K.) Our Children : how to rear them.
Lond. 1895. 16°. Pam. 39.

CHILDREN.—Medicine, etc.—*continued.*

P.P. *London.* Mother's Nursery Guide.
Lond. 1888–92. 8°. P.P. 5992. cd.
PORTER (W. T.) Relation between the Growth of Children and their deviation from the physical type of their sex and age. 1893. 8°. Ac. Saint Louis. *Academy of Science.* Transactions. Vol. 6. No. 10. Ac. 3061.
PRIZE ESSAYS. Essays on feeding School Children. pp. 251. *Lond.* 1890. 8°. 8282. df. 39.
SAUNDERS (G. R.) Food-Management of Infants. pp. 108. *Wanganui*, 1892. 8°. 7581. bbb. 34.
STABLES (W. G.) Mother's Book of Health. pp. 233. *Lond.* 1894. 8°. 07581. f. 4.
STARR (L.) Hygiene of the Nursery. pp. 293.
Lond. 1895. 8°. 7391. de. 7.
SUMNER (M. E.) Nursery Training. pp. 63.
Winchester, 1892. 16°. 7581. a. 9.
WESTLAND (A.) The Wife and Mother. pp. 282.
Lond. 1892. 8°. 7581. bb. 15.

ALLBUTT (H. A.) Infant Mortality and premature Death. pp. 8. *Lond.* 1894. 8°. 7641. c. 5. (5.)
ASHBY (H.) and WRIGHT (G. A.) The Diseases of Children. pp. 757. *Lond.* 1892. 8°. 07581. e. 16.
BALLANTYNE (J. W.) Introduction to the Diseases of Infancy. pp. 242. *Edinb.* 1891. 8°. 07581. e. 4.
BAUMEL (L.) Leçons sur les maladies des enfants. pp. 410. *Paris*, 1893. 8°. 7581. cc. 17.
BOSTON, *Mass. Children's Hospital.* Medical and Surgical Report. pp. 367. *Bost.* 1895. 8°.
7687. eee. 45.
CARMICHAEL (J.) Disease in Children. pp. 591. 1892. 8°. Pentland's Students' Manuals. 7383. d.
COMBY (J.) Traité des maladies de l'Enfance. pp. 872. *Paris*, 1892. 12°. 7580. df. 31.
DONKIN (H. B.) Diseases of Childhood. pp. 433.
Lond. 1893. 8°. 07581. e. 20.
ENCYCLOPÆDIAS. Cyclopædia of the Diseases of Children. 4 vol. *Edinb.* 1889, 90. 8°. 07581. i. 3.
GOODHART (J. F.) Diseases of Children. pp. 740.
Lond. 1894. 8°. 2254. a. 12.
HATFIELD (M. P.) Compend of Diseases of Children. pp. 185. *Edinb.* 1891. 8°. 07581. de. 27.
HENOCH (E. H.) Vorlesungen über Kinderkrankheiten. pp. 875. *Berl.* 1892. 8°. 07581. e. 1.
JACOBI (M. P.) Electricity in diseases of Childhood. 1894. 8°. BIGELOW (H. R.) System of Electro-Therapeutics. 2024. c.
LANNELONGUE (O.) and MÉNARD (V.) Affections congénitales. *Paris*, 1891, *etc.* 8°. 7580. g. 17.
LEFERT (P.) La Pratique des Maladies des Enfants dans les Hôpitaux. pp. 285.
Paris, 1893. 12°. 07581. f. 3.
MACCAW (J.) Aids to Diagnosis and Treatment of Diseases of Children. pp. 181.
Lond. 1894. 8°. 7581. ccc. 3.
MUSKETT (P. E.) Prescribing and Treatment in the diseases of Infants. pp. 334.
Edinb. 1894. 12°. 7509. df. 51.
POWELL (W. M.) Essentials of Diseases of Children. pp. 222. 1893. 8°. Kimpton's Essential Series. 7306. df.
SMITH (J. L.) Treatise on the Diseases of Infancy. pp. 900. *Lond.* 1890. 8°. 07581. e. 11.

BAGINSKY (A.) Paediatrische Arbeiten. pp. 531.
Berl. 1890. 8°. 7580. g. 13.
POLAND (J.) Points of treatment in the deformities of Children. pp. 16. *Edinb.* 1891. 8°.
07305. h. 7. (10.)
POWER (D'A.) Surgical diseases of Children. pp. 548. 1895. 8°. Lewis's Practical Series.
7482. a.

CHILDREN.—Medicine, etc.—*continued.*

BROCA (A.)   Traitement des tumeurs blanches chez l'enfant.   pp. 155.   1893. 8°.   Encyclopédie des aide-mémoire.   8709. g.

NEATBY (E. A.)   Pleural Effusions in Children. pp. 20.   1892. 8°.   Pam. 39.

NUNN (T. W.)   Growing Children and awkward Walking. pp. 106. *Lond.* 1894. 8°. 7581. ccc. 6. *See also* EDUCATION : EYE.

CHILI.   [*See note on page* 1.]
    See also AMERICA, *South.*

Antiquities.   *See infra : Topography :*
    AMERICA, *Central and South.*

Army.

CHILI. Recopilación de leyes concernientes al ejército. pp. 418. *Santiago,* 1888. 8°.
                                                6784. g. 14.

Constitution and Government.

CHILI.   Constitución política, leyes constitucionales, *etc.* pp. 411. *Santiago,* 1886. 8°.
                                                6784. g. 13.

—— Constitución política de la República. pp. 72. *Santiago,* 1888. 8°   8180. h. 24.

LARRAIN ZAÑARTU (J. J.)   El Ciudadano y el Gobierno. Nueva lei del rejimen interior 1886. pp. 226. *Santiago,* 1886. 8°.   6784. f. 17.

RODRIGUEZ BRAVO (J.) Estudios constitucionales. pp. 341. *Santiago,* 1888. 8°.   8180. i. 11.

SAMAMÉ (J. M.)   Disertacion sobre nuestro sistema de gobierno. pp. 28. *Lima,* 1886. 8°.
                                                Pam. 65.

See also infra : History, etc.

History and Politics.

MEDINA (J. T.)   Cosas de la Colonia. Siglo XVIII. pp. 392. *Santiago,* 1889. 8°.   9772. aaa. 25.

GONZALEZ DE NÁJERA (A.)   Desengaño y reparo de la guerra del Reino de Chile. pp. 317. *Santiago,* 1889. 8°..   9781. f. 14.

MITRE (B.)   Historia de San Martin. 3 tom. *Buenos A.* 1887. 8°.   010882. k. 1.

ROLDAN (A.) Las primeras asambleas nacionales, 1811–14. pp. 448. *Santiago,* 1890. 8°. 9771. f. 9.

VALDES (A.)   Revolución chilena y campañas de la independencia. pp. 578.
Santiago, 1888. 8°.   9781. f. 12.

SUAREZ (J. B.)   Rasgos biográficos de hombres notables de Chile. pp. 254.
Valparaiso, 1886. 8°.   10883. aaa. 30.

FIGUEROA (P. P.)   Historia de la revolucion constituyente, 1858–59. *Santiago,* 1889, *etc.* 4°.
                                                9772. f.

AHUMADA MORENO (P.) Guerra del Pacifico. Documentos oficiales. 6 tom.
Valparaiso, 1884–89. fol.   9781. i. 1.

CHILI.   Partes oficiales de las batallas de Chorrillos i Miraflores, Enero, 1881. pp. 420. *Santiago,* 1881. 8°.   9772. g. 10.

FIGUEROA (P. P.)   Atacama en la guerra del Pacífico. pp. 142. *Santiago,* 1888, 8°.
                                            12354. dd. 2. (5.)

PAZ SOLDAN (M. F.)   Narracion de la guerra de Chile contra el Perú y Bolivia. pp. 917. *Buenoe A.* 1884. 8°.   9772. g. 9.

RIQUELME (D.) Recuerdos de la campaña al Perú i Bolivia, 1879–84. pp. 276. *Santiago,* 1890. 8°.   9772. b. 17.

RIVAS (E. A.)   Episodios de la guerra del Pacífico, 1879–83. pp. 153.
Lima, 1891. 8°.   9772. aaa. 35.

SEOANE (G. A.) Tribunales de arbitraje. Contramemorándum sobre algunas reclamaciones francesas. pp. 353. *Santiago,* 1885. 8°.
                                                06955. df. 2.

CHILI.—History and Politics—*continued.*

LARRAIN ZAÑARTU (J. J.) La Convención Independiente. 1890. pp. 180. *Santiago,* 1890. 8°.
                                                8180. i. 13.

A., C. R. Memorandum de la Revolucion de 1891. pp. 530. *Santiago,* 1892. 8°. 9772. g. 12.

ALLENDES (E.)   The Revolution of 1891. pp. 31. *Valparaiso,* 1891. 8°.   Pam. 65.

AMENGUAL N. (R.)   Episodios de la Revolucion chilena. pp. 130. *Buenos A.* 1892. 8°.
                                                9772. b. 14.

BAÑADOS ESPINOSA (J.) Balmaceda y la revolución de 1891. 2 tom. *Paris,* 1894. 8°.
                                                9772. ccc. 15.

FAGALDE (A.) La prensa estranjera y la Dictadura chilena. pp. 212. *Santiago,* 1891. 8°.
                                                9772. dd. 8.

G. B. & I. *War Office.* The Capture of Valparaiso in 1891. pp. 56. *Lond.* 1892. 8°.
                                                9772. ccc. 13.

HERVEY (M. H.)   Dark Days in Chile. Revolution of 1891. pp. 331. *Lond.* 1891–1892. 8°.
                                                9772. ccc. 6.

KUNZ (H.) Der Bürgerkrieg in Chile. pp. 195. *Leipz.* 1892. 8°.   9772. c. 5.

LOPEZ (J. F.) Neutralidad y partidos beligerantes en la guerra civil de Chile. pp. 161. *Paris,* 1892. 8°   8180. h. 25.

MATTE (A.) Memoria presentada á la Excma. Junta de Gobierno. pp. 284. *Paris,* 1892. 8°.
                                                8180. dd. 7.

MONTT (P.) Exposition of the illegal Acts of President Balmaceda. pp. 38. *Wash.* 1891. 8°.
                                                Pam. 65.

CHILI. Recopilación de tratados entre la República y las potencias extranjeras.
Santiago, 1894, *etc.* 8°.   06955. ee.

ARGENTINE REPUBLIC. *M. de Relaciones Exteriores.* Cuestiones de límites entre las repúblicas Argentina, el Brasíl y Chile. pp. 342. *Buenos A.* 1892. 12°.   8180. aa. 17.

SERRANO MONTANER (R.) Límites con la República Arjentina. pp. 50. *Santiago,* 1895. 8°.
                                                Pam. 65.

VALDERRAMA (M.)   La Cuestion de limites entre Chile i la República Arjentina. pp. 99. *Santiago,* 1895. 8°.   8180. aa. 24.

Immigration.   *See infra : Topography.*

Inquisition.   *See* INQUISITION.

Law.

BALLESTEROS (M. E.) La Lei de organizacion de los tribunales. 2 tom. *Santiago,* 1890. 8°.
                                                6784. g. 19.

CHILI.   Recopilación de leyes y decretos vigentes en 21 de Mayo de 1888. pp. 806. *Santiago,* 1888. 8°.   6784. g. 9.

—— Colccion de Códigos de la República. pp. 1016. *Santiago,* 1891, 8°. 6784. aaa. 12.

—— Código civil de la República. pp. 817. *Santiago,* 1889. 8°.   6784. i. 6.

CHACON (J.) Esposicion razonada y estudio comparativo del Código Civil. pp. 370. *Valparaiso,* 1881. 8°.   6784. b. 9

CORREA BRAVO (A.) Estudios legales. pp. 248. *Santiage,* 1890. 8°.   6005. f. 6.

LATORRE (E. C.) Memorias universitarios sobre el Código Civil. 2 tom. *Santiago,* 1888, 89. 8°.
                                                6784. h. 12.

RISOPATRON (C. V.) Diccionario de Lejislacion y Jurisprudencia chilenas. 2 tom. *Santiago,* 1883, 84. fol.   6785. l. 2.

VERA (R.) La Jurisprudencia practica de nuestros tribunales. pp. 500.
Santiago, 1888. 8°.   6784 g. 11.
See also LAW, *Commercial and Criminal.*

CHILI.—Navy.

CHILI. *M. de Marina.* Recopilación de leyes y órdenes referentes á la Marina. 4 tom.
Santiago, 1888, 89. 8°.   8806. ddd. 15.

P.P. *Valparaiso.* Revista de Marina.
Tom. 1–11. *Valparaiso*, 1885–90. 8°. P.P. 4027. g.

Topography.

BRISEÑO (R.) Repertorio de antigüedades chilenas. pp. 580. *Santiago*, 1889. fol.
     1706. a. 20.

CHILI. *Oficina de Estadística.* Sinopsis estadística de Chile. pp. 108. *Santiago*, 1889. 8°.
     8223. de. 43.

ESPINOZA (E.) Geografía descriptiva de Chile. pp. 472. *Santiago*, 1895. 8°.   10481. aaa. 51.

GOMEZ DE VIDAURRE (F.) Historia geográfica del reino de Chile. 2 tom. *Santiago*, 1889. 8°.
     10481. i. 14.

LEMOYNE (J. B.) Péripéties du premier voyage des Missionnaires salésiens au Chili. pp. 164.
Nice, 1891. 8°.   4767. c. 28.

MEDINA (J. T.) Ensayo acerca de una Mapoteca chilena. pp. 254. *Santiago*, 1889. 8°.
     11900. aaa. 50.

AUBERTIN (J. J.) By order of the Sun to Chile. pp. 152. *Lond.* 1894. 8°.   8563. aa. 36.

AKERS (C. E.) Argentine and Chilian Sketches. pp. 190. *Lond.* 1893. 8°.   10481. bbb. 46.

CARRASCO (G.) Del Atlantico al Pacifico. pp. 511. *Buenos A.* 1890. 8°.   10025. e. 3.

DARAPSKY (L.) Las Aguas minerales de Chile. pp. 193. *Valparaiso*, 1890. 8°.   7461. i. 2.

KUNZ (H.) Chile und die deutschen Colonien. pp. 633. *Leipz.* 1891. 8°.   10481. cc. 26.

MORANT (G. C.) Chili and the River Plate. pp. 268. *Lond.* 1891. 8°.   10481. aaa. 47.

VIAL (R.) Costumbres chileñas.
Valparaiso, 1889, *etc.* 8°.   12350. cc.

See also AMERICA, *Central* and *South :* CHILOE.

Trade and Finance.

CHILI. Recopilación de leyes referentes á la recaudación é inversión de fondos públicos. pp. 1172. *Santiago*, 1889. 4°.   6784. g. 10.

OVALLE CORREA (É.) Les Finances du Chili. pp. 170. *Paris*, 1889. 8°.   08227. k. 20.

PARIS. *Exposition Universelle.* Catalogue de la section du Chili. pp. 104. *Paris*, 1889, 8°.
     7959. f. 19.

SANTELICES (R. E.) Los Bancos chilenos. pp. 467. *Santiago*, 1893. 8°.   8225. cc. 46.

CHILIAN DIALECT AND LITERATURE. *See* AMERICAN LITERATURE : POETRY : SPANISH LANGUAGE.

CHILLESFORD. CHILLESFORD. Parish Registers of Chillesford. pp. 33. 1886. 8°.
     9916. f. 35.

CHILOE. BERANGER (C. de) Relacion jeográfica della provincia de Chiloé. pp. 67.
Santiago, 1893. 8°.   Pam. 86.

MORALEDA I MONTERO (J. de) Esploraciones jeográficas e hidrográficas. pp. 533.
Santiago, 1888. 8°.   10480. ccc. 28.

See also CHILI.

CHILOPODA. *See* MYRIOPODA.

CHILTERN HUNDREDS. Ac. Oxford.
Archæological Society. PEARMAN (M. T.) Historical Account of the Hundreds of Chiltern. pp. 20. *Banbury*, 1890. 8°.   Pam. 90.

CHINA. [*See note on page 1.*]

Army and Navy.

PUTYATA (D. V.) Chinas Wehrmacht. pp. 82. *Wien*, 1895. 8°.   8831. m. 2.

Christianity in China. *See* MISSIONS.

History and Politics.

BOULGER (D. C.) Short History of China. pp. 436. *Lond.* 1893. 8°.   9056. ff. 26.

BREBNER (A.) Little History of China. pp. 182. *Lond.* 1895. 8°.   9055. a. 23.

SCHLEGEL (G.) and CORDIER (H.) Archives pour servir à l'étude de l'histoire, *etc.*, de l'Asie Orientale. *Leide*, 1890. 8°.   10058. h.

TERRIEN DE LACOUPERIE (A. É. J. B.) Western Origin of early Chinese Civilisation, 2300 B.C. to 200 A.D. pp. 418. *Lond.* 1894. 8°. 9055. g. 5.

POOLE (S. L.) Life of Sir H. Parkes. 2 vol. *Lond.* 1894. 8°.   10817. dd. 15.

DOUGLAS (R. K.) Li Hungchang. pp. 251. 1895, 8°. Public Men of to-day. Vol. 2.
     10600. c.

GRANT (*Sir* J. H.) Life of Sir Hope Grant. 2 vol. *Edinb.* 1894. 8°.   10817. dd. 16.

HAKE (A. E.) Events in the Taeping Rebellion. pp. 531. *Lond.* 1891, 8°.   9056. ff. 22.

INOUYE (J.) The Japan-China War. Kinchow, Port Arthur and Talienwan. pp. 37.
Yokohama, 1895. 8°   9055. cc. 33.

—— The Fall of Wei-hai-wei. pp. 31.
Yokohama, 1895. 8°.   9055. cc. 32.

MORRIS (J.) War in Korea. pp. 108.
Lond. 1894. 8°.   8023. aaa. 10.

VLADIMIR. The China-Japan War. pp. 449.
Lond. 1895. 8°.   9055. d. 32.

VILLENOISY (F. de) La Guerre Sino-Japonaise, ses conséquences pour l'Europe. pp. 48.
Paris, 1895. 8°.   Pam. 67.

CASTONNET DES FOSSES (H.) Les relations de la Chine et de l'Annam. 1890. 8°. Ac. Paris. *Société indo-chinoise.* Bulletin. Sér 2. Tom. 3.
     Ac. 8812/3.

CHINESE AFFAIRS. La situation actuelle en Chine. pp. 43. *Paris*, 1892. 8°.   8028. de. 30. (16.)

DOUGLAS (R. K.) Society in China. pp 415. *Lond.* 1894. 8°.   2354. e.

GROOT (J. J. M. de) Over het belang der kennis van China voor onze Koloniën. pp. 35.
Leiden, 1891. 8°.   8026. i. 6. (8.)

GUNDRY (R. S.) China and her Neighbours. pp. 408. *Lond.* 1893. 8°.   8028. de. 33.

BUELL (P.) Les Scandales du Quai d'Orsay. pp. 138. *Paris*, 1893. 12°.   8052. cc. 31.

CURZON (*Hon.* G. N.) Problems of the Far East. *Lond.* 1894. *etc.* 8°.   8023. dd. 26.

FERGUSON (J. H.) Juridiction et exterritorialité en Chine. pp. 46. *Brux.* 1890. 8°.
     5319. de. 24. (4.)

HILLIER (W. C.) List of the higher Authorities of China. pp. 34. *Shanghai*, 1889. 4°.
     11100. f. 12.

NORMAN (H.) Peoples and Politics of the Far East. pp. 608. *Lond.* 1895. 8°.   010057. i. 2.

P.P. *Tientsin.* Peking and Tientsin Times. *Tientsin*, 1894, *etc.* fol.   P.P. 9990. ff.

See also infra : Topography.

Inscriptions. *See* INSCRIPTIONS.

Jews in China. *See* JEWS.

Missions. *See* MISSIONS.

Opium Traffic, etc. *See* OPIUM.

CHINA.—Religion and Philosophy.

BOÜINAIS (A.) and PAULUS (A.) Le Culte des Morts dans le Céleste Empire. pp. 267. 1893. 8°. Annales du Musée Guimet. Bibliothèque de Vulgarisation. 7704. a. 37.

BUDDHISM. How in 219 B.C. Buddhism entered China. pp. 9. 1891. 8°. Pam. 41.

DOUGLAS (R. K.) Confucianism and Taouism. pp. 287. 1895. 8°. Non-Christian Religious Systems. 2212. a.

GROOT (J. J. M. de) Religious System of China. Leyden, 1892, etc. 8°. 4503. h. 2.

HARLEZ (C. de) Les Religions de la Chine. pp. 270. Leipz. 1891. 8°. 4504. f. 21.

—— Textes Tâoïstes. pp. 391. 1891. 8°. Annales du Musée Guimet. Tom. 20. 7704. h. 21.

—— L'École philosophique moderne de la Chine. pp. 195. Brux. 1890. 4°. 11100. f. 10.

—— Shēn Siēn-Shū. Mythologie chinoise. pp. 492. 1893. 4°. Ac. Brussels. Acad. Royale. Nouveaux Mémoires. tom. 51. Ac. 985/7.

JUNKER VON LANGEGG (F. A.) Krypto-Monotheismus in den Religionen der alten Chinesen. pp. 79. Leipz. 1892. 8°. Pam. 41.

KUNG-KEW. The Confucian Analects. Translation by W. Jennings. pp. 224. 1895. 8°. Sir J. Lubbock's Hundred Books. Vol. 93. 012207. l. 93.

LAOU-TSZE. Lâo-Tsze the Great Thinker. pp. 131. Lond. 1895. 8°. 4503. de. 12.

LEGGE (J.) The Texts of Tâoism. 2 vol. 1891. 8°. Sacred Books of the East. Vol. 39, 40. 2003. b.

CHWANG-TSZE. Divine Classic of Nan-Hua. Annotations by F. H. Balfour. pp. 425. Shanghai, 1881. 8°. 11099. f. 8.

NANJIO (B.) Cat. of the Chinese translation of the Buddhist Tripitaka. pp. 480. Oxf. 1883. 4°. 4505. g. 2.

SZE-MA TS'EEN. Le Traité sur les Sacrifices. pp. 95. 1890. 8°. Ac. Peking. Oriental Soc. Journal. Vol. 3. Ac. 8823.

TERRIEN DE LACOUPERIE (A. É. J. B.) The Silk Goddess of China. pp. 28. Lond. 1891. 8°. Pam. 41.

—— The Yh-King and its authors. Vol. 1. Lond. 1892. 8°. 7705. aaaa.

See also infra: Topography, etc.

Topography: Social Life, etc.

AC. *Paris. École des Langues Orientales.* Hung-Leang-Keih. Histoire géographique des seize royaumes. *Paris,* 1891, *etc.* 8°. Ac. 8813/18.

BERNIER (F.) Travels in the Mogul Empire A.D. 1656–1668. pp. 497. 1891. 8°. Constable's Oriental Miscellany. Vol. 1. 12205. k.

ODORICUS. Voyages en Asie au XIV° siècle. pp. 602. 1891. 8°. SCHEFER (C.) and CORDIER (H.) Recueil de voyages No. 10. 10024. i.

SHAN-HAI-KING. Antique Géographie chinoise. *Paris,* 1891, *etc.* 8°. 010057. ee. 23.

————————

AC. *Paris. Société des Études Chinoises.* Manuel du Sinologue. *Paris,* 1888, *etc.* 8°. Ac. 8814.

BALL (J. D.) Things Chinese. pp. 497. Lond. 1893. 8°. 010057. f. 16.

BARBER (W. T. A.) Golden Lilies and the Flowery Land. pp. 32. Lond. 1894. 16°. Pam. 88.

BENKO (J. v.) Die Reise S.M. Schiffes "Zrinyi" nach Ost-Asien. pp. 439. Wien, 1894. 8°. 010057. l. 15.

BOUINAIS (A.) De Hanoï à Pékin. pp. 376. Paris, 1892. 8°. 10058. aa. 42.

BRANDT (M. v.) Aus dem Lande des Zopfes. pp. 132. Leipz. 1894. 8°. 010057. c. 33.

—— Sittenbilder aus China. pp. 87. Stuttgart, 1895. 8°. 010057. f. 35.

CANADIAN PACIFIC RAILWAY. Japan and China. pp. 19. Liverpool, 1893. 8°. Pam. 86.

CAUBERT (L. C.) Souvenirs chinois. pp. 180. Paris, 1891. 4°. 010057. ee. 16.

CHINA. China. Von einem früheren Instructeur in der chinesischen Armee. pp. 79. Leipz. 1892. 8°. Pam. 88.

CHING-KE-TUNG. Mon Pays. pp. 294. Paris, 1892. 12°. 10058. aa. 41.

—— Chin-Chin; or, the Chinaman at home. pp. 270. Lond. 1895. 8°. 010057. c. 34.

COLTMAN (R.) The Chinese, their present and future. pp. 212. Phila. 1891. 8°. 010057. ee. 20.

CORDIER (H.) Notice sur la Chine. pp. 111. Paris, 1890. 8°. 10057. ee. 12.

CORNABY (W. A.) A String of Chinese Peach-stones. pp. 479. Lond. 1895. 8°. 010057. h. 9.

CULIN (S.) Gambling Games of the Chinese in America. pp. 17. 1891. 8°. Ac. Philadelphia. University. Publications. Series in Philology. Vol. 1. No. 4. Ac. 2692. p. 2.

CURZON (Hon. G. N.) Problems of the Far East. Lond. 1894, etc. 8°. 8023. dd. 26.

DOUGLAS (R. K.) Society in China. pp. 415. Lond. 1894. 8°. 2354. e.

FERGUSON (J.) From Ceylon to England by way of China, etc. pp. 111. Colombo, 1891. 4°. 10026. k. 13.

FIELDE (A. M.) Pagoda Shadows. pp. 285. Bost. 1890. 8°. 10058. aa. 38.

—— A Corner of Cathay. pp. 286. N.Y. 1894. 8°. 010057. c. 31.

GUNDRY (R. S.) China and her Neighbours. pp. 408. Lond. 1893. 8°. 8028. de. 33.

—— China Present and Past. pp. 414. Lond. 1895. 8°. 010057. k. 9.

HARLEZ (C. de) L'infanticide en Chine. pp. 46. Louvain, 1893. 8°. 8277. e. 45.

HOLCOMBE (C.) The real Chinaman. pp. 350. Lond. 1895. 8°. 10057. c. 4.

HOSIE (A.) Three Years in Western China. pp. 302. Lond. 1890. 8°. 010057. ee. 10.

JENTZSCH (F.) Lebensbilder aus China. pp. 91. Berlin, 1895. 8°. 10058. bbb. 35.

KONOW (H.) I Asiens Farvande. Copenh. 1892–94. 8°. 010057. f.

MAY (C.) L'Empire du Dragon. pp. 284. Paris, 1892. 12°. 010057. c. 12.

MILN (L. J.) When we were Strolling Players in the East. pp. 354. Lond. 1894. 8°. 010057. f. 29.

MORRIS (T. M.) A Winter in North China. pp. 256. Lond. 1892. 8°. 010057. e 11.

MORRISON (G. E.) An Australian in China. pp. 299. Lond. 1895. 8°. 010057. e. 40.

MOULE (A. E.) New China and Old. pp. 312. Lond. 1891. 8°. 010057. ee. 13.

MUTCHMORE (S. A.) The Moghul, Mongol, Mikado and Missionary. 2 vol. N.Y. 1891. 8°. 10058. de. 4.

NORMAN (H.) Peoples and politics of the Far East. pp. 608. Lond. 1895. 8°. 010057. i. 2.

PARKER (E. H.) Up the Yang-tse. pp. 308. Hongkong, 1891. 8°. 010057. c. 5.

CHINA.—Topography—continued.

PRATT (A. E.) To the Snows of Tibet through China. pp. 268. *Lond.* 1892. 8°.
          010057. ee. 29.

PRICE (J. M.) From the Arctic Ocean to the Yellow Sea. pp. 384. *Lond.* 1892. 8°.
          10292. e. 5.

REID (G.) Peeps into China. pp. 191. *Lond.* 1892. 8°.
          4429. df. 7.

ROCKHILL (W. W.) The land of the Lamas. pp. 399. *Lond.* 1891. 8°.
          010057. l. 5.

SADLER (J.) True Celestials, Leaves from a Chinese Sketch-book. pp. 144. *Lond.* 1891. 8°.
          4765. bbb. 42.

SCHLEGEL (G.) and CORDIER (H.) Archives pour servir à l'étude de la geographie, *etc.*, de l'Asie Orientale. *Leide,* 1890, *etc.* 8°.   10058. h.

SELBY (T. G.) The Chinaman in his own stories. pp. 210. *Lond.* 1895. 8°.   10058. de. 11.

SINOLOGICAL VARIETIES. Variétés sinologiques. *Chang-hai,* 1892, *etc.* 8°.   010057. k.

SMITH (A. H.) Chinese Characteristics. pp. 342. *Lond.* 1895. 8°.   010057. h. 8.

—— The Proverbs of the Chinese. pp. 384. *Shanghai,* 1888. 8°.   12304. f. 34.

SCIDMORE (E. R.) Westward to the Far East. pp. 51. *Montreal,* 1892. 8°.   010057. f. 21.

THWING (E. P.) Ex Oriente : studies of Oriental Life. pp. 119. *N.Y.* 1891. 8°.   12352. dd. 2.

TURNER (J. A.) Kwang Tung; five Years in South China. pp. 192. *Lond.* 1894. 8°.
          4767. bbb. 11.

VINCENT (E. G.) Newfoundland to Cochin China. pp. 374. *Lond.* 1892. 8°.   10024. e. 23.

See also MONGOLIA : TIBET.

Trade, Finance, etc.

CASTONNET DES FOSSES (H.) La Chine industrielle et commerciale. pp. 35. *Lyon,* 1888. 8°.
          08227. k. 31. (4.)

GRUNZEL (J.) Die kommerciele Entwickelung Chinas in den letzten 25 Jahren. pp. 97. *Leipz.* 1891. 8°.   08227. ee. 42,

MORRISON (J. K.) The Currency of China. pp. 40. *Lond.* 1895. 8°.   08226. f. 23. (10.)

CHINA SEA. G. B. & I. *Hydrographic Office.* China Sea. Report on the results of dredgings. pp. 16. *Lond.* 1893. fol. Pam. 88.

CHINA WARE. *See* CERAMICS.

CHINESE LANGUAGE AND LITERATURE.

General.

BURDON (J. S.) Colloquial versions of the Chinese Scriptures. pp. 17. *Hongkong,* 1890. 8°.
          3103. df. 1. (5.)

SCHLEGEL (G.) and CORDIER (H.) T'ung pao. Archives pour servir à l'étude des langues de l'Asie Orientale. *Leide,* 1890, *etc.* 8°.
          10058. h.

CORDIER (H.) Half a decade of Chinese studies, 1886–91. pp. 36. *Leyden,* 1892. 8°.
          12903. dd. 33. (9.)

—— Les Études chinoises 1891–1894. pp. 89. *Leide,* 1895. 8°.   12910. g. 34.

PRÉMARE (J. H. de) Notitia Linguæ Sinicæ. pp. 255. *Hong Kong,* 1893. 8°.   12910. b. 47.

VIÑAZA (de la) Escritos de los Portugueses y Castellanos referentes á las lenguas de China. pp. 139. *Lisboa,* 1892. 8°.   011901. ee. 20.

WATTERS (T.) Essays on the Chinese Language. *Shanghai,* 1889. 8°.   12910. f. 33.

CHINESE LANGUAGE—continued.

Dictionaries.

GILES (H. A.) Chinese-English Dictionary. pp. 1416. *Lond.* 1892. 4°.   12910. k. 18.

GOODRICH (C.) Pocket Dictionary Chinese-English and Pekingese syllabary. pp. 237. *Peking,* 1891. 12°.   11099. a. 10.

BALLER (F. W.) Analytical vocabulary of the New Testament. *Chinese and Eng.* pp. 264. *Shanghai,* 1893. 4°.   12910. i. 34.

KERR (J. G.) A Vocabulary of Diseases, English-Chinese. pp. 35. *Shanghai,* 1894. 8°.
          Pam. 39.

BALL (J. D.) English-Cantonese pocket Vocabulary. pp. 23. *Hongkong,* 1894. 8°.
          12910. aa. 74.

CHALMERS (J.) English and Cantonese Dictionary. pp. 296. *Hongkong,* 1891. 8°.
          12910. aa. 49.

DICTIONARIES. English Chinese Vocabulary of the vernacular of Swatow. pp. 302. *Swatow,* 1883. 8°.   12910. dd. 17.

LIN HEUNG-CH'ING. Handbook of the Swatow vernacular. Dictionary. 2 pt. *Singapore,* 1886. 4°.   12910. cc. 1.

GIBSON (J. C.) Swatow Index to the Dictionary of Chinese by S. W. Williams and the Dictionary of the Vernacular of Amoy, by C. Douglas. pp. 171. *Swatow,* 1886. 8°.   12910. dd. 18.

BAILLY ( ) Dictionnaire chinois-françois. 2 tom. *Saigon,* 1889. 4°.   12910. k. 16.

BILLEQUIN (A.) Dictionnaire français-chinois. pp. 830. *Péking,* 1891. 4°.   12910. k. 15.

COUVREUR (S.) Dictionnaire chinois français. pp. 1024. 76. *Ho Kien Fou,* 1890. 4°.
          12910. l. 5.

DICTIONARIES. Dictionnaire chinois-français de la langue Mandarine parlée dans l'ouest de la Chine. pp. 786. *Hongkong,* 1893. 4°.
          12910. dd. 24.

—— Dictionnaire chinois-français. pp. 623. *Peking,* 1893. 4°.   12910. i. 23.

SCHLEGEL (G.) Nederlandsch-chineesch Woordenboek. *Leiden,* 1886–91. 4°.   12910. h. 14.

Grammars, etc.

ARENDT (C.) Handbuch der nordchinesischen Umgangssprache. 1891, *etc.* 8°. SACHAU (C. E.) Lehrbücher des Seminars, *etc.* Bd. 7. 12906. h.

—— Einführung in die nordchinesische Umgangssprache. 2 Abth. 1894. 8°. SACHAU (C. E.) Lehrbücher des Seminars, *etc.* Bd. 12.
          12906. h.

BALLER (F. W.) Mandarin Primer. pp. 326. *Shanghai,* 1891. 8°.   12910. e. 36.

CHOUZY (J. B.) Recueil d'expressions du Style chinois écrit. pp. 152. *Hongkong,* 1894. 8°.
          12910. b. 44.

HESS (E.) Chinesische Phraseologie. pp. 185. *Leipz.* 1891. 8°.   12910. b. 33.

IMBAULT-HUART (C.) Manuel de la langue chinoise parlée. pp. 337. *Hongkong,* 1892. 4°.
          12910. k. 17.

KWAN HWA. Boussole du langage mandarin, traduite par H. Boucher. 2 vol. *Zi-Ka-Wei,* 1887. 8°.   11099. f. 9.

MATEER (C. W.) Course of Mandarin Lessons. pp. 714. *Shanghai,* 1892. 4°.   12910. g. 32.

RUHSTRAT (E.) Index of the characters in Dr. Hirth's "Text Book of documentary Chinese." pp. 41. *Shanghai,* 1892. 4°.   11099. d. 37.

SYDENSTRICKER (A.) Exposition of the construction and idioms of Chinese sentences. pp. 88. *Shanghai,* 1889. 8°.   12902. dd. 27. (4.)

CHINESE.—Grammars—*continued.*
BALL (J. D.) Readings in Cantonese colloquial. pp. 171. *Hongkong,* 1894. 8°.   12910. e. 41.
FRENCH (J. B.) Select phrases in the Canton dialect. pp. 67. *Hongkong,* 1889. 8°.
                                        12901. d, 20. (4.)
BALL (J. D.) The Tung-Kwún dialect: a comparative syllabary of the Tung-Kwún and Cantonese pronunciations. pp. 16.
Hongkong, 1890. 8°.   12902. g. 32. (5.)
—— The San-Wúi dialect. pp. 18.
Hongkong, 1890. 8°.   12902. g. 32. (4.)
ASHMORE (W.) Primary lessons in Swatow grammar. pp. 155. *Swatow,* 1884. 8°.
                                        12910. e. 3.
LIN HEUNG-CH'ING. Handbook of the Swatow vernacular. 2 pt. *Singapore,* 1886. 4°.
                                        12910. cc. 1.

Literature.

LINDSAY (J. L.) *Earl of Crawford.* Catalogue of Chinese Books and Manuscripts. pp. 90.
1895. 4°.   11901. h. 13.
AC. Paris. *Société des Études Chinoises, etc.* Manuel du Sinologue. *Paris,* 1888, *etc.* 8°.
                                        Ac. 8814.
DOUGLAS (R. K.) Chinese Stories. pp. 348.
Edinb. 1893. 8°.   11100. c. 30.
LEGGE (J.) The Chinese Classics.
Oxf. 1893, *etc.* 8°.   11098. a. 1.
—— The Sacred Books of China. Texts of Tâoism. 2 vol. 1891. 8°. MUELLER (F. M.) Sacred Books of the East. Vol. 39, 40.
                                        2003. b.
NANJIO (B.) Catalogue of the Chinese translation of the Buddhist Tripitaka. pp. 480.
Oxf. 1883. 4°.   4505. g. 2.
CHWANG TSZE. Divine Classic of Nan-Hua; with annotations by F. H. Balfour. pp. 425.
Shanghai, 1881. 8°.   11099. f. 8.
SHE KING. The Book of Chinese Poetry. Translated by C. F. R. Allen. pp. 528. *Lond.* 1891. 8°.
                                        11099. c. 4.
—— The Shi King. Translated by W. Jennings. 1891. 8°. Sir J. Lubbock's Hundred Books.
No. 11.   012207. l. 11.
HARLEZ (C. de) Shén-Siēn-Shū. Livre des Esprits et des Immortels. pp. 492. 1893. 4°.
AC. Brussels. *Académie, etc.* Nouveaux Mémoires. Tom. 51.   Ac. 985/7.
TERRIEN DE LACOUPERIE (A. É. J. B.) Oldest Book of the Chinese, the Yh-King. Vol. I.
Lond. 1892. 8°.   7705. aaaa.
KANG HE, *Emperor.* The Sacred Edict, with translation of the colloquial rendering by F. W. Baller. 2 vol. *Shanghai,* 1892. 8°.
                                        11098. b. 15.
See also CHINA: *Topography, etc.*

CHINON. GRIMAUD (H.) Les Origines de l'Imprimerie à Chinon. pp. 6. *Tours,* 1891. 8°.
                                        011900. ee. 5. (12.)

CHINY. FELSENHART (J.) Études sur le Comté de Chiny, 1716–44. 4 pt. 1885–88. 4°.
AC. Arlon. *Société pour la Conservation des Monuments historiques.* Annales. Tom. 17, 18, 19, 20.   Ac. 5514.

CHINYANJA LANGUAGE.
See AFRICAN LANGUAGES.

CHIOGGIA. BELLEMO (V.) Il territorio di Chioggia. pp. 316. *Chioggia,* 1893. fol.
                                        10151. ff. 4.

CHIPEWYAN INDIANS.
See INDIAN LANGUAGES.

CHIPPENHAM.
DANIELL (J. J.) History of Chippenham. pp. 248. *Chippenham,* 1894. 8°.   010358. e.

CHIPPENHAM—*continued.*
DANIELL (J. J.) Chippenham during the Rebellion. pp. 26. *Devizes,* 1880. 8°. 10348. d. 18. (9.)
GOLDNEY (F. H.) Records of Chippenham. pp. 348. *Lond.* 1889. 8°.   10352. dd. 9.

CHIPPING BARNET. BYFORD (S.) Reminiscences of Chipping Barnet. 1816–91. pp. 44. *Barnet,* 1891. 8°.   10348. ccc. 57. (4.)

CHIPPING LAMBOURN. FOOTMAN (J.) History of the Parish Church of Chipping Lambourn. pp. 202. *Lond.* 1894. 8°. 010358. h. 14.

CHIPPING NORTON. BALLARD (A.) Notes on the History of Chipping Norton. pp. 40.
Oxf. 1893. 8°.   10347. d. 7. (5.)

CHIROMANCY. *See* PALMISTRY.

CHISLET. HASLEWOOD (F.) Parish of Chislet, Kent. pp. 193. *Ipswich,* 1887. 8°. 10350. f. 37.

CHITRAL. THOMSON (H. C.) The Chitral Campaign. pp. 312. *Lond.* 1895. 8°.
                                        9057. aaa. 39.
YOUNGHUSBAND (G. J.) The Relief of Chitral. pp. 183. *Lond.* 1895. 8°.   9056. g. 18.

CHIVALRY. *See* FEUDALISM : KNIGHTHOOD, *Orders of.*

CHLOROFORM. *See* ANAESTHETICS.

CHOLERA. BARTH (E.) Die Cholera.
pp. 253. *Breslau,* 1893. 8°.   7561. f. 8.
BELLEW (H. W.) Cholera in India, 1862–81. pp. 218. *Calcutta,* 1884. fol.   7560. k. 5.
BIESE (A. C.) Der Sieg über die Cholera. pp. 42 *Berl.* 1893. 8°.   7560. de. 21.
BOUTET DE SAULNAY ( ) Le Choléra. pp. 32.
Paris, 1892. 8°.   07305. i. 10. (5.)
CHOLERA. Cholera. Immediate treatment.
1892. 8°.   1830. c. 1. (13.)
CUNNINGHAM (D. D.) On Choleraic Comma-Bacilli. 1891. 8°. P.P. *Calcutta.* Scientific Memoirs. Pt. 6.   7305. h.
DAREMBERG (G.) Le Choléra. pp. 189.
Paris, 1892. 8°.   7560. de. 18.
DEATH (J.) My Cholera Experiences, *etc.*
pp. 15. *St. John, N.B.* 1892. 4°.
                                07305. h. 20. (1.)
DRUZYLOWSKI (W.) Pathogénie du Choléra Morbus. pp. 55. *Paris,* 1891. 8°. 07305. k. 14. (4.)
ENGLAND AND WALES. *Local Government Board.* Cholera Regulations: Ports. pp. 7.
Lond. 1890. fol.   7560. k. 7. (4.)
—— Cholera Regulations. Bedding and clothing. pp. 4. *Lond.* 1893. fol.   7560. k. 7. (3.)
ERDMANSDOERFFER (H. G.) Die Juden und die Cholera. pp. 32. *Leipz.* 1892. 8°.
                                4516. c. 5. (10.)
FISCHER (C. H.) Die Saprophyten, unsere natürlichen Helfer gegen die Cholera, *etc.* pp. 28.
Dresd. 1893. 8°.   7305. f. 5. (6.)
FRANÇOIS (A.) Le Choléra. pp. 111.
Lille, 1892. 8°.   7561. h. 29.
GALLIARD (L.) Le Choléra. pp. 186.
Paris, 1894. 8°.   7561. bb. 15.
GOENNER (A.) Die Cholera und ihre Behandlung. pp. 12. *Krems,* 1892. 8°.
                                7306. e. 23. (3.)
GOMEZ (C.) Estudios sobre el Cólera. pp. 24.
Trinidad, 1886. 4°.   7306. k. 19. (4.)
GRONEMAN (I.) Das Kreolin in der Choleratherapie. pp. 55. *Amsterd.* 1894. 8°. Pam. 39.
GÜMPEL (C. G.) On natural Immunity against Cholera, *etc.* pp. 79. *Lond.* 1894. 8°.
                                7561. h. 32.

CHOLERA—*continued.*

HAFFKINE (W. M.) Anti-Choleraic Inoculations in India. pp. 21. 1895. 8°. 7561. k. 26. (13.)

HARKIN (A.) The Vagus Treatment of Cholera. pp. 17. *Lond.* 1890. 8°.   Pam. 39.

HART (E. A.) The Nurseries of Cholera. pp. 35. *Lond.* 1894. 8°.   7561. k. 23.

—— Essays on State Medicine. State aid in relation to Port cholera expenses.
Lond. 1894. 8°.   6095. b. 33.

JANSSEN (A.) Il Colèra. pp. 56.
Firenze, 1893. 8°.   07305. i. 13. (5.)

KOCH (R.) Bacteriological diagnosis of Cholera. pp. 150. *Edinb.* 1894. 8°.   7561. k. 22.

WALL (A. J.) Koch's Komma-Bacillus ist nicht Ursache der Cholera. [Translation of Chapter 6 of Wall's Asiatic Cholera.] pp. 32.
Hamb. 1894. 8°.   Pam. 39.

KRANNHALS (H.) Ueber die Cholera. pp. 32.
Riga, 1892. 8°.   7306. df. 19. (13.)

LESAGE (A.) Le Choléra. pp. 207.   1893. 8°. Encyclopédie des aide-mémoire.   8709. g.

MACNAMARA (N. C.) Asiatic Cholera. pp. 71.
Lond. 1892. 8°.   7561. e. 6.

—— Cholera. 1893. 8°. DAVIDSON (A.) Diseases of Warm Climates.   7686. dd. 2.

MACRAE (R.) Cholera and preventive Inoculation in Gaya Jail. pp. 12. 1894. 8°. 7561. k. 26. (10.)

MAJUMDÁR (P. C.) Therapeutics of Cholera. pp. 102. *Phila.* 1893. 8°.   7561. aaa. 28.

MEYER (R.) Die Behandlung der Cholera im zürcherischen Kantonsspital 1867. pp. 28.
Zürich, 1892. 8°.   7561. k. 26. (4.)

MONOD (H.) Le Choléra. Histoire d'une épidémie, Finistère, 1885-86. pp. 657.
Paris, 1892. 8°.   7560. i. 13.

MONOD (L.) Comment nous préserver du choléra? pp. 16. *Paris,* 1892. 8°.   7006. df. 20. (8.)

MURREL (W.) First Aid in Cholera.
Lond. 1893. fol.   1830. c. 1. (84.)

PETRI (R. J.) Der Cholerakurs im Kaiserlichen Gesundheitsamte. pp. 259. *Berl.* 1893. 8°.
   7560. g. 23.

PETRI (R. J.) Untersuchungen über die durch das Wuchsthum der Cholerabakterien entstehenden chemischen Umsetzungen. 1890. 8°.
GERMANY, *K. Gesundheitsamt.* Arbeiten. Bd. 6.   7440. h.

PHILLIPPO (J. C.) Cholera in Jamaica in 1850-54. pp. 33. *Kingston,* 1892. 8°. 7306. de. 42. (5.)

PROUST (A.) La défense de l'Europe contre le Choléra. pp. 459. *Paris,* 1892. 8°. 7561. k. 18.

RUBINO (A.) Il Colèra. pp. 86.
Milano, 1892. 8°.   7561. aaa. 25.

RUMPF (T.) Behandlung der asiatischen Cholera. 1894. 8°. PENZOLDT (F.) Handbuch der Therapie der Infektionskrankheiten. Bd. 1.
   7620. f.

SAFEGUARDS. Safe-Guards as to Cholera, *etc.*
Liphook, 1893. 4°.   1830. c. 1. (88.)

SCHLEGEL (E.) Homöopathie und Cholera. pp. 30. *Tübingen,* 1892. 8°.   7306. e. 23. (6.)

SCHUESSLER (W. H.) Die Cholera. pp. 13.
Oldenburg, 1892. 8°.   7305. de. 27. (10.)

SIMPSON (W. J. R.) Introduction of Anti-choleraic Vaccination into Calcutta. pp. 5.
Calcutta, 1894. 4°.   Pam. 39.

STRICKER (S.) Studien zur Cholerafrage. pp. 42.
Leipz. 1893. 8°.   Pam. 39.

TUSON (J. E.) Observations on the efficacy of burning Sulphur Fires in epidemics of Cholera. pp. 22. *Lond.* 1884. 8°.
   07305. h. 16. (1.)

CHOLERA—*continued.*

VOUGHT (W.) Chapter on Cholera for lay readers. pp. 107. *Phila.* 1893. 4°.   7561. aa. 12.

WALL (A. J.) Asiatic Cholera. pp. 194.
Lond. 1893. 8°.   7561. k. 14.

WENDT (E. C.) Treatise on Asiatic Cholera. pp. 403. *N.Y.* 1885. 8°.   7561. k. 13.

WOOD (G. B.) Epidemic Cholera. pp. 29.
Kingston, 1892. 8°.   7561. k. 26. (5.)

See also BACTERIOLOGY : DISEASE, *Infectious.*

Epidemic 1892-93.

BJERKNES (M.) Kolerafangerne paa Normannia. pp. 140. *Kristiania,* 1893. 8°.   10413. b. 40.

BOLOGOWSKI (S.) Sur le Choléra de 1892-93 en Russie. pp. 54. *Paris,* 1894. 8°. 7306. h. 15. (6.)

CASSOUTE (É.) Épidémies cholériques de Marseille et de Barrême, 1892-1893. pp. 110.
Paris, 1894. 8°.   7560. d. 6.

CLEMOW (F.) Cholera Epidemic of 1892 in Russia. pp. 123. *Lond.* 1893. 8°. 7560. cc. 22.

DENKSCHRIFT. 'Amtliche Denkschrift über die Choleraepidemie 1892. pp. 129. *Berl.* 1892. fol.
   7560. h. 14.

GAFFKY (G.) Die Cholera in Hamburg in 1892-93. pp. 164. 1894. 8°. GERMANY. *K. Gesundheitsamt.* Arbeiten. Bd. 10. 7440. b.

GLAESER (J. A.) Betrachtungen bei Gelegenheit der letzten Cholera-Epidemie in Hamburg. pp. 59. *Hamb.* 1893. 8°.   7560. i. 14.

HAMBURG. Die Cholera in Hamburg.
Hamb. 1893, *etc.* 4°.   7560. h.

HUEPPE (F.) and (E.) Die Cholera-Epidemie in Hamburg 1892. pp. 118. *Berl.* 1893. 8°.
   7561. k. 16.

KUEBLER ( ) Die Cholera im Elbegebiete ausserhalb Hamburgs. 1895. 8°. GERMANY. *K. Gesundheitsamt.* Arbeiten. Bd. 10.   7440. h.

LANDAU (F.) Chronik der Cholera-Epidemie in Hamburg. pp. 63. *Hamb.* 1892. 8°.
   7306. e. 23. (5.)

MITRA (A.) Cholera Epidemic in Kashmir, 1892. pp. 17. *Calcutta,* 1893. 4°,   Pam. 39.

SPRONCK (C. H. H.) Étude sur les vibrions cholériques rencontrés dans les eaux en Hollande, 1892-93. pp. 54. 1894. 8°. Ac. Amsterdam. *K. Akademie van Wetenschappen.* Verhandelingen. Sectie 2. Deel. III.   Ac. 944/2.

WUTZDORFF ( ) Die Cholera in den westlich vom Elbegebiete. 1895. 8°. GERMANY. *K. Gesundheitsamt.* Arbeiten. Bd. 10.   7440. h.

CHOREA. BROCHET (G.) Chorée infantile. pp. 54. *Montpellier,* 1892. 8°. 07305. h. 19. (9.)

CHOTA NAGPORE. KINU (W.) and POPE (T. A.) Gold, copper and lead in Chota Nagpore. pp. 176. *Calcutta,* 1891. 8°.   7105. aa. 3.

CHRISTIANIA. COLLETT (A.) Gamle Christiania-Billeder. *Christiania,* 1893. 8°. 10281. e.

DAAE (L.) Det gamle Christiania, 1624-1814. pp. 435. *Christiania,* 1891. 8°.   10281. b. 15.

HANSEN (H.) Christiania. 1892. 4°. Les Capitales du Monde. No. 19.   10025. g.

JAEGER (H.) Kristiania og Kristianienserne. pp. 137. *Kristiania,* 1890. 4°.   10281. l. 5.

CHRISTIANITY.

General : Christian Evidences : Christianity and Science.

ABBOTT (L.) The Evolution of Christianity. pp. 258. *Bost.* 1892. 8°.   4376. de. 8.

ALAUX (J. É.) Le Problème religieux au XIX° siècle. pp. 440. *Paris,* 1890. 8°.   4016. f. 32.

ALEXANDER (S. A.) Christ and Scepticism. pp. 308. *Lond.* 1894. 8°.   4018. ff. 4.

CHRISTIANITY.—General—*continued*.

ALEXANDER (W.) *Bp. of Derry.* Primary Convictions. pp. 322. *Lond.* 1893. 8°. 4187. e. 22.

AMÉR (M. V.) Dios y el cosmos. *Palma,* 1889, *etc.* 8°. 4018. c. 16.

ANDRESEN (C.) Wir werden wieder geboren. Theïstischer Monismus. pp. 104. *Hamb.* 1894. 8°. 4371. e. 22.

ANDREWS (T.) Thoughts on Faith and Scepticism. pp. 139. *Lond.* 1894. 8°. 4106. g. 3.

ARNOLDSEN (K. P.) Religionen i forskningens ljus. pp. 691. *Stockholm,* 1891. 8°. 4018. df. 17.

BAKER (R. S.) Rationalism irrational. pp. 150. *Lond.* 1893. 8°. 4018. e. 38.

BALFOUR (R. G.) Central Truths and Side Issues. pp. 238. *Edinb.* 1895. 8°. 4371. b. 42.

BALLARD (F.) The Mission of Christianity. 5 pt. *Lond.* 1891. 8°. 4136. b. 30.

BARRY (A.) *Bp. of Sydney.* Some Lights of Science on the Faith. pp. 348. *Lond.* 1892. 8°. 2208. g. 10.

BATE (G.) How did Christianity and the Gospels originate? pp. 204. *Lond.* 1892. 8°. 4017. f. 17.

BEALE (L. S.) Protoplasm. pp. 285. *Lond.* 1892. 8°. 2254. a. 2.

BEAUGRAND (L.) Philosophie et Religion. pp 328. *Paris,* 1894. 8°. 4018. bbb. 31.

BEET (J. A.) Firm Foundation of the Christian Faith. pp. 127. *Lond.* 1891. 16°. 4018. de. 9.

BEYER (T.) Die von Harnack, Egidy und der ethischen Gesellschaft auf den christlichen Glauben gemachten Angriffe. pp. 64. *Neustettin,* 1893. 8°. 3913. c. 108. (7.)

BIER (T.) Glaube und Wissenschaft. pp. 64. *Berl.* 1891. 8°. 4371. ee. 4. (6.)

BLACKIE (J. S.) Christianity and the Ideal of Humanity. pp. 201. *Edinb.* 1893. 8°. 4371. b. 4.

BONNEY (T. G.) Christian Doctrines and modern Thought. pp. 175. *Lond.* 1891. 8°. 4466. c. 31.

BRIDEL (P. S.) La Foi en Jésus peut-elle constituer la religion définitive? pp. 26. *Lausanne,* 1892. 8°. 4371. ee. 27. (1.)

BRIGGS (C. A.) The Bible, the Church and the Reason. pp. 298. *Edinb.* 1892. 8°. 4376. i. 7.

BROWNJOHN (S. D.) Touching Discrepancy between the Book of Common Prayer and Science. pp. 16. *Lond.* 1892. 8°. 4371. b. 27. (7.)

BRUCE (A. B.) Apologetics. pp. 522. 1892. 8°. International Theological Library. 3605. k.

BULLINGER (A.) Das Christentum im Lichte der deutschen Philosophie. pp. 256. *München,* 1895. 8°. 4371. dd. 9.

BRUNETIÈRE (F.) La Science et la Religion. pp. 106. *Paris,* 1895. 12°. 4018. bbb. 35.

CAILLARD (E. M.) Progressive Revelation. pp. 267. *Lond.* 1895. 8°. 4371. aaaa. 39.

CALL (W. M. W.) Final Causes. pp. 161. *Lond.* 1891. 8°. 4018. f. 24.

CARNEGIE (W. H.) Through Conversion to the Creed. pp. 129. *Lond.* 1893. 8°. 4371. aa. 30.

CARUS (P.) Homilies of Science. pp. 317. *Chicago,* 1892. 8°. 4376. ee. 9.
—— The Religion of Science. pp. 103. *Chicago,* 1893. 8°. 4371. b. 8.

CAVE (A.) The Spiritual World. pp. 254. *Lond.* 1894. 8°. 4371. e. 21.

CHANDLER (A.) The Spirit of Man. pp. 227. *Lond.* 1891. 8°. 8409. ee. 29.

CHAPMAN (C.) Pre-organic Evolution and the Biblical Idea of God. pp. 304. *Edinb.* 1891. 8°. 4018. f. 18.

CHAPMAN (H. B.) Where is Christ? pp. 313. *Lond.* 1890. 8°. 4374. i. 30.

CHRISTIANITY.—General—*continued*.

CHHAJJŪ SIṂHA. Word with non-believers in Revelation. pp. 52. *Lahore,* 1889. 8°. Pam. 77.

CHILD (T.) The Church and Science. pp. 40. *Lond.* 1892. 8°. Pam. 77.

CHRISTIANITY. Is Christianity a Science? pp. 43. *Brighton,* 1891. 8°. 4375. b. 4.
—— Handbook of Christianity. pp. 61. *Chislehurst,* 1892. 8°. 4371. aa. 15.

CHRISTIE (T. W.) "Christianity:" an extract from the "Book of Revelation." pp. 23. *Lond.* 1892. 8°. Pam. 77.

CLIFFORD (J.) The Christian Certainties. pp. 311. *Lond.* 1893. 8°. 4015. e. 2.

COBBE (F. P.) Dawning Lights. pp. 192. *Lond.* 1894. 8°. 4379. cc. 3.
—— A Faithless World, and Health and Holiness. 2 pt. *Lond.* 1894. 8°. 4372. dd. 5.

CONFESSION. A Confession of Faith. pp. 194. *Lond.* 1895. 8°. 4371. aaaa. 37.

COOKE (J. P.) The Credentials of Science the warrant of faith. pp. 324. *Lond.* 1893. 8°. 4017. h. 7.

CRAWFORD (J. H.) From Nature and Life. pp. 185. *Dundee,* 1893. 8°. 4371. df. 19.

DADSON (A. J.) Evolution and Religion. pp. 348. *Lond.* 1893. 8°. 7006. f. 14.

DENNY (J.) Studies in Theology. pp. 272. *Lond.* 1894. 8°. 4371. c. 5.

DE VERE (A. T.) Religious Problems of the Nineteenth Century. pp. 232. *Lond.* 1893. 8°. 4106. aaa. 2.

DIGGLE (J. W.) Religious Doubt: its nature and treatment. pp. 371. *Lond.* 1895. 8°. 4018. ff. 15.

DOWNES (R. P.) Pillars of Our Faith. pp. 312. *Lond.* 1893. 8°. 4016. g. 18.

DRUMMOND (H.) The Greatest Thing in the World. pp. 286. *Lond.* 1894. 8°. 4371. e. 17.
—— The Programme of Christianity. pp. 63. *Lond.* 1892. 8°. 4372. ee. 14.
—— Des Programm des Christentums. pp. 70. *Bielefeld,* 1892. 8°. 4372. ee. 32.

ROCHOLL (H.) Hauptpunkte im Programm des Christentums, Ein Wort zu H. Drummond's neuester Schrift. pp. 92. *Leipz.* 1892. 8°. 3913. aa. 57.

DRUMMOND (J.) Hibbert Lectures, 1894. "Christianity in its most simple form." pp. 331. *Lond.* 1894. 8°. 2212. e. 17.

EAGAR (A. R.) Butler's "Analogy" and modern thought. pp. 220. *Lond.* 1893. 8°. 4429. bb. 33.

EIKONOKLASTES. What has Christianity done for us? pp. 20. *Bombay,* 1889. 8°. 4018. df. 13. (3.)

EVANS (J.) Christian Theology and modern Theories. pp. 375. *Lond.* 1892. 8°. 4371. df. 8.

FAIRBAIRN (A. M.) Religion in History and modern Life. pp. 271. *Lond.* 1894. 8°. 4371. e. 15.

FAITH. Faith and Criticism. pp. 430. *Lond.* 1893. 8°. 4136. aaa. 41.
—— The Faith of Reason. pp. 62. *Lond.* 1895. 8°. 4017. aa. 4.

FARRUGIA (M.) Luce e Tenebre, ossia il Soprannaturale e la Laicizzazione moderne. *Valletta,* 1893. 8°. 4371. ee. 27. (4.)

FINDLAY (G. G.) Christian Doctrine and Morals. pp. 260. *Lond.* 1894. 8°. 4371. dd. 4.

FINCKH (M.) Kritik und Christentum. pp. 234. *Stuttgart,* 1893. 8°. 4017. i. 12.

FISHER (G. P.) Manual of Christian Evidences. pp. 123. *Lond.* 1892. 8°. 4018. e. 37.

FISKE (J.) Evolution and Religion. pp. 12. *Lond.* 1883. 8°. 4371. b. 33. (2.)

CHRISTIANITY.—General—*continued.*

FOLEY (W. M.) Christ in the World. pp. 219. *Dublin*, 1894. 8°.   4456. h. 6.

FRECKELTON (T. W.) Religion and modern Thought. pp. 207. *Lond.* 1893. 8°. 4016. df. 23.

FULTON (J.) The Chalcedonian Decree; or, Historical Christianity confirmed by modern Science. pp. 213. *N.Y.* 1892. 8°. 3506. ee. 10.

GANT (F. J.) The Lord of Humanity. pp. 163. *Lond.* 1891. 8°.   4400. bb. 15.

GERARD (J.) Science or Romance? pp. 136. *Lond.* 1891. 8°.   4017. g. 21.

GERLACH (G. T.) Freie Anschauungen über das Weltall und das Leben. pp. 108. *Leipz.* 1893. 8°.   4371. e 18.

GLADDEN (W.) Burning Questions. pp. 248. *Lond.* 1890. 8°.   4018. f. 12.

GODET (F.) Lectures in defence of the Christian Faith. pp. 295. *Edinb.* 1895. 8°. 4018. ff. 9.

GONDAL (I. L.) Du Spiritualisme au Christianisme. pp. 323. *Paris*, 1894. 8°. 4376. ee. 21.

GRAU (R. F.) Goal of the Human Race. pp. 252. *Lond.* 1892. 8°.   4503. ana. 9.

H., W. R. Is Christianity played out? pp. 8. *Lond.* 1893. 12°.   4422. d. 16. (7.)

HAECKEL (E. H. P. A.) Der Monismus als Band zwischen Religion und Wissenschaft. pp. 46. *Bonn*, 1895. 8°.   8468. k. 28. (7.)

—— Monism. pp. 117. *Lond.* 1894. 8°.
                                 4016. df. 26.

HARDEN (W. D.) Inquiry into The Truth of Dogmatic Christianity. *N.Y.* 1893. 8°.
                                 4015. g. 12.

HARRISON (A. J.) Problems of Christianity and Scepticism. pp. 340. *Lond.* 1892. 8°. 4018. ff. 2.

—— The Church in relation to Sceptics. pp. 348. *Lond.* 1892. 8°   4015. ee. 25.

—— The Ascent of Faith. pp. 302. *Lond.* 1893. 8°.   4018. ff. 1.

HASTINGS (H. L.) The Anti-Infidel Library. *Lond.* 1887, etc. 8°.   4018. df.

HASTINGS (J. B.) Problem of the Ages. pp. 250. *Lond.* 1895. 8°.   4018. c. 23.

HETTINGER (F. L.) Natural Religion. pp. 302. *Lond.* 1890. 8°.   4018. e. 29.

—— Revealed Religion from the "Apologie des Christenthums." pp. 208. *Lond.* 1895. 8°.
                                 4018. bbb. 32.

HILLER (H. C.) Against Dogma and Free-Will and for Weismannism. pp. 30. *Lond.* 1893. 8°.   7006. bb. 33.

HOARE (E.) Great Principles of Divine Truth. pp. 296. *Lond.* 1895. 8°.   4371. c. 4.

HOOPPELL (R. E.) Reason and Religion. pp. 200. *Lond.* 1895. 8°.   4371. aaaa. 40.

HORNER (J.) Did a Hen or an Egg exist first? pp. 96. *Lond.* 1892. 8°.   4429. df. 18.

HOWATT (J. R.) Faith's strong Foundations. pp. 104. *Lond.* 1895. 8°.   4371. aaaa. 41.

HUGHES (H. P.) Essential Christianity. pp. 287. *Lond.* 1894. 8°.   4464. d. 4.

HUXLEY (*Right Hon.* T. H.) Collected Essays. *Lond.* 1894, etc. 8°.   2344. d.

—— Essays upon some Controverted Questions. pp. 625. *Lond.* 1892. 8°.   2210. d. 2.

INGERSOLL (R. G.) The Great Ingersoll Controversy. pp. 256. *N.Y.* 1892. 8°. 4016. df. 18.

IVERACH (J.) Evolution and Christianity. pp. 232. 1894. 8°. NICOLL (W. R.) Theological Educator.   3605. e.

KAFTAN (J.) Das Wesen der christlichen Religion. pp. 490. *Basel*, 1888. 8°.   4374. l. 9.

—— The Truth of the Christian Religion. 2 vol. *Edinb.* 1894. 8°.   4016. g. 19.

CHRISTIANITY.—General—*continued.*

KEENE (J. B.) Power and Force spiritual and natural. pp. 94. *Lond.* 1891. 8°. 4372. ee. 23.

KEIBEL (M.) Die Religion gegenüber dem modernen Moralismus. pp. 85. *Halle*, 1891. 8°.   8409. k. 26.

KELLY (E.) Evolution and Effort. pp. 297. *N.Y.* 1895. 8°.   8009. aaa. 36.

KERR (R. P.) The Voice of God in History. pp. 283. *Richmond*, 1890. 8°.   4534. bbb. 4.

KOENIG (E.) Der Glaubensact des Chr.sten nach Begriff und Fundament untersucht. pp. 173. *Erlangen*, 1891. 8°.   4372. k. 1.

KOESTLIN (J.) Die Begründung unserer sittlich-religiösen Überzeugung. pp. 124. *Berl.* 1893. 8°.   4371. e. 20.

KOPPELMANN (W.) Kant und die Grundlagen der christlichen Religion. pp. 113. *Gütersloh*, 1890. 8°.   3910. ee. 40. (8.)

KUEHN (G.) Naturphilosophische Studien frei von Mysticismus. pp. 187. *Neuwied*, 1895. 8°.
                                 8705. de. 21.

LAKEMAN (G.) The Stone cut out without Hands. pp. 93. *Lond.* 1895. 8°.   4371. c. 12.

LANG (C. R.) "Son of Man"; sequel to evolution. pp. 282. *Bost.* 1892. 8°.   4018. bbb. 30.

LAURIEN (V.) Conventional Christianity: is it the Teaching of the Founder? pp. 353. *Lond.* 1891. 8°.   4372. dd. 2.

LEFÊVRE (J. B.) Confidences d'un Ancien Croyant. pp. 155. *Barneville*, 1891. 8°.
                                 4016. df. 21.

LELLYETT (J.) Letters to Goliath of Gas, R. G. Ingersoll. pp. 155. *Nashville, Tenn.* 1890. 8°.
                                 4017. e. 15.

LILLY (W. S.) The Great Enigma. pp. 334. *Lond.* 1892. 8°.   4016. e. 8.

—— The Claims of Christianity. pp. 258. *Lond.* 1894. 8°.   4016. g. 20.

LINDSAY ( ) Evolution versus Reason and Theology. pp. 96. *Belfast*, 1892. 8°.
                                 7006. bb. 12.

LISLE (W. M.) Evolution of Spiritual Man. pp. 209. *Bost.* 1894. 8°.   4371. df. 27.

LORAINE (N.) The Battle of Belief. pp. 234. *Lond.* 1891. 8°.   4018. f. 26.

LORIMER (G. C.) The Argument for Christianity. pp. 480. *Lond.* 1894. 8°.   4018. ff. 10.

LUFMANN (M.) Modern Scepticism compared with Christian Faith. pp. 64. 1893. 8°. Present Day Tracts. No. 69.   4018. a.

MacCOLL (M.) Christianity in relation to Science and Morals. pp. 346. *Lond.* 1890. 8°.
                                 4376. c. 1.

MacCOSH (J.) Religious Aspect of Evolution. pp. 119. *Lond.* 1890. 8°.   4017. bbb. 33.

MACGREGOR (J.) The Apology of the Christian Religion historically regarded. pp. 544. *Edinb.* 1891. 8°.   4372. i. 36.

MACKINTOSH (W.) The Natural History of the Christian Religion. pp. 607. *Glasg.* 1894. 8°.
                                 4372. cc. 18.

MACQUEARY (H.) Evolution of Man and Christianity. pp. 410. *N.Y.* 1890. 12°. 4018. f. 10.

MADISON (A. W.) The True Theory of Christianity. pp. 86. *N.Y.* 1890. 8°.   Pam. 77.

MAIR (A.) Studies in Christian Evidences. pp. 415. *Lond.* 1894. 8°.   4018. ff. 8.

MARSHALL (W.) Nature as a Book of Symbols. pp. 246. *Lond.* 1893. 8°.   4371. df. 26.

MATTER. Matter, Force and Spirit. pp. 144. *N.Y.* 1895. 8°.   8704. bb. 43.

MITCHELL (J. H.) Christianity is True. pp. 16. *Lond.* 1890. 8°.   Pam. 77.

CHRISTIANITY.—General—continued.

MOLINARI (G. de) Science et Religion. pp. 284. Paris, 1894. 12°. 4018. eee. 5.

MOULE (A. E.) Reasons for the Hope that is in us. pp. 194. Lond. 1891, 8°. 4018. g. 33.

MURPHY (J. J.) Natural Selection and Spiritual Freedom. pp. 241. Lond. 1893. 8°. 4371. a. 27.

NEWNHAM (W. O.) Alresford Essays for the Times. pp. 292. Lond. 1891. 8°. 4378. e. 13.

NORDHEIM (P.) Die Erfüllung des Christenthums auf Grundlage der Entwicklungslehre. pp. 502. Berl. 1894. 8°. 4371. f. 6.

NORTHROP (S. A.) A Cloud of Witnesses. pp. 524. Fort Wayne, 1894. 8°. 4371. f. 2.

PALEY (W.) Paley's View of the Evidences of Christianity. pp. 426. Camb. 1890. 8°. 4018. f. 16.

—— Analysis of Paley's Evidences of Christianity. pp. 115. Camb. 1892. 8°. 4018. a. 51.

PAQUET (L. A.) La Foi et la Raison. pp. 181. Québec, 1890. 8°. 4016. g. 12.

PARKER (J.) Why am I a Christian? pp. 16. Lond. 1890. 8°. Pam. 77.

—— Christianity chronologically confirmed. pp. 27. Lond. 1892. 8°. 4371. de. 3. (9.)

PETERSEN (F.) Religion og Videnskab. pp. 79. Kristiania, 1894. 8°. 4018. h. 6.

PATTEN (A. W.) Facts and Fallacies of " Christian Science." pp. 30. Cincinnati, 189?. 8°. 4371. aaaa. 23. (2.)

PFAFF (A. B. I F.) Gott und die Naturgesetze. pp. 27. 1881. 8°. FROMMEL (W.) Sammlung von Vorträgen. Bd. 5. 12208. e.

PFLEIDERER (O.) Philosophy and development of Religion. Gifford Lectures. 2 vol. Edinb. 1894. 8°. 4371. b. 17.

RAINY (R.) The Supernatural in Christianity: with special reference to the Gifford Lectures of Dr. Pfleiderer. pp. 111. Edinb. 1894. 8°. 4018. ff. 5.

PHILLIPPS (L. F. M.) Lecture on the Cumulative Evidences of Divine Revelation. pp. 408. Lond. 1892. 8°. 4018. b. 3.

PLUMPTRE (E. H.) Christ and Christendom. pp. 281. 1891. 8°. Library of Theological Literature. 3605. g.

PRADIÉ (P.) La Divine Constitution de l'Univers. pp. 487. Paris, 1894. 8°. 4016. dd. 1.

PRINCE (H. J.) The World's Malady. pp. 310. Lond. 1894. 8°. 4371. b. 26.

PUCCINI (R.) Il Soprannaturale e la Scienza. 2 vol. Torino, 1894. 8°. 4017. bbb. 36.

PURINTON (D. B.) Christian Theism. pp. 303. N. Y. 1889. 8°. 4015. cc. 24.

RĀMACHANDRA VASU. Nature and Revelation. pp. 143. Lucknow, 1888. 8°. 4016. g. 13.

RAYMOND (B. P.) Christianity and the Christ. pp. 250. N. Y. 1894. 8°. 4014. bb. 4.

RELIGION. Religion and the Present Hour. pp. 262. Lond. 1893. 8°. 4371. ee. 11.

RENAN (J. E.) The Future of Science; ideas of 1848. pp. 491. Lond. 1891. 8°. 2234. cc. 13.

RÉTHORÉ (F.) Du passé et de l'avenir du Christianisme. pp. 363. Paris, 1894. 8°. 4503. cc. 27.

RETZER (C. F.) Die naturwissenschaftliche Weltanschauung und ihre Ideale. pp. 64. Leipz. 1890. 8°. 4371. ee. 38.

RICKETT (J. C.) Christianity in common Speech. pp. 63. Lond. 1895. 8°. 4371. c. 30.

ROBERT DE LA MENNAIS (H. F.) Essay on Indifference in Matters of Religion. pp. 300. Lond. 1895. 8°. 4377. ff. 7.

ROMANES (G. J.) Thoughts on Religion. pp. 184. Lond. 1895. 8°. 4371. c. 3.

CHRISTIANITY.—General—continued.

RONAY (S.) Das natürliche Christenthum. pp. 62. Leipz. 1894. 8°. 4371. b. 24.

SAVAGE (M. J.) Evolution of Christianity. pp. 178. Bost. 1892. 8°. 4017. g. 19.

—— The Irrepressible Conflict between two World-Theories. pp. 198. Bost. 1892. 8°. 4018. bbb. 28.

SAUTTER (D.) Questions religieuses actuelles. pp. 152. Lausanne, 1893. 8°. 3900. g. 14.

SCHAFFFER (A.) Christianisme. pp. 352. Lausanne, 1891. 8°. 4372. cc. 13.

SCHMIDT (W.) Der alte Glaube und die Wahrheit des Christentums. pp. 374. Berl. 1891. 8°. 3908. f. 26.

—— Schopenhauer in seinem Verhältnis zu den Grundideen des Christentums. pp. 52. Erlangen, 1894. 8°. 8468. k. 27. (11.)

SECRÉTAN (C.) La Civilisation et la Croyance. pp. 474. Lausanne, 1887. 8°. 8467. ff. 43.

SHEPHARD (J. E.) Christianity : what it is. pp. 36. Lond. 1893. 8°. 4476. ee. 1. (7.)

SMITH (H.) What do I believe? pp. 64. Lond. 1895. 8°. 4018. bbb. 37.

SORGE (G. W.) Religion und Naturwissenschaften keine Gegensätze. pp. 80. Berl. 1893. 8°. 8465. ee. 25. (12.)

SOUTHALL (J. E.) Science and Christianity from a Quaker standpoint. pp. 44. Newport, 1890. 8°. Pam. 77.

STENTZEL (A.) Weltschöpfung, Sintfluth und Gott. pp. 183. Braunschweig, 1894. 8°. 4503. ee. 36.

STEWART (A.) Handbook of Christian Evidences. pp. 94. 1891. 8°. Guild and Bible Class Text-Books. 3605. aaa.

STUCKENBERG (J. H. W.) The Age and the Church. pp. 360. Hartford, 1893. 8°. 4182. c. 29.

SWIFT (E.) Spiritual Law in the Natural World. pp. 185. Lond. 1890. 8°. 4380. f. 14.

TAIT (J.) Mind in Matter. pp. 338. Lond. 1892. 8°. 4018. g. 35.

TENAX (J.) Der christliche Staat. pp. 37. Berl. 1894. 8°. 3910. cc. 88. (5)

THOMAS (J. W.) Spiritual Law in the Natural World, etc. pp. 408. Lond. 1894. 8°. 4371. e. 25.

TOLSTOI (L. N.) Count. Ernste Gedanken über Staat und Kirche. pp. 28. Berl. 1891. 8°. Pam. 64.

TURTON (W. H.) The Truth of Christianity. pp. 504. Lond. 1895. 8°. 4014. e. 1.

UNITAS. Unalism, or, new yet old Christianity. pp. 137. Lond. 1892. 8°. 4018. b. 42.

VILLENEUVE (H. de) L' "Amusez-vous" de M. Renan et le Credo du P. Didon. pp. 136. Paris, 1892. 12°. 3900 b. 51.

VISIBLE. The Visible God, and our relation to him. pp. 365. Lond. 1890. 8°. 4227. h. 14.

VORBRODT (G.) Psychologie des Glaubens. pp. 257. Göttingen, 1895. 8°. 4017. h. 10.

Vox. Vox Clamantis. 2 vol. Lahore, 1891. 8°. 4371. df. 10.

WACE (H.) Christianity and Agnosticism. pp. 339. Edinb. 1895. 8°. 4018. ff. 17.

WAINWRIGHT (S.) The Question : " What think ye of Christ?" pp. 335. Lond. 1892. 8°. 4016. g. 16.

WALLACE (C. J.) Analogy of Existences and Christianity. pp. 310. Lond. 1892. 8°. 4372. ee. 30.

WARING (F. R.) The Earth Geist and its Worshippers. pp. 128. Lond. 1895. 8°. 4018. bbb. 38.

CHRISTIANITY.—General—*continued.*

WEBSTER (F. S.) Old-Fashioned Christianity. pp. 104. *Lond.* 1891 8°.   4400. ee. 34.

WELSH (R. E.) In Relief of Doubt. pp. 330. *Lond.* 1895. 8°.   4109. aaaa. 24.

WESTALL (A. St. L.) The Shield of Faith. pp. 159. *Lond.* 1890. 8°.   4109. e. 17.

WEXELSEN (F.) Små Vink til Forståelse af et stort Sporgsmål. pp. 56. *Trondhjem,* 1891. 8°.   Pam. 77.

WHITE (L.) The Democracy of Christianity. pp. 307. *N.Y.* 1892. 8°.   4371. aa. 36.

WILLIAMS (H.) Is Christianity a Superstition? pp. 48. *Melbourne,* 1885. 8°.   4371. de. 4. (5.)

WILLIAMSON (M. B.) The Truth and the Witness. pp. 158. *Lond.* 1895. 8°.   4227. c. 9.

WOOD (C. J.) Survivals in Christianity. pp. 317. *N.Y.* 1893. 8°.   4371. aaa. 26.

WOOD (H.) God's Image in Man. pp. 258. *Lond.* 1892. 8°.   4378. g. 5.

WOODGATE (W. B.) A modern Layman's Faith. pp. 533. *Lond.* 1893. 8°.   3125. ee. 14.

WORLD. God in his World. pp. 270. *N.Y.* 1890. 8°   4378. f. 6.

WRIGHT (C. H. H.) Scripture Proofs of the Doctrines of Christianity. pp. 39. *Lond.* 1893. 16°.   3939. cc. 25. (3.)

WRIGHT (G. F.) The Logic of Christian Evidences. pp. 276. *Lond.* 1881. 8°.   4018. g. 5.

ZOCCHI (G.) Il soprannaturale nella Chiesa e nella Società. pp. 528. *Prato,* 1893. 8°.   4371. ee. 22.

BIBLE. *Ephesians.* What is the Church? By R. Govett. pp. 287. *Norwich,* 1889. 12°.   3266. aa. 49.

CARPENTER (W. B.) *Bp. of Ripon.* Some Thoughts on Christian Reunion. pp. 222. *Lond.* 1895. 8°.   4446. aaa. 10.

HAMMOND (J.) The Christian Church. pp. 288. *Oxf.* 1894. 8°.   4109. aaaa. 13.

—— What does the Bible say about the Church? pp. 61. *Lond.* 1893. 8°.   4109. e. 32.

LUETGERT (W.) Das Reich Gottes nach den Evangelien. pp. 179. *Gütersloh,* 1895. 8°.   3224. cc. 27.

NAVILLE (E.) Le Témoignage du Christ et l'unité du monde chrétien. pp. 341. *Genève,* 1893. 8°.   4371. ee. 16.

ROBERTS (G.) The Marks of Christ's Body. Instructions on the Catholic Church. pp. 132. *Lond.* 1892. 8°.   4109. c. 19.

ROHLEDER (T.) Politisch-religiöse Grundlage für das einige Christentum. pp. 89. *Esslingen,* 1893. 8°.   3908. f. 29.

RUGG (H. W.) The Church. pp. 91. *Bost.* 1891. 8°.   4182. aa. 39.

SPECHT (T.) Die Lehre von der Kirche nach dem h. Augustin. pp. 354. *Paderborn,* 1892. 8°.   4534. ee. 10.

WATSON (M.) Christianity and the Church. pp. 208. *Lond.* 1891. 8°.   4018. c. 20.

BALMFORTH (R.) The New Reformation. pp. 159. *Lond.* 1893. 8°.   08276. e. 50.

CHAPMAN (J.) Jesus Christ and the present Age. pp. 174. *Lond.* 1895. 8°.   4455. dd. 9.

CLIFFORD (J.) The Coming Theology. pp. 43. *Lond.* 1891. 8°.   Pam. 77.

DAWSON (W. J.) The Church of Tomorrow. pp. 283. *Lond.* 1892. 8°.   4478. dd. 20.

DORCHESTER (D.) The Problem of Religious Progress. pp. 768. *N.Y.* 1895. 8°. 4182. bbb. 45.

CHRISTIANITY.—General—*continued.*

GRAY (E. W.) The New Religion. pp. 429. *Chicago,* 1893. 8°.   4376. ee. 1.

HAWEIS (H. R.) The Broad Church: or what is coming. pp. 276. *Lond.* 1891. 8°. 4109. bb. 24.

HENNE-AM-RHYN (O.) Das Christentum und der Fortschritt. pp. 121. *Leipz.* 1892. 8°.   4376. c. 4.

JACOBOWSKI (L.) Der christliche Staat und seine Zukunft. pp. 228. *Berl.* 1894. 8°.   4380. bb. 28.

LINDSAY (J.) Progressiveness of modern Christian Thought. pp. 182. *Edinb.* 1892. 8°.   4371. aaa. 4.

PORUCK (J.) Die Religion der Zukunft. pp. 24. *Berl.* 1894. 8°.   4371. dd. 8. (11.)

STEAD (W. T.) Interview with Mr. Stead on the Church of the Future. pp. 109. *Lond.* 1891. 8°.   4371. ee. 2. (10.)

SWANWICK (A.) Evolution and the Religion of the Future. pp. 66. *Lond.* 1894. 8°.   4018. aa. 12.

VAN NESS (T.) The coming Religion. pp. 228. *Bost.* 1893. 8°.   4018. df. 19.

Y., X. Religion et Progrès. pp. 124. *Brux.* 1891. 4°.   4371. aaa. 7.

See also AGNOSTICISM : ATHEISM : CHURCH AND STATE : CHURCH HISTORY ; CREEDS : DEITY : EVIL : MAN : MIRACLES : RELIGION : THEOLOGY : TRINITY.

Atonement : Incarnation : Resurrection, *Doctrines of.*

BENNETT (J.) Crux Christi. The Doctrine of Atonement. pp. 224. *Lond.* 1892. 8°.   4257. c. 24.

BERTRAND (E.) Une nouvelle conception de la Rédemption. pp. 505. *Paris,* 1891. 8°.   4256. f. 5.

BOVON (J.) Étude sur l'œuvre de la Rédemption. *Lausanne,* 1893, *etc.* 8°.   4225. f.

CHAFY-CHAFY (W. K. W.) The Day of Atonement a shadow of the Day of Atonement of Our Lord. pp. 24. *Lond.* 1895. 8°. 4371. bb. 9. (7.)

DIMOCK (N.) The Doctrine of the Death of Christ, in relation to the sin of man. pp. 136. *Lond.* 1890. 8°.   4225. f. 4.

DOERHOLT (B.) Die Lehre von der Genugthuung Christi. pp. 517. *Paderborn,* 1891. 8°.   4256. dd. 4.

DU BOSE (W. P.) Soteriology of the New Testament. pp. 391. *Lond.* 1892. 8°.   4227. b. 32.

DYMOND (J. J.) Expiation in the Christian Atonement. pp. 16. *Lond.* 1891. 8°.   4371. aaa. 45. (1.)

FREMANTLE (*Hon.* W. H.) The World as the Subject of Redemption. pp. 400. *Lond.* 1895. 8°.   4453. dd. 15.

GOVETT (R.) The Righteousness of God the salvation of the Believer. pp. 556. *Norwich,* 1891. 12°.   3267. bb. 1.

GRACEY (D.) Sin and the Unfolding of Salvation. pp. 291. *Lond.* 1894. 8°.   4371. f. 3.

HALL (C. N.) Atonement the fundamental fact of Christianity. pp. 159. *Lond.* 1893. 8°.   4429. df. 36.

HILLS (A. F.) At-one-ment. pp. 16. *Lond.* 1892. 8°.   8435. bb. 62. (1.)

HORTON (R. F.) The Atonement. 1893. 8°. Faith and Criticism.   4136. aaa. 41.

KIRKMAN (T.) Kaphar: the Atonement Covering. pp. 195. *Liverpool,* 1895. 12°. 4257. c. 19.

MAGUTH (S. S.) The Fall of Adam. 2 vol. *Lond.* 1893. 8°.   4373. k. 13.

CHRISTIANITY.—Atonement—_cont._

MILLS (W.) Investigation into the Atoning Sacrifice of Christ. pp. 65. *Cardiff,* 1890. 8°.
4371. df. 3. (3.)

PATERSON (R.) The Philosophy of the Atonement. pp. 217. *Glasg.* 1892. 8°. 4257. cc. 31.

PICKARD (I.) Germ Thoughts about the Fall of Man. pp. 32. *Lond.* 1893. 8°. 4422. aa. 51. (2.)

SCOTT (A.) Sacrifice, its Prophecy and Fulfilment. pp. 372. *Edinb.* 1894. 8°. 4466. cc. 5.

SEELEY (E.) The great Reconciliation and the Reign of Grace. pp. 306. *Lond.* 1893. 8°.
4257. cc. 34.

SIMMS (A. H.) The Atonement of our Saviour. pp. 71. *Lond.* 1893. 8°. 4479. e. 19.

SMITH (G. V.) Some modern Phases of the Doctrine of Atonement. pp. 44.
Lond. 1894. 8°. 4257. f. 30.

STRAETER (H.) Die Erlösungslehre des hl. Athanasius. pp. 201. *Freiburg,* 1894. 8°.
3623. a. 17.

TERRIEN (J. B.) S. Thomæ Aquinatis Doctrina de Unione Verbi Dei cum humanitate declarata. pp. 216. *Parisiis,* 1894. 8°. 4227. bb. 24.

ATHANASIUS, *Saint.* Athanasius de Incarnatione. pp. 108. *Lond.* 1891. 8°. 3805. bbb. 20.

BILLOT (L.) De Verbo Incarnato. pp. 453. *Romae,* 1892. 8°. 4223. aaa. 25.

GORE (C.) The Incarnation of the Son of God. pp. 276. *Lond.* 1891. 8°. 2208. d. 1.

—— Dissertations on subjects connected with the Incarnation. pp. 323. *Lond.* 1895. 8°.
4225. e. 1.

HOBSON (W. F.) Some Aspects of the Incarnation. pp. 16. *Oxf.* 1891. 8°. 4372. h. 28. (14.)

LAMBRECHT (H. C.) *Bp. of Ghent.* Analysis Tractatus de Incarnatione. pp. 172.
Gandavi, 1887. 8°. 4226. i. 12.

ORR (J.) The Christian View of God and the World as centring in the Incarnation. pp. 541. *Edinb.* 1893 8°. 4371. dd. 2.

STALEY (V.) Plain Words on the Incarnation. pp. 92. *Lond.* 1892. 8°. 4324. bb. 10.

WESTCOTT (B. F.) *Bp. of Durham.* The Incarnation. A charge. pp. 53. *Lond.* 1892. 8°.
4429. b. 36.

—— The Incarnation and Common Life. pp. 428. *Lond.* 1893. 8°. 4477. ee. 7.

ALLEN (D.) The Resurrection of Jesus. pp. 161. *N.Y.* 1893. 8°. 4017. g. 20.

LUXMOORE (H. E.) Layman's argument for the Resurrection of Christ. pp. 31. *Lond.* 1893. 8°.
4429. c. 21. (9.)

RING (T. P.) The most certain Fact in History pp. 101. *Lond.* 1892. 8°. 4224. de. 3.

See also infra: Person and Teaching of Christ: LENT.

Authority in Religious Belief.

CHRISTEN (E.) L'Autorité dans la conception religieuse de Luther. pp. 116. *Genève,* 1893. 8°.
3910. ee. 42.

DOUMERGUE (E.) L'autorité en matière de foi et la nouvelle école. pp. 240. *Lausanne,* 1892. 8°.
3900. a. 55.

MARTINEAU (J.) Seat of Authority in Religion. pp. 664. *Lond.* 1890. 8°. 2009. a.

BRAITHWAITE (R.) True Grounds of religious Faith. Essay on Dr. Martineau's Seat of Authority in Religion. pp. 163. *Lond.* 1890. 8°.
4017. bbb. 35.

MONOD (L.) Le Problème de l'Autorité. pp. 99. *Lyon,* 1891. 8°. 3900. i. 18. (4.)

CHRISTIANITY.—Authority, etc.—_cont._

STANTON (V. H.) The Place of Authority in Matters of religious Belief. pp. 229.
Lond. 1891. 8°. 4372. ee. 21.
See also RELIGION.

Biblical Inspiration : The Higher Criticism, *etc.*

ANDERSON (J.) L'Inspiration divine des Saintes Ecritures. pp. 34. *Brighton,* 1892. 8°. Pam. 5.

ATWOOD (I. M.) The Balance-sheet of Biblical Criticism. pp. 32. *Bost.* 1895. 8°. Pam. 5.

CHALMERS (T.) The evidence of the Christian Revelation. pp. 248. *Phila.* 1887. 12°.
4014. b. 5.

CHISHOLM (A.) The Bible in the light of Nature, *etc. Inverness,* 1891, etc. 8°. 3127. e. 2.

CLIFFORD (J.) Inspiration and Authority of the Bible. pp. 154. *Lond.* 1892. 8°. 3128. ff. 27.

COOK (J.) God in the Bible. pp. 221.
Lond. 1889. 8°. 4487. de. 35.

COXE (A. C.) *Bp. of W. New York.* Holy Writ and modern Thought. pp. 271.
N.Y 1892. 8°. 4486. a. 67.

CROOKER (J. H.) The New Bible and its new uses. pp. 286. *Bost.* 1893. 8°. 3103. aaa. 32.

DE WITT (J.) What is Inspiration? pp. 187. *N.Y.* 1893. 8°. 3125. df. 19.

DIECKHOFF (A. W.) Noch einmal über die Inspiration der heiligen Schrift. pp. 101.
Rostock, 1893. 8°. 3125. ee. 15.

EIK (G. D. K.) De Wetenschap voor de vierschaar van den Bijbel. pp. 180.
Alkmaar, 1890. 8°. 3128 h. 10.

EVANS (L. J.) Biblical Scholarship and Inspiration. pp. 126. *Cincinnati,* 1891. 8°.
3129 ce. 29.

FERRIÈRE (É.) Les Erreurs scientifiques de la Bible. pp. 400. *Paris,* 1891. 12°. 4016. df. 19.

GEIKIE (J. C.) The Bible by modern Light. *Lond.* 1893, etc. 8°. 3125. df. 13.

GESS (W. F.) Die Inspiration der Helden der Bibel. pp. 438. *Basel,* 1892. 8°. 3127. k. 33.

GLADDEN (W.) Who wrote the Bible? pp. 381. *Bost.* 1891. 8°. 3149. de. 30.

GLADSTONE (*Right Hon.* W. E.) The Impregnable Rock of Holy Scripture. pp. 306.
Lond. 1892. 8°. 2202. b. 2.

GONZALEZ (Z.) *Cardinal.* La Biblia y la ciencia. 2 tom. *Madrid,* 1891. 8°. 4016. g. 17.

HOLBOROW (A.) Evolution and Scripture. pp. 334. *Lond.* 1892. 8°. 3129. dd. 23.

HORTON (R. F.) Revelation and the Bible. pp. 412. *Lond.* 1892. 8°. 3109. df. 26.

INSPIRATION. Inspiration and Inerrancy. By C. A. Briggs, *etc.* pp. 274. *Lond.* 1891. 8°.
3128. dd. 9.

—— Inspiration and Inerrancy. History and defense by H. P. Smith. pp. 374.
Cincinnati, 1893. 8°. 3128. g. 4.

JOHANSSON (F. A.) Om Inspirationen. pp. 185. *Lund,* 1889. 8°. 3129. f. 8

HUGHES-GAMES (J.) The Bible and some current sceptical thought. pp. 15. *Liverpool,* 1890. 8°.
Pam. 77.

LUXMOORE (H. E.) Inspiration; why do men not believe the Bible? pp. 24. 1890. 8°.
S. Giles' Hall Lectures. No. 5. 4018. c.

MACGREGOR (J.) The Revelation and the Record. pp. 265. *Edinb.* 1893. 8°. 3109. d. 3.

MacCAIG (A.) The Grand Old Book. pp. 322. *Lond.* 1894. 8°. 3125. df. 20.

MACKENZIE (H.) Evolution illuminating the Bible. pp. 393. *Lond.* 1891. 8°. 3128. d. 1.

CHRISTIANITY. — Biblical Inspiration, etc.—*continued.*

MACKENZIE (H.) Modern Science unlocking the Bible. pp. 217. *Lond.* 1892. 8°. 4371. aaa. 2.

METZGER (G. J.) Der alte Bibelglaube und der moderne Vernunftglaube. pp. 176. *Stuttgart,* 1893. 8°. 3127. l. 26.

MITCHELL (J. H.) The Bible is true. pp. 16. *Lond.* 1890. 8°. 4018. c. 18. (6.)

MUELLER (L.) Bibel und Bibelkritik. pp. 32. *Barmen,* 1895. 8°. Pam. 5.

MYRBERG (O. F.) Die biblische Theologie und ihre Gegner. pp. 115. *Gütersloh,* 1892. 8°. 3125. df. 6.

PIERSON (A. T.) Stumbling Stones removed from the Word of God. pp. 79. *Lond.* 1891. 8°. 3128. f. 12.

REDFORD (R. A.) Bible Revelation. Unity and completness of the Scriptures. pp. 63. 1895. 8°. Present Day Tracts. Vol. 13. 2210. a.

REJECTED. The Transition. The Bible and Science. pp. 54. *Lond.* 1892. 8°. 3104. b. 8. (9.)

RIVIER (T.) Étude sur la Révélation chrétienne. pp. 125. *Lausanne,* 1892. 8°. 4371. ee. 17.

ROGERS (H.) The Superhuman Origin of the Bible inferred from itself. *Lond.* 1893. 8°. pp. 3*.*9. 4017. f. 20.

ROHNERT (W.) Die Inspiration der heiligen Schrift. pp. 284. *Leipz.* 1889. 8°. 3109. df. 30.

ROOKE (T. G.) Inspiration. pp. 261. *Edinb.* 1893. 8°. 3107. df. 6.

RYLE (J. C.) *Bp. of Liverpool.* Is all Scripture inspired? pp. 86. *Lond.* 1891. 8°. 3128. eee. 34.

SANDAY (W.) Inspiration. Bampton Lectures. pp. 640. *Lond.* 1893. 8°. 4456. g. 19.

—— The Oracles of God. pp. 156. *Lond.* 1891. 8°. 3127. ccc. 2.

SAPHIR (A.) The Divine Unity of Scripture. pp. 361. *Lond.* 1892. 8°. 3129. ddd. 17.

SHARR (F. J.) The Inspiration of the Holy Scriptures. pp. 180. *Lond.* 1891. 8°. 3127. m. 13.

SMITH (J. F.) Gains to the Bible from modern criticism. 1893. 8°. FRECKELTON (T. W.) Religion and modern Thought. 4016. df. 23.

SMYTH (J. P.) How God Inspired the Bible. pp. 222. *Dublin,* 1892. 8°. 3125. df. 21.

STEELE (T.) The "Higher Criticism" and the Inspiration of the Bible. pp. 31. *Lond.* 1893. 8°. 3104. b. 8. (11.)

STRETCH (J. F.) Study of Theories of Inspiration. pp. 24. *Lond.* 1890. 8°. Pam. 77.

THOMSON (W. D.) Revelation and the Bible. pp. 270. *Edinb.* 1890. 8°. 4109. e. 21.

TUCK (R.) Handbook of scientific and literary Bible Difficulties. pp. 566. *Lond.* 1890. 8°. 3127. k. 29.

URQUHART (J.) The Inspiration of the Holy Scriptures. pp. 581. *Lond.* 1895. 8°. 3126. ddd. 20.

VERNES (M.) Les Résultats de l'Exégèse biblique. pp. 231. *Paris,* 1890. 18°. 3128. h. 7.

VIGOUROUX (F.) Les Livres Saints et la critique rationaliste. 2 vol. *Paris,* 1890. 18°. 4533. ee. 20.

WADSWORTH (W. M.) The Bible; its origin, growth and descent. pp. 48. *Stockton,* 1895. 8°. 3155. de. 36.

WENSLEY (E. B.) The Higher Criticism. pp. 24. *Lond.* 1892. 8°. 3104. b. 8. (10.)

ZENOS (A. C.) Elements of the Higher Criticism. pp. 255. *N.Y.* 1895. 8°. 3105. de. 7.

CHRISTIANITY. — Biblical Inspiration, etc.—*continued.*

ANDERSON (J. C.) Old Testament and monumental coincidences. pp. 265. *Lond.* 1895. 8°. 7705. a. 35.

BACHMANN (P. J.) Alttestamentliche Untersuchungen. *Berl.* 1894, *etc.* 8°. 3149. i.

BRUGSCH (H.) Steininschrift und Bibelwort. pp. 344. *Berl.* 1891. 8°. 12249. cc. 37.

CARLYLE (G.) Moses and the Prophets. pp. 104. *Lond.* 1890. 8°. 3141. e. 8.

CAVE (A.) The Old Testament and the Higher Criticism. pp. 58. *Lond.* 1890. 8°. 3155. de. 16.

DODEL, afterwards DODEL-PORT (A.) Mozes of Darwin. pp. 139. *Amsterd.* 1890. 8°. 7006. bbb. 28.

GIRDLESTONE (R. B.) The Foundations of the Bible. pp. 215. *Lond.* 1891. 8°. 3128. h. 21.

KINNS (S.) Moses and Geology. pp. 518. *Lond.* 1895. 8°. 3109. dd. 6.

—— Graven in the Rock. 2 vol. *Lond.* 1895. 8°. 3125. dd. 8.

KIRKPATRICK (A. F.) The Divine Library of the Old Testament. pp. 155. *Lond.* 1891. 8°. 3129. ddd. 10.

LARSEN (A. C.) De fem Mose-Bøger. pp. 304. *Kjøbenh.* 1890. 8°. 3155. l. 5.

ROBERTSON (J.) The Old Testament and its contents. pp. 186. 1895. 8°. The Guild Library. 3622. g.

MARKHAM (R. F.) The Inspiration of the Old Testament. pp. 11. *Oswestry,* 1892. 8°. 3149. g. 23. (11.)

SPIERS (W.) The Age and Authorship of the Pentateuch. pp. 395. 1895. 8°. Books for Bible Students. 3125. dd.

VUILLEUMIER (H.) Les résultats des travaux les plus récents relatifs à l'Ancien Testament. pp. 84. *Lausanne,* 1893. 8°. 3149. g. 22. (7.)

WHITE (H. A.) Origin of the Pentateuch in the light of ancient monuments. pp. 304. *Richmond, Va.* 1894. 8°. 3155. k. 34.

ZAHN (J. K. A.) Was lehrt man gegenwärtig auf der Universität Halle-Wittenberg über das Alte Testament? pp. 34. *Gütersloh.* 1894. 8°. 3149. g. 23. (15.)

BRADLAUGH (C.) Genesis. Its authorship and authenticity. pp. 346. 1882. 8°. International Library of Freethought. Vol. 4. 4018. aaa.

CHAMBRUN DE ROSEMONT (A. de) Essai d'un commentaire scientifique de la Genèse. pp. 526. *Lyon,* 1891. 8°. 3155. d. 49.

COGGIN (F. E.) Man's Great Charter. Exposition of the first chapter of Genesis. pp. 210. *Lond.* 1892. 8°. 3155. k. 43.

HUNTINGFORD (E.) Popular Misconceptions about the First Eleven Chapters of Genesis. pp. 229. *Lond.* 1891. 8°. 3155. de. 19.

L., S. J. The First Chapter of Genesis justified by science. pp. 72. *Lond.* 1895. 8°. 3155. l. 20.

RYLE (H. E.) Early Narratives of Genesis. I.–XI. pp. 138. *Lond.* 1892. 8°. 3155. c. 68.

WATSON (F.) The book Genesis a true history, *etc.* pp. 288. *Lond.* 1892. 8°. 4429. aa. 75.

STAERK (W.) Das Deuteronomium. pp. 119. *Leipz.* 1894. 8°. 3155. g. 47.

MONTET (F.) La composition de l'Hexateuque. pp. 36. *Bâle,* 1894. 8°. Pam. 5.

WEDGWOOD (J.) The Message of Israel in the light of modern criticism. pp. 316. *Lond.* 1894. 8°. 4034. k. 28.

BIBLE. New Testament *Gospels.* But how— if the Gospels are historic? pp. 201. *Edinb.* 1891. 8°. 4018. g. 34.

CHRISTIANITY. — Biblical Inspiration, etc.—continued.

Cone (O.) Gospel - Criticism and historical Christianity. pp. 365. *N.Y.* 1891. 8°.
                                3224. k. 26.
Dale (R. W.) The Living Christ and the Gospels. pp. 299. *Lond.* 1890. 8°. 3225. e. 28.
Mead (C. M.) Christ and Criticism. pp. 186. *N.Y.* 1892. 8°.   4017. e. 19.
Wordsworth (C.) *Bp. of Saint Andrews.* Primary Witness to the Truth of the Gospel. pp. 333. *Lond.* 1892. 8°.   4017. f. 19.
Agnostic. Plain Commentary on the First Gospel. pp. 652. *Lond.* 1891. 8°. 3225. dd. 12.
Hervey (*Lord A. C.*) *Bp. of Bath and Wells.* The Authenticity of the Gospel of St. Luke. pp. 76. *Bath*, 1890. 8°.   Pam. 5.
Watkins (H. W.) Modern Criticism in its relation to the Fourth Gospel. Bampton Lectures. pp. 502. *Lond.* 1890. 8°.   4456. g. 16.
See also Earth *and* Creation : and for other works on the New Testament, *see* Church History, *Apostolic Period.*

Canon of the Old Testament.

Buhl (F. P. W.) Kanon des Alten Testamentes. pp. 262. *Leip.* 1891. 8°.   3149. g. 19.
Loisy (A.) Histoire du Canon de l'Ancien Testament. pp. 259. *Paris*, 1890. 8°.   3149. h. 26.
Ryle (H. E.) The Canon of the Old Testament. pp. 304. *Lond.* 1892. 8°.   3149. ddd. 7.
Wildeboer (G.) Het ontstaan van den Kanon des Ouden Verbonds. pp. 170. *Te Groningen*, 1891. 8°.   3149. i. 6.
—— Die Entstehung des alttestamentlichen Kanons. pp. 164. *Gotha*, 1891. 8°.
                                3149. i. 9.
For other works on Biblical Criticism, *etc.*, *see* Church History, and under the heading Bible in the General Catalogue of Printed Books in the British Museum.

Christianity and Non-Christian Religions.

Farrer (J. A.) Paganism and Christianity. pp. 256. *Lond.* 1891. 8°.   4503. bb 31.
Friese (P. C.) Semitic Philosophy. Original Christianity in its conflict with ancient Heathenism. pp. 247. *Chicago*, 1890. 8°. 4372. cc. 11.
Johansson (C. E.) Den bibliska Kristendomen g nt emot Judendomen och Hedendomen. *Upsala*, 1889. *etc.* 8°.   3557. i. 10.
Lewis (A. H.) Paganism surviving in Christianity. pp. 309. *N.Y.* 1892. 8°. 3940. cc. 12.
Parsons (J. D.) Our Sun-God ; Christianity before Christ, *etc.* pp. 214. *Lond.* 1895. 8°.
                                4503. aaa. 14.
Quilliam (W. H.) The Religion of the Sword. Judaism, Christianity and Islam. *Liverp.* 1891, *etc.* 8°.   4503. de.
Stubenvoll ( ) Heidenthum im Christenthum. pp. 191. *Heidelberg*, 1891. 8°.
                                4506. e. 26.
Scott (C. N.) Foregleams of Christianity. pp. 223. *Lond.* 1893. 8°.   4503. aaa. 10.
Wells (J.) Christ and the Heroes of Heathendom. pp. 159. *Lond.* 1891. 8°.   4429. ee. 9.
Wilson (J. M.) Christianity as the crown of the ancient religions. pp. 23. *Lond.* 1893. 8°.
                                4429. c. 21. (13.)

Wolff (M.) Credo ut Intelligam : short studies on early Greek Philosophy and its relation to Christianity. pp. 84. *Oxf.* 1891, 8°.
                                8460. bb. 31.

CHRISTIANITY. — Christianity and Non-Christian Religions—continued.

For comparisons between Christianity and other existing religions, *see* Buddhism ; Hinduism ; Mohammedanism.

Christianity and Social Questions.

See Socialism ; Social Questions.

Miracles. *See* Miracles.

Person and Teaching of Christ.

Aitchison (J.) Signa Christi : evidences of Christianity in the Person of Christ. pp. 296. *Lond.* 1890. 8°.   4016. df. 11.
Avancinus (N.) Vita et Doctrina Jesu Christi ex quatuor Evangelistis collecta. pp. 535. *Lond.* 1894. 16°.   4807. a. 1.
Barrow (E. P.) Regni Evangel'um. Survey of the teaching of Christ. pp. 272. *Lond.* 1892. 8°.
                                3227. df. 37.
Bellett (J. G.) The Son of God. pp. 151. *Lond.* 1895. 8°.   4227. ee. 14.
Bible. *Gospels.* The Great Discourse of Jesus the Christ. pp. 361. *Lond.* 1892. 8°.
                                3227. de. 23.
—— The Master's Guide for His Disciples. pp. 268. *Lond.* 1895. 12°.   3227. de. 38.
Briggs (C. A) The Messiah of the Gospels. pp. 337. *Edinb.* 1894. 8°.   4227. ee. 15.
Broadus (J. A.) Jesus of Nazareth. pp. 105. *N.Y.* 1890. 8°.   4227. h. 13.
Cairns (J.) Christ the central Evidence of Christianity. 6 pt. *Lond.* 1893. 8°.
                                4429. df. 32.
Carpenter (J. E.) Relation of Jesus to his Age and our own. pp. 87. *Lond.* 1895. 8°.
                                4224. a. 40.
Carpenter (W. B.) *Bp. of Ripon.* The Son of Man among the sons of men. pp. 307. *Lond.* 1893. 8°.   4806. c. 3.
—— The Great Charter of Christ. pp. 300. *Lond.* 1895. 8°.   3224. k. 28.
Clarke (J. F.) Christ and Christianity. pp. 16. *Lond.* 1883. 8°,   Pam. 92.
Clarke (R. F.) The Ministry of Jesus. pp. 188. *Lond.* 1890. 8°.   3457. d. 18.
Coultery (P.) Jésus le Christ et sa vie. pp. 386. *Bienne*, 1891. 8°.   4807. ee. 22.
Crooker (J. H.) Different New Testament Vi ws of Jesus. pp. 80. *Bost.* 1891. 8°. 4224. a. 35.
Denniston (J. M.) An Alternative. The Christ of the Fourth Gospel, a miracle of truth, or of falsehood. pp. 160. *Lond.* 1892. 8°.
                                4224. aaa. 49.
Didon (H. N.) La Foi en la Divinité de Jésus-Christ. pp. 260. *Paris*, 1894. 8°.   4225. f. 5.
Dixon (A. C.) The God Man. pp. 64. *Baltimore*, 1891. 8°.   4015. df. 18.
Edwards (T. C.) The God Man. pp. 162. *Lond.* 1895. 8°.   4224. bbb. 27.
Egidy (M. v.) Serious Thoughts. pp. 53. *Lond.* 1891. 8°.   3911. ee. 51. (7.)
Verax. Dogmatisches oder undogmatisches Christentum ? Eine Behandlung des Egidyschen Problems. pp. 18. *Halle*, 1891. 8°.
                                Pam. 93.
Ewald (P.) Der geschichtliche Christus. pp. 35. *Leipz.* 1892. 8°.   4371. ee. 29. (2.)
Eyton (R.) The Beatitudes. pp. 184. *Lond.* 1895. 8°.   4464. i. 18.

CHRISTIANITY.—Person and Teaching of Christ—*continued.*

FAIRBAIRN (A. M.) Place of Christ in modern Theology. pp. 556. *Lond.* 1893. 8°. 4427. h. 23.

FARRAR (F. W.) Life of Christ. pp. 712. *Lond.* 1894. 8°. 4808. f. 1.

—— Life of Christ as represented in Art. pp. 507. *Lond.* 1894. 8°. 2261. d. 1.

FOUARD (C.) The Christ, the Son of God. 2 vol. *Lond.* 1891. 8°. 4808. cc. 12.

GANNETT (W. C.) The Childhood of Jesus. pp. 220. *Lond.* 1890. 8°. 4806. aaa. 7.

GASKELL (W.) The Person of Christ. pp. 32. 1894. 8°. Pages for Religious Inquirers. No. 3. 4378. aaa.

HAEMMERLEIN (T.) *a Kempis.* Meditations on the Life of Christ. pp. 354. *Oxf.* 1892. 8°. 4399. h. 1.

HORTON (R. F.) The Teaching of Jesus. pp. 287. *Lond.* 1895. 8°. 4227. dc. 3.

JESUS CHRIST. As Others Saw Him : A.D. 54. pp. 215. *Lond.* 1895. 8°. 4399. l. 13.

—— Christ and the Creator Glorified. pp. 653. 181. *Glasg.* 1895. 8°. 4016. df. 27.

LAYMAN. Jesus, the Carpenter of Nazareth. pp. 498. *Lond.* 1891. 8°. 4807. c. 2.

LIDDON (H. P.) The Divinity of Our Lord. pp. 585. *Lond.* 1890. 8°. 2208. a. 1.

MILLIGAN (W.) The Ascension and Heavenly Priesthood of Our Lord. pp. 374. *Lond.* 1892. 8°. 4466. c. 30.

MILNER (R.) Lessons on the life of Christ. 2 vol. *Lond.* 1891. 8°. 4808. ee. 5.

MITCHELL (R. M.) Theistic Refutation of the Divinity of Christ. pp. 475. *N.Y.* 1893. 8°. 4227. cc. 13.

MOORHOUSE (J.) *Bp. of Manchester.* The Teaching of Christ. pp. 167. *Lond.* 1891. 8°. 4478. h. 34.

MEYRICK (F.) The Bishop of Manchester on the Limitations of Our Lord's Knowledge. pp. 8. *Lond.* 1891. 8°. Pam. 77.

SWAYNE (W. S.) An inquiry into the Nature of Our Lord's Knowledge as Man. pp. 55. *Lond.* 1891. 8°. 4224. bb. 46.

DE ROMESTIN (H.) An Enquiry into the belief of the Church as to the limitation of Our Lord's Knowledge. pp. 43. *Lond.* 1891. 8°. 4372. h. 28. (13.)

MORETON (F.) The unknown Saviour. pp. 32. *Lond.* 1894. 16°. 4422. aa. 51. (7.)

MOZLEY (T.) The Son. pp. 352. *Lond.* 1891. 8°. 4224. bbb. 20.

NEWTON (B. W.) Ancient Truths respecting the Deity and Humanity of the Lord Jesus. pp. 118. *Lond.* 1893. 8°. 4224. h. 86.

NIPPOLD (F.) Der Entwicklungsgang des Lebens Jesu. pp. 222. *Hamb.* 1895. 8°. 3226. dd. 17.

NOTOVICH (N.) La vie inconnue de Jésus-Christ. pp. 301. *Paris,* 1894. 8°. 4807 b. 2.

—— The unknown Life of Jesus Christ. pp. 288. *N.Y.* 1894. 8°. 4808. aaa. 32.

GIOVANNINI (R.) La Vie inconnue de Jésus-Christ, par N. Notovich. pp. 125. *Lisbonne,* 1894. 8°. 4807. b. 3.

ORD (A. C.) The Blessedness of the Person of Christ. pp. 48. *Lond.* 1895. 8°. 4371. dd. 8. (13.)

OTTLEY (H. B.) Christ and modern Life. pp. 339. *Lond.* 1894. 8°. 4371. df. 20.

PEARSON (A.) Christus Magister. Teachings from the Sermon on the Mount. pp. 305. *Lond.* 1892. 8°. 4371. aa. 11.

PEROWNE (T. T.) Our High Priest in Heaven. pp. 114. *Lond.* 1894. 16°. 4226. a. 13.

CHRISTIANITY.—Person and Teaching of Christ—*continued.*

PICTON (J. A.) The Religion of Jesus. pp. 233. *Lond.* 1893. 8°. 4376. ee. 18.

PORRET (J. A.) Trois Vies de Jésus. Strauss, Renan, Keim. pp. 57. *Genève,* 1893. 8°. 4806. h. 8.

RAUE (S.) Christus als Lehrer und Erzieher. pp. 239. *Freiburg,* 1895. 8°. 4224. bbb. 30.

RÉGLA (P de) Jésus de Nazareth. pp. 404. *Paris,* 1891. 8°. 4807. e. 3.

ROBINSON (A.) The Saviour in the Newer Light. pp. 386. *Edinb.* 1895. 8°. 4227. ee. 16.

ROGERS (A. K.) The Life and Teaching of Jesus. pp. 354. *N.Y.* 1894. 8°. 4808. f. 2.

ROWLEY (A. C.) The Christ in the Two Testaments. pp. 77. *Lond.* 1892. 8°. 4224. dc. 6.

SAVAGE (M. J.) Jesus and modern Life. pp. 229. *Bost.* 1893. 8°. 4227. ee. 12.

SCHAEDER (E.) Die Bedeutung des lebendigen Christus für die Rechtfertigung nach Paulus. pp. 194. *Gütersloh,* 1893. 8°. 3267. d. 38.

SCHMIDT (H.) Zur Christologie. pp. 222. *Berl.* 1892. 8°. 4224. e. 58.

SCHMITZ (B.) Das Leben Jesu unseres göttlichen Heilandes. pp. 669. *Paderborn,* 1893. 8°. 4808. cc. 14.

SEAVER (J.) The Authority of Christ in the Criticism of the Old Testament. pp. 52. *Lond.* 1891. 8°. Pam. 5.

SEELEY (*Sir* J. R.) Ecce Homo. pp. 370. *Lond.* 1895. 8°. 4224. aaa. 52.

SMYTH (E. C.) The Divinity of Jesus Christ. pp. 233. *Bost.* 1893. 8°. 4224. aa. 48.

STALKER (J.) Imago Christi. pp. 332. *Lond.* 1890. 8°. 4227. h. 6.

—— Trial and death of Christ. pp. 309. *Lond.* 1894. 8°. 4807. bb. 4.

STRAUSS (D. F.) Life of Jesus. pp. 784. *Lond.* 1892. 8°. 4807. ee. 20.

UNSWORTH (W.) The Influence of Jesus Christ on Young Men. pp. 248. *Lond.* 1894. 8°. 4224. aaa. 51.

VICKERS (J.) The Real Jesus. pp. 314. *Lond.* 1891. 8°. 4017. f. 18.

VILLENEUVE (H. de) L'Esprit de Jésus ou le christianisme rationaliste. 2 tom. *Paris,* 1890. 12°. 4227. h. 12.

WALLACE (H.) Boyhood of Christ. pp. 110. *Lond.* 1892. 8°. 4808. g. 3.

WATCHMAN. Jesus of Nazareth. His interpretation of the Messiahship. pp. 122. *Lond.* 1894. 8°. 4224. aa. 44.

WEBSTER (W.) Jesus and Democracy. pp. 113. *Manch.* 1895. 8°. 08275. e. 38.

WELLS (J.) Christ and the Heroes of Heathendom. pp. 159. *Lond.* 1891. 8°. 4429. ee. 9.

BIGGS (C. R. D.) Stages in Atonement. The Sayings from the Cross. pp. 74. *Lond.* 1891. 8°. 4257. f. 24.

BURNETT (T. M.) The Wondrous Cross. Seven Last Words. pp. 89. *Lond.* 1895. 8°. 4466. d. 21.

HUBERT (D. G.) Ecce Homo. Meditations on the Passion, *etc.* pp. 196. *Lond.* 1894. 16°. 3456. df. 40.

PASSMORE (T. H.) Crux Heptachorda. Seven last words of our Lord. pp. 87. *Oxf.* 1894. 8°. 4223. aa. 22.

PHILLIPS (F. A.) Mysteries of the Passion. pp. 64. *Lond.* 1893. 8°. 4479. aa. 61.

See also supra: General: Atonement: LENT.

CHRISTIANITY— continued.

Personal: Christianity and Morality.

ARMOUR (J. M.) The Divine Method of Life.
pp. 244. *Bost.* 1887. 8°. 4371. e 8.

BEET (J. A.) The New Life in Christ. pp. 347.
Lond. 1895. 8°. 4403. dd. 37.

BREMOND D'ARS (G. de) *Viscount.* La Vertu du
Christianisme. pp. 438. *Paris,* 1890. 8°.
4379. g. 5.

CARRICK (J.) The Divine Life. pp. 193.
Edinb. 1893. 8°. 4227. ee. 8.

CHRISTIAN ENDEAVOUR. Christian Endeavour
Principles. pp. 106. *Lond.* 1893. 8°.4371. aa. 46.

CHRISTIANITY. Discipleship: the scheme of
Christ anity. pp. 232. *Lond.* 1894. 8°.
4371. ee. 28.

CUYLER (T. L.) Christianity in the Home.
pp. 264. *Lond.* 1893. 8°. 4399. aaaa. 3.

EVERARD (G.) Salvation and Service. pp. 262.
Lond. 1895. 8°. 4371. bb. 14.

GRAY (W. A.) Laws of the Spiritual Life.
pp. 258. *Lond.* 1895. 8°. 4401. dd. 38.

HERMANN (W.) The Communion of the Christian
with God. pp. 261. 1895. 8°. Theological
Translation Library. Vol. IV. 3605. k.

HERRON (G. D.) The Christian Society.
pp. 158. *Lond.* 1894. 8°. 4371. b. 38.

JONES (W.) The Doctrine of Entire Sanctification. pp. 256. *Lond.* 1892. 8°. 4371. a. 13.

KIDD (J.) Morality and Religion. pp. 458.
Edinb. 1895. 8°. 4372. cc. 23.

KIRTON (J. W.) The Christian Growth.
pp. 288. *Lond.* 1893. 8°. 4371. df. 23.

KITTO (J. F.) Religion in Common Life.
pp. 168. *Lond.* 1894. 8°. 4463. dd. 4.

LAMAR (J. S.) First Principles and Perfection.
Cincinnati, 1891. 8°. 4371. e. 10.

LAURIEN (V.) Conventional Religion. pp. 353.
Lond. 1892. 8°. 4371 e. 14.

LAW (W.) Wholly for God. Extracts from the
writings of W. Law. pp. 328. *Lond.* 1894. 8°.
4399. aaaa. 24.

LILLEY (J. P.) The Pathway of Light. pp. 135.
Lond. 1895. 8°. 4371. aaaa. 48.

LITTLE (W. J. K.) The Christian Home.
pp. 287. *Lond.* 1891. 8°. 4402. m. 6.

MACCOLL (M.) Christianity in relation to
Morals. pp. 346. *Lond.* 1890. 8°. 4376. c. 1.

MILLER (J. R.) A Help for the Common Days.
pp. 320. *Edinb.* 1894. 8°. 4371. aaaa. 2.

—— Week-Day Religion. pp. 280.
Lond. 1894. 8°. 4399. aaaa. 4.

—— The Building of Character. pp. 272.
Lond. 1895. 8°. 4399 dd. 2.

MOORE (E. W.) Christ Controlled. pp. 231.
Lond. 1894. 8°. 4399. aa. 49.

PEARSON (S.) Thyself and others. pp. 125.
Lond. 1890. 8°. 4401. f. 32.

—— Week-Day Living. pp. 372.
Lond. 1895. 8°. 4401. dd. 37.

SIMPSON (A. B.) Christ Life. pp. 80.
Lond. 1895. 8°. 4399. bb. 9.

SINCLAIR (W. M.) The Servant of Christ.
pp. 214. *Lond.* 1895. 8°. 4403. ccc. 44.

SMITH (H. W.) Every-day Religion. pp. 242.
Lond. 1894. 8°. 4399. aaaa. 2.

SMITH (H.) The practical Value of Religious
Belief. pp. 31. *Lond.* 1894. 8°. 4018. b. 43.

SPURGEON (C. H.) The Soul-Winner. pp. 343.
Lond. 1895. 8°. 4399. d. 2.

STEARNS (L. F.) The Evidence of Christian Experience. pp. 473. *Lond.* 1890. 8°. 4105. e. 1.

CHRISTIANITY.—Personal, etc.—cont.

STEVENS (G. B.) Doctrine and Life. pp. 247.
Bost. 1895. 8°. 4409. ddd. 3.

TOLSTOI (L. N.) *Count.* 'The Kingdom of God
is within you.' 2 vol. *Lond.* 1894. 8°.
3926. b. 40.

WYNNE (G. R.) Spiritual Life in its earlier
stages. pp.-63. *Lond.* 1895. 8°. 4429. a. 122.
See also supra: General : ETHICS : PRAYER, *etc.*

CHRISTMAS AC. Rouen. *Société des*
Bibliophiles Normands. Noëls normands.
pp. 306. *Rouen,* 1895. 4°. Ac. 8938/54.

IRVING (W.) Old Christmas. Illustrated by R.
Caldecott. pp. 165. *Lond.* 1892. 8°.
12316. m. 4.

KINGSBURY (T. L.) Christmas and Epiphany.
pp. 135. *Lond.* 1894. 8°. 4227. de. 3.

KOEPPEN (W.) Beiträge zur Geschichte der
deutschen Weihnachtsspiele. pp. 132.
Paderborn, 1893, 8°. 011850. h. 35.

ORTWEIN (F.) Deutsche Weihnachten.
pp. 132. *Gotha,* 1892. 8°. 12431. ee. 11.

TILLE (A.) Die Geschichte der deutschen
Weihnacht. pp. 355. *Leipz.* 1893. 8°.
3477. df. 6.

CHRISTMAS CAROLS. Collection of Christmas
Carols. pp. 16. *St. Blazey,* 1880. 8°. Pam. 30.

NEUFCHÂTEL. Noëls en pays neuchâtelois.
pp. 12. *Neuchâtel,* 1891. 4°. 12330. m. 30.

PIERRE (C.) Les noëls populaires. pp. 20.
Paris, 1887. 8°. 11825. g. 21. (1.)

CHRONOLOGY. See CALENDARS.

CHRYSANTHEMUM. BELLAIR (G. A.)
Les Chrysanthèmes. pp. 111.
Compiègne, 1891. 8°. 7054. df. 2.

LONDON. *Chrysanthemum Society.* Catalogue of
Chrysanthemums. 2 pt. *Lond.* 1888, 89. 8°.
7073. de. 13. (6.)

—— Official Catalogue. pp. 107.
Lond. 1890. 8°. Pam. 1.

RAVENSCROFT (B. C.) Chrysanthemum Culture
for Amateurs. pp. 112. *Lond.* 1894. 8°.
7054. df. 23.

RYDER (S.) Successful Chrysanthemum Culture.
pp. 41. *Manch.* 1891. 8°. 7074. e. 10. (7.)

THIBAULT (E.) Note sur la Culture anglaise des
Chrysanthèmes. pp. 23. *Paris,* 1893. 8°. Pam.1.
See also FLOWERS.

CHUR. MOLINIER (É.) Le Trésor de la
Cathédrale de Coire. pp. 106. *Paris,* 1895. fol.
K.T.C. 23. b. 7.

CHURCH AND STATE. BARRY (A.)
Bp. of Sydney. Church and State. pp. 11.
1891. 8°. Church Defence Handy Volume.
4109. c. 21.

BEECHING (H. C.) Church and State. Address
to Villagers. pp. 24. *Lond.* 1887. 8°. Pam. 92.

BENOIST (C.) L'État et l'Église. pp. 67.
Paris, 1892. 8°. 3900. aa. 11.

OULTON (W.) Anti-State-Churchism. pp. 266.
Lond. 1894. 8°. 4109. c. 38.

SEPARAZIONE. Separazione dello Stato dalla
Chiesa. pp. 32. *Torino,* 1891. 8°.
4050. h. 17. (5.)

WIRGMAN (A. T.) The Church and the Civil
Power. pp. 176. *Lond.* 1893. 8°. 4109. c. 34.
See also CHURCH HISTORY : ENGLAND, *Church*
of : LIBERTY, *Religious.* ROMAN CATHOLIC
CHURCH : SCOTLAND, *Church of, etc.*

CHURCH HISTORY.
For the ecclesiastical history of each country,
diocese, parish or sect : *see* under the name
required.

CHURCH HISTORY—*continued.*
General.

BETTANY (G. T.) Sketch of the history of Judaism and Christianity. pp. 456. 1892. 8°. World's Religious Series.   4503. aaa.

GILMARTIN (†.) Manual of Church History. *Dublin*, 1890, *etc.* 8°.   4532. dd. 4.

JOHANSSON (C. E.) Det förkonstantinska Kristendomsförsvaret. pp. 187. *Upsala*, 1889. 8°.   4533. cc. 18.

KNOEPFLER (A.) Lehrbuch der Kirchengeschichte. pp. 748. *Freiburg*, 1895. 8°. 4534. d. 5.

KRAUS (F. X.) Lehrbuch der Kirchengeschichte. pp. 837. *Trier*, 1887. 8°.   4534. f. 15.

MOELLER (W.) History of the Christian Church. pp. 545. *Lond.* 1892. 8°.   4534. ee. 11.

MORENO CEBADA (E.) Las Herejías, los cismas y los errores de todos los siglos. 4 tom. *Barcelona*, 1880. 8°.   4534. c. 28.

MOSHEIM (J. L. v.) Murdock's Translation of Mosheim's Ecclesiastical History. 3 vol. *Bost.* 1892. 8°.   4534. ee. 4.

MUELLER (C.) Kirchengeschichte. 1892, *etc.* 8°. ACHELIS (E. C.) Grundriss der theologischen Wissenschafte n. Reihe 1. Theil IV. 1. 3622. ee.

NEWMAN (H.) Outlines of Church History. pp. 106. *Dublin*, 1894. 8°.   4520. a. 6.

NIELSEN (F.) Ledetraad i Kirkens Historie. 2 pt. *Kjøbenh.* 1889, 87. 8°.   4531. b. 9.

RASMUSSEN (H.) Kortfattet Kirkehistorie for Folkeskolen. pp. 102. *Kjøbenh.* 1891. 8°.   4535. aa. 3.

SCHAFF (P.) History of the Church. 11 vol. *Edinb.* 1891–93. 8°.   2013. g.

SOHM (R.) Outlines of Church History. pp. 254. *Lond.* 1895. 8°.   4531. df. 1.

TARNER (G. E.) Concise tabular view of the Outlines of Christian History. *Lond.* 1890. 4°.   4530. g. 9.

ADAMS (J. C.) Christian Types of Heroism. pp. 208. *Bost.* 1891. 8°.   4530. aa. 7.

BRIGHT (W.) Waymarks in Church History. pp. 436. *Lond.* 1894. 8°.   4532. df. 1.

CANNING (*Hon.* A, S. G.) Thoughts on Religious History. pp. 276. *Lond.* 1891, 8°. 4530. aa. 8.

COMBA (E.) Lezioni di storia della Chiesa. pp. 83. *Firenze*, 1889. 8°.   4532. ee. 16.

CREIGHTON (M.) *Bp. of Peterborough.* Persecution and Tolerance. pp. 140. *Lond.* 1895. 8°.   4455. de. 14.

DUNAND (P H.) Récits de l'histoire de l'Église. 2 series. *Toulouse*, 1893. 8°.   4532. ee. 23.

GAUTIER (L.) Études et tableaux historiques. pp. 403. *Lille*, 1890. 8°.   4534. c. 27.

GWATKIN (H. M.) The Meaning of Ecclesiastical History. pp. 16. *Camb.* 1891. 8°.   4535. c. 10. (5.)

HERZOG (B.) Bilder aus der Kirchengeschichte. pp. 488. *Aarau*, 1890. 8°.   4534. c. 26.

JAMES (C.) Curiosities of Christian History. pp. 522. *Lond.* 1892. 8°.   4534. de. 4.

KNOEPFLER (A.) Kirchengeschichtliche Studien. *Münster*, 1891, *etc.* 8°.   4534. ee.

PIERINI (P.) La Genesi del Liberalismo. pp. 386. *Prato*, 1889. 8°.   3900. c. 8.

SELL (C.) The Church in the Mirror of History. pp. 250. *Edinb.* 1890. 8°.   4530. aaa. 7.

VLIET (J. v. d.) Studia Ecclesiastica. *Lugduni-Bat.* 1891, *etc.* 8°.   3622. b.

WEINGARTEN (H.) Zeittafeln und Überblicke zur Kirchengeschichte. pp. 247. *Leipz.* 1891. 8°.   4531. ee. 11.

CHURCH HISTORY——*continued.*
Dictionaries and Encyclopædias.
See THEOLOGY.

Papacy.

BOSISIO (F.) La difesa dei Sommi Pontefici Romani. *Milano*, 1891, *etc.* 8°.   4050. aa.

BRANCACCIO DI CARPINO (F.) Nuova Cronologia dei Papi. pp. 139. *Torino*, 1895. 8°. 4856. g. 16.

DOBELLI (F.) I Papi da san Pietro a Pio IX. 3 vol. *Roma*, 1889, 90. 8°.   4855. bb. 13.

DUCHESNE (L.) Le Liber Pontificalis. 1884, *etc.* 8°. 2 tom. Ac. Athens. *École Française*. Bibliothèque. 2° série. III.   Ac. 5206/2.

GOYAU (G.) Le Vatican, les Papes et la civilisation. pp. 796. *Brux.* 1895. 4°. K.T.C. 30. b. 7.

MIRBT (C.) Quellen zur Geschichte des Papsttums. pp. 288. *Freiburg*, 1895. 8°. 4571. f. 29.

OLIPHANT (M. O.) Makers of modern Rome. pp. 507. *Lond.* 1895. 8°   2388. i. 21.

WILFRID (H.) Die Geschichte der Päpste. pp. 187. *Basel*, 1894, 8°.   4856. e, 17.

TRIPEPI (L.) Ragioni e Fatti ad apologia di alcuni Papi. pp. 383. *Roma*, 1894. 8°.   4050. h. 21.

PULLER (F. W.) The Primitive Saints and the See of Rome. pp. 428. *Lond.* 1893. 8°.   3940. bb. 28.

GUGLIELMOTTI (A.) Storia della Marina Pontificia. 10 vol. *Roma*, 1886–93. 8°.   8806. e.

GRAF (A.) Le origini del Papato e del Comune di Roma. 1891. 8°. Gli albori della vita italiana. vol. 2.   9166. ccc. 11.

GIRBAL (E. C.) La Rosa de Oro. pp. 87. *Madrid*, 1880. 8°.   4570. aa, 18.

STEINLE (A. M. v.) Der Peterspfennig. 1893. 8°. Frankfurter zeitgemässe Broschüren, *etc.* N. F. Bd. 14.   12209. g.

PINTON (P.) Le donazioni barbariche ai Papi. pp. 230. *Roma*, 1890. fol.   4605. h. 5.

ARDANT (G.) Papes et Paysans. pp. 268. *Paris*, 1891. 12°.   8276. aa. 58.

BLUMENSTOK (A.) Der päpstliche Schutz im Mittelalter. pp. 168. *Innsbruck*, 1890. 8°.   4571. e. 1.

DOELLINGER (J. J. I. v.) Die Papst-Fabeln des Mittelalters. pp. 188. *Stuttgart*, 1890. 8°.   4571. f. 17.

GREENWOOD (A. D.) Empire and Papacy in the middle ages. pp. 227. *Lond.* 1892. 8°.   9076. ccc. 11.

SIMONSFELD (H.) Beiträge zum päpstlichen Kanzleiwesen im Mittelalter. 1890. 8°. Ac. Munich. *K. Akademie der Wissenschaften.* Sitzungsberichte der phil.-philolog. Classe.   Ac. 713/8.

LIGHTFOOT (J. B.) *Bp. of Durham.* The Apostolic Fathers. S. Clement of Rome. 2 vol. *Lond.* 1890. 8°.   2206. f.

LEO I., *Saint, Pope.* Letters and Sermons. 2 pt. 1895. 8°. WACE (H.) and SCHAFF (P.) Select Library of Fathers, *etc.* Vol. 12.   3623. cc.

ALLIES (T. W.) Peter's Rock in Mohammed's Flood from Gregory the Great to Leo III. *Lond.* 1890, 8°.   4533. aaaa. 5.

BONSMANN (T.) Gregor I. der Grosse. pp. 103. *Paderborn*, 1890. 8°.   Pam. 10.

SNOW (T. B.) St. Gregory the Great. pp. 399. *Lond.* 1892. 8°.   4855. bb. 14.

WEYL (R.) Die Beziehungen des Papstthums zum fränkischen Staats- und Kirchenrecht unter den Karolingern. pp. 238. 1892, 8°. GIERKE (O.) Untersuchungen, *etc.* Heft 40. 6025. e. 9.

CHURCH HISTORY.—Papacy—cont.

SCHULTESS (C.) Papst Silvester II. pp. 55.
Hamb. 1891. 4°.   4856. g. 12.

BROECKING (W.) Die französische Politik Papst
Leos IX. pp. 106. *Stuttgart,* 1891. 8°.
                                     4571. ee. 10.

ROBERT (U.) Histoire du Pape Étienne X.
pp. 119. *Brux.* 1892. 8°.   4855. b. 12.

INGRAM (T. D.) England and Rome: from the
Norman Conquest to 1688. pp. 430.
Lond. 1892. 8°.   3940. h. 14.

HILLIGER (B.) Die Wahl Pius' V. zum Papste.
pp. 152. *Leipz.* 1891. 8°.   4571. f. 18.

MIRBT (C.) Die Wahl Gregors VII. pp. 56.
Marburg, 1892. 8°.   4532. g. 12. (4.)

DELARC (O.) Saint Grégoire VII. et la réforme de
l'Église. 3 tom. *Paris,* 1889. 8°. 4571. ee. 8.

LANGEN (J.) Geschichte der Römischen Kirche
von Gregor VII. bis Innocenz III. pp. 720.
Bonn, 1893. 8°.   4571. f. 24.

MARTENS (W.) Gregor VII. 2 Bde.
Leipz. 1894. 8°.   4855. ee. 1.

—— War Gregor VII. Mönch? pp. 52.
Danzig, 1891. 8°.   Pam. 10.

MIRBT (C.) Die Publizistik im Zeitalter Gregors
VII. pp. 629. *Leipz.* 1894. 8°.   05107. g. 3.

SCHNITZER (J.) Die Gesta Romanae Ecclesiae des
Kardinals Beno. pp. 105. 1892. 8°. HEIGEL
(C. T.) Historische Abhandlungen. Heft 2.
                                     9008. i.

ROBERT (U.) Histoire du pape Calixte II.
pp. 262. *Paris,* 1891, 8°.   4856. h. 19.

CALIXTUS II., *Pope.* Bullaire du Pape Calixte II.
1119–1124. 2 tom. *Paris,* 1891. 8°. 5035. aa. 4.

LADAME (E.) Conférence sur Innocent III.
pp. 64. *Neuchâtel,* 1891. 8°.   4864. cc. 23. (6.)

FREDERICK II., *Emperor.* Das Verhältnis
Friedrichs II. zu den Päpsten. 1888. 8°. GIERKE
(O.) Untersuchungen. No. 24.   6025. e. 9.

ROME, *Church of.* Die päpstlichen Kanzlei-
Ordnungen, 1200–1500. pp. 460.
Innsbruck, 1894. 8°.   5018. aa. 27.

TANGL (M.) Das Taxwesen der päpstlichen
Kanzlei vom 13. bis zur Mitte des 15 Jahrhunderts. pp. 106. 1892. 8°. Ac. Vienna. *Universitas.* Mittheilungen. Bd. 13. Heft 1.
                                     Ac. 803.

RODENBERG (C.) Innocenz IV. und das Königreich
Sicilien. pp. 230. *Halle,* 1892. 8°. 4571. ee. 12.

ROME, *Church of.* Alexander IV., *Pope.* Les
Registres d'Alexandre IV. 1895. *etc.* 8°. Ac.
Athens. *École Française.* Bibliothèque des
Écoles Françaises. Sér. 2. Tom. 15. Ac. 5206/2.

LECLÈRE (L.) Les rapports de la Papauté et de
la France sous Philippe III. pp. 138.
Brux. 1889. 8°.   4571. f. 13.

OTTO (H.) Die Beziehungen Rudolfs von Habsburg zu Gregor X. pp. 99. *Innsbruck,* 1895. 8°.
                                     4571. ee. 16.

ZISTERER (A.) Gregor X. und Rudolf von Habsburg. pp. 170. *Freiburg,* 1891. 8°. 4571. ee. 11.

SCHULZ (H.) Papst Coelestin V. *Berl.* 1894, *etc.* 8°.
                                     4856. c.

SIMONSFELD (H.) Analekten zur Papst- und Kon-
ziliengeschichte im 14. und 15. Jhrhndrt. pp. 56.
1892. 4°. Ac. Munich. K. *Akademie der
Wissenschaften.* Abhandlungen der hist. Classe.
Bd. 20. Abt. 1.   Ac. 713/5.

PASTOR (L.) Geschichte der Päpste seit dem
Ausgang des Mittelalters. *Freiburg,* 1891, *etc.* 8°.
                                     4571. f. 20.

—— History of the Popes, from the close of the
Middle Ages. 2 vol. 1891. 8°. Catholic
Standard Library.   3605. i.

CHURCH HISTORY.—Papacy—cont.

KOENIG (L.) Die päpstliche Kammer unter
Clemens V. und Johann XXII. pp. 87.
Wien, 1894. 8°.   4571. ee. 15.

BOUREL DE LA RONCIÈRE (C.) Une Escadre franco-
papale, 1318–1320. pp. 26. *Rome,* 1893. 8°.
                                     Pam. 43.

WURM (H. J.) Cardinal Albornoz, der zweite
Begründer des Kirchenstaates. pp. 280.
Paderborn, 1892. 8°.   4856. b. 13.

JAHR (R.) Die Wahl Urbans VI. pp. 94.
1892. 8°. LINDNER (T.) Hallische Beiträge.
Heft 2.   9007. g.

SAEGMUELLER (J. B.) Die Papstwahlen und die
Staaten von 1447–1555. pp. 238.
Tübingen, 1890. 8°.   4571. bb. 5.

ROME, *Church of.* Sixtus IV., *Pope.* Epistolæ
[between Pope Sixtus IV. and G. Mocenigo, Doge
of Venice], printed by W. Caxton. 1483. pp. 36.
Lond. 1892. 4°.   12204. c.

PÉLISSIER (L. G.) Documenti relativi all' alleanza
tra Alessandro VI. e Luigi XII. 1894, *etc.* 8°.
Ac. Rome. *Società di Storia Patria.* Archivio.
Vol. 17.   Ac. 6540.

BATIFFOL (P.) La Vaticane, de Paul III. à
Paul V. pp. 154. *Paris,* 1890. 8°. 11901. a. 21.

LANGE (C.) Der Papstesel. Ein Beitrag zur
Kunstgeschichte des Reformationszeitalters.
pp. 111. *Göttingen,* 1891. 8°.   7807. h. 31.

MOÜY (C. de) *Count.* Louis XIV. et le Saint-Siège.
2 tom. *Paris,* 1893. 8°.   4571. ec. 14.

ZANELLI (A.) Il Conclave per l'Elezione di
Clemente XII. 1890. 8°. Ac. Rome. *Società
di Storia Patria.* Archivio. Vol 13. Ac. 6540.

MOSCHETTI (A.) Venezia e la elezione di Clemente
XIII. pp. 37. 1890. 4°. Ac. Venice. *Deputa-
zione di Storia Patria.* Monumenti. Ser. 4.
Vol. 11.   Ac. 6580/2.

SCHLITTER (H.) Pius VI. und Josef II. pp. 225.
1894. 8°. Fontes Rerum Austriacarum. Abth. 2.
Bd. 47.   Ac. 810/9.

FRANCLIEU (A. M. de) Pie VI. dans les prisons du
Dauphiné. pp. 378. *Montreuil,* 1892. 8°.
                                     4856. cc. 8.

DUERM (C. v.) Vicissitudes politiques du pouvoir
temporel des Papes de 1790 à nos jours.
pp. 456. *Lille,* 1890. 8°.   4571. f. 14.

BASTIA (G.) Il Dominio temporale dei Papi.
1815–46. pp. 40. *Bologna,* 1890. 8°. Pam. 70.

BITTARD DES PORTES (R.) Histoire des Zouaves
pontificaux. pp. 400. *Paris,* 1894. 8°.
                                     8827. cc. 46.

ROME, *Church of.* Leo XIII. Leonis Papae XIII.
allocutiones, epistolae, constitutiones, *etc.* 4 vol.
Brugis, 1887–94. 8°.   5018. aaa. 3.

BARBIER (P.) Pape Léon XIII. pp. 331.
Paris, 1892. 4°.   4856. h. 20.

FAVERO (F.) Il Pontificato di Leone XIII.
pp. 31. *Ivrea,* 1893. 8°.   Pam. 9.

LEO XIII., *Pope.* Léon XIII. devant ses contemporains. pp. 400. *Paris,* 1892. 12°. 4855. bb. 15.

JOSAPHET. Papst Leo XIII. und seine Namens-
vorgänger auf dem Stuhle des heiligen Petrus.
pp. 61. *Regensburg,* 1893. 8°.   4804. a. 9. (9.)

NORBERT. Vie de Léon XIII. pp. 344.
Saint-Brieuc. 1894. 8°.   4855. aa. 11.

RICARD (A.) Léon XIII. Sa vie, ses œuvres.
pp. 236. *Paris,* 1895. 8°.   4856. f. 10.

SCHLICHTER (H.) Papst Leo's XIII. Leben.
pp. 264. *Münster,* 1892. 8°.   4856. e. 15.

T'SERCLAES (C. de) Le Pape Léon XIII. 2 tom.
Paris, 1894. 4°.   4856. g. 14.

See also AVIGNON: ROMAN CATHOLIC CHURCH,
Papacy.

CHURCH HISTORY.—Various Periods. Apostolic: Early: Mediæval.

BADHAM (F. P.) The Formation of the Gospels. pp. 99. *Lond.* 1891. 8°. 3225. de. 25.

BARROWS (J. H.) Lectures on the credibility of the Gospel Histories. pp. 146. *Bost.* 1891. 8°. 3226. de. 19.

BIRKS (T. R.) Horæ Evangelicæ. pp. 401. *Lond.* 1892. 8°. 3226. dd. 9.

CONE (O.) The Gospel and its earliest interpretations. pp. 413. *N.Y.* 1893. 8°. 3227. c. 32.

FONTAINE (J.) Le Nouveau Testament et les origines du Christianisme. pp. 520. *Paris,* 1890. 8°. 4532. dd. 7.

HOLTZMANN (O.) Neutestamentliche Zeitgeschichte. pp. 200. 1895. 8°. ACHELIS (E. C.) Grundriss der theologischen Wissenschaft n. Abth. 8. 3622. ee.

GLOAG (P. J.) Introduction to the Synoptic Gospels. pp. 298. *Edinb.* 1895. 8°. 3226. cc. 48.

LORIMER (G. C.) People's Bible History. pp. 1241. *Chicago,* 1895. 4°. 3107. e. 5.

NOESGEN (C. F.) Geschichte der neutestamentlichen Offenbarung. *München,* 1891, *etc.* 8°. 3205. ff. 16.

SHAW (W. F.) The Church in the New Testament. pp. 63. *Lond.* 1891. 8°. 4429. aaa. 5.

ALLIES (T. W.) The Formation of Christendom. pp. 328. *Lond.* 1894. 8°. 4533. aa. 5.

BARTLET (J. V.) Early Church History. pp. 160. 1894. 8°. Present Day Primers. 4429. eee.

BUNSEN (E. v.) Die Reconstruction der kirchlichen Autorität. pp. 98. *Leipz.* 1892. 8°. 3910. f. 19. (4.)

BRANDT (W.) Die evangelische Geschichte und der Ursprung des Christenthums. pp. 591. *Leipz.* 1893. 8°. 3226. dd. 13.

CHEETHAM (S.) History of the Christian Church during the first six centuries. pp. 459. *Lond.* 1894. 8°. 4534. aa. 17.

COX (H.) The First Century of Christianity. 2 vol. *Lond.* 1892. 8°. 4534. aaa. 21.

DEISSMANN (G. A.) Bibelstudien. Beiträge zur Geschichte Urchristentums. pp. 297. *Marburg,* 1895. 8°. 3126. g. 17.

DUCHESNE (L.) Les origines chrétiennes. pp. 476. *Paris,* 1891. 4°. 4534. ee. 8.

DUFF (D.) The Early Church. pp. 8. 623. *Edinb.* 1891. 8°. 4534. ee. 1.

FRIEDLAENDER (M.) Zur Entstehungsgeschichte des Christenthums. pp. 172. *Wien,* 1894. 8°. 4516. e. 20.

GWATKIN (H. M.) Selections from Early Writers, illustrative of Church history. pp. 167. *Lond.* 1893. 8°. 3623. aa. 37.

JOHNSON (E.) The Rise of Christendom. pp. 499. *Lond.* 1890. 8°. 4533. ee. 17.

KRUEGER (G.) Sammlung ausgewählter kirchenund dogmengeschichtlicher Quellenschriften. *Freiburg,* 1891, *etc.* 8°. 3623. a. 12.

LARGENT (A.) Études d'histoire ecclésiastique. pp. 277. *Paris,* 1892. 8°. 4535. c. 6.

LE BLANT (E.) Les persécuteurs et les martyrs aux premiers siècles. pp. 372. *Paris,* 1893. 8°. 4530. ee. 24.

LUDWIG (D. A.) Quellenbuch zur Kirchengeschichte. *Davos,* 1891, *etc.* 8°. 4530. ee. 22.

MEHLHORN (P.) Aus den Quellen der Kirchengeschichte. *Berl.* 1894, *etc.* 8°. 4530. eee.

MOXOM (P. S.) From Jerusalem to Nicæa. The Church in the first three centuries. pp. 457. *Bost.* 1895. 8°. 4535. b. 17.

CHURCH HISTORY.—Apostolic.

PÉRATÉ (A.) L'Archéologie chrétienne. pp. 368. *Paris,* 1892. 8°. 2261. c.

P.P. Rome. Römische Quartalschrift für christliche Alterthumskunde und für Kirchengeschichte. *Rom.* 1887, *etc.* 8°. P.P. 1931. dk.

PRYCE (J.) Notes on the history of the Early Church. pp. 90. *Lond.* 1892. 8°. 4429. aa. 57.

ROBINSON (J. A.) Texts and Studies; contributions to Biblical and Patristic literature. *Camb.* 1891, *etc.* 8°. 3605. k.

S., C. The First Years of Christianity. pp. 143. *Lond.* 1893. 8°. 4530. a. 2.

SCHMITT (G.) Die Apologie der drei ersten Jahrhunderte. pp. 138. *Mainz,* 1890. 8°. 4532. cc. 1.

SPITTA (F.) Zur Geschichte und Litteratur des Urchristentums. *Göttingen,* 1893, *etc.* 8°. 4534. d.

STOUGHTON (J.) Lights and shadows of Church Life. pp. 394. *Lond.* 1895. 8°. 4534. c. 29.

STUART (C. E.) Primitive Christianity. pp. 100. *Hamilton,* 1892. 8°. Pam. 77.

TARRANT (W. G.) The Beginnings of Christendom. pp. 121. *Lond.* 1893. 8°. 4531. aa. 23.

ZAHN (T.) Skizzen aus dem Leben der alten Kirche. pp. 338. *Erlangen,* 1894. 8°. 4530. cc. 6.

ZOECKLER (O.) Biblische und kirchenhistorische Studien. *München,* 1893, *etc.* 8°. 4530. cc.

HORT (F. J. A.) Judaistic Christianity. pp. 222. *Camb.* 1894. 8°. 4531. aaa. 30.

TOY (C. H.) Judaism and Christianity. pp. 456. *Bost.* 1891. 8°. 4376. gg. 11.

ALLEN (A. J. C.) The Acts of the Apostles. pp. 157. 1891. 8°. Nisbet's Scripture Handbooks. 3128. h.

BIBLE. *Acts.* The Acts of the Apostles. With introduction by T. E. Page and A. S. Walpole. pp. 229. *Lond.* 1895. 8°. 3227. de. 39.

BUXTON (H. J. W.) Pictures from the Acts of the Holy Apostles. *Oxf.* 1891. 4°. 4827. f. 5.

EDWARDS (F.) These Twelve. [Lectures on the Apostles.] pp. 121. *Lond.* 1895. 8°. 4804. aaa. 25.

FRASER (D.) The Speeches of the Apostles. pp. 258. 1882. 8°. Household Library of Exposition. 3605. d.

HAUSRATH (A.) The time of the Apostles. 4 vol. *Lond.* 1895. 8°. 4534. de. 5.

JUENGST (J.) Die Quellen der Apostelgeschichte. pp. 226. *Gotha,* 1895. 8°. 3267. d. 40.

LE CAMUS (É.) L'œuvre des Apôtres. pp. 368. *Paris,* 1891. 8°. 4534. de. 1.

LIGHTFOOT (J. B.) *Bp. of Durham.* Dissertations on the Apostolic Age. pp. 435. *Lond.* 1892. 8°. 3267. d. 35.

—— Historical Essays. pp. 245. *Lond.* 1895. 8°. 2216. d. 1.

MOORHOUSE (J.) *Bp. of Manchester.* Dangers of the Apostolic Age. pp. 225. *Manch.* 1891. 8°. 4533. ee. 19.

RANKIN (J.) The First Saints. pp. 357. *Edinb.* 1893. 8°. 4828. de. 19.

SPITTA (F.) Die Apostelgeschichte. pp. 380. *Halle,* 1891. 8°. 3266. cc. 40.

STANLEY (A. P.) Sermons and Essays on the Apostolical Age. pp. 373. 1890. 8°. Library of Theological Literature. 3605. g.

STIFLER (J. M.) Introduction to the Study of the Acts. pp. 287. *Lond.* 1894. 8°. 3267. bb. 11.

CHURCH HISTORY.—Apostolic—cont.

STOKES (G. T.) The Acts of the Apostles.
pp. 424. 1891. 8°. NICOLL (W. R.) Expositor's
Bible.   3125. df.

STUART (C. E.) Tracings from the Acts of the
Apostles. pp. 400. Lond. 1894. 8°.
                                3267. bb. 10.

THATCHER (O. J.) Sketch of the history of the
Apostolic Church. pp. 312. Bost. 1893. 8°.
                                4530. aa. 10.

THOMAS (F. E.) Footprints of the Apostles.
pp. 127. Lond. 1892. 8°.   4378. g. 6.

VAUGHAN (C. J.) The Church of the First Days.
pp. 597. Lond. 1890. 8°.   2204. a. 1.

WATSON (R. A.) In the Apostolic Age. pp. 270.
1894. 8°. GREGORY (A. E.) Books for Bible
Students.   3125. dd.

WEIZSAECKER (C. v.) The Apostolic Age of the
Christian Church. 1894, etc. 8°. Theological
Translation Library.   3605. k.

ALLIES (T. W.) St. Peter. His Name and his
Office. pp. 332. Lond. 1895. 8°. 3939. aaa. 51.

ALLNATT (C. F. B.) Was St. Peter Bishop of
Rome. pp. 28. Lond. 1887. 8°. 3939. ccc. 1. (2.)

FOUARD (C.) Saint Pierre et les premières
années du Christianisme. pp. 563.
Paris, 1886. 8°.   4534. cc. 17.

—— Saint Peter. pp. 422. Lond. 1892. 8°.
                                4535. bb. 15.

GALLAGHER (M.) Was the Apostle Peter ever
at Rome? pp. 249. N.Y. 1894. 8°.
                                3939. bb. 25.

HODDER (E.) Simon Peter: his life. pp. 324.
Lond. 1893. 8°.   4808. b. 31.

HENRIOT ( ) Saint Pierre: son apostolat, son
pontificat. pp. 541. Lille, 1891. 8°.
                                4808. i. 21.

ROBINSON (C. S.) Simon Peter. His life and
times. 2 vol. Lond. 1890, 95. 8°. 4807. cc. 5.

SCHMID (J.) Petrus in Rom. pp. 229.
Luzern, 1892. 8°.   4050. g. 38.

BRUCE (A. B.) St. Paul's Conception of Christianity. pp. 404. Edinb. 1894. 8°. 3267. cc. 33.

CALTHROP (G.) St. Paul. A study. pp. 52.
Lond. 1893. 8°.   4808. bb. 23.

CAPPELLI (V.) Sulla persona del Cefa redargui-
tosi dall' Apostolo Paolo in Antiochia. pp. 77.
Milano, 1890. 8°.   Pam. 93.

CLEMEN (C.) Die Chronologie der paulinischen
Briefe. pp. 292. Halle, 1893. 8°. 3267. d. 33.

—— Die Einheitlichkeit der paulinischen Briefe.
pp. 183. Göttingen, 1894. 8°.   3267. f. 3.

EVERETT (C. C.) The Gospel of Paul. pp. 313.
Lond. 1893. 8°.   3267. bb. 9.

FOUARD (C.) Saint Paul and his Missions.
pp. 431. Lond. 1894. 8°.   4808. bbb. 30.

HARDY (E. J.) In the footprints of St. Paul.
pp. 126. Lond. 1895. 8°.   4808. aa. 29.

HASTINGS (H. L.) Pauline Theology.
Lond. 1894. 8°.   4256. de. 7.

KRENKEL (M.) Beiträge zur Aufhellung der
Geschichte des Apostels Paulus. pp. 468.
Braunschweig, 1890. 8°.   3266. d. 36.

MATHESON (G.) Spiritual Development of St.
Paul. pp. 324. Edinb. 1890. 8°. 4808. ee. 4.

RAMSAY (W. M.) St. Paul the Traveller and
Roman Citizen. pp. 394. Lond. 1895. 8°.
                                4806. f. 3.

STEVENS (G. B.) The Pauline Theology.
pp. 383. N.Y. 1894. 8°.   3267. bb. 15.

STOSCH (G.) St. Paulus. pp. 232.
Leipz. 1894. 8°.   4808. bbb. 31.

CHURCH HISTORY.—Apostolic: Early
—continued.

TAYLOR (W. M.) Paul the Missionary. pp. 520.
Lond. 1892. 8°.   4804. bb. 33.

VOLLMER (H.) Die alttestamentlichen Citate
bei Paulus. pp. 103. Frieburg, 1895. 8°.
                                3267. e. 25.

DEANE (W. J.) Pseudepigrapha: account of
apocryphal sacred writings. pp. 348.
Edinb. 1891. 8°.   3166. ee. 32.

LEMM (O. v.) Koptische apokryphe Apostelacten.
1890. 8°. Ac. Saint-Petersburg. Academia
Scientiarum. Bulletin. N.S. No. 4. Ac. 1125/44.

LIPSIUS (R. A.) Acta Apostolorum apocrypha.
Lipsiae, 1891, etc. 8°.   3227. dd.

LIGHTFOOT (J. B.) Bp. of Durham. The Apostolic Fathers. pp. 568. Lond. 1891. 8°.
                                2206. f.

WREDE (W.) Untersuchungen zum ersten Kle-
mensbriefe. pp. 112. Göttingen, 1891. 8°.
                                3623. aa. 28.

VOELTER (D.) Die Ignatianischen Briefe auf
ihren Ursprung untersucht. pp. 125.
Tübingen, 1892. 8°.   3623. aa. 31.

TREPNER (M.) Das Patriarchat von Antiochien
pp. 252. Würzburg, 1891. 8°.   4534. ee. 7.

ADDIS (W. E.) Christianity and the Roman
Empire. pp. 221. 1893. 8°. CARPENTER (J. E.)
Manuals of early Christian History. Vol. 1.
                                4534. a.

COSTELLOE (B. F. C.) The Church and the Cata-
combs. pp. 24. Lond. 1894. 8°.   Pam. 29.

HARDY (E. G.) Christianity and the Roman
Government. pp. 208. Lond. 1894. 8°.
                                4532. df. 2.

LANCIANI (R. A.) Pagan and Christian Rome.
pp. 374. Lond. 1892. 8°.   7705. b. 51.

PULLER (F. W.) The primitive Saints and the
See of Rome. pp. 428. Lond. 1893. 8°.
                                3940. bb. 28.

RAMSAY (W. M.) The Church in the Roman
Empire before A.D. 170. pp. 494. Lond. 1893. 8°.
                                4534. ee. 12.

SCHÜRER (E.) Die ältesten Christengemeinden
im römischen Reiche. pp. 20. Kiel, 1894. 8°.)
                                4534. c. 30. (12.)

BEURLIER (É.) Les Chrétiens et le service militaire pendant les trois premiers siècles. pp. 19.
Paris, 1892. 8°.   4534. c. 30. (8.)

SCHWARZE (A.) Untersuchungen über die äussere Entwicklung der afrikanischen Kirche.
pp. 194. Göttingen 1892. 8°.   4534. f. 18.

ARISTIDES. The Apology of Aristides on behalf
of the Christians. pp. 118. 1891. 8°.
ROBINSON (J. A.) Texts and Studies. 3605. k.

—— Der Apologet Aristides. pp. 67.
Erlangen, 1894. 8°.   3623. aa. 39.

FUEHRER (J.) Ein Beitrag zur Lösung der Feli-
citas-Frage. pp. 162. Leipz. 1890. 8°.
                                4829. df. 19.

KUENSTLE (C.) Hagiographische Studien über
die Passio Felicitatis. pp. 154.
Paderborn, 1894. 8°.   4828. c. 1.

IRENÆUS, Saint. Extracts from the writings of
St. Irenæus. pp. 24. Lond. 1890. 8°. Pam. 78.

CONYBEARE (F. C.) Apology and Acts of Apol-
lonias. pp. 360. Lond. 1894. 8°. 3623. b. 18.

TAYLOR (C.) The Witness of Hermas to the
Gospels. pp. 148. Lond. 1892. 4°. 3226. g. 18.

PERPETUA, Saint. The Passion of S. Perpetua.
pp. 131. 1891. 8°. ROBINSON (J. A.) Texts
and Studies. Vol. 1. No. 2.   3605. k.

EUSEBIUS. Church History, Life of Constantine
the Great, etc. 1890. etc. 8°. WACE (H.) Library of Nicene and Post-Nicene Fathers. N.S.
Vol. 1.   3623. cc.

**CHURCH HISTORY.—Early: Mediae-
val—*continued*.**

GOETZ (C.) Geschichte der cyprianischen Litteratur. pp. 129. *Basel*, 1891. 8°.   3623. a. 14.

PATRICK (J.) The Apology of Origen in reply to
Celsus. pp. 340. *Edinb.* 1892. 8°. 3805. bb. 18.

ALLARD (P.) La Persécution de Dioclétien et le
triomphe de l'Église. 2 tom. *Paris*, 1890. 8°.
                   4533. ee. 16.

BELSER (J.) Zur diokletianische Christenver-
folgung. pp. 107. *Tübingen*, 1891. 4°.
                   4534. f. 16.

STOLLE (F.) Das Martyrium der thebaischen
Legion. pp. 112. *Breslau*, 1891. 8°. Pam. 10.

FICKER (G.) Studien zur Hippolytfrage. pp. 115.
Leipz. 1893. 8°.   4828. cc. 34.

BOISSIER (G.) La Fin du paganisme. 2 tom.
Paris, 1891. 8°.   4530. ee. 21.

PARET (F.) Priscillianus, ein Reformator des
4ᵉⁿ Jährhunderts. pp. 302. *Würzburg*, 1891. 8°.
                   3623. b. 14.

VOIGT (H. G.) Eine verschollene Urkunde des
antimontanistischen Kampfes. pp. 351.
Leipz. 1891. 8°.   4535. c. 5.

THEODORET. Ecclesiastical History, Dialogues
and Letters of Theodoret. 1892. 8°. WACE (H.)
Select Library. Ser. 2, Vol. 3.   3623. cc.

PUECH (A.) St. Jean Chrysostome et les moeurs
de son temps. pp. 334. *Paris*, 1891. 8°.
                   4829. d. 5.

SCHAFF (P.) S. Chrysostom and S. Augustine.
pp. 158. *Lond.* 1891. 8°.   4829. de. 15.

JENKINS (R. C.) From the death of S. Athanasius to the death of S. Basil. pp. 48.
Lond. 1894. 8°.   4535. c. 10. (11.)

SOCRATES, *Scholasticus*. Socrates' Ecclesiastical
History. pp. 343. *Oxf.* 1893. 8°. 2214. a. 2.

THUEMMEL (W.) Zum Beurtheilung des Donatismus. pp. 104. *Halle*, 1893. 8°. 4534. ee. 16.

HOWARD (G. B.) The schism between the
Oriental and Western Churches. pp. 118.
Lond. 1892. 8°.   4535. bb. 14.

BROWN (J. B.) Stoics and Saints: Lectures on
Heathen Moralists and on the life of the
Mediaeval Church. pp. 296. *Glasg.* 1893. 8°.
                   4534. ee. 14.

HENDERSON (E. F.) Select historical documents
of the middle ages. pp. 477. 1892. 8°. Bohn's
Antiquarian Library.   2500. b.

PRÉVOST (G. A.) L'Église et les Campagnes au
moyen âge. pp. 292. *Paris*, 1892. 8°.
                   4534. f. 20.

BONNEFON (J. de) VIIIᵉ centenaire de Saint
Bernard. pp. 298. *Paris*, 1891. 12°.
                   4829. de. 16.

HOPFEN (O. H.) Kaiser Maximilian II. und der
Kompromisskatholizismus. pp. 439.
München, 1895. 8°.   4662. h. 1.

*See also supra: Papacy: FATHERS, Christian:
GNOSTICISM.*

For works on the person and teaching of Christ,
see CHRISTIANITY.

Reformation and Modern.

ALLNATT (C. F. B.) The Bible and the Reformation. pp. 34. *Lond.* 1890. 8°.
              3939. ccc. 1. (5.)

ANELLI (L.) I riformatori nel secoli XVI.
2 vol. *Milano*, 1891. 8°.   4650. aaa. 13.

BAUMGARTEN (H.) Karl der Fünfte und die
deutsche Reformation. pp. 42. *Coburg*, 1893. 8°.
                   Pam. 29.

BERGER (A. E.) Die Kulturaufgaben der Reformation. pp. 300. *Berl.* 1895. 8°. 4888 cc. 9.

**CHURCH HISTORY.—Reformation and
Modern.—*continued*.**

BETTANY (G. T.) Popular history of the Reformation. pp. 512. *Lond.* 1895. 8°. 4650. d. 22.

IRENICUS, *Dr.* Die grundsätzliche Unduldsam-
keit der Reformation. pp. 64. *Trier*, 1890. 8°.
                   Pam. 93.

KREBS (K.) Beiträge zur deutschen Geschichte
im Zeitalter der Reformation.
Leipz. 1895, etc. 8°.   4662. d.

MOORE (A L.) Lectures and Papers on the
history of the Reformation. pp. 525.
Lond. 1890. 8°.   4650. e. 25.

ROCQUAIN (F.) La Cour de Rome et l'Esprit de
Réforme avant Luther. *Paris*, 1893, etc. 8°.
                   4050. h.

ROEHM (J. B.) Zur Tetzel-Legende. pp. 33.
Hildesheim, 1890. 8°.   4535. bb. 17. (4.)

SCHEICHL (F.) Glaubensflüchtlinge im 16.
Jahrhunderte. pp. 26. *Linz*, 1890. 8°. Pam. 29.

FROUDE (J. A.) Life and Letters of Erasmus.
pp. 406. *Lond.* 1894. 8°.   2217. f. 5.

BECKER (J.) Kurfürst Johann von Sachsen und
seine Beziehungen zu Luther, 1520–28. pp 82.
Leipz. 1890. 8°.   4662. d. 18. (2.)

FRIEDRICH (J.) Luther und die Kirchenverfassung der Reformatio Ecclesiarum Hassiae von
1526. pp. 40. *Darmstadt*, 1894. 8°.
               4662. d. 18. (6.)

KOESTLIN (J.) Life of Luther. pp. 499.
Lond. 1895. 8°.   2217. b. 2.

PONS (B) Martino Lutero, riformatore. pp. 428.
Firenze, 1890. 8°.   4888. g. 29.

BURMEISTER (E.) Luther eine Säule der Auc-
torität. *Stettin*, 1891, etc. 8°.   3910. dd. 47.

BEYSCHLAG (W.) Luther's Hausstand. pp. 39.
Barmen, 1888. 8°   4888. a. 35. (2.)

HAUSRATH (A.) Martin Luthers Romfahrt.
pp. 99. *Berl.* 1894. 8°.   4887. de. 42.

BLUEMEL (E.) Luthers Lebensende. pp. 80.
Barmen, 1890. 8°.   4888. a. 35. (3.)

HONEF (M.) Der Selbstmord Luthers. pp. 92.
München, 1890. 8°.   4804. a. 9. (5.)

KOLDE (T.) Luthers Selbstmord. pp. 45.
Erlangen, 1890. 8°.   4888. g. 32. (2.)

—— Noch einmal Luthers Selbstmord. pp. 28.
Erlangen, 1890. 8°.   4888. g. 32. (4.)

MAJUNKE (P.) Luthers Lebensende. pp. 99.
Mainz, 1891. 8°.   4888. d. 2. (1.)

—— Die historische Kritik über Luthers Lebensende. pp. 105. *Mainz*, 1890. 8°.
              4888. d. 2. (2.)

—— Ein letztes Wort an die Luther Dichter.
pp. 52. *Mainz*, 1890. 8°.   4888. g. 32. (3.)

—— Luthers Testament an die deutsche Nation.
pp. 284. *Mainz*, 1892. 8°.   4888. d. 2. (4.)

LORRENZ (L. B.) La Fin de Luther d'après les
dernières recherches historiques. pp. 71.
Paris, 1894. 8°.   4888. g. 34.

STACHELIN (R.) Huldreich Zwingli.
Basel, 1895, etc. 8°.   4888. g.

ADLER (J. B.) Ein Beitrag zur katholischen
Reformation in sechszehnten Jahrhundert.
1892. 8°. Frankfurter zeitgemässe Broschüren,
etc. Bd. 13.   12209. g.

WOLF (G.) Der Augsburger Religionsfriede.
pp. 171. *Stuttg.* 1890. 8°.   4661. dd. 21.

GINDELY (A.) Geschichte der Gegenreformation
in Böhmen. pp. 532. *Leipz.* 1894. 8°.
              4662. f. 8.

WILLIAMSON (A.) Aspects of Faith and religion
in the 17th Century. pp. 139. *Lond.* 1891. 8°.
              4534. ee. 2.

CHURCH HISTORY.—Reformation and Modern—*continued*.

CHAMARD (F.) Annales ecclésiastiques de 1846 à 1869. *Paris*, 1891, *etc.* 8°.   4516. eee. 8.

DORCHESTER (D.) The Problem of Religious Progress. pp. 768. *N.Y.* 1895. 8°.
        4182. bbb. 45.

For other histories of the Reformation, *see* ENGLAND : FRANCE : ITALY : SCOTLAND.

For the ecclesiastical history of each country, *see* under the sub-heading, *History, Ecclesiastical*, of the country required.

History of Dogma, Institutions, Theology.

APOSTLES. The Didache or Teaching of the Twelve Apostles, by C. H. Hoole. pp. 90. *Lond.* 1894. 8°.   3623. aa. 40.

CRUTTWELL (C. T.) Literary history of early Christianity. 2 vol. *Lond.* 1893. 8°. 2214. a. 1.

FUNK (F. X.) Die apostolischen Konstitutionen. pp. 374. *Rottenburg*, 1891. 8°.   05107. ee. 21.

HARNACK (A.) Das apostolische Glaubensbekenntniss. pp. 44. *Berl.* 1892. 8°. Pam. 93.

—— Sources of the Apostolic Canons. pp. 95. *Lond.* 1895. 8°.   4532. e. 6.

—— Dogmengeschichte. pp. 386. 1893. 8°.
ACHELIS (B. C.) Grundriss der theol. Wissenschaft. Abth. 3.   3622. ee.

—— History of Dogma. 1894, *etc.* Theological Translation Library. Vol. 2, *etc.* 3605· k.

—— Précis de l'histoire des dogmes. pp. 481. *Paris*, 1893. 8°.   4532. ee. 22.

—— Geschichte der altchristlichen Litteratur bis Eusebius. *Leipz.* 1893, *etc.* 8°.   3623. a.

SEEBERG (R.) Lehrbuch der Dogmengeschichte. *Erlangen*, 1895, *etc.* 8°.   4534. c.

KRUEGER (G.) Geschichte der altchristlichen Litteratur. pp. 254. 1895. 8°. ACHELIS (E. C.) Grundriss der theologischen Wissenschaften. Abth. 9.   3622. ee.

LIGHTFOOT (J. B.) *Bp. of Durham.* The Apostolic Fathers. pp. 568. *Lond.* 1891. 8°. 2206. f.

MACGREGOR (J.) Studies in the History of Christian Apologetics. pp. 370. *Edinb.* 1894. 8°.
        3224. dd. 26.

HEARD (J. B.) Alexandrian and Carthaginian Theology contrasted. pp. 362. *Edinb.* 1893. 8°.
        4460. aa. 2.

WACE (H.) and SCHAFF (P.) Library of Nicene and Post-Nicene Fathers. *Oxf.* 1890, *etc.* 8°.
        3623. cc.

SLATER (W. F.) Faith and Life of the early Church. pp. 412. *Lond.* 1892. 8°. 4533. ee. 22.

THAMIN (R.) Saint Ambroise et la morale chrétienne au IVᵉ siècle. pp. 492. 1895. 8°. Ac. Lyons. *Université de Lyon.* Annales. Tom. 8.
        Ac. 365.

STOECKL (A.) Geschichte der christlichen Philosophie zur Zeit der Kirchenväter. pp. 435. *Mainz*, 1891. 8°.   4535. cc. 1.

WYNNE (F. R.) The Literature of the Second Century. pp. 270. *Lond.* 1891. 8°. 4530. cc. 5.

CHRISTIAN SECTS. The denominational Reason Why. pp. 376. *Lond.* 1890. 8°.   4520. c. 2.

PFLEIDERER (O.) Die Entwicklung der protestantischen Theologie in Deutschland seit Kant und in Grossbritannien seit 1825. pp. 496. *Freiburg i. B.* 1891. 8°.   4570. ee. 19.

—— The Development of Theology, *etc.* pp. 403. 1890. 8°. MUIRHEAD (J. H.) Library of Philosophy.   8486. h.

FRANK (F. H. R. v.) Geschichte und Kritik der neueren Theologie. pp. 350. *Erlangen*, 1894. 8°.
        3908. f. 31.

CHURCH HISTORY. — Dogma, Institutions. Theology—*continued*.

AHRENDT (C.) Die Entwickelung der Theologie in den letzten 75 Jahren. pp. 21. *Leipz.* 1893. 8°.   4371. ee. 26. (6.)

See also COUNCILS : CREEDS : FATHERS, *Christian*.

CHURCH PLATE. *See* PLATE.

CHURCHWARDENS. SUMNER (G. H.) *Bp. of Guildford.* Churchwardens' Manual. pp. 77. *Lond.* 1890. 8°.   5155. de. 19.

MACKENZIE (W. W.) The Overseer's Handbook. pp. 214. *Lond.* 1889. 8°.   6425. aaa. 49.

PRIDEAUX (C. G.) Guide to the Duties of Churchwardens. pp. 635. *Lond.* 1895. 8°.
        2232. o. 15.

See also LAW, *Ecclesiastical, England.*

CIRCLE. ANDERSON (A. B.) The Secret of the Circle and the Circle squared. pp 26. *Oxf.* 1891. 8°.   8531. cc. 28. (3.)

DINGLE (E.) The Square of the Circle demonstrated from the Cube. pp. 19. *Plymouth*, 1891. 8°.   8531. df. 13.

DINGLE (E.) The Square of the Circle. pp. 35. *Tavistock*, 1894, 8°.   8531. df. 12.

FLOR (O.) Lösung des Problems : die Quadratur des Kreises. *Riga*, 1892. 8°. 8533. d. 27. (10.)

MACCLELLAND (W. J.) A Treatise on the Geometry of the Circle. pp. 299. *Lond.* 1891. 8°.
        8535. b. 40.

OZÉGOWSKI (A.) Die Quadratur des Kreises. pp. 14. *Ostrowo*, 1893. 8°.   8531. c. 47. (5.)

RICHARDSON (J.) How to find the Area and Quadrature of a Circle. pp. 28. *Seaham*, 1890. 12°.   8534. a. 13.

See also GEOMETRY : MATHEMATICS.

CIRCULATION, of the Blood. *See* BLOOD : HEART.

CIRCUMCISION. CLIFFORD (M.) Circumcision. Its advantages, *etc.* pp. 23. *Lond.* 1893. 8°.   7641. e. 5. (2.)

REMONDINO (P. C.) History of Circumcision. pp. 346. *Phila.* 1891. 8°.   7641. b. 30.

SNOW (H. L.) Barbarity of Circumcision as a remedy for congenital abnormality. pp. 58. *Lond.* 1890. 8°.   7641. ee. 7.

See also JEWS.

CIRCUS. OTTO (H. W.) Artisten-Lexikon. Biographische Notizen über berühmte Kunstreiter, *etc.* pp. 128. *Düsseldorf*, 1891. 8°.
        10601. aa. 28.

ROUTLEDGE (G.) and SONS. Book of the Circus. pp. 96. *Lond.* 1892. 8°.   011795. g. 17.

VAUX (C. M. de) *Baron.* Écuyers et Écuyères. pp. 368. *Paris*, 1893. 8°.   7907. dd. 18.

CIRENCESTER. BEECHAM (K. J.) History of Cirencester. pp. 314. *Cirencester*, 1887. 8°.
        010358. g. 20.

CIRRIPEDIA. *See* CRUSTACEA.

CISTERCIAN ORDER. MATTHAEI (A.) Beiträge zur Baugeschichte der Cistercienser Frankreichs und Deutschlands. pp. 67. *Darmstadt*, 1893. 8°.   7817. i. 3.

SIMPSON (W. J. S.) Lectures on S. Bernard of Clairvaux. pp. 257. *Lond.* 1895. 8°. 4829. c. 19.

See also CHATELLIERS : ESHOLT : RELIGIOUS ORDERS : WETTINGEN.

CIUDAD-REAL. HERVÁS Y BUENDÍA (I.) Diccionario de la Provincia de Ciudad-Real. *Ciudad-Real*, 1890, *etc.* 8°.   10160. d. 1.

CIVILIZATION. ADAMS (B.) The Law of Civilization and Decay. pp. 302. *Lond.* 1895. 8°.   9008. k. 2.

CIVILIZATION—*continued.*

CROZIER (J. B.) Civilization and Progress.
pp. 464. *Lond.* 1892. 8°.   8469. dd. 30.

MORRIS (C.) Civilization : historical review of its
elements. 2 vol. *Chicago*, 1890. 4°.
8010. de. 11.

REICH (E.) History of Civilization. pp. 554.
Cincinnati, 1887. 8°.   9009. bb. 23.

ZANONI (E.) La Civiltà. Saggio. pp. 437.
Milano, 1890. 8°.   8009. aaa. 26.

See also ANTHROPOLOGY : ETHNOLOGY : HIS-
TORY, *General :* and under the *History* of each
country.

CLACKMANNAN. EPHEM. Alloa Almanac
and Register for Clackmannan.
Alloa, 1891, *etc.* 8°.   P.P. 2511. bca.

CLACTON-ON-SEA. BENHAM AND CO.
Gazette guide to Clacton-on-Sea. pp. 78.
Colchester, 1892. 8°.   10347. aa. 37. (6.)

LINE, *Brothers.* Guide for Clacton-on-Sea.
pp. 60. *Clacton*, 1893. 8°.   10348. aa. 9. (5.)

CLAIRETS, Abbey. SOUANCÉ (de) *Viscount.* Abbaye de Notre-Dame des Clairets.
pp. 350. *Vannes*, 1894. 8°.   4629. i. 29.

CLAIRVOYANCE. *See* HYPNOTISM.

CLARE, County. FARNHAM (J. E.) Health
and Pleasure Resorts on the Clare Coast.
pp. 75. *Dublin*, 1893. *obl.* 8°.   10390. aaaa. 21.

FROST (J.) History and Topography of the County
of Clare. pp. 654. *Dublin*, 1893. 8°.
10390. e. 22.

H., B. H. Holiday Haunts on the West Coast of
Clare. pp. 87. *Limerick*, 1891. 8°. 10390. de. 2.

LLOYD (J.) Short Tour in the County Clare,
1780. pp. 59. *Camb.* 1893. 12°.   10390. de. 6.

WESTROPP (T. J.) Churches with Round Towers
in Northern Clare. *Dublin*, 1894, *etc.* 8°.
07708. f. 41.

WHITE (P.) History of Clare. pp. 398.
Dublin, 1893. 8°.   10390. f. 11.

CLEETHORPES. CLEETHORPES. Album of
Cleethorpes Views. *Cleethorpes*, 1895. *obl.* 8°.
10360. aa. 41.

CLENT. AMPHLETT (J.) History of Clent.
pp. 203. *Lond.* 1890. 8°.   010358. c. 6.

CLERGY : APOSTOLIC SUCCESSION.
BROWN (J.) The Historic Episcopate. pp. 27
Lond. 1891. 8°.   4108. de. 32. (8.)

EARLE (W.) The Reunion of Christendom in
Apostolic Succession. pp. 310. *Lond.* 1895. 8°.
410.). bb. 32.

FRASER (J.) Episcopacy : historically and legally
considered. pp. 403. *Lond.* 1893. 8°.
4109. e. 31.

GASPARRI (P.) Tractatus Canonicus de Ordina-
tione. 2 vol. *Parisiis*, 1893–94. 8°. 4327. f. 1.

GORE (C.) The Ministry of the Christian Church.
pp. 424. *Lond.* 1893. 8°.   4108. f. 27.

GREGORY (J. R.) The Figment of Apostolical
Succession. pp. 16. *Lond.* 1893. 16°. Pam. 92.

GRUNAU (G.) De Coadjutoribus Episcoporum.
Vratislaviae, 1894, *etc.* 8°.   5063. bb.

IMBART DE LA TOUR (P.) Les Élections episcopales dans l'église de France du IXᵉ au XIIᵉ
siècle. pp. 554. *Paris*, 1891. 8°.   4629. k. 13.

JENKINS (R. C.) The True Apostolic Succession.
pp. 11. *Folkestone*, 1890. 8°. 3940. bb. 31. (4.)

LUCAS (C.) The Threefold Ministry. pp. 8.
Lond. 1892. 8°.   4109. de. 1. (7.)

SACERDOCE. The Ancient Fathers on the Priesthood in the Church. pp. 172. *Lond.* 1891. 8°.
4499. cc. 24.

CLERGY : APOSTOLIC SUCCESSION
—*continued.*

SOBKOWSKI (L.) Episkopat und Presbyterat in
den ersten christlichen Jahrhunderten. pp. 98.
Würzburg, 1893. 8°.   4532. ee. 15.

WALLER (C. H.) Apostolical Succession.
pp. 132. *St. Leonards*, 1895. 12°.   4109. de. 4.

CHAVARD (F.) Le Célibat, le Prêtre et la femme.
pp. 521. *Paris*, 1894. 8°.   8416. f. 49.

CLERICAL CELIBACY. Clerical Celibacy. pp. 46.
Oxf. 1891. 8°.   4108. de. 32. (9.)

BOCQUET (L.) Le Célibat ecclésiastique jusqu'au
Concile de Trente. pp. 277. *Paris*, 1895. 8°.
05107. h. 1.

See also CHURCH HISTORY : EDUCATION, *Ecclesi-
astical :* ENGLAND, *Church of, Anglican Orders :*
ROMAN CATHOLIC CHURCH, *Doctrines, etc. :* THE-
OLOGY, *Pastoral.*

CLERMONT, Oise. DEBAUVE (A.) Histoire
et description du Canton de Clermont. pp. 234.
Paris, 1890. 8°.   10172. f. 11.

CLERMONT - FERRAND. CLERMONT-
FERRAND. Inventaire des archives hospitalières
de Clermont Ferrand. 1887. 8°. Collection des
inventaires-sommaires.   1814–15. b., *etc.*

TARDIEU (A.) Livre d'Or du Cortège des Croisés
à Clermont-Ferrand, 19 Mai 1895. pp. 164.
Clermont-F. 1895. 4°.   9930. k. 3.

CLEVELAND, Ohio. INGHAM (W. A.)
Women of Cleveland and their work. pp. 362.
Cleveland, 1893. 8°.   8415. d. 51.

KENNEDY (J. H.) and DAY (W. M.) Bench and
Bar of Cleveland. pp. 358. *Cleveland*, 1889. 8°.
6006. l. 1.

CLEVELAND. Yorkshire. LEYLAND (J.)
The Yorkshire Coast and the Cleveland Hills.
pp. 334. *Lond.* 1892. 8°.   010358. h. 9.

TWEDDELL (E.) Rhymes and Sketches to illustrate the Cleveland dialect. pp. 104.
Stokesley, 1892. 8°.   011653. i. 90.

CLIFFORD CHAMBERS. MACLEAN
(*Sir* J.) History of the Manor of Clifford
Chambers. pp. 68. *Bristol*, 1890. 8°.
10348. d. 19. (8.)

CLIFTON COLLEGE. OAKLEY (E. M.)
Clifton College Register. pp. 120. 378. 31.
Lond. 1890. 8°.   8366. aaa. 21.

CLIMATOLOGY. ASSMANN (R.) Das
Klima. 1894. 8°. WEYL (T.) Handbuch der
Hygiene. Bd. 1.   7391. dd.

BEBBER (W. v.) Hygienische Meteorologie.
pp. 330. *Stuttgart*, 1895. 8°.   8757. dd. 27.

BRUECKNER (E.) Klimaschwankungen seit 1700.
pp. 324. 1890. 8°. PENCK (A.) Geographische
Abhandlungen. Bd. 4.   10002. i. 2.

CULLIMORE (D. H.) The Book of Climates.
pp. 279. *Lond.* 1891. 8°.   07686. e. 2.

DAVIDSON (A.) Geographical Pathology. Geographical distribution of disease. 2 vol.
Edinb. 1892. 8°.   7686. f. 6.

DUBOIS (E.) Die Klimate der geologischen Vergangenheit. pp. 85. *Nijmegen*, 1893. 8°.
07109. c. 18.

—— The Climates of the Geological Past.
pp. 167. *Lond.* 1895. 8°.   8563. aa. 38.

FRITZ (S.) Bemærkninger om Aarsagerne til
den forskjellige Charakteer hos klimaet i
Jordens forskjellige Egne. pp. 49.
Kjøbenh. 1891. 8°.   Pam. 79.

HILGARD (E. W.) Report on the relations of
Soil to Climate. pp. 59. 1892. 8°. U. S. *Weather
Bureau.* Bulletin. No. 3.   7053. e. 40.

CLIMATOLOGY—*continued.*

HORNBERGER (R.) Grundriss der Meteorologie und Klimatologie. pp. 233. *Berl.* 1891. 8°.
8756. c. 45.

KOEHLER (H.) Die Pflanzenwelt und das Klima Europas seit der geschichtlichen Zeit. *Berl.* 1892, *etc.* 8°. 07028. 1.

MEYER (H.) Anleitung zur Bearbeitung meteorologischer Beobachtungen für die Klimatologie. pp. 187. *Berl.* 1891. 8°. 8756. de. 43.

MIERS (H. A.) The Soil in relation to Health, *etc.* pp. 135. *Lond.* 1893. 8°. 7109. a. 12,

REDWAY (J. W.) Climate and the Gulf Stream. pp. 5. 1890. 8°. 8755. dd. 32. (4.)

MUELINEN (E. F. v.) Beiträge zur Heimathkunde des Kantons Bern. *Bern*, 1880, *etc.* 8°.
10196. cc. 8.

SAN PAULO. *Commissão Geographica.* Dados climatologicos. 2 pt. *S. Paulo*, 1893. 8°.
8757. dd. 25.

ARATA (P. N.) El Clima y las condiciones higiénicas de Buenos Aires. pp. 133. *Buenos A.* 1889. 8°. 07686. 1. 1.

BARROIS (J.) Notice sur le climat du Caïre. 1890. 8°. Ac. Alexandria. *Institut Égyptien.* Bulletin. Sér. 2. No. 10. Ac. 10/4.

Ac. London. *Royal Med. and Chirurgical Society.* Climates and Baths of Great Britain. *Lond.* 1895, *etc.* 8°. 7462. g.

THORNTON (B.) Comparative Climatology of London and the chief English Health Resorts. pp. 15. *Lond.* 1891. 8°. 7686. b. 7.

SCHREIBER (P.) Klimatographie des Königreichs Sachsen. pp. 97. 1893. 8°. LEHMANN (R.) Forschungen zur deutschen Landeskunde. Bd. 8. 10235. i. 10.

See also METEOROLOGY: WATER, *etc.*

CLINICS. *See* MEDICINE: SURGERY.

CLOUDS. *See* METEOROLOGY.

CLUBS. CLUB ACCOUNTS. How to keep Club Accounts. pp. 45. *Westminster*, 1895. 8°.
Pam. 38.

DENE (K.) Clubs: athletic and recreative. pp. 107. *Bristol*, 1890. 8°. 6345. aa. 10.

JOUET (A.) Les Clubs; leur histoire depuis 1789. pp. 239. *Paris*, 1891. 8°. 9226. k. 10.

CHALLAMEL (J. B. M. A.) Les Clubs contre-révolutionnaires. pp. 633. 1895. 8°. PARIS. *Appendix. History.* Collection de documents relatifs à l'histoire de Paris, *etc.* 9231. i.

P.P. *London.* Club Notes. *Lond.* 1894, *etc.* 8°.
896.

CLUBS. Collection of the Rules, *etc.* of London and country Clubs. [Details will be found in the General Catalogue under LONDON. III.] 1885–92. 8°. 10348. ccc. 5–54.

WAUGH (F. G.) The Athenæum Club. pp. 48. *Lond.* 1894. 8°. 10349. e. 21.

—— Members of the Athenæum Club. pp. 162. *Lond.* 1894. 8°. 10349. e. 22.

LONDON. *Constitutional Club.* The Constitutional Club. Architectural description. pp. 16. *Lond.* 1886. 8°. 10349. gg. 24.

—— *Eighty Club.* The "Eighty" Club. Committee. Objects. Rules. 8 pt. *Lond.* 1892. 8°.
8139. b. 35.

—— *National Liberal Club.* The National Liberal Club. A description. pp. 19. *Lond.* 1894. 16°. Pam. 68.

—— *Piccadilly Club.* Rules and Bye-Laws. pp. 20. 1891. 8°. 8275. aa. 62.

—— *White's Club.* History of White's. 2 vol. *Lond.* 1892. 4°. K.T.C. 1. b. 6.

CLUBS—*continued.*

LONDON. *United Brothers' Working Men's Club.* Rules. pp. 12. *Lond.* 1889. 8°. Pam. 82.

ELDERKIN (J.) History of the Lotos Club. pp. 166. *N.Y.* 1895. 8°. 10410. bb. 34. (1.)

NEW YORK, *City of.* Lotos Club. Rules and list of members. pp. 57. *N.Y.* 1895. 8°.
10410. bb. 34. (2.)

PELHAM (*Hon.* T. H. W.) Boys' Clubs. pp. 30. *Lond.* 1890. 8°. 8277. ee. 1. (4.)

CLUNIAC ORDER. CLUNY, *Order of.* Visitations and Chapters-General of the Order of Cluni, in respect of the province of Germany, 1269–1529. pp. 398. *Lond.* 1893. 8°.
4783. dd. 7.

SACKUR (E.) Die Cluniacenser bis zur Mitte des elften Jahrhunderts. *Halle*, 1892, *etc.* 8°.
4782. f.

See also RELIGIOUS ORDERS.

CLUSES. LAVOREL (J. M.) Cluses et le Faucigny. 2 pt. *Annecy*, 1888, 89. 8°.
010171. h. 8.

CLYDE, River. WALKER (R.) The Clyde and Western Highlands. pp. 96. *Lond.* 1892. *obl.* 8°. 10369. e. 10.
See also SCOTLAND, *Highlands.*

COACHING. BAINES (F. E.) On the Track of the Mail-Coach. pp. 351. *Lond.* 1895. 8°.
08247. ee. 6.

BLEW (W. C. A.) Brighton and its Coaches. pp. 354. *Lond.* 1894. 8°. 10349. h. 34.

CAHILL (C.) Anecdotes and reminiscences of the Road in the Coach Days. pp. 100. *Lond.* 1892. 8°. 012330. e. 5.

HOUNSELL (B.) Coach Drives from London. pp. 131. *Lond.* 1894. 8°. 10350. bb. 45.

—— English Coach Drives. pp. 98. *Lond.* 1894. 8°. 10350. bb. 46.

NOBBS (M. J.) Old Coaching Days. pp. 55. *Lond.* 1891. 8° 8235. aa. 62.

PEARSE (H. H. S.) The "Comet" Coach. Illustrated. ff. 31. *Lond.* 1895. *obl. fol.*
1818. a. 9.

SAINT MAUR (*Lord* A.) Driving. Old Coaching Days. 1889. 4°. Badminton Library.
7905. f.

See also HORSEMANSHIP.

COAL AND COAL MINING.
General.

GOOCH (A. W. G. E.) On the Age of the Earth. Anthracite. pp. 32. *Lond.* 1893. 8°. Pam. 27.

MELDOLA (R.) Coal and what we get from it. pp. 210. 1891. 8°. Romance of Science Series.
4421. de.

COLLINS (J. H.) Principles of Coal Mining. pp. 151. 1893. 8°. Collins' Elementary Science Series. 8708. aaa.

HUGHES (H. W.) Text-book of Coal-Mining. pp. 436. *Lond.* 1893. 8°. 07109. g. 46.

JOHNSON (J.) Expeditious Coal Reckoner. pp. 156. *S. Shields*, 1895. 12°. 8505. aa. 62.

JONES (M. V.) Causes of spontaneous Combustion of Coal. pp. 6. *Lond.* 1894. 8°. 8716. cc. 42.

LE CHATELIER (H.) Le Grisou. pp. 187. 1892. 8°. Encyclopédie des aide-mémoire.
8709. g.

LYMAN (B. S.) Folds and Faults in Anthracite-Beds. pp. 43. 1895. 8°. Pam. 27.

MAUCHLINE (R.) Mine Foreman's Handbook of information on Collieries. pp. 337. *Phila.* 1893. 8°. 07109. e. 17.

PAMELY (C.) Colliery Manager's Handbook. pp. 676. *Lond.* 1893. 8°. 7109. g. 34.

COAL AND COAL MINING.—General
—*continued.*

PEEL (R.) Text-Book of Coal Mining. pp. 284. 1893. 8°. Blackie's Science Text Books.
8703. bb.

STUART (D. M. D.) Coal Dust an Explosive Agent. pp. 103. *Lond.* 1894. 4°. 07109. l. 5.

—— Origin and Rationale of Colliery Explosions. *Bristol,* 1895. 8°. 7104. dd. 9.

TAYLOR (E.) New Method for the Ventilation of Coal Mines. pp. 9. *Rochdale,* 1886. 8°.
Pam. 27.

WALKER (W.) Lectures on practical Coal-mining. pp. 32. *Nottingham,* 1892. 8°. Pam. 27.

WALKER (S. F.) How to light a Colliery by Electricity. pp. 36. *Lond.* 1892. 4°. 8757. i. 21.

WILDMAN (J. R.) System of Book-keeping for coal merchants. pp. 58. *Horsforth,* 1893. 8°.
Pam. 38.

See also FUEL.

Coal and Coal Mining in various Countries.

KARPELES (B.) Die Arbeiter des mährischschlesischen Steinkohlen-Revieres. *Leipz.* 1894, *etc.* 8°. 8277. i.

SCHWACKHOEFER (F.) Die chemische Zusammensetzung der in Oesterreich-Ungarn verwendeten Kohlen. pp. 92. *Wien,* 1893. 8°.
7106. i. 17.

JULIN (A.) Recherches sur le salaire des ouvriers des charbonnages belges, 1810–89. pp. 61. *Liège,* 1889. 8°. 08276. f. 23. (5.)

BARTLETT (J. H.) Iron and Coal in Canada. pp. 167. *Montreal,* 1885. 8°. 07109. e. 10.

GRAND' EURY (C.) Géologie du bassin houiller du Gard. pp. 354. *Saint-Étienne,* 1890. 4°.
7109. k. 16.

—— Atlas. fol. 1824. e. 10.

LAPPARENT (A. de) La Question du charbon de terre. pp. 120. *Paris,* 1890. 8°. 7108. a. 19.

AUERBACH (E.) Die Ordnung der Arbeitsverhältnisses in den Kohlengruben von Northumberland und Durham. 1890. 8°. Ac. Leipsic. *Verein für Socialpolitik.* Schriften. No. 45.
Ac. 2322.

CALVERT (J. G.) The Coal Question. pp. 32. *Manch.* 1894. 8°. Pam. 94.

BOYD (R. N.) History of the Coal Trade. pp. 256. *Lond.* 1892. 8°. 8275. c. 85.

KIDSTON (R.) On the Fossil Plants of the Coal Fields, Ayrshire. 1893. 4°. Ac. Edinburgh. *Royal Society.* Transactions. Vol. 37. 2099. g.

—— Fossil Flora of the South Wales Coal Field. 1894. 4°. Ac. Edinburgh. *Royal Society.* Transactions. Vol. 37. 2099. g.

NASSE (R.) Die Bergarbeiter-Verhältnisse in Grossbritannien. pp. 176. *Saarbrücken,* 1891. 8°. 8276. dd. 12.

BRADY (F.) Dover Coal Boring. pp. 41. 1892. 8°. 7106. h. 35.

HARRISON (W. J.) On the Search for Coal in the South-East of England. pp. 28. *Birmingham,* 1894. 8°. Pam. 27.

SOUTH LANCASHIRE AND CHESHIRE COAL ASSOCIATION. Report of Proceedings at the Annual Meeting, Nov. 1894. pp. 141. *Wigan,* 1895. 8°. 08229. e. 34.

OLIVER (S.) Reid's Handy Colliery Guide for Northumberland and Durham. pp. 113. *Lond.* 1891. 8°. 7106. aa. 34.

WILKINS (C.) The South Wales Coal Trade. pp. 405. *Cardiff,* 1888. 8°. 08225. l. 17.

COAL AND COAL MINING.—Various Countries—*continued.*

BROJA (R.) Der Steinkohlenbergbau in der Vereinigten Staaten. pp. 112. *Leipz.* 1894. 8°.
7106. c. 19.

—— Atlas. fol. 7106. d. 3.

SWANK (J. M.) History of Iron and of early Coal mining in the United States. pp. 884. *Phila.* 1892. 8°. 7109. c. 16.

U.S. *Geological Survey.* Coal. pp. 182. *Wash.* 1892. 8°. 07109. h. 35.

—— *Bureau of Labor.* Cost of Production: Coal, *etc.* pp. 1404. 1891. 8°. Annual Report of the Bureau of Labor. No. 6. 8275. k.

—— *Geological Survey.* The Manufacture of Coke. pp. 48. *Wash.* 1892. 8°. Pam. 27.

ALABAMA. *Geological Survey.* Report on the Cahaba Coal Field. pp. 12. 189. *Montgomery,* 1890. 8°. 07109. h. 26.

ILLINOIS. *Bureau of Labour.* Statistics of Coal in Illinois, 1893. pp. 162. *Springfield,* 1894. 8°. 07108. g. 11.

KEYES (C. R.) Coal Deposits of Iowa. pp. 536. 1894. 8°. IOWA. *Geological Survey.* Annual Report. Vol. 2. 7106. i.

WINSLOW (A.) Report on the Coal Deposits of Missouri. pp. 226. 1891. 8°. MISSOURI. *Geological Survey.* Reports. Vol. 1. 07109. l.

EDWARDS (W. S.) Coals and Cokes in West Virginia. pp. 162. *Cincinnati,* 1892. 8°.
7109. b. 18.

LYMAN (B. S.) Coal Measure Sections near Peytona, W. Virginia. *Phila.* 1894. 8°. Pam. 27.

LIST (C.) Westfälische Kohlenformation. pp. 36. 1891. 8°. Sammlung gemeinverständlicher Vortrage. Heft. 126. 12249. m.

See also FUEL : MINERALOGY AND MINING.

COCA : COCAINE. FORSHAW (C. F.) Cocaine for Tooth Extraction. *Bradford,* 1891. 12°.
Pam. 39.

MARTINDALE (W.) Coca and Cocaine. pp. 76. *Lond.* 1894. 8°. 07509. de. 36.

See also ANAESTHETICS.

COCHIN CHINA. BELOT (A.) Cinq cents Femmes pour Un Homme. pp. 345. *Paris,* 1889. 12°. 10056. aaa. 25.

BOURBONNAUD (L.) Madame. Les Indes et l'extrême-Orient. pp. 304. *Paris,* 1892. 8°.
10057. aa. 11.

FAURE (A.) Les Français en Cochinchine au XVIIIᵉ. siècle. pp. 254. *Paris,* 1891. 8°.
4866. h. 14.

SUENSON (E.) Skizzer från Japan och Kochinkina. pp. 211. *Stockholm,* 1890. 8°.
10058. a. 16.

See also ANNAM : FRANCE, *Colonies:* INDO-CHINA : MALAYSIA.

COCKROACH. *See* ORTHOPTERA.

COCOA. HART (J. H.) "Cacao." pp. 76. *Port of Spain,* 1892. 8°. 07076. f. 5.

HATTON (J.) Cocoa. pp. 22. *Lond.* 1892. 8°.
Pam. 1.

HISTORICUS. Cocoa : all about it. pp. 114. *Lond.* 1892. 8°. 07076. e. 33.

COCOA-NUT PALM. COCOA-NUT PALM. All about the "Coconut Palm." pp. 235. *Colombo,* 1885. 8°. 7078. c. 19.

QUINCY (S.) Description de l'arbre cocotier de mer des Îles Seychelles. pp. 10. *Maurice,* 1893. 8°. Pam. 1.

COCOA-NUT PALM—*continued.*

TILAKARATNA (E. R.) List of Products of the Cocoanut Tree. pp. 9. *Colombo*, 1891. 12°.
　　　　　　　　　　　Pam. 1.
See also FORESTRY.

COD FISH. IRELAND. *Fisheries Office.* Hints on the cure of Codfish. pp. 40. *Dubl.* 1891. 8°.
　　　　　　　　　　　Pam. 94.
LITTAYE ( ) Notice sur la Pêche de la Morue. pp. 56. *Paris*, 1891. 8°.　　　7290. f. 21.
MÖLLER (F. P.) Cod-liver Oil and Chemistry. pp. 508. *Lond.* 1895. 8°.　　8906. g. 19.
See also FISH.

COELENTERATA.
See ACTINOZOA : SPONGES : SIPHONOPHORA.

COFFEE. ARNOLD (E. L. L.) Coffee : cultivation and profit. pp. 270. *Lond.* 1886. 8°.
　　　　　　　　　　　07076. g. 20.
—— On the Indian hills : Coffee-planting in Southern India. pp. 350. *Lond.* 1893. 8°.
　　　　　　　　　　　010057. e. 25.
CARÁCAS. *Junta de Aclimatacion.* Cuestionario sobre el cultivo del café. pp. 42.
Carácas, 1895. 8°.　　　　　Pam. 1.
GROENEVELD (J.) Termijnzaken in Koffie te Rotterdam. pp. 15. *Rotterdam*, 1893. 8°.
　　　　　　　　　08226. k. 4. (5.)
KUNEMAN (J.) De Gouvernements Koffiecultuur op Java. pp. 201. *'s Gravenh.* 1890. 8°.
　　　　　　　　　　　07076. g. 1.
LODGE (J. L.) Coffee. pp. 14.
Birmingham, 1894. 8°.　　　　Pam. 1.
ROMUNDE (R. v.) Koffiebladziekte en Koffie Kultuur. pp. 92. *'s Gravenh.* 1892. 8°.
　　　　　　　　　　　07076. l. 7.
SAENZ (N.) Notice sur la culture du Caféier en Colombie. pp. 12!. *Brux.* 1894. 8°. 7075. g. 2.
WESSELS (L.) De opheffing van het monopolie en de vervanging van de geelwongen Koffiecultuur op Java. pp. 72. *'s Gravenh.* 1890. 8°.
　　　　　　　　　8226. ff. 33. (4.)
—— De voorstellen van de Indische Regeering omtrent de gouvernements-Koffiecultur op Java, *etc.* *'s Gravenh.* 1892. 8°.　08227. k. 31. (10.)
See also CAFFEINE.

COFFEE HOUSES. ROBINSON (E. F.) Early history of Coffee Houses in England. pp. 240. *Lond.* 1893. 8°.　　　　7709. b. 46.
See also CLUBS.

COIFFURE. *See* HAIR.

COIMBRA. BRAGA (T.) Historia da Universidade de Coimbra. *Lisboa*, 1892, *etc.* 8°.
　　　　　　　　　　　8356. dd.

COINS AND MEDALS. *See* NUMISMATICS.

COIRE. *See* CHUR.

COKE. *See* COAL.

COLCHESTER. BENHAM (C. E.) Colchester Worthies. pp. 70. *Lond.* 1892. 8°. 10803. g. 11.
—— Guide to Colchester Castle. pp. 19.
Colchester, 1893. 8°.　　10347. d. 7. (6.)
BENHAM (W. G.) The Colchester Oyster Feast. pp. 26. *Colchester* 1893. 8°.　10347. g. 5. (7.)
GOLDING (B. L.) Short account of Colchester Castle. pp. 13. *Bury*, 1892. 8°.
　　　　　　　　　10347. aa. 37. (7.)
LAVER (H.) Colchester. pp. 14.
Colchester, 1892. 8°.　　10349. aa. 37. (7.)

COLEOPTERA.

General.

BEAUREGARD (H.) Les Insectes vésicants. pp. 544. *Paris*, 1890. 8°.　　7297. h. 16.
COLOMBO. *Museum.* Report on the collection of Beetles. pp. 208. *Colombo*, 1890. 8°. 7297. b. 24.

COLEOPTERA.—General—*continued.*

COUPIN (H.) L'amateur de Coléoptères. pp. 352. *Paris*, 1894. 12°.　　　7297. aaa. 41.
HAMILTON (J.) Catalogue of Coleoptera common to N. America, Asia and Europe. 1894. 8°. Ac. *Philadelphia. American Entomological Society.* Transactions. Vol. 21.　Ac. 3688.
PALUMBO (A.) Sulla caccia dei Coleotteri. pp. 10. *Siena*, 1892. 4°.　7004. df. 21. (10.)
CANDÈZE (E.) Catalogue des Élatérides connus en 1890. pp. 246. *Liége*, 1891. 8°. 7298. ee. 22.
PIC (M.) Matériaux pour servir à l'étude des Longicornes. *Lyon*, 1891, *etc.* 8°.　7298. ce.
SCHENKLING (S.) Nomenclator coleopterologicus. pp. 224. *Frankf.* 1894. 8°.　7297. a. 64.
SOMERVILLE (W.) The Pine Beetle (Hylesinus Piniperda L.). pp. 13. 1891. 8°.　Pam. 42.

Local.

European.

HEYDEN (L. v.) Catalogus Coleopterorum Europæ. pp. 420. *Berl.* 1891. 8°.　7297. bb. 24.
REITTER (E.) Tableaux analytiques pour déterminer les coléoptères d'Europe.
Moulins, 1890, *etc.* 8°.　　7297. e. 29.
GANGLBAUER (L.) Die Käfer von Mitteleuropa. *Wien*, 1892, *etc.* 8°.　　7297. dd.
EICHHOFF (W.) Die europäischen Borkenkäfer. pp. 240. *Paris*, 1891. 8°.　7298. bb. 1.
FAIRMAIRE (L.) Coléoptères. pp. 336. 1882. 8°. Histoire naturelle de la France. pt. 8. 7207. cc.
FAUCONNET (L.) Faune des Coléoptères de France. pp. 519. *Autun*, 1892. 8°. 7297. c. 17.
GAVOY (L.) Faunule coléoptérologique du Mont Alaric, Aude. pp. 47. 1892. 8°. Ac. *Carcassone. Société des Arts.* Mémoires. Tom 6.
　　　　　　　　　　　Ac. 262/2.
FOWLER (W. W.) Coleoptera of the British Islands. 3 vol. *Lond.* 1887–89. 8°. 7298. eee.
HEY (W. C.) List of the Coleoptera of Yorkshire. 1886, *etc.* 8°. Ac. *Huddersfield. West Riding Naturalists' Society.* Transactions. Pt. 9, 10, 16, *etc.*　　Ac. 3016/2.
FAVRE (É.) Faune des coléoptères du Valais. pp. 448. 1890. 8°. Ac. *Switzerland. Gesellschaft für die gesammten Naturwissenschaften.* Denkschriften. Bd. 31.　　Ac. 2866/7.

Exotic.

HEYNE (A.) Die exotischen Käfer in Wort und Bild. *Leipz.* 1893, *etc.* 4°.　　7297. l.
GESTRO (R.) Viaggio ad Assab. Coleotteri. 1889. 8°. Ac. *Genoa. Museo di Storia Naturale.* Annali. Ser. 2. Vol. 7.　　Ac. 2809.
PÉRINGUEY (L.) Catalogue of the Coleoptera of S. Africa. 1893, *etc.* 8°. Ac. *Cape Town. South African Philosophical Soc.* Transactions. Vol. 7.
　　　　　　　　　　　Ac. 1993.
HAMILTON (J.) Catalogue of the Coleoptera of Alaska. pp. 38. 1894. 8°. Ac. *Philadelphia. Entomological Soc.* Transactions. Vol. 21.
　　　　　　　　　　　Ac. 3688.
HORN (G. H.) Species of Agrilus of Boreal America. 1891. 8°. Ac. *Philadelphia. Entomological Soc.* Transactions. Vol. 18. No. 4.
　　　　　　　　　　　Ac. 3688.
KNOBEL (E.) Beetles of New England. pp. 45. *Bost.* 1895. obl. 8°.　　7298. a. 8.
KIRSCH (T.) Coleopteren gesammelt auf einer Reise durch Süd Amerika. pp. 58. 1889. 4°. Ac. *Dresden. K. Zoologisches Museum.* Abhandlungen. 1888–89.　　Ac. 3562.
EHNBERG (K.) Beiträge zur Kenntniss der Coleopteren-Fauna Südwest-Siberiens. 1890. 8°. Ac. *Helsingfors. Societas Scientiarum.* Öfversigt. af förhandlingar. No. 32.　　Ac. 1094.

COLEOPTERA.—Local.—*Exotic—cont.*

GAHAN (C. J.) List of the Longicorn Coleoptera collected in Burma. pp. 104. 1894. |8°. Ac. Genoa. *Museo di Storia Naturale.* Annali. Vol. 34.   Ac. 2809.

See also INSECTS: ZOOLOGY.

COLLECTIONS AND COLLECTORS, Private Galleries and Objects of Art and Curiosities. MÉLY (F. de) and BISHOP (E.) Bibliographie des inventaires imprimés. *Paris,* 1892, *etc* 8°.   011900. f.

SWARTE (V. de) Les Financiers amateurs d'art aux XVI°, XVII° et XVIII° siècles. pp. 57. *Paris,* 1890. 8°.   7807. c. 8.

P.P. London. The Artists' Record and Art Collectors' Guide. *Lond.* 1887, 88. 8°.   P.P. 1907. c.

EUDEL (P.) L'Hôtel Drouot en 1881, *etc.* 9 vol. *Paris,* 1882–91. 12°.   7858. a. 29.

P.P. Paris. Répertoire des Ventes publiques de livres, autographes, gravures, estampes et tableaux. *Paris,* 1894, *etc.* 8°.   631.

—— Répertoire des Collectionneurs de la France et de l'Étranger. *Paris,* 1892, *etc.* 8°.   P.P. 2404. l.

ARMAILLÉ (L. d') *Count.* Catalogue des Objets d'art et de riche ameublement composant la collection du Comte d'Armaillé. pp. 55. *Paris,* 1890. 8°.   7806. ee. 31.

BORGHESE (P. M. A.) *Prince de Sulmona.* Catalogue des Objets d'art et d'ameublement du Palais du Prince Borghese à Rome. pp. 143. *Rome,* 1892. 8°.   7808. g. 13.

BERLEPSCH (H. E. v.) Katalog der Sammlung Buchner in Bamberg. pp. 100. *Bamberg,* 1891. 4°.   7806. h. 13.

CATALOGUES. Catalogue des Objets d'art et d'ameublement provenant d'une celebre collection d'Italie. pp. 62. *Paris,* 1891. 8°.   7806. dd. 7.

—— Catalogue d'une collection d'Objets d'art et de bel ameublement. pp. 40. *Paris,* 1894. 8°.   7806. e. 21.

—— Catalogue des Objets d'art et d'ameublement provenant de la collection de Mme. X, pp. 51. *Paris,* 1892. 4°.   7808. g. 5.

DENAIN ( ) *Madame.* Catalogue des Tableaux objets d'art et d'ameublement. pp. 105. *Paris,* 1893. 8°.   7857. k. 31

DUCATEL (C.) Catalogue des Objets d'art et de haute curiosité. pp. 71. *Paris,* 1890. fol.   7806. dd. 5.

CHAFFERS (W.) Catalogue of works of antiquity and art collected by W. H. Forman. 2 pt. *Lond.* 1892. 8°.   C. 54. d. 5.

FONDI (di)' *Prince.* Collection de Tableaux et d'objets d'art au palais du prince de Fondi à Naples. 1895. fol.   7807. m. 9.

FROEHNER (W.) Collection van Branteghem. 2 pt. *Brux.* 1892. fol.   1702. d. 9.

GIOBBE ( ) Catalogo della collezioni Giobbe e Colbacchini di Venezia. pp. 30. *Milano,* 1889. 8°.   Pam. 24.

HOLCOMBE (C.) Chinese Porcelains and other curios belonging to G. A. Hearn. pp. 177. *N.Y.* 1894. 12°.   7805. a. 2.

HAMILTON PALACE. Catalogue of the Pictures, works of art and decorative objects. pp. 234. *Lond.* 1882. 8°.   7806. cc. 1.

—— The Hamilton Palace collection. pp. 244. *Lond.* 1882. 4°.   7806. e. 4.

CHRISTIE AND MANSON. Catalogue of the collection of pictures by old masters formed by Adrian Hope. pp. 151. *Lond.* 1894. 8°.   7858. d. 1.

COLLECTIONS, etc.—*continued.*

JONES (C. C.) Catalogue of the autographic Collection and engraved portraits and views gathered by Colonel Jones. pp. 148. 4. *Phila.* 1894. 8°.   11902. g. 42.

LECLANCHÉ ( ) Catalogue des Objets d'art composant la collection Leclanché. pp. 68. *Paris,* 1892. fol.   7808. f. 4.

MAGNIAC (H.) Catalogue of the collection of Works of art, formed by H. Magniac. pp. 250. *Lond.* 1892. 8°.   K.T.C. 5. a. 11.

P * * * (E. de) Catalogue des Objets d'art et d'ameublement du XVIII° siècle, composant la collection de M. E. de P. pp. 27. *Paris,* 1894. 8°.   7808. f. 16.

MURRAY (C. F.) Catalogue of the Pictures belonging to his Grace the Duke of Portland. pp. 222. *Lond.* 1894. 4°.   K.T.C. 36. b. 1.

SANGIORGI (G.) Catalogo degli Oggetti appartenuti alla famiglia Perez. pp. 64. *Roma,* 1893. 8°.   7808. c. 15.

LUTHMER (F.) Führer durch die K. von Rothschild'sche Kunstsammlung. pp. 96. *Frankfurt.a. M.* 1890. 8°.   Pam. 24.

SEILLIÈRE (A.) *Baron.* Catalogue des Objets d'art provenant de la collection du Baron Seillière. *Paris,* 1890. 4°.   7806. ee. 30.

SPITZER (F.) Catalogue des Objets d'art et de haute curiosité, composant la collection Spitzer. 2 vol. *Paris,* 1893. fol.   K.T.C. 7. b. 9.

STRAHAN (E.) Mr. Vanderbilt's House and collection. 2 vol. *Bost.* 1884. fol.   K.T.C. 21. b. 6.

WEBER (T.) Catalogue des Objets d'art composant la collection de M. T. Weber. pp. 42. 1892. 4°.   7808. g. 7.

See also ART: ART, *Decorative*: FURNITURE, *etc.*

COLLEGIUM GERMANICUM HUNGARICUM, Rome. STEINHUBER (A.) *Cardinal.* Geschichte des Collegium. 2 Bde. *Freiburg,* 1895. 8°.   8357. dd. 9

COLLISIONS, at Sea. *See* LAW, *Maritime.*

COLMAR. BILLING (S.) Chronik der Stadt Colmar. pp. 374. *Colmar,* 1891. 8°. 10255. ee. 3.

COLMER. HERVEY (T.) History of Colmer, Hants. pp. 296. *Colmer,* 1891. 4°. 010358. h. 5.

—— Index to the Parish Registers of Colmer. pp. 60. *Colmer,* 1893. 4°.   9902. f. 45.

COLNE. DAWES (C. E.) The Parish of Colne. 1891. 8°. Occasional Hunts County Sketches. Ser. 2.   10368. aa.

COLOGNE, City. COLOGNE. *Archiv.* Beiträge zur Geschichte Kölns. pp. 406. *Köln,* 1895. 8°.   10250. k. 4.

Ac. Cologne. *Architecten- und Ingenieur-Verein für Niederrhein.* Cölner Thorburgen und Befestigungen 1180–1882. *Cöln,* 1883. *obl.* 4°.   1730. a. 4.

KORTH (L.) Köln im Mittelalter. pp. 91. 1890. 8°. Ac. Cologne. *Historischer Verein.* Annalen. Hft. 50.   Ac. 7335.

Ac. Cologne. *Universitas Coloniensis.* Die Matrikel der Universität Köln, 1389–1559. 1892, *etc.* 4°. Ac. Cologne. *Gesellschaft für Rheinische Geschichtskunde.* Publicationen. Bd. 8, *etc.*   Ac. 7028.

MEYER (C.) Köln im Zeitalter der Reformation. pp. 39. 1892. 8°. Sammlung wissenschaftlicher Vorträge. N,F. Ser. 7. Heft 153. 12249. m.

MERLO (J. J.) Kölnische Künstler in alter und neuer Zeit. pp. 1206. 1893–95. 4°. Ac. Cologne. *Gesellschaft für Rheinische Geschichtskunde.* Publikationen. Bd. 9.   Ac. 7028.

COLOGNE.—City—continued.

MERLO (J. J.) Zur Geschichte des kölner-Theaters. 1890. 8°. Ac. Cologne. *Hist. Verein.* Annalen. Hft. 50. Ac. 7335.

Diocese and Electorate, etc.

LAU (F.) Die erzbischöflichen Beamten in der Stadt Köln während des 12. Jahrhunderts. pp. 89. *Lübeck*, 1891. 8°. Pam. 29.

SAMSON (H.) Die Heiligen als Kirchen Patrone und ihre Auswahl für die Erzdiöcese Köln. pp. 431. *Paderborn*, 1892. 8°. 4824. ccc. 8.

BINTERIM (A. J.) and MOOREN (J. H.) Die Erzdiöcese Köln bis zur französischen Staatsumwälzung. *Düsseldorf*, 1892, etc. 8°. 4662. e.

ENGELSHEYM (D. v.) Liber dissencionum archiepiscopi Coloniensis. 1893, *etc.* 8°. Ac. Munster. *Verein fur Geschichte Westfalens.* Zeitschrift. (Ergänzungshefte.) Ac. 7355.

JANSEN (M.) Die Herzogsgewalt der Erzbischofe von Köln 1180 bis zum Ausgange des 14 Jahrhunderts. pp. 139. 1895. 8°. Historische Abhandlungen aus dem Münchener Seminar. Hft. 7. 9008. i.

DAENELL (E. R.) Die kölner Konföderation. pp. 174. 1894. 8°. ARNDT (W.) Leipziger Studien, *etc.* Bd. 1. 09325. h.

COLOMBIA.

See also AMERICA, *South.*

History and Politics.

BORDA (J. J.) Compendio de historia de Colombia. pp. 224. *Bogota*, 1890. 8°. 9771. aa. 10.

ORTEGA (E.) Historia general de los Chibchas. pp. 103. *Bogota*, 1891. 8°. Pam. 28.

SAMPER AGUDELO (J. M.) Memorias sobre la historia del derecho constitucional de Colombia. pp. 146. *Bogota*, 1881. 8°. Pam. 65.

RESTREPO TIRADO (E.) Estudios sobre los aborigines de Colombia. *Bogotá*, 1892, etc. 8°. 10481. ee.

CORRÁLES (M. E.) Documentos para la historia de la provincia de Cartagena de Indias. 2 tom. *Bogotá*, 1883. 8°. 9772. ccc. 10.

NUÑEZ (R.) La Reforma política en Colombia. pp. 1268. *Bogotá*, 1888. 8°. 8180. c. 7.

COLOMBIA, *Ministerio de Relaciones Exteriores.* Laudo arbitral en que se fija el límite entre la República de Colombia y Venezuela. pp. 10. *Bogotá*, 1892. fol. Pam. 65.

VILLAFAÑA (J. G.) Juicio sobre el Laudo en la cuestion, Límites entre Venezuele y Colombia. pp. 32. *Táriba*, 1891. 8°. Pam. 65.

Topography : Immigration.

CAMACHO ROLDAN (S.) Notas de viaje. Colombia. pp. 896. *Bogotá*, 1890. 8°. 10409. d. 18.

CANDELIER (H.) Rio-Hacha et les Indiens Goajires. pp. 282. *Paris*, 1893. 8°. 10481. c. 34.

CUERVO (A. B.) Coleccion de documentos inéditos sobre la geografia de Colombia. *Bogotá*, 1891, etc. 8°. 10481. de.

MILLICAN (A.) Travels of an Orchid Hunter in Colombia. pp. 222. *Lond.* 1891. 8°. 10481. dd. 21.

RECLUS (J. J. É.) Colombia. Traducida por F. J. Vergara y Velasco. pp. 440. *Bogotá*, 1893. 8°. 10480. dd. 31.

VEDOVELLI-BREGUZZO (C.) Conferenza sulla Colombia. pp. 22. *Milano*, 1892. 8°. 10480. f. 36.

—— Da Puerto Colombia a Bogotà. pp. 35. *Roma*, 1892. 8°. Pam. 86.

—— Programma di una Società per Azioni per la colonizzazione di terreni concessi dal Governo Colombiano nella Sierra Nevada di Santa Marta. pp. 16. *Milano*, 1891. 8°. Pam. 86.

COLOMBIA.—Topography—continued.

VEDOVELLI-BREGUZZO (C.) Italia e Colombia. pp. 8. *Milano*, 1892. 8°. Pam. 86.

VIGLIETTI (C. M.) Avventure di una Spedizione alla Colombia. pp. 200. *Torino*, 1890. 8°. 10481. de. 4.

Trade, Finance, etc.

COLOMBIA. Import duties of Colombia. pp. 17. 1891. 8°. U.S. *Bureau of American Republics.* Bulletin. No. 27. 08225. k. 1.

—— Mining Laws of Colombia. pp. 107. *N.Y.* 1892. 8°. 6616. cc. 4.

MADRID. *Exposición Americana.* Catálogo de los objetos que presenta el Gobierno de Colombia. pp. 136. *Madrid*, 1892. 8°. 7959. f. 24.

COLOMBO. COLOMBO. Colombo Harbour. pp. 73. *Colombo*, 1893. 16°. Pam. 88.

LABUGAMA. A holiday trip to Labugama. pp. 86. *Colombo*, 1891. 12°. Pam. 88.

SKEEN (G. J. A.) Guide to Colombo. pp. 86. *Ceylon*, 1892. 8°. 10057. aa. 16.

RIBEIRO (J.) Account of the Siege of Colombo, 1655–56. pp. 36. 1891. 8°. 9005. d. 26. (8.)

Diocese.

CHAPMAN (J.) *Bp. of Colombo.* Memorials of J. Chapman, Bishop of Colombo. pp. 236. *Lond.* 1892. 8°. 4903. e. 49.

COLOMBO, *Diocese of.* Annual Report of Synod. *Colombo*, 1893, etc. 8°. 4767. dd.

COLONIES AND EMIGRATION.

For the colonies of each country, *see* under the country required.

BONASSIEUX (P.) Les grandes Compagnies de Commerce. pp. 562. *Paris*, 1892. 8°. 9009. h. 4.

DENANCY (E.) De la Colonisation dans ses rapports avec la production, *etc.* pp 131. *Épernay*, 1894. 8°. 8154. aa. 23.

DUBOIS (M.) Systèmes coloniaux et peuples colonisateurs. pp. 290. *Paris*, 1895. 12°. 8154. aaa. 49.

FOCHIFI (V.) Colonie e colonizzazione. pp. 198. *Milano*, 1890. 8°. 8154. aaa. 39.

GATES (E. W.) Hints to Emigrants. pp. 47. *Lond.* 1892. 8°. Pam. 82.

GEFFCKEN (F. H.) Politica della popolazione, emigrazione, colonie. pp. 112. 1889. 8°. Biblioteca dell' economista. Ser. 3. Vol. 13. 8205. l.

GIRAULT (A.) Principes de colonisation. pp. 660. *Paris*, 1895. 12°. 8154. aaa. 26.

ITALY. *Ministero dell' Estero.* Emigrazione e colonie. pp. 660. *Roma*, 1893. 8°. 8154. g. 28.

LEROY-BEAULIEU (P. P.) De la colonisation chez les peuples modernes. pp. 868. *Paris*, 1891. 8°. 8154. dd. 5.

LEWIS (*Sir* G. C.) Essay on the Government of Dependencies. pp. 392. *Oxf.* 1891. 8°. 8154. dd. 6.

LONDON. *Emigrants' Information Office.* Handbooks. *Lond.* 1888, *etc.* 8°. 10025. cc. 18.

—— Summary of Consular Reports. *Lond.* 1891, etc. 8°. 10408. ee.

—— *Self-Help Emigration Society.* The old Country and the new. pp. 19. *Lond.* 1887. 8°. 8282. ff. 9. (7.)

OLTRAMARE (G.) Une nouvelle Orientation de la Politique coloniale. pp. 68. *Genève*, 1892. 8°. 8225. eee. 46.

RICAUD (J. A.) L'Expansion coloniale. pp. 318. *Paris*, 1891. 12°. 8154. aaa. 37.

SACERDOTI (V.) Studi sulla colonizzazione. pp. 248. *Bologna*, 1890. 8°. 8154. dd. 4.

COMMONS.

COMMONS. Hunter (*Sir* R.) Footpaths and Commons and Parish and District Councils. pp. 32. *Lond.* 1895. 8°.   6146. bbb. 26. (13.)

Lefevre (*Right Hon.* G. J. S.) English Commons and Forests. pp. 391. *Lond.* 1894. 8°.
6306. g. 1.

Wirral. · *Footpaths Preservation Society.* Handbook on Public Rights of Way. pp. 29. 1895. 16°.   6426. aaaa. 29.

COMMUNION, Holy. *See* Eucharist.

COMPANIES AND CORPORATIONS.

Bower (G. S.) The Directors Liability Act, 1890, and other provisions relating to public companies. pp. 243. *Lond.* 1890. 8°. 6376. d. 6.

Brice (S. W.) The Law of Corporations and Companies. *Lond.* 1893. 8°.   2232. f. 10.

Buckley (H. B.) Law and practice under the Companies Acts, 1862–90. pp. 803. *Lond.* 1891. 8°.   2018. c.

Cameron (P. H.) Summary of the Law of Joint-stock Companies. pp. 488. *Edinb.* 1892. 8°.
6375. k. 8.

Cook (W. W.) The Corporation Problem. pp. 262. *Lond.* 1891. 8°.   08227. de. 1.

Cummins (C.) Guide to the formation of the accounts of Limited Liability Companies. pp. 48. *Lond.* 1894. 8°.   08227. f. 47.

Dale (B.) How 'are profits for the year to be ascertained? pp. 56. *Lond.* 1895. 8°.
8228. aaa. 28.

Fitzpatrick (J.) and Fowke (V. de S.) Secretary's Manual on the Law of Joint Stock Companies. pp. 290. *Lond.* 1895. 8°. 6376. de. 12.

Foote (A. R.) and Everett (C. E.) Law of Incorporated Companies. *Cincinnati,* 1892, *etc.* 8°.
06616. k.

Fowke (V. de S.) The Companies Acts 1862–90. pp. 403. *Lond.* 1893. 8°.   6376. d. 29.

—— Reminders on Company Law. pp. 68. *Lond.* 1894. 8°.   6375. a. 60.

Fox (W. H.) The Company-Secretary. *Lond.* 1895. fol.   8228. k. 36.

Glotin (H.) Étude sur les syndicats professionnels. pp. 438. *Paris,* 1892. 8°.
5406. de. 10.

Gore-Browne (F.) Concise Precedents under the Companies Acts. pp. 548. *Lond.* 1892. 8°.
6376. d. 21.

Hamilton (W. F.) Manual of Company Law. pp. 468. *Lond.* 1891. 8°.   6376. e. 27.

Harris (G. E.) Treatise on the Law of Damages by Corporations. 2 vol. *Rochester, N.Y.* 1892. 8°.   6616. de. 8.

Haycraft (T. W.) Handy book on the powers & liabilities of Directors. pp. 125. 1891. 12°. Wilson's Legal Handy Books.   6426. aaa. 39.

Healey (C. E. H. C.) Treatise on the Law relating to Joint Stock Companies. pp. 1246. *Lond.* 1894. 8°.   6376. g. 1.

Hurrell (H.) and Hyde (C. G.) Joint Stock Companies Practical Guide. pp. 266. 8. *Lond.* 1890. 8°.   6376. e. 26.

Jordan (R.) The Companies Acts 1862–90. pp. 316. *Lond.* 1893. 8°.   6376. d. 28.

—— Handy book on Joint Stock Companies. pp. 350. *Lond.* 1895. 8°.   6376. de. 13.

Kolff (L. A. C.) Opmerkingen over Naamloozen Vennootschappen in Engeland. pp. 74. *Leiden,* 1891. 8°.   Pam. 23.

Mackenzie (M. J.) Company Law. pp. 443. *Lond.* 1893. 8°.   6376. dd. 5.

Manson (E.) Tinkering Company Law. pp. 8. *Lond.* 1890. 8°.   6190. cc. 4. (3.)

COMPANIES, etc.—*continued.*

Manson (E.) Law of Trading and other Companies. pp. 966. *Lond.* 1893. 8°. 6375. de. 5.

—— Debentures and Debenture Stock of Trading and other Companies. pp. 248. *Lond.* 1894. 8°.
6376. ee. 3.

Paine (T. T.) Formation and Registration of Companies limited by shares and by guarantee. pp. 244. 1890. 8°. Solicitors' Handbooks.
6145. e.

Palmer (F. B.) Company Precedents. *Lond.* 1895, *etc.* 8°.   2232. e. 15.

—— Shareholders', Directors' and Liquidators' Legal Companion. pp. 231. *Lond.* 1894. 8°.
6375. b. 50.

—— Private Companies and Syndicates. pp. 64. *Lond.* 1895. 12°.   Pam. 23.

Peek (*Sir* H. W.) Prospectus-Makers and the Public. pp. 147. *Lond.* 1890. 8°. 6375. de. 4.

Smith (J. W.) Handy book of the Law of Joint Stock Companies. pp. 202. 1893. 12°. Wilson's Legal Handy books.   6426. aaa. 39.

Smith (T. E.) Summary of the Law of Companies. pp. 342. *Lond.* 1891. 8°.   2230. bb. 8.

Tennant (H.) The Companies Act, 1892. pp. 146. *Cape Town,* 1894. 8°.   6376. de. 6.

Thompson (S. D.) Commentaries on the Law of Private Corporations. *San Francisco,* 1895, *etc.* 8°.   06617. cc. 1.

Vindex. Swindling Unlimited. pp. 8. *Lond.* 1891. 8°.   Pam. 23.

Wheeler (P. F.) Partnership and Companies. pp. 300. *Lond.* 1892. 8°.   6376. d. 22.

Hewitt (T.) Treatise on the Law relating to Corporation Duty. pp. 155. *Lond.* 1892. 8°.
6426. cc. 20.

Jackson (M. S.) The Corporation Duty: its history, law and practice. pp. 220. *Lond.* 1892. 12°.   6426. cc. 25.

Emden (A.) Practice and Forms in Winding up Companies. pp. 1034. *Lond.* 1891. 8°.
6376. e. 28.

—— and Snow (T.) Annual Winding up Practice, 1893. pp. 339. *Lond.* 1893. 8°.
6375. dc. 3.

Mackenzie (M. J. M.) and Stewart (C. J.) Companies Winding-up Practice. pp. 372. *Lond.* 1890. 8°.   6376. d. 8.

Palmer (F. B.) Winding-up Forms and Practice. pp. 879. *Lond.* 1893. 8°   6405. f. 6.

Woolf (S.) Winding-up of Companies by the Court. pp. 287. *Lond.* 1891. 8°. 6405. d. 16.

Murfree (W. L.) Law of Foreign Corporations. pp. 376. *St. Louis,* 1893. 8°.   06955. df. 17.

Shepherd (B.) The Companies Ordinances of Hongkong. pp. 110. *Hongkong,* 1891. 8°.
06606. f. 8.

Bouvier Bangillon (A.) La Législation nouvelle sur les Sociétés. Loi du 1er août 1893. pp. 203. *Paris,* 1894. 8°.   5423. e. 20.

Faure (A.) La Nouvelle Loi sur les Sociétés par Actions. pp. 252. *Paris,* 1894. 8°.
5423. de. 19.

Glotin (H.) Étude sur les Syndicats professionnels. pp. 438. *Paris,* 1892. 8°. 5406. de. 10.

Lyon-Caen (C.) and Renault (L.) Traité des Sociétés commerciales. pp. 852. *Paris,* 1892. 8°.
5403. ff. 27.

Pavitt (A.) Les Compagnies limited anglaises et les Sociétés anonymes françaises. pp. 127. *Paris,* 1891. 8°.   6825. b. 6.

Rousseau (R.) Loi du 1er août 1893 sur les Sociétés par actions. pp. 198. *Paris,* 1893. 8°.
5424. dc. 10.

CONGO.—River, State, etc.—*continued.*

BOHL (J.) Nederlands Congo-Behng. pp. 38.
Amsterd. 1890. 8°.　　　　8028. ff. 16. (6.)

BOURDARIE (P.) À la côte du Congo français.
pp. 32. *Paris.* 1894. 8°.　　　　Pam. 89.

CERISIER (C.) Le Congo français en 1892.
pp. 16. *Nancy,* 1892. 8°.　　　　Pam. 89.

CHAPAUX (A.) Le Congo historique, diplomatique
et colonial. pp. 887. *Brux.* 1894. 8°. & fol.
　　　　　　　　　　　　10095. g. 10.

CONGO FREE STATE. Au Congo et au Kassäi.
pp. 60. *Brux.* 1888. 8°.　　　　8027. c. 10.

—— G. (A. M.) Les Congolais. *Paris,* 1890. 8°.
　　　　　　　　　　　　010096. ee. 19.

—— Les Codes du Congo. pp. 360.
Paris, 1892. 8°.　　　　5695. aa. 8.

CORNET (J.) Les formations postprimaires du
bassin du Congo. 1894. 8°. Ac. Liège. *Société
géologique.* Annales. Tom. 21.　　Ac. 3146.

CRUSSOL (J. de) *Duke d'Uzès.* Duchesse d'Uzès.
·Le Voyage de mon fils au Congo. pp. 342.
Paris, 1895. 4°.　　　　10095. g. 11.

DELPORTE (A.) Exploration du Congo. pp. 23.
Brux. 1890. 8°.　　　　Pam. 89.

DESOER (F.) Le Congo belge. pp. 83.
Liège, 1890. 8°.　　　　Pam. 66.

DROOGMANS (H.) Le Congo. pp. 121.
Brux. 1894. 8°.　　　　010095. i. 5.

DUBOIS (P.) L'Éducation des jeunes Congolais en
Belgique. pp. 192. *Liège,* 1893. 8°. 4767. dd. 8.

DUNOD (L.) Le Congo français. pp. 27.
Paris, 1892. 12°.　　　　Pam. 89.

DYBOWSKI (J.) La Route du Tchad. pp. 381.
Paris, 1893. 8°.　　　　10097. i. 36

ÉCŒURÉ. Le Congo Minotaure. pp. 16.
Brux. 1895. 16°.　　　　Pam. 67.

GLAVE (E. J.) Six years of adventure in Congo-
land. pp. 247. *Lond.* 1893. 8°. 10097. dd. 21.

HUBERT (L.) La Conquête du Congo. Liv. 1.
Brux. 1894. 8°.　　　　9061. h. 14.

JOHNSTON (*Sir* H. H.) The River Congo.
pp. 300. *Lond,* 1895. 8°.　　　10095. aaa. 9.

LAMOTTE (É.) Chez les Congolais. pp. 143.
Brux. 1895. 8°.　　　　010096. g. 21.

LEMAIRE (C. F. A.) Congo et Belgique. pp. 253.
Brux. 1894. 4°.　　　　010095. i. 6.

—— Au Congo. Comment les noirs travaillent.
pp. 139. *Brux.* 1895. 8°.　　　010096. ff. 31.

MAGALHÃES (C. de) Occupação do Congo e a conferencia de Berlin. pp. 60. *Lisboa,* 1885. 8°.
　　　　　　　　　　　　Pam. 66.

MARTINI (C.) To danske Kongofarere. pp. 92.
Kφbenh. 1890. 8°.　　　　010096. ff. 10.

MARTRIN-DONOS (C. de) Le Congo et ses affluents.
1891. 4°. BURDO (A.) Les Belges dans l'Afrique
centrale.　　　　　　　　10095. i. 12.

MERILLE DE COLLEVILLE (de) Belgique et
Congo. pp. 24. *Brighton,* 1886. 8°. Pam. 59.

PAQUAIJ (O.) La Verité sur le Congo. pp. 15.
Brux. 1895. 16°.　　　　Pam. 67.

PARYS (L. van) Les Hontes de la civilisation au
Congo belge devoilées. pp. 16.
La Louvière, 1893. 8°.　　　　Pam. 66.

PAYEUR-DIDELOT ( ) Deux ans au continent
mystérieux. 1894, etc. 8°. Ac. Nancy. *Société
de Géographie.* Bulletin. 1894.　　Ac. 6034.

P.P. *Brussels.* Le Congo illustré.
Brux. 1891, etc. 4°.　　P.P. 3936 and 313.

RAAB (R.) Der alte und der neue Kongostaat.
pp. 91. 1892. 8°. Sammlung wissenschaftlicher
Vorträge. N. F. Ser. 7. Hft. 149.　12249. m.

RAMAIX (M. de) Le Congo envisagé au point de
vue belge. 1891, 8°. Ac. Antwerp. *Société
de Géographie.* Bulletin. Tom. 16.　Ac. 6096.

CONGO.—River, State, etc.—*continued.*

RATOIN (E.) Nos nouvelles colonies. pp. 238.
Tours, 1890. 12°.　　　　010096. ee. 14.

REUSEL (C. v.) Notice historique sur le Congo.
pp. 30. *Malines,* 1895. 8°.　　　Pam. 89.

SOMZÉE (L.) Une Condition sine qua non de la
reprise du Congo. pp. 27. *Brux.* 1895. 8°.
　　　　　　　　　　　　Pam. 66.

TRIVIER (E.) Mon Voyage au Continent noir.
pp. 386. *Paris,* 1891. 8°.　　　010096. e. 33.

WARD (H.) Five years with the Congo Cannibals.
pp. 308. *Lond.* 1890. 8°.　　　010096. i. 7.

WAUTERS (A. J.) L'Annexion du Congo. pp. 17.
Brux. 1895. 8°.　　　　Pam. 67.

WINCXTENHOVEN (v.) Exposition d'Anvers,
1894. Les Colonies et l'État Indépendant du
Congo. pp. 100. *Brux.* 1895. 8°. 7957. bb. 1.

See also AFRICA, *Colonisation* and *West* : AFRICAN
LANGUAGES : FRANCE, *Colonies :* MISSIONS.

CONGREGATIONALISM. BRADFORD (A.
H.) The Pilgrim in old England. Independent
Churches in England. pp. 344. *Lond.* 1893. 8°.
　　　　　　　　　　　　4136. aa. 38.

DUKES (E. J.) Principles and polity of Congregational Churches. pp. 48. *Lond.* 1893. 8°.
　　　　　　　　　　　　4136. aaa. 42.

DYER (A. S.) Sketches of English Nonconformity.
pp. 112. *Lond.* 1893. 8°.　　　4109. aa. 42.

GOODRICH (A.) Primer of Congregationalism.
pp. 139. *Lond.* 1894. 16°.　　　4136. a. 41.

INTERNATIONAL CONGREGATIONAL COUNCIL. Record of proceedings, 1891. pp. 418.
Lond. 1891. 8°.　　　　4136. h. 1.

—— International Congregational Council. A
lady's letters. pp. 16. *Lond.* 1891. 8°. 4136. e.

LEPINE (J. F.) Outline of Church Fellowship
and Service. *Lond.* 1893. 16°.　　Pam. 16.

MANN (W. H.) Congregationalism in its Relations. pp. 27. *Natal,* 1885· 8°.　　Pam. 16.

PIERCE (W.) and HORNE (C. S.) Primer of Church
Fellowship. pp. 126. *Lond.* 1893. 8°. 4136. a. 39.

REANEY (G. S.) Why I left Congregationalism.
pp. 133. *Lond.* 1890. 8°.　　　4139. ee. 3.

SUMMERS (W. H.) The Influence of Independency
on the National Life. pp. 16. *Lond.* 1894. 8°.
　　　　　　　　　　　　Pam. 16.

THOMAS (H. A.) Why are we Christians ? Why
are we Congregationalists ? pp. 66.
Lond. 1891. 8°.　　　　4136. aa. 34.

DIXON (R. W.) A Century of village Nonconformity at Bluntisham, Hunts. pp. 311.
Lond. 1887. 8°.　　　　4715. bb. 32.

CUMBERLAND, Maine. *Baptist Association.* Centennial of the Cumberland Association of Congregational Ministers. pp. 75. *Portland,* 1888. 8°.
　　　　　　　　　　　　Pam. 92.

P.P. *Manchester.* Lancashire Congregational
Calendar. *Manch.* 1887, etc. 8°. P.P. 2485. kf.

THOMPSON (J.) Lancashire Independent College.
pp. 220. *Manch.* 1893. 8°.　　　8364. f. 23.

MANCHESTER. *Lancashire Independent College.*
Jubilee, 1893. Addresses and papers. pp. 89.
Manch. 1893. 12°.　　　　8365. c. 84.

HORNE (C. S.) Century of Christian Service.
Kensington Congregational Church. pp. 160.
Lond. 1893. 8°.　　　　4715. df. 5.

JONES (W. H.) History of the Congregational
Churches of Wolverhampton. pp. 178.
Lond. 1894. 8°.　　　　4715. bb. 31.

WALKER (W.) History of Congregational Churches
in the U.S. pp. 451. 1894. 8°. American
Church History Series. Vol. 3.　　4744. g.

See also ENGLAND, *Nonconformists.*

CONIC SECTIONS. Besant (W. H.) Conic Sections. pp. 286. *Lond.* 1895. 8°.
8535. de. 17.

Gundelfinger (S.) Vorlesungen aus der analytischen Geometrie der Kegelschnitte. pp. 434. *Leipz.* 1895. 8535. i. 10.

Macaulay (F. S.) Geometrical Conics. pp. 260. *Camb.* 1895. 8°. 8531. b. 51.

Mac Clelland (W. J.) Treatise on the Geometry of the Circle and some extensions to conic sections. pp. 299. *Lond.* 1891. 8°. 8535. b. 40.

Richter (O.) Über die Systeme derjenigen Kegelschnitte die eine bicirculare Curve vierter Ordnung viermal berühren. pp. 111. *Leipz.* 1890. 8°. 8535. f. 36.

Salmon (G.) Analytische Geometrie der Kegelschnitte. 2 Tle. *Leipz.* 1887, 88. 8°.
8535. i. 5.

Smith (C.) Geometrical Conics. pp. 255. *Lond.* 1894, 8°. 8534. df. 8.

Taylor (C.) Elementary geometry of Conics. 2 pt. *Camb.* 1889, 90. 8°. 8535. b. 31.

Thomae (J.) Die Kegelschnitte in rein projectiver Behandlung. pp. 181. *Halle,* 1894, 8°.
8535. dd. 21.

Weyer (G. D. E.) Ueber die parabolische Spirale. pp. 36. *Kiel,* 1894. 8°. Pam. 38.
See also Mathematics.

CONIFERAE. *See* Forestry.

CONJURING. *See* Legerdemain.

CONNAUGHT. Barnaby (*Sir* N.) Christmas 1892 in Connaught. pp. 35. *Lond.* 1893. 8°. 8146. cc. 5. (15.)
See also Ireland.

CONNECTICUT, State. Connecticut. Public Records of Connecticut. *Hartford,* 1894, *etc.* 8°. 9605. ff.

—— Register and manual of Connecticut. *Hartford,* 1894, *etc.* 8°. P.P. 2525. ce.

Connecticut Women. Selections from the writings of Connecticut Women. pp. 282. *Norwalk,* 1893. 8°. 12295. h. 1.

Gannett (H.) Geographic Dictionary of Connecticut. pp. 67. 1894. 8°. United States. *Geographical Survey.* Bulletin. No. 117.
1829. a. 7.

See also New England.

CONNEMARA. Balfour (*Right Hon.* A. J.) Mr. Balfour's Tours in Connemara and Donegal. pp. 99. *Dublin,* 1890. 8°. 8146. aaa. 39.
Connemara. Through Connemara in a governess cart. pp. 200. *Lond.* 1893. 8°. 10390. cc. 6.

Ward, Lock and Co. Guide to Connemara. pp. 158. *Lond.* 1891. 8°. 10390. bb. 13.

CONSCIENCE. *See* Ethics.

CONSIDERATION, Law of.
See Contract.

CONSTANCE. Bess (B.) Zur Geschichte des konstanzer Konzils. *Marburg,* 1891, *etc.* 8°.
5015. c.

Ludwig (T.) Die konstanzer Geschichtschreibung. pp. 271. *Strassb.* 1894. 8°. 9008. ee. 10.

CONSTANTINE, Algeria. Cadart (C. R.) Souvenirs de Constantine. 1838–39. pp. 385. *Paris,* 1894. 12°. 10095. aaa. 7.
See also Algeria.

CONSTANTINOPLE. Belin (F. A.) Histoire de la Latinité de Constantinople. pp. 547. *Paris,* 1894. 8°. 4534. d. 2.

Ville-Hardouin (G. de) La Conquête de Constantinople. 2 tom. *Paris,* 1891. 8°.
9073. de. 21.

CONSTANTINOPLE—*continued.*

Miyatović (C.) Constantine, the last Emperor of the Greeks. pp. 239. *Lond.* 1892. 8°.
9135. aaa. 18.

Paspates (A. G.) Πολιορκια και ἁλωσις της Κωνσταντινουπολεως ὑπο των 'Οθωμανων, 1453. pp. 255. 'Εν 'Αθηναις, 1890. 8°. 9136. dd. 9.

Carnoy (E. H.) and Nicolaïdès (J.) Folklore de Constantinople. pp. 205. 1894. 12°. Collection internationale de la tradition. Vol. 12, 13.
12430. aaa. 47.

—— Traditions populaires de Constantinople. *Paris,* 1892, *etc.* 8°. 12430. k.

Clement (C. E.) Constantinople. The city of the Sultans. pp. 309. *Boston,* 1895. 8°.
10125. c. 4.

Coufopoulos (D.) Guide to Constantinople. pp. 191. *Lond.* 1895. 8° 10125. aa. 26.

Crawford (F. M.) Constantinople. pp. 79. *Lond.* 1895. 8°. 10125. c. 5.

Elliot (F.) Diary of an idle woman in Constantinople. pp. 12. 425. *Lond.* 1893. 8°.
10125. de. 20.

Grosvenor (E. A.) Constantinople. 2 vol. *Lond.* 1895. 8°. 10125. ff. 11.

Guyot (L. V.) De Montélimar à Constantinople. pp. 306. *Paris,* 1894. 8°. 10106. de. 10.

Lethaby (W. R.) The Church of Sancta Sophia, Constantinople. pp. 307. *Lond.* 1894. 8°.
7814. g. 4.

Loti (P.) Constantinople. 1892. 4°. Les Capitales du Monde. No. 4. 10025. g.

Mordtmann (A.) Esquisse topographique de Constantinople. pp. 91. *Lille,* 1892. 4°.
10125. ff. 10.

Omont (H.) Documents sur l'imprimerie à Constantinople au xviii° siècle. pp. 29. *Paris,* 1895. 8°. Pam. 6.

Paspates (A. G.) The great palace at Constantinople. pp. 381. *Paisley,* 1893. 8°. 10125. e. 10.

Régla (P. de) Les Bas-fonds de Constantinople. pp. 400. *Paris,* 1893. 12°. 10126. aa. 26.

Rendelmann (O.) Le Tremblement de terre de Constantinople, 1894. pp. 23. *Paris,* 1894. 8°.
Pam. 27.

Spry (W. J. J.) Life on the Bosphorus. 2 pt. *Lond.* 1895. 8°. 10125. ff. 12.

Trotignon (L.) L'Orient qui s'en va. pp. 380. *Paris,* 1893. 8°. 10078. aaa. 37.

Wilson (*Sir* C. W.) Murray's Handbook for Constantinople. pp. 38. 166. *Lond.* 1893. 8°.
2364. b. 26.

See also Byzantine Empire : Turkey.

CONSTITUTIONS. Banados Espinosa (J.) Constituciones de Chile, Francia, Estados Unidos, República Argentina, Brasil, Bélgica, España, Inglaterra y Suiza. pp. 626. *Santiago,* 1889. 8°. 8008. h. 11.

Borgeaud (C.) Établissement et revision des Constitutions. pp. 423. *Paris,* 1895. 8°.
8010. ee. 5.

—— Adoption and amendment of Constitutions. pp. 353. *N.Y.* 1895. 8°. 8010. ee. 9.

Dareste de la Chavanne (F. R.) Les Constitutions modernes. 2 tom. *Paris,* 1891. 8°.
2020. g.

Hervieu (H.) Les Ministres leur rôle dans les différents états. pp. 782. *Paris,* 1893. 8°.
8051. g. 19.

Palma (L.) Le Costituzioni dei popoli liberi. 1892, *etc.* 8°. Brunialti (A.) Biblioteca di Scienze Politiche. Vol. 2. 8010. f. 4. & 1140.
See also Government, and for the constitution of each country under the country required.

CONSULS. Cadoux (G.) Les Attachés commerciaux et les Consulats. pp. 72.
Paris, 1891. 8°. Pam. 23.

Contuzzi (F. P.) La Giurisdizione consolare in Oriente. pp. 59. *Milano*, 1889. 8°. Pam. 34.

Flaischlen (G. G.) De l'Initiative consulaire en fait de tutelle et de curatelle. pp. 89.
Paris, 1891. 8°. Pam. 34.

Paulus (J.) Het consulair Recht en de consulaire Werkkring. pp. 286. 's *Gravenh.* 1890. 8°.
06955. ee. 2.

Piggott (F. T.) Exterritoriality. pp. 303.
Lond. 1892. 8°. 06955. ee. 5.

Toda y Güell (E.) Derecho consular de España. pp. 407. *Madrid*, 1889. 8°. 5385. cc. 2.
See also Diplomacy : Law, *International*.

CONSUMPTION AND TUBERCULOSIS.
Consumption.

Alabone (E. W.) The Cure of Consumption. pp. 240. *Lond.* 1894. 8°. 7616. bb. 3.

Allinson (T. R.) Consumption. pp. 20.
Lond. 1892. 8°. 7306. df. 20. (3.)

Alvaro-Alberto ( ) Les composés fluorés dans le traitement de la Tuberculose pulmonaire. pp. 87. *Paris*, 1889. 8°. Pam. 39.

Buckley (J. M.) Hereditary Consumptive's successful battle for life. pp. 99.
N.Y. 1892. 12°. 7616. a. 38.

Burnett (J. C.) Eight years' experience in the cure of Consumption by Bacillinum. pp. 308. *Lond.* 1894. 8°. 7616. a. 4.

Clark (*Sir* A.) Fibroid diseases of the Lung. pp. 199. *Lond.* 1894. 8°. 7616. h. 22.

Congreve (G. T.) On Consumption of the Lungs. pp. 72. 96. *Lond.* 1881, 87. 8°. 7616. aa. 38.

Cutter (E.) Diagnosis of Consumption by means of the microscope. pp. 17. *N.Y.* 1886. 8°.
07305. e. 27. (2.)

—— Food versus bacilli in Consumption.
pp. 22. *N.Y.* 1888. 8°. 07305. e. 27. (5.)

Dale (W.) Inherited Consumption and its remedial management. pp. 37. *Lond.* 1891. 8°.
07305. f. 5. (4.)

Daremberg (G.) Traitement de la Phtisie pulmonaire. 2 vol. *Paris*, 1892. 8°. 7616. a. 39.

Davis (N. S.) Consumption : how to prevent it and how to live with it. pp. 143.
Philadelphia, 1891. 8°. 7616. aa. 39.

Dixon (S. G.) Relationship between Tubercular Diathesis and nitrogenous metabolism. pp. 10.
Detroit, 1894. 8°. 7306. df. 25. (10.)

Durban (F. W.) How I cured myself of Consumption. pp. 8. *Lond.* 1893. 8°.
7306. e. 26. (4.)

Fenwick (W. S.) Dyspepsia of Phthisis. pp. 203.
Lond. 1894. 8°. 7616. f. 11.

Fowler (J. K.) Arrested pulmonary Tuberculosis. pp. 72. *Lond.* 1892. 8°. 7616. f. 4.

Gill (M.) Cure for Consumption. pp. 42.
Manch. 1891. 8°. 7616 aaa. 6.

Grancher (J.) Maladies de l'Appareil respiratoire. pp. 524. *Paris*, 1890. 8°. 7615. d. 3.

Gutteridge (R. S.) Consumption and its cure. pp. 64. 23. *Lond.* 1892. 8°. 7306. df. 19. (12.)

Hambleton (G. W.) The Cure of Consumption. pp. 30. *Lond.* 1889. 8°. 07305. h. 16. (3.)

Hardwicke (H. J.) Alpine climates for Consumption. pp. 65. *Lond.* 1890. 8°.
7616. a. 47.

Harris (T.) The relation of unhealthy Dwellings to the etiology of pulmonary Phthisis. pp. 16. *Manch.* 1892. 8°. 7306. df. 20. (7.)

CONSUMPTION AND TUBERCULOSIS.—*continued.*

Harris (V. D.) and Beale (E. C.) Treatment of pulmonary Consumption. pp. 483. 1895. 8°.
Lewis's Practical Series. 7482. a.

Hartnett (J. J.) Antiseptic dry-air treatment of Consumption. pp. 104. *Lond.* 1892. 8°.
7616. aaa. 9.

Hebon (G. A.) Evidences of the communicability of Consumption. pp. 163. *Lond.* 1890. 8°.
7616. h. 12.

Heryng (T.) La Curabilité de la Phtisie du larynx. pp. 191. *Paris*, 1888. 8°. 7615. f. 32.

Holbrook (M. L.) Hygienic treatment of Consumption. pp. 247. *Lond.* 1892. 8°.
7616. g. 12.

Léon-Petit (E. P.) Le Phthisique et son traitement hygiénique. pp. 303. *Paris*, 1895. 18°.
7616. e. 14.

Moeller (A.) Les sanatoria pour le traitement de la Phtisie. pp. 113. *Bruz.* 1894. 8°.
7615. dd. 2.

Mullens (G. L.) Notes on Phthisis in Australasia. pp. 14. *Sydney*, 1895. 4°. Pam. 39.

Murrell (W.) Clinical lectures on the prevention of Consumption. pp. 103. *Lond.* 1895. 8°.
7616. aaaa. 2.

Panel (G.) Des causes d'extension de la Phtisie dans la population ouvrière de Rouen et de la Seine-Inférieure. 1891. 8°. Ac. Rouen.
Société Libre d'Émulation. Bulletin, 1890–91.
Ac. 527.

Philip (R. W.) Pulmonary Tuberculosis. pp. 55.
Edinb. 1891. 8°. 7615. cc. 13.

Playter (E.) Consumption : its nature, causes and prevention. pp. 343. *Toronto*, 1895. 8°.
7616. ee. 6.

Ransome (A.) Causes and prevention of Phthisis. pp. 146. *Lond.* 1890. 8°. 7616. aaa. 2.

—— Campaign against Phthisis. pp. 8.
1892. 8°. Manchester. *Sanitary Association.*
Pamphlet Series. No. 1. 7404. g.

Reimarus ( ) Die Rettung der Lungenkranken. pp. 20. *Leipz.* 1891. 8°. 07305. h. 8. (8.)

Riffel (A.) Die Erblichkeit der Schwindsucht und tuberkulösen Prozesse. pp. 111.
Karlsruhe, 1891. 8°. 7615. f. 35.

—— Mittheilungen über die Erblichkeit der Schwindsucht. pp. 183.
Braunschweig, 1892. 8°. 7616. i. 7.

Schroetter (L.) Ueber die Lungentuberculose. pp. 28. *Wien*, 1891. 8°. Pam. 39.

Squire (J. E.) Hygienic prevention of Consumption. pp. 194. *Lond.* 1893. 8°. 7616. ee. 3.

Thorne (W. B.) Open-air treatment of Phthisis as practised at Falkenstein. pp. 31.
Lond. 1894. 8°. 07305. f. 17. (15.)

Weber (H.) Traitement de la Phtisie par l'hygiène et le climat. pp. 101. *Paris*, 1886. 8°.
7616. a. 42.

Williams (C. T.) Aero-Therapeutics ; treatment of Lung diseases by climate. pp. 187.
Lond. 1894. 8°. 7461. g. 5.
See also infra, Dr Koch's Treatment : Chest : Lungs : Waters, *etc.*

Tuberculosis.

Burlureaux (C.) La Pratique de l'antisepsie dans la Tuberculose. pp. 274.
Paris, 1892. 12°. 7460. aa. 4.

Cornet (G.) Ueber Tuberculose. pp. 206.
Leipz. 1890. 8°. 7615. d. 4.

Cozzolino (O.) La Tubercolosi sperimentale da inoculazione endermica nei conigli. pp. 72.
1895. 8°. Ac. Rome. *R. Università.* Annali d'igiene. N. S. Vol. 5. Ac. 104. b.

**CONSUMPTION AND TUBERCU-
LOSIS.**—*continued.*

CROOKE (G. F.) Post graduate lectures on the
Pathology of Tuberculosis. pp. 91.
Lond. 1891. 8°.　　　　　　7615. a. 4.

CZAPLEWSKI (E.) Die Untersuchung des Auswurfs auf Tuberkelbacillen. pp. 124.
Jena, 1891. 8°.　　　　　　7615. f. 38.

DIXON (S. G.) Relationship between Tubercular
Diathesis and nitrogenous metabolism. pp. 10.
Detroit, 1894. 8°.　　　　　　Pam. 37.

HELMRICH (V.) Die therapeutischen Wandlungen in der Behandlung der Bauchfelltuber-
culose. pp. 106. *Basel*, 1892. 8°. 7616. i. 5.

JENNER (*Sir* W.) Clinical Lectures and essays.
pp. 329. *Lond.* 1895. 8°.　　7616. h. 23.

KOEHLER (A.) De la Tuberculose oculaire.
pp. 104. *Nancy*, 1892. 4°.　7383. ddd. 1. (5.)

KRAUSE (F.) Die Tuberkulose der Knochen und
Gelenke. pp. 220. *Leipz.* 1891. 8°. 7615. f. 34.

LANNELONGUE (O. M.) Abcès froids et Tuberculose osseuse. pp. 186. *Paris*, 1881. 8°. 7615. d. 9.

—— Coxotuberculose. pp. 220. *Paris*, 1886. 8°.
　　　　　　　　　　　　　7615. d. 8.

—— Tuberculose vertébrale. *Paris*, 1888. 8°.
　　　　　　　　　　　　　7615. d. 7.

—— La Tuberculose chirurgicale. pp. 168.
1894. 8°. Encyclopédie des aide-mémoire.
　　　　　　　　　　　　　8709. g.

LEROUX (H.) La Tuberculose du premier âge.
1890. 8°. VERNEUIL (A. A.) Études sur la
tuberculose. Tom. 2.　　　　7561. k. 1.

LINDFORS (A. O.) Om Tuberculosis Peritonei.
pp. 149. *Lund*, 1889. 8°.　　7620. de. 19.

NOTES. Notes on the intensive treatment of
Tuberculosis. pp. 28. *Lond.* 1895. 8°. Pam. 39.

PHILIPPS (A.) Die Resultate der operativen Behandlung der Bauchfelltuberkulose. pp. 37.
Göttingen, 1890. 4°.　　　　Pam. 39.

PREINDLSBERGER (J.) Die Behandlung der Ge-
lenkstuberculose. pp. 258. *Wien*, 1894. 8°.
　　　　　　　　　　　　　7616. dd. 2.

REIBMAYR (A.) Die ehe Tuberculoser und ihre
Folgen. pp. 315. *Leipz.* 1894. 8°. 7616. i. 4

SEIFERT (R.) On Carbonate of Guaiacol in the
treatment of Tuberculosis. pp. 14.
Lond. 1894. 8°.　　　　　　Pam. 39.

STRAUS (I.) La Tuberculose et son bacille.
pp. 884. *Paris*, 1895. 8°.　　7615. g. 5.

TUBERCULOSIS. Tuberculosis and its treatment.
pp. 16. *Glasg.* 1891. 8°.　　07305. f. 6. (5.)

VERGARA LOPE (D.) La Anoxihemia barométrica.
pp. 95. *México*, 1893. 8°.　　7616. h. 26.

WOLFF (F.) Beiträge zur Kenntniss der Tuberkulose. pp. 124. 1891. 8°. BREHMER (H.)
Mitteilungen. Bd. 3.　　　　7615. ee. 36.

Tuberculosis among Cattle, etc.
See VETERINARY MEDICINE.

Dr. Koch's Treatment : Tuberculin.

KOCH (R.) The Cure of Consumption. pp. 32.
Lond. 1890. 8°.　　　　　　Pam. 39.

ARZT. Was kann die koch'sche Lymphe? pp. 14.
Oldenburg, 1891. 8°.　　　　7305. de 27. (6.)

BECHER (W.) R. Koch. Eine biographische
Studie. pp. 104. *Berl.* 1891. 8°. 010707. f. 5.

BIRNBAUM (M.) De geneeswijze der Tuberculose
van Professor Koch. pp. 72.
Groningen, 1890. 8°.　　　07305. h. 9. (2.)

BRIDGER (A. E.) Dr. Koch's Remedy. pp. 92.
Lond. 1891. 8°.　　　　　　7616. a. 36.

BROWNE (L.) Koch's remedy in relation specially
to Throat Consumption. pp. 114.
Lond. 1891. 8°.　　　　　　7615. cc. 12.

CONSUMPTION, etc. — Dr. Koch's
Treatment—*continued.*

BURNETT (J. C.) Five Years' Experience in the
new Cure of Consumption on a line with the
method of Koch. pp. 116. *Lond.* 1890. 8°.
　　　　　　　　　　　　　7616. a. 31.

CANDELA (N.) La Tubercolosi e la linfa di
Koch. pp. 24. *Napoli*, 1891. 8°.　Pam. 39.

CHIARI (H.) Mittheilungen über das koch'sche
Mittel aus den Medicin. 6 pt. *Berl.* 1891. 8°.
　　　　　　　　　　　　　7616. i. 3.

DAMM (A.) Nochmals gegen Koch. pp. 26.
Wiesbaden, 1890. 8°.　　　07305. h. 8. (4.)

DENISON (C.) Tuberculin and the living Cell.
pp. 24. *Lond.* 1892. 8°.　　07305. f. 14. (8.)

FELLER (H.) Koch's Heilung der Schwindsucht.
pp. 40. *Berl.* 1890. 8°.　　07305. h. 9. (4.)

—— Professor Koch's cure for Consumption.
pp. 61. *Lond.* 1890. 8°.　　7616. aaa. 3.

GATTI (F.) La cura di Koch per la tuberculosi.
pp. 12. *Milano*, 1891. 8°.　07305. h. 10. (4.)

GOETT (E.) Die koch'sche Heilung der Schwindsucht. pp. 16. *Freiburg*, 1890. 8°. 07305. h. 7. (5.)

GRÜN (E. F.) and SEVERN (W. D.) Handbook to
Dr. Koch's Treatment. pp. 58. *Lond.* 1890. 8°.
　　　　　　　　　　　　　7615. f. 29.

HOEVENER (O.) Sectionsbefunde bei Tubercu-
lösen nach koch'scher Methode behandelten.
pp. 30. *Kiel*, 1891. 8°.　　07305. k. 9. (11.)

KOCH (R.) Robert Koch's Heilmittel gegen die
Tuberculose. *Berl.* 1890, *etc.* 8°.　　7615. d.

—— Die Heilung der Schwindsucht durch Prof.
Koch. pp. 23. *Berl.* 1890. 8°. 07305. h. 10. (2.)

—— Schatten im Lichte der koch'schen Schwind-
suchts-Behandlung. pp. 38.
Leipz. 1890. 8°.　　　　　07305. f. 7. (7.)

KRONFELD (A.) R. Koch's Verfahren Tuberculose zu heilen. pp. 100. *Wien*, 1891. 8°.
　　　　　　　　　　　　　7615. f. 33.

LAHMANN (H.) Koch und die Kochianer.
pp. 95. *Stuttgart*, 1890. 8°.　07305. h. 5. (4.)

MIDDENDORP (H. W.) De waarde van Koch's
geneesmiddel tegen Tuberculose. pp. 59.
Te Groningen, 1891. 8°.　　07305. k. 10. (5.)

—— Es giebt keine wahren Tuberkelbacillen.
pp. 39. *Groningen*, 1894. 8°.　　Pam. 39.

—— Der Werth des koch'schen Heilverfahrens
gegen Tuberculose. pp. 54. *Emden*, 1891. 8°.
　　　　　　　　　　　　　07305. k. 10. (6.)

—— Le remède de Koch. pp. 32.
Paris, 1891. 8°.　　　　　07305. k. 9. (13.)

MILBROT ( ) Gegen Dr. R. Koch's Schwind-
suchtsbehandlung. pp. 22. *Berl.* 1890. 8°.
　　　　　　　　　　　　　07305. h. 9. (6.)

ODELL (W.) Scientific Aspect of Dr. Koch's
Remedy. pp. 12. *Lond.* 1891. 8°.
　　　　　　　　　　　　　07305. h. 6. (10.)

PHILIP (R. W.) On Koch's Treatment of Tuberculosis. pp. 36. *Lond.* 1891. 8°.
　　　　　　　　　　　　　07305. h. 17. (5.)

QUEIREL ( ) Rapport sur le traitement de la
tuberculose par la lymphe du Dr Koch. pp. 16.
Marseille, 1891. 8°.　　　　07305. h. 16. (8.)

SCHROETTER (L.) Ueber die Lungentuberculose
und die Mittel zu ihrer Heilung. pp. 28.
Wien, 1891. 8°.　　　　　07305. h. 18. (7.)

SCHWENK (G.) Kochs Heilmethode ein Segen
der Menschheit? pp. 28. *Leipz.* 1891. 8°.
　　　　　　　　　　　　　07305. f. 7. (9.)

SEIFFERT (R.) Kochin-Arbeiten.
Chicago, 1891, *etc.* 8°.　　　7560. i. 9.

SICK (P.) Die koch'sche Tuberkulose-Behand-
lung. pp. 73. *Stuttgart*, 1892. 8°.
　　　　　　　　　　　　　07305. h. 17. (10.)

SPENGLER (C.) Therapeutische Resultate der
Tuberculinbehandlung bei 41 Lungenkranken.
pp. 64. *Davos*, 1892. 8°.　07305. h. 17. (11.)

CONSUMPTION, etc. — Dr. Koch's Treatment.—*continued.*
WIEGER (A.) Die Heilung der Lungenschwindsucht. pp. 84. *Berl.* 1891. 8°. 07305. k. 10. (9.)

CONTAGIOUS DISEASES, *Animals.*
See VETERINARY MEDICINE.

CONTES. CAUVIN (A.) Mémoires pour servir à l'histoire de Contes. pp. 424. *Nice,* 1885. 8°. 10169. de. 19.

CONTRACT, *Law of.* ADDISON (C. G.) Treatise on the Law of Contracts. pp. 1367. *Lond.* 1892. 8°. 2018. e.

ANSON (*Sir* W. R.) Principles of the English Law of Contract. pp. 379. *Oxf.* 1895. 8°. 2320. h. 14.

BUCKLER (W. H.) Origin and history of Contract in Roman Law. pp. 228. *Lond.* 1895. 8°. 5207. aa. 7.

CUNNINGHAM (*Sir* H. S.) and SHEPHARD (H. H.) Indian Contract Act. pp. 532. *Madras,* 1891. 8°. 5319. g. 21.

FRY (*Sir* E.) Treatise on specific performance of Contracts. pp. 836. *Lond.* 1892. 8°. 2017. d.

JENKS (E.) History of the doctrine of Consideration in English law. pp. 225. *Lond.* 1892. 8°. 6375. cc. 16.

LEAKE (S. M.) Digest of principles of the Law of Contracts. pp. 1164. *Lond.* 1892. 8°. 2017. e.

—— Selections from Leake's Elements of the Law of Contracts. 2 vol. *N.Y.* 1891. 8°. 06616. k. 7.

MUḤAMMAD MAJID ALLĀH. Manual of the Law of Contract. pp. 354. *Lond.* 1895. 8°. 6376. de. 15.

POLLOCK (*Sir* F.) Principles of Contract. pp. 760. *Lond.* 1894. 8°. 6376. ee. 5.

RANKING (D. F.) The Law of Contract. pp. 15. *Lond.* 1895. 8°. 6146. bbb. 26. (14.)

VALERY (J.) Des Contrats par correspondance. pp. 461. *Paris,* 1895. 8°. 5423. f. 2.

See also LAW, *Commercial.*

CONUNDRUMS. *See* RIDDLES.

CONVERSANO, Monastery. BENEDICT, *Saint, Monastery of, at Conversano.* Chartularium del Monastero. *Montecassino,* 1892, *etc.* fol. 4785. l.

CONVEYANCING. BROUGHTON (H. M.) Reminders for Conveyancers. pp. 77. *Lond.* 1894. 8°. 6306. a. 26.

BROWN (H. H.) Elements of practical Conveyancing in Scotland. pp. 204. *Edinb.* 1891. 8°. 6306. aa. 36.

CLARK (J. W.) Students' Precedents in Conveyancing. pp. 144. *Lond.* 1893. 8°. 6306. a. 25.

CRAIGIE (J.) Scottish Law of Conveyancing. Heritable Rights. pp. 295. *Edinb.* 1891. 8°. 6583. g. 7.

—— Moveable Rights. pp. 648. *Edinb.* 1894. 8°. 6583. cc. 5.

—— Conveyancing Statutes. pp. 763. *Edinb.* 1895. 8°. 6305. f. 21.

ELPHINSTONE (*Sir* H. W.) Introduction to Conveyancing. pp. 551. *Lond.* 1894. 8°. 2230. c. 7.

GIBSON (A.) and MAC LEAN (R.) The Student's Conveyancing. pp. 624. *Lond.* 1894. 8°. 6306. h. 17.

GOVER (W. H.) Hints as to Advising on Title. pp. 181. *Lond.* 1892. 8°. 6306. f. 8.

GREENWOOD (G. W.) Manual of the practice of Conveyancing. pp. 590. *Lond.* 1891. 8°. 2230. b. 7.

HOOD (H. J.) and CHALLIS (H. W.) Conveyancing and Settled Land Acts. pp. 516. *Lond.* 1895. 8°. 2232. c. 16.

CONVEYANCING—*continued.*
INDERMAUR (J.) Epitome of leading Conveyancing Cases. pp. 172. *Lond.* 1891. 8°. 2230. d. 12.

MARCY (G. N.) Epitome of Conveyancing Statutes. pp. 439. *Lond.* 1893. 8°. 6306. aa. 41.

MURRAY (D.) Conveyancing Reform and the Land Registers Bill. pp. 16. *Glasg.* 1893. 4°. 6583. aaa. 11.

PRIDEAUX (F.) Precedents in Conveyancing. 2 vol. *Lond.* 1895. 8°. 2018. e.

SCOTT (C. E.) Abstract Drawing. pp. 60. *Lond.* 1892. 8°. 6306. aa. 37.

STROUD (F.) Conveyancer's Stamp Duties. pp. 20. *Lond.* 1892. 8°. 6193. cc. 3. (6.)

WOLSTENHOLME (E. P.) Forms and precedents for use under the Conveyancing Acts. pp. 376. *Lond.* 1891. 8°. 6306. h. 5.

—— Conveyancing Acts, 1881, 82, and 92. pp. 499. *Lond.* 1895. 8°. 6306. f. 13.

See also LAND, *Tenures* : PROPERTY.

CONWAY CASTLE. CONWAY CASTLE. History of Conway Castle. *Conway,* 1887. 8°. 10348. bbbb. 14. (5.)

COOKERY.
See also FOOD : HOUSEHOLD MANAGEMENT.

General.

ADDISON (K.) Economical Cookery for the middle classes. pp. 252. *Lond.* 1893. 8°. 07944. e. 14.

ALLEN, *afterwards* MACAIRE (M. L.) Soups, Broths, Purées. pp. 76. *Lond.* 1894. 8°. 7942. a. 67.

ALTING-MEES (H.) Complete Cookery Book, *etc.* pp. 94. *Lond.* 1892. 8°. 07945. e. 84.

ARMOUR (L.) Tested Recipes. pp. 79. *Lond.* 1893. 8°. 7942. aa. 73.

BEETON (S. O.) Every-day Cookery Book. pp. 568. *Lond.* 1890. 8°. 07945. h. 24.

BEETON (I. M.) All about Cookery. pp. 444. 1890. 8°. Beeton's "All about it" books. 12202. ee.

—— Family Cookery Book. pp. 640. *Lond.* 1893. 8°. 07945. h. 39.

BENGTSON (T.) The Gastronomist : alphabetical list of dishes, in French, English, German and Swedish. pp. 85. *Lond.* 1893. 8°. 07944. e. 15.

BETTS (M. E.) Gem Cookery Book. pp. 39. *Sleaford,* 1894. 8°. Pam. 94.

BUCKLAND (A. W.) Our Viands. Whence they come and how they are cooked. pp. 308. *Lond.* 1893. 8°. 07944. e. 1.

BULMER (M.) Home Hints for breakfast, dinner, tea and supper. pp. 107. *Lond.* 1891. 8°. 07945. e. 54.

BUTLER (W. C.) Modern Cook and confectioner. pp. 314. *Edinb.* 1894. 8°. 07944. e. 38.

CAMERON ( ) *Miss.* Soups, Stews and choice ragouts. pp. 199. *Lond.* 1890. 8°. 07945. e. 47.

CARPENTER (A. M.) Popular lessons on Cookery. pp. 247. *Lond.* 1893. 8°. 7942. de. 20.

CHATILLON PLESSIS ( ) La Vie à table. pp. 411. *Paris,* 1894. 8°. 07944. f. 7.

CHEMIN (C.) L'Art de la Cuisine. pp. 246. *Paris,* 1891. 8°. 07945. n. 22.

CHILD (T.) Delicate Dining. pp. 215. *Lond.* 1891. 8°. 07945. e. 64.

CHOLOE, *Aunt.* Methods of Cooking Poultry. pp. 89. *Lond.* 1888. 8°. 07945. e. 78.

COLOMBIÉ (A.) École de Cuisine. pp. 221. *Paris,* 1893. 8°. 7942. g. 30.

COMMON SENSE RECIPE BOOK. The Common sense Recipe Book. pp. 250. *Montreal,* 1895. 8°. 07944. g. 18.

COOKERY.—General—*continued.*

CONTOUR (A.) Le Cuisinier bourguignon. pp. 396. *Beaune,* 1891. 8°. 7942. h. 28.

COOKERY. Cheap Cookery for the artisan. pp. 44. *Lond.* 1892. 8°. 7942. e. 41.

DAVIES (H.) Handbook of plain Cookery. pp. 105. *Lond.* 1892. 8°. 7942. f. 34.

—— Simple Cookery. pp. 80. *Lond.* 1893. 8°. Pam. 94.

DE SALIS (H. A.) Tempting Dishes for small incomes. pp. 88. *Lond.* 1890. 8°. 07945. e. 36.

—— Wrinkles and Notions for every household. pp. 139. *Lond.* 1892. 8°. 7944. d. 14.

—— National Viands à la mode. pp. 92. *Lond.* 1895. 8°. 7945. b. 58.

—— Savouries à la mode. pp. 78. *Lond.* 1890. 8°. 7942. f. 36.

DISHES. 100 Cheap Dishes. pp. 56. *Ipswich,* 1891. 8°. 7942. a. 65. (7.)

—— More tasty Dishes. pp. 156. *Lond.* 1892. 8°. 07945. e. 80.

DUCHARDON (L.) La Cuisine. pp. 410. *Paris,* 1894. 12°. 07944. ee. 11.

DUCKITT (H. J.) Hilda's "Where is it?" of recipes. pp. 265. *Lond.* 1891. 8°. 07945. e. 49.

DURET (E.) Practical household Cookery. pp. 458. *Lond.* 1891. 8°. 07945. e. 50.

EARL (E.) Dinners in Miniature. pp. 141. *Lond.* 1892. 8°. 07945. h. 34.

EDE (W. M.) Cheap Food and cheap Cooking. pp. 20. *Lond.* 1884. 8°. Pam. 94.

FARDELL (M. R.) Easy and economical Cookery. pp. 106. *Lond.* 1892. 8°. 7942. de. 14.

FARE. Our Daily Fare and how to provide it. pp. 140. *Lond.* 1893. 8°. 07944. e. 21.

FERGUSON (J. R.) Chambers's School Cookery. pp. 32. *Lond.* 1892. 8°. Pam. 94.

FILIPPINI (A.) The Delmonico Cook Book. pp. 505. *Lond.* 1890. 8°. 07945. f. 23.

FOODS. Tinned Foods and how to use them. pp. 275. *Lond.* 1893. 8°. 07944. e. 10.

G., E. F. Elegant Dishes and rare receipts. pp. 167. *Lond.* 1894. 8°. 7942. de. 26.

GARRETT (T. F.) Encyclopædia of practical Cookery. 2 vol. *Lond.* 1892–94. 4°. 7954. ee. 12.

GARSTIN (A. M.) Second Series of plain and high-class Cookery. pp. 63. *Lond.* 1892. 8°. 07945. cc. 17.

GIRONCI (M.) Recipes of Italian Cookery. pp. 92. *Lond.* 1892. 8°. 7944. bbb. 43.

GOTHARD (B. W.) Plain Cookery. 1891. 8°. Hughes's Domestic Economy. 07945. e. 46.

—— Bean's Cookery register. *Leeds,* 1892. fol. 1881. b. 20.

GRANDI (F.) Cuisine italienne. pp. 99. *Paris,* 1891. 12°. 07945. e. 63.

"GRID." Real Cookery. pp. 86. *Lond.* 1893. 16°. 7942. de. 17.

GRIGGS (A. M.) Chambers's Cookery for young housewives. pp. 160. *Lond.* 1890. 8°. 07945. e. 41.

HALL ( ) Practical Cookery Book. pp. 59. *Edinb.* 1892. 8°. 07945. e. 79.

HANDY VOLUME CULINARY SERIES. Handy Volume Culinary Series. *Lond.* 1893, *etc.* obl. 8°. 7942. de.

HARRISON (M.) Guide to Cookery. pp. 486. *Lond.* 1891. 8°. 07945. e. 67.

—— Cookery for busy lives and small incomes. pp. 112. *Lond.* 1892. 8°. 7942. de. 9.

COOKERY.—General—*continued.*

HERBERT (A. H. C. K.) Common-sense Cookery. pp. 520. *Lond.* 1894. 8°. 07944. f. 12.

—— Fifty Dinners. pp. 183. *Lond.* 1895. 8°. 07944. e. 51.

HERBERT (T.) Salads and Sandwiches. pp. 31. *Lond.* 1890. 8°. 7944. de. 40.

HERITAGE (L.) Cookery for Schools. pp. 103. *Lond.* 1891. 8°. 07945. e. 69.

—— Cassell's universal Cookery Book. *Lond.* 1895, *etc.* 8°. 7942. f. 44.

HOWARD (*Lady* C. E. C.) Everybody's Dinner Book. pp. 286. *Lond.* 1892. 8°. 7944. df. 37.

KESWICK (J. B.) Health Promoting Food, and how to cook it. pp. 116. *Hexham,* 1895. 8°. 7942. aa. 74.

LEBOUR-FAWSSETT (E.) French Cookery for ladies, pp. 480. *Lond.* 1890. 8°. 07945. e. 45.

LE BRASSEUR (G.) Hints on Cookery. From the French. pp. 180. *Lond.* 1891. 8°. 07945. e. 42.

LENO (M. A.) Western Counties Cookery manual. pp. 56. *Plymouth,* 1893. 8°. 07944. f. 6.

LOVEDAY (J.) First Course of Cookery lessons. pp. 32. *Lond.* 1893. 8°. Pam. 94.

MACDONALD (M. R.) Cookery for schoolgirls. pp. 48. *Lond.* 1893. 8°. 7942. a. 71.

MACNAUGHTAN (M.) Lessons in practical Cookery. pp. 72. *Liverp.* 1895. 8°. Pam. 94.

MARSHALL (A. B.) Mrs. Marshall's Cookery Book. pp. 468. *Lond.* 1890. 8°. 07945. h. 32.

—— Mrs. Marshall's Larger Cookery Book. pp. 656. *Lond.* 1891. 8°. 07945. n. 25.

MURO (Á.) Diccionario general de Cocina. 2 tom. *Madrid,* 1892. 8°. 7954. dd. 13.

—— Conferencias culinarias. *Madrid,* 1891, *etc.* 8°. 07944. e.

—— El Practicón. Tratado completo de Cocina. pp. 862. 110. *Madrid,* 1894. 8°. 07944. g. 16.

NELSON, DALE AND Co. Nelson's Home Comforts. pp. 124. *Lond.* 1890. 8°. 7942. a. 69.

NIAS (J. B.) Cookery of the poor. *Lond.* 1891. 8°. 7942. h. 31. (7.)

NICOL (M. E.) Three hundred and sixty-six Dinners. pp. 186. *N.Y.* 1892. 8°. 7942. de. 12.

NICOLLS, *afterwards* CLARKE (E.) Plain Cookery recipes. pp. 131. *Lond.* 1895. 8°. 07944. ee. 23. (2.)

OBBERGEN (v.) Écoles ménagères dominicales. pp. 24. *Saint-Trond,* 1890. 4°. 7945. k. 42.

PAYNE (A. G.) Cassell's Popular Cookery. pp. 360. *Lond.* 1889. 8°. 7954. aaa. 40.

PEARSON (A. T.) Hand-Book of Cookery. pp. 96. *Lond.* 1892. 8°. 7944. cc. 40.

PITCAIRN (E. H.) Good Fare for little money. pp. 183. *Lond.* 1892. 8°. 7942. e. 38.

RANHOFER (C.) The Epicurean. Treatise on the culinary art. pp. 1183. *N.Y.* 1894. 8°. 7954. f. 32.

RECIPES. Recipes for the million. pp. 212. *Lond.* 1891. 8°. 07945. h. 20.

REYNOLDS (E.) Notes of lessons in Cookery. pp. 31. *Lond.* 1895. 8°. 07944. e. 61.

RICHARDS (A. G.) Cookery. pp. 436. *Montreal,* 1895. 8°. 07944. f. 20.

ROCHFORT (L.) St. James's Cookery Book. pp. 179. *Lond.* 1894. 8°. 07944. f. 3.

RONALD (M.) Century Cook Book. pp. 587. *Lond.* 1895. 8°. 7945. f. 34.

RORER (S. T.) Philadelphia Cook Book. pp. 581. *Lond.* 1892. 8°. 7942. f. 32.

RUNDELL ( ) Domestic Cookery. pp. 159. *Lond.* 1893. 16°. 7942. de. 22.

o

COOKERY.—General—*continued.*

SALA (G. A.) The thorough Good Cook.
pp. 492. *Lond.* 1895. 8°.   07944. g. 17.

SENN (C. H.) Practical Gastronomy and culinary
dictionary. pp. 574. *Lond.* 1892. 8°.
07945. e. 77.

—— Practical Household recipes from "Lessons
in Plain Cooking." *Lond.* 1892, *etc.* 8°.
07945. f.

SHAW (B. L.) Cookery of the day. pp. 62.
Nottingham, 1894. 8°.   07944. f. 10.

SORBY (E.) Handbook of wholesome Cookery.
pp. 88. *Sheffield,* 1894. 8°.   7945. a. 52.

STODDART (L. W.) Plain Cookery recipes.
pp. 63. *Lond.* 1893. 8°.   07944. e. 18.

TENDRET (L.) 1 a table au Pays de Brillat-
Savarin. pp. 283. *Belley,* 1892. 8°.
7942. aa. 72.

THUDICUM (J. L. W.) The Spirit of Cookery.
pp. 701. *Lond.* 1895. 8°.   07944. e. 43.

WELLS (R. B. D.) The Best Food, and how to
Cook it. pp. 144. *Lond.* 1893, 8°.
07944. ee. 7.

WHITCOMBE (*Mrs.* H. P.) "Cheap and Choice."
pp. 40. *Lond.* 1891. 8°.   07944. ee. 5. (4.)

WHITE (S. J.) Cookery in the public schools.
pp. 173. *Bost.* 1890. 8°.   7944. e. 46.

YATES (L. H.) Profession of Cookery from a
French point of view. pp. 228. *Lond.* 1894. 8°.
7942. e. 48.

———————————

ALTING-MEES (H.) La Cuisine au gaz. pp. 27.
Lond. 1892. 8°.   07944. ee. 2. (7.)

SUGG (M. J.) Art of Cooking by gas. pp. 287.
Lond. 1890. 8°.   7945. e. 1.

———————————

COOKERY RECEIPTS. Curious old Cookery receipts.
pp. 90. *Lond.* 1891. 8°.   07945. m. 9.

PUILLAUME (A.) Le Repas à travers les âges.
Paris, 1891, *obl.* 4°.   1876. b. 10.

STRASBURG. *Convent of St. Nicolas-aux-Ondes.*
Küchen-Zettel eines Frauenklosters des XVI.
Jahrhunderts. pp. 50. *Strassb.* 1891. 8°.
7945. e. 34.

TIREL (G.) called TAILLEVENT. Le Viandier de
G. Tirel, 1386–1395. pp. 178.
Paris, 1892. 8°.   07945. f. 32.

Breakfasts and Luncheons.

ALLEN (M. L.) Luncheon Dishes, *etc.* pp. 94.
Lond. 1891. 8°.   07945. e. 70.

HERBERT (A. H. C. K.) Fifty Breakfasts.
pp. 156. *Lond.* 1894. 8°.   07944. e. 29.

SENN (C. H.) Recherché Side Dishes for breakfast and luncheon. pp. 214. *Lond.* 1894. 8°.
07944. e. 26.

SMITH (L. E.) Bonnes Bouches for breakfast,
etc. pp. 110. *Lond.* 1893. 8°.   07944. e. 11.

SWEET (L. G.) New England Breakfast breads.
pp. 129. *Bost.* 1891. *obl.* 8°.   7945. e. 31.

Cape and South African Cookery.
See infra: Indian.

Confectionery: Pastry.

BUTLER (W. C.) Modern Cook and confectioner.
pp. 314. *Edinb.* 1894. 8°.   07944. e. 38.

DAVIES (F.) Cakes and biscuits. pp. 128.
Lond. 1891. 8°.   7942. de. 10.

—— Pastry and confectionery. pp. 127.
Lond. 1891. 8°.   7942. de. 8.

DE SALIS (H. A.) Cakes and Confections à la
mode. pp. 61. *Lond.* 1893. 8°.   07944. e. 5.

DUBOIS (U.) La Pâtisserie d'aujourd'hui.
pp. 445. *Paris,* 1894. 8°.   7944. dd. 5.

COOKERY.—**Confectionery**—*cont.*

EPHEM. "Confectioners' Union" Diary.
Lond. 1892, *etc.* 4°.   P.P. 2505 sl.

GOMMEZ (R.) Piping and Ornamentation.
pp. 104. *Lond.* 1895. 8°.   07944. ee. 20.

HÉRISSE (É.) Manuel du Pâtissier-Confiseur
décorateur. pp. 659. *Paris,* 1894. 8°.
07944. k. 2.

—— The Art of Pastry making. pp. 151.
Lond. 1893. 8°.   07944. e. 2.

LACAM (P.) Le Mémorial de la Patisserie.
pp. 495. *Vincennes,* 1890. 8°.   07945. h. 21.

MARSHALL (A. B.) Fancy Ices. pp. 238.
Lond. 1894. 8°.   7942. g. 26.

PASTRY-COOK. Pastry-cook and confectioner.
pp. 40. *Lond.* 1892. 8°.   7942. g. 23. (10.)

PEDDIE (J.) Dictionary of Confectionery.
pp. 19. *Lond.* 1894. 8°.   Pam. 94.

RYTY ( ) 400 Sweet Dishes. pp. 224.
Lond. 1895. 8°.   07944. ee. 15.

SKUSE (E.) Complete Confectioner. pp. 187.
Lond. 1894. 8°.   07944. g. 1.

SWINBORNE (G. P.) Pastry-Cook and confectioner. pp. 40. *Lond.* 1894. 8°.   Pam. 94.

VINE (F. T.) Practical Pastry. pp. 212.
Lond. 1894. 8°.   07944. e. 37.

WELLS (R.) Ornamental Confectionery. pp. 96.
Lond. 1890. 8°.   07945. m. 11.

—— Modern Flour Confectioner. pp. 113.
Lond. 1891. 8°.   7944. df. 36.

—— Pastrycook and confectioner's guide.
pp. 108. *Lond.* 1892. 8°.   07945. e. 76.

—— Toffy and Sweets. pp. 67.
Manch. 1893. 8°.   07944. de. 1.

WILLY (T.) All about Piping. pp. 64.
Lond. 1891. 8°.   07945. m. 8.

See also BREAD.

Fish.

GEDDES (W. E.) Do you know how to cook Fish?
pp. 64. *Lond.* 1890. 8°.   7942. h. 31. (4.)

GROEN (A. S.) Visch-Kookboek. pp. 40.
Ijmuiden, 1893. 8°.   Pam. 94.

WEALTH. The Wealth of the Ocean. pp. 40.
Glasg. 1894. 8°.   Pam. 42.

See also infra: Vegetarian, etc.

Indian and Colonial Cookery.

HERVEY (H. A.) Anglo-Indian Cookery at home.
pp. 43. *Lond.* 1895. 8°.   07944. ee. 16.

JOHNSON (G.) Anglo-Indian and oriental cookery.
pp. 208. *Lond,* 1893. 8°.   7942. e. 42.

S., F. A. and G., G. Complete Indian Housekeeper and cook. pp. 330. *Edinb.* 1890. 8°.
07945. e. 59.

BALL (J. D.) English-Chinese Cookery Book.
pp. 149. *Hongkong,* 1890. 8°.   11099. d. 24.

S., C. Jamaica Cookery Book. pp. 124.
Kingston, 1893. 8°.   07944. f. 5.

B., A. R. "Colonial Household Guide."
pp. 223. *Capetown,* 1890. 8°.   07945. f. 27.

DIJKMAN (F. J.) Di suid-afrikaanse Koek en
Resepte Boek. pp. 183. *Paarl,* 1895. 8°.
7945. bbb. 38.

HEWITT (A. G.) Cape Cookery. pp. 88.
Cape Town, 1891. 16°.   7942. a. 57.

Invalid Cookery.

BOLAND (M. A.) Handbook of Invalid Cooking.
pp. 323. *N.Y.* 1893. 12°.   07945. h. 36.

BROWNE (P.) Diet and Cookery for common
ailments. pp. 307. *Lond.* 1894. 8°. 7404. e. 4.

CARPENTER (A.) Preparation of Food for the
sick. 1891. 8°. Hughes's Domestic Economy.
07945. e. 46.

COOKERY.—Invalid—continued.

DAVIES (M.) Weld n's Invalid Cookery.
pp. 147. *Lond.* 1894. 8°.   07944. ec. 12.

FEACHEM (M.) Food for the sick and convalescent. pp. 8. *Bristol*, 1895. 8°.   Pam. 94.

POOLE (W. H.) Cookery for the diabetic. pp. 64.
Lond. 1891. 8°.   07945. e. 51.

Menus: Decorations: Waiting, etc.

DE SALIS (H. A.) Floral Decorations. pp. 116.
Lond. 1891. 8°.   07945. e. 55.

LAKE (N.) Menus Made Easy. pp. 237.
Lond. 1894. 8°.   07944. e. 32.

VERBOOM (A.) L'Art de plier les Serviettes de
table. pp. 32. *Brux.* 1889. 8°. 7942. g. 23. (6.)

WAITING. Waiting at Table. pp. 115.
Lond. 1894. 8°.   07944. e. 48.

Military and Naval Cookery.

G. B. & I. *Army School of Cookery.* Instructions
to Military Cooks. pp. 55. *Lond.* 1888. 8°.
    Pam. 94.

—— The Messing of the Soldier. pp. 34.
Lond. 1892. 8°.   Pam. 2.

QUINLAN (A.) and MANN (N. E.) Cookery for
Seamen. pp. 75. *Liverp.* 1894. 8°. 07944. de. 5.

Vegetarian and 'Maigre' Cookery.

ALLINSON (T. R.) Wholesome Cookery; receipts
for vegetarian dishes. pp. 32. *Lond.* 1892. 8°.
    Pam. 94.

BOWDICH (E. W.) New Vegetarian Dishes.
pp. 120. *Lond.* 1892. 8°.   7942. de. 19.

COWEN (E. M.) and POWNALL (S. B.) Fast day
and vegetarian Cookery. pp. 177.
Lond. 1895. 8°.   07944. e. 44.

FORWARD (C. W.) Practical Vegetarian Recipes.
pp. 126. *Lond.* 1891. 8°.   7942. de. 11.

JOHNSON (G.) Fast-day Cookery. pp. 96.
Lond. 1893. 8°.   7942. f. 41.

MAY (*Mrs.* E.) Comprehensive Cookery, as used
in Dr. Allinson's Hygienic Establishment.
pp. 134. *Lond.* 1891. 8°.   07945. e. 52.

PAYNE (A. G.) Cassell's Vegetarian Cookery.
pp. 195. *Lond.* 1891. 8°.   07945. m. 12.

COOLGARDIE GOLDFIELD. *See* GOLD.

COONOOR. NICHOLL (T.) Hand-book to
Coonoor. pp. 22. *Madras*, 1888. *obl.* 8°.
    10058. a. 18. (1.)

CO-OPERATION. BERTRAND (L.) La Co-
opération. pp. 178. *Brux.* 1893. 8°. 08275. e. 8.

BOOKS. Two-hundred-and-fifty books for Co-
operative Libraries. pp. 18. *Manch.* 1894. 8°.
    11903. f. 33. (8.)

BUISSON (H.) Les Associations ouvrières de
production. pp. 32. *Paris*, 1894. 8°. Pam. 82.

BURDINSKI (R.) Die Produktiv-Genossenschaft
als Regenerationsmittel des Arbeiterstandes.
pp. 71. *Leipz.* 1894. 8°.   08276. i. 38.

CO-OPERATION. Competitive Co-operation. pp. 8.
Manch. 1892. 8°.   08226. f. 23. (4.)

—— Universal Co-operation. pp. 191. 1892. 8°.
Common Sense Series.   8277. a.

CRUEGER (H) Die Erwerbs- und Wirthschafts-
Genossenschaften in den einzelnen Ländern.
pp. 375. *Jena*, 1892. 8°.   08276. h. 28.

DAVIES (M. L.) Relations between Co-operation
and socialistic aspirations. pp. 8.
Manch. 1890. 8°.   8276. aa. 59. (4.)

DEANS (J.) The best Method of consolidating
and federating existing Productive Effort.
pp. 11.   08275. ec. 22. (13.)

GARNETT (F.) Co-Operative Classes. pp. 8.
Manch. 1892. 8°.   08275. ce. 22. (15.)

CO-OPERATION—continued.

G. B. & I. *Co-operative Congress.* Address by
Mr. W. Maxwell. pp. 8. *Manch.* 1890. 8°.
    08275. ce. 22. (9.)

HARRISON (W. G.) How best to consolidate the
position of Productive Societies. pp. 11.
Manch. 1892. 8°.   08275. ec. 22. (16.)

HELDT (B. H.) Instellingen op social en co-
öperatief Gebied in Belgie. pp. 144.
Leeuwarden, 1892. 8°.   8275. bbb. 55.

HOBSON (J. A.) Co-operative Labour upon the
land, and other papers. pp. 140.
Lond. 1895. 8°.   08276. ec. 5.

HOLYOAKE (G. J) Co-operative Movement to-
day. pp. 198. 1891. 8°. Social Questions of
to-day.   08276. e.

—— History of the Rochdale Pioneers. pp. 191.
Lond. 1893. 8°.   08276. e. 54.

JONES (B.) Address on Co-Operation. pp. 16.
Manch. 1889. 8°.   8276. aa. 59. (2.)

—— Co-operative Production. 2 vol.
Oxf. 1894. 8°.   2240. aa. 26.

LAMB (C. J.) Something about co-operation as
it is practised at Topolobampo, Mexico.
1890. 8°.   Pam. 82.

LONDON. *National Philanthropic Co-operative
Society.* Programme of the Society. pp. 50.
Lond. 1895. 12°.   Pam. 23.

LONG (J.) Co-operation of Producers in the sale
of farm produce. 1891. 8°. Ac. *Bath. Bath
Society, etc.* Journal. Ser. 4. Vol. 1.
    Ac. 3481/4.

MANCHESTER. *Central Co-operative Board.* Return
relating to the administration of Education
Grants in the various Co-operative Societies.
pp. 36. *Manch.* 1888. 4°.   Pam. 17.

—— Outlines of lessons on Co-operative Book-
keeping and auditing. pp. 36.
Manch. 1889. 4°.   Pam. 38.

MANN (T.) Duties of Co operators in regard to
the hours of labour. pp. 11. *Manch.* 1892. 8°.
    08275. ec. 22. (17.)

MASKERY (A.) How to utilise the increasing
surplus capital of the Movement. pp. 7.
Manch. 1891. 8°.   08275. ec. 22. (11.)

MOTTE (A.) L'avenir des Sociétés coopératives.
pp. 40 *Brux.* 1892. 8°.   08275. ec. 20. (6)

NEW SOUTH WALES. *Commissioners for the Exposition, Chicago.* Social and Co-operative Associations in New South Wales. pp. 24.
Sydney, 1892. 8°.   7958. g. 36.

OUTLINES. Outlines of lessons on the problem of
Co-operation. pp. 36. *Manch.* 1894. 8°.
    Pam. 82.

OWEN (A. K.) Integral Co-operation; its practical
application. pp. 208. *N.Y.* 1885. 8°. 08275. e. 12.

PIZZAMIGLIO (L.) Distributing Co-operative
Societies. pp. 185. *Lond.* 1891. 8°. 08276. e. 12.

PLUNKETT (*Hon.* H. C.) Co-Operative Dairying.
pp. 8. *Lond.* 1890. 8°.   8276. aa. 59. (6.)

—— Co-operation for Ireland. pp. 13.
Manch. 1890. 8°.   8276. aa. 59. (7.)

POTTER aft. WEBB (B.) Co-operative Movement
in Great Britain. pp. 254. *Lond.* 1891. 8°.
    08276. e. 28.

—— Relationship between Co-operation and
trade unionism. pp. 16. *Manch.* 1892. 8°.
    08275. ec. 22. (18.)

—— How best to do away with the Sweating
System. pp. 16. *Manch.* 1892. 12°.
    8277. de. 30. (13.)

PRIMROSE (A. P.) *Earl of Rosebery.* Inaugural
Address at the Co-Operative Congress, 1890.
Manch. 1890. 8°.   8276. aa. 59. (9.)

CO-OPERATION—continued.

REUS (A.) Influencia de la Cooperación en la cuestión social europea. pp. 125.
Madrid, 1891. 8°.   8277. ee. 16.

THIRLAWAY (J.) Cash and Check Systems. pp. 12. *Manch.* 1890. 8°.   Pam. 82.

TRÉMEREL (G.) Des Sociétés Coopératives de consommation à l'étranger et en France. pp. 271. *Paris*, 1894. 8°.   08276. i. 24.

VAUGHAN (H.) *Cardinal.* Co-operation. pp. 7. *Manch.* 1890. 8°.   8276. aa. 59. (12.)

VILLARD (T.) Le Travail collectif en France. pp. 312. *Paris*, 1891. 8°.   08276. g. 31.

WILKINSON (H. B.) Why are Co-operative Stores exempted from Income Tax? 2 pt. *Manch.* 1895. 8°.   Pam. 23.

See also CAPITAL AND LABOUR: GUISE.

COPENHAGEN. COPENHAGEN. Frihavnen
ved Kjøbenhavn. pp. 62. *Kjøbenh.* 1890. 8°.   08227. k. 31. (5.)

—— Illustrerad vägledning för svenska lustresande i Köpenhamn. pp. 62. *Köpenhamn*, 1892. 8°.   10281. aa. 14.

ESMANN (G.) I Kjøbenhavn. pp. 205. *Kjøbenh.* 1891. 8°.   10280. c. 3.

MICHEL (A.) Copenhague. 1892. 4°. Les Capitales du Monde. No. 19.   10025. g.

RASMUSSEN (P.) Copenhagen and environs. pp. 55. *Copenhagen*, 1893. 8°.   10280. aa. 25.

RUBIN (M.) 1807–14. Studier til Københavns Historie. pp. 627. *Kjøbenh.* 1892. 8°. 9424. i. 13.

CHRISTENSEN (H.) Det k. Theater, 1852–59. *Kjøbenh.* 1890. 8°.   011795. g. 11.

Ac. *etc.* Copenhagen. *Universitas Havniensis.* Samling af de for Universitets legater gjældende Bestemmelser. pp. 679. *Kjøbenh.* 1890. 4°.   Ac. 1025/9.

COPEPODA. *See* CRUSTACEA.

COPPER. ARACENA (F. M.) La Industria
del Cobre en las provincias de Atacama y Coquimbo. pp. 372. *Valparaiso*, 1884. 8°.   10481. ff. 32.

BELL (R.) Nickel and Copper Deposits of Sudbury, Canada. *Rochester, N.Y.* 1891. 8°.   Pam. 27.

BROWN (W. L.) Manual of assaying Copper Ores. 1890. 8°. Heinemann's Scientific Handbooks.   8708. f.

FULLER (J.) Art of Coppersmithing. pp. 327. *N.Y.* 1894. 8°.   7944 dd. 4.

KING (W.) Gold and copper in Chota Nagpore. pp. 176. *Calcutta*, 1891. 8°.   7105· aa. 3.

LEGRAND (L.) Notes sur des mines de Cuivre du Roi Génil, Espagne. pp. 64. *Brux.* 1894. 8°.   7108. ee. 15.

PETERS (E. D.) Modern American methods of Copper Smelting. pp. 398. *N.Y.* 1891. 8°.   7106 cc. 21.

WEISS (P.) Le Cuivre. pp. 344. *Paris*, 1894. 12°.   07109. f. 3.

See also METALS.

COPTIC RACE, CHURCH AND LANGUAGE. AMÉLINEAU (E.) Les Actes des
Martyres de l'Église copte. pp. 313. *Paris*, 1890. 8°.   4829. ee. 5.

——Histoire du Patriarche copte Isaac. 1890. 8°. Ac. Algiers. *École Supérieure des Lettres.* Publications. No. 2.   Ac. 5350/2.

—— Géographie de l'Égypte à l'époque copte. pp. 630. *Paris*, 1893. 8°.   10002. h. 14.

BUDGE (E. A. T. W.) Saint Michael the Archangel: three Encomiums. Coptic texts, with a translation. pp. 108, 242. *Lond.* 1894. 4°.   754. f. 7.

COPTIC RACE, etc.—continued.

BUDGE (E. A. T. W.) On a Coptic Grave Shirt. pp. 12. *Westminster*, 1893. 4°. 7705. f. 52. (7.)

CRUM (W. E.) Coptic Manuscripts from the Fayyum. pp. 92. *Lond.* 1893. 4°. 7705. g. 41.

EBERS (G.) Sinnbildliches. Die koptische Kunst. pp. 61. *Leipz.* 1892. 8°.   7706. ee. 38

FORRER (R.) Die frühchristlichen Alterthümer aus Achmin. pp. 29. *Strassb.* 1893. 4°.   7709. k. 24.

HEBBELYNCK (A.) La Langue copte et sa Littérature. pp. 23. *Gand*, 1891. 8°. 12901. d. 33. (8.)

LEMM (O. v.) Koptische apokryphe Apostelacten· 1890. 8°. Ac. Saint-Petersburg. *Academia Scientiarum.* Bulletin. Nouvelle série. 1. No. 4.   Ac. 1125/44.

ROCHEMONTEIX (M. de) Œuvres diverses. pp. 463. 1894. 8°. MASPERO (G.) Bibliothèque égyptologique. Tom. 3.   7702. dd.

ROSSI (F.) Trascrizione con truduzione italiana dal Copto di due Omelie di S. Giovanni Grisostomo. 1890. 4°. Ac. Turin. *Accademia delle Scienze.* Memorie. Ser. 2. Tom. 40. Ac. 2816.

SCHMIDT (C.) Gnostische Schriften in koptischer Sprache aus dem Codex Brucianus. pp. 692. 1892. 8°. GEBHARDT (O. v.) Texte zur Geschichte der altchristlichen Literatur. Bd. 8.   3623. b.

—— De Codice Bruciano. *Lipsiae*, 1892, *etc.* 8°.   4999. c.

SCHULTE (A.) Die koptische Uebersetzung der vier grossen Propheten. pp. 90. *Münster*, 1892. 8°.   3166. ee. 50.

STEINDORFF (G.) Koptische Grammatik. 2 pt. 1894. 8°. PETERMANN (J. H.) Porta Linguarum Orientalium. Pt. 14.   12904. de.

See also EGYPT, *History and Topography.*

COPYHOLDS. *See* LAND, *Tenures, England.*

COPYRIGHT, Law of. ANSORENA (L. de)
Tratado de la propiedad intelectual en España. pp. 315. *Madrid*, 1894. 8°.   5384. aaa. 39.

BODEUX (M.) Le Droit d'Auteur. pp. 45. *Gand.* 1890. 8°.   6005. de. 4. (3.)

CHOSSON (E.) Le Propriété littéraire. Législation en France et à l'étranger. pp. 292. *Paris*, 1895. 12°.   6006. aaa. 37.

COUHIN (C.) La Propriété artistique et littéraire. *Paris*, 1894, *etc.* 8°.   5423. f.

EDMUNDS (L.) Law of Copyright in Designs. pp. 291. *Lond.* 1895. 8°..   6376. f. 21.

FREYDARF (R. v.) Autorrecht und Rechts-system. pp. 240. *Mannheim*, 1894. 8°.   6006. k. 3.

MACK (É.) De la durée du Droit d'auteur. pp. 36. *Paris*, 1893. 8°.   Pam. 34.

MAILLARD (G.) Étude sur le Projet de loi autrichien concernant le droit d'auteur. pp. 24. *Paris*, 1893. 8°.   5551. g. 20. (12.)

SPAIN. *Ministerio de Fomento.* Boletin de la propriedad intelectual. *Madrid*, 1886, *etc.* 8°.   011899. m.

CORACIIDAE. DRESSER (H. E.) Mono-
graph of the Coraciidæ. pp. 111. *Farnborough*, 1893. 4°.   7285. k. 12.

See also BIRDS.

CORALS. Ac. London. *British Museum.*
Depart. of Zoology. Catalogue of Madreporian Corals. *Lond.* 1893, *etc.* 4°.   7207. k. 11.

AGASSIZ (A.) On the Rate of growth of Corals. 1890. 8°. Ac. Cambridge. *Harvard University.* Bulletin. Vol. 20.   Ac. 1736/2.

BOETTGER (L.) Darstellung unserer Kenntnisse und Meinungen von den Korallenbauten. 1890. 8°. Ac. Halle. *Naturwissenschaftlicher Verein.* Zeitschrift. Bd. 63.   Ac. 2942.

CORALS—continued.

DANA (J. D.) Corals and Coral Islands.
pp. 440. *N.Y.* 1890. 8°.   7297. c. 15.

DARWIN (C. R.) Structure and distribution of
Coral Reefs. pp. 549. 1890. 8°. BETTANY (G. T.)
Minerva Library.   012207. h.

KENT (W. S.) The great Barrier Reef of Australia. pp. 387. *Lond.* 1893. fol. K.T.C. 9. b. 3.

REHBERG (H.) Neue und wenig bekannte Ko-
rallen. pp. 50. 1892. 4°. Ac. Hamburg.
Naturwissenschaftlicher Verein. Abhandlungen.
Bd. 12.   Ac. 2885.

CORBIE. DOUILLET (F. A.) Les Gloires de
Corbie. pp. 306. *Amiens,* 1890. 8°. 4629. b. 29.

CORDILLERAS. *See* ANDES.

CORDOVA, Argentine Republic. CUEVA
(C. de la) Un año en Córdoba. pp. 80.
Buenos Aires, 1890. 8°.   Pam. 22.

FONTAINE (G.) La Revolucion de Córdoba.
pp. 15. *Córdoba,* 1891. 8°.   9004. 99. 23. (4.)

CÁRCANO (R. J.) Universidad de Córdoba.
pp. 238. *Buenos Aires,* 1892. 12°. 8356. b. 58.

CORDOVA, Spain. CONTRERAS (R.) Estudio
descriptivo de los monumentos árabes de Granada
y Córdova. pp. 378. *Madrid,* 1885. 8°.
                                7706. b. 35.

COREA. ARNOUS (H. G.) Korea. Märchen
und Legenden. pp. 146. *Leipz.* 1893. 8°.
                                010057. f. 26.

BARBER (W. T. A.) The Land of the Morning
Calm. pp. 31. *Lond.* 1895. 16°.   Pam. 88.

CAVENDISH (A. E. J.) Korea and the sacred
White Mountain. pp. 224. *Lond.* 1894. 8°.
                                10057. d. 3.

CHAILLÉ-LONG (C.) La Corée ou Tchösen.
pp. 73. 1894. 4°. Annales du Musée Guimet.
Tom. 26.   7704. h. 21.

COURANT (M.) Note sur les diverses espéces de
monnaie qui ont été usitées en Corée. 1893. 8°.
Journal Asiatique, *etc.* Série 9. Tom. 2.
                                2098. d.

CURZON (Hon. G. N.) Problems of the Far East.
Lond. 1894, *etc.* 8°.   8023. dd. 26.

DU FIEF (J. B. A. J.) La Corée. 1894. 8°. Ac.
Brussels. *Société de Géographie.* Bulletin.
ann. 18.   Ac. 6098.

FRANCE. *Navy.* Instructions nautiques sur la
mer du Japon, comprenant la Corée. pp. 826.
Paris, 1895. 8°.   10497. b. 46.

GILMORE (G. W.) Korea from its capital.
pp. 328. *Phila.* 1892. 8°.   10057. aa. 13.

HESSE-WARTEGG (E. v.) Korea. Eine Sommer-
reise. pp. 220. *Dresd.* 1895. 4°. 010057. l. 18.

KOLOSSOWSKI (P.) Korea und die ostasiatishe
Frage. pp. 35. *Berl.* 1894. 8°.   Pam. 67.

LANDOR (A. H. S.) Corea; or, Cho-sen.
pp. 304. *Lond.* 1895. 8°.   010057. f. 32.

MILN (L. J.) Quaint Korea. pp. 306.
Lond. 1895. 8°.   010057. e. 39.

PARKER (E. H.) On Race struggles in Corea.
1890. 8°. Ac. Yokohama. *Asiatic Society.*
Transactions. Vol. 18.   Ac. 8828/6.

P.P. London. The Morning Calm. Magazine
of Bishop Corfe's Mission. *Lond.* 1890–93. 8°.
                                P.P. 951. e.

—— Seoul. The Korean Repository.
Seoul, 1892, *etc.* 8°.   P.P. 3803. bl.

POGIO (M. A.) Korea. pp. 248.
Wien, 1895. 8°.   010057. k. 12.

RAMAGET (T.) Vie de M. L. Huin, décapité pour
la foi, en Corée, 1866. pp. 364.
Langres, 1893. 8°.   4864. e. 24.

For the War of 1894-95, *see* CHINA : JAPAN.

COREAN LANGUAGE. SCOTT (J.) Eng-
lish-Corean Dictionary. pp. 345.
Corea, 1891. 8°.   12910. dd. 31.

UNDERWOOD (H. G.) Dictionary of the Korean
language. 2 vol. *Yokohama,* 1890. 8°.
                                12910. aa. 31.

—— Introduction to the Korean spoken language,
etc. pp. 425. *Yokohama,* 1890. 8°. 12910. b. 31.

CORFU. IPPAVIZ (L. C.) Kerkyra. pp. 116.
Roma, 1893. 8°.   10126. cc. 1.

SCHMIDT (B.) Korkyraeische Studien. pp. 102.
Leipz. 1890. 8°.   9004. m. 5. (10.)

MANFRONI (C.) La Marina Pontificia durante la
guerra di Corfù. 1891. 8°. Ac. Rome. *Società
di Storia Patria.* Archivio. Vol. 14. Fasc. 3.
                                Ac. 6540.

CORINTH. JEAN, *le Baron.* Études finan-
cières sur le Canal de Corinthe.
Paris, 1893, *etc.* 4°.   8235. h.

CORK. Ac., *etc.* Cork. *Historical Society.*
Journal. *Cork,* 1892, *etc.* 8°.   Ac. 8323

CORK. Guide to the City of Cork. pp. 172.
Lond. 1894. 8°.   10347. aaa. 38.

CORK TREE. *See* FORESTRY.

CORN : FLOUR. BELFORT DE LA ROQUE
(L. de) Manuel de Meunerie. pp. 426.
Paris, 1891. 8°.   07945. e. 75.

BREVANS (J. de) Le Pain et la Viande. pp. 364.
Paris, 1892. 12°.   7942. de. 23.

DAKOTA. Description of the Corn Belt of South
Dakota. pp. 34. *Yankton,* 1893. 8°.   Pam. 1.

DANSKEN (A. B.) Roller milling. 1892. 8°.
Glasgow. *Insurance and Actuarial Society.*
Transactions. Ser. 3. No. 6.   08227. e.

DUNHAM (R. W.) Structure of Wheat. ff. 26.
Lond. 1892. 8°.   7076. ee. 4.

EWING (P. A.) El Trigo i la molineria en Chile.
pp. 177. *Santiago,* 1890. 8°.   08227. de. 2.

GAROLA (C. V.) Les Céréales. pp. 815.
Paris, 1894. 8°.   7077. ee. 15.

MARINI (A.) La Sericoltura italiana. pp. 261.
Torino, 1891. 8°.   7297. g. 36.

NASH (H. F.) Hay and straw Measurer.
pp. 723. *Swindon,* 1893. 8°.   8548. cc. 7.

QUEENSLAND. *Department of Agriculture.* Wheat-
growing in Queensland. pp. 40.
Lond. 1893. 8°.   Pam. 1.

SERAND (E. H. L.) Les Avoines. pp. 224.
Paris, 1890. 8°.   07076. h. 44.

WESTMORELAND OAT BREAD. Westmoreland Oat
Bread and oat food. pp. 15.
Ravenstonedale, 1890. 8°.   07944. ee. 2. (4.)

———————

G. B. & I. *Board of Agriculture.* Report on
rust or mildew on Wheat plants. pp. 44.
Lond. 1893. 8°.   7074. l. 13. (11.)

LOBERDOS (J.) Les Maladies cryptogamiques
des Céréales. pp. 312. *Paris,* 1892. 8°.
                                07076. e. 38.

See also AGRICULTURE: BOTANY, *Economic :*
BREAD : MAIZE.

Trade : Taxation, etc.

ATHANAS'EV (G.) Le commerce des Céréales en
France au 18e siècle. pp. 576. *Paris,* 1894. 8°.
                                8227. i. 41.

CEYLON. *National Association.* Report of the
Committee on the Grain Tax. pp. 31.
Colombo, 1890. 8°.   Pam. 23.

G. B. & I. *Board of Trade.* Merchant Shipping,
Carriage of Grain Act, 1880.
Lond. 1888, *etc.* 8°.   6835. bb.

CORN.—Trade, Taxation, etc.—*continued.*

HAMILTON (A.) Equivalents of prices for Hay and straw. *Liverp.* 1894. 8°.   1882. d. 2. (106.)

INDIAN WHEAT. Indian Wheat versus American Protection. pp. 44. *Calcutta,* 1883. 8°.
8226. f. 59. (4.)

KOETTGEN (A.) Studien über Getreideverkehr in Deutschland. pp. 67. 1890. 8°. ELSTER (L.) Staatswissenschaftliche Studien. Bd. 3.
8207. h.

KOHN (D.) Der Getreideterminhandel. pp. 189. *Leipz.* 1891. 8°.   08227. ee. 40.

MONTGOMERY, JONES AND Co. Grain fluctuations in Liverpool. 1884–93. *Liverp.* 1894. fol.
1882. d. 2. (98.)

CORNELL UNIVERSITY. Ac. Ithaca.
Cornell University. Addresses at the laying of the Corner Stone of the University Library Building. pp. 32. *Ithaca,* 1889. 8°. Pam. 6.

—— Proceedings at the twenty-fifth Anniversary of the opening of Cornell University. pp. 117. *Ithaca,* 1893. 8°.   8366. g. 25.

PERKINS (F. C.) Cornell University. pp. 78. *N.Y.* 1891. obl. 8°.   8365. de. 24.

CORNWALL. Ac. London. *Society of Antiquaries.* Prehistoric Stone Monuments. Cornwall, by W. C. Lukis. pp. 31. *Lond.* 1885. fol.
7703. b. 31.

BLACK (A.) Guide to Cornwall. Edited by A. R. H. Moncrieff. pp. 186. *Lond.* 1895. 8°.
10347. bb. 40.

BORLASE (W. C.) The Age of the Saints. Early Christianity in Cornwall. pp. 208. *Truro,* 1893. 8°.   4705. e. 30.

BURROW (J. C.) 'Mongst Mines and Miners in Cornish mines. pp. 32. *Lond.* 1893. 4°.
7105. e. 21.

CORNWALL. Murray's Handbook for Cornwall. pp. 51. 181. *Lond.* 1893. 8°.   2364. a. 5.

—— History of Cornwall for children. pp. 71. *Lond.* 1893. 8°.   10351. aa. 61

—— Cornish Holiday Resorts. pp. 16. *Lond.* 1892. 8°.   Pam. 90.

—— Guide to North Cornwall. pp. 61. *Launceston,* 1889. 8°.   10352. e. 2.

COUCH (M. Q.) and (L. M. Q.) Ancient Wells of Cornwall. pp. 217. *Lond.* 1894. 8°.
12430. e. 28.

COWPER (F.) Sailing Tours. Pt. II. Cornwall. *Lond.* 1892, etc. 8°.   10360. e.

DANIELL (J. J.) Compendium of the history and geography of Cornwall. pp. 476. *Truro,* 1894. 8°.   010350. f. 3.

DICKINSON (W. H.) Climate of Cornwall. 1895. 8°. Ac. London. *Medical and Chirurgical Society.* Climates of Great Britain. Vol. 1.   7462. g.

Q. The Delectable Duchy. pp. 343. *Lond.* 1893. 8°.   012357. h. 50.

TREGELLAS (W. H.) Tourists' Guide to Cornwall. pp. 156. *Lond.* 1895. 8°. 10352. a. 55.

WARD (C. S.) and BADDELEY (M. J. B.) South Devon and South Cornwall. pp. 225. 1892. 8°. Thorough Guide Series.   10347. aa.

See also MINERALOGY AND MINES.

CORONATIONS. WORDSWORTH (C.) Manner of the Coronation, 1603, 1625 and 1633. 1892. 8°. Ac. London. *Henry Bradshaw Society.* Publications. Vol. 2.   Ac. 9929/2.

CORONERS: INQUESTS. BINET (C.) Histoire de l'Examen médico-judiciaire des Cadavres en France. pp. 116. *Lyon,* 1893. 8°.
6395. f. 30.

G. B. & I. *Statutes.* Notes of English and Welsh Acts containing the word "Coroner." pp. 33. *Lond.* 1894. fol.   6191. k. 1.

CORONERS—*continued.*

GROSS (C.) History of the Office of Coroner. pp. 16. *N.Y.* 1892. 8°.   6146. d. 22. (4.)

HEKTOEN (L.) Technique of post-mortem Examination. pp. 172. *Chicago,* 1894. 8°.
07482. ee. 14.

HERBERT (T. A.) Law relating to the payment of Coroners. pp. 78. *Lond.* 1891. 8°.
6281. b. 51.

LOWNDES (F. W.) Reasons why the Office of Coroner should be held by a member of the Medical Profession. pp. 23. *Lond.* 1895. 8°.
Pam. 32.

PELISSIER (L. E.) Code des Huissiers et Coroners. pp. 113. *Montréal,* 1891. 8°.   6606. a. 7.

TAYLOR (S.) Digest of the law relating to the office of Coroner. pp. 130. *Lond.* 1893. 8°.
6281. aa. 37.

CORPORATIONS. *See* COMPANIES : GUILDS : TOWNS.

CORPULENCY. DUTTON (T.) Indigestion and Corpulency. pp. 220. *Lond.* 1893. 8°.
7616. aaa. 10.

EBSTEIN (W.) Corpulence and its treatment. pp. 89. *Lond.* 1890. 8°.   7404. d. 6.

CORRÈZE, Department. CORRÈZE. Inventaire-sommaire des Archives antérieures à 1790. 1890, etc. 4°. Collection des Inventaires-Sommaires.   1814. b., etc.

FAGE (R.) 1791–1801. Le Diocèse de la Corrèze pendant la Révolution. pp. 112. *Tulle,* 1889. 8°.   4629. a. 36.

SEILHAC (V. de) Histoire de la Corrèze sous le Directoire, le Consulat, l'Empire et la Restauration. pp. 496. 145. *Tulle,* 1888. 8°. 9226. k. 14.

See also LIMOUSIN.

CORRUPT AND ILLEGAL PRACTICES PREVENTION ACT. *See* ELECTIONS.

CORSICA.

History, etc.

COLONNA DE CESARE ROCCA ( ) Histoire de la Corse. pp. 208. *Paris,* 1890. 8°. 9150. aa. 6.

DONAVER (F.) Colombo e la Corsica, pp. 5. 1889. 8°.   10630. d. 46. (7.)

MORATI (A. de) La Corse. Cosme Ier de Médicis et Philippe II. pp. 160. 1886. 8°. Ac. Bastia. *Société des Sciences.* Bulletin.   Ac. 2861/12.

OGLIASTRO (C. d') Chant de guerre corse. pp. 224. *Marseille,* 1894. 8°. 010663. g. 32.

MARIOTTI (A.) Mémoires sur les campagnes de guerre en Corse, 1731 et 1768–69. 1889. 8°. Ac. Bastia. *Société des Sciences.* Bulletin. An. 9.
Ac. 2861.

VARNHAGEN VON ENSE (C. A. L. P.) Théodore Ier, roi de Corse. pp. 75. 1894. 8°. Ac. Bastia. *Société des Sciences.* Bulletin. An. 14.
Ac. 2861/29.

LETTERON (L.) Pièces pour servir à l'histoire de la Corse 1737–39. pp. 548. 1893. 8°. Ac. Bastia. *Société des Sciences.* Bulletin. An. 13.
Ac. 2861/27.

BARTOLI ( ) Histoire de P. Paoli. pp. 378. *Bastia,* 1889. 8°.   10629. a. 40.

LENCISA (F.) P. Paoli e la Guerra d'indipendenza della Corsica. Sunto storico, etc. pp. 100. *Milano,* 1890. 8°.   9166. dd. 10.

ELLIOT (G.) *Earl of Minto.* Correspondance de Sir G. Elliot avec le Gouvernement anglais. 1892, etc. 8°. Ac. Bastia. *Société des Sciences.* Bulletin. An. 12, etc.   Ac. 2861.

JOLLIVET (M.) La Révolution en Corse. pp. 224. *Paris,* 1892. 8°.   9226. k. 17.

CORSICA.—History—continued.

LETTERON (L.) Pièces pour servir à l'histoire de la Corse pendant la Révolution. 1891, etc. 8°. Ac. Bastia. *Société des Sciences.* Bulletin. An. 10.   Ac. 2861/24.

—— Pièces pour servir à l'histoire de la Corse 1790–91. pp. 338. 1894. 8°. Ac. Bastia. *Société des Sciences.* Bulletin. An. 14.   Ac. 2861/31.

ARDOUIN-DUMAZET (V. E.) L'Armée navale en 1893. La défense de la Corse. pp. 440. *Paris,* 1894. 8°.   8806. b. 44.

COLONNA DE CESARI ROCCA ( ) Armorial corse. pp. 64. *Paris,* 1892. 8°.   9903. bb. 17.

BESSIÈRES (X.) Le recrutement du Clergé en Corse. pp. 50. *Bar-le-Duc,* 1892. 8°.   3900. g. 12. (8.)

Topography.

ANDREI (A.) À travers la Corse. pp. 330. *Paris,* 1893. 8°.   10130. bb. 29.

BARRY (J. W.) Studies in Corsica. pp. 302. *Lond.* 1893. 8°.   10131. ee. 6.

BERGERAT (É.) La Chasse au mouflon. pp. 348. *Paris,* 1893. 12°.   10136. ee. 1.

—— A Wild Sheep Chase. pp. 315. *Lond.* 1894. 4°.   010171. c. 20.

BLACK (C. B.) Itinerary through Corsica. pp. 56. *Lond.* 1892. 8°.   10168. a. 44.

BONAPARTE (R. N.) *Prince.* Une Excursion en Corse. pp. 273. *Paris,* 1891. 4°.   10173. f. 3.

GIROLAMI-CORTONA (F.) Géographie de la Corse. pp. 351. *Ajaccio,* 1893. 8°.   010171. f. 41.

RICHARDSON (R.) Corsica: notes on a recent visit. pp. 34. 1894. 8°.   10171. d. 12.

VUILLIER (G.) Les Iles oubliées. pp. 6. 503. *Paris,* 1893. 4°.   K.T.C. 1. b. 11.

See also AJACCIO.

CORSTORPHINE. SELWAY (G. U.) A Mid-Lothian Village. pp. 48. *Edinb.* 1890. 4°.   10370. dd. 20.

CORTONA. PIERINI (G.) Contributo allo studio della Storia cortonese. pp. 67. *Pergola,* 1894. 8°.   10132. g. 22.

CORUÑA. FAGINAS ARCUAZ (R.) Guia-indicador de la Coruña para 1890–91. pp. 332. *La Coruña,* 1890. 8°.   10161. bbb. 23.

MARTINEZ SALAZAR (A.) Homenaje á la Coruña. pp. 65. *La Coruña,* 1891. 8°.   Pam. 8.

COS. PATON (W. R.) and HICKS (E. L.) Inscriptions of Cos. pp. 407. *Oxf.* 1891. 8°.   7706. e. 39.

COSENZA. ARNONE (N.) Il Duomo di Cosenza. pp. 13. *Siena,* 1893. 8°.   7808. bbb. 29. (6.)

COSMETICS. *See* TOILET.

COSTA RICA. MADRID. *Exposición Americana.* Catálogo de las antigüedades de Costa Rica. pp. 44. *Madrid,* 1892. 8°.   Pam. 18.

—— Etnología Centro-Americana. pp. 112. *Madrid,* 1893. 8°.   07708. g. 17.

—— Catálogo de los objetos que presenta la República. pp. 36. *Madrid,* 1892. 8°. 7959. f. 25.

FERNÁNDEZ (L.) Historia de Costa Rica, 1502–1821. pp. 640. *Madrid,* 1889. 8°. 9772. cc. 15.

MONTERO BARRANTES (F.) Elementos de historia de Costa Rica. pp. 319. *San José,* 1892. 8°.   9772. cc. 2.

COSTA-RICA. Constitución de la República. pp. 86. *San José,* 1889. 8°.   — 8180. a. 24.

BIOLLEY (P.) Costa Rica and her future. pp. 96. *Wash.* 1889. 8°.   10481. e. 30.

—— Costa Rica et son avenir. pp. 127. *Paris,* 1889. 8°.   10481. dc. 2.

COSTA RICA—continued.

CALVO (J. B.) The Republic of Costa Rica. pp. 292. *Chicago,* 1890. 8°.   10481. c. 25.

MONTERO BARRANTES (F.) Geografía de Costa Rica. pp. 350. *Barcel.* 1892. 8°. 10481. dd. 22.

COSTA RICA. Commercial Directory of Costa Rica. pp. 44. 1891. 8°. U.S. *Bureau of American Republics.* Bulletin. No. 28.   08225. k. 1.

—— Import Duties of Costa Rica. pp. 33. 1891. 8°. U.S. *Bureau of American Republics.* Bulletin. No. 11.   08225. k. 1.

See also AMERICA, *South and Central:* AMERICAN DIALECTS, *Spanish.*

COSTUME, General. CHILD (T.) Wimples and Crisping-pins. pp. 209. *Lond.* 1895. 8°.   7743. c. 25.

COCHERIS (P. W.) Les Parures primitives. pp. 266. *Paris,* 1894. 4°.   7743. g. 19.

HOTTENROTH (F.) Trachten der Völker alter u. neuer Zeit. 2 Bde. *Stuttgart,* 1884, 91. 8°.   7743. g. 1.

LEOTY (E.) Le Corset à travers les âges. pp. 110. *Paris,* 1893. 4°.   7743. cc. 8.

KLEINPAUL (R.) Das Mittelalter. Bilder aus dem Treiben aller Stände in Europa. *Leipz.* 1893, etc. 8°.   7709. h.

MASNER (C.) Die Costum-Ausstellung im k. k. oesterreichischen Museum 1891. *Wien,* 1892, etc. obl. fol.   356.

UZANNE (O.) Les Ornements de la Femme. L'éventail, l'ombrelle, le gant, le manchon. pp. 270. *Paris,* 1892. 8°.   7742. bb. 30.

VILLERMONT (M. de) Histoire de la Coiffure. pp. 822. *Brux.* 1891. 8°.   7742. ee. 13.

See also DRESS: FANS: TAILORING: TOILET.

Ecclesiastical.

DUCKETT (*Sir* G. F.) Notices on monastic and ecclesiastical Costume. pp. 24. 1891. 8°.   Pam. 25.

Military.

VALLET (L.) À travers l'Europe. Croquis de cavalerie. pp. 300. *Paris,* 1893. 4°.   8825. h. 28.

See also under the sub-heading *Army* of each country.

National Costume.

Austria. See infra: Hungary.

Denmark.

BERGSÖE (V.) Danske Nationaldragter. pp. 29. *Kjöbenh.* 1890. fol.   1790. a. 5.

France.

MONTAILLÉ ( ) Le Costume féminin depuis l'époque gauloise jusqu'à nos jours. *Paris,* 1894, etc. 4°.   7742. b.

RENAN (A.) Le Costume en France. pp. 274. *Paris,* 1890. 8°.   2261. c.

ROBIDA (A.) Mesdames nos aïeules. pp. 254. *Paris,* 1891. 8°.   7742. bb. 28.

—— "Yester-Year," ten centuries of toilette. pp. 264. *Lond.* 1892. 8°.   7742. bbb. 2.

BOUCHOT (H.) Le Luxe français. L'Empire. pp. 214. *Paris,* 1892. 8°.   K.T.C. 6. b. 13.

—— La Restauration. pp. 324. *Paris,* 1893. 4°.   K.T.C. 1. b. 14.

UZANNE (O.) La Française du siècle. pp. 246. *Paris,* 1892. 8°.   7742. dc. 27.

GRAND-CARTERET (J.) XIXᵉ. siècle en France. pp. 774. *Paris,* 1893. 8°.   K.T.C. 11. b. 12.

Germany.

HOTTENROTH (F.) Handbuch der deutschen Tracht. *Stut'gart,* 1893, etc. 8°.   7743. cc.

COSTUME.—National—*continued.*

Great Britain and Ireland.

G. B. & I. *Royal Household.* Uniforms to be worn by the Queen's Household. *Lond.* 1890. fol.
1860. b. 6.

HOLDING (T. H.) Uniforms of British Army, Navy and Court. pp. 81. *Lond.* 1894. *obl.* fol.
7743. cc. 9.

SCOTCH CLANS. The Scottish Clans and their tartans. *Edinb.* 1892. 16°.　　7743. aa. 19.

STUART (J. S. S.) *pseud.* and (C. E.) *pseud.* Costume of the Clans. pp. 171. *Edinb.* 1892. fol.
Tab. 612. a.

Greece.

POEHLAU (J.) Quaestiones de Re Vestiaria Graecorum. pp. 85. *Wimariae,* 1884, 8°.
7743. c. 20.

EVANS (M. M.) *Lady.* Chapters on Greek Dress. pp. 84. *Lond.* 1893. 8°.　　7705. aaa. 42.

Hungary.

MIKSZÁTH (K.) Scènes hongroises. pp. 99. *Paris,* 1890. 4°.　　1876. f. 16.

Indies, Dutch.

NETHERLANDS. *Colonies.* Tentoonstelling van Kleederdrachten in Nederlandsch Indië. pp. 32. *Leiden,* 1894. 8°.　　7742. bb. 42.

Scotland. See supra: Great Britain and Ireland.

Sicily.

LANZA DI SCALEA (P.) Donne e gioielli in Sicilia nel medio evo e nel rinascimento. pp. 350. *Palermo,* 1892. 4°.　　7742. aa. 15.

Spain.

Ac. Barcelona. *Asociación Arqueológica.* PUIGGARÍ (J.) Estudios de Indumentaria española. pp. 380. *Barcel.* 1890. 8°.　　Ac. 5245.

SPAIN. España. Sus monumentos y artes. *Barcel.* 1884, *etc.* 8°.　　2060. c.d.

CÔTE D'OR. Ac. Dijon. *Commission des Antiquités de la Côte-d'Or.* Catalogue du Musée de la Commission. pp. 389. *Dijon,* 1894. 4°.
7707. h. 21.

GARNIER (N.) La Côte-d'Or. pp. 352. *Moulins,* 1893. 8°.　　10169. f. 3.

See also BURGUNDY: DIJON.

CÔTES-DU-NORD. RIGAUD (J.) Géographie des Côtes-du-Nord. pp. 509. *Saint-Brieuc,* 1890. 8°.　　10174. bb. 19.

See also BRITTANY.

COTTON.

Growth : Spinning, etc.

BLANC (É.) La Culture du coton en Asie et en Algérie. 1895. 8°. Ac. Paris. *Société d'Agriculture.* Mémoires, *etc.* 136.　　Ac. 3408.

BROOKS (C. P.) Cotton Manufacturing. pp. 176. *Blackburn,* 1892. 8°.　　7942. e. 44.

BRYERS (T.) Student's assistant to Cotton Spinning. pp. 101. *Manch.* 1894. 8°.
7945. cc. 1.

CUNLIFFE (R.) Cotton Student's manual. pp. 69. *Manch.* 1892. 8°.　　8767. b. 47.

DELESSARD (E.) La Filature du Coton par les machines modernes. pp. 592. *Paris,* 1893. 8°.
7942. dd. 11.

—— Diagrams. *Paris,* 1893. fol. 7944. i. 11.

DOBSON (B. A.) Humidity in Cotton spinning. pp. 49. *Bolton,* 1894. 8°.　　7913. d. 10.

LISTER (J.) Cotton Manufacture. pp. 222. *Lond.* 1894. 8°.　　07945. h. 43.

MARSDEN (R.) Cotton Weaving. pp. 533. 1895. 8°. WOOD (*Sir* H. T.) Technological Handbooks.　　2266. a. 41

COTTON.—Growth, etc.—*continued.*

MONIE (H.) The Cotton Fibre. pp. 166. *Manch.* 1890. 8°.　　7074. d. 21.

MORTIMER (J.) Cotton : from field to factory. pp. 122. *Manch.* 1894. 8°.　　7077. ee. 13.

—— Cotton Spinning. pp. 134. *Manch.* 1895. 8°.　　8768. c. 36.

NASMITH (J.) Modern Cotton Spinning machinery. pp. 322. *Manch.* 1890. 4°.　　8767. l. 17.

—— Students' Cotton Spinning. pp. 510. *Manch.* 1893. 8°.　　07944. e. 17.

—— Recent Cotton Mill construction. pp. 284. *Manch.* 1894. 8°.　　8767. g. 19.

NUEBLING (E.) Ulms Baumwollweberei im Mittelalter. pp. 207. 1890. 8°. SCHMOLLER (G.) Staats- und socialwissenschaftliche Forschungen. Bd. 9.　　8205. dd.

SCHULZE-GAEVERNITZ (G. v.) Der Grossbetrieb ein wirthschaftlicher und socialer Fortschritt. pp. 281. *Leipz.* 1892. 8°.　　08276. h. 35.

TAYLOR (J. T.) Cotton Weaving and designing. pp. 293. *Lond.* 1893. 8°.　　7742. b. 17.

WALMSLEY (H. E.) Cotton Spinning and weaving. pp. 402. *Manch.* 1893. 8°. 07945. f. 33.

Trade, Prices, etc.

AMERICAN COTTON CROP MOVEMENTS. American Cotton Crop Movements. pp. 12. *Liverpool,* 1892. 8°.　　Pam. 1.

CRISIS. The Crisis in the Cotton Trade. pp. 28. *Liverpool,* 1892. 8°.　　08227. g. 47. (6.)

GORST (H. C.) American Cotton Crop pointer. 1893. 16°.　　1882. d. 2. (27.)

—— American Cotton Price indicator. *Liverpool,* 1894. fol.　　1882. d. 2. (82.)

HALLETT (H. S.) Development of our Eastern Markets for British Cotton manufacturers. pp. 64. *Manch.* 1890. 8°.　　Pam. 23.

LIVERPOOL. *Cotton Association.* Calculation Tables, showing value of American cotton, at 472 lbs. per bale. *Liverpool,* 1892. 8°.
8548. df. 24.

SCHULZE-GAEVERNITZ (G. v.) The Cotton Trade in England and on the Continent. pp. 214. *Lond.* 1895. 8°.　　08229. df. 34.

WILLIAMS (W. D.) Calculation Tables showing the value of cotton at 448 lbs. per bale. *Lond.* 1890. 8°.　　Pam. 23.

See also TEXTILE FABRICS.

COUNCILS AND SYNODS. BRIGHT (W.) Canons of the first four General Councils. pp. 248. *Oxford,* 1892. 8°.　　2206. aa. 2.

LANDON (E. H.) Manual of Councils of the Church. 2 vol. 1893. 8°. The Westminster Library.　　3605. m.

GAVANT (B.) Praxis Synodi Diœcesanæ celebrandæ. pp. 68. *Lond.* 1892. 8°. 5061. aaa. 10.

ORTOLI (J. B. F.) Les Conciles et Synodes. pp. 142. 1890. 18°. BLÉMONT (E.) Collection de la Tradition. Vol. 5.　　12430. aaa. 47.

See also CHURCH HISTORY: ANCYRA: CONSTANCE: EPHESUS: VATICAN COUNCIL.

COUNTER-IRRITATION. GILLIES (H. C.) Theory and practice of Counter-Irritation. pp. 236. *Lond.* 1895. 8°.　　7461. g. 6.

COUNTERPOINT. *See* MUSIC, General.

COUNTY COUNCILS. *See* LOCAL GOVERNMENT.

COUNTY COURTS. DREW (J.) Plaintiff's Handbook of County Courts procedure. *Aldershot,* 1893. 8°.　　6405. aa. 46.

COUNTY COURTS—*continued.*

IRELAND. *Civil Bill Courts.* Rules of Court made in pursuance of the County Courts, Ireland, Act, 1877. pp. 194. *Dublin,* 1892. 8°.
6503. bb. 13.

JONES (C.) Business Man's County Court guide. pp. 276. *Lond.* 1893. 8°. 6405. de. 20.

LOWE (H. N.) County Court costs. pp. 23. *Omagh,* 1892. 8°. 6190. cc. 3. (4.)

See also BANKRUPTCY : ENGLAND, *Law*

COURLAND. LIVONIA. Commentar zu dem vierten Buch des curländischen Privatrechts. *Riga,* 1889, *etc.* 8°. 5756. bbb. 21.

PANTENIUS (T. H.) Kurländische Geschichten. pp. 332. *Leipz.* 1892. 8°. 012554. e. 19.

SERAPHIM (E.) Geschichte Kurlands, *etc.* 2 Bde. *Reval,* 1895–96. 8°. 9456. de. 2.

—— Aus Kurlands herzoglicher Zeit. pp. 248. *Mitau,* 1892. 8°. 10707. f. 30.

—— Aus der kurländischen Vergangenheit. pp. 355. *Stuttgart,* 1893. 8°. 9454. c. 23.

See also BALTIC PROVINCES.

COURMAYER. TUTT (J. W.) Rambles in Alpine valleys. pp. 208. *Lond.* 1895. 8°.
10196. b. 8.

COURSING. CARTER (J.) Lightning Dog handicapper. pp. 40. *Manch.* 1894. 32°.
7912. a. 31.

COX (H.) Coursing and falconry. pp. 439. 1892. 4°. Badminton Library. 7905. f.

G. B. & I. *National Coursing Club.* Constitution and Bye-laws. *Dumfries,* 1895. 24°.
7908. de. 12.

SAUVENIÈRE (A. de) Chronique du Coursing-Club. pp. 155. *Paris,* 1891. 16°. 7912. a. 6.

See also SPORT.

COUTANCES. PIGEON (E. A.) Texte français et latin des vies des Saints du diocèse de Coutances. *Avranches,* 1892, *etc.* 8°. 4829. b.

COVENTRY. COVENTRY. Where to buy at Coventry. pp. 60. *Brighton,* 1891. 4°.
10368. k. 23.

WHITLEY (T. W.) Parliamentary representation of Coventry. *Coventry,* 1892, *etc.* 8°. 8135. i.

COWBRIDGE GRAMMAR SCHOOL.
. P.P. *Cowbridge.* The Bovian. Magazine of Cowbridge Grammar School. *Cowbridge,* 1894, *etc.* 8°. P.P. 6152. bd.

CRAB. *See* CRUSTACEA.

CRACOW. Ac. Cracow. *Uniwersytet.* Album studiosorum Universitatis. *Cracoviae,* 1887, *etc.* 8°. 010795. f.

—— Acta Rectoralia Universitatis Cracoviensis. *Cracoviae,* 1893, *etc.* 8°. 8357. i.

—— Regestrum Bursae Hungarorum Cracoviensis, 1493–1558. pp. 138. *Wien,* 1894. 8°.
8357. dd. 6.

WĘGIERSKI (W.) Chronik der evangelischen Gemeinde zu Krakau bis 1657. pp. 152. *Breslau,* 1880. 8°. 4695. e. 33.

CRAIGMILLAR. SPEEDY (T.) Guide to Craigmillar. pp. 82. *Selkirk,* 1894. 8°.
010370. f. 30.

CRAIL. BEVERIDGE (E.) Churchyard memorials of Crail. pp. 303. *Edinb.* 1893. 4°.
10369. l. 6.

CRAILSHEIM. Ac. Stuttgard. *K. topographisches Bureau.* Beschreibung des Oberamts Crailsheim. pp. 552. *Stuttgart,* 1884. 8°.
10256. cc. 9.

CRANES. *See* MACHINERY, *Lifting, etc.*

CRAON. BERTRAND DE BROUSSILLON (A.) La Maison de Craon, 1050–1480. 2 tom. *Paris,* 1893. 8°. 9906. g. 11.

CRATFIELD. CRATFIELD. Cratfield : accounts of the parish, 1490–1642. pp. 194. *Lond.* 1895. 8°. 010358. l. 42.

CRAVEN, District. *See* YORKSHIRE.

CREATION. *See* EARTH.

CRÉCY-EN-PONTHIEU. CRÉCY-EN-PONTHIEU. Crécy - en - Ponthieu. Inventaire des archives. pp. 39. 1888. 4°. Collection des inventaires, *etc.* 1814–15. b., *etc.*

CREEDS. DEVINE (A.) The Creed : exposition of Catholic doctrine according to the Creeds. pp. 434. *Lond.* 1892. 8°. 3506. ee. 9.

GUMLICH (G. A.) Christian Creeds and Confessions. pp. 136. *Lond.* 1893. 8°. 3505. dd. 39.

HEURTLEY (C. A.) History of the earlier Formularies of Faith of the Western and Eastern Churches. pp. 166. *Lond.* 1892. 8°. 2206. aa. 3.

MOZLEY (T.) The Creed, or a philosophy. pp. 303. *Lond.* 1893. 8°. 4371. df. 14.

APOSTLES' CREED. Lessons on the Creed. pp. 127. *Lond.* 1891. 8°. 4429. b. 33.

BROOK (A.) The Creed of the Christian Church. pp. 47. *Oxf.* 1891. 8°. 4371. de. 4. (10.)

CHRISTIAN CREED. Our Christian Creed. pp. 188. *Lond.* 1894. 8°. 4015. e. 3.

EYTON (R.) Apostles' Creed ; sermons. pp. 206. *Lond.* 1890. 8°. 4479. dd. 16.

HARNACK (A.) Das Apostolische Glaubensbekenntniss. pp. 44. *Berl.* 1892. 8°. Pam. 93.

BAUERFEIND (G. F. C.) Eine Antwort auf des Professor Harnack "Apostolisches Glaubensbekenntnis." pp. 28. *Gütersloh,* 1893. 8°.
3913. c. 108. (6.)

CREMER (H.) Zum Kampf um das Apostolikum. Eine Streitschrift wider D. Harnack. pp. 56. *Berl.* 1893. 8°. Pam. 93.

KATTENBUSCH (F.) Das Apostolische Symbol. *Leipz.* 1894, *etc.* 8°. 3506. g.

MASON (F. A.) Lessons on the Creed. pp. 127. *Lond.* 1891. 8°. 4429. b. 33.

RANKIN (J.) The Creed in Scotland : Exposition of the Apostles' Creed. pp. 366. *Edinb.* 1890. 8°. 3504. f. 24.

SODEN (J. J.) Sermons on the Apostles' Creed. pp. 67. *Lond.* 1891. 8°. 4479. aa. 55.

SWETE (H. B.) The Apostles' Creed. pp. 110. *Lond.* 1894. 8°. 3506. cc. 16.

THAYNE (C.) Instructions on the Creed. pp. 127. *Lond.* 1891. 8°. 3505. de. 55.

WORDSWORTH (E.) Illustrations of the Creed. pp. 333. *Lond.* 1894. 8°. 3505. df. 56.

HOWARD (G. B.) Schism between the Oriental and Western Churches : addition of the " Filioque " to the Creed. pp. 118. *Lond.* 1892. 8°.
4535. bb. 14.

NICENE CREED. The Nicene Creed catechetically explained. pp. 368. *Lond.* 1894. 8°. 3506. c. 70.

KATERJIAN (J.) De fidei Symbolo, quo Armenii utuntur, observationes. pp. 52. *Viennae,* 1893. 8°. 3506. h. 7.

INGRAM (A. F. W.) The Athanasian Creed. pp. 15. *Lond.* 1894. 8°. 4429. c. 21. (20.)

See also CHURCH HISTORY : CHRISTIANITY.

CREE INDIANS. *See* INDIAN LANGUAGES.

CREMA. BARBIERI (L.) Biblioteca storica cremasca. pp. 64. *Crema,* 1891. 8°.
10601. c. 13. (4.)

CREMATION. BRUNETTI (L.) Cremazione. pp. 43. *Padova*, 1884. 8°.   7306. cc. 21. (6.)

COGNARD (J. F.) Chez les anciens à propos de Crémation. pp. 22. *Lyon*, 1893. 8°.
                            7306. e. 23. (9.)

COPE (A. G.) Earth-burial and Cremation. pp. 173. *N.Y.* 1892. 8°.   7391. df. 14.

CRISTOFORIS (M. de) Étude sur la Crémation. pp. 202. *Milan*, 1890. 8°.   7391. df. 11.

ENGLAND. Earth to earth Burial and Cremation. pp. 13. *Lond.* 1890. 8°.   4136. a. 42. (7.)

FICHET (A.) Notice sur l'Appareil crématoire construit pour la ville de Paris. pp. 24. *Paris*, 1891. 8°.   07305. k. 9. (10.)

GOTTI (V.) La Cremazione dei cadaveri. pp. 48. *Bergamo*, 1891. 8°.   07305. f. 15. (3.)

GREIFFENRATH (F.) Die Leichenverbrennung. 1894. 8°. Frankfurter zeitgemässe Broschüren. N. F. Bd. 15.   12209. g.

HADEN (F. S.) Cremation an incentive to crime. pp. 24. *Lond.* 1892. 8°.   07305. k. 13. (8.)

HART (H.) Burning or Burial ? pp. 64. *Lond.* 1892. 8°.   7391. de. 5.

HOLDER (W.) Cremation versus Burial. pp. 44. *Hull*, 1891. 8°.   7404. cc. 13.

KRONFELD (A.) Die Leichenverbrennung. pp. 43. *Wien*, 1890. 8°.   07305. k. 14. (2.)

RICHARDSON (A.) The Law of Cremation. pp. 187. *Lond.* 1893. 8°.   6426. de. 21.

ROTELLA (G.) Cremazione o Inhumazione? pp. 182. *Spoleto*, 1891. 8°.   7404. cc. 18.

SALOMON (F. B.) Ligbrændingssagen for Højesteret. pp. 129. *Kjøbenh.* 1891. 8°.
                            5725. aaa. 10.

SALOMON (G.) La Crémation en France. pp. 50. *Paris*, 1890. 8°.   Pam. 39.

STEIN (H. A. E.) Om Ligbrænding. pp. 28. *Odense*, 1893. 8°.   Pam. 39.

THOMPSON (*Sir* H.) Modern Cremation. pp. 163. *Lond.* 1891. 8°.   7391. df. 12.

WERNICH (A.) Leichenwesen einschliesslich der Feuerbestattung. pp. 148. 1893. 8°. WEYL (T.) Handbuch der Hygiene. Bd. ii. Abth. 2.   7391. dd.

WOTHERSPOON (G.) Cremation. pp. 27. 1886. 8°. London. *Sunday Lecture Society.* Lectures. Selection 5.   4018. c.

See also BURIAL.

CREST, Drôme. ARNAUD (E.) Histoire des Protestants de Crest. pp. 102. *Paris*, 1893. 8°.
                            4629. k. 23.

CRÉ-SUR-LOIR. LA BOUILLERIE (S. de) Cré-sur-Loir. 1891. 8°. Ac. Le Mans. *Société Historique.* Revue. Tom. 29. Livr. 1.
                            Ac. 5321.

CRETE. COMPARETTI (D.) Le Leggi di Gortyna. 1894. 4°. Ac. Rome. *Accademia de' Lincei.* Monumenti. Vol. 3.   Ac. 102/15.

—— Leggi antiche della città di Gortyna in Creta. pp. 59. *Firenze*, 1885. 4°.   7704. l. 12.

EVANS (A. J.) Cretan Pictographs and Prae-Phoenician Script. pp. 146. *Lond.* 1895. 8°.
                            7704. k. 12.

SEMENOFF (A.) Antiquitates iuris publici Cretensium. pp. 129. *Petropoli*, 1893. 8°.
                            5207. b. 4.

PHILHELLÈNE. G. Flourens et l'Insurrection crétoise 1866–68. pp. 402. *Lyon*, 1893. 12°.
                            9136. bb. 17.

CICCOTTI (E.) Le Istituzioni pubbliche cretesi. 1891, *etc.* 4°. Ac. Rome. *Accademia di Conferenze.* Studi. Anno 12, 13, *etc.*   Ac. 6541.

SEEFELD (A. v.) Dem Frühling entgegen! pp. 180. *Hannover*, 1891. 8°.   10126. cc. 13.

CRETE—*continued.*

SKIAS (A. N.) Περι της Κρητικης διαλεκτου. pp. 167. ἐν Ἀθηναις, 1891. 8°. 12923. de 13.

CRETINISM. BLAKE (E. T.) Myxœdema, Cretinism and the goitres. pp. 89. *Bristol*, 1894. 8°.   7616. dd. 1.

LENDVAY (B.) Der Cretinismus in der Schütt. pp. 58. *Pressburg*, 1887. 8°. 07305. e. 27. (3.)

WILKEN. Cretinisme in den indischen Archipel. 1890. 8°. Ac. The Hague. *K. Instituut voor de Volkenkunde van Nederlandsch-Indië.* Bijdragen. Volg. 5. Deel. 5,   Ac. 7519.

See also GOITRE.

CREUSE, Department. TARDIEU (A.) Grand dictionnaire de la Haute-Marche, département de la Creuse. pp. 431. *Herment*, 1894. 4°.   9905. g. 4.

AUTORDE (F.) Creuse. Archives civiles. 1885. 4°. Collection des inventaires, *etc.*
                         1814–15. b, *etc.*

—— Archives révolutionnaires de la Creuse. 1789. pp. 36. *Guéret*, 1890. 8°. 9004. m. 7. (9.)
See also MARCHE.

CRÈVECŒUR, Nord. CRÈVECŒUR. Les lois de Crèvecœur et de Clary. pp. 75. *Paris*, 1894. 8°.   5425. b. 1.

CRÈVECŒUR-LE-GRAND, Oise. SEILLIER (A.) Crèvecœur-Le Grand. 1892, *etc.* 8°. Ac. Beauvais. *Société Académique.* Mémoires. Tom. 15.   Ac. 278/2.

CRIBBAGE. BERKELEY. Bézique and Cribbage. pp. 63. 1890. 8°. Club Series. 7908. ee.

CRAWLEY (R.) Cribbage. pp. 28. *Lond.* 1889. 16°.   7915. de. 17. (2.)
See also CARDS.

CRICKET. CHRISTIAN (E. B. V.) At the Sign of the wicket. Essays. pp. 192. 1894. 8°. Arrowsmith's Bristol Library. Vol. 59.
                            12207. g.

COLOMBO. *Colombo Cricket Club.* Rules. pp. 12. *Colombo*, 1893. 8°.   7907. df. 18. (3.)

CRICKET. How to play Cricket. pp. 24. *Manch.* 1893. 8°.   7912. df. 4. (3.)

CRICKETER. The Cricketer's guide. pp. 24. *Manch.* 1894. 8°.   7912. de. 1. (16.)

DAFT (R.) Kings of Cricket. Reminiscences. pp. 274. *Bristol*, 1893. 8°.   7912. aaa. 1.

—— Hints on Cricket. pp. 52. *Bristol*, 1893. 12°.   7915. de. 18. (7.)

DALE (B.) Some statistics of Cricket. Influence of the weather on the wicket. pp. 31. *Lond.* 1891. 8°.   7912. df. 4. (2.)

EDINBURGH. *Grange Cricket Club.* Reminiscences of the Grange Cricket Club. pp. 114. *Edinb.* 1891. 4°.   7906. e. 39.

GIBBS (J. A.) Improvement of Cricket grounds. pp. 42. *Lond.* 1895. 8°.   07905. f. 35.

GIBSON (A.) County Cricket championship. pp. 148. *Lond.* 1895. 8°.   7912. aaa. 22.

GRACE (W. G.) Cricket. pp. 512. *Bristol*, 1891. 4°.   7905. i. 14.

—— History of a hundred centuries. pp. 135. *Lond.* 1895. 8°.   07905. f. 34.

LONDON. *Marylebone Cricket Club.* Laws of Cricket. *Lond.* 1888, *etc.* 8°.   7912. aa.

MĀṆEKJĪ KĀVASJĪ PAṬEL. History of Parsee Cricket. pp. 101. *Bombay*, 1892. 8°. Pam. 83.

MANUAL. Manual of Cricket. pp. 56. *Lond.* 1892. 8°.   7908. df. 15.

MURDOCH (W. L.) Cricket. pp. 95. 1893. 8°. ALCOCK (C. W.) Oval Series of Games.
                            07905. f.

CRICKET—*continued.*

NYREN (J.) Young Cricketer's tutor. pp. 140. *Lond.* 1893. 8°.   7912. aa. 22.

PENTELOW (J. N.) England v. Australia. Story of the test matches. pp. 180. 1895. 8°. Arrowsmith's Bristol Library. Vol. 64.   12207. g.

SMALL (E. M.) The Canterbury Cricket week. pp. 151. *Canterbury,* 1891. 8°.   7912. a. 7.

STANDING (P. C) Gentlemen v. Players. History of the contest, since 1806. pp. 137. *Lond.* 1892. 8°.   7907. aa. 64.

STEEL (A. G.) Cricket. pp. 420. 1893. 8°. Badminton Library.   2264. aa.

TATE (W. J.) Old Somersetshire cricketing days. pp. 73. *Lond.* 1895. 8°.   7912. aa. 34.

WALMSLEV (E.) Cricket Celebrities of 1890. pp. 76. *Manch.* 1890. 8°.   7912. ee. 2. (4.)

WHITTAM (W.) Modern Cricket and other sports. First year. pp. 85. *Sheffield,* 1883. 16°.   7913. de. 18.

—— Second year. pp. 95. *Sheffield,* 1884. 16°.   7913. de. 13.

WILSON (A.) Comic Cricket. pp. 68. *Lond.* 1891. 8°.   012314. e. 64.

P.P. *Cape Town.* South African Cricketers' Annual. *Cape Town,* 1892, *etc.* 8°. P.P. 2579. l.

—— *Driffield.* Cricket Annual. *Driffield,* 1892, *etc.* 8°.   P.P. 2489. wcc.

—— *London.* Cricket Chat. *Lond.* 1886, *etc.* 8°.   7908. aa. 58.

—— *London.* Famous Cricketers and cricket grounds. 18 pt. *Lond.* 1895. fol. 7912. k. 2.

—— *New York.* American Cricket Annual. *N.Y.* 1890, *etc.* 8°.   P.P. 2523. fd.

—— *Taunton.* Annual glance guide for first-class Cricket. *Taunton,* 1892, *etc.* 8°. P.P. 2489. wcd.

—— *Watson's* Cricket diary. *Lond.* 1892, *etc.* 24°.   P.P. 2489. wea.

BLUES. The Blues and their Battles : scores of all matches between the Universities, 1827-93. pp. 100. *Lond.* 1894. 8°.   7912. a. 35.

EPHEM. Cambridge University Cricket Calendar. *Camb.* 1891, *etc.* 8°.   P. 2489. wcc.

CHARTERHOUSE. Record of all Cricket matches between Charterhouse and other schools, 1850-90. pp. 103. *Lond.* 1891. 8°.   7908. c. 36.

MITCHELL (R. A. H.) Eton Cricket. pp. 22. *Eton,* 1892. 8°.   7912. df. 3. (5.)

RUGBY SCHOOL. Rugby School Cricket scores. pp. 679. *Rugby,* 1894. 8°.   07905. h. 1.

MASON (C. E. S.) Winchester College Cricket matches. pp. 97. *Winchester,* 1893. 8°.   7912. aa. 23.

GALE (N. R.) Cricket Songs. pp. 67. *Lond.* 1894. 8°.   K.T.C. 15. a. 9.

SONGS. Songs of the Bat. pp. 7. *Lond.* 1892. 16°.   Pam. 58.

See also GAMES.

CRICKETTE, Game. Rules. *Lond.* 1890. 8°.   7912. ee. 1. (7.)

CRIME. AUBRY (P.) La contagion du Meurtre. pp. 308. *Paris,* 1894. 8°.   6095. e. 1.

BAER (A.) Der Verbrecher in anthropologischer Beziehung. pp. 456. *Leipz.* 1893. 8°.   6057. bbb. 8.

BAETS (M. de) L'École d'Anthropologie criminelle. pp. 56. *Gand,* 1893. 8°.   6057. a. 37.

CRIME—*continued*

BENTIVEGNI (A. v.) Anthropologische Formeln für das Verbrecherthum, *etc.* pp. 45. 1893. 8°. Ac. Germany. *Gesellschaft für Psychologische Forschung.* Schriften. Hft. 6.   Ac. 3782.

CASTELLI (A.) Del Furto notturno. pp. 45. *Torino,* 1891. 8°.   Pam. 34.

CORRE (A.) Crime et Suicide. pp. 654. *Paris,* 1891. 12°.   8425. e. 13.

—— Documents de Criminologie rétrospective. Bretagne. pp. 580. *Lyon,* 1895. 8°. 6057. e. 24.

CRIMINOLOGY SERIES. Criminology Series. *Lond.* 1895, *etc.* 8°.   6057. aaaa.

FERRI (E.) Estudios de Antropologia criminal. pp. 292. *Madrid,* 1893. 8°.   6057. a. 38.

—— Criminal Sociology. pp. 284. 1895. 8°. Criminology Series. Vol. 2.   6057. uaaa.

FLETCHER (R.) The new School of Criminal Anthropology. pp. 38. *Wash.* 1891. 8°.   6057. e. 23. (7.)

FRANCOTTE (X.) L'Anthropologie criminelle. pp. 368. *Paris,* 1891. 8°.   6057. aaa. 31.

GAROFALO (B. R.) Criminologia. pp. 561. *Torino,* 1891. 8°.   6055. df. 19.

—— La Criminologie. pp. 452. *Paris,* 1890. 8°.   6055. df. 18.

GILES (A. E.) Moral Pathology. pp. 179. *Lond.* 1895. 8°.   08276. ee. 9.

GUENTHER (R.) Über Behandlung der irren Verbrecher. pp. 132. *Leipz.* 1893. 8°.   6056. e. 25.

HAMON (A. F.) De la définition du Crime. pp. 16. *Lyon,* 1893. 8°.   6005. h. 26. (10.)

KURELLA (H.) Naturgeschichte des Verbrechers. pp. 284. *Stuttgart,* 1893. 8°.   6057. bbb. 9.

LAURENT (É.) L'Anthropologie criminelle. pp. 242. *Paris,* 1895. 8°.   6057. e. 14.

LOMBROSO (C.) Il Delitto Politico e le rivoluzioni. pp. 555. *Torino,* 1890. 8°.   7004. df. 17.

—— L'Anthropologie criminelle et ses récents progrès. pp. 185. *Paris,* 1891. 12°.   6055. aa. 12.

—— Nouvelles Recherches d'Anthropologie criminelle. pp. 180. *Paris,* 1892. 12°. 7660. aa. 37.

—— Les applications d'Anthropologie criminelle. pp. 224. *Paris,* 1892. 12°.   6057. aaa. 37.

—— Applicazioni delle psichiatria ed antropologia criminale. pp. 431. *Torino,* 1893. 8°.   6095. g. 5.

—— Les Palimpsestes des prisons. pp. 404. *Lyon,* 1894. 8°.   6056. f. 27.

MACDONALD (A.) Abnormal man. pp. 445. 1893. 8°. UNITED STATES. *Bureau of Education.* Circular. No. 195.   8308. i.

—— Criminology. pp. 416. *N.Y.* 1893. 8°.   6057. aaa. 36.

MORRISON (W. D.) Crime and its causes. pp. 236. *Lond.* 1891. 8°.   08276. e. 24.

P.P. *Pisa.* La Nuova Scienza penale. *Pisa,* 1893, *etc.* 8°.   1112.

PINSERO (N.) Nuovi studi sul problema della Responsabilità penale. pp. 130. *Palermo,* 1894. 8°.   6095. bb. 27.

PUIBARAUD (L.) Les Malfaiteurs de profession. pp. 416. *Paris,* 1893. 12°.   6056. df. 36.

RESTANO (L.) La Negazione del Libero Arbitrio e la responsabilità penale. *Catania,* 1892, *etc.* 8°.   8109. l. 14.

SAINT-AUBIN (J.) Le Criminel et l'Anthropologie criminelle. pp. 61. *Grenoble,* 1889. 8°.   6057. c. 11.

SIGHELE (S) La Coppia criminale. pp. 163. *Torino,* 1893. 8°.   7660. g. 8.

CRIME—*continued.*

STEINMETZ (S. R.) Studien zur ersten Entwicklung der Strafe. 2 Bde. *Leiden,* 1894. 8°.
6055. f. 8.

TARDE (G.) La Philosophie pénale. pp. 566. *Lyon,* 1890. 8°. 6056. f. 23.

TRAEGER (L.) Wille, Determinismus, Strafe. pp. 272. *Berl.* 1895. 8°. 6005. ee. 30.

TRUMBULL (W.) The Problem of Cain. pp. 94. 1890. 8°. 6057. bbb. 7.

WINSLOW (L. S. F.) On Eccentricity of Youth leading to Crime. pp. 54. *Lond.* 1895. 8°.
Pam. 39.

LAURENT (É.) Les Suggestions criminelles. pp. 56. *Lyon,* 1891. 8°. 6005. f. 25.

DELBŒUF (J. R. L.) Die verbrecherischen Suggestionen. 1894. 8°. P.P. *Berlin.* Zeitschrift für Hypnotismus. Jhrg. II. Heft 8.
P.P. 3237. ab.

DUMAS DAVY DE LA PAILLETERIE (A.) Celebrated Crimes. *Phila.* 1895, *etc.* 8°.
K.T.C. 32. a. 2.

SECCOMBE (T.) Lives of twelve Bad Men. pp. 373. *Lond.* 1894. 8°. 10803. g. 14.

VANDAM (A. D.) Masterpieces of Crime. pp. 300. *Lond.* 1892. 8°. 6057. aa. 37.

See also ANTHROPOMETRY: HOMICIDE: INSANITY: LAW, *Criminal:* MEDICINE, *Legal:* POLICE: PRISONS: PUNISHMENT: TOXICOLOGY.

Criminal Women and Children.
See CHILDREN: WOMEN.

Crime in Various Countries.

CABBY. Notorious Bushrangers of Tasmania. pp. 166. *Launceston,* 1891. 8°. 6057. a. 33.

HARE (F. A.) The Last of the Bushrangers. pp. 326. *Lond.* 1892. 8°. 6057. aaa. 30.

WHITT (H. A.) Tales of Crime in Australia. pp. 296. *Lond.* 1894. 8°. 6057. b. 38.

ANDRÉ (L.) La Récidive. pp. 361. *Paris,* 1892. 8°. 6056. ee. 32.

JOLY (H.) Le Combat contre le crime. pp. 435. *Paris,* 1892. 8°. 6057. aa. 36.

LAURENT (É.) Les Habitués des prisons de Paris. pp. 616. *Lyon,* 1890. 8°. 6057. c. 10.

TOMEL (G.) Le Bas du Pavé parisien. pp. 272. *Paris,* 1894. 8°. 12350. aaa. 51.

CORRE (A.) L'Ethnographie criminelle dans les colonies françaises. pp. 521. 1894. 8°. Bibliothèque des Sciences. 19. 8709. b.

GIESE (W.) Die Juden und die deutsche Kriminalstatistik. pp. 107. *Leipz.* 1893. 8°. Pam. 31.

BENT (J.) Reminiscences of forty-two years as a Police Officer. pp. 322. *Manch.* 1891. 8°.
6057. aa. 26.

GRIFFITHS (A.) Secrets of the Prison-House. 2 vol. *Lond.* 1894. 8°. 6056. e. 24.

LONDON. *Saint Giles' Mission.* A River of Mercy. Labour among the criminal classes. pp. 164. *Lond.* 1891. 8°. 4192. ee. 20.

MERRICK (G. P.) Work among the Fallen as seen in the prison cell. pp. 62. *Lond.* 1891. 8°. 8285. aa. 59.

ARTHUR (T. C.) Reminiscences of an Indian Police Official. pp. 285. *Lond.* 1894. 8°.
6057. de. 7.

HERVEY (C. R. W.) Some Records of Crime in India. 2 vol. *Lond.* 1892. 8°. 6057. bb. 32.

KNAVERY. Knavery Unmasked, the confessions of a celebrated dacoit. pp. 313. *Lond.* 1891. 8°. 012628. e. 50.

ALONGI (G.) La Camorra. pp. 237. *Torino,* 1890. 8°. 6025. e. 11.

GIL MAESTRE (M.) Los Malhechores de Madrid. pp. 367. *Gerona,* 1889. 8°. 6057. aa. 31.

BOIES (H. M.) Study of the increase of Criminals in the United States. pp. 318. *N.Y.* 1893. 8°.
8277. ee. 25.

CRIMEA. RUGARD (M.) Krim- und Kaukasus-Fahrt. pp. 240. *Breslau,* 1891. 8°.
10292. f. 5.

SOUDAK (L. de) Voyage en Crimée. pp. 276. *Paris,* 1892. 12°. 10291. aaa. 36.

CRIMEAN WAR. THOUVENEL (L.) Nicolas 1er. et Napoléon III. Préliminaires de la guerre de Crimée 1852–54. pp. 389. *Paris,* 1891. 8°.
9080. cc. 10.

ALEXANDER III., *Emperor of Russia.* Souvenirs de Sébastopol. pp. 390. *Paris,* 1894. 8°.
9078. g. 18.

ADYE (*Sir* J. M.) Recollections of a military Life. pp. 382. *Lond.* 1895. 8°. 10815. ee. 21.

BAMBERG (F.) Geschichte der orientalischen Angelegenheit, *etc.* pp. 622. 1892. 8°. ONCKEN (W.) Allg. Geschichte. Hauptabth. IV. Th. 5.
2068. (30.)

BOSQUET (P. J. F.) Lettres du Maréchal Bosquet. pp. 400. *Paris,* 1894. 8°. 010920. f. 43.

CABROL (J. F. H. B.) Le Maréchal de Saint Arnaud en Crimée. pp. 376. *Paris,* 1895. 8°.
9080. g. 10.

CAMPBELL (C. F.) Letters from Camp during the siege of Sebastopol. pp. 411. *Lond.* 1894. 8°. 9080. e. 11.

CULLET (M. O.) Un Régiment de ligne pendant la Guerre d'Orient. pp. 271. *Lyon,* 1894. 8°.
9080. g. 6.

DU CASSE (P. E. A.) La Crimée et Sébastopol, 1853–56. pp. 99. *Paris,* 1892. 8°. 9080. cc. 26.

HAMLEY (*Sir* E. B.) The War in the Crimea. pp. 312. *Lond.* 1891. 8°. 9080. dd. 14

HERBÉ (J. F. J.) Français et Russes en Crimée. pp. 442. *Paris,* 1892. 8°. 9079. f. 2.

LEBRUN (B. L. J.) Souvenirs des Guerres de Crimée et d'Italie. pp. 336. *Paris,* 1889. 18°.
9080. aaa. 28.

LOIZILLON (P. H.) Campagne de Crimée. Lettres. pp. 302. *Paris,* 1895. 8°. 9079. e. 8.

LYSONS (*Sir* D.) The Crimean War. pp. 298. *Lond.* 1895. 8°. 9080. bb. 37.

REVEL (G. di) La spedizione di Crimea. pp. 191. *Milano,* 1891. 8°. 9079. g. 15.

ROUSSET (C. F. M.) La Bataille d'Inkerman. pp. 78. *Lond.* 1892. 8°. 9080. aaa. 40.

RUSSELL (*Sir* W. H.) The great War with Russia. pp. 324. *Lond.* 1895. 8°. 9080. c. 42.

STERLING (*Sir* A. C.) Story of the Highland Brigade in the Crimea. pp. 393. *Lond.* 1895. 8°. 9078. ff. 32.

THOUMAS (C. A.) Mes Souvenirs de Crimée, 1854–56. pp. 294. *Paris,* 1892. 8°. 9080. bb. 31.

WALKER (*Sir* C. P. B.) Days of a Soldier's Life. pp. 411. *Lond.* 1894. 8°. 9078. dd. 19.

WIMPFFEN (E. F. de) Crimée. pp. 180. *Paris,* 1892. 8°. 9079. i. 8.

WOOD (*Sir* H. E.) The Crimea in 1854 and 1894. pp. 400. *Lond.* 1895. 8°. 9080. g. 7.

See also under the history of ENGLAND, EUROPE, FRANCE, RUSSIA and TURKEY: HISTORY, *Modern.*

CRINOIDEA. See ECHINODERMATA.

CROATIA AND SLAVONIA. BROEKMAN (G. H.) Onze belangen in Croatië en Slavonië. pp. 28. *'s-Hertogenbosch,* 1891. 8°. Pam. 76.

CROATIA AND SLAVONIA—*continued.*

Lukšić (A.) Reiseführer durch Kroatien und Slavonien. pp. 208. *Agram*, 1893. 8°.
10215. a. 6.

Spicer (M.) Blätter aus Kroatiens Gauen. pp. 255. *Berl.* 1894. 8°. 012356. f. 15.

Tkalats (I. I. v.) Jugenderinnerungen aus Kroatien, 1749–1843. pp. 390. *Leipz.* 1894. 8°.
10215. c. 5.

Zay (M.) Croatiae Res. pp. 78. *Budapest*, 1893. 8°. . 8074. g. 6. (8.)
See also Austria.

Language.

Muža (E.) Grammatik der kroatischen Sprache. pp. 214. 1894. 8°. Die Kunst der Polyglottie.
12902. c.

See also Slavonic Languages.

CRONDAL. Ac. Hampshire. *Record Society.* Collection of Records and documents relating to Crondal. *Lond.* 1891, *etc.* 8°.
Ac. 8123/3.

CROQUET. Evelegh (B. C.) Laws of Croquet. pp. 24. *Lond.* 1893. 12°. 7912. de. 1. (4.)

Laws. Laws of Croquet. pp. 23. *Lond.* 1894. 8°. 7907. df. 18. (9.)
See also Games.

CROSCOMBE. Ac., *etc.* Somerset. *Somerset Record Society.* Church-Wardens' accounts of Croscombe. pp. 277. *Lond.* 1890. 4°.
Ac. 8133/4.

CROSS : CROSSES. Ansault ( ) La Croix avant Jésus-Christ. pp. 301. *Paris*, 1894. 8°.
7705. ee. 38.

Forrer (R.) and Mueller (G. A.) Kreuz und Kreuzigung in ihrer Kunstentwicklung. pp. 33. *Strassb.* 1894. 4°. K.T.C. 26. b. 10.

Fréson (J.) Le Crucifiement. pp. 61. *Liége*, 1895. 8°. 4808. bb. 24.

Napier (A. S.) History of the Holy Rood-tree. 1894. 8°. Ac. London. *Early English Text Society.* Original Series, 103. Ac. 9925/77.

Lentzner (C.) Das Kreuz bei den Angelsachsen. pp. 28. *Leipz.* 1890. 8°. 11810. m. 31. (7.)

Friesenegger (J. M.) Die Ulrichs-Kreuze. pp. 67. *Augsburg*, 1895. 4°. 3475. i. 3.

Davidson (J. B.) Ancient Crosses and cross houses. pp. 23. 1881. 4°. Pam. 3.

Lovell (W.) Queen Eleanor's Crosses. pp. 27. 1892. 8°. 07703. h. 1. (9.)

—— Banbury Cross. pp. 8. 1892. 8°.
07703. g. 3. (11.)

Martin (A.) Calvaires en Grès de la vallée du Dun, *etc.* pp. 18. 8. *Paris*, 1890. 18°. Pam. 3.

Peet (H.) The High Cross of Holbeach. pp. 5. *Horncastle*, 1894. 8°. Pam. 90.

Doherty (W. J.) Ancient Crosses of Inishowen, Donegal. *Dublin*, 1891. 8°. 7706. g. 4. (15.)

Graham (R. C.) Carved stones of Islay. pp. 119. *Glasg.* 1895. 4°. 7709. k. 31.

Kermode (P. M. C.) Catalogue of Manks Crosses. pp. 60. *Ramsay*, 1892. 8°. 7708. cc. 50.

Ac. Caerleon. *Antiquarian Association.* Mitchell (E. H.) Crosses of Monmouthshire. pp. 45. *Newport*, 1893. 4°. 7709. h. 35.

Stapleton (A.) Crosses of Nottingham, past and present. *Nottingham*, 1892. 4°. 7702. de. 12. (4.)

—— History of the public Crosses of Old Nottingham. pp. 66. *Nottingham*, 1893. 8°.
10348. ccc. 57. (9.)

See also Art, *Christian.*

CROSSRAGUEL ABBEY. Lawson (R.) Crossraguel Abbey. pp. 66. *Paisley*, 1883. 8°.
4735. aaa. 38.

CROW INDIANS. *See* Indians, *American.*

CROYDON. Croydon. Where to buy at Croydon. pp. 60. *Brighton*, 1891. 4°.
10368. k. 24.

—— Album of Croydon views. *Croydon*, 1895. 4°.
10360. cc. 58.

CROYLAND ABBEY. Searle (W. G.) Ingulf and the Historia Croylandensis. pp. 216. 1894. 8°. Ac. Cambridge. *Antiquarian Society.* Publications. Octavo series. No. 27. Ac. 5624.

CRUSADES. Archer (T. A.) and Kingsford (C. L.) The Crusades. pp. 467. 1894. 8°. Story of the Nations. 9004. ccc. 15.

Riant (P. E. D.) *Count.* Inventaire des lettres historiques des Croisades, 786–1100. pp. 234. *Paris*, 1880. 8°. 11899. i. 38.

Schindler (H.) Die Kreuzzüge in der altprovenzalischen und mittelhochdeutschen Lyrik. pp. 49. *Dresden*, 1889. 4°. Pam. 15.

Michaud (J. F.) Histoire de la première Croisade. pp. 228. *Lond.* 1893. 8°. 9055. aaa. 37.

Wolff (T.) Die Bauernkreuzzüge des Jahres 1096. pp. 194. *Tübingen*, 1891. 8°.
9055. bb. 18.

Klein (C.) Raimund von Aguilers. pp. 146. *Berl.* 1892. 8°. 9055. d. 11.

Gruhn (A.) Der Kreuzzug Richards I. pp. 47. *Berl.* 1892. 8°. 9005. d. 26. (11.)

Paris (G.) La légende de Saladin. pp. 48. *Paris*, 1893. 4°. 11805. m. 24.

Dubois (P.) De recuperatione Terre Sancte. 1891. 8°. Collection de textes pour servir à l'étude de l'histoire. No. 9. 9210. dd.

Gottlob (A.) Die päpstlichen Kreuzzugs-Steuern des 13 Jahrhunderts, *etc.* pp. 278. *Heiligenstadt*, 1892. 8°. 9072. g. 11.

Roehricht (R.) Studien zur Geschichte des fünften Kreuzzuges. pp. 139. *Innsbruck*, 1891. 8°. 9055. d. 10.

Chroust (A.) Tageno, Ansbert und die Historia Peregrinorum. Geschichte des Kreuzzuges Friedrichs I. pp. 205. *Graz*, 1892. 8°.
9055. d. 8.

Wrong (G. M.) The Crusade of 1383. pp. 96. *Lond.* 1892. 8°. 9504. d. 5.

See also Europe : History, *Mediæval and Modern.*

CRUSTACEA. Vogdes (A. W.) Bibliography of the palæozoic Crustacea. pp. 412. 1893. 8°. Ac. San Francisco. *Academy of Natural Sciences.* Occasional Papers. No. IV.
Ac. 3037/4.

Faxon (W.) Reports on Dredging operations off Central America. New Species of Crustacea. 1894. 4°. Ac. Cambridge, *Mass. Museum of Zoology.* Bulletin. Vol. 24. No. 7.
.Ac. 1736/2.

—— Reports of an Exploration off Mexico. Stalk-eyed Crustacea. pp. 292. 1895. 4°. Ac. Cambridge, *Mass. Museum of Zoology.* Memoirs. Vol. 18. Ac. 1736/4.

Friedlaender (B.) Über die markhaltigen Nervenfasern der Crustaceen. 1889. 8°. Ac. Naples. *Zoologische Station.* Mittheilungen. Bd 9.
Ac. 3552/2.

Groult (P.) Acariens, crustacés, *etc.* pp. 248. 1887. 8°. Histoire naturelle de la France. Pt. 15. 7207. cc.

New South Wales. *Commissioners for the Exposition, Chicago.* Edible Crustaceans of N. S. W. pp. 212. *Sydney*, 1893. 8°. 7958. g. 25.

CRUSTACEA—*continued.*

PARKER (G. H.) Compound Eyes in Crustaceans. 1891. 8°. Ac. Cambridge, *Mass. Museum of Zoology.* Bulletin. Vol. 21. No. 2. Ac. 1736/2.

SARS (G. O.) Account of the Crustacea of Norway. *Kristiania*, 1890, etc. 4°. 7298. f. 10.

SKUSE (F. A. A.) British Stalk-eyed Crustacea. pp. 128. 1887. 8°. Young Collector Series. 7001. aaa.

NUSSBAUM (M.) Anatomische Studien an californischen Cirripedien. pp. 97. *Bonn*, 1890. 4°. 7299. l. 17.

CANU (E.) Les Copépodes du Boulonnais. pp. 292. *Lille*, 1892. 4°. 7296. h. 11.

GIESBRECHT (W.) Mittheilungen über Copepoden. 1893, etc. 8°. Ac. Naples. *Zoologische Station.* Mittheilungen. Bd. 11, etc. Ac. 3552/2.

KRAUSE (P. G.) Die Decapoden des Jura. 1891. 8°. Ac. Berlin. *Geologische Gesellschaft.* Zeitschrift. Bd. 43. Heft. 1. Ac. 3137.

ORTMANN (A.) Decapoden und Schizopoden. pp. 120. 1893. 8°. HENSEN (V.) Ergebnisse der Plankton-Expedition. Bd. 2. 1826. b.

THALLWITZ (J.) Decapoden-Studien. pp. 55. 1891. 8°. Ac. Dresden. *K. Zoologisches Museum.* Abhandlungen. 1890-91. Ac. 3562.

ADAMKIEWICZ (A.) Untersuchungen über den Krebs. pp. 134. *Wien*, 1893. 8°. 7640. g. 5.

HECK (C. R.) Der Weisstannenkrebs. pp. 163. *Berl.* 1894. 8°. 7029. e. 1.

PARKER (G. H.) Histology of the eye in the Lobster. pp. 60. 1890. 8°. Ac. Cambridge, *Mass. Museum of Zoology.* Bulletin. Vol xx. no. 1. Ac. 1736/2.

CLAUS (C.) Die Halocypriden des atlantischen Oceans. *Wien*, 1891. fol. 7296. i. 2.

LEICHMANN (G.) Beiträge zur Naturgeschichte der Isopoden. pp. 44. 1891. 4°. LEUCKART (R.) Bibliotheca Zoologica. Heft 10. 7205. f. and 25.

MEINERT (F.) Crustacea malacostraca. 1890. 4°. PETERSEN (C. G. J.) Det Videnskabelige udbytte af Kanonbaaden "Hauchs" togter. III. 7299. l. 15.

STEBBING (T. R. R.) History of Crustacea: recent Malacostraca. pp. 466. 1893. 8°. International Scientific Series. 2324. bb. 11.

GOURRET (P.) Révision des Crustacés Podophthalmes du Golfe de Marseille. pp. 212. 1888. 4°. Ac. Marseilles. *Musée d'Histoire Naturelle.* Annales. Zoologie. Tom. 3. Ac. 2849. b.

See also PALAEONTOLOGY.

CRYPTOGAMIA. *See* ALGAE: BOTANY: FERNS: FUNGI: LICHENS: MOSSES.

CRYPTOGRAPHY. ANDERSEN (C.) Den hemmelige Skrivekunst. pp. 47. *Kjøbenh.* 1889. 8°. 7942. e. 3.

BAZERIES. Chiffre Bazeries. Table chiffrante et déchiffrante. *Paris*, 1893, etc. 8°. 7944. d.

BILLAUDEL (E. A.) La Cryptographie rationnelle. pp. 19. *Charleville*, 1890. 8°. 7942. i. 43. (10.)

BOETZEL ( ) and O'KEENAN ( ) Écriture secrète. pp. 190. *Paris*, 1895. 16°. 7942. b. 52.

CARMONA (J. G.) Tratado de Criptografía. pp. 280. *Madrid*, 1894. 8°. 07944. k. 4.

DELASTELLE (F.) Crytographie nouvelle. pp. 81. *Paris*, 1893. 8°. 07944. g. 6.

E., C. Corrispondenza segreta universale. *Torino*, 1892. 8°. 7942. f. 40.

HERMANN (H.) Nouveau système de Correspondance secrète. 2 pt. *Paris*, 1892. 8°. 7942. l. 37.

JEAN (F.) Le nouveau Sphinx. pp. 356. *Olivet*, 1890. 18°. 012311. i. 28.

CRYPTOGRAPHY—*continued.*

JEAN (F.) L'Inviolable. Système cryptographique. pp. 68. *Olivet*, 1891. 8°. 07945. m. 15.

PELLIGERO (G.) Clave para obtener Secreto en toda clase de correspondencia. *Madrid*, 1893. obl. 8°. 8756. a. 39.

SIMONETTA (F.) Les règles de Cicco Simonetta pour le déchiffrement des Écritures secrètes, 1474. pp. 10. *Nogent*, 1890. 8°. 07703. i. 2. (2.)

VALERIO (P. L. E.) De la Cryptographie. pp. 228. *Paris*, 1893. 8°. 7942. i. 44.

See also TELEGRAPHY, *Telegraph Codes.*

CRYSTALS AND CRYSTALLOGRAPHY. BAUMHAUER (H.) Die Resultate der Aetzmethode in der krystallographischen Forschung. pp. 131. *Leipz.* 1894. 8°. 7109. f. 16.

—— Tafeln. fol. 7109. l. 4.

BERSAUDE (A.) Theorie der optischen Anomalien der regulären Krystalle. pp. 43. *Lissabon*, 1894. 8°. 8716. dd. 12.

BLAKE (J. F.) Geological Optics. pp. 24. 1891. 8°. Pam. 27.

BRAUNS (R.) Die optischen Anomalien der Krystalle. pp. 370. 1891. 8°. Ac. Leipsic. *Fürstliche Jablonowski'sche Gesellschaft.* Preisschriften. Math.-naturwissenschaftl. Section. Nr. 11. Ac. 701/2.

BRUNHES (B.) Étude sur la Réflexion cristalline interne. pp. 146. *Paris*, 1893. 8°. 8715. ee. 48.

FLETCHER (L.) Crystallographic Notes. 8 pt. *Lond.* 1881-87. 8°. 7108. bb. 1. (1.)

—— Dilatation of Crystals on change of temperature. pp. 53. *Lond.* 1883. 8°. 7108. bb. 1. (2.)

—— On Crystals of Percylite, etc. pp. 10. *Lond.* 1890. 8°. 7108. bb. 1. (15.)

—— Optical Indicatrix and transmission of light in crystals. pp. 112. *Lond.* 1892. 8°. 8908. ee. 49.

FOCK (A.) Introduction to chemical Crystallography. pp. 189. *Oxf.* 1895. 8°. 7109. aaa. 30.

—— Krystallographisch-chemische Tabellen. pp. 94. *Leipz.* 1890. 8°. 07109. g. 25.

HECHT (B.) Anleitung zur Krystallberechnung. pp. 76. *Leipz.* 1893. 8°. 7106. c. 15.

HELLMANN (G.) Schneekrystalle. pp. 66. *Berl.* 1893. 8°. 8756. df. 46.

LIEBISCH (T.) Physikalische Krystallographie. pp. 614. *Leipz.* 1891. 8°. 07109. h. 12.

MOREL (J.) Recherches sur les Propriétés optiques des cristaux, etc. pp. 92. *Paris*, 1891. 4°. 8907. g. 20.

PERROT (F. L.) Recherches sur la Réfraction et la dispersion dans une série de cristaux à deux axes. pp. 49. *Genève*, 1890. 8°. Pam. 27.

PULFRICH (C.) Das Totalreflectometer und das Refractometer für Chemiker. pp. 144. *Leipz.* 1890. 8°. 8716. cc. 30.

SCHOENFLIES (A.) Krystallsysteme und Krystallstructur. pp. 638. *Leipz.* 1891. 8°. 07109. h. 21.

THOMSON (W.) *Baron Kelvin.* Molecular Tactics of a Crystal. pp. 59. *Oxf.* 1894. 8°. Pam. 27.

WILLIAMS (G. H.) Elements of Crystallography. pp. 250. *Lond.* 1890. 8°. 7108. a. 22.

See also MINERALOGY.

CUBA. BACHILLER Y MORALES (A.) Cuba: monografía histórica. pp. 214. *Habana*, 1883. 8°. 9771. d. 22.

MANRIQUE (A. M.) Guanahaní. Investigaciones sobre el derrotero de Cristóbal Colón por las Bahamas y costa de Cuba. pp. 228. *Arrecife*, 1890. 8°. 9551. i. 11.

CUBA—*continued.*

CAMPS Y FELIÓ (F. de)' Españoles é Insurrectos. pp. 424. *Habana*, 1890. 8°.   9772. e. 14.

GELPI Y FERRO (G.) Historia de la Revolucion y guerra de Cuba. pp. 312. *Habana*, 1887. 4°.   9772. g. 6.

CEPEDA (F.) Conferencias de Abulí. pp. 304. *Ponce*, 1890. 8°.   8042. aaa. 28.

CUBA. Import Duties of Cuba. pp. 114. 1891. 8°. U.S. *Bureau of American Republics*. Bulletin. No. 10.   08225. k. 1.

ESLAVA (R. G.) Juicio crítico de Cuba en 1887. pp. 200. *Habana*, 1887. 8°.   8180. aaa. 12.

GOVIN Y TORRES (A.) El Enjuiciamiento civil en Cuba. *Habana*, 1886. 8°.   6784. f. 12.

LABRA (R. M. de) La Reforma electoral en las Antillas españolas. pp. 319. *Madrid*, 1891. 8°.   8179. a. 13.

MILLET (G.) La Raza de color de Cuba. pp. 36. *Madrid*, 1894. 8°.   Pam. 81.

MITJANS (A.) Estudio sobre el movimiento científico y literario de Cuba. pp. 395. *Habana*, 1890. 8°.   011850. g. 15.

MORENO (F.) El Pais del Chocolate. pp. 206. *Madrid*, 1887. 8°.   10481. b. 48.

PERPIÑÁ Y PIBERNAT (A.) El Camagüey. Viajes por el interior de Cuba. pp. 448. *Barcelona*, 1889. 8°.   10480. ee. 36.

PUJOL Y DE CAMPS (M.) Apuntes para el presente y porvenir de Cuba. pp. 243. *Habana*, 1885. 4°.   8180. f. 38.

VALDES DOMINGUEZ (F.) El 27 de Noviembre de 1871. pp. 200. *Habana*, 1887. 8°.   8179. aaa. 82.

See also SPAIN, *Colonies :* WEST INDIES.

CUCKOO. BALDAMUS (A. C. E.) Das Leben der europäischen Kuckucke. pp. 224. *Berl.* 1892. 8°.   7285. g. 19.

REY (E.) Altes und Neues aus dem Haushalte des Kuckucks. pp. 108. 1892. 8°. MARSHALL (W.) Zoologische Vorträge. Heft 11.   7204. bb.

See also BIRDS.

CULPHO. CULPHO. Parish Registers of Culpho. pp. 29. 1886. 8°.   9916. f. 34.

CULTER. HENDERSON (J. A.) Annals of Lower Deeside. pp. 271. *Aberdeen*, 1892. 8°.   10369. ccc. 18.

CUMANAGOTA LANGUAGE. *See* INDIAN LANGUAGES.

CUMBERLAND. Ac. Carlisle. *Vale of Derwent Club.* Notes on the History, geology and ornithology of the Vale of Derwent. pp. 106. *Carlisle*, 1891. 8°.   10352. cc. 45.

—— Cumberland. *Antiquarian Society.* TAYLOR (M. W.) Old Manorial Halls of Cumberland. pp. 382. *Kendal*, 1892. 8°.   Ac. 5630/9.

—— JACKSON (W.) Papers and pedigrees relating to Cumberland. 2 vol. *Lond.* 1892. 8°.   Ac. 5630/7.

—— Series of Wills from the registers of the Bishops of Carlisle, 1358–86. *Kendal*, 1893. 8°.   Ac. 5630/10.

BARNES (H.) The Plague in Cumberland. pp. 28. *Kendal*, 1890. 8°.   Pam. 39.

BRUCE (J. C.) Hand-book to the Roman Wall. pp. 279. *Lond.* 1895. 8°.   2368. a. 1.

COTTERELL (C.) Summer holidays in North East England. pp. 143. *Lond.* 1895. 8°.   010358. c. 32.

CUMBERLAND. Pedigrees in the Heralds' Visitations of Cumberland, 1615, 1666. pp. 172. *Carlisle*, 1891. 8°.   9914. cc. 1.

CUMBERLAND—*continued.*

ELLWOOD (T.) The Landnama Book of Iceland as it illustrates the dialect and antiquities of Cumberland. pp. 69. *Kendal*, 1894. 8°.   10280. e. 16.

ENGLAND. Survey of the Debateable and border Lands, 1604. pp. 136. *Alnwick*, 1891. 4°.   10360. h. 25.

FERGUSON (R. S.) Archæological Survey of Cumberland. 1893. 4°. Archæologia. Vol. 53.   2096. g.

See also ENGLAND, *Lake District.*

CUNARD STEAMSHIP COMPANY. *See* NAVAL SCIENCE, *Steamships.*

CUNEIFORM INSCRIPTIONS. *See* ASSYRIA.

CURLING. *See* SKATING.

CUSTOZZA, Battle of. *See* ITALY, *History.*

CYCLING. *See* BICYCLES.

CYNIPIDAE. *See* HYMENOPTERA.

CYPRINIDAE. MULERTT (H.) Der Goldfisch. pp. 104. *Stettin*, 1892. 8°. 7290. de. 7. *See also* FISH.

CYPRIPEDIUM. *See* ORCHIDS.

CYPRUS. COBHAM (C. D.) Attempt at a bibliography of Cyprus. pp. 40. *Nicosia*, 1894. 8°.   Pam. 6.

LONDON. *Cyprus Exploration Fund.* Report of the Committee. *Lond.* 1891, etc. 8°.   7704. aaa. 52.

MERRIAM (A. C.) Geryon in Cyprus. pp. 14. 1894. 8°. DRISLER (H.) Classical Studies.   11312. o. 9.

OHNEFALSCH-RICHTER (M. H.) Kypros, die Bibel und Homer. 2 Bde. *Berl.* 1893. 4°. 7705. g. 44.

—— Kypros, the Bible and Homer. 2 pt. *Lond.* 1893. 4°.   7705. g. 42.

—— Die antiken Cultusstätten auf Kypros. pp. 57. *Berl.* 1891. 4°.   7706. h. 18.

—— Ancient places of Worship in Kypros. pp. 51. *Berl.* 1891. 4°.   7706. h. 21.

'ABD AL-RAḤMĀN IBN ABĪ BAKR. Unternehmungen der Mamluken gegen Cypern, 1423. pp. 43. 16. *Wien*, 1884. 8°.   14555. b.

FAROCHON (P. A.) Chypre et Lépante. pp. 320. *Paris*, 1894. 8°.   9072. h. 9.

CHAMBERLAYNE (T. J.) Lacrimæ Nicossienses. Recueil d'inscriptions funéraires dans l'île de Chypre. *Paris*, 1894, etc. 4°.   7706. h.

CHACALLI (G.) Cyprus and the Cypriot question. pp. 25. *Nicosia*, 1893. 8°.   8022. bb. 27. (8.)

CYPRUS. *Supreme Court.* Cyprus Law Reports. *Nicosia*, 1893, etc. 8°.   06606. h.

LEWIS ( ) Lady's Impressions of Cyprus. pp. 346. *Lond.* 1894. 8°.   10125. aa. 22.

MALLOCK (W. H.) In an Enchanted Island. pp. 407. *Lond.* 1892. 8°.   10125. de. 19.

MOUILLEFERT (P.) Report on the Vineyards of Cyprus. 2 pt. *Nicosia*, 1893. 8°.   7074. l. 13. (12.)

OBERHUMMER (E.) Aus Cypern. 1890. 8°. Ac. Berlin. *Gesellschaft für Erdkunde.* Zeitschrift. Bd. 25.   Ac. 6075/2.

SAKELLARIOS (A. A.) Τα Κυπριακα, ἤτοι γεωγραφια, ἱστορια, κ.τ.λ. Ἐν Ἀθηναις, 1890, etc. 8°.   10076. g.

See also ENGLAND, *Colonies.*

CYPRUS FEVER. *See* FEVERS.

CYSOING, Abbey. CYSOING. Cartulaire de l'abbaye de Cysoing. pp. 1024. *Lille*, 1889. 8°.   4629. b. 30.

CYTISUS, Genus. BRIQUET (J.) Études sur les Cytises des Alpes maritimes. pp. 202. *Genève*, 1894. 8°.   07028. g. 29.

CZARNIKAU. KLEMM (J.) Geschichte der Stadt Czarnikau, *etc.* pp. 112. *Czarnikau*, 1893. 8°.   10255. b. 17.

DAGLINGWORTH. BAZELEY (W.) Notes on Daglingworth. pp. 16. *Gloucester*, 1890. 8°.   10348. d. 19. (5.)

DAHOMEY. ALBÉCA (A. L. d') La France au Dahomey. pp. 236. *Paris*, 1895. 4°.   9061. g. 14.

AUBLET (E.) La Guerre au Dahomey 1888–1893. pp. 350. *Paris*, 1894. 8°. 9061. ccc. 26.

—— La Conquête du Dahomey 1893–1894. pp. 166. *Paris*, 1895. 8°.   9061. ccc. 32.

BADIN (A.) J. B. Blanchard au Dahomey. pp. 307. *Paris*, 1895. 8°.   9061. ee. 33.

BARBOU (A.) Histoire de la Guerre au Dahomey. pp. 154. *Paris*, 1893. 8°.   9061. h. 11.

BERN (J.) L'Expédition du Dahomey, 1892. pp. 432. *Algérie*, 1893. 8°.   9061. ccc. 24.

CHAUDOIN (E.) Trois mois de captivité au Dahomey. pp. 409. *Paris*, 1891. 8°. 10095. de. 16.

CORTEZ DA SILVA CURADO (A. D.) Dahomé. Collecção d'uma serie de artigos. pp. 50. *Lisboa*, 1887. 8°.   Pam. 89.

DAHOMEY. La Conquête de Dahomey. *Paris* 1893. 4°.   9061. eee. 27.

DUMONTEIL (F.) Guerrières et guerriers du Dahomey au Jardin d'Acclimatation. pp. 31. *Paris*, 1891. 12°.   Pam. 89.

FOÀ (E.) Le Dahomey. Histoire, géographie. pp. 429. *Paris*, 1895. 8°.   010096. ff. 29.

GRANDIN (L.) A l'assaut du pays des noirs. 2 tom. *Paris*, 1895. 12°.   010097. e. 1.

LOOY (H. van) Een Reisje in Dahomey. pp. 126. *Mechelen*, 1892. 8°.   10095. a. 5.

MORIENVAL (H.) La Guerre du Dahomey. pp. 240. *Paris*, 1893. 8°.   9061. h. 12.

NICOLAS (V.) L'Expédition du Dahomey en 1890. pp. 152. *Paris*, 1893. 8°. 9061. ccc. 14.

POIRIER (J.) Campagne du Dahomey, 1892-94. pp. 370. *Paris*, 1895. 8°.   9061. ee. 32.

RIOLS (J. de) La Guerre de Dahomey. pp. 107. *Paris*, 1893. 16°.   9061. a. 13.

ROQUES (P. A.) Le Génie au Dahomey en 1892. pp. 52. *Paris*, 1895. 8°.   Pam. 28.

SARMENTO (A.) Portugal no Dahomé. pp. 134. *Lisboa*, 1891. 8°.   8154. e. 24.

VIGNÉ (P.) Terre de Mort—Soudan et Dahomey. pp. 285. *Paris*, 1892. 12°.   10097. ccc. 14.

See also AFRICA, *West*: AFRICAN LANGUAGES.

DAIRY MANAGEMENT AND PRO-DUCE. AIKMAN (C. M.) Milk; its Nature and Composition. pp. 180. *Lond.* 1895. 8°.   07293. g. 21.

ALLEN (E. W.) Derniers progrès en laiterie. pp. 67. *Louvain*, 1895. 8°.   07293. k. 17.

BLACKSHAW (M.) and (J.) Buttermaking for our Pupils. pp. 23. *Macclesfield*, 1894. 8°.   07944. g. 2.

BÖGGILD (B.) Mælkeribruget i Danmark. pp. 626. *Kjøbenh.* 1891. 8°.   07293. i. 5.

BROWN (W.) Science and Practice of Butter Making in Australasia. pp. 267. *Melbourne*, 1889. 8°.   07945. h. 40.

DAIRY MANAGEMENT, etc.—*cont.*

CORNEVIN (A. M. C. I.) De la production du lait. pp. 172. 1894. 8°. Encyclopédie scientifique.   8709. g.

CRUIKSHANK (A. W.) Dairy and Butter-making. pp. 29. *Edinb.* 1891. 8°.   07945. e. 65.

DAKOTA, *North. Dairyman's Association.* Annual Meeting. Proceedings. *Bismarck*, 1891, *etc.* 8°.   7295. ee.

DUCLAUX (É.) Principes de laiterie. pp. 370. *Paris*, 1893. 18°.   7293. bbb. 42.

FLEISCHMANN (W.) Tables pour calculer l'humidité de l'air des caves á fromages. pp. 13. *Brême*, 1892. 8°.   8709. aaa. 5. (8.)

GEORGESON (C. C.) Report on the Dairy Industry of Denmark. pp. 133. 1893. 8°. U.S. *Depart. of Agriculture.* Bulletin. No. 5.   7053. e. 7.

G. B. & I. *Board of Agriculture.* Reports on Dairy Farming in Denmark, Sweden and Germany. pp. 73. *Lond.* 1892. 8°.   7293. i. 10.

GRIFFITHS (M.) Primer on Butter-making. pp. 32. *Lond.* 1892. 8°.   07944. ee. 5. (5.)

JONES (E. M.) Laiterie payante. pp. 100. *Trois-Rivieres*, 1894. 8°.   7293. d. 29.

KLECKI (V. v.) Untersuchungen über das Ranzigwerden und die Säurezahl der Butter. pp. 66. *Leipz.* 1894. 8°.   Pam. 13.

LEFFMANN (H.) Analysis of Milk. pp. 92. *Lond.* 1893. 8°.   07293. i. 22.

LEZÉ (R.) Les industries du lait. pp. 647. *Paris*, 1891. 8°.   07076. f. 2.

LOHEST (C.) Rapport sur l'enseignement laitière en Danemark. pp. 56. *Brux.* 1887. 8°.   Pam. 42.

LONG (J.) Reports on the relation of Dairy-Produce of New Zealand to the English Market. pp. 108. *Wellington*, 1889. 8°. 7293. i. 12. (5.)

MAASSEN (A.) Ueber die Herstellung von Dauermilch. 1891. 8°. GERMANY. *K. Gesundheitsamt.* Arbeiten. Bd. 7.   7440. h.

MAC CALLUM (R. M.) Report on Dairy Factories in New Zealand. pp. 44. *Wellington*, 1888. 8°.   7293. i. 12. (4.)

MACKENZIE (J.) Modern Butter Making. pp. 71. *Lond.* 1888. 8°.   Pam. 94.

MOULTON (J. T.) Butterine. pp. 32. *The Hague*, 1885. 8°.   7942. h. 31. (3.)

MUIR (J.) Manual of Dairy Work. pp. 93. *Lond.* 1893. 8°.   7293. a. 5.

MURRAY (G.) Suggestions on the management and feeding of the Dairy Cow. pp. 18. *Lond.* 1895. 8°.   Pam. 42.

OLIVER (J.) Cheese and Butter Making. pp. 80. *Lond.* 1892. 8°.   7942. e. 31.

—— Milk, Cheese and Butter. pp. 362. *Lond.* 1894. 8°.   07944. f. 8.

OTTO (A.) Die Milch und ihre Produkte. pp. 181. 1892. 8°. Thaer-Bibliothek. Bd. 77.   7078. d.

PLUNKETT (*Hon.* H. C.) Co-operative Dairying. pp. 8. *Lond.* 1890. 8°.   8276. aa. 59. (6.)

ROUVIER (J.) Le Lait : caractères dans l'état de santé et de maladie. pp. 344. *Paris*, 1893. 8°.   7404. bbb. 31.

SARRAN (J.) De la Pasteurisation du lait. pp. 76. *Toulouse*, 1894. 4°. 7383. ddd. 3. (4.)

SHELDON (J. P.) British Dairying. pp. 170. *Lond.* 1893. 8°.   07293. g. 4.

SWITZERLAND. *Société Laitière.* Travaux de concours pour la rédaction d'un manuel de la fabrication du fromage. 2 pt. *Fribourg*, 1890. 8°.   7915. bbb. 37.

DAIRY MANAGEMENT AND PRO-DUCE—continued.

THIERRY (É.) Les Vaches laitières. pp. 352.
Paris, 1895. 12°.   07293. f. 1.
TWEEDIE (E. B.) Danish versus English Butter-making. pp. 78. *Lond.* 1895. 8°. 07944. g. 15.
WARD (R. P.) Dairy Industry and Dairy Farming in Denmark. pp. 34. *Crewe*, 1894. 8°.
                                      7293. i. 12. (13.)
WEIGMANN (H.) Die Methoden der Milchconservirung. pp. 72. *Bremen*, 1893. 8°.
                                      07293. h. 3.
WELPLY (J. J.) Creameries and Infectious Diseases. pp. 59. *Lond.* 1895. 8°. 7561. k. 25.

PHILLIPS (C.) Check-System of Book-keeping for the Dairy trade. pp. 28. *Lond.* 1894. 8°.
                                      Pam. 38.
SCOTT (T.) Creamery Book-keeping. pp. 66.
Limerick, 1893. 8°.   8535. g. 43.
See also CATTLE.

DAKOTA, North. BOOTH (W. S.) Justice's Manual for the State. pp. 168.
Minneapolis, 1891. 8°.   6615. aaa. 6.
DAKOTA, *North. Department of Agriculture.* North Dakota. *Bismarck*, 1892. 8°. Pam. 86.
—— *Board of World's Fair Managers.* North Dakota. *Chicago*, 1893. obl. 8°. Pam. 86.
FINLEY (J. P.) Climatic Features of the two Dakotas. pp. 204. *Wash.* 1893. 4°.
                                      8756. eee. 29.
DAKOTA, South. DAKOTA, *South.* Facts about South Dakota. pp. 64.
Aberdeen, 1890. 8°.   Pam. 8.
DAKOTA. Description of the Corn Belt of South Dakota. pp. 34. *Yankton*, 1893. 8°. Pam. 1.
FINLEY (J. P.) Climatic features of the two Dakotas. pp. 204. *Wash.* 1893. 4°.
                                      8756. eee. 29.
RIVERS (J. D.) Settlers' Guide to the Great Sioux Reservation. pp. 44. *Chicago*, 1890. 8°.
                                      Pam. 86.
SPINK COUNTY. Do you seek a Home? pp. 24.
1892. 8°.   Pam. 86.

DAKOTA LANGUAGE. *See* INDIAN LANGUAGES.

DALE. WARD (J.) Dale and its Abbey. pp. 94.
Derby, 1890. 8°.   010358. e. 4.

DALKEITH. MITCHELL (A.) Political and social movements in Dalkeith. pp. 229.
Edinb. 1882. 8°.   010370. g. 2.

DALMATIA. ERBER (T.) Storia della Dalmazia dal 1797 al 1814. 5 pt.
Zara, 1886-90. 8°.   9315. d. 3.
MASCHEK (L.) Repertorio dei luoghi avitati nel Regno di Dalmazia. pp. 285. *Zara*, 1888. 8°..
                                      8223. de. 44.
MODRICH (G.) La Dalmazia. pp. 506.
Torino, 1892. 8°.   10125. de. 3.
MUNRO (R.) Rambles and Studies in Dalmatia.
pp. 395. *Edinb.* 1895. 8°.   10126. eee. 1.
PISANI (P.) La Dalmatie de 1797 à 1815.
pp. 490. *Paris*, 1893. 8°.   9136. i. 1.
See also AUSTRIA.

DALSLAND. SCHIMMELMANN (I.) Auf Nebenwegen. pp. 108. *Hamburg*, 1895. 8°.
                                      10281. aaa. 21.

DAMAGES, Law of. HARRIS (G. E.) Treatise on the Law of Damages by Corporations. 2 vol.
Rochester, N.Y. 1892. 8°.   6616. de. 8.
MAYNE (J. D.) Treatise on Damages. pp. 642.
Lond. 1894. 8°.   2230. c. 14.

DAMARALAND. LEWIS (R.) The Germans in Damaraland. pp. 31.
Cape Town, 1889. 8°.   Pam. 66.
See also AFRICA, *German Possessions.*

DANBY. ATKINSON (J. C.) Forty Years in a Moorland Parish. pp. 457. *Lond.* 1891. 8°.
                                      010358. e. 11.

DANCE OF DEATH. DANCE OF DEATH. The Dance of Death, by Holbein, 1538.
Lond. 1892. 4°.   K.T.C. 8. a. 14.

DANCING. BERNAY (B.) La Danse au Théâtre. pp. 194. *Paris*, 1890. 8°.
                                      011795. f. 20.
DU VALDOR (J.) La Danse. pp. 118.
Saint-Amand, 1894. 8°.   8410. ccc. 43.
GIRAUDET (E.) Traité de la Danse. pp. 287.
Paris, 1891. 8°.   7913. e. 15.
GROVE (L.) Dancing. pp. 496. 1895. 4°.
Badminton Library.   7905. f.
HEADLAM (S. D.) The Ballet. pp. 16.
Lond. 1894. 8°.   Pam. 50.
HOGAN (J. P.) Method of Dancing.
N.Y. 1892, *etc.* 4°.   7905. cc.
HOW. How to Dance. pp. 49. *Lond.* 1893. 8°.
                                      7912. aa. 18.
IMAGE (S.) The Art of Dancing. pp. 20.
Lond. 1891. 8°.   7912. df. 3. (4.)
LANSDOWN (H. T.) Dance Drill for Girls. pp. 28.
Lond. 1892. 4°.   7906. ee. 33.
P.P. *London.* The Ball Room.
Lond. 1894, *etc.* 4°   PP. 5204. d. & 736.
QUELLIEN (N.) Chansons et Danses des Bretons.
pp. 300. *Paris*, 1889. 8°.   11595. k. 5.
SCOTT (E.) Dancing as an art and pastime.'
pp. 214. *Lond.* 1892. 8°.   07905. f. 2.
—— How to Dance. pp. 102. *Lond.* 1895. fol.
                                      7913. de. 16.
—— Description of Steps and Movements of the Chorolisthu. *Lond.* 1891. fol. 1865. c. 2. (12.)
SHORT ( ) Guide in the Art of Dancing.
pp. 30. *Middlesbrough*, 1892. 16°. 7913. de. 8.
UNGARELLI (G.) Le vecchie Danze italiane.
pp. 78. *Roma*, 1894. 8°.   12431. k. 24.

DANISH LANGUAGE.

Dictionaries.

JESSEN (E.) Dansk etymologisk Ordbog.
Kjøbenh. 1892, *etc.* 8°.   12972. e.
ROSS (H. M. E.) Norsk Ordbog.
Christiania, 1890, *etc.* 8°.   12972. k.
LARSEN (A.) Dictionary of the Dano-Norwegian and English Languages. pp. 693.
Copenhagen, 1888. 8°.   2118. a.
BRYNILDSEN (J.) Tysk-norsk, dansk, Ordbog.
Kristiania, 1895, *etc.* 8°.   12972. dd.

Grammars, etc.

AGERSKOV (C.) Dansk Læsebog. 6 Afd.
Kjøbenh. 1890. 8°.   12972. e. 17.
BENNETT (T.) English-Norwegian Phrasebook.
pp. 235. *Christiania*, 1891. 8°. 12972. bbb. 25.
BERTELSEN (S.) Dansk Læsebog. pp. 175.
Kjøbenh. 1890. 8°.   12972. bbb. 27.
BONDESEN (I.) Ny dansk Læsebog. 2 Del.
Kjøbenh. 1891, 8°.   12260. c. 18.
DAHL (B. T.) Dansk Stillære i sine Grundtræk.
pp. 83. *Kjøbenh.* 1891. 8°.   12972. b. 27.
GROTH (P.) Danish and Dano-Norwegian Grammar. pp. 143. *Bost.* 1894. 8°. 12972. b. 39.
HOFGAARD (S. W.) Omrids af Lydlæren. pp. 78.
Kristiania, 1890. 8°.   12972. bbb. 26.
KROHN (J.) Lidt dansk Grammatik. pp. 9.
Kjøbenh. 1890. 8°.   12901. ccc. 16. (3.)

P

DANISH LANGUAGE.—Grammars—
continued.

LAURSEN (L.) Dansk Læsebog. pp. 128.
Kjøbenh. 1893. 8°.   12972. b. 38.

LUNDE-NIELSSEN (K.) Dansk-norsk Sprog-
Analyse. *Køjbenh.* 1890, *etc.* 8°.
                          12972. ee. 42.

MATTHIESSEN (M. E.) Dansk Sproglære udar-
bejdet til Skolebrug. pp. 36. *Odense,* 1891. 8°.
                          12901. de. 12. (2.)

MATZEN (M.) Vejledning ved Undervisingen i
dan-k Stil i Borger- og Almueskoler. pp. 248.
Kjøbenh. 1891. 8°.   12972. e. 16.

—— Modersmaalets Sproglære. pp. 384.
Kjøbenh. 1893. 8°.   12972. ee. 46.

MIKKELSEN (K.) Dansk Sproglære. pp. 68.
Roskilde, 1893. 8°.   12972. cc. 51.

MÖLLER (A. C. C.) Oversigt over den danske
Sproglære. pp. 32. *Kjøbenh.* 1890. 8°.
                          12972. bb. 48.

OLSVIG (V.) Norse and English words & phrases.
pp. 160. 1890. 8°. Beyer's Tourists' Library.
                          10280. c.

PLATOU (J. M. S.) Norsk Grammatik. pp. 114.
Kristiania, 1890. 8°.   12976. ccc. 4.

POESTION (J. C.) Lehrbuch der norwegischen
Sprache. pp. 183. 1890. 8°. Die Kunst der
Polyglottie. Thl. 28.   12902. c.

ROGSTAD (A.) Modersmaals-undervisningen i
smaaskolen. pp. 79. *Kristiania,* 1890. 8°,
                          Pam. 17.

SARGENT (J. Y.) Grammar of the Dano-Norwegian Language. pp. 172. *Oxford,* 1892. 8°.
                          12972. e. 23.

—— Dano-Norwegian Reader. pp. 176.
1895. 8°. SONNENSCHEIN (E. A.) Parallel
Grammar Series.   12902. aa.

SCHNEEKLOTH (K. A.) Dansk Læsebog. 2 vol.
Kjøbenh. 1890. 8°.   12260. f. 11.

SMITH (M.) Norwegische Grammatik. pp. 60.
Kristiania, 1890. 8°.   12972. bbb. 28.

STRÖM (T.) Dansk Læsebog. 6 Afd.
Kjøbenh. 1890. 8°.   12972. e. 18.

THIMM (T.) Norwegian Self-taught. pp. 79.
Lond. 1892. 8°.   12901. ccc. 16. (4.)

TÖNNESSEN (S. L. J.) Lærebog i norsk Stil.
2 trin. *Kristiania,* 1890. 8°.   12972. e. 15.

VELLESEN (J.) Norsk Grammatik. pp. 32.
Kristiania, 1891. 8°.   12902. bb. 40. (7.)

Orthography.

BILLE (C. S. A.) Den literaire Retskrivning.
pp. 116. *Kjøbenh.* 1889. 8°.   12972. h. 19.

BOYSEN (A.) Danske Retskrivnings-øvelser.
pp. 91. *Kjøbenh.* 1890. 8°.   12972. bbb. 29.

DENMARK. *M. for Undervisningsvæsenet.* Nyeste
Retskrivningsregler. pp. 30. *Kjøbenh.* 1889. 8°.
                          12901. ccc. 16. (2.)

HOUGEN (K.) Retskrivnings-diktater. pp. 70.
Kristiania, 1892. 8°.   12972. cc. 49.

SAABY (V.) Dansk Retskrivningsordbog.
pp. 221. *Kjøbenh.* 1891. 8°.   12972. e. 19.

SCHEELUND (T.) Om dansk Retskrivning.
Kjøbenh. 1892, *etc.* 8°.   12972. bbb.

VODSKOV (H. S.) Dr. E. Jessens "forsmædelige
Skandale.' pp. 101. *Kjøbenh.* 1890. 8°.
                          Pam. 47.

DANISH LITERATURE. ANDERSEN (V.)
Danske Studier. pp. 171. *Kjøbenh.* 1893. 8°.
                          011850. h. 34.

BERNARDINI (L.) La Littérature scandinave.
pp. 280. *Paris,* 1894. 8°.   011850. ccc. 13.

BOYESEN (H. H.) Essays on Scandinavian Literature. pp. 288. *Lond.* 1895. 8°. 011824. e. 64.

DANISH LITERATURE—*continued.*

CHRISTENSEN (F.) Haandbog i dansk Litteratur.
Kjøbenh. 1893, *etc.* 8°.   011850. h.

DANISH AUTHORS. Folkendgave af danske For-
fattere. *Kjøbenh.* 1890, *etc.* 8°.   12260. de.

FENGER (P. B.) Læsestykker af danske Forfat-
tere. *Aarhus,* 1890, *etc.* 8°.   12260. f.

VEDEL (V.) Studier over Gudalderen i dansk
Digtning. pp. 262. *Kjøbenh.* 1890. 8°.
                          011824. f. 22.

WEITEMEYER (H.) Denmark: its language,
literature, *etc.* pp. 268. *Lond.* 1891. 8°.
                          10280. eee. 15

BAIN (R. N.) H. C. Andersen. pp. 461.
Lond. 1895. 8°.   10761. f. 5.

DANUBE. BIGELOW (P.) Paddles and Politics down the Danube. pp. 253.
Lond. 1892. 8°.   10215. aaa. 34.

BIRD (A. F. R.) Boating in Bavaria and down
the Danube. pp. 160. *Hull,* 1893. 8°.
                          10108. f. 4.

DONNER (*Mrs.* J. A.) Down the Danube in an
open Boat. pp. 145. *Lond.* 1895. 12°.
                          10201. cc. 2.

MILLET (F. D.) The Danube. pp. 327.
N.Y. 1893. 8°.   10108. f. 3.

SCHWEIGER-LERCHENFELD (A. v) *Baron.* Die
Donau als Völkerweg und Reiseroute.
Wien, 1895, *etc.* 8°.   10105. ee.

DANZIG. HANS, *Wistulanus.* Geschichte der
Stadt Danzig. pp. 98. *Danzig,* 1891. 8°.
                          10256. a. 20.

LAUFFER (V.) Danzigs Schiffsverkehr am
Ende des xv. Jahrhunderts. 1894. 8°. Ac.
Dantzic. *Westpreussischer   Geschichtsverein.*
Zeitschrift. Hft. 33.   Ac. 7032/3.

SIMSON (P.) Danzig im 30 jährigen Kriege.
1891. 8°. Ac. Dantzic. *Westpreussischer Geschichtsverein.* Zeitschrift. Hft 29. Ac. 7032/3.

KOEHLER (G.) Geschichte der Festungen Danzig, 1814. 2 Thle. *Breslau,* 1893. 8°.
                          9335. dd. 9.

See also WEST PRUSSIA.

DARJEELING. MITCHELL (E.) Guide-
book to Darjeeling. pp. 144. *Calcutta,* 1891. 8°.
                          10057. a. 6.

DARLINGTON. DARLINGTON. Album of
photographic views of Darlington.
Lond. 1895. 8°.   10360. cc. 60.

DART, River. BROWN (W.) The River Dart.
pp. 15. *Lond.* 1892. fol.   10368. l. 3.

DARTMOOR. BURNARD (R.) Dartmoor pictorial Records. *Plymouth,* 1890, *etc.* 8°.
                          010358. f. 12.

—— Acquisition of the Forest of Dartmoor as a
county park. pp. 10. *Plymouth,* 1894. 8°.
                          8282. ff. 9. (18.)

PROWSE (A. B.) Notes on the neighbourhood of
White Tor, West Dartmoor. pp. 5. 1889. 8°.
                          010358. f. 35. (4.)

—— Notes on the neighbourhood of Taw Marsh.
pp. 15. 1890. 8°.   010358 f. 35. (3.)

—— The ancient metropolis of Dartmoor.
pp. 8. 1891. 8°.   010358. f. 35. (2.)

—— Bounds of the Forest of Dartmoor. pp. 15.
1892. 8°,   010358. f 35. (1.)

SPENCER (E.) Remarks on Dartmoor. pp. 78.
Plymouth, 1891. 8°.   10352. aaa. 61.

**DARTMOUTH COLLEGE, New Hamp-
shire.** CHASE (F.) History of Dartmouth
College. *Camb., Mass.* 1891, *etc.* 8°.
                          10412. i. 10.

DAUPHINÉ.
Antiquities and History.
ARNAUD (E.) Bibliographie huguenote du Dauphiné. pp. 109. *Grenoble*, 1894. 8°.
011900. h. 29.
CHANLIAUX (P.) Les Antiquités de l'Allobrogie. pp. 230. *Lyon*, 1890. 8°. 7708. a. 65.
DREVET (L. X.) À travers l'histoire du Dauphiné. pp. 62. *Grenoble*, 1891. 8°.
10106. df. 17. (6.)
P.P. *Grenoble*. Revue du Dauphiné. *Grenoble*, 1894, *etc.* fol. 277.
CHEVALIER (J.) Mémoire sur les hérésies en Dauphiné avant le XVIᵉ siecle. pp. 164. *Valence*, 1890 4°. 4629. i. 13.
TERREBASSE (H. de) Notes pour servir à l'histoire des Protestants du Dauphiné. pp. 217. *Lyon*, 1890. 8°. 4629. b. 27.
MAIGNIEN (E.) Bibliographie du Dauphiné pendant la Révolution, 1787–1806. *Grenoble*. 1891, *etc.* 8°. 011900. f.
CHENAVAS (O.) La Révolution de 1788 en Dauphiné. pp. 235. *Grenoble*, 1888. 8°.
9225. aa. 19.
ROUX (X.) La Révolution en Dauphiné. pp. 216. *Grenoble*, 1888. 4°. 9210. h. 4.
ROCHAS (A.) Journal d'un Bourgeois de Valence, 1789 à 1799. 2 vol. *Grenoble*, 1891, 92. 8°. 9226. k. 22.
DAUPHINY. Mémoire de la marche des brigandages qui se sont commis en Dauphiné en 1789. pp. 206. *Grenoble*, 1891. 8°. 6056. ff. 16.
ACHARD DE GERMANE (A.) Lettres à M. de la Coste, 1791–1793. pp. 275. *Valence*, 1891. 8°.
010920. f. 27.
DICTIONARIES. Dictionnaire des contemporains dauphinois. pp. 132. *Grenoble*, 1891. 8°.
010661. m. 50.
Topography.
JAQUART (E.) Un coin du Dauphiné. pp. 172. *Voiron*, 1892. 8°. 010171. e. 17.
JOANNE (P.) Dauphiné et Savoie. pp. 492. *Paris*, 1894. 8°. 10171. a. 24.
PEZAY (de) *Marquis*. Vallées de la France le long des Grandes Alpes dans le Dauphiné. pp. 104. *Grenoble*, 1894. 8°. 010171. g. 15.
See also ALPS: HAUTES-ALPES *and* ISÈRE, *Departments*.
Dialect and Literature.
DEVAUX (A.) De l'étude des patois du Haut-Dauphiné. 1890. 8°. Ac. Grenoble. *Académie Delphinale*. Bulletin. Sér. 4. Tom. 3.
Ac. 340.
—— Essai sur la langue vulgaire du Dauphiné au moyen âge. pp. 520. *Paris*, 1892. 8°.
12950. d. 2.
MAIGNIEN (E.) Bibliothèque historique du Dauphiné. pp. 379. *Grenoble*, 1892. 8°.
011900. ee. 16.
P.P. *Voiron*. Le Sylphe, organe des écrivains dauphinois. *Voiron*, 1887, *etc.* 8°. P.P. 4382. o.

DAVOS. HARDWICKE (H. J.) Alpine climates for Consumption. pp. 65. *Lond.* 1894. 8°.
7616. a. 47.
MUDDOCK (J. E.) "J. E. M." Guide to Davos-Platz. pp. 154. *Lond.* 1890. 8°. 10196. bb. 10.
SYMONDS (J. A.) Our Life in the Swiss Highlands. pp. 366. *Edinb.* 1892. 8°. 10196. cc. 9.
See also WATERING-PLACES, *etc.*

DAY OF JUDGMENT. *See* ESCHATOLOGY.
DEACONESSES. *See* SISTERHOODS.
DEAF AND DUMB. BELL (A. G.) Facts and opinions relating to the Deaf. pp. 195. *Lond.* 1888. 8°. 7611. bb. 23.

DEAF AND DUMB.—*continued.*
BELL (A. M.) Speech reading and articulation teaching. pp. 37. *N.Y.* 1890. 16°. 12991. h. 29.
BONET (J. P.) Simplification of the letters of the Alphabet and method of teaching Deaf-Mutes. pp. 212. *Harrogate*, 1890. 8°.
8310. cc. 38.
BOYER (A.) De la préparation des organes de la parole chez le jeune sourd-muet. pp. 28. *Paris*, 1894. 8°. 7306. h. 15. (7.)
ELLIOTT (R.) Lessons in Articulation and lip-reading. pp. 116. *Lond.* 1895. 8°. 8307. c. 43.
FAY (E. A.) Histories of American schools for the Deaf. 3 vol. *Wash.* 1893. 8°. 8307. i. 4.
FIEBIG (A.) Die hundertjährige Marter der Taubstummen und ihrer Lehrer. 2 Th. *Breslau*, 1891. 8°. 8309. eee. 10.
FULLER (S.) Helen Keller, a deaf and blind child. *Wash.* 1891. fol. 8310. l. 2.
GOLDSTEIN (M. A.) Possibility of obtaining improvement in the treatment of Deafness and Deaf-Mutism by acoustic gymnastics. pp. 5. 1895. 8°. Pam. 17.
GORDON (J. C.) Education of deaf Children. pp. 261. *Wash.* 1892. fol. 8310. l. 3.
—— Notes upon the education of the Deaf. pp. 90. *Wash.* 1892. 8°. 8308. gg. 18.
HAVSTAD (L. A.) Vore skoler for døve børn. pp. 86. *Kristiania*, 1890. 8°. 8306. de. 20. (7.)
HEALEY (G. F.) Directory of societies of the adult Deaf and Dumb in Great Britain and the U.S. pp. 50. *Liverp.* 1892. 16°. 8310. a. 32.
HOLLENWEGER (C.) Der Taubstumme vor, während und nach seiner Schulbildung. pp. 46. *Marienburg*, 1892. 8°. 3910. ee. 41. (17.)
HUBBARD (H. W.) Deaf-Mutism. pp. 12. *Lond.* 1894. 8°. 7306. e. 22. (16.)
HUTTON (J. S.) Deaf-Mute's question-book. pp. 144. *Halifax, N.S.,* 1895. 8°. 8309. aa. 34.
MACAULAY (J. B.) Deaf and Dumb. pp. 208. *Paignton*, 1892. 8°. 8310. a. 33.
MYGIND (H. R. E.) Die angeborene Taubheit. pp. 119. *Berl.* 1890. 8°. 7611. d. 1.
—— Taubstummheit. pp. 278. *Berl.* 1894. 8°.
7616. dd. 3.
—— Deaf-Mutism. pp. 300. *Lond.* 1894. 8°.
7611. c. 6.
PERINI (C.) Méthode pour enseigner par la parole la langue maternelle aux sourdes-muets. 2 pt. *Currière*, 1891. 8°. 8309. de. 29.
P.P. *Leeds*. The Deaf Chronicle. *Leeds*, 1891, *etc.* 4°. 1538.
STOLTE (H.) Über die Erziehung des Taubstummen zur Religiosität und Sittlichkeit. pp. 86. *Soest*, 1891. 8°. 8304. bb. 10. (4.)
THOLLON (B.) De l'acquisition des idées abstraites par les Sourds-Muets. pp. 55. *Paris*, 1893. 8°. 8304. e. 24. (7.)
YOUNG (*Mrs.* I. S. H.) Vocal Speech and lip-reading for the Deaf-Mute. pp. 30. *Melbourne*, 1883. 8°. 8304. bb. 5. (12.)
X. Delle Cause del dissidio fra i maestri dei Sordo-Muti in Italia. pp. 23. *Città di C.* 1893. 12°. Pam. 17.
See also EAR.

DEAL. FISHER (W. P.) Illustrated guide to Deal. pp. 32. *Manch.* 1891. 8°.
10348 c. 25. (4.)
GIRAUD (E. F.) Guide to Deal. pp. 64. *Deal*, 1891. 8°. 10348. ccc. 57. (6.)

DEAN, Forest of. HYETT (F. A.) Civil War in the Forest of Dean, 1643–45. pp. 15. 1895. 8°. 9001. k. 15. (10.)

P 2

DEATH. ALDEN (H. M.) A Study of Death. pp. 336. *Lond.* 1895. 8°.   8470. df. 10.

BROWNE (O.) On the care of the Dying. pp. 39. *Lond.* 1894. 8°.   7306. df. 22. (8.)

HICKS (A. B.) Hints to medical practitioners concerning granting certificates of Death. pp. 22. *Lond.* 1895. 8°.   Pam. 32.

LABORDE (J. V.) Le traitement physiologique de la Mort. pp. 187. *Paris*, 1894. 8°.   7391. cc. 11.

LIGNIÈRES (D. de) Pour ne pas être enterré vivant. pp. 64. *Paris*, 1893. 8°.   07305. i. 11. (2.)

MAZE (   ) Signes de la Mort. pp. 44. *Paris*, 1892. 8°.   7305. f. 5. (3.)

MONTEVERDI (A.) Vita e Morte. pp. 380. *Cremona*, 1892. 8°.   7442. e. 15.

RIESENFELD (C. E.) Verschollenheit und Todeserklärung nach preussischem Recht. pp. 175. *Breslau*, 1891. 8°.   5604. eee. 7.

SABATIER (A.) Essai sur la Vie et la Mort. pp. 282. *Paris*, 1892. 12°.   7406. aa. 6.

KELLER (J. A.) Vierhundertvierzig merkwürdige und seltene Todes-Arten. pp. 446. *Mainz*, 1890. 8°.   12330. bbb. 51.

T., M. E. Final Triumph; dying sayings.
pp. 64. *Lond.* 1893. 8°.   4804. aaa. 17.

See also BURIAL : DANCE OF DEATH : ESCHATOLOGY.

DEATH DUTIES.
See ENGLAND, *Trade, Finance, etc.*

DECAPODA. *See* CRUSTACEA.

DECIMAL SYSTEM. BACON (G. W.) Handbook to Bacon's Chart of the Metric system. *Lond.* 1892. 8°.   8530. bbb. 27. (10.)

COLLAR (G.) Notes on the Metric System. pp. 16. *Lond.* 1892. 8°.   8506. bb. 52. (4.)

DOWSON (J. E.) Decimal Coinage, weights and measures. pp. 28. *Lond.* 1891. 8°.   8535. gg. 8. (6.)

ELLERY (T. B.) Decimal Coinage and the metric system. pp. 56. *Lond.* 1892. 8°.   8506. bb. 52. (2.)

EVANS (T.) Metric System. pp. 16. *Lond.* 1891. 8°.   8530. bbb. 27. (7.)

LONDON. *Decimal Association.* The Decimal Association. *Lond.* 1891, *etc.* 8°.   08225. ee.

—— Copy of the Memorial to the School Board of London. *Lond.* 1890. fol.   Pam. 38.

MOLESWORTH (*Sir* G. L.) Dec'mal Coinage, weights and measures. pp. 32. *Lond.* 1891. 8°.   8531. dd. 28. (6.)

MONTAGU (S.) A Plea for a British dollar. pp. 8. *Lond.* 1888. 8°.   Pam. 38.

SMITH (W. A.) Decimal Coinage, weights and measures. pp. 23. *Lond.* 1891. 8°.   8531. dd. 28. (7.)

THORNTON (J.) Handbook to Heywood's Chart of metric measures. pp. 20. *Manch.* 1891. 8°.   Pam. 38.

See also MONEY : WEIGHTS AND MEASURES.

DEDHAM, Mass. DEDHAM. Early records of Dedham, 1636–59. pp. 238. *Dedham*, 1892. 8°.   10408. g. 24.

DEE, River. *Aberdeenshire.* DEESIDE. The Deeside Guide. pp. 115. *Aberd.* 1893. 8°.   10369. aaa. 46.

HENDERSON (J. A.) Annals of lower Deeside. pp. 271. *Aberd.* 1892. 8°.   10369. ccc. 18.

DEE, River. *Wales,* HOWSON (J. S.) The River Dee. *Lond.* 1889. 8°.   10358. c. 25.

DEER. BAXTER (G. W.) Elk-hunting in Sweden. pp. 43. *Dundee*, 1893. 16°. Pam. 83.

CHABOT (de) La Chasse du chevreuil et du cerf. pp. 247. *Paris*, 1891. 8°.   7908. f. 18.

CREALOCK (H. H.) Deer-stalking in the Highlands. pp. 194. *Lond.* 1892. fol.   K.T.C. 13. b. 1.

JEFFERIES (R.) Red Deer. pp. 248. *Lond.* 1892. 8°.   7207. cc. 3.

LYDEKKER (R.) Horns and hoofs. pp. 411. *Lond.* 1893. 8°.   7206. h. 21.

WHITAKER (J.) List of Deer-parks and paddocks of England. pp. 204. *Lond.* 1892. 8°.   07293. k. 9.

See also SPORT : ZOOLOGY.

DEGENERATION. HIRSCH (W.) Genie und Entartung. pp. 340. *Berl.* 1894. 8°.   8462. g. 40.

NORDAU (M. S.) Entartung. 2 Bde. *Berl.* 1892, 93. 8°.   012357. i. 39.

—— Degeneration. pp. 500. *Lond.* 1895. 8°.   012357. k. 24.

—— Regeneration : reply to M. Nordau. pp. 315. *Lond.* 1895. 8°.   8409. l. 30.
See also EVOLUTION.

DEHRA DUN. HAWTHORNE (R.) Guide to Mussoorie and Dehra Dun. *Mussoorie*, 1890. 8°.   Pam. 88.

DEIR EL BAHARI.
See EGYPT, *Antiquities.*

DEITY. BARNOUT (H.) Le Monde sans Dieu. pp. 396. *Paris*, 1890. 18°.   4018. c. 15.

BILLOT (L.) De Deo Uno et Trino commentarius. *Romæ*, 1893, *etc.* 8°.   4223. cc.

BLAKENEY (E. H.) The idea of God. pp. 7. *Lond.* 1891. 8°.   4371. e. 6. (1.)

CLARKE (R. F.) The existence of God. pp. 84. *Lond.* 1892. 8°.   3939. ccc. 11.

COURTNEY (W. L.) The reality of God. pp. 45. *Lond.* 1893. 8°.   4018. bb. 42. (8.)

DAVIDSON (W. L.) Theism as grounded in Human Nature. pp. 469. *Lond.* 1893. 8°.   4371. ee. 18.

FARGES (A.) L'Idée de Dieu d'après la raison et la science. pp. 578. *Paris*, 1894. 8°.   4371. g. 3.

FRASER (A. C.) Philosophy of Theism. *Edinb.* 1895, *etc.* 8°.   4018. ff.

GLOSSNER (M.) Der spekulative Gottesbegriff in der neueren Philosophie. pp. 79. *Paderborn*, 1894. 8°.   8467. f. 40.

GOBLET (E.) *Count d'Alviella.* L'idée de Dieu d'après l'anthropologie et l'histoire. pp. 328. *Brux.* 1892. 8°.   4371. ee. 8.

—— Lectures on the origin and growth of the conception of God. pp. 296. *Lond.* 1892. 8°.   2212. e.

KNIGHT (W.) Aspects of Theism. pp. 220. *Lond.* 1893. 8°.   4371. ee. 19.

LE MOYNE (P.) L'Idée de Dieu. pp. 121. *Brux.* 1894. 8°.   4371. aaaa. 52.

LUXMOORE (H. E.) The Existence of God. pp. 24. 1890. 8°. S. Giles' Hall Lectures. No. 7.   4018. c.

MAPLE (W. H.) No "Beginning," or the fundamental fallacy. *Chicago*, 1892. 8°. 4018. df. 20.

PURINTON (D. B.) Christian Theism. pp. 303. *N.Y.* 1889. 8°.   4015. ee. 24.

PHILBROOK (H. B.) What and where is God ? pp. 480. *Chicago*, 1887. 8°.   4371. b. 2.

SAN (L. de) Tractatus de Deo Uno. *Lovanii*, 1894, *etc.* 8°.   4225. f.

DEITY—*continued.*

STEENSTRA (P. H.) The being of God as unity and Trinity. pp. 269. *Bost.* 1891. 8°.
4227. bb. 22.

STENTRUP (F. A.) Synopsis tractatus de Deo uno. pp. 368. *Oeniponte*, 1895. 8°. 4225. f. 6.

VISIBLE. The Visible God, and our relation to him. pp. 365. *Lond.* 1890. 8°. 4227. h. 14.

VOYSEY (C.) Theism. pp. 100.
Lond. 1894. 8°.   4018. ff. 3.

—— Theism as a science of Natural Theology. pp. 134. *Lond.* 1895. 8°. 4371. aaa. 37.

See also ATHEISM: CHRISTIANITY: EARTH, *Creation;* RELIGION: THEOLOGY: TRINITY.

DELAGOA BAY. *See* AFRICA, *Portuguese;* PORTUGAL, *Colonies.*

DELAWARE, River and State. HOFF (J. W.) Two hundred miles on the Delaware River. pp. 180. *Trenton*, 1893. 8°. 10413. k. 26.

HOTCHKIN (S. F.) Early clergy of Delaware. pp. 280. *Phila.* 1890. 8°.   4744. e. 34.

DELHI. MUHAMMAD FAIZ-BAKHSH. Memoirs of Delhi. *Allahabad*, 1888, 89. 8°. 757. e. 41.

SCHROEDER (L. v.) Delhi, das indische Rom. pp. 19. *Mitau*, 1891. 8°.   Pam. 88.

DELOS. HOMOLLE (T.) Comptes des temples déliens en l'année 279. 1890. 8°. Ac. Athens. *École Française.* Bulletin. No. 5, 6.
Ac. 5206/3.

—— Les Travaux de l'École française d'Athènes dans l'Ile de Délos. pp. 45. *Paris*, 1890. 8°.
7705. ee. 25. (4.)

DELPHINIDAE. TRUE (F. W.) Review of the Family Delphinidæ. pp. 191. 1889. 8°. Ac. Washington. *Smithsonian Institution.* Bulletin. No. 36. Ac. 1875/13.

DELUGE. ANDBEE (R.) Die Flutsagen. pp. 152. *Braunschweig*, 1891. 8°. 4503. aa. 42.

DAWSON (*Sir* J. W.) The historical Deluge. pp. 56. 1895. 8°. Present Day Tracts. Vol. 13.
2210. a.

GARBETT (E. L.) Huxley's mendacity and the Bible and Darwin's veracity, on Noah's flood. pp. 16. *Lond.* 1891. 8°.   Pam. 77.

GIRARD (R. de) Études de géologie biblique. Le Déluge. 3 tom. *Fribourg*, 1893-95. 8°.
3107. bb.

HOWORTH (*Sir* H. H.) The glacial nightmare and the flood. 2 vol. *Lond.* 1893. 8°.
7106. c. 14.

PRESTWICH (J.) Phenomena belonging to the last geological period and their bearing upon the tradition of the Flood. pp. 37.
Lond. 1895. 8°.   07109. g. 44.

STUART (A. J.) The World and the Flood. pp. 146. *Shanklin*, 1891. 8°. 8562. aaa. 40.

See also EARTH: GEOLOGY.

DEMARARA. *See* GUIANA, *British.*

DEMOCRACY. *See* GOVERNMENT

DEMONOLOGY. BOIS (J.) Le Satanisme et la Magie. pp. 427. *Paris*, 1895. 8°. 8631. g. 32.

CAMPBELL (C.) Critical studies in St. Luke's Gospel. pp. 318. *Edinb.* 1891. 8°. 3224. 1 13.

HENNE-AM-RHYN (O.) Der Teufels- und Hexenglaube. pp. 159. *Leipz.* 1892. 8°. 8630. ee. 25.

HUDSON (W. H.) The Satan of Theology. pp. 42. *Bost.* 1891. 8°.   4139. bbb. 21. (8.)

IAMBLICHUS. Le Livre de Jamblique sur les mystères. pp. 209. *Paris*, 1895. 8°.
8632. cc. 50.

JACK (T. G.) "The Old Serpent called the Devil." pp. 62. *Lond.* 1892. 16°. 4372. a. 17.

DEMONOLOGY—*continued.*

JANNAWAY (F. G.) Satan's Biography. pp. 48. *Dover*, 1894. 16°. 4371. bb. 9. (4.)

JEWETT (E. H.) Diabolology pp. 197.
N.Y. 1889. 8°.   4257. m. 29.

KNIGHT (E.) Nature versus the Devil. pp. 24. *Lond.* 1894. 8°.   Pam. 49.

LADAME (P.) Les Mandragores ou diables familiers à Genève. 1892. 8°. Ac. Geneva. *Société d'Histoire.* Mémoires et documents. Nouvelle Série. Tom. 3.   Ac. 6941.

LAENGIN (G.) Die biblischen Vorstellungen vom Teufel. pp. 97. *Leipz.* 1890. 8°.
3911. ee. 50. (6.)

MATSON (W. A.) The Adversary. pp. 238.
N.Y. 1891. 8°.   8632. d. 20.

OSBORN (M.) Die Teufellitteratur des XVI. Jahrhunderts. pp. 236. 1893. 8°. HENNING (R.) Acta Germanica. Bd. 3.   12963. dd. 40.

P., C., *le Bibliophile.* Le Diable et ses métamorphoses. pp. 100. *Paris*, 1882. 8°.
4377. aaa. 2.

POGNON (H.) Une incantation contre les génies malfaisants. pp. 47. *Paris*, 1892. 8°. Pam. 3.

STENAY (V. de) Le Diable apôtre par la possession d'Antoine Gay, de Lyon. pp. 282.
Paris. 1894. 8°.   8632. f. 31.

TUCKER (W. H.) The Satan of the Old and New Testament. pp. 237. *Lond.* 1894. 8°.
4257. h. 41.

See also ANGELS: EVIL: EXORCISM: WITCHCRAFT.

DÉMUIN. LEDIEU (A.) Monographie d'un Bourg Picard. 2 pt. *Paris*, 1890. 8°.
10168. cc. 30.

DENEHOLES. *See* CAVES.

DENEUVRE. BERNHARDT (C.) Deneuvre et Baccarat. pp. 296. *Nancy*, 1895. 8°.
10174. f. 24.

DENMARK. [See note on page 1.]

See also SCANDINAVIA.

Antiquities.

See RUNIC INSCRIPTIONS: SCANDINAVIA.

Army.

MEIDELL (F.) Militarismen i Danmark. pp. 66. *Kjøbenh.* 1892. 8°.   9007. g. 22. (5.)

See also infra: HISTORY.

Church of.

BANG (V.) Præstegaardsliv i Danmark. pp. 317. *Kjøbenh.* 1891. 8°.   4685. aaa. 27.

KOCH (H. L. S. P.) and RØRDAM (H. F.) Fortællinger af Danmarks Kirkehistorie, 1517-1848. 2 pt. *Kjøbenh.* 1889. 8°.   4685. aaa. 25.

COPENHAGEN. *Udvalget for Kirkesagens Fremme.* Smaaskrifter til Belysning af Kirkens Tarv og Trang. *Kjøbenh.* 1893, *etc.* 8°.   3925. bb.

ELMQVIST (T. J. A.) Kirken og dens hellige Handlinger. pp. 194. *Odense*, 1892. 8°.
3477. dg. 1.

MATZEN (H.) Haandbog i den danske Kirkeret. pp. 988. *Kjøbenh.* 1891. 8°.   5125. e. 12.

PALUDAN-MÜLLER (J.) Folkekirke og evangelisk Tro. pp. 110. *Kjøbenh.* 1890. 8°. 3925. f. 27.

SCHARLING (C. H.) Grundtvig eller Luther? pp. 145. *Kjøbenh.* 1891. 8°.   3925. cc. 33.

SEVERINSEN (P.) Den danske Kirkes Stilling i den danske Stat. pp. 84. 1893. 16°. COPENHAGEN. *Udvalget for Kirkesagens Fremme.* Smaaskrifter. VI.   3925. bb.

See also infra: HISTORY.

DENMARK—*continued.*

Constitution: Government: Politics.

Duus (A.)   Under Fremskridtets Fane.
Kjøbenh. 1892, *etc.* 8°.   8092. de.

Goos (A. H. F. C.)   Grundtræk af den danske
Statsret. pp. 343. *Kjøbenh.* 1890. 8°. 5705. h. 9.

Jörgensen (J. P.)   Landsognenes Forvaltning
fia 1660.   pp. 195.   *Kjøbenh.* 1890. 8°.
    08276. g. 11.

—— Bondestanden og Socialdemokratiet.
pp. 19.   *Kjøbenh.* 1890. 8°.   Pam. 82.

Matzen (H.)   Forelæsninger over den danske
Tingsret. pp. 640. *Kjøbenh.* 1891. 8°.
    5705. i. 11.

Nyholm (C. C. V.)   Grundtræk af Danmarks
Statsforvaltning. pp. 317. *Kjøbenh.* 1893. 8°.
    8092. de. 41.

Torp (C.)   Dansk Tingsret.   pp. 770.
Kjøbenh. 1892. 8°.   5725. d. 10.

Ussing (J.)   Om afgørelsen af Tvistigheder med
Forvaltningen.   pp. 310.   *Kjøbenh.* 1893. 8°.
    5725. b. 20.

See also infra: History : Socialism : Social
Science.

History.

Fabricius (A. K.)   Fædrelandshistorie for Folkeskolen.   pp. 127.   *Kjøbenh.* 1893. 8°.
    9425. aaa. 12.

Holm (R. J.)   Danmarkshistorie.   pp. 205.
Kjøbenh. 1890. 8°.   9424. bb. 9.

Jorgensen (A. D.)   Fortævellinger af Nordens
Historie.   *Kjøbenh.* 1892, *etc.* 8°. 9425. bbb. 17.

Jörgensen (L.)   Afholdssagens Historie i Danmark.   *Odder,* 1891, *etc.* 8°.   8435. de.

Mollerup (W.)   Danmarks Historie i Billeder.
Kjøbenh. 1893, *etc. obl.* fol.   668.

P.P. *Copenhagen. Musæum.* Tidsskrift for Historie. *Kjøbenh.* 1889, *etc.* 8°.   P.P. 3552. bda.

Rom (N. C.)   Fædrelandshistorie.   pp. 123.
Kjøbenh. 1890. 8°.   9425. aaa. 10.

Sidgwick (C. S.)   Story of Denmark.   pp. 312.
Lond. 1890. 8°.   9425. aaa. 8.

Weitemeyer (H.)   Denmark : its history, *etc.*
pp. 268. *Lond.* 1891. 8°.   10280. eee. 15.

Saxo, *Grammaticus.*   Nine Books of the Danish
History of Saxo Grammaticus.   pp. 435.
Lond. 1894. 8°.   9424. f. 1.

Ac. *Copenhagen. Selskab for Udgivelse af Kilder
til Dansk Historie.*   Repertorium Diplomaticum
Regni Danici Mediævalis. *Kjøbenh.* 1894, *etc.* 8°.
    Ac. 7634/9.

Olrik (H.)   Konge og Præstestand i den danske
Middelalder.   *Kjøbenh.* 1892, *etc.* 8°.   9424. ee.

Barfod (P. F.)   Danmarks Historie, 1536–1670.
Kjøbenh. 1891, *etc.* 8°.   9424. cc. 7.

Vaupell (O. F.)   Den nordiske Syvaaiskrig,
1563–70.   pp. 203.   *Kjøbenh.* 1891. 8°.
    9431. g. 7.

Bering Lüsberg (H. C.)   Christian iv., Danmarks
Konge. *Kjøbenh.* 1890, *etc.* 8°.   10761. h. 12.

Lind (H. D.)   Kong Christian den fjerde.
pp. 449. *Kjøbenh.* 1889. 8°.   8807. c. 42.

Rördam (H. F.)   Historiske Samlinger vedrø-
rende danske Forhold og Personligheder især i
det 17. Aarhundrede. *Kjøbenh.* 1890, *etc.* 8°.
    9424. bb. 8.

Nyrop (C.)   Oplysninger om Grev Valdemar
Kristians Ruslandsfærd 1643–45.   1891. 8°.
Ac. *Copenhagen. Dansk Historisk Forening.*
Tidsskrift.   Række 6.   Bd. 3.   Ac. 7630.

Brasch (C. H.)   Prins Georg af Danmark i hans
Ægteskab med Anna af Storbrittannien.
pp. 99. *Kjøbenh.* 1890. 8°.   10805. f. 15.

DENMARK.—History—*continued.*

Holm (P. E.)   Danmark-Norges Historie, 1720–
30. *Kjøbenh.* 1890, *etc.* 8°.   9424. ee. 5.

Brown (J.)   Memoirs of the Sovereigns of Denmark, 1766–1818.   2 vol.   *Lond.* 1895. 8°.
    10600. f. 1.

Koch (H. L. S. P.)   Kong Christian vi. Historie.
pp. 354. *Kjøbenh.* 1886. 8°.   9424. bb. 5.

Blangstrup (J. C.)   Christian vii. og Caroline
Mathilde.   pp. 238.   *Kjøbenh.* 1891. 8°.
    10761. h. 13.

Rubin (M.)   1807–14.   Studier til Danmarks
Historie.   pp. 627.   *Kjøbenh.* 1892. 8°.
    9424. i. 13.

Thrige (S. B.)   Frederik den sjettes Historie.
pp. 190. *Kjøbenh.* 1891. 8°.   10761. cc. 23.

Lütken (O.)   Les Danois sur l'Escaut, 1809–13.
pp. 172. *Copenhague,* 1891. 8°.   9080. bbb. 35.

Woynar (C.)   Österreichs Beziehungen zu Dänemark, 1813–14.   1891.   8°.   Ac. *etc.*   Vienna.
K. Akademie.   Archiv für österreichische Geschichte.   Bd. 77.   Ac. 810/8.

Nielsen (Y.)   Diplomatiske Aktstykker vedkommende Norges Opgjør med Danmark, 1818–19.
pp. 77. *Christiania,* 1889. 8°.   Pam. 74.

Rosenberg (C. F. V. M.)   Danmark i Aaret
1848.   pp. 338.   *Kjøbenh.* 1891. 8°.
    9431. aaa. 12.

Wilde (O. A. K.)   Fra Krigen i 1848–49.
pp. 190. *Kjøbenh.* 1892. 8°.   9080. e. 7.

Neergaard (N.)   Under Junigrundloven, 1848–
66.   *Kjøbenh.* 1892, *etc.* 8°.   9424. bb. 7.

Albrectsen (S.)   Fra den tyske Invasion i 1864.
pp. 37. *Randers,* 1889. 8°.   9007. ff. 4. (5.)

Denmark.   Den dansk-tydske Krig, 1864.
Kjøbenh. 1890, *etc.* 8°.   9424. i. 12.

Hoffmann (C. A.)   Erindringer fra Krigen 1834.
pp. 299. *Kjøbenh.* 1892. 8°.   9080. e. 10.

Sörensen (C. T. v.)   Erindringer fra Første
Regiment 1864.   pp. 124.   *Kjøbenh.* 1891. 8°.
    8823. ddd. 22.

Thorsander (G.)   Dansk-tyska Kriget 1864.
pp. 111. *Stockholm,* 1890. 8°.   9080. c. 27.

Wille (R.)   Lose Tagebuchblätter aus dem
Feldzug gegen Dänemark.   pp. 283.
Berl. 1895. 8°.   9080. ee. 11.

Brandes (E.)   Fra 85 til 91.   pp. 87.
Kjøbenh. 1891. 8°.   Pam. 74.

Berg (C. P.)   Fra Rigsdagen 1890–91.
Kjøbenh. 1891, *etc.* 8°.   8094. b.

Nelson (O. N.)   History of Scandinavians in the
United States.   *Minneapolis,* 1893, *etc.* 8°.
    010882. k. 15.

See also supra : Constitution : Norway.

History, Ecclesiastical.
See supra : Church of.

Law.

Ac. *Copenhagen. Selskab for Udgivelse til dansk
Historie.*   Forarbejderne til Kong Kristian v.'s
danske Lov. *Kjøbenh.* 1891, *etc.* 8°. Ac. 7634/8.

Ahlmann (O. F.)   Om umiddelbare Fogedforret-
ninger. pp. 112. *Kjøbenh.* 1892. 8°. 5705. a. 2.

Deuntzer (J. H.)   Kort Fremstilling af den
danske Personret.   pp. 86.   *Kjøbenh.* 1889. 8°.
    5725. bb. 19. (5.)

—— Den danske Familieret.   pp. 368.
Kjøbenh. 1892. 8°.   5705. c. 15.

—— Kort Fremstilling af den danske Næringsret.
pp. 48. *Kjøbenh.* 1890. 8°.   5725. bb. 19. (4.)

Hude (A.)   Danehoffet og dets Plads i Danmarks
Statsforfatning. pp. 224. *Kjøbenh.* 1893. 8°.
    8092. b. 3.

DENMARK—Law—continued.

LASSEN (J. S. V.) Haandbog i Obligationsretten.
pp. 710. *Kjøbenh.* 1892. 8°.　　　5725. d. 7.

MATZEN (H.) Forelæsninger over den danske
Retshistorie. *Kjøbenh.* 1893, *etc.* 8°. 9424. dd.

MÖLLER (E. J.) Forudsætninger. pp. 311.
Kjøbenh. 1894. 8°.　　　　　5725. bb. 16.

RICHTER (V.) Juridisk Stat, 1892. pp. 92.
Kjøbenh. 1892. 8°.　　　　　6005. g. 16.

UTKE DAMM (J. F.) Om Betingelserne for Er-
statnings- og Straffeansvar. pp. 166.
Kjøbenh. 1889. 8°.　　　　　6025. aaa. 7.

See also LAW, *Commercial : Criminal.*

Topography.

BAEDEKER (C.) Norway and Denmark. 2 pt.
Leips. 1895. 8°.　　　　　2352. a.

COOK (T.) Guide to Norway and Denmark.
pp. 206. *Lond.* 1893. 8°.　　10280. aa. 24.

DENMARK. Murray's Handbook for Denmark.
pp. 22, 153.　　　　　　　　2364. a. 7.
—— Denmark, its Medical Organization, Hygiene and Demography. pp. 474.
Copenhagen, 1891. 8°　　　　7391. g. 13.

GINISTY (P.) De Paris au Cap Nord. pp. 252.
Paris, 1892. 8°.　　　　　10280. f. 11.

MALATIER (L.) and SAILÈS (A.) Au Pays
d'Hamlet. pp. 174. *Villefranche,* 1894. 8°.
　　　　　　　　　　　　10281. l. 9.

THYE (R.) Danmarks Geografi. pp. 61.
Kjøbenh. 1892. 8°.　　　　　10280. c. 4.

WEITEMEYER (H.) Denmark: its history and
topography. pp. 268. *Lond.* 1891. 8°.
　　　　　　　　　　　　10280. eee. 15.

Trade. Finance, etc.

GREEN (T.) Danske Fonds og Aktier, 1891.
pp. 194. *Kjøbenh.* 1892. 8°. 08227. de. 39.

THOMSON (C.) Les conditions du travail en
Danemark. pp. 84, *Paris,* 1891. 8°.
　　　　　　　　　　08276. k. 4. (6.)

DENT. THOMPSON (W.) Sedbergh, Garsdale
and Dent. pp. 280. *Leeds.* 1892. 8°..
　　　　　　　　　　　　10360. k. 12.

DENTISTRY. *See* TEETH.

DEPTFORD. STURDEE (T.) Reminiscences
of old Deptford. *Lond.* 1895. obl. 8°.
　　　　　　　　　　　　10352. f. 6.
See also TRINITY HOUSE, *Corporation of the.*

DERBY AND DERBYSHIRE. ANDREWS
(W.) Bygone Derbyshire. pp. 256.
Derby, 1892. 8°.　　　　010358. f. 38.

BRADBURY (E.) The Way about Derbyshire.
pp. 176. 1893. 8°. Way-About Series. No. 4.
　　　　　　　　　　　　010358. e.

COX (J. C.) Three centuries of Derbyshire Annals. 2 vol. *Lond.* 1890. 8°. 010358. l. 28.

DERBY. Murray's Handbook for Derbyshire.
pp. 38. 229. *Lond.* 1892, 8°.　2364. a. 8.
—— Photographs of Derby. *Lond.* 1895. obl. 8°.
　　　　　　　　　　　　10360. aa. 44.

FOSTER (A. J.) Round about the Crooked Spire.
pp. 203. *Lond.* 1894. 8°.　010358. e. 27.

KEYS (J.) Sketches of old Derby. pp. 203.
Lond. 1895. 4°.　　　　　10352. k. 8.

LEYLAND (J.) The Peak of Derbyshire. pp. 310.
Lond. 1891. 8°.　　　　　10368. g. 42.

MELLO (J. M.) Handbook to the geology of
Derbyshire. pp. 89. *Lond.* 1891. 8°.
　　　　　　　　　　　　7109. aa. 22.

PAYNE (C. J.) Derby Churches old and new.
pp. 158. *Derby,* 1893. 8°.　10360. c. 30.

DERBY AND DERBYSHIRE—cont.

P.P. *Derby.* Notts and Derbyshire notes and
queries. *Derby,* 1892, *etc.* 8°.
　　　　　　　　P.P. 6065. f. and 2210.

SHELDON (J. P.) Through Staffordshire stiles
and Derbyshire dales. pp. 21. *Derby,* 1894. 4°.
　　　　　　　　　　　　10368. h. 33.

STONE (J. S.) Woods and dales of Derbyshire.
pp. 180. *Phila.* 1894. 8°.　10358. h. 27.

T, J. Old Halls and families of Derbyshire.
Lond. 1892, *etc.* 4°.　　　10351. k. 18.

WARD (J.) Pleasant rambles around Derby.
pp. 131. *Derby,* 1895. 8°　10358. bbb. 68.

DERMATOLOGY. *See* SKIN.

DERRICKS. *See* MACHINERY, *Hoisting. etc.*

DERWENT, Cumberland. Ac. Carlisle.
Vale of Derwent Field Club. Notes on the Vale
of Derwent. pp. 106. *Carlisle,* 1891. 8°.
　　　　　　　　　　　　10352. cc. 45.

ROBINSON (J. F.) Guide to the Vale of Derwent.
pp. 24. *Newcastle,* 1892. 8°.
　　　　　　　　　　10348. ccc. 59. (6.)

DESIGN. *See* ART, *Decorative.*

DETERMINANTS. BALTZER (R.) Theorie
und Anwendung der Determinanten. pp. 278.
Leipz. 1881. 8°.　　　　　8531. e. 40.

WELD (L. G.) Course in the theory of Determinants. pp. 238. *Lond.* 1893. 8°.
　　　　　　　　　　　　8535. bb. 20.

WEICHOLD (G.) Lehrbuch der Determinanten.
1893, *etc.* 8°. Kleyer's mathematische Encyclopädie.　　　　　　　　8705. g.
See also ALGEBRA : MATHEMATICS.

DETROIT, River. BAILLAIRGÉ (G. F.) Le
Détroit et la baie Hudson. pp. 54.
Joliette, 1888. 8°.　　　　Pam. 86.

DETROIT, Town. BATES (G. C.) By-gones
of Detroit. 1894. 8°. Ac. Lansing. *Pioneer
Society.* Pioneer Collections. Vol. 22.
　　　　　　　　　　　　Ac. 8403.

DEVANÂGARI. *See* SANSCRIT.

DEVELOPMENT. *See* EVOLUTION.

DEVENTER. BEEKMAN (B. A.) Verorde-
ningen der gemeente Deventer. pp. 227.
Deventer, 1890. 8°.　　　　5686. a. 25.

DEVIL. *See* DEMONOLOGY.

DEVONPORT, Tasmania. BALFE (O.)
Devonport and its surroundings. pp. 54.
Launceston, 1893. 4°.　　　Pam. 87.

DEVONSHIRE. DREDGE (J. I.) Sheaves
of Devon Bibliography. 2 pt.
Plymouth, 1889, 90. 4°.　　11899. e. 42.

BLACK (A.) Guide to Devonshire. Edited by
A. R. H. Moncrieff. pp. 232. *Lond.* 1895, 8°.
　　　　　　　　　　　　10351. bb. 66.

BROWNLOW (W. R. B.) *R.C. Bp. of Clifton.* Life
in Devon in 1287. pp. 23. *Lond.* 1894. 8°.
　　　　　　　　　　　　Pam. 29.

CHUDLEIGH (J.) Devonshire Antiquities. pp. 123.
Exeter, 1893. 8°.　　　　7705. aaaa. 38.

DEVON. Murray's Handbook for Devon. pp. 291.
Lond. 1895. 8°.　　　　　2364. a. 9.

DREDGE (J. I.) Devon Booksellers in the 17th
and 18th centuries. 3 pt. *Plymouth,* 1885, 87. 4°.
　　　　　　　　　　　　11899. e. 43.

HEARDER and SON. Illustrated guide to sea fishing and the rivers of S. Devon. pp. 115.
Plymouth, 1892. 16°.　　　Pam. 83.

PAGE (J. L. W.) Coasts of Devon. pp. 444.
Lond. 1895. 8°.　　　　　010358. e. 34.

DEVONSHIRE—continued.

PAGE (J. L. W.) The Rivers of Devon. pp. 348.
Lond. 1893. 8°.   010358. h. 6.

REICHEL (O. J.) The Hundred of Hartland and
the Geldroll. pp. 3. *Plymouth*, 1894. 8°.
                    10348. d. 20. (13.)

—— Suggestions to aid in identifying the Place-
Names in the Devonshire Domesday. pp. 35.
Plymouth, 1894. 8°.   Pam. 90.

ROGERS (W. H. H.) West-Country stories and
sketches. pp. 203. *Exeter*, 1895. 4°.
                    010358. h. 21.

THOMPSON (E. S.) Climate of Devonshire.
1895. 8°. Ac. London. *Medical and Chirurgical Society.* Climates of Great Britain. Vol.1.
                    7462. g.

VIVIAN (J. L.) Visitations of the County of
Devon, 1531, 1564 and 1620. pp. 899.
Exeter, 1895. 4°.   9914. dd. 14.

WADE (Z. E. A.) Pixy-led in N. Devon.
pp. 322. *Lond.* 1895. 8°.   10352. b. 46.

WARD (C. S.) and BADDELEY (M. J. B.) South
Devon. pp. 225. 1892. 8°. Thorough Guide
Series.   10347. aa.

WHITE (W.) History and Directory of Devon.
pp. 1303. *Sheffield*, 1890. 8°.   N.R.

WORTH (R. N.) History of Devonshire. pp. 347.
Lond. 1895. 8°.   10358. d. 49.

—— Tourist's guide to N. Devon. pp. 119.
Lond. 1894. 8°.   10352. a. 70.

—— Suggested identifications of Domesday
Manors of Devon. pp. 29. 1892. 8°.
                    10348. d. 20. (4.)

Dialect.

Ac. London. *English Dialect Society.* CHOPE
(R. P.) Dialect of Hartland, Devonshire.
pp. 123. *Lond.* 1891. 8°.   Ac. 9934/30.

HEWETT (S.) Peasant speech of Devon. pp. 184.
Lond. 1892. 8°.   12315. e. 39.

DEWSBURY. CHADWICK (S. J.) Handbook
to Dewsbury. pp. 46. *Dewsbury*, 1893. 8°.
                    10347. d. 7. (7.)

DHARWAR. JUKES (T.) Supplement to
reminiscences in Dharwar. pp. 24.
Bombay, 1894. 8°.   Pam. 88.

DIABETES. EBSTEIN (W.) Über die Lebens-
weise der Zuckerkranken. pp. 144.
Wiesbaden, 1892. 8°.   7620. e. 22.

GONZALEZ HERNANDEZ (R.) La Cachexie bronzée
dans le diabète. pp. 73. *Montpellier*, 1892. 8°.
                    7641. dd. 10.

HOFMEISTER (B.) Diabetes Mellitus. 1894. 8°.
Ac. London. *New Sydenham Society.* Clinical
Lectures. Ser. 3.   Ac. 3838/27.

PAVY (F. W.) Physiology of the Carbohydrates:
their relation to diabetes. pp. 280.
Lond. 1894. 8°.   7406. f. 10.

POOLE (W. H.) Cookery for the diabetic. pp. 64.
Lond. 1891. 8°.   07945. e. 51.

PURDY (C. W.) Diabetes. pp. 184.
Phila. 1890. 8°.   7630. e. 7.

SAUNDBY (R.) Lectures on Diabetes. pp. 232.
Bristol, 1891. 8°.   7630. e. 9.
See also GENITO-URINARY ORGANS: KIDNEYS.

DIAGNOSIS, Medical. BUM (A.) and
SCHNIRER (M. T.) Diagnostisches Lexikon.
Wien, 1893, *etc.* 8°.   7441. d.

DA COSTA (J. M.) Medical Diagnosis. pp. 995.
Lond. 1890. 8°.   7460. ff. 16.

FENWICK (S.) Medical Diagnosis. pp. 352.
Lond. 1891. 8°.   2254. a. 9.

GIBSON (G. A.) and RUSSELL (W.) Physical
Diagnosis. pp. 383. *Edinb.* 1893. 8°. 7440. de. 8.

DIAGNOSIS, Medical—continued.

JAKSCH (R. v.) Clinical Diagnosis. pp. 460.
Lond. 1893. 8°.   7442. g. 25.

MAUREL (E.) Manuel de séméiologie technique.
pp. 558. *Paris*, 1890. 12°.   7321. hbb. 20.

MUSSER (J. H.) Treatise on Medical Diagnosis.
pp. 881. *Edinb.* 1894. 8°.   7320. dd. 7.

VIERORDT (O.) Clinical text-book of Medical
Diagnosis. pp. 700. *Edinb.* 1891. 8°. 7460. f. 7.

WESENER (F.) Lehrbuch der chemischen Unter-
suchungsmethoden zur Diagnostik innerer
Krankheiten. pp. 280. 1890. 8°. Wreden's
Sammlung. Bd. 15.   7321. h.
See also MEDICINE.

DIAMONDS. AFRICA. Diamond industry of
South Africa. pp. 18. *Lond.* 1893. 8°.
                    Pam. 27.

AFRICAN DIAMOND MINES. Sketch of the African
Diamond Mines. *N.Y.* 1890. 4°.   7107. e. 13.

LOOS (D. de) Diamant. 1890. 8°. Ac. Haarlem.
Nederlandsche Huishondelijke Maatschappij. Ko-
loniaal Museum te Haarlem. Catalogus. Dl. 6.
Sk. 2.   Ac. 4441/5.

MIDDLEBROOK (J. E.) Diamond industry of South
Africa. *Kimberley*, 1892. *obl.* 8°. 7106. de. 1.

REDMAN (W.) Hall Marks, illustrated. And
list of great Diamonds. pp. 48.
Bradford, 1893. 8°.   7709. bb. 65.

REUNERT (T.) Diamonds in South Africa.
pp. 242. *Cape Town*, 1893. 8°.   7106. ff. 22.

STREETER (E. W.) Koh-i-Nûr Diamond. pp. 81.
Lond. 1895. 16°.   7106. de. 6.
See also GEMS.

DIARRHŒA: DYSENTERY. FAYRER
(*Sir* J.) Diarrhœa. 1893. 8°. DAVIDSON (A.)
Diseases of Warm Climates.   7686. dd. 2.

DAVISON (D. M.) Dysentery. 1893. 8°.
DAVISON (A.) Diseases of Warm Climates.
                    7686. dd. 2.

DIATOMACEAE. HABIRSHAW (F.) Cata-
logue of the Diatomaceæ. ff. 299.
Geneva, N.Y., 1888. 4°.   7298. g. 11.

HÉRIBAUD-JOSEPH (F.) Les Diatomées d'Auvergne.
pp. 255. *Clermont-F.* 1893. 8°.   7299. g. 26.

MILLS (F. W.) Introduction to the study of
Diatomaceæ. pp. 243. *Lond.* 1893. 8°.
                    07028. l. 13.

MOELLER (J. D.) Lichtdrucktafeln hervorragend
schöner Möller'scher Diatomaceen-Präparate.
Wedel, 1891. fol.   1819. b. 10.

P.P. *Paris.* Le Diatomiste. *Paris*, 1890, *etc.* fol.
                    52.

WOLLE (F.) Diatomaceæ of North America.
pp. 47. *Bethlehem*, 1890. 8°.   7298. ee. 18.

DEBY (J.) Analysis of the diatomaceous genus
Campylodiscus. pp. 95. *Lond.* 1890. 8°. 7298. e. 5.
See also ALGAE.

DICTATION. DICTATION BOOK. New Dic-
tation book. pp. 112. *Lond.* 1893. 8°.
                    12981. aa. 61.

—— Suggestive Dictation book.
Lond. 1894. *etc.* 8°.   12981. bb. 52.

DICTATION EXERCISES. Dictation exercises.
pp. 96. *Lond.* 1891. 8°.   12981. aa. 46.

DICTATION TESTS. Dictation Tests. pp. 48.
Lond. 1891. 8°.   12200. aaa. 16.

EVANS (T.) Dictation exercises.
Lond. 1891, *etc.* 8°.   12981. cc.

GREEN (J.) Spelling and Dictation exercises.
Manch. 1891, *etc.* 8°.   12981. bbb. 47.

LOAD (F. C.) Exercises in Dictation, *etc.* pp. 29.
Lond. 1894. 8°.   12901, bbb. 45. (5.)

DICTATION—*continued.*

LUCAS (H.) Unseen exercises in Dictation. pp. 19. *Leeds*, 1892. 8°. 12901. ccc. 17. (11.)

SKERRY (G. E.) Graduated exercises in Dictation. pp. 95. *Lond.* 1894. 8°. 12981. b. 63.

TEACHER. Handbook of Dictation exercises. pp. 36. 1891. 8°. Guide Series. 12203. ccc.

DICTIONARIES. For Encyclopædic Dictionaries, *see* ENCYCLOPÆDIAS: for Biblical and Theological Dictionaries, *see* THEOLOGY: and for Dictionaries of Languages, *see* under the language required.

DIET. *See* FOOD.

DIGESTION. Ac. London. *New Sydenham Society.* EWALD (C. A.) Lectures on diseases of the Digestive Organs. *Lond.* 1891, *etc.* 8°. Ac. 3838/54.

ALLINSON (T. R.) Diet and Digestion. pp 46. *Lond.* 1892. 8°. 7306. df. 49. (9.)

CHELTHAM (A.) Indigestion. *Rhyl*, 1893. 8°. 07305. f. 17. (7.)

DEWAR (J.) Dyspepsia. pp. 88. 1891. 8°. "Red Cross" Series. 7404. d.

DUTTON (T.) Digestion rationally discussed. pp. 124. *Lond.* 1892. 8°. 7404. c. 38.

—— Indigestion explained, treated and dieted. pp. 220. *Lond.* 1893. 8°. 7616. aaa. 10.

GROSJEAN (A.) Recherches sur l'action de la propeptone et de la peptone. pp. 80. 1892. 8°. Ac. Brussels. *Académie.* Mémoires couronnés. Tom. 46. Ac. 985/4.

HALL (W. W.) Indigestion, how to cure it. pp. 162. *Glasg.* 1892. 8°. 7620. a. 14.

HERSCHELL (G. A.) Indigestion. pp. 343. *Lond.* 1895. 8°. 7620. de. 33.

INDIGESTION. Indigestion: homœopathic treatment. pp. 23. *Lond.* 1885. 24°. 7620. a. 22.

ROBERTS (*Sir* W.) Contributions on Digestion. pp. 261. *Lond.* 1891. 8°. 7391. df. 10.

ROSENHEIM (T.) Pathologie und Therapie der Krankheiten des Verdauungsapperates. *Wien*, 1891, *etc.* 8°. 7620. cc.

RUSSELL (J. R.) On Digestion. pp. 86. *Lond.* 1890. 8°. 07305. e. 17. (3.)

SIGAUD (C.) Traité des troubles fonctionnels de l'appareil digestif. pp. 240. *Paris*, 1894. 8°. 7630. g. 25.

SINCLAIR (W. J.) Indigestion. 1890. 8°. MANCHESTER. *Sanitary Association.* Health Lectures. Ser. 1. No. 4. 7404. bbb.

STACPOOLE (F.) Indigestion. pp. 29. *Paisley*, 1891. 8°. 07305. f. 5. (8.)

STARR (L.) Diseases of the Digestive Organs in infancy. pp. 396. *Edinb.* 1891. 8°. 7620. de. 21.

VAN VALZAH (W. H.) Chronic disorders of the Digestive Tube. pp. 151. *N.Y.* 1893. 8°. 7620. de. 24.

See also ABDOMEN: BILE: FOOD: LIVER: STOMACH.

DIJON. BENIGNUS, *Monastery of, at Dijon.* Le Trésor de l'Abbaye Saint-Bénigne de Dijon. pp. 469. 1894. 8°. Ac. Dijon. *Société Bourguignonne.* Mémoires, Tom. 10. Ac. 6024.

BRESSON (J.) Histoire de l'eglise Notre-Dame de Dijon. pp. 576. *Dijon*, 1891. 8°. 4629. i. 23.

CHABEUF (H.) Dijon. Monuments et souvenirs. *Dijon*, 1892, *etc.* 4°. 10173. g.

CLÉMENT-JANIN (M. H.) Les vieilles maisons de Dijon. pp. 216. *Dijon*, 1890. 8°. 10169. c. 14.

CORNEREAU (A.) Le Palais des États de Bourgogne. 1890. 8°. Ac. Dijon. *Société Bourguignonne.* Mémoires. Tom. 6. Ac. 6024.

DIJON—*continued.*

DORMOY (P. A) Guerre de 1870–71. Les trois batailles de Dijon. pp. 600. *Paris*, 1894. 8°. 9079. k. 7.

GARNIER (J.) Les anciens orfèvres de Dijon. pp. 47. *Dijon*, 1889. 8°. 7943. i. 43. (8.)

MOREAU (J.) Dijon à la fin du XVIII° siècle. pp. 144. *Dijon*, 1893. 4°. 10173. h. 22.

SELLENET (J. B.) La Sainte Hostie de Dijon. pp. 59. *Dijon.* 1894. 12°. 4324. e. 12.

See also BURGUNDY.

DINAN. LE SAGE (J.) Considérations sur quelques questions municipales touchant les intérêts de la cité. pp. 16. 80. *Dinan*, 1890. 8°. 010171. f. 24. (2.)

DINANT. HACHEZ (H.) Histoire de Dinant. pp. 269. *Court St. Étienne*, 1893. 8°. 010271. h. 2.

PIRENNE (H.) Histoire de la Constitution de Dinant au moyen-âge. pp. 119. 1889. 8°. Ac. Ghent. *Université.* Recueil de travaux. Fasc. 2. Ac. 2647/3.

DINAS MAWDDWY. ASHTON (C.) Guide to Dinas Mawddwy. pp. 37. *Aberystwith*, 1893. 8°. 10348. ccc. 59. (7.)

DIPHTHERIA. ARLOING (S.) Sérumthérapie et diphthérie. 1895. 8°. Ac. Lyons. *Académie des Sciences.* Mémoires. Sciences et Lettres. Sér. 3. Tom. 3. Ac. 364/5.

BEHRING (E.) Die Geschichte der Diphtherie. pp. 208. *Leipz.* 1893. 8°. 7616. i. 9.

BERDOE (E.) Microbes and Disease Demons. Anti-toxin treatment of diphtheria. pp. 93. *Lond.* 1895. 8°. 7561. aa. 18.

BOURGES (H.) La Diphtérie. pp. 226. *Paris*, 1892. 8°. 7616. c. 40.

BROWNE (L.) Diphtheria and its associates. pp. 272. *Lond.* 1895. 8°. 7615. bb. 1.

DELTHIL (P. L. É.) Traité de la Diphtérie. pp. 686. *Paris*, 1891. 8°. 7616. h. 13.

ESCHERICH (T.) Ätiologie und Pathogenese der Diphtherie. *Wien*, 1894, *etc.* 8°. 7615. dd.

—— Diphtherie. pp. 155. *Wien*, 1895. 8°. 7615. dd. 3.

GALLEZ (L.) Diphthérie animale et humaine. 1895. 8°. Ac. Brussels. *Académie de Médecine.* Bulletin. Sér. IV. Tom. 9. Ac. 3794.

GILLET (H.) La pratique de la Sérothérapie. pp. 293. *Paris.* 1895. 12°. 7616. a. 52.

GOTTSTEIN (A.) Immunität, Infektionstheorie und Diphtherie-Serum. pp. 69. *Berl.* 1894. 8°. 7616. f. 17.

HARRISON (H. F. E.) Diphtheria. pp. 16. *Lond.* 1893. 8°. 7306. e. 22. (8.)

HUEBNER (J. B. O.) Studien über die Behandlung der Diphtherie mit dem Behringschen Heilserum. pp. 124. *Leipz.* 1895. 8°..

JENNER (*Sir* W.) Lectures and essays on Diphtheria. pp. 581. *Lond.* 1893. 8°. 7561. dd. 27.

LANDAU (R.) Zur Geschichte des Diphtherieheilserums Behrings. pp. 23. *München*, 1895. 8°. Pam. 39.

MARTIN (B. R.) Practical treatise on Diptheria. pp. 64. *Lond.* 1895. 8°. 7616. aaaa. 3.

PARKER (R. W.) Diphtheria: its nature and treatment. pp. 182. *Lond.* 1891. 8°. 7616. f. 1.

POPE (H. C.) Discussion on Diphtheria. pp. 24. *Lond.* 1895. 8°. 7561. k. 26. (14.)

POPLAR. *Sanitary Committee.* Report on the cause of Diphtheria. pp. 21. *Poplar*, 1894. 8°. 7561. k. 26. (11.)

SYMPSON (E. M.) Causes of death in Diphtheria. pp. 28. *Lond.* 1891. 8°. 07305. h. 7. (11.)

DIPHTHERIA—continued.

TALBOT (R. M.) Diphtheria. pp. 11.
Poplar, 1894. 8°. 7561. k. 26. (12.)

THORNE (R. T.) Diphtheria : pp. 266.
Lond. 1891. 8°. 7616. ee. 2.

TORDEUS (E.) Note sur le traitement de la diph-
térie par la sérothérapie. pp. 7.
Brux. 1895. 8° Pam. 39.
See also DISEASE, *Infectious :* THROAT.

DIPLOMACY. U.S. *Department of State.*
Index to the literature of Diplomacy.
1887, *etc.* 4°. 11899. c. 30.

BENITEZ Y FERNANDEZ (A.) Nomografía diplo-
mático consular. *Madrid*, 1893, *etc.* 8°.
5384. de.

CHEVREY-RAMEAU (P.) Répertoire diplomatique
et consulaire. 4 pt. *Paris*, 1883–88. 8°.
6916. b. 6.

DIPLOMATEN KLATSCH. Diplomaten-Klatsch.
pp. 350. *Berl.* 1890. 8°. 8026. ee. 22.

FÉRAND-GIRAUD (L. J. D.) États et Souverains ;
personnel diplomatique, *etc.* devant les tribunaux étrangers. 2 tom. *Paris*, 1895. 8°.
06955. df. 25.

MAULDE-LA-CLAVIÈRE (A. R. de) La Diplomatie
au temps de Machiavel. *Paris*, 1892, *etc.* 8°.
9072. f. 16.

ODIER (P. G.) Des privilèges des agents diplomatiques en pays de chrétienté. pp. 467.
Paris, 1890. 8°. 06955. df. 1.

VERCAMER (E.) Des franchises diplomatiques.
pp. 333. *Paris*, 1891. 8°. 06955. df. 3.
See also CONSULS : LAW, *International.*

DIPTERA. BECKER (T.) Dipterologische
Studien. 1894, *etc.* 8°. Berliner entomologische
Zeitschrift. Bd. 39. Ac. 3625.

BIGOT (J. M. F.) Descriptions de diptères nouveaux. 1892, *etc.* 8°. Ac. Paris. *Société
Zoologique.* Mémoires. Tom. 5. Ac. 3556/3.

BUCKTON (G. B.) Natural History of the Drone-
Fly. pp. 91. *Lond.* 1895. 8°. 7297. c. 20.

LYNCH ARRIBÁLZAGA (F.) Dipterologia argentina.
Mycetophilidae. pp. 75. *Buenos A.* 1892. 8°.
7296. d. 2.

—— Dipterologia Argentina. Syrphidæ.
pp. 181. *Buenos A.* 1891. 8°. 7298. eee. 11.

OSTEN-SACKEN (C. R.) Characters of the three
Divisions of Diptera. 1893. 8°. Berliner entomologische Zeitschrift. Bd. 37. Ac. 3625.

ROEDER (V. v.) Dipteren gesammelt auf einer
Reise durch Süd-Amerika. *Berl.* 1892. 8°.
7002. f. 16. (8.)

STROBL (G.) Die Dipteren von Steiermark.
1893. 8°. Ac. Gratz. *Naturwissenschaftlicher
Verein.* Mittheilungen. Hft. 29, 30. Ac. 2905.

THEOBALD (F. V.) Account of British Flies.
Vol. 1. Pt. 1–8. *Lond.* 1892–93. 8°.
7298. ee. 28.

WILLISTON (S. W.) Synopsis of North American
Syrphidæ. pp. 335. 1886. 8°. Ac. Washing-
ton. *Smithsonian Institution.* Bulletin of the
National Museum. No. 31. Ac. 1875/13.
See also MOSQUITO.

DIPTERACEAE. *See* FORESTRY.

DISCOBOLI. GARMAN (S.) The Discoboli.
pp. 96. 1892. 4°. Ac. Cambridge. *Harvard
University. Museum of Zoology.* Memoirs.
Vol. XIV. Ac. 1736/4.
See also FISH.

DISEASE : ÆTIOLOGY.
General.

BURDETT (H. C.) Helps in Sickness, *etc.*
pp. 484. *Lond.* 1894. 8°. 7404. cc. 23.

DISEASE : ÆTIOLOGY—continued.

BRAMWELL (J. B.) Exciting causes of Disease.
1886. 8°. EDINBURGH. *Health Society.* Health
Lectures. Ser. 6. 7404. g.

EYSOLDT (W.) Lehrbuch der inneren Krankheiten. *Merseburg*, 1894, *etc.* 8°. 7630. i.

GILLIES (H. C.) Interpretation of Disease.
Lond. 1891, *etc.* 8°. 7305. e.

JADROO. Disease and Race. pp. 120.
Lond. 1894. 8°. 07305. i. 6.

KUEHNER (A.) Der Staub als Krankheitserreger.
pp. 56. *Neuwied*, 1894. 8°. 7616. i. 16.

SMITH (P. H. P.) Lumleian Lectures on certain
points in the ætiology of Diseases. pp. 236.
Lond. 1895. 8°. 7442. ee. 2.

TANNER (T. H.) Index of Diseases and treatment.
pp. 512. *Lond.* 1891. 8°. 2254. a. 25.

THAMODARAMPILLAY (C.) Essay on the chief
causes of Diseases. pp. 72. *Colombo*, 1894. 8°.
7460. a. 4.

DAVIDSON (A.) Geographical Pathology. 2 vol.
Edinb. 1892. 8°. 7686. f. 6.

FELKIN (R. W.) Geographical distribution of
Tropical Diseases in Africa. *Edinb.* 1895. 8°.
7687. ee. 23.

HAVILAND (A.) Geographical distribution of
Disease in Great Britain. *Lond.* 1892, *etc.* 8°.
7686. dd. 1.

See also BACTERIOLOGY : DIAGNOSIS : MEDICINE :
PATHOLOGY, *etc.*

Infectious Diseases.

Ac. London. *Clinical Society.* Report of a
Committee appointed to investigate the periods
of incubation of infectious Diseases. pp. 225.
Lond. 1892. 8°. Ac. 3826.

BEHRING (E.) Abhandlungen zur ätiologischen
Therapie von ansteckenden Krankheiten.
pp. 366. *Leipz.* 1893. 8°. 7560. i. 15.

—— Die Bekämpfung der Infectionskrankheiten.
Leipz. 1894, *etc.* 8°. 7561. l.

BERNHEIM (S.) Immunisation et Sérumthérapie.
pp. 340. *Paris*, 1895. 8°. 7561. aa. 19.

BOUCHARD (C.) Rapport sur les Épidémies qui
ont sévi en France, 1889. pp. 64. 1891. 8°.
Ac. Paris. *Académie de Médecine.* Mémoires.
Tom. 36. Fasc. 2. Ac. 3725.

CREIGHTON (C.) History of Épidemics in Britain.
2 vol. *Camb.* 1891–94. 8°. 2255. f. 8.

CURGENVEN (J. B.) On the oil of Eucalyptus
Globulus in the treatment of infectious Diseases.
pp. 12. *Lond.* 1891. 8°. 07305. e. 23. (10.)

DAVIDSON (A.) Geographical Pathology : geographical distribution of infective Diseases.
2 vol. *Edinb.* 1892. 8°. 7686. f. 6.

ENGLAND AND WALES. *Local Government Board.*
Memorandum on the circumstances under which
the closing of Public Elementary Schools may
be required, *Lond.* 1893. fol. 7560. k. 7. (2.)

FESSLER (J.) Klinisch-experimentelle Studien
über chirurgische Infectionskrankheiten.
pp. 176. *München*, 1891. 8°. 07482. g. 10.

FRACASTORO (G.) Les trois livres de J. Fracastor
sur la contagion. pp. 372. *Paris*, 1893. 8°.
7561. aa. 13.

GOTTSTEIN (A.) Immunität, Infektionstheorie
und Diphtherie-Serum. pp. 69. *Berl.* 1894. 8°.
7616. f. 17.

HART (E. A.) Essays on State Medecine. 2 pt.
Lond. 1894. 8°. 6095. b. 33.

JANKE (H.) Embryologie und Infections-Krankheits-Uebertragung. pp. 104. *Berl.* 1894. 8°.
7580. cc. 12.

DISEASE.—Infectious Diseases.—cont.

Kocher (T.) and Tavel (E.) Vorlesungen über chirurgische Infectionskrankheiten.
Basel, 1895, *etc.* 8°.   07482. k.

London. *Medical Officers of Schools Association.* Rules for the prevention of infectious Diseases in schools. pp. 35. *Lond.* 1891. 8°.
                                              07305. h. 8. (6.)

Mac Neill (R.) The Prevention of Epidemics. pp. 247. *Lond.* 1894. 8°.   7087. ee. 22.

Mullins (G. L.) Epidemic Diseases and their prevention in Sydney. pp. 8. *Sidney*, 1895. 8°.
                                                     Pam. 39.

Nuttall (G. H. F.) Hygienic measures in relation to infectious Diseases. pp. 112.
Lond. 1893. 8°.   7561. aaa. 23.

Ollivier (A.) Rapport général sur les Épidémies qui ont régné en France, 1888, *etc.* pp. 91.
1891. 4°. Ac. Paris. *Académie de Médecine.* Mémoires. Tom. 36. Fasc. 2.   Ac. 3725.

Parkes (L. C.) Infectious Diseases. Notification. pp. 185. *Lond.* 1894. 8°.   7561. a. 29.

Penzoldt (F.) Handbuch der Therapie der Infektionskrankheiten. *Jena*, 1894, *etc.* 8°.
                                                      7620. f.

Reich (E.) Studien über die epidemischen Krankheiten. pp. 397. *Leipz.* 1894. 8°.
                                              7560. cc. 23.

Russell (*Hon.* F. A. R.) Epidemics, plagues and fevers. pp. 508. *Lond.* 1892. 8°.
                                                   7561. k. 5.

Sworder (H.) Information concerning infectious Diseases. pp. 82. *Lond.* 1893. 8°. 7561. aa. 11.

Welply (J. J.) Creameries and infectious Diseases. pp. 59. *Lond.* 1895. 8°. 7561. k. 25.

Woodhead (G. S.) Pathological Mycology. Etiology of infective Diseases. pp. 174.
Edinb. 1885. 8°.   7561. k. 6.

Aikman (C. M.) Air, Water and Disinfectants. pp. 128. 1895. 12°. Manuals of Health.
                                                      7404. a.

Arnould (J.) La Désinfection publique. pp. 255. *Paris*, 1893. 8°.   7561. aaa. 26.

Cadel (A.) La fognatura delle città in rapporto alle Malattie endemiche ed epidemiche.
pp. 4. 284. *Torino*, 1891. 8°.   8777. bbb. 20.

Curgenven (J. B.) Disinfection of infectious Diseases by antiseptic inunction, *etc.* pp. 25.
Lond. 1891. 8°.   7561. f. 4.

Gay (J.) Disinfection and Disinfectants. pp. 16. *Lond.* 1895. 8°.   07305. i. 14. (4.)

Helbing (H.) and Passmore (F. W.) Facts about Disinfectants, *etc.* pp. 20.
Lond. 1893. 8°.   07305. i. 11. (1.)

Kemp (P. H. v. d.) De quarantaine- en epidemievoorschriften in Nederlandsch-Indie.
pp. 327. *Batavia*, 1892. 8°.   5686. dd. 1.

Rideal (S.) Disinfection and Disinfectants. pp. 328. *Lond.* 1895. 8°.   7561. dd. 29.

Sisley (R.) Study of Influenza and the Law concerning infectious Diseases. pp. 119.
Lond. 1892. 8°.   6426. e. 9.

See also Cholera : Diphtheria : Fevers : Hospitals : Influenza : Plague : Small Pox.

Septic Diseases. *See* Septic Diseases.

Tropical and sub-tropical Diseases.

British Medical Association, *Leeward Islands Branch.* Leeward Islands Medical Journal.
Lond. 1891, *etc.* 8°.   07305. f.

Brun (H. de) Maladies des pays chauds. 1893, *etc.* 8°. Encyclopédie des aide-mémoire.
                                                      8709. g.

DISEASE.—Tropical, etc.—*continued*.

Davidson (A.) Hygiene and Diseases of warm climates. pp. 1016. *Edinb.* 1893. 8°.
                                                 7686. dd. 2.

Etterlé (J.) Les Maladies de l'Afrique tropicale. pp. 192. *Brux.* 1892. 8°.   7390. f. 8.

Felkin (R. W.) Geographical distribution of tropical Diseases in Africa. pp. 79.
Edinb. 1895. 8°.   7687. ee. 23.

Fisch (R.) Tropische Krankheiten. pp. 262. *Basel*, 1894. 8°.   07686. e. 10.

Hardie (D.) Notes on some Diseases in Queensland in relation to atmospheric conditions.
pp. 132. *Brisbane*, 1893. 8°.   07686. k. 7.

Kelsch (A.) and Kiener (P. L.) Traité des Maladies des pays chauds. pp. 908.
Paris, 1889. 8°.   07686. k. 1.

Kohlstock (P.) Ärztlicher Ratgeber für Ostafrika. pp. 344. *Berl.* 1891. 8°. 7390. de. 13.

Sibthorpe (C.) Clinical Manual for India. pp. 420. *Madras*, 1890. 8°.   07686. k. 2.

See also Beriberi : Fevers : Hygiene, *of Tropical Countries* : Liver.

DISINFECTANTS. *See* Disease, *Infectious*.

DISSECTION. Brodie (C. G.) Dissections illustrated. *Lond.* 1892, *etc.* 8°.   7419. l. 9.

Cooke (T.) Dissection Guides. pp. 118. *Lond.* 1891. 8°.   7419. f. 5.

Girod (P.) Manipulations de Zoologie, guide pour les travaux de dissection. 2 pt.
Paris, 1889, 92. 8°.   7206. k. 26.

See also Anatomy ; Coroners.

DISTILLATION. Sorel (E.) La distillation. pp. 244. 1894. 8°. Encyclopédie des aide-mémoire.   8709. g.

See also Alcohol.

DISTOMIDAE. *See* Parasites.

DISTRESS, Law of. Daniels (G. St. L.) Handbook of the Law of Distress. pp. 132.
Lond. 1894. 8°.   6325. de. 27.

See also Land.

DISTRICT COUNCILS.
See Local Government.

DISTRICT VISITING. District Visitors. District Visitors, Deaconesses, *etc.* pp. 89.
Lond. 1891. 8°.   4192. aa. 35.

Sewell (M. A.) District Visiting. pp. 16. *Lond.* 1893. 8°.   4429. c. 21. (10.)

See also Charities.

DITMARSCHEN. Nehlsen (R.) Dithmarscher Geschichte. pp. 639. *Hamb.* 1895. 8°.
                                                10255. ee. 12.

DIVINATION. *See* Fortune-Telling.

DIVORCE. *See* Marriage.

DJERID. *See* Sahara.

DOCKS. *See* Ports and Harbours.

DODONA. Warsberg (A. v.) *Baron.* Eine Wallfahrt nach Dodona. pp. 149.
Graz, 1893. 8°.   10125. ccc. 7.

DOG. Boston (F. J.) Dogs great and small. *N.Y.* 1895. fol.   12809. w. 2.

—— Children's Book of Dogs. *N.Y.* 1895. fol.
                                                12809. w. 3.

C——, *Major.* Indian notes about Dogs. pp. 118. *Calcutta*, 1889. 8°.   7293. aa. 18.

De Salis (H. A.) Dogs: manual for amateurs. pp. 120. *Lond.* 1893. 8°.   07293. g. 10.

Dog Stories. Dog Stories from the "Spectator." pp. 261. *Lond.* 1895. 8°.   07293. h. 1.

DOG—*continued.*

EERELMAN (O.) Horses and Dogs. pp. 39.
Lond. 1895. 4°.   7295. k. 4.

HILL (J. W.) Our Canine Companions. pp. 297.
Lond. 1891. 8°.   7291. aa. 13.

JONES (H.) Dogs I have known. pp. 116.
Lond. 1893. 8°.   4429. a. 53.

LEONARD (R. M.) The Dog in British Poetry.
pp. 350. *Lond.* 1893. 8°.   11601. ee. 38.

LITTLEDALE (H.) Notes on Wild Dogs, *etc.*
Bombay, 1892. 8°.   7004. df. 21. (11.)

MILLAIS (E.) Two Problems of reproduction.
pp. 21. *Manch.* 1895. 8°.   Pam. 42.

MIVART (St. G.) Dogs, Jackals, Wolves and
Foxes. pp. 216. *Lond.* 1890, 4°. 7206. dd. 7.

P.P. *London.* Dog Owners' annual.
Lond. 1890, *etc.* 8°.   P.P. 2489. yca.

PERTUS (J.) Le Chien. pp. 297.
Paris, 1893. 8°.   7293. b. 40.

PRICE (R. J. L.) Dogs ancient and modern.
pp. 82. *Lond.* 1893. 8°.   7293. c. 36.

SHAW (V. K.) Illustrated book of the Dog.
Lond. 1889-91. 4°.   7291. d. 11.

STABLES (W. G.) The Dog. pp. 44.
Lond. 1893. *obl.* 16°.   7293. a. 7.

—— Our Friend the Dog. pp. 354.
Lond. 1895. 8°.   7291. aaa. 34.

KENNEL PEDIGREE BOOKS. Kennel Pedigree
Books. *Lond.* 1889, *etc.* 8°.   7293. aaa.

LONDON. *Kennel Club.* Rules. *Lond.* 1893. 4°.
                                        1865. c. 2. (26.)

LEE (R. B.) History and description of modern
Dogs (sporting division). pp. 584.
Lond. 1893. 8°.   07291. i.

CAILLARD (P.) Les Chiens d'Arrêt. pp 148.
Paris, 1890. *obl.* 4°.   1821. c. 9.

H., H. Scientific education of Dogs for the gun.
pp. 217. *Lond.* 1890. 8°.   7905. c. 48.

BELL (E. W.) The Scottish Deerhound.
pp. 137. *Edinb.* 1892. 4°.   7293. l. 17.

CUPPLES (G.) Scotch Deer-hounds and their
masters. pp. 336. *Edinb.* 1894. 8°. 7291. d. 14.

GRAHAM (G. A.) Pedigrees of Scottish Deer-
hounds. pp. 78. *Dursley*, 1894. 8°. 7293. l. 18.

BEVAN (F. R.) Observations on breaking Re-
trievers. pp. 23. *Lond.* 1891. 8°.
                                        7293. f. 12. (1.)

MERCER (F. H. F.) The Spaniel and its training.
pp. 143. *N.Y.* 1890. 8°.   7293. bbb. 30.

BROWN (D.) The Greyhound Stud Book.
Dalry, 1882, *etc.* 8°.   7906. df.

LLOYD (F.) The Whippet Stud Book.
Lond. 1894. 8°.   7293. c. 37.

—— The Whippet : how to breed, race and
exhibit it. pp. 204. *Lond.* 1894. 8°.
                                               07293. g. 24.

LONDON. *National Whippet Club.* Official Stud
Book and racing calendar. *Lond.* 1894, *etc.* 8°.
                                               7906. ccc.

LEE (R. B.) History and description of modern
Dogs. Non-sporting division. pp. 376.
Lond. 1894. 8°.   07293. i. 26.

JACKSON (C. F. W.) and BOWERS (E. H.) Bull
Dog pedigrees. pp. 237. *Bath*, 1892. 8°.
                                               07293. i. 13.

DALZIEL (H.) Collie Stud Book and show record.
pp. 130. 1891. 8°. Kennel Pedigree Books.
                                               7293. aaa.

JONES (E. W. H.) Sheep-dog Trials and the
Sheep-dog. pp. 102. *Brecon*, 1892. 8°.
                                               7293. bb. 44.

DOG—*continued.*

LEE (R. B.) History and description of the
Collie. pp. 157. *Lond.* 1890. 4°.   7291. d. 7.

WYNN (M. B.) History of the Mastiff. pp. 222.
Melton Mowbray, 1886. 8°.   7294. ccc. 1.

HUGHES-HUGHES (W. O.) Guide to pedigrees of
St. Bernard Dogs. pp. 358.
Tunbridge, 1893. 8°.   07293. g. 11.

LEE (R. B.) History and description of the
Modern Dogs. The Terriers. pp. 426.
Lond. 1894. 8°.   07293. i. 27.

—— History and description of the Fox Terrier.
pp. 239. *Lond.* 1895. 8°.   07293. i. 30.

BUNGARTZ (J.) Der Hund im Dienste des rothen
Kreuzes. pp. 63. *Leipz.* 1892. 8°. 7291. aaa. 31.

CHRISTENSEN (M.) Krigshunden. pp. 102.
Aalborg, 1892. 8°.   7291. aa. 25.

JUPIN (L. S. M. J. J.) Tactique et chiens de
guerre. pp. 153. *Paris*, 1890. 8°. 8823. dd. 39.
See also ANIMALS, *Domestic:* HUNTING.

Diseases, Hygiene, etc.

See HYDROPHOBIA : VETERINARY MEDICINE.

Law relating to Dogs.

MANSON (E.) Law relating to Dogs. pp. 84.
Lond. 1893. 8°.   6345. aaa. 6.

LONDON. *Dog Owners' Protection Association.*
Kent Dog Owners and the Muzzling Order.
pp. 53. *Lond.* 1890. 8°.   7293. i. 12. (7.)

DOGMA. *See* CHURCH HISTORY, *Christian
Institutions, etc.* : THEOLOGY.

DOL, Brittany. KERBEUZEC (H. de) Locutions populaires du pays de Dol-en-Bretagne.
2 pt. *Rennes*, 1894. 8°.   12954. d. 49.

DÔLE. LURION (R. de) Notice sur la
Chambre des Comptes de Dôle. pp. 322.
Besançon, 1892. 8°.   08227. g. 40.
See also FRANCHE-COMTÉ.

DOLLAR, Clackmannan. TAIT (J.) Dollar,
past and present. pp. 51. *Edinb.* 1894. 8°.
                                               10370. aa. 65.

DOLOMITES. *See* ALPS, *Eastern.*

DOLPHIN. *See* DELPHINIDAE.

DOMBURG. KESTELOO (H. M.) Domburg
en zijn geschiedenis. pp. 157.
Middelburg, 1890. 8°.   010271. f. 8.

DOMESDAY BOOK. BIRCH (W. de G.)
Materials for the re-editing of the Domesday
Book. *Lond.* 1892. 4°.   7704. i. 11. (7.)

REICHEL (O. J.) The Leuca or Lug of Domesday, *etc.* pp. 5. *Plymouth*, 1894. 8°. Pam. 90.

—— Suggestions to aid in identifying the place-
names in the Devonshire Domesday. pp. 35.
Plymouth, 1894. 8°.   Pam. 90.

DOMESDAY BOOK. Notes on the Oxfordshire
Domesday. pp. 31. *Oxf.* 1892. 8°. 10368. f. 43.

DOMESTIC ECONOMY.
See HOUSEHOLD MANAGEMENT.

DOMINICAN ORDER. CHAPOTIN (M. D.)
Études historiques sur la province dominicaine
de France. Le Couvent de Saint Louis d'Évreux.
Paris, 1890. 8°.   4629. i. 12.

—— Les Dominicains d'Auxerre. pp. 418.
Paris, 1892. 8°.   4629. d. 5.

—— La Guerre de la succession de Poissy,
1660-1707. pp. 176. *Paris*, 1892. 8°.
                                               4629. d. 9.

—— Le dernier prieur du dernier couvent, 1736-
1806. (J. Faitot.) pp. 529. *Paris*, 1893. 8°.
                                               4629. d. 12.

DOMINICAN ORDER—continued.

DOMINICANS. Acta capitulorum provincialium ordinis Fratrum Praedicatorum.
Toulouse, 1894, etc. 8°.   4071. l.

—— Collection of extracts from magazines relating to the Dominicans in England and Wales.
4705. e. 32. (1.)

FINKE (H.) Ungedruckte Dominikanerbriefe des 13. Jahrhunderts. pp. 174.
Paderborn, 1891. 8°.   4784. e. 57.

MANDONNET (P. F.) Les Dominicains et la découverte de l'Amérique. pp. 255.
Paris, 1893. 12°.   9551. bb. 24.

NICOLAS (C.) L'ancien couvent des Dominicains de Marseille. pp. 70. *Nimes, 1894.* 8°.
4629. h. 19.

PALMER (C. F. R.) Friar-Preachers of Leicester, *etc. Leicester, 1884.* 8°.   4705. e. 32. (2.)

THIRIOT (G.) Recherches sur l'ordre des Dominicains à Metz. 1893. 8°. Ac. Metz. *Gesellschaft für Lothringische Geschichte.* Jahrbuch. Jahrg. 5.   Ac. 7112.

See also RELIGIOUS ORDERS.

DOMO D'OSSOLA. DE-VIT (V.) La provincia romana dell' Ossola. pp. 333.
Firenze, 1892. 8°.   10135. f. 4.

DOMREMY.
See FRANCE, *History, House of Valois.*

DONATISM. *See* HERESIES.

DONEGAL. BALFOUR (*Right Hon.* A. J.) Mr. Balfour's Tours in Donegal. pp. 99.
Dublin, 1890. 8°.   8146. aaa. 39.

DOHERTY (W. J.) Inis-Owen and Tirconnel. pp. 211. *Dublin, 1891.* 8°.   10390. df. 6.

—— Some Ancient Crosses and other antiquities of Inishowen. *Dublin,* 1891. 8°. 7706. g. 4. (15.)

DONEGAL. Illustrated edition of the Donegal Highlands. pp. 314. *Dublin, 1894.* 8°.
10390. df. 11.

MUSGRAVE (J.) Letter to A. J. Balfour on South-West Donegal. pp. 19. *Belfast, 1890.* 8°.
8282. ff. 12. (2.)

DORDOGNE, Department. GOULD (S. B.) The deserts of southern France. 2 vol.
Lond. 1894. 8°.   010171. h. 41.

See also PÉRIGORD.

DORSETSHIRE. BRUCE (J. M.) Climate of Dorset. 1895. 8°. Ac. London. *Medical and Chirurgical Society.* Climates of Great Britain. Vol. 1.   7462. g.

DORSET. Dorset Records. *Lond.* 1894, *etc.* 8°.
010350. k.

MOULE (H. J.) Old Dorset. pp. 240.
Lond. 1893. 8°.   010358. g. 32.

WORTH (R. N.) Tourist's guide to Dorsetshire. pp. 112. *Lond. 1894.* 8°.   10352. a. 73.

DORTMUND. Ac. Dortmund. *Historischer Verein.* Dortmunder Urkundenbuch.
Dortmund, 1881, *etc.* 8°.   Ac. 7336.

RUEBEL (C.) Dortmunder Finanz- und Steuerwesen. *Dortmund,* 1892, *etc.* 8°.   8248. g.

See also WESTPHALIA.

DOUAI. Ac. Douai. *Société d'Agriculture, Science et Arts.* Douai, son histoire militaire. pp. 273. *Douai, 1892.* 4°.   10173. h. 20.

CARDON (G.) La fondation de l'Université de Douai. pp. 543. *Paris, 1892.* 8°. 8355. df. 16.

DOUBS, Department. THURIET (C.) Traditions populaires du Doubs. pp. 111.
Besançon, 1889. 8°.   12430. k. 33.

DOUGLAS, Isle of Man. DOUGLAS. Douglas.
Birmingham, 1893. 16°.   10349. a. 31. (4.)

DOUVRES. DOUVRES. Les Chartes de la Tour de Douvres, 1250–1624. pp. 238.
Bourg, 1881. 8°.   010171. g. 4.

DOUVRIN. FANIEN (H.) Histoire du Douvrin. pp. 248. *Arras, 1891.* 8°.   10172. b. 3.

DOVER. DOVER. Where to buy at Dover. pp. 52. *Brighton, 1891.* 4°.   10368. k. 25.

FOLKESTONE. Handbook of Folkestone and Dover. pp. 176. *Folkestone, 1894.* 8°.
10350. aaa. 55.

MINET (W.) Fourth foreign church at Dover, 1685–1731. 1893. 8°. Ac. London, *Huguenot Society.* Proceedings. Vol. 4. No. 2.
Ac. 2073.

DOVERCOURT. BLOOM (J. H.) Heraldry and monumental inscriptions in Dovercourt, *etc.* pp. 127. *Hemsworth, 1893.* 4°.   9902. g. 24.

DOWN, County. BASSETT (G. H.) County Down guide. pp. 414. *Dubl. 1886.* 4°.
10390. df. 9.

DRAGONFLIES. BRITISH DRAGONFLIES. Handbook of British Dragonflies. pp. 98.
Birmingham, 1890. 8°.   7297. a. 45.

DRAGONFLIES. Collecting, preserving, and rearing Dragonflies. pp. 8. *Birmingham, 1891.* 8°.
7004. de. 23. (5.)

KIRBY (W. F.) Catalogue of Neuroptera Odonata. pp. 202. *Lond. 1890.* 8°.   7297. f. 15.

DRAINAGE AND SEWERAGE.

AULT (E.) Paper on the Shone Hydro-Pneumatic Sewerage System. pp. 26.
Lond. 1888. 8°.   8827. bbb. 28. (2.)

BEARDMORE (W. L.) Drainage of habitable Buildings. pp. 89. 1892. 8°. Specialist's Series.   8708. k.

BROWN (G. P.) Drainage Channel and waterway. pp. 480. *Chicago, 1894.* 8°.   8777. cc. 10.

CLARKE (C. H) Practical Drain inspection. pp. 16. *Lond.* 1894. 8°.   8777. bbb. 28. (11.)

DEMPSEY (G. D.) On the Drainage of lands, towns and buildings. pp. 351. *Lond.* 1890. 8°.
8777. aaa. 23.

MAGUIRE (W. R.) Domestic Sanitary Drainage and plumbing. pp. 437. *Lond.* 1890. 8°.
8777. cc. 26.

MIDDLETON (G. A. T.) House Drainage. pp. 63. *Lond.* 1892. 8°.   8777. aaa. 35.

MILLE (A.) Assainissement des Villes par l'eau, les égouts, les irrigations. pp. 271.
Paris, 1885. 8°.   8777. h. 26.

NADIÉÏNE (M. P.) New System of sanitary Drainage. pp. 23. *Lond.* 1893. 8°.
8709. c. 10. (15.)

REEVES (R. H.) Reports on sewer air and ventilation. pp. 16. *Lond.* 1894. 8°.   Pam. 79.

SMEATON (J.) Plumbing, Drainage. *etc.* pp. 236. *Lond.* 1893. 8°.   8777. b. 46.

VACHER (F.) Defects in Plumbing and drainage work. pp. 83. *Manch.* 1894. 8°.   8777. d. 37.

JACKSON (D. W.) Discussion on the drainage of Chicago. pp. 138. *Chicago,* 1892. 8°.
8777. g. 11.

LONDON. *County Council.* Main drainage of London. pp. 35. *Lond.* 1891. 8°.   N.R.

RICHMOND, *Surrey.* Richmond main sewerage. pp. 14. *Lond.* 1891. 4°.   8706. f. 23. (8.)

See also PLUMBING : SANITATION.

Farm Drainage.

SCOTT (J.) Farm engineering text-books. Draining. pp. 133. *Lond.* 1883. 8°.   8703. ccc. 43.

DRAINAGE.—Farm Drainage—*continued.*

WRIGHTSON (J.) Soils and Manures. With chapters on drainage. 1892. 8°. Cassell's Agricultural Readers. 7077. de.

See also AGRICULTURE.

Sewage Disposal: Purification, etc.

BANNEHR (J.) The Sewage difficulty solved. pp. 38. *Lond.* 1892. 8°. 8777. bbb. 28. (5.)

BURGHARDT (C. A.) Sewage and its purification. pp. 18. *Lond.* 1892. 8°. 8709. c. 10. (10.)

BURNLEY. Description of the Sewage disposal works. pp. 38. *Burnley,* 1893. 4°. 8777. cc. 32.

CRIMP (W. S.) Sewage treatment and sludge disposal. pp. 26. *Lond.* 1893. 8°. 8777. bbb. 28. (7.)

—— Sewage disposal works. pp. 349. *Lond.* 1894. 8°. 8777. g. 9.

HOUSTON (A. C.) Report upon the Scott Moncrieff system for the bacteriological purification of sewage. pp. 27. *Lond.* 1893. 8°. 8776. ee. 52.

JONES (C.) Refuse Destructors. pp. 73. *Lond.* 1894. 8°. 8777. bbb. 23.

LOMAX (C. J.) Collection, treatment and disposal of town refuse. pp. 113. *Bolton,* 1892. 8°. 8777. bbb. 22.

LONDON. *Local Government Board.* Report on the destruction of town refuse. pp. 48. *Lond.* 1888. 8°. 8768. l. 23. (2.)

RAFTER (G. W.) and BAKER (M. N.) Sewage disposal in the U.S. pp. 598. *N.Y.* 1894. 8°. 8777. i. 6.

WARDLE (T.) On Sewage Treatment and disposal. pp. 426. *Manch.* 1893. 8°. 8776. ee. 50.

WARING (G. E.) Modern methods of sewage disposal. pp. 252. *N.Y.* 1894. 8°. 8777. aaa. 39.

WOLLHEIM (A.) Modern Sewage precipitation works. pp. 9. *Lond.* 1892. 8°. 8709. c. 10. (13.)

—— Foreign Sewage precipitation works, *etc.* *Lond.* 1893. 8°. 8777. b. 45.

DRAMA AND STAGE.

General Works.

ARCHER (F.) How to write a good Play. pp. 224. *Lond.* 1892. 8°. 11794. f. 39.

BENOIST (A.) Les Théories dramatiques avant les discours de Corneille. 1891. 8°. Ac. Bordeaux. *Faculté des Lettres.* Annales. an. 1891. No. 4. Ac. 8917.

BLUMENTHAL (O.) Theatralische Eindrücke. pp. 351. *Berlin,* 1885. 8°. 11795. d. 50.

CALMOUR (A. C.) Practical Play-writing and cost of production. pp. 62. *Bristol,* 1891. 8°. 011795. e. 41.

CREIZENACH (W.) Geschichte des neueren Dramas. *Halle,* 1893, *etc.* 8°. 011795. f.

DOUMIC (R.) De Scribe à Ibsen. pp. 352. *Paris,* 1893. 12°. 011850. f. 21.

GARTELMANN (H.) Dramatik. Kritik des Aristotelischen Systems. pp. 186. *Berlin,* 1992. 8°. 11312. f. 54.

HAM (J. P.) The Stage and the Drama in their relation to society. pp. 20. 1880. 8°. LONDON. *Sunday Lecture Society.* Selection. No. 4. 4018. c.

HENNEQUIN (A.) The Art of Play-writing. pp. 187. *Boston,* 1890. 8°. 11824. dd. 43.

JULLIEN (J.) Le Théâtre vivant. pp. 421. *Paris,* 1894. 8°. 11740. aaa. 39.

MATTHEWS (J. B.) Books and Play-books. pp. 250. *Lond.* 1895. 8°. 011805. f. 2.

DRAMA.—General Works—*continued.*

MUELLER (H. F.) Beiträge zum Verständnis der tragischen Kunst. pp. 273. 1893. 8°. Aufsätze und Vorträge. Bd. 8. 12356. l.

PEREIRA DA SILVA (J. M.) Considerações sobre Poesia dramatica. pp. 300. *Rio de J.,* 1889. 18°. 11824. df. 44.

P.P. *London.* The Dramatic Year book. *Lond.* 1892, *etc.* 8°. P.P. 2496. hb.

POLTI (G.) Les trente-six Situations dramatiques. pp. 202. *Paris,* 1895. 12°. 12516. de. 33.

POUGIN (A.) Le Théâtre à l'Exposition Universelle de 1889. pp. 125. *Paris,* 1890. 8°. 011795. g. 13.

SCHROEDER (H.) Rousseau's Brief über die Schauspiele. pp. 16. *Berl.* 1894. 4°. 11825. k. 7. (12.)

SITTENBERGER (H.) Die Wahrheit auf der Bühne. pp. 34. *Wien,* 1893. 8°. Pam. 50.

SMITH (B. E.) Cyclopædia of Names. pp. 1083. *Lond.* 1894. fol. 2112. g.

TREE (H. B.) Some Fallacies of the modern stage. pp. 36. *Lond.* 1892. 8°. Pam. 50.

ULLRICH (T.) Kritische Aufsätze über Kunst und Theater. pp. 352. *Berl.* 1894. 4°. 11850. dd. 37.

VIENNA. *Internationale Ausstellung für Musik- und Theaterwesen.* Catalogue. pp. 281. *Wien,* 1892. 8°. 7958. bbb. 16.

—— Jugend-Führer. pp. 44. *Wien,* 1892. 8°. Pam. 24.

Amateur Acting. *See* THEATRICALS.

Art of Acting, etc.

ADAMS (F. A. F.) Gesture and pantomimic action. pp. 221. *N.Y.* 1891. 8°. 11794. h. 33.

AYRES (A.) Acting and actors. pp. 287. *N.Y.* 1894. 8°. 011805. de. 2.

COQUELIN (B. C.) L'Art du comédien. pp. 72. *Paris,* 1894. 12°. 011805. de 1.

DUPONT-VERNON (H.) Diseurs et comédiens. pp. 246. *Paris,* 1891. 12°. 011795. e. 38.

FITZGERALD (P.) The Art of acting. pp. 194. *Lond.* 1892. 8°. 011795. c. 39.

IRVING (*Sir* J. H. B.) The Drama. pp. 164. *Lond.* 1893. 8°. 11795. dg. 32.

KIELBLOCK (A.) The Stage Fright. pp. 69. *Bost.* 1891. 8°. 11795. de. 38.

MAC LAUGHLIN (E. L.) Handy book upon elocution and dramatic art. pp. 179. *Lond.* 1892. 8°. 011795. e. 34.

MARTINET (A.) Histoire du Conservatoire de Musique et de Déclamation. pp. 302. *Paris,* 1893. 8°. 7898. cc. 22.

SOLLY (J. R.) Acting and the art of speech at the Paris Conservatoire. pp. 63. *Lond.* 1891. 8°. 11805. dd, 31.

FOX (C. H.) The Art of making-up. pp. 106. *Lond.* 1892. 8°. Pam. 50.

Fires in Theatres. *See* FIRES.

History. *See supra: General* ; *infra: Drama of Various Countries:* MIRACLE PLAYS.

Miracle Plays. *See* MIRACLE PLAYS.

Musical Drama. *See* MUSIC: OPERA.

Theatre Construction, etc.

BUCKLE (J. G.) Theatre construction and maintenance. pp. 157. *Lond.* 1888. 8°. 7817. k. 12.

LEFÈVRE (J.) L'Électricité au théâtre. pp. 345. *Paris* 1894. 8°. 8758. b. 3.

MOYNET (G.) La Machinerie théâtrale. pp. 408. *Paris,* 1893. 8°. 011795. i. 6.

DRAMA—*continued*.

Drama and Theatres of Various Countries.

See also under the Literature of each country.

Australia.

NEW SOUTH WALES. *Commissioners for the Exposition, Chicago*. The Drama in New South Wales. pp. 95. *Sydney*, 1892. 8° 7958. g. 24

Austria. See infra : Bohemia : Germany.

Belgium.

CLAEYS (P.) Histoire du Théâtre à Gand. 3 tom. *Gand*, 1892. 8°.   011795. h. 3.

Bohemia.

ŠUBERT (F. A.) Das böhmische National-Theater in der Musik- und Theater-Ausstellung zu Wien. pp. 258. *Prag*, 1892. 8°. 11795. g. 29.

Denmark. See infra : Scandinavia.

France.

MERLET (G.) Études sur les Classiques français. pp. 504. *Paris*, 1894. 8°.   011850. f. 77.

TESTARD (H.) Théâtre français. Selection of French plays. *Lond.* 1893, *etc.* 8°. 11740. aaaa.

CHASSIGNET (L. M. M.) Essai sur les foires françaises au moyen âge. 1892. 8°. Ac. Nancy. *Société des Sciences*. Mémoires. 5ᵉ sér. Tom. 7.   Ac. 383/2.

RIGAL (E.) A. Hardy et le Théâtre français à la fin du XVIᵉ siècle. pp. 715. *Paris*, 1889. 8°.   011795. f. 25.

FOURNEL (V.) Le Théâtre au XVIIᵉ siècle. pp. 416. *Paris*, 1892. 12°.   11795. dg. 31.

MONTCHRESTIEN (A. de) Les Tragédies de Montchrestien. pp. 330. *Paris*, 1891. 8°.   12234. bbb. 6.

BRUNETIÈRE (F.) Les Époques du Théâtre français. pp. 373. *Paris*, 1892. 12°.   11795. dg. 29.

BÉNARD (P.) Molière et sa troupe ont-ils donné des représentations en Picardie ? pp. 14. *Saint-Quentin*, 1892. 8°.   Pam. 50.

LODGE (L. D.) A Study in Corneille. pp. 313. *Baltimore*, 1891. 8°.   011824. e. 45.

DU BLED (V.) La Comédie de société au XVIIIᵉ siècle. pp. 326. *Paris*, 1893. 12°.   11795. dg. 39.

MARCELLO (B.) Le Théâtre à la mode au XVIIIᵉ siècle. pp. 156. *Paris*, 1890. 8°. 011795. e. 49.

HUOT DE GONCOURT (E. L. A.) La Guimard. pp. 331. *Paris*, 1893. 12°.   010662. g. 21.

LUMIÈRE (H.) Marie Joly, sociétaire de la Comédie-Française, 1761-98. pp. 29. *Paris*, 1891. 8°.   010661. m. 48.

GROUCHY (E. H. de) Les abonnés de l'Opéra en 1778. pp. 13. *Paris*, 1891. 8°.   Pam. 50.

LUMIÈRE (H.) Le Théâtre Français pendant la Révolution, 1789-99. pp. 438. *Paris*, 1894. 12°.   011795. e. 50.

MAZZONI (G.) Il Teatro della Rivoluzione, *etc.* pp. 438. *Bologna*, 1894. 8°.   011795. e. 60.

SOUBIES (A.) La Comédie-Française. 1825-94. pp. 158. *Paris*, 1895. 8°.   11795. k. 26.

—— Soixante-neuf ans à l'Opéra-Comique en deux pages. pp. 30. *Paris*, 1894. 4°.   11794. i. 30.

—— Le Théâtre à Paris 1870-71. pp. 15. *Paris*, 1892. 8°.   Pam. 50.

—— Le Théâtre en France de 1871 à 1892. pp. 208. *Paris*, 1893. 12°.   11795. a. 36.

—— Le Théâtre à Paris, 1872 et 73. pp. 28. *Paris*, 1892. 8°.   Pam. 50.

DRAMA.—France—*continued*.

ADERER (A.) Le Théâtre à côté. pp. 269. *Paris*, 1894. 12°.   011795. e. 59.

GINISTY (P.) Choses et gens de Théâtre. pp. 270. *Paris*, 1892. 8°.   11795. dg. 26.

KNIGHT (J.) Theatrical Notes. pp. 321. *Lond.* 1893. 8°.   011795. i. 5.

LAMBERT (A.) Sur les planches. pp. 376. *Paris*, 1894. 12°.   011795. e. 54.

LAROQUE (A.) Acteurs et actrices de Paris. pp. 138. *Paris*, 1891. 12°.   10660. bbb 29.

LARROUMET (G.) Études d'histoire dramatique. pp. 324. *Paris*, 1892, 8°.   11795. dg. 25.

LEMONNIER (A.) Les petits mystères de la vie théâtrale. pp. 232. *Paris*, 1895. 18°.   011795. e. 62.

—— Les Abus du théâtre. pp. 178. *Paris*, 1895. 8°.   011795. e. 61.

ODÉON. Conférences faites aux matinées du Théâtre de l'Odéon. 2 vol. *Paris*, 1889-90. 12°.   011795. e. 32.

PARIGOT (H.) Le Théâtre d'hier. pp. 448. *Paris*, 1893. 12°.   011850. f. 35.

WEISS (J. J.) Autour de la Comédie Française. pp. 328. *Paris*, 1892. 12°.   11795. dg. 28.

—— Le Drame historique et le drame passionnel. pp. 383. *Paris*, 1894. 12°.   011795. e. 52.

DESPIERRES (*Mme.* G.) Le Théâtre et les comédiens à Alençon au 16ᵉ et 17ᵉ siècle. pp. 15. *Paris*, 1892. 8°.   Pam. 50.

BOURGES (E.) Notes sur le théâtre de la Cour à Fontainebleau, 1747-87. pp. 82. *Paris*, 1892. 8°.   Pam. 50.

ROUSSET (H.) Le Théâtre à Grenoble. 1500-1890. pp. 172. *Grenoble*, 1891. 8°.   011795. f. 35.

LEFEBVRE (L.) Le Théâtre de Lille au XVIIIᵉ siècle. pp. 114. *Lille*, 1894. 8°.   011795. e. 53.

—— Un Chapitre de l'histoire du Théâtre de Lille. 1708-1872. pp. 94. *Lille*, 1890. 8°.   Pam. 50.

DECLÈVE (J.) Le Théâtre à Mons. 1891. 8°. Ac. Mons. *Société de Sciences*. Mémoires. Sér. 5. Tom. 4.   Ac. 1013.

DESTRANGES (É.) Le Théâtre à Nantes. pp. 504. *Paris*, 1893. 8°.   011795. e. 45.

NOURY (J.) Les Comédiens à Rouen, au XVIIᵉ siècle. pp. 41. *Rouen*, 1893. 8°.   Pam. 50.

—— Le Théâtre-Français de Rouen en 1793. pp. 67. *Rouen*, 1893. 8°.   Pam. 50.

See also MIRACLE PLAYS.

Germany.

FLUEGGEN (O. G.) Biographisches Bühnen-Lexikon der deutschen Theater. *München*, 1892, *etc.* 8°.   10705. c. 44.

KIRCHBACH (W.) Deutsche Schauspieler. pp. 51. 1892. 8°. WOLFF (E.) Deutsche Schriften. Rhe. 2. Hft. 2.   12250. i.

P.P. *Leipsic*. Deutsche Dramaturgie. *Leipz.* 1895, *etc.* 8°.   19.

WYSOCKI (L. G.) A. Gryphius et la tragédie allemande. pp. 456. *Paris*, 1893. 8°. 011824. k. 19.

ULRICH (W.) Ueber den Zustand der dramatischen Poesie Deutschlands, 17. Jahrhundert. pp. 44. *Leipz.* 1891. 8°.   Pam. 15.

REULING (C.) Die komische Figur in den deutschen Dramen bis zum Ende des XVII. Jahrhunderts. pp. 181. *Stuttgart*, 1890. 8°.   011840. i. 55.

DRAMA.—Germany—continued.

HEITMUELLER (F,) Hamburgische Dramatiker zu Zeit Gottscheds. pp. 101. *Dresden*, 1891. 8°.
011824. h. 7.

MORSCH (H.) Goethe und die griechischen Bühnendichter. pp. 55. 1891. 4°.
011824. i. 20. (14.)

RABANY (C.) Kotzebue. pp. 536.
Paris, 1893. 8°.   010707. k. 3.

ADLER (G.) Die Sozialreform und das Theater. pp. 48. *Berl.* 1891. 8°.   8277. ee. 1. (8.)

AUERBACH (B.) Dramatische Eindrücke. pp. 326. *Stuttgart*, 1893. 8°.   11795. dg. 38.

BETTELHEIM (A.) Die Zukunft unseres Volkstheaters. pp. 94. *Berl.* 1892. 8°.   011795. h. 5.

ERDMANN (G. A.) Theater-Reformen? pp. 82. *Bern*, 1892. 8°.   Pam. 50.

LANDWEHR (H.) Dichterische Gestalten in geschichtlicher Treue. pp. 191. *Bielefeld*, 1893. 8°.
011850. g. 31.

LITZMANN (B.) Das deutsche Drama in den litterarischen Bewegungen der Gegenwart. pp. 216. *Hamburg*, 1894. 8°.   11825. f. 49.

MUELLER (A.) Dramaturgische Gänge. pp. 216. *Dresden*, 1892. 8°.   011795. ee. 14.

NELTEN (L.) Dramaturgie der Neuzeit. pp. 152. *Halle*, 1894. 8°.   011795. h. 13.

RACHÉ (P. B.) Die deutsche Schulkomödie. pp. 79. *Liebertwolkwitz*, 1891. 8°.
011850. h. 14. (5.)

SCHAUMBERGER (J.) Die Volksbühne und das moderne Drama. pp. 15. 1891. 8°. Münchener Flugschriften. Ser. I. 4.   743.

SCHLOSSAR (A.) Deutsche Volksschauspiele. 2 Bde. *Halle*, 1891. 8°.   11747. cc. 41.

SONNTAG (O.) Wie kommt man zum Theater? pp. 114. *Berl.* 1891. 8°.   11795. dg. 20.

SOUTH GERMAN. Das deutsche Theater als Erzieher. pp. 48. *Leipz.* 1893. 8°.   Pam. 50.

WESTENBERGER (B.) Die Nothlage unseres Bühnenschritthums. pp. 40. 1890. 8°. Deutsche Zeit- und Streit-Fragen. N. F. Hft. 76.
12209. f.

MERLO (J. J.) Zur Geschichte des kölner Theaters. 1890. 8°. Ac. Cologne. *Historischer Verein.* Annalen, *etc.* Hft. 50.   Ac. 7335.

ALLERS (C. W.) Die Meininger. *Leipz.* 1890. fol.   11795. k. 23.

WAHLE (J.) Das weimarische Hoftheater unter Goethes Leitung. pp. 29. *Braunschweig*, 1891. 8°.   Pam. 50.

WEDDIGEN (O.) Geschichte des Theaters in Wiesbaden. pp. 125. *Wiesbaden*, 1894. 8°.
011795. h. 12.

See also MIRACLE PLAYS.

Great Britain and Ireland.

CREIZENACH (W.) Die Schauspiele der englischen Komödianten. pp. 352. *Berl.* 1895. 8°.
011805. f. 3.

FISCHER (R.) Zur Kunstentwicklung der englischen Tragödie bis zu Shakespeare. pp. 192. *Strassb.* 1893. 8°.   011850. i. 28.

FLEAY (F. G.) Biographical chronicle of the Drama, 1559-1642. 2 vol. *Lond.* 1891. 8°.
2302. b.

GOLDEN (W. E.) Brief history of the Drama. pp. 227. *N.Y.* 1890. 8°.   11795. dg. 19.

HAZLITT (W. C.) Manual for the collector of old English Plays. pp. 284. *Lond.* 1892. 4°.
11824. i. 40.

HUNT (J. H. L.) Dramatic Essays. pp. 241. *Lond.* 1894. 8°.   11795. dg. 44.

DRAMA.—Great Britain and Ireland— *continued.*

LOWELL (J. R.) Old English Dramatists. pp. 132. *Lond.* 1892. 8°.   2308. aa. 22.

SCHACK (A. F. v.) *Count.* Die englischen Dramatiker vor, neben und nach Shakespeare. pp. 500. *Stuttgart*, 1893. 8°.   11773. c. 1.

BAYNES (T. S.) Shakespeare Studies. pp. 409. *Lond.* 1894. 8°.   11764. c. 14.

BRANDES (G. M. C.) W. Shakespeare. *Paris*, 1895, etc. 8°.   011765. h.

BRINK (B. ten) Five lectures on Shakespeare. pp. 248. *Lond.* 1895. 8°. Bohn's Standard Library.   2504. k.

BLAZE DE BURY (Y.) Profils Shakespeariens. pp. 118. *Paris*, 1891. 8°.   11763. df. 40.

BRANDL (A.) Shakspere. pp. 232. 1894. 8°.

BETTELHEIM (A.) Führende Geister. Bd. 8.
12253. h.

CALDECOTT (H. E.) Spoils. Studies in Shakespeare. pp. 44. *Lond.* 1891. 8°.   Pam. 80.

CALMOUR (A. C.) Fact and fiction about Shakespeare. pp. 112. *Stratford-on-A.* 1894. 4°.
11763. i. 13.

CUNLIFFE (J. W.) Influence of Seneca on Elizabethan Tragedy. pp. 155. *Lond.* 1893. 4°.
11825. h. 28.

DARMESTETER (J.) Shakespeare. pp. 238. *Paris*, 1892. 12°.   11764. f. 10.

DOWDEN (E.) Introduction to Shakespeare. pp. 136. *Lond.* 1893. 8°.   11763. e. 59.

EEKHOUD (G.) Au siècle de Shakespeare. pp. 170. *Brux.* 1893. 12°.   11763. e. 60.

LEWES (L.) Women of Shakespeare. pp. 384. *Lond.* 1894. 8°.   011765. h. 3.

MACDONALD (G.) A Dish of Orts. Paper on Shakspere. pp. 322. *Lond.* 1893. 8°.
12354. ee. 28.

MARTIN (H.) *Lady.* On some of Shakespeare's female characters. pp. 410. *Edinb.* 1891. 8°.
11763. i. 6.

MARX (T.) Der dichterische Entwickelungsgang Shakespeares. pp. 27. 1895. 8°. Sammlung wissenschaftlicher Vorträge. Hft. 211.
12249. m.

MOULTON (R. G.) Shakespeare as a dramatic artist. pp. 443. *Oxf.* 1893. 8°.   2300. c. 1.

OECHELHAEUSER (W.) Shakespeareana. pp. 251. *Berl.* 1894. 8°.   11766. i. 42.

SHAKSPERE (W.) Shakespeare Adversaria. *Stratf.* 1890, etc. 4°.   2040.

THAYER (W. R.) The best Elizabethan Plays. pp. 611. *Bost.* 1890. 8°.   11771. bbb. 9.

WAGENER (B.) Shakespeare's Einfluss auf Goethe. *Halle*, 1890, etc. 8°.   11766. cc.

WENDELL (B.) W. Shakspere. pp. 439. *Lond.* 1894. 8°.   11764. cc. 24.

WILLIAMS (J. L.) Homes and haunts of Shakespeare. 5 pts. *Lond.* 1892. fol.   K.T.C. a. 7.

GREENSTREET (J. H.) The Whitefriars Theatre in the time of Shakspere. pp. 15.
Lond. 1888. 8°.   Pam. 50.

—— Documents relating to the players at the Red Bull and the Cockpit in the time of James I. pp. 19. *Lond.* 1885. 8°.   Pam. 50.

ORDISH (T. F.) Early London Theatres in the fields. pp. 298. 1894. 8°. The Camden Library. No. 2.   7709. cc.

HAMILTON (W.) Sketch of the Drama in England during the last three centuries. pp. 79. *Lond.* 1890. 8°.   011795. c. 34.

ARCHER (W.) The Theatrical 'World.' *Lond.* 1894, *etc.* 8°.   011795. ee.

DRAMA—Great Britain and Ireland—
continued.

ADAMS (W. D.) With Poet and player. pp. 228.
Lond. 1891. 8°.   011824. e. 31.

EDWARDS (F.) Playbills. A collection and
comments. pp. 37. *Lond.* 1893. 8°. Pam. 50.

ERLE (T. W.) Letters from a theatrical Scene-
Painter; minor theatres of London twenty years
ago. pp. 116. *Lond.* 1880. 12°. 011795. e. 55.

IRVING (*Sir* J. H. B.) The Drama. Addresses.
pp. 164. *Lond.* 1893. 8°.   11795. dg. 32.

JONES (H. A.) The Renascence of the English
Drama. pp.343. *Lond.* 1895. 8°. 11795. c. 44.

KNIGHT (J.) Theatrical Notes. pp. 321.
Lond. 1893. 8°.   011795. i. 5.

MATTHEWS (J. B.) Books and playbooks.
pp. 250. *Lond.* 1895. 8°.   011805. f. 2.

P.P. London. The Dramatic Year-book.
Lond. 1892, *etc.* 8°.   P.P. 2496. hb.

ROBINS (E.) Echoes of the Playhouse. pp. 331.
N.Y. 1895. 8°.   11795. dg. 4.

SCOTT (C. W.) Thirty years at the play, pp. 246.
Lond. 1892. 8°.   12602. bbb. 21.

SINGER (H. W.) Das bürgerliche Trauerspiel in
England. pp. 128. *Leipz.* 1892. 8°.
                                  011795. f. 37.

STREATFEILD (W. E.) Theatrical notices. Collected by W. E. S. 1847-92. 27 vol.
fol. & 4°.   314. b, *etc.*

WALKLEY (A. B.) Playhouse Impressions.
pp. 261. *Lond.* 1892. 8°.   11781. df. 39.

HAMLYN (C. A.) Manual of theatrical Law.
pp. 216. *Lond.* 1891. 8°.   6426. cc. 29.

KNIGHT (J.) David Garrick. pp. 346.
Lond. 1894. 8°.   10825. f. 36.

BOADEN (J.) Memoirs of Mrs. Siddons. pp. 471.
Lond. 1893. 8°.   10825. f. 35.

GOODMAN (W.) The Keeleys. pp. 357.
Lond. 1895. 8°.   10825. i. 4.

PEMBERTON (T. E.) Life and writings of T. W.
Robertson. pp. 320. *Lond.* 1893. 8°.
                                  10856. f. 6.

BANCROFT (S. B.) and (M. E.) Mr. and Mrs.
Bancroft. pp. 410. *Lond.* 1891. 8°.
                                  10827. aaa. 40.

CALVERT (W.) Souvenir of Sir H. Irving. pp. 46.
Lond. 1895. 8°.   10825. i. 5.

FITZGERALD (P. H.) Sir H. Irving. pp. 149.
Lond. 1895. 8°.   10825. aaa. 46.

DALE (A.) Familiar Chats with the queens of
the Stage. pp. 399. *N.Y.* 1890. 4°.
                                  011795. i. 1.

DIRCKS (R.) Players of to-day. pp. 150.
Lond. 1892. 8°.   11795. dg. 27.

ENGLISH ACTRESSES. Leading English actresses.
Lond. 1892. fol.   10804. ee. 14.

FITZGERALD (P.) The Savoy Opera and the
Savoyards. pp. 248. *Lond.* 1894. 8°.
                                  11795. dg. 46.

GODDARD (A.) Players of the period.
Lond. 1891, *etc.* 8°.   011795. ee.

P.P. London. Pearson's photographic Portfolio
of footlight favourites. *Lond.* 1894. fol. 1763. c.

—— The Pantomime Annual.
Lond. 1892, *etc.* 8°.   P.P. 2496. ib.

REID (E.) and COMPTON (H.) The Dramatic
Peerage, 1891. pp. 266. 1890. 8°. The "Peerage" Series.   012202. eeee.

WINGATE (C. E. L.) Shakespeare's Heroines on
the stage. pp. 355. *N.Y.* 1895. 8°. 011765. gg. 2.

DRAMA.—Great Britain and Ireland—
continued.

WAGNER (L.) Roughing it on the stage. pp. 20.
Lond. 1895. 12°.   11795. aa. 33.

PENLEY (B. S.) The Bath Stage. pp. 180.
Lond. 1892. 8°.   11795. dg. 41.

BAYNHAM (W.) The Glasgow Stage. pp. 221.
Glasg. 1892. 8°.   11795. dg. 21.
See also MIRACLE PLAYS.

Greece.

BLAYDES (F. H. M.) Adversaria in Tragicorum
Graecorum fragmenta. pp. 423.
Halis S. 1894. 8°.   11312. p. 11.

CAMPBELL (L.) Guide to Greek tragedy.
pp. 335. *Lond.* 1891. 8°.   11312. e. 21.

CAPPS (E.) The Greek Stage. 1891. 8°.
Ac. U.S. *American Philological Association.*
Transactions. Vol. 22.   Ac. 9965.

CHURCH (A. J.) Stories from the Greek comedians.
pp. 344. *Lond.* 1893. 8°.   11312. d. 53.

LARROUMET (G.) Études d'Histoire dramatique.
pp. 324. *Paris,* 1892. 8°.   11795. dg. 25.

MUNK (E.) Student's manual of Greek tragedy.
pp. 324. *Lond.* 1891. 8°.   2280. aa. 4.

MORSCH (H.) Goethe und die griechischen
Bühnendichter. pp. 55. 1891. 8°.
                                  011824. i. 20. (14.)

NAVARRE (O.) Dionysos. Étude sur l'organisation du théâtre athénien. pp. 320.
Paris, 1895. 8°.   011795. ee. 17.

SMITH (G.) Specimens of Greek tragedy in
English verse. 2 vol. *N.Y.* 1893. 8°.
                                  11705. de. 21.

STEIGER (H.) Der Eigenname in der attischen
Komödie. pp. 64. 1891. 8°. Ac. Erlangen.
Academia Fridericiana. Acta. Vol. 5.
                                  Ac. 2629.

RICHTER (P.) Zur Dramaturgie des Äschylus.
pp. 287. *Leipz.* 1892. 8°.   11312. i. 66.

WEIL (H.) Des traces de remaniement dans les
drames d'Eschyle. pp. 28. *Paris,* 1890. 4°.
                                  Pam. 14.

DECHARME (P.) Euripide et l'esprit de son
théâtre. pp. 568. *Paris,* 1893. 8°.
                                  11312. dd. 34.

BUSSLER (E.) Frauencharaktere aus den Tra-
gödien des Euripides. pp. 43. 1892. 8°.
Sammlung wissenschaftlicher Vorträge. N. F.
Hft. 158.   12249. l.

COUAT (A.) Aristophane et l'ancienne comédie
attique. pp. 392. *Paris,* 1892. 12°.
                                  11312. bb. 14.

PUECH (H.) Les Comédies d'Aristophane.
pp. 38. *Montpellier,* 1892. 12°. 11312. p. 1. (14.)

GARTELMANN (H.) Kritik des Aristotelischen
Systems, *etc. Berl.* 1892. 8°.   11312. f. 54.

PICKARD (J.) Der Standort der Schauspieler
und des Chors im griechischen Theater.
München, 1892, *etc.* 8°.   011795. f.

BOURDON (G.) Le Théâtre grec moderne.
pp. 123. *Paris,* 1892. 8°.   011795. i. 3.

India.

LEVI (S.) Le Théâtre Indien. pp. 122.
1890. 8°. Ac. Paris. *École des Hautes Études.*
Bibliothèque. Sciences philol. et hist.
Fasc. 83.   Ac. 8929.

Italy.

ANCONA (A. d') Origini del Teatro italiano.
2 vol. *Torino,* 1891. 8°.   011795. h. 1.

DRAMA.—Italy—*continued.*

MASI (E.) Sulla storia del Teatro italiano nel secolo XVIII. pp. 424. *Firenze,* 1891. 8°.
11795. dg. 35.

COSTETTI (G.) La Compagnia reale sarda e il Teatro italiano dal 1821 al 1855. pp. 230.
Milano, 1893. 8°. 11794. g. 28.

SALVINI (T.) Leaves from the Autobiography of T. Salvini. pp. 240. *Lond.* 1893. 8°.
10629. c. 35.

CROCE (B.) I teatri di Napoli del secolo XV–XVIII. 1889, *etc.* 8°. Ac. Naples. *Società di Storia Patria.* Archivio storico. An. 14, *etc.* Ac. 6534.

GIACOMO (S. di) Cronaca del Teatro S. Carlino. *Napoli,* 1890, *etc.* 4°. 930.

RADICIOTTI (G.) Teatro in Sinigaglia. pp. 229. *Milano,* 1893. 8°. 7895. dd. 13.

CAMBIASI (P.) Teatro di Varese, 1776–1891. pp. 51. *Milano,* 1891. 8°. Pam. 50.

ROSMINI (E.) Legislazione e giurisprudenza dei Teatri. pp. 898. *Milano,* 1893. 8°. 5373. ee. 34.
See also infra : Rome.

Japan.

MACCLATCHIE (T. R. H.) Japanese Plays versified. pp. 141. *Lond.* 1890. 8°. 11100. b. 12.

Latin. See infra : Rome.

New South Wales. See supra : Australia.

Norway. See infra : Scandinavia.

Persia.

FATH 'ALĪ ĀKHŪNDZĀDAH, *Mirzā.* Neupersische Schauspiele. *Pers.* and *Germ.*
Wien. 1889, *etc.* 8°. 757. f. 33.

Philippine Islands.

BARRANTES (V.) El Teatro tagalo. pp. 299. *Madrid,* 1889. 8°. 011795. g. 12.

Rome : Latin.

SAINT-SAËNS (C.) Note sur les décors de Théâtre dans l'antiquité romaine. pp. 23.
Paris, 1886. 8°. 7705. e. 36.

SCHOENE (A.) Das historische Nationaldrama der Römer. pp. 18. *Kiel,* 1893. 8°. Pam. 14.

BAHLMANN (P.) Die lateinischen Dramen von Wimphelings Stylpho. 1480–1550. pp. 114.
Münster, 1893. 8°. 011850. i. 30.

See also MIRACLE PLAYS.

Russia.

CORVIN DE KRUKOVSKOI (P.) Le Théâtre en Russie. pp. 358. *Paris,* 1890. 12°.
011795. e. 18.

VIENNA. *Internationale Ausstellung für Theaterwesen.* Russland. Direction der Hoftheater.
pp. 84. *Wien,* 1892. 8°. 7958. bbb. 15.

Scandinavia.

HEDBERG (F.) Skådespelarekonst och dramatik. pp. 408. *Stockholm,* 1890. 12°. 11795. dg. 22.

Ac. Upsal. *Svenska Literatursällskapet.* Bref rörande Teatern under Gustaf III.
Upsala, 1891, *etc.* 8°. Ac. 9072/9.

OTTERSTRÖM (L.) Från salong och scen.
pp. 146. *Stockholm,* 1891. 8°. 011795. ee. 11.

HANSEN (P.) Den danske skueplads illustreret Theaterhistorie. *Kjøbenh.* 1890, *etc.* 8°.
011795. g.

CHRISTENSEN (H.) Det kongelige Theater i Aarene 1852–59. pp. 344. *Kjøbenh.* 1890. 8°.
011795. g, 11.

HANSEN (C. F.) Dansk Theater handbog.
pp. 176. *Kjøbenh.* 1891. 8°. 011795. e. 44.

DRAMA.—Scandinavia—*continued.*

JAEGER (H.) H. Ibsen og hans Værker.
pp. 230. *Kristiania,* 1892. 8°. 011850. g. 22.

BOM (E. de) H. Ibsen en zijn werk. pp. 107.
Gent, 1893. 8°. 011850. g. 18.

BOYESEN (H. H.) Commentary on the works of H. Ibsen. pp. 317. *Lond.* 1894. 8°.
011850. g. 27.

SAROLEA (C.) H. Ibsen. pp. 102.
Paris, 1891. 8°. 011824. g. 6.

SHAW (G. B.) Quintessence of Ibsenism. pp. 161.
Lond. 1891. 8°. 011824. g. 15.

SIMONS (L.) Besproken Plaatsen. [Essays on Ibsen, *etc.*] pp. 280. *Amsterdam,* 1891. 8°.
011824. g. 29.

TISSOT (E.) Le Drame norvégien. pp. 294.
Paris, 1893. 8°. 011850. f. 37.

WICKSTEED (P. H.) Four lectures on H. Ibsen. pp. 112. *Lond.* 1892. 8°. 011824. ee. 2.

ZANONI. Ibsen and the drama. pp. 192.
Lond. 1895. 8°. 011850. eee. 25.

BOCCARDI (A.) La Donna nell' opera di H. Ibsen. pp. 51. *Milano,* 1893. 8°. 011824. f. 67. (8.)

GILLILAND (M. S.) Ibsen's Women. pp. 32.
Lond. 1894. 4°. 011824. f. 66. (4.)

Scotland. See supra : Great Britain.

Spain.

Ac. Madrid. *R. Academia Española.* VEGA CARPIO (L. F. de) Obras. *Madrid,* 1890, *etc.* 8°.
11726. m.

CORRAL Y MAIRÁ (M.) Boceto crítico del teatro moderno. pp. 36. *Madrid,* 1892. 8°. Pam. 50.

SEPÚLVEDA (E.) El Teatro del Príncipe Alfonso.
pp. 38. *Madrid,* 1892. 8°. Pam. 50.

VIENNA. *Internationale Ausstellung für Theaterwesen.* Katalog der Ausstellung des Königreiches Spanien. pp. 95. *Wien,* 1892. 8°.
7958. bbb. 14.

YXART (J.) El Arte escénico en España.
Barcelona, 1894, *etc.* 8°. 011795. e.

Switzerland.

Ac. Zurich. *Stiftung von Schnyder von Wartensee.* Schweizerische Schauspiele des 16ᵗᵉⁿ Jahrhunderts. *Zürich,* 1890, *etc.* 8°. 11747. f.

United States of America.

HUTTON (L.) Curiosities of the American Stage.
pp. 347. *N.Y.* 1891. 8°. 011795. g. 16.

GROSSMANN (E.) E. Booth. Recollections.
pp. 292. *Lond.* 1894. 8°. 010882. g. 18.

WINTER (W.) Life and Art of E. Booth.
pp. 308. *Lond.* 1893. 8°. 10883. bb. 29.

—— Ada Rehan. pp. 80. *N.Y.* 1891. 4°.
K.T.C. 5. b. 6.

BURROUGHS (M.) Art Portfolio of stage celebrities. *Chicago,* 1894. 8°. 10604. g. 14.

DALE (A.) Chats with queens of the Stage.
pp. 399. *N.Y.* 1890. 4°. 011795. i. 1.

DRAUGHTS. ATKINSON (M.) New Bristol [a move at draughts]. *Bristol,* 1889, *etc.* 8°.
7913. ee. 23.

CHEQUERIST. How to play Draughts well.
pp. 32. *Lond.* 1894. 8°. 7912. df. 4. (4.)

CUNNINGHAM (J. G.) The Draughts pocket manual. pp. 183. *Lond.* 1894. 8°. 7913. c. 55.

DUNNE (F.) Draughts-Player's guide. pp. 212.
Warrington, 1890. 8°. 7913. ee. 24.

GOULD (J.) The Game of Draughts. Problems. *etc.* pp. 350. *Lond.* 1884. 8°. 7913. df. 6.

—— Important matches from 1847.
Lond. 1888. 8°. 7913. df. 5.

DRAWING. B., J. A Few words about Drawing for beginners. pp. 47.
Edinb. 1893. 8°.   7855. c. 52.

DRAWING—*continued.*

HARWOOD (A.) Systematic course of Shading from the cast. *Lond.* 1892. *obl.* fol.   7857. e. 4.

HEALD (F. B.) Sedgebrook Series of 2nd Grade freehand Drawing cards. 3 sets. 1892. 4°.
Brown's School Series.   12210. g. 1.

HILLIER (D. E.) Guide to the Drawing examinations. pp. 38. 1892. 8°. A. L. Educational Series.   12203. cc.

LEDSHAM (J. B.) Drawing Examination cards. 1891, *etc.* 16°. World School Series. 12200. m.

LONGMANS, GREEN AND Co. Drawing Books. *Lond.* 1890, *etc.* 8°.   7856. de.

METCALFE (T.) Pleasant Drawing for the standards. 5 pt. *Lond.* 1887. 8°. 7854. bb. 59.

MINOR (I. S.) Drawing book.
Port-of-Spain, 1893. *obl.* 4°.   1880. a. 64.

MORTIMER (E. M.) Conversational Drawing Lessons for infants. pp. 32. *Lond.* 1893. 4°.   7855. dd. 27.

PEARL SERIES. Pearl Series of Drawing copies for infant schools. *Lond.* 1893, *etc.* 8°. 7856. a.

PETTY (J.) Drawing Series. *Leeds*, 1890, *etc.* 8°.   7854. aaa.

—— Government Exam. Test Papers. Second grade Freehand. *Leeds*, 1894. 8°. 7855. cc. 51.

—— Teachers' Guide to Drawing.
Leeds, 1894, *etc.* 8°.   7855. aa. 47.

PETTY (L.) Manual Instruction Drawing cards. *Manch.* 1891. 8°.   7854. ccc. 37.

PHILLIPS (L. J.) Drawing for infants and junior schools. 3 sets. *Lond.* 1890. 8°. 7854. aaa. 37.

RICHMOND (E.) Kinder-Garten Drawing lessons. pp. 33. 1890. 12°. Gill's School Series.
    12202. g.

RIDGE (E. B.) Standard Drawing lessons.
Lond. 1891, *etc.* 4°.   7856. de.

RUSHMORE (F. M.) Practical hints on Teaching Drawing. *Leeds*, 1892, *etc.* 8°. 7854. aa. 11.

SHEFFIELD (E.) Artistic Drawing cards for infants. *Lond.* 1893. 4°.   7855. aaa. 45.

SPARKES (W. E.) How to shade from Models and casts. pp. 62. *Lond.* 1890. 8°.
    7857. aa. 55.

STADE (P.) Ein neuer Lehrplan für den Zeichenunterricht in der Volksschule. pp. 23.
1892. 8°. MEYER (J.) Pädagogische Zeit- und Streitfragen. Hft. 28.   8310. c.

STEELEY (F.) and TROTMAN (B. H.) " Excelsior" Drawing test cards. 5 pt. *Lond.* 1891. 8°.
    7856. de. 20.

—— Excelsior graduated Drawing charts.
Lond. 1894, *etc.* fol. & 8°.   1801. d.

—— Excelsior first grade Drawing cards.
Lond. 1892. 8°.   7855. c. 50.

—— Excelsior straight line Drawing cards.
Lond. 1893. 8°.   7857. d. 9.

—— Excelsior Kindergarten Drawing cards.
Lond. 1893. 8°.   7856. de. 29.

TRAINER (P. E.) Practical Series of Drawing cards. *Lond.* 1891, *etc.* 8°.   7854. ccc.

VAUGHAN (J.) Freehand Course for the elementary stage. *Lond.* 1893. fol. 7854. k. 12.

WALKER (J. A.) Standard Drawing books.
Glasg. 1893, *etc.* *obl.* 4°.   7858. gg. 8.

—— Second Grade freehand Drawing book.
pp. 24. *Glasg.* 1893. fol.   7858. l. 13.

WARREN (S. E.) Industrial science Drawing. pp. 152. *N.Y.* 1893. 8°.   7857. d. 13.

WOOD (R. S.) Analytic Drawing series.
Lond. 1892, *etc.* fol.   7858. c.

WYSE (H. T.) Brushwork Series. Second Grade freehand Drawing cards. *Dundee*, 1891. 8°.
    7855. b. 53.

See also ART : PAINTING : PERSPECTIVE.

DRAWING—*continued.*

Geometrical, Mechanical Drawing, etc.

BARRODALE (T. H.) Code Geometrical Drawing. *Birmingham*, 1890. 4°.   Pam. 38.

BRADBURY (A. A.) Cusack's How to draw the Geometrical Models and Vases. pp. 12.
Lond. 1895. 4°.   Pam. 24.

BRYANS (E.) Examples in Geometrical Drawing and scales for preliminary examination for Woolwich and Sandhurst. *Oxford*, 1893. 8°.
    8531. aa. 47.

BURN (R. S.) Architectural and Engineering Drawing Book. pp. 155. *Lond.* 1893. 8°.
    7855. c. 53.

COX (E. J.) Complete Geometry revision Sheets. ff. 12. *Lond.* 1890. 8°.   Pam. 38.

DAVY (C. R.) Mechanical Drawing for beginners. *Leeds*, 1891. *obl.* 8°.   8767. cc. 24.

DONALDSON (J.) Drawing for marine engineers. 2 pt. *Lond.* 1895. 8°.   8806. e. 40.

DRAUGHTSMAN. Geometrical Draughtsman. pp. 150. *Lond.* 1892. 8°.   8535. de. 10.

FISH (J. C. L.) Lettering of working Drawings. *N.Y.* 1894. *obl.* 4°.   1752. a. 5.

HALLIDAY (G.) First Course in mechanical Drawing. 2 pt. *Lond.* 1891. *obl.* fol.
    1807. a. 10.

HARRIS (R.) Note-book on plane geometrical Drawing. pp. 230. *Lond.* 1895. 8°.
    8534. df. 14.

HARWOOD (A.) Geometry work book.
Lond. 1893, *etc.* 8°.   1879. a. 5.

MAC LAY (A.) Elementary course of mechanical Drawing, *etc. Munch.* 1891, *etc.* 8°. 7857. d. 4.

MOFFATT (W.) Geometrical Drawing test papers. *Lond.* 1893. 8°.   7855. cc. 50.

MORRIS (I. H.) Geometrical Drawing for art students. pp. 183. *Lond.* 1890. 8°.
    8535. b. 34.

PETTY (J.) Government test papers in Geometrical Drawing. 32 papers.
Leeds, 1894. fol.   7856. g. 1.

PRATT (R.) Sciography : or, parallel and radial projection of shadows. pp. 39.
Lond. 1891. *obl.* 4°.   7854. f. 49.

PRESSLAND (A. J.) Geometrical Drawing. pp. 144. *Lond.* 1892. 8°.   8535. b. 50.

ROBSON (J. H.) Geometrical Drawing. pp. 178. *Lond.* 1890. 8°.   8535. b. 33.

TUCK (F. J.) First lessons in Geometrical Drawing. pp. 32. *Eton*, 1893. 8°. 8533. bb. 44.

WELLS (S. H.) Engineering Drawing and Design. 2 pt. *Lond.* 1893. 8°. 8768. bbb. 37.

DRAWINGS, Collections of.

Ac. London. *British Museum.* Guide to the Exhibition of Drawings in the Print and Drawing Gallery. pp. 111. *Lond.* 1891. 8°.
    7854. e. 37.

—— Guide to an Exhibition of Drawings by old Masters, from the Malcolm Collection. pp. 118. *Lond.* 1895. 8°.   7858. b. 50.

—— Paris. *Bibliothèque Nationale.* Inventaire de la collection de Dessins sur Paris formée par M. H. Destailleur. pp. 72. *Paris*, 1891. 8°.
    7858. g. 35.

—— Inventaire des Dessins exécutés pour R. de Gaignières. 2 tom. *Paris*, 1891. 8°.
    7858. gg. 2.

SCHÉFER (G.) Catalogue des Dessins, *etc.* composant le Cabinet des Estampes de la Bibliothèque de l'Arsenal. *Paris*, 1894, *etc.* 8°.
    7857. dd.

DRAWINGS.—Collections of—*continued.*

CINCINNATI. *Museum Association.* Cat. of an exhibition of Etchings and Drawings. pp. 26. *Cincinnati*, 1892. 8°.   Pam. 24.

FLORENCE. *Galleria.* Catalogo della racolta di Disegni posseduta dalla R. Galleria degli Uffizi di Firenze. 1890, *etc.* 8°. ITALY. *M. dell' Istruzione.* Indici e Cataloghi. XII. 011903. k.

HEFNER-ALTENECK (J. H. v.) Original-Zeichnungen deutscher Meister des 16ten Jahrhunderts. pp. 8. *Frankfurt*, 1889. fol. 1759. c. 12.

CHAMPFLEURY. Catalogue des Eaux-fortes et Dessins formant la collection Champfleury. pp. 127. *Paris*, 1891. 4°.   7858. c. 17.

EISENMANN (O.) Handzeichnungen älterer Meister aus der Sammlung E. Habich. *Lübeck*, 1890, *etc.* fol.   1756. b.

GRATET-DUFLESSIS (G.) Collection de Dessins sur Paris. 1891. 8°. Ac. Paris. *Société de l'Histoire de Paris.* Mémoires. Tom. 17.
Ac. 6883/2.

BOURCARD (G.) Dessins, *etc.* du dix-huitième siècle. pp. 675. *Paris*, 1893. 8°. 7858. gg. 20.

DREAMS. *See* SLEEP.

DRENTHE. JOOSTING (J. G. C.) Ordelen van den Etstoel van Drenthe, 1518–1604. pp. 474. 1893. 8°. Ac. Utrecht. *Vereeniging tot Uitgaaf der Bronnen van het Oude Vaderlandsche Recht.* Oude Werken. Reeks 1. No. 16.
5685. e.

DRESDEN. KRAUSE (B.) Die geschichtliche Entwickelung der Residenzstadt Dresden. 2 Hft. *Dresden*, 1893. 8°.   10255. f. 29.

DRESS AND DRESSMAKING.

Dress.

BALLIN (A. S.) Health and beauty in Dress. pp. 244. *Lond.* 1893. 8°.   7404. df. 7.

BLANC (A. A. P. C.) L'Art dans la parure et dans le Vêtement. pp. 294. *Paris*, 1890. 4°.
7742. de. 26.

HOLDING (T. H.) Comfort & economy in Clothes. pp. 60. *Lond.* 1891. 16°.   7742. aaa. 16.

JAEGER (G.) Dr. Jaeger's Health-Culture. pp. 317. *Lond.* 1887. 8°.   7391. aa. 6.

KRATSCHMER (F.) Die Bekleidung. 1894. 8°. WEYL (T.) Handbuch der Hygiene. Bd. 1.
7391. dd.

LEOTY (E.) Le Corset à travers les âges. pp. 110. *Paris*, 1893, 4°.   7743. cc. 8.

SCHURTZ (H.) Grundzüge einer Philosophie der Tracht. pp. 146. *Stuttgart*, 1891. 8°.
7743. c. 17.

STEELE (F. M.) Beauty of form and grace of Vesture. pp. 231. *Lond.* 1892. 8°.
7743. bbb. 60.

WILLIAMS (W. M.) Philosophy of Clothing. pp. 155. *Lond.* 1890. 8°.   7404. cc. 15. *See also* COSTUME.

Dressmaking.

BALHATCHET (G.) Dress Cutting and making on tailors' principles. pp. 16. *Bristol*, 1895. 8°.
Pam. 24.

BANKS (A. M.) Instructions for drafting Bodice pattern on the paper folding plan. *Leeds*, 1895. 8°. & fol.   1810. d. 1. (58.)

BELLHOUSE (*Mrs.* J.) Be your own Dress-maker. pp. 36. *Rochdale*, 1893. 8°.   Pam. 24.

CARLISLE (E. M. F.) Practical method of Dress cutting. *Lond.* 1893, *etc.* 8°.   7742. aaa. 21.

CHART. Improved scientific Dressmaking chart. *Lond.* 1890. fol.   1801. d. 1. (144.)

COOKE (S. A.) Ladies' own charts. *Lond.* 1891. fol.   1810. d. 1. (8.)

DRESS.—Dressmaking—*continued.*

DAVIS (J. E.) Elements of modern Dressmaking. pp. 193. *Lond.* 1894. 8°.   7742. bb. 33.

FURNISS (*Mrs.* C.) Burton-on-Trent Excelsior System of cutting ladies' and children's clothing. *Burton-on-Trent*, 1889.   Tab. 1800. b.

GAUNT ( ) Instructions for cutting out clothing for the baby. pp. 64. *Glasg.* 1895. 8°.
7743. bb. 75.

GREEN (H. M.) Dressmaking simplified. *Walsall*, 1895. 4°.   7743. f. 31.

GRENFELL (A. L.) Dressmaking. pp. 83. *Lond.* 1892. 8°.   7742. aa. 10.

—— Dress cutting-out. *Lond.* 1893. fol.
7743. e. 4.

—— Under-Linen cutting-out. pp. 16. *Lond.* 1894. 8°.   Pam. 24.

GRIFFITHS ( ) Teacher of Dressmaking. pp. 12. *Manch.* 1894. 8°.   Pam. 94.

HEATH (F.) Pattern-making by paper folding. pp. 64. *Lond.* 1894. 8°.   7743. bbb. 69.

HENRY (S.) Paragon system of drafting dress bodice, collar and sleeve. pp. 11. *Manch.* 1894. 8°.   Pam. 24.

HICKS (R.) Dress Cutting and making on tailors' principles. pp. 47. *Lond.* 1894. 8°.
7743. bbb. 70.

HOLDING (T. H.) Ladies' Garment cutting. pp. 90. *Lond.* 1890. 4°.   7742. de. 25.

KENDALL (E. G.) Cosmopolitan improved system of Dress-cutting. *Leeds*, 1892. fol. & 8°.
1812. d. 5.

KIRKHOPE (G.) Draper's and tailor's Measurement book. pp. 132. *Lond.* 1894. 8°.
8548. bbb. 61.

KLEMM (H.) Volledige handleiding van het Dames-Kleedermaken. 4 pt. *Leiden*, 1890. 8°.
7743. ee. 16.

LOEFVALL (J. H.) How to cut, fit and finish a Dress. pp. 70. *Lond.* 1891. 8°.   7743. a. 4.

LOW (E.) Technical and practical lessons in Dressmaking. pp. 37. *Carshalton*, 1893. 8°.
7743. bbb. 67.

LUDLOW ( ) Practical Tailor dress cutting system. pp. 8. *Rawtenstall*, 1894. 8°. Pam. 24.

P., C. J. Popular Dress making. pp. 12. *Lond.* 1895. 8°.   Pam. 24.

P.P. *London.* London Journal. Fashions for the month. *Lond.* 1886, *etc.* 4°.   N. R.

P.P. *London.* Metropolitan Fashions for autumn and winter. *Lond.* 1892, *etc.* obl. fol.
1807. b.

P.P. London. *Lady.* Lady handbooks of Dressmaking, *etc.* *Lond.* 1893, *etc.* 8°.   P.P. 5174.

P.P. *London,* The Millinery Journal. *Lond.* 1893, *etc.* fol.   1740.

P.P. *Paris. La Mode pratique.* Fashions of to-day. *Lond.* 1892, 94. fol.   P.P. 5231 h.

ROSEVEAR (E.) Needlework, knitting and cutting out. 3 pt. *Lond.* 1894 8°. 7743. bb. 66.

ROSÉE ( ) Handbook of Millinery. pp. 62. *Lond.* 1895. 8°.   7743. bb. 76.

SCHILD (M.) New Skirts. How to cut them. pp. 14. *Lond.* 1893. 4°.   7743. f. 28.

SCISSORS. Why Dressmaking does not pay. pp. 16. *Lond.* 1895. 8°.   08226. b. 13. (19.)

SMITH (L. E.) Practical Dressmaking. pp. 65. *Lond.* 1895. 8°.   7743. aaa. 77.

STIRLING (M.) Practical Dress-cutting. *Lond.* 1890. 8°.   7742. b. 15.

SUTCLIFFE (*Mrs.* G. M.) Dress-cutting and making. pp. 49. *Leeds*, 1893. 8°.   7743. bb. 67.

TOMLIN (J.) Dressmakers' Guide. pp. 16. 1892. 8°.   Pam. 24.

DRESS.—Dressmaking—*continued.*

WELDON AND CO. Home Dressmaker. pp. 15.
Lond. 1888. 4°.   Pam. 24.

WHITE (F.) Easy Dressmaking. pp. 62.
Lond. 1892. 4°.   7743. bbb. 61.

WORTH (G.) La couture des Vêtements de
femme. pp. 113. *Paris*, 1895. 8°. 7743. e. 27.

YOUNG (J. W.) Unique System for cutting ladies'
garments. *Leeds*, 1893. fol.
    Tab. 11747. b (70.)
See also NEEDLEWORK : TAILORING.

DREUX. COYNART (C. A. de) L'Année 1562
et la bataille de Dreux. pp. 47.
Paris, 1894. 8°.   9007. g. 23. (7.)

DRIVING. *See* COACHING : HORSE.

DROITWICH. GARROD (A. E.) Medical
Springs of Droitwich, *etc.* 1895. 8°. Ac. London. *Medical and Chirurgical Society.* Climates
of Great Britain. Vol. 1.   7462. g.

TOMLINS (W. H.) Droitwich Brine Baths as
therapeutic agents. pp. 22.   *Lond.* 1895. 8°.
    7306. e. 26. (13.)

DROME, Department. BRUN-DURAND (J.)
Dictionnaire du Département de la Drôme.
pp. 502. *Paris*, 1891. 4°.   10172. g. 6.

DRUGS, Adulteration of. *See* PHARMACY.

DRUIDS. *See* CELTIC RACES : STONEHENGE.

DRUIDS, Ancient Order of. *See* FRIENDLY
SOCIETIES.

DRUNKENNESS. *See* ALCOHOL.

DUBLIN.

City.

COSGRAVE (E. M.) Dictionary of Dublin. 2 pt.
Dublin, 1895. 8°.   10390. de. 9.

DIGNAM (J.) Dignam's Dublin guide. pp. 134,
Dublin, 1891. 8°.   10390. c. 27.

JOYCE (W. St. J.) Rambles around Dublin.
pp. 46. 1890. 8°. P.P. *Dublin.* Evening
Telegraph Reprints. No. 3.   P.P. 6159. ac.

—— Rambles near Dublin. pp. 75. 1890. 8°.
P.P. *Dublin.* Evening Telegraph Reprints.
No. 9.   P.P. 6159. ac.

MAC CREADY (C. T.) Dublin street names.
pp. 160. *Dublin*, 1892. 8°.   10390. aaaa. 20.

R., F. E. Historical reminiscences of Dublin
Castle. pp. 111. *Dublin*, 1895. 16°. 9509. a. 14.

WAKEMAN (W. F.) Old Dublin. 2 pt. 1888. 8°.
P.P. *Dublin.* Evening Telegraph Reprints.
No. 2, 4.   P.P. 6159. ac.

Churches and University.

LEEPER (A.) Historical handbook to the Cathedral Church of St. Patrick. pp. 119.
Dublin, 1891. 8°.   10390. de. 1.

HUGHES (S. C.) Church of S. Werburgh, Dublin.
pp. 156. *Dublin*, 1889. 8°.   4735. aa. 30.

HOLY TRINITY, *Priory of the, at Dublin.* Account
Roll of the Priory of the Holy Trinity, Dublin
1337-46. pp. 231. 1891. 8°. Ac. Kilkenny.
Archæological Society. The Annuary. Extra
vol. 1891.   Ac. 5785/2.

Ac. Dublin. *Trinity College.* Book of Trinity
College, Dublin. 1591-1891. pp. 316.
Belfast, 1892. 4°.   8364. i. 2.

—— Records of the tercentenary festival of the
University. pp. 328. *Dublin*, 1894. 8°
    8364. h. 12.

OLDHAM (C. H.) Trinity College pictorial. pp. 70.
Dublin, 1892. 4°.   8365. f. 33.

URWICK (W.) Early history of Trinity College,
Dublin. pp. 99. *Lond.* 1892. 8°. 8364. bb. 70.

DUCKS. COOK (W.) Ducks, and how to
make them pay. pp. 128.
St. Mary Cray, 1895. 8°.   7293. aaa. 28.

DUTCHER (W.) The Labrador Duck ; list of the
extant specimens. pp. 15. 1891. 8°.
    7004. df. 22. (10.)

—— The Labrador Duck ; another specimen.
Camb. Mass. 1894. 8°.   7004. df. 22. (14.)

PARKER (W. K.) Morphology of the Duck Tribe.
pp. 132. 1890. 4°. Ac. Dublin. *Royal Irish
Academy.* Cunningham Memoirs. No. 6.
    Ac. 1540/6.

See also ANIMALS, *Domestic :* BIRDS : POULTRY.

DUELLING. BERGER (A.) Das sogenannte
americanische Duell. pp. 48. *Leipz.* 1892. 8°.
    05604. g. 6. (3.)

CARDENAL Y GOMEZ (M.) Las Armas y el Duelo.
pp. 49. *Habana*, 1886. 8°. 8425. bbb. 42. (7.)

CROABBON (A.) La science du Point d'Honneur.
pp. 593. *Paris*, 1888. 8°.   8425. i. 32.

FERRÉUS ( ) Annuaire du Duel. 1888–89.
pp. 290. *Paris*, 1891. 8°.   8425. e. 14.

HERGSELL (G.) Duell-Codex. pp. 203.
Wien, 1891. 8°.   8425. g. 21.

LETAINTURIER-FRADIN (G.) Le Duel à travers
les âges. pp. 14. 300. *Paris*, 1892. 8°.
    8425. i. 31.

—— Les Jurys d'honneur et le Duel. pp. 120.
Nice, 1895. 8°.   8425. aa. 43.

MURZ (F.) Degen- Säbel- und Duell-Fechten.
pp. 231. *Debreczen*, 1890. 8°.   7907. dd. 2.

PRÉVOST (C.) and JOLLIVET (G.) L'Escrime et
le Duel. pp. 257. *Paris*, 1891. 8°. 7908. eee. 5.

ROBAGLIA (A.) L'Escrime et le Duel. pp. 294.
Paris, 1890. 18°.   7908. c. 34.

TARDE (G.) El Duelo. pp. 350.
Madrid, 1893. 8°.   8425. aa. 36.

VIDAL DE SAINT-URBAIN ( ) Le Duel sous
l'ancien régime et de nos jours. pp. 75.
Dijon, 1892. 8°.   5423. g. 1. (7.)

WIESINGER (A.) Das Duell vor dem Richterstuhle der Religion, der Moral, *etc.* pp. 184.
Graz, 1895. 8°.   8425. bbb. 45.

YÑIGUEZ (E.) Ofensas y desafíos : las leyes que
rigen en el Duelo. pp. 190. *Madrid*, 1890. 8°.
    8425. f. 16.

See also FENCING.

DUISBURG. AVERDUNK (H.) Geschichte
der Stadt Duisburg, 1666.
Duisburg, 1894, *etc.* 8°.   10261. g.

BORHECK (A. C.) Versuch einer Geschichte der
Stadt Duisburg. pp. 64. *Duisburg*, 1893. 8°.
    10107. ff. 26. (7.)

DULWICH. STOCKS (W. H.) Short history
of the organ and services at the Chapel of
Alleyn's College at Dulwich. pp. 28.
Lond. 1891. 8°.   7897. l. 13. (9.)

See also EXHIBITIONS, *Part I. :* LONDON, *Environs.*

**DUMBARTON AND DUMBARTON-
SHIRE.** MAC LEOD (D.) Dumbarton, ancient
and modern. *Glasg.* 1893. 4°.   1790. b. 7.

—— Historic Families and memorabilia of the
Lennox. pp. 232. *Dumbarton.* 1891. 8°.
    10369. ccc. 4.

—— Past Worthies of the Lennox. pp. 216.
Edinb. 1894. 8°.   012330. g. 68.

DUMFRIESSHIRE. CHRISTISON (D.) View
of the Forts, camps, and motes of Dumfriesshire.
1891. 4°. Ac. Edinburgh. *Society of Antiquaries.* Proceedings. Vol. 25.   Ac. 5770/2.

GRAY (P.) Dumfriesshire illustrated.
Dumfries, 1894, *etc.* 8°.   10370. dd. 21.

DUMFRIESSHIRE—*continued.*

PATERSON (J.) Nithsdale. pp. 63.
Glasg. 1893. fol.   K.T.C. 21. b. 2.

DUNBAR. MACDONALD (J.) Burgh Register and guide to Dunbar. pp. 51.
Haddington, 1893. 8°.   10369. cc. 30.

DUNDEE. MAXWELL (A.) Old Dundee.
pp. 424. *Edinb.* 1891. 4°.   010370. f. 24.
See also FORTH BRIDGE.

DUNEDIN, N.Z. BATHGATE (A.) Picturesque Dunedin. pp. 300. *Dunedin,* 1890. 8°.
10492. ee. 21.

DUNKIRK. RAHLENBECK (C. A.) Une Ville belge perdue. pp. 16. *Brux.* 1891. 8°.
10105. ee. 10. (6.)

DUN-LE-ROI. MOREAU (P.) Histoire de Dun-le-Roi. *Saint Amand,* 1895, *etc.* 8°.
010171. i.

DUNNOTTAR CASTLE. LONGMUIR (J.) Dunnottar Castle. pp. 114.
Stonehaven, 1894. 8°.   10369. ccc. 31.

DUNOON. DUNOON. Gaelic topography of Dunoon. pp. 47. *Kirkintilloch,* 1892. 8°.
12901. ccc. 17. (9.)

DURANCE River. FÉRAUD-GIRAUD (L. J. D.) Notes sur la Durance. pp. 206.
Aix, 1893. 8°.   10171. d. 11.

DURBAN. ROBINSON (*Sir* J.) Sketches of Durban and its harbour. pp. 15.
Durban, 1891. 4°.   10096. i. 16.

DURBON. Ac. Gap. *Société d'Études.* Chartes de Durbon. pp. 904.
Montreuil, 1893. 8°.   4782. i. 28.

DURHAM, City and County. FOWLER (J. T.) Excavations on the site of the Chapter-House of Durham Abbey. 1883. 8°. Ac. Durham. *Architectural Society,* Transactions.
Ac. 5635.

GREENWELL (W.) Durham Cathedral. 1883. 8°. Ac. Durham. *Architectural Society.* Transactions.   Ac. 5635.

TALBOT (R. T.) Durham Cathedral. 1893. 8°.
FARRAR (F. W.) Our English Minsters.
07816. ee. 2.

SAINT OSWALD, *Durham.* Parish Registers of St. Oswald's, Durham. pp. 293. *Durham,* 1891. 8°.
9916. ee. 4.

Ac. Durham. *Surtees Society.* Publ. Vol. 85. English Miscellanies illustrating the history and language of the northern counties. pp. 100.
Durham, 1890. 8°.   Ac. 8045/65.

BARNES (H.) On Quarter Sessions Orders relating to the Plague in Durham, 1665.
1890. 8°.   Pam. 39.

BOYLE (J. R.) Guide to the County of Durham. pp. 733. *Lond.* 1892. 8°.   10351. d. 40.

COTTERELL (C.) Summer Holidays in N.E. England. pp. 143. *Lond.* 1895. 8°.
010358. e. 32.

DURHAM, *County.* Geography of Durham.
pp. 32. *Lond.* 1892. 8°.   10348. ccc. 57. (8.)

—— Murray's Handbook for Travellers in Durham. By T. E. Espin. pp. 342. *Lond.* 1890. 8°.
2364. a. 10.

—— Pedigrees at the Visitations of the County of Durham, 1575, 1615, 1666. *Lond.* 1887. 8°.
9904. cc. 2.

NORTHUMBERLAND. Collectanea Curiosa. pp. 64. *Newcastle,* 1892. 8°.   010358. l. 39.

ROWELL (H.) Cycling Mileage Guide and Diary, 1891. pp. 48. *Lond.* 1891. 16°.   7906. a. 69.

DÜSSELDORF. REDLICH (O. R.) Anwesenheit Napoleons I. in Düsseldorf, 1811, *etc.*
pp. 78. *Düsseldorf,* 1892. 8°.   9079. i. 12.

DÜSSELDORF—*continued.*

LACHMANSKI (H.) Düsseldorf und Heine.
pp. 31. *Berl.* 1893. 8°.   10601. ff. 10. (11.)

DUTCH LANGUAGE.

Dialects.

JELLINGHAUS (H.) Die niederländischen Volksmundarten. pp. 132. 1892. 8°. Ac. Hamburg. *Verein für Niederdeutsche Sprachforschung.* Forschungen.   Bd. 5. Ac. 9822/5.

Dictionaries.

MANHAVE (J.) Beknopt woordenboek der Nederlandsche taal. pp. 576. *'s-Gravenhage,* 1892. 8°.
12972. bbb. 33.

SCHLEGEL (G.) Nederlandsch-chineesch Woordenboek. *Leiden,* 1886–91. 8°.   12910. h. 14.

CALISCH (I. M.) Nieuw engelsch Woordenboek. 2 pt. *Arnhem,* 1893. 8°.   12972. e. 24.

DICTIONARIES. Pocket-Dictionary of English and Dutch. 2 pt. *Leipz.* 1893. 16°. 12972. aa. 21.

PICARD (H.) Pocket Dictionary of English-Dutch and Dutch-English. pp. 1250.
Gouda, 1890. 8°.   12972. aaa. 23.

CALISCH (I. M.) Nieuw fransch Woordenboek. 2 pt. *Arnhem,* 1893. 8°.   12950. e. 37.

Grammars, etc.

BRUINS (F.) De practische Taalmeester, *etc.* 4 pt. *Groningen,* 1891. 8°.   12972. c. 43.

CRAMER (B.) Geheel vernieuwde en verbeterde Trap der Jeugd. pp. 96. *Cape Town,* 1894. 8°.
12972. aa. 24.

DESMET (A.) Pratique de la Langue flamande. pp. 162. *Paris,* 1892. 8°.   12972. ee. 44.

DU TOIT (S. J.) Afrikaans ons volkstaal. pp. 126. *Paarl,* 1891. 8°.   12972. c. 42.

ELFFERS (H.) Practische hollandsche Spraakkunst. pp. 257. *Kaapstad,* 1894. 8°.
12972. cc. 50.

—— Grammar of the Dutch Language. pp. 200. *Cape Town,* 1890. 8°.   12972. c. 39.

—— Leesboek voor Zuid-Afrika. 3 Dltj. *Kaapstad,* 1895. 8°.   12972. b. 41.

—— South African letter-writer. pp. 125. *Cape Town,* 1895. 8°.   10921. bbb. 40.

GELDEREN (I. v.) Ons Nederlandsch. Grammatica-cursus. 3 pt. *Groningen,* 1894-5. 8°.
12972. d. 28.

HERTOG (C. H. d.) Nederlandsche Spraakkunst, *etc.* 2 Stuk. *Amsterdam,* 1892. 8°.
12972. e. 22.

KALFF (G.) Het onderwijs in de Moedertaal. pp. 149. *Amsterdam,* 1893. 8°.   12935. e. 20.

KOLLEWIJN (R. A.) Onaannemelik? [Answer to C. H. d. Hertog.] pp. 42. *Zutphen,* 1893. 8°.
12903. c. 52. (7.)

REINHARDSTOETTNER (C. v.) Holländische Konversations-Grammatik. pp. 348.
Heidelberg, 1886. 8°.   12972. cc. 52.

ROSSOUW (E. H.) Leesboekje voor onze Zuid-Afrikaansche Kinderen. pp. 60.
Kaapstad, 1893. 8°.   12972. aa. 22.

TUNK (J. v. d.) Nederlandsche Spraakkunst voor Zuid Afrika. pp. 179. *Kaapstad,* 1891. 8°.
12972. dd. 22.

VALETTE (T. G. G.) Nouvelle Grammaire néerlandaise. pp. 321. *Paris,* 1894. 8°.
12972. cc. 54.

—— Corrigé des thèmes de la Grammaire néerlandaise. pp. 52. *Paris,* 1894. 8°.
12972. cc. 53.

DUTCH LANGUAGE—*continued.*

Elffers (H.) Course of Dutch Composition.
pp. 186. *Cape Town*, 1894. 8°.   12972. b. 40.

Tuuk (J. v. d.) Manual of Dutch Composition.
pp. 200. *Cape Town*, 1893. 8°.   12972. c. 45.

Koch (W.) Course of translation from Flemish
into English. pp. 99. *Ghent*, 1891. 8°.
12972. c. 44.

Franck (J.) Notgedrungene Beiträge zur Etymologie. pp. 49. *Bonn*, 1893. 8°.
12903. e. 28. (7.)

History.

Verdam (J.) De Geschiedenis der nederlandsche
taal. pp. 224. *Leeuwarden*, 1890. 8°.
12972. e. 11.

Backer (L. de) La langue flamande en France.
pp. 200. *Gand*, 1893. 8°.   12950. e. 36.

Synonyms and Idioms.

Delinotte (L. P.) Dictionnaire des Idiotismes
de la langue hollandaise. pp. 312.
Amsterdam, 1891. 8°.   12972. ccc. 1.

Hendriks (J. V.) Handwoordenboek van nederlandsche Synoniemen. pp. 335. *Tiel*, 1890. 8°.
12972. dd. 24.

Hofman (C. A.) Formes idiomatiques comparées. pp. 161. *Amsterdam.* 1890. 8°.
12902. ccc. 21.

Willem. Samesprake in Afrikaans en Engels.
2 Nos. *Paarl*, 1890. 8°.   12972. c. 40.

DUTCH AND FLEMISH LITERA-TURE.

Bibliography.

Ac. Ghent. *K. Vlaamsche Academie.* Potter
(F. de) Vlaamsche Bibliographie.
Gent, 1893, *etc.* 8°.   Ac. 7556/2.

Meulen (R. v. d.) Brinkman's Catalogus der
boeken, plaat- en kaartwerken, 1882-91.
Amsterd. 1892, *etc.* 8°.   011904. h.

History, Criticism, etc.

Bots (P. M.) Handboek der Stijlleer, schoone
letteren en nederlandsche Letterkunde.
pp. 208. *Rotterdam*, 1892. 8°.   11825. dd. 53.

Brink (J. ten) De oude Garde en de jongste
School. 2 vol. *Amsterd.* 1891. 8°.
011824. g. 28.

Hasebroek (J. P.) Een Dichter-Album.
pp. 333. *Amsterd.* 1890. 8°.   10760. c. 25.

Hofdijk (W. J.) Geschiedenis der nederlandsche
Letterkunde. pp. 367. *'s Gravenh.* 1886. 8°.
11850. dd. 32.

Jonckbloet (G.) Uit Nederland en Insulinde.
Amsterd. 1893, *etc.* 8°.   011850. g.

Kleine (F. S.) Schrijvers en schrifturen.
pp. 224. *Haarlem*, 1891. 8°.   011840. e. 70.

Leopold (L.) Nederlandsche Schrijvers der vier
laatste eeuwen. pp. 336. *Groningen*, 1891. 8°.
12258. h. 17.

Low German Classics. Illustr. Bibliothek
niederdeutscher Klassiker. *Leipz.* 1891, *etc.* 8°.
12253. h.

Luzac (C. J.) De nederlandsche sentimenteele
Roman. pp. 116. *Amersfoort*, 1890. 8°.
011824. h. 23.

Martinet (J. v. L.) Het fatalisme in onze jongste
Letterkunde. pp. 29. *Haarlem*, 1891. 8°.
Pam. 15.

Ruyten (A.) Bloemlezing uit nederlandsche
Dichters en prozaschrijvers.
Roermond, 1891, *etc.* 8°.   11557. h. 24.

Segers (G.) J. van den Vondel. pp. 398.
Antwerpen, 1895. 8°.   10759. i. 48.

Tideman (J.) Studien en schetsen. pp. 308.
's Gravenh. 1892. 8°   11825. h. 29.

DUTCH LITERATURE—*continued.*

Verwijs (E.) Nederlandsche Klassieken.
Leeuwarden, 1885, *etc.* 8°.   12258. bb.

Werner (A.) The Humour of Holland.
pp. 398. *Lond.* 1893. 8°.   012314. g.

DWALLO LANGUAGE.

See African Languages.

DWARFS. Haliburton (R. G.) Dwarfs of

Mount Atlas. pp. 41. *Lond.* 1891. 8°. Pam. 89.

—— The Holy Land of Punt. 2 pt.
Lond. 1893. 8°.   10007. bb. 17.

—— Survivals of Dwarf races in the New World.
pp. 14. *Salem*, 1894. 8°.   Pam. 86.

Panckow (H.) Über Zwergvölker in Afrika
und Süd-Asien. 1892. 8°. Ac. Berlin. *Gesellschaft für Erdkunde.* Zeitschrift. Bd. 27.
No. 2.   Ac. 6075/2.

Quatrefages de Bréau (J. L. A. de) The Pygmies. pp. 255. *Lond.* 1895. 8°.   10007. bbb. 26.

Tyson (E.) Philological essay concerning the
Pygmies of the Ancients. pp. 103. 1894. 8°.
Bibliothèque de Carabas. Vol. 9.   12204. hh.

Paltauf (A.) Über den Zwergwuchs. pp. 106.
Wien, 1891. 8°.   7419. l. 5.

DYEING. Brannt (W. T.) Practical Scourer

and garment dyer. pp. 203. *Phila.* 1893. 8°.
07944. f. 2.

Dépierre (J.) Traité de la Teinture et de l'impression des matières colorantes artificielles.
Paris, 1891, *etc.* 8°.   07945. f.

Garçon (J.) La Pratique du Teinturier.
Paris, 1893, *etc.* 8°.   07944. g.

Grison (T.) La Teinture au dix-neuvième siècle.
2 tom. *Paris*, 1884. 8°.   7743. e. 28.

Hurst (G. H.) Handbook of garment Dyeing
and cleaning. pp. 180. *Lond.* 1895. 8°.
07944. f. 14.

—— Silk Dyeing, *etc.* pp. 226. 1892. 8°.
Wood (*Sir* H. T.) Technological Handbooks.
2266. a. 38.

Knecht (E.) A Manual of Dyeing. 3 pt.
Lond. 1893. 8°.   07945. g. 7.

Nietzki (R.) Chemistry of the organic Dyestuffs.
pp. 313. *Lond.* 1892. 8°.   8909. d. 6.

Prud'homme ( ) Teinture et impression.
pp. 195. 1894. 8°. Encyclopédie des aide-
memoire.   8709. g.

Sansone (A.) Recent progress in Dyeing.
pp. 136. *Lond.* 1895. 8°.   07945. f. 34.

Tassart (C. L.) L'Industrie de la Teinture.
pp. 305. *Paris*, 1890. 18°.   7942. cc. 31.

—— Les Matières colorantes et la chimie de la
teinture. pp. 296. *Paris*, 1890. 12°.
8906. de. 25.

Villon (A. M.) Nouveau manuel du Teinturier.
pp. 399. 1890. 8°. Encyclopédie-Roret.
12207. l. 7.

Vinant (M. de) Traité de Teinture. pp. 713.
Lyon, 1890. 8°.   07945. m. 6.
See also Colours.

DYNAMICS. Besant (W. H.) Treatise on

Dynamics. pp. 448. *Camb.* 1893. 8°.
2242. aa. 3.

Blaikie (J.) Elements of Dynamics. pp. 208.
Edinb. 1893. 8°.   2242. aa. 4.

Burton (C. V.) Introduction to Dynamics.
pp. 302. *Lond.* 1890. 8°.   8767. cc. 19.

Cattaneo (C.) Dinamica elementare. pp. 145.
Milano, 1884. 8°.   012200. h. 55.

Geldard (C.) Statics and Dynamics. pp. 308.
Lond. 1893. 8°.   8767. f. 28.

Greenhill (A. G.) Notes on Dynamics.
pp. 138. *Lond.* 1893. fol.   8767. m. 4.

DYNAMICS—*continued.*

LOCK (G. H.) Key to J. B. Lock's Elementary Dynamics. pp. 228. *Lond.* 1892. 8°.
8767. f. 15.

LONEY (S. L.) Treatise on elementary Dynamics. pp. 348. *Camb.* 1891. 8°. 8767. g. 5.

—— Solutions of examples. pp. 200. *Camb.* 1892. 8°. 8767. f. 16.

—— Elements of Dynamics. 2 pt. 1893. 8°. Pitt Press Mathematical Series. 2322. cc. 37.

ROBINSON (J. L.) Elements of Dynamics. pp. 431. *Lond.* 1894. 8°. 8767. g. 16.

ROUTH (E. J.) Elementary part of a Treatise on the Dynamics of a system of rigid bodies. pp. 412. *Lond.* 1891. 8°. 2242. c. 10.

TAIT (P. G.) Dynamics. pp. 361. *Lond.* 1895. 8°. 8768. bb. 13.

WORTHINGTON (A. M.) Dynamics of Rotation. pp. 154. *Lond.* 1892. 8°. 8767. f. 7.

See also FORCE: MATHEMATICS: MECHANICS.

DYNAMOMETERS. *See* MACHINERY.

DYSENTERY. *See* DIARRHŒA.

DYSPEPSIA. *See* DIGESTION.

————

EAR. ALLEN (H.) Diseases of the Ear. 1893. 8°. Handbook of Local Therapeutics.
7442. g. 26.

ALLEN (S. E.) The Mastoid Operation. pp. 111. *Cincinnati*, 1892. 8°. 7482. aa. 5.

BEZOLD (F.) Ueberschau ueber den gegenwärtigen Stand der Ohrenheilkunde. pp. 196. *Wiesbaden*, 1895. 8°. 7611. h. 7.

BING (A.) Vorlesungen über Ohrenheilkunde. pp. 286. *Wien*, 1890. 8°. 7611. d. 2.

BUERKNER (K.) Lehrbuch der Ohrenheilkunde. pp. 368. *Stuttgart*, 1892. 8°. 7615. f. 41.

BURCHARDT (M.) Praktische Diagnostik der Simulationen von Schwerhörigkeit. pp. 51. *Berl.* 1891. 8°. Tab. 1800. b.

BURNETT (C. H.) System of diseases of the Ear, *etc.* 2 vol. *Lond.* 1893. 8°. 7615. cc. 14.

COZZOLINO (V.) Hygiene of the Ear. pp. 52. *Lond.* 1892. 8°. 7611. de. 47.

DALBY (*Sir* W. B.) Diseases and injuries of the Ear. pp. 279. *Lond.* 1893. 8°. 7610. de. 43.

DESCOURTIS (G.) Des Hallucinations de l'ouïe. pp. 110. *Paris*, 1889. 4°. 7660. dd. 10.

FIELD (G. P.) Manual of diseases of the Ear. pp. 422. *Lond.* 1894. 8°. 2024. bb.

—— Pathology and treatment of suppurative diseases of the Ear. pp. 85. *Lond.* 1893. 8°.
7611. aaaa. 6.

FORBES (A. L. A.) On Deafness. pp. 99. *Lond.* 1893. 8°. 7611. b. 47.

GARNAULT (P.) Précis des maladies de l'Oreille. pp. 549. *Paris*, 1895. 8°. 7611. c. 8.

GEHUCHTEN (A. van) Le Bulbe olfactif chez quelques mammifères. 1891. 8°. CARNOY (J. B.) La Cellule. Tom. 7. Fasc. 2. 7121. i.

GRUBER (J.) Text-book of diseases of the Ear. pp. 648. *Lond.* 1893. 8°. 7610. g. 15.

HAUG (R.) Die Krankheiten des Ohres. pp. 296. *Wien*, 1893. 8°. 7611. g. 40.

—— Klinische Vorträge aus dem Gebiete der Otologie. *Jena*, 1895, *etc.* 8°. 7615. dd.

HOVELL (T. M.) Treatise on the diseases of the Ear. pp. 720. *Lond.* 1894. 8°. 7611. d. 7.

JONES (H. M.) Subjective noises in the Ears. pp. 152. *Lond.* 1891. 8°. 7611. c. 1.

EAR—*continued.*

JONES (H. M.) Practitioner's Handbook of diseases of the Ear. pp. 396. *Lond.* 1894. 8°. 7610. g. 17.

KAFEMANN (R.) Ueber die Behandlung der chronischen Otorrhoe. pp. 59. *Danzig*, 1891. 8°.
Pam. 39.

LEDOUBLE (A.) Malformations des muscles de l'Oreille. *Paris*, 1894. 8°. Pam. 39.

MACBRIDE (P.) Diseases of the Throat and Ear. pp. 640. 1892. 8°. Pentland's Medical Series. Vol. 3. 7641. ee.

MARTHA (A.) Des Microbes de l'Oreille. pp. 52. *Paris*, 1893. 8°. 7305. ee. 21. (6.)

NICHOLSON (J. H.) Artificial Ear Drums. pp. 80. *Lond.* 1890. 8°. Pam. 39.

—— Treatise on how to cure Deafness. pp. 104. *Lond.* 1893. 8°. 7306. df. 19. (16.)

PEIRSON (A. M.) Deafness. pp. 124. *Forest Hill*, 1893. 8°. 7611. aaaa. 8.

POLITZER (A.) Anatomical and histological dissection of the human Ear. pp. 272. *Lond.* 1892. 8°. 7611. d. 4.

—— Text-book of diseases of the Ear. pp. 739. *Lond.* 1894. 8°. 2024. bb.

PRITCHARD (U.) Handbook of diseases of the Ear. pp. 238. 1891. 8°. Lewis's Practical Series. 7482. a.

ROHRER (F.) Lehrbuch der Ohrenheilkunde. pp. 240. *Leipz.* 1891. 8°. 7611. g. 28.

ROOSA (D. B. S. J.) Practical treatise on diseases of the Ear. pp. 741. *Lond.* 1892. 8°.
7610. g. 8.

SCHWALBE (G.) Beiträge zur Anthropologie des Ohres. 1891. 8°. VIRCHOW (R.) Internationale Beiträge. Bd. 1. 7383. g. 7.

SEXTON (S.) Deafness and discharge from the Ear. pp. 89. *N.Y.* 1891. 8°. 7611. bb. 22.

SHEILD (A. M.) Diseases of the Ear. pp. 266. *Lond.* 1895. 8°. 7611. aaaa. 17.

STEWART (W. R. H.) Aids to Otology. pp. 110. *Lond.* 1893. 8°. 7611. aaaa. 9.

See also DEAF AND DUMB.

EARTH: CREATION: COSMOGONY.

ALDERSON (C.) The Aldersonian-Mosaic system of Creation. pp. 149. *Huddersfield*, 1880. 4°.
3155. k. 48.

ANTIMOLEK. Natur und Wesen der Ursubstanz, *etc.* pp. 124. *Regensburg*, 1892. 8°.
8705. c. 21.

BERGMANN (H.) Die Einheit in der Schöpfung. pp. 179. *Danz.* 1892. 8°. 8757. k. 5.

BOGROS (M.) La Genèse: origine du monde. pp. 341. *Nevers*, 1894. 8°. 3155. l. 19.

BONNEY (T. G.) Microscope's contributions to the Earth's physical history. pp. 16. *Camb.* 1892. 8°. Pam. 27.

—— Story of our Planet. pp. 592. *Lond.* 1893. 8°. 07109. h. 36.

CALLEJA (C.) General Physiology, or physiological theory of Cosmos. pp. 391. *Lond.* 1890. 8°. 8706. aaaa. 31.

CLODD (E.) The Story of Creation. pp. 242. *Lond.* 1894. 8°. 7004. aaa. 17.

DAWSON (*Sir* J. W.) Some salient Points in the science of the Earth. pp. 499. *N.Y.* 1894. 8°.
07109. f. 4.

DORMAN (M. R. P.) From Matter to Mind. pp. 319. *Lond.* 1895. 8°. 8462. c. 27.

DRAYSON (A. W.) Untrodden ground in Astronomy and Geology. pp. 305. *Lond.* 1890. 8°.
8561. h. 38.

FAYE (H. A. É. A.) Sur l'origine du Monde. pp. 309. *Paris*, 1885. 8°. 7004. c. 8.

EARTH, etc.—*continued.*

FELTON (H.) Creation, its law and religion.
pp. 301. *Lond.* 1894. 8°.   4018. ff. 6.

GLEANER. Mosaic record of the Creation.
pp. 320. *Lond.* 1893. 8°.   3155. de. 31.

GREGORY (R. A.) The Planet Earth. pp. 108.
Lond. 1894. 8°.   8562. aaa. 48.

GUNKEL (H.) Schöpfung und Chaos in Urzeit
und Endzeit. pp. 431. *Göttingen,* 1895. 8°.
                                          3155. k. 49.

GUTBERLET (C.) Der mechanische Monismus.
pp. 306. *Paderborn,* 1893. 8°.   8705. e. 23.

GUYARD (É.) Histoire du Monde. pp. 689.
Paris, 1894. 8°.   10002. h. 16.

HAAS (H. J.) Aus der Sturm- und Drangperiode
der Erde. *Berl.* 1892, *etc.* 8°.   07109. i.

HAECKEL (E. H. P. A.) History of Creation.
2 vol. *Lond.* 1892. 8°.   7006. c. 10.

HARTMANN (J.) Creation of God. pp. 432.
N.Y. 1893. 8°.   3125. df. 17.

HUTCHINSON (H. N.) Autobiography of the
Earth. pp. 290. *Lond.* 1890. 8°.   7109. a. 8.

JESSOP (C. M.) Saturn's Kingdom. pp. 294.
Lond. 1891. 8°.   7003. aa. 6.

KAISER (F. C.) Neue Bahnen in der Weltanschauung. pp. 127. *Dresd.* 1892. 8°.
                                          8705. d. 31.

LEHMANN (R.) Schopenhauer und die Entwickelung der monistischen Weltanschauung. pp. 25.
Berl. 1892. 4°.   Pam. 49.

LORIDAN (J.) Voyages des astronomes français
à la recherche de la figure de la Terre.
pp. 285. *Lille,* 1890. 8°.   8561. k. 5.

MAC LENNAN (E.) Cosmical Evolution.
pp. 399. *Lond.* 1890. 8°.   8563. aaa. 21.

MEYER (E. H.) Die Eddische Kosmogonie.
pp. 118. *Freiburg,* 1891. 8°.   4503. ee. 4.

MIFFRE (J.) Action sur les mouvements locaux
et généraux de la Terre. pp. 10.
Paris, 1893. 4°.   8566. e. 1.

—— Résumé d'un mémoire sur l'action éloignée.
pp. 4. *Paris,* 1893. 4°.   8566. e. 3.

—— Moyens physiques de l'action éloignée.
pp. 36. *Paris,* 1894. 4°.   8566. e. 2.

NAEGELI (C. W. v.) Mechanisch-physiologische
Theorie der Abstammungslehre. pp. 822.
München, 1884. 8°.   7002. f. 19.

ORDER. Order in the physical World and its
First Cause. pp. 231. *Lond.* 1891. 8°.
                                          7003. aa. 7.

PERRINI (C.) Il Mondo e l' uomo. pp. 218.
Trani, 1893. 8°.   7001. aa. 31.

POYNTING (J. H.) Mean density of the Earth.
pp. 156. *Lond.* 1894. 8°.   8563. b. 44.

PRIDHAM (C.) Twilight and Dawn. pp. 389.
Lond. 1892. 8°.   3165. df. 36.

SIMMONS (H. M.) The Unending Genesis.
pp. 111. *Chicago,* 1890. 8°.   4017. a. 14.

SLYTHE (J. D.) The Cosmos. pp. 34.
Chichester, 1894. 8°.   8708. b. 23. (11.)

SMALL (E. W.) The Earth. pp. 220. 1894. 8°.
University Extension Series.   012202. g.

STARS. The Stars and the Earth. pp. 60.
Lond. 1895. 16°.   8562. aa. 33.

STOEHR (A.) Gedanken über Weltdauer und
Unsterblichkeit. pp. 14. *Berl.* 1894. 8°.
                                          Pam. 49.

STRECKNER (W.) Welt und Menschheit vom
Standpunkte des Materialismus. pp. 243.
Leipz. 1892. 8°.   08464. ee. 1.

TJERA (M.) Origen y constitución mecánica del
Mundo. pp. 407. *Barcelona,* 1889. 8°.
                                          8563. c. 6.

EARTH, etc.—*continued.*

TURPIN (E.) L'Univers. pp. 374.
Paris, 1893. 12°.   8705. aaa. 48.

TUTTLE (H.) Arcana of Nature. pp. 248.
Lond. 1895. 8°.   7001. aa. 33.

VAUCHEZ (E.) La Terre. Évolution de la vie.
2 tom. *Paris,* 1893. 8°.   7004. de. 21.

WINKLER (R.) Ein neues Weltsystem. pp. 150.
Nürnberg, 1891. 8°.   8716. cc. 31.

WILSON (J. M.) Evolution, Creation and the
Fall. pp. 29. *Lond.* 1893. 8°.
                                       4429. c. 21. (14.)

WILSON (J. S.) The Creation Story by W. E.
Gladstone, investigated by J. S. W. pp. 84.
Manch. 1890. 8°.   4016. df. 10.

WOLFF (H.) Die Weltentwickelung, *etc.*
2 Bde. *Leipz.* 1890. 8°.   8466. gg. 30.

ZIEMSSEN (O.) Makrokosmus. Grundideen zur
Schöpfungsgeschichte. pp. 127.
Gotha, 1893. 8°.   8462. bb. 33.

———

BIGELOW (F. H.) Terrestrial Magnetism. 1890. 4°.
U.S. *Expedition to West Africa.* Bulletin, 18.
                                          Pam. 79.

DINGLE (E.) The Earth's ecliptic angle demonstrated to be the standard universal. pp. 51.
Lond. 1887. 8°.   8535. ccc. 32.

HARTMANN (J.) Die Vergrösserung des Erd-
schattens bei Mondfinsternissen. 1891. 8°. Ac.
Leipsic. *Gesellschaft der Wissenschaften.* Abhandlungen. Bd. 29.   Ac. 700/4.

SAUBERT (B.) Der Erdmagnetismus. pp. 44.
Hannover, 1895. 8°.   8756. de. 52.

SCHUECK (A.) Magnetische Beobachtungen an
der deutschen Bucht der Nordsee. pp. 22.
Hamb. 1895. 12°.   Pam. 79.

WILDE (H.) On Causes of phenomena of Terres-
trial Magnetism. 2 pt. 1891. 4°.   8757. l. 10.
See also ASTRONOMY : DELUGE : EARTHQUAKES :
GEOGRAPHY : GEOLOGY : GRAVITATION : PHYSIO-
GRAPHY : SUN : VOLCANOES, *etc.*

EARTHQUAKES. Ac. Yedo. *Seismolo-*
gical Society. Seismological Journal of Japan.
Yokohama, 1893, *etc.* 8°.   Ac. 1945.

HOERNES (R.) Erdbebenkunde. pp. 452.
Leipz. 1893. 8°.   07109. h. 34.

HUGUENEL (E.) Beitrag zur Erklärung der
Erdbeben und der schlagenden Wetter. pp. 56.
Potsdam, 1893. 8°.   8755. dd. 7. (11.)

LONGRAIRE (L. de) Séismes et Volcans. 1894. 8°.
Ac. Paris. *Société des Ingénieurs Civils.* Mémoires. Sér. 5. Ann. 47.   Ac. 4305.

MILNE (J.) Earthquakes. pp. 367. 1893. 8°.
International Scientific Series.   2324. b. 23.

VINOT (L.) Étude sur les tremblements de terre.
pp. 232. *Paris,* 1893. 8°.   07109. h. 30.

———

KEELER (J. E.) Earthquakes in California,
1889. pp. 24. 1890. 8°. U.S. *Geological*
Survey. Bulletin. No. 68.   1829. a. 7.

HOLDEN (E. S.) Earthquakes in California, 1890-
91. pp. 31. 1892. 8°. U.S. *Geological Survey.*
Bulletin. No. 95.   1829. a. 7.

PERRINE (C. D.) Earthquakes in California, 1892,
93. 2 pt. 1893, 94. 8°. U.S. *Geological Survey.*
Bulletin. No. 112, 114.   1829. a. 7.

RENDELMANN (O.) Le Tremblement de terre de
Constantinople, 1894. pp. 23. *Paris,* 1894. 8°.
                                          Pam. 27.

ESSEX, *East.* Account of the earthquake in East
Essex, April 22, 1884. pp. 126.
Colchester, 1892. 8°.   7106. aa. 39.

EARTHQUAKES—*continued.*

MILNE (J.) The Earthquake in Japan, 1891. pp. 70. *Yokohama*, 1891. *obl.* 4°.   1824. b. 5.

HOERNES (R.) Das Erdbeben von Laibach und seine Ursachen. pp. 61. *Graz*, 1895. 8°.
       Pam. 27.

ABELLA Y CASARIEGO (E.) Terremotos de Nueva Vizcaya, Filipinos, 1881. pp. 31. *Madrid*, 1884. 8°.   Pam. 27.

—— Terremotos experimentados en la Isla de Luzón, 1892. pp. 110. *Manila*, 1893. 8°.
       7109. dd. 13.

See also EARTH.

EASEMENTS, Law of. GODDARD (J. L.) Treatise on the Law of Easements. pp. 605. *Lond.* 1891. 8°.   6306. g. 3.

GRIFFITH (W.) Commentaries on the Indian Easements Act, 1882. pp. 114. *Madras*, 1886. 8°.   5319. aaa. 32.

INNES (L. C.) Digest of the Laws of Easements. pp. 127. *Lond.* 1895. 12°.   6306. aaa. 2.

MICHELL (R. B.) Law of Easements in India. pp. 182. *Madras*, 1891. 8°.   5318. aaa. 3.

See also LAND TENURES, *England.*

EASTBOURNE. EASTBOURNE. Views of Eastbourne. 1893. 12°.   10360. a. 18.

EASTBOURNE PICTORIAL. Eastbourne Pictorial. pp. 44. *Eastbourne*, 1890. fol.   1787. aa. 20.

PASCOE (C. E.) Eastbourne. pp. 86. *Lond.* 1891. 8°.   10360. a. 14.

BEATSON (W. B.) Water supply of Eastbourne. pp. 12. *Eastbourne*, 1895. 8°.   Pam. 79.

EASTER. BROWNING (R.) Easter interpreted. pp. 28. *N.Y.* 1891. 8°.   011653. i. 53.

FREYBE (A.) Ostern in deutscher Sage und Dichtung. pp. 137. *Gütersloh*, 1893. 8°.
       3477. df. 3.

LIDDON (H. P.) Easter in St. Paul's. Sermons. pp. 459. *Lond.* 1891. 8°.   4465. f. 18.

LIFE. Daily life in Resurrection Light. pp. 63. *Lond.* 1891. 16°.   3457. d. 26.

PRIEST. Outlines for Holy Week and Easter. pp. 16. *Rugeley*, 1894. 8°.   3456. dd. 43.

————————

BERFRIED (E.) Die Ausgestaltung der christlichen Osterberechnung, *etc.* pp. 60. *Mittelwalde*, 1893. 8°.   8561. aaa. 31.

—— Tafeln zur Veranschaulichung der Ausgestaltung der Osterberechnung. *Mittelwalde*, 1893. 4°.   8563. aa. 31.

GERARD (J.) The Date of Easter. pp. 8. 1895. 8°.   Pam. 4.

HIND (W. M.) Easter Cycles, as exhibited by the calendars. pp. 15. *Lond.* 1891. 8°. Pam. 4.

TONDINI (C.) La question de la Pâque dans la réforme du calendrier russe. pp. 15. *Paris*, 1892. 8°.   Pam. 4.

See also CALENDARS : SEASONS.

EASTER ISLAND. CARROLL (A.) Easter Island Inscriptions. 1892. 8°. Ac. Wellington. *Polynesian Society.* Journal. Vol. 1. Ac. 1991.

JAUSSEN (F. É.) *Bp. of Axieri.* L'Île de Pâques. pp. 32. *Paris*, 1893. 8°.   07703. i. 2. (14.)

EASTERN CHURCHES. *See* ARMENIA : GREEK CHURCH : JACOBITE CHURCH : NESTORIANS : RUSSIA.

EASTERN QUESTION. *See* ARMENIA : ASIA : ENGLAND, *Politics :* EUROPE : INDIA : RUSSIA : TURKEY, *etc., etc.*

EAST FRIESLAND. *See* FRIESLAND, *East.*

EAST LONDON. EAST LONDON. Guide to East London. *Cape Town*, 1893, *etc.* 8°.
       10097. d. 6.

EAST PRUSSIA. HORN (A.) Die Verwaltung Ostpreussens, 1525–1875, *etc.* pp. 653. *Königsberg*, 1890. 8°.   9385. h. 7.

EATON HALL. MORRIS (R. H.) Guide to Eaton Hall. pp. 48. *Manch.* 1892. 8°.
       10347. aa. 37. (8.)

ÉCARTÉ. DORMOY (É.) Traité mathématique de l'Écarté. pp. 278. *Paris*, 1891. 8°.
       7913. ee. 27.

DRAYSON (A. W.) Whist.—Écarté. 1891. 8°.

HOFFMANN (L.) Cyclopædia of Card Games.
       2264. b. 20.

See also CARDS.

ECHINOCOCCUS. *See* PARASITES.

ECHINODERMATA. Ac. London. *British Museum.* Catalogue of British Echinoderms. pp. 202. *Lond.* 1892. 8°.   7207. g. 19.

DREYER (F.) Die Principien der Gerüstbildung bei Echinodermen. 1891. 8°. Jenaische Zeitschrift für Naturwissenschaft. Bd. 26. Heft 2.
       Ac. 3760.

HAMAN (F. O.) Beiträge zur Histologie der Echinodermen. 4 Hfte. *Jena*, 1884–89. 8°.
       7299. h. 4.

KENT (W. S.) The great Barrier Reef of Australia. pp. 387. *Lond.* 1893. fol.
       K.T.C. 9. b. 3.

LORIOL (P. de) Notes pour servir à l'étude des Échinodermes. pp. 31. 1891. 4°. Ac. Geneva. *Société de Physique.* Mémoires. Vol. suppl.
       Ac. 2870.

PERRIER (E.) Échinodermes. 1891. 8°. HORN, *Cape.* Mission scientifique. Tom. 6. 8709. d.

—— Expéditions scientifiques du Travailleur et du Talisman. Échinodermes. pp. 431. 1894. 4°. FRANCE. *Ministère de l'Instruction.* Expéditions scientifiques.   1826. b.

AGASSIZ (A.) Notice of Calamocrinus Diomedæ, *etc.* 1890. 8°. Ac. Cambridge. *Harvard University.—Museum.* Bulletin. Vol. 20.
       Ac. 1736/2.

WACHSMUTH (C.) and SPRINGER (F.) Perisomic plates of the Crinoids. *Phila.* 1890. 8°.
       7297. c. 18. (3.)

HÉROUARD (E.) Recherches sur les Holothuries de France. pp. 170. *Paris*, 1890. 8°.
       7299. g. 22.

ÉCIJA. ROA (M. de) Écija. pp. 349. *Écija*, 1890. 8°.   4629. i. 25.

ECLIPSE. *See* SUN.

ÉCOLE DES CHARTES. Ac. Paris. *École des Chartes.* Livret de l'École des Chartes, 1821–91. pp. 312. *Paris*, 1891. 8°.
       Ac. 8930/14.

ECUADOR. GONZALEZ SUAREZ (F.) Historia de la república del Ecuador. *Quito*, 1890, *etc.* 8°.   9772. dd.

—— Atlas. *Quito*, 1892. *obl.* fol. 14001. a. 21.

KAUFMANN (A. G.) Don G. G. Moreno, Präsident der Republik Ecuador. pp. 283. *Freiburg*, 1891. 12°.   010882. c. 11.

LAMBEL (A. P. F. de) Garcia Moreno. pp. 144. *Lille*, 1891. 18°.   10883. aa. 28.

ALFARO (E.) Ecuador. La Revolución, 1884. pp. 79. *San Salvador*, 1885. 8°.   9771. cc. 22.

PERU. *Ministerio de Relaciones Exteriores.* Negociaciones sobre límites con el Ecuador. pp. 243. *Lima*, 1890. fol.   8179. k. 4.

VAZQUEZ (H.) Límites entre el Ecuador y el Perú. pp. 384. *Quito*, 1892. fol. 8180. i. 19.

ECUADOR—*continued.*

CEVALLOS (P. F.) Geografía del Ecuador.
pp. 371. *Lima*, 1888. 8°.   10480. dd. 35.

WOLF (T.) Geografía y geología del Ecuador.
pp. 671. *Leipz.* 1892. fol.   10481. i. 26.

ECUADOR. Import Duties of Ecuador. pp. 12.
1891. 8°. U.S. *Bureau of American Republics.*
Bulletin. No. 25.   08225. k. 1.

MADRID. *Exposición Histórico-Americana.* Catálogo del Ecuador. pp. 43. *Madrid*, 1892. 8°.
    Pam. 18.

See also AMERICA, *South and Central.*

ECZEMA. *See* SKIN.

EDDAS. *See* ICELANDIC LITERATURE.

EDESSA. BUFFA, (A.) La Légende d'Abgar
et les origines de l'Église d'Édesse. pp. 109.
Genève, 1893. 8°.   4530. c. 2.

EDINBURGH, City. BARTHOLOMEW (J.)
Pocket guide to Edinburgh. pp. 87.
Edinb. 1892. 8°.   10369. aaa. 42.

COLSTON (J.) Incorporated Trades of Edinburgh.
pp. 237. *Edinb.* 1891. 4°.   8248. f. 23.

—— History of the Scott Monument, Edinburgh.
pp. 120. *Edinb.* 1881. 8°.   10856. aa. 10.

EDINBURGH. Graphic guide to Edinburgh.
pp. 169. *Glasg.* 1893. 32°.   10349. a. 35. (1.)

—— History of the ancient City Cross, Edinburgh. pp. 14. *Edinb.* 1885. 8°.
    010358. l. 12. (3.)

—— Some Edinburgh shops. pp. 84.
Edinb. 1894. 8°.   010370. e. 7.

—— *Greyfriars Churchyard.* Epitaphs and
monumental inscriptions in the Greyfriars
Churchyard. pp. 54. *Edinb.* 1893. 8°.
    10369. c. 52.

HARRISON (W.) Memorable Edinburgh houses.
pp. 122. *Edinb.* 1893. 8°.   10369. ccc. 24.

HUTTON (L.) Literary landmarks of Edinburgh.
pp. 80. *Lond.* 1891. 8°.   010370. f. 21.

LIVINGSTON (J.) Memories of Buccleuch Place.
pp. 79. *Edinb.* 1893. 8°.   010370. e. 6.

MASSON (D.) Edinburgh Sketches and memories.
pp. 438. *Lond.* 1892. 8°.   2368. f. 1.

NORRIE (W.) Edinburgh Newspapers. pp. 48.
Earlston, 1891. 8°.   011902. m. 19. (12.)

OLIPHANT (M. O.) Royal Edinburgh. pp. 520.
Lond. 1891. 8°.   10370. c. 38.

REID (J.) New lights on old Edinburgh.
pp. 208. *Edinb.* 1894. 8°.   10369. aaa. 48.

ROSE (A.) Accompt of Expenses in Edinburgh,
1715. 1893. 8°. Ac. Edinburgh. *Scottish
History Society.* Publications. Vol. 15.
    Ac. 8256.

WARRENDER (M.) Walks near Edinburgh.
pp. 200. *Edinb.* 1895. 8°.   10369. aaa. 52.

WILSON (*Sir* D.) Memorials of Edinburgh in
the olden time. 2 vol. *Edinb.* 1891. 8°.
    10370. ff. 27.

Edinburgh Academy.

EDINBURGH. *Academy.* Edinburgh Academy
chronicle. *Edinb.* 1893, *etc.* 8°.
    P.P. 6199. bc. & 725.

—— Edinburgh Academy army list, 1824–94.
pp. 30. *Edinb.* 1894. 8°.   8365. c. 22.

University.

Ac. Edinburgh. *University.* List of members
of the General Council of the University.
Edinb. 1893, *etc.* 8°.   8367. de.

—— Edinburgh University Lecture-Extension
Association. pp. 8. *Edinb.* 1891. 4°.
    8365. f. 34.

EDINBURGH—*continued.*

County.

BELL (J. M.) Castles of the Lothians. pp. 97.
Edinb. 1893. 4°.   10370. i. 4.

DICKSON (J.) Ruined Castles of Mid-Lothian.
pp. 308. *Edinb.* 1894. 8°.   010370. ff. 1.

RICHARDSON (R.) The County of Edinburgh. Its
geology. pp. 40. *Edinb.* 1895. 8°.
    10369. dd. 5.

EDUCATION.

Pt. I. General.

Bibliography.

HALL (G. S.) and MANSFIELD (J. M.) Hints
toward a Bibliography of Education. pp. 309.
Bost. 1893. 8°.   011901. e. 24.

U.S. *Bureau of Education.* Catalogue of educational literature. *Wash.* 1892, *etc.* 8°.
    8308. k.

General Works.

ACLAND (A. H. D.) and SMITH (H. L.) Studies
in secondary Education. pp. 334.
Lond. 1892. 8°.   8364. de. 31.

ARDIGÒ (R.) La scienza della Educazione.
pp. 590. *Verona*, 1893. 8°.   8308. gg. 19.

BERGSTRÖM (O.) Vetenskaplig uppfostrings-
lära. pp. 156. *Lund*, 1891. 8°.   8311. b. 7.

BILLIA (L. M.) Della Legge suprema dell'
Educazione. pp. 183. *Torino*, 1891. 8°.
    8311. g. 3.

BOEHM (J.) Grundzüge der Erziehungs- und
Unterrichtslehre. pp. 296. 16.
München, 1891. 8°.   8310. cc. 44.

BRUNETIÈRE (F.) Éducation et instruction.
pp. 107. *Paris*, 1895. 12°.   8310. a. 39.

BUTLER (N. M.) The Function of the secondary
School. pp. 18. 1890. 8°.   8304. c. 23. (7.)

COMPAYRÉ (G.) Psychology applied to Education.
pp. 216. 1895. 8°. Heath's Pedagogical Library.
    8311. aaa.

CRY. The Cry of the Children. pp. 123.
Lond. 1892. 8°.   8277. de. 17.

DOERING (A.) System der Pädagogik im Umriss.
pp. 299. *Berl.* 1894. 8°.   8311. ee. 3.

DONALDSON (H. H.) Growth of the Brain. Study
of the nervous system in relation to education.
pp. 374. 1895. 8°. Contemporary Science Series.
Vol. 29.   8709. i.

DÜHRING (J.) Mental Life and culture.
pp. 256. *Phila.* 1893. 8°.   012357. h. 45.

DURELL (F.) A New life in Education.
pp. 288. *Phila.* 1894. 8°.   8311. c. 13.

ESSAYS. Thirteen essays on Education.
pp. 321. *Lond.* 1891. 8°.   8311. e. 2.

FÉRARD (C. D.) Mémoires d'un vieux maître
d'école. pp. 224. *Paris*, 1894. 8°. 8311. aaa. 11.

FISCHER (C. A.) Grundzüge einer Sozialpädagogik. pp. 429. *Eisenach*, 1892. 8°. 8277. dd. 12.

FRICK (O.) Sammlung pädagogischer Abhandlungen. *Halle*, 1889, *etc.* 8°.   8310. d.

—— Pädagogische und didaktische Abhandlungen. *Halle*, 1893, *etc.* 8°.   8307. i.

GAUSSERON (B. H.) Comment élever nos Enfants?
pp. 368. *Paris*, 1891. 8°.   8415. df. 23.

GIACOMO (G. de) La Scuola. pp. 65.
Cosenza, 1894. 8°.   8311. g. 13.

GINER (F.) Educación y enseñanza. pp. 216.
Madrid, 1889. 8°.   8310. a. 29.

GRASBY (W. C.) Teaching in three Continents.
pp. 344. *Lond.* 1891. 8°.   8310. cc. 39.

GUYAU (J. M.) Education and Heredity. pp. 306.
1891. 8°. Contemporary Science Series. 8079. i.

EDUCATION.—General Works—*cont.*

HART (J.) Die Schule im socialdemokratischen Zukunftstaate. 1895. 8°. Frankfurter zeitgemässe Broschüren. N. F. Bd. 16. 12209. g.

HAUFFE (G.) Welche Berührungspunkte bieten hinsichtlich ihrer Erziehungs-Grundsätze Herbart-Ziller und Diesterweg? pp. 220.
Leipz. 1891. 8°. 8310. c. 43.

HERBART (J. F.) The science of Education. pp. 268. *Lond.* 1892. 8°. 8311. b. 4.

FELKIN (H.M.) and (E.) Introduction to Herbart's Science of Education. pp. 193. *Lond.* 1895. 8°. 8311. c. 20.

LANG (O. H.) Outlines of Herbart's Pedagogics. pp. 72. *N.Y.* 1894. 8°. 8311. aaa. 14.

MARKE (L. J. W.) Vor Skole og Herbarts Pædagogik. pp. 78. *Kjøbenh.* 1891. 8°. 8311. aa. 11.

UFER (C.) Introduction to the Pedagogy of Herbart. pp. 123. 1895. 8°. Heath's Pedagogical Library. 8311. aaa.

HERTZBERG (N. C. E.) Opdragelse og Undervisning. pp. 114. *Kristiania,* 1891. 8°. 8311. b. 2.

HERZOG (J. A.) Die Schule und ihr neuer Aufbau auf natürlicher Grundlage. pp. 153.
Zürich, 1892. 8°. 8357. f. 15.

HOCHEGGER (R.) Die Bedeutung der Philosophie für die Pädagogik. pp. 132. 1893. 8°. Pädagogische Zeit- und Streitfragen. Hft. 32-34. 8310. c.

—— Über Individual- und Sozialpädagogik. pp. 36. 1891. 8°. Pädagogische Zeit- und Streitfragen. Hft. 19. 8310. c.

HOPKINS (L. P.) Spirit of the new Education. pp. 282. *Bost.* 1892. 8°. 8311. b. 10.

JAEGER (O.) Aus der Praxis. Ein pädagogisches Testament. pp. 168. *Wiesbaden,* 1885. 8°. 8311. g. 16.

JOLLY (W.) Ruskin on Education. pp. 167. *Lond.* 1894. 8°. 8310. bbb. 4.

KLEIMENHAGEN (H.) Rathgeber für Eltern und Lehrer in Erziehungsfragen. pp. 125.
Braunschweig, 1894. 8°. 8311. cc. 4.

KLYKKEN (O.) Om Barnesjelen og dens udvikling. pp. 113. *Trondhjem,* 1892. 8°. 8357. aa. 15.

KNOKE (C.) Grundriss der Pädagogik seit dem Zeitalter des Humanismus. pp. 226.
Berl. 1894. 8°. 8311. g. 11.

KOONINGS (J.) De School practische Paedagogiek. pp. 235. *Zutphen,* 1890. 8°. 8311. g. 1.

KRAUSE (C. C. F.) Abhandlungen über Erziehung und Unterricht. 2 Bde. *Berl.* 1894. 8°. 8311. g. 14.

KRIEG. Krieg, Friede und Erziehung. pp. 132. *Leipz.* 1891. 8°. 8425. f. 18.

KRIEG (C.) Lehrbuch der Pädagogik. pp. 376. 1893. 8°. Wissenschaftliche Handbibliothek. Reihe 3. Bd. 1. 3558. c.

LAIGLE (A.) L'Éducation au point de vue de la lutte pour la vie. pp. 292. *Paris,* 1891. 8°. 8311. aa. 12.

LAURIE (S. S.) Institutes of Education. pp. 272. *Edinb.* 1892. 8°. 8311. b. 9.

LENTZNER (C.) Three Essays. pp. 62. *Halle,* 1890. 8°. 8304. e. 23. (8.)

LEVERSON (M. R.) Thoughts on Institutions of the higher Education. pp. 114. *N.Y.* 1893. 8°. 8311. g. 9.

LIGUE. Ligue internationale de l'Enseignement. Bulletin. *Paris,* 1889, *etc.* fol. 8355. f. 42.

LONDON. *Society for the Extension of University Teaching.* Aspects of modern Study. pp. 187. *Lond.* 1894. 8°. 8367. aa. 19.

—— *Teachers' Guild.* Papers read, 1888-90. pp. 146. *Lond.* 1890. 8°. 8311. c. 1.

EDUCATION.—General Works—*cont.*

MACVICAR (M.) Principles of Education. pp. 178. *Bost.* 1892. 8°. 8311. aa. 25.

MAILLET (E.) L'Éducation. Éléments de psychologie appliquée à la pédagogie. pp. 678. *Paris,* 1890. 8°. 8310. cc. 36.

MARTINAZZOLI (A.) and CREDARO (L.) Dizionario di pedagogia. *Milano,* 1894, *etc.* 4°. 8310. h.

MAUDSLAY (A.) Old Thoughts for young brains. pp. 216. *Lond.* 1890. 8°. 8310. cc. 34.

NOETLING (W.) Notes on Education. pp. 195. *N.Y.* 1894. 8°. 8311. bb. 2.

OLMI (G.) Nuovo teatro di Educazione. 4 vol. *Modena,* 1894. 8°. 8311. aaa. 21.

PARIS. *Exposition Universelle,* 1889. Rapports du jury. Éducation. pp. 482. *Paris,* 1891. fol. 7959. h. 24.

BUTLER (N. M.) Education at the Paris Exposition. pp. 7. *N.Y.* 1889. 8°. Pam. 17.

PARKER (F. W.) Talks on Pedagogics. pp. 491. *Lond.* 1894. 8°. 8311. aaa. 4.

PATRICK (J. N.) Elements of Pedagogics. pp. 224. *Syracuse,* 1895. 8°. 8311. aaa. 28.

P.P. *London.* The Educational Review. *Lond.* 1891, *etc.* 8°. P.P. 1187. id.

—— *New York.* Educational Review. *N.Y.* 1891, *etc.* 8°. P.P. 1225. ga.

POSADA (A.) Ideas pedagógicas modernas. pp. 354. *Madrid,* 1892. 8°. 8311. c. 6.

PREYER (W.) Mental Development in the child. pp. 170. *Lond.* 1894. 8°. 8311. aa. 33.

PUTNAM (D.) A Manual of Pedagogics. pp. 330. *Bost.* 1895. 8°. 8311. b. 27.

QUEYRAT (F.) L'Abstraction et son rôle dans l'éducation. pp. 143. *Paris,* 1895. 8°. 8462. aa. 24.

QUINET ( ) *Madame.* Le vrai dans l'Éducation. pp. 375. *Paris,* 1891. 12°. 012357. e. 61.

REIN (W.) Outlines of Pedagogics. pp. 199. *Lond.* 1893. 8°. 8311. aa. 27.

RICCARDI (P.) Antropologia e Pedagogia. *Modena,* 1892, *etc.* 4°. 8310. l.

RICHTER (A.) Neudrucke pädagogischer Schriften. *Leipz.* 1890, *etc.* 8°. 8308. aaa.

RIJKENS (R. R.) De Invloed van de school, *etc.* pp. 125. *Groningen,* 1893. 8°. 8311. g. 10.

ROOPER (T. G.) Apperception; or, the mental operation in the act of learning. pp. 52. *Syracuse,* 1891. 8°. 8310. aa. 52.

SALLWAERK (E. v.) Volksbildung. pp. 41. 1891. 8°. Pädagogische Zeit- und Streitfragen. Hft. 22. 8310. c.

SALVADORI (C.) Saggi pedagogici. pp. 258. *Fermo,* 1894. 8°. 8311. cc. 8.

SANTI GIUFFRIDA ( ) Monografie pedagogiche. pp. 126. *Milano,* 1892. 8°. 8311. b. 16.

SEARLE (F. C.) To a Boy leaving School for the University. pp. 50. *Lond.* 1892. 8°. 8411. e. 5.

SMELIK (J.) Schetsen voor opstellen over Paedagogiek. *'s-Gravenh.* 1891, *etc.* 8°. 8311. b. 3.

SMITH (N.) Education without deformity. *Lond.* 1891, *etc.* 8°. 8304. aaa. 10.

THAMIN (R.) Éducation et Positivisme. pp. 186. *Paris,* 1892. 12°. 8311. aa. 19.

THRING (E.) Erziehung und Schule. pp. 128. 1891. 8°. Pädagogische Sammelmappe. Hft. 140. 8304. dd.

TOLSTOI (L. N.) *Count.* La Liberté dans l'École. pp. 285. *Paris,* 1888. 12°. 8311. aa. 9.

TRIER (H.) Pædagogiske Tids- og Stridsspørgsmaal. *Kjøbenh.* 1892, *etc.* 8°. 8311. c.

EDUCATION.—General Works—*cont.*

TRUMBULL (H. C.) Hints on Child-training.
pp. 312. *Lond.* 1891. 8°.   8310. bbb. 2.

U.S. *Bureau of Education.* Educational Exhibits at the Exposition, New Orleans, 1884–85.
3 pt. *Wash.* 1886. 8°.   8366. de. 32.

URUSOV (M.) *Princess.* Education from the cradle.
pp. 168. *Lond.* 1890. 8°.   7581. a. 7.

VESSIOT (A.) Chemin Faisant. Notes et réflexions sur l'éducation. pp. 383.
Paris, 1891. 12°.   8311. aa. 8.

VILLARI (P.) Nuovi scritti pedagogici. pp. 374.
Firenze, 1891. 8°.   8311. aa. 2.

VERNIER (C.) La dissertation de Pédagogie.
pp. 334. *Paris,* 1891. 12°.   8310. c. 44.

VESSIOT (A.) Pages de Pédagogie. pp. 409.
Paris, 1895. 12°.   8311. c. 22.

WARREN (T. H.) Education and Equality.
pp. 44. *Lond.* 1895. 8°.   Pam. 17.

WREN (W.) What is Education? pp. 46.
Lond. 1894. 8°.   Pam. 17.

See also CHILDREN.

Agricultural. *See* AGRICULTURE.

Artistic. *See* ART.

Classical.

ADAM (J.) Intellectual and ethical value of Classical Education. pp. 20. *Camb.* 1895 8°.
        8304. c. 5. (4.)

D., H. Les Humanités. pp. 50.
Tongres, 1891. 8°.   8304. e. 21. (14.)

LEVERSON (M. R.) Thoughts on higher Education, with chapter on classical studies. pp. 114.
N.Y. 1893. 8°.   8311. g. 9.

RÉFORME. La Réforme des études classiques.
pp. 94. *Paris,* 1891. 8°.   8305. g. 11. (4.)
See also infra: Pt. II. *England: France: Germany:* GREEK LANGUAGE: LATIN LANGUAGE.

Commercial. *See infra:* TECHNICAL.

Ecclesiastical: Seminaries.

AUBRY (J. B.) Essai sur la méthode des études ecclésiastiques en France. *Lille,* 1891, *etc.* 8°.
        8356. f.

BERTRAND (L.) Histoire des Séminaires de Bordeaux et de Bazas. 3 tom. *Bordeaux,* 1894. 8°.
        8356. dd. 10.

BOURNE (F. A.) Diocesan Seminaries, *etc.*
pp. 66. *Lond.* 1893. 8°.   8365. dd. 17. (16.)

DECHEVRENS (A.) Les Universités catholiques.
pp. 396. *Paris,* 1894. 8°.   8356. b. 63.

DUCELLIER (A. X.) *Archb. of Besançon.* Derniers conseils aux séminaristes au moment de leur départ pour le régiment. pp. 15.
Besançon, 1890. 8°.   4422. d. 18. (2.)

DURIEU (P.) Traité de l'administration temporelle des Séminaires. pp. 604. *Paris,* 1890. 8°.
        05107. f. 3.

RICORDEL ( ) L'Enseignement ecclésiastique dans le diocèse de Nantes après la Révolution.
2 fasc. *Vannes,* 1891–93. 8°.   8356. g. 23.

S., C. W. Det theologiska doktoratet i Sverige resp. 1593–1893. pp. 145. *Lund,* 1893. 8°.
        8357. aa. 18.

SYLVIA (A. de) Séminaires et séminaristes.
pp. 319. *Paris,* 1892. 12°.   8356. aa. 23.

ZSCHOKKE (H.) Die theologischen Studien der Kirche in Österreich. pp. 1235.
Wien, 1894. 8°.   8357. i. 2.

See also COLLEGIUM GERMANICUM, *Rome:* MAYNOOTH COLLEGE: USHAW COLLEGE: WARE.

EDUCATION—*continued.*

Education of the Deaf and Dumb.
See DEAF AND DUMB.

Engineering Education. *See* ENGINEERING.

Female.

ALTCHEVSKY (C.) Rapport sur l'École féminine à Kharkov. pp. 8. *Paris,* 1890. 8°.
        8304. e. 22. (6.)

BARNETT (E. A.) Training of Girls for work.
pp. 215. *Lond.* 1894. 8°.   8415. de. 39.

BURSTALL (S. A.) Education of Girls in the United States. pp. 204. *Lond.* 1894. 8°.
        8311. aaa. 7.

FRANCE. *Ministère de l'Instruction.* Plan d'études de l'Enseignement secondaire des jeunes filles.
pp. 70. *Paris,* 1891. 12°.   8356. aa. 19.

GILLANT ( ) Les Écoles de filles avant la Révolution. pp. 23. *Verdun,* 1893. 8°.
        8304. aa. 18. (7.)

GUIDE. Guide for Governesses. pp. 65.
York, 1885. 12°.   8310. a. 35.

HEALEY (E.) Educational systems of Sweden, Norway and Denmark, with special reference to girls. pp. 36. *Lond.* 1892. 8°.
        8304. e. 23. (12.)

HARADEVĪ. Pamphlet on female Education.
pp. 15. *Allahabad,* 1893. 8°.   Pam. 37.

LEGOUVÉ (G. J. B. E. W.) Une élève de seize ans. pp. 388. *Paris,* 1891. 12°. 8415. de. 18.

LEMAISTRE (A.) Nos jeunes filles aux examens et à l'École. pp. 383. *Paris,* 1891. 8°.
        8356. f. 38.

MASSY (H.) Notions de Morale et d'éducation civique à l'usage des jeunes filles.
Paris, 1892. 12°.   8411. cc. 25.

POSADA (A.) La amistad y el Sexo. pp. 32.
Madrid, 1893. 8°.   Pam. 37.

REICHEL (H. R.) Intermediate education of Girls in Wales. pp. 8. *Bangor,* 1890. 8°.
        8304. e. 21. (12.)

REPORT. Report of a Committee to collect statistics as to Salaries paid to Assistant Mistresses in High Schools. pp. 16. *Lond.* 1890. 8°.
        8277. ee. 1. (5.)

RIDLEY (A. E.) F. M. Buss and her work for Education. pp. 399. *Lond.* 1895. 8°.
        4906. de. 34.

ROCHARD (J.) L'Éducation de nos filles.
pp. 350. *Paris,* 1892. 8°.   8311. aa. 18.

SOULSBY (L. H. M.) School Work. pp. 18.
Oxf. 1890. 32°.   Pam. 17.

SWEDEN. *Schools.* Underdåniga utlåtanden angående undersökning af Sveriges högre flickskolor. pp. 180. *Stockholm,* 1889. 8°.
        8357. f. 11.

WARD (H. O.) Social Ethics and society duties.
pp. 310. *Bost.* 1892. 8°.   8411. ee. 2.

WORDSWORTH (E.) First principles in Women's Education. pp. 18. *Oxf.* 1894. 32°. Pam. 37.

GNAUCK-KUEHNE (E.) Das Universitätsstudium der Frauen. pp. 60. *Oldenburg,* 1891. 8°.
        Pam. 37.

LONDON. *University Association of Women Teachers.* Journal. *Lond.* 1892, *etc.* fol. 1510.

SCHUBERT-FEDER (C.) Das Leben der Studentinnen in Zürich. pp. 29. *Berl.* 1893. 8°.
        8304. bb. 6. (10.)

THWING (C. F.) The College Woman. pp. 169.
N.Y. 1894. 8°.   8415. de. 43.

History, *General.*

BERGSTRÖM (O.) Uppfostrans Historia.
Göteborg, 1892, *etc.* 8°.   8311. cc.

EDUCATION.—History—*continued.*

EDUCATORS. The Great Educators.
Lond. 1892, *etc.* 8°.   8311. de.

PONCE (M. A.) Nociones de historia de la Pedagojía. pp. 225. *Valparaiso,* 1889. 8°.
        8309. e. 38.

QUICK (R. H.) Essays on educational Reformers. pp. 560. *Lond.* 1890. 8°. 8308. aaa. 21.

ROUSSELOT (P.) Pédagogie historique. pp. 288. *Paris,* 1891. 12°.   8311. aa. 23.

SCHMID (C. A.) Geschichte der Erziehung. *Stuttgart,* 1884, *etc.* 8°.   8309. g.

TARSOT (L.) Les Écoles et les écoliers à travers les âges. pp. 339. *Paris,* 1893. 8°. 8356. h. 17.

LAURIE (S. S.) Historical survey of Pre-Christian Education. pp. 436. *Lond.* 1895. 8°.
       8306. de. 21.

DAVIDSON (T.) The Education of the Greek People. pp. 229. *Lond.* 1895. 8°. 8311. aa. 36.

STADELMANN (F.) Erziehung und Unterricht bei den Griechen und Römern. pp. 216. *Triest,* 1891. 8°.   10921. aa. 30.

WEST (A. F.) Alcuin and the rise of Christian Schools. pp. 205. 1893. 8°. The Great Educators. Vol. 3.   8311. de.

COMPAYRÉ (G.) Abelard and the origin of Universities. pp. 315. 1893. 8°. The Great Educators. Vol. 5.   8311. de.

HARTFELDER (C.) Melanchthoniana paedagogica. pp. 287. *Leipz.* 1892. 8°. 8309. eee. 11.

KOMENSKÝ (J. A.) Zwei Abhandlungen des J. A. Comenius. pp. 55. *Hannover,* 1894. 8°.
        Pam. 17.

BUTLER (N. M.) Place of Comenius in the history of Education. pp. 20. *Syracuse,* 1892. 8°.
        Pam. 17.

GRILLENBERGER (G.) Comenius. pp. 48. *Fürth,* 1893. 8°.   Pam. 9.

GRUNDIG (F.) J. A. Comenius. pp. 89. *Gotha,* 1892. 8°.   10759. i. 43.

KOMENSKÝ (J. A.) Comenius-Studien. *Znaim,* 1892, *etc.* 8°.   4888. c.

LAURIE (S. S.) J. A. Comenius. pp. 272. *Syracuse,* 1893. 8°. 4886. aaa. 25.

LINDNER (G. A.) J. A. Comenius. pp. 43. *Wien,* 1892. 8°.   4888. f. 19.

PATERSON (M.) J. A. Comenius. pp. 48. *Lond.* 1892. 8°.   Pam. 9.

REBER (J.) J. A. Comenius. pp. 61. *Leipz.* 1895. 8°.   8311. c. 21.

SCHUMANN (G.) Zur 300 jährigen Jubelfeier des J. A. Comenius. pp. 40. *Neuwied,* 1892. 8°.
       4888. f. 24. (8.)

STAEHELIN (R.) A. Comenius. pp. 65. *Basel,* 1893. 8°. 4888. e. 17. (8.)

WITTE (J.) J. A. Comenius. pp. 51. *Ruhrort,* 1892. 8°.   Pam. 9.

MILTON (J.) John Milton's Essay " Of education." pp. 46. 1893. 8°. 8304. bb. 10. (12.)

FECHTNER (E.) J. Locke's "Gedanken über Erziehung" dargestellt. pp. 43. *Wien,* 1894. 8°.   Pam. 17.

GERINI (G. B.) Le Dottrine pedagogiche di G. Locke. pp. 34. *Torino,* 1893. 8°. Pam. 17.

ROUSSEAU (J. J.) Émile, or Treatise on Education. pp. 355. *N.Y.* 1893. 8°. 8311. aa. 30.

STARACE (G.) Rousseau e i criterii della sua Educazione. pp. 87. *Bari,* 1894. 8°. 8311. c. 23.

SEYFFARTH (L. W.) Pestalozzi in Preussen. pp. 70. *Liegnitz,* 1894. 8°. 8357. c. 54.

DIEBOW (P.) Die Pädagogik Schleiermachers. pp. 177. *Halle,* 1894. 8°. 8311. g. 12.

For the Educational History of each country, *see infra:* Pt. II. *National Education.*

EDUCATION—*continued.*

Hygiene, etc. of Schools. *See* HYGIENE.

Infants and Kindergarten.

BARTH (E.) and NIEDERLEY (W.) Pleasant Work for busy fingers. pp. 322. *Lond.* 1891. 8°.
       8308. aaa. 25.

BOOK. Second Book for the Kindergarten in school. pp. 171. *Aberd.* 1885. 8°.
      12204. aaa. 15.

COMPOSITION. Composition for the Kindergarten. pp. 48. *Lond.* 1893. 8°. 011824. ee. 9.

FOSTER (M. J. C.) The Kindergarten of the church. pp. 227. *N.Y.* 1894. 8°. 8311. b. 28.

FROEBEL (F. W. A.) Letters on the Kindergarten. pp. 331. *Lond.* 1891. 8°. 8310. bb. 48.

—— Froebel Letters. pp. 182. *Bost.* 1893. 8°.
      10921. b. 42.

—— The Student's Froebel. *Lond.* 1893, *etc.* 8°.
      8311. b. 14.

BOWEN (H. C.) Froebel and Education. pp. 209. 1893. 8°. The Great Educators. Vol. 4.
      8311. de.

HILL (L.) Brush work for the Kindergarten. pp. 75. *Lond.* 1894. 8°. 7855. e. 47.

KINDERGARTEN DRAWING BOOK. Drawing and painting Book. *Lond.* 1894. 4°. 7856. df. 43.

LEDSHAM (J. B.) Kindergarten Drawing cards, *etc. Manch.* 1892. 8°. 7855. a. 45.

MORTIMER (E. M.) Practical Kindergarten lessons. pp. 125. *Lond.* 1891. 8°. 8310. cc. 41.

ORLANDONI (G.) La Scuola fröbelianizzata. pp. 47. *Lecco,* 1890. 8°. Pam. 17.

PESTALOZZI (J. H.) How Gertrude teaches her Children. pp. 256. *Lond.* 1894. 8°. 8311. b. 24.

P.P. *London.* Child Life: Kindergarten journal. *Lond.* 1891, *etc.* 8°. P.P. 1182.

POULSSON (E.) In the Child's world. pp. 443. *Springfield,* 1893. 8°. 12807. r. 43.

ROBERTS (A. E.) The Child in school. pp. 60. *Lond.* 1895. 8°. 8309. de. 26.

SCHRADER (H.) Häusliche Beschäftigungen als Erziehungsmittel im Pestalozzi-Fröbel-Hause zu Berlin. pp. 90. *Berl.* 1893. 8°. 8311. b. 20

WALKER (L.) Varied Occupations for infants. pp. 139. *Lond.* 1894. 8°. 7942. e. 46.

WIGGIN (K. D.) Relation of the Kindergarten to the Public School. pp. 25. *San Fran.* 1891. 8°. 8304. b. 21. (6.)

See also infra: Manual: CHILDREN; OBJECT LESSONS. For biographies of Pestalozzi and Froebel, *see supra: History.*

Legal. *See* LAW.

Manual: Sloyd.

BARTER (S.) Manual Instruction. Woodwork. pp. 343. *Lond.* 1892. 8°. 7817. f. 26.

—— "English" Sloyd. Paper on Barter's Woodwork, *etc.* 1892. *s. sh.* 8°. Pam. 17.

HUDSON (J. C.) Barter's "Woodwork." A critique. pp. 4. *Lond.* 1892. 8°. Pam. 17.

BENSON (W. A. S.) Elements of Handicraft and design. pp. 151. *Lond.* 1893. 8°. 7808. df. 4.

BEVIS (A. W.) Hand and eye Training. *Birmingham,* 1893, *etc.* 16°. 8311. a. 4.

—— Course of practical Lessons on hand and eye Training. *Lond.* 1895, *etc.* 4°. 7858. f. 26.

BROWNE (*Sir* J. C.) Training of the hand. *N.Y.* 1890. 8°.   Pam. 17.

BUTLER (N. M.) Manual Training. pp. 20. *Newport,* 1888. 8°. 8304. aa. 17. (7.)

—— The Manual Training movement. pp. 5. *N.Y.* 1889. 8°. 8304. bb. 7. (2.)

EDUCATION.—Manual, etc.—*continued.*

DUPUY (P.) L'Enseignement manuel de l'Enfant. pp. 53. *Montréal, 1889. 8°.*   8304. bb. 9. (2.)

GOETZE (W.) Illustrated manual of hand and eye Training. pp. 229. *Lond. 1894. 8°.*   8304. aaa. 13.

—— Manual Training made serviceable to the School. pp. 157. *Lond. 1894. 8°.* 7820. aaa. 41.

GOSS (W. F. M.) Bench Work in wood. pp. 161. *Bost. 1890. 8°.*   7817. bb. 3.

HAYCOCK (G. S.) Clay-Modelling for schools. pp. 26. *Lond. 1894. obl. 8°.*   7875. a. 41.

HEATH (C.) and THORNTON (J. S.) Directory of Sloyd classes in Great Britain and Ireland. pp. 8. *Lond. 1893. 8°.*   8365. dd. 17. (18.)

HEATON (W.) Manual of Cardboard modelling. pp. 158. *Lond. 1894. 8°.*   7817. i. 6.

HEERWART (E.) Course of Paper-plaiting or Mat-weaving. pp. 23. *Lond. 1895. 8°.*   7944. d. 16.

HEWITT (G. C.) Cardboard Sloyd. *Leeds, 1894. 4°.*   7942. k. 40.

—— Swedish Course of cardboard Modelling. pp. 128. *Halifax, 1895. 8°.*   7817. e. 29.

HEWITT (W.) Graduated course of Manual Training exercises. *Lond. 1892, etc. 8°.*   7915. c. 50.

HOFFMAN (B. B.) Sloyd System of wood working. pp. 242. *N.Y. 1892. 8°.*   7820. aaa. 38.

HOLMAN (H.) Varied occupations, their principles and purposes. pp. 93. *Lond. 1895. 8°.*   7942. aaa. 56.

HOLT (T. E.) Smith's Work. Primer of manual training. pp. 14. *Manch. 1893. 8°.*   07944. ee. 3. (7.)

HUGHES (E. P.) The Slöjd System. pp. 7. *1889. 8°.*   Pam. 17.

—— Manual Instruction in schools. pp. 11. *York, 1888. 8°.*   Pam. 17.

JOHANSSON (A.) Practical directions for making the High School series of Slöjd Models. pp. 58. *Lond. 1892. 8°.*   7820. aaa. 35.

KALB (G.) First Lessons in hand and eye training. pp. 143. *Lond. 1894. 8°.* 7817. bb. 1.

KELLOGG (A. M.) Forty Lessons in clay modelling. pp. 52. *N.Y. 1894. 8°.*   7875. aa. 57.

KILBON (G. B.) Knife Work in the school-room. pp. 64. *Springfield, 1890. 8°.*   7820. bbb. 34.

LATTER (L. R.) Cane Weaving for children. pp. 31. *Lond. 1894. 8°.*   Pam. 94.

—— Open or Cross Weaving in paper and cane. pp. 38. *Lond. 1894. 8°.*   7943. aa. 46.

—— Weaving in straw, cloth, or felt. pp. 19. *Lond. 1894. 8°.*   Pam. 94.

—— Knotting, looping and plaiting. pp. 24. *Lond. 1892. 12°.*   7942. a. 65. (8.)

—— Paper folding for schools. pp. 44. *Lond. 1893. 8°.*   Pam. 94.

LONDON. *Union of Slöjd Teachers.* Report of the General Meeting. *York, 1889, etc. 8°.*   8366. aa.

MAGNUS (*Sir* P.) Manual Training in English schools. pp. 6. *N.Y. 1890. 8°.*   Pam. 17.

—— National Association of Manual Training teachers. Address. pp. 21. *Lond. 1894. 8°.*   Pam. 17.

P.P. *Nääs.* Slöjdundervisningsblad. *Nääs, 1887, etc. 4°.*   472.

NÄXS. *Slöjdlärareseminarium.* Information about the Courses. *Nääs, 1891. 8°.*   Pam. 17.

T., J. S. Visit to the Headquarters of Sloyd, the Slöjdlärareseminarium at Nääs. pp. 4. *Manch. 1892. 8°.*   Pam. 17.

EDUCATION.—Manual, etc.—*continued.*

NELSON (W.) Working diagrams of the English series of Sloyd Models. *Lond. 1895. fol.*   7815. d. 9.

NEW YORK. *College for the Training of Teachers.* Art in Manual Training schools. pp. 5. *N.Y. 1889. 8°.*   Pam. 17.

P.P. *London. Hand & Eye.* Monthly journal. *Lond. 1892, etc. 8°.*   P.P. 1182. b. and 2182.

R., J. M. Slöjd. *Nääs, 1894. 8°.*   8304. bb. 6. (11.)

REYNOLDS (J. H.) Place of Manual Training in education. pp. 8. *Lond. 1889. 8°.*   Pam. 17.

RICKS (G.) Hand and eye Training. *Lond. 1894, etc. 8°.*   7808. cc. 4.

RUSSELL (J.) Sloyd Values. pp. 15. *Lond. 1893. 8°.*   Pam. 17.

SALOMON (O.) Manual Training. pp. 16. *Lond. 1890. 8°.*   Pam. 17.

—— Progressive Steps taken by the Swedish Sloyd instruction. pp. 7. *N.Y. 1890. 8°.*   Pam. 17.

—— Teacher's Hand-book of Slöjd. pp. 270. *Lond. 1894. 8°.*   7817. e. 26.

—— Theory of educational Sloyd. pp. 150. *Lond. 1894. 8°.*   8304. aaa. 14.

SCHERER (H.) Der Handfertigkeitsunterricht. pp. 22. *1893. 8°.* Pädagogische Zeit- und Streitfragen. Hft. 35.   8310. c.

SHUTTLEWORTH (C. B.) Manual Instruction in schools. pp. 54. *Lond. 1894. 8°.*   8304. bb. 5. (19.)

SLATER (J. W.) Clay Modelling for the standards. pp. 62. *Lond. 1895. 8°.*   7875. cc. 5.

SNELL (A.) Geometrical Instruction through hand and eye. pp. 98. *Lond. 1895. 8°.*   8533. bb. 49.

STURM (P.) The Art of Modelling in clay and other pliable materials. pp. 39. *Lond. 1894. 8°.*   7808. df. 16. (7.)

SWITZERLAND. *Société pour la propagation des travaux manuels.* Les Travaux manuels en Suisse. pp. 92. *Fribourg, 1888. 8°.*   7942. i. 43. (7.)

THORNTON (J. S.) Manual Training in Germany. pp. 8. *Lond. 1891. 8°.*   Pam. 17.

UNWIN (M. L. H.) Manual of Clay-modelling, etc. pp. 88. *Lond. 1895. 8°.*   7875. aa. 59.

WOODWARD (C. M.) Manual Training in education. pp. 310. *1890. 8°.* Contemporary Science Series.   8709. i.

YOUNG (C. S.) Manual Training for standards. *Leeds, 1895. obl. 4°.*   7817. l. 12.

Medical. *See* MEDICINE.

Military. *See* MILITARY SCIENCE.

Musical. *See* MUSIC.

Moral. *See infra :* RELIGIOUS.

Physical. *See* GYMNASTICS.

Religious and Moral.

BROMBY (C. H.) *Bp. of Tasmania.* What is real Education? pp. 16. *Lond. 1895. 8°.*   4421. aa. 58. (5.)

DOWDEN (J.) *Bp. of Edinburgh.* Systematic instruction in Religion. pp. 6. *Derby, 1890. 8°.*   8304. e. 20. (4.)

EMMETT (J. T.) Religious Education. pp. 39. *Lond. 1895. 8°.*   4109. bb. 34.

KEFERSTEIN (H.) Religionsunterricht und Erziehung zur Religion. pp. 64. *1891. 8°.* Deutsche Zeit- und Streit-Fragen. Hfte. 93 & 94.   12209. f.

EDUCATION.—Religious, etc.—continued.

LAYARD (E. B.) Religion in boyhood: hints on the training of boys. pp. 79. *Lond.* 1894. 8°.
4399. aaaa. 14.

PHILIPP (J.) Der Religions-Unterricht in den vorzüglichsten biblischen Geschichten. pp. 142. *Igló*, 1880. 8°. 3125. ee. 13.

SOULSBY (L. H. M.) Religious side of secular Teaching. pp. 26. *Oxf.* 1891. 16°. Pam. 17.

WELLDON (J. E. C.) Religious Education of boys. 1891. 8°. Thirteen Essays on education.
8311. e. 2.

ADLER (F.) Moral instruction of children. pp. 270. *N.Y.* 1892. 8°. 8311. aa. 31.

BRAY (C.) The Education of the Feelings. pp. 167. *Lond.* 1894. 8°. 8306. ccc. 25.

MASSY (H.) Notions de morale à l'usage des jeunes filles. *Paris*, 1892. 12°. 8411. cc. 25.

NOTES. Notes of lessons on Morals. pp. 37. *Birmingham*, 1893. 8°. 8415. d. 52.

REYNOLDS (E.) Sketches of lessons in Moral Instruction. pp. 45. *Lond.* 1895. 8°.
8409. d. 17.

SCHOOLBOY MORALITY. Schoolboy Morality. pp. 23. *Lond.* 1892, 16°. Pam. 85.

SHIRREFF (E. A. E.) Moral Training. pp. 20. *Lond.* 1892. 8°. 8304. bb. 9. (10.)

TRAINING. The Training of children. pp. 18. *Lond.* 1894. 16°. 4371. a. 40. (6.)
See also supra: Ecclesiastical: infra: Pt. II. under Australia: England: France: Germany: Italy: Spain: Sweden: United States: SUNDAY SCHOOLS.

School Libraries. *See* LIBRARIES.

School Management: Teaching, etc.

ARNOLD (S. L.) Waymarks for Teachers. pp. 276. *Bost.* 1894. 8°. 8311. aaa. 5.

BERRY (T. W.) Complete pocket record of the Class. *Lond.* 1895. 8°. 8308. bb. 59.

COWHAM (J. H.) New school method for Pupil Teachers and Students. 3 pt. *Lond.* 1894. 8°.
8311. aaa. 10.

FLUX (A. T.) Scholarship school Management. pp. 146. *Lond.* 1893. 8°. 8311. b. 19.

LANDON (J.) Principles and practice of Teaching. pp. 462. *Lond.* 1894. 8°. 8311. c. 9.

ODELL (W.) Recreation. pp. 44. *Torquay*, 1893. 8°. 8305. cc. 6.

PRINCE (J. J.) School Management and method. pp. 375. *Manch.* 1894. 8°. 8311. aaa. 3.

RINGDAL (R. I.) Disciplin. pp. 88. *Kristiania*, 1892. 8°. 8309. c. 55.

WILSON (J.) Manual of methods of Teaching. pp. 440. *Lond.* 1892. 8°. 8311. b. 8.
See also supra: General: LANGUAGE : OBJECT LESSONS.

School Savings Banks. *See* BANKING.

Science Teaching. *See infra: Technical:* CHEMISTRY : PHYSICS.

Teaching, *Profession of.*

ANDREAE (C.) Zur Entwicklungsgeschichte der deutschen Lehrerbildungs-Anstalten. pp. 162. *Kaiserslautern*, 1893. 8°. 8357. f. 18.

ATKINSON (F. W.) Professional preparation of secondary Teachers in the U.S. pp. 64. *Leipz.* 1893. 8°. 8365. dd. 17. (15.)

BRAMWELL (A. B.) Training of Teachers in the U.S. pp. 198. *Lond.* 1894. 8°. 8311. aaa. 6.

EDUCATION.—Teaching, etc.—continued.

BUTLER (N. M.) Duty of the University to the Teaching Profession. pp. 8. *Saratoga*, 1890. 8°.
8304. bb. 8. (4.)

DISNEY (H. W.) Law relating to Schoolmasters. pp. 128. *Lond.* 1893. 8°. 6345. aaa. 7.

KAUFFMANN-HARTENSTEIN (J.) Zur Lehrerbildungsfrage. pp. 65. *Solothurn*, 1889. 8°.
8357. f. 8.

NEWTON (J. W.) How to become a Pupil Teacher. pp. 12. *Sheffield*, 1885. 8°. Pam. 17.

REPORT. Statistics of Salaries paid to Assistant Mistresses in High Schools. pp. 16. *Lond.* 1891. 8°. 8277. ee. 1. (5.)
See also supra: General: School Management: EXAMINATIONS.

Technical : Commercial.

AC. Oxford. *University.* County Councils and Technical Education. Report. *Oxf.* 1892, etc. 8°. 8366. b.

ASHBEE (C. R.) Manual of the Guild and School of Handicraft. pp. 95. *Lond.* 1892. 8°.
07945. m. 16.

BARTH (E.) and NIEDERLEY (W.) Die Schulwerkstatt. pp. 308. *Bielefeld*, 1882. 8°.
8311. ee. 5.

BENSON (E. W.) *Archbp. of Canterbury.* Technical Education and its Influence on Society. pp. 31. *Lond.* 1892. 8°. 8311. aa. 20.

BRUHNS (A.) Die Schulwerkstätte in ihrer Verbindung mit dem theoretischen Unterrichte. 2 pt. *Wien*, 1895. 8°. 8311. d. 1.

BUCKMASTER (J. C.) County Councils and Technical Education. pp. 42. *Lond.* 1891. 8°.
8306. de. 19. (9.)

G. B. & I. *Association of Technical Institutions.* Proceedings at the Annual Meeting, 1895, *etc.* *Bristol*, 1895, etc. 8°. 8311. cc.

HAMPSHIRE. Technical Education for Hampshire. pp. 10. *Southampton*, 1891. 8°.
8304. aa. 18. (6.)

INNES (T.) Technical Instruction in agriculture. pp. 23. *Edinb.* 1891. 8°. 7074. e. 10. (6.)

LÉAUTEY (E.) L'Enseignement commercial. pp. 774. *Paris*, 1886. 8°. 8356. o. 40.

LITTLE (M.) Manual of recent Acts of Parliament relating to Technical Education. pp. 51. *Edinb.* 1893. 8°. 6583. aaa. 10.

LONDON. *National Association for Technical Education.* Guide to evening classes in London. pp. 81. *Lond.* 1890. 8°. 8364. aaa. 40.

LUEDERS (K.) Denkschriften über die Entwickelung der gewerblichen Fachschulen in Preussen. pp. 318. *Berl.* 1891. 4°. 8356. l. 4.

MICHELL (G. J.) and SMITH (E. H.) Technical Education in the counties. pp. 144. *Lond.* 1892. 8°. 8311. aa. 6.

NEW ZEALAND. *Department of Education.* Technical Education. *Wellington*, 1885. fol.
8365. h. 25.

P.P. London. Record of Technical Education. *Lond.* 1891, etc. 8°. P.P. 1187. ie.

ROBINS (E. C.) Memorandum of proceedings at a drawing-room meeting for the promotion of Technical Education. pp. 41. *Lond.* 1887. 8°.
Pam. 17.

SCHAUERMANN (F. L.) Ornament applied to the work of technical schools. pp. 208. *Lond.* 1892. 8°. 7808. e. 11.

SEXTON (A. H.) The first Technical College. pp. 188. *Lond.* 1894. 8°. 8366. aa. 28.

SOUTHAMPTON. Technical and secondary Education. pp. 12. *Southampton*, 1891. 8°.
8304. bb. 5. (14.)
R

EDUCATION.—Belgium—_continued._

HIRSCH (A.) and HUISMAN (M.) L'Extension Universitaire belge. pp. 21. *Brux.* 1895. 8°.
Liège. 1893. 8°.   Pam. 17.

MOLITOR (L.) Notes pour l'amélioration de la discipline dans les établissements d'enseignement m yen en Belgique. pp. 107.
Liège, 1893. 8°.   8304. bb. 6. (8.)

Canada.

BOURINOT (J. G.) Our intellectual strength and weakness. 1894. 8°. Ac. Ottawa. *Royal Society of Canada.* Proceedings. Vol. 11.
Ac. 1883.

CHAPAIS (T.) Les Congrégations enseignantes. pp. 50. *Québec,* 1893. 8°.   8304. b. 21. (9.)

DAVIN (N. F.) Speech of Mr. Davin on Schools of the N.W. Territories. pp. 18.
Ottawa, 1894. 8°.   Pam. 45.

LEGENDRE (N.) Nos Écoles. pp. 95.
Québec, 1890. 8°.   Pam. 17.

MANITOBA. Manitoba School Case, 1894. pp. 286.
Lond. 1895. 8°.   06606. f. 22.

PRENDERGAST (J. E. P.) Manitoba School Question. pp. 25. *Winnipeg,* 1893. 8°.   Pam. 17.

QUEBEC. Lois de l'Instruction publique de la province de Québec. pp. 295.
Montreal, 1894. 8°.   06606. h. 3.

—— Lettre pastorale des Archevêques et Évêques de Québec, de Montréal et d'Ottawa, sur l'Education. pp. 52. *Québec,* 1894. 8°.
Pam. 96.

ROULEAU (T. G.) Catéchisme des lois scolaires. pp. 47. *Québec,* 1893. 12°.   Pam. 17.

TACHÉ (A. A.) *Archp. of Saint Boniface.* Mémoire sur la question des écoles. pp. 64.
Montréal, 1894. 8°.   Pam. 17.

TARDIVEL (J. P.) Polémique à propos d'Enseignement. pp. 110. *Québec,* 1894. 8°.
8311. cc. 6.

Cape of Good Hope.

SHEA (J. M.) Analysis of school examinations in Cape Colony. pp. 275. *Capetown,* 1893. 8°.
8364. aaaa. 51.

Ceylon. See infra : India.

Denmark : Iceland.

BAGGER (S.) Om Folkeskolens Reform. pp. 54.
Kjøbenh. 1890. 8°.   8304. e. 21. (9.)

BANG (V.) Latinskoleliv i Danmark og Norge, 16ᵈᵉ og 17ᵈᵃ Aarhundrede. pp. 299.
Kjøbenh. 1892. 8°.   8357. aa. 16.

BIILMANN (L.) Er Skolens Gjerning forfeilet? pp. 29. *Odense,* 1891. 8°.   8304. c. 21. (13.)

HEALEY (E.) Educational systems of Sweden, Norway and Denmark. pp. 36.
Lond. 1892. 8°.   8304. e. 23. (12.)

HOLM (P. A.) and SAUTER (E.) Skolelovene, samt en Del Bekjendtgjørelser. pp. 200.
Kjøbenh. 1890. 8°.   5725. a. 7.

LARSEN (J.) Bidrag til den Folkeskoles Historie 1784–1818. pp. 322. *Kjøbenh.* 1893. 8°.
8357. d. 5.

TIDEMAND (O. W.) Det kongelige Blaagaard-Jonstrupske Skolelærerseminarium, 1790–1890. pp. 204. *Kjøbenh.* 1890. 8°.   8357. bb. 31.

WEIS (A. P.) and HAGE (H. F.) De gældende Retsregler for det højere Skolevæsen i Danmark. 2 Afd. *Kjøbenh.* 1891. 4°.   5705. i. 10.

ICELAND. Reglugjörð fyrir búnaðarskólann á Hólum. pp. 12. *Reykjavík,* 1891. 8°.
867. l. 4. (17.)

See also supra : Pt. I., Female : School Management.

EDUCATION.—_continued._

England. See also Pt. I. General : School Management : Teaching.

General and Higher.

AC. Oxford. *University.* Report of a Conference on secondary Education in England. pp. 234. *Oxf.* 1893. 8°.   8311. cc. 2.

FLEISCHNER (L.) Zur Geschichte des englischen Bildungswesens. pp. 40. 1893. 8°. Sammlung wissenschaftlicher Vorträge. N. F. Serie 8. Hft. 175.   12249. l.

JACOB (H. P.) Public School life in England. pp. 33. *Karachi,* 1893. 8°.   Pam. 17.

LECLERC (M.) L'Éducation en Angleterre. pp. 368. *Paris,* 1894. 12°.   8309. aaa. 47.

MALGAT (J.) Essai sur l'Élevage des enfants en Angleterre. pp. 59. *Nice,* 1894. 12°.
8311. aaa. 20.

P.P. *Glasgow.* The School Monthly.
Glasg. 1893, *etc.* 8°.   1866. b. 6.

—— *London.* The School-World. Vol. 1.
Lond. 1890, 91. 4°.   1865. a. 8.

PRESCOTT (P.) Reform in Education. pp. 41.
Lond. 1890. 8°.   8304. aa. 16. (7.)

PUBLIC SCHOOLS. Great Public Schools. pp. 344.
Lond. 1893. 8°.   8364. d. 34.

SCHOOLS. Private Schools and schoolmasters. pp. 118. *Lond.* 1892. 8°.   8311. aa. 15.

—— Schools and Colleges : selected list. pp. 37.
Birmingham, 1893. 8°.   8304. bb. 6. (9.)

SHARPLESS (I.) English Education. pp. 193.
Lond. 1893. 8°.   8311. aa. 26.

WILLIAMS (J.) Education. Manual of practical law. pp. 348. *Lond.* 1892. 8°. 6426. aaaa. 12.

Elementary.

ALFORD (B. H.) Free Education. 1891. 8°.
MACKAY (T.) A Plea for Liberty. 8276. g. 44.

BOUSFIELD (W.) Elementary Schools, how to increase their utility. pp. 189. *Lond.* 1890. 8°.
8309. de. 27.

BRUNNER (J. T.) and ELLIS (T. E.) Public Education in Cheshire. pp. 144.
Manch. 1890. 8°.   8366. aaa. 20.

COOPER (J.) Compulsory Attendance clauses of the Education Acts. *Farnworth,* 1894. 12°.
1865. c. 1. (8.)

EMERY (W.) Free Education Act, 1891. pp. 15.
Lond. 1891. 8°.   8304. e. 20. (12.)

ENGLAND AND WALES. *Local Government Board.* Memorandum on the circumstances under which the closing of Public Elementary Schools may be required in order to prevent the spread of disease. *Lond.* 1893. fol.   7560. k. 7. (2.)

FAWCETT (*Right Hon.* H.) Free Education in its relation to the social condition of the People. pp. 16. *Westminster,* 1890. 8°.   Pam. 17.

FLOWER (J. E.) Evening Continuation Schools. pp. 8. *Lond.* 1894 8°.   8304 e. 23. (15.)

GIBBS (H. J.) and DOWN (T. C.) School Board Election manual. pp. 119. *Lond.* 1891. 12°.
8308. aaa. 23.

G. B. *Committee on Education.* The New Code, 1893-4, of regulations of the Education Department. pp. 280. *Lond.* 1893. 8°.   8311. b. 15.

—— Memorandum as to Free Education.
Lond. 1893. fol.   1865. c. 1. (21.)

—— Rules to be observed in planning and fitting up Public Elementary Schools. pp. 8.
Lond. 1893. fol.   8365. h. 28.

—— How to carry out Circular 332 and the requirements of the New Code, 1895. pp. 16.
Lond. 1895. 8°.   8310. a. 37.

EDUCATION.—England—*continued.*

GREGORY (R.) Elementary Education in England. pp. 192. *Lond.* 1895. 8°.　　8311. bb. 1.

HOWATT (J. R.) Sketch of 50 years' work by the Ragged School Union. pp. 45.
Lond. 1894. 8°.　　　　　　　4192. g. 4.

KASPARY (J.) Humanitarian appeal to the London School Board electors. pp. 8.
Lond. 1894. 8°.　　　　　　　Pam. 17.

LEDSHAM (J. B.) Register of Attendance and Fees. *Manch.* 1890. fol.　　1881. a. 18.

LENZ (A.) Die Zwangserziehung in England. Reformatory and Industrial Schools. pp. 136.
Stuttgart, 1894. 8°.　　　　6056. ee. 36.

LONDON. *School Board.* Report.
Lond. 1887, *etc.* 8°.　　　　　　N.R.

—— Report of Bye-Laws Committee.
Lond. 1887, *etc.* fol.　　　　　　N.R.

—— Report of School Accommodation and Attendance Committee. *Lond.* 1892, *etc.* fol.
　　　　　　　　　　　　　　　N.R.

—— Report of School Management Committee.
Lond. 1887, *etc.* fol.　　　　　　N.R.

—— Report of the Industrial Schools Committee.
Lond. 1887, *etc.* fol.　　　　　　N.R.

—— Report of the Statistical Committee.
Lond. 1887, *etc.* 4°.　　　　　　N.R.

—— Annual Report of the Evening Classes Committee. *Lond.* 1887, *etc.* fol.　　N.R.

—— Reports of Debates of School Board, 1891–1894, *etc. Lond.* 1895, *etc.* 8°.　　8311. ccc.

—— Directory of Evening Continuation Schools held north of the Thames, *etc.* pp. 98.
Lond. 1894. 8°.　　　　　　8367. aa. 18.

—— Report on the administration of the Bye-Laws. pp. 229. *Lond.* 1891. 8°.　　N.R.

HEADLAM (S. D.) The London School Board in 1890. pp. 16. *Lond.* 1890. 8°. 8365. bbb. 66. (3.)

HELBY (J. T.) London School Board. How the money goes and who spends it. pp. 24.
Lond. 1891. 8°.　　　　　8304. e. 20. (13.)

LOBB (J.) London School Board : its expenditure. pp. 24. *Lond.* 1891. 8°.　8304. e. 21. (16.)

—— London School Board. Twelve Years' Experience. pp. 16. *Lond.* 1894, 8°.　Pam. 17.

BRUCE (G. L.) Report on eighteen months' work at the London School Board. pp. 8.
Lond. 1893. 8°.　　　　8365. bbb. 66. (8.)

LOWNDES (F. S.) The Education Question.
} p. 30. *Lond.* 1893. 8°.　　8304. bb. 9. (13.)

LYON (E. H.) Royal Education Commission, 1886–8. Summary of the final report. pp. 128.
Lond. 1888. 8°.　　　　　　8364. co. 61.

MACKENZIE (W. W.) Treatise on the Elementary Education Acts, 1870–1891. pp. 347.
Lond. 1892. 8°.　　　　　　6426. cc. 18.

MARGESSON (*Lady* I. A.) Principles and Working of the New Education. pp. 45.
Lond. 1894, 8°.　　　　8304. bb. 5. (18.)

MOORE (T.) The Church the Educator of the English Nation. pp. 212. *Lond.* 1891. 8°.
　　　　　　　　　　　　4192. bb. 47.

MOSS (J. F.) Handbook of the New Code of Regulations. pp. 164. *Lond.* 1890. 8°. 8309 e. 39

NUNN (J.) Voluntary Schools. Schemes for Rate-Aid considered. pp. 27. *Manch.* 1895. 8°.
　　　　　　　　　　　　　Pam. 17.

—— Rate-Aid or State-Aid. pp. 21.
Manch. 1895. 8°.　　　　　　Pam. 17.

OWEN (*Sir* H.) Elementary Education Acts, 1870–1891. pp. 753. *Lond.* 1891. 8°. 2230. f. 4

P.P. London. The Voluntary Teacher. Journal in the interests of voluntary schools.
Lond. 1890–92. 8°.　　　　P.P. 1180. de.

EDUCATION.—England—*continued.*

RIDDELL (C. J. B.) District Organizations for Church of England elementary schools. pp. 19.
Lond. 1895. 8°.　　　　　　Pam. 17.

ROOPER (T. G.) The Lines on which Standards I. and II. should be taught. pp. 31. *Hull,* 1894. 8°.
　　　　　　　　　　　8304. aa. 19. (9.)

SING (G. H.) "Can we save our Schools?"
pp. 16. *Lond.* 1893. 8°.　　4429. c. 21. (11.)

STEINTHAL (A. E.) Elementary Education Act 1891. pp. 135. *Lond.* 1891. 8°. 6426. aaaa. 5.

STOTT (F.) The "Carlisle" absence-attendance register. *Manch.* 1891. fol.　　1881. b. 17.

TRENCH (H. F. C) A new Educational Policy for the Church. *Lond.* 1894, 8°. 8304. bb. 5. (20.)

TUCKWELL (G. M.) The State and its Children. pp. 164. 1894, 8°. GIBBINS (H. de B.) Social Questions of to-day.　　　　　　08276. e.

WENHAM (J. G.) The School Manager. pp. 250.
Lond. 1892. 8°.　　　　　8038. aaa. 29.

See also EXAMINATIONS.

　　Females. See supra : Pt. I. Female.

　　Infants. See supra : Pt. I. Infants.

　　Manual. See supra : Pt. I. Manual.

　　　　　Religious.

HAWKES (J. H.) A Liberal's Appeal for the toleration of the Christian religion in schools.
pp. 57. *Lond.* 1892, 8°.　　8304. bb. 5. (15.)

HOBBS (S.) Conscience. Illustrated by an official correspondence with the Education Department.
pp. 15. *Lond.* 1892, 8°.　　8304. bb. 6. (4.)

LONDON. *Central Society for Higher Religious Education.* Report of a Conference on religious Teaching in higher Schools. pp. 44.
Lond. 1892. 8°.　　　　　4429. c. 21. (2.)

OXFORD, *Diocese of. Board of Education.* Syllabus of religious Instruction for schools.
Oxf. 1890. 8°.　　　　　8304. e. 20. (8.)

SHEFFIELD. Scriptural Education. Speeches delivered at Sheffield, at two meetings. pp. 66.
Sheffield. 1887. 16°.　　　4136. c. 10. (10.)

SINCLAIR (W. M.) Christian Teaching. An address. pp. 15. *Lond.* 1892. 8°. 4429. aa. 60. (9.)

—— Sacred Studies : or, higher religious Education. pp. 47. *Lond.* 1893, 8°. Pam. 95.

WILKINSON (T. E.) *Bp. of Zululand.* Does England wish her boys and girls to grow up Atheists?
pp. 16. *Lond.* 1895. 8°.　　4421. aa. 58. (11.)

　　Technical. See supra : Pt. I. Technical.

　　　　　University.

JEBB (R. C.) The work of the Universities for the nation. pp. 52. *Camb.* 1893. 8°.
　　　　　　　　　　　　8366. aa. 24.

MACKINDER (H. J.) and SADLER (M. E.) University Extension, past, present and future.
pp. 144. *Lond.* 1891. 8°.　　8364. aa. 49.

PEARSON (K.) The New University for London.
pp. 139. *Lond.* 1892. 8°.　　8366. aaa. 24.

ROBERTS (W. R.) British Universities. pp. 89.
Manch. 1892. 8°.　　　8365. bbb. 66. (7.)

VARIGNY (H. de) L'University Extension Movement en Angleterre. pp. 14. *Paris,* 1893, 8°.
　　　　　　　　　　　8304. e. 24. (8.)

See also supra : Pt. I. University, and under the name of each English University.

　　　　　France.

　　　General and Higher.

AC. New York. *University.* School system of France. pp. 20. *N.Y.* 1893, 8°.　　Pam. 17.

ARNOLD (M.) A French Eton. pp. 416.
Lond. 1892. 8°.　　　　　8355. de. 4.

EDUCATION.—France—*continued.*

BAHLSEN (L.) Der französische Unterricht nach den Grundsätzen der Reformer. pp. 36.
Berl. 1892. 4°.   Pam. 17.

CAILL (A.) La Question des Vacances scolaires.
pp. 41. *Paris*, 1891. 8°.   8304. b. 21. (4.)

CLAMADIEU (J. A.) La Question de la Philosophie au Lycée à la fin du xixᵉ siècle.
pp. 72. *Paris*, 1892. 12°.   8461. aaa. 28. (6.)

DEJOB (C.) L'Instruction publique en France au dix-neuvième siècle. pp. 455.
Paris, 1894. 12°.   8356. b. 61.

FOUILLÉE (A.) L'Enseignement au point de vue national. pp. 451. *Paris*, 1891. 8°.
                                  8310. cc. 40.

—— Education from a national standpoint.
pp. 332. *Lond.* 1892. 8°.   8311. aa. 13.

FRANCE. *Ministère de l'Instruction.* Plan d'Études et programmes de l'Enseignement secondaire classique. pp, 168. *Paris*, 1892. 12°.
                                  8356. aa. 21.

GARNIER ( ) L'Anglomanisme dans l'enseignement secondaire. pp. 10. *Langres*, 1890. 8°.
                                  8304. e. 21. (11.)

GUILLAUME (L.) Les Jésuites et les classiques chrétiens. pp. 184. *Gand*, 1894. 8°. 4092. e. 2.

LAVISSE (E.) À propos de nos Écoles. pp. 250.
Paris, 1895. 12°.   8356. aaa. 45.

LEFÈVRE (É.) L'Éducation en France. pp. 172.
Verviers, 1888. 8°.   8310. cc. 37.

LOT (F.) L'Enseignement supérieur en France.
pp. 144. *Paris*, 1892. 12°.   8356. b. 62.

LOWUM (A.) Den franske Latinskole. pp. 165.
Christiania, 1891. 8°.   8355. df. 15.

MEY (O.) Die Schulen und der organische Bau der Volksschule in Frankreich. pp. 226.
Berl. 1893. 8°.   8311. g. 8.

PARIS. *École Monge.* Rapport du Directeur.
Paris, 1890, *etc.* 8°.   8356. cc.

—— *Lycée Louis-le-Grand.* Lycée Louis-le-Grand. pp. 18. *Paris*, 1891. 8°.
                                  8356. g. 21. (6.)

—— *Société de Sainte-Barbe.* Sainte-Barbe.
Prospectus general. pp. 30.
Villefranche, 1890. 8°.   8356. g. 21. (1.)

—— Sainte-Barbe. École préparatoire aux écoles du gouvernement. pp. 15. *Paris*, 1890. 8°.
                                  Pam. 17.

PARIS (G.) Le haut Enseignement en France.
pp. 61. *Paris*, 1894. 12°.   Pam. 17.

P.P. *Paris.* Revue de l'Enseignement secondaire et supérieur. *Paris*, 1884, *etc.* 8°.
                                  P.P. 1199. d.

PETIT (É.) Alentour de l'École. pp. 388.
Paris, 1890. 12°.   8356. aa. 15.

—— L'École moderne. pp. 422. *Paris*, 1892. 12°.
                                  8310. aa, 53.

RAGANASSE (Z.) Fabrique de Pions. L'École Normale. pp. 245. *Paris*, 1893. 8°.
                                  8311. aaa. 2.

ROUSSELET (L.) Nos grandes Écoles d'Application. pp. 485. *Paris*, 1895. 8°. 8356. i. 16.

ROUX (F.) Histoire de l'École Normale spéciale de Cluny. pp. 319. *Alais*, 1889. 8°. 8356. f. 35.

SPULLER (E.) Éducation de la démocratie.
pp. 332. *Paris*, 1892. 12°.   8311. aa. 24.

—— Au Ministère de l'instruction. Discours, allocutions, circulaires. pp. 298.
Paris, 1895. 8°.   8310. d. 11.

TEEGAN (T. H.) Technical, industrial and commercial Education in France. pp. 223.
Lond. 1891. 8°.   8356. aa. 16.

VILLERS (L.) Des Libéralités scolaires. pp. 308.
Paris, 1892. 8°.   5123. aa. 5.

EDUCATION.—France—*continued.*

ZED. Notes et souvenirs d'Inspection. pp. 107.
Deville, 1891. 8°.   8311. b. 6.
See also infra : History.

Ecclesiastical. See supra : Pt. I. Ecclesiastical.

Elementary.

COMPAYRÉ (G.) Organisation des écoles primaires. pp. 392. *Paris*, 1890. 18°.
                                  8356. aaa. 42.

COYNE (É.) L'Éducation obligatoire.
Annecy, 1894. 8°.   Pam. 17.

KEMENY (F.) Beiträge zur Kenntnis des Volksschulwesens von Frankreich. pp. 57.
1890. 8°. Pädagogische Zeit- und Streitfragen.
Bd. 3.   8310. c.

NOËL (F.) Jurisprudence des écoles primaires.
pp. 37. *Paris*, 1895. 8°.   Pam. 17.

P.P. *Paris.* Journal des Instituteurs des écoles primaires. *Paris*, 1891, *etc.* 8°. P.P. 1199. ea.

RIVET (A.) La Législation de l'Enseignement primaire libre. pp. 332. *Lyon*, 1891. 8°.
                                  8356. g. 19.

TEEGAN (T. H.) Elementary education in France.
pp. 255. *Lond.* 1891. 8°.   8356. aaa. 43.

WEIGERT (M.) Die Volksschule und der gewerbliche Unterricht. pp. 63. 1890. 8°. Volkswirthschaftliche Zeitfragen. Hft. 90, 91.
                                  8207. i.

See also infra : History.

Female. See supra : Pt. I. Female.

History.

TARSOT (L.) Les Écoles et les écoliers à travers les âges. pp. 339. *Paris*, 1893. 8°. 8356. h. 17.

DENK (V. M. O.) Geschichte des gallo-fränkischen Unterrichts- und Bildungswesens.
pp. 276. *Mainz*, 1892. 8°.   8355. df. 17.

BERNARD (P. C.) De l'Enseignement élémentaire aux xiᵉ et xiiᵉ siècles. pp. 457. *Paris*, 1894. 8°.
                                  8356. c. 31.

CLERVAL (A.) Les Écoles de Chartres du vᵉ au xviᵉ siècle. pp. 572. 1895. 8°. Ac. Chartres.
Société archéologique. Mémoires. Tom. 11.
                                  Ac. 5293/3.

ALLAIN (E.) L'œuvre scolaire de la Revolution.
pp. 436. *Paris*, 1891. 8°.   8355. df. 13.

FRANCE. *Comité d'Instruction Publique.* Procès-Verbaux du Comité d'Instruction de la Convention Nationale. *Paris*, 1891, *etc.* 8°. 8356. h.

BONNEL (A.) Réorganisation de l'Instruction publique en 1802. pp. 57. *Lyon*, 1894. 8°.
                                  Pam. 17.

Ac, *Paris. École normale.* Le Centenaire de l'École normale. 1795–1895. pp. 699.
Paris, 1895. 8°.   8356. i. 17.

FIERVILLE (C.) Archives des Lycées. 1802–93.
pp. 526. *Paris*, 1894. 8°.   8356. i. 14.

MAURIN (J.) Les Écoles primaires protestantes avant la Révocation de l'Edit de Nantes.
pp. 53. *Montauban*, 1892. 8°. 8304. e. 23. (14.)

NICOLET (G. E.) L'École primaire protestante jusqu'en 1789. pp. 76. *Auxerre*, 1891. 8°.
                                  Pam. 17.

URSEAU (C.) L'Instruction primaire avant 1789 dans les paroisses d'Angers. pp. 344.
Angers, 1890. 12°.   8355. df. 9.

ROTGÈS (E.) Histoire de l'Instruction primaire dans l'arrondissement de Bazas. pp. 366.
Bordeaux, 1893. 4°.   8356. d. 14.

BRUNEAU (M.) L'Enseignement secondaire & supérieur à Bourges, 1762–92. 1890. 8°. Ac.
Bourges. *Commission Historique.* Mémoires, *etc.* Ser. 4. Vol. 6.   Ac. 6780.

PLIEUX (A.) Étude sur l'instruction publique à Lectoure. pp. 216. *Agen*, 1890. 8°. 8356. h. 12.

EDUCATION.—France—_continued._

ANGOT (A.) L'Instruction populaire dans la
Mayenne avant 1790. pp. 277. _Paris_, 1890. 8°.
8356 d. 13.

—— La Révolution et l'instruction populaire
dans la Mayenne. pp. 31. _Laval_, 1891. 8°.
8304. bb. 9. (4.)

NARBONNE (L.) L'Instruction publique à Narbonne avant 1789. pp. 104. _Narbonne_, 1891. 8°.
8356. f. 39.

DEMANGE (F. J.) Les Écoles d'un village toulois,
XVIII° siècle. pp. 310. _Paris_, 1892. 8°
8356. b. 59.

LITTON (A.) L'Instruction publique en Vendée
pendant la Révolution. 1890. 8°. Ac. Napoléon. _Société d'Émulation._ Annuaire. Sér.3.
Vol. 10.   Ac. 395.

See also supra: Pt. I. History.

Religious.

BONNOT (A.) Les Fruits de l'école sans Dieu.
pp. 151. _Paris_, 1890. 18°.   3900. b. 42.

BOUGE (A.) Les Instituteurs et les institutrices
laïques. pp. 288. _Paris_, 1891. 12°.
8355. aaa. 53.

LAVEILLE (A.) L'Église institutrice de la France.
1887, _etc._ 8°. Ac. Coutances. _Académie de
Saint Thomas d'Aquin._ Académie, _etc._
Ac. 2012.

MARTIN (G.) Dix ans de laïcisation. pp. 96.
Paris, 1890. 8°.   8305. ff. 7. (9.)

PARIS. _Institut Catholique._ Lettre des arché-
vêques et évêques fondateurs de l'Institut catholique. pp. 12. _Paris_, 1891. 8°.
3900. g. 12. (7.)

VEUCLIN (E. V.) A propos de la bénédiction des
Écoles chrétiennes libres de Bernay. pp. 4.
Bernay, 1891. 8°.   8304. bb. 9. (8.)

Technical. See supra: Pt. I. Technical.

University.

FRANCE. _Universities._ Les Statuts et privilèges
des Universités françaises jusqu'en 1789.
Paris, 1890, _etc._ fol.   8356. l.

LEFRANC (A.) Histoire du Collège de France.
pp. 432. _Paris_, 1893. 8°.   8355. df. 18.

DENIFLE (H. S.) Les Universités françaises au
moyen-âge. pp. 99. _Paris_, 1892. 8°.
8356. g. 20

JOUVENCY (J.) L'élève de rhétorique au collège
Louis le-Grand au XVIII° siècle. pp. 136.
Paris, 1892. 8°.   11805. bb. 32.

Ac. Paris. _Université._ Le livret de l'étudiant
de Paris. 2 pt. _Paris_, 1891. 12°.   8355. aa. 20.

BIBLIOGRAPHIE. Bibliographie des Thèses.
Paris, 1892, _etc._ 8°.   11902. g.

BOIRAC (É.) La Dissertation philosophique.
pp. 458. _Paris_, 1892. 8°.   8462. f. 24.

DUPUY (A.) L'État et l'Université. pp. 288.
Paris, 1890. 8°.   8310. bbb. 3.

ENSEIGNEMENT. Pour et contre l'Enseignement
philosophique. pp. 178. _Paris_, 1894. 12°.
8311. aaa. 12.

FOLLEVILLE (D. de) La question des Universités régionales. pp. 72. _Paris_, 1890. 8°.
8304. e. 22. (8.)

IZOULET (J.) L'Âme française et les Universités
nouvelles. pp. 79. _Paris_, 1892. 8°. 8356. a. 14.

MARION (H.) L'Éducation dans l'Université.
pp. 400. _Paris_, 1893. 12°.   8356. aa. 24.

NICATI (W.) À propos de la Constitution d'une
Université à créer en Province. pp. 47.
Paris, 1891. 8°.   8304. e. 24. (5.)
See also supra: Pt. I. University.

EDUCATION—_continued._

Germany.

General and Higher.

BACKES ( ) Festschrift zur Jubelfeier des
hessischen Landes-Lehrer-Vereins. pp. 164.
Darmstadt, 1894. 8°.   8357. d. 6.

CLAUSNITZER (L.) Geschichte des preussischen
Unterrichtsgesetzes. pp. 339. _Berl._ 1892. 8°.
8356. e. 38.

DAHN (F.) Moltke als Erzieher. pp. 209.
Breslau, 1892. 8°.   10707. aaa. 36.

DOERPFELD (F. W.) Das Fundamentstück einer
gerechten Schulverfassung.
Hilschenbach, 1892, _etc._ 8°.   8310. d. 6.

FAUTH (F. C.) Gedanken zur Schulreform.
pp. 29. _Grünberg_, 1894. fol.   Pam. 17.

FRANZ (A.) Das preussische Zwangserziehungs-
Gesetz von 13. März 1878. 1894. 8°. Frankfurter zeitgemässe Broschüren. N. F. Bd. 15.
12209. g.

HAMMERSTEIN (L. v.) Das preussische Schul-
monopol. pp. 295. _Freiburg_, 1893. 8°.
8357. cc. 49.

HARTMANN (F.) Der deutsche Unterricht und
die Schulreform. pp. 56. 1890. 8°. Deutsche
Zeit- und Streitfragen. No. 67.   12209. f.

HILDEBRAND (H. R.) Vom deutschen Sprachunterricht in der Schule. pp. 278. _Leipz._ 1890. 8°.
8357. cc. 46.

HORN (J. F.) Das Zukunftsgymnasium. pp. 27.
1893. 8°. Pädagogische Zeit- und Streitfragen.
Bd. 5.   8310. c.

HORNEMANN (F.) Bemerkungen über den gegenwärtigen Stand der Schulreformbewegung.
1889. 8°. GERMANY. _Deutscher Einheitsschul-
verein._ Schriften. Hft. 5.   8357. cc.

KAPPES (C.) Zur Schulfrage. pp. 74.
Karlsruhe, 1883. 8°.   8304. d. 13. (7.)

KEFERSTEIN (H.) Ideale und Irrthümer der
Unterrichtsprogramme. pp. 59. 1890. 8°.
Deutsche Zeit- und Streit-Fragen. N. F.
Jhrg. 5.   12209. f.

KUKULA (R. C. W.) Bibliographisches Jahrbuch
der deutschen Hochschulen. pp. 1071.
Innsbruck, 1892. 8°.   011900. ee. 14.

LASSON (A.) Für das alte Gymnasium wider die
Neuerer. pp. 81. _Berl._ 1890. 8°. 8304. e. 20. (7.)

MEYER (L.) Die Reform der höheren Schulen.
1890. 8°. GERMANY. _Deutscher Einheitsschul-
verein._ Schriften, _etc._ Heft 6.   8357. cc.

PARSONS (J. R.) Prussian Schools through
American eyes. pp. 21. _Syracuse_, 1891. 8°.
8357. k. 6.

P.P. _Berlin._ Jahres-Verzeichniss der an den
deutschen Schulanstalten erschienen Abhandlungen. _Berl._ 1890, _etc._ 8°.   P.P. 6513. lc.

P.P. _Leipsic._ Neuphilologische Blätter.
Leipz. 1894, _etc._ 8°.   P.P. 5044. cc.

—— Zeitschrift für den deutschen Unterricht.
Leipz. 1887, _etc._ 8°.   P.P. 1212. ee.

PINLOCHE (A.) La réforme de l'éducation en
Allemagne au dix-huitième siècle. pp. 597.
Paris, 1889. 8°.   8357. f. 3.

RICHTER (G.) Das höhere bürgerliche Schul-
wesen. 1889. 8°. GERMANY. _Deutscher Ein-
heitsschulverein._ Schriften. Hft. 5. 8357. cc.

SCHMIDT (C.) Die Confession der Kinder nach
den Landesrechten. pp. 550.
Freiburg, 1890. 8°.   5604. eee. 22.

SCHMITT (E.) Hochschulen, Universitäten und
technische Hochschulen. pp. 66. 1894. 8°.
DURM (J.) Handbuch der Architektur. Nr. 4.
7815. bb. 12.

EDUCATION.—Germany.—*continued.*

STILLBAUER (J.) Das Volksschulwesen in Deutschland. pp. 32. 1891. 8°. Frankfurter zeitgemässe Broschüren. N. F. Bd. 12.
                                    12209. g.
TREITSCHKE (H. v.) Die Zukunft des deutschen Gymnasiums. pp. 81. *Leipz.* 1890. 8°.
                                    8310. c. 47.
WALTER (H.) Bildung, nicht Gelehrsamkeit! pp. 64. *Gotha,* 1890. 8°.   8304. e. 19. (12.)
See also supra: Alsace-Lorraine: infra: University.

Elementary.

CLAUSNITZER (L.) Zeiten der Reaktion für die preussische Volksschule. pp. 72.
Spandau, 1881. 8°.   8357. d. 4. (2.)
FISCHER (C.) Geschichte des deutschen Volksschullehrerstandes. 2 Bde.
Hannover, 1892. 8°.   8357. e. 50.
FLUEGEL (G.) Gesetze über die Volksschulen in Preussen. pp. 710.
Saarlouis, 1894. 8°.   05604. g. 8.
GNEIST (H. R. v.) Die staatsrechtlichen Fragen des preussischen Volksschulgesetzes. pp. 122.
Berl. 1892. 8°.   8310. d. 7.
MUELLER (C.) Die preussischen Kultusminister und das Volksschulwesen. pp. 89.
Bernburg, 1884. 8°.   8357. d. 4. (1.)
POGGE ( ) Die neueren Gesetze auf dem Gebiete des preussischen Volksschulwesens. pp. 250. *Berl.* 1893. 8°.   05604. i. 16.
PRUSSIA. Die Volksschule in Ostpreussen. pp. 431. *Königsberg,* 1892. 8°. 05604. g. 2.
RICHTER (A.) Kursächsische Volksschulordnungen. 1891. 8°. Neudrucke pädagogischer Schriften. No. 4.   8308. aaa.
SCHROEER (H.) Die Volksschule als Grundbedingung zur endgiltigen Lösung der Schulreform-Frage. pp. 54. *Erfurt,* 1891. 8°.
                                    8304. b. 21. (5.)
SCHWALB (M.) Das preussische Volksschulgesetz. Vortrag, *etc.* Bremen, 1892. 8°.
                                    8304. bb. 6. (6.)
TREITSCHKE (H. v.) Der Entwurf des preussischen Volksschulgesetzes. pp. 32.
Stuttgart, 1892. 8°.   8304 bb. 6. (7.)

Female. See supra: Pt. I. Female.

Manual. See supra: Pt. I. Manual.

Religious.

BOETTGER (H.) Christenthum und Atheismus? Geschichte der preussischen Volksschulgesetzgebung. pp. 47. *Hildesheim,* 1892. 8°.
                                    8304. bb. 7. (9.)
H., *Dr.* Der katholische Standpunkt in Bezug auf den Entwurf des Volksschulgesetzes. pp. 45. *Köhr,* 1892. 8°.   8304. aa. 17. (8.)
JODL (F.) Moral, Religion und Schule. pp. 36. *Stuttgart,* 1892. 8°.   Pam. 17.
PINKAVA (F.) Bildung des Willensvermögens in der Volksschule. pp. 156. *Olmütz,* 1894. 8°.
                                    8311. c. 17.
POETSCH (J.) Religion oder Litteratur als Centrum des Volksschulunterrichts? 1892. 8°. Frankfurter zeitgemässe Broschüren. N. F. Bd. 13. Hft. 5.   12209. g.
PRUSSIA. *Volksschulen.* Der Religionsunterricht in der Volksschule. pp. 24. *Strassb.* 1892. 8°.
                                    Pam. 17.
WEBER ( ) Für die Konfessionschule. 1894. 8°. Sammlung theologischer und sozialer Reden. Ser. 5. Lief. 6–9.   4224. ff. 25.
WURTEMBERG. Statistisches Handbuch über die kath. Volksschulen Württembergs. pp. 509.
Horb, 1893. 8°.   8357. f. 27.

EDUCATION.—Germany—*continued.*

Technical. See supra: Pt. I. Technical.

University.

ALTMANN (W.) Die Doktordissertationen der deutschen Universitäten, 1885–90. pp. 64.
Berl. 1891. 8°.   8304. e. 22. (11.)
DIPPE (A.) Sozialismus und Philosophie auf den deutschen Universitäten. pp. 38.
Leipz. 1895. 8°.   Pam. 82.
FOCK (G.) Catalogus Dissertationum philologicarum classicarum. 3 pt. *Leipz.* 1893. 8°.
                                    011900. ee. 31.
CHRIST (W. v.) Reform des Universitätsunterrichtes. pp. 28. *München,* 1891. 4°. Pam. 17.
FABRICIUS (W.) Die Studentenorden des 18. Jahrhunderts. pp. 102. *Jena,* 1891. 8°.
                                    8357. h. 32.
HOFFMANN (M.) Grundsätze für die Habilitation. als Privatdozent bei den philosophischen Fakultäten der Universitäten. pp. 39.
Leipz. 1890. 8°.   8304. e. 19. (10.)
KAEHLER (M.) Die Universitäten und das öffentliche Leben. pp. 129. *Erlangen,* 1891. 8°.
                                    8357. e. 46.
KALB (W.) Die alte Burschenschaft. pp. 160. *Erlangen,* 1892. 8°.   8357. e. 51.
KAPPES (M.) Die philosophische Bildung unserer gelehrten Berufe. pp. 41. *Münster,* 1892. 8°.
                                    8468. k. 28. (3.)
LAUFBAHN. Die akademische Laufbahn und ihre ökonomische Regelung. pp. 184.
Berl. 1895. 8°.   8357. cc. 52.
LEXIS (W.) Die deutschen Universitäten. 2 Bde. *Berl.* 1893. 4°.   8357. i. 1.
PAULSEN (F.) The German Universities. pp. 254. *N.Y.* 1895. 8°.   8357. bb. 37.
PETERSDORFF (H. v.) Die Vereine deutscher Studenten. pp. 301. *Leipz.* 1895. 8°.
                                    8357. e. 55.
REINKE (J.) Die preussischen Universitäten. pp. 23. *Kiel,* 1891. 8°.   8305. ff. 6. (15.)
SCHMIDT (L.) Der philologische Universitätslehrer. pp. 30. *Marburg,* 1892. 8°. Pam. 17.
SCHMITT (E) Hochschulen und Universitäten. pp. 66. 1894. 8°. DARM (J.) Handbuch der Architektur   7815. bb. 12.
STEIN (F.) Die akademische Gerichtsbarkeit in Deutschland. pp. 151. *Leipz.* 1891. 8°.
                                    05604. h. 12.
ZIEGLER (T.) Der deutsche Student am Ende des 19. Jahrhunderts. pp. 240.
Stuttgart, 1895. 8°.   8357. aa. 20.
See also supra: Pt. I. University, and under the name of each German University.

Greece. See supra: Pt. I. History.

Iceland. See supra: Pt. II. Denmark.

India and Ceylon.

THOMAS (F. W.) History and prospects of British Education in India. pp. 158. *Camb.* 1891. 8°.
                                    8365. de. 23.
JAYARĀMA RĀU. Christianity and Education in India. pp. 31. *Madras,* 1888. 8°. Pam. 40.
P.P *Lahore.* "The Student's Guide": a monthly journal for Entrance Students at the Universities. *Lahore,* 1891, *etc.* 8°.
                                    P.P. 1219. laa.
MADRAS DIRECTORY. Madras Directory of Public Instruction. *Madras,* 1893, *etc.* 8°.   8366. f.
MAHESACHANDRA NYĀYARATNA. Report on the Tols of Bengal, Bihár and Orissa. pp. 31.
Calcutta, 1892. fol.   7705. g. 40.

EDUCATION.—India—continued.

P.P. *Madras.* Journal of Education.
Madras, 1891, etc. 8°.   P.P. 1219. lc.

CEYLON. *Schools.* Ceylon Schools. Government
and grant-in-aid. pp. 54. *Colombo,* 1893. 8°.
                                   8304. aa. 19. (7.)

See also supra : Pt. I. Female.

Ireland.

HOUSTON (T. G.) School and home. pp. 133.
Belfast, 1895. 8°.   8309 de. 32.

HUMPHREYS (D.) Evidence submitted to the
Commissioners of the Educational Endowments,
Ireland Act. pp. 71. *Dublin,* 1889. 8°.
                                   8309. de. 28.

CLARKE (R. F.) University Education in Ireland.
pp. 70. *Lond.* 1890. 8°.   8354. de. 39.

See also supra : Pt. II. England.

Italy.

ALLIEVO (G.) Lo Stato educatore ed il ministro
Boselli. pp. 47. *Torino,* 1889. 8°.
                                   8305. ff. 6. (4.)

BERTINI (G. M.) Per la Riforma delle Scuole
medie. pp. 223. *Torino,* 1889. 8°. 8355. b. 51.

BÈRTOLI (A.) Voci al deserto. pp. 288.
Palermo, 1890. 8°.   8308. bb. 49.

CARBONE (A.) La libertà e la Scuola, *etc.*
pp. 39. *Vallo della L.* 1890. 8°. 8305. ff. 7. (5.)

DEJOB (C.) L'Instruction publique en France
et en Italie au 19ᵐᵉ siècle. pp. 455.
Paris, 1894. 12°.   8356. b. 61.

GABELLI (A.) L' Istruzione in Italia.
Bologna, 1891, etc. 8°.   8356. aa. 18.

HORNEMANN (F.) Einheitschulbestrebungen in
Italien. 1890. 8°. GERMANY. *Deutscher Ein-
heitsschulverein.* Schriften. Hft. 6. 8357. cc.

MARTINI (F.) Ordinamento degli Istituti d' istruzione superiore. pp. 233. *Milano,* 1895. 8°.
                                   8311. d. 2.

MIRAGLIA (B.) Le Pédagogiste italiane. pp. 95.
Firenze, 1894. 8°.   8310. bbb. 5.

PAGLIUCA (C.) Fra Scuola e maestri. pp. 138.
Caserta, 1894. 16°.   8311. aaa. 19.

POLIDORI (E.) Il Cristianesimo escluso dall' Insegnamento in Italia. pp. 30.
Bologna, 1891. 32°.   Pam. 17.

ROMANO (S.) La Scuola primaria e popolare in
relazione ai bisogni della vita presente. pp. 15.
Palermo, 1884. 8°.   8304. e. 23. (3.)

TURIELLO (P.) Saggio sull' Educazione nazionale
in Italia. pp. 170. *Napoli,* 1891. 8°.
                                   8355. de. 5.

ZUPPELLI (V.) La Scuola del popolo. pp. 215.
Città di C. 1891. 8°.   8310. c. 45.

See also supra : Pt. I. Infants : University.

Japan.

AC. Yedo. *Educational Society.* Account of
the Educational Society. pp. 19.
Tokyo, 1890. 8°.   8304. aa. 16. (5.)

JAPAN. *Department of Education.* Instruction
of the Department of Education.
Tokyo, 1886, etc. 8°.   11099. b. 15.

—— Notification No. 3 of the Department of
Education. *Tokyo,* 1886. 8°.   11099. b. 18.

—— History of the Department of Education.
pp. 52. *Tokyo,* 1887. 8°.   11099. b. 19.

—— Collection of Imperial Ordinances issued by
the Department. *Tokyo,* 1887. etc. 8°.
                                   11099. b. 14.

—— Cabinet Ordinance relating to the titles,
and treatment of Public School Officials.
Tokyo, 1887. 8°.   11099. b. 22.

EDUCATION.—Japan—continued.

JAPAN. *Department of Education.* Ordinances
of the Department of Education.
Tokyo, 1887, etc. 8°.   11099. b. 17.

—— Descriptive outlines of the Schools in Japan.
pp. 31. *Tokyo,* 1887. 8°.   11099. b. 20.

—— Imperial Ordinance relating to Elementary
Schools. pp. 41. *Tokyo,* 1891. 8°. 11099. b. 26.

—— General regulations relating to local education. pp. 6. 1891. 8°.   11099. b. 27.

—— Annual report of the Minister for Education. *Tokyo,* 1892, etc. 8°.   11098. c. 5.

—— Outlines of modern Education in Japan.
pp. 218. *Tokyo,* 1893. 8°.   8355. df. 19.

Jews.

WIESEN (J.) Geschichte des Schulwesens im
Talmudischen Altertume. pp. 49.
Strassb. 1892. 8°.   Pam. 17.

SIMON (J.) L'Éducation chez les Juifs au moyen
âge. pp. 16. *Nîmes,* 1893. 8°.
                                   4516. f. 9. (10.)

SIENNA, *Università Israelitica.* Statuto e regolamento. pp. 26. *Siena,* 1890. 8°. Pam. 17.

Netherlands.

GON (W. H. D. v. d.) Staats of Gemeente-
School ? pp. 54. *Arnhem,* 1892. 8°.
                                   8304. bb. 6. (3.)

GOUKA (M.) De Kweekschool. pp. 335.
Rotterdam, 1894. 8°.   8311. cc. 9.

HUSEN (R.) Opvoed- en onderwijskunde ten be-
hoeve van Kweekscholen. pp. 182.
Gorinchem, 1890. 8°.   8357. b. 55.

SCHAEPMAN (H. J. A. M.) De wet op het lager
Onderwijs. pp. 134. *Utrecht,* 1890. 8°.
                                   5686. a. 26.

UIJTENVIERE. Weinig Geacht, toch Groot van
Kracht. *Amsterd.* 1893, etc. 8°. 8311. c.

Norway, See infra : Sweden.

Prussia. See supra : Germany.

Rome. See supra : Pt. I. History.

Roumania.

MICHAILESCŬ (S. C.) Incercări critice asupra
Invčţămêntului nostru primaru. pp. 267.
Bucuresci, 1888. 8°.   8357. f. 7.

NICOLESCŬ (I.) Scoala moderna şi principiul
naţional. pp. 113. *Bucuresci,* 1887. 8°.
                                        Pam. 17

Russia.

KOKHOVSKY (W. de) Saint-Pétersbourg. Bases
caractéristiques de l'organisation et de l'activité
du Musée pédagogique. pp. 22.
St. Pétersbourg, 1889. 8°.   8304. e. 23. (5.)

TOLSTOI (L. N.) *Count.* Le Progrès et l'Instruction publique en Russie. pp. 315.
Paris, 1890. 18°.   8357. b. 53.

See also supra : Pt. I. Female.

Scotland.

EDGAR (J.) History of early Scottish Education. pp. 333. *Edinb.* 1893. 8°. 8364. f. 21.

P.P. *Aberdeen.* Scottish Educational Year-book.
Aberdeen, 1895, etc. 12°.   P.P. 2510. vb.

SCOTLAND. *Education Department.* Secondary
Education. Circulars. Papers set at Examinations, *etc.* pp. 59. *Lond.* 1891. 8°. Pam. 17.

—— Secondary Education. Report, 1892, on the
inspection of Higher Class Schools. pp. 8.
Lond. 1891. 8°.   Pam. 17.

WENLEY (R. M.) University Extension movement in Scotland. pp. 54. *Glasg.* 1895. 8°.
                                        Pam. 17.

See also supra : England.

EDUCATION—*continued.*

Spain.

RIBERA (J.) La Enseñanza entre los Musulmanes españoles. pp. 99. *Zaragoza*, 1893. 8°.
  8357. i. 3.

SISAY AILLAUD (E.) Consideraciones generales sobre la Instrucción pública. pp. 60. *Madrid*, 1888. 8°. Pam. 1.

GUTIERREZ Y DIEZ (A.) Conveniencia de la Enseñanza religiosa. pp. 204. *Santander*, 1889. 8°.
  3900. bb. 35.

See also supra: Pt. I. Female.

Sweden and Norway.

FASTING (G.) Vor religiøse Opdragelse. pp. 104. *Bergen*, 1892. 8°. 4373. aa. 5.

HEALEY (E.) Educational Systems of Sweden and Norway. pp. 36. *Lond.* 1892. 8°.
  8304. e. 23. (12.)

SVENSON (A.) Skolan och folkupplysningen. pp. 35. *Stockholm*, 1892. 8°. Pam. 17.

SWEDEN. *Komitén för utredning angående studieväsendet inom de filosofiska fakulteterna vid Universiteten.* Underdåniga förslag afgifna af den Komité. pp. 247. *Stockholm*, 1889. 8°.
  8463. e. 29.

WESTLING (G.) Metodik för undervisningen inom Folkskolan. pp. 94. *Linköping*, 1893. 8°.
  8311. cc. 7.

BEER (J.) Om undervisningen i naturkundskab i Folkeskolen. pp. 72. *Kristiania*, 1890. 8°.
  8304. ee. 22. (7.)

HERTZBERG (N.) Pædagogikens Historie samt den norske Skoles udvikling. pp. 156. *Kristiania*, 1890. 8°. 8357. bb. 32.

NICOLAISEN (J.) Om Modersmaalsundervisningen i Folkeskolen. pp. 184. *Kristiania*, 1889. 8°. 8357. e. 44.

ODHNER (H.) Den nordiska Folkhögskolan. pp. 143. *Linköping*, 1891. 8°. 8357. bb. 33.

P.P. *Christiania.* Universitets- og skole-Annaler. *Kristiania*, 1886, *etc.* 8°. P.P. 1165. aa.

See also supra: Pt. I., Ecclesiastical: Female: Manual.

Switzerland.

FINSLER (G.) Die Lehrpläne und Maturitätsprüfungen der Gymnasien der Schweiz. pp. 390. *Bern*, 1893. 8°. 8357. e. 52.

GEISER (C.) Die Bestrebungen zur Gründung einer eidgenössischen Hochschule. pp. 198. *Bern*, 1890. 8°. 8357. f. 1.

HESS (J. W.) Geschichte des Schulwesens der Landschaft Basel. 1894. 8°. Ac. Basle. *Historische Gesellschaft.* N. F. Bd. 4. Ac. 6924.

SPENGLER (C.) L'Avenir de nos enfants. pp 116. *Lausanne*, 1890. 8°. 8306. de. 19. (8.)
See also supra: Pt. I. Female.

United States of America.

ADAMS (H. B.) Contributions to American Educational History. 1887, *etc.* 8°. U.S. *Bureau of Education.* Circular of Information.
  8308. i.

BALCH (G. T.) Methods of teaching patriotism in Public Schools. pp. 109. *N.Y.* 1890. 8°.
  8365. d. 39.

HARCOURT (R.) The great Conspiracy against our American Public Schools. pp. 325. *San Francisco*, 1890. 8°. 4182. bbb. 41.

HART (A. B.) Studies in American Education. pp. 150. *N.Y.* 1895. 8°. 8311. aaa. 13.

JAY (J.) Moral Education in the Public Schools. pp. 7. *Katonah*, 1891. 8°. 8304. e. 24. (4.)

KINNEY (A.) Tasks by twilight. pp. 211. *N.Y.* 1893. 8°. 12354. de. 1.

EDUCATION.—United States—*cont.*

PAGE (M. H.) Graded Schools in the U.S. pp. 71. *Lond.* 1894. 8°. 8311. aaa. 8.

RICE (J. M.) The Public-School system of the U.S. pp. 308. *N.Y.* 1893. 8°. 8366. aa. 23.

U.S. *Bureau of Education.* Report on secondary School Studies. pp. 249. *Wash.* 1895. 8°.
  8308. i.

ZIMMERN (A.) Methods of Education in the U.S. pp. 178. *Lond.* 1894. 8°. 8311. aaa. 9.

CLARK (W. G.) History of Education in Alabama, 1702–1889. pp. 281. 1889. 8°. U.S. *Bureau of Education.* Circular, 1889. 8308. i.

U.S. *Bureau of Education.* Report on Education in Alaska. pp. 88. *Wash.* 1886. 8°.
  8366. de. 31.

WOODBURN (J. A.) Higher Education in Indiana. pp. 200. 1891. 8°. U.S. *Bureau of Education.* Circular, 1891. 8308. i.

Ac. Topeka. *Kansas Historical Society.* History of Education in Kansas. pp. 231. *Topeka*, 1893. 8°. Ac. 8531/2.

MARTIN (G. H.) Evolution of the Massachusetts Public School system. pp. 284. *N.Y.* 1894. 8°.
  8311. aa. 37.

NEW JERSEY. *Council of Education.* Report of the Standing Committee on pedagogics. pp. 18. *Jersey City*, 1889. 8°. 8304. bb. 7. (3.)

SMITH (E.) History of the schools of Syracuse. pp. 347. *Syracuse*, 1893. 8°. 8365. dd. 16.

AMERICAN UNIVERSITIES. Four American Universities. pp. 202. *N.Y.* 1895. 4°. 8364. i. 9.

BLACKMAR (F. W.) History of Federal and State Aid to higher Education. pp. 343. 1890. 8°. U.S. *Bureau of Education.* Circular, 1890.
  8308. i.

COUBERTIN (P. de) Universités transatlantiques. pp. 379. *Paris*, 1890. 8°. 8367. aa. 14.

STEINER (B. C.) History of University Education in Maryland. pp. 37. 1891. 8°. Johns Hopkins University Studies. Ser. 9. No. 3–4. Ac. 2689.

TOLMAN (W. H.) History of higher Education in Rhode Island. pp. 210. 1894. 8°. 8366. bb. 43.

WHARTON (J.) Is a College education advantageous to a business man? pp. 36. *Phila.* 1890. 8°. Pam. 17.
See also supra: Pt. I. Female: Infants: Manual: School Management: Profession of: University.

Uruguay. See supra: America, South.

Victoria. See supra: Australasia.

Wales.

BEVAN (J. O.) The Welsh Act and the English Bill. pp. 16. *Lond.* 1894. 8°. Pam. 17.

ROBERTS (W. R.) British Universities: notes and summaries contributed to the Welsh University discussion. pp. 89. *Manch.* 1892. 8°.
  8365. bbb. 66. (7.)

WALES. *Joint Education Committees.* Welsh Intermediate Act, 1889. General Conference of the Committees. *Wrexham*, 1890. 8°. 8311. c.
See also supra: Pt. I. Female.

Wurtemburg. See supra: Germany.

EDZELL. EDWARDS (D. H.) Historical Guide to Edzell. pp. 135. *Brechin*, 1893. 8°.
  10369. aaa. 49.

EGER, *Bohemia.* GRADL (H.) Geschichte des Egerlandes, bis 1437. pp. 433. *Prag*, 1893. 8°.
  10210. ff. 1.

EGYPT. [*See note on page 1.*]

Antiquities.

Ac. Cairo. *Musée Égyptien.* Recueil de Monuments et de notices sur les fouilles en Égypte. *Le Caire*, 1890, *etc.* fol. 598.

—— London. *Burlington Fine Arts Club.* Exhibition of the Art of ancient Egypt. pp. 129. *Lond.* 1895. 4°. Ac. 4644/37.

—— *S. K. Museum.* Supplemental Catalogue of Tapestry-woven and embroidered Egyptian textiles. pp. 57. *Lond.* 1891. 8°. 7958. d. 9.

BERLIN. *K. Museen.* Verzeichniss der aegyptischen Altertümer, Gipsabüsse und Papyrus. pp. 398. *Berl.* 1894. 8°. 7705. a. 34.

—— Aegyptische und vorderasiatische Alterthümer. *Berl.* 1895. fol. K.T.C. 25. a. 1.

—— Aegyptische Urkunden aus den koeniglichen Museen zu Berlin. *Berl.* 1892, *etc.* 4°. 7703. h.

BLACKDEN (M. W.) Collection of hieratic graffite from the Alabaster Quarry of Hat-Nub. ff. 15. 1892. *obl.* fol. 1702. a. 8.

BRIMMER (M.) Egypt. Essays on ancient Egypt. pp. 86. *Lond.* 1892. 8°. K.T.C. 11. b. 4.

BRUGSCH (É.) La tente funéraire de la Princesse Isimkheb. pp. 8. *Le Caire*, 1889. fol. 7702. k. 18.

BRUGSCH (H.) Die Aegyptologie. pp. 535. *Leipz.* 1891. 8°. 7702. f. 42.

BUDGE (E. A. T. W.) The Mummy. pp. 404. *Camb.* 1893. 8°. 2258. d. 13.

—— Prefatory remarks on Egyptian Mummies. pp. 26. *Lond.* 1890. 8°. 7706. g. 4. (19.)

—— The Nile. Notes for travellers. pp. 374. *Lond.* 1892. 8°. 2259. b. 14.

—— Catalogue of the Egyptian Collection in the Fitzwilliam Museum. pp. 138. *Camb.* 1893. 8°. 7702. bb. 46.

—— Account of the collection of Egyptian Antiquities, in the possession of Lady Meux. pp. 119. *Lond.* 1893. 4°. 7704. k. 9.

—— On Egyptian Bronze Weapons in the collection of Sir J. Evans and the British Museum. pp. 12. *Westminster*, 1892. 4°. 7705. f. 37.

EDWARDS (A. B.) Pharaohs, Fellahs and Explorers. pp. 325. *Lond.* 1891. 8°. 7704. cc. 29.

GRIFFITH (F. L.) and PETRIE (W. M. F.) Two Hierog. Papyri from Tanis. pp. 25. 1889. 4°. Egyptian Exploration Fund. Extra Memoir. 7703. h.

NAVILLE (E.) Mound of the Jew. Antiquities of Tell-el-Yahudiyeh. pp. 76. 1890. 4°. Egyptian Exploration Fund. Memoir 7. 7703. h.

EGYPT. *Exploration Fund.* Season's work at Ahnas and Beni Hasan, 1890-91. pp. 22. *Lond.* 1891. 4°. 7703. g. 29.

NAVILLE (E.) Festival Hall of Bubastis. pp. 40. 1892. 4°. Egyptian Exploration Fund. Memoir 10. 7703. h.

EGYPT. *Exploration Fund.* Archæological Report, comprising the recent work of the Fund. *Lond.* 1893, *etc.* 4°. 7702. dd.

NAVILLE (E.) Ahnas el Medineh, Heracleopolis, Tomb of Paheri. pp. 40. 1894. 4°. Egyptian Exploration Fund. Memoir 11. 7703. h.

—— Temple of Deir el Bahari. pp. 32. Egyptian Exploration Fund. Memoir 12. 7703. h.

EGYPT. *Exploration Fund.* Wall Drawings and Monuments of El Kab. By J. J. Tylor. pp. 23. *Lond.* 1895. fol. 1700. d. 4.

—— Archaeological Survey of Egypt. *Lond.* 1893, *etc.* 4°. 7703. g.

NEWBERRY (P. E.) and FRASER (G. W.) El Bersheh. 1893, *etc.* 4°. Archaeol. Survey of Egypt. 7703. g.

—— Beni Hasan. 2 pt. 1893-94. 4°. Archaeol. Survey of Egypt. 7703. g.

EGYPT. *Service des Antiquités.* Catalogue des Monuments et Inscriptions de l'Égypte. *Vienne*, 1894, *etc.* fol. 7701. h.

—— Note on excavations executed by the Department, 1893. pp. 16. *Cairo*, 1893. 8°. Pam. 3.

VIREY (E.) Service des antiquités. Notice des principaux monuments exposés au Musée de Gizeh. pp. 341. *Le Caire*, 1892. 8°. 7704. a. 44.

ERMAN (A.) Life in ancient Egypt. pp. 570. *Lond.* 1894. 8°. 7704. d. 13.

FINLAYSON (J.) Ancient Egyptian Medicine. pp. 55. *Glasg.* 1893. 8°. 7306. e. 22. (6.)

FORRER (R.) Die Graeber- und Textilfunde von Achmim-Panopolis. pp. 27. *Strassb.* 1891. 4°. 7705. h. 22.

—— Die frühchristlichen Alterthümer aus dem Gräberfelde von Achmin-Panopolis. pp. 29. *Strassb.* 1893. 4°. 7709. k. 24.

—— Mein Besuch in El-Achmin. pp. 104. *Strassb.* 1895. 8°. 10096. cc. 14.

GAYET (A.) Le Temple de Louxor. 1894, *etc.* fol. FRANCE. *M. l'Instruction.* Mémoires par les membres de la mission archéologique française. Tom. 15. 7703. k.

JOHNSON (V. E.) Egyptian Science from the monuments and ancient books. pp. 198. *Lond.* 1892. 8°. 7702. aa. 42.

LEFÉBURE (E.) Rites égyptiens. Construction et protection des édifices. pp. 104. 1890. 8°.

Ac. Algiers. *École supérieure des Lettres d'Alger.* Publications, *etc.* No. 4. Ac. 5350/2.

LUMBROSO (G.) Progressi della Egittologia greco-romana. pp. 32. *Roma*, 1893. 4°. Pam. 6.

MASPERO (G.) Catalogue du Musée Égyptien de Marseille. pp. 208. *Paris*, 1889. 8°. 7704. cc. 28.

—— Life in ancient Egypt. pp. 376. *Lond.* 1892. 8°. 7702. a. 39.

—— Bibliothèque égyptologique, comprenant les œuvres des Égyptologues français dispersées dans divers recueils. *Paris*, 1893, *etc.* 8°. 7702. dd.

—— The Dawn of Civilization. pp. 800. *Lond.* 1894. 8°. 4430. dd. 1.

MOLDENKE (C. E.) The New York Obelisk. pp. 202. *N.Y.* 1891. 8°. 7704. aaa. 53.

JULIEN (A. A.) Notes of research on the New York Obelisk. 2 pt. 1893. 8°. 7702. e. 39.

MONACO (A.) Orientalia. pp. 189. *Roma*, 1891. 8°. 4506. bb. 30.

MORGAN (J. de) Le Trésor de Dahchour. pp. 11. *Cairo*, 1894. 8°. Pam. 3.

—— Fouilles à Dahchour. pp. 165. *Vienne*, 1895. 4°. 7701. h. 7.

MUELLER (W. M.) Asien und Europa nach altägyptischen Denkmälern. pp. 403. *Leipz.* 1893. 8°. 7704. cc. 32.

MYER (I.) Scarabs. History, manufacture and religious symbolism. pp. 177. *Lond.* 1894. 8°. 7704. aa. 40.

PETRIE (W. M. F.) Egyptian Decorative Art. pp. 128. *Lond.* 1895. 8°. 7704. aa. 45.

—— Ten Years' digging in Egypt, 1881-91, *etc.* pp. 201. *Lond.* 1892. 8°. 7702. aaa. 40.

—— Illahun, Kahun and Gurob. pp. 59. *Lond.* 1891. 4°. 7705. h. 21.

EGYPT.—Antiquities—_continued._

PETRIE (W. M. F.) Medum. pp. 52.
  Lond. 1892. 4°.   7702. k. 19.
—— Tell El Amarna. pp. 46. _Lond._ 1894. 4°.
         7702. k. 21.
—— Catalogue of antiquities from Tel el Amarna.
  pp. 19. _Lond._ 1893. 8°.   Pam. 3.
RYAN (C.) Egyptian Art : elementary handbook.
  pp. 115. _Lond._ 1894. 8°.   7704. aa. 38.
SCHACK-SCHACKENBURG (H.) Aegyptologische
  Studien. _Leipz._ 1893, etc. 4°.   7702. i.
THUDE (L.) Führer durch das Museum von
  Gizeh. pp. 164. _Kairo_, 1891. 8°. 7704. aa. 34.
  See also infra : History : Pyramids : ART, _An-_
  cient ; EGYPTIAN LANGUAGE.

Antiquities relating to Biblical History, etc.

BOYD (T. H.) A Crisis in Egypt. What hap-
  pened on the day of the Exodus. pp. 36.
  Dublin, 1893. 8°.   Pam. 5.
BUXTON (C. M.) Side lights upon Bible History.
  pp. 299. _Lond._ 1892. 8°.   3149. d. 6.
EIK (G. D. K.) De Schrittuur bewezen uit de
  huidige Archæologie van Egypte en Palæstina.
  pp. 401. _Alkmaar_, 1891. 8°.   3149. dd. 5.
FRASER (A. T.) Darkness and light in the Land
  of Egypt. pp. 55. _Lond._ 1891. 8°.
         8716. bbb. 46.
KINNS (S.) Graven in the Rock ; accuracy of the
  Bible confirmed, by reference to Egyptian monu-
  ments. 2 vol. _Lond._ 1895. 8°.   3125. dd. 8.
KITCHIN (J. G.) Bible Student in the British
  Museum. pp. 88. _Lond._ 1892. 8°. 7702. aa. 43.
LANDRIEUX (M.) Aux Pays du Christ. Études
  bibliques en Égypte, _etc._ pp. 645.
  Paris, 1895. 8°.   10077. l. 17.
NETELER (B.) Die Zeitstellung des israelitischen
  Auszugs in der ägyptischen Geschichte. pp. 16.
  Münster, 1895. 8°.   Pam. 3.
ROUGIER OLANIER (F.) Biblia y Egiptología.
  pp. 94. _Barcelona_, 1893. 8°. 3105. de. 1. (7.)
SAYCE (A. H.) The "Higher Criticism" and the
  verdict of the Monuments. pp. 575.
  Lond. 1894. 8°.   4429. d. 2.
WILLIAMSON (A.) Light from Eastern Lands on
  Abraham, Joseph and Moses. pp. 242.
  Edinb. 1892. 8°.   3155. de. 24.
WRIGHT (G. H. B.) Was Israel ever in Egypt ?
  pp. 382. _Lond._ 1895. 8°.   4516. c. 23.

History.
General and Ancient.

AMÉLINEAU (E.) Résumé de l'histoire de l'Égypte.
  pp. 323. 1894. 4°. Annales du Musée Guimet.
         7704. e.
PETRIE (W. M. F.) History of Egypt.
  Lond. 1894, etc. 8°.   2378. b.
P.P. _Cairo._ Revue d'Égypte.
  Le Caire, 1894, etc. 8°.   P.P. 3807. c.
BRIMMER (M.) Egypt. Essays. pp. 86.
  Lond. 1892. 8°.   K.T.C. 11. b. 4.
BRUGSCH (H.) Egypt under the Pharaohs.
  pp. 469. _Lond._ 1891. 8°.   7704. cc. 30.
MACDONALD (M.) Harmony of ancient History
  of the Egyptians and Jews. pp. 301.
  Phila. 1891. 12°.   9009. cc. 4.
MARIETTE (F. A. F.) Outlines of ancient Egyptian
  History. pp. 155. _Lond._ 1892. 8°. 9061. c. 7.
MASPERO (G.) Historie ancienne des peuples de
  l'Orient. pp. 811. _Paris_, 1893. 8°. 9055. bb. 34.
—— The Dawn of Civilization. pp. 800.
  Lond. 1894. 8°.
         4430. dd. 1.

EGYPT.—History—_continued._

MASPERO (G.) Histoire de l'Orient. pp. 240.
  Paris, 1891. 8°.   9055. aa. 10.
SAYCE (A. H.) Egypt of the Hebrews and
  Herodotos. pp. 342. _Lond._ 1895. 8°.
         9061. aa. 1.
WIEDEMANN (A.) Geschichte von Alt-Ägypten.
  pp. 319. 1891. 8°. Reiche der Alten Welt.
  Bd. 1.   9008. aaa. 5.
GAMBARDELLA (S.) L'Egitto e l'Etiopia. pp. 40.
  Napoli, 1890. 8°.   9004. m. 6. (8.)
SPIEGELBERG (W.) Studien zum Rechtwesen des
  Pharaonenreiches de Dynast. XVIII.-XXI. pp. 132.
  Hannover, 1892. 4°.   7702. g. 44.
Ac. London. _British Museum._ Tell el-Amarna
  Tablets in the British Museum. Introduction
  by C. Bezold and E. A. T. W. Budge. pp. 157.
  Lond. 1892. 4°.   7703. aa. 30.
BEZOLD (C.) Oriental Diplomacy : the trans-
  literated text of the Cuneiform Despatches dis-
  covered at Tell el-Amarna. pp. 124.
  Lond. 1893. 8°.   7704. aaa. 54.
PALESTINE. _Palestine Exploration Fund._ Tell
  Amarna Tablets. Translated by C. R. Conder.
  pp. 212. _Lond._ 1893. 8°.   2356. b. 5.
SCHEIL (F. V.) Tablettes d'El-Amarna publiées
  par F. V. Scheil. 1893. fol. Mémoires publiés
  par les membres de la Mission archéologique au
  Caire. Tom. 6.   7703. k.
MALLET (D.) Les premiers établissements des
  Grecs en Égypte. pp. 499. 1893. 4°. Mémoires
  publiés par les membres de la mission archéo-
  logique au Caire. Tom. 12.   7703. k.
MAHAFFY (J. P.) Empire of the Ptolemies.
  pp. 533. _Lond._ 1895. 8°.   2382. b. 5.
SIMAIKA ('A. A.) La Province romaine d'Égypte.
  pp. 234. _Paris_, 1892. 8°.   9061. d. 4.
AMÉLINEAU (E.) Géographie de l'Égypte à
  l'époque copte. pp. 630. _Paris_, 1893. 8°.
         10002. h. 14.
ABU ṢĀLIḤ. Churches and Monasteries of Egypt.
  pp. 382. 1895. 4°. Anecdota Oxoniensia. Semitic
  Series. Part VII.   12204. f.
AMÉLINEAU (E.) Histoire des Monastères de la
  Basse-Égypte. pp. 429. 1894. 8°. Annales du
  Musée Guimet. Tom. 25.   7704. h. 21.
  See also supra : Antiquities : COPTIC RACE :
  HISTORY, _Ancient._

Mediæval and Modern.

BROOKS (E. W.) Chronology of the conquest of
  Egypt by the Saracens. _Leipz._ 1895. 8°.
         Pam. 28.
MALUS (É. L.) Souvenirs de l'expédition d'Egypte
  1798–1801. pp. 224. _Paris_, 1892. 8°.
         9061. ccc. 11.
PEYRE (R.) L'Expédition d'Égypte 1798–1800.
  pp. 220. _Paris_, 1890. 8°.   9061. ee. 25.
CHENNELLS (E.) Recollections of an Egyptian
  Princess. 2 vol. _Edinb._ 1893. 8°. 10606. e. 16.
RUSSELL (H.) The Ruin of the Soudan : 1883–
  1891. _Lond._ 1892. 8°.   9061. dd. 4.
CHAILLÉ-LONG (C.) L'Égypte et ses provinces
  perdues. pp. 327. _Paris_, 1892. 12°. 9061. ccc. 12.
—— The Three Prophets : Gordon, El Maahdi,
  Arabi Pasha. pp. 235. _N.Y._ 1884. 12°.
         9061. de. 16.
TABARIÉ (M.) C. G. Gordon, le défenseur de
  Khartoum. pp. 233. _Paris_, 1886. 12°.
         10817. aaa. 49.
WINGATE (F. R.) Mahdiism and the Egyptian
  Soudan. pp. 617. _Lond._ 1891. 8°. 2386. f. 2.
JEPHSON (A. J. M.) Emin Pasha and the re-
  bellion at the Equator. pp. 490. _Lond._ 1890. 8°.
         010096. f. 18.

EGYPT.—History—continued.

GOODRICH (C. F.) Report of the British operations in Egypt. 1882. 2 pt. *Wash.* 1883. 8°.
9061. dd. 8.

OHRWALDER (J.) Ten Years' captivity in the Mahdi's Camp, 1882–92. pp. 471.
Lond. 1893. 8°.   9061. ccc. 15.

BORELLI (O.) Choses politiques d'Égypte 1883–95. pp. 602. *Paris,* 1895. 8°.   8028. ff. 22.

PALAT (B. E.) Campagne des Anglais au Soudan, 1884–85. pp. 130. *Paris,* 1894. 8°. 9061. ccc. 25.

MALE (A.) Scenes through the Battle Smoke. pp. 484. *Lond.* 1891. 8°.   9009. cc. 1.

BORELLI (O.) La chute de Khartoum, 26 jan. 1885. pp. 235. *Paris,* 1893. 8°.   9061. c. 8.

VUGLIANO (C.) Gli ultimi avvenimenti du Sudan. pp. 28. *Frosinone,* 1891. 4°.   Pam. 67.

MILNER (A.) England in Egypt. pp. 448.
Lond. 1894. 8°.   9061. cc. 36.

BÉRARD (E.) Rapport sur l'Égypte. pp. 27.
Lyon, 1892. 4°.   8028. f. 30.

HRON (C.) Ägypten und die ägyptische Frage. pp. 278. *Leipz.* 1895. 8°.   8028. ee. 30.

P.P. *Alexandria.* The Egyptian Gazette.
Alexandria, 1893, *etc.* fol.   P.P. 9101. ab.
See also ARABS : MOHAMMEDANISM.

Law.

BORELLI (O.) La Législation égyptienne annotée.
Brux. 1892, *etc.* 8°.   5310. e.

FĪLĪB JALLĀD. Répertoire de la Législation égyptienne. *Alexandrie,* 1888, *etc.* 4°.
14528. ee. 1.

SIMAIKA ('A. A.) De la compétence des Tribunaux mixtes d'Égypte. pp. 171.
Paris, 1892. 8°.   5319. aaa. 34.

Pyramids.

ADAMS (W. M.) The House of the Hidden Places. pp. 249. *Lond.* 1895. 8°. 7704. a. 49.

FRASER (M. D.) The Pyramids, *etc.* pp. 111.
Glasg. 1894. 8°.   10078. aa. 23.

GORDON (H. F.) The Great Pyramid in, but not of, Egypt. pp. 68. *Lond.* 1890. 8°.   Pam. 3.

JAROLIMEK (A.) Der mathematische Schlüssel zu der Pyramide des Cheops. pp. 7.
Wien, 1890. 4°.   Pam. 3.

LAGRANGE (C.) Sur la concordance entre la chronologie de la Bible et celle de la Grande Pyramide. pp. 226. *Brux.* 1893. 8°. 3155. h. 51.

—— The Great Pyramid a witness to the literal chronology of the Hebrew Bible, and British-Israel identity. pp. 278. *Lond.* 1894. 8°.
07703. e. 1.

LANGLEY (W. C.) Lecture on the Great Pyramid, the probable foundation of Freemasonry, *etc.* pp. 36. *Stockton-on-T.* 1890. 8°.   Pam. 25.

MAYOU (L.) Les secrets des Pyramides de Memphis. pp. 55. *Paris,* 1894. 8°. 07703. g. 1. (19.)

MORGAN (J. de) Le Trésor de Dahchour. pp. 11.
Cairo, 1894. 8°.   07703. i. 2. (19.)

PARSONS (A. R.) New light from the Great Pyramid. pp. 420. *N.Y.* 1893. 8°. 4371. ee. 34.

WARD (J. J.) The hidden Pyramid. pp. 32.
Leeds, 1894. 8°.   7704. a. 47.
See also supra: Antiquities.

Religion, Ancient.

BUDGE (E. A. T. W.) Bibliography of texts and monographs on the Book of the Dead and religion of Egypt. *Lond.* 1895. 4°.   Cat. Desk. B.

AC. London. *British Museum.* The Book of the Dead. Papyrus of Ani. Egyptian text with transliteration and translation by E. A. W. Budge. pp. 377. *Lond.* 1895. 4°. 7701. h. 5.

EGYPT.—Religion, Ancient—continued.

PER-M-HRU. Book of the Dead. Edited, with translation, by C. H. S. Davis. pp. 186.
N.Y. 1894. 8°.   7701. i. 3.

BOSC (E.) Isis dévoilée ou l'Égyptologie sacrée. pp. 304. *Paris,* 1891. 8°.   4503. aaa. 5.

BRIMMER (M.) Egypt. Essays. pp. 86.
Lond. 1892. 8°.   K.T.C. 11. b. 4.

BUDGE (E. A. T. W.) The Mummy. Egyptian funereal archæology. pp. 404. *Camb.* 1893. 8°.
2258. d. 13.

FRADENBURGH (J. W.) Fire from strange Altars. pp. 324. *Cincinnati,* 1891. 8°.   4503. bb. 27.

JÉQUIER (G.) Le Livre de ce qu'il y a dans l'Hadès. pp. 163. 1894. 8°. Ac. Paris.
École des Hautes Études. Bibliothèque. Sciences philologique, *etc.* Fasc. 97.   Ac. 8929.

LANZONE (R. V.) Dizionario di Mitologia egizia. *Torino,* 1881, *etc.* 4°.   4504. h.

LOCKYER (J. N.) The Dawn of Astronomy. Study of the temple-worship of the Egyptians. pp. 432.
Lond. 1894. 8°.   2258. d. 14.

MALLET (D.) Le culte de Neit à Saïs. pp. 252.
Paris, 1888. 8°.   4503. f. 32.

MASPERO (G.) Bibliothèque égyptologique.
Paris, 1893, *etc.* 8°.   7702. dd.

MYER (I.) Scarabs : history and religious symbolism of the Scarabaeus. pp. 177.
Leipz. 1894. 8°.   7704. aa. 40.

RENOUF (*Sir* P. le P.) Priestly character of the earliest Egyptian Civilization. 3 pt.
Lond. 1890. 8°.   7704. e. 17. (27.)

—— The Name of Isis and Osiris, *etc.* 2 pt.
Lond. 1890. 8°.   7704. e. 17. (24.)

REVILLOUT (E.) Rituel funéraire de Pamonth. 3 fasc. *Paris,* 1880–89. 4°.   7703. g. 24.

TIELE (C. P.) Histoire des anciennes religions de l'Égypte et des peuples sémitiques. pp. 510.
Paris, 1882. 8°.   4504. h. 8.

WIEDEMANN (A.) Die Religion der alten Ägypter. pp. 175. 1890. 8°. Darstellungen aus dem Gebiete der nichtchristlichen Religionsgeschichte. Bd. 3.   4506. f.

—— Index der Goetter- und Daemonennamen zu Lepsius, Denkmaeler aus Aegypten. pp. 75.
Leipz. 1892. 8°.   Pam. 44.

See also supra: Antiquities : RELIGION.

Topography.

DUEMICHEN (J.) Zur Geographie des alten Ägypten. pp. 80. *Leipz.* 1894. 4°.   7701. g.

EGYPT. *Exploration Fund.* Atlas of ancient Egypt. *Lond.* 1894. 4°.   7702. h. 20.

ROUGÉ (J. de) Géographie ancienne de la Basse-Égypte. pp. 176. *Paris,* 1891. 8°.
7702. bb. 44.

AMÉLINEAU (E.) La Géographie de l'Égypte à l'époque copte. pp. 630. *Paris,* 1893. 8°.
10002. h. 14.

AḤMAD IBN 'ALI IBN 'ABD AL ḰĀDIR. Description de l'Égypte. 1895, *etc.* fol. Mémoires publiés par les membres de la mission archéologique du Caire. Tom. 17.   7703. k.

ADAMS (F. W. L.) The new Egypt. pp. 297.
Lond. 1893. 8°.   010096. e. 61.

ALIS (H.) Promenade en Égypte. pp. 352.
Paris, 1895. 8°.   010097. e. 3.

BAEDEKER (C.) Egypt. pp. 293.
Leipz. 1895. 8°.   2352. a.

BENTLEY (A. J. M.) and GRIFFINHOOFE (C. G.) Wintering in Egypt. pp. 104. *Lond.* 1895. 8°.
10096. b. 4.

BERNSTEIN-STEGLITZ ( ) Auf der Wanderschaft in Egypten. pp. 240. *Berl.* 1895. 8°. 010097. g. 7.

EGYPT.—Topography—*continued*.

BREWSTER (M. A.) Three months' travels in Egypt. pp. 233. *Lond.* 1894. 8°. 10078. b. 20.

BROOK (*Mrs.* C. J.) Six weeks in Egypt. pp. 238. *Lond.* 1893. 8°. 010096. e. 57.

BUDGE (E. A. T. W.) The Nile. pp. 374. *Lond.* 1892. 8°. 2259. b. 14.

BUXTON (H. M.) On either side of the Red Sea. pp. 163. *Lond.* 1895. 8°. 10076. ee. 11.

C., F. A. Egypt; its highways and byways. pp. 84. *Lond.* 1882. 8°. 010096. e. 26.

CHÉLU (A.) De l'Équateur à la Méditerranée. pp. 507. *Paris*, 1891. 8°. 10096. i. 5.

COOK (T.) Tourists' handbook for Egypt. pp. 355. *Lond.* 1892. 8°. 10095. aaa. 6.

—— Programme of Cook's International tickets to Egypt. pp. 62. *Lond.* 1891-92. 8°. 010096. e. 37.

COOPER (C. A.) Seeking the Sun. An Egyptian holiday. pp. 181. *Edinb.* 1892. 8°. 10096. ee. 5.

COURET (A.) En Terre Promise. pp. 259. *Paris*, 1891. 12°. 10078. aa. 19.

DAVIS (R. H.) The rulers of the Mediterranean. pp. 228. *N.Y.* 1894. 8°. 10025. de. 5.

EBERS (G.) Aegypten. Heliogravuren. *Berl.* 1893. fol. K.T.C. 17. a. 2.

EDWARDS (A. B.) Pharaohs, Fellahs and Explorers. pp. 325. *Lond.* 1891. 8°. 7704. cc. 29.

EGYPT. Murray's Handbook for Egypt. pp. 568. *Lond.* 1895. 8°. 2364. a. 11.

FLOYER (E. A.) Étude sur le Nord-Etbai. pp. 192. *Le Caire*, 1893. 4°. 10095. i. 11.

FRASER (M. D.) The Pyramids, Palestine, Pompeii. pp. 111. *Glasg.* 1894. 8°. 10078. aa. 23.

GAYET (A.) Itinéraire de la Haute Égypte. pp. 290. *Paris*, 1894. 12°. 10097. c. 39.

H., W. H. Carnatic to Canaan. pp. 131. *Madras*, 1891. 12°. 10077. a. 6.

H. (William) Letters from Egypt. pp. 89. *Manch.* 1891. 8°. 010096. e. 31.

HARCOURT (H. d') *Duke.* L'Égypte et les Égyptiens. pp. 305. *Paris*, 1893. 8°. 10095. de. 20.

HARTUNG (B.) Sommertage im Heiligen Lande, *etc.* pp 150. *Leipz.* 1895. 8°. 10078. bb. 1.

JANEWAY (C.) Ten Weeks in Egypt. pp. 158. *Lond.* 1894. 8°. 10078. aaa. 40.

JOÛBERT (J.) En Dahabièh du Caire aux Cataractes. pp. 476. *Paris*, 1894. 8°. 010096. m. 20.

KAYSER (F.) Ägypten einst und jetzt. pp. 237. *Freiburg i. B.* 1884. 8°. 10097. dd. 13.

KING (A.) Dr. Liddon's Tour in Egypt. pp. 213. *Lond.* 1891. 8°. 010096. e. 38.

LAVERRENZ (C.) Zwei Wanderungen durch das nördliche Afrika. pp. 172. *Berl.* 1891. 8°. 010096. f. 23.

LEGRAND (M.) La Vallée du Nil. pp. 253. *Paris*, 1892. 8°. 10095. ee. 16.

MAG DALAH. Un Hiver en Orient. pp. 298. *Paris*, 1892. 8°. 010096. m. 14.

MARIETTE (F. A. F.) Itinéraire de la Haute-Égypte. pp. 237. *Paris*, 1880. 16°. 10095. a. 1.

MARTRIN-DONOS (J. de) Au Pays du Sauveur. Impressions de voyage. pp. 278. *Fontenay-l.-C.* 1893. 8°. 10078. c. 36.

MATTHES (A.) Reisebilder aus dem Morgenlande. pp. 356. *Gutersloh*, 1891. 8°. 10024. ccc. 2.

MONTBARD (G.) En Égypte. pp. 348. *Paris*, 1892. 8°. 10096. i. 14.

EGYPT.—Topography—*continued*.

MONTBARD (G.) The Land of the Sphinx. pp. 341. *Lond.* 1894. 8°. 010096. m. 23.

MONTGOMERY (A. N.) Hints about Egypt. pp. 88. *Lond.* 1882. 8°. 010096. aa. 10.

NEUMANN (T.) Das moderne Ägypten. pp. 352. *Leipz.* 1893. 8°. 010096. m. 19.

PENSA (H.) L'Égypte et le Soudan égyptien. pp. 403. *Paris*, 1895. 8°. 10097. cc. 29.

P.P. *Cairo.* Revue d'Égypte. *Le Caire*, 1894, etc. 8°. P.P. 3807. c.

PETRIE (W. M. F.) Ten Years' Digging in Egypt. pp. 201. *Lond.* 1892. 8°. 7702. aaa. 40.

RAE (W. F.) Egypt To-day. pp. 331. *Lond.* 1892. 8°. 010096. ff. 19.

REVEL (J.) Chez nos Ancêtres. pp. 494. *Paris*, 1888. 18°. 10078. b. 16.

SAINT CLAIR (G.) Buried Cities and Bible countries. pp. 378. *Lond.* 1891. 8°. 10078. c. 29.

SCHARLING (C. H.) Reisestudier fra Ægypten. *Kjøbenh.* 1891, etc. 8°. 10078. cc.

SILVA PRADO (E. da) Viagens. A Sicilia o Egypto. pp. 246. *Paris*, 1886. 8°. 10026. a. 6.

SOURBECK (T.) Egyptische Strassenbilder. pp. 240. *Basel*, 1891. 8°. 10095. de. 14.

STANLEY (H. M.) My early Travels. 2 vol. *Lond.* 1895. 8°. 10027. ee. 4.

STECKNER (H.) Beim Fellah und Khedive. pp. 180. *Halle a. S.*, 1892. 8°. 010096. e. 51.

TESTOIN (É.) L'Égypte, ou le pays des Coptes. pp. 256. *Tours*, 1894. 8°. 010095. i. 9.

THOMAS (G.) En Égypte. pp. 174. *Paris*, 1894. 8°. 010096. cc. 44.

TIRARD (H. M.) and (N.) Sketches from a Nile steamer. pp. 275. *Lond.* 1891. 8°. 010096. c. 32.

TROTIGNON (L.) L'Orient qui s'en va. pp. 380. *Paris*, 1893. 8°. 10078. aaa. 37.

UKHTOMSKY (E. E.) *Prince.* Voyage en Orient de son Altesse le Césarevitch. pp. 392. *Paris*, 1893. 4°. 1789. d. 1.

USSING (J. L.) Nedre-Ægypten. pp. 194. *Kjøbenh.* 1889. 8°. 7704. aaa. 47.

See also NILE: SOUDAN.

Trade and Finance.

EGYPT. Report on the finances of Egypt, 1884. *Cairo*, 1885. 4°. 8223. dh. 3.

—— Rapport sur les opérations monétaires, 1886. pp. 7. *Le Caire*, 1886. 4°. 08229. g. 40.

—— *Direction des douanes.* Rapport du Directeur Général, 1889, *etc. Alexandrie*, 1890, *etc.* 12°. 8226. i.

—— Le commerce extérieur de l'Égypte. Statistique, 1884-89, *etc. Alexandrie*, 1891, *etc.* fol. 8228. l. 8.

KAUFMANN (W.) Egyptian State Debt and its relation to International Law. pp. 308. *Lond.* 1892. 8°. 08227. g. 41.

—— Das internationale Recht der egyptischen Staatsschuld. pp. 189. *Berl.* 1891. 8°. 8228. f. 49.

EGYPTIAN LANGUAGE AND LITE-RATURE.

BUDGE (E. A. T. W.) First steps in Egyptian. pp. 321. *Lond.* 1895. 8°. 2268. d. 19.

ERMAN (A.) Ägyptische Grammatik. pp. 200. 70. 1894. 8°. PETERMANN (J. H.) Porta Linguarum Orientalium. Pars 15. 12904. dc.

—— Egyptian Grammar. pp. 201. 70. *Lond.* 1894. 8°. 012904. cc. 7.

EGYPTIAN LANGUAGE, etc.—cont.

RENOUF (*Sir* P. le P.) Elementary grammar of the Egyptian language. pp. 78. 1890. 4°. Archaic Classics.   2268. e. 26.

ABEL (C.) Offener Brief in Sachen der ägyptisch-indogermanischen Sprachverwandtschaft. pp. 35. *Leipz.* 1891. 8°.   12901. d. 33. (6.)
—— Nachtrag zum offenen Brief. pp. 26. *Leipz.* 1891. 8°.   12901. d. 33. (6.)

BRUGSCH (H.) Die Aegyptologie. pp. 535. *Leipz.* 1891. 8°.   7702. f. 42.

EBERS (G.) Die hieroglyphischen Schriftzeichen der Aegypter. pp. 55. *Leipz.* 1890. 8°.
                                              7702. dd. 18.

PLEYTE (W.) Zur Geschichte der Hieroglyphenschrift. 1890. 8°. Einzelbeiträge zur allgemeinen Sprachwissenschaft. Heft 8. 12902. g.

RENOUF (*Sir* P. le P.) Egyptian Phonology. *Lond.* 1889, *etc.* 8°.   7702. bb. 40.

SCHACK-SCHACKENBURG (H.) Aegyptologische Studien. *Leipz.* 1893, *etc.* 4°.   7702. i.

AC. London. *British Museum.* Book of the Dead. By E. A. W. Budge. pp. 377. *Lond.* 1895. 4°.   7701. h. 5.
—— Book of the Dead. Facsimile of the Papyrus. pp. vii. 37 pl. *Lond.* 1894. fol. Tab. 819. b.

PER-M-HRU. Book of the Dead. By C. H. S. Davis. pp. 186. *N.Y.* 1894. 8°.   7701. i. 3.

AHMES. Ein mathematisches Handbuch der alten Aegypter, Papyrus-Rhind. pp. 278. *Leipz.* 1891. 4°.   7705. g. 39.

AMÉLINEAU (E.) La Morale égyptienne. Étude sur le papyrus de Boulaq No. 4. pp. 261. 1892. 8°. AC. Paris. *École des Hautes Études.* Bibliothèque. Sciences religieuses. Vol. 4.
                                              AC. 8929/7.

BERLIN. *K. Museen.* Aegyptische Urkunden aus den Museen zu Berlin. *Berl.* 1892, *etc.* 4°.
                                              7703. h.

WESSELY (C.) Einige Urkunden des Berliner k. ägyptischen Museums. pp. 26. *Berl.* 1890. 8°.   Pam. 3.

EBERS (G.) Papyros Ebers. Aus dem Aegyptischen übersetzt von H. Joachim. pp. 214. *Berl.* 1890. 8°.   7704. aaa. 48.

GRIFFITH (F. L.) Two Hieroglyphic Papyri from Tanis. pp. 25. 1889. 4°. EGYPT. *Exploration Fund.* Memoirs.   7703. h.

KUPKA (P. F.) Wiener "Papyri." Skizzen aus Aegypten. pp. 217. *Dresd.* 1894. 8°.
                                              7704. aaa. 56.

MAHAFFY (J. P.) On the Flinders Petrie Papyri. 2 vol. 1891. 4°. Ac. Dublin. *R. Irish Academy.* Cunningham Memoirs. No. viii. Ac. 1540/6.

PETRIE (W. M. F.) Egyptian tales from the Papyri. *Lond.* 1895, *etc.* 8°.   7704. aa. 43.

RAINERUS, *Archduke of Austria.* Papyrus Erzherzog Rainer. Führer durch die Ausstellung. *Wien,* 1892, *etc.* 8°.   754. c. 8.

REVILLOUT (E.) Notice des Papyrus démotiques et autres textes juridiques ou historiques. *Paris,* 1893, *etc.* 4°.   7702. h. 19.

VATICAN LIBRARY. Monumenta papyracea Bibliothecae Vaticanae. pp. 136. *Romae,* 1891. 4°.
                                              7702. h. 18.

LIEBLEIN (J. D. C.) Le livre égyptien, Que Mon Nom Fleurisse. pp. 47. *Leipz.* 1895. 8°.
                                              7705. b. 53.

See also supra: Antiquities.

EHINGEN. Ac. Stuttgard. *K. statistisch-topographisches Bureau.* Beschreibung des Oberamts Ehingen. pp. 261. *Stuttgart,* 1893. 8°.   Ac. 2432/5.

EIFEL. HECKING ( ) Die Eifel in ihrer Mundart. pp. 112. *Prüm,* 1890. 8°.
                                              12962. aaa. 37.

EIFFEL TOWER, Paris. FEVRIER (J. F.) La Tour Eiffel. pp. 21. *Paris,* 1890. 8°.
                                              Pam. 77.

GIRARD (H.) La Tour Eiffel. pp. 111. *Paris,* 1890. 8°.   7959. bb. 47.

HERRERA Y FAYOS (M.) La Torre Eiffel. Reflexiones meteorológicas. pp. 23. *Barcelona,* 1889. 8°.   Pam. 79.

LALLEMAND (C.) Guide to the Eiffel Tower. pp. 47. *Paris,* 1890. 8°.   Pam. 18.

TISSANDIER (G.) La Tour Eiffel. pp. 81. *Paris,* 1889. 8°.   7958. bb. 13.

EINDHOVEN. SMITS (F. N.) Geschiedenis van Eindhoven. *Eindhoven,* 1887, *etc.* 8°.
                                              010271. f.

EISENACH. WENIGER (L.) Die Dominikaner in Eisenach. pp. 44. 1894. 8°. Sammlung wissenschaftlicher Vorträge. Hft. 199.
                                              12249. m.

EJECTMENT, Law of. *See* LAND, *Tenures, England:* LANDLORD AND TENANT.

ELAM. *See* SUSA.

ELASTICITY. KECK (W.) Vorträge über Elasticitäts-Lehre. 2 Th. *Hannover,* 1892. 8°.
                                              8768. f. 10.

LOVE (A. E. H.) Treatise on the Theory of Elasticity. *Camb.* 1892, *etc.* 8°.   8768. l. 13.

POINCARÉ (H.) Leçons sur la Théorie de l'Élasticité. pp. 208. *Paris,* 1892. 8°.   8768. f. 3.

REIFF (R.) Elasticität und Elektricität. pp. 181. *Freiburg,* 1893. 8°.   8757. e. 15.

See also BUILDING : ENGINEERING : MECHANICS : STRAINS AND STRESSES.

ELATEIA. PARIS (P.) Élatée. pp. 320. 1891. 8°. Ac. Athens. *École Française.* Bibliothèque. Fasc. 60.   Ac. 5206/2.

ELATERIDAE. *See* COLEOPTERA.

ELBA. MELLINI PONÇE DE LEON (V.) I Francesi all' Elba. pp. 319. *Livorno,* 1890. 8°.
                                              9079. cc. 28.

ELBING. DORR (R.) Uebersicht über die prähistorischen Funde in Elbing. pp. 42. *Elbing,* 1893. 4°.   7704. k. 10. (3.)

ELECTIONS.
General: Proportional Representation.

BERRY (J. M.) Proportional Representation. The Gove System. pp. 32. *Worcester, Mass.,* 1892. 8°.   Pam. 65.

BURCH (G. v. der) *Count.* Représentation proportionnelle. pp. 16. *Brux.* 1894. 4°. Pam. 73.

GENEVA. *Association Réformiste.* Étude des différents méthodes de Représentation proportionnelle. pp. 27. *Genève,* 1890. 8°. Pam. 67.

HOFFSCHMIDT (A. d') Les Systèmes minoritaires. pp. 183. *Brux.* 1891. 4°.   8081. h. 6.

HONDT (V. d') Le pourquoi de Représentation proportionnelle. pp. 43. *Brux.* 1895. 8°.
                                              Pam. 73.

LARGIADÈR (A. P.) Untersuchung über die Proportional-Vertretung. pp. 45. 1891. 8°. Schweizer Zeitfragen. No. 20.   8074. f.

MAERE-LIMNANDER (de) De la Représentation proportionnelle. pp. 19. *Gand,* 1894. 8°.
                                              Pam. 73.

MASSAU (J.) La Représentation proportionnelle. pp. 19. *Gand,* 1891. 8°.   Pam. 73.

ROSIN (H.) Minoritätenvertretung und Proportionalwahlen. pp. 54. *Berl.* 1892. 8°. Pam. 64.

WILLEMS (P.) La Représentation proportionnelle. pp. 20. *Gand,* 1894. 8°.   Pam. 73.

ELECTIONS—*continued.*

Law and History of.

Belgium.

MANUEL. Manuel de l'Électeur. Opérations électorales. pp. 15. *Gand*, 1894. 16°.
Pam. 73.

—— Revision des listes électorales. pp. 15. *Gand*, 1894. 16°. Pam. 73.
See also supra: General.

France.

CHALLETON (F.) Histoire électorale de la France, 1789-1890. 3 tom. *Paris*, 1891. 8°. 9230. cc. 10.

HOFFSCHMIDT (A. d') Exposé des règles concernant les opérations électorales. pp. 386. *Brux.* 1890. 8°. 8081. g. 16.

Great Britain and Ireland, Parliamentary Elections.

GREGO (J.) History of Parliamentary Elections. pp. 403. *Lond.* 1892. 8°. 8132. eee. 11.

BLAIR (P. J.) Manual for Parliamentary Elections. pp. 495. *Edinb.* 1893. 8°. 6583. f. 24.

DAY (S. H.) Election Cases in 1892 and 1893. pp. 184. *Lond.* 1894. 8°. 6325. df. 24.

ELLIS (A. J.) Handbook for Electors and election agents. pp. 156. 1892. 8°. RUMSEY (A.) Legal Handbooks. 6191. de.

FANE (W. V. R.) and GRAHAM (A. H.) Qualifications and registration of Electors. pp. 142. *Lond.* 1892. 8°. 6325. de. 31.

HEDDERWICK (T. C. H.) Parliamentary Election manual. pp. 324. *Lond.* 1892. 12°.
6325. cc. 21.

LAWSON (W.) Notes of decisions under the Representation of the People Acts and Registration Acts, 1885-93. pp. 374. *Dublin*, 1894. 8°. 6325. df. 26.

—— Notes of decisions under the Representation of the People Acts and Registration Acts, 1894. pp. 54. *Dublin*, 1895. 8°. 6503. aaa. 22.

LEEDS. *Union of Conservative Associations.* Elections: how they should be conducted. pp. 36. *Leeds*, 1895. 8°. Pam. 68.

MURRAY (A. G.) Qualification of Voters and Digest of registration cases. pp. 100. *Edinb.* 1891. 8°. 6425. e. 27.

PARKER (F. R.) Parker's Election Manuals. 4 pt. *Lond.* 1892. 8°. 6345. aa. 6.

—— Powers and liabilities of an Election Agent and of a Returning Officer. pp. 899. *Lond.* 1891. 8°. 6325. df. 15.

RICHARDS (H. C.) Candidates' guide in contested Elections. pp. 104. *Lond.* 1894. 8°. 6345. aa. 9.

ROGERS (F. N.) Rogers on Elections. Vol. 2, 3. *Lond.* 1895. 8°. 6325. cc. 27.

ROSS-OF-BLADENSBURG (J. F. G.) "Simplex" Chart for recording Election results. pp. 20. *Lond.* 1892. 8°. Pam. 68.

ROWE (W. H.) Manual on the conduct of Parliamentary Elections. pp. 161. *Lond.* 1890. 8°. 8139. c. 10.

SEAGER (J. R.) Law of Elections, in the light of the election petitions of 1892. pp. 64. *Lond.* 1893. 8°. 6345. aaa. 5.

JELF (E. A.) Corrupt and Illegal Practices Prevention Act, 1883. pp. 179. *Lond.* 1895. 8°. 6325. de. 43.

RICHARDS (H. C.) Corrupt and Illegal Practices Prevention Act, 1883. pp. 122. *Lond.* 1893. 8°. 6345. aa. 8.

LEADER (R. E.) The Press and the Corrupt Practices Bill. pp. 27. *Sheffield*, 1883. 8°. 8139. bb. 48. (1.)

ELECTIONS.—Great Britain—*continued.*

GRAHAM (J. E.) Manual of the Elections, Scotland. Corrupt and Illegal Practices, Act, 1890. pp. 108. *Edinb.* 1891. 8°. 6583. c. 5.

CARLETON (J. W.) Parliamentary Elections in Ireland. pp. 543. *Dublin*, 1885. 8°.
6503. aaa. 16.
See also ENGLAND, *Parliament.* For County, District, and Parish Council elections, *see* LOCAL GOVERNMENT.

Prussia.

GNEIST (H. R. v.) Die nationale Rechtsidee von den Ständen und das preussische Dreiklassenwahlsystem. pp. 272. *Berl.* 1894. 8°.
8008. dd. 7.

Spain.

FREIXA Y RABASO (E.) Manual de Elecciones de diputados. pp. 93. *Madrid*, 1891. 8°.
8042. aaa. 31.

TAPIA (A.) El Derecho electoral. pp. 203. *Madrid*, 1891. 8°. 5384. aa. 9.

VIVANCO Y ARGÜELLES (D.) La Reforma electoral. pp. 209. *Madrid*, 1890. 8°. 8042. a. 24.

United States of America.

BISHOP (C. F.) History of Elections in the American Colonies. pp. 297. 1893. 8°. Ac. New York. *Columbia College.* Studies in History. Vol. 3. Ac. 2688/2.

STANWOOD (E.) History of Presidential Elections. pp. 452. *Bost.* 1888. 8°. 9602. de. 11.

O'NEIL (C. A.) The American Electoral system. pp. 284. *N.Y.* 1889. 8°. 8176. bbb. 15.

PRYOR (J. W.) Statement of the Election Law as in force in New York City. pp. 62. *N.Y.* 1894. 12°. Pam. 65.

REMSEN (D. S.) Suffrage and the Ballot. 1892. 8°. Ac. Brooklyn. *Ethical Association.* Evolution Series. No. 21. 7006. bbb.

—— Primary Elections. pp. 121. *N.Y.* 1894. 8°. 8176. bbb.
See also UNITED STATES OF AMERICA, *Constitution.*

ELECTRICITY AND MAGNETISM.

Bibliography.

SZCZEPANSKI (F. v.) Bibliotheca Electrotechnica. pp. 75. *St. Petersburg*, 1892. 8°. Pam. 6.

General: Theoretical: Electrical Engineering.

Ac. *Internationaler Elektrotechniker-Congress.* Bericht über die Verhandlungen der Hauptversammlungen des Congresses, 1891. *Frankf.* 1892, *etc.* 8°. 8757. l.

—— London. *University College.* Account of the new engineering and electrical Laboratories. pp. 32. *Lond.* 1893. 4°. 8757. i. 26.

—— Palo Alto. *Leland Stanford Junior University.* Studies in Electricity, *etc.* *Palo Alto*, 1892, *etc.* 8°. Ac. 2692. n./2.

ALLARA (V.) Il Magnetismo. pp. 138. *Milano*, 1893. 8°. 8757. a. 51.

ANGELL (J.) Elements of Magnetism and electricity. pp. 264. 1892. 8°. Collins's Elementary Science Series. 8783. aaa.

ATKINSON (P.) Electricity for everybody. pp. 239. *N.Y.* 1895. 8°. 8758. bbb. 1.

—— Elements of dynamic Electricity and magnetism. pp. 405. *Lond.* 1891. 8°.
8757. bbb. 8.

BARBAT (C.) Dictionnaire d'électricité. pp. 994, 234. *Paris*, 1894. 12°. 8768. bb. 12.

ELECTRICITY.—General—_continued._

BARCKHAUSEN (H.) Einige Betrachtungen über Magnetismus und Elektricität.
Bremen, 1892. 8°.　　　　　　8755. dd. 7. (7.)

BEAUMONT (W. W.) Practical electrical Engineering. 2 vol. _Lond._ 1894. 4°. 8757. m. 5.

BENJAMIN (P.) Intellectual rise in Electricity. pp. 611. _Lond._ 1895. 8°.　　　8758. ccc. 9.

BERTOLINI (G.) Nozioni di Elettricità e di magnetismo. _Genova_, 1892, etc. 8°.　　8757. e.

BIGGS (C. H. W.) First principles of electrical Engineering. pp. 203. _Lond._ 1892. 8°.
　　　　　　　　　　　　　　　　8757. aa. 38.

BONNEY (G. E.) Electrical experiments. pp. 252. _Lond._ 1893. 8°.　　8757. cc. 29.

BOTTONE (S. R.) Electricity and Magnetism. pp. 203. 1893. 8°. Whittaker's Library of Popular Science.　　　　　　8709. aa.

BURCH (G. J.) Manual of Electrical Science. pp. 260. 1893. 8°. SYMES (J. E.) University Extension Series.　　　　012202. g.

CAILLARD (E. M.) Electricity, the science of the 19th century. pp. 310. _Lond._ 1891. 8°.
　　　　　　　　　　　　　　　　8757. aa. 28.

COLOMBO (G.) and FERRINI (R.) Manuale dell' Elettricista. pp. 204. _Milano_, 1891. 8°.
　　　　　　　　　　　　　　　012200. h. 4.

COULOMB (C. A. de) Vier Abhandlungen über die Elektricität und den Magnetismus. pp. 88. 1890. 8°. Ostwald's Klassiker der exacten Wissenschaften. Nr. 13.　　　8706. de.

CUMMING (L.) Electricity treated experimentally. pp. 405. _Lond._ 1893. 8°.　8757. a. 46.

—— Introduction to the theory of Electricity. pp. 318. _Lond._ 1894. 8°.　8757. b. 20.

DAHLANDER (G. R.) Elektriciteten. _Stockholm_, 1890, etc. 8°.　　8757. f. 19.

DARY (G.) L'Électricité dans la nature. pp. 440. _Paris_, 1892. 8°.　8756. b. 52.

DU BOIS (H.) Magnetische Kreise. pp. 382. _Berl._ 1894. 8°.　　　　8757. cc. 42.

DUHEM (P.) Leçons sur l'Électricité et le magnétisme. _Paris_, 1891, etc. 8°. 8756. f. 38.

DUMONT (G.) Annales d'Électricité et de magnétisme. 13 fasc. _Paris_, 1889, 90. 8°.
　　　　　　　　　　　　　　　　8757. l. 14.

—— Dictionnaire d'Électricité et de magnétisme. pp. 1020. _Paris_, 1887. 8°.　8757. l. 7.

EMTAGE (W. T. A.) Introduction to the Theory of Electricity and magnetism. pp. 254. 1894. 8°. Clarendon Press Series.　　2319. a. 29.

EWING (J. A.) Magnetic induction in Iron and other metals. pp. 351. _Lond._ 1891. 8°.
　　　　　　　　　　　　　　　　8757. f. 23.

GERARD (E.) Leçons sur l'Électricité. 2 tom. _Paris_, 1893. 8°.　　8757. i. 24.

G. B. _Priry Council. Department of Science and Art._ Outline of Experiments suitable for illustrating instruction in magnetism and electricity. pp. 93. _Lond._ 1893. 8°.　Pam. 18.

G. B. and I. _Army. Corps of Royal Engineers._ Notes on Electricity. pp. 61. _Lond._ 1891. 8°.
　　　　　　　　　　　　　　　8709. aaa. 5. (7.)

GUILLEMIN (A.) Electricity and magnetism. pp. 976. _Lond._ 1891. 8°.　8757. i. 20.

HEAVISIDE (O.) Electrical Papers. 2 vol. _Lond._ 1892. 8°.　　　　8758. d. 2.

—— Electromagnetic Theory. _Lond._ 1893, etc. 8°.　　　　8757. e.

HERTZ (H.) Electric Waves. pp. 278. _Lond._ 1893. 8°.　　　8757. f. 32.

INFANTE (P.) Un Avviamento allo studio del magnetismo. pp. 92. _Bari_, 1893. 8°.
　　　　　　　　　　　　　　　　8757. b. 19.

ELECTRICITY.—General—_continued._

JACKSON (D. C.) Text-book on Electro-Magnetism. _N.Y._ 1893, etc. 8°.　8757. bbb. 30.

JAMIESON (A.) Elementary Manual of Magnetism and electricity. pp. 297. _Lond._ 1894. 8°.
　　　　　　　　　　　　　　　　8757. cc. 37.

JERROLD (W.) Electricians and their marvels. pp. 160. _Lond._ 1894. 8°.　8757. bb. 34.

JOCELYN (J. R. J.) Notes on Electricity for the use of Garrison Artillery. pp. 208.
Lond. 1891. 8°.　　　　　　8757. aa. 37.

KENNELLY (A. E.) Evolution of Electric and magnetic Physics. 1891. 8°. Ac. Brooklyn. _Ethical Association._ Evolution Series. No. 6.
　　　　　　　　　　　　　　　　7006. bbb.

KNOTT (C. G.) Electricity and magnetism. pp. 239. _Lond._ 1893. 8°.　8757. aa. 45.

KOLKIN (N.) Ethereal Matter, electricity and akasa. pp. 75. _Sioux City_, 1891. 8°. Pam. 36.

LAFLAMME (J. C. K.) Notions sur l'Électricité et le magnétisme. pp. 84. _Québec_, 1893. 8°.
　　　　　　　　　　　　　　　　8757. aaa. 11.

LEBLOND (H.) Électricité expérimentale et pratique. 3 tom. _Paris_, 1889–91. 8°.
　　　　　　　　　　　　　　　　8757. h. 17.

—— Cours élémentaire d'Électricité pratique. pp. 449. _Paris_, 1894. 8°.　8758. ccc. 1.

LEFÈVRE (J.) Dictionnaire d'Électricité et de magnétisme. _Paris_, 1890, etc. 8°.　8757. i.

LEMSTRÖM (S.) Expériences sur l'influence de l'Électricité sur les végétaux. pp. 71. 1890. 4°. Ac. Helsingfors. _Finska Universitet._ Commentationes variae, etc. No. 1.　Ac. 1095.

LODGE (O. J.) Modern views of Electricity. pp. 480. 1892. 8°. Nature Series. 2244. b. 30.

MAXWELL (J. C.) Treatise on Electricity and magnetism. 1892, etc. 8°. Clarendon Press Series.　　　　　　　　2320. h. 16.

BOLTZMANN (L.) Vorlesungen über Maxwells Theorie der Elektricität. _Leipz._ 1891, etc. 8°.
　　　　　　　　　　　　　　　　8757. g. 31.

FOEPPL (A.) Einführung in die Maxwell'sche Theorie der Elektricität. pp. 413.
Leipz. 1894. 8°.　　　　　　8757. e. 19.

POINCARÉ (H.) Électricité et optique. Les théories de Maxwell. pp. 314. _Paris_, 1890. 8°.
　　　　　　　　　　　　　　　　8757. h. 15.

THOMSON (J. J.) Notes on recent researches in Electricity. A sequel to Clerk-Maxwell's Treatise on Electricity. pp. 578. 1893. 8°. Clarendon Press Series.　　2320. g. 24.

MAYCOCK (W. P.) First Book of Electricity and magnetism. pp. 233. _Lond._ 1895. 8°.
　　　　　　　　　　　　　　　　8758. b. 10.

—— Practical Electrical notes and definitions. pp. 286. _Lond._ 1890. obl. 8°. 8757. a. 28.

MOELLER (M.) Das räumliche Wirken der Elektrizität und des Magnetismus. pp. 73.
Hannover, 1892. 8°.　　　　8757. f. 30.

MUNRO (J.) The Romance of Electricity. pp. 320. _Lond._ 1893. 8°.　　4429. f. 7.

NABER (H. A.) Standard methods in Physics and Electricity criticised. pp. 114.
Lond. 1894. 8°.　　　　　　8757. f. 33.

NEUMANN (F. E.) Ueber ein allgemeines Princip der Theorie inducirter elektrischer Ströme. pp. 96. 1892. 8°. Ostwald's Klassiker, etc. Nr. 36.　　　　　　　　8706. de.

OHM (G. S.) The Galvanic Circuit investigated mathematically. pp. 269. _N.Y._ 1891. 12°.
　　　　　　　　　　　　　　　　8757. a. 41.

P.P. _Chicago._ Electricity. _Chicago_, 1891, etc. fol.　　　P.P. 1612. ga.

—— _London._ The Electrician Primers. _Lond._ 1894, etc. 8°.　　　8757. e.

ELECTRICITY.—Appliances, etc.—*cont.*

GRAWINKEL (C.) and STRECKER (C.) Hilfsbuch für die Elektrotechnik. pp. 567.
Berl. 1891. 8°.   8757. cc. 23.

HOSPITALIER (É.) Recettes de l'Électricien. pp. 352. *Paris,* 1895. 12°.   8758. aaa. 3.

KEIGNART (E.) Guide de l'Amateur électricien pour la construction de tous les appareils électriques. pp. 492. *Paris,* 1894. 8°. 8758. cc. 1.

KENNELLY (A. E.) Theoretical elements of electro-dynamic Machinery. *N.Y.* 1893, *etc.* 8°.
                                                8757. k. 6.

MUELLER (E. R.) Die elektrischen Maschinen. pp. 39. 1890. 8°. Sammlung wissenschaftlicher Vorträge. N. F. Ser. 5.   12249. m.

NIBLETT (J. T.) Portative Electricity. pp. 234. *Lond.* 1893. 8°.   8757. cc. 34.

SAYER (G. H.) Electrical Apparatus for amateurs. pp. 104. 1894. 8°. Ward and Lock's Amateurs' Aid Series.   07944. ee.

SNIJDERS (J. A.) De vorderingen der Electrotechniek in de laatste jaren. pp. 313.
's-Gravenh. 1894. 8°.   8757. dd. 29.

UNWIN (W. C.) Development and transmission of Power from central stations. pp. 312.
Lond. 1894. 8°.   8768. e. 26.

ARNOLD (E.) Die Ankerwicklungen der Gleichstrom-Dynamomaschinen. pp. 129.
Berl. 1891. 8°.   8757. cc. 20.

BIŠĆAN (W.) Die Dynamomaschine. pp. 107. *Leipz.* 1892. 8°.   8757. g. 37.

BOTTONE (S. R.) How to manage the Dynamo. pp. 47. *Lond.* 1893. 8°.   8757. a. 42.

CROCKER (F. B.) and WHEELER (S. S.) Practical management of Dynamos and Motors. pp. 205. *N.Y.* 1894. 8°.   8757. bbb. 32.

CROFTS (A.) How to make a Dynamo. pp. 104. *Lond.* 1890. 8°.   8757. aa. 31.

GATEHOUSE (T. E.) The strange history of a Dynamo. pp. 64. *Lond.* 1891. 8°.
                                            8767. cc. 30. (8.)

GIBBINGS (A. H.) Dynamo Attendants and their dynamos. pp. 58. *Lond.* 1894. 8°. 8757. aa. 47.

HALLIDAY (G.) Notes on design of small Dynamo. pp. 79. *Lond.* 1892. 8°. 8757. cc. 24.

HAWKINS (C. C.) and WALLIS (F.) The Dynamo: its theory, design and manufacture. pp. 520. 1893. 8°. Specialist's Series.   8708. k.

HERING (C.) Principles of Dynamo-Electric Machines. pp. 279. *N.Y.* 1890. 8°.
                                                8757. bbb. 33.

HOPKINSON (J.) Original Papers on Dynamo Machinery. pp. 249. *Lond.* 1893. 8°.
                                                8757. bb. 34.

KAPP (G.) Dynamos, Alternators and Transformers. pp. 483. *Lond.* 1893. 8°. 8757. cc. 35.

PATERSON (G. W. L.) Management of Dynamos. pp. 214. *Lond.* 1895. 8°.   8758. bb. 5.

URQUHART (J. W.) Dynamo construction. pp. 368. *Lond.* 1895. 8°.   8758. b. 2.

WALKER (F.) Practical Dynamo-building for amateurs. pp. 63. *Lond.* 1892. 8°. 8757. aa. 41.

WILKES (G.) Practical hints in Dynamo design. 1894. 8°. Ac. Madison. *University of Wisconsin.* Bulletin. Engineering Series. Vol. 1. No. 2.   Ac. 1792.

ATKINSON (P.) Electric Transformation of power and its application by the Electric Motor. pp. 244. *Lond.* 1894. 8°.   8757. bbb. 31.

BOTTONE (S. R.) Electro-Motors. pp. 135. *Lond.* 1890. 8°.   8757. bb. 29.

KRIEG (M.) Die elektrischen Motoren und ihre Anwendungen in der Industrie. pp. 252.
Leipz. 1891. 8°.   8757. f. 21.

ELECTRICITY.—Appliances, etc.—*cont.*

LEBLOND (H.) Les Moteurs électriques à courant continu. pp. 494. *Paris,* 1894. 8°. 8757. cc. 39.

MINEL (P.) Régularisation des Moteurs des machines électriques. pp. 192. 1894. 8°. Encyclopédie des aide-mémoire. No. 95A. 8709. g.

NIAUDET (A.) Elementary treatise on Electric Batteries. pp. 266. *N.Y.* 1886. 8°. 8757. cc. 19.

NIBLETT (J. T.) Secondary Batteries. pp. 267. *Lond.* 1892. 8°.   8757. bbb. 12.

PARDOE (G. T.) Paper on the advantage of hydraulic Storage as applied to Electric Supply Stations. pp. 24. *Brighton,* 1895. 8°. Pam. 79.

SACK (J.) Die elektrischen Accumulatoren und ihre Verwendung in der Praxis. pp. 256. 1892. 8°. Elektrotechnische Bibliothek. Bd. 45.
                                                8757. b.

ZACHARIAS (J.) Die Accumulatoren zur Aufspeicherung des elektrischen Stromes. pp. 251. *Jena,* 1892. 8°.   8757. h. 22.

DUMONT (G.) and BAIGNÈRES (G.) Étude sur le transport de l'énergie à grand distance par l'Électricité. pp. 114. *Paris,* 1895. 8°.
                                                8757. dd. 28.

HERTZ (H.) Untersuchungen ueber die Ausbreitung der elektrischen Kraft. pp. 295.
Leipz. 1892. 8°.   8757. h. 24.

KAPP (G.) Electric transmission of Energy. pp. 445. 1894. 8°. Specialist's Series. 8708. k.

KILGOUR (M. H.) Electrical Distribution. pp. 424. *Lond.* 1893. 8°.   8757. cc. 31.

LONDON. *Electrical Company.* Electrical Transmission and distribution of power. pp. 203. *Lond.* 1895. 8°.   8758. bb. 2.

PICOU (R. V.) La Distribution de l'Électricité. 2 pt. 1892. 8°. Encyclopédie des aide-mémoire.
                                                8709. g.

ROBINSON (H.) Comparisons between the different systems of distributing Electricity. pp. 21. *Lond.* 1893. 8°.   8756. cc. 43. (10.)

ALLSOP (F. C.) Induction Coils and coil-making. pp. 162. *Lond.* 1894. 8°.   8757. cc. 36.

BONNEY (G. E.) Induction Coils. pp. 231. *Lond.* 1892. 8°.   8757. a. 38.

BEDELL (F.) and CREHORE (A. C.) Alternating Currents. pp. 325. 1893. 8°. Specialist's Series.   8708. k.

BLAKESLEY (T. H.) Papers on Alternating Currents. pp. 140. 1891. 8°. Specialist's Series.
                                                8708. k.

EMMET (W. Le R.) Alternating Current Wiring and distribution. pp. 76. *N.Y.* 1894. 8°.
                                                8757. a. 54.

LOPPÉ (F.) and BOUQUET (R. P.) Traité des Courants Alternatifs industriels.
Paris, 1894, *etc.* 8°.   8757. e.

THOMPSON (S. P.) Polyphase Electric Currents. pp. 261. 1895. 8°. Finsbury Technical Manuals.   7945. cc.

BENJAMIN (P.) The Voltaic Cell. pp. 562. *N.Y.* 1893. 8°.   8757. e. 16.

JAUMANN (G.) Absolutes Elektrometer mit Knppelsuspension. 1892. 8°. Ac. Vienna. *K. Akademie.* Sitzungsberichte. Math.-naturwissenschaftl. Classe. Bd. 101. Hft. 1. Ac. 810/6.

SILVERTOWN. *India Rubber and Telegraph Works Company.* Silvertown Patent Portable Testing Set. pp. 23. *Lond.* 1891. 8°.   8757. aa. 29.

TOMMASI (D.) Traité des Piles électriques. pp. 680. *Paris,* 1889. 8°.   8757. f. 15.

WEYMOUTH (F. M.) Drum Armatures and commutators. pp. 294. *Lond.* 1894. 8°. 8757. e.

MAY (O.) Belting Table. *Lond.* 1890. fol.
                                                8766. ccc. 3.

ELECTRICITY—*continued.*

Applications of Electricity.

BOUQUET (R. P.) Notes et formules d'Électricité industrielle. pp. 405. *Paris,* 1893. 12°.
8757. aaa. 61.

BRACKETT (C. F.) Electricity in daily life. pp. 288. *Lond.* 1891. 8°.   8757. f. 17.

LAFFARGUE (J.) Les Applications Mécaniques de l'énergie électrique. pp. 363. *Paris,* 1895. 8°.
8758. bbb. 2.

LEA (F. B.) Electricity in every-day life. pp. 26. *Lond.* 1890. obl. 8°.   Pam. 79.

LEBIEZ (L.) L'Électricien amateur. pp. 220 *Paris,* 1894. 12°.   8758. b. 6.

MINEL (P.) Introduction à l'Électricité industrielle. 2 pt. 1893. 8°. Encyclopédie des aide-mémoire.   8709. g.

N.Y. *General Electric Company.* General Electric Company. pp. 16. *N.Y.* 1893. 8°.
8755. dd. 32. (8.)

NICHOLS (E. L.) Laboratory manual of applied Electricity. *N.Y.* 1894, *etc.* 8°.   8704. ff. 15.

NIPHER (F. E.) Electrical Industries in St. Louis. pp. 8. *St. Louis,* 1891. 8°.
8708. l. 8. (6.)

OFFOR (G.) Lecture on Electricity as applied to domestic purposes. pp. 8. *Lewisham,* 1893. 4°.
8706. f. 23. (10.)

TAINTURIER (C.) Manuel d'Électricité industrielle. pp. 297. *Paris,* 1895. 8°. 8758. bb. 6.

TREVERT (E.) Electricity and its recent applications. pp. 346. *Lynn, Mass.,* 1891. 8°.
8757. a. 34.

UPPENBORN (F.) Der gegenwärtige Stand der Elektrotechnik und ihre Bedeutung für das Wirthschaftsleben. pp. 32. 1892. 8°. Volkswirthschaftliche Zeitfragen. Hft. 108. 8207. i.

URBANITZKY (A. R. v.) Electricity in the service of man. *Lond.* 1892, *etc.* 8°.   8757. h. 23.

VERITY (J. B.) Electricity up to date. pp. 226. *Lond.* 1894. 8°.   8757. cc. 38.

MONTILLOT (C. J.) and (L.) La Maison électrique. pp. 488. *Paris,* 1893. 8°. 8757. l. 15.

WALKER (S. F.) Electricity in our homes and workshops. pp 350. *Lond.* 1895. 8°. 8758. b. 12

GORDON (*Mrs.* J. E. H.) Decorative Electricity. pp. 178. *Lond.* 1891. 8°.   8757. bb. 31.

PABST (C.) Électricité agricole. pp. 376. *Paris,* 1894. 8°.   8758. ccc. 2.

CINDERFORD. *Electric Blasting Apparatus Company.* Instructions re Electric Blasting. *Cinderford,* 1891. 8°.   8756. cc. 44. (7.)

ALLSOP (F. C.) Electric Bell construction. pp. 131. *Lond.* 1890. 8°.   8757. bb. 27.

—— Practical Electric Bell fitting. pp. 170. *Lond.* 1895. 8°.   8757. aaaa. 53.

BOTTONE (S. R.) Electric-Bells and all about them. pp. 201. *Lond.* 1892. 8°. 8757. bb. 32.

EDWINSON (G.) The Electrician at home. Electric Bells. pp. 126. 1894. 8°. Ward and Lock's Amateurs' Aid Series.   07944. ee.

FAVARGER (A.) L'Électricité et ses applications à la chronométrie. pp. 198. *Genève,* 1892. 8°.
8757. dd. 21.

DARY (G.) L'Électricité et la défense des côtes. pp. 318. *Paris,* 1894. 12°.   8806. bb. 29.

THOMPSON (S. P.) Electricity in mining. pp. 45. *Lond.* 1891. 8°.   8756. ccc. 26. (13.)

CALLOU (L.) Applications de l'Électricité dans la marine. pp. 347. *Paris,* 1894. 8°.
8757. dd. 22.

MINEL (P.) Électricité appliquée à la marine. pp. 203. 1894. 8°. Encyclopédie des aide-mémoire.   8709. g.

ELECTRICITY.—Applications—*cont.*

PESCHARD (A.) Les premières applications de l'Électricité aux grandes orgues. pp. 73. *Paris,* 1890. 8°.   7895. g. 11.

LIESEGANG (R. E.) Beiträge zum Problem des electrischen Fernsehens. pp. 130. 1891. 8°. Probleme der Gegenwart. Bd. 1.   8708. l. 6.

LEFÈVRE (J.) L'Électricité au théâtre. pp. 345. *Paris,* 1894. 8°.   8758. b. 3.

SLOANE (T. O'C.) Electric Toy making. pp. 140. *Lond.* 1892. 8°.   8757. aa 40.

BOUSSAC (A.) Construction des Lignes Électriques aëriennes. pp. 313. *Paris,* 1894. 8°.
8757. k. 10.

KEASBEY (E. Q.) Law of Electric Wires in streets and highways. pp. 190. *Chicago,* 1892. 8°.   6617. aaa. 13.

See also RAILWAYS, *Electric:* PHONOGRAPH : TELEGRAPH : TELEPHONE : TRAMWAYS.

Electric Light.

ALLSOP (F. C.) Practical Electric-Light fitting. pp. 275. *Lond.* 1892. 8°.   8757. cc. 30.

BAX (E. I.) Popular Electric Lighting. pp. 159. *Lond.* 1892. 8°.   8757. cc. 33.

BOTTONE (S. R.) Guide to Electric Lighting. pp. 189. *Lond.* 1893. 8°.   8757. aaa. 60.

BOULT (W. S.) Electricity v. Gas. Comparative cost of gas and electric-light. *Liverp.* 1892. 4°.
1811. a. 1. (70.)

CROWTHER (F. J.) Orders of the Board of Trade in reference to Electric Light Undertakings. pp 48. *Lond.* 1893. 8°.   6426. aaaa. 18.

DE SEGUNDO (E. C.) Domestic Electric Lighting. pp. 115. *Lond.* 1892. 8°.   8757. a. 39.

ELECTRICITY. Electricity, the light of to-day. *Lond.* 1893. 4°.   8757. i. 23.

FAHIE (A.) House Lighting by electricity. pp. 80. *Lond.* 1892. 8°.   8757. bbb. 19.

FODOR (E de) Experimente mit Strömen hoher Wechselzahl und Frequenz. pp. 291. *Wien,* 1894. 8°.   8757. cc. 40.

FOX (S. G. L.) On the future of Electric Lighting. pp. 16. *Lond.* 1892. 8°.
8756. ccc. 26. (14.)

GALINE (L.) Traité général d'Éclairage. pp. 412. *Paris,* 1894. 8°.   8715. dd. 30.

GUY (A. F.) Electric Light and power. pp. 316. *Lond.* 1894. 8°.   8757. a. 52.

HASKINS (C. D.) Transformers. Their theory, construction, and application. pp. 150. *Lynn, Mass.,* 1892. 8°.   8757. aa. 42.

HEDGES (K.) Continental Electric Light central stations. pp. 240. *Lond.* 1892. 4°. 8757. l. 12.

HEIM (C.) Die Einrichtung elektrischer Beleuchtungsanlagen für Gleichstrombetrieb. pp. 503. *Leipz.* 1892. 8°.   8757. g. 36.

HERZOG (J.) and FELDMANN (C. P.) Die Berechnung elektrischer Leitungsnetze. pp. 364. *Berl.* 1893. 8°.   8757. bbb. 28.

KENNEDY (R.) Photographic and optical Electric Lamps. pp. 59. *Lond.* 1895. 8°. 8758. ccc. 6.

KNIGHT (J. H.) Electric Light for country houses. pp. 75. *Lond.* 1895. 8°.   8758. b. 5.

KRUEGER (E. A.) Die Herstellung der elektrischen Glühlampe. pp. 103. *Leipz.* 1894. 8°.
8757. g. 38.

LEWANDOWSKI (R.) Das elektrische Licht in der Heilkunde. pp. 295. *Wien,* 1892. 8°.
7460. ff. 25.

LONDON. *Phœnix Fire Office.* Rules for Electric Light installations. pp. 23. *Lond.* 1892. 8°.
Pam. 23.

ELECTRICITY.—*Medical—continued.*

HEDLEY (W. S.) The Hydro-Electric methods in medicine. pp. 156. *Lond.* 1892. 8°. 7461. f. 6.

HIRT (L.) Lehrbuch der Elektrodiagnostik und Elektrotherapie. pp. 224. *Stuttgart,* 1893. 8°. 7460. dd. 3.

HODGKINSON (T. C.) Electro-Neurotone apparatus. pp. 98. *Lond.* 1893. 8°. 7462. de. 30.

JONES (H. L.) Medical Electricity. 1892. 8°. Lewis's Practical Series. 7482. a.

LEWANDOWSKI (R.) Das elektrische Licht in der Heilkunde. pp. 295. *Wien,* 1892. 8°. 7460. ff. 25.

LIEBIG (G. A.) and ROHÉ (G. H.) Practical Electricity in medicine and surgery. pp. 383. *Phila.* 1890. 8°. 7461. h. 18.

MATTEI (C.) *Count.* Médecine Électro-homéo-pathique. pp. 508. *Nice,* 1883. 8°. 7461. cc. 5.

—— Electro-homœopathic Medicine. pp. 352. *Lond.* 1888. 8°. 07305. e. 9.

BÉRARD (S.) Count Mattei's Electro-homœo-pathic specifics. pp. 281. *Lond.* 1889. 8°. 7461, c. 17.

GENTY DE BONQUEVAL (J.) Traité de l'Électro-homéopathie. pp. 352. *Paris,* 1891. 8°. 7461. cc. 4.

GLIDDON (A. J. L.) Stepping stones to Electro-homœopathy. pp. 251. *Lond.* 1892. 8°. 7390. de. 15.

KENNEDY (A. S.) Notes on Count Mattei's Electro-homœopathic remedies. pp. 147. *Lond.* 1891. 8°. 7410. df. 35.

MACHADO (V.) As applicaçõs medicas e cirurgi-cas da electricidade. pp. 463. *Lisboa,* 1895. 8°. 7461. h. 24.

MILLICAN (K. W.) Electro-Therapeutics. pp. 43. *Lond.* 1893. 8°. 7461. bb. 16.

MORTON (W. J.) Franklinic Interrupted Current. pp. 8. *N.Y.* 1891. 8°. 7306. k. 20. (2.)

—— Electric medicamental Diffusion. pp. 27. *Chicago,* 1895. 8°. 7306. df. 25. (6.)

MUELLER (C. W.) Beiträge zur praktischen Elek-trotherapie. pp. 118. *Wiesbaden,* 1891. 8°. 7460. f. 8.

ODIARDI (E. S. d') Medical Electricity. pp. 66. *Lond.* 1893. 8°. 7460. a. 3.

RYLEY (J. B.) Physical and nervous exhaustion in man. Treatment by "Electro-kinetics." pp. 72. *Lond.* 1892. 8°. 7461. de. 7.

STEAVENSON (W. E.) and JONES (H. L.) Medical Electricity. pp. 446. 1892. 8°. Lewis's Practical Series. 7482. a.

STEWART (D. D.) and LAWRANCE (E. S.) Essen-tials of Medical Electricity. pp. 158. 1893. 8°. Kimpton's Essential Series. 7306. df.

TURNER (D. F. D.) Manual of Medical Electri-city. pp. 315. *Lond.* 1893. 8°. 7460. ee. 23.

WEISS (G.) Technique d'Électrophysiologie. pp. 214. 1892. 8°. Encyclopédie des aide-mémoire. 8709. g.

MAC DONALD (C. F.) Infliction of the death-penalty by means of Electricity. pp. 37. *N.Y.* 1892. 8°. 07305. h. 19. (11.)

ELECTROLYSIS. *See* ELECTRICITY, *Electro-Metallurgy, etc.*

ELECTRO-PLATING. BONNEY (G. E.) Electro-Platers' handbook. pp. 208. *Lond.* 1891. 8°. 8757. bb. 30.

BOUANT (É.) La Galvanoplastie, *etc.* pp. 384. *Paris,* 1894. 12°. 7106. e. 12.

URQUHART (J. W.) Electro-Plating. pp. 226. *Lond.* 1894. 8°. 2266. aa. 18.

See also ELECTRICITY, *Electro-Metallurgy, etc.*

ELEPHANT. CHERVILLE (G. G. de) *Marquis.* Les Éléphants. pp. 260. *Paris,* 1895. 8°. 7206. dd. 12.

REES (J. D.) The Duke of Clarence in Southern India. With a narrative of Elephant-catching in Mysore. pp. 213. *Lond.* 1891. 8°. 010057. l. 6.

ELEPHANTIASIS. MAITLAND (J.) Ele-phantiasis and allied disorders. pp. 54. *Madras,* 1891. 8°. 7640. i. 7.

ELEUSINIAN MYSTERIES. *See* GREECE, *Religion.*

ELGINSHIRE. *See* MORAY.

ELIZABETH, N.J. ELIZABETHTOWN, *Pres-byterian Church.* Sextons' Record Book, 1766-1800. pp. 20. *Bost.* 1890. 8°. Pam. 26.

ELK. *See* DEER.

ELLEZELLES. DEGAND (E.) La Commune d'Ellezelles, 1792-1814. pp. 28. *Renaix,* 1891. 8°. 9004. gg. 26. (4.)

ELMHAM, North. NORTH ELMHAM. An-cient Churchwardens' accounts of North Elm-ham, 1539-77. pp. 144. *Norwich,* 1891. 4°. 010358. h. 2.

ELMSTONE. ELMSTONE. Parish Registers, 1552-1812. pp. 67. *Canterbury,* 1891. 8°. 9903. c. 11.

ELM TREE. *See* FORESTRY.

ELOCUTION. BAYNHAM (G. W.) Elocution. pp. 448. *Lond.* 1892. 8°. 011824. g. 13.

BELL (A. M.) Faults of Speech. pp. 71. *N.Y.* 1889. 12°. 12991. h. 28.

BELL (D. C.) Standard Elocutionist. pp. 600. *Lond.* 1892. 8°. 12272. bbb. 17.

BROOKFIELD (A. M.) Speaker's A B C. pp. 125. *Lond.* 1892. 16°. 011824. de. 31.

BUCHANAN (R. C.) Elocution up-to date. pp. 158. *Lond.* 1894 8°. 12273. e. 12.

CAMPBELL (H.) Voice, Speech and Gesture. pp. 888. *Lond.* 1895. 8°. 011805. f. 1.

CLEGG (C. E.) Elements of Elocution. pp. 239. *Lond.* 1890. 8°. 11805. dd. 30.

—— Clegg's Elocutionist. pp. 352. *Lond.* 1895. 8°. 12273. aaa. 23.

—— Elocutionary Specimens. pp. 236. *Lond.* 1891. 8°. 12273. f. 20.

CONRAD (M. G.) Die moderne öffentlicher Vor-trag. pp. 15. 1891. 8°. Münchener Flug-schriften, *etc.* Ser. 1. 1. 743.

FAVRE (L.) Traité de diction. 2 tom. *Paris,* 1894. 8°. 011805. e. 1.

FORSYTH (J.) The practical Elocutionist. pp. 455. *Lond.* 1895. 8°. 011824. de. 52.

FOSTER (J. E.) Lessons in Elocution. pp. 64. *Lond.* 1894. 8°. 011824. h. 37

—— The new Elocution. pp. 51. *Lond.* 1895. 8°. 11805. cc. 41.

GATTIE (W. H.) Text book of Elocution. pp. 56. *Lond.* 1895. 16°. 011805. e. 2.

GOSS (J.) Forensic Eloquence. pp. 260. *San Francisco,* 1891. 8°. 11805. dd. 32.

HARTLEY (C.) The English Elocutionist. pp. 328. *Lond.* 1892. 8°. 11603. bb. 34.

HAWKINS (C. H.) Hints on the art of Reading and Reciting. pp. 48. *Lond.* 1891. 8°. 11805. bb. 49.

HOLYOAKE (G. J.) Public Speaking and debate. pp. 266. *Lond.* 1895. 8°. 11824. bb. 55.

MAC LAUGHLIN (E. L.) Handy book upon Elocu-tion. pp. 179. *Lond.* 1892. 8°. 011795. e. 34.

MILES (A. H.) The New Standard Elocutionist. pp. 640. *Lond.* 1895. 8°. 12273. f. 27.

ELOCUTION—*continued.*

MORISON (R. C. H.) Chambers's Elocution. pp. 512. *Lond.* 1894. 8°.   12273. f. 26.

RAYMOND (G. L.) The Orator's Manual. pp. 342. *Bost.* 1892. 8°.   11805. ccc. 30.

RICHARDSON (J.) Speaking : its philosophy and practice. Pt. 1. pp. 170. *Lond.* 1889. 8°.   7898. aaaa. 11.

SCHNEIDEWIN (M.) Gedanken über antike und moderne Staatsberedsamkeit. pp. 48. *Leipz.* 1895. 8°.   Pam. 72.

SKRAUP (C.) Die Kunst der Rede und des Vortrags. pp. 284. *Leipz.* 1894. 8°.   11826. e. 33.

See also HOMILETICS : RECITATIONS : RHETORIC : VOICE.

Selected Speeches, etc.

JEBB (R. C.) The Attic Orators from Antiphon to Isaeus. 2 vol. *Lond.* 1893. 8°.   2280. f. 1.

CUCHEVAL (V.) Histoire de l'Éloquence romaine. 2 tom. *Paris*, 1893. 8°.   11805. dd. 34.

STEPHENS (H. M.) Principal Speeches of Statesmen of the French Revolution. 2 vol. 1892. 8°. Clarendon Press Series.   2319. b. 3.

REINACH (J.) Le "Conciones" français. L'éloquence française depuis la Révolution. pp. 473. *Paris*, 1894. 12°.   011824. de. 51.

STANLEY (E. H. S.) *Earl of Derby.* Speeches and Addresses. 2 vol. *Lond.* 1894. 8°.   012301. f. 21.

ELTON, Huntingdonshire. WHISTLER (R. F.) The History of Ailington or Elton. pp. 146. *Lond.* 1892. 8°.   10351. g. 30.

ELY, City and Diocese. JAMES (M. R.) The Sculptures in the Lady Chapel at Ely. pp. 68. *Lond.* 1895. 4°.   7875. e. 29.

WARD, LOCK AND Co. Illustrated handbook to Ely Cathedral. pp. 32. *Lond.* 1890. 8°.   010358. l. 23.

ELY, *Diocese of.* Ely Episcopal Records. pp. 558. *Lincoln*, 1891. 8°.   4999. d. 12.

EMBALMING. PARCELLY ( ) Étude des Embaumements. pp. 189. *Lyon*, 1891. 12°.   7391. e. 4.

EMBOLISM. *See* BLOOD.

EMBROIDERY. Ac. London. *South Kensington Museum.* Supplemental descriptive catalogue of Embroideries. pp. 49. *Lond.* 1891. 8°.   Pam. 18.

CATANEA PARASOLE (I.) Musterbuch für Stickerein und Spitzen. 1616. ff. 46. *Berl.* 1891. obl. fol.   1810. a. 25.

FARCY (L. de) La Broderie du XIᵉ siècle jusqu'à nos jours. *Angers*, 1890, *etc.* fol.   K.T.C. 4. a. 3.

FLEUSS (O.) Designs for Church Embroidery. *Lond.* 1894, *etc.* 4°.   2231.

GUERLIN (R.) Notice sur les Broderies exécutées par les Ursulines d'Amiens. pp. 15. *Paris*, 1891. 8°.   7807. cc. 4. (7.)

LAWLEY, afterwards WEIL (*Hon.* A. J.) Designs for Church Embroidery. *Lond.* 1894. 4°.   7742. ee. 17.

LONDON. *Society for the Encouragement of Indian Art.* Catalogue of a Loan Exhibition of Embroidery by Indian Women. pp. 44. *Lond.* 1893. 8°.   7743. c. 22.

MANUAL. Manual of modern Embroidery. pp. 27. *Lond.* 1893. 16°.   7742. a. 8.

MARSHALL (F.) and (H.) Old English Embroidery. pp. 138. *Lond.* 1894. 4°.   7743. e. 11.

MÜNTZ (E.) Tapisseries, broderies et dentelles. pp. 43. *Paris*, 1890. 4°.   7743. g. 17.

See also NEEDLEWORK.

EMBRYOLOGY. HELLIN (D.) Die Ursache der Multiparität der uniparen Tiere und der Zwillingsschwangerschaft beim Menschen. pp. 70. *München*, 1895. 8°.   7406. g. 24.

HERTWIG (O.) Text-book of Embryology of man and mammals. pp. 670. *Lond.* 1892. 8°.   7005. ccc. 8.

JANKE (H.) Embryologie und Infections-Krankheits-Uebertragung. pp. 104. *Berl.* 1894. 8°.   7580. cc. 12.

KORSCHELT (E.) and HEIDER (C.) Text-book of the Embryology of invertebrates. *Lond.* 1895, *etc.* 8°.   7299. c.

MANTON (W. P.) Syllabus of Lectures on human Embryology. pp. 125. *Phila.* 1894. 8°.   7580. aaa. 6.

MARSHALL (A. M.) Vertebrate Embryology. pp. 640. *Lond.* 1893. 8°.   07581. e. 19.

P.P. *Leipsic.* Archiv für Entwickelungsmechanik der Organismen. *Leipz.* 1894. *etc.* 8°.   P.P. 3208. d.

PRENANT (A.) Éléments d'Embryologie de l'homme et des vertébrés. *Paris*, 1891, *etc.* 8°.   7419. i. 15.

ROULE (L.) L'Embryologie générale. pp. 510. 1893. 8°. Bibliothèque des Sciences Contemporaines.   8709. b.

—— L'Embryologie comparée. pp. 1162. *Paris*, 1894. 8°.   7203. cc. 13.

ROUX (W.) Beitrag zur Entwickelungsmechanik des Embryo. 1892. 8°. Ac. Vienna. K. *Akademie.* Sitzungsberichte. Math. - naturwissenschaftliche Classe. Bd. 101. Hft. 1.   Ac. 810/6.

SCHUMANN (K.) Morphologische Studien. *Leipz.* 1892, *etc.* 8°.   7029. dd.

See also BIOLOGY.

EMDEN. FUERBRINGER ( ) Die Stadt Emden. pp. 323. *Emden*, 1892. 8°. 10256. aaa. 33.

MEER (B. v.) De Synode te Emden 1571. pp. 267. *'s Gravenhage*, 1892. 8°. 5015. ee. 6.

EMIGRATION. *See* COLONIES.

EMMAUS. SCHIFFERS (M. J.) Amwâs, das Emmaus des hl. Lucas. pp. 236. *Freiburg*, 1890. 12°.   10078. c. 26.

EMMENDINGEN. MAURER (H.) Emmendingen. pp. 112. *Emmendingen*, 1890. 8°.   10261. g. 5.

EMPLOYERS' LIABILITY ACT.
See CAPITAL AND LABOUR, *Laws, etc.*

ENAMELS. Ac. Troyes. *Musée de Troyes.* LE CLERT (L.) Émaux peints. Catalogue. pp. 43. *Troyes*, 1890. 8°.   Ac. 261/4.

BOWES (J. L.) Japanese Enamels. pp. 111. *Lond.* 1886. 4°.   7943. i. 18.

—— Notes on Shippo. Sequel to "Japanese Enamels." pp. 109. *Liverp.* 1895. 8°.   7807. l. 45.

GARDNER (J. S.) English Enamels. 1894. fol. CHURCH (A. H.) Some Minor Arts.   K.T.C. 24. b. 3.

GAUTIER (T.) Émaux et Camées. pp. 192. *Paris*, 1895. 12°.   11483. de. 43.

KONDAKOV (N. P.) Geschichte und Denkmäler des byzantinischen Emails. pp. 412. *Frankf.* 1892. 4°.   K.T.C. 25. b. 4.

LUTHMER (F.) Das Email. pp. 204. 1893. 8°. Seemanns kunstgewerbliche Handbücher. No. 9.   7805. de. 3.

RUPIN (E.) L'Œuvre de Limoges. *Paris*, 1890, *etc.* 4°.   7806. ee. 33.

WYZEWA (T. de) Dessins et modèles. Les Arts du Feu. pp. 143. *Paris*, 1892. 8°. 7944. h. 32.

See also CERAMICS : GLASS.

ENBORNE. Money (W.) Early History of the Parish of Enborne. pp. 17.
Newbury, 1893. 8°.   10348. e. 15. (7.)

ENCAUSTIC. *See* CERAMICS.

ENCYCLOPÆDIAS. Balch (W. R.) Ready Reference: the universal cyclopædia. pp. 812.
Lond. 1894. 8°.   012215. e. 1.

Beeton (S. O.) Illustrated Encyclopædia.
Lond. 1888, *etc.* 8°.   495.

Bruder (A.) Staatslexikon.
Freiburg, 1889, *etc.* 8°.   ˋ 012216. i.

Cooley (A. J.) Cyclopædia of practical Receipts. 2 vol. *Lond.* 1892. 8°.   2022. e.

Eastwick (R. W. E.) The Oracle Encyclopædia.
Lond. 1895, *etc.* 8°.   12215. ccc.

ENCYCLOPÆDIAS. Cassell's Storehouse of Information. *Lond.* 1891, *etc.* 8°.   1907.

—— Cassell's New Technical Educator.
Lond. 1892, *etc.* fol.   197.

—— The National Encyclopædia. 14 vol.
Lond. 1884–88. 8°.   12217. g.

—— The New Popular Educator. 8 vol.
Lond. 1888–92. 8°.   012215. f.

—— Ogilvie's Encyclopædia. pp. 653.
Lond. 1891. 4°.   012217. h. 5.

—— The Popular Encyclopedia.
Lond. 1890, *etc.*. 8°.   012217. h.

Johnson (A. J.) Johnson's Universal Cyclopædia. *N.Y.* 1893, *etc.* 8°.   2107. e.

Stevans (C. M-) Lee's Condensed Cyclopedia. pp. 384. *Chicago*, 1895. 16°.   12217. a. 8.

Smith (B. E.) Cyclopædia of Names.
pp. 1085. *Lond.* 1894. fol.   2112. g.

ENCYCLOPEDIAS. Sijthoff's Woordenboek voor Kennis en Kunst. *Leiden*, 1890, *etc.* 8°.
   012217. g.

Beleze (G.) Dictionnaire universel de la vie pratique. *Paris*, 1890, *etc.* 8°.   012216. i.

Bouant (É.) Dictionnaire-Manuel-illustré des sciences. pp. 807. *Paris*, 1894. 12°. 8706. a. 37.

ENCYCLOPÆDIAS. Encyclopédie Scientifique des aide-mémoire. *Paris*, 1892, *etc.* 8°.   8709. g.

Moulidars (T. de) Dictionnaire Encylopédique des connaissances utiles. pp. 1596.
Paris, 1891. 4°.   012217. h. 1.

P.P. *Paris.* Revue Encyclopédique.
Paris, 1891, *etc.* 4°.   P.P. 4283. k.

ENCYCLOPÆDIAS. Brockhaus' Konversations-Lexikon. *Leipz.* 1892, *etc.* 8°.   012215. l.

—— Gernandts Konversationslexikon.
Stockholm, 1891, *etc.* 8°.   012217. h.

—— Nordisk Conversationslexikon. 6 Bde.
Kjøbenh. 1884–90. 8°.   012216. m. 2.

Konow (S.) Norsk Lomme-Konversations-Lexikon. pp. 1073. *Kristiania*, 1891. 16°.
   12217. aa. 1.

Lütken (G.) Allers illustrerede Konversationsleksikon. *Kjøbenh.* 1892, *etc.* 8°.   012217. f.

ENCYCLOPÆDIAS. Diccionario Enciclopedico hispano-americano. *Barcelona*, 1887, *etc.* 4°.
   1878. c.

For Biblical and Theological Dictionaries and Encyclopædias, *see* THEOLOGY.

ENDOWMENTS. Geouffre de Lapradelle (A.) Théorie et pratique des Fondations perpétuelles. pp. 476. *Paris*, 1895. 8°.
   5408. aaa. 10.

ENGADINE. Strickland (F. de B.) The Engadine. A guide. pp. 339. *Lond.* 1891. 8°.
   10196. aa. 18.

P.P. *Saint Moritz.* The Alpine Post.
St. Moritz, 1892, *etc.* fol.   P.P. 9508. ab.

Wise (A. T. T.) Alpine Winter in its medical aspects. pp. 114. *Lond.* 1892. 8°. 7686. aa. 4.

ENGADINE—*continued.*

Heathcote (E. D.) Flowers of the Engadine. pp. 22. Pl. 224. *Winchester*, 1891. 8°.
   7054. g. 13.

See also ALPS: GRISONS: ROMANSCH LANGUAGE: SWITZERLAND.

ENGANO. Modigliani (E.) L' Isola delle Donne-Viaggio ad Engano. pp. 312.
Milano, 1894. 8°.   010055. h. 3.

ENGINEERING.

Bibliography.

Ac. *London. Institution of Civil Engineers.* Catalogue of the Library. 3 vol.
Lond. 1895. 8°.   BB.E. a. 10.

Galloupe (F. E.) Index to engineering periodicals, 1883–87. pp. 294. *Bost.* 1888. 8°.
   2022. a.

General.

Ac. *Madison. University of Wisconsin.* Bulletin. Engineering series.
Madison, 1894, *etc.* 8°.   Ac. 1792.

—— *Toronto. School of Practical Science.* Papers read before the Engineering Society.
Toronto, 1893, *etc.* 8°.   Ac. 4490.

Adams (H.) Designing wrought and cast Iron Structures. *Lond.* 1883, *etc.* 8°.   8767. cc.

Anglin (S.) The Design of Structures. pp. 503.
Lond. 1895. 8°.   8767. g. 32.

Baker (T.) Rudimentary treatise on engineering Surveying. pp. 231. *Lond.* 1891. 8°.
   8767. f. 1.

Baker (W. L.) The Beam; technical elements of girder construction. pp. 213.
Lond. 1892. 8°.   8765. b. 49.

Barberot (E.) Traité de Constructions civiles. pp. 917. *Paris*, 1895. 8°.   8768. ccc. 3.

Boulnois (H. P.) The Municipal Engineer's handbook. pp. 445. *Lond.* 1892. 8°.
   8777. bbb. 21.

Brewer (J. S.) Elementary Engineering.
pp. 136. *Lond.* 1893. 8°.   8767. f. 27.

Colombo (G.) Manuale dell' Ingegnere.
pp. 472. *Milano*, 1890. 8°.   012200. h. 14.

Dye (F.) Popular Engineering. pp. 469.
Lond. 1895. 8°.   8768. f. 14.

Longmans, Green and Co. Civil Engineering series. *Lond.* 1893, *etc.* 8°.   8768. f.

Martin (H. M.) Statically indeterminate Structures and the principle of least work.
pp. 71. *Lond.* 1895. 8°.   8768. bb. 14.

Masselin (O.) Dictionnaire des Connaissances utiles. pp. 612. *Paris*, 1891. 8°. 8767. l. 23.

Newman (J.) Scamping Tricks practised upon public works. pp. 129. *Lond.* 1891. 8°.
   7820. aa. 22.

Oslet (G.) Cours de Construction.
Brux. 1885, *etc.* 8°.   8767. l. 16.

P.P. *London.* The Engineering Magazine.
Lond. 1894, *etc.* 8°.   P.P. 1653. b.

—— *London.* The Engineering Review.
Lond. 1891, *etc.* 4°.   N.R.

—— *London.* Manufacturers' engineering Journal. *Lond.* 1892, *etc.* fol.   N.R.

—— *New York.* Cassier's Magazine. Engine r. ing, *etc.* *N.Y.* 1892, *etc.* 8°.   P.P. 1612. ca.

Reynolds (O.) Syllabus of lectures in Engineering at the Owens College. pp. 102.
Manch. 1894. 8°.   8767. f. 42.

Steiner (F.) Die Photographie im Dienste des Ingenieurs. *Wien*, 1891, *etc.* 8°.   8908. m.

Warren (W. H.) Engineering Construction. pp. 379. *Lond.* 1894. 8°.   8768. f. 13.

ENGINEERING.—General—*continued.*

WRAY (H.) Instruction in Construction.
pp. 453. *Lond.* 1891. 8°.   8831. c. 21.

See also BRIDGES : CEMENTS : ELASTICITY : HIGH-
WAYS : MACHINERY : SLIDE RULE : STRAINS AND
STRESSES.

Chemistry. *See* CHEMISTRY, *Applied.*

Drawing. *See* DRAWING.

Education.

Ac. London. *Institution of Civil Engineers.*
Engineering Education in the British Dominions. pp. 76. *Lond.* 1891. 8°. Ac. 4313/9.

—— London. *University College.* Account of
the new engineering Laboratories. pp. 32.
Lond. 1893. 4°.   8757. i. 26.

BAILEY (W. H.) Outside the Class-room;
thoughts for young engineers. pp. 20.
Manch. 1891. 8°.   8409. f. 31.

EWING (J. A.) University training of Engineers.
pp. 20. *Camb.* 1891. 8°.   8304. e. 19. (13.)

RIEDLER (A.) Zur Frage der Ingenieur-Erzie-
hung. pp. 35. 1895. 8°. Volkswirthschaftliche
Zeitfragen. Hft. 126.   8207. i.

Hand-books : Rules : Formulae, etc.

BENTLEY (W.) Rules and definitions arranged
for the use of students in Engineering. pp. 30.
Halifax, 1894. 8°.   8708. b. 23. (9.)

ENGINEER. Engineer's and Draughtsman's data
book. *Lond.* 1893. 8°.   8767. f. 31.

GANGĀRĀMA. Pocket book of Engineering. 2 pt.
Lahore, 1894. *obl.* 12°.   14117. a. 32.

HENDERSON (R.) Data for Engineers. pp. 28.
Lond. 1891. 8°.   8708. h. 16. (6.)

HURST (J. T.) Spons' Tables and Memoranda
for Engineers. pp. 278. *Lond.* 1893. 32°.
     8548. a. 32.

LEANING (J.) Specifications for the use of Engineers and builders. pp. 140. *Lond.* 1894. 8°.
     7817. b. 5.

MANAGER. Examples of engineering Estimates
and accounts. pp. 44. *Huddersfield,* 1887. fol.
     8228. l. 4.

MATHESON (E.) and GRANT (R. C.) Handbook
for Engineers. pp. 188. *Lond.* 1893. 12°.
     8767. e. 2.

MOLESWORTH (*Sir* G. L.) Pocketbook of Formulæ for Civil and Mechanical Engineers.
pp. 783. *Lond.* 1893. *obl.* 8°.   8767. de. 1.

P.P. *London.* The Engineer's Year book of
formulæ, *etc. Lond.* 1894, *etc.* 8°.
     P.P. 2491. cdb.

PIRRIE (J. S.) Practical Handy book for the use
of Engineers. pp. 289. *Melbourne,* 1890. 12°.
     8766. eee. 5.

TRAUTWINE (J. C.) Civil Engineer's pocket book.
pp. 866. *N.Y.* 1888. 8°.   8767. aa. 23.

WESTERN (R. W.) Simple Explanations of engineering formulae. pp. 75. *Lond.* 1892. 8°.
     8768. cc. 22.

History.

Ac. London. *Society of Engineers.* Facsimile
copy of the Society of Civil Engineers' proceedings from 1771. *Westminster,* 1893. 4°.
     Ac 4314/2.

DEBAUVE (A.) Les Travaux Publics et les ingénieurs des ponts et chaussées. pp. 443.
Paris, 1893. 8°.   8768. f. 11.

DUMONT (J. B.) Les grands Travaux du siècle.
pp. 480. *Paris,* 1891. 8°.   8766. g. 22.

FRITH (H.) Romance of Engineering. pp. 364.
Lond. 1892. 8°.   08235. e. 7.

FRITH (H.) Triumphs of modern Engineering.
pp. 323. *Lond.* 1891. 8°.   8767. cc. 14.

ENGINEERING.—History—*continued.*

HARCOURT (L. F. V.) Achievements in Engineering during the last half century. pp. 311.
Lond. 1891. 8°.   8768. cc. 11.

HOLMES (F. M.) Engineers and their triumphs.
pp. 160. *Lond.* 1894. 8°.   8767. g. 24.

WATT (J.) Story of Watt and Stephenson.
pp. 136. *Lond.* 1892. 8°.   10827 aa. 37.

Law relating to Engineers.

HUDSON (A. A.) Law of engineering contracts.
pp. 880. *Lond.* 1891. 8°.   6375. k. 10.

Marine. *See* NAVAL SCIENCE.

Materials, *Strength and Resistance of.*

BOVEY (H. T.) Theory of Structure and strength
of materials. pp. 817. *N.Y.* 1893. 8°.
     8767. k. 1.

DUQUESNAY ( ) Résistance des Matériaux.
pp. 187. 1892. 8°. Encyclopédie des aide-
mémoire.   8709. g.

DURAND (L.) La résistance des Matériaux simplifiée. pp. 142. *Saint-Étienne,* 1894. 4°.
     8534. f. 25.

FERNANDEZ FRIAS (R.) Resistencia de Materiales. pp. 511. *Santiago,* 1886. 8°.
     8768. m. 5.

GALLIZIA (P.) Resistenza dei Materiali e stabi-
lità delle costruzioni. pp. 336.
Milano, 1892. 8°.   012200. h. 13.

MADAMET (A.) Résistance des Matériaux.
pp. 486. *Paris,* 1891. 8°.   8767. dd. 15.

See also supra : Handbooks : STRAINS AND
STRESSES.

Mechanical. *See* MACHINERY : RAILWAYS, *etc.*

Military. *See* MILITARY SCIENCE.

Mining. *See* COAL : MINERALOGY.

Railway. *See* MACHINERY : RAILWAYS.

Sanitary. *See* DRAINAGE : SANITATION.

Tables. *See supra :* Hand-books.

Water.

SLAGG (C.) Water Engineering. pp. 309.
Lond. 1895. 8°.   8776. aaaa. 25.

See also CANALS : HYDRAULICS : RIVERS.

ENGINES, Steam, Gas, etc.
See MACHINERY.

**ENGLAND : GREAT BRITAIN AND
IRELAND.** [*See note on page 1.*]

Antiquities.

Ac. London. *Society of Antiquaries.* Prehistoric
Stone Monuments, Cornwall, by W. C. Lukis.
pp. 31. *Lond.* 1885. fol.   7703. b. 31.

BELL (A. M.) The later Age of Stone, in connection with remains found near Limpsfield.
pp. 54. *Westerham,* 1888. 8°.   Pam. 3.

SMITH (W. G.) Man, the primeval savage. His
haunts and relics from Bedfordshire to Blackwall. pp. 349. *Lond.* 1894. 8°.   07708. g. 23.

Ac. London. *School of Mines.* Handbook to
the Collection of British Pottery and Porcelain.
pp. 178. *Lond.* 1893. 8°.   7957. d. 8.

EVANS (A. J.) On a late-Celtic Urn-Field at
Aylesford. 1890. 4°. Ac. London. *Society of
Antiquaries.* Archæologia. Vol. 52, pt. 2.
     Cat. Dsk. I.

THOMAS (T. H.) Inscribed Stones. Pre-Norman
inscribed monumental stones of Glamorganshire.
pp. 13. *Cardiff,* 1893. 8°.   Pam. 3.

ASHLEY (W. J.) The Anglo-Saxon "Township."
pp. 19. *Bost., Mass.,* 1894. 8°.   Pam. 82.

FILES (G. T.) The Anglo-Saxon house. pp. 65.
Leipz. 1893. 8°.   7709. e. 8.

ENGLAND.—Antiquities—*continued.*

ANDREWS (W.) Old Church Lore. pp. 255.
Hull, 1891. 8°.   7709. b. 41.
TAYLOR (J.) Antiquarian Essays. pp. 383.
Bristol, 1895. 8°.   07708. g. 44.
See also ROME, *Antiquities, in England :* STONE-HENGE.

Army.

Bibliography.

G. B. & I. *Army.* Catalogue of English official
Military Works on sale, 1893.
Lond. 1894, *etc.* 8°.   011901. e.

General Works : History of the Army, etc.

ADYE (*Sir* J. M.) Recollections of a Military
Life. pp. 382. *Lond.* 1895. 8°.   10815. ee. 21.
ARNOLD-FORSTER (H. O.) Our Home Army.
pp. 152. *Lond.* 1892. 8°.   8831. f. 33.
CARTER (T.) War Medals of the British Army.
pp. 656. *Lond.* 1893. 8°.   8828. ff. 21.
CHICHESTER (H. M.) and SHORT (G. B.·) Records
and Badges of every Regiment in the Army.
pp. 568. *Lond.* 1895. 8°.   8829. cc. 26.
CLARKE (*Sir* A.) The Significance of the pro-
posed Barracks Loan. pp. 7. 1890. 4°.
         8830. k. 31. (4.)
DAVIES (W. W.) Tommy Atkins ; at home and
abroad. pp. 50. *Cadoxton Barry,* 1893. 4°.
         8829. h. 37. (3.)
ENGLAND. England's Battles by sea and land.
2 vol. *Lond.* 1888–90. 8°.   9502. g. 10.
GRANT (J.) British Battles. *Lond.* 1890–94. 4°.
         9503. i. 3.
G. B. & I. *Army.* The Army Book for the
British Empire. pp. 612. *Lond.* 1893. 8°.
         8830. d. 8.
—— English Army Lists, 1661–1714.
Lond. 1892, *etc.* 8°.   8829. l. 13.
—— Nicknames and traditions in the Army.
pp. 117. *Chatham,* 1891. 8°.   8831. f. 34.
—— Soldiers' Grievances. pp. 30.
Lond. 1891. 8°.   8831. f. 32. (3.)
IGNOTUS. Essential Foundation of real Army
Reform. pp. 48. *Lond.* 1892. 8°.
         8831. f. 32. (8.)
KILLEEN (L.) Soldiers at Sea. pp. 211.
Lond. 1893. 8°.   012330. f. 27.
KING (C. C.) The British Army and Auxiliary
Forces. *Lond.* 1892, *etc.* 4°.   8826. i.
MAC HARDY (W. B.) Scheme for establishing a
Society for each county to improve the status
of the Soldier on his return to civil life. pp. 26.
Lond. 1893. 8°.   8830. h. 26. (9.)
KNOLLYS (W. W.) Dashing Deeds afloat and
ashore. 8 pt. *Lond.* 1892. 8°.   10602. b. 24.
—— and ELLIOTT (W. J.) Heroes of the
Battlefield. pp. 440. *Lond.* 1895. 8°.
         9009. aaa. 24.
LONDON. *National Association for the Employ-
ment of Reserve Soldiers, etc.* Objects. Annual
Report. pp. 12. *Lond.* 1891. 8°. 8830. g. 32.
LLOYD (W. W.) On Active Service. Pl. 20.
Lond. 1890. *obl.* 8°.   1852. a. 7.
MAUDE (A.) A Plea for the Private. pp. 24.
Lond. 1890. 8°.   8831. l. 10. (9.)
MILNE (S. M.) Standards and Colours of the
Army, 1661–1881. pp. 257. *Leeds,* 1893. 8°.
         8830. l. 23.
P.P. *London.* Home District Military Guide.
Lond. 1894, *etc.* 8°.   P.P. 2486. kma.
—— The War Medal Record.
Lond. 1895, *etc.* 4°.   P.P. 4014. b. & 988.
PERRY (O. L.) Rank and Badges in Her
Majesty's Army and Navy. pp. 424.
Lond. 1888. 8°.   2249. a. 26.

ENGLAND.—Army—*continued.*

SIMKIN (R.) The Army. Illustrated in colours.
pp. 16. *Lond.* 1891. *obl.* fol.   8831. c. 17.
—— Our Armies illustrated and described.
Lond. 1894. *obl.* 4°.   8827. ee. 43.
SPALDING (H. S.) Epochs of the British Army.
Illustrated. pp. 52. *Lond.* 1891. 8°.
         8829. l. 9.
TANCRED (G.) Historical Record of Medals and
honorary distinctions conferred on the British
Army. pp. 483. *Lond.* 1891. 4°. 7757. e. 17.
VETUS. Letters on the administration of the
War Office. pp. 103. *Lond.* 1893. 8°.
         8829. aa. 19.
WALTON (C.) History of the British Standing
Army, 1660–1700. pp. 887. *Lond.* 1894. 8°.
         8830. l. 26.
WHITE (C. W.) Short Service and employment
of reserve soldiers. pp. 48. *Lond.* 1885. 8°.
         Pam. 2.
WOLSELEY (G. J.) *Viscount Wolseley.* Standing
Army of Great Britain. 1893. 8°. Armies of
to-day.   8829. i. 9.
WRIGHT (S.) Non-Commissioned Officer's Ex-
aminer. pp. 63. *Lond.* 1895. 8°. 8823. g. 30.
YOUNGHUSBAND (G. J.) The Queen's Commission.
pp. 254. *Lond.* 1891. 8°.   8824. c. 17.
See also MILITARY SCIENCE : VICTORIA CROSS.

Artillery. See infra : Queen's Regulations : GUNNERY.

Musketry Instruction. See GUNNERY.

Queen's Regulations : Warrants, etc.

G. B. & I. *Army.* List of and general index to
the Army Regulations and Instructions.
pp. 363. *Lond.* 1894. 8°.   6875. de. 16.
—— Queen's Regulations and Orders, 1893.
pp. 788. *Lond.* 1893. 8°.   2249. e. 3.
—— Field Army Establishments. Home defence.
pp. 161. *Lond.* 1892. 8°.   8829. aaa. 33.
—— Field Army Establishments. Service
abroad. pp. 207. *Lond.* 1892. 8°. 8829. aaa. 34.
—— Military Administration and staff duties.
pp. 53. *Lond.* 1891. 8°.   8831. f. 32. (4.)
—— Regulations for Mobilization for home
defence.—Regular Forces. pp. 67.
Lond. 1892. 8°.   Pam. 2.
—— Mobilization Tables for home defence.
List of Militia, Yeomanry, and Volunteer Units.
pp. 30. *Lond.* 1893. 8°.   Pam. 2.
—— Regulations for the equipment of her
Majesty's Army. 3 pt. *Lond.* 1890, 91. 8°.
         8830. bb. 24.
—— Regulations for equipment. Pt. 2. Details
of equipment, *etc. Lond.* 1890, *etc.* 8°.
         8830. bb. 24.
—— Regulations for Equipment. Pt. 3. War.
12 pt. *Lond.* 1893. 8°.   8830. aaa. 51.
—— Instructions for fitting the Valise equip-
ment. pp. 9. *Lond.* 1890. 8°.   Pam. 2.
—— Regulations for Encampments. pp. 50.
Lond. 1889. 16°.   8831. aa. 32.
—— Trumpet and Bugle Sounds. pp. 163.
Lond. 1891. 8°.   8830. bb. 42.
—— Royal Warrant for the pay, appointment,
promotion, *etc.* of the Army. 1893, *etc.* pp. 518.
Lond. 1893. 8°.   8830. bb. 41.
—— Regulations for the allowances of the Army.
pp. 208. *Lond.* 1895. 8°.   8832. aa. 2.
—— Financial Instructions in relation to army
accounts. pp. 203. *Lond.* 1892. 8°. 8831. f. 37.
—— Report on the system adopted for testing
the tactical fitness of Majors for command.
Lond. 1895, *etc.* fol.   8826. i. 31. (4.)

ENGLAND.—Army—*continued.*

G. B. & I. *Army.* Dress Regulations for Officers of the army. pp. 168. *Lond.* 1894. 8°. 8832. bb. 3.

—— Regulations for Recruiting. 1895. pp. 76. *Lond.* 1895. 8°. 8830. aaa. 64.

—— A Guide to Meat Inspection for officers in Bengal. pp. 12. *Calcutta,* 1893. 8°. 8831. f. 45.

—— Messing of the Soldier. pp. 34. *Lond.* 1892. 8°. Pam. 2.

—— Cavalry Drill. 1891. *Lond.* 1891, *etc.* 8°. 8831. aa. 39.

—— *Corps of Royal Engineers.* Regulations for Engineer services. pp. 369. *Lond.* 1892. 8°. 8830. bb. 30.

—— Royal Engineers, Dismounted. Field kit. *Lond.* 1892. fol. 1865. c. 4. (1.)

—— Garrison Artillery Drill. *Lond.* 1892, *etc.* 16°. 8831. aa. 44.

—— Field Artillery Drill. pp. 336. *Lond.* 1893. 16°. 8831. aa. 46.

—— Siege Artillery Drill. pp. 341. *Lond.* 1891. 16°. 8831. aa. 38.

—— Mountain Artillery Drill. pp. 176. *Lond.* 1891. 16°. 8831. aa. 37.

—— Handbook for Military Artificers. pp. 498. *Lond.* 1889. 16°. 8831. aa. 33.

—— Army Regulations for Ordnance Store Services. pp. 209. *Lond.* 1890. 8°. 8831. g. 56.

—— Infantry Sword Exercise. pp. 78. *Lond.* 1895. 8°. 8824. b. 47.

—— Infantry Drill. pp. 269. *Lond.* 1893. 16°. 8831. e. 11.

—— Regimental Transport. Infantry. pp. 19. *Lond.* 1889. 8°. Pam. 2.

—— Regulations for Army Medical Services. pp. 248. *Lond.* 1894. 8°. 8832. bb. 4.

—— Manual for the Medical Staff Corps. pp. 275. *Lond.* 1894. 8°. 8830. bb. 41.

—— Standing Orders for the Army Medical Staff. pp. 110. *Lond.* 1894. 8°. 8829. bb. 33.

—— Army Service Corps. Drills and Exercises. pp. 397. *Lond.* 1891. 16°. 8831. aa. 36.

—— Regulations for Army Service Corps Duties. pp. 144. *Lond.* 1893. 8°. 8830. aaa. 54.

—— Supply Handbook for the Army Service Corps. pp. 235. *Lond.* 1895. 8°. 8830. aaa. 63.

—— Regulations for Army Veterinary Services. pp. 86. *Lond.* 1894. 8°. 8831. aaa. 48.

—— Army School Regulations, 1891. pp. 85. *Lond.* 1891. 8°. Pam. 2.

—— Regulations for the Militia. 1894. pp. 379. *Lond.* 1894. 8°. 8829. aaa. 37.

—— Regulations under which Commissions in the Army may be obtained by officers of the Militia. pp. 10. *Lond.* 1893. 8°. Pam. 2.

—— Regulations for the Honourable Artillery Company. pp. 166. *Lond.* 1895. 8°. 8832. aa. 1.

—— Notes on Foot Drill for artillery volunteers. pp. 23. *Leeds,* 1891. 16°. 8831. cc. 13.

—— Orders and Regulations for Volunteers in brigade and regimental camps. pp. 23. *Lond.* 1893. 16°. 8831. aa. 1. (7.)

—— Regulations for the Volunteer Force, 1895. pp. 429. *Lond.* 1895. 8°. 8830. bb. 51.

—— Purchase of Land by volunteer corps. Extracts from the Military Lands Act, 1892. pp. 15. *Lond.* 1893. 8°. Pam. 2.

See also EXAMINATIONS : GUNNERY.

Regimental Histories and Standing Orders.

G. B. & I. *Army. Corps of Gentlemen-at-Arms.* History of Her Majesty's Body Guard, 1509–1892. pp. 242. *Lond.* 1892. 8°. 8829. m. 10.

ENGLAND.—Army—*continued.*

G. B. & I. *Army. Brigade of Foot Guards.* Brigade of Guards' Magazine. *Lond.* 1888, *etc.* 8°. P.P. 4039. d.

—— *Sixth Dragoon Guards.* Continuation of the historical Records, 1839–88, of the Carabiniers. pp. 76. *Chatham,* 1888. 8°. 8829. cc. 13.

LIDDELL (R. S.) Memoirs of the Tenth Royal Hussars. pp. 566. *Lond.* 1891. 8°. 8825. g. 24.

MOLE (E.) A King's Hussar : military memoirs, 1863–88, of a Troop Serjeant-Major of the 14th Hussars. pp. 360. *Lond.* 1893. 8°. 012330. g. 46.

FORTESCUE (Hon. J. W.) History of the 17th Lancers. pp. 245. *Lond.* 1895. 8°. 8829. l. 26.

CLEAVELAND (F. D.) Notes on the early History of the Royal Regiment of Artillery. pp. 271. 1892. 8°. 8823. dd. 42.

G. B. & I. *Royal Artillery.* Standing Orders of the Royal Regiment of Artillery. pp. 272. *Lond.* 1893. 8°. 8830. d. 9.

Ac. Woolwich. *Royal Military Academy.* Records of the Royal Military Academy. 2 pt. *Woolwich,* 1895. 4°. 8365. h. 31.

GROVES (J. P.) Illustrated histories of the Scottish Regiments. *Edinb.* 1893, *etc.* 4°. 8826. i.

CROMB (J.) The Highland Brigade. pp. 320. *Edinb.* 1893. 8°. 8829. bb. 31.

IVES (J. C.) The Buffs, E. K. Regt. pp. 60. *Canterbury,* 1891. 8°. Pam. 7.

G. B. & I. *Army. Northumberland Fusiliers.* Standing Orders. *Dover,* 1893. 8°. 8829. cc. 18.

—— St. George's Gazette. *Dublin, etc.,* 1883, *etc.* fol. P.P. 4039. m.

—— *The King's (Liverpool Regiment).* Historical record of the King's, Liverpool Regiment of Foot. pp. 361. *Lond.* 1883. 8°. 8829. k. 16.

—— *The Prince of Wales's Own (West Yorkshire Regiment).* Historical records of the 14th Regiment. pp. 415. *Devonport,* 1893. 8°. 8829. i. 14.

—— *Royal Scots Fusiliers.* Historical record of the Royal Scots Fusiliers. pp. 185. *Edinb.* 1885. 8°. 8829. cc. 14.

PATON (G.) Historical records of the 24th Regiment. pp. 370. *Lond.* 1892. 8°. 8830. cc. 21.

G. B. & I. *Army. King's Own Scottish Borderers.* Borderers' Chronicle. *Plymouth,* 1893, *etc.* 4°. N.R.

—— *Royal Inniskilling Fusiliers.* The Sprig of Shillelagh. *Portsmouth,* 1890, *etc.* 4°. N.R.

EVERARD (H. E. E.) History of T. Farrington's Regiment, the 29th, Worcestershire, Foot. pp. 598. *Worcester,* 1891. 4°. 8829. cc. 1.

G. B. & I. *Army. Thirtieth Regiment.* Records of the xxx. Regiment. pp. 283. *Lond.* 1887. 8°. 8829. cc. 16.

—— *East Surrey Regiment.* 1st Battalion, East Surrey Regiment. Battalion List. *Agra,* 1894, *etc.* 4°. 8829. b.

TRIROCHE (G.) Un congé au Queen's Royal Surrey Regiment. pp. 181. *Paris,* 1893. 8°. 8824. c. 38.

SWINEY (G. C.) Records of the 32nd (Cornwall) Light Infantry. pp. 386. *Lond.* 1893. 8°. 8824. dd. 40.

G. B. & I. *Army. South Staffordshire Regiment.* Extracts from the records of the First Battalion South Staffordshire Regiment. pp. 24. *Gibraltar,* 1887. 8°. 8830. d. 11. (6.)

—— *South Staffordshire Regiment.* History of the 2nd Battalion South Staffordshire Regiment. pp. 8. *Lichfield,* 1892. 8°. Pam. 2.

—— Historical Records of the 40th Regiment. pp. 620. *Devonport,* 1894. 8°. 8829. d. 43.

ENGLAND.—Army—*continued.*

G. B. & I. *Army. Oxfordshire Light Infantry.* History of the Oxford Lt. Infantry. pp. 19. *Wycombe*, 1892. 8°.　　　8830. d. 11. (9.)

—— *Oxfordshire Light Infantry.* The 43rd and 52nd Light Infantry Chronicle. *Lond.* 1893, etc. 8°.　　　8829. cc. 17.

—— Standing Orders of the 1st Battalion Oxfordshire Light Infantry. pp. 38. *Portsmouth*, 1890. 8°.　　　8830. bb. 40.

—— *Oxfordshire Light Infantry.* Oxfordshire Light Infantry Almanac. 1893. *Lond.* 1893. s. sh. fol.　　　1882. c. 1. (170.)

FYLER (A. E.) History of the 50th Regiment. pp. 380. *Lond.* 1895. 8°.　　　8829. i. 22.

ROGERSON (W.) Historical Records of the 53rd, Shropshire, Regiment. pp. 248. *Lond.* 1891. 8°.　　　8830. k. 14.

WOOLLRIGHT (H. H.) History of the Fifty-Seventh, West Middlesex, Regiment. pp. 406. *Lond.* 1893. 8°.　　　8829. cc. 15.

G. B. & I. *Army. Duke of Edinburgh's (Wiltshire) Regiment.* "The Nines." A paper for all interested in the Wiltshire Regiment. *Mandalay*, 1892, etc. 4°.　　　8825. b.

—— *North Staffordshire Regiment.* History of the Prince of Wales's North Staffordshire Regiment. pp. 9. *Lichfield*, 1892. 8°.　　　8830. d. 11. (10.)

—— *York and Lancaster Regiment.* Roll of the Officers of the York and Lancaster Regiment. 2 pt. *Lond.* 1885. 8°.　　　8831. k. 31.

—— *York and Lancaster Regiment.* The Tiger and the Rose. A monthly Journal. *Sheffield*, 1887, etc. 4°.　　　P.P. 4039. i.

—— *Welsh Regiment.* Men of Harlech. Newspaper for the men of the 2nd Battalion the Welsh Regiment. *Trimulgherry*, 1893, etc. 4°.　　　P.P. 4039. q. & 1549.

—— *Highland Light Infantry.* Highland Light Infantry Chronicle. *Glasg.* 1893, etc. 4°.　　　P.P. 4039. l.

—— *Gordon Highlanders.* 1st Battalion Gordon Highlanders. Standing Orders. pp. 37. *Colombo*, 1890. 8°.　　　8824. ccc. 11.

—— *Queen's Own Cameron Highlanders.* The 79th News. *Edinb.* 1891, etc. 4°.　　　P.P. 4039. la. & 950.

—— *Princess Victoria's Royal Irish Fusiliers.* Historical Record of the Eighty-ninth, Princess Victoria's, Regiment. pp. 235. *Chatham*, 1888. 8°.　　　8829. cc. 12.

GOFF (G. L. J.) Historical Records of the 91st Argyllshire Highlanders. pp. 361. *Lond.* 1891. 8°.　　　8829. k. 31.

G. B. & I. *Army. Prince of Wales's Leinster Regiment.* The Maple Leaf. A monthly paper. *Deesa, Poona, Tipperary*, etc., 1892, etc. 4°.　　　P.P. 4039. o. & 1462.

—— *Army. Royal Munster Fusiliers.* The Bengal Tiger, Regimental Paper. *Mandalay, Cawnpore*, etc., 1888, etc. fol. & 4°.　　　P.P. 4039. p.

—— *Rifle Brigade.* Rifle Brigade Chronicle. *Lond.* 1891, etc. 8°.　　　8830. d.

VERNER (W. W. C.) The First British Rifle Corps. The Rifle Brigade. pp. 149. *Lond.* 1890. 8°.　　　8831. aaa. 46.

G. B. & I. *Army Service Corps.* Standing Orders of the Army Service Corps. pp. 117. *Lond.* 1895. 8°.　　　8831. aaa. 60.

LLOYD-VERNEY (G. H.) Records of the Infantry Militia Battalions of the county of Southampton. pp. 447. *Lond.* 1894. 8°.　　　8829. l. 20.

ENGLAND.—*Army*—*continued.*

G. B. & I. *Army. Marines.* The Globe and Laurel. Journal of the Royal Marines. *Chatham*, 1892, etc. 4°.　　　N.R.

EDYE (L.) Historical records of the Royal Marines. *Lond.* 1893, etc. 8°.　　　8829. i.

Royal Military Academy, Woolwich. See WOOLWICH.

Royal Military College, Sandhurst. See SANDHURST.

Volunteers.

GRANT (C.) "Memo"s for the Volunteer Forces. pp. 91. *Glasg.* 1891. 16°.　　　8831. a. 82.

MAYHEW (C. G. A.) Guide to the training of Infantry Volunteers. pp. 47. *Lond.* 1893. 32°.　　　8823. aa. 33.

P.P. *London.* Volunteer Service Magazine. *Lond.* 1892, etc. 8°.　　　P.P. 4039. ba.

SCOTLAND. *West of Scotland Tactical Society.* Present Condition and future organisation of the Volunteer Force. pp. 431. *Lond.* 1891. 8°.　　　8830. bb. 27.

WILKINSON (H. S.) Citizen Soldiers. pp. 99. *Lond.* 1894. 8°.　　　8829. aaa. 38.

G. B. & I. *Army. Honourable Artillery Company of London.* The Ancient Vellum Book of the Honourable Artillery Company, 1611–82. pp. 186. *Lond.* 1890. 8°.　　　8823. cc. 55.

HAYHURST (T. H.) History and Records of the Volunteer movement in Bury, Heywood and Ramsbottom. pp. 332. *Bury*, 1887. 8°.　　　8829. aa. 26.

P.P. *Liverpool.* The Lancashire and Cheshire Volunteer. *Liverp.* 1895, etc. 8°.　　　P.P. 4039. hb. & 902.

MERRICK (E.) History of the Civil Service Rifle Volunteers. pp. 95. *Lond.* 1891. 8°. 8831. f. 35.

G. B. & I. *Army. Third Middlesex Rifle Volunteers.* Our Own Gazette. *Lond.* 1885–87. 4°.　　　P.P. 4038. c.

—— *Sixteenth Middlesex (London Irish).* London Irish Rifles Magazine. *Lond.* 1894, etc. 8°. 879.　　　P.P. 4038. d.

—— *Seventeenth Middlesex Rifle Volunteer Corps.* Our Gazette. *Lond.* 1889, etc. 8°. 8830. k. & 1934.

WILDE (E. T. R.) The Tower Hamlets Rifle Volunteer Brigade. pp. 41. *Lond.* 1892. 8°.　　　8830. g. 31.

ANDERSON (J. E.) Short account of the Mortlake Company of the Royal Putney and Mortlake Volunteer Corps, 1803–6. pp. 16. *Richmond*, 1893. 4°.　　　8829. h. 37. (2.)

See also supra : Queen's Regulations.

Yeomanry.

FELLOWS (G.) History of the South Notts. Yeomanry Cavalry. pp. 165. *Nottingham*, 1895. 4°.　　　8829. l. 22.

THOMSON (J. A.) History of the Fife Light Horse. pp. 283. *Edinb.* 1892. 4°. 8829. k. 17.

Chancery, Court of. *See infra : Law :* EQUITY.

Church of.

General : Doctrine, etc.

ADDERLEY (C. B.) *Baron Norton.* High and low Church. pp. 72. *Lond.* 1893. 8°. 4109. c. 29.

BATHE (A.) What I should believe. pp. 143. *Lond.* 1894. 8°.　　　4373. de. 42.

BLIGH (*Hon.* E. V.) Lord Ebury as a church reformer. pp. 363. *Lond.* 1891. 8°. 4109. g. 20.

BOUCHER (J. S.) Manual of Doctrine for Church teachers. pp. 280. *Lond.* 1891. 8°. 4109. c. 23.

BROOKE (S. A.) Reasons for secession from the Church of England. 2 pt. *Lond.* 1891. 8°.　　　4139. bbb. 21. (7.)

ENGLAND.—Church of—*continued.*

TREBLE (E. J.) Plain Teaching about the Church of England. pp. 187. *Lond.* 1893. 8°.
           4108. aa. 91.

VERITY (E. A.) Treason in the Camp. pp. 24. *Oldham,* 1894. 8°.   4109. k. 13. (11.)

WALSH (W.) Secret work of the Ritualists. pp. 44. *Lond.* 1895. 8°.   4109. aaaa. 20. (15.)

WANSTALL (C. L.) Why I belong to the Church of England. pp. 8. *Bedford,* 1885. 8°. Pam. 92.

WESTON (F. H.) The Church handy Dictionary. pp. 110. *Birmingham,* 1892. 8°. 4109. aaaa. 11.

WHITTUCK (C. A.) The Church of England and recent religious thought. pp. 308.
Lond. 1893. 8°.   4109. aaaa. 4.

WORDSWORTH (C.) *Bp. of Lincoln.* Theophilus Anglicanus. pp. 344. *Lond.* 1890. 8°.
           3939. aaa. 43.

———

ARBUTHNOT (R. K.) The Church and the working classes. pp. 32. *Lond.* 1893. 8°. Pam. 92.

BURNE (J. B.) Parson and peasant. pp. 260.
Lond. 1891. 8°.   012357. e. 4.

DAY (E. H.) Considerations for Church workers. pp. 47. *Lond.* 1895. 8°.   4421. aa. 58. (7.)

FRY (T. C.) Social Policy for the Church. pp. 128. *Lond.* 1893. 8°.   08275. e. 3.

JACOB (E.) The Divine Society; or, the Church's care of large populations. pp. 183.
Lond. 1890. 8°.   4421. c. 48.

MOORHOUSE (J.) *Bp. of Manchester.* Church Work: its means and methods. pp. 231.
Lond. 1894. 8°.   4499. cc. 29.

TRENCH (W. R.) The Church of the people. pp. 230. *Lond.* 1894. 8°.   4464. cc. 5.
See also THEOLOGY, *Pastoral.*

Anglican Orders.

BUTLER (M. R.) Brief catechism on English Orders. pp. 29. *Lond.* 1895. 16°.   Pam. 78.

——— Rome's Tribute to Anglican Orders. pp. 54. *Lond.* 1893. 8°.   Pam. 78.

BELLASIS (E.) Was Barlow a Bishop? pp. 16. *Lond.* 1890. 8°.   3939. ccc. 1. (6.)

CLARK (J.) De Successione Apostolica necnon missione et jurisdictione Hierarchiæ Anglicanæ et Catholicæ. pp. 509. *Georgiopoli,* 1890. 8°.
           3940. i. 6.

DALBUS (F.) Les Ordinations anglicanes. pp. 43. *Arras,* 1894. 8°.   3942. f. 4.

DENNY (E.) Anglican Orders and jurisdiction. pp. 237. *Lond.* 1893. 8°.   4429. c. 10.

——— De Hierarchia Anglicana dissertatio apologetica. pp. 265. *Londini,* 1895. 8°. 4109. c. 30.

FIRMINGER (W. K.) The Attitude of the Church of England to Non-Episcopal 'Ordinations.' pp. 75. *Lond.* 1894. 8°.   4109. k. 10.

——— Purity of the Apostolic Succession in the Church of England. pp. 28.
Zanzibar, 1895. 8°.   4109. bb. 35.

GREGORY (J. R.) Anglican Orders and Apostolical Succession. pp. 24. *Lond.* 1893. 16°.
           Pam. 92.

HADDAN (A. W.) Lectures on the Apostolical Succession in the Church of England. pp. 115. *N.Y.* 1893. 8°.   4109. aaaa. 15.

SMITH (J. B.) English Orders: whence obtained. pp. 133. *Lond.* 1893. 8°. 4109. aaaa. 7.

SMITH (S. F.) Reasons for rejecting Anglican Orders. pp. 150. *Lond.* 1895. 8°. 3939. aaa. 49.

WORDSWORTH (J.) *Bp. of Salisbury.* De validitate ordinum Anglicanorum Responsio ad Batavos. pp. 23. *Sarisburiae,* 1894. 8°. Pam. 92.
See also supra : General.

ENGLAND.—Church of—*continued.*

Catechism. See CATECHISMS.

Church of England and Dissent.

DYER (A. S.) Comparative table of English Nonconformity and the English Church.
Lond. 1893. *s. sh.* fol.   1897. c. 8. (106.)

FREE (R. W.) Church and Dissent. pp. 160.
Lond. 1893. 8°.   4109. e. 33.

HAMMOND (J.) Church or Chapel? pp. 390.
Lond. 1893. 8°.   4109. aaaa. 1.

HENSON (H. H.) " Is it honest?" Remarks on Archdeacon Sinclair's plea for "courtesy" between Churchmen and Dissenters. pp. 16.
Lond. 1892. 8°.   Pam. 92.

PROCTER (M. J.) Points of difference between the English, Roman and Protestant Churches. pp. 204 *Camb.* 1894. 8°.   3940. b. 10.

See also supra : General. Infra : Establishment : History, Ecclesiastical : Nonconformists.

Church of England in the Colonies.

ANSON (A. J. R.) *Bp. of Qu'Appelle.* The Church and her Work in new settlements. pp. 16.
Lond. 1893. 8°.   4475. g. 39. (20.)

BARRY (A.) *Bp. of Sydney.* Ecclesiastical expansion of England. pp. 387.
Lond. 1895. 8°.   4460. b. 1.

G. B. & I. *Colonies.* Ecclesiastical Provinces. pp. 39. *Lond.* 1888. 8°.   4109. c. 16. (5.)

WIRGMAN (A. T.) History of the English Church in South Africa. pp. 276. *Lond.* 1895. 8°.
           4744. bb. 11.

P.P. *Cape Town.* The Cape Church Monthly. *Cape Town,* 1892, *etc.* 8°.   P.P. 910. fh.

LANGTRY (J.) History of the Church in Eastern Canada and Newfoundland. pp. 256. 1892. 8°. Colonial Church Histories.   4421. dd.

EATON (A. W. H.) The Church of England in Nova Scotia. pp. 320. *Lond.* 1892. 8°.
           4745. cc. 41.

LEE (G. H.) Historical sketch of the first fifty years of the Church of England in the Province of New Brunswick. pp. 141.
Saint John, 1880. 8°.   4744. bb. 10.

ELLIS (J. B.) Sketch of the history of the Church of England in Jamaica. pp. 136.
Kingston, 1891. 8°.   4745. c. 36.

FARRAR (T.) Notes on the history of the Church in Guiana. pp. 226. *Berbice,* 1892. 8°.
           4745. bbb. 41.

GOODMAN (G.) The Church in Victoria, during the Episcopate of C. Perry, first Bp. of Melbourne. pp. 476. *Lond.* 1892. 8°. 4744. g. 13.

ROSS (C. S.) Story of the Otago Church. pp. 449. *Dunedin,* 1887. 8°.   4745. b. 34.
See also UNITED STATES OF AMERICA, *Protestant Episcopal Church.*

Church of England in Wales. See WALES.

Churchwardens. See CHURCHWARDENS.

Ecclesiastical Courts. See LAW, *Ecclesiastical.*

Establishment and Endowment, etc.

CRITICUS. The established Church and its Endowments. pp. 31. *Lond.* 1892. 8°.   Pam. 92.

ELWELL (E. S.) Abuse of public patronage in the Church. pp. 23. *Lond.* 1893. 8°.   Pam. 92.

ENGLAND, *Church of.* The Case for Disestablishment. pp. 276. *Lond.* 1894. 8°.
           4109. aaaa. 10.

——— *Church Defence Institution.* Church Defence handy volume. *Lond.* 1894. 8°.
           4109. bb. 29.

ENGLAND.—Churches—*continued.*

BALDWIN (F.) The old Churches of our Land. pp. 167. *Lond.* 1894. 8°. 4429. c. 46.

BONNEY (T. G.) Cathedrals, Abbeys and Churches of England and Wales. 2 vol. *Lond.* 1894, *etc.* 4°. 7814. h. 6.

FARRAR (F. W.) Our English Minsters. pp. 351. *Lond.* 1893. 8°. 07816. ee. 2.

MILNE (F. A.) Ecclesiology. pp. 327. 1894. 8°. Gentleman's Magazine Library. 2324. e. 9.

STATHAM (H. H.) The Cathedrals of England and Wales. pp. 79. *Lond.* 1894. fol. K.T.C. 16. a. 2.

VAN RENSSELAER (M. G.) English Cathedrals. pp. 395. *Lond.* 1892. 8°. K.T.C. 5. b. 20.

VENABLES (E.) Episcopal Palaces of England. pp. 253. *Lond.* 1895. 4°. 4705. f. 21.

Ac. Manchester. *Chetham Society.* Remains. Vol. 32. N. S. Notes on the Churches of Cheshire. pp. 152. *Manch.* 1894. 4°. Ac. 8120.

CRANAGE (D. H. S.) Architectural account of the Churches of Shropshire.
Wellington, 1894, *etc.* 4°. 7814. h.

SOIL (E. J.) Le Yorkshire et le nord-est de l'Angleterre. Excursion de la Gilde de Saint-Thomas. pp. 52. *Bruges*, 1894. 4°. 10368. h. 34.
See also infra : Topography : ARCHITECTURE.

Civil Service.

CHASTER (A. W.) The Powers, duties and liabilities of Executive Officers. pp. 307. *Lond.* 1891. 8°. 6281. g. 17.

CIVIL SERVANT. Heads and tails in the Civil Service. pp. 35. *Lond.* 1887. 8°. Pam. 67.

JOHNSTON (R.) Civil Service guide. pp. 223. *Lond.* 1891. 8°. 8006. aaa. 9.

PITMAN (I.) Civil Service guide. pp. 77. *Lond.* 1893. 8°. 8008. bbb. 22.

P.P. *London.* Clark's Civil Service Annual. *Lond.* 1894, *etc.* 8°. P.P. 2486. kpa.
See also EXAMINATIONS.

Colonies and Dependencies.

See also under the name of each Colony and Dependency.

Bibliography.

Ac. London. *Royal Colonial Institute.* Catalogue of the Library. pp. 543. *Lond.* 1895. 8°. 011900. k. 9.

CAMPBELL (F. B. F.) Imperial Federation series of Colonial State-Paper Catalogues. *Lond.* 1893, *etc.* 8°. 011900. ee.

P.P. *London.* Torch and Colonial Book Circular. *Lond.* 1887–92. 8°. P.P. 6481. fa.

Church of England in. See supra, Church of : MISSIONS.

History, Geography, etc.

Ac. London. *Royal Colonial Institute.* Journal of the Royal Colonial Institute. *Lond.* 1890, *etc.* 8°. Ac. 2270/3.

LONDON. *Imperial Institute.* Imperial Institute. Description and Prospectus. pp. 64. *Lond.* 1892. 8°. 8154. g. 25.

—— Year Book of the Imperial Institute. *Lond.* 1892, *etc.* 8°. 2121. d.

CALDECOTT (A.) English Colonization and Empire. pp. 277. 1891. 8°. KNIGHT (W.) University Extension Manuals. Vol. 1. 12204. f.

CLAYDEN (A.) British Colonisation. pp. 40. *Lond.* 1891. 8°. Pam. 66.

GIBBINS (H. de B.) British Commerce and Colonies. pp. 136. 1893. 8°. Methuen's Commercial Series. 08227. de.

G. B. & I. *Colonies.* Arms or Badges of the Colonies. *Lond.* 1881. fol. 1861. d. 23.

ENGLAND.—Colonies—*continued.*

GRESWELL (W. H. P.) Outlines of British Colonisation. pp. 358. *Lond.* 1893. 8°. 8154. dd. 10.

LECKY (W. E. H.) The Empire, its value and its growth. pp. 48. *Lond.* 1893. 8°. 8139. aaa. 46.

MAZEPPA (H. T.) A new yet ancient System of Politics. *Lond.* 1892, *etc.* 8°. 8154. aaa. 42.

NAVEZ (L.) Les causes et les conséquences de la Grandeur coloniale de l'Angleterre. pp. 56. *Bruxelles*, 1890. 8°. Pam. 66.

O'RELL (M.) John Bull & Co. The colonial branches of the Firm. pp. 322. *Lond.* 1894. 8°. 10025. de. 6.

PAUL (A.) A short view of Greater Britain. *Lond.* 1895. 4°. 1865. c. 9. (10.)

—— How Great Britain became Greater Britain. pp. 14. *Lond.* 1895. 8°. 9005. d. 26. (14.)

PELHAM (H. F.) The Imperial Domains and the Colonate. pp. 28. *Lond.* 1890. 8°. 9004. m. 4. (7.)

ROBINSON (H. J.) Colonial Chronology. pp. 304. *Lond.* 1892. 4°. 9009. m. 2.

SEELEY (*Sir* J. R.) The Expansion of England. pp. 359. *Lond.* 1895. 8°. 9525. aa. 17.

TEMPLE (A.) The making of the Empire. pp. 288. *Lond.* 1895. 8°. 9009. c. 17.

THWAITE (B. H.) The Electoral Government of Greater Britain. pp. 27. *Lond.* 1895. 8°. Pam. 66.

———————————

BRITAIN. Broader Britain. Photographs. 12 pt. *Lond.* 1895. *obl.* fol. 1787. aa. 30.

DAWSON (G. M.) and SUTHERLAND (A.) Geography of the British Colonies. pp. 330. 1892. 8°. Macmillan's Geographical Series. 10004. b. 3.

HUGHES (W.) and WILLIAMS (J. F.) Geography of the British Colonies. pp. 232. 1892. 8°. Philips' Geographical Manuals. 10006. de.

LAWSON (W.) Geography of the British Colonies. pp. 36. *Edinb.* 1894. 16°. 10003. aaaa. 48.

MEIKLEJOHN (J. M. D.) The British Empire : its geography, *etc.* *Lond.* 1891. 8°. 10024. cc. 12.

NIOX (G. L.) Géographie. Empire britannique. pp. 472. *Paris*, 1893. 8°. 10004. cc. 1.

PARKIN (G. R.) Round the Empire. pp. 263. *Lond.* 1892. 8°. 10005. aaa. 24.

JENKYNS (C. C.) Hard Life in the Colonies. pp. 365. 1892. 8°. The Adventure Series. 012207. k.

WORLD. The English-Speaking world. Photographs. pp. 192. *Lond.* 1895. *obl.* 4°. 1787. aa. 29.

Imperial Federation, Defence, etc.

Ac. Edinburgh. *Scottish Geographical Society.* Britannic Federation. pp. 180. *Lond.* 1892. 8°. Ac. 6182/2.

BENNETT (A.) The Dream of an Englishman. pp. 190. *Lond.* 1893. 8°. 8154. aa. 17.

BRASSEY (T.) *Baron Brassey.* Papers and Addresses. Imperial Federation. 5 vol. *Lond.*, 1894–95. 8°. 8806. ccc. 15.

CUNINGHAM (G. C.) Scheme for Imperial Federation. pp. 116. *Lond.* 1895. 8°. 8154. aaa. 48.

DILKE (*Sir* C. W.) and WILKINSON (H. S.) Imperial Defence. pp. 234. *Lond.* 1892. 8°. 8830. bb. 29.

G. B. & I. Decadence of Imperial Britain. pp. 56. *Dublin*, 1893. 8°. 8139. aaa. 11.

HERVEY (M. H.) Trade policy of Imperial Federation. pp. 182. *Lond.* 1892. 8°. 08276. e. 27.

ENGLAND.—Colonies—*continued.*

DE LABILLIÈRE (F. P.) British Federalism.
Lond. 1893. 8°.   Pam. 66.

LITTLE (J. S.) The United States of Britain.
pp. 32. *Guildford*, 1887. 8°.   Pam. 66.

—— A Vision of empire. pp. 24.
Guildford, 1889. 8°.   Pam. 66.

MEDLEY (G. W.) Fiscal federation of the Empire.
Lond. 1892. 8°.   8228. bb.

PARKIN (G. R.) Imperial Federation. pp. 314.
Lond. 1892. 8°.   8154. aaa. 41.

STUART-CANSDELL (C.) Federation, Colonial and
British. pp. 116. *Sydney*, 1891. 8°.
                                       8154. cc. 11.

TAYLOR (H. D'E.) Disruption of the Empire.
pp. 8. *Melbourne*, 1886. 8°.   Pam. 66.

Law, Constitutions, etc.

FEURTADO (W. A.) Index to the Laws relating
to the Colonies. pp. 52. *Kingston*, 1890. 8°.
                                       6605. aaa. 5.

MILLS (A.) Colonial Constitutions. pp. 55.
Lond. 1891. 8°.   Pam. 66.

TARRING (C. J.) Chapters on the Law relating
to the Colonies. pp. 478. *Lond.* 1893. 8°.
                                       6605. bb. 20.

TODD (A.) Parliamentary Government in the
British Colonies. *Lond.* 1894. 8°. 8155. ee. 20.

Trade and Finance.

CHALMERS (R.) History of Currency in the
British Colonies. pp. 496. *Lond.* 1893. 8°.
                                       08229. g. 46.

FUCHS (C. J.) Die Handelspolitik Englands
und seiner Kolonien in den letzten Jahrzehnten.
pp. 358. 1893. 8°. Ac. Leipsic. *Verein für
Socialpolitik.* Schriften. Bd. 57. Ac. 2322.

GRESWELL (W. H. P.) British Colonies and
their Industries. pp. 132. *Lond.* 1893. 8°.
                                       10003. aaaa. 47.

GREY (H. G.) *Earl Grey.* Commercial policy of
the British Colonies and the McKinley Tariff.
pp. 79. *Lond.* 1892. 8°.   08227. g. 28.

LYDE (L. W.) Commercial geography of the
British Empire. pp. 156. 1894. 8°. Methuen's
Commercial Series.   08227. de.

SCOTT (B. J.) Colonial Government securities.
pp. 4. *Lond.* 1887. 4°.   Pam. 23.

Commons, House of. *See infra, Parliament.*

Constitution and Government.

ANSON (*Sir* W. R.) Law and custom of the
Constitution. *Oxf.* 1892, *etc.* 8°.   2228. cc. 9.

BOUTMY (É. G.) Studies in constitutional Law.
pp. 183. *Lond.* 1891. 8°.   8008. bbb. 20.

—— The English Constitution. pp. 212.
Lond. 1891. 8°.   8008. bbb. 19.

CARBONNAT (C. de) Les Institutions de l'Angleterre œuvre du temps et des circonstances.
pp. 16. *Toulouse*, 1891. 8°. 9004. gg. 27. (7.)

DICEY (A. V.) Introduction to the study of the
Law of the Constitution. pp. 454.
Lond. 1893. 8°.   2230. bb. 2.

DISRAELI (B.) *Earl of Beaconsfield.* Vindication
of the English Constitution. pp. 307.
Lond. 1895. 12°.   8133. aa. 21.

FROMAGEOT (H.) Étude sur les pouvoirs des
Commissions politiques d'enquête en Angleterre.
pp. 39. *Paris*, 1893. 8°.   6605. h. 26. (9.)

GOODNOW (F. J.) Analysis of the administrative
systems of the U.S., England, France and
Germany. 2 vol. *N.Y.* 1893. 8°. 6005. h. 10.

HALL (W. E.) Treatise on the foreign powers
and jurisdiction of the British Crown. pp. 304.
Oxf. 1894. 8°.   06955. df. 18.

ENGLAND.—Constitution, etc.—*cont.*

HAYNES (T. H.) The Veto of the Crown.
pp. 15. *Lond.* 1893. 8°.   8139. aa. 53. (19.)

INDERMAUR (J.) and THWAITES (C.) Student's
Guide to constitutional Law. pp. 128.
Lond. 1894. 8°.   6005. b. 2.

PORRITT (E.) The Englishman at Home.
pp. 379. *N.Y.* 1893. 8°.   8139. aa. 54.

REGIDOR Y JURADO (A. M.) La Gran Bretaña.
pp. 20. *Madrid*, 1893. 8°.   Pam. 68.

TUCKERMANN (F.) Upon the Royal Prerogative
in England. pp. 108. *Heidelberg*, 1894. 8°.
                                       8139. dd. 4.

WENDT (G.) England. Seine Geschichte und
Verfassung. pp. 349. *Leipz.* 1892. 8°.
                                       10348. e. 22.

WENZEL (J.) Comparative view of the executive
and legislative Departments of the U.S., France,
England and Germany. pp. 22.
Bost. 1891. obl. 8°.   8010. a. 3.

WICKS (F.) The British Constitution and
government. pp. 149. *Lond.* 1892. 8°.
                                       8009. aa. 17.

BROWNING (O.) The Citizen, his rights and
responsibilities. pp. 233. *Lond.* 1893. 8°.
                                       8139. de. 3.

HUGHES AND Co. Constitutional Reader. pp. 212.
Lond. 1893. 8°.   8139. aaa. 43.

MALDEN (H. E.) Life and duties of a Citizen.
pp. 206. *Lond.* 1894. 8°.   8009. b. 31.

PARROTT (J. E.) Life and duties of the Citizen.
Handbook for teachers. pp. 136.
Lond. 1893. 8°.   8139. a. 32.

—— Industrial and social life and duties of the
Citizen. pp. 128. *Lond.* 1894. 8°. 8139. b. 41.

—— The Waterloo Citizen Reader. pp. 136.
Lond. 1893. 8°.   8139. b. 39.

SMITH (G. A.) The Citizen of England. pp. 192.
Lond. 1895. 8°.   8139. aaa. 49.

STONE (J. H.) and JONSON (B.) The Civic
Reader. pp. 240. *Lond.* 1893. 8°. 8139. b. 40.

WYATT (C. H.) The English Citizen. pp. 348.
Lond. 1893. 8°.   8139. a. 33.

See also infra: Parliament: CONSTITUTIONS;
GOVERNMENT.

Constitutional History.

FEILDEN (H. St. C.) Short constitutional History
of England. pp. 358. *Oxf.* 1895. 8°.
                                       09504. h. 1.

GNEIST (H. R. v.) History of the English
Constitution. pp. 791. *Lond.* 1891. 8°.
                                       2394. f. 1.

MEDLEY (D. J.) Student's manual of English
constitutional History. pp. 583. *Oxf.* 1894. 8°.
                                       09504. ee. 4.

MONTAGUE (F. C.) Elements of English constitutional History. pp. 240. *Lond.* 1894. 8°.
                                       9504. c. 3.

POLLOCK (*Sir* F.) and MAITLAND (F. W.) History
of English Law before Edward I. 2 vol.
Camb. 1895. 8°.   2228. cc. 1.

WAKEMAN (H. O.) and HASSALL (A.) Essays
introductory to the study of English constitutional History. pp. 349. *Lond.* 1891. 8°.
                                       9505. bbb. 10.

VINOGRADOV (P. G.) Villainage in England.
pp. 464. *Oxf.* 1892. 8°.   2240. d. 23.

PROTHERO (G. W.) Select Statutes, *etc.* illustrative of the reigns of Elizabeth and James I.
pp. 464. *Oxf.* 1894. 8°.   2230. a. 19.

MAC CULLAGH TORRENS (W. T.) History of
Cabinets. From the Union with Scotland.
2 vol. *Lond.* 1894. 8°.   09504. f. 13.

See also infra: History.

ENGLAND—*continued.*

County Councils. *See* LOCAL GOVERNMENT.

County Courts. *See* COUNTY COURTS.

Finance. *See infra : Trade.*

Geography. *See infra : Topography.*

Harbours. *See* PORTS.

History.

Bibliography.

CHEVALIER (C. U. J.) Angleterre. Topo-bibliographie. pp. 79. *Montbéliard*, 1893. 8°.
          Pam. 6.

GARDINER (S. R.) and MULLINGER (J. B.) Introduction to the study of English History. pp. 468. *Lond*. 1894. 8°.   BB.M. a. 8.

ENGLAND AND WALES. *Public Record Office.* Descriptive Catalogue of ancient deeds in the Public Record Office. *Lond*. 1890, *etc*. 8°.
       Cat. Desk. D.

—— Calendar of Patent Rolls. *Lond*. 1891, *etc*. 8°.   2076. g.

—— Lists and Indexes. *Lond*. 1892, *etc*. fol.
       9505. i.

—— Catalogue of English, Scotch and Irish Record Publications. *Lond*. 1888. *etc*. 8°.
       011901. f.

BIRD (S. R. S.) Guide to documents in the Public Record Office. pp. 355. *Lond*. 1891. 8°.
       Cat. Desk. B.

LIEBERMANN (F.) Literatur von etwa 1890–1892 zur Geschichte Englands.
Freiburg, 1892. 8°.   Pam. 6.

General.

ACLAND (A. H. D.) and RANSOME (C.) Handbook of the political History of England. pp. 318. *Lond*. 1894. 8°.   2394. b. 3.

AIRY (O.) Text-book of English History. 3 pt. *Lond*. 1893. 8°.   9503. ccc. 18.

AUBREY (W. H. S.) Rise and growth of the English Nation. *Lond*. 1895, *etc*. 8°. 9502. e. 2.

BAIN (F. W.) The English Monarchy. pp. 226. *Lond*. 1894. 8°.   8139. dd. 3.

BARTLE (G.) Synopsis of English History. pp. 318. *Lond*. 1893. 8°.   9503. b. 25.

BAYLIS (M. S.) Churchman's History of England. pp. 268. *Lond*. 1895. 8°.   9503. b. 38.

BLACKIE (W. G.) Comprehensive History of England. *Lond*. 1894, *etc*. 8°.   9504. h.

BREWSTER (H. P.) and HUMPHREY (G. H.) England and its rulers. pp. 313.
Chicago, 1892. 8°.   9504. d. 9.

BRITISH EMPIRE. Graphic History of the British Empire. pp. 803. *Lond*. 1890. 8°. 9503. ee. 15.

—— Brief History of the British Empire. pp. 287. 1891. 8°. Nelson's School Series. 12202. dd.

BUCKLEY, *aft.* FISHER (A. B.) High school History of England. pp. 427. *Toronto*, 1891. 8°.
       9503. c. 34.

—— History of England. pp. 151. 1892. 8°. History Primers.   2378. a.

BURROWS (M.) Commentaries on the History of England. pp. 533. *Edinb*. 1893. 8°. 2394. d. 2.

CARPENTER (H. J. B.) and GREEN (G. E.) Outlines of British History. pp. 262.
Lond. 1892. 8°.   9503. cc. 24.

CARTER (G.) Outlines of English History, 1066–1815. pp. 130. *Lond*. 1891. 8°. 9503. bb. 37.

CURTIS (J. C.) Outlines of English History. pp. 48. *Lond*. 1891. 8°.   9503. aaa. 11.

ENGLAND. Little History of England. pp. 204. *Lond*. 1895. 8°.   9504. cc. 8.

—— A short History of England. pp. 172. *Lond*. 1890. 8°.   9503. cc. 19.

ENGLAND.—History—*continued.*

FALLON (D.) Outlines of English History. *Malta*, 1890, *etc*. 8°.   9503. cc.

FEARENSIDE (C. S.) Intermediate text-book of English History. 1893, *etc*. 8°. Tutorial Series.
       12205. c. 165.

GARDINER (S. R.) Student's History of England. *Lond*. 1892, *etc*. 8°.   9502. e. 1.

GIBSON (J.) History made easy. pp. 192. *Lond*. 1893. 8°.   9503. cc. 26.

GREEN (J. R.) History of the English People. 4 vol. *Lond*. 1895. 8°.   9504. ddd. 1.

HIGGINSON (T. W.) and CHANNING (E.) English History for American Readers. pp. 334. *N.Y*. 1893. 8°.   9504. e. 4.

HOSMER (J. K.) Short History of Anglo-Saxon freedom. pp. 420. *Lond*. 1890. 8°. 8008. d. 3.

LINGARD (J.) The History of England. 10 vol. *Dublin*, 1888. 8°.   09504. ee. 3.

LONGMANS, GREEN AND Co. Summary of English History. pp. 160. *Lond*. 1892. 8°.
       9503. cc. 25.

LOW (S. J. M.) and PULLING (F. S.) Dictionary of English History. *Lond*. 1895, *etc*. 8°.
       9505. e, 9.

M., J. M. D. Outlines of the History of England. pp. 82. *Lond*. 1890. 8°.   9503. cc. 18.

MAJOR (J.) History of Greater Britain. pp. 476. 1892. 8°. Ac. Edinburgh. *Scottish History Society*. Publications. Vol. 10.   Ac. 8256.

MALDEN (H. E.) English Records. pp. 239. *Lond*. 1894. 8°.   9504. e. 5.

OMAN (C. W. C.) History of England. pp. 760. *Lond*. 1895. 8°.   9502. ee. 1.

PITT (G.) English History, with its wars left out! pp. 114. *Mitcham*, 1893. 8°. 9505. b. 26.

PRINGLE (R. S.) Junior History of England. pp. 56. *Manch*. 1891. 8°. 9004. gg. 24. (11.)

—— Local Examination History. pp. 199. *Manch*. 1894. 8°.   9503. bbb. 36.

RANSOME (C.) Elementary History of England. pp. 250. *Lond*. 1894. 8°.   9503. aa. 15.

—— Advanced History of England. pp. 1069. *Lond*. 1895. 8°.   9503. cc. 33.

SANDERSON (E.) The Story of England. pp. 256. *Lond*. 1892. 8°.   9503. bb. 41.

—— Our Country. pp. 208. *Lond*. 1892. 8°.
       9503. bb. 40.

—— History of England. pp. 1098. *Lond*. 1893. 8°.   09504. f. 12.

—— Summary of British History. pp. 206. *Lond*. 1893. 8°.   9504. ccc. 13.

SMITH (E. J. S.) Historica Prima. Class-book of English history. pp. 148. *Lond*. 1891. 12°.
       9503. aaa. 14.

SPRY (J.) Student's note-book of English History. pp. 290. *Lond*. 1891. 8°. 9505. bbb. 9.

TRAILL (H. D.) Social England. *Lond*. 1894, *etc*. 8°.   2083. a.

WENDT (G.) England. Seine Geschichte. pp. 349. *Leipz*. 1892. 8°.   10348. e. 22.

WHITE (F. A.) Civil Service History of England. pp. 192. 1890. 8°. Civil Service Series.
       2238. a. 10.

WRIGHT (H. F.) Intermediate History of England. pp. 461. *Lond*. 1892. 8°. 9503. ccc. 22.

Ac. London. *University.* Questions on English History. pp. 50. 1891. 8°. Tutorial Series.
       12205. c. 50.

—— Oxford. *University.* Oxford and Cambridge Local Examination Papers in English History. *Lond*. 1891. 8°.   9503. c. 31.

ENGLAND.—History—*continued.*

Chronological Tables, Dates, etc.

ASHTON (J.) Letts's Date Book and chronological diary. pp. 294. *Lond.* 1893. 8°. 09504. g. 3.

BEETON (S. O.) Date Book. When was it? pp. 282. *Lond.* 1892. 8°. 9505. aaa. 5.

ENGLISH HISTORY. Note-book of English History. pp. 39. *Morija*, 1893. 8°. 9503. ccc. 21.

—— Fifty notes on English History. pp. 27. *Sudbury*, 1891. 8°. 9004. m. 4. (10.)

GREEN (F. L.) Main facts and dates of British History. pp. 93. *Lond.* 1893. 8°. 9504. cc. 3.

GRICE (W.) Dates and data of English History. *Bognor*, 1893, *etc.* 4°. 9503. ee. 18.

LOGAN (R.) Genealogical chart of the Royal Family of Great Britain. *Edinb.* 1891. fol. 1850. d. 14.

MACKECHNIE (A. L.) Dates of the Sovereigns of England. *Lond.* 1895. 8°. 11601. d. 24. (18.)

MĀDHOPRASĀDA. Chronological pocket History of England. pp. 16. *Mirzapur*, 1891. 8°. Pam. 28.

SCAIFE (A. H.) Synoptical chart of English History. *Canada*, 1894. *s. sh.* fol. Tab. 1700 d.

TIMMIS (I. A.) Chronological and heraldic Charts of the Royal House of England. *Lond.* 1890. fol. 1850. c. 17.

Constitutional History. See supra : Constitution.

History of Various Periods : Essays, etc.

ARCHER (T.) Stories and biographies from English History, 1066-1485. pp. 208. 1890. 8°. Century Historical Readers. No. 4. 9503. d.

ARNOLD-FORSTER (H. O.) Things new and Old. 2 pt. 1893. 8°. Cassell's Modern School Series. 12205. aa.

ASKIN (P.) Lectures on four great Rulers. 4 pt. *Dublin*, 1893. 8°. 9512. bb. 14.

BURROWS (M.) History of the foreign policy of Great Britain. pp. 372. *Edinb.* 1895. 8°. 9073. d. 13.

DALGLEISH (W. S.) Periods of English History. *Lond.* 1892, *etc.* 8°. 9504. d. 22.

ENGLISH HISTORY. Great deeds in English History. pp. 118. 1891. 8°. Bell's Reading Books. 12203. cc.

—— Stories from English History for young Americans. pp. 784. *N.Y.* 1892. 8°. 9503. c. 32.

GEORGE (H. B.) Battles of English History. pp. 334. *Lond.* 1895. 8°. 2394. d. 3.

GRANT (J.) British Battles on land and sea. *Lond.* 1890-94. 4°. 9503. i. 3.

HARDY (W. J.) Handwriting of the Kings and Queens of England. pp. 176. *Lond.* 1893. 8°. 7709. k. 21.

LEADMAN (A. D. H.) Prœlia Eboracensia. Battles fought in Yorkshire. pp. 192. *Lond.* 1891. 8°. 9510. g. 2.

LEGG (J. W.) The Sacring of the English Kings. pp. 17. *Lond.* 1894. 8°. 3477. e. 10.

LINDSAY (J. L.) *Earl of Crawford.* Bibliotheca Lindesiana. Hand-List of Proclamations. *Aberd.* 1893, *etc.* fol. 11901. i.

LONGMANS, GREEN AND Co. 'Ship' Historical Readers. *Lond.* 1893, *etc.* 8°. 9503. d.

W., E. A. Old England : sketches of English history. pp. 232. *Lond.* 1892. 4°. 9503. g. 3.

WALL (J. C.) Tombs of the Kings of England. pp. 485. *Lond.* 1891. 8°. 9503. ee. 16.

WARNER (B. E.) English History in Shakespeare's Plays. pp. 321. *N.Y.* 1894. 8°. 011765. f. 3.

WILMOT (S.) The Queens of England. 2 vol. *Lond.* 1887–89. 4°. 10805. g. 3.

ENGLAND.—History—*continued.*

Earliest Period to the 15th Century.

OWEN (R.) The Kymry : their origin and history. pp. 296. *Carmarthen*, 1891. 8°. 10007. i. 6.

ARCHER (T.) Stories from early English History. pp. 175. 1890. 8°. Century Historical Readers. No. 3. 9503. d.

CHURCH (A. J.) Stories from English History from Julius Cæsar to the Black Prince. pp. 240. 1895. 8°. Seeley's First Lesson Books. 012202. ff.

MACDERMOT (T. B.) English History Course, from the earliest times to A.D. 1399. pp. 56. *Lond.* 1892. 8°. 9504. cc. 4.

ROBERTSON (C. G.) The making of the English Nation. B.C. 55-1135 A.D. pp. 113. 1894. 8°. OMAN (C. W. C.) Oxford Manuals. No. 1. 9503. b. 27.

ERDMANN (A.) Über die Heimat und den Namen der Angeln. pp. 118. 1890. 8°. Ac. Upsal. *Humanistiska Vetenskapssamfundet.* Skrifter. Bd. 1. Ac. 1078.

WEIR (P.) The Invaders of Britain. pp. 184. *Clifton*, 1893. 8°. 9504. d. 8.

ANGLO-SAXON CHRONICLE. Two of the Saxon Chronicles Parallel. *Oxf.* 1892, *etc.* 8°. 2394. b. 2.

WINKELMANN (E.) Geschichte der Angelsachsen bis zum Tode König Alfreds. pp. 185. 1883. 8°. ONCKEN (W.) Allgemeine Geschichte. Hauptabth. II. Th. 3. 2068. (9.)

MACKINLAY (J. B.) Saint Edmund, King and Martyr. pp. 435. *Lond.* 1893. 8°. 4829. f. 2.

MORRISON (W.) Site of the Battle of Ashdown. *Lond.* 1893. 8°. Pam. 90.

DUCKETT (*Sir* G. F.) Hastings v. Senlac. pp. 3. 1892. 8°. 9005. d. 26. (10.)

HENDERSON (E. F.) Historical documents of the Middle Ages. pp. 477. 1892. 8°. Bohn's Antiquarian Library. 2500. b.

HOVEY (R.) Outlines of English History, 1066-1485. *Lond.* 1889. 8°. 9004. bbb. 14. (6.)

JEWETT (S. O.) The Normans in relation to their Conquest of England. pp. 373. 1891. 8°. Story of the Nations. 9004. ccc. 3.

PENDER (E.) *Lady.* Norman and English History, 11th and 12th Cent. pp. 300. *Edinb.* 1891. fol. K.T.C. 1. b. 3.

ROUND (J. H.) Fendal England, XI. and XII. cent. pp. 587. *Lond.* 1895. 8°. 2394. h. 3.

—— Geoffrey de Mandeville. pp. 461. *Lond.* 1892. 8°. 9510. h. 8.

HUTTON (W. H.) King and Baronage. A.D. 1135-1327. pp. 117. 1895. 8°. OMAN (C. W. C.) Oxford Manuals. No. 2. 9503. b. 27.

KINDT (A. R.) Gründe der Gefangenschaft Richards I. pp. 54. *Halle*, 1892. 8°. 10803. cc. 12. (9.)

GRUHN (A.) Der Kreuzzug Richards I. pp. 47. *Berl.* 1892. 8°. 9005. d. 26. (11.)

NEEDLER (G. H.) Richard Cœur de Lion in Literature. pp. 75. *Leipz.* 1890. 8°. 011824. h. 11.

KNELLER (C. A.) Des Richard Löwenherz deutsche Gefangenschaft, 1192-1194. pp. 128. *Freiburg*, 1893. 8°. 10806. d. 10.

BÉMONT (C.) Chartes des libertés anglaises, 1100-1305. pp. 132. 1892. 8°. Collection de textes pour servir à l'étude de l'histoire. 09210. de.

MICHEL (F.) Rôles gascons. 1885, *etc.* 8°. FRANCE. Collection de documents. Sér. I. 9210. g.

TOUT (T. F.) Edward the First. pp. 238. 1893. 8°. Twelve English Statesmen. 10803. c.

ENGLAND.—History—*continued.*

ENGLAND. *Parliament.* Records of the Parliament holden at Westminster, 1305. pp. 373. 1893. 8°. Rerum Britannicarum Scriptores.
2073/98

G. B. & I. *Commission for printing State Papers.* Calendar of the Close Rolls A.D. 1307–13, *etc. Lond.* 1892, *etc.* 8°. 2076. g.

—— Calendar of Patent Rolls, A.D. 1327–30, *etc. Lond.* 1891, *etc.* 8°. 2076. g.

MOISANT (J.) Le Prince Noir en Aquitaine 1355–70. pp. 294. *Paris,* 1894. 8°. 9072. dd. 1.

Ac. London. *Camden Society.* N.S. 52. Expeditions to Prussia and the Holy Land made by Henry Earl of Derby, 1390–3. pp. 360. *Lond.* 1894. 4°. Ac. 8113/137.

COSNEAU (E.) Le Connétable de Richemont, 1393–1458. pp. 712. *Paris,* 1886. 8°.
010661. i. 21.

RAMSAY (*Sir* J. H.) Lancaster and York, A.D. 1399–1485. 2 vol. *Oxf.* 1892. 8°. 2394. e. 1.

CHARLES (R.) L'invasion anglaise dans le Maine, 1417–28. 1889. 8°. Ac. Le Mans. *Société Historique.* Revue. Tom. 25. Ac. 5321/3.

VILLARET (A. de) Campagnes des Anglais dans l'Orléanais, 1421–1428. pp. 168. *Orléans,* 1893. 8°. 9079. g. 22.

JOUBERT (A.) Négociations relatives à l'échange de Charles, duc d'Orléans et du comte d'Angoulême contre les seigneurs anglais faits prisonniers à la bataille de Baugé. pp. 11. *Angers,* 1890. 8°. 9004. m. 7. (15.)

JARRY (L.) Le Compte de l'Armée anglaise au siège d'Orléans, 1428–29. pp. 240. *Orléans,* 1892. 8°. 9072. f. 9.

THOMPSON (E.) Wars of York and Lancaster, 1450–1485. pp. 165. *Lond.* 1892. 8°.
9503. aaa.

OMAN (C. W. C.) Warwick, the Kingmaker. pp. 243. 1891. 8°. English Men of Action.
10803. bbb.

KRIEHN (G.) The English Rising in 1450. pp. 131. *Strassb.* 1892. 8°. 9510. h. 10.

FEARENSIDE (C. S.) Synopsis of English History, A.D. 1485–1580. 1890. 8°. Tutorial Series.
12205. c. 21.

See also DOMESDAY BOOK: FRANCE, *History.*

16th Century.

BUSCH (W.) England unter den Tudors. *Stuttgart,* 1892, *etc.* 8°. 2394. e. 2.

—— England under the Tudors. *Lond.* 1895, *etc.* 8°. 2394. g. 1.

FROUDE (J. A.) History of England from the fall of Wolsey to the defeat of the Spanish Armada. 12 vol. *Lond.* 1893. 8°. 9510. de.

JORDAN (F.) Body, parentage and character in history: notes on the Tudor Period. pp. 82. *Lond.* 1890. 8°. 9503. c. 29.

HUTTON (W. H.) Sir Thomas More. pp. 283. *Lond.* 1895. 8°. 10815. bb. 31.

EHSES (S.) Römische Dokumente zur Geschichte der Ehescheidung Heinrichs VIII. von England, 1527–1534. pp. 284. 1893. 8°. Ac. Bonn. *Görres-Gesellschaft.* Quellen und Forschungen. Bd. 2. Ac. 2026/6.

FROUDE (J. A.) Divorce of Catherine of Aragon. pp. 543. *Lond.* 1893. 8°. 9510. bbb. 6.

HOPE (A.) The First Divorce of Henry VIII. pp. 375. *Lond.* 1894. 8°. 9410. bbb. 7.

HAMILTON PAPERS. The Hamilton Papers. A.D. 1532–1543, *etc. Edinb.* 1890, *etc.* 8°.
2075. d.

GASQUET (F. A.) Henry VIII. and the English Monasteries. *Lond.* 1892, *etc.* 8°. 4707. cc. 12.

ENGLAND.—History—*continued.*

BLAZE DE BURY ( ) Un Divorce royal. Anne Boleyn. pp. 238. *Paris,* 1890. 8°.
10805. bbb. 19.

G. B. & I. *Commission for printing State Papers.* Acts of the Privy Council of England. 1542, *etc. Lond.* 1890, *etc.* 8°. 2075. g.

ENGLAND. Discourse of the Common Weal of this realm of England. [Written about 1549.] pp. 208. *Camb.* 1893. 8°. 8009. aaa. 33.

GUARAS (A. de) Accession of Queen Mary. pp. 152. *Lond.* 1892. 4°. 12204. e.

HAUDECŒUR (A.) Marie la Sanglante. pp. 20. *Paris,* 1890. 8°. 10803. f. 2. (1.)

BEESLY (E. S.) Queen Elizabeth. pp. 245. 1892. 8°. Twelve English Statesmen. 10803. c.

RYDE (P. W.) Cusack's Reign of Queen Elizabeth for scholarship candidates. pp. 118. *Lond.* 1895. 8°. 9510. c. 5.

PROTHERO (G. W.) Select Statutes and other documents illustrative of the reigns of Elizabeth and James I. pp. 464. *Oxf.* 1894. 8°.
2230. a. 19.

SEELEY (*Sir* J. R.) The Growth of British Policy. 2 vol. *Camb.* 1895. 8°. 2394. d. 1.

FROUDE (J. A.) English Seamen in the sixteenth century. pp. 309. *Lond.* 1895. 8°. 9510. aaa. 8.

HINDS (A. B.) The Making of the England of Elizabeth. pp. 152. *Lond.* 1895. 8°.
9512. b. 6.

BRUGMANS (H.) Engeland en de Nederlanden. 1558–67. pp. 235. *Groningen,* 1892. 8°.
9079. h. 21.

SCOTLAND. *General Register House.* Calendar of Letters and papers relating to the affairs of the Borders of England and Scotland. *Edinb.* 1894, *etc.* 8°. 2075. e.

BEKKER (E.) Elisabeth und Leicester. pp. 131. 1890. 8°. Giessener Studien. No. 5.
9072. f. 4.

BOURNE (H. R. F.) Sir P. Sidney. pp. 384. 1891. 8°. ABBOTT (E.) Heroes of the Nations.
10603. dd.

STEBBING (W.) Sir W. Ralegh. pp. 413. *Oxf.* 1891. 8°. 2101. c. 8.

ATKINSON (E. G.) The Cardinal of Châtillon in England, 1568–71. pp. 116. *Lond.* 1890. 8°.
4863. ce. 20.

SCOTT (*Hon.* M. M. M.) The Tragedy of Fotheringay. pp. 271. *Lond.* 1895. 8°. 10806. ee. 4.

KRETZSCHMAR (J.) Die Invasionsprojekte der katholischen Mächte gegen England. pp. 215. *Leipz.* 1892. 8°. 9077. ccc. 13.

FROUDE (J. A.) Spanish Story of the Armada, and other essays. pp. 394. *Lond.* 1892. 8°.
9009. aa. 21.

LAUGHTON (J. K.) State Papers relating to the defeat of the Spanish Armada. 1894, *etc.* 8°. Ac. London. *Navy Records Society.* Publications. Vol. 1, *etc.* Ac. 8109.

GREEN (E.) Preparations in Somerset against the Spanish Armada, A.D. 1558–88. pp. 137. *Lond.* 1888. 8°. 9510. f. 23.

TILTON (W. F.) Die Katastrophe der spanischen Armada. pp. 150. *Freiburg,* 1894. 8°.
9077. ccc. 39.

17th Century.

THORNTON (P. M.) The Stuart Dynasty. pp. 326. *Lond.* 1891. 8°. 9525. aaa. 4.

LAFFLEUR DE KERMAINGANT (P. P.) L'Ambassade de France en Angleterre sous Henri IV. 1602–05. 2 vol. *Paris,* 1895. 8°. 9079. l. 12.

PROTHERO (G. W.) Select Statutes, *etc.,* illustrative of the reign of James I. pp. 464. *Oxf.* 1894. 8°. 2230. a. 19.

ENGLAND.—History—*continued*.

WAKELING (G. H.) King and Parliament. A.D. 1603–1714. pp. 135. 1894. 8°. OMAN (C. W. C.) Oxford Manuals. No. 5. 9503. b. 27.

SAYOUS (E.) Les deux Révolutions d'Angleterre, 1603–1689. pp. 256. *Paris*, 1891. 8°. 9512. e. 7.

DIGBY (*Sir* E.) The Life of a Conspirator. Biography of Sir E. Digby. pp. 306. *Lond.* 1895. 8°. 10825. h. 9.

HOWELL (J.) Epistolæ Ho-elianæ. Familiar Letters of J. Howell. pp. 850. *Lond.* 1890, 92. 8°. 010920. f. 22.

RYDFORS (A.) De diplomatiska förbindelserna mellan Sverige och England 1624–30. pp. 154. *Upsala*, 1890. 8°. 9080. cc 15.

MOTIER DE LA FAYETTE (M. M.) Histoire d'Henriette d'Angleterre. pp. 300. *Paris*, 1890. 8°. 010661. f. 22.

Ac. London. *Browning Soc.* Browning's Life of Strafford. pp. 319. *Lond.* 1892. 8°. 10815. eee. 17.

FIRTH (C. H.) Papers relating to T. Wentworth, Earl of Strafford. pp. 31. 1890. 4°. Ac. London. *Camden Soc.* XXXIX., *etc.* Camden Miscellany. Vol. 9. Ac 8113/39.

CAMPBELL (D.) The Puritan in Holland, England and America. 2 vol. *Lond.* 1892. 8°. 9602. dd. 1.

GREGORY (J.) Puritanism in the Old World and in the New. pp. 406. *Lond.* 1895. 8°. 4715. df. 7.

GRIFFIS (W. E.) Influence of the Netherlands in the making of the English Commonwealth. pp. 40. *Bost.* 1891. 8°. Pam. 28.

SCOTT (B.) The Pilgrim Fathers neither Puritans nor Persecutors. pp. 52. *Lond.* 1891, 8°. 4535. c. 10. (6.)

BORGEAUD (C.) The Rise of Modern Democracy in old and new England. pp. 168. *Lond.* 1894. 8°. 08276. e. 60.

FEARENSIDE (C. S.) History of England, 1640–1670. pp. 136. 1892. 8°. Tutorial Series. 12205. c. 92.

GARDINER (S. R.) History of the Civil War, 1642–1649. 4 vol. *Lond.* 1893. 8°. 2077. cc.

HYDE (E.) *Earl of Clarendon.* History of the Rebellion. Book VI. pp. 331. 1894. 8°. Clarendon Press Series. 2320. aa. 34.

MALBON (T.) Memorials of the Civil War in Cheshire. pp. 275. 1889. 8°. Ac. Manchester. *Record Soc.* Publications. Vol. 19. Ac. 8121.

HYETT (F. A.) The Civil War in the Forest of Dean, 1643–45. pp. 15. 1895. 8°. 9004. k. 15. (10.)

KINGSTON (A.) Hertfordshire during the Civil War. pp. 212. *Lond.* 1894. 4°. 10358. dd. 26.

GRAINAGE (W.) Battles and Battle Fields of Yorkshire. pp. 184. *Ripon*, 1895. 8°. 09504. h. 2.

BEAUFORT (W. H. de) O. Cromwell. pp. 90. *Amersfoort*, 1890. 8°. 10803. e. 18. (7.)

CHURCH (S. H.) O. Cromwell: a history. pp. 524. *N.Y.* 1894. 8°. 10815. eee. 18.

CLARK (G. H.) O. Cromwell. pp. 258. *Bost.* 1893. 8°. 10815. de. 4.

HOARE (W. E.) Note on F. Harrison's Oliver Cromwell. pp. 106. *Madras*, 1890. 8°. 10815. aaa. 32.

MACAULAY (J.) Cromwell Anecdotes. pp. 158. *Lond.* 1891. 8°. 10815. aaa. 31.

BLEIBTREU (C.) Cromwell bei Marston Moor. pp. 98. *Leipz.* 1890. 8°. 9072. c. 9. (7.)

MITSUKURI (G.) Englisch - niederländische Unionsbestrebungen im Zeitalter Cromwells. pp. 107. *Tübingen*, 1891. 8°. 9079. i. 6.

ENGLAND.—History—*continued*.

LUDLOW (E.) Memoirs of E. Ludlow. 2 vol. *Oxf.* 1894. 8°. 2407. e. 1.

VERNEY (F. P.) *Lady.* Memoirs of the Verney Family during the Civil War. 2 vol. *Lond.* 1892. 8°. 2404. g. 7.

ENGLAND. *Committee for Compounding*, 1643–1660. Yorkshire Royalist Composition Papers. 1893, *etc.* 8°. Ac. Huddersfield. *Yorkshire Archæological Association.* Record series. Vol. 15, *etc.* Ac. 5652/8.

Ac. London. *Camden Society.* N.S. XLIX. The Clarke Papers. 1647–60. *Lond.* 1891, *etc.* 4°. Ac. 8113/135.

GARDINER (S. R.) History of the Commonwealth and Protectorate, 1649–60. *Lond.* 1894, *etc.* 8°. 2077. cc.

BLOUNT (T.) Boscobel, or the History of the preservation of King Charles II. pp. 167. *Lond.* 1894. 8°. 9512. b. 5.

CHARLES II., *King.* King Charles the Second and the Cogans of Coaxdon Manor. pp. 15. *Lond.* 1891. 4°. 9512. g. 5.

INDERWICK (F. A.) The Interregnum, A.D. 1648–1660. pp. 310. *Lond.* 1891. 8°. 9512. e. 6.

ELLIS (J. J.) T. Cromwell. pp. 106. 1891. 8°. Men with a Mission. 4804. a.

WAYLEN (J.) The House of Cromwell and the Story of Dunkirk. pp. 389. *Lond.* 1891. 8°. 9916. ee. 2.

HAMILTON (A.) *Count.* Memoirs of the Court of King Charles II. pp. 599. 1891. 8°. Bohn's Standard Library. 2504. k.

JUSSERAND (J. J.) A French Ambassador at the Court of Charles the Second. pp. 259. *Lond.* 1892. 8°. 010661, l. 26.

CUNNINGHAM (P.) Story of Nell Gwyn and the sayings of Charles II. pp. 224. *Lond.* 1892. 8°. 10825. f. 32.

CARTWRIGHT, *afterwards* ADY (J.) Sacharissa. D. Sidney, Countess of Sunderland. pp. 314. *Lond.* 1893. 8°. 10825. g. 5.

WOLSELEY (G. J.) *Viscount Wolseley.* Life of J. Churchill, Duke of Marlborough, to the accession of Queen Anne. 2 vol. *Lond.* 1894. 8°. 2406. d. 1.

HUMPHREYS (A. L.) Some sources of history for the Monmouth Rebellion and the Bloody Assizes. pp. 20. *Taunton*, 1892. 4°. Pam. 28.

BENT (J.) The Bloody Assizes. pp. 121. *Edinb.* 1890. 4°. 9512. g. 7.

ASKIN (P.) King William III. and his times. pp. 35. *Dublin*, 1890. 8°. 9005. d. 26. (5.)

GREEN (E.) March of William of Orange through Somerset, 1688. pp. 78. *Lond.* 1892. 8°. 9510. f. 24.

DAWSON (C.) Description of the Battle of Beachy Head. pp. 16. *Lewes*, 1895. 12°. Pam. 28.

FORBES (A. W. H.) English History, William III., Anne, George I., George II. pp. 94. *Lond.* 1892. 8°. 9525. aaa. 5.

FREETH (F.) English History Notes, 1688–1727. pp. 120. *Lond.* 1890. 12°. 9512. a. 5.

RANKING (D. F.) Student's Special History, 1689–1832. pp. 112. *Lond.* 1894. 8°. 9525. aa. 16.

18th Century.

LECKY (W. E. H.) History of England in the eighteenth century. 7 vol. *Lond.* 1891. 8°. 9525. bb. 10.

BRETT (*Hon.* R. B.) Footprints of Statesmen during the 18th century. pp. 197. *Lond.* 1892. 8°. 8139. aa. 51.

ENGLAND.—History—_continued._ '

OLIPHANT (M. O.) Historical Sketches of the reign of Queen Anne. pp. 381. _Lond._ 1894. 8°.
10803. bbb. 7.

MAC CULLAGH TORRENS (W. T.) History of Cabinets. From the Union with Scotland. 2 vol. _Lond._ 1894. 8°. 09504. f. 13.

LEGRELLE (A.) Une négociation entre Berwick et Marlborough, 1708-09. pp. 99.
Paris, 1893. 8°. 9525. df. 13.

KOCH (G.) Bolingbrokes politische Ansichten und die Squirarchie. pp. 14. _Brl._ 1890. 4°.
9004. n. 10. (7.)

SALOMON (F.) Geschichte des letzten Ministeriums Königin Annas von England, 1710-14. pp. 359. _Gotha,_ 1894. 8°. 9525. df. 14.

WEBER (O.) Der Friede von Utrecht. pp. 485. _Gotha,_ 1891. 8°. 9077. ccc. 10.

INNES (A. D.) Britain and her Rivals in the 18th century, 1712-89. pp. 419. _Lond._ 1895. 8°.
9078. c. 26.

G. B. History of Great Britain from George I. pp. 190. 1887. 8°. Blackwood's Educational Series. 12204. bbbb.

LLOYD (R. D.) Historical Chart and notes on the origin of the Victorian Monarchy. pp. 8. _Lond._ 1892. 8°. 9904. dd. 5.

FREETH (F.) English History for examination purposes, 1727-88. pp. 125. _Lond._ 1894. 8°.
9504. ccc. 12.

JEPHSON (H.) The Platform; its rise and progress. 2 vol. _Lond._ 1892. 8°. 8138. g. 14.

DALY (J. B.) The Dawn of Radicalism. pp. 252. _Lond._ 1892. 8°. 08276. e. 63.

AC. Edinburgh. _Scottish History Society._ Publications. Vol. 19. The Jacobite attempt of 1719. Letters of the duke of Ormonde. pp. 306. _Edinb._ 1895. 8°. Ac. 8256.

WIESENER (L.) Le Régent, l'abbé Dubois et les Anglais. pp. 518. _Paris,_ 1891. 8°. 7079. f. 1.

AC. Edinburgh. _Scottish History Society._ Publications. Vol. 20, _etc._ The Lyon in Mourning; speeches, letters, _etc.._ relative to the affairs of Prince Charles Edward Stuart.
Edinb. 1895, _etc._ 8°. Ac. 8256.

BOYER (A. J. B. de) _Marquis d'Aguilles._ Un Protégé de Bachaumont. Correspondance du Marquis d'Éguilles. pp. 179. _Paris,_ 1887. 8°.
10920. ccc. 24.

LUCAS (F. W.) Appendiculæ Historicæ; shreds of history [of the struggles between England and France in N. America]. pp. 216. _Lond._ 1891. 4°.
9555. h. 1.

BRADLEY (A. G.) Wolfe. pp. 214. 1895. 8°. English Men of Action. 10803. bbb.

WALPOLE (H.) _Earl of Orford._ Memoirs of the Reign of George the Third. 4 vol.
Lond. 1894. 8°. 2394. h. 2.

ANDERSON (J. H.) History of George the Third's reign. pp. 138. _Lond._ 1891. 8°. 9425. b. 13.

FEARENSIDE (C. S.) and EVANS (A. J.) History of England from 1760 to 1798. pp. 172. 1891. 8°. Tutorial Series. 12205. c. 26.

RUVILLE (A. v.) W. Pitt (Chatham) und Graf Bute. pp. 119. _Berl._ 1895. 8°. 9512. e. 17.

BURKE (_Right Hon._ E.) Burke's Speeches. Edited by F. G. Selby. pp. 328. _Lond._ 1895. 8°.
12301. bb. 32.

HOWE (W.) _Viscount Howe._ General Howe's Orderly Book, June 17, 1775 to 26 May, 1776. pp. 357. _Lond._ 1890. 8°. 9605. ff. 8.

PRIMROSE (A. P.) _Earl of Rosebery._ Pitt. pp. 297. 1891. 8°. Twelve English Statesmen. 10803. c.

JACOB (T. E.) Life of W. Pitt. pp. 312. _Lond._ 1890. 8°. 10815. aa. 18.

ENGLAND.—History—_continued._

COTTIN (P.) L'Angleterre devant ses Alliés, 1793-1814. pp. 100. _Paris,_ 1893. 8°.
9087. ccc. 17.

19th Century.

LATIMER (E. W.) England in the nineteenth century. pp. 451. _Chicago,_ 1894. 8°
9525. df. 15.

OMPTEDA (C. F. W. v.) _Baron._ A Hanoverian-English Officer a hundred years ago. pp. 320. _Lond._ 1892. 8°. 010707. ee. 9.

INGRAM (T. D.) History of the Union of Great Britain and Ireland. pp. 220.
Westminster, 1890. 8°. 9509. aa. 20.

BROWNE (G. L.) Nelson. Public and private life. pp. 472. _Lond._ 1891. 8°. 10817. f. 17.

LAUGHTON (J. K.) Nelson. pp. 240. 1895. 8°. English Men of Action. 10803. bbb.

NELSON (H.) _Viscount Nelson._ Nelson's Words and Deeds. pp. 224. _Lond._ 1890. 8°. 10921. e. 16.

SOUTHEY (R.) Life of Nelson. pp. 326. _Lond._ 1891. 8°. 10817. e. 13.

KEY ÅBERG (C. V. V.) De diplomatiska Förbindelserna mellan Sverige och Storbritannien. 1807-09. pp. 100. _Upsala,_ 1891. 8°. 9435. dd. 7.

ROBERTS (F. S.) _Baron Roberts._ The Rise of Wellington. pp. 198. 1895. 8°. Pall Mall Magazine Library. Vol. 2. 012208. f.

NAPIER (_Sir_ W. F. P.) History of the War in the Peninsula, _etc._ 3 pt. _Lond._ 1893. 8°.
9080. e. 2.

LAGERHJELM (G. R.) Napoleon och Wellington på Pyreneiska Halfori. _Stockholm,_ 1889. 8°.
9080. e. 26.

CRAWFORD (A. H. G.) General Crawford and his light division. pp. 298. _Lond._ 1891. 8°.
10817. i. 27.

TOMKINSON (W.) Diary of a cavalry officer. 1807-15. _Lond._ 1894. 8°. 9080. dd. 19.

CLERC (J. C. A.) Campagne du Maréchal Soult dans les Pyrénées, 1813-14. pp. 464.
Paris, 1894. 8°. 9180. ee. 5.

For the Battle of Trafalgar and the Campaign of Waterloo. _See_ TRAFALGAR : WATERLOO.

Reign of Queen Victoria.

GRANT (D.) Royalty at home. pp. 128.
Lond. 1894. 8°. 10806. f. 20.

HARDY (E. J.) People's life of their Queen. pp. 190. _Lond._ 1895. 8°. 10806. aaa. 17.

JEAFFRESON (J. C.) Victoria, Queen and Empress. 2 vol. _Lond._ 1893. 8°. 10806. f. 17.

JOHNSTON (R.) Short History of the Queen's Reign. pp. 87. _Lond._ 1892. 8°. 9525. aa. 15.

VICTORIA, _Queen._ Queen Victoria. pp. 144.
Lond. 1894. 8°. 10805. aa. 41.

WILSON (R.) Life and times of Queen Victoria. 2 vol. _Lond._ 1891-93. 8°. 10806. f. 21.

WARREN (M. S.) The Princess of Wales. pp. 264. _Lond._ 1895. 8°. 10806. aaa. 18.

VINCENT (J. E.) H.R.H. the Duke of Clarence. pp. 289. _Lond._ 1893. 8°. 10806. aaa. 16.

GAMMAGE (R. G.) History of the Chartist Movement. 1837-54, _etc._ pp. 438.
Newcastle, 1894. 8°. 9525. ee. 12.

BOLTON (S. K.) Famous English Statesmen of Victoria's Reign. pp. 460. _N.Y._ 1891. 8°.
10803. de. 2.

REID (S. J.) Prime Ministers of Queen Victoria. _Lond._ 1890, _etc._ 8°. 10803. cc.

DUNCKLEY (H.) Lord Melbourne. pp. 248. 1890. 8°. Prime Ministers of Queen Victoria.
10803. cc.

MAC CARTHY (J.) Sir R. Peel. pp. 176. 1891. 8°. Prime Ministers of Queen Victoria.
10803. cc.

ENGLAND.—History—*continued.*

PARKER (C. S.) Sir R. Peel. *Lond.* 1891, *etc.* 8°.
　　　　　　　　　　　　　　　10815. ccc. 13.
THURSFIELD (J. R.) Peel. pp. 246. 1891. 8°.
Twelve English Statesmen.　　　　　10803. c.
WALPOLE (S.) Life of Lord J. Russell. 2 vol.
Lond. 1891. 8°.　　　　　　　　　2406. e. 1.
SAINTSBURY (G. E. B.) The Earl of Derby.
pp. 223. 1892. 8°. Prime Ministers of Queen
Victoria, *etc.*　　　　　　　　　　10803. cc.
GLADSTONE (*Right Hon.* W. E.) Speeches and
Public Addresses. *Lond.* 1892. 8°. 2238. cc. 13.
JERROLD (W.) W. E. Gladstone. pp. 160.
Lond. 1893. 8°.　　　　　　　　10815. b. 80.
LUCY (H. W.) Right Hon. W. E. Gladstone.
pp. 252. 1895. 8°. Statesmen Series. 10602. e.
ROBBINS (A. F.) Early public Life of W. E.
Gladstone. pp. 464. *Lond.* 1894. 8°.
　　　　　　　　　　　　　　　10815. de. 9.
RUSSELL (G. W. E.) Right Hon. W. E. Glad-
stone. pp. 289. 1891. 8°. Prime Ministers of
Queen Victoria.　　　　　　　　　10803. cc.
BREWSTER (F. C.) Disraeli in Outline. pp. 394.
Phila. 1890. 8°.　　　　　　　10816. e. 20.
FRASER (*Sir* W. A.) Disraeli and his day.
pp. 500. *Lond.* 1891. 8°.　　　10815. cc. 14.
BRIGHT (*Right Hon.* J.) Public Letters.
pp. 304. *Lond.* 1895. 8°.　　　　8139. aa. 55.
MAC CULLAGH TORRENS (W. T.) Twenty Years
in Parliament. pp. 381. *Lond.* 1893. 8°.
　　　　　　　　　　　　　　　8139. e. 8.
MARTIN (A. P.) Life and Letters of R. Lowe,
Viscount Sherbrooke. 2 vol. *Lond.* 1893. 8°.
　　　　　　　　　　　　　　　10817. dd. 10.
WOLFF (*Sir* H. D.) Some Notes of the Past,
1870–91. pp. 140. *Lond.* 1893. 8°. 9080. c. 35.
LANG (A.) Life, letters and diaries of Sir S.
Northcote. pp. 413. *Edinb.* 1891. 8°.
　　　　　　　　　　　　　　　10815. cc. 13.
JEYES (S. H.) Life of the Marquis of Salisbury.
4 vol. *Lond.* 1895, 96. 8°.　　　　10816. h.
TRAILL (H. D.) The Marquis of Salisbury.
pp. 224. 1892. 8°. Prime Ministers of Queen
Victoria.　　　　　　　　　　　10803. cc.
MAXWELL (*Sir* H. E.) Life of the Right Hon.
W. H. Smith. pp. 378. *Edinb.* 1894. 8°.
　　　　　　　　　　　　　　　10815. b. 82.
ESCOTT (T. H. S.) R. Spencer-Churchill, as a
product of his age. pp. 408. *Lond.* 1895. 8°.
　　　　　　　　　　　　　　　10815. d. 17.
FILON (A.) Profils anglais. R. Churchill. J.
Chamberlain. J. Morley. Parnell. pp. 293.
Paris, 1893. 8°.　　　　　　　10803. bb. 27.
JEYES (S. H.) Right Hon. J. Chamberlain.
pp. 258. 1895. 8°. Public Men of to-day.
　　　　　　　　　　　　　　　10600. e.
STATESMEN. Statesmen Past and Future.
pp. 211. *Lond.* 1894. 8°.　　　10815. df. 7.
C., A. Quinquennial Proceedings of two Ad-
ministrations. 1881–91. pp. 62.
Lond. 1892. 8°.　　　　　　　　Pam. 68.
CLAYDEN (P. W.) England under the Coalition.
1885–92. pp. 575. *Lond.* 1892, 93. 8°.
　　　　　　　　　　　　　　　9525. bbb. 4.
LUCY (H. W.) Diary of the Salisbury Parlia-
ment, 1886–92. pp. 530. *Lond.* 1892. 8°.
　　　　　　　　　　　　　　　8139. f. 6.
P.P. *London.* The Times Annual. 1890, *etc.*
Lond. 1891, *etc.* 8°.　　　　　P.P. 3435. dda.
RUSSELL (T. B.) Last Year : events of 1890.
pp, 97. *Lond.* 1891. 8°.　　　　9009. c. 11.
O'CONNOR (T. P.) Sketches in the House.
Story of a Memorable Session. pp. 288.
Lond. 1893. 8°.　　　　　　　8139. c. 13.
See also CRIMEAN WAR : INDIA, *History, etc.*

ENGLAND—*continued.*

History, *Ecclesiastical.*

General.

BUXTON (E. M. W.) Founded upon a Rock.
Stories from English Church History. pp. 134.
Lond. 1895. 8°.　　　　　　　4705. aaa. 36.
CUTTS (E. L.) History of the Church of England.
pp. 227. 1895. 8°. Public School Text-Books
of Religious Instruction.　　　　3605. bb.
—— Turning points of English Church History.
pp. 334. *Lond.* 1895. 8°.　　　4430. cc. 15.
FOWLER (M.) Notable Archbishops of Canter-
bury. pp. 222. *Lond.* 1895. 8°. 4429. dd. 9.
FRANCIS (*Mrs.* C. D.) Story of the Church of
England. pp. 160. *Lond.* 1891. 8°. 4429. b. 28.
GARNIER (T. P.) The Story of the Church of
England. pp. 43. *Lond.* 1891. 8°.
　　　　　　　　　　　　　4429. c. 21. (I.)
HORE (A. H.) History of the Church of England.
pp. 544. *Lond.* 1893. 8°.　　　4707. de. 3.
LATHAM (J.) Catechism concerning the History
of the Church of England. pp. 32.
Lond. 1891. 8°.　　　　　　　　Pam. 29.
LIGHTFOOT (J. B.) *Bp. of Durham.* Leaders in
the northern Church. pp. 203.
Lond. 1890. 8°.　　　　　　　　2217. b. 1.
LYNN (W. T.) Short catechism of English Church
History. pp. 14. *Lond.* 1892. 8°.　Pam. 29.
MAKOWER (F.) Die Verfassung der Kirche von
England. pp. 560. *Berl.* 1894. 8°. 4705. f. 19.
—— Constitutional History of the Church of
England. pp. 545. *Lond.* 1895. 8°. 4705. d. 18.
MILNE (F. A.) Ecclesiology. pp. 327.
1894. 8°. Gentleman's Magazine Library.
　　　　　　　　　　　　　　　2324. c. 9.
NYE (G. H. F.) The Church and her story.
pp. 227. *Lond.* 1894. 8°.　　　4707. b. 29.
—— Short catechism of English Church History.
pp. 20. *Lond.* 1893. 8°.　　4705. b. 46. (8.)
PINNOCK (W. H.) Analysis of English Church
History. pp. 448. *Camb.* 1892. 8°.
　　　　　　　　　　　　　　　4705. aaa. 35.
STEDMAN (A. M. M.) English Leaders of Re-
ligion. *Lond.* 1891, *etc.* 8°.　　4907. d.
WOODWARD (H. H.) History of the Church of
England in the form of question and answer.
pp. 20. *Lond.* 1894. 8°.　　4705. b. 46. (10.)

Pre-Reformation.

PRESBYTER. The Buried Church in Silchester.
pp. 10. *Reading,* 1892. 8°.　　　Pam. 3.
Ac. London. *Early English Text Soc.* 95, *etc.*
Old English Version of Bede's Ecclesiastical
History. *Lond.* 1890, *etc.* 8°.　Ac. 9925/72.
ALLIES (M. H.) History of the Church in Eng-
land to the accession of Henry VIII. pp. 371.
Lond. 1892. 8°.　　　　　　　4707. bb. 13.
ANDERDON (W. H.) Britain's early Faith.
pp. 244. *Lond.* 1888. 8°.　　　3940. aaa. 17.
BREEN (J. D.) The Church of old England.
pp. 48. *Lond.* 1888. 8°.　　3939. ccc. 1. (4.)
BROWNE (G. F.) Lessons from early English
Church History. pp. 115. *Lond.* 1893. 8°.
　　　　　　　　　　　　　　　4429. bb. 15.
CATHCART (W.) The Ancient British and Irish
Churches. pp. 347. *Lond.* 1894. 8°.
　　　　　　　　　　　　　　　4705. cc. 13.
CHARLES (E.) Early Christian Missions of Ire-
land, Scotland and England. pp. 425.
Lond. 1893. 8°.　　　　　　　　4429. c. 1.
CLARE (A.) Foundation-Stones : lessons on the
founding of the Church in England. pp. 187.
Lond. 1895. 8°.　　　　　　　4429. a. 102.
G., L. First teachings about the early English
Church. pp 155. *Lond.* 1891. 8° 4707. aa. 39.

ENGLAND.—History, *Ecclesiastical—cont.*

BROWNE (G. F.) *Bp. of Stepney.* Augustine and his Companions. pp. 201. *Lond.* 1895. 8°.
                   4430. aaa. 10.

CUTTS (E. L.) Augustine of Canterbury. pp. 207. 1895. 8°. English Leaders of Religion.
                   4907. d.

AC. Christiania. *Norsk Historisk Forening.* TARANGER (A.) Den angelsaksiske Kirkes Indflydelse paa den Norske. pp. 459. *Kristiania,* 1890–91. 8°.   4707. b. 30.

CRAKE (A. D.) Stories of the old Saints and the Anglo-Saxon Church. pp. 173. *Oxf.* 1895. 8°.
                   4399. h. 42.

G. B. & I. *Commission for printing State Papers.* Calendar of entries in the Papal Registers relating to Great Britain and Ireland. *Lond.* 1893, *etc.* 8°.   2078. c.

HALL (M. H.) Builders of the Church in Northumbria. pp. 111. *Lond.* 1890. 8°.
                   4828. aaa. 18.

RAGEY ( ) Eadmer. pp. 314. *Paris,* 1892. 8°.
                   4902. h. 1.

INGRAM (T. D.) England and Rome: relations from the Norman Conquest to 1688. pp. 430. *Lond.* 1892. 8°.   3940. h. 14.

RADFORD (L. B.) Thomas of London before his consecration. pp. 270. 1894. 8°. AC. Cambridge. *University.* Cambridge Historical Essays. No. 7.   2378. b. 7.

L'HUILLIER (A.) Saint Thomas de Cantorbéry. *Paris,* 1891, *etc.* 8°.   4829. ee.

WALLACE (W.) Life of St. Edmund of Canterbury. pp. 638. *Lond.* 1893. 8°. 4829. df. 34.

AC. London. *Camden Society.* N. S. LV. Visitations of churches belonging to St. Paul's Cathedral, 1297–1488. pp. 130. *Lond.* 1895. 4°.   Ac. 8113/138.

GASQUET (F. A.) The Great Pestilence, A.D. 1348–9. pp. 244. *Lond.* 1893. 8°. 7561. k. 20.

MOBERLY (G. H.) Life of William of Wykeham. pp. 365. *Winchester,* 1893. 8°. 4902. g. 27.

SERGEANT (L.) J. Wycliff. pp. 377. 1893. 8°.

ABBOTT (E.) Heroes of the Nations. 10601. f.

BAKER (J.) A Forgotten Great Englishman: Peter Payne, the Wycliffite. pp. 100. *Lond.* 1894. 8°.   4902. de. 4.

WOODHOUSE (R. I.) Life of J. Morton, Archbishop of Canterbury. pp. 168. *Lond.* 1895. 8°.   4856. aaaa. 22.

CAVENDISH (G.) Life of T. Wolsey, Cardinal. pp. 287. *Hammersmith,* 1893. 8°.
                K.T.C. 6. a. 16.

Reformation: 16th and 17th Centuries.

BECKETT (W. H.) English Reformation of the sixteenth century. pp. 312. 1890. 8°. Church History Series. Vol. 7.   4421. i.

CHILD (G. W.) Church and State under the Tudors. pp. 429. *Lond.* 1890. 8°. 2217. d. 1.

FOSTER (J.) Index Ecclesiasticus: lists of ecclesiastical dignitaries in England and Wales since the Reformation. *Oxf.* 1890, *etc.* 8°.
                   2121. e.

INGRAM (T. D.) England and Rome, from the Norman Conquest to 1688. pp. 430. *Lond.* 1892. 8°.   3940. h. 14.

MOORE (A. L.) Lectures on the History of the Reformation in England. pp. 525. *Lond.* 1890. 8°.   4650. e. 25.

RYLE (J. C.) *Bp. of Liverpool.* What do we owe to the Reformation? pp. 27. *Lond.* 1891. 8°.   Pam. 78.

WORSLEY (H.) The Dawn of the English Reformation. pp. 380. *Lond.* 1890. 8°. 4707. e. 20.

ENGLAND.—History, *Ecclesiastical—cont.*

ENGLISH MARTYRS. The English Martyrs under Henry VIII. and Elizabeth. pp. 139. *Lond.* 1890. 8°.   4828. aa. 15.

KING (A. J.) The English Martyrs, included in the decree of beatification of the Congregation of Sacred Rites. pp. 36. *Bath,* 1887. 8°.
                   Pam. 10.

GASQUET (F. A.) Henry VIII. and the English Monasteries. 2 vol. *Lond.* 1892–93. 8°.
                   4707. cc. 12.

—— The Last Abbot of Glastonbury. pp. 195. *Lond.* 1895. 8°.   4902. f. 31.

MANNING (H. E.) *Cardinal.* Henry VIII. and the English Monasteries. pp. 16. *Lond.* 1890. 8°.
           3939. ccc. 1. (16.)

DOREAU (V. M.) Henri VIII. et les martyrs de la Chartreuse de Londres. pp. 435. *Paris,* 1890. 8°.   4829. ee. 6.

LUPTON (J. H.) Influence of Dean Colet upon the Reformation. pp. 68. *Lond.* 1893. 8°.
                   4707. d. 5.

MASON (A. J.) Lectures on Colet, Fisher and More. pp. 118. *Lond.* 1895. 8°. 4429. a. 97.

BRIDGETT (T. E.) Life of Blessed J. Fisher. pp. 508. *Lond.* 1890. 8°.   2217. c.

JACOBS (H. E.) The Lutheran Movement in England. pp. 376. *Lond.* 1892. 8°. 4707. ee. 18.

WILLINGTON (J. R.) T. Cranmer, Archbishop of Canterbury. pp. 44. *Lond.* 1893. 8°.
          4906. de. 25. (5.)

ZIMMERMANN (A.) Kardinal Pole. pp. 390. *Regensburg,* 1893. 8°.   4856. c. 15.

DIXON (R. W.) History of the Church of England. Vol. 3. Edward VI. pp. 584. *Lond.* 1893. 8°.   2214. f.

VETTER (T.) J. Hooper, Bischof von Gloucester und Worcester. *Zurich,* 1891. 8°.
          4804. d. 1. (8.)

LEE (F. G.) The Church under Queen Elizabeth. pp. 376. *Lond.* 1892. 8°. 4705. bb. 38.

BELLASIS (E.) Was Barlow a Bishop? pp. 16. *Lond.* 1890. 8°.   3939. ccc. 1. (6.)

BATESON (M.) Collection of Letters from the Bishops to the Privy Council, 1564. pp. 83. 1893. 4°. The Camden Miscellany. Vol. 9.
               Ac. 8113/39.

COLLETTE (C. H.) Queen Elizabeth and the Penal Laws. pp. 192. *Lond.* 1890. 8°.
               3940. g. 11.

BREEN (J. D.) 189: or, the Church of Old England protests. pp. 16. *Lond.* 1890. 8°.
          3939. ccc. 1. (7.)

THURSTON (H.) Catholic writers and Elizabethan readers. pp. 52. *Lond.* 1894–95. 8°.
         11825. q. 21. (11.)

COLLINS (W. E.) Archbishop Laud Commemoration, 1895. Lectures. pp. 344. *Lond.* 1895. 8°.   4906. f. 31.

LAUD (W.) *Archbp. of Canterbury.* Life of Archbishop Laud. pp. 490. *Lond.* 1894. 8°.
          4905. df. 21.

SIMPKINSON (C. H.) Life and Times of W. Laud. pp. 307. *Lond.* 1894. 8°. 4903. ee. 41.

LONDON. *Laudian Exhibition.* Laud Commemoration, 1895. Catalogue of Laudian Relics, *etc.* pp. 36. *Lond.* 1895. 16°.
          4902. aa. 28.

OTTLEY (R. L.) L. Andrewes. pp. 216. *Lond.* 1894. 8°.   4906. df. 24.

SHAW (W. A.) Financial administration of the revenues of the disendowed Church under the Commonwealth. pp. 52. *Lond.* 1893. 8°.
         4705. cc. 14. (11.)

GREGORY (J.) Puritanism in the Old World and the New. pp. 406. *Lond.* 1895. 8°. 4715. df. 7.

ENGLAND.—History, *Ecclesiastical—cont.*

SCOTT (B.) The Pilgrim Fathers neither puritans nor persecutors. pp. 52. *Lond.* 1891. 8°.
Pam. 29.

KETTLEWELL (J.) Life of J. Kettlewell with details of the history of the nonjurors. pp. 273. *Lond.* 1895. 8°.　　　　4903. eee. 27.

19th Century.

OVERTON (J. H.) The English Church in the 19th century, 1800–33. pp. 350.
Lond. 1894. 8°.　　　　4707. e. 25.

ZAHN (J. K. A.) Geschichte der evangelischen Kirke in britischen Reich im 19ten Jahrhundert. pp. 147. *Stuttgart,* 1891. 8°.　　4715. aaa. 44.

WORLEY (G.) The Catholic Revival of the 19th Century. pp. 152. *Lond.* 1894. 8°.
4707. aaaa. 30.

WAKELING (G.) The Oxford Church Movement. pp. 309. *Lond.* 1895. 8°. 4707. c. 28.

RIGG (J. H.) Oxford high Anglicanism. pp. 348. *Lond.* 1895. 8°.　　　　4705. cc. 15.

FLÖYSTRUP (C. E.) Den anglokatholske Bevægelse i det 19 de Aarhundrede. pp. 168. *Kjøbenh.* 1891. 8°.　　　　4705. d. 19.

LIDDON (H. P.) Life of E. B. Pusey.
Lond. 1893, *etc.* 8°.　　　　2217. f. 2.

LOCK (W.) J. Keble. pp. 245. *Lond.* 1893. 8°.
4903. eee. 19.

PROTHERO (R. E.) Life and correspondence of A. P. Stanley. 2 vol. *Lond.* 1893. 8°.
2217. f. 3.

DAVIDSON (R. T.) *Bp. of Winchester* and BENHAM (W.) Life of A. C. Tait, Archbp. of Canterbury. 2 vol. *Lond.* 1891. 8°. 2217. f. 1.

DIGGLE (J. W.) Lancashire Life of Bishop Fraser. pp. 400. *Lond.* 1891. 8°. 4907. d. 24.

KITCHEN (G. W.) E. H. Browne, Bishop of Winchester. pp. 519. *Lond.* 1895. 8°. 4905. df. 23.

LIGHTFOOT (J. B.) *Bp. of Durham.* Bishop Lightfoot. pp. 139. *Lond.* 1894. 8°
4903. ccc. 48.

See also supra: Church of: BAPTISTS: CHURCH HISTORY: CONGREGATIONALISM: METHODISM: MISSIONS: PRESBYTERIANISM: ROMAN CATHOLIC CHURCH, in England: UNITARIANISM.

Lake District.

ARMISTEAD (W.) Tales and legends of the English Lakes. pp. 289. *Lond.* 1891. 8°.
12331. h. 32.

BADDELEY (M. J. B.) English Lake District. pp. 254. 1895. 8°. Thorough Guide Series. No. 1.　　　　10347. aaa.

BLACK (A.) Guide to the English Lakes. pp. 293. *Edinb.* 1888. 8°.　　10347. aa. 38.

ENGLISH LAKE DISTRICT. English Lake District. pp. 144. 1895. 8°. Concise Series of Guides No. 1.　　　　10348. aaa.

FORSHAW (C. F.) Ten Days in Lakeland. pp. 32. *Lond.* 1892. 8°.　10348. ccc. 59. (4.)

GARNETT (J.) Guide to the highways of the Lake District. pp. 184. *Windermere,* 1891. 8°.
10360. d. 22.

HUSON (T.) Round about Helvellyn. pp. 51. *Lond.* 1895. fol.　　　　K.T.C. 25. b. 2.

BARBER (S.) Beneath Helvellyn's shade. pp. 166. *Lond.* 1892. 8°.　　010358. e. 18.

JENKINSON (H. I.) Practical guide to the English Lake District. pp. 407. *Lond.* 1893. 8°.
2366. b. 1.

KNIGHT (W.) The English Lake District as interpreted in Wordsworth. pp. 270. *Edinb.* 1891. 8°.　　　　10351. aa. 52.

RAWNSLEY (H. D.) Coach-Drive at the Lakes. pp. 96. *Keswick,* 1891. 12°.　10368. aa. 45.

ENGLAND.—Lake District—*continued.*

RAWNSLEY (H. D.) Literary associations of the English Lakes. 2 vol. *Glasg.* 1894. 8°..
10368. ccc. 40.

RUMNEY (A. W.) Cycling in the English Lake District. pp. 18. *Bradford,* 1894. 8°.
10347. aa. 37. (5.)

WAUGH (E.) Rambles in the Lake Country. pp. 290. *Manch.* 1893. 8°.　010358. e. 23.

See also infra: Topography: WESTMORELAND.

Law.

Bibliography. See LAW.

General.

BRETT (T.) Commentaries on the present Laws of England. 2 vol. *Lond.* 1891. 8°. 6146. k. 10.

DILLON (J. F.) Laws and Jurisprudence of England and America. pp. 431.
Lond. 1894. 8°.　　　　6616. de. 10.

HERKLESS (W. R.) Law Reform. pp. 33. *Glasg.* 1893. 8°.　　　6190. cc. 3. (18.)

INDERMAUR (J.) Principles of the Common Law. pp. 576. *Lond.* 1895. 8°.　　2230. d. 23.

—— Student's Guide to the principles of Common Law. pp. 108. *Lond.* 1893. 8°. 6146. h. 38.

LEHR (P. E.) Éléments de Droit civil anglais. pp. 774. *Paris,* 1885. 8°.　　6146. d. 16.

LESTER (H. F.) Lessons in our Laws.
Lond. 1893, *etc.* 8°.　　　　8139. de.

NEALE (J. A.) Exposition of English Law by English Judges, 1886–91. pp. 224.
Lond. 1892. 8°.　　　　6190. h. 6.

P.P. *London.* The Law Library. Nos. 1–10. *Lond.* 1892–93. 8°.　　　　1866. b. 6.

S., J. J. Shortcomings of the machinery for Pauper Litigation. pp. 88. *Lond.* 1891. 8°.
6146. f. 24.

STEPHEN (H. J.) New Commentaries on the Laws of England. 4 vol. *Lond.* 1895. 8°.
2016. d.

WALPOLE (C. G.) Rubric of the Common Law. pp. 358. *Lond.* 1891. 8°.　　6146. k. 9.

WETHERFIELD (F.) Hints upon Law. pp. 96. *Lond.* 1890. 8°.　　　　6145. a. 38.

WILLIAMS (J.) Institutes of Justinian illustrated by English Law. pp. 351. *Lond.* 1893. 8°.
5254. aa. 29.

HOLDSWORTH (W. A.) The practical Lawyer. pp. 648. *Lond.* 1884. 8°.　　6146. d. 15.

JONES (C.) The Solicitor's clerk. pp. 252. *Lond.* 1892. 8°.　　　　6190. aa. 27.

—— Companion to the Solicitor's clerk. pp. 182. *Lond.* 1895. 8°.　　6190. aa. 35.

STIFF (H. W.) New Guide for articled clerks. pp. 239. *Lond.* 1895. 8°.　　6190. a. 24.

See also infra: Statutes: JURY.

Barristers-at-Law. See LAW, Profession of.

Commercial. See LAW, Commercial.

Constitutional. See supra: Constitution.

County Courts. See COUNTY COURTS.

Criminal. See LAW, Criminal.

Dictionaries: Handbooks.

BARRISTER. Every Man's own Lawyer. pp. 736. *Lond.* 1895. 8°.　　　　2232. a. 2.

BARRISTER-AT-LAW. My Lawyer. pp. 568. *Lond.* 1894. 8°.　　　　6146. f. 30.

BEETON (S. O.) Everybody's Lawyer. pp. 777. *Lond.* 1891. 8°.　　　　2232. a. 5.

MERRILL (J. H.) American and English Encyclopædia of Law. *Northport,* 1887, *etc.* 8°.
2016. a. and aa.

ENGLAND.—Law—*continued.*

DEMBITZ (L. N.) Law Language. pp. 209. *Louisville*, 1892. 8°.   12991. ddd. 8.

RAWSON (H. G.) Pocket Law-Lexicon. pp. 372. *Lond.* 1893. 8°.   6005. a. 6.

WETHERFIELD (F.) Useful Law for men and women of business, pp. 92. *Lond.* 1889. 8°.   6145. a. 37.

WHARTON (J. J. S.) Wharton's Law Lexicon. pp. 793. *Lond.* 1892. 8°.   2228. cc. 8.

Ecclesiastical. See LAW, *Ecclesiastical.*

Equity. See EQUITY.

History.

GOUDY (H.) Inaugural lecture on the fate of the Roman Law north and south of the Tweed. pp. 33. *Lond.* 1894. 8°.   Pam. 32.

INDERWICK (F. A.) The King's Peace. Historical sketch of the English Law Courts. pp. 254. 1895. 8°. Social England Series.   9503. ccc.

INDERMAUR (J.) and THWAITES (C.) Student's Guide to legal History. pp. 128. *Lond.* 1894. 8°.   6005. b. 2.

MAITLAND (F. W.) Why the History of English Law is not written. pp. 20. *Lond.* 1888. 8°.   Pam. 32.

POLLOCK (*Sir* F.) and MAITLAND (F. W.) History of English Law before Edward I. 2 vol. *Camb.* 1895. 8°.   2228. cc. 1.

QUADRIPARTITUS. Quadripartitus, ein englisches Rechtsbuch von 1114. pp. 168. *Halle*, 1892. 8°.   5805. a. 2.

LIEBERMANN (F.) Über die Leges Anglorum saeculo XIII. pp. 105. *Halle a. S.*, 1894. 8°.   5805. a. 5.

BAILDON (W. P.) Court of Star Chamber. pp. 38. *Lond.* 1894. 8°.   6146. bbb. 26. (5.)

Legal Forms.

CLAY (W. G.) Law relating to Writs of Summons. pp. 231. *Lond.* 1894. 8°. 6190. aa. 34.

MARCY (G. N.) Forms of originating summons. pp. 149. *Lond.* 1895. 8°.   6190. df. 23.

MOORE (H.) Handbook of practical Forms. pp. 509. *Lond.* 1895. 8°.   6190. f. 11.

SMITH (J. W.) Legal Forms for common use. pp. 323. *Lond.* 1893. 8°.   6145. a. 39.

Magisterial.

ATKINSON (C. M.) Magistrate's Annual Practice for 1895. pp. 897. *Lond.* 1895. 8°. 6282. e. 24.

GIBSON (A.) and WELDON (A.) Student's Criminal and magisterial Law. pp. 338. *Lond.* 1895. 8°.   6485. f. 9.

GLEN (W. C.) Summary Jurisdiction Acts. pp. 618. *Lond.* 1894. 8°.   2232. a. 9.

OKE (G. C.) Magisterial Formulist. pp. 775. *Lond.* 1893. 8°.   2232. cc. 5.

—— Magisterial Synopsis. 2 vol. *Lond.* 1893. 8°.   2017. b.

PALEY (W.) Law and practice of Summary Convictions. pp. 618. *Lond.* 1892. 8°. 6281. g. 20.

STONE (S.) The Justice's Manual. pp. 1286. *Lond.* 1895. 8°.   2232. a. 20.

TROTTER (J. G.) Appeals from Convictions and Orders of Justices. pp. 391. *Lond.* 1891. 8°.   6281. g. 18.

WIGRAM (W. K.) Justice's Note-book. pp. 646. *Lond.* 1892. 8°.   6281. dd. 8.

WRIGHT (H.) The Office of Magistrate. pp. 90. *Lond.* 1892. 8°..   6282. aa. 23.

See also LAW, *Criminal :* POLICE.

Privy Council, Judicial Committee of.

BEAUCHAMP (J. J.) Jurisprudence of the Privy Council. pp. 920. *Montreal*, 1891. 8°. 6005. f. 7.

ENGLAND.—Law—*continued.*

WHEELER (G.) Privy Council Law. pp. 1044. *Lond.* 1893. 8°.   6125. i. 5.

   PROFESSION OF (*Barristers and Solicitors.*)

See LAW, *Profession of.*

   Star Chamber, Court of. See supra : History.

Statutes.

CHITTY (J.) The Statutes of practical utility. *Lond.* 1894, *etc.* 8°,   2017. c.

GIBSON (A.) and WELDON (A.) Student's Statute Law. pp. 932. *Lond.* 1893. 8°.   2230. e. 7.

G. B. & I. *Statutes.* Index to the Statutes in force, 1892. pp. 1332. *Lond.* 1893. 8°.   BAR. A. y.

HARDCASTLE (H.) Treatise on the construction and effect of Statute Law. pp. 659. *Lond.* 1892. 8°.   6145. e. 26.

POOLE (R. T.) Parliamentary Legislation in brief. Epitome of Public Acts. *Lond.* 1893, *etc.* 8°.   6190. a.

STRICKLAND (P.) Chronological Table of Public General Acts in force, 1894. pp. 82. *Lond.* 1895. 8°.   6145. g. 18.

See also supra: General.

Supreme Court of Judicature.

CAVANAGH (C.) Law and procedure of Summary Judgment on specially endorsed writ. pp. 229. *Lond.* 1887. 8°.   6281. c. 30.

CLAY (W. G.) Law and practice relating to Writs of Summons. pp. 231. *Lond.* 1894. 8°.   6190. aa. 34.

COOTE (H. C.) Coote's Common Form Practice and Tristram's Contentious Practice. pp. 895. *Lond.* 1891. 8°.   2018. a.

DAVIS (E. J.) Whose Fault? Story of a trial at Nisi Prius. pp. 254. *Lond.* 1892. 8°.   6282. c. 15.

EPHEM. Lawyer's Diary and Courts of Justice Directory. *Lond.* 1892, *etc.* 8°.   P.P. 2494. b.

FRANQUET DE FRANQUEVILLE (C.) *Count.* Le Système judiciaire de la Grande Bretagne. 2 tom. *Paris*, 1893. 8°.   6190. df. 16.

GIBSON (A.) and WELDON (A.) Student's Practice of the Courts. pp. 389. *Lond.* 1894. 8°.   6281. g. 23.

G. B. & I. Statutory Rules and Orders. *Lond.* 1891, *etc.* 8°.   2022. f.

—— Index to the Statutory Rules and Orders. *Lond.* 1891, *etc.* 8°.   2022. f.

INDERMAUR (J.) Manual of the practice of the Supreme Court of Judicature. pp. 371. *Lond.* 1894. 8°.   2230. d. 22.

—— and THWAITES (C.) Student's guide to procedure in the Queen's Bench. pp. 97. *Lond.* 1894. 8°.   6190. f. 10.

ODGERS (W. B.) Principles of Pleadings in civil actions. pp. 315. *Lond.* 1894. 8°. 6190. df. 18.

OSWALD (J. F.) Contempt of Court. pp. 295. *Lond.* 1895. 8°.   6190. df. 25.

PIGGOTT (F. T.) Service out of the Jurisdiction. pp. 262. *Lond.* 1892. 8°.   6281. g. 21.

SETON (*Hon. Sir* H. W.) Forms of Judgments and Orders in the High Court of Justice and Court of Appeal. *Lond.* 1891, *etc.* 8°.   2230. e. 13.

Law Reports. *See* LAW REPORTS.

Local Government. *See* LOCAL GOVERNMENT.

Lords, *House of. See infra : Parliament.*

Navy.

BRASSEY (T.) *Baron Brassey.* Papers and addresses, naval and maritime. 5 vol. *Lond.* 1894, 95. 8°.   8806. ccc. 15.

ENGLAND.—Navy—*continued.*

CLOWES (W. L.) All about the Royal Navy. pp. 187. *Lond.* 1891. 8°. 8807. aa. 43.

COLOMB (P. H.) Essays on Naval Defence. pp. 328. *Lond.* 1893. 8°. 8807. dd. 37.

G. B. & I. *Navy.* Another view of the British Navy. pp. 151. *Lond.* 1886. 8°. 8807. aa. 30.

—— The Needs of the Navy. pp. 29. *Lond.* 1894. 4°. 8806. ccc. 14.

—— Justice to Naval Officers. pp. 64. *Lond.* 1893. 8°. Pam. 43.

HEWETT (W. W.) Order Book for Executive Officers. pp. 140. *Portsmouth,* 1894. 8°. 8806. dd. 24.

HOLMAN (J.) Life in the Royal Navy. pp. 152. *Lond.* 1892. 8°. 8805. bbb. 34.

LONDON. *Navy League.* Constitution. Suggested Programme. *Lond.* 1895. 4°. Pam. 43.

P.P. *Devonport.* Naval Brigade News. *Lond.* 1886, *etc.* fol. P.P. 1138. o.

—— *London.* Royal Naval Warrant Officers' Annual. *Lond.* 1893, *etc.* 8°. P.P. 2486. va.

PERRY (O. L.) Rank and Badges in the Army and Navy. pp. 424. *Lond.* 1888. 8°. 2249. a. 26.

ROBINSON (C. N.) The British Fleet. pp. 560. *Lond.* 1894. 8°. K.T.C. 33. a. 1.

WILKINSON (H. S.) The Brain of the Navy. pp. 122. *Lond.* 1895. 8°. 8806. a. 64.

—— The Command of the Sea. pp. 122. *Lond.* 1894. 8°. 8806. a. 65.

—— The Secret of the Sea. pp. 27. *Lond.* 1895. 8°. Pam. 68.

WILLIAMS (H.) The Steam Navy of England. pp. 312. *Lond.* 1895. 8°. 8806. h. 30.

See also NAVAL SCIENCE : SHIPBUILDING.

Examinations. See EXAMINATIONS.

Gunnery. See GUNNERY.

Naval History.

ENGLAND. England's Battles by sea and land. 2 vol. *Lond.* 1888–90. 8°. 9502. g. 10.

LOW (C. R.) England's Sea victories. pp. 241. *Lond.* 1893. 8°. 9025. c. 2.

ROBINSON (C. N.) The British Fleet. pp. 560. *Lond.* 1894. 8°. K.T.C. 33. a. 1.

SOUTHEY (R.) English Seamen. Howard, Clifford, Hawkins, Drake, Cavendish. pp. 403. *Lond.* 1895. 8°. 10804. b. 22.

WILLIAMS (H.) Britain's Naval Power. History of the British Navy. pp. 265. *Lond.* 1894. 8°. 8806. bb. 32.

FROUDE (J. A.) English Seamen in the sixteenth century. pp. 309. *Lond.* 1895. 8°. 9510. aaa. 8.

LEAKE (S. M.) Life of Captain S. Martin, 1666–1740. pp. 223. 1895. 8°. Ac. London. *Navy Records Society.* Publications. Vol. 5. Ac. 8109.

HANNAY (D.) Rodney. pp. 222. 1891. 8°. English Men of Action. 10803. bbb.

MAHAN (A. T.) Influence of Sea Power upon the French Revolution and Empire, 1793–1812. 2 vol. *Lond.* 1892. 8°. 9079. g. 21.

BROWN (G. L.) Nelson. pp. 472. *Lond.* 1891. 8°. 10817. f. 17.

LAUGHTON (J. K.) Nelson. pp. 240. 1895. 8°. English Men of Action. 10803. bbb.

NELSON (H.) *Viscount Nelson.* Nelson's Words and Deeds. Edited by W. Clark Russell. pp. 224. *Lond.* 1890. 8°. 10921. e. 16.

SOUTHEY (R.) The Life of Nelson. pp. 326. *Lond.* 1891. 8°. 10817. e. 13.

RUSSELL (W. C.) Collingwood. pp. 271. *Lond.* 1891. 8°. 10817. k. 17.

FORTESCUE (*Hon.* J. W.) Dundonald. pp. 227. 1895. 8°. English Men of Action. 10803. bbb.

DAVIS (N. D.) The Fight between the "Peacock" and the "Hornet," 1813. pp. 20. *Demerara,* 1889. 8°. Pam. 28.

BRIGHTON (J. G.) Admiral Sir Provo W. P. Wallis. pp. 299. *Lond.* 1892. 8°. 10816. bbb. 26.

KNOLLYS (W. W.) Our Soldiers and Sailors. Dashing Deeds, *etc.* 8 pt. *Lond.* 1892. 8°. 10602. b. 24.

DON (W. G.) Reminiscences of the Baltic Fleet of 1855. pp. 138. *Brechin,* 1894. 8°. 9080. aa. 23.

S., C. S. Reminiscences of a Midshipman's Life. 1850–56. 2 vol. *Lond.* 1893. 8°. 10817. dd. 11.

See also supra : History.

For the Spanish Armada, *see supra :* History : for the Battle of Trafalgar, *see* TRAFALGAR.

Queen's Regulations, etc.

G. B. & I. *Admiralty.* Queen's Regulations and Admiralty Instructions. pp. 1329. *Lond.* 1893. 8°. 8806. ddd. 1.

—— List of Her Majesty's Ships engaged in the Naval Manœuvres. *Lond.* 1889, *etc.* 8°. 8807. dd.

—— Uniform Regulations for Officers of the Fleet. pp. 29. *Lond.* 1893. fol. 8805. h. 11.

—— Watch, Station, Quarter and Fire Bills. pp. 300. *Lond.* 1890. 4°. 8807. d. 16.

—— Boats' Signals. pp. 351. *Lond.* 1890. 16°. 8807. dd. 21.

—— Handbook of gymnastic exercises. pp. 107. *Lond.* 1891, 8°. 8807. dd. 24,

—— Regulations for carrying into effect the Act for the Royal Naval Artillery Volunteers. pp. 65. *Lond.* 1889. 8°. 8807. b. 56.

Royal Marines. See supra : Army.

Nonconformists.

GAIDOZ (H.) Les religions en Grande-Bretagne. pp. 36. *Paris,* 1895. 8°. Pam. 92.

HAMMOND (J.) Church or Chapel ? pp. 390. *Lond.* 1893. 8°. 4109. aaaa. 1.

—— Mistakes of modern Nonconformity. pp. 87. *Lond.* 1895. 8°. 4109. aaaa. 22.

HAYWARD (J.) Phases of a Nonconformist forward movement, *etc.* pp. 28. *Lond.* 1891. 8°. Pam. 16.

HOLLOWELL (J. H.) Why we cannot leave Nonconformity. pp. 8. *Lond.* 1895. 8°. Pam. 16.

MACKENNAL (A.) Story of the English separatists. pp. 139. *Lond.* 1893. 8°. 4715. df. 6.

NYE (G. H. F.) How Dissent is established and endowed. pp. 80. *Lond.* 1894. 8°. 4109. bb. 30.

P.P. *London.* Review of the Churches. *Lond.* 1891, *etc.* 4°. P.P. 268. cac.

PIKE (E. C.) Lectures on English Nonconformity. pp. 144. *Lond.* 1895. 8°. 4715. bb. 34.

ROGERS (J. G.) Church Systems of England in the 19th Century. pp. 683. 1891. 8°. Congregational Lectures. 4462. i.

SKEATS (H. S.) History of the free churches of England. pp. 757. *Lond.* 1894. 8°. 4715. b. 38.

STEAD (F. H.) The English Church of the future. pp. 40. *Lond.* 1892. 8°. Pam. 92.

ZAHN (J. K. A.) Abriss einer Geschichte der Evangelischen Kirche im britischen Weltreich. pp. 147. *Stuttgart.* 1891. 8°. 4715. aaa. 41.

See also supra: Church of England and Dissent : History, Ecclesiastical : BAPTISTS : CONGREGATIONALISM : FRIENDS, *Society of :* METHODISM : PRESBYTERIANISM : SWEDENBORGIANISM : UNITARIANISM.

ENGLAND—*continued.*

Parliament.

See also supra: Constitution: History. Infra: Politics: GOVERNMENT: PARLIAMENT.

JENNINGS (G. H.)   Anecdotal History of the British Parliament.   pp. 718.   *Lond.* 1892. 8°.
2238. f. 7.

MAY (T. E.) *Baron Farnborough.* Treatise on the law, privileges and usage of Parliament.
pp. 898.   *Lond.* 1893. 8°.   2017. b.

SMITH (G. B.)   History of the English Parliament.   2 vol.   *Lond.* 1892. 8°.   09504. f. 10.

TODD (A.)   Parliamentary Government in England.   2 vol.   *Lond.* 1892. 8°.   8139. aa. 52.

WALPOLE (S.)   The Electorate and the Legislature.   pp. 163.   1892. 8°.   The English Citizen.   2238. bb.

DICKINSON (G. L.)   Development of Parliament during the 19th century.   pp. 183.
Lond. 1895. 8°.   8139. dd.5.

Commons, House of.

G. B. & I.   *Commons, House of.*   Rules, orders and forms of Procedure.   pp. 212.
Lond. 1891. 8°.   8139. a. 27.

BEAN (W. W.)   Parliamentary Representation of the six northern counties of England, 1603–1886.   pp. 1208.   *Hull,* 1890. 8°.   8133. f. 3.

MAC CALMONT (F. H.)   Parliamentary Poll Book of all elections 1832–95.   2 pt.   *Lond.* 1895. 8°.
8139. a. 36.

G. B. & I.   *Commons, House of.*   Sittings of the House of Commons for eleven years, 1880–90.
Lond. 1891. *s. sh.* fol.   Pam. 68.

DUNCAN (J. A.)   Payment of Members.   pp. 8.
1892. 8°.   National Reform Union Pamphlets.
8139. b.

HAWKEN (H.)   Payment of Members.   pp. 16.
Lond. 1892. 8°.   8139. aa. 53. (13.)

MAC CULLAGH TORRENS (W. T.)   Twenty years in Parliament.   pp. 381.   *Lond.* 1893. 8°.
8139. e. 8.

COOKE (C. W. R.)   Four Years in Parliament.
pp. 142.   *Lond.* 1891. 8°.   8139. aa. 44.

TEMPLE (*Sir* R.)   Life in Parliament. 1886–92.
pp. 391.   *Lond.* 1893. 8°.   8139. bbb. 12.

BOYER (E. A.)   Comparison of results of General Elections, 1885–86–92.   pp. 72.
Manch. 1892. 8°.   8139. a. 31.

CRAWSHAY (W. S.)   The Politics of the Commons. Compiled from election addresses, *etc.*   1886.
pp. 359.   *Lond.* 1886. 8°.   8138. g. 13.

G. B. & I.   *Commons, House of.*   Collection of election addresses, *etc.*   1886.   1856. d.

—— *Parliament.*   Parliamentary Pictures and personalities 1890–93.   pp. 96.
Lond. 1893. *obl.* fol.   1850. a. 6.

WATKINSON (J.)   Guide to electorial Changes since 1886.   pp. 26.   *Lond.* 1891. 8°. 8139. aa. 50.

G. B. & I.   *Commons, House of.*   Handbook to the General Election, 1892.   pp. 60.
Lond. 1892. 8°.   8138. aa. 20. (4.)

—— The Race for the Majority, 1892.
Lond. 1892. fol.   1889. d. 3. (226.)

M.   An Election Journal, 1892.   pp. 350.
Lond. 1894. 8°.   8139. c. 16.

G. B. & I.   *Commons, House of.*   The New House of Commons.   July 1892.   pp. 328.
Lond. 1892. 8°.   8139. a. 30.

—— List of Members of the House of Commons. July 1892–94.   pp. 82.   *Lond.* 1895. 8°.
8139. b. 42.

BOYER (E. A.)   General Election.   Book for marking results and comparing 1885–86–92.
pp. 68.   *Manch.* 1892. 8°.   8139. a. 29.

ELECTION RECORDER.   The Election Recorder; giving the names of Members of Parliament at the dissolution.   *Lond.* 1895, *etc.* 8°.   8139. a. 39.

G. B. & I.   *Commons, House of.*   General Election, July 1895.   Address of every Candidate.
Lond. 1895, *etc.* fol.   1850. d.

—— General Election, 1895.   Members returned to the House of Commons.   pp. 78.
Lond. 1895. 8°.   8139. aa. 59.

—— The New House of Commons.   July 1895.
pp. 368.   *Lond.* 1895. 16°.   8139. a. 37.

See also supra: History.   Infra: Politics.

Elections, Law of, etc.   See ELECTIONS.

Lords, House of.

BOURNE (H. R. F.)   The House of Lords.
pp. 79.   *Lond.* 1881. 8°.   8139. aa. 53. (2.)

BREAKERS.   Drifting towards the Breakers!   By a Sussex Peer.   pp. 197.   *Lond.* 1895. 8°.
8139. b. 13.

CHARLEY (*Sir* W. T.)   The Crusade against the Constitution: vindication of the House of Lords.
pp. 552.   *Lond.* 1895. 8°.   8139. aa. 56.

COMMONER.   The House of Lords.   pp. 20.
Lond. 1894. 8°.   Pam. 68.

FIELDING (T.)   The House of Lords: its history, rights and uses.   pp. 59.   *Lond.* 1893. 8°.
8131. bb. 51. (13.)

HOUFE (C. A.)   The Question of the Houses.
pp. 130.   *Lond.* 1895. 8°.   8139. a. 38.

MAC NEILL (J. G. S.)   Titled Corruption: origin of some Irish peerages.   pp. 140.
Lond. 1894. 8°.   8146. b. 28.

MAC PHERSON (W. C.)   The Baronage and the Senate.   pp. 414.   *Lond.* 1893. 8°.   8139. dd. 1.

PIKE (L. O.)   Constitutional history of the House of Lords.   pp. 405.   *Lond.* 1894. 8°. 8139. e. 10.

SPALDING (T. A.)   The House of Lords: a retrospect and forecast.   pp. 281.   *Lond.* 1894. 8°.
8139. e. 9.

See also infra: Politics.

Politics, *Domestic and General.*

BUXTON (S. C.)   Handbook to Political Questions of the day.   pp. 436.   *Lond.* 1892. 8°.
2238. cc. 10.

ROBBINS (A. F.)   Practical Politics; or, the Liberalism of to-day.   pp. 224.   *Lond.* 1888. 8°.
8139. aa. 45.

SMITH (Goldwin)   Essays on Questions of the day.   pp. 360.   *N.Y.* 1893. 8°.   8139. c. 12.
1890.

NONCONFORMIST.   Mr. Gladstone exposed!
pp. 11.   *Lond.* 1890. 8°.   Pam. 78.

TREMENHEERE (H. C.)   What to avoid and why.
pp. 34.   *Lond.* 1890. 8°.   Pam. 68.
1891.

BRITISH POLITICS.   British politics.   By a Member of the Reform Club.   pp. 23.   *Lond.* 1891. 12°.
8139. aa. 53. (7.)

DORINGTON (*Sir* J. E.)   The Unionist Cause in the Tewkesbury division.   pp. 24.
Cheltenham, 1891. 8°.   Pam. 68.

DYER (J.)   Liberal Measures and tory doings.
pp. 97.   *Lond.* 1891. 8°.   8139. aa. 53. (8.)

FORDHAM (G.)   Annual Parliaments, and universal suffrage recommended, 1817.   pp. 23.
Lond. 1891. 12°.   8133. a. 9. (7.)

GLADSTONE (*Right Hon.* W. E.)   Religious Disabilities Bill.   Speech in moving the Second Reading.   pp. 16.   *Westminster,* 1891. 8°.
Pam. 68.

LIBERAL SPEAKERS.   Facts and figures for Liberal Speakers.   No. 1–3.   *Westminster,* 1891. 8°.
8139. bb. 48. (11.)

ENGLAND —Politics—*continued.*

MEREDYTH (W. H.) The Brief for the Government. pp. 210. *Edinb.* 1891. 8°. 8139. aa. 47.

NONCONFORMIST. Liberalism and Liberty. pp. 16. *Lond.* 1891. 8°. 8139. aa. 53. (9.)

TREMENHEERE (H. S.) Why have I a vote? and how should I use it? pp. 30. *Lond.* 1891. 8°. 8139. bb. 48. (15.)

1892.

ARGUMENT. Argument from Nationality to disestablishment and federalism. pp. 8. *Lond.* 1892. 8°. 8139. bb. 47. (1.)

BALFOUR (*Right Hon.* A. J.) Lies and Replies: exposure of some Gladstonian fallacies. Letters. pp. 100. *Westminster*, 1892. 8°. 8139. bb 47. (2.)

BOTTOMLEY (J. H.) General Election, 1892. Political Progress. pp. 30. *Doncaster*, 1891. 8°. 8139. aa. 48. (2.)

CARFAX. The Coming Election. How shall I vote? pp. 30. *Lond.* 1892. 8°. 8146. bb. 33. (12.)

DAVIDSON (J. M.) Politics for the people. Ser. 1. pp. 127. 1892. 8°. Bellamy Series. No. 11. 12205. e.

FISCHER (T.) Essay on the Primrose League. pp. 15. *Lond.* 1892. 8°. 8139. bb. 47. (7.)

GREAT BRITAIN. The Union and the Unionists. *Reading*, 1892. 8°. 8146. cc. 6. (12.)

INNES (C. R.) Middle Class organisation. pp. 19. 49. *Lond.* 1892. 8°. 08227. i. 29. (9.)

IRELAND. Hang "Home Rule!" *Lond.* 1892, etc. 8°. 8285. aa.

JACOBS. Scheming Jacobs. What they do! pp. 123. *Lond.* 1892. 16°. 8277. a.

LIVERPOOL. *Liberal Federal Council.* General Election. The Liberal Programme. pp. 8. *Liverpool*, 1892. 8°. 8139. bb. 47. (12.)

NOBLE (J.) Facts for Politicians. pp. 335. *Lond.* 1892. 8°. 8139. aa. 49.

OGILVIE-FORBES (J. C. M.) The Coming Elections from the point of view of a Unionist and a Catholic. pp. 28. *Aberdeen*, 1892. 8°. 8146. cc. 6. (15.)

PRATT (W.) Conservatism. pp. 15. *Manchester*, 1892. 8°. 8139. aa. 53. (14.)

PRESENT DAY QUESTIONS. Present Day Questions. *Lond.* 1892, etc. 8°. 8139. df.

SCOTLAND. *National Union of Conservative Associations.* The Campaign Guide. Election handbook. pp. 348. *Edinb.* 1892. 8°. 8139. c. 11.

SMITH (R.) What will be the first move in the new Parliament, 1892? pp. 16. *Lond.* 1892. 8°. 8146. cc. 6. (6.)

TORY DEMOCRACY. Tory Democracy and conservative policy. pp. 241. *Lond.* 1892. 8°. 8139. b. 36.

WARNING. A Warning to Workers. pp. 4. *Lond.* 1892. 8°. Pam. 68.

WATCHMAN. The Coming Crisis. Is Mr. Gladstone the Foe of Protestantism. pp. 23. *Lond.* 1892. 16°. 3939. a. 6. (5.)

1893.

CANDIDATE. A Candidate's Speeches. pp. 233. *Lond.* 1893. 8°. 8139. aaa. 44.

GLADSTONE (*Right Hon.* W. E.) Mr. W. E. Gladstone; a life misspent. pp. 283. *Lond.* 1893. 8°. 8139. b. 37.

LONDON. *Eighty Club.* The "Eighty" Club. Report for 1893. Speeches, etc. 4 pt. *Lond.* 1894. 8°. 8139. aaa. 47.

P.P. *London.* The Liberal Magazine. *Lond.* 1893, etc. 8°. P.P. 3558. k. & 845.

PHILLIMORE (W. P. W.) Suggestions for a constitutional Reform Bill. pp. 22. *Lond.* 1893. 8°. 8139. bb. 47. (20.)

POWELL (G. H. C.) Electoral Reform. pp. 24. *Lond.* 1893. 8°. Pam. 68.

SAUNDERS (W.) The political Situation: how it strikes a Radical. pp. 31. *Lond.* 1893. 8°. 8139. bb. 47. (21.)

TREMENHEERE (H. S.) How good Government grew, and how to preserve it. pp. 28. *Lond.* 1893. 8°. Pam. 68.

WOLSEY-SEAMAN (W.) England's Rights and demands before Irish Home Rule. pp. 42. *Lond.* 1893. 8°. 8139. bb. 51. (15.)

1894.

CONSERVATIVE POLICY. Conservative Policy of the future. pp. 8. *Westminster*, 1894. 8°. 8139. bb. 51. (16.)

CONSTABLE (H. S.) Some Hints for political leaflets. pp. 169. *Lond.* 1894. 8°. 8139. bb. 50.

D., J. N. Progress of Democratic Power, and its effect on England. pp. 16. *Lond.* 1894. 32°. Pam. 82.

HAMBER (H.) An Impeachment of Party Government. pp. 14. *Lond.* 1894. 8°. 8139. bb. 51. (17.)

HILL (W.) Labour and Liberalism. pp. 43. *Lond.* 1894. 8°. 8139. bb. 51. (18.)

LIBERALS. What the Liberals have done, 1892-94. [Eight blank leaves.] *Lond.* 1894. 24°. Pam. 68.

MAXSE (F. A.) Judas! A political tract. pp. 19. *Lond.* 1894. 8°. 8138. aa. 20. (9.)

WHITE (A.) The English Democracy. pp. 251. *Lond.* 1894. 8°. 8139. dd. 2.

1895.

BREAKERS. Drifting towards the Breakers! pp. 197. *Lond.* 1895. 8°. 8139. b. 13

FACTS. Facts for Electors. Handbook for Unionist committee men. pp. 86. *Edinb.* 1895. 8°. 8139. aaa. 51.

GOULD (F. C.) Cartoons of the Election campaign, 1895. pp. 47. *Lond.* 1895. fol. 12314. l. 10.

HALLETT (T. G. P.) Union versus Home Rule. pp. 68. *Lond.* 1895. 8°. 8146. cc. 7.

PARNELL (*Hon.* A.) British Policy from Home and Imperial points of view. pp. 179. *Lond.* 1895. 8°. 8139. a. 35.

REID (A.) The New Party described. pp. 310. *Lond.* 1895. 8°. 08276. f. 84.

ROBINSON (W. P.) Burning Questions. pp. 151. *Lond.* 1895. 8°. 8139. aaa. 48.

ROSE (W. K.) and SMITH (R. M.) The Liberal Platform. pp. 772. *Lond.* 1895. 8°. 8139. df. 14.

SNELL (W. E.) The Cabinet and party politics. pp. 95. *Lond.* 1895. 8°. 8139. aaa. 52.

See also supra: Parliament: CAPITAL AND LABOUR : IRELAND : SOCIALISM : SOCIAL SCIENCE.

Politics, Foreign.

FRANC (C.) La Sécurité nationale. L'Angleterre et la triple alliance. pp. 335. *Paris*, 1893. 8°. 8026. aaa. 43.

LUND (J. K.) England and the continental Powers. pp. 95. *Lond.* 1894. 8°. 8026. bbb. 37.

MARTIN (E.) L'Angleterre et le Canal de Suez. pp. 30. *Paris*, 1892. 8°. 8028. de. 30. (14.)

PARNELL (*Hon.* A.) British Policy from Home and Imperial points of view. pp. 179. *Lond.* 1895. 8°. 8139. a. 35.

WEIL (G. D.) L'attitude de l'Angleterre vis-à-vis de la France en 1870-1871. pp. 88. *Paris*, 1891. 8°. 8026. i. 6. (11.)

WILKINSON (H. S.) The Great Alternative. Plea for a national policy. pp. 331. *Lond.* 1894. 8°. 8026. ee. 28.

ENGLAND.—Politics—_continued._

Asia. Antagonismus der englischen und russischen Interessen in Asien. pp. 187.
Wien, 1890. 8°.   8028. e. 21.

Campbell (W. F.) _Baron Stratheden and Campbell._ The Eastern Question. Speeches 1871-91. pp. 304. _Lond._ 1894. 8°.   8028. ee. 28.

Marvin (C.) Letters to the "Morning Post." pp. 427. _Allahabad_, 1891. 8°.   8023. ec. 23.

Popowski (J.) The rival Powers in Central Asia. pp. 235. _Westminster_, 1893. 8°. 8028. de. 29.

Portugal. _Ministerio dos Negocios Estrangeiros._ Documentos. Negocios da Africa. Correspondencia com a Inglaterra. pp. 269.
Lisboa, 1890. fol.   8028. g. 16.

—— Documentos apresentados ás Cortes. Negociações do Tratado com a Inglaterra 20 Aug., 1890. pp. 227. _Lisboa_, 1890. fol. 8028. g. 17.

G. B. & I. Victoria, _Queen._ O Ultimatum Britannico. Correspondencia. 1890. 8°. Ac.
Lisbon. _Sociedade de Geographia._ Boletim. Ser. 9. Nos. 1-5.   Ac. 6020.

Gromier (M. A.) Portugal, Angleterre & France. pp. 48. _Paris_, 1890. 16°.   Pam. 67.

Lisboa (C.) Apreciações ao Tratado anglo-portuguez, 1890. _Lisboa_, 1890. 8°.
         8028. de. 31. (7.)

Mello (C. de.) A Questão ingleza. O tratado. _Lisboa_, 1890, _etc._ 8°.   8027. bb. 11.

Barjona de Freitas (A. C.) A questão ingleza. Discurso. pp. 24. _Lisboa_, 1891. 8°. Pam. 71.

Barros Gomez (H. de) As Negociações com a Inglaterra no periodo de 1886-89. pp. 59. _Lisboa_, 1891. 8°.   Pam. 71.

Hintze Ribeiro (E. R.) Portugal e a Inglaterra. pp. 48. _Lisboa_, 1891. 8°.   Pam. 71.

See also Behring Sea : Europe : India.

Privy Council, _Judicial Committee of._

See supra : Law.

Queen's Bench, _Court of._

See supra : Law.

Rivers, _etc._

G. B. The Rivers of Great Britain. 2 vol.
Lond. 1892. 4°.   10348. k. 18.

Hope (R. C.) Legendary Lore of the Holy Wells of England. pp. 222. _Lond._ 1895. 8°.
        12431. i. 34.

See also infra : Topography : Thames.

Roman Catholic Church, _in England._

See supra : History, Ecclesiastical : Roman Catholic Church.

Social Life.

England. Social England Series.
Lond. 1895, _etc._ 8°.   9503. ccc.

Traill (H. D.) Social England.
Lond. 1894, _etc._. 8°.   2077. b.

Andrews (W.) Bygone England. Social studies pp. 258. _Lond._ 1892. 8°.   7709. aaa. 24.

Ditchfield (P. H.) Old English sports and customs. pp. 132. _Lond._ 1891. 8°. 7912. aa. 6.

Kebbel (T. E.) Old and new English country life. pp. 234. _Edinb._ 1891. 8°.   08276. f. 17.

Balch (E.) Glimpses of old English homes. pp. 223. _Lond._ 1890. 4°.   010358. g. 10.

Hodges (E.) Some ancient English homes. pp. 280. _Lond._ 1895. 4°.   10348. d. 21.

Hutton (B.) Castles and their heroes. pp. 270. _Lond._ 1891. 8°.   10349. cc. 17.

Baye (J. de) _Baron._ Industrial Arts of the Anglo-Saxons. pp. 135. _Lond._ 1893. 4°.
        7709. k. 20.

ENGLAND.—Social Life—_continued._

Clavering. The Duties of Baronial Life in England during the middle ages. fol. 39.
1891. 4°.   7709. k. 15.

Jusserand (J. J.) English Wayfaring Life in the middle ages. pp. 451. _Lond._ 1892. 8°.
        7709. aaa. 22.

Gasquet (F. A.) The Great Pestilence, A.D. 1348-9, known as the Black Death. pp. 244. _Lond._ 1893. 8°.   7561. k. 20.

Green (A. S.) Town Life in the 15th Century. 2 vol. _Lond._ 1894. 8°.   2258. b. 23.

Carrington (W. A.) Selections from the Stewards' Accounts at Haddon Hall, 1549-1671. pp. 56. _Derby._ 1894. 8°,   Pam. 3.

Winter (W.) Shakespeare's England. pp. 254. _N.Y._ 1893. 8°.   10349. d. 24.

Sydney (W. C.) Social Life in England 1660-90. pp. 463. _Lond._ 1892. 8°.   9525. aaa. 6.

Hervey (J.) _Earl of Bristol._ Letter-books of J. Hervey, Earl of Bristol. 1651-1750. 3 vol. _Wells_, 1894. 8°.   10921. dd. 14.

—— The Diary of J. Hervey, Earl of Bristol. With extracts from his Book of Expenses, 1688-1742. pp. 312. _Wells_, 1894. 4°.
        10921. dd. 15.

Pepys (S.) The Diary of S. Pepys. Edited by H. B. Wheatley. _Lond._ 1893, _etc._ 8°.
        Banks. 3. e. 2.

Sydney (W. C.) England and the English in the 18th century. 2 vol. _Lond._ 1891. 8°.
        9525. ee. 11.

Robinson (E. F.) Early history of Coffee Houses in England. pp. 240. _Lond._ 1893. 8°.
        7709. b. 46.

Kalm (P.) Kalm's account of his visit to England in 1748. pp. 480. _Lond._ 1892. 8°.
        010358. h. 7.

Kingston (A.) Fragments of two Centuries. pp. 200. _Royston_, 1893. 8°.   10350. de. 26.

Join-Lambert (A.) Londres et les Anglais en 1771. pp. 50. _Paris_, 1890. 8°.   10349. gg. 20.

Robinson (J. R.) "Old Q." W. Douglas, fourth Duke of Queensberry. pp. 362. _Lond._ 1895. 8°.
        10825. cc. 29.

—— The Last Earls of Barrymore. 1769-1824. pp. 272. _Lond._ 1894. 8°.   10817. dd. 14.

Gossip. Gossip of the Century. 2 vol.
Lond. 1892. 8°.   012330. l. 1.

Besant (_Sir_ W.) Fifty Years ago. pp. 244. _Lond._ 1892. 8°.   9525. df. 12.

Tuckley (H.) Under the Queen. pp. 278. _Cincinnati_, 1891. 8°.   10348. cc. 22.

Dallas (G. M,) Diary of G. M. Dallas, U.S. Minister to England 1856-61. pp. 443. _Phila._ 1892. 8°.   010882. e. 16.

Fowler (J. K.) Echoes of old Country Life. _Lond._ 1892. 4°.   12352. g. 31.

Gavard (C.) Un Diplomate à Londres. Lettres et notes. 1871-77. pp. 322. _Paris_, 1895. 12°.
        9080. e. 17.

Horizon. The Social Horizon. pp. 163. _Lond._ 1892. 8°.   08276. e. 41.

Leclerc (M.) Les Professions et la société en Angleterre. pp. 294. _Paris_, 1894. 12°.
        10348. c. 27.

Woods (R. A.) English social Movements. pp. 277. _Lond._ 1892. 8°.   08276. f. 29.

See also infra : Topography, Travels, _etc._: Social Questions.

Sport. _See_ Sport.

Statutes. _See supra :_ Law.

Supreme Court of Judicature.

See supra : Law.

ENGLAND—*continued.*

Topography.

Bibliography.

CHEVALIER (C. N. J.) Angleterre. Topo-bibliographie. pp. 79. *Montbéliard*, 1893. 8°.
11903. b. 44. (4.)

General.

BERLYN (A.) Sunrise Land. pp. 315.
Lond. 1894. 8°.   10350. bb. 48.

CORNISH (C. J.) Wild England of to-day.
pp. 310. *Lond.* 1895. 8°.   7002. g. 20.

ENGLAND AND WALES. Sights and scenes in England and Wales. *Lond.* 1894, *etc. obl.* 4°.
1787. aa. 25.

G. B. & I. Our own Country.
Lond. 1891, *etc.* 8°.   10348. i. 8.

—— Round the Coast. Pictures from photographs. *Lond.* 1895, *etc. obl.* fol. 1787. aa. 33.

—— *Hydrographic Office.* Sailing directions for the West Coast of England. *Lond.* 1891. 8°.
10496. ff. 21.

HOPE (R. C.) Legendary Lore of the Holy Wells of England. pp. 222. *Lond.* 1893. 8°.
12431. i. 34.

HUISH (M. B.) The Southern Coast of England,
Lond. 1891. fol.   K.T.C. 2. a. 5.

JEWRY, afterwards VALENTINE (L.) Picturesque England. pp. 512. *Lond.* 1894. 8°.
10352. dd. 7.

MILNE (F. A.) English Topography.
1891, *etc.* 8°. Gentleman's Magazine Library.
2324. c. 9.

NEELMEYER-VUKASSOWITSCH (H.) Grossbritannien und Irland. pp. 914. *Leipz.* 1886. 8°.
10026. k. 10.

RUSKIN (J.) The Harbours of England.
pp. 134. *Orpington*, 1895. 8°.   2340. f.

BALCH (E.) Glimpses of old English homes.
pp. 223. *Lond.* 1890. 4°.   010358. g. 10.

G. B. & I. Historic Houses of the United Kingdom. *Lond.* 1891. 8°.   7814. h. 10.

HODGES (E.) Some ancient English homes.
pp. 280. *Lond.* 1895. 4°.   10348. d. 21.

HUTTON (B.) Castles and their heroes. pp. 270.
Lond. 1891. 8°.   10349. cc. 17.

VENABLES (E.) Episcopal Palaces of England.
pp. 253. *Lond.* 1895. 4°.   4705. f. 21.

WHITAKER (J.) Descriptive List of the deerparks and paddocks of England. pp. 204.
Lond. 1892. 8°.   07293. k. 9.

See also supra : Lake District : Rivers.

Gazetteers : Geography : Guide Books.

BARTHOLOMEW (J.) Gazetteer of the British Isles. pp. 880. *Edinb.* 1893. 8°.   2059. c.

BRABNER (J. H. F.) Comprehensive Gazetteer of England and Wales. *Lond.* 1894, *etc.* 8°.
10348. i. 6.

CASSELL (J.) Gazetteer of Great Britain and Ireland. *Lond.* 1893, *etc.* 8°.   10348. i.

BEVAN (G. P.) Home geography of England and Wales. pp. 248. *Lond.* 1893. 8°. 10347. c. 35.

HALL (M.) Notes on the geography of the British Isles. pp. 110. *Dubl.* 1895. 8°.
10348. b. 27.

HAUGHTON (T.) Geography of England and Wales. pp. 525. *Lond.* 1893. 8°. 10348. cc. 23.

JOHNSTON (R.) Competitive geography of the British Isles. pp. 151. *Lond.* 1893. 8°.
10347. c. 36.

MEIKLEJOHN (J. M. D.) The British Empire.
pp. 336. *Lond.* 1891. 8°.   10024. cc. 12.

RAMSAY (*Sir* A. C.) Physical Geology and Geography of Great Britain. pp. 421.
Lond. 1894. 8°.   2030. d.

WARD (M. J. B.) About England : first lessons in English Geography. pp. 166. *Lond.* 1892. 8°.
10347. cc. 21.

———

BAEDEKER (C.) Great Britain. Handbook.
pp. 547. *Leipz.* 1894. 8°.   2352. a.

BOSTON. A Summer in England : hand-book for American women. pp. 82. *Bost.* 1892. 8°.
10360. a. 19.

G. B. & I. Inland Watering-Places. pp. 211.
Lond. 1891. 8°.   7470. aaa. 2.

PASCOE (C. E.) American Roads through England. pp. 80. *Lond.* 1891. 8°.   10360. a. 10.

SPURRIER (W. J.) Cyclists' route book for Great Britain and Ireland. pp. 188. *Lond.* 1893. 8°.
10348. cc. 24.

SUMMER RESORTS. Summer Resorts in Great Britain and Ireland. pp. 64. *Lond.* 1895. 8°.
10348. d. 22

WHERE. Where shall we go? Guide to the Watering-places of England, Scotland, Ireland, and Wales. Edited by A. R. Hope Moncrieff.
pp. 348. *Lond.* 1892. 8°.   10347. c. 33.

Travels, etc.

BURNABY (E. H. V.) Ride from Land's End to John o' Groat's. pp. 146. *Lond.* 1893. 8°.
10351. e. 42.

COTTERELL (C.) Summer holidays in N.E. England. pp. 143. *Lond.* 1895. 8°.
010358. e. 32.

HARPER (C. G.) From Paddington to Penzance. A summer tramp. pp. 272. *Lond.* 1893. 8°.
010358. f. 43.

HISSEY (J. J.) Across England in a dog-cart.
pp. 413. *Lond.* 1891. 8°.   010358. f. 26.

—— Through ten English Counties. pp. 406.
Lond. 1894. 8°.   010350. i. 2.

HOUNSELL (B.) English Coach drives. pp. 98.
Lond. 1894. 8°.   10350. bb. 46.

KNIGHT (F. A.) Rambles of a Dominie. pp. 193.
Lond. 1891. 8°.   10348. bbb. 32.

SMITH (G.) A Trip to England. pp. 140.
Toronto, 1891. 8°.   010350. ee. 1.

STABLES (W. G.) Leaves from the Log of a Gentleman Gipsy. pp. 430. *Lond.* 1891. 8°.
10350. ee. 31.

———

DAVIS (R. H.) Our English Cousins. pp. 228.
N.Y. 1894. 8°.   10347. d. 9.

DODGE (W. P.) As the Crow flies. From Corsica to Charing Cross. pp. 132. *N.Y.* 1893. 12°.
10106. dd. 5.

DORR (J. C. R.) The Flower of England's face.
pp. 259. *N.Y.* 1895. 16°.   10348. aa. 10.

THWAITES (R. G.) Our Cycling Tour in England.
pp. 315. *Chicago*, 1892. 8°.   10349. cc. 20.

DECRAIS (J.) L'Angleterre contemporaine. Notes et récits. pp. 378. *Paris*, 1893. 12°.
10347. cc. 25.

POISSON ( ) Angleterre, Écosse, Irlande.
pp. 324. *Orleans*, 1895. 8°.   10348. d. 25.

ROTHSCHILD (H. de) Notes sur l'Angleterre.
pp. 65. *Lille*, 1889. 8°.   10348. g. 7.

VILLARS (P.) Sketches of England. pp. 180.
Lond. 1891. 4°.   10348. k. 17.

BRAND (W. F.) Allerlei aus Albion. pp. 156.
Leipz. 1891. 8°.   10349. d. 18.

ULLRICH (T.) Reise-Studien aus England und Schottland. pp. 417. *Berl.* 1893. 8°.
12249. ccc. 2.

STEFFEN (G. F.) Från det moderna England.
pp. 415. *Stockholm*, 1891. 8°.   10348. e. 28.

ENGLAND.—Topography—*continued.*

STEFFEN (O. F.) Aus dem modernen England. Deutsche Ausgabe. pp. 436. *Leipz.* 1895. 8°.
    10349. gg. 22.

FERREIRA (B.) Em Viagem. Traços de uma excursão pela Inglaterra. pp. 133.
Coimbra, 1895. 8°.   10360. b. 62.

OLIVEIRA MARTINS (J. P.) A Inglaterra de hoje. pp. 257. *Lisboa,* 1893. 8°.   10347. c. 38.

AMṚITALĀLA RĀYA. Reminiscences, English and American. *Calcutta,* 1883, *etc.* 8°. 10409. aa. 31.

BEHARĀMAJĪ MIHRBĀNJĪ MALĀBARI. The Indian eye on English Life. pp. 231.
Westminster, 1893. 8°.   10348. e. 25.

NANDALĀLA DĀSA. Reminiscences, English and Australian. pp. 242. *Calcutta,* 1893. 8°.
    10492. ee. 29.

NANDALĀLA GHOSHA. Englishmen at home. pp. 194. *Calcutta,* 1888. 8°.   10350. o. 49.

VAIDYANĀTHA, *Chief Justice of Indore.* England and India: impression of persons and things. pp. 234. *Bombay,* 1893. 8°.   10027. e. 6.

YUEN SEANG-FOO. "Those Foreign Devils!" A Celestial on England. pp. 191.
Lond. 1891. 8°.   11099. b. 28.

Trade: Finance: Taxation.
National Finance.

HALL (H.) Antiquities and curiosities of the Exchequer. pp. 230. 1891. 8°. Camden Library.   7709. cc.

BERNARD (W. L.) and REID (A.) Bold Retrenchment; or the Liberal Policy. pp. 222.
Lond. 1888. 8°.   8139. b. 44.

FARRER (T. H.) *Baron Farrer.* Mr. Goschen's Finance, 1887–90. pp. 162. *Lond.* 1891. 8°.
    8228. bb. 21.

GOSCHEN (*Right Hon.* G. J.) Speech on the insufficiency of our Cash Reserves and central stock of gold. pp. 31. *Lond.* 1891. 8°.
    08227. g. 36. (9.)

HARCOURT (*Right Hon. Sir* W. G. G. V. V.) The Budget of 1891. pp. 19. *Westminster,* 1891. 8°.
    8139. bb. 48. (10.)

MARTINUZZI (P.) La Banca d'Inghilterra nei riguardi del servizio del Tesoro. pp. 152.
Livorno, 1892. 8°.   08227. h. 29.

Tariffs, etc.

G. B. & I. *Customs.* Warehousing Regulations. pp. 139. 69. *Lond.* 1891. 8°.   8244. aaa. 45.

Taxation and Rating.

TAXATION. Taxation. 1891–92. pp. 173.
Lond 1892. 8°.   8226. aaa. 50.

BLAKE (W. H. J.) The new Death Duties, 1894. pp. 14. *Lond.* 1894. 8°.   Pam. 23.

CARTMELL (J. A.) The Finance Act, 1894, so far as it relates to the Estate and other Death Duties. pp. 128. *Lond.* 1894. 8°. 6355. df. 15.

FREETH (E.) Guide to the new Death Duty. pp. 187. *Lond.* 1894. 8°.   6355. df. 16.

GRIFFITH (G. C.) Digest of the Death Duties. pp. 318. *Lond.* 1894. 8°.   2230. a. 5.

HARMAN (J. E.) The Finance Act, 1894, so far as it relates to the Death Duties. pp. 144.
Lond. 1894. 8°.   6425. aaaa. 5.

HARRIS (E.) Synopsis of the new Estate Duty. pp. 80. *Lond.* 1894. 8°.   6125. h. 10.

LORIMER (J. C.) The new Death Duties. pp. 92. *Edinb.* 1894. 8°.   6425. aaaa. 6.

MUNRO (J. E. C.) The Finance Act, 1894, so far as it relates to Estate and Succession Duty. pp. 110. *Lond.* 1894, 8°.   6426. ee. 4.

NORMAN (A. W.) Digest of the Death Duties. pp. 335. *Lond.* 1892. 8°.   6355. f. 2.

BLANCH (W. H.) Shall I appeal against my Income Tax Assessment? pp. 62.
Lond. 1890. 8°.   Pam. 23.

CHAPMAN (A.) Income Tax: how to get it refunded. pp. 60. 1894, 5. 12°. Wilson's Legal Handy books.   6426. aaa. 39.

—— "Copyright" Income Tax Tables at 7d. and 6d. in the pound. pp. 7. *Lond.* 1893. 8°
    8225. ee. 45.

DOWELL (S.) Acts relating to the Income Tax. pp. 448. *Lond.* 1895. 8°.   6425. ee. 3.

ELLIS (A. M.) Guide to the Income Tax Acts. pp. 359. *Lond.* 1893. 12°.   6426. cc. 33.

FLINT (S. W.) Schedule D, and how to deal with it. pp. 18. *Lond.* 1893. 16°. Pam. 23.

INCOME TAX. Income Tax, to pay or not? pp. 70. *Lond.* 1890. 8°.   Pam. 23.

MITCHELL (G. B.) Hints to taxpayers, how to appeal against Income Tax assessments. pp. 115. *Wolverhampton,* 1891. 8°.   8226. cc. 49.

MURRAY (A.) and CARTER (R. N.) Guide to Income-tax practice. pp. 280. *Lond.* 1895. 8°.
    6425. aaaa. 9.

RHODES (J.) Income Tax assessments. pp. 31. *Lond.* 1889–90. 8°.   Pam. 23.

ROBINSON (A.) The Law relating to Income Tax. pp. 504. *Lond.* 1895. 8°.   6425. h. 9.

BOURDIN (M. A.) Exposition of the Land Tax. pp. 228. *Lond.* 1894. 8°.   6426. df. 23.

DOWELL (S.) Acts relating to the Tax on Inhabited Dwelling-Houses. pp. 39.
Lond. 1893. 8°.   6425. df. 22.

ALPE (E. N.) Digest of the Law relating to Stamp Duties. pp. 264. *Lond.* 1890. 8°.
    6376. b. 45.

—— Law of Stamp Duties. pp. 333.
Lond. 1894. 8°.   6376. de. 8.

GRIFFITH (G. C.) Digest of the Stamp Duties of the Death Duties, *etc.* pp. 318.
Lond. 1894. 8°.   2230. a. 5.

HIGHMORE (N. J.) The Stamp Act, 1891. pp. 152. *Lond.* 1891. 8°.   6425. e. 28.

BOYLE (E.) and DAVIES (G. H.) The Principles of Rating. pp. 1163. *Lond.* 1895. 8°. 6425. e. 30.

CASTLE (E. J.) Law and Practice of Rating. pp. 655. *Lond.* 1895. 8°.   6426. df. 24.

CLEAVER (H. P.) and ROHRWEGER (F.) Parochial Assessment rules. pp. 213. *Lond.* 1894. 8°.
    6426. aaaa. 20.

LAWRIE (A. P.) How to appeal against your Rates,—outside the Metropolis. pp. 97.
1892. 12°. Wilson's Legal Handy books.
    6426. aaa. 39.

O'MEARA (J. J.) Municipal Taxation at home and abroad. pp. 310. *Lond.* 1894. 8°.
    08225. ec. 12.

PENFOLD (C.) Penfold on Rating. pp. 554.
Lond. 1893. 8°.   6426. e. 14.

RYDE (W. C.) Reports of Rating Appeals heard during 1886–90. pp. 420. *Lond.* 1890. 8°.
    6425. cc. 12.

BAUMANN (A. A.) Betterment, the Law of special assessment for benefits in America. pp. 110. *Lond.* 1893. 8°.   8277. de. 25.

For the Taxation of Land and Ground Rents. *See* LAND, *Tenures, England.*

Trade.

ASHLEY (W. J.) Introduction to English Economic history and theory. *Lond.* 1892, *etc.* 8°.
    2240. aa. 1.

CUNNINGHAM (W.) Growth of English industry and commerce. 2 vol. *Camb.* 1890–92. 8°.
    2020. d.

ENGLAND.—Trade, etc.—*continued.*

CUNNINGHAM (W.) and MAC ARTHUR (E. A.) Outlines of English industrial History. pp. 274. 1895. 8°. Cambridge Historical Series. 2378. b.

HEWINS (W. H. S.) English Trade and finance, chiefly in the 17th century. pp. 174. 1892. 8°. University Extension Series. 012202. g.

ROGERS (J. E. T.) Industrial and commercial History of England. Lectures. pp. 473. *Lond.* 1892. 8°. 2020. d.

TRAILL (H. D.) Social England. Record of the progress of the people. *Lond.* 1894, *etc.* 8°. 2077. b.

HAHL (A.) Zur Geschichte der volkswirtschaftlichen Ideen in England. pp. 59. 1893. 8°. ELSTER (L.) Staatswissenschaftliche Studien. Bd. 5. 8207. h.

BEER (G. L.) Commercial policy of England toward the American Colonies. pp. 167. 1893. 8°. Ac. New York. *Columbia College.* Studies in History, *etc.* Vol. 3. Ac. 2688/2.

FUCHS (C. J.) Die Handelspolitik Englands in den letzten Jahrzehnten. pp. 358. 1893. 8°. Ac. Leipsic. *Verein für Socialpolitik.* Schriften. Bd. 57. Ac. 2322.

GIBBINS (H. de B.) Industrial history of England. pp. 232. 1890. 8°. University Extension Series. 012202. g.

BOWLEY (A. L.) Short account of England's Foreign Trade in the 19th century. pp. 152. *Lond.* 1893. 8°. 08276. e. 57.

ANSON (L.) English Manufactures and Australasian trade. pp. 99. *Lond.* 1893. 8°. 08227. e. 46.

BRITISH TRADE. British Trade and English ports. pp. 64. *Lond.* 1889. 8°. 08226. h. 14. (8.)

BURGIS (E.) Perils to British Trade. pp. 251. *Lond.* 1895. 8°. 08276. ee. 4.

MAC CORMICK (R. S.) Future trade relations between Great Britain and the United States. pp. 48. *Lond.* 1892. 8°. 08226. k. 6. (8.)

MAHONY (J. W.) England's falling workshop, *etc.* pp. 158. *Lond.* 1893. 8°. 8228. c. 52.

SIMMONDS (P. L.) Handbook of British commerce, *etc.* pp. 204. *Lond.* 1892. 8°. 8228. cc. 45.

SMITH (C. W.) Commercial Gambling: causes of depression in agriculture and trade. pp. 170. *Lond.* 1893. 8°. 08227. de. 32.

VARON. Fair Play: England for the English, *etc.* pp. 24. *Manch.* 1891. 8°. Pam. 82.

WILLIAMSON (A.) British Industries and foreign competition. pp. 311. *Lond.* 1894. 8°. 08226. f. 11.

See also BANKING : CAPITAL AND LABOUR : INDIA : LAW, *Commercial* : MINERALOGY, *etc.* For works on Free Trade and Protection, *see* TRADE.

ENGLISH CHANNEL, TUNNEL, etc.

BROWN (S. H.) Tables showing the approximate magnetic direction and rate of the tidal streams in the Dover straits. pp. 11. *Lond.* 1894. 8°. Pam. 79.

ENGLISH CHANNEL. Sailing Directions. pp. 259. *Lond.* 1892. 8°. 10496. aaa. 17.

G. B. & I. *Hydrographic Office.* Notes on tidal streams at the entrance to the English Channel, 1889–90. pp. 12. *Lond.* 1891. fol. 10498. k. 10.

HOUETTE (P. A. A.) Les courants de La Manche. pp. 30. *Paris,* 1894. 4°. 10497. f. 22.

JACKSON (R.) Channel Pilot text-book. pp. 43. *Portsmouth,* 1894. 8°. Pam. 43.

PATERSON (J. D.) By Dover and Calais. pp. 355. *Dover,* 1894. 8°. Pam. 43.

ENGLISH CHANNEL, etc.—*continued.*

RUSSELL (W. C.) The British Seas. With etchings and engravings. pp. 88. *Lond.* 1892. fol. K.T.C. 3. b. 10.

UNDERHILL (A.) Our Silver Streak; Yachtsman's Guide from Harwich to Scilly. pp. 141. *Lond.* 1892. 8°. 10498. b. 14.

BRAMWELL (*Sir* F. J.) The Channel Tunnel. pp. 34. *Lond.* 1883. 8°. Pam. 76.

FRANCE. Correspondence between France and England respecting the proposed Channel Tunnel and railway. pp. 199. *Lond.* 1880. 8°. 08235. e. 14.

BRASSEUR (A.) Le Pont sur la Manche. pp. 61. *Brux.* 1893. 8°. 8768. l. 23. (9.)

LONDON. *Channel Bridge and Railway Company.* Le Pont sur la Manche. pp. 185. *Paris,* 1892. 8°. 08235. h. 32.

See also SOLENT.

ENGLISH LANGUAGE.

General : History.

ANGLOPHIL. The Queen's English up to date. pp. 192. *Lond.* 1892. 8°. 12981. ccc. 8.

BUELBRING (C. D.) Wege und Ziele der englischen Philologie. pp. 38. *Groningen,* 1893. 8°. 12901. f. 43. (3.)

CHAMPNEYS (A. C.) History of English. pp. 414. *Lond.* 1893. 8°. 12981. ccc. 17.

EARLE (J.) English prose. pp. 530. *Lond.* 1890. 8°. 2308. b. 26.

—— Philology of the English Tongue. pp. 744. 1892. 8°. Clarendon Press Series. 2320. d. 36.

EMERSON (O. F.) History of the English Language. pp. 415. *N.Y.* 1894. 8°. 12981. ccc. 33.

FALLON (D.) On the Importance of the Study of English. pp. 20. *Malta,* 1892. 8°. 12903. e. 27. (3.)

HEWITT (H. M.) Manual of our Mother Tongue. 2 vol. *Lond.* 1894. 8°. 12981. ccc. 38.

JESPERSEN (O.) Progress in Language, with special reference to English. pp. 370. *Lond.* 1894. 8°. 12981. e. 12.

KITTREDGE (G. L.) Brief history of the English Language. 1890. 4°. Webster's International Dictionary. 2112. g.

LOUNSBURY (T. R.) History of the English Language. pp. 505. *N.Y.* 1894. 8°. 12981. cc. 49.

LOW (W. H.) The English Language, its history and structure. pp. 207. 1893. 8°. Tutorial Series. 12205. c. 160.

MEAD (T. H.) Our Mother Tongue. pp. 328. *N.Y.* 1890. 8°. 011824. e. 3.

MEIKLEJOHN (J. M. D.) Book of the English Language. pp. 128. *Lond.* 1891. 8°. 12981. cc. 35.

MOLEE (E.) Germanik English. pp. 64. *Bristol, Dakota,* 1889. 8°. 12901. e. 38.

RAMSEY (S.) The English Language. Historical Study. pp. 571. *N.Y.* 1892. 8°. 12982. e. 26.

STORM (J.) Englische Philologie. *Leipz.* 1892, *etc.* 8°. 2272. f. 14.

WYATT (A. J.) Matriculation answers. London University : English Language. 1891. 8°. Tutorial Series. 12205. c. 30.

See also infra : Anglo-Saxon : *Early and Middle English.*

Anglo-Saxon (Language and Literature). Early, Middle and Modern English (to 18th Century).

HALL (J. R. C.) Concise Anglo-Saxon Dictionary pp. 369. *Lond.* 1894, 8°. 12981. f. 15.

WYATT (A. J.) and JOHNSON (H. H.) Glossary of Aelfric's Homilies. pp. 72. 1890. 8°. Tutorial Series. 12205. c. 22.

ENGLISH.—Composition—_continued._

SYDDALL (J.) Evans's first step in Composition. pp. 16. _Lond._ 1892. 8°. 011824. g. 38.

THOMSON (W. S.) Practical guide to English Composition. pp. 302. _Aberd._ 1894. 8°. 011824. g. 37.

—— Short essays on Public Examination topics. pp. 209. _Aberd._ 1894. 8°. 012356. f. 17.

—— Guide to English Composition. pp. 273. _Aberd._ 1891. 8°. 011824. de. 19.

WALTON (J. H.) English Synthesis: a practical method of prose-writing. pp. 212. _Madras_, 1894. 8°. 011824. f. 62.

See also infra: Grammar.

Dialects, etc.

PAGET (C.) _Lady._ Notes on northern Words. pp. 19. _Camb._ 1891. 8°. 12901. ccc. 17. (6.)

Ac. London. _English Dialect Society._ BUELBRING (C. D.) Ablaut in the modern dialects of the South of England. pp. 23. _Lond._ 1891. 8°. Ac. 9935/11.

—— CHOPE (R. P.) Dialect of Hartland, Devonshire. pp. 123. _Lond._ 1891. 8°. Ac. 9934/30.

HEWETT (S.) Peasant speech of Devon. pp. 184. _Lond._ 1892. 8°. 12315. c. 39.

Ac., etc. London. _English Dialect Society._ NORTHALL (G. F.) Folk-phrases of four counties (Glouc., Staff., Warw., Worc.). pp. 43. _Lond._ 1894. 8°. Ac. 9934/36.

—— HESLOP (O.) Northumberland Words. _Lond._ 1892, etc. 8°. Ac. 9934/31.

—— GOWER (G. W. G. L.) Glossary of Surrey Words. pp. 46. _Lond._ 1893. 8°. Ac. 9934/34.

—— WORDSWORTH (C.) Rutland Words. pp. 43. _Lond._ 1891. 8°. Ac. 9934/29.

—— DARTNELL (G. E.) and GODDARD (E. H.) Glossary of words used in Wiltshire. pp. 235. _Lond._ 1893. 8°. Ac. 9934/33.

—— SALISBURY (J.) Glossary of words used in S.E. Worcestershire. pp. 92. _Lond._ 1894. 8°. Ac 9934/35.

MORRIS (M. C. F.) Yorkshire Folk-Talk. pp. 408. _Lond._ 1892. 8°. 12981. ccc. 1.

TWEDDELL (E.) Rhymes and sketches to illustrate the Cleveland dialect. pp. 104. _Stokesley_, 1892. 8°. 011653. i. 90.

Ac. London. _English Dialect Society._ WRIGHT (J.) Grammar of the dialect of Windhill, West Riding of Yorkshire. pp. 255. _Lond._ 1892. 8°. Ac. 9934/32.

LENTZNER (C.) Wörterbuch der englischen Volkssprache in Australien. pp. 237. _Halle_, 1892. 8°. 12982. f. 15.

WRIGHT (A.) Baboo English as 'tis writ. pp. 108. _Lond._ 1891. 8°. 012314. e. 45.

See also AMERICAN DIALECT: SCOTCH DIALECT.

Dictionaries.

WILLIAMS (R. O.) Our Dictionaries, and other topics. pp. 174. _N.Y._ 1890. 8°. 12981. c. 47.

ANNANDALE (C.) Concise Dictionary of the English Language. pp. 818. _Lond._ 1892. 8°. 2274. e. 1.

DICTIONARIES. The Encyclopædic Dictionary. 7 vol. _Lond._ 1892. 8°. 12981. i. 4.

—— Standard Dictionary of the English Language. _N.Y._ 1893, etc. 4°. 12982. k. 12.

FUNK AND WAGNALLS. Compounding of Words in Funk and Wagnalls' Standard Dictionary of the English Language. pp. 82. _N.Y._ 1892. 4°. 12981. k. 2.

DYCE (A.) Glossary to the Works of Shakespeare. pp. 519. _Lond._ 1894. 8°. 011765. h. 1.

ENGLISH.—Dictionaries—_continued._

FENNELL (C. A. M.) Stanford Dictionary of Anglicised Words and phrases, _etc._ pp. 826. _Camb._ 1892. 4°. 2112. f.

MACLAGAN (T. T.) Royal English Dictionary. pp. 714. _Lond._ 1894. 8°. 12981. ccc. 31.

MURRAY (J. H.) Companion Dictionary of the English Language. pp. 672. _Lond._ 1892. 12°. 12981. aa. 50.

NUTTALL (P. A.) Routledge's pronouncing Dictionary of the English Language. pp. 756. _Lond._ 1892. 8°. 2274. b. 22.

—— Standard Dictionary of the English Language. pp. 816. _Lond._ 1894. 8°. 12981. d. 1.

OGILVIE (J.) Comprehensive English Dictionary. pp. 1376. _Lond._ 1893. 8°. 12983. h. 15.

—— Student's English Dictionary. pp. 864. _Lond._ 1895. 4°. 12981. f. 16.

PITMAN (I.) and SONS. Pocket Dictionary of the English Language. pp. 362. _Lond._ 1893. 12°. 12981. a. 49.

WEBSTER (N.) International Dictionary of the English Language. pp. 2011. _Lond._ 1891. 8°. 12981. k. 1.

—— Dictionary. Abridged from Webster's International Dictionary. pp. 324. _Lond._ 1894. 8°. 12981. aa. 68.

—— Brief International Dictionary. pp. 530. _Lond._ 1894. 8°. 12982. cc. 36.

—— High School Dictionary. pp. 530. _Lond._ 1892. 8°. 12982. ccc. 30.

—— Dictionary of the English Language, for use in common schools. pp. 422. _Lond._ 1892. 8°. 12983. e. 21.

—— Practical Dictionary of the English Language. pp. 634. _Lond._ 1894. 8°. 12981. e. 11.

—— Academic Dictionary. pp. 704. _Lond._ 1895. 8°. 12981. dd. 1.

WILLIAMS (J.) Cassell's English Dictionary. pp. 1100. _Lond._ 1892. 8°. 12981. e. 8.

See also supra: Anglo-Saxon, etc.; infra: Idioms: Orthography: Synonyms.

English and other Languages.

STACE (E. V.) English-Arabic Vocabulary. pp. 218. _Lond._ 1893. 8°. 012904. g. 1.

WORTABET (J.) and PORTER (H.) English-Arabic Dictionary. 2 pt. _Cairo_, 1894. 8°. 12904. f. 2.

DURGĀCHARANA VANDYOPĀDHYĀYA. Illustrated Bengali-and-English Dictionary. pp. 1114. _Calcutta_, 1889. 16°. 12906. bb. 34.

RĀMACHANDRA GHOSHA. Student's Dictionary in English and Bengali. pp. 1080. _Calcutta_, 1891. 8°. 12907. cc. 34.

BENNETT (C.) Vocabulary in English and Burmese. pp. 155. _Rangoon_, 1886. 8°. 760. dd. 12.

JUDSON (A.) English and Burmese Dictionary. pp. 930. _Rangoon_, 1894. 8°. 12907. ee. 49.

—— English and Burmese Dictionary, abridged. pp. 544. _Rangoon_, 1893 8°. 12910. c. 9.

KITTEL (F.) A Kannada English Dictionary. pp. 1752. _Mangalore_, 1894. 4°. 12907. ff. 21.

DICTIONARIES. English Chinese Vocabulary of the vernacular of Swatow. pp. 302. _Swatow_, 1883. 8°. 12910. dd. 17.

GOODRICH (C.) Pocket Dictionary Chinese-English. pp. 237. _Peking_, 1891. 12°. 11099. a. 10.

BALLER (F. W.) Analytical Vocabulary of the New Testament, _Chinese_ and _Eng._ pp. 264. _Shanghai_, 1893. 4°. 12910. i. 34.

SCOTT (J.) English-Corean Dictionary. pp. 345. _Corea_, 1891. 8°. 12910. dd. 31.

LARSEN (A.) Dictionary of the Dano-Norwegian and English Languages. pp. 693. _Copenhagen_, 1888. 8°. 2118. a.

ENGLISH.—Dictionaries—*continued.*

CALISCH (I. M.) and (N. S.) Nieuw Engelsch Woordenboek Engelsch-Nederlandsch—Nederlandsch-Engelsch. 2 pt. *Arnhem*, 1893. 8°.
12972. e. 24.

DICTIONARIES. Pocket-Dictionary of the English and Dutch Languages. 2 pt. *Leipz.* 1893. 16°.
12972. aa. 21.

PICARD (H.) Dictionary of the English-Dutch and Dutch-English languages. pp. 1250. *Gouda*, 1890. 8°. 12972. aaa. 23.

VALKHOFF (J. N.) Vocabulary, Dutch-English. pp. 144. *Groningen*, 1892. 8°. 12981. bb. 49.

KELLY (J. W.) English-Eskimo and Eskimo-English Vocabularies. 1890. 8°. U.S. *Bureau of Education.* Circular of Information. No. 165.
8308. i.

GASC (F. E A.) Concise Dictionary of the French and English Languages. pp. 1214. *Lond.* 1892. 8°. 2272. d. 2.

JAESCHKE (R.) Nutt's Conversation Dictionaries. English-French. pp. 490. *Lond.* 1892. 16°.
12953. b. 57.

LALLEMAND (H.) and LUDWIG (A.) New English and French Vocabulary. pp. 670. *Lond.* 1894. 16°. 12950. a. 53.

LA QUESNERIE (G. de) Vocabulaire anglais. pp. 97. *Paris*, 1895. 8°. 12984. ff. 13.

SPIERS (A.) Nouveau Dictionnaire anglais-français. 2 pt. *Paris*, 1889. 4°. 12950. l. 1.

MOISY (H.) Glossaire anglo-normand donnant plus de 5,000 mots, qui sont communs au dialecte normand et à l'anglais. *Caen*, 1889, *etc.* 8°.
12954. e.

BARRÈRE (A. M. V.) Dictionary of English and French military terms. *Lond.* 1895, *etc.* 8°.
8823. h. 49.

FLETCHER (J. J.) Pocket Glossary of technical terms. French-English. pp. 203. *Lond.* 1893. 32°. 12954. a. 54.

PIRRIE (W.) Technical Dictionary, English-French and French-English, of sea-terms. pp. 354. *Lond.* 1895. 8°. 8806. a. 66.

FLUEGEL (J. G.) Universal English-German and German-English Dictionary. 3 Bd. *Lond.* 1891. 8°. 2116. f.

—— Praktisches Wörterbuch der englischen und deutschen Sprache. 2 Thle. *Leipz.* 1891. 8°.
12962. f. 22.

JAESCHKE (R.) Nutt's Conversation Dictionaries. English-German. pp. 570. *Lond.* 1893. 16°.
12962. a. 28.

KRUMMACHER (M.) Wörterbuch der englischen und deutschen Umgangssprache. 3 pt. *N.Y.* 1892. 8°. 12962. ccc. 22.

MURET (E.) Encyclopædic English-German and German-English Dictionary. *Berl.* 1891, *etc.* 8°.
12962. m. 8.

WEIR (E.) Cassell's new German Dictionary. *Lond.* 1891. 8°. 12963. bbb. 46.

EITZEN (F. W.) Wörterbuch der Handelsprache, Deutsch-Englisch. pp. 915. *Leipz.* 1893. 8°.
12962. o. 4.

HICKIE (W. J.) Greek-English Lexicon to the New Testament. pp. 213. *N.Y.* 1893. 8°.
12924. a. 54.

GIANNARES (A. N.) Concise Dictionary of English and Modern Greek. pp. 436. *Lond.* 1895. 8°. 12923. bbb. 46.

JAYASIMHA RATNACHANDRA PĀNDE. Pocket Dictionary of Gujarati and English. 2 pt. *Ahmedabad*, 1892. 8°. 12906. a. 53.

LALUBHĀI GOKALADĀSA PATEL. Pocket Gujarati-English Dictionary. pp. 1040. *Ahmedabad*, 1892. 8°. 12907. a. 56.

ENGLISH.—Dictionaries—*continued.*

MĀNEKJĪ PESTANJĪ RANDERIĀ. English-Gujarati Dictionary. pp. 602. *Ahmedabad*, 1886. 8°.
12906. de. 6.

MOTIRĀMA TRIKAMDĀSA. Pronouncing pocket English and Gujarati Dictionary. pp. 1186. *Bombay*, 1891. 16°. 12907. a. 53.

GESENIUS (F. H. W.) Hebrew and English Lexicon of the Old Testament. *Oxf.* 1892, *etc.* 4°. 012904. k. 2.

BLUMHARDT (J. F.) English Hindustani Vocabulary. pp. 23. 1892. 8°. Military vocabularies. I. 12902. ccc.

JAESCHKE (R.) Nutt's Conversation Dictionaries. English-Italian. pp. 424. *Lond.* 1894. 16°.
12942. a. 50.

MELZI (B.) Nuovo Dizionario inglese-italiano e italiano-inglese. 2 pt. *Milano*, 1892. 8°.
12943. bb. 41.

ROBERTS (J. P.) Dizionario italiano-inglese e inglese-italiano. 2 pt. *Firenze*, 1891. 8°.
12942. cc. 20.

ANSTRUTHER (R. H.) and SETTEMBRINI (R.) Seafaring Phrases, English and Italian. pp. 134. *Portsmouth*, 1894. 8°. 8806. bb. 31.

DAVIS (J. F.) Latin-English Vocabulary to Caesar's Gallic War, Book VII. pp. 96. *Lond.* 1894. 8°. 12934. cc. 36.

MARCHANT (J. R. V.) and CHARLES (J. F.) Cassell's Latin Dictionary. pp. 927. *Lond.* 1892. 8°. 12935. c. 39.

BĀBĀ PADAMANJĪ. Dictionary, English and Marathi. pp. 668. *Bombay*, 1889. 8°.
12906. dd. 29.

MOLESWORTH (J. T.) Compendium of Molesworth's Marathi and English dictionary. pp. 611. *Bombay*, 1890. 8°. 12907. cc. 33.

'ABD AL-KARĪM. Dictionary of Anglo-Persian homogeneous words. pp. 68. *Bombay*, 1889. 8°.
757. d. 38. (4.)

RICHARDSON (J.) Persian-English Dictionary. pp. 1539. *Lond.* 1892. 8°. 12906. i. 17..

SOHRĀBSHĀH BEHRĀMJĪ. Student's enlarged English-Persian Dictionary. pp. 733. *Surat*, 1892. 8°. 12907. ccc. 41.

CASTRO DE LA FAYETTE (L.) Diccionario inglez-portuguez e portuguez inglez. 2 pt. *Pariz*, 1892. 16°. 12941. b. 42.

MICHAELIS (H.) Dictionary of the Portuguese and English languages. 2 vol. *Lond.* 1893. 8°. 12943. dd. 3.

DICTIONARIES. Pocket-Dictionary of the English and Russian Languages. 2 pt. *Leipz.* 1893. 16°. 12976. ccc. 7.

LAKSHMAṆA RĀMACHANDRA VAIDYA. Standard Sanskrit-English Dictionary. pp. 889. *Bombay*, 1889. 8°. 12906. dd. 23.

MACDONNELL (A. A.) Sanskrit English Dictionary. pp. 384. *Lond.* 1893. 4°. 12906. i. 19.

VĀMANA SIVRĀMA ĀPTE. Practical Sanskrit-English Dictionary. pp. 1196. *Poona*, 1890. 4°. 12906. i. 16.

—— Student's English-Sanskrit Dictionary. pp. 462. *Bombay*, 1893. 8°. 12907. cc. 48.

MICHELL (E. B.) Siamese-English Dictionary. *Bangkok*, 1892. 4°. 12910. cc. 11.

DICTIONARIES. English-Siamese Dictionary. pp. 400. *Bangkok*, 1890. 8°. 12906. df. 39.

CLOUGH (B.) Sinhalese-English Dictionary. pp. 824. *Colombo*, 1892. 4°. 12906. dd. 44.

DE SILVA (D. S.) English-Sinhalese pronouncing Dictionary. *Colombo*, 1885, *etc.* 8°.
12906. df. 21.

BEALE (A. M. A.) English-Spanish and Spanish-English Dictionary. pp. 314. 342. *Lond.* 1895. 8°. 12943. aa. 50.

ENGLISH.—Dictionaries—*continued.*

LOPES (J. M.) and BENSLEY (E. R.) Diccionario
inglése-español y español-inglés. 2 pt.
Paris, 1891. 8°.　　　　　12942. k. 8.

BJÖRKMAN (C. G.) Svensk-engelsk Ordbok.
pp. 1360. *Stockholm*, 1889. 8°.　12972. e. 13.

DICTIONARIES. Pocket-Dictionary of the English
and Swedish Languages. 2 pt. *Leipz.* 1894. 16°.
　　　　　　　　　　　　　12972. a. 20.

ANKETELL (C. P.) Pronouncing English-Tamil
Dictionary. pp. 332. *Madras*, 1888. 16°.
　　　　　　　　　　　　　12907. aa. 66.

LINCOLN (J. H.) English-Tamil Vocabulary.
pp. 87. *Singapore*, 1895. 8°.　　12910. aa. 73.

PERCIVAL (P.) Dictionary of English and Tamil.
pp. 492. *Madras*, 1893. 8°.　　12907. b. 45.

VIṢVANĀTHA PILLAI. Dictionary, Tamil and
English. pp. 735. *Madras*, 1888. 8°.
　　　　　　　　　　　　　12906. dd. 36.

ṢAṄKARANĀRĀYANA. English-Telugu Dictionary.
pp 726. *Madras*, 1894. 8°.　　12907. bbb. 45.

For Dictionaries of English and African and
English and American-Indian Languages, *see*
AFRICAN LANGUAGES : INDIAN LANGUAGES.

Early and Middle English.

See supra : Anglo-Saxon, etc.

Etymology.

JOHNSON (C. F.) English Words. pp. 255.
N.Y. 1891. 8°.　　　　　12981. b. 62.

SHEPPARD (R. S.) English Word-lore. pp. 176.
Madras, 1894. 12°.　　　　12982. aaa. 56.

SKEAT (W. W.) Primer of English Etymology.
pp. 112. 1895. 8°. Clarendon Press Series.
　　　　　　　　　　　　　2319. a. 40.

TEALL (F. H.) English Compound Words and
Phrases. pp. 309. *Lond.* 1892. 8°. 12982. cc. 32.
See also supra : Ango-Saxon, etc.

Grammar, Analysis, etc.

ADAMS (E.) Elements of the English Language.
pp. 326. *Lond.* 1892. 8°.　　　2112. b.

ATKINSON (H. S.) English for the lower
standards. *Singapore*, 1894, *etc.* 8°. 12981. aa. 67.

BEACH (G.) Elements of English. pp. 257.
Lond. 1891. 8°.　　　　　12981. cc. 29.

BLACKWOOD (W.) and SONS. English Grammar
and analysis. *Lond.* 1889, *etc.* 8°.　12981. ccc.

BOND (F.) Introduction to English Grammar.
pp. 166. *Lond.* 1893. 8°.　　　12981. ccc. 11.

BROCKINGTON (A. A.) Notes on English Grammar. pp. 101. *Toronto*, 1895. 8°. 12981. c. 48.

BRUCE (R. H.) Note book of English Grammar.
pp. 24. *Lond.* 1894. 8°.　　　12981. cc. 45.

CAMPBELL (D.) Higher English for secondary
schools. pp. 186. *Lond.* 1895. 8°. 12981. b. 66.

CARTER (G.) Explanation of Grammatical
Terms. pp. 29. *Lond.* 1892. 8°.
　　　　　　　　　　　　　12901. ccc. 17. (7.)

COLES (J.) Geography, Arithmetic and examples
in parsing. *Lond.* 1891. 8°.　　12200. ee. 5.

DALGLEISH (W. S.) Progressive English Grammar. pp. 152. *Edinb.* 1892. 8°. 12981. bbb. 54.

DICKINSON (W. J.) Difficulties of Grammar
simplified. pp. 185. 1891. 8°. Hughes's Educational Course.　　　　　　　12200. b.

DOUGLAS (J.) English Grammar and Analysis.
pp. 198. *Edinb.* 1891. 12°.　　12981. aa. 45.

DUNLOP (W. W.) Principles of English Grammar. pp. 144. *Lond.* 1893. 8°. 12981. ccc. 21.

DYSON (J.) Plain Facts of Grammar and
analysis. pp. 18. *Hertford*, 1890. 8°.
　　　　　　　　　　　　　12901. ccc. 17. (2.)

ENGLISH. Lower-grade English grammar.
pp. 102. 1890. 8°. Royal English Class-
Books.　　　　　　　　　　12203. ee.

ENGLISH.—Grammar—*continued.*

ENGLISH GRAMMAR. Summary of English Grammar. pp. 150. *Lond.* 1890. 8°.　12981. cc. 27.

ENGLISH LANGUAGE. Handbook of English.
pp. 56. *Blackburn*, 1893. 8°. 12901. ccc. 16. (7.)

EVANS (T.) Midland Grammar for the standards.
Lond. 1887, *etc.* 8°.　　　　12981. bb. 50.

GOW (J.) Method of English for secondary
schools. *Lond.* 1892, *etc.* 8°.　12981. ccc. 10.

GRAMMAR. Elementary Grammar. pp. 170.
Lond. 1891. 8°.　　　　　12981 bbb. 46.

HASLAM (T. J.) Good English for beginners.
pp. 246. *Dublin*, 1892. 8°.　011824. de. 29.

HORN (J. S.) Elementary Grammar. pp. 48.
Manch. 1891. 8°.　　　　　12981. aa. 44.

JACKSON (R.) English Grammar. pp. 280.
Lond. 1893. 8°.　　　　　12981. bbb. 56.

KELLNER (L.) Historical outlines of English
Syntax. pp. 336. *Lond.* 1892. 8°. 12981. cc. 43.

KIRWAN (G. R.) Primer of English Grammar.
pp. 39. *Lond.* 1892. 8°.　　　12981. aa. 16.

LENNIE (W.) Principles of English Grammar.
pp. 220. *Edinb.* 1894. 12°.　　12981. aa. 64.

—— Key. pp. 235. *Edinb.* 1894. 12°.
　　　　　　　　　　　　　12981. aa. 65.

LYDE (L. W.) Notes on English Grammar.
pp. 60. *Lond.* 1893. 8°.　　　12981. aa. 60.

M., J. M. D. Short Grammar of the English
tongue. pp. 176. *Lond.* 1890. 8°. 12981. cc. 34.

MATHEWS (H.) Outlines of English Grammar.
pp. 250. *Bost.* 1892. 8°.　　　12981. ccc. 22.

MEIKLEJOHN (J. M. D.) Fifty new lessons in
English. pp. 102. *Lond.* 1895. 8°. 12981. c. 11.

MERINGTON (M. H.) English Primer. pp. 57.
Lond. 1892. 8°.　　　　　12981. ccc. 24.

MORELL (J. D.) The New Morell ; a Grammar
of the English Language. pp. 256.
Lond. 1893. 8°.　　　　　12981. ccc. 20.

MORRIS (R.) Historical outlines of English Accidence. pp. 463. *Lond.* 1895. 8°.　2274. a. 21.

PUPIL. Pupil's English Grammar. pp. 207.
Lond. 1892. 8°.　　　　　12981. ccc. 9.

RAMSEY (S.) English Language and English
grammar. pp. 571. *N.Y.* 1892. 8°. 12982. e. 26.

RIGDON (J.) Grammar of the English sentence.
pp. 281. *Danville, Ind.* 1890. 8°.　12981. f. 4.

ROGERS (J. W. F.) Grammar and logic in the
Nineteenth Century. pp. 211. *Lond.* 1892. 8°.
　　　　　　　　　　　　　12982. ccc. 31.

ROYAL GRAMMAR BOOKS. Royal Grammar books.
[2 pt. *Lond.* 1887. 8°.　　　12981. aaa. 65.

SOMERVELL (R.) The Structure of sentences.
pp. 50. *Lond.* 1891. 8°.　　　12981. b. 65.

SONNENSCHEIN (E. A.) English Grammar for
schools. 1889. 8°. Parallel Grammar Series.
　　　　　　　　　　　　　12902. aa.

STEEL (G.) English Grammar and analysis.
pp. 300. *Lond.* 1894. 8°.　　　12981. ccc. 32.

STRONGE (S. E.) and EAGER (A. R.) English
Grammar, with analysis. pp. 239.
Lond. 1892. 8°.　　　　　12981. cc. 42.

SWEET (H.) New English Grammar.
1892, *etc.* 8°. Clarendon Press Series.
　　　　　　　　　　　　　2320. f. 40.

—— Short historical English Grammar. pp. 264.
1892. 8°. Clarendon Press Series. 2319. a. 48.

TURNER (J. A.) and HALLIDIE (A. R. S.) Primary
English Grammar. pp. 166. *Lond.* 1894. 8°.
　　　　　　　　　　　　　12981. ccc. 36.

—— English Grammar. pp. 148.
Lond. 1894. 8°.　　　　　12981. ccc. 34.

—— Primary English Grammar. pp. 138.
Lond. 1893. 8°.　　　　　12981. ccc. 26.

ENGLISH.—Grammar—*continued*.

VALENTINE (E. S.) Atlas of English Grammar. ff. 18. *Lond.* 1890. 4°.   12981. f. 2.

WATSON (W.) English. *Preston*, 1894. 8°.   12901. bbb. 45. (7.)

WEST (A. S.) Elements of English Grammar. pp. 288. 1893. 8°. Pitt Press Series.   2322. cc. 45.

—— English Grammar. pp. 120. 1895. 8°. Pitt Press Series.   2322. d. 6.

WHITEHEAD (L.) The Home Grammar. pp. 190. *Lond.* 1892. 8°.   12981. ccc. 6.

ARNOLD (E. J.) "Practical" examination tests. *Leeds*, 1889, *etc.* 12°.   12204. bbbb.

EVANS (T.) Grammar Test cards. 3 pt. *Lond.* 1890. 8°.   12210. bbb.

RICHARDSON (J. L.) Watson's Department examination questions. 6 pt. *Lond.* 1887, 88. 8°.   12204. bbbb. 15.

—— Watson's graduated Exercises in parsing. 2 pt. *Lond.* 1887. 8°.   12981. aa. 63.

SHEWAN (J. S.) Exercises in the correction of grammatical Errors. pp. 39. *Aberd.* 1890. 8°.   12901. ccc. 12. (5.)

TURNER (J. A.) and HALLIDIE (A. R. S.) Exercises in Grammar and analysis. pp. 122. *Lond.* 1893. 8°.   12981. ccc. 25.

WOODS (M. A.) English Examples and exercises. 1890, *etc.* 8°. SONNENSCHEIN (E. A.) Parallel Grammar Series.   12902. aa.

ALMOND (H. H.) English Prose extracts. pp. 68. *Edinb.* 1895. 8°.   12272. a. 15.

ARNOLD (E.) Unseen Readers. *Lond.* 1892, *etc.* 8°.   12201. c. 50.

NECK (M. G. v.) Advanced Prose for class-reading. pp. 234. *Groningen*, 1891. 8°.   12274. aaa. 30.

Grammars, etc., for foreigners.

STOFFEL (C.) Studies in English, for continental students. *Zutphen*, 1894, *etc.* 8°.   12981. b. 1.

WEINECK (O.) Common Sense guide to English for foreigners. pp. 265. *N.Y.* 1893. 8°.   12981. ccc. 28.

SHANGHAI. *St. Francis Xavier's School.* Method of learning English for Chinese pupils. 2 pt. *Zi-Ka-Wei*, 1882, 83. 8°.   11099. f. 10.

BREKKE (K.) Engelsk Læsebog. pp. 295. *Kristiania*, 1893. 8°.   12272. b. 18.

HALS (C. A.) Engelsk Lærebog for begyndere. pp. 212. *Kristiania*, 1891. 8°. 12981. ccc. 23.

JESPERSEN (O.) Studier over engelske Kasus. *Kjøbenh.* 1891, *etc.* 8°.   12981. ee.

LAURSEN (M.) Engelsk Læsebog. *Kjøbenh.* 1893, *etc.* 8°.   12272. cc.

LÖFVING (C.) Elementarbok i engelska Språket. 2 pt. *Upsala*, 1881. 8°.   12982. c. 27.

MATHESIUS (N. A.) Engelsk Skolgrammatik. pp. 210. *Stockholm*, 1893. 8°.   12981. b. 64.

—— Engelsk Elementarbok. *Stockholm*, 1893, *etc.* 8°.   12981. cc. 46.

OLSVIG (V.) Engelske ord og vendinger. pp. 149. *Bergen*, 1890. 8°.   12972. b. 37.

ROSING (S.) Kortfattet engelsk Formlære til skolebrug. pp. 36. *Kjøbenh.* 1889. 8°.   12981. aa. 48.

WADDY (S. D.) Engelske Samtaleøvelser. pp. 152. *Throndhjem*, 1891. 8°.   12972. ccc. 3.

WESTERN (A.) De engelske Bisætninger. pp. 145. *Kristiania*, 1893. 8°.   12981. f. 13.

BRUGGENCATE (K. ten) De hoofdzaken der Engelsche Grammatica. pp. 68. *Groningen*, 1890. 8°.   12981. c. 39.

ENGLISH.—Grammar—*continued*.

COWAN (F. M.) and MAATJES (A. B.) Leercursus ter beoefening der Engelsche Taal. 4 Gdlte. *Amsterd.* 1891. 8°.   12981. c. 45.

DUINEN (R. v.) Course of English Reading-lessons. 3 vol. *Amsterd.* 1890–91. 8°.   12981. cc. 36.

GUENTHER (J. H. A.) Handbook of the English Language. pp. 296. *Groningen*, 1891. 8°.   12981. f. 5.

HOFMAN (C. A.) Practisch Leerboek der Engelsche Taal. 2 Gdlten. *'s Gravenh.* 1894. 8°.   12981. ccc. 44.

HOOG (W. de) Hints and questions for the use of candidates. pp. 98. *Dordrecht*, 1890. 8°.   12981. cc. 37.

BERNON (A.) Grammaire anglaise pour les enfants. pp. 16. *Ile Maurice*, 1894. 8°.   12903. c. 52. (9.)

BUÉ (R.) Faits et gestes de deux Écoliers. Conversations en français et en anglais. pp. 86. *Lond.* 1895. 8°.   12950. b. 38.

CHASLES (É.) Grammaire anglaise. 2 pt. *Paris*, 1887, 83. 8°.   12982. c. 28.

BIERBAUM (F. J.) Lehrbuch der englischen Sprache. *Leipz.* 1892, *etc.* 8°.   12282. cc.

BOENSEL (O.) Lesebuch für den englischen Unterricht. pp. 273. *Leipz.* 1894. 8°.   12981. f. 14.

DEUTSCHBEIN (C.) and WILLENBERG (G.) Leitfaden für den englischen Unterricht. *Cöthen*, 1893, *etc.* 8°.   12981. f.

DUNKER (W.) and BELL (W.) Englische Gesprächs- und Wiederholungs-Grammatik. pp. 664. *Stettin*, 1891. 8°.   12981. f. 3.

HENRY (V.) Précis de Grammaire comparée de l'anglais et de l'allemand. pp. 418. *Paris*, 1893. 8°.   12901. d. 41.

—— A Short comparative Grammar of English and German. pp. 394. *Lond.* 1894. 8°.   12962. cc. 48.

PENNER (E.) and MASSEY (C. C.) Englisch. 1892. 8°. Methode Schliemann zur Erlernung fremder Sprachen.   12901. k.

SEIDEL (A.) Praktisches Lehrbuch der englischen Umgangssprache. pp. 182. 1894. 8°. Die Kunst der Polyglottie. Thl. 44. 12902. c.

WILKE (E.) Anschauungsunterricht im Englischen. pp. 108. *Leipz.* 1894. 8°.   12984. ff. 12.

HASUM ALIDINA CONTRACTOR. The English Teacher. pp. 97. *Bombay*, 1887. 8°.   12981. c. 46.

SALMON (D.) and OAKLEY (A. J. C.) Junior school Grammar for India. pp. 134. *Lond.* 1892. 8°.   12981. cc. 40.

UPENDRANĀTHA MUKHOPĀDHYĀYA. Rajbhasha. Guide to writing and speaking English correctly. pp. 252. *Calcutta*, 1891. 12°. 14131. c. 21. (2.)

PAVIA (L.) Grammatica inglese. pp. 260. *Milano*, 1895. 8°.   012200. i. 5.

RICCARDO (F.) Dialoghi inglesi-italiani. pp. 225. *Lond.* 1891. 16°.   12941. de. 9.

DIXON (J. M.) New Conversations written for Japanese Schools. pp. 116. *Tokyo*, 1889. obl. 8°.   12910. a. 25.

FALLON (D.) Elementary English Grammar. pp. 115. *Malta*, 1893. 8°.   12981. bbb. 55.

FRENDO DE MANNARINO (S.) Graduated Readers for Maltese pupils. *Valetta*, 1895, *etc.* 8°.   12981. bbb.

CASWELL (J.) Elementary Lessons, to assist Siamese in the acquisition of English. pp. 70. *Bangkok*, 1881. 12°.   12981. aaa. 67.

ENGLISH.—Grammar, etc.—*continued.*

CORZANEGO (A.) Gramática inglesa. pp. 278.
Valencia, 1881. 8°.   12982. cc. 33.

GURRIN (T. E.) Gramática inglesa. pp. 160. 32.
Londres, 1890. 8°.   12981. cc. 28.

PEÑA (E. M.) Gramática inglesa. pp. 237.
Madrid, 1894. 8°.   12982. bb. 1.
See also infra : Idioms.

History. *See supra : General : Anglo-Saxon, etc.*

Idioms.

BERRINGTON (R. S.) Peculiar English expressions
explained. pp. 48. *The Hague*, 1893. 12°.
                                    12901. de. 17. (8.)

DIXON (J. M.) Dictionary of idiomatic English
phrases. pp. 384. *Lond.* 1891. 8°.
                                    12981. cc. 30.

KOOP (A.) Dictionary of English Idioms with
their German equivalents. pp. 157.
Lond. 1891. 8°.   12963. b. 23.

MAIR (J. A.) Sayings and phrases frequently
occurring. pp. 155. *Lond.* 1891. 8°.
                                    12305. d. 40.

MAYER (A. v) Manual of English-French-
German Idioms. pp. 326. *Lond.* 1895. 8°.
                                    12950. df. 51.

MEADMORE (R.) Les Idiotismes de la Conversation anglaise. pp. 160. *Paris*, 1892. 8°.
                                    12981. bbb. 51.

MAC MORDIE (W.) English Idioms and how to
use them. pp. 400. *Bombay*, 1890. 8°.
                                    12981. c. 41.

PETERSON (P.) English Idioms set out and explained. pp. 380. *Bombay*, 1893. 8°.
                                    12981. f. 18.

Orthography.

Ac. Cambridge. *Philological Society.* SWEET
(H.) Spelling reform and English Literature.
pp. 8. *Lond.* 1884. 8°.   Pam. 47.

ASHMAN (R.) Ashman's Spelling book. pp. 68.
Manch. 1891. 8°.   12981. c. 42.

BAILLAIRGÉ (C. P. F.) Vocabulary of English
homonyms. pp. 190. *Quebec*, 1891. 16°.
                                    12981. bbb. 52.

COWARD (E.) Practical Spelling guide. pp. 20.
Lond. 1891. 8°.   12901. ccc. 12. (7.)

DICTIONARIES. The Spelling Vocabulary.
pp. 79. *Lond.* 1894. 8°.   1158. b.

EVANS (T.) Word-Building Spelling book.
pp. 33. *Lond.* 1894. 8°.   Pam. 47.

GREEN (J.) and SON. Spelling and Dictation
exercises. *Manch.* 1891, *etc.* 8°. 12981. bbb. 47.

GUIDE. Handy Guide to Spelling.
Lond. 1892. 16°.   12981. aa. 56.

LEDSHAM (J. B.) Word Building Spelling lessons.
ff. 32. *Manch.* 1893. 8°.   Pam. 47.

LOAD (F. C.) Exercises in Spelling. pp. 29.
Lond. 1894. 8°.   12901. bbb. 45. (5.)

PHYFE (W. H. P.) Five Thousand Words often
misspelled. pp. 303. *N.Y.* 1894. 8°.
                                    12981. ccc. 37.

SHEARER (J. W.) The Combination Speller.
pp 168. *Richmond, Va.,* 1894. 8°.
                                    12981. bbb. 59.

THOMSON (W. S.) Public Examination Spelling
key. pp. 78. *Aberd.* 1893. 8°. 12981. ccc. 19.

YOXALL (J. H.) and GREGORY (B.) The Word
Builder and speller. pp. 60. *Lond.* 1891. 8°.
                                    12901. ccc. 12. (10.)
See also DICTATION.

Pronunciation : Phonetics.

BOWEN (E. W.) Historical Study of the ē-vowel
in accented syllables in English. pp. 78.
Baltimore, 1893. 8°.   12981. f. 12.

ENGLISH.—Pronunciation, etc.—*cont.*

CLARK (J.) Manual of Linguistics. General
phonology. pp. 315. *Edinb.* 1893. 8°.
                                    12901. ccc. 20.

MAYHEW (A. L.) Synopsis of old English
Phonology. pp. 327. 1891. 8°. Clarendon
Press Series.   2319. a. 28.

HEMPL (G.) Chaucer's Pronunciation. pp. 37.
Bost. 1893. 8°.   12981. d. 4.

GIETMANN (G.) Die Aussprache des Englischen
in systematischer Vollständigkeit. pp. 108.
Freiburg, 1892. 8°.   12981. ccc. 5.

GUIDE. Handy Guide to correct Pronunciation
and Spelling. pp. 85. *Lond.* 1892. 16°.
                                    12981. aa. 56.

PAYNE (F. M.) How to Pronounce 10,000
difficult Words. pp. 116. *N.Y.* 1893. 12°.
                                    12981. a. 50.

PHYFE (W. H. P.) The Test Pronouncer.
pp. 82. *N.Y.* 1892. 8°.   12981. bbb. 53.

RAMSAY-CRAWFORD (W.) Common Words commonly mispronounced, *etc.* pp. 140.
Lond. 1894. 8°.   12981. cc. 47.

SKEAT (B. M.) Word-list illustrating the correspondence of modern English with Anglo-French
vowel-sounds. 1884. 8°. Ac. London. *English
Dialect Society.* Miscellanies Ac. 9935/3.

WESTERN (A.) Englische Lautlehre für Studierende und Lehrer. pp. 98. *Heilbronn*, 1885. 8°.
                                    Pam. 47.

SPANTON (J.) Letter H : its old and modern
uses. pp. 15. *Ramsey*, 1894. 8°.
                                    12901. de. 17. (11.)

Synonyms.

BECHTEL (J. H.) Practical Synonyms. pp. 226.
Phila. 1893. 8°.   12981. aa. 62.

CRABB (G.) English Synonyms explained.
pp. 638. *Lond.* 1893. 8°.   12981. e. 9.

ROGET (P. M.) Thesaurus of English Words.
pp. 670. *Lond.* 1894. 8°.   2274. c. 23.

WORD. Just the Word wanted. pp. 126.
Lond. 1892. 16°.   12981. aa. 55.

ENGLISH LITERATURE.

Bibliography.

P.P. *London.* Book Review Index.
Lond. 1892, *etc.* 4°.   1865. a. 16.

—— Torch and Colonial Book Circular.
Lond. 1887–92. 4°.   P.P. 6481. fa.

SONNENSCHEIN (W. S.) Reader's Guide to com-
temporary Literature. pp. 16. 775. *Lond.* 1895. 8°.
                                    Cat. Desk. C.

History and Criticism.

BAGEHOT (W.) Literary Studies. 3 vol.
Lond. 1895. 8°.   011850. eee. 44.

BIRRELL (A.) Res Judicatæ. pp. 280.
Lond. 1892. 8°.   012357. e. 57.

BLANCŒIL (A.) Les grands Poètes anglais.
pp. 383. *Paris*, 1893. 8°.   011850. g. 28.

BOUCHER (L.) Histoire de la Littérature anglaise.
pp. 512. *Paris*, 1890. 18°.   011840. i. 56.

CANN (T. C.) Manuale di Litteratura inglese.
pp. 466. *Firenze*, 1889. 8°.   12981. e. 7.

CHOATE (I. B.) Wells of English. pp. 310.
Bost. 1892. 8°.   011824. e. 44.

COLLES (W. M.) Literature and the Pension
List. pp. 101. *Lond.* 1889. 8°.   11899. e. 25.

COLLINS (J. C.) Essays and Studies. pp. 369.
Lond. 1895. 8°.   12824. h. 31.

COURTHOPE (W. J.) History of English Poetry.
Lond. 1895, *etc.* 8°.   2049. bb.

DAWSON (W. J.) The makers of Modern English.
pp. 375. *Lond.* 1891. 8°.   011840. h. 60.

ENGLISH,—History, etc.—*continued.*

Dulcken (H. W.) English Literature. pp. 120. *Lond.* 1892. 8°.   011824. g. 9.

Fischer (T. A.) Die Studien zur englischen Litteraturgeschichte. pp. 177. *Gotha,* 1892. 8°.   011824. h. 75.

Gayley (C. M.) The Classic Myths in English Literature. pp. 539. *Bost.* 1893. 8°. 4503. bb. 39.

Gosse (E. W.) Gossip in a Library. pp. 337. *Lond.* 1891. 8°.   011824. f. 20.

Hales (J. W.) Handbooks of English Literature. *Lond.* 1894, *etc.* 8°.   011850. eee.

—— Folia Litteraria. Essays. pp. 367. *Lond.* 1893. 8°.   011850. f. 27.

Hill (G. B.) Writers and readers. pp. 211. *Lond.* 1892. 8°.   011824. e. 37.

Howitt (W.) Homes and haunts of British Poets. pp. 642. *Lond.* 1894. 8°. 10803. e. 14.

Hunt (T. W.) Ethical teachings in old English literature. pp. 384. *N.Y.* 1892, 8°. 011824. g. 4.

Innes (A. D.) Seers and Singers: study of English poets. pp. 223. *Lond.* 1893. 8°.   011850. eee. 3.

Jusserand (J. A. A. J.) Histoire littéraire du peuple anglais. *Paris,* 1894, *etc.* 8°. 2308. f. 16.

—— Literary History of the English people. pp. 545. *Lond.* 1895. 8°.   2366. e. 1.

—— English Essays from a French pen. pp. 215. *Lond.* 1895. 8°.   012356. f. 44.

Kirk (J. F.) Supplement to Allibone's Critical dictionary of English literature. 2 vol. *Phila.* 1890. 8°.   2050. f.

Koerting (G.) Grundriss der Geschichte der englischen Litteratur. pp. 404. 1893. 8°. Sammlung von Kompendien für das Studium. Ser. 1. Bd. 1.   12205. i.

Laing (F. A.) History of English Literature for junior classes. pp. 304. 1893. 8°. Collin's School Series.   12204 bbb.

Lang (A.) Letters to dead Authors. pp. 194. *Lond.* 1892. 8°.   011824. h. 34.

Low (W. H.) Intermediate text-book of English Literature. 1893, *etc.* 8°. Tutorial Series.   12205. c. 159.

Lowell (J. R.) Conversations on some old Poets. pp. 294. *Phila.* 1893. 8°. 011850. h. 29.

Mabie (H. W.) Essays in literary Interpretation. pp. 222. *Lond.* 1894. 8°.   011824. de. 53.

Mac Mahan (A. B.) The Study Class. pp. 278. *Chicago,* 1891. 8°.   011824. ee. 4.

Miller (J. O.) Condensed table of English Literature. *Toronto,* 1895. 8°   11766. aa. 6.

Milsand (J.) Littérature anglaise et philosophie. pp. 502. *Dijon,* 1893. 8°.   011824. k. 23.

Mitchell (D. G.) English Lands, letters and kings. 2 vol. *Lond.* 1890. 8°.   011840. f. 56.

Pancoast (H. S.) Introduction to English Literature. pp. 473. *N.Y.* 1894. 8°.   011850. ee. 8.

Raleigh (W.) The English novel. pp. 298. 1894. 8°. University Extension Manuals.   12204. f.

Renton (W.) Outlines of English Literature. pp. 548. 1893. 8°. University Extension Manuals.   02204. f.

Robertson (J. L.) History of English Literature for schools. pp. 372. *Edinb.* 1894. 8°.   011850. eee. 12.

Ryland (F.) Chronological outlines of English Literature. pp. 351. *Lond.* 1890. 8°.   011840. f. 74.

Sainte-Beuve (C. A.) Select Essays on English literature. pp. 268. *Lond.* 1895. 8°.   011850. eee. 33.

ENGLISH.—History, etc.—*continued.*

Saintsbury (G. E. B.) Miscellaneous Essays. pp. 429. *Lond.* 1895. 8°.   012357. h. 68.

Scherer (E.) Essays on English Literature. pp. 272. *Lond.* 1891. 8°.   011824. f. 13.

Smith (G. J.) Synopsis of English and American Literature. pp. 125. *Bost.* 1890. 8°. 011840. h. 59.

Stephen (L.) Hours in a Library. 3 vol. *Lond.* 1892. 8°.   2308. b. 19.

Swinburne (A. C.) Studies in Prose and Poetry. pp. 298. *Lond.* 1894. 8°.   2308. b. 28.

Taine (H. A.) Histoire de la Littérature anglaise. 5 tom. *Paris,* 1892. 8°.   2308. e.

Tiel (C .v.) Short history of English Literature. pp. 142. *Leiden,* 1890. 8°. 011840. l. 39.

Traill (H. D.) Social England. *Lond.* 1894, *etc.* 8°.   2077. b.

White (G.) Outline of the philosophy of English Literature. *Bost.* 1895, *etc.* 8°. 011850. eee. 77.

Wright (H. C.) Stories in English Literature. pp. 286. *Lond.* 1891. 8°.   011840. g. 83.

Wylie (L. J.) Studies in the evolution of English Criticism. pp. 212. *Bost.* 1894. 8°.   011850. g. 51.

Various Periods.

For Anglo - Saxon Literature, *see* English Language, *Anglo-Saxon, etc.*

Brooke (S. A.) History of early English Literature. 2 vol. *Lond.* 1892. 8°.   2308. f. 15.

Jusserand (J. A. A. J.) L'épopée mystique de William Langland. pp. 275. *Paris,* 1893. 8°.   011850. f. 46.

—— Piers Plowman. pp. 262. *Lond.* 1894. 8°.   K.T.C. 15. a. 6.

Ac. London. *Chaucer Society.* Ser. 2. No. 27. Chronology of Chaucer's writings. pp. 89. *Lond.* 1890. 8°.   Ac. 9924/32.

Kaluza (M.) Chaucer und der Rosenroman. pp. 253. *Berl.* 1893. 8°.   011850. h. 18.

Lounsbury (T. R.) Studies in Chaucer. 3 vol. *Lond.* 1892. 8°.   011824. h. 22.

Pollard (A. W.) Chaucer. pp. 142. 1893. 12°. Green (J. R.) Literature Primers.   2322. a.

Low (W. H.) History of English Literature, 1485–1580. pp. 71. 1890. 8°. Tutorial Series.   12205. c.

—— History of English Literature, 1580–1620. pp. 100. 1891. 8°. Tutorial Series.   12205. c. 68.

—— History of English Literature, 1714–98. pp. 124. 1891. 8°. Tutorial Series.   12205. c. 35.

Koeppel (E.) Geschichte der italienischen Novelle in der englischen Litteratur des 16. Jahrhunderts. pp. 100. 1892. 8°. Brink (B. ten) and Scherer (W.) Quellen und Forschungen. Hft. 70.   2338. h.

Scott (M. A.) Elizabethan translations from the Italian. pp. 47. *Baltimore,* 1895. 8°. Pam. 15.

Gosse (E. W.) Jacobean Poets. pp. 226. 1894. 8°. Knight (W.) University Extension Manuals.   12204. f.

Beljame (A.) Le Public et les Hommes de lettres en Angleterre, 1660–1744. pp. 506. *Paris,* 1883. 8°.   011824. h. 60.

Garnett (R.) The Age of Dryden. pp. 292. 1895. 8°. Hales (J. W.) Handbooks of English Literature.   011850. eee.

Dennis (J.) The Age of Pope. pp. 258. 1894. 8°. Hales (J. W.) Handbooks of English Literature.   011850. eee.

Dobson (H. A.) Eighteenth century Vignettes. pp. 261. *Lond.* 1892. 8°.   012357. f. 71.

ENGLISH.—Various Periods.—*continued*.

ROWLAND (P. F.) A comparison, criticism and estimate of the English Novelists, 1700–1850. *Oxf.* 1894. 8°.   Pam. 15.

MINTO (W.) Literature of the Georgian Era. pp. 315. *Edinb.* 1894. 8°.   011850. eee. 24.

PHELPS (W. L.) Beginnings of the English romantic movement. pp. 192. *Bost.* 1893. 8°.   011850. g. 49.

BROWN (J. M.) Manual of English Literature, 1750–1850. pp. 406. *Christchurch,* 1894. 8°.   011850. f. 70.

SAINTSBURY (G. E B.) Essays in English Literature, 1780–1860. pp. 451. *Lond.* 1891. 8°.   011840. g. 84.

BROOKE (S. A.) Development of theology as illustrated in English Poetry, 1780–1830. pp. 35. *Lond.* 1893. 8°.   011824. ec. 8.

BOLTON (S. K.) Famous English Authors of the Nineteenth Century. pp. 451. *N.Y.* 1892. 8°.   108 3. e. 3

NICOLL (W. R.) and WISE (T. J.) Literary anecdotes of the Nineteenth Century. *Lond.* 1895, *etc.* 8°.   11852. gg. 36.

OLIPHANT (M. O.) Victorian Age of English Literature. 2 vol. *Lond.* 1892. 8°. 011828. g. 10.

SAINTSBURY (G. E. B.) Corrected Impressions. Essays on Victorian writers. pp. 218. *Lond.* 1895. 8°.   011850. eee. 26.

DIXON (W. M.) English Poetry from Blake to Browning. pp. 204. *Lond.* 1894. 8°.   011850. g. 35.

MATHER (J.M.) Popular studies of 19th Century Poets. pp. 184. *Lond.* 1892. 8°. 011824. f. 44.

SCUDDER (V. D.) Life of the Spirit in modern English Poets. pp. 349. *Bost.* 1895. 8°.   011824. f. 63.

SHARP (A.) Victorian Poets. pp. 207. 1891. 8°.

SYMES (J. E.) University Extension Series.   012202. g.

WALKER (H.) The Greater Victorian Poets. pp. 332. *Lond.* 1895. 8°.   011824. i. 41.

BLAKENEY (E. H.) The Teaching of Tennyson. pp. 8. 1893. 8°.   11825. g. 22. (5.)

BROOKE (S. A.) Tennyson. pp. 490. *Lond.* 1891. 8°.   011850. i. 34.

COLLINS (J. C.) Illustrations of Tennyson. pp. 186. *Lond.* 1891. 8°.   011824. f. 14.

JENKINSON (A.) Lord Tennyson. pp. 127. *Lond.* 1892. 8°.   10856. aa. 6.

JENNINGS (H. J.) Lord Tennyson. pp. 178. *Lond.* 1892. 8°.   2408. a. 1.

LUCE (M.) Handbook to the works of Lord Tennyson. pp. 454. *Lond.* 1895. 8°.   011850. e. 10.

—— New Studies in Tennyson. pp. 96. *Clifton,* 1893. 8°   011850. f. 43.

OATES (J.) Teaching of Tennyson. pp. 257. *Lond.* 1894. 8°.   011850. g. 53.

PARSONS (E.) Tennyson's Life and poetry. *Chicago,* 1893. 8°.   10803. cc. 12. (15.)

BERDOE (E.) The Browning Cyclopædia. pp. 572. *Lond.* 1892. 8°.   2308. c. 22.

—— Browning Studies. pp. 331. *Lond.* 1895. 8°.   011805. h. 1.

BURRIDGE (B. M.) Browning as an exponent of a philosophy of life. pp. 55. *Cleveland,* 1893. 8°.   011850. i. 24.

COOKE (G. W.) Guide book to the works of R. Browning. pp. 450. *Bost.* 1891. 8°. 011824. e. 6.

EALAND (F.) Sermons from Browning. pp. 106. *Lond.* 1892. 8°.   011824. de. 33.

REVELL (W. F.) Browning's criticism of Life. pp. 116. *Lond.* 1892. 8°.   011824. de. 31.

ENGLISH.—Various Periods—*continued*.

TRIGGS (O. L.) Browning and Whitman. pp. 145. *Lond.* 1893. 8°.   011824. ee. 3.

WILSON (F. M.) A Primer on Browning. pp. 248. *Lond.* 1891. 8°.   11840. c. 54.

NETTLESHIP (J. T.) R. Browning. pp. 454. *Lond.* 1895. 8°.   011850. eee. 40.

LILLY (W. S.) Four English Humorists of the 19th century. pp. 192. *Lond.* 1895. 8°.   011850. h. 62.

MONTÉGUT (E.) Écrivains modernes de l'Angleterre. Série 3. pp. 356. *Paris,* 1892. 8°.   011824. de. 37.

SKELTON (J.) The Table-Talk of Shirley. pp. 344. *Edinb.* 1895. 8°.   10885. e. 21.

I. Letters to Eminent Hands. [Criticisms on contemporary authors]. pp. 74. *Derby,* 1892. 8°.   011840. h. 64.

STEUART (J. A.) Letters to living Authors. pp. 271. *Lond.* 1890. 8°.   10921. d. 21.

See also BALLADS : DRAMA : FICTION : POETRY.

Selections and Extracts.

CRAIK (H.) English Prose selections. *Lond.* 1893, *etc.* 8°.   2308. c. 23.

ENGLISH WRITERS. Library of early English Writers. *Lond.* 1895, *etc.* 8°.   2324. f. 17.

HENLEY (W. E.) and WHIBLEY (C.) Book of English Prose. 1387–1649. pp. 395. *Lond.* 1894. 8°.   012357. h. 62.

JEWRY, afterwards VALENTINE (L.) Cameos of English Literature. 12 vol. *Lond.* 1894. 8°.   12273. ff. 2.

MILES (A. H.) Poets and the poetry of the Century. *Lond.* 1891, *etc.* 8°.   11603. cc.

VOLLMOELLER (C.) Englische Sprach- und Literaturdenkmale des 16. 17. und 18. Jahrhunderts. *Heilbronn,* 1883, *etc.* 8°.   12204. d.

WRIGHT (J. C.) Readings from great English writers. pp. 338. *Lond.* 1893. 8°. 12273. f. 24.

See also BALLADS : POETRY.

Study and Teaching of Literature, etc.

BOWEN (H. C.) English Literature teaching in schools. pp. 56. *Lond.* 1891. 8°. 8310. aa. 50.

COLLINS (J. C.) Study of English Literature. pp. 167. *Lond.* 1891. 8°.   11840. dd. 32.

ENGLISH LITERATURE. English Literature. pp. 32. 1887. 4°. Pall Mall Gazette "Extras." No. 32.   N.R.

GLAZEBROOK (M. G.) Teaching of English Literature. 1891. 8°. Thirteen Essays on Education.   8311. e. 2.

Ac. London. *University.* Questions on English history and literature. 7th Series. Intermediate English, 1892. pp. 50. 1891. 8°. Tutorial Series.   12205. c. 50.

—— 8th series. B.A. English, 1892. 1891. 8°. Tutorial Series.   12205. c. 51.

ENGRAVING AND ILLUSTRATION.

See also ART : DRAWING : PRINTS.

General: Copper and Wood Engraving.

ADELINE (J.) Les Arts de Reproduction vulgarisés. pp. 379. *Paris,* 1894. 8°. 7858. gg. 27.

BLACKBURN (H.) The Art of Illustration. pp. 240. *Lond.* 1894. 8°.   7858. gg. 12.

BROUGH (W. S.) Book Illustration. pp. 42. *Leek,* 1891. 8°.   7807. i. 4. (10.)

CHAPIN (W. O.) The Masters and masterpieces of Engraving. pp. 266. *N.Y.* 1894. 8°.   K.T.C. 19. a. 10.

CUNDALL (J.) Brief history of Wood Engraving. pp. 132. *Lond.* 1895. 8°.   7858. aa. 40.

HAMERTON (P. G.) Drawing and Engraving. pp. 172. *Lond.* 1892. 8°.   K.T.C. 6. a. 7.

EPILEPSY—*continued.*

HARE (H. A.) Epilepsy : Pathology and treatment. pp. 228. *Phila.* 1890. 8°.   7630. de. 13.

SUTTER (J.) A Colony of Mercy. [Description of a home for epileptics at Bethel, Bielefeld] pp. 351. *Lond.* 1893. 8°.   4192. ee. 27.
See also NERVES.

EPILOBIUM. TRELEASE (W.) Revision of the American species of Epilobium. 1891. 8°. SAINT LOUIS. *Missouri Botanical Garden.* Second Report,   7054. h.

EPINAL. CLAUDOT (C.) Notice sur la forêt communale d'Épinal. pp. 64. 1891. 8°. Ac. Épinal. *Société d'Émulation.* Annales. Année 67.   Ac. 585.
See also VOSGES.

EPISCOPACY. *See* CLERGY.

EPITAPHS. BOX (C.) Elegies and Epitaphs. pp. 299. *Gloucester,* 1892. 8°.   11601. i. 4.

HILTON (J.) On some chronogrammatic Epitaphs in England. pp. 13. 1888. 8°. 07703. f. 3. (8.)

MUNBY (A. J.) Faithful Servants: epitaphs and obituaries. pp. 400. *Lond.* 1891. 8°.   10803. cc. 7.

T., E. M. Into the Silent Land. Epitaphs. pp. 127. *Lond.* 1893. 4°.   7709. f. 28.

WARD (F. W. F.) Tombstone Poetry and scriptural quotations. pp. 218. *Lond.* 1895. 8°.   11602. ccc. 26.

BEVERIDGE (E.) Churchyard Memorials of Crail. pp. 303. *Edinb.* 1893. 4°.   10369. l. 6.

EDINBURGH. *Greyfriars Churchyard.* Epitaphs and monumental Inscriptions in the Greyfriars Churchyard. pp. 54. *Edinb.* 1893. 8°.   10369. c. 52.

COWPER (H. S.) Monumental Inscriptions in the church and churchyard of Hawkshead, Lancashire. pp. 84. *Kendal,* 1892. 8°. 9905. aaa. 27.

HIGH HALDEN. Inscriptions in the church and churchyard of High Halden. pp. 76. *Tenterden,* 1895. 8°.   9905. bbb. 47.

MARY, *the B. V., Church of, Newington.* Monumental Inscriptions in the Old Churchyard of Newington. *Lond.* 1880, *etc.* 8°.   9906. b. 5.

RYE (W.) The Monumental Inscriptions in the Hundred of Tunstead. pp. 190. *Norwich,* 1891. 8°.   9914. h. 15.

HARRIS (E. D.) Copy of the Epitaphs in the Burying Ground of Block Island, R.I. pp. 66. *Camb.* 1883. 8°.   9914. ff. 5.

KINGMAN (B.) Epitaphs from Burial Hill, Plymouth, Mass. pp. 330. *Brookline, Mass.,* 1892. 8°.   9902. e. 28.

RAUNIÉ (É.) Épitaphier du vieux Paris. 1890, *etc.* 4°. PARIS. Histoire générale. 10174. l.

EPPING. BEDFORD (J. T.) Story of the preservation of Epping Forest. pp. 31. *Lond.* 1882. 8°.   10348. d. 18. (14.)

WINSTONE (B.) Extracts from the minutes of the Epping Highway Trust. pp. 303. *Lond.* 1891. 8°.   10368. h. 29.
See also LONDON, *Environs.*

EQUATIONS. AUTONNE (L.) Sur la théorie des Équations différentielles. 1891, *etc.* 4°. Journal de l'École Polytechnique. Cahier 61, *etc.*   T.C. 1. b.

—— Sur la théorie des Équations différentielles. pp. 120. 1892. 8°. Ac. Lyons. *Université.* Annales. Tom 3.   Ac. 365.

—— Sur la limitation du degré pour les intégrales algébriques de l'Équation différentielle. 1893, *etc.* 4°. Ac. Paris. *École Centrale des Travaux Publics, etc.* Journal de l'École Polytechnique. Cahier 63.   T.C. 1. b.

EQUATIONS—*continued.*

BASHFORTH (F.) Reprint of a "Description of a Machine for finding the numerical roots of equations," communicated to the British Association, 1845. 2 pt. *Camb.* 1892. 8°.
     8533. dd. 11. (3.)

BENOIT (P.) Über Differentialgleichungen. pp. 19. *Berl.* 1891. 4°.   8535. i. 3. (5.)

BLAKE (E. M.) Method of indeterminate Coefficients and Exponents applied to differential Equations. pp. 41. *N.Y.* 1893. 8°.
     8533. dd. 11. (6.)

BURNSIDE (W. S.) and PANTON (A. W.) Theory of Equations. pp. 496. 1892. 8°. Dublin University Press Series.   2322. f.

BOBEK (C. J.) Lehrbuch der Ausgleichsrechnung nach der Methode der kleinsten Quadrate. pp. 176. 1891. 8°. KLEYER (A.) Mathematisch-naturwissenschaftliche Encyklopädie. 8705. g.

CWOJDZIŃSKI (T.) Anwendung der fuchsschen Theorie auf die Differentialgleichung. pp. 45. *Brody,* 1894. 8°.   Pam. 38.

FORSYTH (A. R.) Theory of differential Equations. *Camb.* 1890, *etc.* 8°.   8535. f. 30.

GULDBERG (A.) Sur une certaine classe d'Équations différentielles. pp. 8. 1893. 8°. Ac. Christiania. *Videnskabs-Selskab.* Forhandlinger. Aar 1893. No. 18.   Ac. 1054.

HAENTZSCHEL (E.) Studien über die Reduction der Potentialgleichung auf gewöhnliche Differentialgleichungen. pp. 180. *Berl.* 1893. 8°.
     8533. dd. 7.

HEFFTER (L.) Einleitung in die Theorie der linearen Differentialgleichungen. pp. 258. *Leipz.* 1894. 8°.   8535. dd. 24.

HEYMANN (W.) Studien über die Transformation der Differential- und Differenzengleichungen. pp. 436. *Leipz.* 1891. 8°.   8535. g. 35.

HORN (J.) Ueber Systeme linearer Differentialgleichungen mit mehreren Veränderlichen. pp. 123. *Berl.* 1891. 8°.   8535. d. 5.

LA VALLÉE POUSSIN (C. J. de) Mémoire sur l'intégration des Équations différentielles. pp. 82. 1892. 8°. Ac. Brussels. *Académie.* Mémoires couronnés. Tom 47.   Ac. 985/4.

LEROUX (J.) Sur les intégrales des Équations linéaires, *etc.* pp. 92. *Paris,* 1894. 4°.
     8535. h. 34.

LIE (M. S.) Vorlesungen über Differentialgleichungen. pp. 568. *Leipz.* 1891. 8°. 8535. h. 26.

MICHELSEN (P.) Die bestimmten algebraischen Gleichungen. pp. 306. *Hannover,* 1893. 8°.
     8535. d. 21.

POCKELS (F.) Über die partielle Differentialgleichung $\Delta u + K^2 u = 0$. pp. 339. *Leipz.* 1891. 8°.   8535. g. 41.

RIVEREAU (P.) Sur les invariantes de certaines classes d'Équations différentielles. pp. 133. *Paris,* 1890. 4°.   8535. h. 19.

SCHLESINGER (L.) Handbuch der Theorie der linearen Differentialgleichungen. *Leipz.* 1895. 8°.   8535. i.

SCHUELER (W. F.) Lehrbuch der unbestimmten Gleichungen. 1891, *etc.* 8°. KLEYER (A.) Mathematisch-naturwissenschaftliche Encyklopädie.   8705. g.

SEGUIER (J. de) Formes quadratiques et multiplication complexe. pp. 339. *Berl.* 1894. 8°.
     8534. dd. 12.

VESSIOT (E.) Sur l'intégration des Équations différentielles linéaires. pp. 84. *Paris,* 1892. 4°.
     8535. gg. 1.

See also ALGEBRA : MATHEMATICS.

EQUITY. BRETT (T.) Leading Cases in modern Equity. pp. 386. *Lond.* 1891. 8°. 6125. a. 6.

EQUITY—*continued.*

FOSTER (R.) Treatise on pleading and practice in Equity in the Courts of the U.S. pp. 822. *Bost.* 1890. 8°.   06616. df. 12.

GIBSON (A.) Aids to Equity. pp. 356. *Lond.* 1893. 8°.   2230. b. 23.

INDERMAUR (J.) Manual of the principles of Equity. pp. 481. *Lond.* 1894. 8°. 6190. df. 19.

—— Epitome of leading Conveyancing and Equity Cases. pp. 172. *Lond.* 1891. 8°. 2230. d. 12.

—— and THWAITES (C.) Student's guide to the principles of Equity. pp. 128. *Lond.* 1894. 8°.   6191. b. 29.

KERLY (D. M.) Sketch of the equitable jurisdiction of the Court of Chancery. pp. 303. *Cumb.* 1890. 8°.   6190. aa. 25.

SNELL (E. H. T.) Principles of Equity. Eleventh edition. pp. 790. *Lond.* 1894. 8°. 6190. df. 21.

—— Analysis of the eleventh edition of Snell's Principles of Equity. pp. 191. *Lond.* 1894. 8°.   2230. bb. 10.

STORY (J.) Commentaries on Equity Jurisprudence. pp. 1089. *Lond.* 1892. 8°. 2018. e.

See also ENGLAND, *Law.*

ERFURT. Der Jesuitenstreit in Erfurt. pp. 43. *Leipz.* 1891. 8°.   Pam. 93.

PICK (A.) Hohenzollern-Besuche in Erfurt. pp. 67. *Erfurt,* 1891. 8°.   9008. g. 8. (8.)

ERISTALIS. *See* DIPTERA.

ERITREA. ALAMANNI (E. Q. M.) L'Avvenire della colonia Eritrea. pp. 45. *Asti,* 1890. 8°.   Pam. 70.

—— La colonia Eritrea. pp. 911. *Torino,* 1891. 8°.   08227. h. 8.

BORSARI (F.) Le zone colonizzabile dell' Eritrea. pp. 96. *Milano,* 1890. 8°.   010096. ee. 18.

ERITREO. Pro Africa Italica. pp. 62. *Roma,* 1891. 8°.   Pam. 67.

LUCIANO (G. B.) Colonizzazione nell' Eritrea. pp. 46. *Roma,* 1891. 8°.   Pam. 66.

SCHWEINFURTH (G.) Il presente e l'avvenire della colonia Eritrea. pp. 63. *Milano,* 1894. 8°.   010096. ff. 30.

ASSAB. Da Assab al Mareb. pp. 94. *Roma,* 1891. 8°.   8028. cc. 40.

See also ABYSSINIA : AFRICA, *Central and East.*

ERLANGEN. Ac. Erlangen. *Academia Fridericiana.* Fest-Zeitung zur Jubelfeier der Universität Erlangen. pp. 6. *Erlangen,* 1893. fol.   1879. c. 1. (16.)

STRUEMPELL (A. v.) Bericht über die Feier des 150jährigen Bestehens der Friedrich-Alexander-Universität zu Erlangen. pp. 45. *Erlangen,* 1894. 4°.   Pam. 17.

ERNE, Lough. HENRY (W.) Upper Lough Erne in 1739. pp. 95. *Dublin,* 1892. 8°. 10390. f. 8.

ERYTHRAE. GAEBLER (H.) Erythrä. pp. 126. *Berl.* 1892. 8°.   9026. c. 14.

ERZGEBIRGE. SCHURTZ (H.) Der Seifenbergbau im Erzgebirge. 1890. 8°. LEHMANN (R.) Forschungen zur deutschen Lands- und Volkskunde, Bd. 5.   10235. i. 10.

ESCHATOLOGY. ALDEN (H. M.) A Study of Death. pp. 336. *Lond.* 1895. 8°. 8470. df. 10.

ARNOLD (H.) Was wird aus uns nach dem Tode ? pp. 147. *Leipz.* 1891. 8°.   4257. i. 36.

B., F. H. Eternal Life. pp. 32. *Lond.* 1891. 32°. 4122. c. 30. (4.)

BASIS. The Basis of every individual's Immortality shown. ff. 32. 1893. 4°.   8462. k. 3.

ESCHATOLOGY—*continued.*

CHAMBERS (A.) "Our Life after Death." pp. 213. *Lond.* 1894. 8°.   4257. f. 34.

CHEEVER (H. T.) Biblical Eschatology. pp. 241. *Bost.* 1893. 8°.   4257. cc. 39.

CHILD (T.) Is there an Unseen World. pp. 16. *Lond.* 1889. 8°.   Pam. 84.

CLARKE (T.) The Fate of the Dead. pp. 196. *Lond.* 1892. 8°.   4257. f. 28.

COBBE (F. P.) The Hopes of the human race. pp. 221. *Lond.* 1894. 8°.   4380. a. 7.

DENIS (L.) Après la Mort. pp. 411. *Paris,* 1891. 12°.   8632. de. 4.

DENNY (J.) Studies in Theology. pp. 272. *Lond.* 1894, 8°.   4371. c. 5.

DREW (E. M.) The Fuller Life. Thoughts in memory of the departed. *Lond.* 1895. 8°. 4399. cc. 2.

ENGLISH (C. D.) Philosophy of a Future State. pp. 16. *Phila.* 1885. 8°.   Pam. 77.

FINCH (A. E.) The Belief in Immortality. pp. 32. 1888. 8°. LONDON. *Sunday Lecture Society.* Selection 5.   4018. c.

FIGUIER (L.) Les Bonheurs d'outre-tombe. pp. 370. *Paris,* 1892. 12°.   4257. e. 16.

FLEMING (J.) Recognition in Eternity. pp. 16. *Lond.* 1892. 8°.   4475. de. 29.

GORDON (G. A.) Witness to Immortality in literature, philosophy and life. pp. 310. *Bost.* 1893. 8°.   4257. cc. 38.

HAUPT (E.) Die eschatologischen Aussagen Jesu. pp. 167. *Berl.* 1895. 8°.   4256. ee. 2.

HIBBARD (F. G.) Eschatology, or the Doctrine of the Last Things. pp. 360. *N.Y.* 1890. 8°. 4257. g. 42.

HOCKING (W. J.) Mors Janua Vitæ. pp. 60. *Lond.* 1891. 8°.   4257. f. 21.

HUDSON (T. J.) Scientific demonstration of the Future Life. pp. 326. *Lond.* 1895. 8°. 4257. bb. 25.

JUSTAMON (A.) Étude sur l'Eschatologie de Jésus et de Saint Paul. pp. 92. *Montauban,* 1895. 8°.   4257. dd. 10.

KABISCH (R.) Die Eschatologie des Paulus. pp. 338. *Göttingen,* 1893. 8°.   4257. d. 12.

KUECHENMEISTER (G. F. H.) Die Todtenbestattungen der Bibel und die Feuerbestattung. pp. 163. *Stuttgart,* 1893. 8°.   4257. d. 14.

LEIGHTON (C. C.) Intimations of Eternal Life. pp. 139. *Bost.* 1891, 8°.   4257. e. 14.

LESCŒUR (L.) Le Dogme dela Vie future et la libre pensée. pp. 476. 1892. 8°. *Bibliothèque Oratorienne.* Vol. 13.   3622. cc.

LYTTELTON (*Hon.* W. H.) The Life of Man after death. pp. 134. *Lond.* 1893. 8°. 4372. c. 46.

MALTUS (J. A.) The Everlasting Life and Love of Jesus. pp. 46, 51. *Lond.* 1893. 16°. 4399. a. 30.

MARSH (F. E.) Where are the Dead. pp. 16. *Lond.* 1895. 8°.   4371. aaaa. 45. (4.)

NAISMITH (W.) Lux Dei. pp. 120. *Paisley,* 1895. 8°.   4371. de. 14.

MUḤAMMAD. Le Paradis de Mahomet, suivi de l'Enfer. pp. 229. *Paris,* 1892. 8°. 14516. a. 9.

NICOLL (W. R.) The Key of the Grave. pp. 189. *Lond.* 1894. 8°.   4257. cc. 35.

OEHLER (H.) Wie wird's nach dem Tode sein ? pp. 22. *Reutlingen,* 1890. 8°. 4371. e. 1. (8.)

PÉTAVEL-OLLIFF (E.) The Problem of Immortality. pp. 597. *Lond.* 1892. 8°. 4256. e. 9.

REDE (W.) The Communion of Saints. pp. 167. *Lond.* 1893. 8°.   4257. e. 18.

REYNOLDS (J. W.) Natural history of Immortality. pp. 389. *Lond.* 1891. 8°. 4256. de. 3.

ESCHATOLOGY—*continued.*

RUNZE (G.) Die Psychologie der Unsterblich-keitsglaubens. pp. 224. 1894, 8°. Studien zur vergleichenden Religionswissenschaft. pt. 2.
4503. e.

SABATIER (A.) Essai sur l'Immortalité au point de vue du naturalisme évolutioniste. pp. 291. *Paris*, 1895. 8°. 4257. bb. 23.

SALMOND (S. D. F.) Christian Doctrine of Im-mortality. pp. 703. *Edinb.* 1895. 8°. 4256. ee. 1.

SCHWALLY (F.) Die Leben nach dem Tode nach den Vorstellungen des alten Israel. pp. 204. *Giessen*, 1892. 8°. 4257. dd. 6.

SEYMOUR (A. J.) Glimpses of the far-off Land. pp. 215. *Lond.* 1893. 8°. 4257. f. 33.

SILL (E. R.) The Same after Death as before. pp. 15. *Lond.* 1892. 8°. Pam. 95.

SPRATLY (W. J.) Scientific Basis for a future state. pp. 196. *Lond.* 1894. 8°. 4018. eee. 3.

STEVENSON (J. F.) God and a Future Life. pp. 78. *Lond.* 1895. 8°. 4256. de. 8.

STOCKWELL (T. H.) Our Dead : where are they ? pp. 171. *Lond.* 1890, 8°. 4257. f. 17.

STOCKWELL (C. T.) Evolution of Immortality. pp. 104. *Chicago*, 1890. 8°. 4257. f. 32.

STRONG (J.) The doctrine of a Future Life. pp .128. *N.Y.* 1891, 8°. 4257. bb. 14.

TEMPLER (B.) Die Unsterblichkeitslehre bei den judischen Philosophen des Mittelalters. pp. 79. *Leipz.* 1895. 8°. 4257. dd. 7.

W., W. T. A few words on Eternal Life. pp. 16. *Lond.* 1894. 8°. 4422. ddd. 53. (12.)

WEBB (A. W.) Does the Soul live after Death ? pp. 71. *Auckland*, 1881. 8°. 4371. e. 5. (7.)

WIEDEMANN (A.) Ancient Egyptian doctrine of the Immortality of the Soul. pp. 71. *Lond.* 1895. 8°. 4503. aaa. 26.

WILLINK (A.) The World of the Unseen. pp. 184. *Lond.* 1893. 8°. 4256. de. 5.

—— Not "Death's Dark Night." pp. 76. *Lond.* 1892. 8°. 4257. k. 31.
See also SOUL.

Day of Judgment.

DEERING (W.) Anglosaxon Poets on the Judg-ment Day. pp. 84. *Halle*, 1890. 8°.
011840. h. 57. (8.)

HAMPDEN-COOK (E.) The Christ has Come. The Second Advent an event of the past. pp. 163. *Lond.* 1894. 8°. 3187. e. 2.

JONES (J.) called IDRISYN. Catechism on the Second Advent. pp. 111. *Lond.* 1880. 8°.
3505. d. 51.

MILLIGAN (W.) The Resurrection of the Dead. pp. 246. *Edinb.* 1894. 8°. 4257. aa. 13.

Heaven.

FRY (H. J.) Thoughts about Heaven. pp. 45. *Lond.* 1892. 8°. 4372. aaa. 48.

RYLE (J. C.) Bp. of Liverpool. Shall we know one another in Heaven ? pp. 136. *Lond.* 1890. 8°. 4256. a. 2.

S., G. J. The Heavenly Jerusalem. pp. 48. *Lond.* 1891. 8°. Pam. 77.

WEAVER (G. S.) Heaven. pp. 100. *Bost.* 1891. 8°. 4257. aa. 12.

Hell : Eternal Punishment : Conditional Immortality.

AGAPEE (A.) Adam's Duration as created the measure of man's duration in punishment. pp. 57. *Lond.* 1890. 8°. Pam. 77.

AKED (C. F.) Eternal Punishment. pp. 52. *Lond.* 1892. 8°. 4371. e. 6. (4.)

BÈS (J.) Étude sur une théorie contemporaine de l'Immortalité conditionnelle. pp. 64. *Lyon*, 1890, 8°. Pam. 77.

ESCHATOLOGY—*continued.*

BROCHMANN (J. H. H.) Om Evigheden Begreb og den evige Straf. pp. 15. *Kristiania*, 1890. 8°.
Pam. 93.

CAMERON (F. M.) On the meaning of the Word Eternal. Heb. xi. 3. pp. 29. *Lond.* 1891. 8°.
4371. de. 4. (12.)

COUNTRY. That Unknown Country ; what men believe concerning Punishment after death. pp. 960. *Springfield*, 1889. 8°. 4257. m. 31.

FALKE (R.) Die Lehre von der ewigen Ver-dammnis. pp 180. *Eisenach*, 1892. 8°. 4257. d. 11.

FARRAR (F. W.) Eternal Hope. pp. 227. *Lond.* 1892. 8°. 2206. a. 1.

KING (G. W.) Κολασις αιωνιος ; or future Retri-bution. pp. 267. *N.Y.* 1891. 8°. 4257. bb. 15.

MACPHERSON (J.) The Larger Hope. pp. 152. *Lond.* 1890. 8°. 4257. f. 19.

PÉTAVEL-OLLIFF (E.) Le Salut universel et l'universalisme conditionnel. pp. 124. *Paris*, 1891. 8°. 4257. dd. 7.

PHILLIPSON (J.) Natural history of Hell. pp. 112. *N.Y.* 1894. 8°. 4257. f. 35.

SEARCHER. Eternal Punishment. Are the souls of the wicked to be destroyed after death ? pp. 71. *Lond.* 1894. 8°. 4257. d. 16.

SOLLY (H. S.) Punishment for Sin : is it eternal ? 1893. 8°. FRECKLETON (T. W.) Religion and Modern Thought. 4016. df. 23.

VARLEY (H.) Death and Afterwards : nature and duration of punishment of the wicked. pp. 64. *N.Y.* 1893. 8°. 4257. aaa. 23.
See also UNIVERSALISM.

Purgatory : Paradise : Intermediate State.

ANDERSON (A. J.) Is it right to pray for the Dead. pp. 32. *Lond.* 1889. 8°. Pam. 92.

BULLINGER (E. W.) "The Spirits in Prison." pp. 29. *Lond.* 1891. 8°. Pam. 77.

CONSTABLE (H.) Hades ; or, the Intermediate State of man. pp. 383. *Lond.* 1893. 8°. 4257. c. 27.

D'ARCY (G.) From Death to the Judgment Day. pp. 46. *Lond.* 1892. 8°. 4371. e. 6. (6.)

BRINQUANT (J. F.) De la Beauté du corps des bienheureux. pp. 180. *Lime*, 1892. 8°.
4371. ee. 13.

LUCKOCK (H. M.) Intermediate State between death and judgment. pp. 258. *Lond.* 1890. 8°.
4257. g. 41.

MUMFORD (J.) Two ancient treatises on Purga-tory. pp. 360. 1893. 8°. P.P. *London.* Quarterly Series. Vol. 87. 3605. dd.

PELLS (S. F.) Sheol versus Hades. pp. 216. *Lond.* 1891. 8°. 4257. d. 9.

SCHOUPPE (F. X.) Purgatory. pp. 312. *Lond.* 1894. 8°. 4257. cc. 37.

SCOTT (D. W.) Hades and beyond. pp. 491. *Lond.* 1892. 8°. 4257. f. 31.

SISTER OF MERCY. To-day in Paradise. pp. 48. *Oxf.* 1894. 8°. 4257. a. 23.

WALKER (J. E.) The blessed Dead in Paradise. pp. 305. *Lond.* 1891. 8°. 4257. cc. 29.

WILLIAMSON (A.) The intermediate State. pp. 82. *Lond.* 1890. 8°. 4378. e. 8.

ESK. *Forfarshire, N. and S., Rivers.* See GLENESK.

ESK. *Midlothian, N. and S., Rivers.* CHAP-MAN (T.) and STRATHESK (J.) The Mid-Lothian Esks. pp. 45. *Edinb.* 1895. 4°. K.T.C. 30. b. 9.

ESKIMOS. GRENFELL (W. T.) Vikings of To-day. Labrador. pp. 240. 10460. bb. 27.

HORDEN (J.) Bp. of Moosonee. Forty-two years amongst the Eskimo. pp. 223. *Lond.* 1893. 8°. 4429. eee. 6.

ESKIMOS—*continued.*

KELLY (J. W.) Eskimo Vocabularies, preceded by ethnographical memoranda. 1890. 8°. *U.S. Bureau of Education.* Circular of information. No. 165.   8308. a.

NANSEN (F.) Eskimoliv. pp. 293. *Kristiania,* 1891. 8°.   10460. ee. 41.

—— Eskimo Life. pp. 350. *Lond.* 1893. 8°.   10460. ee. 42.

PAYNE (F. F.) Eskimo of Hudson's Strait. pp. 18. *Toronto,* 1889. 8°.   Pam. 86.

PEARY (J. D.) My Arctic Journal. A year among ice fields and Eskimos. pp. 240. *Lond.* 1893. 8°.   10460. e. 32.

RINK (H. J.) Eskimo tribes. 1891, *etc.* 8°. DENMARK. *Commission for Ledelsen af de Undersøgelser i Grønland.* Meddelelser. Bd. 11, *etc.*   10460. dd.

Language.

KELLY (J. W.) English-Eskimo and Eskimo-English Vocabularies. 1890. 8°. UNITED STATES. *Bureau of Education.* Circular of Information. No. 165.   8308. i.

KJER (J.) and RASMUSSEN (C.) Danskgrønlandsk Ordbog. *Kjøbenh.* 1893. 8°.   12972. k. 3.

BOURQUIN (T.) Grammatik der Eskimo-Sprache. pp. 415. *Lond.* 1891. 8°.   12975. k. 38.

ESQUIMAUX PRIMER. Western Esquimaux Primer. pp. 72. *Lond.* 1891. 8°.   12910. a. 28.

RINK (H. J.) Eskimo tribes. With comparative vocabulary. 1891, *etc.* 8°. DENMARK. *Commission for Ledelsen af de Undersøgelser i Grønland.* Meddelelser. Bd. 11, *etc.*   10460. dd.

RYBERG (C. J. P.) Dansk-grønlandsk Tolk. pp. 378. *Kjøbenh.* 1891. 8°.   12910. aa. 54.

SCHULTZE (A.) Brief grammar and vocabulary of the Eskimo Language. pp. 21. *Bethlehem, Pa.* 1889. 8°.   12910. d. 31. (2.)

See also ARCTIC REGIONS : GREENLAND.

ESPERANTO. *See* VOLAPÜK.

ESSEN. HUMANN (G.) Der Westbau des Münsters zu Essen. pp. 44. *Essen.* 1890. 4°.   7814. ee. 21.

ESSEX. ANDREWS (W.) Bygone Essex. pp. 249. *Colchester,* 1892. 8°.   010358. i. 2.

BENHAM (W. G.) The Essex Labourer. pp. 18. *Colchester,* 1888. 8°.   8282. g. 28. (4.)

BERLYN (A.) Sunrise-Land. pp. 345. *Lond.* 1894. 8°.   10350. bb. 48.

CHANCELLOR (F.) Ancient sepulchral Monuments of Essex. pp. 418. *Lond.* 1890. fol.   1707. c. 8.

COWPER (F.) Sailing Tours. Pt. 1. Coast of Essex. *Lond.* 1892, *etc.* 8°.   18360. e.

EPHEM. Essex County Annual. *Forest Gate,* 1891, *etc.* 8°.   P.P. 2507. cfc.

ESSEX. Murray's Handbook for Essex, *etc.* pp. 78. 482. *Lond.* 1892. 8°.   2364. a. 13.

JONES (H. L.) Swin, swale, and swatchway : Cruises down the Thames, *etc.* pp. 203. *Lond.* 1892. 4°.   10358. e. 26.

LINDLEY (P.) New holidays in Essex. pp. 70. *Lond.* 1891. obl. 16°.   10358. bb. 66.

P.P. *Chelmsford.* The Essex Review. *Chelmsford,* 1892, *etc.* 8°.   P.P. 6081. eb.

—— London. The Essex Notebook. No. 2–12. *Lond.* 1884–85. 4°.   P.P. 6081. l.

ESTE, House of. Ac. London. *Burlington Fine Arts Club.* Exhibition of Pictures of the school of Ferrara-Bologna, also of Medals of members of the house of Este. pp. 57. *Lond.* 1894. 4°.   7858. c. 25.

ESTEPA. AGUILAR Y CANO (A.) Estepa. Nueva colección de documentos. pp. 138. *Estepa,* 1891. 8°.   10161. c. 7.

ESTHONIA. Ac. Riga. *Gesellschaft für Geschichte der Ost-See Provinzen.* Goldschmiedearbeiten in Estland, *etc.* pp. 24. *Lübeck,* 1892. fol.   1811. a. 8.

LIVONIA. Commentar zu dem vierten Buch des liv-, est- und curländischen Privatrechts. *Riga,* 1889, *etc.* 8°.   5756. bbb. 21.

SERAPHIM (E.) Geschichte Liv-, Est- und Kurlands. 2 Bde. *Reval,* 1895, 96. 8°. 9456. de. 2.

Language and Literature.

Ac. Saint Petersburg. *Academia Scientiarum.* WIEDEMANN (F. J.) Ehstnisch-deutsches Wörterbuch. pp. xii. coll. 1406. *St. Petersburg,* 1893. 8°.   12963. m. 10.

KIRBY (W. F.) The Hero of Esthonia. Study of the Kalewipoeg. 2 vol. *Lond.* 1895. 8°.   12431. ee. 29.

WIEDEMANN (F. J.) Ehstnisch-deutsches Wörterbuch. pp 1406. 2 vol. *St. Petersburg,* 1893. 8°.   12963. m. 9.

JORDAN (P.) Geschichte der ehstländischen literärischen Gesellschaft 1842–92. pp. 92. *Reval,* 1892. 8°.   11851. f. 35.

See also BALTIC PROVINCES.

ESTOPPEL, Law of. BROUGHTON (L. P. D.) Estoppel in civil suits in India. pp. 168. *Lond.* 1893. 8°.   5318. bb. 30.

ETAIYAPURAM. GAṆAPATI PIḶḶAI. Etaiyapuram past and present. pp. 147. *Madras,* 1890. 12°.   10058. a. 20.

ÉTAMPES. LEGRAND (M.) and MARQUIS (L.) Les trois états du bailliage d'Étampes aux États généraux. *Étampes,* 189 *,* *etc.* 8°.   9225. bb. 21.

ETCHING. *See* ENGRAVING : PRINTS.

ETHER. *See* AIR : ANAESTHETICS.

ETHICS.

General.

ABBOTT (J.) A Primer of Ethics. *Bost.* 1891. 8°.   8409. e. 18.

ARISTOTLE. Aristotelis Ethica Nicomachea recognovit I. Bywater. pp. 264. *Oxonii,* 1890. 8°.   8408. g. 27.

—— Introduction to Aristotle's Ethics. By E. Moore. pp. 300. *Lond.* 1890. 8°.   2234. b. 2.

FILKUKA (L.) Die metaphysischen Grundlagen der Ethik bei Aristoteles. pp. 138. *Wien,* 1895. 8°.   8460. f. 28.

STEWART (J. A.) Notes on the Nicomachean Ethics of Aristotle. 2 vol. *Oxf.* 1892. 8°.   2234. cc. 14.

HÄGERSTRÖM (A.) Aristoteles etiska grundtankar. pp. 196. *Upsala,* 1893. 8°. 8460. f. 27.

BAKER (A.) Outlines of Logic and Ethics. pp. 161. *Lond.* 1891. 8°.   8462. b. 21.

BARONZIO (A.) La Morale positiva. pp. 88. *Mantova,* 1890. 8°.   8408. h. 29.

BLONDEL (M.) L'Action. Essai d'une critique de la vie. pp. 495. *Paris,* 1893. 8°. 8470. c. 14.

BOEHMER (G.) Ethische Essays. *München,* 1890, *etc.* 8°.   8409. ee. 24.

BOWNE (B. P.) Principle of Ethics. pp. 309. *N.Y.* 1892. 8°.   8409. l. 13.

CALIDORE. Sir Calidore. pp. 96. *Edinb.* 1892. 8°.   8404. ccc. 38.

CATHREIN (V.) Philosophia Moralis. pp. 396. *Friburgi,* 1895. 8°.   8409. h. 20.

—— Moralphilosophie. *Freiburg,* 1890, *etc.* 8°.   8467. h. 15.

ETHICS—*continued*.

Cée (J. P.) Avant-projet d'un code des Lois Morales. pp. 185. *Paris*, 1890. 8°. 8285. cc. 41.

Cook (A. B.) Metaphysical basis of Plato's Ethics. pp. 160. *Camb.* 1895. 8°. 8460. bb. 40.

Cook (W.) Ethics of Bishop Butler and Kant. pp. 52. 1888. 8°. Ac. Ann Arbor. *University.* Philosophical Papers. Ser. 2. No. 4.
　　　　　　　　　　　　　　　　Ac. 2685/7.

D'Arcy (C. F.) Short study of Ethics. pp. 278. *Lond.* 1895. 8°. 8409. i. 2.

Dewey (J. H.) The Study of Ethics. pp. 151. *Ann Arbor*, 1894. 8°. 8409. k. 28.

Duboc (J.) Grundriss einer einheitlichen Trieblehre vom Standpunkte des Determinismus. pp. 308. *Leipz.* 1892. 8°. 8409. f. 34.

Dugard (M.) La Culture morale. pp. 404. *Paris*, 1892. 12°. 8405. cc. 40.

Elsenhans (T.) Wesen und Entstehung des Gewissens. pp. 334. *Leipz.* 1894. 8°. 8465. ff. 29.

Eschenauer (A.) La Morale universelle. pp. 467. *Paris*, 1882. 8°. 8408. h. 33.

Ferretti (A.) Institutiones Philosophiæ Moralis. *Romæ*, 1893, *etc.* 8°. 8411. cc.

Foerster (F. W.) Der Entwicklungsgang der kantischen Ethik. pp. 106. *Berl.* 1893. 8°. 8462. e. 32.

Fowler (T.) Progressive Morality. pp. 192. *Lond.* 1895. 8°. 8409. d. 10.

Friso (L.) Filosofia Morale. pp. 335. *Milano*, 1893. 8°. 012200. h. 67.

Gallwitz (H.) Das Problem der Ethik in der Gegenwart. pp. 272. *Göttingen*, 1891. 8°. 8467. cc. 41.

Gilman (N. P.) The Laws of daily conduct. pp. 230. *Bost.* 1891. 8°. 8409. ee. 28.

Giżycki (G. v.) Vorlesungen über soziale Ethik. pp. 88. *Berl.* 1895. 8°. 8275. f. 36.

—— Introduction to the Study of Ethics. pp. 304. *Lond.* 1891. 8°. 8409. ee. 26.

Guttzeit (H.) Der Verbildung-Spiegel. *Grossenhain*, 1893. *etc.* 8°. 8410. dd.

Hegel (G. W. F.) System der Sittlichkeit. pp. 71. *Osterwieck*. 1893. 8°. 8408. h. 34. (7.)

—— The Ethics of Hegel. pp. 216. *Bost.* 1893. 8°. 8409. ee. 35.

Hoekstra (S.) Zedenleer. 3 dl. *Amsterdam*, 1894. 8°. 8408. dd. 3.

Höffding (H.) Etiske Undersøgelser. pp. 83. *Kjøbenh.* 1891. 8°. 8411. cc. 30. (5.)

Huxley (*Right Hon.* T. H.) Evolution and Ethics. pp. 57. *Lond.* 1893. 8°. 8409. f. 37.

Hyslop (J. H.) Elements of Ethics. pp. 470. *Edinb.* 1895. 8°. 8409. h. 28.

Janet (P.) Cours de Psychologie et de Morale. pp. 486. *Paris*, 1891. 12°. 8470. df. 2.

Jouin (L.) Elementa philosophiæ moralis. pp. 400. *Neo-Eboraci*, 1886. 12°. 8409. ee. 22.

Kant (I.) Fundamental Principles of the Metaphysic of Ethics. pp. 102. *Lond.* 1895. 8°. 8411. cc. 32.

Koessing (F.) Über die Wahrheitsliebe. *Paderborn*, 1893, *etc.* 8°. 4371. ee.

Larsen (S. C.) Studia critica in Plutarchi Moralia. pp. 151. *Hauniæ*, 1889. 8°. 11312. k. 52.

Leinbach (C. A.) Untersuchungen über die verschiedenen Moralsysteme. pp. 125. *Fulda*, 1894. 8°. 8409. l. 26.

Letourneau (C. J. M.) L'Évolution de la Morale. pp. 478. 1887. 8°. Bibliothèque Anthropologique. Tom. 3. 7004. de.

Lilly (W. S.) On Right and wrong. pp. 284. *Lond.* 1891. 8°. 8409. g. 42.

ETHICS—*continued*.

Mac Cosh (J.) Our Moral Nature. pp. 53. *Lond.* 1892. 8°. 8409. cc. 25.

Macdonald (W. A.) Science and Ethics. pp. 182. *Lond.* 1895. 8°. 8411. cc. 28.

Mackenzie (J. S.) Manual of Ethics. pp. 355. 1894. 8°. Tutorial Series. 12205. c. 217.

—— Manual of Ethics. pp. 339. 1893. 8°. 12205. c. 108.

Manmathanātha Chaṭṭopadhyaya. Science of Ethics. pp. 102. *Lahore*, 1891. 8°. 8409. l. 8.

Marion (H.) De la Solidarité morale. pp. 359. *Paris*, 1890. 8°. 8467. dd. 32.

Martineau (J.) The Law of Duty : a suggested moral text-book. pp. 136. *Madras*, 1889. 8°. 8410. e. 4.

Stephen (H.) Complete analysis of Martineau's "Types of Ethical Theory." Vol. ii. pt. 1. *Calcutta*, 1890. 8°. 8409. l. 27.

Stephens (H.) Notes on Martineau's Types of Ethical Theory. *Calcutta*, 1890, *etc.* 8°. 8409. ccc. 25.

Muirhead (J. H.) Elements of Ethics. pp. 239. 1892. 8°. Knight (W.) University Extension Manuals. 12204. f.

Murray (J. C.) Introduction to Ethics. pp. 407. *Paisley*, 1891. 8°. 8409. ee. 27.

Pagnani (C.) *Bp. of Kandy.* First notions of Logic and Ethics. pp. 272. *Colombo*, 1891. 8°. 8470. ccc. 17.

Rickaby (J.) Moral Philosophy. pp. 380. 1892. 8°. Manual of Catholic Philosophy. 8470. ccc.

Ritter (P. H.) Ethische Fragmenten. pp. 228. *Utrecht*, 1892. 8°. 8409. ee. 33.

Robertson (J. D.) Conscience. *Lond.* 1894, *etc.* 8°. 8409. l. 19.

Rod (É.) Les Idées morales du temps présent. pp. 318. *Paris*, 1891. 8°. 8409. cc. 8.

Runze (G.) Ethik. *Berl.* 1891, *etc.* 8°. 8408. h. 30.

Ryland (F.) Ethics. pp. 220. *Lond.* 1893. 8°. 8409. e. 27.

Saint-André (L.) Notes sur la Morale de H. Spencer, de Littré, de A. Fouillée. pp. 65. *Paris*, 1892. 8°. Pam. 49.

Salter (W. M.) What can Ethics do for us ? pp. 32. *Chicago*, 1891. 8°. Pam. 49.

Schubert (J.) Smith's Moralphilosophie. 1891. 8°. Wundt (W.) Philosophische Studien. Bd. 6. 8463. e. 12.

Scott (W. R.) Introduction to Cudworth's treatise concerning Eternal Morality. pp. 67. *Lond.* 1891. 8°. 8405. cc. 33.

Scotus Novanticus. Ethica. pp. 356. *Lond.* 1891. 8°. 8411. cc. 13.

Seth (J.) A Study of Ethical Principles. pp. 460. *Edinb.* 1895. 8°. 8409. h. 29.

—— Freedom as Ethical Postulate. pp. 48. *Edinb.* 1891. 8°. 8461. bbb. 48. (5.)

Sidgwick (H.) The Methods of Ethics. pp. 523. *Lond.* 1893. 8°. 2023. c.

—— Outlines of the history of Ethics. pp. 288. *Lond.* 1892. 8°. 8486. bb. 13.

Simmel (G.) Einleitung in die Moralwissenschaft. *Berl.* 1892, *etc* 8°. 8411. cc. 17.

Spencer (H.) Principles of Ethics. *Lond.* 1892, *etc.* 8°. 2023. b.

Spinoza (B. de) Ethic. Translated by W. H. White. pp. 297. *Lond.* 1894. 8°. 8408 d. 8.

Friedlaender (J.) Spinoza ein Meister der Ethik. pp. 30. *Berl.* 1895. 8°. Pam. 85.

Worms (R.) La Morale de Spinoza. pp. 334. *Paris*, 1892. 8°. 8411. e. 4.

ETHICS—continued.

WRZECIONKO (R.) Der Grundgedanke der Ethik des Spinoza. pp. 57. Wien, 1894. 8°.
8409. l. 28.

STIEGLITZ (T.) Über den Ursprung des Sittlichen. pp. 130. Wien, 1894. 8°. 8409. l. 29.

VORBRODT (G.) Principien der Ethik Lotzes. pp. 186. Dessau, 1891. 8°. 8409. cc. 4.

WILLIAMS (C. M.) Review of Systems of Ethics founded on Evolution. pp. 581. Lond. 1893. 8°.
8409. k. 15.

WILSON (J. M.) and FOWLER (T.) Principles of Morals. pp. 370. Oxf. 1894. 8°. 8468. k. 23.

WOLFF (H.) Handbuch der Ethik. pp. 94. Leipz. 1890. 8°. 8468. k. 26. (4.)

WULCKOW (R.) Die ethischen Erziehungsaufgaben unserer Zeit. pp. 93. Giessen, 1894. 8°.
8408. bb. 37.

WUNDT (W.) Ethik. pp. 684. Stuttg. 1892. 8°.
8408. h. 35.

ZIEGLER (T.) Social Ethics. pp. 140. Lond. 1892. 8°. 8409. ee. 30.

See also MORALS : PHILOSOPHY.

Christian Ethics : Ethics and Religion.

C., B. F. C. Ethics or Anarchy. pp. 100. Lond. 1895. 8°. 3939. ccc. 17.

FLETCHER (A. E.) Christian Ethics. 1894. 8°.
REID (A.) Vox Clamantium. 8409. h. 19.

GUTBERLET (C.) Ethik und Religion. pp. 376. Münster, 1892. 8°. 8408. g. 30.

KAY (S. W.) Resist not Evil. pp. 204. Manch. 1893. 8°. 4371. aa. 26.

KNIGHT (W.) The Christian Ethic. pp. 178. Lond. 1893. 8°. 4371. df. 21.

LEENDERTZ (A. C.) Het ethisch-evangelisch standpunkt in het christelijk-godsdienstig geloof. 2 vol. Rotterdam, 1891. 8°. 4371. aaa. 12.

RICKABY (J.) Aquinas Ethicus ; moral teaching of St. Thomas. Lond. 1892. 8°. 3605. dd.

ROBINS (H. E.) Harmony of Ethics with Theology. pp. 100. N.Y. 1891. 8°. 4257. aaa. 22.

ROTHE (R.) Uebersicht der theologischen Ethik. pp. 302. Bremen, 1895. 8°. 4371. ee. 37.

SHELDON (W. L.) Ethics and belief in a God. pp. 42. St. Louis, 1892. Pam. 85.

SMYTH (T.) Christian Ethics. pp. 498. 1892. 8°. SALMOND (S. D. F.) International Theological Library. 3605. k.

STANGE (C.) Die christliche Ethik in ihrem Verhältnis zur modernen Ethik. pp. 99. Göttingen, 1892. 4°. 8409. m. 6.

UPTON (C. B.) Religion and Ethics. 1891. 8°. BARTRAM (R.) Religion and Life. 4372. ee. 10.

WEISS (H.) Einleitung in die christliche Ethik. pp. 238. 1889. 8°. Sammlung theologischer Lehrbücher. 3554. i.

See also supra: General: CHRISTIANITY, Practical, etc.

ETHIOPIC LANGUAGE. BACHMANN

(P. J.) Aethiopische Lesestücke. pp. 50. Leipz. 1892. 8°. 754 b. 18.

GOLDSCHMIDT (L.) Bibliotheca Æthiopica. pp. 63. Leipz. 1893. 8°. 11906. b. 1.

ETHNOLOGY : ETHNOGRAPHY. Ac.

Basle. Academia Ethnographische Kommission. Mitteilungen aus der ethnographischen Sammlung. Basel, 1894, etc. 8°. 10007. bb.

ANDRIAN (F. v.) Der Höhencultus asiatischen und europäischen Völker. pp. 385. Wien, 1891. 8°. 4503. cc. 16.

BABINGTON (W. D.) Fallacies of Race theories. pp. 277. Lond. 1895. 8°. 9004. g. 24.

ETHNOLOGY—continued.

BAHNSON (K.) Etnografien, fremstillet i dens Hovedtræk. Kjøbenh. 1892, etc. 8°. 10007. d.

BASTIAN (A.) Ideale Welten, etc. 3 Bde. Berl. 1892. 8°. 4503. h. 1.

—— Controversen in der Ethnologie. Berl. 1893, etc. 8°. 10006. e.

BRINTON (D. G.) Races and Peoples. pp. 313. N.Y. 1890. 8°. 10007. bbb. 25.

CHIJS (J. A. v. d.) Catalogus der ethnologische verzameling van het Bataviaasch Genootschap van Kunsten. pp. 195. Batavia, 1894. 8°.
10007. l. 3.

GOMME (G. L.) Ethnology in folk-lore. pp. 200. 1892. 8°. LUBBOCK (Rt. Hon. Sir J.) Modern Science. 8709. f.

KOLLMANN (J.) and RUETIMEYER (L.) Bericht über die ethnographische Sammlung der Universität Basel. pp. 44. 1894. 8°. Ac. Basle. Academia Ethnographische Kommission. Mitteilungen. I. 10007. bb.

LANGKAVEL (B.) Der Mensch und seine Rassen. pp. 644. Stuttgart, 1892. 8°. 10007. g. 46.

LEFÈVRE (A.) Les Races et les Langues. pp. 301. Paris, 1893. 8°. 8708. cc.

—— Race and Language. pp. 424. 1893. 8°. International Scientific Series. Vol lxxvi.
2324. bb. 13.

PARIS. Exposition Universelle, 1889. Histoire du Travail et des Sciences anthropologiques. Paris, 1889. fol. 7958. k. 2.

P.P. Leipsic. Zeitschrift für Volkskunde. Bd. 1–4. Leipz. 1889–92. 8°. P.P. 3863. d.

P.P. Lunden. Am Ur-Quell. Monatschrift für Volkskunde. Hamb. 1890, etc. 8°. 897.

RECLUS (É.) Primitive Folk. pp. 339. 1891. 8°. ELLIS (H. H.) Contemporary Science Series.
8709. i.

BRINTON (D. G.) Protohistoric ethnography of Western Asia. pp. 32. Phila. 1895. 8°.
Pam. 88.

SAYCE (A. H.) Races of the Old Testament. pp. 180. 1891. 8°. By-Paths of Bible Knowledge, XVI. 2002. a.

HEWITT (J. F.) Ruling Races of prehistoric times in India, S.Western Asia and S. Europe. pp. 627. Westminster, 1894. 8°. 9056. ee. 19.

OPPERT (G.) On the Original Inhabitants of India. pp. 711. Westminster, 1893. 8°.
10007. cc. 15.

P.P. Boston. Journal of American Ethnology and Archæology. Bost. 1891, etc. 4°.
P.P. 3862. c.

See also ANTHROPOLOGY : ARYANS : SEMITIC RACES, and for the Ethnology of each country under the country required.

ETIQUETTE. ARMSTRONG (L. H.) Etiquette

of party giving, etc. pp. 81. Lond. 1893. 8°.
8411. cc. 24.

BRYSON (L. F.) Everyday Etiquette. pp. 145. N.Y. 1890. 8°. 8410. dd. 7.

ETIQUETTE. Etiquette of good society. pp. 224. Lond. 1893. 8°. 8409. ccc. 16.

—— Etiquette for ladies. pp. 96. 1894. 8°. Warne's Bijou Books. 7913. aa. 19.

FORM. Good Form. Dinners. pp. 80. N.Y. 1890. 8°. 8411. aa. 46.

GRANDMAISON (de) Le Savoir-vivre et ses usages. pp. 355. Paris, 1893. 12°. 8411. cc. 26.

GREVILLE (B. V.) Baroness Greville. The Gentlewoman in society. pp. 271. 1892. 8°. Victoria Library. 012208. f.

HABITS. The Habits of good society. pp. 378. Lond. 1890. 8°. 8407. cc. 33.

ETIQUETTE—*continued.*

LONGSTREET (A. B.) Social Etiquette of New
York. *N.Y.* 1887. 8°. 8411. aa. 31.

MORTON (A. H.) Etiquette. pp. 203.
Phila. 1892. 8°. 8409. ccc. 15.

VERNON (A.) La Distinction française. pp. 188.
Paris, 1893. 8°. 8409. ccc. 17.

ETNA, Mount. *See* VOLCANOES.

ETON COLLEGE. DRAGE (G.) Eton and
the Empire. pp. 40. *Eton,* 1890. 8°.
8364. aaa. 43.

ETON COLLEGE. Eton of old, 1811–22. pp. 244.
Lond. 1892. 8°. 8365. f. 38.

ETON. Loan Collection of Portraits, views and
other objects connected with Eton. pp. 115.
Eton College, 1891. 4°. 8365. f. 36.

ÉTOUY. P., A. Étouy, ses origines et ses
anciens seigneurs. pp. 85. *Paris,* 1894. 8°.
10171. g. 2.

ETRETAT. BACON (H.) Etretat. pp. 132.
Paris, 1895. 8°. 10170. aa. 2.

ETRURIA, Kingdom of, 1801–1807.
See FLORENCE.

ETRUSCANS. BUGGE (E. S.) Etruskisch
und Armenisch. Sprachvergleichende Forschung-
en. *Christiania,* 1890, *etc.* 8°. 12933. dd.

CORDENONS (F.) Un po' più di luce sulle origini
e sistema di scrittura degli Euganei-Veneti.
pp. 212. *Padova,* 1894. 8°. 12902. dd. 43.

FALCHI (I.) Sulla questione etrusca. pp. 12.
Firenze, 1893. 8°. 07703. g. 1. (17.)

LELAND (C. G.) Etruscan Roman Remains in
popular tradition. pp. 385. *Lond.* 1892. 4°.
4504. i. 7.

PAULI (C.) Corpus Inscriptionum Etruscarum.
Lipsiæ, 1893, *etc.* fol. 7701. k.

—— Altitalische Forschungen.
Leipz. 1885, *etc.* 8°. 7706. de.

—— Altitalische Studien.
Hannover, 1883, *etc.* 8°. 7706. e. 16.

SEEMANN (T.) Die Kunst der Etrusker. pp. 72.
Dresden, 1890. 8°. 7708. cc. 48.

See also ITALY, *Antiquities :* VASES.

EUCALYPTUS. COWAN (F.) Check-List of
the common names of the Eucalypts. pp. 26.
Greenesburgh, 1894. 8°. Pam. 1.

CURGENVEN (J. B.) On the use of the oil of
Eucalyptus Globulus in the treatment of infectious diseases. pp. 12. *Lond.* 1891. 8°.
07305. e. 23. (10.)

MAC ALPINE (D.) and REMFREY (J. R.) Trans-
verse sections of petioles of Eucalypts as aids in
the determination of Species. pp. 64. 1891. 8°.
Ac. Melbourne. *Royal Society.* Transactions.
New Series. Vol. 2. Pt. 1. Ac. 1908/8.

S., M. R. C. Essay on the essential oil of
Eucalyptus. pp. 8. *Lond.* 1889. 8°.
07305. h. 6. (1.)

EUCHARIST. ANGLICANUS. The Eucharist :
is it a sacrifice, a sacrament, or neither ? pp. 63.
Lond. 1891. 8°. 4109. c. 15. (2.)

BATES (A. N) On Holy Communion and ritual-
ism. pp. 23. *Lond.* 1889. 8°. 4109. e. 18.

BICKELL (G.) The Lord's Supper and the Pass-
over Ritual. pp. 219. *Edinb.* 1891. 8°.
4324. g. 36.

BEECHEY (S. V.) Excuses of non-Communicants.
pp. 20. *Lond.* 1895. 8°. 4462. aa. 14.

BIRCH (E. J.) The Sacrament of the Lord's
Supper. pp. 35. *Lond.* 1891. 8°. 4324. f. 29.

BONA (J.) De sacrificio Missæ tractatus.
pp. 228. *Augustæ T.* 1891. 16°. 4324. a. 10.

EUCHARIST—*continued.*

BRIDGETT (T. E.) Faith of the ancient English
Church concerning the Holy Eucharist. pp. 24.
Lond. 1890. 8°. 3939. ccc. 1. (19.)

CASSEL (S. afterwards P.) Missa und Selicha.
pp. 26. *Berl.* 1891. 8°. Pam. 77.

CHURCHILL (S.) Holy Communion. pp. 162.
Lond. 1891. 8°. 4327. cc. 1.

CLARE (A.) The Perfect Sacrifice. pp. 224.
Lond. 1888. 8°. 4324. g. 40.

CLARKE (G.) The Lord's Supper. pp. 63.
Lond. 1894. 8°. 4324. a. 30.

CLARKE (R. F.) The weekly Communicant.
pp. 67. *Lond.* 1895. 16°. Pam. 75.

COSTELLOE (B. F. C.) The Mass. pp. 28.
Lond. 1890. 8°. 3939. ccc. 1. (11.)

DAVIDSON (W. T.) The Lord's Supper. pp. 174.
Lond. 1895. 8°. 4324. c. 31.

DEACON. The Holy Supper. pp. 49.
Lond. 1894. 8°. 3716. df. 23.

DIMOCK (N.) "Dangerous Deceits." Examination of the teaching of Article thirty-one.
pp. 126. *Lond.* 1895. 8°. 3940. i. 10.

EN DE. Those Holy Mysteries. *Lond.* 1893. 16°.
4324. a. 28.

EX-PRIEST. The Eucharist. pp. 63.
Lond. 1895. 8°. 4323. aa. 3.

FALCONI (J.) Notre Pain Quotidien, c'est-a-dire
le Sacrement de l'autel. pp. 256. *Paris,* 1890. 8°.
4324. g. 28.

GIBSON (H.) Instructions on first Communion.
pp. 96. *Lond.* 1892. 16°. 4324. aa. 15.

GIRDLESTONE (R. B.) The Lord's Supper.
1895. 8°. Four foundation Truths. 4109. aa. 44.

GOUGH (E. J.) Simple thoughts on the Holy
Eucharist. pp. 40. *Edinb.* 1893. 8°.
4371. b. 14. (6.)

HAINES (E. W.) The Lord's Supper. pp. 105.
Lond. 1895. 8°. 4324. aaa. 21.

HALL (H. A.) Duty and Service. Instructions
on the Supper of the Lord. pp. 127.
Lond. 1895, 16°. 4399. bb. 10.

HAMMOND (J.) Seal and Sacrament ; a guide to
Holy Communion. pp. 256. *Lond.* 1892. 8°.
4429. aa. 48.

JENKINS (R. C.) A few words on the Eucharist.
pp. 15. *Folkestone,* 1890. 8°. 3940. bb. 31. (2.)

JOOS (W.) Anatomie der Messe. pp. 560.
Schaffhausen, 1891. 8°. 3476. h. 22.

LAMBERT (J. M.) Le Congrès Eucharistique de
Naples. pp. 57. *Bar-le-Duc,* 1892. 8°.
4371. bb. 33. (4.)

LANCASTER (J.) "This is My Body." Teaching
of the Church of England, respecting the Real
Presence. 1889. 8°. STUART (E. A.) The City
Pulpit. No. 100. 4478. k.

LILLEY (J. P.) The Lord's Supper. pp. 329.
Edinb. 1891. 8°. 4324. g. 32.

LINKLATER (R.) The Lord's Day and the Holy
Eucharist. Essays by various authors. pp. 226.
Lond. 1892. 8°. 4355. aaa. 9.

LITURGIES. England, *Church of.* Altar Book :
containing the Order of Holy Communion, with
additions from the Sarum Missal. pp. 234.
Lond. 1894. fol. 3406. f. 28.

—— *Ritual and Ceremonial Books.* Catechism
on the Communion Service. pp. 29.
Oxf. 1892. 32°. Pam. 11.

—— Rome, *Church of. Missals.* The Stranger's
guide at High Mass. pp. 43. *Lond.* 1890. 24°.
3366. c. 12.

LOBSTEIN (P.) La doctrine de la Sainte Cène.
pp. 206. *Lausanne,* 1889. 8°. 4325. cc. 15.

x

EUCHARIST.—Prayers, etc.—*continued.*

FRANCIS (J. L.) Office for use at Classes for the Instruction of Communicants. pp. 10.
Lond. 1895. 12°.   3457. bb. 63. (7.)

HALLET (F.) Explanation of the prayers and ceremonies of the Mass. pp. 83.
Lond, 1895. 16°.   3477. a. 4.

H., C. J. The Great Christian service. pp. 32.
Lond. 1894. 8°.   Pam. 75.

HUNT (A. L.) The King's Table of blessing.
pp. 144. *Lond.* 1893. 8°.   4324. a. 26.

L., C. Short meditations on the Holy Eucharist.
pp. 128. *Lond.* 1894. 32°.   4324. a. 31.

LEONARD, *Saint.* Prayers for Mass. pp. 56.
Lond. 1893. 24°.   3456. df. 39. (2.)

LERCARI (X.) Jesus in the Blessed Sacrament.
pp. 92. *Lond.* 1893. 32°.   4324. a. 27.

—— Helps to worship; Manual for Holy Communion. pp. 108. *Oxf.* 1888. 16°. 3456. df. 3.

LORD'S SUPPER. The Blessed Sacrament. Preparation, attendance, etc. pp. 133.
Oxf. 1893. 8°.   4324. aaa. 9.

—— A Year of Eucharists. Suggestions for prayer. pp 105. *Lond.* 1891. 8°. 4327. aaa. 9.

—— Office of preparation for Holy Communion.
pp. 8. *Lond.* 1894. 16°.   Pam. 75.

MOULE (H. C. G.) The Cup of the Covenant.
pp. 16. *Lond.* 1890. 16°.   Pam. 77.

—— At the Holy Communion. pp. 180.
Lond. 1892. 8°.   4324. a. 13.

PAGANI (G. B.) Devotion to the holy Sacrament. pp. 148. *Lond.* 1892. 12°. 4324. aaa 10.

RUSSELL (M.) At home near the Altar. pp. 83.
Lond. 1893. 8°.   4324. e. 11.

SHARPE (G. H.) Easter thoughts for Holy Communion. pp. 16. *Lond,* 1892. 16°. Pam. 77.

SKEY (F. C.) A Round of Eucharists. pp. 63.
Oxf. 1895. 8°.   4324. bb. 12.

STAVERT (A. A.) Preparations for rightly receiving the Holy Communion. 2 pt.
Lond. 1892. 12°.   3457. bb. 63. (5.)

WELLS (J.) My First Communion. pp. 80.
Lond. 1894. 8°.   4429. de. 41.

WOTHERSPOON (H. J.) The Divine Service. Eucharistic office. pp. 30. *Glasg.* 1893. 8°.
    3408. bbb. 35.

See also LITURGIOLOGY: MEDITATIONS: PRAYERS.

EUCHRE.
BOUGHER, *Lieut.* Euchre : its methods and maxims. pp. 16. *Lond.* 1889. 32°.
    7915. de. 16. (2.)

CAVENDISH. Pocket guide to Euchre. pp. 22.
Lond. 1890. 16°.   7915. de. 17. (4.)
See also CARDS.

EUPHRATES.
NERSES, *Patriarch of Armenia.* Promenade sur les bords de l'Euphrate. pp. 24.
Rochefort-s.-M. 1891. 8°.   Pam. 88.

EURE, Department.
Inventaire des archives départementales. Eure. Archives ecclésiastiques. pp. 364. 1886. 4°. Collection des inventaires.
    1815. b, *etc.*

BOIVIN-CHAMPEAUX (L.) Notices sur la Révolution dans le département de l'Eure. 2 vol.
Évreux, 1893, 94. 8°.   9231. k. 4.

See also NORMANDY: PERCHE: VEXIN.

EUROPE. [*See note on page* 1.]

History.

EUROPEAN HISTORY. Cartoons of European History. *Lond.* 1891, *etc.* fol. Tab. 11747. a. (46.)

FYFFE (C. A.) History of modern Europe.
pp. 1088. *Lond.* 1895. 8°.   9080. e. 18.

HASSALL (A.) Periods of European history.
Lond. 1893, *etc.* 8°.   9073. aaa.

EUROPE.—History—*continued.*

JACKSON (L.) Ten Centuries of European progress. pp. 364. *Lond.* 1891. 8°. 9080. bbb. 22.

LAVISSE (E.) General view of the political History of Europe. pp. 188. *Lond.* 1891. 8°.
    9073. cc. 4.

LORENZ (O.) Genealogischer Hand- und Schul-Atlas. pp. 43. *Berl.* 1892. 8°. 9914. bb. 12.

OMAN (C. W. C.) Europe. 476–918. pp. 532.
1895. 8°. HASSALL (A.) Periods of European History. Period I.   9073. aaa.

PEUTZ (H. G.) Staatengeschichte des Abendlandes im Mittelalter. 2 Bde. 1885–87. 8°.
ONCKEN (W.) Allgemeine Geschichte.
Hauptabth. II. Th. 6.   2068. (12.)

EMERTON (E.) Mediæval Europe. 814–1300.
pp. 607. *Bost.* 1894. 8°.   9073. aaa. 17.

ADAMS (G. B.) Civilization during the Middle Ages. pp. 463. *Lond.* 1894. 8°. 9073. c. 2.

KLEINPAUL (R.) Das Mittelalter. Bilder aus dem Leben aller Stände in Europa.
Leipz. 1893, *etc.* 8°.   7709. h.

BOURGEOIS (É.) Manuel historique de Politique étrangère. *Paris,* 1892, *etc.* 8°. 8009. aaa.

PHILIPPSON (M.) Westeuropa im Zeitalter von Philipp II., Elisabeth und Heinrich IV. 2 pt.
1882, 83. 8°. ONCKEN (W.) Allgemeine Geschichte. Hauptabth. III. Th. 2. 2068. (18.)

WAKEMAN (H. O.) Europe. 1598–1715.
pp. 394. 1894. 8°. HASSALL (A.) Periods of European History. Period 5. 9073. aaa.

MELIN ( ) Histoire de l'Europe de 1610 à 1789. pp. 736. *Moulins,* 1890. 8°. 9076. ccc. 7.

HAUMANT (É.) La Guerre du Nord. 1655–60.
Paris, 1893. 8°.   9078. ff. 31.

WEBER (O.) Der Friede von Utrecht. pp. 485.
Gotha, 1891. 8°.   9077. ccc. 10.

BROGLIE (J. V. A. de) *Duke,* Maurice de Saxe et le Marquis d'Argenson. 2 vol.
Paris, 1893. 12°.   010663. f. 2.

LEGRELLE (A.) Notes et documents sur la paix de Ryswick. pp. 136. *Lille,* 1894. 8°.
    9078. g. 16.

BROGLIE (A. L. V. C. de) *Duke.* La Paix d'Aix-la-Chapelle, 1748. pp. 346. *Paris,* 1895. 12°.
    9078. ee. 39.

ROSE (J. H.) Century of continental History, 1780–1880. pp. 408. *Lond.* 1895. 8°.
    9078. ce. 40.

LUMBROSO (A.) Saggio di una Bibliografia per servire alla storia dell' epoca napoleonica.
Modena, 1894, *etc.* 8°.   011900. e.

CORRÉARD (F.) Histoire contemporaine de l'Europe, 1789–1889. pp. 832. *Paris,* 1892. 8°.
    9080. e. 1.

GUÉROULT (G.) Le Centenaire de 1789. Évolution de l'Europe depuis cent ans. pp. 399.
Paris, 1889. 12°.   9225. aaa. 20.

PELLETAN (C.) Les guerres de la Révolution.
pp. 201. *Paris,* 1894. 12°.   9226. bb. 38.

OMPTEDA (C. F. W. v.) A Hanoverian-English Officer a hundred years ago. Memoirs of Baron Ompteda. pp. 320. *Lond.* 1892. 8°. 010707. ee. 9.

OMPTEDA (L. F. C. C.) *Baron.* Irrfahrten eines mittelstaatlichen Diplomaten. pp. 435.
Leipz. 1894. 8°.   9080. g. 8.

ZWIEDINECK-SUEDENHORST (H. v.) Erzherzog Johann von Österreich im Feldzuge von 1809.
pp. 200. *Graz,* 1892. 8°.   10704. f. 33.

JOHN BAPTIST JOSEPH FABIAN SEBASTIAN, *Archduke of Austria.* Aus dem Tagebuch Erzherzog Johanns von Oesterreich, 1810–1815. pp. 251.
Innsbruck, 1891. 8°.   9314. cc. 9.

EUROPE.—History—*continued.*

BLEIBTREU (C.) Der russische Feldzug 1812. pp. 143. *Leipz.* 1893. 8°.   9079. g. 14.

SCHIMPFF (G. v.). 1813. Napoleon in Sachsen. pp. 278. *Dresden,* 1894. 8°.   9080. k. 9.

FANE (P. A. W.) *Countess of Westmorland.* Letters of Lady Burghersh, from Germany and France, 1813–14. pp. 241. *Lond.* 1893. 8°.
          010920. e. 27.

ROLOFF (G.) Politik und Kriegführung während des Krieges von 1814. pp. 92. *Berl.* 1891. 8°.
          9080. bbb. 33.

WEIL (M.) La Campagne de 1814 d'après les documents des Archives à Vienne. *Paris,* 1891, *etc.* 8°.   9080. cc. 11.

DEBIDOUR (A.) Histoire diplomatique de l'Europe, 1814–1878. 2 tom. *Lond.* 1891. 8°.
          9079. h. 11.

STERN (A.) Geschichte Europas, 1815–71. *Berl.* 1894, *etc.* 8°.   9079. k.

LORD (J.) Modern European statesmen. pp. 623. *N.Y.* 1891, 8°.   9080. cc. 12.

LOFTUS (*Lord* A. W. F. S.) Diplomatic Reminiscences, 1837–62. 2 vol. *Lond.* 1892. 8°.
          10815. e. 12.

CROWE (*Sir* J. A.) Reminiscences of thirty-five years of my life. pp. 445. *Lond.* 1895. 8°.
          10815. e. 19.

LA VALLÉE DE RARÉCOURT (G. de) *Marquis de Pimodan.* Souvenirs du général Marquis de Pimodan, 1847–49. 2 tom. *Lond.* 1891. 8°.
          010661. f. 42.

LINTON (W. J.) European Republicans. pp. 344. *Lond.* 1893. 8°.   10601. ee. 16.

ROTHAN (G.) L'Europe et l'avènement du Second Empire. pp. 439. *Paris,* 1892. 12°.
          9076. ccc. 16.

POLITIKOS. Sovereigns and courts of Europe. pp. 439. *Lond.* 1891. 8°.   10603. de. 7.

SCHLICHTEGROLL (C. F. v.) and ZOLLER (E. v.) Portrait-Gallerie der regierenden Fürsten und Fürstinnen Europas. *Stuttgart,* 1890, *etc.* fol.
          1764. c.

EUROPEAN COURTS. Liebes- und Eheleben an europäischen Höfen. pp. 253. *Berl.* 1893. 8°.
          10703. de. 38.

See also CRIMEAN WAR: CRUSADES; FRANCE, *Wars of the Revolution.* HISTORY: TREATIES: THIRTY YEARS' WAR: WATERLOO, *etc.*

Politics, etc.

ALVISI (G. G.) Intenti dei diversi Stati d'Europa nelle questioni orientali. pp. 596. *Firenze,* 1889–90. 8°.   8026. aaa. 34.

APPLETON (L.) Foreign Policy of Europe. pp. 408. *Lond.* 1892. 8°.   9076. ee. 13.

BLOCK (M.) L'Europe politique et sociale. pp. 586. *Paris,* 1892. 8°.   8008. f. 5.

CESTARO (F. P.) Frontiere e nazioni irredente. pp. 183. *Torino,* 1891. 8°.   8026. c. 5.

DIPLOMATE. Les grandes puissances militaires devant la France et l'Allemagne. pp. 266. *Paris,* 1893. 8°.   8026. ee. 27.

EUROPEAN ANXIETY. Die europäische Angst und die neue Politik. pp. 102. *Dresden,* 1890. 8°.   8026. f. 14.

GRAND-CARTERET (J.) Crispi, Bismarck et la Triple-Alliance en caricatures. pp. 319. *Paris,* 1891. 8°.   012314. e. 76.

HENRY (L. E.) Europe in 1882 : out of the shadow. pp. 98. *Wellington College,* 1882. 8°.
          8051. de. 20.

KERR (H.) Will there be Peace or War in Europe ? pp. 8. *Lond.* 1892. 8°.   8026. ee. 24. (15.)

LABBÉE (E·) Les États-Unis de l'Europe. pp. 213. *Paris,* 1895. 8°.   8026. aa. 50.

EUROPE.—Politics—*continued.*

MAC DARGUS (J.) Who are the Disturbers of the peace in Europe ? pp. 248. *Lond.* 1892. 8°.
          8026. bb. 33.

MAZADE (C. de) L'Europe et les neutralités. pp. 117. *Paris,* 1893. 12°.   8026. bbb. 36.

P., J. La Triple Alliance en Europe. pp. 88. *Paris,* 1890. 8°.   8026. bbb. 32.

ROBOLSKY (H.) Die mitteleuropäische Friedensliga. pp. 304. *Leipz.* 1891. 8°.   8026. f. 15.

SCHLIEF (E.) Der Friede in Europa. pp. 511. *Leipz.* 1892. 8°.   8026. f. 19.

SENTUPÉRY (L.) L'Europe politique en 1892. *Paris,* 1893, *etc.* 8°.   8026. i.

TARNER (G. E.) A future Roman Empire. pp. 62. *Lond.* 1895. 8°.   8026. bbb. 41.

V., D. Berlin—Wien—Rom. pp. 273. *Leipz.* 1892. 8°.   8026. f. 18.

VIGOUREUX (C. E.) L'Avenir de l'Europe. pp. 308. *Paris,* 1891. 8°.   8026. bb. 24.

WICKERSHEIMER (E.) L'Europe en 1890. pp. 316. *Paris,* 1890. 18°.   8026. bb. 28.

DÉROULÈDE (P.) Désarmement. pp. 16. *Paris,* 1891. 8°.   8026. ee. 25. (6.)

DÉSARMEMENT. Le désarmement général. pp. 16. *Paris,* 1891. 8°.   8026. ee. 25. (7.)

DU PUY (C.) How can Europe disarm ? pp. 8. *Lond.* 1890. 8°.   8026. ee. 24. (6.)

See also WAR *and* PEACE *and under the sub-heading* Politics, Foreign, *of each country.*

Topography.

EUROPE. Picturesque Europe. *Lond.* 1892, *etc.* 4°.   1127.

NEAR HOME. Near Home : or, Europe described. pp. 535. *Lond.* 1888. 8°.   10106. de. 2.

RECLUS (J. J. É.) Hégémonie de l'Europe. pp. 13. *Bruxelles,* 1894. 8°.   Pam. 67.

WEST. "From West to East." pp. 102. *Lond.* 1894. 8°.   10107. aa. 10.

EVANS (T.) Geography of Europe. pp. 32. *Lond.* 1888. 8°.   10106. df. 17. (2.)

LANIER (L.) L'Europe (sans la France). Lectures de géographie. pp. 992. *Paris,* 1895, 8°.
          10107. aa. 11.

LAWSON (W.) Geography of Europe. pp. 48. *Edinb.* 1894. 8°.   Pam. 91.

APPLETON (D.) European Guide book. 2 pt. *N.Y.* 1890. 8°.   2352. a.

EUROPE. Useful notes for Travellers in Europe. pp. 79. *N.Y.* 1892. 16°.   Pam. 91.

GIDDINS (G. H.) The Christian Traveller's continental handbook. pp. 162. *Lond.* 1895. 8°.   10108. aa. 41.

KING (E.) Cassell's Pocket-guide to Europe. pp. 505. *Lond.* 1893. 8°.   10106. a. 5.

KNOX (T. W.) Pocket guide for Europe. pp. 223. *N.Y.* 1891. 16°.   10108. b. 10.

MEUGENS, *afterwards* BELL (N.) Tourist's Art guide to Europe. pp. 328. *Lond.* 1893. 8°.
          10107. aa. 9.

MONCRIEFF (A. R. H.) Where to go Abroad. pp. 466. *Lond.* 1893. 8°.   10108. b. 12.

TIEDEMAN (H.) The Continent by Queenboro' viâ Flushing ! pp. 566. *Lond.* 1894. 8°.
          10106. ccc. 33.

AMERICANS. Americans in Europe. pp. 241. *Lond.* 1893. 8°.   10408. bbb. 31.

BISHOP (W. H.) House-hunter in Europe. pp. 370. *N.Y.* 1893. 8°.   10106. dd. 4.

BLAKE (M. E.) Summer holiday in Europe. pp. 203. *Dublin,* 1890. 8°.   10106. ee. 4.

x 2

EVOLUTION—*continued.*

MERKEL (F.) and BONNET (R.) Referate und Beiträge zur Anatomie und Entwickelungsgeschichte. *Wiesbaden,* 1891, *etc.* 8°.   7419 g.

MEUNIER (V.) Sélection et perfectionnement animal. pp. 224. 1894. 8°. Encyclopédie des aide-mémoire.   8709. g.

MITCHELL (H. W.) Evolution of life. pp. 460. *N.Y.* 1891. 8°.   7006. c. 9.

MOLL (J. W.) De invloed van Darwin's afstammingsleer op de Botanie. pp. 29. *Te Groningen,* 1890. 8°   Pam. 1.

NAEGELI (C. W. v.) Mechanisch-physiologische Theorie der Abstammungslehre. pp. 822. *München,* 1884. 8°.   7002. f. 19.

NATURE. Nature's Method in the Evolution of life. pp. 88. *Lond.* 1894. 8°.   7006. bb. 19.

ORR (H. B.) Theory of Development and Heredity. pp. 255. *N.Y.* 1893. 8°. 7006. c. 14.

OSBORN (H. F.) From the Greeks to Darwin. Development of the evolution idea. pp. 259. 1894. 8°. Ac. New York. *Columbia College.* Biological Series. No. 1.   7002. e.

PARKYN (E. A.) Darwin; his work and influence. pp. 49. *Lond.* 1894. 8°. 7006. e. 23.

PASCOE (F. P.) Darwinian theory of the Origin of species. pp. 130. *Lond.* 1890. 8°.   7006. bbb. 27.

PFEFFER (G.) Versuch über die Entwickelung der jetzigen Verbreitungsverhältnisse unserer Tierwelt. pp. 62. *Hamburg,* 1891. 8°. Pam. 42.

POCOCK (W. W.) Darwinism a fallacy. pp. 160. *Lond.* 1891. 8°.   7006. b. 46.

PRIEM (F.) L'Évolution des formes animales avant l'apparition de l'homme. pp. 383. *Paris,* 1891. 8°.   7006. bb. 31.

QUATREFAGES DE BREAU (J. L. A. de) Les Émules de Darwin. 2 vol. *Paris.* 1894. 8°. 7006. e. 24.

ROMANES (G. J.) Darwin, and after Darwin. pp. 460. *Lond.* 1893. 8°.   7006. e. 18.

SPENCER (H.) Inadequacy of Natural Selection. pp. 69. *Lond.* 1893. 8°.   8462 d. 20. (7.)

SPITZER (H.) Beiträge zur Descendenztheorie. pp. 538. *Leipz.* 1886. 8°.   7006. f. 18.

STIRLING (J. H.) Darwinism. pp. 358. *Edinb.* 1894. 8°.   7006. e. 22.

SYME (D.) On the Modifications of organisms. pp. 164. *Melbourne,* 1891. 8°.   7004. c. 7.

VARIGNY (H. de) Experimental Evolution. pp. 271. 1892. 8°. Nature Series. 2244. c. 9.

WALLACE (A. R.) Natural Selection and tropical nature. pp. 492. *Lond.* 1891. 8°. 2250. a. 20.

WEISMANN (A.) Die Allmacht der Naturzüchtung. pp. 96. *Jena,* 1893. 8°.   8462. f. 38.

—— Effect of external Influences upon Development. pp. 69. *Lond.* 1894. 8°.   7006. e. 25.

ROMANES (G. J.) Examination of Weismannism. pp. 221. *Lond.* 1893. 8°.   7006. c. 13.

SPENCER (H.) A Rejoinder to Prof. Weismann. pp. 29. *Lond.* 1893. 8°.   7002. e. 11. (15.)

—— Weismannism once more. pp. 24. *Lond.* 1894. 8°.   Pam. 42.

See also ANTHROPOLOGY: HEREDITY: NATURAL HISTORY: ZOOLOGY.

Christianity and Evolution.

See CHRISTIANITY.

Philosophy, Politics, etc., and Evolution.

Ac. Brooklyn. *Ethical Association.* Evolution in Science, philosophy, and art. pp. 475. *N.Y.* 1891. 8°.   7006. e. 20.

CROLL (J.) Philosophical basis of evolution. pp. 204. *Lond.* 1890. 8°.   7006. e. 8.

EVOLUTION.—*continued.*

FOUILLÉE (A.) L'Évolutionnisme des Idées-forces. pp. 303. *Paris,* 1890. 8°.   8463. de. 43.

FUERST (H.) Die neuen Ideale. pp. 133. *Dresden,* 1893. 8°.   8462. e. 23.

MARICHAL (H.) Essai de Philosophie évolutive. pp. 177. *Brux.* 1891. 8°.   7006. h. 2.

WILSON (J. M.) Evolution as a reply to Materialism, pessimism and agnosticism. pp. 30. *Lond.* 1892. 8°.   4421. aa. 58. (1.)

WINCHELL (A.) Speculative consequences of Evolution. pp. 24. 1888. 8°. Ac. Ann Arbor. *University of Michigan.* Philosophical Papers. Ser. 2. No. 2.   Ac. 2685 17.

HUXLEY (*Right Hon.* T. H.) Evolution and Ethics. *Lond.* 1893. 8°.   8409. f. 37.

WILLIAMS (C. M.) Review of Systems of Ethics founded on the theory of Evolution. pp. 581. *Lond.* 1893. 8°.   8409. k. 15.

GAILHARD (G.) Darwinisme et Spiritualisme. pp. 371. *Paris,* 1891. 8°.   7006. bbb. 31.

AMMON (O.) Der Darwinismus gegen die Sozialdemokratie. pp. 112. *Hamburg,* 1891. 8°.   8277. ce. 28. (1.)

RITCHIE (D. G.) Darwinism and politics. pp. 141. *Lond.* 1891. 8°.   08276. e. 67.

BONARDI (E.) Evoluzionismo e socialismo. pp. 56. *Firenze,* 1894. 8°.   7006. f. 16.

BUECHNER (F. C. C. L.) Darwinismus und Sozialismus. pp. 72. *Leipz.* 1894. 8°. Pam. 82.

ÉVREUX. AVRIL DE BUREY (R. A. L.) *Viscount.* Les Archives héraldiques d'Évreux. pp. 376. *Évreux,* 1890. 4°.   9902. i. 30.

FERRAY (E.) Le trésor militaire d'Évreux. pp. 21. *Paris,* 1892. 8°.   Pam. 44.

EWE LANGUAGE. *See* AFRICAN LANGUAGES.

EXAMINATIONS.

Board of Trade. *See infra : Marine.*

Civil Service, Home, India, *etc.*

ATKINSON (R. W.) Popular guide to Professions. pp. 131. *Lond.* 1895. 8°.   8007. bbb. 4.

G. B. & I. *Civil Service Commissioners.* Rules and regulations respecting examinations for the Civil Service, the Army, the Navy, *etc.* pp. 136. *Lond.* 1891. 8°.   8009. dd. 7.

—— Home Civil Service. Statistical tables relating to Examinations. *Lond.* 1884, *etc.* 8°.   8009. dd. 6.

—— Seven Years' Examinations for second-class Clerkships. pp. 233. *Lond.* 1892. 8°.   8530. h. 32.

BEARD (W. S.) Guide to Employment for boys. Information respecting clerkships in the Civil Service, *etc.* pp. 148. *Lond.* 1890. 8°.   8310. a. 27.

CHOICE. Choice of a Profession. Guide to Government and other appointments. pp. 27. *Oxf.* 1891. 8°.   8304. aa. 16. (10.)

G. B. & I. *Civil Service.* Guide to employment in the Civil Service. pp. 112, *Lond.* 1894. 8°.   8008. a. 2.

JOHNSTON (R.) Civil Service guide. pp. 223. *Lond.* 1893. 8°.   8006. aaa. 11.

MACNAMARA (N. C.) Regulations as to physical defects which disqualify candidates for admission into the Civil Service, *etc.* pp. 31. *Lond.* 1894. 8°.   Pam. 39.

PITMAN (*Sir* I.) Civil Service Guide. pp. 77. *Lond.* 1893. 8°.   8008. bbb. 22.

P.P. *London.* Clark's Civil Service Annual and calendar. *Lond.* 1894, *etc.* 8°.   P.P. 2186. kpa.

EXAMINATIONS.— Civil Service, etc.—
continued.

SAVILL (S.)   The Civil Service coach.   pp. 208.
1892. 8°.   Civil Service Series.   2238. a. 36.

SKERRY (G. E.)   Hints to Civil Service candidates.   pp. 58.   *Lond.* 1895. 8°.   8008. b. 5.

G. B. & I.   *Civil Service Commissioners.*   Competition for the situation of Assistant in the Nautical Almanac Office.   *Lond.* 1893, *etc.* 8°.
8009. dd. 30.

—— Competition for situations as assistant Cashier in H.M. Naval Yards.
Lond. 1893, *etc.* 8°.   8009. d. 30.

—— Competition for the situation of Assistant, Board of Agriculture.   *Lond.* 1895. *etc.* 8°.
8009. dd. 28.

—— Competitions for situations as Assistant in the British Museum.   pp. 72.   *Lond.* 1891. 8°.
8009. d. 3.

—— Competitions for situations as Clerk in the Ecclesiastical Commission.   *Lond.* 1893, *etc.* 8°.
8009. dd. 3.

—— Limited competition of candidates nominated to the situation of Assistant at the Royal Observatory.   pp. 22.   *Lond.* 1892. 8°.   8009. d.

—— Competition for appointments as Inspector of Factories.   *Lond.* 1890, *etc.* 8°.   8009. dd.

—— Competition for appointment as Inspector of Mines.   pp. 12.   *Lond.* 1892. 8°.   8009. d. 10.

—— Competition for situation of Clerk in the Legacy Duty Office.   *Lond.* 1893, *etc.* 8°.
8009. d. 14.

—— Competition for situations as assistant Surveyor of Taxes in the Inland Revenue Department.   *Lond.* 1892, *etc.* 8°.   8009. d. 13.

—— Competition for the situation of assistant Librarian at the Museum of Practical Geology.   *Lond.* 1895, *etc.* 8°.   8009. dd. 31.

—— Competition for situations as junior Examiner in H.M. Office of Works.   pp. 48.
Lond. 1891. 8°.   8009. d. 16.

—— Specimens of Papers set to candidates for situations in the Post Office.
Lond. 1893, *etc.* 8°.   8009. d. 20.

—— Competition for female Sorterships.
Lond. 1885, *etc.* 8°.   8009. dd. 2.

—— Competition for a Clerkship in the Judicial Department of the Privy Council.
Lond. 1893, *etc.* 8°.   8009. d. 21.

—— Competition for Clerkships in the Public Record Office.   pp. 70.   *Lond.* 1891. 8°. 8009. d. 22.

—— Competitions for Assistants in the Science and Art Department.   pp. 27.   *Lond.* 1892. 8°.
8009. d. 25.

—— Examination for situations as assistant Surveyor in the Royal Engineer Civil Staff.
pp. 38.   *Lond.* 1891. 8°.   8009. d. 27.

—— Competition for situations as Clerk in the Dublin Metropolitan Police Courts.
Lond. 1893, *etc.* 8°.   8009. d. 32.

—— Examinations for promotion in the Dublin Metropolitan Police Force.   *Lond.* 1895, *etc.* 8°.
8009. dd. 29.

—— Competition for situations as assistant Surveyor in the Public Works Office, Ireland.
Lond. 1893, *etc.* 8°.   8009. d. 29.

—— Competition for the situation of Valuer and Surveyor, Ireland.   *Lond.* 1893, *etc.* 8°.   8009. d.

SATYANĀTHA (S.)   Four years in an English University, with a chapter on the Indian Civil Service Examination.   pp. 120.
Madras, 1890. 8°.   8366. aaa. 25.

G. B. & I.   *Civil Service Commissioners.*   Examination for appointments in the India Forest Service.   *Lond.* 1885, *etc.* 8°.   8009. d.

EXAMINATIONS—*continued.*

Holy Orders.

HUGHES (M. J.)   Guide to preparation for Cambridge and Oxford preliminary Examination of candidates for Holy Orders.   pp. 47.
Lond. 1892. 8°.   4499. bbb. 10.

Legal.

CLARK (E. C.)   The Law Examinations.
pp. 60.   *Camb.* 1891. 8°.   8304. a. 8. (7.)

A., M., and B., LL.   Guide to the Bar.
pp. 215.   *Lond.* 1893. 8°.   6190. aa. 30.

GIBSON (A.)   Intermediate Law Examination made easy.   pp. 548.   *Lond.* 1893. 8°. 2230. d. 6.

—— and WELDON (A.)   Intermediate Examination digest.   pp. 332.   *Lond.* 1894. 8°. 6190. df. 20.

GOVER (J. M.)   London Intermediate Laws guide.   pp. 46.   1891. 8°.   Tutorial Series. 12205. c. 31.

—— Intermediate Laws.   Roman Law Papers, Jurisprudence papers.   3 pt.   1891. 8°.   Tutorial Series.   12205. c. 32.

INDERMAUR (J.)   Articled Clerk's guide to the Intermediate Examination.   pp. 255.
Lond. 1894. 8°.   6146. d. 19.

GIBSON (A.)   Aids to the Final.   pp. 79.
Lond. 1895. 8°.   6146. aa. 40.

HALLILAY (R.)   Digest of the questions at the final pass examination of Articled Clerks.
pp. 867.   *Lond.* 1895. 8°.   6146. d. 21.

INDERMAUR (J.)   Articled Clerk's guide to the Final Examination.   pp. 112.   *Lond.* 1894. 8°.
2230. c. 4.

STIFF (H. W.)   New guide for Articled Clerks.
pp. 239.   *Lond.* 1895. 8°.   6190. a. 24.

LAW AGENT.   Examination Questions for students preparing for the Examination in Law, Scotland.
pp. 131.   *Edinb.* 1894. 8°.   6583. cc. 8.

PLEADER.   Guide to the study of Law.   pp. 223.
Lucknow, 1890. 8°.   5318. aaa. 4.

BOMBAY, *Attorneys.*   Questions at the Attorneys' Examination, 1892.   pp. 12.   *Bomb.* 1892. 8°.
6146. bbb. 26. (2.)

Marine.

G. B. & I.   *Board of Trade.*   Regulations relating to examinations of Masters and Mates.
pp. 104.   *Lond.* 1888. 8°.   8807. b. 55.

ALLEN (L.)   Guide book to the examination for extra Master.   pp. 255.   *Dundee*, 1893. 8°.
8805 c. 81.

NEWTON (J.)   Guide to the Board of Trade examinations.   pp. 193.   *Lond.* 1892. 8°.
8807. dd. 32.

REED (T.)   Guide to the Local Marine Board examinations.   pp. 371.   *Sunderland*, 1891. 8°.
8807. dd. 23.

—— Key.   pp. 250.   *Sunderland*, 1891. 8°.
8807. dd. 22.

G. B. & I.   *Board of Trade.*   Regulations relating to the examinations of engineers.
pp. 45.   *Lond.* 1890. 8°.   Pam. 43.

—— Examination of Engineers.   pp. 20.
Lond. 1893. 8°.   Pam. 43.

DAVIES (E. J. M.)   Solutions to Questions given at the Extra First Class Engineers' Examinations.   pp. 274.   *Lond.* 1890. 8°. 8768. cc. 15.

THORN (W. H.)   Engineers' Hand-book to Board of Trade examinations.   pp. 639.
Sunderland, 1895. 8°.   8768. dd. 17.

—— Key.   pp. 336.   *Sunderland*, 1895. 8°.
8768. dd. 8.

See also infra : Military and Naval.

Medical.

MACLEOD (M.)   Edinburgh University.   Medical Preliminary examination papers.   2 pt.
Edinb. 1889. 8°.   8367. aa. 16.

EXAMINATIONS.—Medical—*continued.*

SMITH (W. R.) University of Edinburgh. Examination Questions in chemistry, physiology, materia medica, anatomy, etc.. 6 pt.
Edinb. 1892. 8°. 8366. aa. 25.

Ac. London. *R. College of Physicians.* Papers set for the examinations for the Diploma in Public Health. *Lond.* 1890, *etc.* 8°.
Ac. 3848/7.

WALSH (D.) Questions and Answers on materia medica, medicine, midwifery, pathology and forensic medicine. pp. 96. *Lond.* 1892. 8°.
7321. aaaa. 26.

LONDON. *St. Mary's Hospital.* Regulations for preliminary examinations. *Lond.* 1895, *etc.* 8°.
7688. c.

Ac. London. *R. College of Surgeons.* Papers set for the examinations for the Diploma of Fellow and Licence in Dental Surgery.
Lond. 1894, *etc.* 8°. Ac. 3848/8.

SLEMAN (R. R.) Papers set for examinations for the qualification of Licentiate of the Society of Apothecaries. pp. 25. *Lond.* 1892. 8°.
07305. h. 19. (12.)

Military and Naval.

G. B. & I. *Civil Service Commissioners.* Rules respecting Exams. for the Army and Navy.
pp. 136. *Lond.* 1891. 8°. 8009. dd. 7.

—— *Army.* Regulations under which Commissions may be obtained by University Candidates. pp. 8. *Lond.* 1893. 8°. 8830. d. 11. (15.)

—— *Civil Service Commissioners.* Specimens of papers set at the Army preliminary examination 1882–87. *Lond.* 1888. 8°. 8831. f. 20.

—— Specimens of Papers set at the Army preliminary examination, 1886–93. *Lond.* 1893. 8°.
8831. aaa. 55.

—— *Army.* Regulations under which Commissions may be obtained by Officers of the Militia. pp. 12. *Lond.* 1891. 8°.
8831. f. 32. (5.)

—— Questions set at the Militia competitive examination, 1891. pp. 32.
Lond. 1891. 8°. 8831. l. 8. (8.)

—— *Civil Service Commissioners.* Literary examination of Officers of the Auxiliary Forces, for Commissions in the Army.
Lond. 1889, *etc.* 8°. 8009. d.

—— *Army.* Report on result of examination of Officers in Tactics, Military Law, Fortification, Artillery, *etc. Lond.* 1892, *etc.* 8°. 8830. d.

Ac. Woolwich. *R. Military Academy.* Regulations respecting admission. pp. 8.
Lond. 1893. 8°. 8830. aaa. 58.

—— Woolwich Mathematical papers, 1885–94.
Lond. 1895. 8°. 8533. e. 44.

SANDHURST. *R. Military College.* Regulations respecting examinations for admission. pp. 16.
Lond. 1887. 8°. 8830. bb. 25.

YOUNGHUSBAND (G. J.) The Queen's Commission : how to prepare for it, *etc.* pp. 254.
Lond. 1891. 8°. 8824. c. 15.

MACNAMARA (N. C.) Regulations as to physical defects which disqualify candidates, *etc.* pp. 31.
Lond. 1894. 8°. 7306. e. 25. (13.)

BANNATYNE (J. M.) Guide to Professional examinations in the Infantry. *Paris,* 1892, *etc.* 8°.
8829. aaa. 31.

PRATT (S. C.) Guide to Promotion. An aid to officers. *Lond.* 1892, *etc.* 8°. 8831. f. 39.

WRIGHT (S.) Non-Commissioned Officer's examiner. pp. 63. *Lond.* 1895. 8°. 8823. g. 30.

BEARD (W. S.) Guide to Employment. Appointments in the Royal Navy, *etc. Lond.* 1890. 8°.
8310. a. 27.

EXAMINATIONS.—Military, etc.—*cont.*

WALKER (T. P.) Seamanship examination questions of the Training Squadron, *etc.* pp. 49.
Portsmouth, 1894. 8°. 8806. ccc. 11.

Musical. *See* MUSIC.

Scholastic and Educational.

CLOUGH (G. B.) Guide to the Scholarship examination. pp. 316. *Lond.* 1890. 8°.
8364. c. 86.

EVANS (T.) Scholarship examination questions, 1883–91, *etc.* pp. 110. *Lond.* 1891. 8°.
8503. c. 34.

GEDDES (R. F.) and ROUTER (S. H.) Queen's Scholarship examination questions, 1888–93.
pp. 213. 1894. 12°. Brown's School Series.
12204. b.

MOFFATT (W.) Queen's Scholarship questions, July 1894. pp. 40. *Lond.* 1894. 8°. Pam. 17.

SCHOLARSHIP QUESTIONS. Scholarship questions 1887–90. *Lond.* 1891. 8°. 12201. ee. 15.

—— Scholarship Questions, 1892. pp. 31.
Lond. 1893. 8°. 12201. ee. 17.

SMITH (A. C.) Guide to Queen's Scholarship examination. pp. 118. *Lond.* 1894. 8°.
8364. aaa. 49.

GREAT BRITAIN. *Committee on Education.* Four Years' Certificate questions, 1884–87. pp. 208.
Lond. 1888. 8°. 8364. aaa. 46.

—— Questions proposed to candidates for admission into Training Colleges, *etc.*
Lond. 1890, *etc.* 8°. 8365. bbb.

PUPIL TEACHERS. Six years' Pupil Teachers' questions, 1886–91. pp. 188. *Lond.* 1892. 8°.
8308. aaa. 27.

—— Book of examination questions for the use of Pupil-Teachers. pp. 196. *Lond.* 1895. 8°.
012200. gg. 4.

LONDON. *City and Guilds Institute for the Advancement of Technical Education.* Technological Examinations. pp. 4. *Lond.* 1892. 8°.
8367. b. 16.

GREAT BRITAIN. *Committee on Education.* An examination under the New Code, 1891. pp. 46.
Lond. 1891. 8°. 8304. aa. 16. (12.)

GUIDE. Guide to the Elementary Examinations and standard v. pp. 72. *Lovedale,* 1892. 8°.
12204. b. 17.

Science and Art Department.

BURGESS (A. T.) The "Classified" Series of Science and Art questions. pp. 16.
Lond. 1894. 8°. Pam. 39.

GREAT BRITAIN. *Department of Science and Art.* Examination Papers with answers.
Blackburn, 1893. *etc.* 8°. 7958. aa.

—— Art Examination papers.
Lond. 1892, *etc.* 8°. 7959. cc.

—— South Kensington Questions in physiology, magnetism, electricity, agriculture, chemistry, *etc.* 5 pt. *Lond.* 1869. 8°. 8703. aaa. 35.

HARRISON (W. J.) Blackie's Guides to the Science examinations. *Lond.* 1892, *etc.* 8°. 8703. aa.

University.

Ac. Cambridge. *University.* Examination papers for Entrance and Minor Scholarships and Exhibitions in the Colleges of Cambridge.
Camb. 1891, *etc.* 4°. 8365. f. 30.

BURN (R.) The Classical Tripos. pp. 50.
Camb. 1891. 8°. 8304. aa. 22. (1.)

Ac. Cambridge. *University.* Local Examinations. Examination for commercial certificates.
Camb. 1889, *etc.* 8°. 8367. f.

EXHIBITIONS.—Denmark—*continued.*

OLSEN (B.) Katalog over dansk Folke-museum i Kjøbenhavn. pp. 91. *Kjøbenh.* 1892. 8°.
07708. g. 27.

England.

Ac. London. *British Museum.* Guide to the Exhibition Galleries. pp. 343. *Lond.* 1895. 8°.
7702. b. 42.

FAGAN (L. A.) An easy walk through the British Museum. pp. 98. *Lond.* 1891, 8°.
7706. g. 4. (16.)

KITCHEN (J. G.) The Bible student in the British Museum. pp. 88. *Lond.* 1892. 8°.
7702. aa. 43.

LEE (W. J.) Treasures of the British Museum. pp. 79. *Lond.* 1892. 8°.   7704. a. 42.

LONDON. *National Gallery.* Catalogue of the Pictures. British and Modern schools. pp. 215. *Lond.* 1890. 8°.   7856. de. 14.

—— Catalogue of the Pictures. Foreign schools. pp. 529. *Lond.* 1890. 8°.   7856. de. 15.

—— Abridged Catalogue of the Pictures. Foreign schools. pp. 251.
Lond. 1890. 8°.   7856. de. 13.

COOK (E. T.) Popular handbook to the National Gallery. pp. 832. *Lond.* 1893. 8°. 2262. b. 1.

MONKHOUSE (W. C.) In the National Gallery. pp. 303. *Lond.* 1895. 8°.   7858. aa. 41.

Ac. London. *S. Kensington Museum.* Catalogue of the National Gallery of British Art. 2 pt. *Lond.* 1893. 8°.   7958. cc. 4.

—— Catalogue of the Prescott-Hewett gift of water-colour Paintings. pp. 8. *Lond.* 1891. 8°.
Pam. 18.

—— Catalogue of Pictures of the Dutch and Flemish Schools lent by Lord F. P. Clinton-Hope. pp. 16. *Lond.* 1891. 8°.   Pam. 18.

—— *Bethnal Green Branch Museum.* Brief guide to the various Collections. pp. 47.
Lond. 1891. 8°.   Pam. 18.

—— Catalogue of a Collection of Oil Paintings bequeathed by J. Dixon. pp. 18.
Lond. 1890. 8°.   Pam. 18.

SOANE (*Sir* J.) General description of Sir John Soane's Museum. pp. 98. *Lond.* 1893. 8°.
7705. aa. 36.

GRAVES (A.) Dictionary of Artists who have exhibited works in the principal London Exhibitions, 1760-1893. pp. 314. *Lond.* 1895. 4°.
7808. g. 21.

Ac. London. *Burlington Fine Arts Club.* Exhibition of Pictures by masters of the Netherlandish Schools of XV. and early XVI. centuries. *Lond.* 1894. 4°.   Ac. 4644 33.

—— Exhibition of Pictures of the school of Ferrara-Bologna, 1440-1540. pp. 57.
Lond. 1895. 4°.   7858. c. 25.

LONDON. *Corporation. Art Gallery.* Reproductions of Pictures presented to the Gallery by Sir J. Gilbert. pp. 32. *Lond.* 1893. 4°.
7858. cc. 3.

—— Catalogue of the loan collection of Pictures, 1892. *Lond.* 1892. 8°.   7855. f. 48.

—— Catalogue of the loan collection, 1894. pp. 126. *Lond.* 1894. 8°.   7856. aa. 47.

—— Reproductions by collotype process of some of the works in the loan Exhibition, 1894. pp. 80. *Lond.* 1894. 4°.   K.T.C. 26. b. 12.

BLACKBURN (H.) The Royal Academy Bijou. *Lond.* 1891, *etc.* 8°.   7854. aa.

P.P. London. *Magazine of Art.* Royal Academy Pictures. *Lond.* 1888, *etc.* 4°.   P.P. 1931. pci.

—— "Black & White" handbook to the Royal Academy and New Gallery Pictures.
Lond. 1893, *etc.* 8°.   7858. l.

EXHIBITIONS.—England—*continued.*

LONDON. *New Gallery.* Summer Exhibition. Catalogue. *Lond.* 1889, *etc.* 8°.   7854. aa.

—— Victorian Exhibition. 1837-87. Catalogue. pp. 219. *Lond.* 1891. 4°.   7959. b. 54.

—— Catalogue of the Exhibition of early Italian Art, 1300-1550. pp. 180.
Lond. 1893. 8°.   7959. b. 55.

—— *Grafton Galleries.* Catalogue of the Exhibition. *Lond.* 1893, *etc.* 16°. & fol.
7854. aa. & h.

—— *Hanover Gallery.* Catalogues of Exhibitions of Paintings. *Lond.* 1894, *etc.* 8°. 7854. a.

—— *New English Art Club.* Catalogue.
Lond. 1886, *etc.* 8°.   7857. b.

ROGET (J. L.) History of the "Old Water-Colour" Society. 2 vol. *Lond.* 1891. 8°.
7854. e. 35.

LONDON. *Royal Institute of Painters in Water Colours.* Catalogue of the Exhibition.
Lond. 1887, *etc.* 8°.   7858. aaa.

Ac. London. *Society of British Artists.* Exhibition of Sketches, Studies and decorative design. pp. 52. *Lond.* 1890. 16°. 7854. b. 26.

—— *Society of Painter-Etchers.* Catalogue of the Exhibition. *Lond.* 1882, *etc.* 8°. 7857. cc. 16.

TOOTH (A.) and SONS. Catalogue of the spring Exhibition Pictures. *Lond.* 1884, *etc.* 8°. 7857. c.

—— Catalogue of the winter Exhibition of Pictures. *Lond.* 1889, *etc.* 8°.   7857. cc.

LONDON. *International Horticultural Exhibition.* Catalogue of Fine Arts. pp. 45. *Leed.* 1892. 8°.
Pam. 24.

—— *Italian Exhibition,* 1888. Catalogue of Fine Art Department. pp. 80. *Lond.* 1888. 8°.
Pam. 18.

—— *Southwark Loan Picture Exhibition.* Catalogue. *Lond.* 1890, *etc.* 8°.   7854. ccc.

BIRMINGHAM. *Museum and Art Gallery.* Illustrated Catalogue of the collection of Paintings, *etc.* pp. 296. *Birmingham,* 1892, 4°. 7807. b. 11.

—— Catalogue with descriptive notes of the collection of Paintings, *etc.* pp. 60.
Birmingham, 1892. 8°.   Pam. 24.

—— Catalogue of the loan collection of. Paintings by Animal Painters. pp. 58.
Birmingham, 1892. 8°.   7855. c. 49

BRIGHTON. *Public Museum.* Report.
Brighton, 1892, *etc.* 8°.   7956. c.

BRISTOL. *Museum.* Guide. pp. 32.
Bristol, 1894. 8°.   Pam. 18.

RICHTER (J. P.) and SPARKES (J. C. L.) Catalogue of Pictures in the Dulwich College Gallery. pp. 220. *Lond.* 1880. 8°.   7856. c. 43.

SPARKES (J. C. L.) Catalogue of the Cartwright collection and other pictures at Dulwich College. pp. 52. *Lond.* 1890. 8°.   7856. c. 42.

LEEDS. *Municipal Art Gallery.* Catalogue of the Artists' spring Exhibition, 1894. pp. 115. *Leeds,* 1894. 16°.   7854. aa. 17.

MANCHESTER. *Art Gallery.* Catalogue of the permanent collection of Pictures. pp. 121. *Manchester.* 1894. 8°.   7857. dd. 18.

NOTTINGHAM. *Museum.* Catalogue of classical Antiquities from the Temple of Diana, Nemi. pp. 82. 1891. 8°.   7705. aaa. 39.

ACLAND (*Sir* H. W.) and RUSKIN (J.) The Oxford Museum. pp. 112. *Lond.* 1893. 4°. 7808. f. 12.

RUGBY. *Exhibition of Local Art.* Rugby Exhibition of Local Art. pp. 68. *Rugby,* 1891, 8°.
7958. aaa. 18.

SHEFFIELD. *Mappin Art Gallery.* Catalogue of the permanent collection of Pictures, *etc.* pp. 32. *Sheffield,* 1892. 8°.   Pam. 24.

EXHIBITIONS—*continued.*

France.

BABEAU (A.)   Le Louvre et son histoire.
pp. 349.   *Paris*, 1895. 4°.   10172. i. 14.

PARIS.   *Louvre.*   Catalogue des peintures exposées dans les galeries du Louvre.   pp 232.
Paris, 1890. 8°.   7854. aaa. 36.

DOUGLASS (R. B.)   The Palace of Art.   Guide to the Louvre.   pp. 148.   *Paris*, 1891. 8°.
7808. a. 35.

GAUTIER (T.)   Guide au Musée du Louvre.
pp. 360.   *Paris*, 1882. 18°.   7858. a. 30.

GRUYER (F. A.)   Voyage autour du Salon Carré au Musée du Louvre.   pp. 496.
Paris, 1891. 4°.   K.T.C. 4. b. 4.

LAFENESTRE (G.) and RICHTENBERGER (E.)   Le Musée national du Louvre.   pp. 379.
Paris, 1893. 8°.   7856. de. 36.

O'SHEA (H.)   Les Musées du Louvre.   pp. 446.
Paris, 1892. 12°.   7706. a. 43.

PETROZ (P.)   Esquisse d'une histoire de la peinture au Louvre.   pp. 290.   *Paris*, 1890. 8°.
7858. g. 30.

BENEDITE (L.)   Le Musée du Luxembourg.
Paris, 1894. 4°.   189.

PARIS.   *Luxembourg.*   Notice des peintures, sculptures et dessins.   pp. 84.   *Paris*, 1887. 8°.
7807. aaaa. 11. (4.)

—— *Musée du garde-meuble.*   Catalogue.
pp. 103.   *Paris*, 1892. 8°.   7709. aa. 25.

STEIN (H.)   État des objets d'art dans les monuments religieux et civils de Paris au début de la révolution française.   *Paris*, 1890, *etc.* 8°.
7807. aaaa.

HUOT DE GONCOURT (E. L. A.) and (J. A.)   Le Salon de 1852, *etc.*   pp. 222.   *Paris*, 1893. 12°.
7858. a. 40.

CASTAGNARY (J. A.)   Salons, 1857-1870.   2 tom.
Paris, 1892. 12°.   7808. a. 48.

P.P.   *Paris. Journal des Débats.*   Les Salons de 1894, *etc.   Paris*, 1894, *etc.* 4°.   146.

PARIS.   *Salon.*   Explication, *etc.*   1895,
pp. 412.   *Paris*, 1895. 12°.   7854. a. 43.

—— Paris Salons of 1895, *etc.*
Lond. 1895, *etc.* fol.   1751, a. 1.

—— *Société des Beaux-Arts.*   Catalogue illustré des ouvrages de peinture, sculpture et gravure, 1890, *etc.   Paris*, 1890, *etc.* 8°.   7858. e. 24.

—— *Exposition Universelle*, 1889.   L'Art français.
pp. 184.   *Paris*, 1890. 4°.   7958. i. 20.

GONSE (L.)   Exposition de 1889.   L'Art français retrospectif au Trocadero.   pp. 592.
Paris, 1889. 4°.   7875. ee. 15.

WALTON (W.)   Chefs-d'œuvre de l'Exposition universelle, 1889.   pp. 118.   *Paris*, 1889. fol.
K.T.C. 23. b. 2.

LASTEYRIE (R. de)   Album archéologique des Musées de province.   *Paris*, 1890, *etc.* 4°.
K.T.C. 3. b. 1.

STEIN (H.)   Le Musée d'Ajaccio.   pp. 16.
Paris, 1894. 8°.   Pam. 24.

PERALDI (F.) and NOVELLINI (P.)   Musée d'Ajaccio.   Catalogues des tableaux et des statues.   pp. 160.   *Ajaccio*, 1892. 8°.   7808. aa. 47.

ANGERS.   *Musée.*   Peintures, sculptures, Musée David.   pp. 306.   *Angers*, 1881. 12°.   7808. aa. 46.

VALLET (E.)   Catalogue des tableaux, *etc.*, exposés dans le Musée de Bordeaux.   pp. 252.
Bordeaux, 1894. 12°.   7857. a. 43.

GRUYER (F. A.)   Le Peinture au Château de Chantilly.   *Paris*, 1895. 4°.   K.T.C. 30. b. 10.

ROUEN.   *Musée.*   Catalogue des ouvrages de peinture, *etc.*   pp. 132.   *Rouen*, 1890. 8°.
7854. a. 35.

EXHIBITIONS.—France—*continued.*

SAINT-GERMAIN EN LAYE.   *Exposition des Beaux-Arts.*   Catalogue des ouvrages de peinture, *etc.*
Saint Germain, 1891, *etc.* 8°.   7808. df.

PALUSTRE (L.)   Album de l'Exposition rétrospective de Tours, 1890.   pp. 124.
Tours, 1891. 4°.   7957. g. 10.

Ac.   Troyes.   *Musée.*   Catalogue des tableaux.
pp. 97.   *Troyes*, 1886. 8°.   Ac. 261.

VERSAILLES.   *Musée National.*   Guide illustré du Musée.   pp. 72.   *Versailles*, 1893. 12°. 7807. e. 32.

Germany.

BLANCHET (J. A.)   Rapport sur les Musées d'Allemagne.   pp. 44.   *Paris*, 1893. 8°.
07703. i. 1. (15.)

BERLIN.   *K. Museen.*   Handbücher der Museen, *etc.*
Berl. 1891, *etc.* 8°.   7808. a. 41.

—— Beschreibendes Verzeichnis der Gemälde.
pp. 407.   *Berl.* 1891. 8°.   7856. de. 28.

—— *Verein Berliner Künstler.*   Internationale Kunst-Ausstellung.   pp. 156.   *Berl.* 1891. 8°.
7854. ccc. 35.

DARMSTADT.   *Museum.*   Verzeichniss der Erwerbungen.   1890, *etc.* 8°.   7808. aaa.

DRESDEN.   *K. Sammlungen.*   Führer durch die königlichen Sammlungen.   pp. 305.
Dresd. 1894. 8°.   7706. a. 49.

WOERMANN (C.)   Verzeichnis der älteren Gemälde der Galerie Weber in Hamburg.
pp. 240.   *Dresd.* 1892. 8°.   7858. f. 14.

Ac.   Hamburg.   *Museum für Kunst.*   Führer durch die Sammlungen.   pp. 828.
Hamb. 1894. 8°.   7807. m. 11.

ROSENBERG (M.)   Die Kunstkammer im grossherzoglichen Residenzschlosse zu Karlsruhe.
Karlsruhe, 1892. fol.   K.T.C. 2. a. 6.

VOGEL (J.)   Das städtische Museum zu Leipzig.
pp. 100.   *Leipz.* 1892. 4°.   7808. g. 8.

STUTTGARD.   *K. Staats-Sammlung vaterländischer Kunst-Denkmale.*   Beschreibender Katalog.
Stuttg. 1883, *etc.* 8°.   7709. bb. 50.

KEUNE (J. B.)   Führer durch das Provinzial-Museum zu Trier.   pp. 47.   *Trier*, 1891. 8°.
Pam. 91.

India.

LUCKNOW.   *Provincial Museum.*   Minutes of the Managing Committee 1883-88.   pp. 417.
Allahabad, 1889. 8°.   7001. f. 7.

Ac.   Calcutta.   *Indian Museum.*   Notes.
Calcutta, 1889, *etc.* 8°.   Ac. 3693.

Ireland.

DUBLIN.   *National Gallery.*   Catalogue of works of art.   pp. 188.   *Dublin*, 1890. 8°.   7854. ccc. 32.

—— *Science and Art Museum.*   General Guide.
pp. 75.   *Dublin*, 1892. 8°.   Pam. 18.

Italy.

ITALY.   *Ministero dell' Istruzione Pubblica.*   Le Gallerie nazionali italiane.   Notizie e documenti.
Roma, 1894, *etc.* 4°.   7808. h.

GATTI (A.)   Catalogue du Musée de Saint Pétrone.
pp. 58.   *Bologne*, 1894. 8°.   07707. e. 2.

Ac.   Brescia.   *Accademia di Scienze ed Arti.*   Illustrazione dei civici musei di Brescia.   2 pt.
Brescia, 1889, 91. 8°.   07708. g. 4.

COMO.   *Civico Museo.*   Cataloghi.
Como, 1890, *etc.* 8°.   7706. cc. 11.

KÁROLY (K.)   Guide to the Paintings of Florence.
pp. 344.   *Lond.* 1893. 8°.   7857. a. 41.

MONACO (D.)   Handbook to the Naples Museum.
pp. 274.   *Naples*, 1893. 8°.   7705. a. 32.

STELLA (A.)   Pittura e scultura in Piemonte, 1842-91.   pp. 667.   *Torino*, 1893. 8°. 7814. b. 3.

EXHIBITIONS.—Italy—*continued.*

MASSI (H. J.) Description of the Museums of ancient sculpture in the Vatican, pp. 232. *Rome*, 1892. 8°.　　　　　7875. aa. 51.

Ac. Venice. *R. Accademia di Belle Arti.* Catalogue. pp. 211. *Lond.* 1894. 8°. 7858 aa. 32.

B., G. Catalogue de la Galerie Royale de Venise. pp. 199. *Venise*, 1890. 8°.　　　7856. a. 49.

Jamaica.

Ac. Kingston. *Institute of Jamaica.* General guide to the Museum. pp. 26. *Kingston*, 1893. 8°.
Pam. 42.

Netherlands.

OBREEN (F. D. O.) Wegwijzer door 's Rijks Museum te Amsterdam. pp. 188.
Schiedam, 1890. 8°.　　　　7807. h. 32.

HAGUE. *K. Museum.* Catalogue of the Pictures, etc. pp. 76. *The Hague*, 1893. 8°. 7858. aa. 33.

New South Wales. See supra: Australia.
Norway. See Sweden.
Scotland.

EDINBURGH. *National Gallery.* Catalogue. pp. 200. *Edinb.* 1886. 8°.　　7858. a. 45.

Sweden and Norway.

Ac. Stockholm. *Nordiska Museet.* Führer durch die Sammlungen. pp. 50. *Stockholm*, 1888. 8°.
Pam. 3.

STOCKHOLM. *National Museum.* Konstskatter i National Museum. *Stockholm*, 1890, *etc.* 8°.
7857. dd. 14.

UNDSET (I. M.) University-Museum of northern Antiquities in Christiania. pp. 23.
Christiania, 1889. 8°.　　　　Pam. 3.

BÆHRENDTZ (F. J.) Teckningar ur Kalmar Museum. *Kalmar*, 1890, *etc.* 4°.　07708. g.

United States of America.

BOSTON. *Museum of Fine Arts.* Department of Japanese Art. Catalogue. pp. 37.
Bost. 1894. 8°.　　　　　7858. b. 46.

CHICAGO. *Columbian Exposition.* Extracts from Rules governing the administration of the Department of Fine Arts. *Chicago*, 1891. 8°. Pam. 18.

—— Official Catalogue. Part x. Fine Arts. pp. 196. *Chicago*, 1893. 8°.　　7958. bb. 26.

—— Official Illustrations from the Art Gallery. pp. 383. *Phila.* 1893. 8°. 7958. bb. 34.

—— Pennsylvania Art Contributions. pp. 61. *Harrisburg*, 1893. 8°.　　　7958. bb. 36.

CINCINNATI. *Museum Association.* Catalogue of Oil Paintings and Sculpture. pp. 77.
Cincinnati, 1892. 8°.　　　　7854. d. 39.

SAN FRANCISCO. *Memorial Museum.* Guide to the halls and galleries of the Memorial Museum. pp. 123. *San Fran.* 1895. 8°. 7959. aaa. 58.

Ac. Philadelphia. *Academy of Fine Arts.* Descriptive Catalogue of the permanent collections. pp. 111. *Phila.* 1892. 8°. 7854. d. 38.

Victoria. See supra : Australia.

PRIVATE ART COLLECTIONS. *See* COLLECTIONS AND COLLECTORS.

Pt. II.　International and Industrial Exhibitions.

For the Art Sections of International Exhibitions, *see supra : Pt. I.* For Exhibitions of Electricity, *see* ELECTRICITY.

Chicago Exposition, 1893.

CHICAGO. *Exposition.* Official Catalogue. 12 pts. *Chicago*, 1893. 8°. 7958. bb. 16–18. and 24–32.

—— Classification of the Exposition. pp. 122. *Chicago*, 1891. 8°.　　　　7958. bb. 21.

EXHIBITIONS.—International—*cont.*

CHICAGO. *Columbian Exposition.* Department of Literature. *Chicago*, 1892. 8°.　　Pam. 18.

—— Department of Science and Philosophy. Division of African ethnology. *Chicago*, 1892. 8°.
1879. c. 1. (8.)

ARBEL (P.) Rapport sur l'Exposition de Chicago concernant la métallurgie, les mines et les industries diverses. pp. 100.
Saint-Étienne, 1894. 8°.　　　7958. bbb. 18.

DREDGE (J.) Record of the Transportation exhibits. pp. 779. 1894. 8°. Engineering Series.
8755. m.

CHICAGO. *Columbian Exposition.* Catalogue of the exhibit of the Bureau of the American Republics. pp. 245. *Chicago*, 1893. 8°.
7958. bb. 22.

—— Special-Katalog der österreichischen Abtheilung. pp. 122. *Wien*, 1893. 8°. 7959. bb. 23.

—— Catalogue of the Brazilian Section. pp. 145. *Chicago*, 1893. 8°.　　　　7958. bb. 37.

—— Catalogue of the exhibits of British Guiana. pp. 44. *Chicago*, 1893. 8°.　　Pam. 18.

—— Section française. Catalogue. pp. 255. *Paris*, 1893. 8°.　　　　7958. h. 32.

—— Catalogue de l'Exposition des souvenirs franco-américains de la guerre de l'Independance. pp. 108. *Paris*, 1893. 4°.　7959. h. 25.

—— Exposition de la Librairie française. *Chicago*, 1893. 8°.　　　　7958. h. 33.

—— Katalog der Ausstellung des deutschen Reiches. pp. 256. *Berl.* 1893. 8°. 7958. h. 34.

—— Bericht des Sonderkomitees der " Deutschen Frauen-Abteilung bei der Weltausstellung in Chicago." pp. 253. *Berl.* 1893. 8°. 7958. bb. 35.

G. B. & I. *Royal Commission for the Chicago Exhibition.* Handbook of Regulations and general information. pp. 123. *Lond.* 1892. 8°.
7958. aaa. 21.

—— Official catalogue of the British Section. pp. 544. *Lond.* 1893. 8°.　7958. aaa. 20.

CHICAGO. *Columbian Exposition.* Industrial Art manufactures of the Indian Empire. pp. 36. 1893. 8°.　　　　　　　　Pam. 24.

—— Catalogue of the exhibits in the New South Wales Courts. pp. 782. *Sydney*, 1893. 8°.
7956. k. 20.

—— Report of the Executive Commissioner for N.S.W. pp. 671. *Sydney*, 1894. 8°. 7956. k. 21.

—— Catalogue of the exhibit of Norway. pp. 79. *Chicago*, 1893. 8°.　　Pam. 18.

—— Catalogue of the Russian Section. pp. 572. *St. Petersburg*, 1893. 8°.　7956. l. 8.

—— Catálogo de la Sección española. pp. 1053. *Madrid*, 1893. 8°.　　　　7959. f. 39.

—— Swedish Catalogue. 2 pt. *Stockholm*, 1893. 8°.　　　　　7959. e. 3.

—— Catalogue of the exhibit of the U.S. Navy Department. pp. 233. *Chicago*, 1893. 8°.
7958. bb. 20.

—— Catalogue of the Illinois Woman's Exposition Board. pp. 143. *Chicago*, 1893. 8°.
7958. bb. 23.

VENEZUELA. World's Columbian Exposition. United States of Venezuela in 1893. pp. 149. *N.Y.* 1893. 8°.　　　　　7959. cc. 14.

CHICAGO. *World's Congress.* General programme of the series of World's Congresses. pp. 16. *Chicago*, 1893. 8°.　　　　Pam. 18.

—— *Columbian Exposition.* The City of Chicago and her Exposition of 1893. *Lond.* 1892, *etc.* 8°.　　　　　　7958. f

—— International Guide to the Exposition. pp. 168. *Lond.* 1893. 8°.　　7959. d. 42.

EXHIBITIONS.—International—cont.

CHICAGO. *Columbian Exposition.* A Scamper through the States : guide to the World's Fair, 1893. pp. 120. *Lond.* 1892. 8°. 10409. cc. 32.

—— Chicago and its Environs. pp. 523. 48. *Chicago.* 1893. 8°. 10413. bb. 35.

—— Useful notices for visitors. pp. 32. *Lond.* 1893. 8°. Pam. 18.

—— Souvenir of World's Fair, 1893. *Lond.* 1892. obl. 8°. 7957. de. 6.

—— Chicago and the World's Columbian Exposition. *Chicago*, 1893. fol. 7958. h. 31.

—— Leaflets describing the buildings of the Exhibition. *Chicago*, 1893. fol. 1882. c. 2. (192.)

BOETTCHER (O.) Weltausstellungs-Briefe. pp. 190. *Leipz.* 1893. 8°. 10412. a. 49.

BOHLIN (K. J.) Genom den stora västern. pp. 216. *Stockholm*, 1893. 8°. 10460. aaa. 31.

BURNHAM (D. H.) and MILLET (F. D.) Columbian Exposition. The book of the builders. Vol. 1. No. 1-6. *Chicago*, 1894. fol. 1736. b. 8.

DIBBLE (W. E.) Columbian Exposition pocket record book. pp. 55. *Chicago*, 1893. 8°. Pam. 18.

EMERSON (W.) The World's Fair buildings, Chicago. *Lond.* 1893. 4°. 7959. k. 22.

FLINN (J. J.) Handbook of the Columbian Exposition. pp. 350. *Chicago*, 1892. 8°. 7958. aa. 20.

GOTTSCHALK (L. M.) and OSTERBERG-VERAKOFF (M.) 20 Tage durch Chicago. pp. 72. *Stuttgart*, 1893. 8°. 10411. aa. 50. (3.)

GRANDIN (L.) Impressions d'une Parisienne à Chicago. pp. 334. *Paris*, 1895. 12°. 10412. aaa. 44.

HAWTHORNE (J.) Humors of the Fair. pp. 205. *Chicago*, 1893. 8°. 012330. g. 49.

JENKS (T.) Century World's Fair book. pp. 215. *N.Y.* 1893. 4°. 7959. ff. 11.

P.P. *Chicago.* World's Columbian Exposition illustrated. *Chicago*, 1891, *etc.* fol. P.P. 9091. da.

RALPH (J.) Chicago and the World's Fair. pp. 244. *N.Y.* 1893. 8°. 7958. f. 17.

RIEDLER (A.) Ein Rückblick auf die Weltausstellung in Chicago. pp. 35. 1894. 8°. Volkswirthschaftliche Zeitfragen. Heft 117. 8207. i.

For the Parliament of Religions at the Chicago Exposition, *see* RELIGION, *History, etc.*

Paris Exposition, 1889.

For the Eiffel Tower, *see* EIFFEL TOWER.

FRANCE. *Ministère du Commerce.* Exposition Internationale de 1889. Monographie; palais, jardins, constructions diverses, *etc.* 2 tom. *Paris*, 1892-95. 8°. Atlas. fol. Tab. 1294. a.

PARIS. *Exposition Universelle*, 1889. Rapport général. *Paris*, 1891, *etc.* 8°. 7957. g. 13.

MONOD (É.) L'Exposition de 1889. Grand ouvrage illustré. *Paris*, 1890, *etc.* 4°. 7958. i. 19.

VIBERT (P.) Les Musées commerciaux et l'Exposition, 1889. pp. 208. *Paris*, 1892. 12°. 7956. b. 2.

Other Exhibitions.

ANTWERP. *Wereldtentoonstelling*, 1894. Kijkjes op de Antwerpsche Wereldtentoonstelling. pp. 64. *'s-Gravenhage*, 1894. 8°. 7956. bb. 9.

STIEGLER (G.) Deutsche Weltausstellung zu Berlin. pp. 48. *Berl.* 1892. 8°. Pam. 18

GROSCH (H. A.) Kunstindustrimuseum Kristiania. pp. 95. *Kristiania*, 1892. 8°. 7808. df. 20.

EDINBURGH. *International Exhibition*, 1890. Official daily programme. *Edinb.* 1890. 8°. 7959. d. 34.

LOWE (C.) Four national Exhibitions in London and their organiser. pp. 548. *Lond.* 1892. 8°. 7956. cc. 8.

EXHIBITIONS.—International—cont.

LONDON. *Italian Exhibition*, 1888. Italian Exhibition. Catalogue, exclusive of fine art department. pp. 145. *Lond.* 1888. 8°. 7959. d. 37.

LYONS. *Exposition Universelle*, 1894. Catalogue général. 10 pt. *Lyon*, 1894. 8°. 7958. f. 18.

MELBOURNE. *Centennial International Exhibition*, 1888. Official Record. pp. 1138. *Melbourne*, 1890. 8°. 7958. g. 16.

P.P. *Paris.* L'Exposition de Moscou de 1891. Pt. 1-8. *Paris*, 1891. fol. P.P. 9024. bb.

PLARR (L.) La France à Moscou. Exposition de 1891. pp. 298. *Paris*, 1891. 4°. 7957. f. 4.

FRANCE. *Ministère du Commerce.* Exposition internationale de 1900 à Paris. Actes organiques. pp. 158. *Paris*, 1895. 8°. 7959. h. 28.

PARMA. *Esposizione Industriale.* Catalogo ufficiale. pp. 96. *Parma*, 1887. 8°. 7959. b. 53.

—— Regolamento i Programmi. pp. 31. *Parma*, 1887. 8°. Pam. 18.

—— Elenco dei giurati e dei premiati. pp. 44. *Parma*, 1887. fol. Pam. 18.

SAN FRANCISCO. *California Midwinter International Exposition.* Official History. pp. 259. *San Fran.* 1894. fol. 1790. b. 11.

TASMANIA. *International Exhibition.* Official Record. pp. 137. *Launceston*, 1893. 8°. 7956. h. 6.

TURIN. *Esposizione Generale.* Relazione generale. 2 pt. *Torino*, 1886. 8°. 7958. h. 27.

EXMOOR. JEFFERIES (R.) Red Deer. pp. 248. *Lond.* 1892. 8°. 7207. cc. 3.

PAGE (J. L. W.) Exploration of Exmoor. pp. 318. *Lond.* 1890. 8°. 010358. g. 14.

RAWLE (E. J.) Annals of the Forest of Exmoor. pp. 163. *Taunton*, 1893. 4°. 10368. l. 4.

EXORCISM. BISCHOFBERGER (T.) Die Verwaltung des Exorcistats nach Massgabe des römischen Benediktionale. pp. 57. *Stuttgart*, 1893. 12°. Pam. 36.

See also DEMONOLOGY: WITCHCRAFT.

EXPLORATION. *See* VOYAGES.

EXPLOSIVES. *See* GUNPOWDER: MELANITE.

EXPRESSION: GESTURE. ADAMS (F. A. F.) Gesture and pantomimic action. pp. 221. *N.Y.* 1891. 8°. 11794. h. 33.

BOURDON (B.) L'Expression des émotions. pp. 374. *Paris*, 1892. 8°. 12901. dd. 35.

HACKS (C.) Le geste. Illustrations. pp. 492. *Paris*, 1893. 8°. 11794. i. 29.

MAIN (W.) On Expression in nature. pp. 197. *Lond.* 1894. 8°. 7006. bb. 34.

WARMAN (E. B.) Gestures and attitudes. pp. 422. *Bost.* 1892. 4°. 11794. f. 40.

See also PHRENOLOGY.

EXTRADITION, Law of. DELIUS (H.) Die Auslieferung flüchtiger Verbrecher. pp. 122. *Berl.* 1890. 8°. 5655. ee. 17.

FÉRAUD-GIRAUD (L. J. D.) De l'Extradition. pp. 142. *Paris*, 1890. 8°. 5425. eee. 16.

RICHBERG (J. C.) International Extradition case. Extradition of J. L. Adutt, a fugitive from justice of Austro-Hungarian Government. pp. 85. *Chicago*, 1893. 8°. 06955. df. 20.

See also LAW, *Criminal* and *International.*

EXTREME UNCTION. SCHMITZ (I.) De effectibus Sacramenti Extremae Unctionis. pp. 86. *Friburgi*, 1893. 8°. 4326. d. 1.

See also SACRAMENTS.

EYAM. WOOD (W.) History and antiquities of Eyam. pp. 128. *Sheffield*, 1895. 8°. 10358. cc. 57.

EYE.

General : Anatomy, etc.

BERNHEIMER (S.) Das Wurzelgebiet des Oculomotorius beim Menschen. pp. 80.
Wiesbaden, 1894. 8°.   7611. f. 40.

BROWN (A. C.) Relation between the movements of the Eyes and the movements of the Head. pp. 28. *Lond.* 1895. 8°.   7306. e. 26. (3.)

CAMPBELL (H.) The Eye. pp. 99. 1883. 8°. Popular Physiology Series.   7404. df.

GUNN (R. M.) The Eye. 1893. 8°. MORRIS (H.) Treatise on Anatomy.   7419. l. 10.

KOENIG (A.) Beitrage zur Psychologie und Physiologie der Sinnesorgane. pp. 388.
Hamb. 1891. 8°.   8462. f. 15.

PRENTICE (C.) The Eye in its relation to health. pp. 214. *Bristol*, 1895. 8°.   7611. cc. 11.

RAMON Y CAJAL (S.) Die Retina der Wirbelthiere. pp. 179. *Wiesbaden*, 1894. 8°.   7406. i. 2.

BAYER (J.) Bildliche Darstellung des gesunden Auges unser Hausthiere. *Wien*, 1891, *etc.* 8°.   07293. m. 6.

EXNER (S.) Physiologie der facettirten Augen von Krebsen und Insecten. pp. 206.
Leipz. 1891. 8°.   7296. d. 1.

See also infra : Refraction : OPTICS.

Colour Vision.

ABNEY (W. de W.) Colour Vision. pp. 231.
Lond. 1895. 8°.   8716. cc. 43.

DREHER (E.) Drei psycho physiologische Studien. pp. 108. *Leipz.* 1891. 8°.   7410. dh. 62.

GREEN (F. W. E.) Colour-blindness and Colour-perception. pp. 311. 1891. 8°. International Scientific Series. Vol. 71.   2324. bb. 8.

HUNT (E.) Colour Vision. pp. 122.
Glasg. 1892. 4°.   7610. g. 7.

Diseases and Defects : Ophthalmoscopy.

ALLEN (T. F.) and NORTON (G. S.) Ophthalmic Diseases and therapeutics. pp. 555.
Phila. 1892. 8°.   7610. g. 13.

BERRY (G. A.) Elements of ophthalmoscopic Diagnosis. pp. 83. *Edinb.* 1891. 8°. 7610. de. 37.

—— Diseases of the Eye. pp. 727. 1893. 8°. Pentland's Medical Series.   7641. ee.

BUXTON (A. St. C.) Ophthalmic Hints. pp. 51.
Lond. 1890. 8°.   7610. de. 38.

EVERSBUSCH (O.) Behandlung der bei Infektions-krankheiten vorkommenden Erkrankungen des Sehorgans. 1894. 8°. PENZOLDT (F.) Handbuch der Therapie der Infektionskrankheiten. Bd. 1.   7620. f.

—— Die neue Heilanstalt für Augenkranke in Erlangen. pp. 87. *Wiesbaden*, 1893. 8°.   7687. eee. 37.

FEUER (N.) Relation between affections of the Teeth and Eyes. pp. 53. *Lond.* 1894. 8°.   7306. e. 25. (7.)

FICK (A. E.) Lehrbuch der Augenheilkunde. pp. 486. *Leipz.* 1894. 8°.   7611. d. 9.

FORD (A. V.) Ophthalmic Notes. pp. 107.
Lond. 1891, 8°.   7610. de. 39.

FOX (L. W.) and GOULD (G. M.) Compend of Diseases of the Eye. pp. 164. *Edinb.* 1892, 8°.   7611. aaaa. 3.

FUCHS (E.) Lehrbuch der Augenheilkunde. pp. 810. *Leipz.* 1891. 8°.   7611. g. 30.

—— Text-book of Ophthalmology. pp. 788.
Lond. 1892. 8°.   7611. g. 35.

—— Intorno alle cause della cecità ed al modo di prevenirla. pp. 205. *Firenze*, 1890. 8°.   7611. d. 3.

EYE.—Diseases, etc.—*continued.*

GAYET (A.) Éléments d'Ophtalmologie. pp. 488.
Paris, 1893. 8°.   7610. ee. 38.

HAAB (O.) Atlas of Ophthalmoscopy.
Lond. 1895. 8°.   7611. c. 9.

HANSELL (H. F.) and BELL (J. H.) Manual of clinical Ophthalmology. pp. 231. *Phila.* 1892. 8°.   7610. de. 44.

HARLAN (G. G.) Diseases of the Eye. 1893. 8°. ALLEN (H.) Handbook of local Therapeutics.   7442. g. 26.

HIRSCHBERG (J.) Einführung in die Augenheilkunde. *Leipz.* 1892, *etc.* 8°.   7611. h. 2.

JACOBSON (J.) Briefe an Fachgenossen. pp. 599.
Königsberg, 1894. 8°.   10921. l. 29.

JULER (H. E.) Handbook of Ophthalmic Science and practice. pp. 549. *Lond.* 1893. 8°.   7610. g. 12.

LANG (W.) Guide to the practice of Ophthalmology. *Lond.* 1895, *etc.* 8°.   7611. aaaa. 20.

LAPERSONNE (F. de) Ophtalmologie. pp. 199.
1893. 8°. Encyclopédie des aide-mémoire.   8709. g.

MACNAMARA (N. C.) Diseases and refraction of the Eye. pp. 604. *Lond.* 1891, 8°.   7610. de. 40.

MAGNUS (H. F.) Leitfaden für Begutachtung von Unfallsbeschädigungen der Augen. pp. 176.
Breslau, 1894. 8°.   7615. c. 5.

MELLINGER (C.) Beiträge zur Augenheilkunde. pp. 64. *Basel*, 1893. 8°.   7611. g. 39.

NORRIS (W. F.) and OLIVER (C. A.) Text-book of Ophthalmology. pp. 641. *Edinb.* 1894. 8°.   7610. d. 2.

NOYES (H. D.) Text-book on diseases of the Eye. pp. 812. *Lond.* 1894. 8°.   7610. g. 18.

OWEN (D. C. L.) Elements of ophthalmic Therapeutics. pp. 68. *Birmingham*, 1890. 4°.   7611. g. 32.

PANAS (P.) Traité des Maladies des Yeux. 2 tom. *Paris*, 1894. 8°.   7610. f. 26.

P.P. *Copenhagen.* Nordisk ophthalmologisk Tidsskrift. *Kjøbenh.* 1888, *etc.* 8°. P.P. 3286. ch.

SCHULEK (V.) Ungarische Beiträge zur Augenheilkunde. *Leipz.* 1895. 8°.   7611. h.

SCHWEINITZ (G. E. de) Diseases of the Eye. pp. 641. *Lond.* 1893. 8°.   7610. g. 14.

SHAW (C. E.) Diseases of the Eye. pp. 103.
Lond. 1895, 8°.   7611. aaaa. 18.

STEER (H.) The Eyes and their sufferings. pp. 35. *Derby*, 1891. 24°.   7321. aa. 22. (2.)

SWANZY (H. R.) Handbook of the diseases of the Eye. pp. 582. *Lond.* 1895. 8°.   7611. cc. 9.

WECKER (L. de) and MASSELON (J.) Manuel d'Ophthalmologie. pp. 991. *Paris*, 1889. 8°.   7611. f. 39.

DIMMER (F.) Die ophthalmoscopischen Lichtreflexe der Netzhaut. pp 240. *Leipz.* 1891. 8°.   7611. f. 37.

HARTRIDGE (G.) The Ophthalmoscope. pp. 156.
Lond. 1894. 8°.   7611. aaaa. 12.

JAEGAR (E. v.) Ophthalmoskopischer Hand-Atlas. pp. 88. *Leipz.* 1890. 8°.   7611. g. 33.

MADDOX (E. E.) Clinical use of Prisms. pp. 170.
Bristol, 1893. 8°.   7611. aaaa. 10.

WAKEFIELD (J.) Eye-sight Testing in relation to defective vision. pp. 16. *Brighouse*, 1892. 8°.   7306. df. 19. (15.)

FOURNET (A. M. A.) Medical spectacles and the London Ophthalmic Hospital. pp. 22.
Lond. 1894. 8°.   7306. g. 18. (5.)

CLARKE (E.) Eye strain, commonly called Asthenopia. pp. 168. *Lond.* 1892. 8°. 7611. aa. 4.

EYE.—Diseases, etc.—continued.

BAEUERLEIN (A.) Meine Erfahrungen über Staar und Staaroperationen. pp. 145.
Wiesbaden, 1894. 8°.   7611. h. 4.

FINK (G. H.) Methods of operating for Cataract. pp. 77. *Lond*. 1894. 8°.   7611. aa. 30.

HALL (G. C.) Complications of cataract operations. *Calcutta*, 1887. 8°.   7611. bb. 21.

SCHOEN (W.) Ursache und Verhütung des grauen und grünen Staares. pp. 307.
Wiesbaden, 1893. 8°.   7611. h. 3.

ZENKER (H.) Tausend Staaroperationen. pp. 158. *Wiesbaden*, 1895. 8°.   7610. f. 31.

SMITH (P.) Pathology and treatment of Glaucoma. pp. 198. *Lond*. 1891. 8°.   7611. g. 27.

BOCK (E.) Die angeborenen Kolobome des Augapfels. pp. 212. *Wien*, 1893. 8°. 7610. ee. 40.

WATSON (W. S.) Anatomy and diseases of the Lachrymal Passages. pp. 55. *Lond*. 1892. 8°.
     7610. ee. 37.

LEVINÇON (J.) Étude sur les Maladies des voies lacrymales produisant le larmoiement. pp. 197. *Paris*, 1893. 8°.   7610. g. 16.

NIEDEN (A.) Der Nystagmus der Bergleute. pp. 140. *Wiesbaden*, 1894. 8°.   7611. g. 41.

SNELL (S.) Miner's Nystagmus. pp. 143. *Bristol*, 1892. 8°.   8715. h. 25.

BRAUNSTEIN (E. P.) Zur Lehre von der Innervation der Pupillenbewegung. pp. 142.
Wiesbaden, 1894. 8°.   7611. h. 5.

BORYSIEKIEWICZ (M.) Untersuchungen über den feineren Bau der Netzhaut. pp. 64.
Leipz. 1894. 8°.   7611. df. 28.

FISCHER (R.) Über die Embolie der Arteria centralis retinae. pp 246. *Leipz*. 1891. 8°.
     7610. cc. 3.

MACKAY (G.) On blinding of the Retina by direct Sunlight. pp. 52. *Lond*. 1894. 8°. 7306. e. 25. (12.)

PANSIER (P.) Les manifestations oculaires de l'hystérie. pp. 171. *Paris*, 1892. 8°. 7410. d. 32.

WILBRAND (H.) and SAENGER (A.) Über Sehstörungen bei functionellen Nervenleiden. pp. 190. *Leipz*. 1892. 8°.   7630. g. 22.

KOEHLER (A.) De la tuberculose oculaire. pp. 104. *Nancy*, 1892. 4°.   7383. ddd. 1. (5.)

VALUDE (E.) De la tuberculose oculaire. 1887. 8°.

VERNEUIL (A. A.) Études sur la tuberculose. Tom. 1.   7561. k. 1.

FROELICH (L.) Pelade et lésions oculaires. pp. 12. *Genève*, 1890. 8°.   07305. h. 9. (5.)

GRIFFITH (A. H.) Diagnosis of intra-ocular Growths. pp. 24. *Lond*. 1892. 8°,
     07305. h. 19. (10.)

COLLINS (W. J.) Associated and related ocular and dental Diseases. pp. 23. *Lond*. 1891. 8°.
     07305. h. 6. (3.)

FICK (A. E.) Die Bestimmung des Brechzustandes eines Auges durch Schattenprobe. pp. 67. *Wiesbaden*, 1891. 8°.   7611. f. 38.

JEAFFERSON (C. S.) Notes on nursing in Eye Diseases. pp. 90. *Bristol*, 1894. 8°. 7611. aaaa. 11.

STEPHENSON (S.) Ophthalmic Nursing. pp. 188. *Lond*. 1894. 8°,   7611. aaaa. 13.

BURCHARDT (M.) Diagnostik der Simulationen von Schwachsichtigkeit. pp. 51. *Berl*. 1891. 8°.
     Tab. 1800. b.

FROELICH (L.) Des Procédés modernes pour reconnaître la simulation de la faiblesse visuelle. *Genève*, 1891. 8°.   07305. h. 17. (1.)

BAYER (J.) Bildliche Darstellung des gesunden und kranken Auges unserer Hausthiere. *Wien*, 1891, *etc.* 8°.   07293. m. 6.

Hygiene of the Eye.

COHN (H. L.) Lehrbuch der Hygiene des Auges. pp. 855. *Wien*, 1892. 8°.   7610. g. 11.

EYE.—Hygiene of—continued.

TROUSSEAU (A.) Hygiène de l'Œil. pp. 214. 1892. 8°. Encyclopédie des aide-mémoire.
     8709. g.

Refraction of the Eye.

HARTRIDGE (G.) Refraction of the Eye. pp. 259. *Lond*. 1894. 8°.   7611. aaaa. 16.

JACKSON (E.) Skiascopy and its application to the study of refraction. pp. 112.
Phila. 1895. 8°.   8715. i. 4.

MACNAMARA (N. C.) Diseases and refraction of the Eye. pp. 604. *Lond*. 1891. 8°. 7610. de. 40.

MORTON (A. S.) Refraction of the Eye. pp. 72. *Lond*. 1894. 8°.   7611. aaaa. 15.

SCHIÖTZ (H. A.) Øiets Refraktionstilstande. pp. 85. *Kristiania*, 1891. 8°.   Pam. 39.

See also supra : *General* : OPTICS.

Short and Defective Sight in Children.

FERDINANDS (G.) School Teacher's ophthalmic guide. pp. 10. *Aberd*. 1892. 8°. 7611. aaaa. 2.

GELPKE (T.) Die Augen der Elementarschüler. pp. 136. *Tübingen*, 1891. 8°.   7610. g. 3.

GUSSE (C. J.) De la Vision chez les élèves d'un lycée. pp. 38. *Limoges*, 1895. 4°. 7610. f. 30.

MARTIN (G.) Étiologie et prophylaxie de la myopie scolaire. pp. 28. *Paris*, 1894. 8°.
     7306. e. 23. (17.)

SNELL (S.) Eyesight and school life. pp. 70. *Bristol*, 1895. 8°.   7611. cc. 12.

EYSSES, Abbey. EYSSES, *Abbey*. L'abbaye d'Eysses en Agenais. pp. 114.
Bordeaux, 1893. 8°.   4629. k. 20.

FABLES. BÉDIER (J.) Les Fabliaux : études de littérature au moyen âge. pp. 485. 1893. 8°. Ac. *Paris*. *École des Hautes Études*. Bibliothèque. Sciences philologiques. Fasc. 98.
     Ac. 8929.

BABRIUS. Babrius et ses Fables. 1891. 8°. Ac. *Bordeaux*. *Faculté des Lettres*. Annales.
     Ac. 8917.

HERVIEUX (L.) Les Fabulistes latins. 2 tom. *Paris*, 1893, 94. 8°.   11312. o. 13.

LESSING (G. E.) Abhandlungen über die Fabel. pp. 222. *Wien*, 1890. 8°.   011840. l. 42.

LÉVÊQUE (E.) Iconographie des Fables de la Fontaine, La Motte, Dorat, Florian. pp. 229. *Paris*, 1893. 8°.   7858. gg. 29.

MICHELSSON (M.) Russischer Fabelschatz. pp. 111. *St. Petersburg*, 1890. 8°. 011586. e. 39.

NEWBIGGING (T.) Fables and fabulists. pp. 152. *Lond*. 1895. 8°.   011850. eee. 41.

FACTORIES. ASHBEE (C. R.) Chapters in Workshop re-construction and citizenship. pp. 166. *Lond*. 1894. 8°.   08276. i. 29.

AUSTIN (E.) Law relating to Factories and Workshops. pp. 364. *Lond*. 1895. 8°.
     6425. aaaa. 21.

GARCKE (E.) and FELLS (J. M.) Summary of the Factory and Workshop Acts, 1878–91. pp. 40. *Lond*. 1893. 8°.   8282. cc. 48. (8.)

—— Factory Accounts. pp. 264. *Lond*. 1893. 8°.   8535. df. 31.

JEANS (V.) Factory Act Legislation. Industrial and commercial effects. pp. 96. *Lond*. 1892. 8°.
     8275. c. 84.

LONDON. *Liberty and Property Defence League*. Women and Factory legislation. Debates in the House of Lords. pp. 7. *Lond*. 1891. 8°.
     Pam. 82.

MATHESON (E.) Depreciation of Factories. pp. 143. *Lond*. 1893. 8°.   08229. k. 7.

FACTORIES—*continued*.

MULHAUSEN. *Association pour prévenir les accidents de fabrique.* Collection of Appliances for the prevention of accidents in factories. pp. 92. *Mulhouse,* 1895. fol.   8765. h. 28.

REDGRAVE (A.) The Factory Acts. pp. 356. *Lond.* 1895. 8°.   6426. dh. 1.

TAYLOR (R. W. C.) The modern Factory System. pp. 476. *Lond.* 1891. 8°.   08276. g. 15.

—— Factory System and Factory Acts. pp. 184. 1894. 8°. GIBBINS (H. de B.) Social Questions, etc. Vol. 12.   08276. e.

See also CAPITAL AND LABOUR : INDUSTRIES : MACHINERY, *etc.*

FAIENCE. *See* CERAMICS.

FAIRFORD. CARBONELL (F. R.) Handbook to Fairford Church. *Oxf.* 1893. 8°. 7856. de. 31.

FAIRS. *See* DRAMA, *France.*

FAITH. STRUTT (P.) The Nature of Faith. pp. 187, 23. *Lond.* 1891. 8°   4017. f. 14.

SWETE (H. B.) Faith in its relation to Creed, thought and life. pp. 48. *Lond.* 1895. 8°.   4429. a. 100.

See also CHRISTIANITY : THEOLOGY.

FAITH HEALING. AMBROSE (R. G.) Prayer-healing. pp. 74. *Lond.* 1890. 8°.   4324. g. 30.

BUCKLEY (J. M.) Faith-healing and kindred phenomena. pp. 291. *Lond.* 1892. 8°.   7410. df. 45.

PORTER (N. L.) Experience of Healing by Faith. pp. 8. *Bost.* 1885. 32°.   Pam. 39.

SCHOFIELD (A. T.) Faith healing. pp. 128. *Lond.* 1892. 8°.   4429. df. 2.

FALAISE. MERIEL (A.) Histoire de Falaise. pp. 490. *Bellême.* 1890. 18°. 10169. cc. 12.

FALCONRY. HARTING (J. E.) Bibliotheca Accipitraria. Catalogue of books relating to Falconry. pp. 289. *Lond.* 1891. 8°. 011903. l. 10.

BELVALLETTE (A.) Traité d'Autourserie. pp. 137. *Paris,* 1887. 8°.   7912. aaa. 4.

BERT (E.) Treatise of Hawks and hawking, 1619. pp. 109. *Lond.* 1891. 4°. 7908. ee. 15.

BOOK. Booke for Kepinge of Sparhawkes or Goshawkes. Written about 1575. pp. 51. 1886. 4°. Quaritch's Reprints.   12204. h.

CHAPPEVILLE (P. C. de) Petit traité du Fauconnerie. pp. 26. *Paris,* 1885. 8°. Pam. 83.

LASCELLES (*Hon.* G.) Falconry. 1892. 8°. Badminton Library.   7905. f.

PARIS. *Exposition de* 1889. Fauconnerie. Catalogue illustré. pp. 92. *Paris,* 1890. 4°. 7905. i. 10.

FALKENSTEIN. THORNE (W. B.) Open-air treatment of Phthisis as practised at Falkenstein. pp. 31. *Lond.* 1894. 8°.   Pam. 39.

FALKLAND ISLANDS. FALKLAND ISLANDS. Laws and Ordinances. pp. 139. 1885. fol.   6605. h. 5.

MURDOCH (W. G. B.) From Edinburgh to the Antarctic. pp. 364. *Lond.* 1894. 8°.   10460. f. 29.

STIRLING (W. H.) *Bp. of the Falkland Islands.* Brief account of the Falkland Islands. pp. 27. *Buenos Aires,* 1891. 8°.   4745. aa. 46.

FALL, Doctrine of the. *See* EVIL.

FALL RIVER. EARL (H. H.) Fall River and its manufactories. 1803–90. pp. 56. *Fall River, Mass.* 1890. 24°.   Pam. 86.

FALMOUTH. BUCKINGHAM (J. S.) Falmouth and Flushing a hundred years ago. pp. 20. *Falmouth,* 1895. 8°.   Pam. 90.

FAMILY. Ac. Turin. *Università.* BOBBIO (G.) Sulle Origini della Famiglia. pp. 108. *Torino,* 1891. 8°.   6025. f. 4.

CUNOW (H.) Die Verwandtschafts-Organisationen der Australneger. pp. 190. *Stuttgart,* 1894. 8°.   10007. l. 1.

GIRAUD-TEULON (A.) Les Origines de la Famille. pp. 525. *Genève,* 1884. 12°.   8416. df. 22.

HARTMANN (C. R. E. v.) The Sexes compared and other essays. pp. 164. *Lond.* 1895. 8°.   8415. df. 31.

KOVALEVSKY (M. M.) Tableau des origines et de l'évolution de la Famille. pp. 202. 1890. 8°. Ac. Stockholm. *Lorénska Stiftelse.* Skrifter. No. 2.   Ac. 3475.

MUCKE (J. R.) Horde und Familie in ihrer urgeschichtlichen Entwickelung. pp. 308. *Stuttgart,* 1895. 8°.   8223. dh. 22.

POSADA (A.) Teorías acerca del Origen de la Familia. pp. 74. *Madrid,* 1892. 8°.   8282. ff. 12. (7.)

SANCTIS (G. de) La Famiglia ed il prossimo. pp. 159. *Milano,* 1892. 8°.   8285. aa. 61.

STARCKE (C. N.) La Famille primitive. pp. 287. *Paris,* 1891. 8°.   8708. cc.

See also ANTHROPOLOGY : MARRIAGE.

Law.

HRUZA (E.) Geschichte des griechischen und römischen Familienrechtes. *Erlangen,* 1892, *etc.* 8°.   5254. cc. 17.

LELOIR (G.) Code de la Puissance paternelle. 2 tom. *Paris,* 1892. 12°.   5423. de. 14.

PASCAUD (H.) De l'Autorité paternelle. pp. 96. *Paris,* 1893. 8°.   5423. d. 3.

BARAZETTI (C.) Die Vormundschaft (la Tutelle), die Pflegschaft (la Curatelle), *etc.* pp. 662. *Hannover,* 1894. 8°.   05604. k. 7.

FUCHS (W.) Der Hausmeister und sein Recht. pp. 47. *Wien,* 1891. 8°.   Pam. 34.

TRUEPER (J.) Die Familienrechte an der öffentlichen Erziehung. pp. 104. *Langensalza,* 1892. 8°.   8310. d. 10.

DEANS (R. S.) The Law of Parent and Child, guardian and ward. pp. 166. *Lond.* 1895. 8°.   6325. cccc. 2.

GEARY (W. N. M.) Law of Family Relations. pp. 637. *Lond.* 1892. 8°.   5176. bb. 22.

CODERCH MANAU (S.) El Consejo de Familia en España. pp. 526. *Barcelona,* 1893. 8°.   5383. e. 11.

See also MARRIAGE, *Law of.*

FANS. Ac. London. *British Museum. Department of Prints and Drawings.* Catalogue of the collection of Fans presented by Lady Charlotte Schreiber. pp. 138. *Lond.* 1893. 8°.   7855. ff. 50.

B., E. Collection d'Eventails des XVII° and XVIII° siècles. *Paris,* 1890. obl. fol.   1754. b. 3.

BIRCH, afterwards SALWEY (C. M.) Fans of Japan. pp. 149. *Lond.* 1894. 4°. 7808. g. 17.

FLORY (M. A.) Book about Fans. pp. 141. *N.Y.* 1895. 8°.   7742. b. 52.

MELANI (A.) Svaghi artistici femminili. pp. 348. *Milano,* 1891. 4°. K.T.C. 5. b. 19.

UZANNE (A.) Petites monographies d'Art. pp. 270. *Paris,* 1892. 8°.   7742. bb. 30.

See also COSTUME.

FARCIENNES. KAISIN (J.) Annales de la Commune de Farciennes. 2 tom. *Tamines,* 1889. 8°.   10270. ee. 21.

FARMING. *See* AGRICULTURE : ANIMALS, *Domestic* : BOTANY, *Economic* : CATTLE : GRASSES : SHEEP, *etc.*

FAROE ISLANDS. Ac. Copenhagen. *Samfund til Udgivelse af gammel Nordisk Litteratur.* Færøsk Anthologi. 2 vol. *Kjøbenh.* 1886–91. 8°.
Ac. 9057.

—— *Føringafelänun.* Føriskar Vysur irktar o sungnar äv Føringun y Kjøpinhavn, 1876–92.
pp. 67. *Kjøbenh.* 1892. 8°. Ac. 9875.

FRANCE. *Navy.* Instructions nautiques sur les Fœroe. pp. 172. *Paris,* 1894. 8°. 10197. cc. 7.

G. B. & I. *Hydrographic Office.* Færoe Islands Pilot. pp. 40. *Lond.* 1891. 8°. 10496. g. 2.

TOFLSEN (P.) Fuglakväje. pp. 26.
Kjøbenh. 1892. 8°. Pam. 62.

FASTING. LOCK (W.) Fasting. A paper. pp. 16. *Lond.* 1892. 8°. 4429. aa. 60. (7,)

PULLER (F. W.) Concerning the Fast before Communion. pp. 56. *Lond.* 1891. 8°.
4371. de. 4. (15.)

FATHERS, Christian. HORT (F. J. A.) Lectures on the Ante-Nicene Fathers. pp. 138. *Lond.* 1895. 8°. 3623. de. 1.

LIGHTFOOT (J. B.) *Bp. of Durham.* The Apostolic Fathers. pp. 568. *Lond.* 1891. 8°. 2206. f.

WACE (H.) and SCHAFF (P.) Library of Nicene and Post-Nicene Fathers. *Oxf.* 1890, etc. 8°.
3623. cc.

ALZOG (J. B.) Grundriss der Patrologie. pp. 590. *Freiburg,* 1888. 8°. 3623. aa. 25.

BARDENHEWER (O.) Patrologie. pp. 635. *Freiburg,* 1894. 8°. 3622. f. 2.

NIRSCHL (J.) Lehrbuch der Patrologie und Patristik. 3 Bde. *Mainz,* 1881–85. 8°.
3623. aa. 24.

RÉZBÁNYAY (J.) Compendium Patrologiae et patristicae. pp. 704. *Quinque Ecclesiis,* 1894. 8°.
3622. b. 5.

STOECKL (A.) Geschichte der christlichen Philosophie zur Zeit der Kirchenväter. pp. 435. *Mainz,* 1891. 8°. 4535. cc. 1.

BRIGHT (W.) Lessons from the lives of three Great Fathers. pp. 318. *Lond.* 1890. 8°.
4829. b. 6.

See also CHURCH HISTORY : THEOLOGY.

FATS AND OILS. BEAUVISAGE (G.) Les Matières grasses. pp. 324. *Paris,* 1891. 12°.
8909. aaa. 41.

BENEDIKT (R.) Chemical analysis of Oils, Fats, Waxes, etc. pp. 683. *Lond.* 1895. 8°.
07945. h. 2.

CARPENTER (W. L.) Treatise on the manufacture of lubricants, etc. pp. 446. *Lond.* 1895. 8°.
07944. e. 53.

GROSSMANN (J.) Die Bekämpfung der Sturzwellen durch Öl. pp. 140. *Wien,* 1892. 8°.
8805. bbb. 37.

WRIGHT (C. R. A.) Animal and vegetable Oils, Fats, Butters and Waxes. pp. 570. *Lond.* 1894. 8°. 7942. h. 33.

MARAZZA (E.) L'Industria stearica. pp. 283. *Milano,* 1893. 8°. 012200. h. 106.

See also COD : GLYCERINE : ICHTHYOL ; OLIVE : PETROLEUM : SOAP.

FAVIÈRES. BOUILLET (A.) Description de l'église de Saint-Sulpice de Favières. pp. 44. *Paris,* 1891. 8°. 10105. ff. 4. (6.)

FAYOUM. BROWN (R. H.) The Fayûm and Lake Mœris. pp. 110. *Lond.* 1892. 8°.
7705. ee. 28.

WHITEHOUSE (F. C.) Ptolemaic Maps, with reference to Lake Mœris. pp. 4. *Lond.* 1890. 8°. Pam. 89.

See also EGYPT.

FEAR. MOSSO (A.) La Paura. pp. 334. *Milano,* 1892. 8°. 7616. b. 25.

FÉCAMP. MARTIN (A.) Histoire de Fécamp. *Fécamp,* 1893, etc. 8°. 010171. i.

FEDERAL GOVERNMENT. *See* GOVERNMENT.

FELIXSTOWE. TAYLOR (J. E.) Story of the Felixstowe cliffs. pp. 22. *Ipswich,* 1891. 8°.
Pam. 27.

FELKIRK. FELKIRK. Registers of the Parish Church of Felkirk. pp. 275.
Rochdale, 1894. 8°. 9904. f. 11.

FELSTED GRAMMAR SCHOOL. BEEVOR (R. J.) Alumni Felstedienses. pp. 104. *Lond.* 1890. 8°. 8364. aaa. 44.

FELTHAM. FELTHAM. Short Guide to Feltham. pp. 12. *Lond.* 1889. 16°. Pam. 25.

FENCING. THIMM (C. A.) Complete Bibliography of the Art of Fence. pp. 261.
Lond. 1891. 8°. 011902. e. 9.

ALLANSON-WINN (R. G.) Broad-Sword and Single-Stick. pp. 116. 1890. 8°. All-England Series. 7908. df.

BAUDRY (A.) L'Escrime pratique au XIX° siècle. pp. 150. *Paris,* 1894. 8°. 07905. l. 4.

BROUTIN (C. L.) El arte de la Esgrima. pp. 179. *Madrid,* 1893. 8°. 07905. h. 28.

CARDENAL Y GOMEZ (M.) Las Armas y el duelo. pp. 49. *Habana,* 1886. 8°. Pam. 85.

CASTLE (E.) Schools and masters of Fence. pp. 355. *Lond.* 1892. 8°. 7906. ccc. 31.

—— L'Escrime et les escrimeurs. pp. 281. *Paris,* 1888. 4°. 7908. f. 15.

CIVRY (U. G. de) *Viscount.* Discours sur l'escrime. pp. 8. *Paris,* 1893. 16°.
07905. f. 38. (3.)

EEKHOUD (G.) L'Escrime à travers les âges. pp. 76. *Brux.* 1894. 12°. 7912. aaa. 16.

GELLI (J.) Scherma italiana. pp. 193. *Milano,* 1891. 8°. 7912. a. 8.

G. B. & I. *Army.* Infantry Sword Exercise. 1895. pp. 78. *Lond.* 1895. 8°. 8824. b. 47.

HÉBRARD DE VILLENEUVE ( ) Propos d'Épée. 1882–94. pp. 207. *Paris,* 1894. 8°.
7912. aaa. 12.

HEREDIA (N. A. J. G. J. N. de) *Marquis de Heredia.* Verdades en pocas palabras. pp. 112. *Madrid,* 1892. 8°. 8823. aa. 31.

HERSGELL (G.) Die Fechtkunst. pp. 415. *Wien,* 1892. 8°. 7908. dd. 27.

HUTTON (A.) The Swordsman. A manual of fence. pp. 126. *Lond.* 1891. 8°. 7908. df. 12.

—— Old Sword-play. pp. 36. *Lond.* 1892. 4°.
7908. f. 19.

LECOMTE (C.) L'Escrime au point de vue médical. pp. 91. *Paris,* 1895. 8°. 7906. ee. 35.

LEGUINA (E. de) *Baron de la Vega.* Libros de Esgrima. pp. 165. *Madrid,* 1891. 8°.
011901. g. 8.

MASIELLO (F.) La Scherma italiana. pp. 593. *Firenze,* 1887. 8°. 07905. l. 3.

—— La scherma di sciabola a cavallo. pp. 104. *Firenze,* 1891. 8°. 7912. a. 11.

MURZ (F.) Degen-, Säbel- und Duell-Fechten. pp. 231. *Debreczen,* 1890. 8°. 7907. dd. 2.

P.P. *Milan.* Scherma italiana.
Milano, 1891, etc. fol. 62.

—— *Nancy.* Annuaire des Maîtres d'escrime. *Nancy,* 1894, etc. 8°. P.P. 2436. cd.

POLLOCK (W. H.) Fencing. pp. 304. 1893. 8°. Badminton Library. 2264. aa.

PRÉVOST (C.) and JOLLIVET (G.) L'Escrime et le duel. pp. 257. *Paris,* 1891. 8°. 7908. eee. 5.

ROBAGLIA (A.) L'Escrime et le duel. pp. 294. *Paris,* 1890. 18°. 7908. c. 34.

FEVERS—*continued.*

JOHANNESSEN (A.) Die epidemische Verbreitung des Scharlachfiebers in Norwegen. pp. 214. *Kristiana*, 1884. 8°.   7560. i. 10.

MALCOLM (J. D.) Physiology of death from traumatic Fever. pp. 129. *Lond.* 1893. 8°.   7561. k. 19.

ANDERSON (A. M.) Antiseptic treatment of typhoid Fever. pp. 23. *Dundee*, 1892. 8°.   7560. i. 11.

BARR (J.) The Treatment of typhoid Fever. pp. 212. *Lond.* 1892. 8°.   7561. k. 3.

MARSTON (J. A.) Notes on typhoid Fever. pp. 165. *Lond.* 1890. 8°.   7561. aaa. 22.

WHITEHEAD (H. R.) Tropical typhoid Fever. 1893. 8°. DAVIDSON (A.) Hygiene of Warm Climates.   7686. dd. 2.

WORTHING. Report on the Epidemic of enteric Fever, 1893, in Worthing, *etc.* pp. 59. *Brighton*, 1894. 8°.   7561. h. 33.

YEO (I. B.) Treatment of typhoid Fever by "antiseptic" remedies, *etc.* pp. 70. *Lond.* 1891. 8°.   7561. aa. 9.

DREWITT (F. G. D.) Gangrene of the limbs following typhoid fever. pp. 12. *Lond.* 1894. 8°.   7561. k. 26. (9.)

BÉRENGER-FÉRAUD (L. J. B.) Traité de la Fièvre jaune. pp. 985. *Paris*, 1890. 8°. 7560. i. 6.

CUERVO MÁRQUEZ (L.) La Fiebre amarilla en el interior de Colombia. pp. 340. *Curazao*, 1891. 8°.   7560. d. 2.

JONES (J.) Investigations on the natural history of yellow Fever. pp. 311. *Chicago*, 1894. 8°.   7561. bb. 17.

STERNBERG (G. M.) Yellow Fever. 1893. 8°. DAVIDSON (A.) Hygiene of Warm Climates.   7686. dd. 2.

See also DISEASE, *Infectious:* MALARIA. For Puerperal Fever, *see* OBSTETRICS.

FICTION.

Bibliography.

JERSEY CITY. *Public Library.* Title list of Fiction. pp. 35. *Jersey City*, 1891. 8°.   011901. ce. 7.

MANCHESTER, *N.H. City Library.* Catalogue of English Fiction. pp. 111. *Manch.* 1894. 8°.   011901. ee. 32.

RUSSELL (P.) Guide to British and American novels. pp. 314. *Lond.* 1894. 8°. 011850. g. 44.

ST. LOUIS. *Mercantile Library Association.* Catalogue. English Fiction. pp. 211. *St. Louis*, 1892. 8°.   011901. ee. 8.

GRISWOLD (W. M.) Descriptive List of Novels dealing with American city life. pp. 70. *Camb. Mass.* 1891. 8°.   011902. m.

—— Descriptive List of Novels dealing with American country life. pp. 49. *Camb.* 1890. 8°.   011902. m.

—— Descriptive List of British Novels. pp. 297. *Camb.* 1891. 8°.   011902. m.

—— Descriptive List of Novels dealing with life in France. *Camb.* 1892. 8°.   011902. m.

—— Descriptive List of Novels dealing with life in Norway. pp. 9.11. *Camb.* 1892. 8°. 011902. m.

—— Descriptive List of Novels dealing with life in Russia. *Camb.* 1892. 8°.   011902. m.

—— Descriptive List of international Novels. pp. 53. *Camb.* 1891. 8°.   011902. m.

History, Criticism, etc.

SALVERTE (F. de) Le Roman dans la Grèce ancienne. pp. 403. *Paris*, 1894. 12°. 11312. n. 2.

RALEIGH (W.) The English Novel. pp. 298. 1894. 8°. University Extension Manuals.   12201. f.

FICTION.—History, etc.—*continued.*

ROWLAND (P. F.) Comparison and estimate of English Novelists, 1700–1850. *Oxf.* 1894. 8°.   11825. cc. 57. (12.)

SIMONDS (W. E.) Introduction to the study of English Fiction. pp. 240. *Bost.* 1894. 8°.   011850. cee. 48.

S., J. A. The New Fiction. A protest against sex-mania. pp. 122. 1895. 8°. Westminster Gazette Library. Vol. 3.   012200. 1.

KOERTING (H.) Geschichte des französischen Romans im XVII. Jahrhundert. 2 Bde. *Oppeln.* 1891. 8°.   011824. h. 4.

LE BRETON (A.) Le Roman au 17ᵐᵉ siècle. pp. 322. *Paris*, 1890. 8°.   011824. de. 8.

MORILLOT (P.) Le Roman en France depuis 1610. pp. 611. *Paris*, 1893. 8°. 011850. f. 2.

SAINTSBURY (G. E. B.) Essays on French Novelists. pp. 460. *Lond.* 1891. 8°. 011850. g. 9.

KLINCKSIECK (F.) Zur Entwicklungsgeschichte des Realismus im französischen Roman. pp. 56. *Marburg*, 1891. 8°.   Pam. 15.

VELDE (M. S. v. de) French Fiction of to-day. 2 vol. *Lond.* 1891. 8°.   011840. h. 63.

HEINE (C.) Der Roman in Deutschland, 1774–78. pp. 140. *Halle*, 1892. 8°.   011850. i. 10.

MIELKE (H.) Der deutsche Roman des 19. Jahrhunderts. pp. 351. *Braunschweig*, 1890. 8°.   011840. h. 50.

MORSIER (E. de) Romanciers allemands contemporains. pp. 404. *Paris*, 1890. 8°.   011824. de. 2.

LUZAC (C. J.) De Nederlandsche sentimenteele Roman. pp. 116. *Amersfoort*, 1890. 8°.   011824. h. 23.

ADAM (P.) Le Conte futur. pp. 55. *Paris*, 1893. 8°.   12515. h. 33.

BOWEN (Sir C. S. C.) Novel reading. pp. 24. *Walsall*, 1891. 8°.   011824. h. 29. (10.)

BRUNETIÈRE (F.) Le Roman naturaliste. pp. 370. *Paris*, 1883. 12°.   11840. aa. 7.

GERSCHMANN (H.) Studien über den modernen Roman. pp. 120. *Königsberg*, 1894. 8°.   011850. i. 55.

GREGOROVIUS (L.) Die Verwendung historischer Stoffe in der erzählenden Literatur. pp. 71. *München*, 1891. 8°.   Pam. 15.

HOWELLS (W. D.) Criticism and Fiction. pp. 188. *Lond.* 1891. 8°.   11851. aaa. 8.

MOULTON (R. G.) Four Years of Novel reading. pp. 100. *Lond.* 1895. 8°.   011850. eee. 68.

PERRET (É.) Le Roman. pp. 231. *Lausanne*, 1892. 8°.   011824. h. 70.

THOMPSON (D. G.) Philosophy of Fiction. pp. 226. *N.Y.* 1890. 8°.   011840. g. 85.

TOWNSEND (M. E.) Great characters of Fiction. pp. 226. *Lond.* 1893. 8°.   011850. g. 17.

ZOLA (É. É. C. A.) The experimental Novel. pp. 413. *N.Y.* 1893. 8°.   011850. g. 55.

ART. On the Art of writing Fiction. pp. 138. *Lond.* 1894. 8°.   011850. g. 46.

FICTION. How to write Fiction. ff. 157. 1894. 8°.   11850. dd. 35.

SMITH (B. E.) Cyclopædia of Names. pp. 1085. *Lond.* 1894. fol.   2112. g.

WHEELER (W. A.) Dictionary of the names of noted Fictitious Persons and Places. 1890. 4°. Webster's International Dictionary.   2112. g.

See also under the Literature of each country.

FIDDICHOW. GLOEDE (H.) Heimathlich Bilder aus alter Zeit. pp. 150. *Berl.* 1892. 8°.   10357. f. 23.

FIFE. Geddie (J.) The fringes of Fife.
pp. 184. *Edinb.* 1894. 8°. 010370. eee. 1.

Mackay (Æ. J. G.) Sketch of the history of
Fife. pp. 268. *Edinb.* 1890. 8°. 10369. f. 6.

Millar (A. H.) Fife : pictorial and historical.
2 vol. *Cupar-Fife*, 1895. 4°. 10370. g. 18.

Thomson (J. A.) History of the Fife Light
Horse. pp. 283. *Edinb.* 1892. 4°. 8829. k. 17.

FIGURES. See Numbers.

FIJI. Fiji. The Land tenure of Fiji. pp. 48.
Leruka, 1882. 8°. 10492. cc. 21. (13.)

Levey (G. C.) Handy guide to Australasia.
pp. 392. *Lond.* 1891. 8°. 10192. aaa. 49.

Melbourne. *International Exhibition*, 1880.
Fijian Court. Catalogue, etc. pp. 23.
Melbourne, 1880. 8°. 10492. cc. 24. (10.)
See also Australasia : England, *Colonies:*
Pacific Ocean.

FINANCE. See Trade.

FINCHAMPSTEAD. Lyon (W.) Chronicles
of Finchampstead. pp. 321. *Lond.* 1895. 8°.
10352. i. 38.

FINGALS CAVE. Mac Lean (J. P.) Historical examination of Fingal's Cave. pp. 49.
Cincinnati, 1890. 8°. 010370. f. 17.

FINGERS. See Hand.

FINISTÈRE, Department. Finisterre.
Inventaire-sommaire des archives antérieures à
1790. 1889, *etc.* 4°. Collect on des inventaires-
sommaires. 1814. b, *etc.*

Peyron (É.) Documents pour servir à l'histoire
du Clergé dans le Finistère pendant la Révolution. *Quimper*, 1892, *etc.* 8°. 4629. d.

Du Rusquec (H.) Dictionnaire du dialecte de
Léon. pp. 320. *Paris*, 1895. 8°. 12978. k. 9.
See also Brittany.

FINLAND.

Antiquities.

Aspelin (J. R.) Finlands arkeologiska Myn-
dighet. pp. 10. *Helsingfors*, 1891. 8°.
07703. g. 1. (6.)

Brown (J. C.) People of Finland in archaic
times. pp. 290. *Lond.* 1892. 8°. 7709. aa. 27.

History, Constitution, etc.

Finland. Attioåriga minnen. Deklarationer,
utfärdade i Finland under kriget, 1808–9.
pp. 155. 34. *Helsingfors*, 1890. 8°. 9080. bbb. 30.

Danielson (J. R.) Finlands förening med
Ryska Riket. pp. 196. *Borgå*, 1890. 8°.
8092. e. 2.

—— Finland's Union with the Russian Empire.
pp. 181. *Borgå*, 1891. 8°. 9454. b. 16.

Neovius (A.) Ur Finlands historia.
Borgå, 1890, *etc.* 8°. 9455. de.

Finland. Validity of the Fundamental Laws
of Finland. pp. 62. *Stockholm*, 1892. 8°.
8093. a. 2.

Hermanson (R. F.) Finlands Statsrättsliga
Ställning. pp. 318. *Helsingfors*, 1892. 8°.
8091. k. 1.

—— Bemötande i frågan om Finlands statsrättsliga ställning. pp. 126. *Helsingfors*, 1894. 8°.
8092. d. 2.

Meurman (A.) La Finlande d'autrefois et d'aujourd'hui. pp. 67. *Helsingfors*, 1890. 8°.
10281. f. 8.

Mechelin (L. H. S.) Står Finlands rätt i strid
med Rysslands fördel? pp. 55.
Helsingfors, 1890. 8°. Pam. 74.

Palme (S.) Ställningar och förhållanden i
Finland. pp. 67. *Stockholm*, 1891. 8°.
9007. ff. 4. (10.)

S., E. Finland i 19de seklet. pp. 8.
Helsingfors, 1893. 24°. Pam. 74.

FINLAND—*continued.*

Law. See Law, *Criminal.*

Topography : Social Life.

Ac. Helsingfors. *Suomen Maantieteellinen Seura.*
Fennia. Helsingfors, 1889, *etc.* 8°. Ac. 6113.

Bayley (A. M. C.) Vignettes from Finland.
pp. 301. *Lond.* 1895. 8°. 10290. bb. 20.

Ignatius (C E. F.) Finlands Geografi.
pp. 589. *Helsingfors*, 1881–90. 8°. 10292. h. 12.

Finland. Under Splitflag til Finland som
Passager. pp. 153. *Kjøbenh.* 1892. 8°.
10290. bb. 19.

—— Turistföreningen i Finland.
Helsingfors, 1891. 8°. Pam. 91.

Finnish Women. Finska Qvinnor, *etc.*
Helsingfors, 1892. 8°. 10790. bbb. 39.

Hagström (K. A.) Från Sverige och Finland.
pp. 108. 1891. 8°. Wadström (B.) Nytt
bibliotek. No. 2. 012581. f.

Mechelin (L. H. S.) Finland in 19ten Jahrhundert. pp. 405. *Helsingfors*, 1894. 4°.
10290. i. 5.

—— Finland in the Nineteenth Century.
pp. 367. *Helsingfors*, 1894. 4°. 10290. i. 4.

Meyer (A.) Finnerne og deres Land. pp. 55.
Kjøbenh. 1891. 8°. 10107. c. 13. (6.)

Reedtz-Thott (O.) Fem uger i Finland.
pp. 169. *Kjøbenh.* 1892. 8°. 10292. h. 18.

Reuter (O. M.) Finlands natur, folk och kultur.
pp. 173. *Borgå*, 1889. 8°. 10290. aaa. 14.

Whishaw (F. J.) Romance of the Woods.
pp. 298. *Lond.* 1895. 8°. 012330. g. 87.

Trade, Finance, etc.

Finland. Berättelse afgifven af Finans-Ex-
peditionens i Kejserliga Senaten.
Helsingfors, 1888, *etc.* 8°. 08229. f. 47.

Boxström (A.) Jemförande Befolknings Statistik. pp. 398. *Helsingfors.* 1891. 8°. 8223. de. 4.

FINMARK. Friis (J. A.) Skildringer fra
Finmarken. pp. 155. *Kristiania*, 1891. 8°.
12581. d. 38.

Hagemann (A. O. C.) Engelskmanden under
Finmarken. pp. 145. *Kristiania*, 1891. 8°.
9431. aaa. 7.

Magnus (A.) Finmarken. pp. 139.
Kjøbenh. 1889. 8°. 9454. bb. 13.

**FINNISH LANGUAGE AND LITERA-
TURE.** Ac. Helsingfors. *Suomalais Ugri-
laisen Seura. Apuneuvoja suomalais-ugrilaisten
Kielten opintoja varten. Helsingfors*, 1894, *etc.* 8°.
Ac. 9081/4.

Duka (T.) Essay on Ugor Languages. pp. 67.
Lond. 1889. 8°. 12976. dd. 28.

Eliot (C. N. E.) A Finnish Grammar. pp. 279.
Oxf. 1890. 8°. 2272. a. 24.

Swedish and Finnish School - Interpreter.
Svensk och Finsk Skoltolk. pp. 169.
Helsingfors, 1890. 8°. 12972. aa. 19.

Thomsen (V.) Beröringer mellem de finske.
Sprog. pp. 308. 1890. 8°. Ac. Copenhagen.
Kjøbenhavnsk Selskab. Skrifter. 6. Række.
Bd. 1. Ac. 1023/2.

Wellewill (M.) Praktische Grammatik der
finnischen Sprache. pp. 199. 1890. 8°. Die
Kunst der Polyglottie. Thl. 30. 12902. c.

Krohn (J. L. F.) Finska Litteraturens Historia.
Helsingfors, 1891, *etc.* 8°. 011850. h.

Kalewala. Kalevalson esityöt. 1891, *etc.* 8°.
P.P. *Helsingfors.* Suomi. Jakso III. Osa 4,
etc. P.P. 4852. d.

—— Extracts from the Kalewala. pp. 19.
Camb. 1892. 8°. Pam. 62.

FINNISH LANGUAGE, etc.—*cont.*

BROWN (J. C.) People in Finland. Sketches given in the Kalevala. pp. 290. *Lond.* 1892. 8°.
7709. aa. 27.

COMPARETTI (D.) Der Kalewala. pp. 327. *Halle,* 1892. 8°. 011840. l. 54.

SCHWANENFLUEGEL (H.) Kalevala. En Kulturhistorisk Skitse. pp. 62. *Kjøbenh.* 1891. 8°.
011850. g. 7. (4.)

FIRES AND FIRE BRIGADES. BAYLIS (T. H.) Fire Hints. pp. 30. *Lond.* 1884. 8°.
8715. aa. 54.

BELLAMY (H. F.) Formation and duties of the Selangor Fire Brigade. pp. 9. *Kuala Lumpur,* 1891. 8°. Pam. 79.

BOURNAND (F.) Le régiment de Sapeurs-pompiers de Paris. pp. 34. *Paris,* 1887. fol.
8825. h. 25.

BRAYLEY (A. W.) History of the Boston Fire Department. pp.729. *Bost.* 1889. 8°. 8715. ee. 45.

FALLER (L.) Das Feuerlösch- und Rettungswesen in Elsass-Lothringen. pp. 223. *Rappoltsweiler,* 1893. 8°. 8716. d. 8.

GAUTSCH (C.) Das chemische Feuer-Löschwesen. pp. 167. *München,* 1891. 8°. 8715. f. 42.

GORDON (J. E. H.) Fire risks of electric Lighting. 1891. 8°. GORDON (J. E. M.) Decorative Electricity. 8757. bb. 31.

JONES (A.) Causes of and precautions against Fire. pp. 47. *Lond.* 1894. 8°. 8716. aaa. 46.

LAIDLAW (D. L.) Growing Fire hazard of central City Districts. pp. 24. 1891. 8°. GLASGOW. *Insurance Soc.* Transactions. Ser. 3. No. 3.
08227. e.

LONDON. *Fire Brigade.* Report on the Fires in London during 1890, etc. *Lond.* 1891, etc. 8°. N.R.
—— *National Fire Brigades' Union.* Drill book. pp. 89. *Guildford,* 1894. 16°. 8716. a. 16.
—— *International Fire Tournament.* Official Catalogue and programme. pp. 88. *Lond.* 1893. 8°. 8716. bbb. 47.

MANCHESTER. *Mutual Fire Insurance Corporation.* Automatic Sprinklers. *Manch.* 1889. 12°.
Pam. 79.

MERRYWEATHER (J. C.) Hints on Fire-protection of towns and buildings. pp. 8. *Lond.* 1892. 4°.
8715. k. 17.

MESERVE (A. I.) Fireman's Handbook. pp. 128. *Chicago,* 1890. 8°. 8716. a. 14.

PARIS. *Sapeurs-Pompiers.* Théorie des Sapeurs-Pompiers. pp. 69. 1891. 8°. Encyclopédie-Roret. 12208. b.

PATERSON (W.) Fire Extinction. 1887. 8°. GLASGOW. *Insurance Soc.* Transactions. Ser. 2. No. 9.
08227. e.

P.P. *London,* The Phœnix Gazette. *Lond.* 1885, 86. 4°. P.P. 1691. d.

PHILLIPS (H. J.) The Handling of dangerous Goods. pp. 362. *Lond.* 1895. 8°. 8909. h. 1.

SHAND, MASON AND Co. Occasional Circular. Progress in fire-extinguishing apparatus. *Lond.* 1893, etc. fol. 8715. k.

SHAW (E. M.) Fire Protection. pp. 348. *Lond.* 1890. 8°. 8715. h. 20.

TURIN. *Mostra Internazionale di Macchine per Estinzione di Incendi,* 1887. Catalogo. pp. 127. *Torino,* 1887. 8°. 7956. k. 9.

VALUE. Value of private Fire Brigades. pp. 12. *Lond.* 1891. 24°. Pam. 79.

WELSCH (J. A.) Les Incendies dans les manufactures. pp. 167. *Gand,* 1893. 8°. 8715. bb. 64

EXETER. *Theatre Royal.* Narrative of the fire at the Theatre Royal, Exeter, 1887. pp. 16. *Exeter,* 1887. 8°. Pam. 90.

FIRES, etc.—*continued.*

RÉSUCHE (R.) Crushes and crowds in theatres and other buildings in cases of Fire. pp. 32. *Lond.* 1891. 8°. Pam. 79.

FIRE INSURANCE. See INSURANCE.

FIREWORKS. SONZOGNO (C.) Il Pirotecnico moderno. *Milano,* 1892. 8°. 8716. aaa. 43.

BORY DE LIÈGE (J.) La Pyrotechnie militaire, 1591. pp. 68. *Paris,* 1892. 8°. 8830. g. 33. (6.)

FIROZPUR. FIROZPUR. Gazetteer of the Ferozepore District. pp. 142. *Lahore,* 1889. 8°. 10056. k. 34.
See also PUNJAB.

FIR TREES. See CONIFERA.

FISH AND FISHING.

Fish.

Ac. London. *British Museum. Department of Zoology.* Catalogue of the Fishes in the British Museum. *Lond.* 1895, etc. 8°. 7207. gg. 3.
—— Guide to the Galleries of Reptiles and Fishes. *Lond.* 1893. 8°. 7206. f. 10.

Ac. Plymouth. *Marine Biological Association.* Account of the Marine Biological Association. pp. 7. *Plymouth,* 1894. 8°. Pam. 42.

BOWDICH, afterwards LEE (S.) Anecdotes of the habits of Fishes. pp. 323. *Lond.* 1891. 8°.
7204. a. 21.

CHICAGO. *Colombian Exposition.* Catalogue Part IV. Fisheries Building and Aquaria. pp. 28. *Chicago,* 1893. 8°. 7958. bb. 32.

COWAN (F.) Dictionary of Proverbs relating to the Sea, etc. pp. 144. *Greensburgh, Pa.* 1894. 8°.
12304. g. 34.

DEAN (B.) Fishes, living and fossil. pp. 300. 1895. 8°. Ac. New York. *Columbia College. Biological Series.* Vol. 3. 7002. e.

See also AQUARIUM: COD FISH: CYPRINIDAE: MYXINE.

Local Fish Fauna.

GILL (T. N.) Bibliography of Fishes of the Pacific Coast. pp. 64. 1882. 8°. Bulletin of the U.S. National Museum. No. 11.
Ac. 1875/13.

JORDAN (D. S.) and GILBERT (C. H.) Synopsis of Fishes of North America. pp. 1018. 1882. 8°. Bulletin of the U.S. National Museum. No. 16. Ac. 1875/13.

PENNSYLVANIA. *Fish Commissioners.* Pensylvania's Fish exhibit at the Exposition, Chicago, 1893. pp. 106. *Harrisburg,* 1893. 8°.
7290. bb. 13.

SHIELDS (G. O.) American Game Fishes. pp. 58. *Chicago,* 1892. 8°. 7490. f. 24.

PERUGIA (A.) Appunti sopra alcuni Pesci sud-americani. 1890. 8°. Ac. Genoa. *Museo Civico.* Annali. Ser. 2. Vol. 10. Ac. 2809.

NEW SOUTH WALES. *Commissioners for the Columbian Exposition.* Marine Fish and fisheries of New South Wales. pp. 30. *Sydney,* 1892. 8°. 7958. g. 27.
—— Edible Fishes of New South Wales. pp. 212. *Sydney,* 1893. 8°. 7958. g. 25.

KENT (W. S.) The great Barrier Reef of Australia. pp. 387. *Lond.* 1893. fol. K.T.C. 9. b. 3.

MOREAU (E.) Manuel d'Ichthyologie française. pp. 650. *Paris,* 1892. 8°. 7290. de. 8.

SCHULZE (E.) Fauna Piscium Germaniae. 1890. 8°. Ac. Magdeburg. *Naturwissenschaftlicher Verein.* Jahresbericht, 1889. Ac. 2947/2.

HOUGHTON (W.) British fresh-water Fishes. pp. 231. *Hull,* 1895. 8°. 7290. g. 12.

LUBERTA. List of Fishes of the Great Yarmouth district. pp. 62, *Lowestoft,* 1892. 8°. 7290. aa. 23.

FISH.—Local Fish Fauna—*continued.*

DUBLIN. *Science and Art Museum.* Catalogue of Collection of Irish Fishes. pp. 34. *Dublin,* 1889. 8°.   7204. c. 17. (6.)

WEBER (M.) Die Süsswasser-Fische des indischen Archipels. 1894. 8°. Zoologische Ergebnisse einer Reise in niederländisch Ost-Indien. Bd. 3.   7205. f. 4.

COCKERELL (T. D. A.) List of the Fishes of Jamaica. pp. 16. 1892. fol. Ac. Kingston. *Institute of Jamaica.* Bulletin. No. 1.   Ac. 1958/4.

GOURRET (P.) Les Pêcheries et les Poissons de la Méditerranée. pp. 360. *Paris,* 1894. 12°.   7290. a. 28.

FRIES (B. F.) Scandinaviens Fiskar målade af W. von Wright. *Stockholm,* 1893, *etc.* 4°.   7290. k.

—— History of Scandinavian Fishes. *Stockholm,* 1893, *etc.* 4°.   7290. k.

ASPER (G.) Les Poissons de la Suisse et la pisciculture. pp. 192. *Lausanne,* 1891. 8°.   7290. e. 25.

See also infra : FISHERIES.

'Cookery. *See* COOKERY.

Fish Culture.

BETTONI-CAZZAGO (E.) Piscicoltura d' acqua dolce. pp. 318. *Milano,* 1895. 12°.   012200. i. 15.

BORNE (M. v. d.) Teichwirtschaft. pp. 190. 1894. 8°. Thaer-Bibliothek. Bd. 89. 7078. aaa.

BULLO (G. S.) Piscicultura marina. *Padova,* 1891, *etc.* 8°.   7290. e. 28.

—— Atlante. fol.   1819. a. 26.

FRANCE. *Ministère de l'Agriculture.* Annales de la Station aquicole de Boulogne. *Bologne,* 1892, *etc.* 4°.   7290. g.

FRITSCH (A.) Der Elbelachs. pp. 113. *Prag,* 1893. 8°.   7290. g. 13.

GOODE (G. B.) Fishery Exhibition, Berlin, 1880. Exhibit of fisheries and fish culture of the U.S. pp. 263. 1890. 8°. Bulletin of the U.S. National Museum. No. 18. Ac. 1875/13.

GOBIN (A.) La Pisciculture en eaux salées. pp. 353. *Paris,* 1891. 12°.   7290. a. 19.

HALFORD (F. M.) Making a Fishery. pp. 212. *Lond.* 1895. 8°.   K.T.C. 32. b. 4.

MAITLAND (*Sir* J. R. G.) On stocking Rivers with Salmonidae. pp. 75. *Stirling,* 1892. 8°.   7290. e. 26.

PALACKY (J.) Die Verbreitung der Fische. pp. 239. *Prag,* 1891. 8°.   7290. f. 22.

P.P. *Sézanne.* Étangs et Rivières. Bulletin de pisciculture. *Paris,* 1888, *etc.* 8°.   P.P. 1950. ae.

TRYBOM (F.) Fiskevård och Fiskodling. pp. 199. *Stockholm,* 1893. 8°.   7290. a. 25.

Fishing and Fisheries.

Angling : Amateur Fishing.

AMPHLETT (F. H.) The Lower and Mid Thames. pp. 128. *Lond.* 1894. 8°.   7912. aaa. 13.

ANGLER. The complete Angler. pp. 141. *N.Y.* 1891. 8°.   7908. ee. 22.

BEEVER (J.) Practical Fly-fishing. pp. 54. *Lond.* 1893. 8°.   7906 dd. 11.

BERNES (J.) An older form of the Treatyse of Fysshynge with an angle. pp. 37. 1883. 8°. Ac. London. *English Dialect Society.* Miscellanies.   Ac. 9935/3.

BICKERDYKE (J.) Sea Fishing. pp. 562. 1895. 8°. Badminton Library.   7905. f.

—— Days of my Life on waters fresh and salt. pp. 227. *Lond.* 1895. 8°.   07905. g. 6.

FISH.—Angling, etc.—*continued.*

BRADLEY (T.) The Yorkshire Anglers' Guide. pp. 143. *Leeds,* 1893. 8°.   7907. ff. 3.

BURGESS (J. T.) Angling and how to angle. pp. 212. *Lond.* 1895. 8°.   07905. ee. 2.

CLARKE (K.) The Practical Angler. pp. 207. *N.Y.* 1892. 8°.   7907. df. 11.

FISHER (A. T.) Rod and River. pp. 375. *Lond.* 1892. 8°.   7908. d. 34.

FOLIN (L. de). Pêches et chasses zoologiques. pp. 332. *Paris,* 1893. 8°.   7206. e. 15.

GRAHAM (P. A.) Country Pastimes for boys. pp. 448. *Lond.* 1895. 8°.   07905. f. 32.

GRIMBLE (A.) Shooting and Salmon fishing. pp. 259. *Lond.* 1892. 4°.   7908. f. 17.

HALFORD (F. M.) Dry-Fly Fishing in theory and practice. pp. 289. *Lond.* 1889. 8°.   K.T.C. 5. b. 15.

HEARDER AND SON. Illustrated Guide to Sea Fishing. pp. 115. *Plymouth,* 1892. 16°   7915. de. 19. (2.)

—— Trout and Salmon Fishing in the neighbourhood. pp. 16. *Plymouth,* 1893. 16°.   7915. de. 19. (4.)

HOPKINS (F. P.) Fishing Experiences of half a century. pp. 225. *Lond.* 1893. 8°. 07905. f. 7.

KEENE (J. H.) Boy's own guide to Fishing. pp. 200. *Bost.* 1894. 8°.   07905. f. 31.

LA BLANCHÈRE (P. R. M. H.) La Pêche aux bains de mer. pp. 323. *Paris,* 1894. 4°.   7290. g. 11.

LANG (A.) Angling Sketches. pp. 185. *Lond.* 1895. 8°.   07905. f. 28.

LOCARD (A.) La Pêche et les poissons des eaux douces. pp. 352. *Paris,* 1891. 12°. 7290. aa. 21.

MAC CARTHY (E.) The Leaping Ouananiche : what it is, where to catch it. pp. 66. *N.Y.* 1894. 8°.   7290. de. 9.

MAC VINE (J.) Sixty-three Years' angling. pp. 263. *Lond.* 1891. 8°.   7908. ee. 14.

MOLL (R.) Illustrated guide to Fishing in Norfolk waters. pp. 111. *Lond.* 1893. 8°.   7912. aa. 24.

NIVEN (R.) British Angler's lexicon. pp. 270. *Bp. Auckland,* 1892. 8°.   07905. f. 5.

PASKE (C. T.) and AFLALO (F. G.) The Sea and the Rod. pp. 224. *Lond.* 1892. 8°. 7906. df. 26.

PATTERSON (A.) Fish-Hook and float. Salt water Fishing. pp. 62. *Great Yarmouth,* 1891. 4°.   7908. ee. 20.

PENNELL (H. C.) Fishing. pp. 481. 1893, *etc.* 8°. Badminton Library.   2264. aa.

RASHLEIGH (E. W.) "Where to Fish"—"When to fish." pp. 57. *Fowey,* 1894. 8°.   7204. c. 17. (14.)

RED SPINNER. A Mixed Bag : medley of angling stories. pp. 252. *Lond.* 1895. 12°.   012629. de. 13.

SAMUELS (E. A.) With Fly-rod and camera. pp. 477. *N.Y.* 1890. 8°.   7907. i. 21.

SANDEMAN (F.) Angling Travels in Norway. pp. 286. *Lond.* 1895. 4°.   7905. i. 29.

—— By Hook and by crook. pp. 255. *Lond.* 1892. 8°.   7908. f. 22.

SHIELDS (G. O.) American Game Fishes. pp. 580. *Chicago,* 1892. 8°.   7290. f. 24.

SHRUBSOLE (E. S.) Long Casts and sure rises. pp. 159. *Lond.* 1893. 8°.   07905. f. 11.

SPACKMAN (W. H.) Trout in New Zealand. pp. 99. *Wellington,* 1892. 8°. 10492. bb. 39.

STODDART (T. T.) The Angler's Companion. pp. 207. *Lond.* 1892. 8°.   7908. eee. 10.

T., J. Yorkshire Fishing and shooting. pp. 40. *Lond.* 1894. 8°.   07905. h. 22.

FISH.—Angling, etc.—*continued.*

TAYLER (J.) Red Palmer: a treatise on fly-fishing. pp. 88. *Folkestone*, 1893. 8°. 7912. aaa. 5.

WALTON (I.) The Complete Angler. Edited by G. W. Bethune. 2 vol. *Lond.* 1891. 8°.
7908. dd. 9.

—— The Complete Angler. Edited by J. E. Harting. 2 vol. *Lond.* 1893. 8°.
K.T.C. 19. a. 4.

MARSTON (R. B.) Walton and some earlier writers on Fishing. pp. 264. 1894. 8°.
WHEATLEY (H. B.) Book-Lover's Library.
11900. aa.

HALE (J. H.) How to tie Salmon Flies. pp. 123. *Lond.* 1892. 8°. 7908. dd. 19.

KELSON (G. M.) The Salmon Fly. *Lond.* 1895. 8°. 7907. i. 27.

MARBURG (M. O.) Favourite Flies and their histories. pp. 522. *Bost.* 1892. 4°. 7907. dd. 17.

Fisheries.

CHICAGO. *Exposition.* Catalogue. Pt. IV. Fish, Fisheries, etc. *Chicago*, 1893. 8°. 7958. bb. 32.

ERNAULT (L.) and JAUBERT (E.) La conquête de la Mer. pp. 280. *Paris*, 1895. 4°.
10497. f. 23.

G. B. & I. *Meteorological Office.* Fishery Barometer manual. pp. 81. *Lond.* 1887. 8°.
8754. cc. 26.

HAYNES (T. H.) International Fishery disputes. pp. 24. *Lond.* 1891. 8°. 8026. i. 6. (9.)

—— Territorial Waters and ocean fishery rights, etc. pp. 20. *Lond.* 1893. 8°. 6190. aa. 31. (14.)

America.

AMERICAN HISTORY. Winnowings in American history. Fisheries Series. *Brooklyn*, 1890, etc. 8°.
9551. aaa.

GOODE (G. B.) Fishery Exhibition, Berlin. Exhibit of the Fisheries of the U.S. 1880. 8°. Bulletin of the U.S. Nat. Museum. No. 18.
Ac. 1875/13.

GRENFELL (W. T.) Vikings of to-day: Life among the fishermen of Labrador. pp. 240. *Lond.* 1895. 8°. 10460. bb. 27.

PENNSYLVANIA. *Fish Commissioners.* Fisheries of Pennsylvania. pp. 106. *Harrisburg*, 1893. 8°.
7290. bb. 13.

RATHBUN (R.) Summary of Fishery investigations in the North Pacific Ocean and Behring Sea, 1888–92. 1894. 8°. U.S. *Commission of Fisheries.* Bulletin. Vol. 12. 7290. dd.

U.S.A. *Commission of Fish and Fisheries.* Bulletin. Vol. 8, etc. *Wash.* 1890, etc. 8°. 7290. dd.

—— Report of the Commissioner. *Wash.* 1891, etc. 8°. 7290. c.
See also BEHRING SEA.

Australasia.

KENT (W. S.) The great Barrier Reef of Australia. pp. 387. *Lond.* 1893. fol. K.T.C. 9. b. 3.

NEW SOUTH WALES. Marine Fisheries. pp. 30. *Sydney*, 1892. 8°. 7958. g. 27.

—— History of the Fisheries of New South Wales. pp. 126. *Sydney*, 1893. 8°. 7953. g. 26.

—— Edible Fishes, etc. pp 212. *Sydney*, 1893. 8°. 7958. g. 25.

Europe.

ALMEIDA (G.) Os Açores e a industria piscatoria. pp. 28. *S. Miguel*, 1893. 8°. Pam. 23.

BERTHOULE (A.) Rapport sur un projet de constitution d'assurances mutuelles entre marins-pêcheurs. pp. 102. *Paris*, 1892. 8°. 8282. cc. 48. (5.)

LITTAYE ( ) Notice sur la Pêche de la Morue. pp. 56. *Paris*, 1891. 8°. 7290. f. 21.

MEYS (M.) La Pêche du Hareng à Boulogne. pp. 30. *Abbeville*, 1894. fol. 7290. i. 2.

FISHERIES.—Europe—*continued.*

ROCHÉ (G.) Les grandes Pêches maritimes de la France. pp. 164. 1894. 8°. Encyclopédie des aide-mémoire. 8709. g.

SCHWAPPACH (A.) Fischereipolitik. pp. 396. 1894. Handbuch der Staatswissenschaft. Bd. 10. 8009. k.

BIBRA (v.) and LICHTENBERG ( ) Das Gesetz für Elsass-Lothringen betreffend die Fischerei, 2 Juli 1891. pp. 156. *Strassb.* 1893. 8°.
5604. de. 11.

AFLALO (F. G.) Sea-Fishing on the English Coast. pp. 190. *Lond.* 1891. 8°. 7908. ee. 11.

G. B. & I. *Board of Trade.* Regulations for lettering, numbering and registering British Sea Fishing Boats. pp. 16. *Lond.* 1893. 8°.
Pam. 43.

CALDERWOOD (W. L.) Mussel Culture and the bait supply. pp. 121. *Lond.* 1895. 8°.
7290. a. 24.

SALMOND (J. B.) Silvaceas, or the manners and superstitions of the Fisher folks of Scotland. pp. 9. *Lowestoft*, 1892. 8°. Pam. 90.

STEWART (C.) Treatise on the Law of Scotland relating to rights of Fishing. pp. 582. *Edinb.* 1892. 8°. 6583. g. 10.

HOLT (E. W. L.) Survey of Fishing grounds. West Coast of Ireland. 1893. 8°. Ac. Dublin. *Dublin Society.* Scientific Transactions. Vol. v. Ser. II. Ac. 3505/7.

IRELAND. *Fisheries Office.* Digest of principal sections in Acts of Parliament relating to the Irish Fisheries. pp. 149. *Dublin*, 1891. 8°.
6503. a. 13.

—— Useful hints on the cure of Codfish and Herrings. pp. 40. *Dublin*, 1891. 8°. Pam. 94.

DRECHSEL (C. F.) Samling af Islandske Love gældende for Fiskeriet. pp. 40. *Kjøbenh.* 1892. 8°. Pam. 34.

GICQUEL (F.) Les Pêcheries sur les côtes d'Islande. pp. 42. *Saint-Brieuc*, 1893. 8°.
7004. df. 22. (12.)

ICELAND. Íslenzka síldarveiða-lögin með norskr i þýðing eftir J. Olafsson. pp. 15. *Eskifirði*, 1880. 8°. 867. i. 46. (3.)

GOURRET (P.) Les Pêcheries de la Méditerranée. pp. 360. *Paris*, 1894. 12°. 7290. a. 28.

HOOGENDIJK (A.) De Grootvisscherij op de Noordzee. pp. 349. *Haarlem*, 1893. 8°.
7290. f. 27.

VERHEIJ (A.) and FILLEKES (H.) Seinboekje voor Nederlandsche Visschersschepen. pp. 95. *Vlaardingen*, 1891. 8°. 8807. b. 60.

Ac. Paris. *Société d'Acclimatation, etc.* Les grandes Pêches en Norvège. pp. 58. *Paris*, 1892. 8°. Ac. 3555/6.

DRECHSEL (C. F.) Oversigt over vore Saltvandsfiskerier i Nordsøen. pp. 146. *Kjøbenh.* 1890. 4°.
7290. k. 6.

CORONEL (S.) Précis d'une monographie d'un Pêcheur-côtier du Finmark. 1891. 8°. Ac. Paris. *Société des études pratiques.* Les ouvriers des deux mondes. Sér. 2. Fasc. 31. 8282. f. 18.

FISTULA. *See* RECTUM.

FIUME. FEST (A.) Fiume zur Zeit der Uskokenwirren. pp. 88. *Triest*, 1893. 8°.
10210. f. 6.

FIVES. AINGER (A. C.) Fives. 1894. 8°. Badminton Library. 2264. aa. 11.
See also GAMES.

FLAGELLATA. *See* PROTOZOA.

FLAGS. BLAND (W.) National Banners; their history and construction. pp. 2. 1892. 8°. 9900. b. 9. (14.)

FLORENCE.—Topography—_continued._

MARCOTTI (J.) Guide-souvenir de Florence. pp. 417. _Florence_, 1892. 8°.   10135. aaa 11.

SCOTT (L.) Echoes of old Florence. pp. 326. _Lond._ 1894. 8°.   10132. aaa. 13.

—— The Orti Oricellari. pp. 278. _Florence_, 1893. 8°.   10135. g. 11.

FRANCESCHINI (P.) L'Oratorio di San Michele in Orto in Firenze. pp. 108. _Firenze_, 1892. 8°.   4605. bb. 13.

CAVALLUCCI (C. J.) S. Maria del Fiore e la sua facciata. pp. 173. _Firenze_, 1887. 8°. 4605. c. 10.

GODKIN (G. S.) The Monastery of San Marco. pp, 90. _Florence_, 1892. 8°.   4865. bbb. 51.

GOTTI (A.) Storia del Palazzo Vecchio in Firenze. pp. 392. _Firenze_, 1889. 4°. 10131. i. 6.

KÁROLY (K.) Guide to the paintings of Florence. pp. 344. _Lond._ 1893. 8°.   7857. a. 41.

Dialect.

FRIZZI (G.) Dizionario dei frizzetti popolari fiorentini. pp. 267. _Città di C._ 1890. 8°.   12941. de. 8.

FLORIDA. FLORIDA. _Department of Agriculture._ Report of the Commissioner of Agriculture. pp. 133. _Tallahassee_, 1893. 8°.   7074. k. 14.

NORTON (C· L.) Handbook of Florida. pp. 380. _Lond._ 1891. 8°.   10409. aa. 29.

PIO (L.) The east coast of Florida. pp. 37. 1893. 12°.   Pam. 86.

RUIDÍAZ Y CARAVIA (E.) La Florida. 2 tom. _Madrid_, 1893. 8°.   9615. dd. 6.

STUART (H. W. V.) Adventures amidst the forests and rivers of South America and in Florida. pp. 268. _Lond._ 1891. 8°. 10481. i. 23.

TORREY (B.) A Florida Sketch-book. pp. 242. _Bost._ 1894. 8°.   10413. b. 39.

WILLIAMS (F. H.) Florida. Practical information. pp. 16. _Lond._ 1894! 8°.   Pam. 86.

—— Florida for fruit farming. _Lond._ 1890. 8°   Pam. 86.

———————

FLORIDA. Table of Florida cases. pp. 89. _Charleston_, 1892. 8°.   06616. k. 10.

FLOUR. _See_ CORN.

FLOWERS. COOKE (M. C.) Across the common after wildflowers. pp. 98. _Lond._ 1895. 8°.   7029. a. 16.

—— Around a cornfield in a ramble after wild flowers. pp. 98. _Lond._ 1895. 8°. 7029. a. 17.

—— Down the lane and back, in search of wild flowers. pp. 114. _Lond._ 1895. 8°. 7029. a. 19.

—— A stroll on a marsh, in search of wild flowers. pp. 94. _Lond._ 1895. 8°. 7029. a. 18.

—— Through the copse. pp. 106. _Lond._ 1895. 8°.   7029. a. 20.

CONDER (J.) Flowers of Japan and the art of floral arrangement. pp. 136. _Tokio_, 1891. fol.   K.T.C. 4. b. 16.

GORDON (W. J.) Our Country's Flowers. pp. 154. _Lond._ 1891. 8°.   07028. g. 10.

HEATHCOTE (E. D.) Flowers of the Engadine. pp. 22. pl. 224. _Winchester_, 1891. 8°. 7054. g. 13.

HENSLOW (G.) The Making of Flowers. pp. 168. 1891. 8°. Romance of Science Series. 4421. de.

HIBBERD (S.) Field Flowers. pp. 156. _Lond._ 1894. 8°.   7055. aaa. 6.

GORI (P.) L'Amore per i Fiori. pp. 333. _Firenze_, 1894. 8°.   7029. b. 29.

HIBBERD (S.) The Amateur's Flower Garden. pp. 310. _Lond._ 1892. 8°.   2252. b. 14.

HULME (F. E.) Familiar wild Flowers. Ser. 5. _Lond._ 1894. 8°.   07028. e. 43.

FLOWERS—_continued._

KEELER (H. L.) Wild Flowers of early spring. pp. 69. _Cleveland_, 1894. 8°.   Pam. 1.

MACDONALD (D.) Sweet-scented Flowers and fragrant leaves. pp. 136. _Lond._ 1895. 8°.   7030. bbb. 4.

MATHEWS (F. S.) Familiar Flowers of field and garden. pp. 308. _N.Y._ 1895. 8°.   07028. k. 28.

MILLER (E.) and WHITING (M. C.) Wild flowers of the North-Eastern States. pp. 622. _N.Y._ 1895. 4°.   7029. k. 16.

N.. J. W. Town Flowers. pp. 32. _Lond._ 1893. 8°.   Pam. 1.

PLANCHON (G.) Rapport sur la coloration artificielle des Fleurs. pp. 7. _Paris_, 1892. 4°.   Pam. 13.

PITTS (H.) Flowers and their lessons. pp. 46. _Lond._ 1891. 8°.   Pam. 95.

PLUES (M.) Rambles in search of wild flowers. pp. 368. _Lond._ 1892. 8°.   07028. e. 37.

ROBINSON (W.) Hardy Flowers. pp. 341. _Lond._ 1893. 8°.   7029. aa. 37.

—— The English Flower garden. pp. 751. _Lond._ 1895. 8°.   2251. e. 13.

ROOZEN (A.) Notes on the cultivation of Dutch and Cape bulbs. pp. 148. _Lond._ 1894. 8°.   07028. e. 44.

SPARKES (J. C. L.) and BURBIDGE (F. W.) Wild Flowers in art and nature. _Lond._ 1894, etc. 4°.   7029. i. 16.

STEP (E.) Wayside and woodland Blossoms. pp. 173. _Lond._ 1895. 8°.   7030. de. 4.

SUTTON AND SONS. Culture of Flowers from seeds and roots. pp. 425. _Lond._ 1895. 8°.   07028. f. 54.

WEED (C. M.) Ten New England Blossoms and their insect visitors. pp. 142. _Bost._ 1895. 8°.   07028. e. 56.

See also BEGONIA : BOTANY : CARNATION : CHRYSANTHEMUM : GARDENING : HEPATICA : LILIACEAE : PRIMULACEAE, _etc._

Floral Decoration.

DE SALIS (H. A.) Floral Decorations. pp. 116. _Lond._ 1891. 8°.   07945. e. 55.

CONDER (J.) Flowers of Japan and the art of floral arrangement. pp. 136. _Tokio_, 1891. fol.   K.T.C. 4. b. 16.

Flower Painting. _See_ PAINTING.

Language of Flowers.

AUSTRALIAN FLOWERS. Language of Australian Flowers. pp. 27. _Melbourne_, 1891. 16°.   7054. de. 1.

GRANT (M. K.) Language of Flowers birthday book. pp. 271. _Lond._ 1895. 16°. 7030. a. 6.

LANGUAGE. The Language of Flowers. _Lond._ 1890. 16°.   7054. aa. 23.

READER (E. E.) Voices of Flower-land. _Lond._ 1893. 8°.   11601. aaa. 42.

Artificial Flowers.

USES. Uses of coloured Tissue Paper. pp. 32. _Lond._ 1889. 8°.   7942. i. 43. (9.)

FLUTE. ROCKSTRO (R. S.) Treatise on Construction, history, and practice of the Flute. pp. 664. _Lond._ 1890. 8°.   7898. k. 35.

WELCH (C.) History of the Boehm Flute. pp. 269. _Lond._ 1892. 8°.   7898. l. 31.

See also MUSICAL INSTRUMENTS.

FLYING MACHINES. _See_ BALLOONS.

FOIX. LESCAZES (J. J.) Mémorial historique contenant la narration des troubles dans le païs de Foix, 1490-1640. pp. 280. _Foix._ 1894. 4°.   4629. cc. 5.

FOIX—*continued.*

DOUBLET (G.) Incidents de la vie à Foix sous Louis XIV. pp. 44. *Foix*, 1894. 8°.   Pam. 91.

—— Incidents de la vie à Foix sous Louis XV. pp. 47. *Foix*, 1895. 12°.   Pam. 91.

—— Incidents de la vie à Foix sous Louis XVI. pp. 34. *Foix*, 1895. 12°.   Pam. 91.

DARNAUD (É.) Une Révolte à Foix, 1840. pp. 37. *Foix*, 1890. 8°.   9072. c. 9. (9.)

—— L'Évolution des villageois dans l'arrondissement de Foix. pp. 3. *Foix*, 1895. 4°. Pam. 82.

FOLIGNO. FALOCI PULIGNANI (M.) Le Relazioni tra S. Francesco d'Assisi et la città di Foligno. pp. 49. *Foligno*, 1893. 8°. Pam. 10.

FOLKESTONE. BIRCH (W. P.) Pocket guide to Folkestone. *Folkestone*, 1891. 32°.   Pam. 90.

ENGLISH (J.) Reminiscences of old Folkestone smugglers. pp. 72. *Folkestone*, 1885. 8°.   10348. bbbb. 14. (4.)

FOLKESTONE. Handbook of Folkestone. pp. 176. *Folkestone*, 1894. 8°.   10350. aaa. 55.

WATFORD (R. J.) Photographs of Folkestone. *Folkestone*, 1895. obl. 8°.   10350. aa. 33.

WOODWARD (M.) Past and present of the Parish Church of Folkestone. pp. 138. *Lond.* 1892. 8°.   010358. e. 17.

FOLK LORE.

General.

AC. Boston, *Mass. American Folk-Lore Society.* Memoirs. *Bost.* 1894, *etc.* 8°.   Ac. 9959/2.

—— London. *Folk Lore Society.* Cox (M. R.) Cinderella. Three hundred and forty-five variants. pp. 535. *Lond.* 1893. 8°. Ac. 9938/13.

—— Denham Tracts. A collection of folklore. *Lond.* 1892, *etc.* 8°.   Ac. 9938/12.

—— GOMME (G. L.) Handbook of Folklore. pp. 193. *Lond.* 1890. 8°.   Ac. 9938/10.

—— Europe. *Congrès des traditions populaires.* Première Session, 1889. Compte rendu des séances. pp. 168. *Paris*, 1891. 8°. Ac. 9796.

CHARENCY (H. de) *Count.* Le Folklore dans les deux mondes. pp. 424. *Paris*, 1894. 8°.   12430. k. 42.

COX (M. R.) Introduction to Folklore. pp. 320. *Lond.* 1895. 8°.   12431. cc. 39.

FAURE ( ) Récits et légendes du moyen-âge. pp. 514. *Saint-Amand.* 1893. 8°.   4532. df. 3.

GOMME (G. L.) Ethnology in Folklore. pp. 200. 1892. 8°. LUBBOCK (*Sir J.*) Modern Science.   8709. f.

GAIDOZ (H.) Un vieux rite médical. pp. 84. *Paris*, 1892. 8°.   4503. de. 6.

GRAF (A.) Miti e superstizioni del medio evo. 2 vol. *Torino*, 1892, 93. 8°.   12430. bb. 39.

GRÜN (C.) Les Esprits élémentaires. pp. 263. *Verviers*, 1891. 8°.   8632. ccc. 16.

HENNE-AM-RHYN (O.) Eine Reise durch das Reich des Aberglaubens. pp. 175. *Leipz.* 1893. 8°.   8632. d. 25.

INWARDS (R.) Weather Lore. pp. 190. *Lond.* 1893. 8°.   8755. cc. 58.

JACOBS (J.) Science of Folk-Tales and the problem of diffusion. *Lond.* 1892. 8°. 12430. g. 39. (5.)

—— Problem of diffusion of Folk-Tales. pp. 20. *Lond.* 1894. 8°.   12410. ccc. 12. (4.)

KIRK (R.) Secret Commonwealth of elves, fauns, and fairies. pp. 92. *Lond.* 1893. 8°. 8632. g. 20.

KOEHLER (R.) Aufsätze über Märchen und Volkslieder. pp. 152. *Berl.* 1894. 8°.   12430. i. 48.

LUND (L.) Tolv Fragmenter om Hedenskabet med særligt Hensyn til Forholdene i Nord-og-Mellem-Europa. *Kjøbenh.* 1891, *etc.* 8°. 4506. g.

FOLK LORE.—**General**—*continued.*

PAULUCCI DE' CALBOLI (L.) Maggio e calendimaggio. pp. 218. *Roma*, 1894. 8°. 12430. a. 36.

P.P. *Leipsic.* Zeitschrift für Volkskunde. Bd. 1–4. *Leipz.* 1888–92. 8°.   P.P. 3863. d.

—— *Lunden.* Am Ur-Quell. Monatschrift für Volkskunde. *Hamb.* 1890, *etc.* 8°.   897.

PLOIX (C.) Le surnaturel dans les Contes populaires. pp. 211. *Paris*, 1891. 12°. 12430. cc. 30.

SÉBILLOT (P.) Légendes et curiosités des métiers. *Paris*, 1895, *etc.* 8°.   12430. i.

—— Les Travaux publics et les Mines dans les traditions. pp. 623. *Paris*, 1894. 8°.   12431. k. 22.

SEPP (J.) Völkerbrauch bei Hochzeit, Geburt und Tod. pp. 176. *München*, 1891. 8°.   12431. cc. 7.

SUPERSTITIONS. Strange and curious Superstitions. pp. 24. *Lond.* 1891. 8°. 12431. d. 41. (6.)

WAGNER (L.) Manners, customs and observances. pp. 318. *Lond.* 1895. 8°. 12431. b. 54.

CRAMPON ( ) Le Juif-Errant. 1893. 8°. Ac. Amiens. *Académie des Sciences.* Mémoires. Tom. 40.   Ac. 540.

COMPARETTI (D.) Vergil in the Middle Ages. pp. 376. *Lond.* 1895. 8°.   011824. e. 62.

HULME (F. E.) Natural History lore and legend. pp. 350. *Lond.* 1895. 8°.   12411. ccc. 1.

STEINER (C. J.) Die Tierwelt nach ihrer Stellung in Mythologie und Volksglauben. pp. 323. *Gotha*, 1891. 8°.   12431. ee. 8.

GLOCK (J. P.) Die Symbolik der Bienen in Sage, Dichtung, *etc.* pp. 411. *Heidelb.* 1891. 8°.   011824. h. 41.

FRIEND (H.) Flowers and flower lore. 2 vol. *Lond.* 1892. 8°.   12431. ee. 9.

ROSENKRANZ (C.) Die Pflanzen im Volksaberglauben. pp. 415. *Kassel*, 1893. 8°.   12430. c. 36.

SLOET VAN DE BEELE (L. A. J. W.) De Planten in het germaansche Volksgeloof. pp. 98. *'s Gravenh.* 1890. 8°.   12431. f. 49.

See also CHARMS : EVIL EYE.

Folk Lore of various Countries.

Africa.

ARTIN (Y.) Contes populaires de la vallée du Nil. pp. 287. 1895. 8°. Les Littératures populaires. Tom. 32.   2318. aa.

BUETTNER (C. G.) Lieder und Geschichten der Suaheli. pp. 202. 1894. 8°. Beiträge zur Völkerkunde. Bd. 3.   10007. f.

CHATELAIN (H.) Folk-tales of Angola. pp. 315. 1894. 8°. Ac. Boston. *American Folk-Lore Society.* Memoirs. Vol. 1.   Ac. 9959/2.

FERRAND (G.) Contes populaires malgaches. pp. 266. 1893. 8°. Collection de contes.   2348. a.

JACOTTET (E.) Contes populaires des Bassoutos. pp. 292. 1895. 8°. Collection de Contes populaires. 20.   2348. aa. 30.

KAFIR FOLK LORE. Specimens of Kaffir Folklore. 1893. 8°. TONGA. Ethnographical Notes in Tonga, *etc.*   Ac. 9808.

STANLEY (H. M.) My dark Companions and their stories. pp. 335. *Lond.* 1893. 8°.   12430. dd. 24.

Albania. See infra : Turkey.

Basques.

MONTEIRO (M.) Legends and popular tales of the Basque people. pp. 274. *Lond.* 1890. 8°.   12431. ee. 12.

Basutoland. See supra : Africa.

FOLK LORE—*continued.*

Belgium.

HAROU (A.) Contributions au Folklore de la Belgique. pp. 88. 1892. 12°. Collection de La Tradition. Vol. 9.   12430. aaa. 47.

Ac. Liége. *Société du Folklore wallon.* Bulletin de Folklore. *Brux.* 1891, *etc.* 8°. Ac. 9871/2.

—— Questionnaire de Folklore. pp. 153. *Liége,* 1891. 8°.   Ac. 9871.

GITTÉE (A.) and LEMOINE (J.) Contes populaires du Pays wallon. pp. 176. *Gand,* 1891. 8°.   12430. h. 44.

MONSEUR (E.) Le Folklore wallon. pp. 144. *Brux.* 1892. 12°.   12431. ee. 23.

Bengal. See infra : India.

Bohemia.

KRAUSS (F. S.) Böhmische Korallen aus der Götterwelt. pp. 147. *Wien,* 1893. 8°.   12430. k. 39.

Brazil.

MELLO-MORAES (A. J. de). Festas e tradiçoes populares do Brazil. pp. 480. *Rio de J.* 1895. 8°.   12430. i. 49.

ROMERO (S.) Contos populares do Brazil. pp. 235. *Lisboa,* 1885. 8°.   12431. ccc. 12.

SANTA ANNA NERY (F. J. de) Folk-Lore brésilien. pp. 272. *Paris,* 1889. 8°.   12430. cc. 28.

Brittany. See infra : France.

Bukowina.

WLISLOCKI (H. v.) Märchen und Sagen der Bukowinaer. pp. 188. *Hamburg,* 1891. 8°.   12430. g. 38.

Cambodia.

LECLÈRE (A.) Cambodge. Contes et légendes. pp. 308. *Paris,* 1895. 8°.   12411. h. 10.

Celtic. See infra : France : Ireland : Scotland : Wales.

Denmark. See infra : Scandinavia.

England.

GOULD (S. B.) Old English fairy tales. pp. 400. *Lond.* 1895. 8°.   12411. c. 38.

—— Book of nursery songs and rhymes. pp. 160. *Lond.* 1895. 8°.   11602. d. 37.

GOMME (G. L.) Dictionary of British Folklore. *Lond.* 1894. *etc.* 8°.   2348. d. 1.

HARTLAND (E. S.) English fairy and folk tales. pp. 282. *Lond.* 1893. 8°.   12411. ee. 20.

HAZLITT (W. C.) Tales and legends of national origin. pp. 486. *Lond.* 1892. 8°. 12411. h. 2.

HOPE (R. C.) Legendary Lore of the Holy Wells of England. pp. 222. *Lond.* 1893. 8°.   12431. i. 34.

JACOBS (J.) English Fairy Tales. pp. 253. *Lond.* 1890. 8°.   12411. h. 7.

—— More English Fairy Tales. pp. 243. *Lond.* 1894. 8°.   12411. h. 8.

NORTHALL (G. F.) English folk-rhymes. pp. 565. *Lond.* 1892. 8°.   12431. ee. 14.

GOMME (A. B.) Traditional games of England. 1894, *etc.* 8°. GOMME (G. L.) Dict. of British Folk Lore.   2348. d. 1.

YEATMAN (E. F. E.) "On the Green." Village games. pp. 47. *Lond.* 1894. 16°. 7912. a. 32.

Faroe Islands. See infra : Scandinavia.

Finland.

Ac. Helsingfors. *Suomalaisen Kirjallisuuden Seura.* Les Collections folk-loristes. pp. 34. *Helsingfors,* 1891. 8°.   Ac. 9080/3.

France.

Ac. Nantes. *Société des Bibliophiles Bretons.* Contes et légendes de Basse-Bretagne. pp. 198. *Nantes,* 1891. 4°.   Ac. 8926/15.

FOLK LORE.—France—*continued.*

CANTELOU (S. de) Au Pays des Farfadets. pp. 250. *Paris,* 1891. 8°.   12431. k. 27.

LE BRAZ (A.) La Légende de la Mort en Basse-Bretagne. pp. 495. *Paris,* 1893. 12°.   12431. cc. 29.

ROUSSEY (C.) Société des Parlers de France. Contes populaires. pp. 303. *Paris,* 1894. 8°.   12431. l. 4.

THURIET (C.) Traditions populaires du Doubs. pp. 111. *Besançon,* 1889. 8°.   12430. k. 33.

—— Traditions populaires de la Haute-Saone et du Jura. pp. 652. *Paris,* 1892. 8°. 12411. c. 7.

LAROCHE (P.) Folklore du Lauraguais. *Albi,* 1891, *etc.* 8°.   12431. ce. 2.

FERTIAULT (F.) Des traditions populaires dans les Noëls bourguignons. pp. 15. *Paris,* 1890. 8°.   Pam. 22.

LA SICOTIÈRE (L. de) Bibliographie des usages et des traditions de l'Orne. pp. 35. *Vannes,* 1892. 8°.   Pam. 6

PINEAU (L.) Le Folk-Lore du Poitou. pp. 547. 1892. 8°. Collection de Contes.   2348. a.

Georgia. See infra : Slavonic, etc.

Germany.

BIELSCHOWSKY (A.) Geschichte der deutschen Dorfpoesie im 13. Jahrhundert. 1890, *etc.* 8°. HENNING (R.) and HOFFORY (J.) Acta Germanica. Bd. 2.   12963. dd. 40.

KLEE (G. L.) Sieben Bücher deutscher Volkssagen. 2 Thle. *Gütersloh,* 1885. 8°.   12431. cc. 33.

LIST (G.) Deutsch-mythologische Landschafts-Bilder. pp. 264. *Berl.* 1891. 8°. 12430. k. 28.

NOVER (J.) Unsre Vorzeit. Deutsche Volkssagen. pp. 378. 1891. 8°. WAEGNER (W.) Unsre Vorzeit. pt. 3.   12411. h. 1.

ROGGE (C.) Aberglaube, Volksglaube und Volksbrauch der Gegenwart. pp. 32. *Leipz.* 1890. 8°.   Pam. 41.

PROEHLE (H.) Brockensagen. pp. 70. *Harzburg,* 1888. 8°.   12430. a. 37.

GANDER (C.) Niederlausitzer Volksagen. pp. 197. *Berl.* 1894. 8°.   12430. l. 14.

GILLHOFF (J.) Das mecklenburgische Volksrätsel. pp. 142. *Parchim,* 1892. 8°.   12304. g. 33.

JAHN (U.) Volksmärchen aus Pommern und Rügen. 1891. *etc.* 8°. Ac. Hamburg. *Verein für Niederdeutsche Sprachforschung.* Forschungen. Heft 2.   Ac. 9822/5.

P.P. *Stettin.* Blätter für pommersche Volkskunde. *Stettin,* 1892, *etc.* 8°.   1056.

KNOOP (O.) Sagen und Erzählungen aus der Provinz Posen. pp. 363. 1893. 8°. Ac. Posen. *Historische Gesellschaft.* Sonder-Veröffentlichungen. Bd. 2.   Ac. 7365/2.

HAAS (A.) Rügensche Sagen und Märchen. pp. 263. *Greifswald,* 1891. 8°. 12430. bbb. 20.

MEICHE (A.) Sagenbuch der sächsischen Schweiz. pp. 139. *Leipz.* 1894. 8°.   12430. c. 37.

Greece.

RODD (J. R.) Customs and lore of Modern Greece. pp. 294. *Lond.* 1892. 8°. 12431. ee. 6.

GEORGEAKIS (G.) and PINEAU (L.) Le Folk-Lore de Lesbos. pp. 372. 1894. 8°. Les Littératures populaires. Tom. 31.   2348. aa.

Hungary.

CURTIN (J.) Myths of the Russians and Magyars. pp. 555. *Lond.* 1890. 8°.   12430. f. 33.

HUNGARIAN FAIRY TALES. Old Hungarian fairy tales. pp. 95. *Lond.* 1895. 4°. 12411. f. 33.

FOLK LORE—*continued.*

India.

CROOKE (W.) Introduction to the Folklore of Northern India. pp. 420. *Allahabad*, 1894. 8°.
4503. ec. 31.

JACOBS (J.) Indian Fairy tales. pp. 255.
Lond. 1892. 8°. 12411. h. 9.

SWYNNERTON (C.) Indian Night's Entertainment. pp. 380. *Lond.* 1892. 4°. 14162. f. 16.

MAHEṢACHANDRA DATTA. Folklore in Bengal.
Calcutta, 1893, etc. 8°. 12430. k.

LEWIS (A.) Bilochi Stories. pp. 45.
Allahabad, 1885. 8°. 761. c. 7.

GAṄGĀDATTA UPRETI. Proverbs and folk-lore of Kumaun and Garhwal. pp. 413.
Lodiana, 1894. 8°. 14156. h. 51.

CAMPBELL (A.) Santal Folk tales. pp. 127.
Pokhuria, 1891. 8°. 14178. g. 24.

Indians, American. See infra : United States of America.

Ireland.

CURTIN (J.) Hero-tales of Ireland. pp. 558.
Bost. 1894. 8°. 12411. d. 1.

—— Tales of the Fairies and of the ghost world. pp. 196. *Lond.* 1895. 8°. 12431. c. 45.

GOMME (G. L.) Dictionary of British Folklore.
Lond. 1894, etc. 8°. 2348. d. 1.

GOMME (A. B.) Traditional games of England, Ireland, etc. 1894, etc. 8°. GOMME (G. L.) Dictionary of British Folklore. 2348. d. 1.

HYDE (D.) Beside the Fire : Irish Gaelic folk stories. pp. 203. *Lond.* 1890. 8°. 12431. k. 16.

JACOBS (J.) Celtic Fairy Tales. pp. 267.
Lond. 1892. 8°. 12411. h. 5.

—— More Celtic Fairy Tales. pp. 234.
Lond. 1894. 8°. 12411. h. 6.

JOYCE (P. W.) Old Celtic romances. pp. 446.
Lond. 1894. 8°. 2348. c. 1.

LARMINIE (W.) West Irish Folk-tales and romances. pp. 258. 1893. 8°. GOMME (G. L.) Camden Library. 7709. cc.

YEATS (W. B.) The Celtic twilight. pp. 212.
Lond. 1893. 8°. 12431. aa. 42.

—— Irish Fairy and Folk tales. pp. 326.
Lond. 1893. 8°. 12411. ee. 22.

Italy.

FINAMORE (G.) Tradizioni popolari abruzzesi. pp. 241. 1894. 8°. PITRÉ (G.) Curiosità popolari. Vol. 13. 12450. f. 16.

PIGORINI-BERI (C.) Costumi e superstizioni dell' Appenino Marchigiano. pp. 304.
Città di C. 1889. 8°. 12431. k. 14.

LELAND (C. G.) Legends of Florence.
Lond. 1895, etc. 8°. 12411. ccc.

ROSA (G.) Tradizioni e costumi Lombardi. pp. 107. *Bergamo*, 1891. 4°. 12431. l. 2.

MUSONI (F.) Gli studi di folk-lore in Friuli. pp. 40. *Udine*, 1894. 8°. 12450. dd. 4.

GIGLI (G.) Superstizioni, pregiudizi e tradizioni in Terra d' Otranto. pp. 290. *Firenze*, 1893. 8°.
12431. cc. 30.

SEVES (F.) Ninne-nanne. Filastrocche e sorteggi. pp. 106. *Pinerolo*, 1890. 8°. 12430. aa. 30.

MANGO (F.) Novelline popolari sarde. pp. 144.
1890. 8°. PITRÉ (G.) Curiosità popolari. Vol. IX. 12450. f. 16.

Japan.

RINDER (F.) Old-World Japan. Legends. pp. 195. *Lond.* 1895. 8°. 12411. eee. 3.

Kafirs. See supra : Africa.

FOLK LORE—*continued.*

Letts.

AUNING (R.) Ueber den lettischen Drachen-Mythus, Puhkis. pp. 128. *Mitau*, 1892. 8°.
12431. c. 43.

BIELENSTEIN (H.) Das lettische Thiermärchen. 1891. 8°. Ac. Mitau. *Lettisch-litterärische Gesellschaft*. Magazin. Bd. 19. Stück 1. Ac. 9085.

Madagascar. See supra : Africa.

New Zealand and Polynesia.

TREGEAR (E.) Fairy Tales and Folk-lore of New Zealand. pp. 165. *Wellington, N.Z.* 1891. 8°.
12431. cc. 26.

Philippine Islands.

RETANA (W. E.) Supersticiones de los Indios filipinos. pp. 104. *Madrid*, 1894. 12°.
12489. e. 20.

Roumania.

Ac. Bucharest. *Academia Romána*. Texte Macedo-Române. Basme şi poesii poporale de la Cruşova. pp. 380. *Bucuresci*, 1891. 8°.
11586. dd. 15.

Russia. See infra : Slavonic Races.

Scandinavia.

BERGSTRÖM (R.) Ur folksagans rosengårdar.
Stockholm, 1889, etc. 8°. 12431. ce.

KRISTENSEN (E. T.) Gamle folks fortællinger om det jyske almueliv. *Kjøbenh.* 1891, etc. 8°.
10280. dd.

—— Moskonen brygger. pp. 152.
Kjøbenh. 1891. 8°. 12430. dd. 25.

LAGERLOF (S.) Ur Gösta Berlings Saga. pp. 16.
Stockholm, 1891. fol. Pam. 19.

HENRIKSSON (J.) Plägseder och skrock bland Dalslands. pp. 114. *Åmål*, 1889. 8°.
12331. h. 35.

Ac. Upsal. *Vestgöta Landsmålsföreningen*. Allmogelif i Vestergötland. pp. 127.
Stockholm, 1891. 8°. Ac. 9885.

POULSEN (P.) Fuglakväje. pp. 26.
Kjøbenh. 1892. 8°. Pam. 62.

Scotland.

BARBOUR (J. G.) Unique traditions of West and South Scotland. pp. 255. *Lond.* 1886. 8°.
12431. k. 15.

CAMPBELL (*Lord* A.) Waifs and strays of Celtic Tradition. *Lond.* 1889, etc. 8°. 12341. k.

DOUGLAS (*Sir* G. B. S.) Scottish Fairy and Folk tales. pp. 301. *Lond.* 1893. 8°. 12411. ee. 21.

GOMME (G. L.) Dictionary of British Folklore.
Lond. 1894, etc. 8°. 2348. d. 1.

GOMME (A. B.) Traditional games of England, Scotland, and Ireland. 1894, etc. 8°. GOMME (G. L.) Dictionary of British Folklore.
2348. d. 1.

JACOBS (J.) Celtic Fairy tales. pp. 267.
Lond. 1892. 8°. 12411. h. 5.

—— More Celtic Fairy tales. pp. 234.
Lond. 1894. 8°. 12411. h. 6.

KIRK (R.) Secret Commonwealth of elves, fauns and fairies. pp. 92. 1893. 8°. Bibliothèque de Carabas. Vol. 5. 12204. hh.

MACDOUGALL (J.) Folk and Hero tales. pp. 311. 1891. 8°. CAMPBELL (*Lord* A.) Waifs and Strays of Celtic Tradition. No. 3. 12431. k.

MACKINLAY (J. M.) Folklore of Scottish lochs and springs. pp. 364. *Glasg.* 1893. 8°.
12430. dd. 26.

SAXBY (J. M. E.) Birds of omen in Shetland. pp. 32. 1893. 8°. 12430. g. 39. (7.)

Slavonic Races : Russia.

BAIN (R. N.) Cossack Fairy tales. pp. 290.
Lond. 1894. 8°. 12431. f. 51

FOLK LORE.—Slavonic Races—cont.

CURTIN (J.) Myths and Folk-tales of the Russians. pp. 555. *Lond.* 1890. 8°.
     12430. f. 33.

GERBER (A.) Great Russian Animal tales. pp. 101. 1891. 8°. Ac. Baltimore. *Modern Language Association.* Publications. Vol. VI. No. 2.   !Ac. 2683/2.

POLEVOI (P. N.) Russian Fairy tales. pp. 264. *Lond.* 189;. 8°.   12431. ee. 18.

GEORGIAN FOLK TALES. Georgian Folk tales. pp. 175. 1894, 8°. Grimm Library. No. 1.   12431. ee.

KRAUSS (F. S.) Volksglaube der Südslaven. pp. 176. 1890. 8°. Darstellungen aus dem Gebiete der nichtchristlichen Religionsgeschichte. Bd. 2.   4506. f.

MURKO (M.) Die Geschichte von den sieben Weisen bei den Slaven. pp. 138. 1890. 8°. Ac. Vienna. *K. Akademie.* Sitzungsberichte. Philosoph.-historische Classe. Bd. 122. Ac. 810/6.

Turkey.

CARNOY (É. H.) and NICOLAÏDES (J.) Traditions populaires de Constantinople. *Paris,* 1892, *etc.* 8°.
     12430. k.

—— Folklore de Constantinople. pp. 205. 1894. 8°. BLÉMONT (E.) Collection internationale de la tradition. Vol. 12, 13.
     12430. aaa. 47.

DOZON (L. A. H.) Contes albanais. pp. 264. 1881. 12°. Collection de Chansons, *etc.* Vol. 3.
     2348. a.

United States : Indians.

FORTIER (A.) Bits of Louisiana Folklore. 1888. 8°. Ac. Baltimore. *Modern Language Association.* Translations and Proceedings. Vol. III.   Ac. 2683/2.

BRINTON (D. G.) Reminiscences of Pennsylvania Folklore. 1892. 8°.   12430. k. 40. (8.)

RAND (S. T.) Legends of the Micmacs. pp. 452. 1894. 8°. Wellesley Philological Publications.
     12430. l.

LUMMIS (C. F.) The Man who married the Moon. pp. 239. *N.Y.* 1894. 8°. 12431. ee. 28.

Wales.

GOMME (G. L.) Dictionary of British Folklore. *Lond.* 1894, *etc.* 8°.   2348. d. 1.

EMERSON (P. H.) Welsh Fairy-tales. pp. 87. *Lond.* 1894. 8°.   12411. e. 35.

JACOBS (J.) Celtic Fairy tales. pp. 267. *Lond.* 1892. 8°.   12411. h. 5.

—— More Celtic Fairy tales. pp. 234. *Lond.* 1894. 8°.   12411. h. 6.

FONTAINEBLEAU. BOURGES (E.) Les anciennes maisons de Fontainebleau. pp. 39. *Fontainebleau,* 1893. 12°.   10106. de. 4. (4.)

BOURGES (E.) Notes sur le Théâtre de la Cour à Fontainebleau. pp. 82. *Paris,* 1892. 8°.
     Pam. 50.

LHUILLIER (T.) Érection de la paroisse Saint-Louis de Fontainebleau. pp. 20. *Fontainebleau,* 1893. 8°.   4629. bbb. 17. (7.)

THOMAS-MARANCOURT (É.) Mes fouilles au Croc-Marin. pp. 68. *Fontainebleau,* 1891. 8°.
     10107. ff. 27. (10.)

See also GÂTINAIS.

FONTAINE-DANIEL, Abbey. LEBLANC (E.) L'Abbaye de Fontaine-Daniel. pp. 114. *Mayenne,* 1892. 8°.   4629. c. 11.

FONTAINE-FRANÇAISE. GASCON (R. É.) Histoire de Fontaine-Française. pp. 502. *Dijon,* 1892. 8°.   010171. f. 38.

FONTAINE-JEAN. JAROSSAY (E.) Histoire de l'abbaye de Fontaine-Jean. 1891. 8°. Fontainebleau. *Société historique.* Annales, 1891.   Ac. 6791/2.

FONTAINE-LES-DIJON. CHOMTON ( ) Saint Bernard et le château de Fontaine-Les-Dijon. *Dijon,* 1891, *etc.* 8°.   4824. do

FONTAINE SUR SOMME. LE SUEUR (A.) Fontaine sur Somme. 1891. 8°. Ac. Amiens. *Société d'Archéologie.* Mémoires. Sér. 4. Tom. 1.   Ac. 5343.

FONTENOY-LE-CHÂTEAU. OLIVER (C.) Fontenoy-le-Château. pp. 440. 1894. 8°. Ac. Épinal. *Société d'Émulation.* Annales. Ann. 70.   Ac. 585.

FONTEVRAULT. BOSSEBŒUF (L. A.) Fontevrault. pp. 104. *Tours,* 1890. 8°.
     4629. aaa. 22.

FOOD. ALLINSON (T. R.) Diet and digestion. pp. 46. *Lond.* 1892. 8°.   7306. df. 19. (9.)

BELLOWS (A. J.) Philosophy of eating. pp. 275. *Glasg.* 1892. 8°.   7391. df. 13.

BON-SENS. Devoir et Bonheur. Alimentation. pp. 8. *Liège,* 1893. 8°.   Pam. 39.

BOURDEAU (L.) Histoire de l'alimentation. pp. 372. *Paris,* 1894. 8°.   07945. h. 44.

BREVANS (J. de) Le Pain et la viande. pp. 364. *Paris,* 1892. 12°.   7942. de. 23.

BUCKLAND (A. W.) Our Viands. pp. 308. *Lond.* 1893. 8°.   07944. e. 1.

CUTTER (E.) Food Diseases. pp. 12. *Nashville,* 1888. 8°.   07305. e. 24. (9.)

DURHAM (W.) Food, Physiology, *etc.* pp. 123. 1891. 8°. Science in plain language. 2709. aaa.

DUTTON (T.) Food and Drink rationally discussed. pp. 124. *Lond.* 1894. 8°. 7404. aa. 78.

EDE (W. M.) Cheap Food and cheap cooking. pp. 20. *Lond.* 1884. 8°.   Pam. 94.

FOODS. Tinned Foods and how to use them. pp. 275. *Lond.* 1893. 8°.   07944. e. 10.

GRANDEAU (L. N.) L'Alimentation de l'Homme et des animaux. *Paris,* 1893, *etc.* 8°. 07293. i.

GRIFFITHS (W.) Principal starches used as Food. pp. 62. *Cirencester,* 1892. 8°.
     07076. e. 39.

HAMMERICH (E.) Vejledning til Behandling af Alimentations sager. pp. 137. *Kjøbenh.* 1891. 8°.   5725. a. 9.

HART (A. M.) Diet in sickness and in health. pp. 219. *Lond.* 1895. 8°.   7390. f. 10.

KNIGHT (J.) Food and its functions. pp. 282. *Lond.* 1895. 8°.   07944. ee. 18.

LEPPER (S.) Dietetic Way to health and beauty. pp. 20. *Lond.* 1895. 8°.   Pam. 39.

MARTHA (A.) Les Intoxications alimentaires. pp. 218. *Paris,* 1894. 8°.   7405. aaaa. 1.

ROBERTS (*Sir* W.) Collected Contributions on digestion and diet. pp. 261. *Lond.* 1891. 8°.
     7391. df. 10.

RUSSELL (J. R.) Hints on Diet. pp. 70. *Lond.* 1890. 8°.   07305. e. 17. (1.)

SCHWAAB (E. F.) Secrets of Canning. pp. 150. *Lond.* 1890. 8°.   7945. aaa. 59.

SECRETS. Secrets of the Fasting Men. *Lond.* 1891. 8°.   7321. aaa. 22. (5.)

STUTZER (A.) Nahrungs- und Genussmittel. 1894. 8°. WEYL (T.) Handbuch der Hygiene. Bd. 3.   7391. dd.

TSCHIRCH (A.) and OESTERLE (O.) Anatomischer Atlas der Pharmakognosie und Nahrungsmittelkunde. *Leipz.* 1893, *etc.* fol.   7029. i.

FOOD—*continued.*

WELLES (C. S.) Practical Dietetics. pp. 79.
N.Y. 1893. 8°.   07305. f. 16. (8.)
See also COOKERY : DIGESTION.

Adulteration, etc.

ENGLAND AND WALES. *Local Government Board.*
Sale of Food and Drugs Act. Extract from the
Annual Report. pp. 29. *Lond.* 1890. 8°.
                                    7404. h. 1.

BELL (*Sir* W. J.) Sale of Food and Drugs Acts,
1875–79. pp. 146. *Lond.* 1894. 8°.
                                    6426. aaaa. 25.

HEDDERWICK (T. C. H.) Sale of Food and Drugs.
Acts of 1875–79. pp. 101. *Lond.* 1894. 8°.
                                    6425. c. 33.

ROBINSON (H. M.) and CRIBB (C. H.) Law and
chemistry of Food. pp. 499.   *Lond.* 1895. 8°.
                                    6425. de. 33.

BARTLEY (D. C.) Adulteration of Food. pp. 200.
Lond. 1895. 12°.   6426. de. 25.

BONNET (V.) Précis d'Analyse microscopique
des denrées alimentaires. pp. 200.
Paris, 1890. 8°.   7404. cc. 11.

BOWER (J. A.) Simple method for detecting
food adulteration. pp. 118. *Lond.* 1895. 8°.
                                    4430. cc. 7.

BURCKER (E.) Traité des falsifications des substances alimentaires. pp. 471. *Paris*, 1892. 8°.
                                    07945. g. 4.

DOUMERC (A.) and LEYMARIE (L. de) Législation
concernant les falsifications alimentaires.
pp. 247. *Paris*, 1895. 8°.   5405. aa. 5.

GIRARD (C.) Analyse des matières alimentaires.
pp. 727. 1894. 8°. FREMY (E.) Encyclopédie
chimique. Tom. 10.   8907. i.

MACÉ (E.) Les substances alimentaires étudiées
au microscope. pp. 512. *Paris*, 1891. 8°.
                                    7404. de. 6.

PEARMAIN (T. H.) and MOOR (C. G.) Aids to
the analysis of food. pp. 160. *Lond.* 1895. 8°.
                                    8909. eee. 1.

POLIN (L. H. A. M.) and LABIT (H. J. J. P.)
Examen des aliments suspects. pp. 229. 1892. 8°.
Encyclopédie des aide-mémoire.   8709. g.

SMITH (J. B.) Food-stuffs. *Dulwich*, 1892, *etc.* 8°.
                                    7404. bbb. 30.

WEDDERBURN (A. J.) Report on food adulteration. pp. 64. 1894. 8°. U.S. *Department of
Agriculture. Chemical Division.* Bulletin. No. 41.
                                    7053. e. 9.

Chemistry of Food.

See CHEMISTRY, *Applied.*

Diet for Invalids and Children.

ART. Art of Feeding the invalid. pp. 264.
Lond. 1893. 8°.   7688. c. 25.

BROWNE (P.) Diet and cookery for common ailments. pp. 307. *Lond.* 1894. 8°.   7404. e. 4.

BURNET (R. W.) Foods and dietaries. pp. 196.
Lond. 1892. 8°.   7404. d. 10.

CUTTER (E.) Feeding in the wasting diseases.
pp. 20. *N.Y.* 1890. 8°.   07305. l. 6. (5.)

EBSTEIN (W.) Über die Lebensweise der Zuckerkranken. pp. 144. *Wiesbaden*, 1892. 8°.
                                    7620. e. 22.

FEACHEM (M.) Food for the sick and convalescent. pp. 8. *Bristol*, 1895. 8°.   Pam. 94.

LEWIS (H. K.) Lewis's Diet charts.
Lond. 1893. fol.   •   7391. g. 19.

MELLIN (G.) How to Feed babies and invalids.
pp. 155. 1893. 8°.   7688. a. 51.

OERTEL (F.) Pfarrer Kneipps Kraftnährmittel.
pp. 95. *Kempten*, 1891. 8°.   Pam. 39.

SÉE (G.) Du régime alimentaire. pp. 744.
Paris, 1887. 8°.   7442. e. 13.

FOOD.—Diet for Invalids, etc.—*cont.*

DUKES (C.) Essentials of school diet. pp. 187.
Lond. 1891. 8°.   7944. ee. 45.

SAUNDERS (G. R.) The Food-Management of
infants and young children. pp. 108.
Wanganui, 1892. 8°.   7581. bbb. 34.
See also COOKERY.

Meat.

ADLER (G.) Die Fleisch-Teuerungspolitik der
deutschen Städte beim Ausgange des Mittelalters. pp. 125. *Tübingen*, 1893. 8°. 08227. h. 38.

FROZEN MEAT INDUSTRY. The frozen meat industry. pp. 40. *Sydney*, 1892. 8°.
                                    8282. e. 43. (15.)

G. B. & I. *Army.* Guide to Meat inspection
for regimental officers. pp. 52. *Lond.* 1894. 8°.
                                    8831. aaa. 56.

—— Guide to Meat inspection for officers in
Bengal. pp. 12. *Calcutta*, 1893. 8°. 8831. f. 45.

OSTERTAG (R.) Handbuch der Fleischbeschau.
pp. 568. *Stuttgart*, 1892. 8°.   07293. l. 1.

PAUTET (L.) Précis de l'Inspection des viandes.
pp. 364. *Paris*, 1892. 12°.   7404. e. 2.

POSTOLKA (A.) and TOSCANO (A.) Die animal-
ischen Nahrungs- und Genussmittel des Menschen. pp. 437. *Wien*, 1893. 8°. 07293. k. 12.

WYLDE (W.) The inspection of Meat. pp 105.
Lond. 1890. 8°.   7404. de. 4.

Vegetarianism.

BECHĀRĀMA CHAṬṬOPĀDHYĀYA. Lectures on
Vegetarianism. pp. 30. *Sukkur*, 1893. 8°.
                                    4503. aaa. 20.

BONNEJOY (E.) Le Végétarisme et le régime
végétarien. pp. 341. *Paris*, 1891. 8°. 8436. cc. 1.

BOWDICH (E. W.) New Vegetarian dishes.
pp. 120. *Lond.* 1892. 8°.   7942. de. 19.

DENSMORE (E.) The natural Food of man.
pp. 66. *Lond.* 1890. 8°.   7404. d. 4.

—— How Nature cures : the natural food of man.
pp. 413. *Lond.* 1892. 8°.   7391. ee. 1.

DUNCAN (A. W.) The chemistry of Food. pp. 6.
Manch. 1887. 8°.   07305. f. 14. (4.)

FARNETI (R.) Frutti freschi e secchi ortaggi.
pp. 712. *Milano*, 1892. 8°.   07076. e. 37.

FORWARD (C. W.) Practical Vegetarian recipes.
pp. 126. *Lond.* 1891. 8°.   7942. de. 11.

HILLS (A. F.) Essays on Vegetarianism. pp. 248.
Lond. 1895. 8°.   8425. c. 71.

—— Natural Food of man. *Lond.* 1891. 8°.
                                    8425. bbb. 43. (12.)

—— Reaction. A speculation. pp. 29.
Lond. 1891. 8°.   8425. bbb. 43. (13.)

—— Principles and practices. pp. 33.
Lond. 1892. 8°.   8435. bb. 62. (3.)

—— Vital Food. pp. 8. *Lond.* 1892. 8°.
                                    8435. bb. 62. (6.)

LONDON. *Northern Heights Vegetarian Society.*
Best Food for athletes. pp. 30. *Lond.* 1895. 8°.
                                    Pam. 85.

MACDONALD (W. A.) Reformed Dietetics. pp. 60.
Lond. 1895. 8°.   7404. aaaa. 1.

O., I., and A., M. Arguments from Scripture
for pure Diet and living. pp. 12. *Paris*, 1890. 8°.
                                    4136. a. 42. (9.)

OLDFIELD (J.) The Cost of living. pp. 9.
Lond. 1892. 8°.   8435. bb. 62. (8.)

—— The Ideal Diet. pp. 8. *Lond.* 1892. 8°.
                                    8435. bb. 62. (9.)

P.P. *Manchester.* Daisy Basket. Magazine of
the children's branch of the Vegetarian Society.
Manch. 1893, *etc.* 8°.   P.P. 1146. h. and 2219.

—— *London.* Natural Food. *Lond.* 1890, *etc.* fol.
                         P.P. 2706. aga. and 1096.

FOOD.—Vegetarian—_continued._

SALT (H. S.) A Plea for Vegetarianism. pp. 115. _Manch._ 1886. 8°.   7390. aa. 3.

WINCKLER (A.) Kritik des Vegetarismus. pp. 30. _Berl._ 1891. 8°.   8409. l. 23. (4.)

WINTLE (A. T.) The Dietary of troops. pp. 10. _Lond._ 1892. 8°.   8435. bb. 62. (11.)

YATES (M.) The Staff of life. pp. 9. _Lond._ 1892. 8°.   8435. bb. 62. (12.)

See also COOKERY.

FOOT. ADAMS (W.) On Contractions of the fingers and on "Hammer-toe." pp. 154. _Lond._ 1892. 8°.   7482. g. 18.

BLAKE (E.) Ankle Strain. pp. 16. _Lond._ 1895. 8°.   Pam. 39.

BRODHURST (B. E.) Nature and treatment of Club-foot. pp. 60. _Lond._ 1893. 8°. 07482. ee. 10.

FREIBERG (A. H.) Treatment of the Club-foot. pp. 17. 1892. 8°.   7306. df. 22. (5.)

JUDSON (A. B.) Weight of the body in relation to Club-foot. pp. 15. _Bost._ 1892. 8°. 07305. 13. i. (2.)

MOORE (A. J.) That uncomfortable Shoe. Treatise on the Foot. pp. 138. _N.Y._ 1891. 8°.   7944. de. 45.

WALSHAM (W. J.) and HUGHES (W. K.) Deformities of the human Foot. pp. 550. _Lond._ 1895. 8°.   07482. ee. 15.

See also BOOTMAKING.

FOOT AND MOUTH DISEASE. _See_ VETERINARY MEDICINE.

FOOTBALL. ALCOCK (C. W.) Football. Association Game. pp. 80. 1890. 8°. All England Series.   7908. df.

CAMP (W.) American Football. pp. 175. _N.Y._ 1891. 8°.   7905. aaa. 51.

CAMSELL ( ) Game of Football. _Lond._ 1890. 8°.   7912. ee. 1. (6.)

FLOYD (A. E.) Football Guide. Handbook of the Devon County Football Association. _Plymouth,_ 1893, _etc._ 16°.   7908. de.

FOOTBALL. Football. Its laws, rules, _etc._ pp. 56. _Manch._ 1893. 8°.   7907. df. 18. (5.)

HOWARD (N.) Football. How to become a player. pp. 24. _Liverpl._ 1894. 12°. 7912. d. 1. (8.)

LAWS. Laws of Football. Association. pp. 27. _Lond._ 1894. 32°.   7915. de. 13. (5.)

LONDON. Laws of the Football Association. _Lond._ 1888, _etc._ 8°.   7912. a.

MARRIOTT (C. J. B.) Rugby Union Game. Association Game. pp. 120. 1894. 8°. ALCOCK (C. W.) "Oval" Series.   07905. f.

MARSHALL (F.) Football. pp. 560. _Lond._ 1893, 94. 8°.   07905. i. 6.

PARIS. _Union des Sociétés françaises de Sports._ Règles du jeu de football, Rugby. pp. 35. _Paris,_ 1891. 16°.   7915. de. 15. (3.)

P.P. _London._ Famous Footballers and athletes. _Lond._ 1895. _etc._ fol.   1431.

—— Rugby Union Football handbook. _Lond._ 1894. _etc._ 8°.   P.P. 2489. wfb.

POE ( ) Poe's Football. American Rules. pp. 64. _N.Y._ 1891. 8°.   7908. df. 16.

RUGBY UNION. Laws of the Rugby Union. _Lond._ 1888, _etc._ 12°.   7912. a.

—— Rugby Union Scoring Book. _Lond._ 1892. 8°.   7906. d. 35.

SAINT-CLAIR (G. de) and SAINT-CHAFFRAY (E.) Football, Rugby. pp. 114. _Paris._ 1894. 12°.   7912. aa. 32.

SHEARMAN (M.) Athletics and Football. pp. 464. 1894. 8°. Badminton Library.   2264. aa. 1.

FOOTBALL—_continued._

BRISTOL. _Bristol Football League._ Rules, Fixtures, _etc._ _Bristol,_ 1892, _etc._ 16°.   7912. a. 16.

LANCASHIRE LEAGUE. Football Scoring card. 1892. 8°.   1865. c. 2. (14.)

HIGSON (J.) History of the Salford Football Club. pp. 148. _Salford,_ 1892. 8°.   7912. aa. 13.

LEIGHTON (J. A.) North-Western Rugby Football League card. _Kendal,_ 1892. fol.   1865. c. 2. (22.)

ROBERTS (G. A.) Somerset Rugby Football. pp. 66. _Bath,_ 1894. 8°.   7912. aa. 30.

YORK. _Rugby Football Union._ Official Guide, Season 1893-4. pp. 311. _Leeds,_ 1893. 24°.   7912. a. 38.

SCOTLAND. _Football League._ Scottish League Handbook, 1890-91. _Glasg._ 1890. 16°.   7912. a. 30.

—— Scottish League fixtures, 1892. _Leith,_ 1892, 12°.   7908. a. 102.

See also GAMES.

FORAMINIFERA. _See_ PROTOZOA.

FORBACH. BESLER (M.) Geschichte des Schlosses und der Stadt Forbach. pp. 144. _Forbach,_ 1895. 8°.   10261. f. 6.

FORCE: ENERGY. ARNDT (R.) Bemerkungen über Kraft. pp. 50. _Greifswald,_ 1892. 8°.   8768. f. 8.

BRYANT (W. M.) The World-Energy and its self-conservation. pp. 304. _Chicago,_ 1890. 8°.   8703. de. 37.

HILLER (H. C.) Rhythmic Heredity. Matter a property of energy. pp. 355. _Lond._ 1894. 8°.   7006. e. 26.

MAJOR (F.) Spacial and atomic Energy. pp. 62. _Lond._ 1889. 8°.   8708. c. 16.

MEWES (R.) Kraft und Masse. _Berl._ 1892, _etc._ 8°.   8704. ff.

SCHEFFLER (H.) Die Äquivalenz der Naturkräfte. pp. 585. _Leipz._ 1893. 8°. 8768. cc. 30.

See also DYNAMICS: PHYSICS.

FORDOUN. CRAMOND (W.) Annals of Fordoun. pp. 108. _Montrose,_ 1894. 8°.   10369. ccc. 32.

MOLLYSON (C. A.) The Parish of Fordoun. pp. 341. _Aberd._ 1893. 8°.   010370. e. 5.

FORDWICH. WOODRUFF (C. E.) History of the Town and Port of Fordwich. pp. 291. _Canterbury,_ 1895. 8°.   010358. f. 60.

FORESHORE. LĀLAMOHANA DĀSA GHOSHA. Law of Riparian Rights. pp. 439. _Calcutta,_ 1891. 8°.   5319. c. 11.

FORESTERS, Order of. _See_ FRIENDLY SOCIETIES.

FORESTRY AND TREES. ALHEILIG ( ) Recette, conservation et travail des Bois. pp. 197. 1892. 8°. Encyclopédie des aide-mémoire. 8709. g.

BRETON (L.) Du Rôle des forêts en temps de guerre. pp. 168. _Paris,_ 1894. 8°. 8828. c. 55.

BROWN (J.) The Forester. 2 vol. _Edinb._ 1894. 8°.   2252. e. 3.

BUEHLER (A.) Mittheilungen der schweizerischen Centralanstalt für das forstliche Versuchswesen. _Zürich,_ 1891, _etc._ 8°.   07076. k.

CANTANI (A.) Elementi di economia basati sul Rimboschimento. pp. 604. _Torino,_ 1895. 8°.   7001. g. 6.

CHRISTY (R. M.) Why are the Prairies treeless? pp. 22. _Lond._ 1892. 8°.   Pam. 1.

DEMONTZEY (P.) La restauration des terrains en montagne au Pavillon des Forêts. pp. 168. _Paris,_ 1889. 8°.   7078. cc. 36.

FORESTRY.—*continued.*

DEMONTZEY (P.) L'extinction des torrents en France par le Reboisement. 2 tom.'
Paris, 1894. 4°.   8776. g. 44.

DES CARS (A.) Tree Pruning. pp. 61. 1893. 8°. Rider's Technical Series. No. 2.   7078. e.

DIDIER-MONGEOT (A.) Notions sur la clôture et la plantation des Arbres. pp. 110.
Paris, 1894. 8°.   7078. bbb. 51.

ECKERT (F.) Resultate forstlich-meteorologischer Beobachtungen 1885-1887., 1890. 4°. AUSTRIA. *Staatliches Forstliches Versuchswesen.* Mittheilungen. Heft 12.   7073. eee. 7.

ECKSTEIN (C.) Bericht über die Leistungen auf dem Gebiete der Forst- und Jagdzoologie.
Frankf. 1892, etc. 8°.   7208. aaa.

ENDRES (M.) Lehrbuch der Waldwertrechnung und Forststatik. pp. 286. Berl. 1895. 8°.
       07077. i. 2.

GRISARD (J.) and VANDEN-BERGHE (M.) Les Bois industriels indigènes et exotiques.
Paris, 1893, etc. 8°.   7054. h.

HANSEN (C.) Hovedregningsopgaver. 3 pt.
Kjøbenh. 1891, 93, 92. 8°.   8507. cc. 5.

HELFERICH (J. A. R.) Economia forestale.
1886, 87. 8°. Biblioteca dell' economista. Ser. 3. Vol. 12.   8205. l.

HUFFEL (G.) Les Arbres et les peuplements forestiers. pp. 200. Paris, 1893. 8°. 7077. h. 2.

INDIA. *Forest Department.* Notes on the preparation of Forest working-plans. pp. 162.
Calcutta, 1892. 8°.   7077. f. 4.

KAUSCHINGER (G.) Protection of Woodlands against dangers arising from organic and inorganic causes. pp. 252. Edinb. 1893. 8°.
       07076. g. 26.

NISBET (J.) On Mixed Forests, and their advantages. pp. 30. Lond. 1893. 8°.
       7077. g. 9. (3.)

—— On the advantages of underplanting light-demanding Forest Trees. pp 30.
Lond. 1893. 8°.   7077. g. 9. (5.)

—— The climatic and national-economic Influence of Forests. pp. 24. Lond. 1893. 8°.
       7077. g. 9. (1.)

—— Concerning the enhancement of Increment which takes place in Tree-Forest, *etc.* pp. 18.
Lond. 1893. 8°.   7077. g. 9. (6.)

—— On the Selection of species of Trees for woodland crops. pp. 38. Lond. 1893. 8°.
       7077. g. 9. (4.)

—— Soil and situation in relation to Forest growth. pp. 31. Lond. 1893. 8°.
       7077. g. 9. (2.)

—— Studies in Forestry. pp. 335.
Oxf. 1894. 8°.   07076. e. 55.

PINCHOT (G.) Government Forestry abroad. 1891. 8°. Ac. Saratoga. *American Economic Association.* Publications. Vol. 6. No. 3.
       Ac. 2388.

RANSOME (J. S.) How to select wood-working Machinery. pp. 246. 1893. 8°. Timber Trade Handbooks. No. 3.   7078. aa.

SCHWAPPACH (A.) Forstpolitik, Jagd- und Fischereipolitik. pp. 396. 1894. 8°. FRANKENSTEIN (K.) Hand- und Lehrbuch der Staatswissenschaften. Bd. 10.   8009. k.

SCHWARZ (F.) Forstliche Botanik. pp. 513.
Berl. 1892. 8°.   07028. h. 33.

SOIGNIE (J. de) Plantations le long des voies de communication. pp. 75. Brux. 1894. 8°.
       07028. h. 35.

THIÉRY (E.) Restauration des montagnes, reboisement. pp. 413. 1891. 8°. Encyclopédie des travaux publics.   012216. i.

FORESTRY—*continued*

VIENNA. *Land- und forstwirthschaftlicher Congress.* Bericht über die Verhandlungen des Congresses, 1890. Wien, 1890. 8°. 07076. i. 1.

WEBSTER (A. D.) Practical Forestry. pp. 118. 1894. 8°. Rider's Technical Series. No. 3.
       7078. e.

WEISE (W.) Mündener forstliche Hefte.
Berl. 1892, etc. 8°.   7078. dd.

ALGERIA. *Ligue du Reboisement de l'Algérie.* La Colonisation et la question forestière. pp. 117.
Alger, 1891. 8°.   07076. g. 5.

BULARD (C.) Avant de reboiser protégeons nos Forets contre les incendies. pp. 27.
Alger, 1881. 8°.   8755. dd. 33. (3.)

COMBE (A.) Les Forêts de l'Algérie. pp. 72.
Alger, 1889. 8°.   Pam. 1.

MATHIEU (A.) Le Service forestier dans le département d'Oran. pp. 44. Alger, 1892. 8°.
       Pam. 1.

DIMITZ (L.) Oesterreichs Forstwesen, 1848-1888. pp. 330. Wien, 1890. 8°. 07076. h. 46.

LEFEVRE (Rt. Hon. G. J. S.) English Commons and Forests. pp. 391. Lond. 1894. 8°. 6306. g. 1.

RAWLE (E. J.) Annals of the Royal Forest of Exmoor. pp. 163. Taunton, 1893, 4°.
       10368. l. 4.

NAIRNE (D.) Notes on Highland Woods. 1892. 8°. Ac. Inverness. *Gaelic Society.* Transactions. Vol. 17.   Ac. 8260.

U.S. *Department of Agriculture.* Report on Forestry. pp. 421. Wash. 1884. 8°. 7053. e. 53.
—— *Department of Agriculture. Forestry Division.* Circular. Wash. 1892, etc. 8°.
       7053. e. 51.

BOWERS (E. A.) Condition of the Forests on the public lands. 1891. 8°. Ac. Saratoga. *American Economic Association.* Publications. Vol. 6. No. 3.   Ac. 2388.

FERNOW (B. E.) Practicability of an American Forest administration. 1891. 8°. Ac. Saratoga. *American Economic Association.* Publications. Vol. 6. No. 3.   Ac. 2388.

See also BOTANY : COCOA NUT : GARDENING.

Diseases of Trees.

ADMIRAAL (K.) De Kankerziekte der boomen. pp. 103. Amsterdam, 1889. 8°. 07076. h. 40.

CURTIS (C. E.) Manifestation of disease in Forest Trees. pp. 49. Lond. 1892. 8°.
       07076. e. 36.

HARTIG (R.) Text-book of the diseases of Trees. pp. 331. Lond. 1894. 8°.   7075. f. 2.

Laws relating to Forestry, etc.

POWELL (B. H. B.) Forest Law. A course of lectures. pp. 495. Lond. 1893. 8°. 05319. i. 4.

CHANCEREL (L.) L'Usufruit des Domaines forestiers. pp. 241. Paris, 1894. 8°. 5405. e. 2.

NAQUET (E.) Traité des droits de timbre. pp. 512. Paris, 1894. 8°.   5423. e. 19.

GRANER (F.) Forstgesetzgebung und Forstverwaltung. pp. 501. Tübingen, 1892. 8°.
       5604. d. 3.

LAGASI (P.) Studii sulla legislazione forestale. pp. 461. Borgotaro, 1890. 8°. 5373. ee. 23.

Forest Flora.

BOULGER (G. S.) Familiar Trees.
Lond. 1891-94. 8°.   07028. k. 18.

LASLETT (T.) Timber and Timber Trees. pp. 442. Lond. 1894. 8°.   2252. b. 18.

JESPERSEN (J. F. W.) Fortsatte Studier over Bøgebevoxningernes Pleie og Anlæg.
Kjøbenh. 1893, etc. 8°.   7055. cc.

FORESTRY.—Forest Flora—_continued._

Heim (F.) Recherches sur les Diptérocarpacées. Introduction à la monographie générale de la famille. pp. 186. _Paris_, 1892. 4°. 7054. g. 18.

Schwappach (A.) Wachstum und Ertrag normaler Rotbuchenbestände, etc. pp. 104. _Berl._ 1893. 8°. 7077. h. 3.

Lamey (A.) Le Chêne-liège. pp. 289. _Paris_, 1893. 8°. 7077. g. 8.

Beissner (L.) Handbuch der Nadelholzkunde. pp. 576. _Berl._ 1891. 8°. 07076. m. 11.

Eckstein (C.) Die Kiefer, Pinus silvestris L. und ihre tierischen Schädlinge. _Berl._ 1893, etc. 8°. 7074. m.

Wagler (P.) Die Eiche in alter und neuer Zeit. 2 Tle. _Wurzen_, 1891. 4°. & 8°. 4503. g. 5.

Ward (H. M.) The Oak. pp. 175. 1892. 8°.

Lubbock (_Sir J._) Modern Science. 8709. f.

America.

Sargent (C. S.) Silva of North America. _Bost._ 1891, etc. 8°. 7074. m.

Ac. Salem. _Essex Institute._ Robinson (J.) Our Trees. pp. 120. _Salem_, 1891. 8°. 7070. ee. 9.

Apgar (A. C.) Trees of the northern United States, etc. pp. 224. _N.Y._ 1892. 8°. 7078. e. 1.

Colmeiro (M.) Arboles de origen americano, existentes en el Jardin Botánico de Madrid. pp. 54. _Madrid_, 1892. 8°. Pam. 1.

Dame (L. L.) Typical Elms of Massachusetts. pp. 89. _Bost._ 1890. 4°. 7074. m. 5.

Newhall (C. S.) Trees of North-eastern America. pp. 250. _N.Y._ 1892. 8°. 07076. g. 25.

See also supra : General.

Algeria. See supra : General.

Asia.

Friedrich (T.) Die Holz-Tektonik Vorder-Asiens. pp. 55. _Innsbruck_, 1891. 4°. 7703. g. 26.

Talbot (W. A.) Systematic list of the Trees of the Bombay Presidency. pp. 230. _Bombay_, 1894. 8°. 07076. g. 27.

Mendis (A.) called Senānāyka. List of timber Trees in Ceylon. pp. 9. 1891. obl. 8°. Pam. 1. _See also supra : General._

Australasia.

Melbourne. _Public Library._ Descriptive catalogue of the specimens in the Museum illustrating the economic Woods of Victoria. pp. 48. _Melbourne_, 1894. 8°. 7078. cc. 36.

Russell (H. C.) Notes on the rate of growth of some Australian trees. pp. 4. _Sydney_, 1891. 8°. Pam. 4.

Warren (W. H.) Australian Timbers. pp. 67. _Sydney_, 1892. 8°. 7078. f. 40.

Victoria. Giant trees of Victoria. 1888. fol. 1827. d. 2.

Kirk (T.) Forest flora of New Zealand. pp. 345. _Wellington_, 1889. fol. 1827. c. 7.

Europe.

Gadeau de Kerville (H.) Les vieux Arbres de la Normandie. 1891, etc. 8°. Ac. Rouen. _Société des Amis des Sciences Naturelles._ Bulletin, Année 26, etc. Ac. 2859.

Hoeck (F.) Nadelwaldflora Norddeutschlands pp. 55. 1893. 8°. Lehmann (R.) Forschungen zur deutschen Lands- und Volkskunde. Bd. 7. 10235. i. 10.

Koehne (E.) Deutsche Dendrologie. pp. 601. _Stuttgart_, 1893. 8°. 07076. l. 8.

Krause (E. H. L.) Die fremden Bäume der rostocker Anlagen. 1890. 8°. Ac. Neubrandenburg. _Verein der Freunde der Naturgeschichte._ Archiv des Vereins. Ac. 2890.

FORESTRY.—Forest Flora—_continued._

Nisbet (J.) British Forest Trees and their characteristics. pp. 352. _Lond._ 1895. 8°. 07076. e. 46.

Piccioli (L.) Le piante legnose italiane. _Firenze_, 1890, etc. 8°. 07028. g.

Laguna (M.) Flora forestal española. 2 pt. _Madrid_, 1883, 90. 8°. 7078. i. 33.

—— Atlas. 1824. e. 6.

See also Botany, Local Flora. _Supra : General._

Timber Measurement.

Burt (E. A. P.) Railway Rates standard timber measurer and calculator. pp. 311. _Lond._ 1888. 8°. 8548. c. 49.

—— Standard Stave measurer and calculator. pp. 112. _Lond._ 1891. 8°. 8548. de. 18.

Carter (P. J.) Treatise on the Mensuration of Timber and timber crops. pp. 67. _Calcutta_, 1893. 8°. 8533. dd. 8.

Cotsworth (M. B.) Railway and Timber Trades' measurer and calculator. pp. 225. _Leeds_, 1893. 12°. 8548. de. 26.

FOREZ. Montégut (E.) Tableaux de la France. En Bourbonnais et en Forez. pp. 336. _Paris_, 1888. 12°. 10171. dc. 5.

FORLÌ. Merlini (A.) _Marquis_, and Bornandini (A.) Le Acque e i vini della provincia di Forlì. pp. 39. _Forlì_, 1886. fol. 7470. i. 6.

Brandi (B.) L'Archivio di Forlì. pp. 57. _Roma_, 1892. 8°. 10107. ff. 28. (3.)

FORMARTINE. _See_ Aberdeen.

FORMOSA. Cordier (H.) Bibliographie des ouvrages relatifs à l île Formose. pp. 59. _Chartres_, 1893. 8°. 11900. g. 21.

Garnot (E. G.) L'Expédition française de Formose, 1884-85. pp. 10. 234. _Paris_, 1894. 8°. 9055. d. 29.

—— Atlas. 4°. 9055. f. 21.

Imbault-Huart (C.) L'île Formose, histoire et description. pp. 323. _Paris_, 1893. 4°. 10058. k. 31.

Mackay (G. L.) From far Formosa. pp. 346. _Edinb._ 1895. 8°. 010057. ee. 87.

FORTH BRIDGE. Phillips (P.) Sketches of the Forth Bridge. pp. 36. _Edin._ 1890. 8°. Pam. 79.

FORTIFICATION. Ac. Chatham. _Royal Engineer Institute._ Lewis (J. F.) Permanent Fortification for English engineers. pp. 323. _Chatham_, 1890. 8°. Ac. 4354/3.

—— Notes on Land and coast Fortification. pp. 106. _Chatham_, 1894. 8°. 8228. c. 54.

Asklund (J. G.) Några uppgifter om de europeiska Staternas nyare fästningsbyggnader. pp. 70. _Stockholm_, 1891. 8°. 8831. l. 10. (13.)

Azibert (F.) Sièges célèbres. pp. 391. _Paris_, 1890. 8°. 9072. h. 1.

Béthuys (G.) and Manceau (C.) L'Outillage d'une Armée, canons et fortresses. pp. 320. _Paris_, 1892. 8°. 8824. k. 16.

Brialmont (A. H.) Les Régions fortifiées. 2 pt. _Brux._ 1890. 8°. & fol. 8026. h. 18.

—— Atlas. 1788. c. 30.

—— La Défense des États et la fortification. pp. 349. _Brux._ 1895. 8°. 8825. e. 29.

—— Atlas. fol. 8825. i. 12.

Cugnac (G. G. M. de) Défense d'un plateau. pp. 40. _Paris_, 1893. 8°. Pam. 2.

Dary (G.) L'Électricité et la défense des côtes. pp. 348. _Paris_, 1894, 12°. 8806. bb. 29.

Deguise (V.) Cours de Fortification passagère. _Brux._ 1893, etc. 8°. & fol. 8826. h. & 8825. i.

z

FRANCE.—Antiquities, etc.—*continued*.

PERRIER DU CARNE ( ) L'Arrondissement de Mantes aux temps préhistoriques. pp. 136. *Mantes*, 1894. 8°. 07708. k. 1.

—— Armes et objets de l'époque de bronze recueillis à Mantes. pp. 24. *Versailles*, 1892. 8°. 07703. i. 2 (9.)

PETITOT (É.) La Sépulture dolménique de Mareuil-les-Meaux. pp. 202. *Paris*, 1892. 12°. 7708. aa. 62.

PILLOY (J.) La Picardie souterraine. *Saint-Quentin*, 1892. 4°. 7707. g. 37.

SAINT-VENANT (J. de) Tumulus néolithiques avec incinérations près d'Uzès. pp. 24. *Nimes*, 1894. 8°. Pam. 3.

Ac. etc. Paris. *Comité des travaux historiques.* L'Épigraphie chrétienne en Gaule. pp. 140. *Paris*, 1890. 8°. 07708. f. 24,

—— *Société de l'Art Français.* La France artistique et monumentale. *Paris*, 1892 etc. 4°. 1755. g.

—— Toulouse. *Société archéologique du Midi.* Album des monuments du Midi. *Toulouse*, 1893, etc. 4°. Ac. 5344/3.

ARBOIS DE JUBAINVILLE (M. H. d') Les Noms gaulois chez César et Hirtius. *Paris*, 1891, *etc.* 12°. 12978. c. 19.

BAZIN (H.) Vienne et Lyon gallo-romains. pp. 407. *Paris*, 1891. 8°. 7708. cc. 53.

BERTRAND (A.) La Gaule avant les Gaulois. *Paris*, 1891, *etc.* 8°. 07708. f.

—— Archéologie celtique et gauloise. *Paris*, 1889, etc. 8°. 07708. f.

BIÉLAWSKI (J. B. M.) Le Plateau central de la France dans les temps anciens. pp. 276. *Paris*, 1890. 8°. 7708. aa. 52.

BLADÉ (J. F.) Géographie historique du sud-ouest de la Gaule. 1893. 8°. Ac. Bordeaux. *Faculté des Lettres.* Annales, année 1893. No. 3-4. Ac. 8917.

BLANCHET (J. A.) Mélanges d'archéologie gallo-romaine. *Paris*, 1893, *etc.* 8°. 7706. d.

BONNEJOY (E.) De l'Érection par les anciens Gaulois des men-hirs. pp. 30. *Carentan*, 1889. 8°. 07703. i. 1. (4.)

FOURDRIGNIER (E.) Étude sur les bracelets et colliers gaulois. pp. 28. *Paris*, 1892. 8°. 07703. i. 1. (9.)

JOUBERT (L.) La Gaule jusqu'à la conquête romaine. pp. 254. *Paris*, 1890. 8°. 09200. c. 1.

GABUT (F.) Archéologie préhistorique et gallo-romaine. pp. 52. *Lyon*, 1894. 8°. 7706. f. 31.

LE BLANT (E.) Nouveau recueil des Inscriptions chrétiennes de la Gaule. pp. 483. *Paris*, 1892. 4°. 7709. i. 22.

LIÈVRE (A. F.) Les Chemins gaulois et romains entre la Loire et la Gironde. 1892. 8°. Ac. Poitiers. *Société des Antiquaires.* Mémoires. Sér. 2. Tom. 14. Ac. 5326.

LOMBARD–DUMAS (A.) Nouvelle hypothèse sur le rôle de l'Hipposandale. pp. 17. *Nimes*, 1893. 8°. Pam. 3.

MALÈGUE (H.) Antiquités gallo-romaines de la Haute-Loire. pp. 99. *Le Puy*, 1894. 8°. 07708. k. 2.

MENTIENNE ( ) L'ancien pays du Parisis. Un cimetière gallo-romain à Bry-sur-Marne. pp. 48. *Paris*, 1892. 8°. 07703. i. 1. (11.)

MOLLIÈRE (H.) Recherches sur l'Évaluation de la population des Gaules et de Lugdunum. pp. 102. *Lyon*, 1892. 8°. 09200. cc. 6.

REINACH (S.) L'Histoire du travail en Gaule à l'Exposition de 1889. pp. 73. *Paris*, 1890. 12°. 7708. a. 66.

FRANCE.—Antiquities, etc.—*continued*.

STOKES (G. T.) Greek in Gaul down to A.D. 700. *Dublin*, 1892. 8°. Pam. 47.

WILLIAMS (C. A.) Die französischen Ortsnamen keltischer Abkunft. pp. 87. *Strassb.* 1891. 8°. 12903. dd. 33. (7.)

ZANGEMEISTER (C.) Zur Geographie des römischen Galliens nach den tironischen Noten. pp. 36. *Heidelburg*, 1892. 8°. Pam. 2.

ROBIDA (A) La vieille France. Texte, dessins, etc. *Paris*, 1890, etc. 4°. 10171. i.

LARNED (W. C.) Churches and castles of mediæval France. pp. 236. *Lond.* 1895. 8°. 010171. i. 5.

See also infra: History: Topography : INSCRIPTIONS : NUMISMATICS.

Army.
General.

ARDOUIN-DUMAZET (V. E.) and GERS (P.) Au Régiment. pp. 304. *Paris*, 1894. 4°.8829. l. 21.

B. Dix Mois de caserne, par un Séminariste-Soldat. pp. 70. *La Chapelle*, 1894. 12°. 8823. h. 48.

BAUER (L.) Devoirs des municipalités en ce qui concerne l'Armée. pp. 842. *Montargis*, 1894. 8°. 5408. e. 31.

CHAPUIS (F.) Catéchisme du soldat. pp. 125. *Paris*, 1892. 8°. 8823. a. 13.

CHOPPIN (H.) Trente ans de la vie militaire. pp. 248. *Paris*, 1891. 8°. 010661. f. 38.

—— L'Armée française, 1870-90. pp. 306. *Paris*, 1890. 18°. 8823. aaa. 40.

DALLY (F. J. M. A.) La France militaire illustrée. pp. 430. *Paris*, 1893. 8°. 8831. l. 16.

DELAPERRIERRE (E.) La France économique et l'Armée. pp. 612. *Paris*, 1893. 8°. 8226. h. 41.

DES ECORRES (C.) Au Pays des Étapes. Notes d'un légionnaire. pp. 365. *Paris*, 1892. 12°. 012330. f. 37.

DESPLANTES (F.) Les Sous-Officiers. pp. 336. *Limoges*, 1894. fol. 10659. h. 27.

DILKE (*Sir* C. W.) Les Armées françaises jugées par un Anglais. pp. 64. *Paris*, 1892. 8°. 8830. g. 33. (7.)

FRANCE. Militärisches Allerlei aus Frankreich. pp. 136. *Berl.* 1890. 8°. 12331. i. 24.

—— Army. L'Armée et son budget en 1890. pp. 336. *Paris*, 1890. 8°. 8823. g. 10.

—— Répartition et emplacement des troupes. pp. 74. *Paris*, 1893. 8°. 8829. l. 24. (5.)

—— Carte de la répartition et de l'emplacement des troupes, 1893. pp. 34. *Paris*, 1893. 8°. Pam. 2.

G. B & I. *War Office.* Handbook of the French Army. pp. 155. *Lond.* 1891. 8°. 8831. ee. 14.

JUNG (H. F. T.) La République et l'Armée. pp. 362. *Paris*, 1892. 12°. 8823. aaa. 47.

LASSALLE (C.) Manuel de l'Organisation de l'Armée. pp. 1292. *Paris*, 1892. 8°. 8831. bb. 34.

—— Tableaux de la division militaire de la France. pp. 134. *Paris*, 1894. 8°. 8828. i. 35.

LEROY (A.) Notice sur la fabrication des draps de troupe. pp. 265. *Paris*, 1889. 8°. 7743. c. 13.

LEWAL (J. L.) The French Army. 1893. 8°. Armies of to-day. 8829. i. 9.

LUCAS-CHAMPIONNIÈRE (H.) La Vie militaire. pp. 149. *Paris*, 1893. 12°. 8823. a. 17.

MANGEOT (H.) Des Causes de nos revers de 1870-71 au point de vue de notre armement. pp. 39. *Nancy*, 1895 8°. 8830. bbb. 13. (8.)

MAUROY (V.) L'Armée française. *Rennes*, 1893, *etc.* 8°. 8828. cc.

FRANCE.—Army—*continued.*

Mermeix ( ) La France sous les armes.
pp. 252. *Paris,* 1886–89. fol. 8825. i. 6.

Messin (C.) L'Armée française. pp. 232.
Paris, 1890. 8°. 8823. l. 42.

Monmillion (V.) Trois ans au Régiment.
pp. 316. *Paris,* 1894. 12°. 8831. aaa. 61.

Morand (C. A. L. A.) *Count.* De l'Armée selon
la Charte, *etc.* pp. 210. *Paris,* 1894. 8°.
8830. f. 37.

N., O. Armee-Liste des französischen Heeres.
pp. 88. *Berl.* 1889. fol. 8826. h. 25.

P., L. L'Armée sans chef. pp. 291.
Paris, 1891. 12°. 8823. g. 25.

Pardiellan (P. de) Aide-mémoire de l'Officier
français en Allemagne. pp. 14.
Paris, 1890. 16°. 8823. a. 10.

P.P. *Paris.* Annuaire du service d'État-major.
pp. 104. *Paris,* 1889. 8°. P.P. 2406. bb.

Robert (F.) Réformes nécessaires. pp. 200.
Paris, 1894. 8°. 8823. o. 31.

Roche (J.) L'Armée française et l'armée allemande. pp. 57. *Paris,* 1895. 8°. Pam. 2.

Saumur (J.) Armées de Terre et de Mer.
pp. 567. *Paris,* 1891. 8°. 8823. n. 13.

Schott (A.) Die französische Wehrsteuer.
pp. 128. 1892. 8°. Staatswissenschaftl. Studien.
Bd. 4. 8207. h.

———

Philebert (C.) À propos des Manœuvres de
1889. pp. 37. *Paris,* 1890. 8°. 8831. l. 10. (10.)

G. B. & I. *War Office.* Cavalry Manœuvres in
France, 1890. pp. 23. *Lond.* 1891. 8°. Pam. 2.

Ardouin-Dumazet (V. E.) Les grandes Manœuvres de l'Est en 1891. pp. 352.
Paris, 1891. 8°. 8823. g. 23.

Reinach (J.) Les grandes Manœuvres de l'Est.
pp. 85. *Paris,* 1891. 12°. 8823. aaa. 44.

—— Reponse à M. J. Reinach. pp. 88.
Paris, 1892. 8°. 8823. g. 24.

Ardouin-Dumazet (V. E.) Les grandes Manœuvres de 1892. pp. 280. *Paris,* 1892. 12°.
8828. aaa. 23.

—— L'Armée en 1894. Grand Manœuvres de
Beauce. pp. 374. *Paris,* 1895. 8°. 8806. bb. 33.

Gers (P.) Voyage de M. le Président à Châteu-
dun. Grandes Manœuvres des 4ᵉ et 11ᵉ corps.
pp. 12. *Paris,* 1894. 8°. 9930. g. 36.

———

Chrétien (E.) La Taxe militaire. Commentaire de l'article 35 de la loi sur le recrutement.
pp. 143. *Paris,* 1891. 8°. 08227. g. 24.

Nicolas (V.) Manuel d'Administration et de
comptabilité militaires. pp. 532.
Paris, 1892. 12°. 6875. de. 15.

Pavitt (A.) Guide to the French Laws of 1889,
on nationality and military Service. pp. 42.
Lond. 1893. 8°. 5405. de. 6. (5.)

Rabany (C.) La Loi sur le recrutement. 2 tom.
Paris, 1890. 8°. 6875. cc. 16.

———

Gélinet (J. N. L.) La Frontière menacée.
Étude militaire. pp. 120. *Paris,* 1895. 8°.
8830. bbb. 14.

Hennebert (E.) La Défense du territoire.
pp. 281. *Paris,* 1890. 18°. 8026. bb. 29.

Luzeux (A. F.) De l'introduction du service de
deux ans dans l'Armée. pp. 64.
Paris, 1895. 8°. 8830. bbb. 17.

Patiens. La Défense nationale et la Défense
des côtes. pp. 264. *Paris,* 1894. 8°. 8828. c. 57.

Pierron (É.) La Défense des frontières.
Paris, 1892, *etc.* 8°. 8829. l.

FRANCE.—Army—*continued.*

Poullin (M.) Les Forteresses françaises en
1870–71. 2 pt. *Paris,* 1890. 8°. 9080. cc. 7.

Ténot (E.) Les nouvelles Défenses de la France.
La Frontière. pp. 392. *Bordeaux,* 1893. 8°.
8829. i. 12.

Chotard (H.) Louis xiv. Louvois, Vauban, et
les fortifications du nord de la France. 1890. 8°.
Ac. Dunkirk. *Comité Flamand.* Annales.
Tom. 18. Ac. 5298.

X., *Général.* Étude de la Frontière nord-est.
pp. 63. *Paris,* 1892, 8°. 8830. f. 38. (2.)

Richou (G.) Construction des forts de la Meuse.
pp. 68. *Paris,* 1892. 4°. 8824. k. 22·

Jacquemin (M.) À la Frontière de l'Est.
pp. 184. *Paris,* 1894. 12°. 10105. cc. 4.

Mizraki (J.) and Soulier (E.) Les Servitudes
militaires et les Fortifications de Paris. pp. 320.
Paris, 1893. 12°. 8830. aaa. 56.

Perrin (E.) Topographie et défense des Alpes
françaises. pp. 758. *Périgueux,* 1894. 8°.
8830. l. 30.

Aguiton (d') Guerre de la France contre le
Piémont, et du Piémont contre la France.
pp. 34. 3. *Grenoble,* 1891. 8°. 8823. dd. 41.

See also infra: Navy: Military Science:
Fortification.

History.

Champeaux (J. de) Honneur et patrie, la Noblesse
aux Armées. *Nevers,* 1893, *etc.* 4° 10659. h.

Hardy de Périni (M. J. F. É.) Batailles françaises. *Châteauroux,* 1894, *etc.* 8°. 9220. ccc.

Jablonski (L.) L'Armée française à travers les
âges. *Paris,* 1890, *etc.* 12°. 8824. c. 14.

Lonlay (D. de) Notre Armée; histoire populaire. pp. 1138. *Paris,* 1890. 8°. 09200. h. 2.

Quarré de Verneuil (A. H. R.) L'Armée en
France depuis Charles vii. pp. 368.
Paris, 1880. 8°. 8823. ddd. 24.

Romagny (C. M.) Histoire générale de l'Armée
nationale, 1214–1892. pp. 331.
Paris, 1893. 12°. 8828. aaa. 24.

Choppin (H.) La Cavalerie française. pp. 480.
Paris, 1893. 8°. 8824. k. 32.

Belhomme (V. L. J. F.) Histoire de l'Infanterie
en France. *Paris,* 1892, *etc.* 8°. 8830. bbb.

Du Bois-Melly (C.) Mœurs soldatesques de
Louis xii. à Henri ii. 1894. 8°. Ac. Geneva.
Institut National. Bulletin. Tom. 32. Ac. 610.

Belhomme (V. L. J. F.) L'Armée française en
1690. pp. 206. *Paris,* 1895. 8°. 8824. dd. 43.

Lioret (G.) La Compagnie de Milice bourgeoise, 1779–89. pp. 33.
Moret-sur-L. 1892. 8°. 8826. g. 42.

Du Bourget (C. C. M. J.) Campagnes modernes,
1792–1892. pp. 262. *Paris,* 1892. 8°.
9009. d. 14.

Vigneron (H.) La France militaire du xixᵉ
siècle. *Paris,* 1890, *etc.* 8°. 9231. h. 12.

Titeux (E.) Histoire de la Maison militaire du
Roi, 1814–30. 2 tom. *Paris,* 1890. fol.
8825. h. 16.

For the history of the Army, 1793–1815, *see
infra:* Military History, 1789–1815.

Regimental Histories, etc.

Hennet (L.) Notices historiques sur l'État-
major général. pp. 160. *Paris,* 1892. 8°.
8824. ccc. 31.

Poli (O. de) Le Régiment de la Couronne,
1643–1791. pp. 370. *Paris,* 1891. 8°.
8830. l. 12.

Verly (A.) L'Escadron des Cent-Gardes.
pp. 307. *Paris,* 1894. 8°. 8830. cc. 27.

FRANCE.—Army—*continued.*

BOURGUE (M.) Historique du 3ᵉ régiment d'Infanterie ex-Piémont. pp. 448. *Paris*, 1894. 8°.   8829. i. 19.

DEMIAU ( ) Historique du 5ᵉ régiment d'Infanterie. pp. 368. *Caen*, 1890. 8°.   8830. l. 14.

TARRAGON (M. L. A. de) Historique du 15ᵉ régiment d'Infanterie. pp. 450. *Paris*, 1895. 8°.   8830. e. 18.

FRANCE. *Army.* Historique du 24ᵉ régiment d'Infanterie. pp. 323. *Paris*, 1893. 8°.   8829. f. 44.

PIÉRON (G. L. E.) Histoire d'un régiment, la 32ᵉ demi-brigade. pp. 381. *Paris*, 1890. 8°.   8824. k. 18.

MAUGENRE (L. M. A.) Trente et un ans au 36ᵐᵉ de la ligne. pp. 753. *Saint-Dié*, 1891. 8°.   010661. f. 30.

FAIVRE D'ARCIER (C. S.) and ROYÉ (A. H.) Historique du 37ᵉ régiment d'Infanterie. pp. 15. 344. *Paris*, 1895. 8°.   8830. e. 22.

CHAPERON (H.) Historique du 46ᵉ régiment d'Infanterie. pp. 200. *Paris*, 1894. 8°. 8831. h. 18.

GERTHOFFER (J. G.) Historique du 52ᵉ régiment d'Infanterie. pp. 334. *Paris*, 1890. 8°.   8831. e. 18.

DUVAL (J. C.) Historique du 53ᵐᵉ régiment d'Infanterie. pp. 121. *Pau*, 1892. 8°. 8823. dd. 43.

FRANCE. *Army.* Historique du 74ᵉ régiment d'Infanterie. pp. 207. *Paris*, 1890. 8°.   8831. k. 21.

GÉROME ( ) Historique du 75ᵉ régiment d'Infanterie. pp. 284. *Paris*, 1891. 12°.   8823. aaa. 42.

DOLLIN DU FRESNEL (H. V.) Le 76ᵉ ex 1ᵉʳ Léger. pp. 752. *Paris*, 1894. 4°.   8824. k. 36.

MALAGUTI ( ) Historique du 87ᵉ régiment d'Infanterie. pp. 647. *Saint-Quentin*, 1892. 8°.   8824. k. 28.

BOUVIER (J. B.) Historique du 96ᵉ régiment d'Infanterie. pp. 426. *Lyon*, 1892. 8°.   8824. k. 23.

DUCHATELET (A. V.) Historique du 106ᵐᵉ régiment d'Infanterie. pp. 172. *Châlons*, 1890. 8°.   8830. l. 15.

GYVÈS (H. J. A. de) Historique du 122ᵐᵉ régiment d'Infanterie. pp. 394.
Montpellier, 1890. 8°.   8826. ee. 2.
—— Croquis. fol.   8826. i. 17.

JAGUIN (L. O.) Historique du 137ᵉ régiment d'Infanterie. pp. 172. *Fontenay-le-C.* 1890. 8°.   8824. e. 11.

RICHARD (A. J. C.) Les Chasseurs à pied. pp. 510. *Paris*, 1890. 8°..   8829. i. 20.

GANGLOFF (G.) Les Zouaves. 2 tom. *Rambervilliers*, 1893. 8°.   8829. l. 23.

BLANC (M. S. J. A.) La Légion étrangère. pp. 272. *Paris*, 1890. 18°.   9080. aaa. 36.

NORDECK (E. v.) Sibirien in Frankreich. Enthüllungen über die Fremdenlegion. pp. 48. *Berl.* 1894. 12°.   8830. e. 11. (5.)

ALBERT (A.) Le Manuscrit des Carabiniers. 1792-1814. pp. 290. *Paris*, 1894. 8°. 8829. k. 26.

FOUCART ( ) L'armement des Cuirassiers en 1811. pp. 39. *Paris*, 1894. 8°. 8829. l. 24. (6.)

AMONVILLE (M. F. J. B. d') Les Cuirassiers du Roy, le 8ᵉ Cuirassiers. pp. 342. *Paris*, 1892. 8°.   8830. l. 18.

SAINT-JUST (V. E. M. de) Historique du 5ᵉ régiment de Dragons. pp. 420. *Paris*, 1891. 8°.   8824. k. 9.

FRANCE. *Army.* Historique du 10ᵉ régiment de Dragons. pp. 614. *Paris*, 1893. 8°. 8824. k. 34.

CASTÉRAS-VILLEMARTIN (J. A. M. P. F. de P.) Historique du 16ᵉ regiment de Dragons. pp. 208. *Paris*, 1892, 4°.   8826. i. 27.

FRANCE.—Army—*continued.*

HACHE (É.) Historique du 23ᵉ régiment de Dragons. pp. 236. *Paris*, 1890. 4°. 8826. i. 16.

BOURQUENEY (M. V. C. de) Historique du 25ᵉ régiment de Dragons. pp. 294. *Tours*, 1890. 4°.   8824. k. 10.

QUINEMONT (de) Historique du 2ᵉ régiment de Chasseurs à cheval. pp. 294. *Paris*, 1889. 8°.   8823. o. 29.

WOLF (F. S. A.) Historique du 10ᵉ régiment de Chasseurs à cheval. pp. 342. *Paris*, 1890, 8°.   8824. e. 45.

LEPAGE (P. J.) and PARROT (R. P. M.) Historique du 19ᵉ régiment de Chasseurs. pp. 435. *Lille*, 1893. 4°.   8825. h. 26.

CASTILLON DE SAINT-VICTOR (M. J.) Historique du 5ᵉ régiment de Hussards. pp. 210. *Paris*, 1889. 4°.   8825. h. 14.

PAULTRE DE LAMOTTE (C. H. P.) Historique du 8ᵉ régiment de Hussards. pp. 186. *Valence*, 1891. 8°.   8825. g. 31.

LASSUS (H. de) Historique du 11ᵉ régiment de Hussards. pp. 253. *Valence*, 1890. 8°.   8823. dd. 37.

DURAND (A. H. V.) Historique du 3ᵉ régiment de Spahis. pp. 230. *Paris*, 1892. 8°. 8826. ee. 22.

DAUVÉ (H. P. E.) Historique du 12ᵉ régiment d'Artillerie. pp. 332. *Paris*, 1890. 8°. 8831. k. 19.

ROSWAG (H.) Historique du 13ᵉ régiment d'Artillerie. pp. 298. *Paris*, 1891. 8°.   8823. n. 12.

FRANCE. *Army.* Historique du 2ᵉ régiment du Génie. pp. 413. *Paris*, 1894. 8°. 8828. aaa. 25.

M., G. L. La Question des Pontonniers et le projet de loi qui les supprime. pp. 32. *Paris*, 1894. 8°.   8830. f. 38. (6.)

BOURNAND (F.) Le régiment de Sapeurs-pompiers de Paris. pp. 34. *Paris*, 1887. fol.   8825. h. 25.

Church of. See *infra*: HISTORY, *Ecclesiastical*: ROMAN CATHOLIC CHURCH, *in France.*

Colonies.

BOUCHIÉ DE BELLE (A.) Le régime commercial des Colonies françaises. pp. 130. *Paris*, 1894. 12°.   08226. g. 10.

BOUTMY (É. G.) Le Recrutement des administrateurs coloniaux. pp. 127. *Paris*, 1895. 12°.   8154. aa. 27.

CANU (A. H.) La Pétaudière coloniale. pp. 316. *Paris*, 1894. 12°.   8154. aa. 25.

CERISIER (C.) Impressions coloniales, 1868-1892. pp. 357. *Paris*, 1893. 8°. 8155. ee. 16.

CHESSÉ (I.) Vérités coloniales. pp. 154. *Paris*, 1895. 8°.   8154. aa. 30.

COOK (A.) Les Colonies françaises. pp. 141. *Bordeaux*, 1889. 4°.   10024. f. 22.

DAUBIGNY (E.) Choiseul et la France d'outre-mer après le Traité de Paris. pp. 352. *Paris*, 1892. 8°.   9555. ee. 9.

DENANCY (E.) De la Colonisation dans ses rapports avec la production et la consommation. pp. 131. *Épernay*, 1894. 8°.   8154. aa. 23.

DESCHAMPS (L.) Histoire de la question coloniale. pp. 405. *Paris*, 1891. 8°.   8144. ee. 27.

—— Histoire de la Colonisation française. pp. 156. *Paris*, 1894. 12°.   8155. de. 13.

DUBOIS (M.) Géographie de la France et de ses Colonies. pp. 645. *Paris*, 1892. 8°.   10025. ce. 26.

FRANCE. L'Expansion de la France et la diplomatie. pp. 298. *Paris*, 1895. 8°. 8026. aa. 38.

GASQUET (A.) Géographie de la France et de ses Colonies. pp. 444. *Paris*, 1892. 8°.   10024. aa. 23.

Constitution and Government.

FRANCE.—Constitution, etc.—*continued.*

Durand (J.) Les Étrangers devant la Loi française. pp. 198. *Paris,* 1890. 8°. 5403. de. 2.

Delanney (L.) Les Occupations temporaires et la loi du 29 déc. 1892. pp. 300. *Paris,* 1893. 8°. 5425. a. 1.

Lachau (C.) De la Compétence des tribunaux français à l'égard des étrangers. pp. 468. *Paris,* 1893. 8°. 5423. e. 18.

Constitutional History.

Nys (E.) Les théories politiques en France jusqu'au XVIIIᵉ siècle. pp. 208. *Brux.* 1891. 8°. 8009. f. 14.

Fustel de Coulanges (N. D.) Histoire des institutions politiques de l'ancienne France. pp. 572. *Paris,* 1891. 8°. 09200. e. 4.

Luchaire (A.) Manuel des Institutions, période des Capétiens. pp. 638. *Paris,* 1892. 8°. 5406. de. 12.

Perrier (J.) Histoire des Sénéchaux et Connétables de France. 978–1789. pp. 212. *Lyon,* 1893. 8°. 010662. i. 17.

Luchaire (A.) Histoire des Institutions monarchiques de la France. 987–1180. 2 tom. *Paris,* 1891. 8°. 09200. ee. 2.

Aubert (F.) Histoire du Parlement de Paris. 1250–1515. 2 tom. *Paris,* 1894. 8°. 09200. a. 7.

Petiet (R.) Du Pouvoir législatif en France depuis Philippe le Bel jusqu'en 1789. pp. 295. *Paris,* 1891. 8°. 8050. f. 7.

Spont (A.) De Cancellariæ regum Franciæ officiariis, 1440–1523. pp. 86. *Vesontione,* 1894. 8°. 5408. aaa. 9.

Weill (G.) Les théories sur le Pouvoir Royal pendant les guerres de religion. pp. 315. *Paris,* 1891. 8°. 8051. d. 24.

Babeau (A.) La Province sous l'ancien régime. 2 tom. *Paris,* 1894. 8°. 9231. g. 25.

Julienne (J.) Recueil des Droits seigneuriaux avant 1789. pp. 35. *Le Mans,* 1890. 8°. Pam. 34.

Muel (L.) Gouvernements, Ministères et Constitutions de la France depuis cent ans. pp. 557. *Paris,* 1893. 8°. 9231. g. 19.

Challeton (F.) Histoire électorale et parlementaire de la France, 1789–1890. 3 tom. *Paris,* 1891. 8°. 9230. cc. 10.

Weil (G. D.) Les Élections législatives depuis 1789. pp. 294. *Paris,* 1895. 8°. 9230. ccc. 4.

—— Un Siècle d'Histoire. Le Droit d'Association et le droit de réunion devant les Chambres et les Tribunaux. pp. 340. *Paris,* 1893. 12°. 8052. cc. 35.

Louis Philip Albert, *Count de Paris.* Le Droit à l'association. pp. 49. *Paris,* 1894. 12°. 8051. ccc. 27.

See also infra: History: Politics: Constitutions : Elections : Local Government.

Constitutional Church.

See infra : History, *Ecclesiastical.*

Église Réformée. *See infra :* Protestants.

Finance. *See infra :* Trade.

Frontiers. *See supra :* Army.

History.

General and Miscellaneous.

Charmes (X.) Le Comité des Travaux historiques. Histoire et documents. 3 tom. 1886. 4°. France. Collection des documents, *etc.* 9210. g.

Langlois (C. V.) and Stein (H.) Les Archives de l'histoire de France. *Paris,* 1891, *etc.* 8°. 011902. h.

P.P. *Paris,* L'Archiviste. Revue historique et documentaire. *Paris,* 1893, *etc.* 8°. P.P. 3551. va.

FRANCE.—History—*continued.*

Corner (J.) History of France. pp. 195. *Lond.* 1869. 8°. 9210. c. 6.

Creighton (L.) First history of France. pp. 301. *Lond.* 1893. 8°. 9200. bb. 19.

Duruy (V.) Histoire de France. pp. 945. *Paris,* 1892. 4°. 9200. i. 11.

Kitchin (G. W.) History of France. 1892, *etc.* 8°. Clarendon Press Series. 2320. e. 25.

Roget (F. F.) First steps in French History. pp. 328. *Lond.* 1892. 8°. 9200. c. 9.

Bennassi-Desplantes (F. J.) Patrie! Contes et récits. pp. 63. *Rouen,* 1891. 8°. 9230. cc. 12.

Charmes (F.) Études historiques. pp. 400. *Paris,* 1893. 8°. 012356. f. 16.

Fustel de Coulanges (N.) Nouvelles Recherches sur quelques problèmes d'histoire. pp. 482. *Paris,* 1891. 8°. 9009. l. 3.

French History. Stories from French History. Ser. 2. pp. 128. *Lond.* 1886. 8°. 4429. c. 13.

Guizot (F. P. G.) Récits historiques. *Lond.* 1891, *etc.* 8°. 9220. ccc.

Koenig (B. E.) Die Geschichte des Cabinet noir Frankreichs. pp. 57. *Leipz.* 1895. 8°. Pam. 28.

Lecoy de la Marche (A.) La Guerre aux erreurs historiques. pp. 360. *Paris,* 1891. 8°. 9210. cc. 18.

Michelet (J.) France et Français. Textes patriotiques. pp. 174. *Paris,* 1893. 12°. 9210. cc. 18.

Paul (N. M.) True stories from French History. pp. 254. *Lond.* 1890. 8°. 9200. c. 8.

Seignobos (C.) Scènes et épisodes de l'histoire nationale. pp. 315. *Paris,* 1891. 4°. 9200. i. 10.

Reinach (J.) La France et l'Italie devant l'histoire. pp. 244. *Paris,* 1893. 8°. 9079. h. 20.

Vacheron (A.) Mémorial poétique de l'Histoire de France. pp. 172. *Paris,* 1895. 12°. 9220. ccc. 17.

For the Constitutional History of France, *see supra : Constitution.*

Gauls to the House of Capet.

Martin (B. L. H.) Les Origines de la France jusqu'aux Maires du Palais. pp. 234. *Paris,* 1891. 8°. 09200. ee. 1.

Brémaud (P.) Les Origines de la nationalité française, *etc.* 1892. 8°. Ac. Brest. *Société Académique.* Bulletin. Sér. 2. Tom. 17. Ac. 300.

Bertrand (A.) La Gaule avant les Gaulois. *Paris,* 1891, *etc,* 8°. 07708. f.

Joubert (L.) La Gaule jusqu'à la conquête romaine. pp. 254. *Paris,* 1890. 8°. 09200. c. 1.

Stoffel (E. G. H. C.) Guerre de César et d'Arioviste. pp. 163. *Paris,* 1890. 4°. 9041. dd. 9.

Jullian (C.) Gallia. Tableau sommaire de la Gaule. pp. 312. *Paris,* 1892. 8°. 9210. c. 10.

Rabillon (V.) Les Empereurs provinciaux des Gaules. 1891. 8°. Ac. Rennes. *Société Archéologique.* Tom. 20. Pt. 2. Ac. 5341.

Schiber (A.) Die fränkischen und alemannischen Siedlungen in Gallien. pp. 109. *Strassb.* 1894. 8°. 9225. b. 39.

Pfister (H. v.) Vom Ursprunge der Franken. pp. 43. *Darmstadt,* 1891. 8°. Pam. 28.

Jouvencel (P. d.) L'Indépendance des Gaules et l'Allemagne. pp. 134. *Paris,* 1890. 12°. 9200. b. 3.

Lipp (M.) Die Marken des Frankenreiches unter Karl dem Grossen. *Königsberg,* 1892, *etc.* 8°. 9220. d.

Weyl (R.) Die Beziehungen des Papstthums zum fränkischen Staats- und Kirchenrecht unter den Karolingern. pp. 238. 1892. 8°. Gierke (O.) Untersuchungen, *etc.* Hft. 40. 6025. c. 9.

FRANCE.—History—*continued*.

MARTIN (B. L. H.) Les Capétiens jusqu'à la mort de Philippe-Auguste. pp. 246.
Paris, 1892. 8°. 09200. ce. 5.

FAVRE (E.) Eudes, Roi de France, 882-898. pp. 284. 1893. 8°. Ac. Paris. *École des Hautes Études*. Bibliothèque. Sciences philologiques. Fasc. 99. Ac. 8929.

GIRY (A.) Les derniers Carolingiens. 1891. 8°. Ac. Paris. *École des Hautes Études*. Bibliothèque. Sciences philologiques. Fasc. 87.
Ac. 8929.

BROECKING (W.) Die französische Politik Papst Leos IX. pp. 106. *Stuttg.* 1891. 8°. 4571. ee. 10.

HIRSCH (R.) Studien zur Geschichte König Ludwigs VII. 1119-60. pp. 116. *Leipz.* 1892. 8°.
09210. e. 16.

PETIT-DUTAILLIS (C.) Étude sur Louis VIII., 1187-1226. pp. 568. 1895. 8°. Ac. Paris. *École des Hautes Études*. Bibliothèque. Sciences philologiques. Fasc. 101. Ac. 8929.

BERGER (É.) Histoire de Blanche de Castille. pp. 428. 1895. 8°. Ac. Athens. *École Française*. Bibliothèque. Fasc. 70. 5206/2.

DOINEL (J. S.) Histoire de Blanche de Castille. pp. 228. *Tours*, 1887. 12°. 10631. de. 34.

MICHEL (F.) Rôles gascons. 1885, *etc.* 4°. FRANCE. Collection de documents. Sér. I. 9210. g.

LECLÈRE (L.) Les rapports de la Papauté et de la France sous Philippe III. pp. 138.
Brux. 1889. 8°. 4571. f. 13.

Ac. Paris. *Société de l'Histoire*. Chronographia Regum Francorum. *Paris*, 1891, *etc.* 8°.
Ac. 6884/80.

HENNEBERG (H.) Die politischen Beziehungen zwischen Deutschland und Frankreich unter Albrecht I. 1289-1303. pp. 164.
Strassb. 1891. 8°. 9073. cc. 5.

House of Valois, 1328-1589.

PARIS (G.) and JEANROY (A.) Extraits des Chroniqueurs. pp. 474. *Paris*, 1892. 8°.
9220 aa. 7.

DEBIDOUR (A.) and ÉTIENNE (E.) Les Chroniqueurs français du moyen âge. Études. pp. 408. *Paris*, 1895. 12°. 9220. ccc. 16.

IMBERT DE SAINT AMAND (A. L.) Women of the Valois Court. pp. 356. *Lond.* 1894. 8°.
010661. ee. 48.

LUCE (S.) Histoire de la Jacquerie. pp. 368. *Paris*, 1894. 8°. 09210. df. 9.

DUCKETT (*Sir* G. F.) Documents relating to the hostages of John, King of France, 1360. pp. 78. *Lond.* 1890. 8°. 9220. eec. 16.

LEROUX (A.) Nouvelles recherches sur les relations de la France avec d'Allemagne, 1378-1461. pp. 367. *Paris*, 1892. 8°. 9079. h. 16.

Ac. Paris. *Société de l'Histoire*. GRUEL (G.) Chronique d'A. de Richemont. pp. 313.
Paris, 1890. 8°. 09200. c. 2.

COSNEAU (E.) Le Connétable de Richemont. 1393-1458. pp. 712. *Paris*, 1886. 8°.
010661. i. 21.

COVILLE (A.) Les Cabochiens et l'Ordonnance de 1413. pp. 456. *Paris*, 1888. 8°
09210. de. 10.

CHARLES (R.) L'Invasion anglaise dans le Maine, 1417-28. 1889. 8°. Ac. Le Mans. *Société Historique*. Revue. Tom. 25. Ac. 5321/3.

ADAMS (W. H. D.) The Maid of Orleans. pp. 339. *Lond.* 1889. 8°. 010661. f. 36.

ARC (J. d') Jeane Dare l'héroïne de la France. pp. 488. *Paris*, 1895. 8°. 10658. l. 9.

FRANCE.—History—*continued*.

AYROLES (J. B. J.) La vraie Jeanne d'Arc. pp. 25. 754. *Paris*, 1890. 8°. 10660. k. 11.

BLAZE DE BURY (H.) Jeanne d'Arc. pp. 525. *Paris*, 1890. 8°. 010661. h. 16.

BOURBON-LIGNIÈRES (H. de) Étude sur Jeanne d'Arc. pp. 622. *Paris*, 1894. 12°. 010662. f. 24.

BOUTEYRE (J.) Pourquoi Jeanne d'Arc n'a pas encore de poète. pp. 31. *Gand*, 1892. 8°.
10601. d. 32. (4.)

BOUTHORS (L.) La vénérable Jeanne d'Arc. pp. 236. *Orléans*, 1895. 8°. 010663. k. 11.

BRETTES ( ) La France du XX. siècle et Jeanne d'Arc. pp. 47. *Paris*, 1894. 24°. Pam. 8.

CHAPOTIN (M. D.) Jeanne d'Arc et les Dominicains. pp. 31. *Paris*, 1894. 8°.
10601. ce 21. (14.)

CHARLES (E.) Joan the Maid. pp. 318. *Paris*, 1894. 8°. 4429. cc. 12.

CHESNELONG (P. C.) Jeanne d'Arc et la vocation chrétienne de la France. pp. 24.
Paris, 1894. 8°. 010603. g. 40. (8.)

COCHARD (T.) Existe-t-il des reliques de Jeanne d'Arc? 1892. 8°. Ac. Orleans. *Société Archéologique*. Mémoires. Tom. 23. Ac. 5324/2.

—— La mémoire de Jeanne d'Arc à Orléans. pp. 32. *Orléans*, 1892. 8°. 10601. d. 32. (5.)

COUSINOT (G.) Chronique de La Pucelle. pp. 476. *Paris*, 1892. 12°. 9225. a. 19.

DEFOURNY (P.) Jeanne d'Arc et le Droit des gens. pp. 94. *Paris*, 1888. 8°.
10660. aa. 38. (4.)

DEBOUT (H.) and EUDE (É.) L'Histoire de Jeanne d'Arc. pp. 433. *Paris*, 1895. 8°.
10660. i. 27.

—— Discours prononcé au pèlerinage de Domrémy, 1891. pp. 14. *Paris*, 1891. 8°.
10601. ee. 21. (5.)

DEBRAY (G.) Les Monuments de Jeanne Darc. pp. 89. *Rouen*, 1890. 8°. 10603. e. 16. (3.)

DOINEL (J.) Jeanne d'Arc, telle qu'elle est. pp. 83. *Orléans*, 1892. 8°. 10601. ff. 7. (3.)

DRAPEYRON (L.) Jeanne d'Arc. *Paris*, 1892, *etc.* 8°. 09200. ee. 4.

FABRE (J.) Jeanne d'Arc. pp. 355. *Paris*, 1892. 8°. 010662. h. 9.

—— Le mois de Jeanne d'Arc. pp. 344. *Paris*, 1892. 12°. 010662. ff. 33.

FESCH (P.) Jeanne d'Arc. pp. 12. 440. *Paris*, 1894. 8°. 010662. i. 30.

GÉNOT (H.) Jeanne d'Arc en France et à Domremy. pp. 14. *Neufchâteau*, 1890. 8°. Pam. 8.

GLOUVET (J. de) France. 1418-29. pp. 362. *Paris*, 1895. 12°. 9225. aa. 30.

GEORGES (É.) Jeanne d'Arc considérée au point de vue franco-champenois. pp. 538.
Troyes, 1894. 8°. 010662. i. 21.

GRAVILLON (A. de) Le génie de Jeanne Darc. pp. 152. *Paris*, 1895. 8°. 010663. i. 33.

GRÈZES (H. de) Jeanne d'Arc, franciscaine. pp. 36. *Paris*, 1895. 8°. 010663. i. 40. (10.)

HAUDECŒUR (A.) Jeanne d'Arc dans la littérature en Angleterre. pp. 55. *Reims*, 1895. 8°.
010663. i. 34.

HUET (E.) Jeanne d'Arc et la musique. pp. 152. 1894. 8°. Ac. Orleans. *Société d'Agriculture*, *etc.* Sér. 2. Tom. 32. Ac. 415.

HIRSCH (W.) Betrachtungen über die Jungfrau von Orleans vom Standpunkte der Irrenheilkunde. pp. 35. *Berl.* 1895. 8°. Pam. 8.

HUMBLOT (H.) Jeanne d'Arc et le clergé français pp. 54. *Paris*, 1891. 12°. 10601. e. 12. (2.)

JANVIER (M. A.) Panégyrique de Jeanne d'Arc. pp. 477. *Paris*, 1894. 8°. Pam. 8.

FRANCE.—History.—continued.

KERR (*Lady* A.) Joan of Arc. pp. 169.
Lond. 1895. 8°.   010663. f. 35.

LA BALLE (de) Jeanne d'Arc et le pays
d'Évreux. pp. 29. *Évreux*, 1893. 8°.
     10601. tt. 12. (9.)

LECOY DE LA MARCHE (A.) À la gloire de
Jeanne d'Arc. pp. 242. *Paris*, 1895. 8°.
     010663. i. 20.

LEMIRE (C.) Jeanne d'Arc et le sentiment national. pp. 266. *Paris*, 1891. 12°. 010662. ff. 16.

LE MOYNE DE LA BORDERIE (L. A.) Une préten-
due compagne de Jeanne d'Arc. Pierrone et
Perrinaïc. pp. 19. *Paris*, 1894. 8°.   Pam. 8.

LESIGNE (E.) Vie de Jeanne Darc. pp. 252.
Paris, 1889. 8°.   010661. h. 20,

L'HOTE (E.) Jeanne d'Arc la bonne Lorraine.
pp. 114. *Saint-Dié*, 1895. 8°.   010663. k. 16.

MAHRENHOLTZ (R.) Jeanne Darc in Geschichte,
Legende, Dichtung. pp. 174. *Leipz.* 1890. 8°.
     010661. i. 19.

MISSET (E.) Jeanne d'Arc champenoise. pp. 80.
Paris, 1895. 8°.   010662. k. 21.

MOUROT (V.) Jeanne d'Arc. pp. 138.
Saint-Amand, 1890. 12°.   10660. bb. 39.

PAU (M. E.) Histoire de notre petite sœur
Jeanne d'Arc. pp. 166. *Paris*, 1891. 8°.
     10663. bb. 43.

QUIS. Jeanne d'Arc eine Heilige? pp. 147.
München, 1893. 8°.   010661. g. 52.

THEVET (A.) Jeanne d'Arc. pp. 41.
Orléans, 1890. 8°.   10601. g. 3. (7.)

VALLÉE ( ) Jeanne d'Arc. pp. 74.
Paris, 1894. 8°.   010663. g. 33.

WALLON (H. A.) Sénat. Discours par M. H.
Wallon, Président de la commission de la Fête de
Jeanne d'Arc. pp. 16. *Paris*, 1894. 8°. Pam. 8.

WYNDHAM (F. M.) The Maid of Orleans.
pp. 87. *Lond.* 1894. 8°.   010662. g. 37.

DEBOUT (H.) Jeanne d'Arc et les archives
anglaises. pp. 25. *Paris*, 1894. 8°.
     10600. eee. 1. (7.)

RABBE (F.) Jeanne d'Arc en Angleterre.
pp. 376. *Paris*, 1891. 12°.   010662. ff. 8.

DEBOUT (H.) Appréciation du duc de Bedford,
sur Jeanne d'Arc. pp. 29. *Paris*, 1895. 8°.
     10600. eee. 1. (6.)

SEVIN (A. M.) Jeanne d'Arc dans la littérature
anglaise contemporaine. pp. 100.
Lille, 1894. 8°.   010662. k. 4.

LEROY (O.) Jeanne d'Arc à Domremy. pp. 72.
Saint-Dié, 1890. 12°.   Pam. 8.

LA VALLÉE DE RARÉCOURT (G.) *Marquis de
Pimodan*. La première étape de Jeanne d'Arc.
pp. 57. *Paris*, 1890. 8°.   9225. l. 17.

ROUETTE (C.) Itinéraire de Jeanne la Pucelle.
2 tom. *Vulaines*, 1894. 8°.   010663. f. 33.

VILLARET (A. de) Compagnes des Anglais,
1421–28. Compagnes de Jeanne d'Arc sur la
Loire postérieures au siège d'Orléans. pp. 168.
Orléans, 1893. 8°.   9079. g. 22.

DUBOIS (F. N. A.) Histoire du siège d'Orléans,
1428–29. pp. 444. *Orléans*, 1894. 8°.
     09210. df. 8.

BOUCHER DE MOLANDON ( ) and BEAUCORPS
(A. de) L'Armée anglaise vaincue par Jeanne
d'Arc. Documents inédits. 1892. 8°. Ac.
Orleans. *Société Archéologique*. Mémoires.
Tom. 23.   Ac. 5324/2.

JARRY (L.) Le compte de l'Armée anglaise au
siège d'Orléans, 1428–29. pp. 240.
Orléans, 1892. 8°.   9072. f. 9.

DEVELLE (E.) Jeanne d'Arc. Blois. Selles-en-
Berni, 1429. pp. 100. *Blois*, 1894. 8°.
     10662. cc. 41.

FRANCE.—History—continued.

BADEL (É.) Jeanne d'Arc à Nancy. pp. 102.
Orléans, 1890. 8°.   10663. i. 25.

LEDAIN (B.) Jeanne d'Arc à Poitiers. pp. 91.
Paris, 1894. 12°.   010663. f. 36.

PERNIN (C. R.) Jeanne d'Arc à Troyes. pp. 46.
Paris, 1894. 8°.   Pam. 8.

DEBOUT (H.) Jeanne d'Arc, prisonnière à Arras.
pp. 40. *Arras*, 1894. 8°.   10601. aa. 35. (7.)

ARC (J. d') Les Procès de Jehanne la Pucelle.
pp. 212. *Saint-Brieuc*, 1890. 12°. 010661. f. 15.

—— Procès de condamnation de Jeanne d'Arc.
pp. 432. *Paris*, 1895. 12°.   010663. f. 48.

ROBILLARD DE BEAUREPAIRE (C. de) Notes sur
les Juges du procès de Jeanne d'Arc. pp. 135.
Rouen, 1890. 8°.   10658. d. 20.

Ac. Paris. *Société de l'Histoire.* LESEUR (G.)
Histoire de Gaston IV., Comte de Foix.
Paris, 1893, *etc.* 8°.   Ac. 6884/84.

BASIN (T.) *Archbishop of Cæsarea*. Fragments
de l'histoire de Louis XI. tirés d'un manuscrit
de Goettingue par M. L. Delisle, *etc.* pp. 33.
Paris, 1893. 8°.   9009. m. 9. (3.)

Ac. Paris. *Société de l'Histoire,* ROYE (J. de)
Journal de Jean de Roye, 1460–83.
Paris, 1894, *etc.* 8°.   Ac. 6884/86.

—— AUTON (J. d') Chroniques de Louis XII.
Paris, 1889, *etc.* 8°.   Ac. 6884/79.

LEDIEU (A.) Notice et documents sur le marriage
de Louis XII. 1889. 8°. Ac. Abbeville.
Société d'Émulation. Mémoires. Sér. 4. Tom. 1.
     Ac. 230.

PÉLISSIER (L. G.) Trois relations sur la situation
de la France en 1498–99 envoyées par Ludovic
Sforza au duc de Ferrare. pp. 28.
Montpellier, 1894. 8°.   Pam. 28.

—— Documents pour l'histoire de la domination française dans le Milanais, 1499–1513.
pp. 371. 1891. 8°. Bibliothèque meridionale.
Sér. 2. Tom. 1.   12238. ee.

MARCHAND (C.) Le maréchal F. de Scépeaux de
Vieilleville et ses Mémoires. pp. 369.
Paris, 1893. 8°.   010661. ff. 45.

WRANGEL (F. U.) Liste des diplomates français
en Suède, 1541–1891. pp. 95.
Stockholm, 1891. 8°.   10664. l. 16.

STRINDBERG (A.) Les relations de la France avec
la Suède. pp. 249. *Paris*, 1891. 8°. 9080. cc. 17.

CORLIEU (A.) La mort des rois de France depuis
François Ier. pp. 384. *Paris*, 1892. 8°.
     010662. g. 20.

POTIQUET ( ) La Maladie et la mort de François II. pp. 103. *Paris*, 1893. 8°. 10661. bbb. 52.

DU BOIS MELLY (C.) Les Ordonnances royales
et les mœurs sous les derniers Valois. 1892. 8°.
Ac. Geneva. *Institut National.* Bulletin.
Tom. 31.   Ac. 610.

ARMSTRONG (E.) The French Wars of religion.
pp. 128. *Lond.* 1892. 8°.   09225. f. 1.

GOBAT (A.) La République de Berne et la
France pendant les guerres de religion. pp. 242.
Paris, 1891. 8°.   9304. ee. 21.

LAYARD (*Right Hon. Sir* A. H.) Despatches of
M. Suriano and M. A. Barbaro, 1560–63.
1891. 4°. Ac. London. *Huguenot Society.*
Publications. Vol. 6.   Ac. 2073/4.

COYNART (C. A. de) L'Année 1562 et la bataille
de Dreux. pp. 47. *Paris*, 1894. 8°. Pam. 28.

LA FERRIÈRE-PERCY (H. de) La Saint-Barthélemy. pp. 288. *Paris*, 1892. 8°.   9220. g. 4.

CRUE (F. de) Le Parti des Politiques au lendemain de la Saint-Barthélemy. pp. 365.
Paris, 1892. 8°.   9226. h. 22.

FRANCE.—History—*continued.*

NOLHAC (P. de) and SOLERTI (A.) Il viaggio in Italia di Enrico III. pp. 343. *Torino,* 1890. 8°.
010661. f. 44.

Ac. Paris. *Société de l'Histoire de France.* LA HUGUERYE (M. de) Éphéméride de l'expédition des Allemands en France, 1587. pp. 553.
Paris, 1892. 8°. Ac. 6884/83.

House of Bourbon, 1589–1789.

LA FERRIÈRE-PERCY (H. de) Henri IV. pp. 401.
Paris, 1890. 12°. 010661. cc. 36.

BLAIR (E. T.) Henry of Navarre and the religious wars. pp. 307. *Phila.* 1895. 4°.
010662. k. 12.

WILLERT (P. F.) Henry of Navarre and the Huguenots. pp. 478. 1893. 8°. ABBOTT (E.) Heroes of the Nations. 10601. f.

MARGARET DE VALOIS, *Queen.* Memoirs of Margaret de Valois. pp. 286. *Lond.* 1895. 8°.
010663. i. 15.

ESTOC (M. d') Les Réquisitoires de l'histoire de France, 1600–1892. pp. 332. *Paris,* 1891. 12°.
09200. de. 1.

HENRY IV., *King.* Lettres du roi Henry IV. à Monsieur de Béthune, 1602. pp. 42.
Paris, 1890. 8°. Pam. 35.

ZELLER (B.) La minorité de Louis XIII., 1610–12. pp. 394. *Paris,* 1892. 8°. 9220. cc. 2.

BESANT (W.) Gaspard de Coligny. pp. 232.
Lond. 1894. 8°. 010662. f. 21.

HANOTAUX (G.) Histoire du Cardinal de Richelieu. *Paris,* 1893, *etc.* 8°. 4863. cc. 23.

FAGNIEZ (G.) Le Père Joseph et Richelieu. 2 tom. *Paris,* 1894. 8°. 4867. gg. 16.

CASTONNET DES FOSSES (H.) Les relations de la France avec le Perse. pp. 52. *Angers,* 1889. 8°.
9007. ff. 6. (5.)

SALOMON (F.) Frankreichs Beziehungen zu dem schottischen Aufstand, 1637–40. pp. 58.
Berl. 1890. 8°. Pam. 28.

Ac. Paris. *Société de l'Histoire.* BESANÇON (B. de) *Seigneur du Plessis.* Mémoires. pp. 400.
Paris, 1892. 8°. Ac. 6884/82.

—— HÉRAULT DE GOURVILLE (J.) Mémoires de Gourville. *Paris,* 1894, *etc.* 8°. 010663. k.

MAZZARINI (G.) *Cardinal.* Carnet de Mazarin. pp. 134. *Tours,* 1893. 16°. 010662. e. 10.

COSNAC (G. J. de) Mazarin et Colbert. 2 tom.
Paris, 1892. 8°. 010662. h. 11.

DENIS (J.) Littérature politique de la Fronde. pp. 69. *Caen,* 1892. 8°. 11826. d. 46. (4.)

ROY (M.) Un épisode de la Fronde. Chesnoy, 1652. *Sens,* 1893. 8°. Pam. 28.

CHÉROT (H.) La première jeunesse de Louis XIV. 1649–53. pp. 194. *Lille,* [1893.] 8°.
010661. ff. 35.

IMBERT DE SAINT-AMAND (A. L.) *Baron.* Court of Louis XIV. pp. 266. *Lond.* 1894. 8°.
010661. cc. 49.

VAST (H.) Les grands traités du Règne de Louis XIV. pp. 187. 1893. 8°. Collection de textes. *etc.* 09210. de.

CARTWRIGHT, afterwards ADY (J.) Madame Henrietta, daughter of Charles I. pp. 406.
Lond. 1894. 8°. 10805. cc. 34.

MOTIER DE LA FAYETTE (M. M.) Mémoires. pp. 300. *Paris,* 1890. 8°. 010661. f. 22.

PARDAILLAN DE GONDRIN (F. A. de) *Marchioness de Montespan.* Memoirs of Madame de Montespan. 2 vol. *Lond.* 1895. 8°. 010663. g. 31.

GÉRIN (C.) Louis XIV. et le Saint-Siège. 2 tom.
Paris, 1894. 8°. 4571. f. 25.

MOÜY (C. de) Louis XIV. et le Saint-Siège. 1662–65. 2 tom. *Paris,* 1893. 8°. 4571. cc. 14.

FRANCE.— History—*continued.*

BURGAUD (É.) and BAZERIES (É.) Le Masque de Fer. pp. 302. *Paris,* 1893. 12°. 9210. c. 11.

CHARLOTTE ELIZABETH, *Duchess d'Orléans.* Aus den Briefen der Herzogin Elisabeth Charlotte von Orléans. 2 Bde. *Hannover,* 1891. 8°.
010920. h. 6.

LEGRELLE (A.) La Diplomatie française et la Succession d'Espagne. 3 tom.
Paris, 1888–90. 8°. 9072. g. 9.

Ac. Carlsruhe. *Badische historische Commission.* Ludwig Wilhelm von Baden und der Reichskrieg gegen Frankreich, 1693–1697. 2 Bde. *Karlsruhe,* 1892. 8°. Ac. 7066/5.

LEGRELLE (A.) Notes sur la paix de Ryswick. pp. 136. *Lille,* 1894. 8°. 9078. g. 16.

BAUDRILLART (A.) Philippe V. et la cour de France 1700–15. pp. 711. 1889. 8°. Revue d'histoire diplomatique. Supp. tom. 3. Ac. 6885.

WEBER (O.) Der Friede von Utrecht. pp. 485.
Gotha, 1891. 8°. 9077. ccc. 10.

MALLESON (G. B.) History of the French in India. pp. 614. *Lond.* 1893. 8°. 2386. g.

Ac. Paris. *École des Langues Orientales Vivantes.* ĀNANDARAÑGA PILLAI. Les Français dans l'Inde. 1736–48. *Paris,* 1894. 8°. 752. f. 33.

HOUSSAYE (A.) La Régence. pp. 364.
Paris, [1890.] 18°. 9226. b. 21.

PERKINS (J. B.) France under the Regency. pp. 603. *Lond.* 1892. 8°. 9210. c. 9.

LESCURE (M. F. A. de) Les Maîtresses du Régent. pp. 256. *Paris,* 1892. 8°. 010662. e. 5.

WIESENER (L.) Le Régent, l'abbé Dubois et les Anglais. pp. 518. *Paris,* 1891. 8°. 9079. f. 1.

PARIS. *Parlement.* Remonstrances du Parlement de Paris au XVIIIe siècle. 1888, *etc.* 4°.
FRANCE. Collection de documents. 9210. g.

CARRÉ (H.) La France sous Louis XV., 1723–74. pp. 256. *Paris,* 1891. 8°. 9230. g. 4.

DU HAUSSET ( ) Private memoirs of Louis XV. pp. 282. *Lond.* 1895. 8°. 10658. dd. 13.

SOULANGE-BODIN (A.) La diplomatie de Louis XV. pp. 286. *Paris,* 1894. 8°. 9077. dd. 13.

DES RÉAULX ( ) *Marchioness.* Le Roi Stanislas et Marie Leczinska. pp. 415. *Paris,* 1895. 8°.
010795. e. 38.

IMBERT DE SAINT-AMAND (A. L.) Court of Louis XV. pp. 285. *Lond.* 1894. 8°. 010661. ee. 51.

—— Last years of Louis XV. pp. 220.
Lond. 1894. 8°. 010661. ee. 50.

MAUGRAS (G.) Le Duc de Lauzun et la cour intime de Louis XV. pp. 469. *Paris,* 1893. 8°.
010661. ff. 36.

—— The Duc de Lauzun and the court of Louis XV. pp. 365. *Lond.* 1895. 8°. 010663. i. 12.

OGLE (A.) The Marquis d'Argenson. pp. 254.
Lond. 1893. 8°. 010661. g. 51.

BROGLIE (J. V. A. de) *Duke.* Maurice de Saxe et le Marquis d'Argenson. 2 vol.
Paris, 1893. 12°. 010663. f. 2.

LUCAS (F. W.) Appendiculæ Historicæ [on the struggles between England and France in N. America]. pp. 216. *Lond.* 1891. 4°. 9555. h. 1.

FAUCHILLE (P.) La diplomatie française et la Ligue des Neutres de 1780. pp. 619.
Paris, 1893. 8°. 9079. f. 9.

BARRALL MONTFERRAT (de) *Marquis.* Dix ans de paix armée entre la France et l'Angleterre, 1783–93. *Paris,* 1893, *etc.* 8°. 9080. k.

Period immediately before, and causes of the Revolution.

BASCOUL (L.) Étude sur la décomposition. Avant 89. pp. 438. *Saint-Amand,* 1892. 8°.
9226. bbb. 28.

FRANCE.—History—_continued._

GOMEL (C.) Des Causes financières de la Révolution française. pp. 548.
Paris, 1892. 8°.   9226. d. 4.

LOWELL (E. J.) Eve of the French Revolution. pp. 408. _Bost._ 1892. 8°.   9226. e. 10.

MACDONALD (F.) Studies in the France of Voltaire and Rousseau. pp. 254.
Lond. 1895. 8°.   010663. i. 22.

PELLISSIER (P. A.) Le dix-huitième siècle. pp. 359. _Paris_, 1893. 8°.   9225. d. 3.

PICARD (A.) La veille de la Révolution. pp. 236. _Paris_, 1895. 4°.   9230. l. 1.

ROCQUAIN (F.) The revolutionary Spirit preceding the Revolution. pp. 186.
Lond. 1891. 8°.   08276. e. 29.

SEPET (M.) Les préliminaires de la Révolution. pp. 358. _Paris_, 1890. 8°.   9226. bbb. 19.

WARD (H.) Literary antecedents of the French Revolution. pp. 28. _Oxf._ 1890. 8°.
     011840. h. 55. (17.)

Revolution.

Bibliography.

DUCOIN (A.) Catalogue d'une collection de pièces relatifs à la Révolution. pp. 83.
Paris, 1895. 8°.   11901. g. 43.

TUETEY (A.) Répertoire des sources manuscrites de l'histoire de Paris pendant la Révolution.
Paris, 1890, _etc._ 8°.   10174. i.

FRANCE. Histoire officielle de la France, depuis 1789. Table du "Moniteur" et du Journal Officiel. _Paris_, 1891, _etc._ 4°.   712.

TOURNEUX (M.) Bibliographie de l'histoire de Paris pendant la Révolution. _Paris_, 1890, _etc._ 8°.
     10174. i.

General History : Political Works, etc.

ADLER (J. B.) Die französische Revolution und die pariser Commune. pp. 61. _Mainz_, 1892. 16°.
     9230. a. 6.

ALGER (J. G.) Glimpses of the Revolution. pp. 303. _Lond._ 1894. 8°.   9231. f. 7.

AULARD (F. A.) Études sur la Révolution. pp. 300. _Paris_, 1893. 8°.   9226. b. 34.

BARBOU (A.) Les trois Républiques françaises. pp. 352. _Paris_, 1892. 8°.   9226. aa. 19.

BARDOUX (A.) La Bourgeoisie française, 1789–1848. pp. 442. _Paris_, 1893. 12°.   08275. f. 7.

BAUDRY (F. P.) Révolution française, 1789–99. pp. 122. _Rouen_, 1890. 8°.   9226. cc. 3.

BERTEZÈNE (A.) Histoire de cent ans, 1792–1892. 2 vol. _Paris_, 1893, 94. 12°.   9226. bbb. 30.

BIRÉ (E.) Légendes révolutionnaires. pp. 388. _Paris_, 1893. 8°.   9231. g. 23.

BONNEVILLE DE MARSANGY (L.) Autour de la Révolution. pp. 282. _Paris_, 1895. 12°. 9230. b. 19.

BOURSIN (E.) and CHALLAMEL (A.) Dictionnaire de la Révolution française. pp. 935.
Paris, 1893. 8°.   9226. m. 10.

BRIOSCHI (P. A.) Una página de historia, ó la Revolución francesa. pp. 411. _Milán_, 1894. 8°.
     9231. bb. 1.

BROC (H. de) _Viscount._ La France pendant la Révolution. 2 tom. _Paris_, 1891. 8°. 9226. h. 19.

CARLYLE (T.) The French Revolution. 3 vol. 1891. 8°. Sir J. Lubbock's Hundred Books. Vol. 7.   012207. l. 7.

CHALLETON (F.) Cent ans d'Élections. 3 tom. _Paris_, 1891. 8°.   9230. cc. 10.

CORRÉARD (F.) Histoire de l'Europe et de la France, 1789–1889. pp. 842. _Paris_, 1892. 8°.
     9080. e. 1.

CRANE (T. F.) and BRUN (S. J.) Tableaux de la Révolution française. Historical French reader. pp. 311. _N.Y._ 1894. 8°.   9226. a. 4.

FRANCE.—History—_continued._

DARLES (P.) and JANIN (E.) Histoire de la France, 1789–1889. pp. 664. _Paris_, 1889. 12°.
     9009. aa. 15.

DICKINSON (G. L.) Revolution and reaction in France. pp. 300. _Lond._ 1892. 8°. 9226. e. 8.

DU BLED (V.) Les Causeurs de la Révolution. pp. 416. _Paris_, 1890. 18°.   010661. f. 26.

FOUÉRÉ-MACÉ ( ) Époque révolutionnaire. Curiosités historiques. pp. 106. _Rennes_, 1894. 4°.
     9226. e. 16.

FRENCH REVOLUTION. Documents pour servir à l'histoire de la Révolution. _Lyon_, 1893, _etc._ 8°.
     010920. m.

GEOFFROY DE GRANDMAISON (C. A.) L'ambassade en Espagne pendant la Révolution, 1789–1804. pp. 356. _Paris_, 1892. 8°.   9079. f. 5.

GERMONT (L.) Histoire de la Révolution, 1774–1804. pp. 272. _Paris_, 1892. 8°. 9225. c. 22.

HEDIN (A.) Studier i franska Revolutionens historia. _Stockholm_, 1890, _etc._ 8°.   9226. e. 4.

HOUSSAYE (A.) La Révolution. pp. 259.
Paris, 1891. 12°.   9226. e. (5.)

JEAN-BERNARD. Les Lundis révolutionnaires. _Paris_, 1889, _etc._ 18°.   9226. bbb. 21.

JANET (P.) Histoire de la Révolution. pp. 287. _Paris_, 1889. 12°.   9225. a. 18.

LENÔTRE (G.) La France révolutionnaire. pp. 420. _Paris_, 1895. 8°.   9226. c. 29.

MALLET (C. E.) The French Revolution. pp. 307. 1893. 8°. University Extension Manuals.
     12204. f.

MIGNET (F. A. M.) Histoire de la Révolution. pp. 364. _Londres_, 1894. 8°.   9226. e. 11.

MINZES (B.) Die Nationalgüterveräusserung während der französischen Revolution. pp. 167. 1892. 8°. Staatswissenschaftliche Studien, _etc._ Bd. 4.   8207. h.

MOSSÉ (B.) La Révolution et le Rabbinat français. pp. 283. _Avignon_, 1890. 8°. 4034. l. 24.

MUEL (L.) Gouvernements et Constitutions de la France depuis cent ans. pp. 557.
Paris, 1893. 8°.   9231. g. 19.

NAUROY (C.) Révolutionnaires. pp. 318.
Paris, 1891. 12°.   010661. f. 37.

NORTHROP (H. H.) History of the Revolution, 1789–95. pp. 725. _Richmond, Va._, 1890. 8°.
     9225. i. 21.

ONCKEN (W.) Das Zeitalter der Revolution, des Kaiserreiches, _etc._ 2 Bde. 1884, _etc._ 8°. Allgemeine Geschichte.   2068. (26.)

POUJOULAT (J. J. F.) Histoire de la Révolution. 2 tom. _Tours_, 1884. 8°.   9226. d. 3.

ROSE (J. H.) Revolutionary and Napoleonic era, 1789–1815. pp. 388. 1895. 8°. Cambridge Historical Series.   2378. b. 29.

SOLERIO (G. P.) La Rivoluzione francese, 1789–99. pp. 176. _Milano_, 1894. 16°.   012200. i. 10.

STEPHENS (H. M.) Europe: 1789–1815. pp. 423. 1893. 8°. HASSELL (A.) Periods of European History. Vol. 7.   9073. aaa.

SYMES (J. E.) The French Revolution 1789–95. pp. 160. 1890. 8°. University Extension Series.
     012202. g.

THIERS (L. A.) History of the Revolution. 5 vol. _Lond._ 1895. 8°.   09225. g. 1.

TROUSSET (J.) Histoire d'un siècle. 12 tom. _Paris_, 1890–92. 8°.   9225. d. 2.

BOURGEOIS (J.) L'Histoire et le Centenaire de 1792. pp. 104. _Chambéry_, 1891. 8°. 9226. b. 22.

ÉTRANGER. Thèses antirévolutionnaires à propos du Centenaire. pp. 120. _Leide_, 1889. 8°.
     8052. ccc. 2.

FRANCE.—History.—*continued.*

Guéroult (G.) Le Centenaire de 1789.
pp. 399. *Paris*, 1889. 12°.   9225. aaa. 20.

Harrison (F.) Centenary of the French Revolution. *Lond.* 1889. 8°.   8470. f. 9. (6.)

Paris. *Société d'Économie Sociale.* La Réforme sociale et la Centenaire de la Révolution. pp. 645. *Paris*, 1890. 8°.   8275. k. 3.

Balsillie (D.) The lesson of the Revolution. pp. 124. *Edinb.* 1891. 8°.   8275. aaa. 52.

Bascoul (L.) Étude sur la décomposition de la France après 89. pp. 368. *Paris*, 1893. 8°.   3900. bb. 50.

Birot (E.) La Révolution d'après M. H. Taine. pp. 107. *Paris*, 1894. 8°.   9231. k. 5.

Brettes (F.) Les Principes de 89. pp. 312. *Paris*, 1889. 12°.   8009. b. 28.

Chauffard (A.) La Révolution dans l'ensemble de ses phases et le triomphe de l'unité catholique. pp. 302. *Avignon*, 1893. 8°.   3900. b. 60.

Constant (P.) La Révolution et la liberté. pp. 305. *Paris*, 1895. 8°.   8050. g. 7.

Gresland (J.) Rien, Rien, Rien! 1789–1889. pp. 446. *Paris*, 1889. 12°.   9226. b. 25.

Guyot (Y.) Les Principes de 89 et le socialisme. pp. 281. *Paris*, 1894. 12°.   08275. f. 11.

Joyau (E.) La philosophie en France pendant la Révolution, 1789–95. pp. 305. *Paris*, 1893. 12°.   8486. b. 12.

Lagoutte ( ) De la Révolution. pp. 344. *La Chapelle-Montligeon*, 1894. 8°.   8009. k. 24.

Leroy Beaulieu (A.) La Révolution et le libéralisme. pp. 351. *Paris*, 1890. 8°.   8051. ccc. 19.

Previti (L.) La Rivoluzione e la civiltà nuova. pp. 170. *Prato*, 1887. 8°.   8009. aaa. 25.

Saint-Poncy (L. de) *Count.* Les Fruits de la Révolution. pp. 160. *Paris*, 1893. 12°.   8050. cc. 16.

Trogan (É.) L'Équivoque sur la Révolution. Réponse à Monseigneur Freppel. pp. 67. *Paris*, 1889. 8°.   8051. ccc. 22.

See also Europe, and for the Wars of the Republic *infra : Military History.*

Biographies and Mémoires.

Ac. Paris. *Société d'Histoire contemporaine.* Captivité et derniers moments de Louis XVI. *Paris*, 1892, *etc.* 8°.   Ac. 6885. c./2.

Delaporte (V.) Le Roi-Martyr. pp. 212. *Paris*, 1893. 8°.   010661. ff. 41.

Ac. Paris. *Société d'Histoire contemporaine.* Lettres de Marie Antoinette. *Paris*, 1895, *etc.* 8°.   010920. f.

La Rocheterie (M. de) Histoire de Marie-Antoinette. 2 tom. *Paris*, 1890. 8°.   10660. gg. 27.

—— Life of Marie Antoinette. 2 vols. *Lond.* 1893. 8°.   010661. h. 41.

Campan (J. L. H.) Memoirs of the court of Marie Antoinette. 2 vol. *Lond.* 1895. 8°.   K.T.C. 15. a. 17.

Proelss (R.) Königin Marie Antoinette. pp. 244. *Leipz.* 1894. 8°.   010663. h. 6.

Imbert de Saint-Amand (A. L.) Marie-Antoinette et la fin de l'ancien régime, 1781–89. pp. 330. *Paris*, 1891. 12°.   010663. f. 57.

—— Marie Antoinette at the Tuileries, 1789–91. pp. 296. *Lond.* 1891. 8°.   010661. oe. 58.

Schwarz (F.) Mirabeau und Marie Antoinette. pp. 85. *Basel*, 1891. 8°.   10601. d. 35. (6.)

Bishop (M. C.) Prison life of Marie Antoinette and her children. pp. 313. *Lond.* 1893. 8°.   10658. b. 35.

Bloy (L.) La Chevalière de la Mort [Trial of Marie Antoinette]. pp. 62. *Gand*, 1891. 8°.   10601. f. 7. (7.)

Armaillé (M. C. A. d') *Countess.* Madame Élisabeth. pp. 509. *Paris*, 1886. 8°. 010662. g. 16.

Imbert de Saint-Amand (A. L.) Youth of the Duchess of Angoulême. pp. 316. *Lond.* 1892. 8°.   010661. ee. 62.

—— Duchess of Angoulême and the two Restorations. pp. 403. *Lond.* 1892. 8°. 010661. ee. 61.

Mary Theresa Charlotte, *Duchess of Angoulême.* Journal, 1789–92. pp. 167. *Paris* 1894. 8°.   010663. g. 7.

—— Mémoire écrit par Marie Thérèse de France, 1792–95. pp. 167. *Paris*, 1893. 8°.   10661. g. 25.

Chantelauze (R. de) Louis XVII. Son enfance, sa prison et sa mort. pp. 377. *Paris*, 1895. 12°.   010663. f. 52.

Gaugler (G. de) L'enfant du Temple, Louis XVII. pp. 391. *Paris*, 1891. 12°. 010661. f. 50.

Le Normant des Varannes (É.) Histoire de Louis XVII. pp. 472. *Orléans*, 1890. 8°.   10660. gg. 29.

Ac. Paris. *Société d'Études sur la Question Louis XVII.* Bulletin. *Paris*, 1893, *etc.* 8°.   772.

Delrosay (F.) La question Louis XVII. [Identity of C. G. Naeundorff with Louis XVII.] pp. 208. *Paris*, 1890. 8°.   10660. b. 41.

Lepingleux-Deshayes (A.) Naundorff était Louis XVII. pp. 10. *Paris*, 1892. 8°. Pam. 69.

Evans (E. E.) Story of Louis XVII. of France. [Identification with Eleazar Williams.] pp. 360. *Lond.* 1893. 8°.   010882. g. 17.

Mary Theresa Louisa, *Princess de Lamballe.* Secret memoirs of the Royal Family of France. 2 vol. *Lond.* 1895. 8°.   010663. g. 25.

Bégis (A.) Le massacre de la Princesse de Lamballe. pp. 25. *Paris*, 1891. 8°.   10601. f. 8. (1.)

Gaulot (P.) Marie Antoinette, M. de Fersen. pp. 379. *Paris*, 1892. 12°.   10761. cc. 25.

—— A Friend of the Queen. 2 vol. *Lond.* 1894. 8°.   2402. c. 15.

Courdemanche ( ) Le Duc de Penthièvre. pp. 399. *Paris*, 1889. 8°.   010661. f. 40.

Ac. Paris. *Société d'Histoire contemporaine.* Lambert (P. T.) Mémoires de l'abbé Lambert, confesseur du duc de Penthièvre, 1791–99. pp. 330. *Paris*, 1894. 8°.   Ac. 6885. c./5.

Pérusse (J. F. de) *Duke des Cars.* Mémoires du duc des Cars. 2 tom. *Paris*, 1890. 8°.   010663. i. 2.

Rouquet (A.) Les Chénier. pp. 30. *Paris*, 1891. 8°.   10662. i. 32.

Bardoux (A.) La jeunesse de La Fayette, 1757–92. pp. 409. *Paris*, 1892. 8°.   010661. h. 36.

—— Les dernières années de La Fayette, 1792–1834. pp. 431. *Paris*, 1893. 8°. 010662. h. 26.

Maugras (G.) Le Duc de Lauzun et la Cour de Marie-Antoinette. pp. 550. *Paris*, 1895. 8°.   010663. k. 8.

Vallette (G.) Mallet du Pan et la Révolution. pp. 101. *Genève*, 1893. 8°.   9231. g. 24.

Holst (H. v.) The French Revolution, tested by Mirabeau's career. 2 vol. *Chicago*, 1894. 8°.   9226. e. 18.

Larivière (C. de) Mirabeau et ses détracteurs. pp. 51. *Paris*, 1892. 8°.   Pam. 8.

FRANCE.—History—*continued.*

MÉZIÈRES (A. J. F.) Vie de Mirabeau. pp. 344.
Paris, 1892. 8°.   010662. ff. 10.

RAYEUR (J. A.) Mirabeau. pp. 268.
Moulins, 1892. 12°.   010662. ff. 32.

ROUSSE (E.) Mirabeau. pp. 224. 1891. 8°. Les
grands écrivains français.   10664. c.

SCHWARZ (F.) Mirabeau und Marie Antoinette.
pp. 85. *Basel*, 1891. 8°.   10601. d. 35. (6.)

IRISSON D'HÉRISSON (M. d') *Count.* Un constituant, J. J. Mounier. pp. 382.
Paris, 1892. 12°.   9226. b. 24.

SÉGUR (A. de) *Marquis.* Le Maréchal de Ségur,
1724-1801. pp. 398. *Paris*, 1895. 8°.
       010663. k. 9.

BIGEON (A.) Sieyès. L'homme—le constituant.
pp. 245. *Paris*, 1893. 8°.   010661. ff. 46.

BLENNERHASSETT (C. J.) *Lady.* Talleyrand.
pp. 572. *Berl.* 1894. 8°.   010663. k. 7.

—— Talleyrand. Translated from the German.
2 vol. *Lond.* 1894. 8°.   010663. h. 5.

TALLEYRAND PÉRIGORD (C. M. de) Mémoires,
lettres et papiers secrets. pp. 291.
Paris, 1891. 8°.   010661. ee. 44.

—— Memoirs of C. M. Talleyrand to 1805.
2 vol. *Lond.* 1895. 8°.   010663. i. 24.

CUGNAC (de) *Marquis.* Souvenirs historiques.
1789-1871. pp. 321. *Lille*, 1891. 18°.
       9230. c. 19.

MÉMOIRES. Les Mémoires d'une Inconnue.
1780-1816. pp. 419. *Paris*, 1894. 8°.
       010663. g. 11.

Ac. Paris. *Société d'Histoire contemporaine.*
Correspondance du Mis et de la M^{lse} de Raige-
court pendant l'émigration 1790-1800. pp. 445.
Paris, 1892. 8°.   Ac. 6885. c.

PINGAUD (L.) Un agent secret sous la Révolution. Le comte d'Antraigues. pp. 441.
Paris, 1894. 12°.   010663. f. 3.

DELACHENAL (R.) Un agent politique sous la Révolution. Pierre Chépy. pp. 80. 1892. 8°.
Ac. Grenoble. *Académie Delphinale.* Bulletin. Sér. 4. Tom. 5.   Ac. 340.

COSTA DE BEAUREGARD (A.) *Marquis.* Souvenirs
du Cte. de Virieu. pp. 414. *Paris*, 1892. 8°.
       010662. h. 14.

LE GENTIL (J. P. G.) *Count de Paroy.* Mémoires du Comte de Paroy. 1789-97. pp. 479.
Paris, 1895. 8°.   010663. g. 36.

BADER (C.) Mme. Roland d'après des lettres et
des manuscrits. pp. 55. *Paris*, 1892, 8°.
       010662. h. 19.

LACROIX (C. de) Souvenirs du Comte de Mont-
gaillard. pp. 336. *Paris*, 1895. 8°.
       010663. i. 36.

TREILHES (A.) Étude sur le triumvirat girondin.
Vergniaud, Gaudet, Gensonné. pp. 56.
Bordeaux, 1891. 8°.   9008. g. 8. (10.)

BARRAS (P. F. J. N. de) *Count.* Memoirs of
Barras. 4 vol. *Lond.* 1895, 96. 8°. 010663. k. 3.

BILLAUD VARENNE (J. N.) Billaud Varenne.
Mémoires inédits. *Paris*, 1893. 8°.
       010661. ff. 42.

DREYFOUS (M.) Les trois Carnot. pp. 294.
Paris, 1888. 8°.   010661. m. 7.

REGNARD (A.) Chaumette et la Commune de 93.
Paris, 1889. 8°.   9004. m. 7. (8.)

FOUCHÉ (J.) *Duke d' Otranto.* Memoirs of
J. Fouché. pp. 474. *Lond.* 1892. 8°.
       010662. i. 5.

LA REVELLIÈRE DE LÉPEAUX (L. M. de) Mémoires. 3 tom. *Paris*, 1895. 8°. 010663. i. 35.

CHARAVAY (E.) La Revellière-Lépeaux et ses
mémoires. pp. 46. *Paris*, 1895. 8°. 010663. i. 17.

FRANCE.—History—*continued.*

ASHBEE (H. S.) Marat en Angleterre. pp. 31.
Paris, 1890. 8°.   10601. g. 2. (5.)

CABANÈS (A.) Marat inconnu. pp. 328.
Paris, 1891. 12°.   010661. ee. 43.

WITT (P. de) La jeunesse de Marat. pp. 59.
Paris, 1892. 8°.   010662. f. 3.

MARAT (J. P.) Marat, l'ami du peuple aux
braves Parisiens, 26 août, 1792. Huitième
placard. pp. 17. 6. *Londres*, 1892. 8°. Pam. 69.

FOCKE (R.) Charlotte Corday. Eine kritische
Darstellung ihres Lebens. pp. 162.
Leipz. 1895. 8°.   010663. i. 32.

JEAFFRESON (M.) Marie Charlotte Anne de
Corday. pp. 73. *Lond.* 1893. 8°. 010662. f. 17.

JEAN-BERNARD. Quelques poésies de Robespierre.
pp. 69. *Paris*, 1890. 16°.   Pam. 59.

BÉGIS (A.) Saint-Just, son emprisonnement sous
Louis XVI. pp. 50. *Paris*, 1892. 8°. 010662. ff. 26.

BAGUENIER DESORMEAUX (H.) Un conventionnel
choletais, M.-L. Talot. pp. 98. *Angers*, 1891. 8°.
       010661. m. 49.

For memoirs of Military Officers, *see infra :
Wars of the Republic, etc.;* for memoirs of civil
officials, *etc.,* of the Consulate and first Empire,
see infra : Napoleon I.

Ecclesiastical History of the Revolution. See
infra : Ecclesiastical History.

Education and the Revolution. See EDUCATION.

Revolution in the Provinces.

VASCHALDE (H.) L'Ardèche à la Convention
Nationale. pp. 300. *Paris*, 1893. 8°. 9225. d. 4.

SERRES (J. B.) Histoire de la Révolution en
Auvergne. *Saint Amand*, 1895, *etc.* 8°.
       9231. aaa.

BOUDON (A.) Les Municipalités du Puy pendant
la période révolutionnaire.
Le Puy, 1894, *etc.* 8°.   9231. dd.

MÉNARD ( ) Un Chapitre de l'histoire de la
Terreur à Avranches. pp. 44.
Avranches, 1894. 8°.   Pam. 28.

AUTUN. Cahiers des paroisses d'Autun. pp. 407.
Autun, 1895. 8°.   9231. k. 9.

LOCHARD (J.) Quelques pages d'un manuscrit
sous la Terreur en Béarn. pp. 220.
Paris, 1893. 8°.   9226. b. 30.

SOUCAILLE (A.) Béziers pendant la Révolution.
pp. 360. *Béziers*, 1894. 8°.   9231. k. 8.

—— Historique de la Société populaire de
Béziers. pp. 102. *Béziers*, 1892. 8°. 9226. i. 15.

JONGLEUX (E.) Bourges et la Révolution.
pp. 338. *Bourges*, 1895. 8°.   9226. c. 28.

CAU-DURBAN (D.) La Période révolutionnaire à
Castelnau-Durban. pp. 56. *Foix*, 1892. 8°.
       9008. g. 11. (7.)

FORESTIER (L.) Société populaire de Chaumont.
1790-94. pp. 67. *Chaumont*, 1892. 8°. Pam. 28.

JOLLIVET (M.) La Révolution en Corse. pp. 224.
Paris, 1892. 8°.   9226. k. 17.

LETTERON ( ) Pièces pour servir à l'histoire de
la Corse pendant la Révolution, 1891, *etc.* 8°.
Ac. Bastia. *Société des sciences, etc.* Bulletin. An. 10.   Ac. 2861.

AUTORDE (F.) Archives révolutionnaires de la
Creuse. *Guéret*, 1890. 8°.   Pam. 28.

MAIGNIEN (E.) Bibliographie historique du
Dauphiné pendant la Révolution.
Grenoble, 1891, *etc.* 8°.   011900. f.

ROCHAS (A.) Journal d'un Bourgeois de Valence,
1789 à 1799. 2 vol. *Grenoble*, 1891, 92. 8°.
       9226. k. 23.

ROUX (X) La Révolution en Dauphiné. pp. 216.
Grenoble, 1888. 4°.   9231. m. 16.

FRANCE.—History—*continued.*

DAUPHINY. *Députés.* Mémoire de la marche des brigandages qui se sont commis en Dauphiné en 1789. pp. 206. *Grenoble, 1891.* 8°.
6056. ff. 16.

CHEVALIER (J. A. U.) Le Comité de Surveillance révolutionnaire de Romans en 1793-94. pp. 48. *Valence, 1890.* 8°. 9004. m. 7. (11.)

ROCHAS (A.) Journal d'un bourgeois de Valence, 1789-99. 2 vol. *Grenoble, 1891, 92,* 8°.
9226. k. 22.

SÉRANON (J. de) Une vallée des Alpes pendant la révolution : la Vallouise. pp. 150.
Aix, 1891. 8°. 10169. aaa. 2.

BOIVIN-CHAMPEAUX (L.) Notices sur la Révolution dans l'Eure. 2 vol. *Évreux, 1893, 94.* 8°.
9231. k. 4.

BÉNÉTRIX (P.) Les conventionnels du Gers. pp. 143. *Auch, 1894.* 8°. 10661. bbb. 53.

—— Le vandalisme révolutionnaire dans le Gers. pp. 49. *Bordeaux, 1891.* 8°. Pam. 28.

TARBOURIECH (A.) Curiosités révolutionnaires du Gers. pp. 102. *Auch, 1892.* 8°. 9226. c. 25.

BÉNÉTRIX (P.) Lazare Carnot à Auch. pp. 15. *Auch, 1891.* 8°. Pam. 28.

BOCERET (E. de) Guérande pendant la période révolutionnaire. pp. 32. *Vannes, 1895.* 8°.
Pam. 91.

VIENNE, *Upper* Société des archives du Limousin. Archives révolutionnaires.
Limoges, 1893, etc. 8°. 9226. g. 24.

C., E. Histoire de la persécution révolutionnaire dans le Jura, 1789-1800. pp. 357.
Lons-le-Saunier, 1893. 8°. 4630. df. 3.

LAPEYRE (E.) Les insurrections du Lot en 1790. pp. 130. *Cahors, 1892.* 8°. 9231. g. 20.

FALGAIROLLE (E.) Le tribunal révolutionnaire de la Lozère, 1793, *etc.* pp. 183.
Paris, 1893. 8°. 9225. c. 21.

CASTONNET DES FOSSES (H.) Le siège de Lyon en 1793. 8°. Ac. Angers. *Société d'Agriculture.* Mémoires. Sér. 4. Tom. 6. Ac. 245.

GALLI (H.) Les Représentants de la Marne aux assemblées de la Révolution. pp. 55.
Châlons-s.-M. 1894. 8°. 10661. c. 43.

BÈGUE (J.) Notice sur le district de Meaux sous la Révolution. pp. 39. *Argenteuil, 1891.* 8°.
9007. ff. 5. (3.)

MEUNIER (P.) Le Révolution en Nivernais.
Nevers, 1891, etc. 12°. 9226. aa. 8.

DUVAL (L.) Éphémérides de la moyenne Normandie, 1789. pp. 234. *Alençon, 1890.* 12°.
9226. aaa. 38.

Ac. Paris. *Société d'Histoire contemporaine.*
MOULIN (M.) Mémoires sur la chouannerie normande. pp. 403. *Paris, 1893.* 8°. 9226. f. 3.

LOUVET (L.) Rouen et la révolution. pp. 33.
Rouen, 1892. 8°. 9226. h. 20.

FLOUR DE SAINT-GENIS ( ) L'Esprit public et les élections au Havre, 1787-90. 1889. 8°. Ac., *etc.* Havre. *Société Havraise.* Recueil, 1889.
Ac. 2612.

PAS-DE-CALAIS. Cahiers de doléances de 1789. 2 tom. *Arras, 1891.* 8°. 9226. k. 16.

FRANCE. *États-Généraux.* Assemblées du Boulonnais : Cahiers des trois ordres. pp. 628.
Boulogne, 1889. 4°. 9231. m. 15.

POITOU. Cahiers de 1789. Assemblée provinciale du Poitou. pp. 389. *Poitiers, 1889.* 12°.
9230. cc. 6.

VISSAC (M. de) Les Révolutionnaires du Rouergue. pp. 284. *Riom, 1893.* 8°. 09200. e. 6.

MASSE (J.) Histoire de l'annexion de la Savoie, 1792. *Grenoble, 1891, etc.* 8°. 9080. f.

FRANCE.—History—*continued.*

BURDIN (C.) L'Annexion de 1792 et son centenaire. pp. 132. *Chambéry, 1890.* 8°. 9226. aa. 7.

F., H. Aperçu sur la Révolution de 1792 dans la vallée du Giffre. pp. 139. *Annecy, 1892.* 16°.
9226. a. 3.

LEGRAND (M.) and MARQUIS (L.) 1789. Les trois états du bailliage d'Étampes aux États généraux.
Étampes, 1892, etc. 8°. 9225. bb. 21.

BERTAUTS-COUTURE (L.) Histoire de Villiers-le-Bel pendant la Révolution. pp. 141.
Paris, 1891. 8°. 9226. k. 13.

BONNAULT (de) Un village, Mérélessart, pendant la Révolution. pp. 63.
Abbeville, 1892. 8°. 09210. e. 1. (4.)

DENIS (A.) Le Club des Jacobins de Toul. pp. 130. *Paris, 1895.* 8°. 9231. l. 5.

BOUGLON (R. de) Les reclus de Toulouse sous la Terreur. Registres officiels concernant les citoyens emprisonnés. *Toulouse, 1893, etc.* 8°.
10660. gg. 32.

DUBOUL (A.) Le Tribunal révolutionnaire de Toulouse, 1794. pp. 168. *Toulouse, 1894.* 8°.
9231. i. 13.

CARRÉ DE BUSSEROLLE (J. X.) La Chouannerie en Touraine. 1799-1801. pp. 20.
Montsoreau, 1890. 8°. 9072. cc. 4. (5.)

DUHAMEL (L.) Documents sur la Révolution dans Vaucluse, 1793-1800. 2 pt.
Paris, 1894, 95. 8°. 9231. g. 11.

CHASSIN (C. L.) La préparation de la Guerre de Vendée, 1789-93. 3 tom. *Paris, 1892.* 8°.
9231. l. 1.

—— La Vendée patriote, 1793-1800.
Paris, 1893, etc. 8°. 9231. k.

ROUILLÉ (A.) Guerres de Vendée et chouannerie. 1793-96. pp. 80. *La Roche, 1891.* 4°.
7757. g. 18.

DU VERGIER DE LAROCHEJAQUELEIN (H.) *Count.* H. de La Rochejaquelein et la guerre de la Vendée. pp. 345. *Paris, 1890.* 8°. 010662. h. 2.

GUINEY (L. I.) "Monsieur Henri." A footnote to French history. pp. 139. *N.Y. 1892.* 8°.
10661. aa. 28.

PORT (C.) La Légende de Cathelineau. pp. 350.
Paris, 1893. 8°. 010662. h. 36.

GAZEAU (A. C.) *Countess de La Bouëre.* Souvenirs, la guerre de La Vendée, 1793-96. pp. 363. *Paris, 1890.* 8°. 9231. g. 13.

CARRÉ DE BUSSEROLLE (J. X.) Les Vendéens à Thouars, 1793. pp. 60. *Montsoreau, 1890.* 8°.
9072. cc. 4. (6.)

CONTADES (G. de) *Count.* Émigrés et chouans. pp. 373. *Paris, 1895.* 8°. 010663. f. 54.

JULLIEN (M. A.) Une mission en Vendée, 1793. pp. 347. *Paris, 1893.* 12°. 9226. bbb. 29.

VALLETTE (R.) La Commission militaire de Fontenay. pp. 22. *Fontenay, 1894.* 8°.
9004. l. 36. (5.)

CHASSIN (C. L.) Ville de Nantes. Centenaire national du 29 Juin 1793. pp. 45.
Nantes, 1893. 8°. Pam. 28.

BLOCQUEL DE CROIX (G.) *Baron de Wismes.* Une page de la Terreur à Nantes. pp. 55.
Vannes, 1894. 8°. 4629. cc. 4.

YONNE. Département de l'Yonne. Procès-verbaux de l'administration départementale, 1790-1800. *Auxerre, 1889, etc.* 8°. 9225. dd.

MONCEAUX (H.) La Révolution dans le département de l'Yonne, 1788-1800. pp. 734.
Paris, 1890. 8°. 011902. f. 21.

MEMAIN (T.) Histoire de la commune de Pourrain, 1789-1800. pp. 94. *Auxerre, 1892.* 12°.
9225. a. 20.

FRANCE.—History—*continued.*

Events, 1789–1799.

Ac. Paris. *Société de l'histoire de la Révolution.*
SIEYES (E. J.) Qu'est-ce que le Tiers État.
Avec une introduction par E. Champion. pp. 93.
Paris, 1888. 8°.   Ac. 6885. b./2.

GAUTIER (H.) L'An 1789. Événements, mœurs,
et caractères. pp. 804. *Paris,* 1888. 4°.
                  9200. i. 8.

DUGUET (É.) Les Députés et les cahiers de
1789. pp. 423. *Pari,* 1890. 12°. 8052. cc. 13.

Ac. Paris. *Société de l'histoire contemporaine.*
DUQUESNOY (A. C.) Journal sur l'Assemblée
Constituante 1789–90. 2 tom. *Paris,* 1894. 8°.
                 Ac. 6885. c./6.

DU BLED (V.) Orateurs et tribuns 1789–94.
pp. 320. *Paris,* 1891. 12°.   011824. e. 17.

STEPHENS (H. M.) Speeches of statesmen and
orators of the French Revolution. 2 vol.
1892. 8°. Clarendon Press Series.   2319. b. 3.

GÉRAUD (E.) Journal d'un étudiant pendant la
Révolution. 1789–93. pp. 393.
Paris, 1890. 18°.   9226. aaa. 36.

ROBINSON (J. H.) French Revolution, 1789–91.
pp. 32. 1894. 8°. Ac. Philadelphia. *University of Pennsylvania.* Translations, *etc.* Vol. 1.
                 Ac. 2692. p./5.

Ac. Paris. *Société de l'histoire de la Révolution.*
Le Serment du Jeu de Paume. Facsimilé du
texte et des signatures. pp. 63.
Paris, 1893. 8°.   9226. m. 11.

—— PITRA (L. G.) La Journée du 14 Juillet
1789. pp. 68. *Paris,* 1892. 8°. Ac. 6885. b./5.

FOURNEL (V.) Les hommes du 14 Juillet.
pp. 347. *Paris,* 1890. 12°.   9226. bb. 35.

—— Le Patriote Palloy et l'exploitation de la
Bastille. pp. 363. *Paris,* 1892. 8°. 010661. h. 37.

MAGGIOLO (L.) Les Fêtes de la Révolution.
1894. 8°. Ac. Nancy. *Société des Sciences.*
Mémoires. 5° Série. tom. 11.   Ac. 383/2.

ACHARD DE GERMANE (A) Lettres à M. de la
Coste, président du Parlement de Dauphiné,
1791–93. pp. 275. *Valence,* 1891. 8°.
                 010920. f. 27.

ECKARDT (J.) Figuren der pariser Schreckens-
zeit, 1791–94. pp. 449. *Leipz.* 1893. 8°.
                 010661. h. 39.

BROWNING (O.) The Flight to Varennes.
pp. 348. *Lond.* 1892. 8°.   9080. c. 12.

FOURNEL (V.) L'Événement de Varennes.
pp. 404. *Paris,* 1890. 8°.   9231. g. 16.

PINEL ( ) 25 Avril 1892. Le Centenaire de la
guillotine. pp. 10. *Paris,* 1892. 8°. Pam. 39.

Ac. Paris. *Société de l'histoire de la Révolu-
tion.* CHAUMETTE (P. G.) Mémoires sur la
Révolution du 10 Août 1792. pp. 66.
Paris, 1893. 8°.   Ac. 6885. b./6.

MUELINEN (W. F. von) Das französische
Schweizer-Garderegiment 10 Aug. 1792.
pp. 214. *Luzern,* 1892. 8°.   8823. ddd. 28.

BIRÉ (E.) Paris pendant la Terreur. pp. 440.
Paris, 1890. 8°.   9226. aaa. 35.

BOURNAND (F.) La Terreur à Paris. pp. 296.
Paris, 1891. 12°.   9230. c. 18.

WALLON (H. A.) La Terreur: études critiques.
2 tom. *Paris,* 1881. 8°.   9226. bbb. 27.

EVERITT (G.) Guillotine the Great and her
successors. pp. 302. *Lond.* 1890. 8°. 9226. bb. 36.

LENÔTRE (G.) La Guillotine et les exécuteurs
pendant la Révolution. pp. 378.
Paris, 1893. 8°.   6056. ee. 33.

DURFORT (L. H. C. P. de) *Duchess de Duras.*
Prison journals during the French Revolution.
pp. 233. *N.Y.* 1891. 8°.   9226. b. 27.

FRANCE.—History—*continued.*

BOUCHEZ (E.) Francs-maçons Septembriseurs.
pp. 136. *Paris,* 1892. 8°.   04785. k. 7.

DELBREL (J.) Les Martyrs de Septembre.
pp. 98. *Paris,* 1892. 12°.   4629. de. 9.

PARIS. *Église de Carmes.* Le Centenaire des
massacres de Septembre. pp. 100.
Paris, 1892. 8°.   4629. c. 14.

Ac. Paris. *Société de l'histoire de la Révolution.*
GUIFFREY (J. J.) Listes des députés et des
suppléants à la Convention nationale. pp. 169.
Paris, 1889. 8°.   Ac. 6885. b.

BAUDOT (M. A.) Notes historiques sur la Convention, le Directoire, *etc.* pp. 356.
Paris, 1893. 8°.   9231. k. 1.

GROS (J.) Le Comité de Salut Public de la Convention. pp. 352. *Paris,* 1893. 12°. 9225. a. 21.

SCHUETTE (M.) Aus dem Jahre des Schreckens
(1793). pp. 40. *Stralsund,* 1894. 8°. Pam. 28.

AULARD (F. A.) Le Culte de la Raison et le
culte de l'Être suprême, 1793–94. pp. 371.
Paris, 1892. 12°.   9226. aa. 16.

HESDIN (R.) Journal of a spy in Paris during the
Reign of Terror. 1794. pp. 209. *Lond.* 1895. 8°.
                 9230. ccc. 5.

HAMEL (E.) Thermidor d'après les sources
originales. pp. 363. *Paris,* 1891. 8°.
                 9226. bbb. 23.

TOFT (L. F.) Statskoupet den 9 Thermidor
Aar II. pp. 371. *Kjøbenh.* 1890, 8°.
                 010661. f. 52.

KERVILER (R.) Le Procès des 132 Nantais.
pp. 297. *Vannes,* 1894. 8°.   09225. k. 1.

SCIOUT (P. L.) Le Directoire. 2 tom.
Paris, 1895. 8°.   9231. f. 9.

BARRAS (P. F. J. N. de) Memoirs of Barras.
4 vol. *Lond.* 1895, 96. 8°.   010663. k. 3.

LA REVELLIÈRE DE LÉPEAUX (L. M. de) Mémoires. 3 tom. *Paris,* 1895. 8°. 010663. i. 35.

CHARAVAY (E.) La Revellière-Lépeaux et ses
Mémoires. pp. 46. *Paris,* 1895. 8°. 010663. i. 17.

CARNOT (L. N. M.) Correspondance de Carnot.
Paris, 1892, *etc.* 8°.   9225. m.

TALLEYRAND-PÉRIGORD (C. M.) Correspondance
diplomatique de Talleyrand. pp. 465.
Paris, 1891. 8°.   8026. i. 1.

BURKE (*Right Hon.* E.) Burke's Letters on a
Regicide Peace. pp. 176. *Lond.* 1893. 8°.
                 12268. c. 8.

Ac. Paris. *Société d'Histoire Contemporaine.*
18 Fructidor. Documents. pp. 516.
Paris, 1893. 8°.   Ac. 6885. c. 14.

LA RUE (I. E. de) Histoire du dix-huit Fructidor.
pp. 174. *Paris,* 1895. 8°.   9230. d. 1.

See also supra : General: Biographies.

*Military History of the Republic, Consulate and
Empire,* 1792–1815.

For biographies, *etc.,* of Napoleon I., *see infra :
Napoleon I.*

CHUQUET (A.) Les Guerres de la Révolution.
Paris, 1886, *etc.* 8°.   9080. aaa. 38.

DELLARD (J. P.) Mémoires sur les guerres de la
République et de l'Empire. pp. 290.
Paris, 1892. 8°.   010662. h. 23.

DU BOURGET (C. C. M. J.) Campagnes modernes,
1792–1892. pp. 262. *Paris,* 1892. 8°.
                 9009. d. 14.

HAUTERIVE (E. d') L'Armée sous la Révolution,
1789–94. pp. 366. *Paris,* 1894. 8°. 8830. e. 12.

MAHAN (A. T.) Influence of Sea Power upon
the Revolution and Empire, 1793–1812. 2 vol.
Paris, 1892. 8°.   9079. g. 21.

FRANCE.—History—*continued.*

PELLETAN (C.) Les guerres de la Révolution. pp. 201. *Paris*, 1894. 12°.   9226. bb. 38.

AMBERT (J. M. J. J. A. J.) Les généraux de la Révolution, 1792–1804. pp. 387. *Paris*, 1892. 8°.   010662. h. 10.

GRIFFITHS (A.) French revolutionary generals. pp. 259. *Lond.* 1891. 8°.   010661. ee. 38.

THOUMAS (C .A.) Les grands Cavaliers du Premier Empire. *Paris*, 1890, *etc.* 8°.   010661. m. 41.

MASSON (F.) Cavaliers de Napoléon. pp. 235. *Paris*, 1895. 4°.   K.T.C. 36. b. 3.

—— 1782–1809. Aventures de guerre. pp. 162. *Paris*, 1895. 4°.   1871. d. 8.

MOREAU DE JONNÈS (A.) Aventures de guerre au temps de la République et du Consulat. pp. 469. *Paris*, 1893. 8°.   10661. ff. 24.

BOULART ( ) Mémoires militaires du général Bon. pp. 368. *Paris*, 1892. 8°.   9080. cc. 27.

BRICARD (L. J.) Journal du canonnier Bicard, 1792–1802. pp. 494. *Paris*, 1891. 8°.   010661. f. 34.

—— Extrait du "Journal du canonnier Bricard." La discipline aux armées de la première république. pp. 128. *Paris*, 1894. 8°. 010663. f. 5.

BIGOT (C.) Gloires et souvenirs militaires d'après les mémoires du canonnier Bricard, du Maréchal Bugeaud, *etc.* pp. 272. *Paris*, 1894. 8°.   K.T.C. 22. c. 3.

BRUNSCHVIGG (L.) Cambronne. pp. 374. *Nantes*, 1894. 8°.   010662. h. 44.

CARNOT (L. N. M.) *Count.* Correspondance de Carnot. *Paris*, 1892, *etc.* 8°.   9225. m.

MONTÉGUT (É.) Le maréchal Davout. pp. 351. *Paris*, 1895. 8°.   010663. f. 61.

FONT-RÉAULX (H. de) Desaix et Marceau. pp. 156. *Paris*, 1890. 8°.   10661. i. 29.

CONSAL (S.) Vie du général Drouot. 1774–1847. pp. 256. *Paris*, 1892. 8°.   010662. i. 8.

WELSCHINGER (H.) Le Roman de Dumouriez. pp. 331. *Paris*, 1890. 12°.   9226. aaa. 37.

DUPUY (V.) Souvenirs militaires, 1794–1816. pp. 316. *Paris*, 1892. 12°.   9080. aaa. 44.

GIROD DE L'AIN (M.) Le général Éblé, 1758–1812. pp. 222. *Paris*, 1893. 8°. 010662. i. 28.

GODART (R.) Mémoires du général Roch Godart, 1792–1815. pp. 371. *Paris*, 1895. 8°.   010663. h. 12.

LE HARIVEL DE GONNEVILLE (A. O.) Souvenirs militaires. pp. 393. *Paris*, 1895. 8°.   010663. f. 60.

FONT-RÉAULX (H. de) Le général Kleber. pp. 141. *Limoges*, 1891. 8°.   010661. f. 45.

LAHURE (L. J.) Souvenirs de la vie militaire, 1787–1815. pp. 350. *Paris*, 1895. 8°.   010663. g. 35

LANDRIEUX (J.) Mémoires de l'adjudant-général J. Landrieux, 1795–97. *Paris*, 1893, *etc.* 8°.   010663. g. 2.

THOUMAS (C. A.) Le maréchal Lannes. pp. 388. *Paris*, 1891. 8°.   010661. f. 31.

LAVAUX (F.) Mémoires de F. Lavaux, sergent, 1793–1814. pp. 344. *Paris*, 1895. 12°.   010663. f. 42.

CHARAVAY (É.) Le général Alexis Le Veneur, 1746–1833. pp. 111. *Paris*, 1895. 8°.   010662. i. 36.

MACDONALD (É. J. J. A.) *Duke de Tarente.* Souvenirs. pp. 423. *Paris*, 1892. 8°. 10817. ee. 18.

—— Recollections. 2 vol. *Lond.* 1892. 8°.   010663. i. 7.

MARBOT (M. de) *Baron.* Mémoires. 2 vol. *Paris*, 1891. 8°.   010661. f. 29.

FRANCE.—History—*continued.*

MARBOT (M. de) *Baron.* Memoirs of Baron de Marbot. *Lond.* 1892. 8°.   010661. f. 53.

PARFAIT (N.) Le général Marceau. pp. 467. *Paris*, 1892. 8°.   010661. h. 34.

OUDINOT (M. C. J. E.) *Duchess de Reggio.* Le maréchal Oudinot duc de Reggio. pp. 566. *Paris*, 1894. 8°.   010663. g. 13.

PARQUIN (D. C.) Souvenirs et Campagnes d'un vieux soldat, 1803–14. pp. 394. *Paris*, 1892. 8°.   010662. h. 33.

—— Souvenirs du capitaine Parquin, 1803–14. pp. 168. *Paris*, 1892. 4°.   K.T.C. 18. b. 1.

PEYRUSSE (G. J. R.) *Baron.* Lettres inédites du baron Peyrusse, 1809–14. pp. 256. *Paris*, 1894. 8°.   10921. aaa. 42.

PAULIN (J. A.) *Baron.* Les Souvenirs du général Bon Paulin 1782–1876. pp. 335. *Paris*, 1895. 12°.   010663. f. 46.

SÉGUR (P. P. de) *Count.* De 1800 à 1812. Mémoires du général de Ségur. pp. 451. *Paris*, 1894. 8°.   010663. f. 26.

—— General Count de Ségur. pp. 440. *Lond.* 1895. 8°.   010663. g. 27.

SÉRUZIER (T. J. J.) *Baron.* Mémoires militaires. pp. 360. *Paris*, 1895. 12°.   010663. f. 40.

THIÉBAULT (P. C. F. A. H. D.) *Baron.* Mémoires. 5 tom. *Paris*, 1893, 95. 8°. 010663. g. 1.

THIRION (A.) Souvenirs militaires. pp. 359. *Paris*, 1892. 8°.   9076. ccc. 10.

CÈRE (É.) Madame Sans-Gêne (T. Figueur.) 1782–1815. pp. 320. *Paris*, 1894. 12°.   010663. f. 16.

BOISSONNADE (P.) Histoire des Volontaires de la Charente, 1791–94. pp. 364. *Angoulême*, 1890. 8°.   9231. dd. 1.

KREBS (L.) and MORIS (H.) Campagnes dans les Alpes pendant la Révolution. 1792–93. pp. 399. *Paris*, 1891. 8°.   9079. k. 2.

FOUCART (P.) and FINOT (J.) La Défense nationale dans le Nord, 1792 à 1802. *Lille*, 1890, *etc.* 8°.   9226. m.

MARMOTTAN (P.) Le général Fromentin et l'Armée du Nord, 1722–94. pp. 260. *Paris*, 1891. 8°.   9226. k. 15.

PETIT (M.) Les Prussiens en Champagne, 1792. pp. 64. *Paris*, 1890. 12°.   9080. aaa. 33.

CHUQUET (A.) La Retraite de Brunswick. pp. 271. *Paris*, 1887. 8°.   9080. aaa. 38.

DUBOUL (A.) L'Armée révolutionnaire de Toulouse. pp. 265. *Toulouse*, 1891. 8°. 9226. e. 6.

VICCHI (L.) Les Français à Rome, 1792–95. pp. 182. *Rome*, 1892. 4°   9167. m. 3.

CHUQUET (A.) Jemappes et la conquête de la Belgique. pp. 255. *Paris*, 1890. 8°. 9414. e. 3.

LANZAC DE LABORIE (L. de) La domination française en Belgique. 2 tom. *Paris*, 1895. 8°.   9414. h. 18.

DURIEUX (A.) La Défense nationale dans le Cambresis. 1793–94. 1890. 8°. Ac. Cambray. *Société d'Émulation.* Mémoires. Tom. 45. Ac. 307.

K., J. Die Schlacht bei Kaiserslautern Nov. 1793. pp. 59. *Kaiserslautern*, 1893. 8°.   9080. d. 39.

FRENCH REVOLUTION. La Révolution française en Hollande. pp. 398. *Paris*, 1894. 8°.   9414. e. 5.

SAHRON (F. H. A.) De Oorlog von 1794–95 op het grondgebied van de Republiek de Vereenigde Nederlanden. *Te Breda*, 1892, *etc.* 8°.   9079. f.

ARESIN-FATTON (J. M. R.) Historische Essays. pp. 357. *Wien*, 1894. 8°.   9080. dd. 22.

FRANCE.--History—*continued.*

KRACAUER (I.) Frankfurt am Main und die französische Republik 1795-97. 1891. 8°. Ac. Frankfurt. *Gesellschaft für Frankfurts Geschichte.* Archiv. Folge. 3. Bd. 3. Ac. 7049.

TROLARD (E.) Pèlerinage aux champs de bataille d'Italie. De Rivoli à Marengo et à Solferino. pp. 410. *Paris,* 1893. 8°.
                      10136. bbb. 29.

GRIBAYÉDOFF (V.) The French invasion of Ireland in '98. pp. 192. *N.Y.* 1890. 8°.
                      9509. bbb. 15.

CHALAMET (A.) Guerres de Napoléon, 1800-1807. pp. 288. *Paris,* 1895. 8°.   9079. m. 6.

THIERS (L. A.) History of the Consulate and Empire of France. 12 vol.
Lond. 1893. 94, 8°.   9231. d.

GUENTHER (R.) Geschichte des Feldzuges von 1800. pp. 210. *Frauenf.* 1893. 8°. 9080. i. 13.

LETTOW-VORBECK (O. v.) Der Krieg von 1806 und 1807. 2 Bde. *Berl.* 1891. 8°. 9079. k. 1.

NAPIER (*Sir* W. F. P.) History of the war in the Peninsula. 3 pt. *Lond.* 1893. 8°.
                      9080. c. 2.

LAGERHJELM (G. R.) Napoleon och Wellington, på Pyreneiska Halfön. pp. 213.
Stockh. 1889. 8°.   9080. c. 26.

G., L. F. Les prisonniers de Cabrera. Mémoires d'un conscrit de 1808. *Paris,* 1892. 12°.
                      9078. b. 18.

CLERC (J. C. A.) Campagne du Maréchal Soult dans les Pyrénées 1813-14. pp. 464.
Paris, 1894. 8°.   9180. ee. 5.

VANDAL (A.) Napoléon et Alexandre Ier.
Paris, 1891, *etc.* 8°.   9079. i. 5.

ROBINET DE CLÉRY (A.) D'Essling à Wagram. Lasalle. Correspondance. pp. 222.
Paris, 1891. 8°.   010661. f. 56.

JOHN BAPTIST JOSEPH FABIAN SEBASTIAN, *Archduke of Austria.* Aus dem Tagebuch Erzherzog Johanns von Oesterreich, 1810-1815. pp. 251. *Innsbruck,* 1891. 8°.   9314. cc. 9.

BERTIN (G.) La Campagne de 1812. pp. 338. *Paris,* 1895. 8°.   9079. c. 5.

JENSEN (N. P. v.) Napoleons Felttog i Rusland, 1812. pp. 395. *Kjøbenh.* 1893. 8°. 9079. k. 8.

KAUSLER (F. v.) Campagne de Russie, 1812. pp. 319. *Paris,* 1895. 8°.   9079. l. 15.

MARENZI (F.) *Count.* Kritische Beiträge zum Studium des Feldzuges des Jahres 1812. pp. 23. *Wien,* 1895. 8°.   Pam. 2.

SCHALLER (H. de) Histoire des troupes suisses au service de France sous le règne de Napoléon 1er. pp. 236. *Lausanne,* 1883. 8°. 8823. o. 12.

MAAG (A.) Die Schicksale der schweizer Regimenter in Napoleons I. Feldzug nach Russland, 1812. pp. 315. *Biel,* 1890. 8°. 9080. bbb. 24.

WOLSELEY (G. J.) *Viscount Wolseley.* Decline and fall of Napoleon. pp. 203. 1895. 8°. Pall Mall Magazine Library. No. 1.   012208. f.

LAGERHJELM (G. R.) Napoleon och Carl Johan under kriget i Tyskland 1813. pp. 421.
Stockh. 1891. 8°.   9080. cc. 18.

WIEHR (E.) Napoleon und Bernadotte in Herbstfeldzuge 1813. pp. 496. *Berl.* 1893. 8°.
                      9080. ee. 7.

FANE (P. A. W.) *Countess of Westmorland.* Letters of Lady Burghersh from Germany and France, 1813-14. pp. 241. *Lond.* 1893. 8°.
                      010920. e. 27.

JENSEN (N. P. v.) Napoleons Felttog, 1814. pp. 339. *Kjøbenh.* 1891. 8°.   9079. g. 18.

BOUVIER (F.) Les premiers Combats de 1814. pp. 161. *Paris,* 1895. 18°.   9077. dd. 23.

FRANCE.—History—*continued.*

WURTEMBURG. *Kommission für Landesgeschichte.* Geschichte des Feldzuges 1814 gegen Frankreich. pp. 481. *Stuttgart,* 1893. 8°. 9080. dd. 21.

ROLOFF (G.) Politik und Kriegführung während des Krieges von 1814. pp. 92. *Berl.* 1891. 8°.
                    9080. bbb. 33.

HOUSSAYE (H.) 1815. Les Cent Jours. pp. 636. *Paris,* 1893. 8°.   9226. b. 28.

VILLEMAIN (A. F.) Souvenirs des Cent Jours. pp. 188. *Lond.* 1892. 8°.   9226. aa. 12.

MONGE (O.) La Capitulation de Lapalud. Campagne du duc d'Angoulême dans Vaucluse, 1815. pp. 55. *Avignon,* 1894. 8°. 09210. e. 1. (6.)

WELSCHINGER (H.) Le Maréchal Ney, 1815. pp. 427. *Paris,* 1893. 8°.   010662. i. 10.

WESTON (J. A.) Historic doubts as to the execution of Marshal Ney. pp. 310.
N.Y. 1895. 8°.   010663. g. 28.

See also infra : Napoleon I.

For the Campaign of Waterloo, *see* WATERLOO, *Battle of.*

Napoleon I. Biographies and Memoirs.

See also supra : Military History of the Republic, Consulate, and Empire.

AIGLENID DE LIONNE (V. d') L'Empire. pp. 66. *Auxerre,* 1890. 8°.   10601. e. 5. (2.)

BONDOIS (P.) Napoléon et la société de son temps. pp. 445. *Paris,* 1895. 8°. 010661. h. 50.

CHAMANS DE LAVALETTE (A. M.) *Count.* Memoirs of Count Lavalette, Adjutant and Secretary to Napoleon. pp. 460. *Lond.* 1894. 8°. 010662. k. 5.

CHAPTAL (J. A. C.) *Count de Chanteloup.* Mes souvenirs sur Napoléon. pp. 413.
Paris, 1893. 8°.   010661. h. 47.

DAYOT (A.) Napoléon raconté par l'image. pp. 497. *Paris,* 1895. 4°.   K.T.C. 26. b. 18.

—— Napoleon I. in Bild und Wort.
Leipz. 1895, *etc.* 8°.   10659. i.

DUMAS DAVY DE LA PAILLETERIE (A.) Napoleon. pp. 250. *N.Y.* 1894. 8°.   010663. h. 4.

FAUVELET DE BOURRIENNE (L. A.) Memoirs of Napoleon Bonaparte. 4 vol. *Lond.* 1893. 8°.
                      2402. d. 16.

FROEHLICH (F.) Napoleon I. und seine Beziehungen zum klassischen Altertum. pp. 28.
Zürich, 1892. 8°.   10601. d. 27. (11.)

GRAND-CARTERET (J.) Napoléon en images. Estampes anglaises. pp. 190. *Paris,* 1895. 8°.
                      010662. k. 19.

JUNOT (L.) *Duchess d'Abrantès.* Mémoires. 6 tom. *Paris,* 1893. 8°.   010662. f. 28.

—— Home and court life of the Emperor Napoleon. 4 vol. *Lond.* 1893. 8°.   2402. c. 14.

LETELLIER (E.) Encore une singulière découverte. D'où vient le nom de Napoléon et celui de Bonaparte? pp. 19. *Paris,* 1894. 8°.
                      12316. ee. 36.

LÉTY (M.) Bonaparte à Valence. pp. 60. *Tournon,* 1895. 8°.   010661. g. 33.

LÉVY (A.) Napoléon intime. pp. 656. *Paris,* 1893. 8°.   010661. ff. 38.

—— Private life of Napoleon. 2 vol.
Lond. 1894. 8°.   010661. ff. 50.

LUMBROSO (A.) Miscellanea Napoleonica. pp. 205. *Roma,* 1895. 8°.   010663. i. 37.

MASSON (F.) Napoléon chez lui. La journée de l'Empereur aux Tuileries. pp. 355.
Paris, 1894. 8°.   010663. g. 12.

—— Napoleon at home. 2 vol. *Lond.* 1894. 8°.
                      010663. g. 24.

—— Napoléon et les femmes. pp. 334.
Paris, 1894. 8°.   010661. ff. 49.

—— Napoleon and the fair sex. pp. 320.
Lond. 1894. 8°.   010663. g. 15.

FRANCE.—History—_continued._

MASSON (F.) and BIAGI (G.) Napoléon inconnu. Papiers inédits. 2 vol. _Paris_, 1895. 8°.
    010663. i. 45.

MÉNEVAL (C. F. de) _Baron._ Mémoires pour servir à l'histoire de Napoléon 1er, 1802-15. 3 tom. _Paris_, 1894. 8°.   010663. g. 5.

—— Memoirs to serve for the History of Napoleon I. 3 vol. _Lond._ 1894. 8°. 010663. g. 4.

MIRACLE Y CARBONNELL (F.) Napoleón I. y su escritura. pp. 258. _Barcelona_, 1892. 8°.
    7942. h. 32.

MORRIS (W. O'C.) Napoleon and the military supremacy of revolutionary France. pp. 433. 1893. 8°. ABBOTT (E.) Heroes of the Nations. No. 8.   10601. f.

NAPOLEON I., _Emperor._ Les Monologues de Napoléon 1er. pp. 157. _Paris_, 1891. 8°.
    12357. bb. 47.

RÉMUSAT (C. É. J. de) _Countess._ Memoirs of Madame de Rémusat. 1802-1808. pp. 707. _Lond._ 1895. 8°.   010663. h. 7.

RICARD (J. B. H. L. A. de) Autour des Bonaparte. pp. 353. _Paris_, 1891. 12°.
    010662. g. 31.

RIOLS (J. de) Napoléon peint par lui-même. pp. 142. _Paris_, 1895. 12°.   010662. de. 2.

SEPET (M.) Napoléon, son caractère, son rôle historique. pp. 192. _Paris_, 1894. 8°.
    010663. f. 37.

SILVAGNI (U.) Napoleone Bonaparte e i suoi tempi. _Roma_, 1895, etc. 8°.   9080. k.

WAIRY (L. C.) Mémoires de Constant sur la vie privée de Napoléon. 4 tom. _Paris_, 1894. 8°.
    010663. f. 13.

NAPOLEON I., _Emperor._ Die militärischen Proklamationen Napoleons I., 1796-1815. pp. 81. _Oppeln_, 1890. 8°.   Pam. 45.

SARGENT (H. H.) Napoleon's first Campaign. pp. 231. _Lond._ 1895. 8°.   9080. e. 13.

GAFFAREL (P.) Bonaparte et les Républiques italiennes, 1796-99. pp. 303. _Paris_, 1895. 8°.
    9079. f. 14.

FLEINER (F.) Die Ehescheidung Napoleons I. Antrittsrede. pp. 41. _Leipz._ 1893. 8°.
    10601. e. 21. (9.)

WOLSELEY (G. J.) _Viscount Wolseley._ Decline and fall of Napoleon. pp. 203. 1895. 8°. Pall Mall Magazine Library.   012208. f.

SCHIMPFF (G. v.) 1813. Napoleon in Sachsen. pp. 278. _Dresden_, 1894. 8°.   9080. k. 9.

PIERRON (É.) Napoléon de Dresde à Leipzig. pp. 36. _Paris_, 1891. 8°.   9072. cc. 4. (10.)

BLEIBTREU (C.) Der Imperator, Napoleon, 1814. pp. 452. _Leipz._ 1891. 8°.   9076. ee. 14.

USSHER (_Sir_ T.) Napoleon's last Voyages, diaries of Sir T. Ussher, etc. pp. 203. _Lond._ 1895. 8°.
    10658. d. 4.

FIRMIN-DIDOT (G.) La captivité de Sainte-Hélène. pp. 330. _Paris_, 1894. 8°.
    010663. g. 10.

LAS CASES (M. J. E. A. D. de) _Marquis de La Caussade._ Le Mémorial de Sainte-Hélène. _Paris_, 1894, etc. 12°.   010663. f.

IMBERT DE SAINT-AMAND (A. L.) _Baron._ Citizeness Bonaparte. pp. 306. _Lond._ 1891. 8°.
    010661. ee. 57.

DUCREST (G.) Memoirs of the Empress Josephine. 2 vol. _Lond._ 1893. 8°.   010661. h. 48.

GEAREY (C.) Three Empresses: Josephine, Marie-Louise, Eugenie. pp. 316. _Lond._ 1893. 8°.   010662. f. 15.

LE NORMAND (M. A. A.) Historical Memoirs of the Empress Josephine. 2 vol. _Lond._ 1895. 8°.
    010663. i. 14.

FRANCE.—History—_continued._

TURQUAN (J.) La Générale Bonaparte. D'après les témoignages des contemporains. pp. 352. _Paris_, 1895. 18°.   010662. ff. 50.

IMBERT DE SAINT-AMAND (A. L.) _Baron._ Happy days of the Empress Marie Louise. pp. 383. _Lond._ 1890. 8°.   010661. ee. 59.

—— Marie Louise. The Island of Elba and the Hundred Days. pp. 283. _Lond._ 1891. 8°.
    010661. ee. 60.

DU CASSE (P. E. A.) Souvenirs d'un aide de camp du roi Jérôme. pp. 315. _Paris_, 1890. 18°.
    010661. ee. 49.

FREDERICA, _Queen Consort of Jerome Napoleon._ Correspondance inédite de la Reine Catharine. pp. 398. _Paris_, 1893. 8°.   010920. f. 37.

PULITZER (A.) Le Roman du Prince Eugène de Beauharnais. pp. 422. _Paris_, 1895. 8°.
    010662. k. 6.

MAZE-SENCIER (A.) Les Fournisseurs de Napoléon 1er et des deux Impératrices. pp. 367. _Paris_, 1893. 8°.   7743. e. 9.

Civil History of the Consulate and Empire.

For the Military History, see _supra_: _Military History._

LUMBROSO (A.) Saggio di una bibliografia per servire alla storia dell' epoca Napoleonica. _Modena_, 1894, etc. 8°.   011900. c.

PASQUIER (E. D.) _Duke._ Histoire de mon temps. _Paris_, 1893, etc. 8°.   010662. i.

—— A History of my time. _Lond._ 1893, etc. 8°.
    010661. g. 41.

THIERS (L. A.) History of the Consulate and Empire. 12 vol. _Lond._ 1893, 94. 8°. 9231. d.

BAUDOT (M. A.) Notes historiques sur l'Empire, etc. pp. 356. _Paris_, 1893. 8°.   9231. k. 1.

DAUDET (E.) La Police et les chouans sous le Consulat et l'Empire. pp. 359. _Paris_, 1895. 12°.   9230. bbb. 35.

STEWARTON ( ) Secret History of the Court and Cabinet of St. Cloud, 1805. 2 vol. _Lond._ 1895. 8°.   010663. g. 30.

IRISSON D'HÉRISSON (M. d') _Count._ Les Girouettes politiques. Un Secrétaire de Napoléon 1er, C. P. E. Mounier. pp. 452. _Paris_, 1894. 12°.
    9226. b. 33.

GUILLON (É.) Les Complots militaires sous le Consulat et l'Empire. pp. 279. _Paris_, 1894. 12°.   9226. b. 32.

TALLEYRAND-PÉRIGORD (C. M. de) Talleyrand intime d'après sa correspondance avec la Duchesse de Courlande. 1814. pp. 282. _Paris_, 1891. 8°.   010662. ff. 3.

1815-1870.

For the History of the "Hundred Days," see _supra_: _Military History_: WATERLOO.

PELLETAN (C.) De 1815 à nos jours. pp. 370. _Paris_, 1891. 12°.   9230. cc. 8.

HOUSSAYE (H.) 1815. La première restauration. pp. 636. _Paris_, 1893. 8°.   9078. b. 16.

DALBARET (C.) Un assassinat juridique, 1815. Les généraux Faucher. pp. 351. _Paris_, 1894. 12°.   010662. f. 27.

IMBERT DE SAINT-AMAND (A. L.) _Baron._ Duchess of Berry and the court of Louis XVIII. pp. 301. _Lond._ 1892. 8°.   010661. ee. 64.

PASQUIER (E. D.) _Duke._ Histoire de mon temps. _Paris_, 1893, etc. 8°.   010662. i.

—— History of my Time. _Lond._ 1893, etc. 8°.
    010661. g. 49.

IRISSON D'HÉRISSON (M. d') _Count._ Les Girouettes politiques. Un pair de France policier, J. J. Mounier. 1815-22. pp. 499. _Paris_, 1894. 12°.   9226. e. 13.

FRANCE.—History—*continued.*

GONTAUT-BIRON (A. H. S. de) *Duchess.* Memoirs. 2 vol. *Lond.* 1894. 8°.   010663. g. 16.

MAZADE (C. de) L'Opposition royaliste. pp. 304. *Paris*, 1894. 12°.   9226. b. 31.

NICOULLAUD (C.) Casimir Périer député de l'opposition, 1817-30. pp. 496. *Paris*, 1894. 8°.   010663. k. 5.

IMBERT DE SAINT-AMAND (A. L.) *Baron.* The Duchess of Berry and the court of Charles x. pp. 305. *Lond.* 1893. 8°.   010661. cc. 63.

DU CASSE (P. E. A.) *Baron.* La chute des monarchies en France au XIX° siècle. pp. 170. *Paris*, 1890. 12°.   9226. aa. 15.

IMBERT DE SAINT-AMAND (A. L.) *Baron.* The The Duchess of Berry and the Revolution of 1830. pp. 331. *Lond.* 1893. 8°. 010661. ee. 65.

—— La Duchesse de Berry en Vendée, à Nantes et à Blaye. pp. 586. *Paris*, 1893. 8°.   10659. i. 11.

—— Les dernières années de la Duchesse de Berry. pp. 424. *Paris*, 1891. 12°.   10659. bbb. 49.

RASTOUL (A.) Histoire de France depuis la Révolution de Juillet. 2 tom. *Paris*, 1891, 92. 8°.   9231. g. 17.

LA MOTTE-ANGO (H. C. S. F. de P. de) *Marquis de Flers.* Le Roi Louis-Philippe. pp. 476. *Paris*, 1891. 8°.   10658. h. 22.

IMBERT DE SAINT-AMAND (A. L.) *Baron.* La Jeunesse de Louis-Philippe et de Marie-Amélie. pp. 410. *Paris*, 1894. 4°.   10659. i. 14.

—— Marie-Amélie et la Cour de Palerme 1806-14. pp. 255. *Paris*, 1891. 12°.   10658. cc. 9.

—— Marie Amélie et la duchesse d'Orléans. pp. 398. *Paris*, 1893. 12°.   10658. e. 6.

—— Marie-Amélie au Palais-Royal. pp. 410. *Paris*, 1892. 12°.   10658. bbb. 27.

—— Marie-Amélie et la Cour des Tuileries. pp. 406. *Paris*, 1893. 12°.   10659. b. 43.

—— Marie Amélie et l'apogée du règne de Louis-Philippe. pp. 307. *Paris*, 1894. 8°. 10658. e. 10.

—— Les Exils. pp. 322. *Paris*, 1895. 12°.   010663. f. 56.

—— FRANCIS FERDINAND PHILIP, *Prince de Joinville.* Vieux Souvenirs, 1818-48. pp. 454. *Paris*, 1894. 12°.   010663. f. 18.

—— Memoirs of the Prince de Joinville. pp. 340. *Lond.* 1895. 8°.   010663. g. 14.

TALLEYRAND-PÉRIGORD (C. M. de) Correspondance diplomatique de Talleyrand. *Paris*, 1891, *etc.* 8°.   8026. i.

MIRABEAU (M. de) *Countess.* Le Prince de Talleyrand et la Maison d'Orléans. pp. 290. *Paris*, 1890. 18°.   8052. cc. 10.

ZEVORT (E.) Thiers. pp. 239. *Paris*, 1892. 12°.   010662. h. 21.

THOUVENEL (É. A.) Épisodes d'histoire contemporaine tirés des papiers de M. Thouvenel, 1844-45, 1851-52. pp. 316. *Paris*, 1892. 8°.   9080. b. 47.

IMBERT DE SAINT AMAND (A. L.) *Baron.* La Révolution de 1848. pp. 384. *Paris*, 1894 12°.   10659. b. 44.

MONTRÉAL (F. de) Les dernières heures d'une Monarchie. pp. 230. *Paris*, 1893. 8°.   9225. h. 22.

JOIGNEAUX (P.) Souvenirs historiques. *Paris*, 1891, *etc.* 8°.   9226. aa.

TAILHANDIER (J. de) Lamartine et 1848. pp. 22. *Lyon*, 1890. 8°.   9004. gg. 20. (10.)

RISQUONS-TOUT. La risquons-tout en 1848. pp. 62. *Mouscron*, 1890. 16°.   Pam. 28.

FRANCE.—History—*continued.*

DUVAL (G.) Napoléon III. Enfance—jeunesse. pp. 335. *Paris*, 1895. 12°.   010663. f. 41.

THIRRIA (H.) Napoléon III. avant l'Empire. *Paris*, 1895, *etc.* 8°.   010663. k.

HACHET-SOUPLET (P.) Louis-Napoléon prisonnier au fort de Ham. pp. 290. *Paris*, 1894. 12°.   010663. f. 14.

SPULLER (E.) Histoire parlementaire de la Seconde République. pp. 376. *Paris*, 1891. 8°.   9226. bbb. 26.

DU CASSE (P. E. A.) *Baron.* Les dessous du Coup d'État, 1851. pp. 316. *Paris*, 1891. 12°.   9230. cc. 11.

MARX (C.) Le Dix-huit Brumaire de Louis Bonaparte. pp. 115. *Lille*, 1891. 8°.   8051. ccc. 25.

WAUWERMANS (P.) Les proscrits du Coup d'État en Belgique. pp. 228. *Brux.* 1892. 16°.   10662. aaa. 29.

GALLOIS (J. É.) Mémoires d'une victime du 2 décembre, 1851. pp. 172. *Arbois*, 1889. 8°.   010661. m. 51.

ROTHAN (G.) L'Europe et l'avènement du Second Empire. pp. 439. *Paris*, 1892. 12°. 9076. ccc. 16.

BULLE (C.) Geschichte des zweiten Kaiserreichs. pp. 652. 1890, *etc.* 8°. ONCKEN (W.) Allgemeine Geschichte. Hauptabth. IV. Th. 3.   2068. (28.)

LA GORCE (P. de) Histoire du second Empire. 2 tom. *Paris*, 1894. 8°.   9231. k. 6.

EBELING (A.) Napoleon III. und sein Hof. 3 vol. *Köln*, 1891, 94. 8°.   010661. g.

LAMY (É.) Études sur le second Empire. pp. 483. *Paris*, 1895. 8°.   9231. l. 6.

NAUROY (C.) Les secrets des Bonaparte. pp. 370. *Paris*, 1889. 12°.   8052. cc. 11.

LANO (P. de) Le secret d'un Empire. Napoléon III. pp. 365. *Paris*, 1893. 12°.   010662. g. 23.

—— La cour de Napoléon III. pp. 357. *Paris*, 1892. 8°.   9226. b. 26.

—— The secret of an Empire. The Empress Eugénie. pp. 270. *Lond.* 1895. 8°.   010662. g. 39.

CARETTE ( ) *Madame.* Souvenirs intimes de la Cour des Tuileries. Sér. 2. pp. 340. *Paris*, 1890. 18°.   9226. aaa. 34.

—— Souvenirs intimes. Sér 3. pp. 338. *Paris*, 1891. 12°.   9226. b. 23.

—— My mistress the Empress Eugénie. pp. 336. *Lond.* 1893. 8°.   010662. g. 36.

TASCHER DE LA PAGERIE (S. de) *Countess.* Mon Séjour aux Tuileries, 1852-58. pp. 311. *Paris*, 1893. 12°.   010662. ff. 38.

MARTINET (A.) Le Prince Impérial, 1856-79. pp. 347. *Paris*, 1895. 8°.   010663. i. 38.

LARROUMET (G.) Notice sur le Prince Napoléon. pp. 25. *Paris*, 1892. 4°.   10601. g. 5. (4.)

GUYHO (C.) Études d'histoire parlementaire, 1852. Les Hommes de 1852. pp. 349. *Paris*, 1889. 12°.   9230. c. 17.

—— Les beaux jours du Second Empire. pp. 345. *Paris*, 1891. 12°.   9230. c. 16.

BAILLEHACHE (M. de) Souvenirs intimes d'un lancier de la Garde Impériale. pp. 316. *Paris*, 1894. 8°.   9080. c. 40.

MERSON (E.) Confessions d'un journaliste. pp. 324. *Paris*, 1890. 18°.   010661. f. 17.

THOUVENEL (L.) Nicolas I. et Napoléon III. Les préliminaires de la guerre de Crimée. pp. 389. *Paris*, 1891. 8°.   9080. cc. 10.

LEBRUN (B. L. J.) Souvenirs des guerres de Crimée et d'Italie. pp. 336. *Paris*, 1889. 18°.   9080. aaa. 28.

FRANCE.—History—*continued.*

MORNY (C. A. L. J. de) *Count.* Une ambassade en Russie, 1856. pp. 244. *Paris*, 1892. 8°.
9080. bbb. 36.

AUSTRIA. *Army.* Der Krieg im Jahre 1859. pp. 272. *Bamberg*, 1894. 8°. 9080. l. 7.

GRANDIN (L.) Campagne de 1859. Les Français en Italie. pp. 449. *Paris*, 1891. 8°.
9080. g. 1.

ROTHAN (G.) La France et sa politique extérieure en 1866. 2 tom. *Paris*, 1893. 12°.
8026. aa. 30.

OLLIVIER (O. É.) L'Empire libéral.
Paris, 1895, etc. 8°. 9231. l.

WEISS (J. J.) Combat constitutionnel. 1868–86. pp. 334. *Paris*, 1893. 8°. 8052. cc. 27.

MAUGNY (de) *Count.* Souvenirs du Second Empire. pp. 308. *Paris*, 1889. 12°. 9230. cc. 7.

—— Souvenirs of the Second Empire. pp. 247. *Lond.* 1891. 8°. 9231. h. 11.

PESCATORE (G.) L'Incidente Hohenzollern e la diplomazia francese nel luglio 1870. pp. 183. *Torino*, 1894. 8°. 9080. f. 8.

DARIMON (A.) L'Agonie de l'Empire. pp. 354. *Paris*, 1891. 12°. 9079. e. 1.

See also CRIMEAN WAR : MEXICO.
For the history of the French German War of 1870–71, *see* GERMAN-FRENCH WAR, and for that of the Commune of Paris, 1871, *see* PARIS.

1870, etc.

BERTEZÈNE (A.) Histoire de la Basse-République 1870–90. pp. 361. *Paris*, 1891. 8°.
9231. k. 7.

LANO (P. de) Aprés l'Empire. pp. 328. *Paris*, 1894. 12°. 9226. c. 14.

ZEVORT (E.) La France sous le régime du suffrage universel. pp. 263. *Paris*, 1894. 8°.
8050. g. 6.

HORN (J. É.) La Grande Nation 1870–71. pp. 340. *Paris*, 1891. 12°. 9080. bbb. 28.

WEIL (G. D.) L'attitude de l'Angleterre vis-à-vis de la France en 1870–71. pp. 88. *Paris*, 1891. 8°.
8026. i. 6. (11.)

SAVARY (É.) M. Rouher à Cerçay aprés la Guerre. pp. 156. *Paris*, 1893. 12°. 9080. ee. 6.

DREUX-BRÉZÉ (S. de) *Marquis.* Notes pour servir à l'histoire du parti royaliste. pp. 308. *Paris*, 1895. 8°. 9231. h. 14.

GRANDIN (L.) Les gloires de la patrie. Le maréchal de Mac-Mahon. 2 tom. *Paris*, 1894. 12°.
010663. f. 8.

FERRY (J.) Discours et opinions.
Paris, 1893, etc. 8°. 8051. dd.

TOURNIER (A.) Gambetta ; souvenirs anecdotiques. pp. 332. *Paris*, 1893. 8°. 010662. g. 24.

RAIBAUD (A.) Quinze Ans d'opportunisme.
pp. 105. *Évreux*, 1893. 12°. 8052. ccc. 4.

DAUDET (E.) Histoire diplomatique de l'Alliance franco-russe. 1873–93. pp. 339. *Paris*, 1894, 8°.
9079. f. 12.

HAMON (A.) and BACHOT (G.) La France politique et sociale, 1890. 2 vol. *Paris*, 1891, 12°.
9230. cc. 9.

LENGLÉ (P.) Souvenirs de nos campagnes politiques avec le Prince N. Bonaparte, 1879–91. pp. 336. *Paris*, 1893. 8°. 010662. g. 25.

BERTOL-GRAIVIL (E.) Voyage de M. Carnot, Président de la République, dans le midi et la Corse. pp. 164. *Paris*, 1890. 8°. 9930. gg. 31.

—— Les Voyages présidentiels illustrés. Septième et huitième voyage de M. Carnot. pp. 124. *Paris*, 1890, 4°. 9930. gg. 34.

P.P. *Paris.* L'Annuaire Universel illustré.
Paris, 1893, etc. 4°. P.P. 2316. ab.

FRANCE.—History—*continued.*

BERTRAND (A.) La Chambre de 1893. Biographies. pp. 672. *Paris*, 1893. 12°. 010662. f. 23.

—— Le Sénat de 1894. Biographies. pp. 430.
Paris, 1894. 8°. 010663. f. 32.

ÉTARD (G.) Le Sénat illustré. 1894–97. pp. 815. *Paris*, 1895. 8°. 10658. l. 8.

GRENIER ( ) Nos Sénateurs. Biographies et portraits. pp. 452. *Paris*, 1895. 32°.
8052. a. 5.

See also infra : Politics.

History, *Ecclesiastical.*

RICARD (A.) La mission de la France. pp. 312.
Paris, 1894. 4°. 4630. f. 5.

SMITH (R. T.) The Church in France. pp. 487. 1895. 8°. DITCHFIELD (P. H.) The National Churches. 4534. de.

BOURGAIN (L.) Études sur les Biens ecclésiastiques avant la Révolution. pp. 402.
Paris, 1890. 8°. 4629. e. 27.

MAYNARD (L.) Rapports de l'État et de l'Église, des origines à 1789. *Lyon*, 1894, etc. 8°. 4534. cc.

MÉRIC (É.) Le Clergé sous l'ancien régime.
pp. 502. *Paris*, 1890. 12°. 4629. dc. 5.

DUCHESNE (L.) Mémoire sur les diocèses épiscopaux dans l'ancienne Gaule. 1890. Ac. Paris. *Société des Antiquaires.* Mémoires. Sér. 5. Tom. 10. Ac. 5331.

—— Fastes épiscopaux de l'ancienne Gaule.
Paris, 1894, etc. 8°. 4629. ee.

SCULLARD (H. H.) Martin of Tours. pp. 173.
Manch. 1891. 8°. 4827. aaa. 2.

ARNOLD (C. F.) Caesarius von Arelate und die gallische Kirche. pp. 607. *Leipz.* 1894. 8°.
4629. e. 35.

HOPE (A.) Conversion of the Teutonic Race.
pp. 466. *Lond.* 1892. 8°. 4535. b. 12.

DU MOULIN-ECKART (R.) *Count.* Leudegar, Bischof von Autun. pp. 108. *Breslau*, 1890. 8°.
4829. df. 23.

CHAMARD (F.) Histoire ecclésiastique du Poitou.
pp. 166. *Poitiers*, 1890. 8°. 4629. k. 8.

ESPITALIER (H.) Les premiers Évêques de Fréjus. pp. 120. *Draguignan*, 1891. 8°. 4864. ff. 4.

—— Les Évêques de Fréjus du VIIᵉ au XIIIᵉ siècle. pp. 210. *Draguignan*, 1894. 8°. 4864. ff. 1.

IMBART DE LA TOUR (P.) Les Élections episcopales du IXᵉ au XIIᵉ siècle. pp. 554.
Paris, 1891. 8°. 4629. k. 13.

MARBODUS, *Bp. of Rennes.* Marbode. 1035–1123. 1889. 8°. Ac. Rennes. *Société archéologique.* Bulletin. Tom. 20. Ac. 5341.

SULLY (M. de) *Bp. of Paris.* M. de Sully. Étude sur l'administration épiscopale du XIIᵉ siècle. 1890. 8°. Ac. Paris. *Société de l'Histoire de Paris.* Mémoires. Tom. 16. Ac. 6883/2.

SCHUERMANS (H.) La Pragmatique Sanction de Saint-Louis. *Brux.* 1890, etc. 8°. 4529. c.

GÉRIN (C.) Louis XIV. et le Saint Siège. 2 tom. *Paris*, 1894. 8°. 4571. f. 25.

MOÏY (C. de) *Count.* Louis XIV. et le Saint-Siège. 1662–65. 2 tom. *Paris*, 1893. 8°. 4571. ee. 14.

CROUSLÉ (L.) Fénelon et Bossuet.
Paris, 1894, etc. 8°. 011850. h.

SANVERT (P. A.) Massillon. pp. 278.
Châlon-sur-S. 1891. 8°. 4865. dd. 14.

JEAN (A.) Les Évêques de France, 1682–1801. pp. 544. *Paris*, 1891. 8°. 4888. g. 32.

MENTION (L.) Documents relatifs aux rapports du Clergé avec la Royauté, 1682–1705. 1893, *etc.* 8°. Collection de textes. 09210. dc.

Ac. Louvain. *Academia Lovaniensis.* Jansenius, évêque d'Ypres. pp. 228. *Louvain*, 1893. 8°.
4887. ee. 15.

FRANCE.—History, *Ecclesiastical—cont.*

TOLLEMACHE (M.) French Jansenists. pp. 256.
Lond. 1893. 8°.   4867. de. 40.
LE ROY (A.) Le Gallicanisme au XVIIIᵉ siècle.
pp. 794. Paris, 1892. 8°.   4629. d. 8.
GILARDONI (C.) La Bulle Unigenitus en Champagne. pp. 252. Vitry-le-F. 1892. 8°. 4629. d. 7.
SÉCHÉ (L.) Les derniers Jansénistes, 1710-1870.
3 tom. Paris, 1891. 8°.   4629. i. 21.

CHAMARD (F.) La Révolution, le Concordat et la
liberté religieuse. pp. 296. Paris, 1891. 12°,
                                        4629. b. 28.
PRESSENSÉ (E. de) L'Église et la Révolution
française. pp. 576. Paris, 1889. 8°. 4629. i. 10.
MAURY (J. S.) Cardinal. Correspondance diplomatique et mémoires inédits. 2 tom.
Lille, 1891. 8°.   4863. dd. 21.
BONET-MAURY (G.) Le Cardinal Maury d'après
ses mémoires et sa correspondance. pp. 24.
Paris, 1892. 8°.   4804. h. 2. (4.)
BROC (H. de) Un Évêque sous la Révolution,
M. de Maillé La Tour-Landry. pp. 354.
Paris, 1894. 8°.   4867. dd. 31.
MÉRIC (E.) Histoire de M. Émery et de l'Église,
1789-1815. 2 pt. Paris, 1885. 8°. 4629. b. 30.
SALAMON (L. S. J. de) Bp. of Saint Flour.
Mémoires de l'Internonce à Paris pendant la
Révolution, 1790-1801. pp. 376. Paris, 1890. 8°.
                                        4629. e. 26.
VEUCLIN (E. V.) La Constitution civile du
Clergé. pp. 4. Bernay, 1891. 8°.
                                      4629. bbb. 17. (5.)
BEAUFOND (E. de) P. Suzor, évêque constitutionnel, l'Indre-et-Loire. pp. 36.
Tours, 1890. 12°.   4804. g. 3. (4.)
LE COQ (F.) Documents pour servir à l'histoire
de la constitution civile du clergé dans la Mayenne. Laval, 1890, etc. 8°.   4629. d. 3.
QUERNAU-LAMERIE (E.) L'Église constitutionnelle de la Mayenne après la Terreur. pp. 69
Angers, 1891. 8°.   4629. ee. 7. (6.)
BOURNAND (F.) Le Clergé sous la Terreur.
pp. 160. Tours, 1895. 8°.   4629. ee. 9.
MEIGNAN (G.) Archb. of Tours. Un Prêtre déporté en 1792. pp. 288. Tours, 1891. 8°.
                                         4865. f. 1.
MOREAU (P. G.) Le centenaire du martyre des
Carmélites de Compiègne, 1794. pp. 58.
Compiègne, 1894. 8°.   4864. bbb. 47.
ALENÇON (É. d') Martyrologe de l'ordre des
Frères Mineurs pendant la Révolution, 1792-
1800. pp. 47. Paris, 1892. 8°. 4804. c. 33. (10.)
APOLLINAIRE, de Valence. Études franciscaines
sur la Révolution dans l'Isère. 1893. 8°. Ac.
Grenoble. Académie Delphinale. Bulletin.
Sér. 4. Tom. 6.   Ac. 310.
—— Études franciscaines sur la Révolution dans
le Vaucluse. pp. 84. Avignon, 1895. 8°. 4629. f. 34.
MAFFRE (J.) Histoire des prêtres du diocèse
d'Alby mis à mort pendant la Révolution.
pp. 316. Alby, 1891. 8°.   4866. ee. 9.
TRESVAUX DU FRAVAL (F. M.) Histoire de la
persécution révolutionnaire en Bretagne. 2 tom.
Saint-Brieuc, 1892. 12°.   4629. aaa. 27.
LEURIDAN (T.) Le Clergé de la Flandre-
Wallonne pendant la Révolution. 1890. 8°. Ac.
Roubaix. Société d'Émulation. Mémoires.
Sér. 2. Tom. 5.   Ac. 520.
FRANCLIEU (A. M. de) Les Martyrs de l'Église de
Grenoble, 1794. pp. 262. Lyon, 1890. 8°.
                                         4867. c. 4.
PEYRON (É.) Documents pour servir à l'histoire
du Clergé dans le Finistère pendant la Révolution. Quimper, 1892, etc. 8°.   4629. d.

FRANCE.—History, *Ecclesiastical—cont.*

SAUREL (F.) Histoire religieuse de l'Hérault
pendant la Révolution. Paris, 1894, etc. 8°.
                                         4629. d.
LECLER (A.) Martyrs du diocèse de Limoges
pendant la Révolution. Limoges, 1892, etc. 8°
                                         4867. gg.
BRUGIÈRE (H.) Le Livre d'Or des diocèses de
Périgueux et de Sarlat pendant la période révolutionnaire. pp. 326. Montreuil, 1893. 8°.
                                         4629. e. 34.
POITOU. Clergé du Poitou en 1789. Procès-
verbaux, cahier des doléances, etc. pp. 290.
Fontenay-le-C. 1890. 8°.   4629. k. 11.
ABSAC (G.) Prêtres du diocèse du Puy mis à
mort en 1794. 4 pt. Le Puy, 1894, etc. 16°.
                                         4864. aaa.
LOTH (J.) Histoire du Cardinal de La Rochefoucauld pendant la Révolution. pp. 756.
Évreux, 1893. 8°.   4863. ee. 24.
MARTIN (A.) Le Clergé normand, 1791-1802.
pp. 45. Évreux, 1892. 8°.   Pam. 29.
SAINT-BRIEUC. Le Clergé du diocèse de Saint-
Brieuc pendant la Révolution. 1889. 8°. Ac.
Saint-Brieuc. Société Archéologique. Mémoires.
Sér. 2. Tom. 3.   Ac. 5294/2.
ARNAULT (V.) Le Clergé de Touraine pendant
la Révolution. pp. 409. Tours, 1893. 8°.
                                         4629. d. 11.
Ac. Paris. Société d'Histoire Diplomatique.
Documents sur la négociation du Concordat.
2 tom. Paris, 1891, 92. 8°.   Ac. 6885/3.
BROGLIE (J. V. A. de) Duke. Le Concordat.
pp. 239. Paris, 1893. 12°.   3900. b. 55.
SÉCHÉ (L.) Les Origines du Concordat. 2 tom.
Paris, 1894. 8°.   4630. df. 1.
GEOFFROY DE GRANDMAISON (C. A.) La Congrégation, 1801-1830. pp. 409. Paris, 1889. 8°.
                                         4784. e. 55.
DROCHON (J. E. B.) La Petite Église. pp. 416.
Paris, 1894. 16°.   4629. de. 10.
DESURMONT ( ) Le R.P. J. Passerat et les Rédemptoristes pendant les guerres de l'Empire.
pp. 416. Montreuil, 1893. 8°.   4864. e. 25.
LESUR (É.) and BOURNAND (F.) Nos grands
Évêques au XIXᵉ siècle. pp. 113.
Tours, 1895. 8°.   4864. e. 26.
RICARD (A.) Les grands Évêques au XIXᵉ siècle.
Lille, 1890, etc. 8°.   4867. gg. 11.
PARIS. Les Archevêques de Paris au dix-
neuvième siècle. pp. 211. Tournai, 1895. 8°.
                                         4864. ee. 2.
SERRES (J. B.) Vie de Monseigneur C. de Douhet
d'Auzers évêque de Nevers. pp. 264.
Toulouse, 1893. 8°.   4864. e. 22.
SUBILEAU (J.) Cinquante ans d'autorité épiscopale en Anjou. Mgr. Angebault et Mgr. Freppel.
2 pt. Paris, 1894. 8°.   4865. ff. 28.
BOURNAND (F.) Le Clergé pendant la guerre
1870-71. pp. 366. Paris, 1891. 8°.
                                         9080. cc. 20.
—— Le Clergé pendant la Commune, 1871.
pp. 374. Paris, 1892. 8°.   4629. i. 26.
See also ALBIGENSES : CHURCH HISTORY. *Infra :*
PROTESTANTS.

Language and Literature.
See FRENCH LANGUAGE AND LITERATURE.

Law.
DRAMARD (E.) Bibliographie du Droit français
et étranger. pp. 120. Paris, 1893. 8°.
                                         011900. ee. 17.
COQUILLE (J. B. V.) La France et le Code Napoléon. pp. 427. Paris, 1894. 8°. 5408. e. 29.
FRANCE. The French Civil Code. pp. 611.
Lond. 1895. 8°.   5423. df. 7.

FRANCE.—Law—*continued*.

Huc (T.) Commentaire du Code Civil. 2 tom. *Paris*, 1892. 8°.   5423. df.

TRIPIER (L.) Les Codes français. 10 pt. *Paris*, 1892. 8°.   2018. a.

BERTIN (J. L. H.) Chambre du Conseil. 2 tom. *Paris*, 1894. 8°.   5403. dd. 6.

CHAILLEY-BERT (J.) and FONTAINE (A.) Lois sociales. pp. 407. *Paris*, 1895. 8°. 5408. c. 32.

CROME (C.) Allgemeiner Theil der modernen französischen Privatrechtswissenschaft. pp. 514. *Mannheim*, 1892. 8°.   5423. c. 15.

MACHELARD (E.) Dissertations de Droit romain et de droit français. pp. 768. *Paris*, 1882. 8°.   5206. d. 12.

MANCELLE (E. H.) Dictionnaire des délais, préscriptions, péremptions en matière civile, commerciale, criminelle, *etc.* pp. 702. *Paris*, 1890. 8°.   5403. ff. 26.

MENGUY (E.) Les Actes et conventions. pp. 578. *Paris*, 1892. 12°.   5424. b. 15.

P.P. *Paris*. Revue du Droit public, *etc.* *Paris*, 1894, *etc.* 8°.   P.P. 1370. ga.

RIVIÈRE (H. F.) Pandectes françaises. *Paris*, 1885, *etc.* 4°.   5402. k.

SARRAUTE (P.) Manuel du Juge d'Instruction. pp. 550. *Paris*, 1890. 8°.   5403. dd. 2.

TISSIER (T.) La Réforme des frais de justice. pp. 274. *Paris*, 1892. 12°.   5423. de. 15.

VALLET (G.) and MONTAGNON (É.) Manuel des Magistrats du Parquet et des officiers de police judiciaire. 2 tom. *Paris*, 1890. 8°. 5403. de. 3.

VAULABELLE (G. de) Les Lois caduques. pp. 279. *Paris*, 1891. 8°.   8282. de. 45.

See also supra: Constitution: JURY: LAW, Commercial, Criminal, Profession of: LAW REPORTS.

Legal History.

BRUNNER (H.) Forschungen zur Geschichte des französischen Rechtes. pp. 750. *Stuttgart*, 1894. 8°.   6005. h. 22.

FOURNIER (M.) Histoire de la science du Droit en France. *Paris*, 1892, *etc.* 8°.   6005. de.

MICHELET (J.) Origines du Droit français. pp. 359. *Paris*, 1890. 8°.   5423. de 13.

TARDIF (A.) Histoire des sources du Droit français. pp. 527. *Paris*, 1890. 8°. 6005. de. 3.

VIOLLET (P.) Histoire du Droit civil français. pp. 912. *Paris*, 1893. 8°.   5423. dd. 9.

OMONT (H.) Inventaire de la collection du Parlement conservée à la Bibliothèque Nationale. pp. 39. *Paris*, 1891. 8°.   Pam. 6.

AUBERT (F.) Histoire du Parlement de Paris, 1250-1515. 2 tom. *Paris*, 1894. 8°. 09200. e. 7.

GUILHIERMOY (P.) Étude sur la procédure et le fonctionnement du Parlement au XIV° siècle. pp. 646. *Paris*, 1892. 8°.   5406. f. 1.

SPONT (A.) De Cancellariæ regum Franciæ officiariis, 1440-1523. pp. 86. *Vesontione*, 1894. 8°.   5408. aaa. 9.

ROBILLARD DE BEAUREPAIRE (C. de) Notes sur les Juges du Procès de Jeanne d'Arc. pp. 135. *Rouen*, 1890. 8°.   10658. e. 6.

FAGNIEZ (G.) Fragment d'un répertoire de Jurisprudence parisienne au XV° siècle. pp. 94. 1891. 8°. Ac. Paris. *Société de l'Histoire de Paris.* Mémoires. tom. 17.   Ac. 6883/2.

Ac. Paris. *Bibliothèque Nationale.* Catalogue des factums et d'autres documents judiciaires antérieurs à 1790. *Paris*, 1890, *etc.* 8°.   11899. ff. 50.

ESPINAY (G. d') Les réformes de la Coutume de Touraine au XVI° siècle. pp. 246. *Tours*, 1891. 8°.   5406. c. 3.

FRANCE.—Law—*continued*.

CAREL (P.) Étude historique sur le Barreau de Caen. pp. 249. *Caen*, 1889. 12°. 6005. aa. 7.

GRELLET-DUMAZEAU (A.) Les exilés de Bourges, 1753-1754. pp. 422. *Paris*, 1892. 8°. 9226. d. 2.

DUBOUL (A.) La Fin du Parlement de Toulouse. pp. 430. *Toulouse*, 1890. 8°.   9231. i. 9.

REYNAUD ( ) Discours. La Constituante et le Tribunal de Cassation. pp. 85. *Paris*, 1891. 8°.   5408. aa. 10.

DESMAZE (C.) La Magistrature française. 1802-89. pp. 400. *Paris*, 1889. 12°. 5423. aa. 6.

See also supra: Constitution.

Local Government. *See* LOCAL GOVERNMENT.

Navy.

ARDOUIN-DUMAZET (V. E.) L'Armée navale en 1893. pp. 440. *Paris*, 1894. 8°. 8806. b. 44.

—— Au Régiment. En Escadre. pp. 304. *Paris*, 1894. 4°.   8829. l. 21.

—— Les grandes Manœuvres navales de 1892. pp. 280. *Paris*, 1892. 12°.   8828. aaa. 23.

—— L'Armée et la Flotte en 1894. pp. 374. *Paris*, 1895. 8°.   8806. bb. 33.

BENASSI-DESPLANTES (F. J.) Cronstadt et Portsmouth. pp. 192. *Rouen*, 1892. 8°.   10105. bbb. 10.

BERTIN (L. E.) État de la Marine de guerre. pp. 188. 1893. 8°. Encyclopédie des aide-mémoire.   8709. g.

DREDGE (J.) Modern French Artillery, with illustrations of French Warships. pp. 458. 1892. 4°. Engineering Series.   8755. m.

GIRARD (B.) Souvenirs maritimes, 1881-83. pp. 664. *Paris*, 1895. 8°. 010096. ce. 46.

GUEYDON (L. H. de) Idées maritimes d'hier. pp. 292. *Paris*, 1891. 8°.   8807. dd. 26.

LANESSAN (J. L. de) La Marine française, 1890. pp. 427. *Paris*, 1890. 8°.   8807. dd. 15.

LOIR (M.) La Marine française. Illustrations. pp. 620. *Paris*, 1893. 4°.   8805. ff. 30.

MARINE. La Marine. Croquis humoristiques. pp. 148. *Paris*, 1890. 4°.   12330. m. 23.

VIGNERON (H.) La France militaire et maritime du XIX° siècle. *Paris*, 1890, *etc.* 8°. 9231. h. 12.

WEYL (É.) La Flotte de guerre et les arsenaux. pp. 250. *Paris*, 1894. 12°.   8806. b. 48.

X. Marine contemporaine. pp. 174. *Paris*, 1893. 12°.   8806. b. 46.

BENNASSI-DESPLANTES (F. J.) Les cinq ports militaires de la France. pp. 157. *Limoges*, 1894. 8°.   10174. g. 29.

History.

QUESNEL (G.) Histoire maritime de la France depuis Colbert. pp. 276. *Paris*, 1894. 8°.   8807. bbb. 43.

DUCÉRÉ (É.) Histoire maritime de Bayonne. pp. 395. *Bayonne*, 1895. 8°.   10172. i. 13.

LOIR (M.) Gloires et souvenirs maritimes. pp. 331. *Paris*, 1895. 4°.   8806. k. 6.

SAINTE-CROIX (L. de) Essai sur l'histoire de l'administration de la Marine, 1689-1792. pp. 457. *Paris*, 1892. 8°.   8805. cc. 43.

LOIR (M.) La Marine royale en 1789. pp. 319. *Paris*, 1892. 8°.   8807. aa. 46.

GRANDIN ( ) Le vice-amiral Jurien de la Gravière. pp. 363. *Paris*, 1895. 8°.   010662. i. 37.

COSTE (G.) Les anciennes Troupes de la marine, 1622-1792. pp. 323. *Paris*, 1893. 8°.   8824. k. 31.

NICOLAS (V.) Le livre d'or de l'Infanterie de la marine. 2 tom. *Paris*, 1891. 8°. 8824. c. 43.

See also NAVAL SCIENCE.

FRANCE—*continued.*

Parlements. *See supra: Law.*

Politics, *Domestic.*

General.

AYNARD (E.) Discours prononcés à la Chambre des Députés, 1889–93. pp. 386.
Paris, 1894. 8°.   8051. d. 26.

DELAFOSSE (J.) Études et portraits. pp. 354.
Paris, 1894. 12°.   012356. f. 21.

HAMON (A. F.) and BACHOT (G.) La France politique. *Paris,* 1891, *etc.* 12°.   9230. cc. 9.

PASCAL (E.) Discours politiques, 1878–87.
pp. 590. *Paris,* 1889. 18°.   8052. cc. 14.

P.P. *Paris.* Revue politique et parlementaire.
Paris, 1894, *etc.* 8°.   P.P. 3555. a.

REINACH (J.) La Politique opportuniste, 1880–89.
pp. 378. *Paris,* 1890. 8°.   8051. aa. 39.

See also supra: Constitution: History, 1870, *etc.:* SOCIALISM : SOCIAL SCIENCE, *etc.*

Monarchy and Bonapartism.

BÉRAUD (E.) Un seul Chef, un seul parti.
pp. 62. *Paris,* 1891. 8°.   Pam. 69.

BOULY DE LESDAIN (L.) Comte de Paris ou duc de Madrid ? pp. 59. *Paris,* 1891. 8°. Pam. 69.

CIVIS. Histoire de la famille d'Orléans. pp. 30.
Paris, 1890. 8°.   Pam. 69.

CLÉRON (O. B. P. G. de) *Count d'Haussonville.*
Lettre à M. d'Haussonville à l'adresse de M. le comte de Paris et du parti monarchique. pp. 3.
Londres, 1892. 4°.   1850. c. 6. (71.)

DELORY (M.) Démonstration de la supériorité de la République sur la Monarchie en France.
pp. 199. *St.-Omer,* 1891. 8°.   8052. cc. 20.

DREUX-BRÉZÉ (S. de) *Marquis.* Notes pour servir à l'histoire du parti royaliste. pp. 308.
Paris, 1895. 8°.   9231. h. 14.

—— Henri v. et le comte de Paris. Réponse au Marquis de Dreux-Brézé. pp. 41.
Paris, 1895. 8°.   Pam. 69.

DU MAGUÉ (L.) L'Idée moderne agonisante.
pp. 174. *Paris,* 1894. 8°.   8052. cc. 33.

FRANCE. Dieu, la Royauté et le salut de France.
228. *Paris,* 1890. 12°.   8051. ccc. 18.

HÉLION DE BARRÈME (L. M. J. E.) *Viscount.*
Catholiques avec le Pape, royalistes avec le Roi.
pp. 8. *Nice,* 1892. 12°.   Pam. 45.

HESSE (H.) Monarchie, République ? pp. 79.
Paris, 1893. 8°.   8051. h. 3.

LUCHAPT (X. de) Le Duc d'Orléans. pp. 31.
Paris, 1890. 8°.   Pam. 69.

PRINCIPES. Nos vieux Principes légitimistes en regard des élections, 1893. pp. 73.
Paris, 1894. 8°.   8050. g. 4.

S., L. de. Pourquoi M. le comte de Chambord n'est pas monté sur le trône de France. pp. 101.
Paris, 1891. 12°.   8052. cc. 17.

STIEGLITZ (A. de) De l'Équilibre politique du Légitimisme. *Paris,* 1893, *etc.* 8°.   8010. dd.

TESTE (L.) Les Monarchistes sous la République.
pp. 251. *Paris,* 1891. 8°.   8052. cc. 19.

AUDIBERT (W.) La troisième République et les Napoléon. pp. 103. *Langres,* 1890. 8°. Pam. 69.

BERRUYER (R.) Les Mémoires d'une Bonapartiste. pp. 358. *Grenoble,* 1894. 8°. 10663. h. 15.

CUNEO D'ORNANO (G.) La République de Napoléon. pp. 636. *Paris,* 1894. 8°. 9226. c. 15.

LENGLÉ (P.) Souvenirs de nos campagnes politiques avec le Prince N. Bonaparte, 1879–91.
pp. 336. *Paris,* 1893. 8°.   010662. gg. 31.

VILLOT (É. C. É.) L'Empereur de demain.
pp. 336. *Paris,* 1891. 12°.   8052. cc. 18.

General Boulanger.

AIMELAFILLE (H.) Comment on devient Boulangiste. pp. 159. *Paris,* 1890. 8°. 010661. h. 13.

BOULANGER (G. E. J. M.) Mémoires. pp. 341.
Paris, 1890. 8°.   010661. ee. 41.

BOULANGER (G. E. J. M.) Collection of speeches, election manifestos, *etc.,* relating to General Boulanger. *Paris,* 1888, 89. 12°, *etc.*
     8051. aa. 43.

—— Collection of placards issued in connection with the election of the Department of the Seine, Jan. 27, 1889. 1889. fol.   1850. d. 13. (298.)

—— Collection of various publications relating to General Boulanger. *Paris,* 1888, 89. 8°.
     8051. d. 27.

—— Haute Cour de Justice. Affaire Boulanger, Dillon et Rochefort. Compte rendu des Audiences. pp. 73. *Paris,* 1889. fol. 5425. h. 2.

—— Haute Cour de Justice. Affaire Boulanger, Dillon-Rochefort. Réquisitoire du Procureur général. pp. 118. *Bordeaux,* 1889. 8°.
     8052. cc. 12.

DÉMOCRATE. La Philosophie du Boulangisme.
pp. 48. *Paris,* 1890. 8°.   Pam. 69.

MAGUÉ (A.) Le Proscrit de Jersey. pp. 24.
Neuilly sur S. 1890. 12°.   Pam. 69.

MILLOT (M.) La Comédie boulangiste. pp. 352.
Paris, 1891. 12°.   8051. ccc. 9.

MORPHY (M.) Mon Rôle dans le Boulangisme.
pp. 14. *Paris,* 1892. 8°.   Pam. 69.

PARIS. Broadsides relating to the Paris Élections Législatives of Sept. 22. 1889, concerning General Boulanger. 10 pts. *Paris,* 1889. fol.
     1850. d. 13. (270.)

MERMEIX ( ) Les Coulisses du Boulangisme.
pp. 379. *Paris,* 1890. 18°.   8051. ccc. 17.

VERLY (A.) Le Général Boulanger et la Conspiration monarchique. pp. 324.
Paris, 1893. 12°.   9230. cc. 15.

1889–1890.

BORIE (L.) Une Élection législative au centenaire de 1789. pp. 146. *Tulle,* 1890. 8°.
     9226. aa. 6.

HUSSON (F.) Le Catéchisme du XIX° siècle.
pp. 77. *Paris,* 1890. 18°.   8052. aa. 18.

LEROY BEAULIEU (P. P.) Un Chapitre des mœurs électorales, 1889 et 1890. pp. 31.
Paris, 1890. 8°.   Pam. 69.

SOLLIER (L.) Catholicisme et démocratie constitutionnelle. pp. 129. *Paris,* 1890. 18°.
     8051. ccc. 20.

See also supra: General Boulanger.

1891.

GALLUS. La République et les républicains.
pp. 62. *Nancy,* 1891. 8°.   Pam. 69.

HAMON (A. F.) and BACHOT (G.) Ministère et nclinite. pp. 556. *Paris,* 1891. 12°. 8823. g. 22.

QUATRELLES. Un an de Règne. Mes décrets, lois, *etc.* pp. 230. *Paris,* 1891. 12°
     8051. aa. 42.

SAILLARD (F.) Du seul Moyen pour fonder en France la Démocratie. pp. 73.
Paris, 1891. 12°.   Pam. 69.

VÉDRENNE (P.) Vive la République! pp. 152.
Paris, 1891. 8°.   8072. de. 25.

1892.

ASSÉZAT DE BOUTEYRE (E.) Aperçus politiques.
pp. 35. *Le Puy,* 1892. 8°.   Pam. 69.

DRUMONT (E. A.) Gambetta et sa Cour. pp. 36.
Paris, 1892. 8°.   4031. g. 45. (9.)

FINET (A.) Grandeur de la France par l'émancipation des travailleurs. pp. 63.
Paris, 1892. 8°.   08276. k. 19.

FRANCE.—Politics—*continued.*

FRENCH ANARCHY. L'Anarchie française.
pp. 316. *Paris*, 1892. 12°.　　8052. cc. 25.

MAIGNEN (C.) La Souveraineté du peuple est
une hérésie. pp. 119. *Paris*, 1892. 8°.
　　　　　　　　　　　8010. de. 14.

MARCHAND (E.) La France aux Français!
pp. 93. *Paris*, 1892. 12°.　　8052. bb. 10.

PATRIOTE. La France de demain. pp. 144.
Paris, 1892. 12.　　　　　8052. cc. 26.

VACHEROT (É.) La Démocratie libérale.
pp. 376. *Paris*, 1892. 12°.　　8009. aa. 18.

BELIN (L.) État du radicalisme dans l'Yonne.
pp. 141. *Vitry-le-F.* 1893. 8°.　　8052. b. 2.

CHASSAGNE (M.) Les Élections de 1893 et le
Panamo-Boulangisme. pp. 90.
Paris, 1893. 8°.　　　　　8051. d. 25.

DESJARDINS (A.) Questions sociales et politiques.
pp. 490. *Paris*, 1893. 8°.　　8009. h. 22.

FIAUX (F. L.) H. Brisson et les révisionnistes.
pp. 15. *Paris*, 1893. 8°.　　　Pam. 69.

FRANC (J.) La France et son gouvernement.
pp. 46. *Bayonne*, 1893. 8°.　　Pam. 69.

GRÉZEL (　) Par ici la Sortie, ou les Conserva-
teurs et les Catholiques font fausse route.
pp. 343. *Paris*, 1893. 8°.　　8051. de. 19.

JAUBERT (D.) La Crise nationale. pp. 430.
Paris, 1893. 12°.　　　　8051. ccc. 26.

MARIELD (J.) Mélanges patriotiques. pp. 233.
Paris, 1893. 12°.　　　　8026. bb. 34.

MAUMUS (É. V.) La Pacification politique et
religieuse. pp. 73. *Paris*, 1893. 8°. 8052. cc. 32.

RÉFORME. Réforme du Suffrage universel.
pp. 58. *Paris*, 1893. 8°.　　　Pam. 69.

　　　　　　　1894-95.

DES ASPRES (G.) Un Peuple exproprié.
pp. 317. *Paris*, 1894. 12°.　　08275. f. 14.

LAFFITTE (P.) Lettres d'un Parlementaire.
pp. 256. *Paris*, 1894. 8°.　　8052. cc. 37.

OLLIVIER (O. É.) Solutions politiques. pp. 310.
Paris, 1894. 12°.　　　　8009. b. 32.

REINACH (J.) Pages républicaines. pp. 353.
Paris, 1894. 12°.　　　　8052. cc. 38.

SICARD (J.) Expiation. Étude politique.
pp. 280. *Paris*, 1894. 8°.　　8052. cc. 36.

CASTELLANE (M. E. P. A. B. de) *Marquis.* Les
Temps nouveaux. pp. 324. *Paris*, 1895. 12°.
　　　　　　　　　　　8051. cc. 36.

CHAUDORDY (　de) *Count.* Considérations sur
l'état de la France. pp. 67. *Paris*, 1895. 12°.
　　　　　　　　　　　8051. cc. 35.

COURCOURAL (P.) La Décentralisation et la
Monarchie nationale. pp. 45.
Rochefort, 1895. 8°.　　　　Pam. 69.

GAMBETTA (L.) A B C de la Démocratie.
pp. 126. *Paris*, 1895. 8°.　　8051. d. 28.

HUMANUS (O.) *pseud.* L'Union fait la force.
pp. 28. *Berl.* 1895. 8°.　　　Pam. 67.

VITRAC-DESROZIERS (M.) Les Dessous minis-
tériels. pp. 275. *Paris*, 1895. 12°. 8051. aa. 44.

See also supra: History, 1870, *etc.*

　　　　　Politics, *Foreign.*

BOURGEOIS (É.) Manuel de Politique étrangère.
Paris, 1892, *etc.* 8°.　　　8009. aaa.

ÉTRANGER. Le Prestige de la France en Europe.
pp. 29. *Paris*, 1890. 8°.　　　Pam. 69.

FLOURENS (L. É.) Politique extérieure. pp. 36.
Paris, 1893. 8°.　　　　Pam. 69.

AUBŒUF (J.) Cri de Guerre. pp. 411.
Paris, 1891. 12°.　　　　8026. bb. 31.

CONSULES. Videant Consules. La guerre est-
elle inévitable? pp. 159. *Paris*, 1890. 12°.
　　　　　　　　　　　8026. aaa. 38.

FRANCE.—Politics—*continued.*

DÉROULÈDE (P.) Désarmement? pp. 16.
Paris, 1891. 8°.　　　8026. ee. 25. (6.)

DREYFUS (F. C.) La Guerre nécessaire. pp. 40.
Paris, 1890. 8°.　　　8026. i. 5. (5.)

LANGLOIS (E.) La Guerre inutile. Réponse à
M. Dreyfus. pp. 42. *Paris*, 1890. 8°.
　　　　　　　　　　8026. ee. 25. (5.)

PEMJEAN (L.) La Paix nécessaire; réponse à
M. Dreyfus. pp. 19. *Paris*, 1890. 8°. Pam. 67.

DIPLOMATE. Les Puissances militaires devant la
France et l'Allemagne. pp. 266.
Paris, 1893. 8°.　　　　8026. ee. 27.

FIORE (P.) L'Empereur d'Allemagne, la France,
etc. pp. 40. *Paris*, 1890. 8°. 8026. ee. 24. (7.)

HEIMWEH (J.) Triple Alliance et Alsace-Lorraine. pp. 138. *Paris*, 1892. 8°. 8026. b. 22.

WALDTEUFEL (É.) Six mois de Paix armée.
pp. 454. *Paris*, 1894. 12°.　　8026. b. 23.

CASTONNET DES FOSSES (H.) La France, l'Angleterre et l'Italie dans la mer Rouge.
Lille, 1889. 8°.　　　8026. i. 6. (6.)

FRANC (C.) L'Angleterre et la Triple Alliance.
pp. 335. *Paris*, 1893. 8°.　　8026. aaa. 43.

POLIGNAC (　de) La France vassale de l'Angleterre. pp. 73. *Alger*, 1894. 8°.　8026. ee. 29.

M., R. de. La France et l'Italie. pp. 13.
1891. 8°.　　　　8026. ee. 24. (13.)

NARJOUX (F.) Français et Italiens. pp. 288.
Paris, 1891. 12°.　　　　8026. aa. 24.

NEGRO (M.) Quelles sont les causes de la Haine
française contre l'Italie? *Lond.* 1893. 8°.
　　　　　　　　　　　　Pam. 67.

PALADINI (L.) Pas d'Équivoque. Lettres [on
the antipathy between France and Italy].
pp. 50. *Turin*, 1890. 8°　　　Pam. 70.

CHANNEBOT (A.) L'Empire ottomane, l'Italie et
la France. pp. 24. *Paris*, 1891. 12°.
　　　　　　　　　　8028. f. 32. (4.)

MONVOISIN (É.) France et Turquie. pp. 32.
Paris, 1894. 8°.　　　　Pam. 67.

BERTOL-GRAIVIL (E.) and BOYER (P.) Le Livre
d'Or des fêtes franco-russes. pp. 215.
pp. 215. *Paris*, 1894. 4°.　　9930. gg. 35.

BOURNAND (F.) Le Livre d'Or franco-russe.
pp. 382. *Tours*, 1894. 8°.　　8026. e. 9.

FRAENKEL (H.) Eine Frage an das französische
Volk: Ist der Verrath der Kultur an die
Barbarei eine Thatsache? pp. 33.
Weimar, 1892.. 8°.　　8026. i. 5. (10.)

CATTEY (A.) Manuel en vue de faire obtenir
l'union franco-américaine-russophile.
Paris, 1893. 8°.　　　　08275. f. 12.

CYON (E. de) Histoire de l'Entente franco-russe.
pp. 494. *Paris*, 1895. 8°.　　8026. h. 19.

GEFFCKEN (F. H.) Frankreich, Russland und
der Dreibund. pp. 179. *Berl.* 1893. 8°.
　　　　　　　　　　　8026. e. 7.

HÉNAUT (F. de) Douze ans d'alliance franco-
russe. pp. 186. *Paris*, 1892. 8°. 8026. d. 4.

VACHON (M.) Les marins russes en France.
pp. 204. *Paris*, 1893. 4°.　　9930. k. 1.

MAZINGHIEN (G.) and TERRADE (A.) Les Officiers
de l'escadre russe à Versailles. pp. 160.
Versailles, 1894. 8°.　　　9930. ccc. 26.

POPOWSKI (J.) Die französisch-russische Allianz.
pp. 30. *Wien*, 1891. 8°.　　8026. i. 6. (10.)

ROY (C.) Le Livre de propagande de l'Alliance
française. pp. 80. *Paris*, 1894, 12°. 8026. b. 25.

MUSSET (E. S. B.) Union helléno-latine. pp. 32.
Paris, 1890. 8°　　　8026. ee. 24. (10.)

WOESTE (C.) La Neutralité belge. pp. 85.
Brux. 1891. 8°.　　　　8026. i. 2.

FRANCE.—Politics—*continued*.

P.P. *Paris*. Revue franco-sud-américaine.
Paris, 1891, *etc*. fol.   P.P. 1423. d.
See also EUROPE.

Population.

SCHOENE (L.) Histoire de la population française. pp. 428. *Paris*, 1893. 12°. 8207. aa. 35.

FRANCE. *M. de l'Intérieur*. Dénombrement de la population. 1891. pp. 876.
Paris, 1892. 8°.   2060. d.

LEVASSEUR (É.) Esquisse de l'ethnographie de la France. 1888. 8°. Ac. Paris. *Académie des Sciences Morales*. Mémoires. Tom. 16. 2098. f.

BAUDRILLART (H. J. L.) Les populations agricoles de la France, Maine, Anjou, Touraine, *etc*. pp. 643. *Paris*, 1888. 8°.   08276. h. 27.

—— Normandie et Bretagne. pp. 638.
Paris, 1885. 8°.   10168. h. 29.

—— Les populations du Midi. pp. 654.
Paris, 1893. 8°.   08276. h. 52.

LAINÉ (A.) De la dépopulation en France.
pp. 60. *Tours*, 1891. 12°.   08276. f. 24. (3.)

RABAUD (C.) Le Péril national ou la dépopulation croissante de la France. pp. 55.
Paris, 1891. 8°.   08276. f. 22. (8.)

Protestants.

BERSIER (E.) Projet de révision de la Liturgie des églises réformées. pp. 248. *Paris*, 1888. 8°.
3900. i. 14.

CHICAGO. *Columbian Exposition*. Les œuvres du Protestantisme français au XIX° siècle.
pp. 480. *Paris*, 1893. 4°.   3902. k. 1.

COURTOIS (D.) La Musique sacrée dans l'Église réformée. pp. 101. *Paris*, 1888. 8°.
7895. e. 10.

FULLIQUET (G.) La Crise théologique dans l'Église réformée. pp. 61. *Lyon*, 1892. 8°.
3900. dd. 2, (2.)

MAURY (L.) Le Réveil religieux dans l'Église réformée. 2 pt. *Paris*, 1892. 8°. 4660. de. 1.

PENEL BEAUFIN ( ) Législation des cultes protestants en France. pp. 275.
Paris, 1893. 12°.   5107. aaa. 18.

P.P. *Montauban*. Revue de Théologie et des questions religieuses. *Montauban*, 1891, *etc*. 8°.
P.P. 37. caa.

POZZY (B.) Les Origines de l'Église et des œuvres de Laforce. pp. 192. *Paris*, 1894. 8°.
4629. a. 51.

RÉVEILLAUD (E.) L'établissement d'une colonie de Vaudois français en Algérie. pp. 118.
Paris, 1893. 12°.   10096. bb. 12.

RUSSIER (A.) L'Œuvre de la Société centrale protestante d'Évangélisation. pp. 114.
Montauban, 1892. 8°.   3900. i. 17.

SABATIER (L. A.) La France et le protestantisme. pp. 12. *Paris*, 1894. 8°.
3900. dd. 2. (5.)

TRIGANT-GENESTE (E) Dictionnaire d'administration à l'usage des Églises protestantes.
pp. 562. *Paris*, 1895. 8°.   05107. h. 4.

History.

Ac. NEW YORK. *Huguenot Society*. Catalogue of books, pamphlets and manuscripts belonging to the Society. pp. 107. *N.Y.* 1890. 8°.
011902. l. 29.

ARNAUD (E.) Bibliographie huguenote du Dauphiné. pp. 109. *Grenoble*, 1894. 8°.
011900. h. 29.

FISCH (A.) Une Galerie de Portraits empruntés à l'histoire de la réforme en France. pp. 258.
Toulouse, 1893. 12°.   010663. f. 19.

PUAUX (N. A. F.) Histoire du Protestantisme français. pp. 591. *Paris*, 1894. 8°. 4630. f. 7.

FRANCE.—Protestants—*continued*.

JANE II., *Queen of Navarre*. La Prédication du Protestantisme en Ossau imposée par Jeanne d'Albret. pp. 12. *Pau*, 1895. 8°.   Pam. 29.

WILLERT (P. F.) Henry of Navarre and the Huguenots. pp. 478. 1893. 8°. ABBOTT (E.) Heroes of the Nations.   10601. f.

SCHMIDT (C.) Poésies huguenotes du 16° siècle.
pp. 44. *Strassb.* 1882. 8°.   11474. b. 18.

TYLOR (C.) The Huguenots in the 17th century.
pp. 316. *Lond.* 1892. 8°.   4629. aaa. 24.

LALOT (J. A.) Essai sur la conférence tenue à Fontainebleau entre Duplessis-Mornay et Duperron, 1600. pp. 303. *Paris*, 1889. 8°.
4629. k. 6.

GALTIER DE LAROQUE (A. de) Le Marquis de Ruvigny et les protestants à la cour de Louis XIV., 1643–85. pp. 310. *Paris*, 1892. 12°.
010662. ff. 19.

BENOÎT (D.) Du caractère huguenot. pp. 63.
Paris, 1892. 8°.   3900. i. 18. (7.)

BAIRD (H. M.) The Huguenots and the Revocation of the Edict of Nantes. 2 vol.
Lond. 1895. 8°.   2216. b. 3.

DOUEN (E. O.) La Révocation de l'Édit de Nantes. 3 tom. *Paris*, 1894. 8°.   4630. f. 6.

SMILES (S.) Huguenots in France after the Revocation of the Edict of Nantes. pp. 528.
Lond. 1893. 8°.   4629. aaa. 28.

BRUN (P.) Les Assemblées illicites des Protestantes dans le pays de Foix. pp. 29.
Foix, 1894. 8°.   4629. cc. 7. (12.)

CAMISARDS. Précis de la guerre des Camisards, 1702–10. pp. 268. *Nimes*, 1892. 8°. 9226. k. 21.

VIDAL ( ) Les Camisards en action. pp. 147.
Rodez, 1890. 8°.   9226. d. 1.

SCHOTT (T.) Die Kirche der Wüste, 1715–87.
pp. 213. 1893. 8°. Ac. Halle. *Verein für Reformationsgeschichte*. Schriften, Nr. 43, 44.
Ac. 2027.

LOMBARD (S.) La vie des Étudiants au désert, 1756–63. pp. 109. *Genève*, 1893. 8°. 4629. a. 39.

READ (C.) Lafayette, Washington et les Protestants de France. pp. 58. *Paris*, 1893. 8°.
4629. e. 40.

MAURIN (J.) Les Écoles primaires protestantes avant la Révocation de l'Édit de Nantes.
pp. 53. *Montauban*, 1892. 8°.   Pam. 17.

NICOLET (G. E.) L'École primaire protestante jusqu'en 1789. pp. 76. *Auxerre*, 1891. 8°.
Pam. 17.

PASCAL (P.) É. Benoist et l'Église réformée d'Alençon. pp. 207. *Paris*, 1892. 8°. 4866. g. 14.

CADÈNE (J.) L'Église réformée de Bordeaux.
pp. 88. *Bordeaux*, 1892. 8°.   4629. aa. 32.

FLORIS (U.) La Réforme à Aumessas. pp. 91.
Nimes, 1893. 8°.   4629. a. 49.

TERREBASSE (H. de) Notes pour servir à l'histoire des Protestants du Dauphiné. pp. 217.
Lyon, 1890. 8°.   4629. b. 27.

ARNAUD (E.) Histoire des Protestants de Crest en Dauphiné. pp. 102. *Paris*, 1893. 8°.
4629. k. 23.

PHILIP DE BARJEAU (J.) Le Protestantisme dans la vicomté de Fezensaguet. pp. 114.
Auch, 1891. 8°.   4629. k. 19.

AMPHOUX (H.) Essai sur l'histoire du Protestantisme au Havre. pp. 463. *Havre*, 1894. 8°.
4629. e. 39.

JOUBERT (A.) Histoire de l'Église réformée de Laval. 1889. 8°. MAYENNE. *Commission historique*. Procès-verbaux. Sér. 2. Tom. 1.
010171. m. 18.

FRANCE.—Protestants—_continued._

BOWER (H. M.) The Fourteen of Meaux : an account of the earliest " Reformed Church " in France. pp. 124. _Lond._ 1894. 8°.
4629. d 13.

THIRION (M.) Étude sur l'histoire du Protestantisme à Metz. pp. 480. _Nancy_, 1884. 8°.
4629. e. 28.

BOURGEON (G.) La Réforme à Nérac. 1530-60. pp. 118. _Toulouse_, 1880. 8°.   4629. i. 9.

PICANON (A. E.) Notice sur l'Église réformée de Sauzé-Vaussais. pp. 12. _Paris_, 1892. 8°.
Pam. 29.

DUPIN DE SAINT-ANDRÉ (A.) Le Protestantisme en Touraine. pp. 11. _Paris_, 1882. 8°. Pam. 29.

—— Les Églises réformées disparues en Touraine. pp. 58. _Paris_, 1894. 8°.   4629. f. 33.
See also LA ROCHELLE.

Huguenot Emigration.

WEDEKIND (O.) Die Réfugiés. pp. 93. _Hamb._ 1886. 8°.   4629. f. 32.

SCHICKLER (F. de) Les Églises du Refuge en Angleterre. 3 tom. _Paris_, 1892. 8°.
4629. dd. 14.

LONDON. _French Protestant School._ Records of the French Protestant School. pp. 112. _Lymington_, 1894. 8°.   8364. e. 47.

DE GRAVE (J. W.) Notes on the Register of the Walloon Church of Southampton. _1885, etc._ 8°. Ac. London. _Huguenot Society._ Proceedings. Vol. 5.   Ac. 2073.

MINET (W.) Account of the Huguenot Family of Minet, from their coming out of France. pp. 240. _Lond._ 1892. 4°.   9914. dd. 13.

PUAUX (N. A. F.) Histoire de l'établissement des Protestants français en Suède. pp. 212. _Paris_, 1891. 8°.   4629. i. 20.

COMBE (E.) Les Réfugiés en Suisse. pp. 238. _Lausanne_, 1885. 8°.   4650. cc. 23.

Social Life.

GRISWOLD (W. M.) List of Novels dealing with life in France. _Camb._ 1892. 8°.
011902. m.

ELLIOT (F.) Old Court life in France. 2 vol. _N.Y._ 1893. 8°.   012612. g. 6.

JUNOT (L.) _Duchess d'Abrantès._ Histoire des Salons de Paris. 4 tom. _Paris_, 1893. 8°.
9230. ccc. 2.

POSTEL (R.) Nos Aïeux. pp. 215. _Paris_, 1892. 8°.   7709. f. 25.

MANNEVILLE (C. A. A. de) De l'état des Terres et des personnes dans la paroisse d'Amblainville. pp. 389. _Beauvais_, 1890. 8°. 10174. g. 27.

LA TRÉMOILLE (G. de) Livre de comptes, 1395-1406. Guy de la Trémoille et Marie de Sully. pp. 276. _Nantes_, 1887. 4°.   7709. k. 33.

BOURCIEZ (É.) Les Mœurs polies sous Henri II. pp. 437. _Paris_, 1886. 8°.   011824. i. 24.

SWARTE (V. de) Les Financiers amateurs d'art. pp. 57. _Paris_, 1890. 8°.   7807. c. 8.

VÉRICEL (G.) Vieux Usages lyonnais. pp. 72. _Lyon_, 1893. 12°.   12430. c. 36.

GASQUET (A.) Lectures sur la Société française aux XVIIe et XVIIIe siècles. pp. 314. _Paris_, 1894. 12°.   9225. a. 31.

GIDEL (A. C.) Les Français du XVIIe siècle. pp. 453. _Paris_, 1893. 8°.   9225. b. 25.

GAHIER (J.) La Journée d'une dame au XVIIe siècle. pp. 23. _Nantes_, 1894. 8°.   Pam. 3.

FERRIER (R.) Journal of Major Ferrier, while travelling in France, 1687. pp. 48. 1894. 8°. Ac. London. _Camden Society._ Camden Miscellany. Vol. 9.   Ac. 8113/39.

FRANCE.—Social Life—_continued._

VOYER (M. R. de) _Marquis d'Argenson._ Rapports du Lieutenant de police, 1697-1715. pp. 418. _Paris_, 1891. 8°.   12234. bbb. 5.

MAUGRAS (G.) The Duc de Lauzun and the Court of Louis XV. pp. 365. _Lond._ 1895. 8°.
010663. i. 12.

THIRION (H.) La Vie privée des Financiers au XVIIIe siècle. pp. 531. _Paris_, 1895. 8°.
08226. i. 6.

TORNEZY (A.) Un Bureau d'esprit au XVIIIe siècle. Le salon de Madame Geoffrin. pp. 274. _Paris_, 1895. 8°.   012356. i. 7.

DU BLED (V.) La Société française avant et après 1789. pp. 337. _Paris_, 1892. 12°. 9230. c. 16.

CASTERAS (P. de) La Société toulousaine à la fin du 18e siècle. pp. 363. _Toulouse_, 1891. 8°.
010171. e. 8.

YOUNG (A.) Travels in France, 1787-89. pp. 366. 1889. 8°. Bohn's Standard Library.
2504. i.

—— Voyages en France. 2 tom. _Paris_, 1882. 8°.   010171. g. 11.

NOTELLE (L.) The French Peasantry since the Revolution. pp. 64. _Birmingham_, 1892. 8°.
8275. aa. 57.

SWINBURNE (H.) The Courts of Europe at the close of the last century. 2 vol. _Lond._ 1895. 8°.
10600. f. 2.

BERTIN (E.) La Société du Consulat et de l'Empire. pp. 344. _Paris_, 1890. 8°. 9226. bb. 34.

BOUCHOT (H.) Le Luxe français. L'Empire. pp. 214. _Paris_, 1892. 8°.   K.T.C. 6. b. 13.

BROC (H. de) _Viscount._ La Vie en France sous le premier Empire. pp. 524. _Paris_, 1895. 8°.
9231. l. 4.

MAZE-SENCIER (A.) Les Fournisseurs de Napoléon Ier. pp. 367. _Paris_, 1893. 8°. 7743. e. 9.

GRAND-CARTERET (J.) XIXe siècle. Classes—mœurs—usages—costumes—inventions. pp. 774. _Paris_, 1893. 8°.   K.T.C. 11. b. 12.

BOUCHOT (H.) Le Luxe français. La Restauration. pp. 324. _Paris_, 1893. 4°.
K.T.C. 1. b. 14.

FRANCE. Manners and customs of the French. 1815. pp. 43. _Lond._ 1893. 8°. 12350. g. 23.

UZANNE (O.) La Française du siècle. pp. 246. _Paris_, 1892. 8°.   7742. de. 27.

AYNARD (T.) Les Salons d'autrefois. 1828-48. pp. 31. _Lyon_, 1887. 8°.   12352. g. 34.

SICHEL (E.) Story of two Salons. pp. 320. _Lond._ 1895. 8°.   010663. h. 10.

ENGLISHMAN. An Englishman in Paris. 2 vol. _Lond._ 1892. 8°.   9231. f. 4.

LANO (P. de) Les Bals travestis et les tableaux vivants sous le Second Empire. pp. 99. _Paris_, 1893. 8°.   K.T.C. 11. b. 11.

VENTO (C.) Les Salons de Paris en 1889. pp. 425. _Paris_, 1891. 12°.   10169. aaa. 3.

BOUCARD (M.) La Vie de Paris. pp. 375. _Paris_, 1892. 8°.   10171. de. 4.

EDWARDS (M. B.) France of to-day. 2 vol. _Lond._ 1892, 94. 8°.   10168. f. 24.

FRANCE. Frankreich an der Zeitwende. pp. 379. _Hamburg_, 1895. 8°.   10174. bb. 29.

GIRAUDEAU (F.) Les Vices du jour et les vertus d'autrefois. pp. 294. _Paris_, 1891. 8°.
8409. cc. 12.

HAMON (A. F.) and BACHOT (G.) L'Agonie d'une société. pp. 346. _Paris_, 1894. 8°.
8228. aaaa. 13.

MAGUÉ (A.) La France bourgeoise actuelle. pp. 279. _Paris_, 1892. 12°.   8051. de. 14.

MANSUY (É.) La Misère en France à la fin du XIXe siècle. pp. 303. _Paris_, 1889. 12°. 8285. b. 59.

FRANCE.—Social Life—*continued.*

PARIS NOTE-BOOK. My Paris Note-Book.
pp. 384. *Lond.* 1894. 8°.   010171. k. 12.

TUCKLEY (H.) In Sunny France: present-day
life. pp. 249. *Cincinnati*, 1894. 8°.
                                  010168. e. 3.

UZANNE (O.) La Femme à Paris. pp. 328.
Paris, 1894. 4°.   K.T.C. 28. b. 1.

VANDAM (A. D.) French Men and French manners. pp. 305. *Lond.* 1895. 8°. 010171. e. 24.

See also COSTUME : INVENTORIES : PARIS : SOCIAL
SCIENCE, *etc., etc.*
    Taxation. *See infra* : TRADE.

Topography.

Geographies : Guide Books, etc.

AC. Paris. *Société de l'Art français.* La France
artistique, *etc. Paris*, 1892, *etc.* 4°.   1755. g.

DUBOIS (M.) Géographie de la France. pp. 645.
Paris, 1892. 8°.   10025. cc. 26.

GASQUET (A.) Géographie de la France.
pp. 444. *Paris*, 1892. 8°.   10024. aa. 23.

GINDRE DE MANCY (J. B.) Dictionnaire des
Communes de la France. pp. 783.
Paris, 1890. 32°.   10171. aa. 22.

GOURDAULT (J.) La France pittoresque.
pp. 478. *Paris*, 1893. 4°. !   10172. i. 9.

LALANNE (E.) La France et ses colonies.
pp. 380. *Paris*, 1893. 4°.   10026. m. 3.

LEROY (A. L.) Géographie de la France.
pp. 406. *Paris*, 1890. 8°.   10004. dd. 4.

LEVASSEUR (É.) La France. Géographie et statistique. 2 tom. *Paris*, 1890. 8°. 10168. ccc. 26.

MAILHOL (D. de) Dictionnaire géographique des
Communes. pp. 796. *Paris*, 1890. 4°.
                                  10172. i. 6.

MEYRAT (J.) Dictionnaire des Communes de
France. pp. 721. *Tours*, 1895. 8°. 10174. c. 18.

NIOX (G. L.) Géographie. La France. pp. 433.
Paris, 1893. 8°.   10168. cc. 35.

PARIS. *Association de Topographie.* Annuaire.
pp. 407. *Paris*, 1891. 8°.   10171. c. 6.

———

BERTOT (J.) Guides du cycliste en France.
De Paris à Bordeaux, *etc.* pp. 131.
Paris, 1895. 16°.   10174. a. 26.

—— De Paris à Grenoble, Lyon et Marseille.
pp. 185. *Paris*, 1895. 12°.   10174. a. 25.

BRIMONT (de) *Count*, and GIBERT (F.) Dictionnaire routier de France.
pp. 349. *Paris*, 1894. 8°.   10174. b. 38.

FRANCE. Murray's Handbook for Travellers in
France. 2 vol. *Lond.* 1892. 8°.   2364. a. 14.

MARTIN (A.) Les Étapes d'un touriste en France.
pp. 317. *Paris*, 1890. 8°.   10174. aa. 35.

RICHARD. Guide du voyageur en France. 5 pt.
Paris, 1890. 8°.   10168. cc. 26.

    Travels.

AMÉRO (C.) Le Tour de France d'un petit
Parisien. pp. 795. *Paris*, 1890. 4°. 10172. f. 8.

ARDOUIN-DUMAZET (V. E.) Voyage en France.
Paris, 1893, *etc.* 8°.   10169. c. 19.

BARKER (E. H.) Wayfaring in France. pp. 431.
Lond. 1890. 8°.   010171. h. 32.

BLASCO (E.) Recuerdos. Notas de Francia, *etc.*
pp. 241. *Madrid*, 1894. 8°.   12354. de. 22.

EDWARDS (M. B.) France of to-day. 2 vol.
Lond. 1892, 94. 8°.   10168. f. 24.

FRANCE. Across France in a caravan from Bordeaux to Genoa. pp. 408. *Edinb.* 1892. 8°.
                                  010171. g. 10.

GUBERNATIS (A. de) La France. Lectures, *etc.*
pp. 293. *Florence*, 1891. 8°.   10174. g. 24.

FRANCE.—Topography—*continued.*

LAMI (E. O.) Voyages pittoresques et techniques
en France. pp. 547. *Paris*, 1892. 8°.
                                  10172. g. 8.

MIGEON (G.) Sac au Dos. Paysages et impressions. pp. 157. *Paris*, 1892. 8°.
                                  10171. dd. 4.

PENNELL (J.) and (E. R.) Our Sentimental
Journey through France. *Lond.* 1893. 8°.
                                  010168. e. 1.

TUCKLEY (H.) In Sunny France. pp. 249.
Cincinnati, 1894. 8°.   010168. e. 3.

VAGABOND. An Original Wager. pp. 318.
Lond. 1895. 8°.   07905. f. 40.

See also supra : *Antiquities* : *Social Life.*

    Coasts.

AC. Hamburg. *Norddeutsche Seewarte.* Segelhandbuch der französischen Westküste.
pp. 270. *Hamb.* 1894. 8°.   10496. aaa. 61.

FILOZ (N.) Les Mers de France. pp. 293.
Paris, 1894. 12°.   7005. aaa. 23.

TROUESSART (É. L.) Au Bord de la Mer. Géologie, faune et flore des côtes. pp. 344.
Paris, 1893. 8°.   7002. aa. 2.

VATTIER D'AMBROYSE (V.) Le Littoral de la
France. *Paris*, 1890, *etc.* 8°.   10172. f.

    Northern France.

BAEDEKER (C.) Northern France. pp. 411.'
Leipz. 1894. 8°.   2352. a.

JOANNE (P.) Itinéraire de la France. Le Nord.
pp. 416. *Paris*, 1890. 8°.   2362. a.

PASCOE (C. E.) Roads to Paris from London.
pp. 82. *Lond.* 1891. 8°.   10360. a. 12.

    Southern France.

BAEDEKER (C.) South-Eastern France. pp. 294.
Leipz. 1895. 8°.   10108. d. 18.

—— South-Western France. pp. 293.
Leipz. 1895. 8°.   10108. d. 19.

BLACK (C. B.) South of France. West half.
pp. 248. *Lond.* 1895. 8°.   10174. aa. 44.

COOK (T.) Handbook to health resorts of the
South of France. pp. 174. *Lond.* 1893. 8°.
                                  10174. aa. 38.

GOULD (S. B.) The Deserts of Southern France.
2 vol. *Lond.* 1894. 8°   010171. h. 41.

See also RIVIERA : SPORT : WATERING PLACES.

Trade : Finance : Taxation.

General : National Finances and Taxation.

BERTHAUT (A.) and AMIAUD (A.) Manuel des
certificats de propriété, et des opérations concernant les rentes sur l'État. pp. 480.
Paris, 1893. 8°.   8227. dd. 31.

BESSON (E.) Les livres fonciers et la réforme
hypothécaire. pp. 552. *Paris*, 1891. 8°.
                                  6825. c. 11.

BIDOIRE (P.) and SIMONIN (A.) Les Budgets
français. *Paris*, 1895, *etc.* 12°.   08226. f.

BONNEAUD (J. J.) Pétition aux deux Chambres
pour doter la France de un milliard. pp. 60.
Paris, 1890. 16°.   8277. a. 58. (2.)

COHEN (É.) Le Budget. pp. 310.
Paris, 1892. 12°.   08227. de. 15.

DUVAL (E.) Des Inconvénients de la limitation
légale du Taux de l'Intérêt. pp. 94.
Paris, 1892. 8°.   8226. cc. 54.

FRANCE. Les finances de la République.
Paris, 1889. fol.   8245. d. 3. (230.)

GORGES (J. M.) and BEZARD (V. A.) Manuel des
transferts et mutations de rentes sur l'État.
pp. 528. *Paris*, 1891. 8°.   08227. f. 24.

HUMBLOT (C.) Les Banqueroutes de la République. pp. 56. *Paris*, 1893. 8°.   Pam. 69.

FRANCE.—Trade, etc.—*continued.*

JOUBERT (A.) La conversion de la Rente.
pp. 23. *Paris*, 1893. 8°. 8227. i. 40. (S.)

LAPIERRE (W.) Les Finances opportunistes.
pp. 23. *Langres*, 1893. 8°. Pam. 23.

LEVERDAYS (E.) Les Causes de l'effondrement
économique. pp. 360. *Paris*, 1893. 12°.
8277. de. 46.

MARCILLAC (C. de) La Caisse centrale du Trésor
public. pp. 650. *Paris*, 1890. 8°. 08227. k. 19.

REMY (V. H. A.) Traité de la comptabilité
publique. pp. 623. *Paris*, 1894. 8°.
08227. k. 33.

ROBERT-COUTELLE (É.) Le Crédit foncier de
France jugé par lui-même. pp. 439.
Paris, 1890. 12°. 08227. e. 18.

ROCHE (J.) La Politique économique de la
France. pp. 382. *Paris*, 1894. 8°. 08207. f. 1.

ROUSSEN (L. de) Des Fissures du Budget. pp. 60.
Paris, 1892. 8°. 8228. aaaa. 19. (5.)

SAINT-ANDRÉ (J. A. de) La Question de monopoles. pp. 337. *Paris*, 1890. 8°. 08227. ee. 15.

SCHOTT (A.) Die französische Wehrsteuer nach
dem Gesetze vom 15 Juli 1889. pp. 128.
1892. 8°. ELSTER (L.) Staatswissenschaftliche
Studien. Bd. 4. 8207. h.

STOURM (R.) Le Budget. pp. 623.
Paris, 1891. 8°. 08227. g. 33.

TROLARD (E.) Mémoires d'un Inspecteur des
Finances. pp. 363. *Paris*, 1892. 8°.
08227. de. 28.

WORMS (É.) Doctrine, pratique et réforme
financière. pp. 401. *Paris*, 1891. 8°.
08227. h. 20.

—— Le Budget de la France. pp. 550.
Paris, 1893. 8°. 08227. i. 16.

COHEN (É.) Réformes dans le régime des impôts.
pp. 358. *Paris*, 1895. 8°. 08226. f. 21.

COURTRAY (L.) Les Impôts sur le luxe. pp. 196.
Paris, 1895. 8°. 08226. k. 8.

ISAURE-TOULOUSE ( ) Manuel des droits de
timbre, d'enregistrement, et d'hypothèques.
pp. 319. *Paris*, 1894. 12°. 5405. a. 4.

JOBIT (M.) Les Législations d'impôt. pp. 573.
Poitiers, 1893, 8°. 5424. df. 10.

LEHOUX (D.) L'Impôt : études budgétaires.
pp. 47. *Tours*, 1892. 8°. 8228. aaaa. 20. (5.)

LYON (C.) and TEISSIER (G.) Les Opérations de
Bourse et l'impôt du timbre. pp. 451.
Paris, 1894. 8°. 08226. f. 22.

MAGUÉRO (É.) Traité des droits d'enregistrement
de timbre et d'hypothèques. *Paris*, 1893, *etc.* 4°.
5424. f.

P.P. *Paris.* Revue de l'Enregistrement du
timbre et du domaine. *Paris*, 1894, *etc.* 8°.
P.P. 1362. d.

—— *La France Commerciale et Industrielle.*
Tarif général des Douanes. pp. 146.
Paris, 1892. 8°. P.P 1423. zg.

PLANTEAU (F. É.) La Réforme des impôts.
pp. 273. *Paris*, 1890. 18°. 8228. aaaa. 15.

ROCHE (J.) L'Impôt général sur le revenu.
pp. 48. *Paris*, 1894. 12°. 08226. f. 19.

GUYOT (Y.) La Suppression des octrois. pp. 72.
Paris, 1886. 12°. Pam. 23.

TRAMUSET (E.) La Réforme de l'octroi et l'impôt sur les boissons. pp. 219. *Paris*, 1892. 12°.
8228. c. 51.

VAGOGNE (M.) Recueil des instructions et lettres
sur les octrois 1809-91. *Abbeville*, 1891, *etc.* 8°.
08227. ee. 38.

For the Bank of France and the Caisse d'Épargne,
see Banking.

FRANCE.—Trade, etc. —*continued.*

Financial and Commercial History.

STOURM (R.) Bibliographie historique des
Finances de la France au 18° siècle. pp. 311.
Paris, 1895. 8°. 011900. h. 30.

BOUCHARD (L.) Système financier de l'ancienne
monarchie. pp. 502. *Paris*, 1891. 8°.
08227. ee. 30.

BESSON (E.) L'Enrégistrement et la ferme générale. pp. 102. *Paris*, 1893. 8°. 08229. k. 8.

JOUBERT (A.) Les Finances. La rente et
l'impôt : leur histoire. pp. 520.
Paris, 1893. 12°. 08226. f. 2.

PITON (C.) Les Lombards en France. pp. 259.
Paris, 1892. 8°. 8248. g. 14.

SPONT (A.) La gabelle du sel en Languedoc au
15° siècle. pp. 57. *Toulouse*, 1891. 8°. Pam. 23.

ATHANAS'EV (G.) Le Commerce des céréales en
France au 18° siècle. pp. 576. *Paris*, 1894. 8°.
8227. i. 41.

MALON (B.) L'Agiotage de 1715 à 1870.
pp. 62. *Paris*, 1885. 8°. 8275. i. 5.

BOINET (H.) Le Budget départemental. Essai
sur son histoire. *Lanniou*, 1890. 8°.
08227. ee. 28.

MARCÉ (V.) La comptabilité publique pendant
la Révolution. pp. 94. *Paris*, 1893. 8°.
08227. h. 40.

XAU (F.) La Question des Huissiers. Le tarif de
1807. pp. 314. *Paris*, 1890. 18°. 8229. aaa. 44.

CALMON (A.) Histoire parlementaire des finances
de la Monarchie de juillet. *Paris*, 1895, *etc.* 8°.
08229. df.

DEVERS (A.) La Politique commerciale de la
France depuis 1860. 1892. 8°. Ac. *Leipsic.*
Verein für Socialpolitik. Schriften. No. 51.
Bd. 3. Ac. 2322.

RENAUD (F.) Discours. Les Finances de la
France pendant la guerre, 1870-71. pp. 59.
Paris, 1894. 8°. Pam. 23.

—— Discours du développement des dépenses
publiques en France depuis 1870. pp. 62.
Paris, 1890. 8°. 8226. ff. 33. (7.)

CUCHEVAL-CLARIGNY (A.) Les Finances de la
France, 1870-91. pp. 492. *Paris*, 1891. 8°.
08227. f. 23.

BOURBON (P.) Commentaire des chiffres sur la
Rançon de la France en 1871. pp. 74.
Le Vésinet, 1889. 8°. Pam. 23.

Public Works.

HENRY (E.) Les formes des enquêtes administra-
tives en matière de travaux publics. pp. 166.
Paris, 1891. 8°. 5406. e. 2.

RAMEL (E. de) and LOISON (E.) Travaux
Publics, occupation temporaire et extraction de
matériaux. pp. 106. *Paris*, 1893. 12°.
5424. b. 17.

Trade.

CHICAGO. *Columbian Exposition.* Section française. Catalogue officiel. pp. 255.
Paris, 1893. 8°. 7958. h. 32.

COQUEUGNIOT (E.) L'Avocat des commerçants
et des industriels. *Paris*, 1892. 8°. 5405. de. 5.

DEVILLE (V.) Manuel de géographie commerciale. 2 tom. *Paris*, 1893. 8°. 10004. i. 5.

FRANCE. *Direction des Douanes.* Tableau
général du commerce de la France, 1892.
pp. 796. *Paris*, 1893. 4°. 8225. g. 29.

—— *Ministère des Travaux Publics.* Album de
Statistique graphique, 1889. *Paris*, 1890. 4°.
8223. f. 30.

—— *Ministère des Affaires étrangères.* Conférence monétaire entre la Belgique, la France,
la Grèce, l'Italie et la Suisse en 1893. pp. 131.
Paris, 1894. fol. 8228. i. 77.

FRANCE.—Trade, etc.—*continued*.

LAFFAILLE (J.) Hypothécation. Moyen d'augmenter la fortune publique et particulière. pp. 100. *Paris*, 1891. 8°.   08227. k. 30.

LOQUES (P.) and DELEAU (E.) Le Commerce extérieur de la France et la concurrence dans l'Amérique latine et les Antilles. pp. 31. *Paris*, 1886. 8°.   Pam. 23.

P.P. *Havre-de-Grâce*. Annuaire de la Marine de commerce. *Havre*, 1890, *etc.* 8°. P.P. 2406. ia.

RAVALOVICH (A.) Le Marché financier en 1892. pp. 174. *Paris*, 1893. 8°.   8225. eee. 48.

VIBERT (E. C. P.) La Concurrence étrangère. Industries parisiennes. Politique coloniale. pp. 485. *Paris*, 1887. 8°.   8246. eee. 19.

XAU (F.) La Question des huissiers. Les affaires commerciales. pp. 314. *Paris*, 1890. 18°.   8229. aaa. 44.

See also Supra: Colonies: CAPITAL AND LABOUR: BANKING: LAW, *Commercial:* MONEY: PANAMA: TRADE.

FRANCHE - COMTÉ.

FRANCHE-COMTÉ. Notes pour servir à la bibliographie franc-comtoise. 2 pt. *Vesoul*, 1889, 90. 8°. 011902. g. 38.

ESTIGNARD (A.) Le parlement de Franche-Comté, 1674-1790. *Paris*, 1892, *etc.* 8°. 5406. de.

LURION (R. de) Notice sur la Chambre des comptes de Dole. pp. 322. *Besançon*, 1892. 8°.   08227. g. 40.

LAMBERT (M.) Les Fédérations en Franche-Comté et la fête du 14 juillet 1790. pp. 116. *Paris*, 1890, 8°.   9231. dd. 2.

GAUTHIER (J.) Dictionnaire des Artistes franc-comtois antérieurs au XIXᵉ siècle. pp. 24. *Besançon*, 1892. 8°.   Pam. 24.

PANÇA (S.) La Franche-Comté de M. Bouchot. pp. 17. *Dole*, 1890. 8°.   Pam. 15.

PERRON (A.) Les Franc-Comtois. pp. 198. *Besançon*, 1892. 8°.   010171. g. 14.

SICARD (J.) Franche-Comté. pp. 157. *Besançon*, 1895. fol.   1789. d. 4.

See also BESANÇON: BURGUNDY: DOLE: JURA.

FRANCISCAN ORDER.

LE MONNIER (L.) History of S. Francis of Assisi. pp. 524. *Lond.* 1894. 8°.   4829. f. 7.

ALVAREZ LUGIN (R.) Catalogus Superiorum min. observant. provinciæ Tusciæ. pp. 85. *Ad Claras Aquas*, 1892. 8°.   4783. bbb. 33.

METS (B.) Geschiedenis van de orde der Minderbroeders. pp. 256. *Gent*, 1893. 8°. 04785. k. 14.

HUETTEBRAEUKER (O.) Der Minoritenorden zur Zeit des grossen Schismas. pp. 93. *Berl.* 1895. 8°.   Pam. 25.

WEARE (G. E.) Collectanea relating to the Bristol Friars Minors. pp. 111. *Bristol*, 1893. 8°.   4707. e. 24.

Ac. Oxford. *Historical Society*. LITTLE (A. G.) The Grey Friars in Oxford. pp. 369. *Oxf.* 1892. 8°.   Ac, 8126/12.

STONE (J. M.) Faithful unto Death. Sufferings of English Franciscans during the 16th and 17th centuries. pp. 260. *Lond.* 1892. 8°. 4707. cc. 11.

MARCELLINO and DOMENICHELLI (T.) Epistolae missionariorum Ordinis S. Francisci ex Frisia et Hollandia. pp. 403. *Ad Claras Aquas*, 1888. 8°.   4685. h. 8.

ALENÇON (É. d.) Martyrologe des frères mineurs pendant la Révolution, 1792-1800. pp. 47. *Paris*, 1892. 8°.   4804. c. 33. (10.)

APOLLINAIRE, *de Valence*. Études franciscaines sur la Révolution dans l'Isère. 1893. 8°. Ac. GRENOBLE. *Acad. Delphinale*. Bulletin. Sér. 4. Tom. 6.   Ac. 340.

FRANCISCAN ORDER—*continued*.

APOLLINAIRE, *de Valence*. Études franciscaines sur la Révolution dans Vaucluse. pp. 84. *Avignon*, 1895. 8°.   4629. f. 34.

SPILA (B.) Memorie storiche della Provincia riformata romana. *Roma*, 1890, *etc.* 8°. 4782. dd.

SURREL DE SAINT-JULIEN (H. de) Le Père J. Aréso, Restaurateur des franciscains. pp. 312. *Montreuil*, 1892. 8°.   4866. h. 20.

HAMMER (B.) Die Franciscaner in den Vereinigten Staaten Nordamerica's. pp 143. *Köln*, 1892. 8°.   4744. f. 27.

GRÈZES (H. de) Le Sacré-Cœur. Études franciscaines. pp. 396. *Lyon*, 1890. 12°.   4223. aa. 21.

MARIOTTI (C.) Il Laterano e l'ordine francescano. pp. 158. *Roma*, 1893. 8°. 4782. h. 23.

ROME, *Church of*. Leo XIII., *Pope*. Di San Francesco d'Assisi e della propagazione del terz' ordine francescano. Lettera Enciclica. pp. 31. *Brescia*, 1882. 16°.   Pam. 25.

EZERVILLE (F. J. d') Le Tiers-ordre de Saint François. pp. 36. *Lille*, 1887. 32°.   Pam. 25.

FRANCISCANS. Abridgement of the rule of the Third Order of St. Francis. pp. 32. *Bombay*, 1883. 16°.   Pam. 25.

GRECCIO (P. B. da) Il Terz' Ordine di San Francesco d'Assisi secondo la costituzione di Leone XIII. pp. 304. *Quaracchi*, 1888. 8°.   4071. bbb. 26.

See also CAPUCHINS: RELIGIOUS ORDERS.

FRANCO-GERMAN WAR.

See GERMAN FRENCH WAR.

FRANKFORT-ON-THE-MAIN.

BATTENBERG (F. W.) Die Peterskirche zu Frankfurt. pp. 338. *Leipz.* 1895. 8°.   4662. b. 3.

COLLISCHONN (P.) Frankfurt im schmalkaldischen Kriege. pp. 108. *Strassburg*, 1890. 8°.   9327. d. 8.

ELKAN (E.) Das frankfurter Gewerberecht von 1617-1631. pp. 183. *Tübingen*, 1890. 8°.   5604. ccc. 24.

KRACAUER (I.) Frankfurt und die französische Republik 1795-97. 1891. 8°. Ac. Frankfurt. *Gesellschaft für Frankfurts Geschichte. Archiv.* Folge 3. Bd. 3.   Ac. 7049.

KOCH (H. H.) Das Dominikanerkloster zu Frankfurt, 13 bis 16 Jahrhundert. pp. 166. *Freiburg*, 1892. 8°.   4662. e. 16.

SCHMIDT-SCHARFF (W.) Die Wallservitut in Frankfurt. pp. 152. *Frankf.* 1894. 8°.   05604. k. 6.

WOLFF (C.) Der Kaiserdom in Frankfurt. pp. 150. *Frankf.* 1892. 8°.   7814. ee. 19.

ZIEGLER (J.) Storchnester in Frankfurt. 1893. 8°. Ac. Frankfort. *Senckenbergische Naturforschende Gesellschaft.* Bericht, 1893.   Ac. 2878-3.

FRAUD: CHEATING.

HASTINGS (S.) Short treatise on the Law relating to Fraud and misrepresentation. pp. 133. *Lond.* 1893. 8°.   6325. cc. 23.

MONCREIFF (*Hon.* F. C.) Treatise on the Law relating to Fraud and misrepresentation. pp. 614. *Lond.* 1891. 8°.   6325. c. 23.

ARGUS. L'Étouffage pratiqué par caissiers et croupiers de certains cercles. pp. 50. *Paris*, 1893. 8°.   Pam. 83.

DUCRET (E.) Le Charlatanisme dévoilé. pp. 319. *Paris*, 1892. 12°.   012330. f. 42.

REUSCHEL (R.) Knights of Industry. Revelations about foreign long-firms in London. pp. 280. *Lond.* 1895. 8°.   6057. a. 44.

FREEDOM.

See LIBERTY.

FREEMASONRY.

Bibliography.

BAIN (G. W.) Catalogue of Masonic Books, engravings, etc. in possession of G. W. Bain. pp. 39. *Sunderland*, 1893. 8°.   Pam. 25.

FREEMASONS. Catalogue of Works on Freemasonry. pp. 65. *Lond.* 1891. 8°.   011900. f. 9. (8.)

HUGHAN (W. J.) Histories of Lodges, England. Bibliography. pp. 20. *Lond.* 1892. 8°. Pam. 25.

WHYMPER (H. J.) Catalogue of Bibliographies on Freemasonry. pp. 16. 1891. 4°.
       11901. g. 33. (3.)

WIGAN. *Public Library.* Works relating to Freemasonry. pp. 64. *Wigan*, 1892. 8°.
       011902. i. 11.

Ceremonies: Controversy: General History.

BOIS (G.) Maçonnerie du Grand-Orient de France. pp. 521. *Paris*, 1892. 8°. 04785. k. 1.

BOOS (H.) Geschichte der Freimaurerei. pp. 308. *Aarau*, 1894. 8°.   04785. k. 17.

BOUCHEZ (E.) Francs-maçons septembriseurs. pp. 136. *Paris*, 1892. 8°.   04785. k. 7.

BROUWERS (A.) L'Action de la Franc-maçonnerie dans l'histoire moderne. pp. 172. *Liège*, 1892. 8°.   04785. m. 2.

BRUDER. Pfarrer und Freimaurer. pp. 23. *Budapest*, 1890. 8°.   4783. a. 34. (3.)

COPIN-ALBANCELLI (P.) La Question franc-maçonnique devant les électeurs. pp. 31. *Paris*, 1893. 8°.   Pam. 25.

—— La Franc-maçonnerie et la question religieuse. pp. 235. *Paris*, 1892. 8°. 04785. h. 1.

CROWE (F. J. W.) Master Mason's Handbook. pp. 77. *Lond.* 1890. 8°.   4785. cc. 40.

—— Scottish Master Mason's handbook. pp. 72. *Lond.* 1894. 8°.   4785. cc. 41.

—— Irish Master Mason's handbook. pp. 95. *Lond.* 1895. 8°.   4782. e. 5.

DALMEDICO (A.) La Massoneria e la repubblica di Venezia. pp. 28. 1891. 8°.   Pam. 25.

DAYMONAZ (B.) Le Décalogue et la Franc-maçonnerie. pp. 78. *Paris*, 1889. 8°.
       4783. c. 59. (11.)

ESTOC (M. d') Les Jésuites rouges de la Franc-maçonnerie. pp. 316. *Paris*, 1894. 12°.
       4782. c. 4.

FINDEL (J. G.) Dunkle Punkte im Maurerleben. pp. 116. *Leipz.* 1892. 8°.   4784. e. 56.

FREEMASONS. History of the Fraternity of Free and Accepted Masons. pp. 904. *Bost.* 1891. 8°.
       04785. m. 7.

—— Perfect ceremonies of Craft Masonry. pp. 152. *Lond.* 1884. 8°.   4785. cc. 14.

—— Etiquette of Freemasonry. pp. 281. *Lond.* 1890. 8°.   4784. aa. 46.

—— Una setta infernale. pp. 68. *Torino*, 1893. 8°.   Pam. 25.

HALL (W. E.) Freemasonry: its origin, nature and relation to Religion. pp. 15. *Dumfries*, 1895. 8°.   Pam. 25.

L., D. New Year's gift to the Pope; or, the Freemasons vindicated. pp. 56. *York*, 1882. 8°.
       Pam. 25.

LANGLEY (W. C.) Lecture on the Great Pyramid, suggesting a relationship with the foundation of Freemasonry. pp. 36. *Stockton*, 1890. 8°.
       Pam. 25.

LEONI (L.) La Massoneria e le annessioni degli Stati Pontificii. 3 vol. *Viterbo*, 1892, 93. 8°.
       04785. k. 10.

LEITH (J.) Origin and purpose of Freemasonry. pp. 8. *Lond.* 1893. 8°.   Pam. 25.

MEURIN (L.) La Franc-maçonnerie. Synagogue de Satan. pp. 556. *Paris*, 1893. 8°. 04785. k. 8.

FREEMASONRY. — Ceremonies, etc.—
continued.

PAPILLAUD (A.) Les Crimes maçonniques. pp. 273. *Paris*, 1891. 12°.   10659. cc. 29.

RIVAL ( ) Le Drame contemporain. pp. 471. *Paris*, 1891. 12°.   4785. cc. 22.

ROMAIN (G.) Le Péril franc-maçon. pp. 42. *Paris*, 1895. 12°.   3900. c. 35.

ROSEN (P.) L'Ennemie Sociale. Histoire de la Franc-maçonnerie. pp. 428. *Paris*, 1890. 8°.
       4782. f. 7.

ROUSTAN (H. J. F.) À bas les Franc-maçons comme compromettant notre alliance avec la Russie. pp. 40. *Paris*, 1894. 8°. Pam. 69.

SPETH (G. W.) Royal Freemasons. pp. 75. *Phila.* 1885. 16°.   4783. a. 32. (5.)

STEVENS (J.) Evolution of Symbolic Masonry. pp. 84. *Lond.* 1892. 8°.   4785. cc. 37.

TAUTE (R.) Die katholische Geistlichkeit und die Freimaurerei. pp. 94. *Leipz.* 1895. 8°.
       4785. cc. 45.

TAXIL (L.) Pie IX. Franc-maçon? pp. 140. *Paris*, 1892. 8°.   4856. c. 14.

X. La Iglesia y la Masoneria. pp. 218. *Valencia*, 1890. 8°.   4785. cc. 30.

CLARIN DE LA RIVE (A.) La Femme et l'enfant dans la maçonnerie. pp. 746. *Paris*, 1894. 8°.
       04785. k. 11.

TAXIL (L.) Y a-t-il des femmes dans la Franc-maçonnerie? pp. 404. *Paris*, 1891. 8°.
       4782. k. 13.

—— Les Sœurs maçonnes. pp. 388. *Paris*, 1895. 8°.   4785. bbb. 56.

Charitable Institutions.

FREEMASONS. *Royal Masonic Institution for Girls.* Pocket booklet of the Institution. *Lond.* 1893. 32°.   Pam. 25.

TYSON (J. H.) Masonic charities of West Lancashire. pp. 5. *Liverp.* 1889. 8°.
       4783. c. 59. (12.)

History of Freemasonry in various countries, and of separate Lodges.

FREEMASONS. *South African Lodges.* S. African Freemason's Directory. *Cape Town*, 1892, etc. 8°.   P.P. 2579. q.

P.P. *Cape Town.* South African Masonic record. *Cape Town*, 1893, etc. 4°.   P.P. 1069.

ABAFI (L.) Geschichte der Freimaurerei in Oesterreich-Ungarn. 2 Bde. *Budapest*, 1890, 91. 8°.
       4782. g.

ERBRÉE (J. d') La Maçonnerie canadienne-française. pp. 189. *Quebec*, 1893. 8°. 4785. a. 28.

—— La Franc-maçonnerie dans la province de Quebec. pp. 276. *Ottawa*, 1883. 12°.
       4784. bbb. 47.

GRAHAM (J. H.) History of Freemasonry in the province of Quebec. pp. 645. *Montreal*, 1892. 8°.
       04785. m. 1.

MAC CALLA (C. P.) Freemasonry in America. pp. 23. *Phila.* 1890. 8°.   Pam. 25.

PHILADELPHIA. *St. John's Lodge.* Phototypes from Liber B. of St. John's Lodge, Philadelphia. *Phila.* 1884. fol.   Pam. 25.

ROBERTSON (J. R.) The Cryptic Rite in Canada and the United States. pp. 253. *Toronto*, 1888. 8°.   04785. k. 12.

MAMOZ (D.) Histoire de la Franc-maçonnerie à Angoulême au XVIIIe siècle. pp. 40. *Angoulême*, 1888. 8°.   4783. c. 59. (10.)

BROECKER (C.) Die Freimaurer-Logen Deutschlands. pp. 195. *Berl.* 1894. 8°. 04785. m. 6.

CONDER (E.) Records of the hole Crafte and fellowship of Masons. pp. 312. *Lond.* 1894. 8°.   8248. i. 5.

FREEMASONRY. — History of Free-masonry, etc.—*continued.*

FREEMASONS. Masonic Records 1717–1894. England. pp. 544. *Lond.* 1895, 4°.   4784. h. 9.

—— Reminiscences of twenty-six years of Freemasonry. pp. 50. *Lond.* 1890. 8°. 4782. g. 19.

—— *Prince of Wales's Lodge.* List of Members from the time of its constitution, *etc.* pp. 103. *Lond.* 1890. 8°.   4785. cc. 31.

—— *Shadwell Clerke Lodge.* List of Members. *Lond.* 1892. 8°.   4784. bbb. 48.

LANE (J.) Centenary Warrants and jewels: comprising an account of the Lodges under the Grand Lodge of England. pp. 126.
Lond. 1891. 8°.   4782. c. 6.

MARTIN (L.) L'Angleterre et la Franc-Maçonnerie. pp. 436. *Paris,* 1894. 12°. 4785. d. 34.

NEWTON (J.) History of the Lodge of Sincerity, No. 174. pp. 126. *Lond.* 1888. 8°. 04785. m. 8.

RILEY (J. R.) Masonic Certificates: notes and illustrations. pp. 85. 1895. 4°. FREEMASONS. *Lodge Quatuor Coronati.* Quatuor Coronatorum Antigrapha. Vol. 8.   4784. h. 6.

HOPE (A.) History of St. John the Baptist Lodge, Exeter. pp. 135. *Exeter,* 1894. 8°.   4785. cc. 43.

ABBOTT (G. B.) History of Freemasonry in Hertfordshire. pp. 467. *Lond.* 1893. 8°.   4782. g. 32.

HUGHAN (W. J.) Royal Arch chapters in Kent. *Torquay,* 1892. s. sh. 8°.   Pam. 25.

SCARTH (A.) and BRAIM (C. A.) History of the Lodge of Fidelity. pp. 240. *Leeds,* 1894. 8°.   4785. g. 45.

BROWN (R.) Combermere Lodge of Union. pp. 74. *Macclesfield,* 1893. 8°.   4782. f. 15.

HOWELL (A.) History of the Phœnix Lodge, Chapter of Friendship, and Royal Naval Preceptory of Knights Templar. pp. 273. *Portsmouth,* 1894. 4°.   1880. b. 28.

HUGHAN (W. J.) Sketch of the Chapter of Friendship, Portsmouth. pp. 7. 1890. 8°.   Pam. 25.

CHAPMAN (J.) History of St. John's Lodge, Torquay. pp. 32. *Lond.* 1894. 8°. Pam. 25.

RILEY (J. R.) The Yorkshire Lodges. pp. 119. *Leeds,* 1885. 4°.   4785. i. 14.

HUGHAN (W. J.) Histories of Lodges, Scotland. pp. 4. *Glasg.* 1892. 8°.   Pam. 25.

LEON (E. X.) History of the Royal Lodge, Kingston, Jamaica. pp. 46. *Jamaica,* 1894. 8°.   Pam. 25.

TIRADO Y ROJAS (M.) La Masoneria en España. 2 tom. *Madrid,* 1892–93. 8°.   4782. e. 3.

FREEMASONS. *Grande Oriente Nacional de Venezuela.* Folleto del Grande Oriente nacional de Venezuela. pp. 164. *Carácas,* 1894. 8°.   04785. k. 16.

Reproductions of MSS. and Reprints of Books.

FREEMASONS. Grand Lodge No 1, Manuscript roll of the old constitutions. *Margate,* 1893. fol.   Tab. 11747. c. 2.

—— Grand Lodge No. 2, Manuscript roll of the old constitutions. *Lond.* 1893. fol.   Tab. 11747. c. 3.

—— "Buchanan" Manuscript roll of the old constitutions. *Lond.* 1893. fol. Tab. 11747. c. 1.

—— Reproduction of the "Clapham Masonic MS." of the 17th century. pp. 14.
Leeds, 1892. 8°.   Pam. 25.

EMBLETON (T. W.) Old charges of British Freemasons. "T. W. Embleton" Masonic MS. pp. 20. *Leeds,* 1893. 8°.   Pam. 25.

FREEMASONRY. — Reproductions of MSS., and Reprints of Books—*continued.*

HUGHAN (W. J.) Old charges, including reproduction of the "Haddon Manuscript." pp. 191. *Lond.* 1895. 8°.   04785. k. 22.

—— The "Hope," "Waistell" and "Probity" Masonic MSS. pp. 31. *Leeds,* 1892. 8°. Pam. 25.

FREEMASONS. The Newcastle College roll, D. 37. pp. 11. 14. 14. 12. *Newcastle,* 1894. 4°. 4783. e. 20.

—— Scarborough Manuscript Roll of the old constitutions. *Margate,* 1894. fol.
Tab. 11747. c. 4.

—— Reproduction of the "Stanley-Masonic MS." pp. 18. *Leeds,* 1893. 8°.   Pam. 25.

TEW (T. W.) Reproduction of the "T. W. Tew Masonic MS. pp. 18. *Leeds,* 1892. 8°. Pam. 25.

FREEMASONS. Reproduction of the "W. Watson MS." pp. 20. 1891. 8°.   Pam. 25.

—— The W. Watson Manuscript roll. Facsimile. *Margate,* 1891.   Tab. 11747. c. 5.

ANDERSON (J.) New Book of constitutions. 1738. pp. 230. 1890. 8°. FREEMASONS. *Lodge Quatuor Coronati.* Quartuor Coronatorum Antigraphia. Vol. 7.   4784. h. 6.

FREEMASONS. R. Holme's Academie of Armory, Dr. Plot's Staffordshire, Diary of Elias Ashmole, *etc.* pp. 26. *Calcutta,* 1892. 8°.   04785. h. 2.

HUGHAN (W. J.) Reprints of articles on the constitutions of Freemasonry. pp. 31. 1889. 8°.   Pam. 25.

PRESTON (W.) Reprint of the 1772 edition of W. P.'s Illustrations of Masonry. pp. 11. 264. *Lond.* 1887. 12°.   4785. cc. 19.

FREE TRADE. *See* TRADE.

FREE-WILL. *See* LIBERTY.

FREEZING MACHINERY. — *See* REFRIGERATION.

FREIBURG, in the Breisgau. Ac. Freiburg. *Städtische Archivcommission.* POINSIGNON (A.) Geschichtliche Ortsbeschreibung der Stadt Freiburg. *Freiburg,* 1891, *etc.* 8°. Ac. 7055.

HANSJAKOB (H.) St. Martin zu Freiburg. pp. 206. *Freiburg,* 1890. 8°. 4662. bbb. 23.

POINSIGNON (A.) Die Urkunden des hl. Geist-Spitals zu Freiburg. *Freiburg,* 1890, *etc.* 8°.   7688. f.

KOENIG (J.) Beiträge zur Geschichte der Universität Freiburg. 1893. 8°. Ac. Freiburg. *Kirchlich-historischer Verein.* Diöcesan-Archiv. Bd. 23.   Ac. 2025.

MAYER (H.) Geschichte der Universität Freiburg in der ersten Hälfte des XIX. Jahrhunderts. *Bonn,* 1892, *etc.* 8°.   8357. dd.

FRENCH LANGUAGE.
General.

BELLEROCHE (E.) French Terms and quotations. pp. 16. *Blackheath,* 1892. 16°. 12901. de. 12. (3.)

CASSAL (H. C. S.) State and prospects of the study of French in England. pp. 19.
Lond. 1885. 8°.   Pam. 17.

EGLI (G.) Wörter für den Unterricht in der französischen Sprache an Sekundarschulen. pp. 40. *Zürich,* 1893. 8°. 12901. bbb. 45. (3.)

Argot.

GABILLAUD (L.) Le Nouveau Dictionnaire d'Argot. pp. 7. *Paris,* 1893. 8°.
12901. bbb. 45. (4.)

KOSCHARTZ (E.) Les Parlers parisiens. pp. 147. *Paris,* 1893. 8°.   12950. cc. 30.

LARCHEY (L.) Nouveau supplément du Dictionnaire d'Argot. pp. 284. *Paris,* 1889. 12°.   2272. b. 13.

FRENCH.—Argot—*continued.*

LA RUE (J.) La Langue Verte. Dictionnaire d'Argot. pp. 186. *Paris*, 1894. 8°.
12952. de. 23.

PLOWERT (J.) Glossaire pour servir à l'intelligence des auteurs décadents et symbolistes. pp. 98. *Paris*, 1888. 12°. 12954. d. 23.

SAINT CYR. L'Argot de Saint-Cyr. pp. 71. *Paris*, 1893. 12°. 12954. a. 55.

TIMMERMANS (A.) L'Argot parisien. pp. 318. *Paris*, 1892. 8°. 12953. f. 25.

VILLATTE (C.) Parisismen. pp. 326. *Berlin*, 1890. 8°. 12952. e. 17.

VIRMAITRE (C.) Dictionnaire d'Argot fin-de-siècle. pp. 336. *Paris*, 1894. 12°. 12954. dd. 1.

Commercial French.

BALLY (S. E.) Manual of French commercial Correspondence. pp. 114. 1894. 8°. Methuen's Commercial Series. 08227. de.

CARROUÉ (P.) New book of commercial French. pp. 35. *Lond.* 1895. 8°. 12950. aaa. 48.

HOSSFELD (C.) and VATON (E.) Le Correspondant commercial francais-anglais. pp. 400. *Londres*, 1891. 16°. 10920. aa. 26.

THUM (R.) French commercial Dialogues. pp. 194. *Lond.* 1891. 8°. 12950. c. 38.

WOODHOUSE GROVE SCHOOL. French commercial Phrases. pp. 11. 1892. 4°. 12950. c. 34.

ZUELOW (R. v.) Lehrbuch der französischen Sprache für Post- und Telegraphenbeamte. pp. 246. 1890. 8°. Die Kunst der Polyglottie. Th. 27. 12902. c.

See also infra : Grammars.

Composition. *See infra:* TRANSLATION.

Conversation.

ANTOINE (A.) Lessons in colloquial French. pp. 93. *Lond.* 1892. 8°. 12954. ccc. 1.

BOOTH (H.) Railway journey to Switzerland, with French and English dialogues. pp. 109. *Lond.* 1891. 4°. 12952. de. 18.

BUÉ (B.) La Conversation en Classe à l'usage des jeunes filles. *Lond.* 1890, *etc.* 8°.
12952. df.

—— Easy French Dialogues. pp. 80. *Lond.* 1892. 8°. 12954. d. 28.

—— Faits et gestes de deux Écoliers en vacances, *Fr. and Eng.* pp. 86. *Lond.* 1895. 8°.
12950. b. 38.

DELINOTTE (L. P.) Mots et expressions les plus usités dans la conversation. *Dutch and Fr.* pp. 112. *Groningue*, 1891. 8°. 12953. e. 28.

HOSSFELD (C.) French Dialogues and idiomatic phrases. pp. 193. *Lond.* 1894. 8°. 12952. de. 24.

LADELL (H. R.) French conversation Sentences. pp. 62. *Lond.* 1893. 8°. 12954. d. 35.

PASSY (P.) Le Français parlé. Morceaux choisis. pp. 121. *Leipz.* 1892. 8°. 12950. cc. 21.

PELLISSIER (E.) Vivâ-Voce French class book. pp. 235. *Lond.* 1892. 8°. 12950. cc. 15.

STORM (J.) French Dialogues. pp. 218. *Lond.* 1892. 8°. 12954. d. 4.

SEIDEL (A.) Lehrbuch der französischen Umgangssprache. pp. 182. 1894. 8°. Die Kunst der Polyglottie. Th. 45. 12902. c.

SWAN (H.) Traveller's colloquial French. pp. 128. *Lond.* 1891. 8°. 12952. aaa. 56.

THUM (R.) French commercial Dialogues. pp. 194. *Lond.* 1891. 8°. 12950. c. 38.

VUILLARD (A.) and ARMSTRONG (P. J.) French-English vade-mecum. pp. 303. *Lond.* 1893. 8°.
12953. df. 25.

See also infra : GRAMMAR.

FRENCH—*continued.*

Dialects.

BEHRENS (D.) Bibliographie des Patois gallo-romans. pp. 255. 1893. 8°. KOERTING (G.) and KOSCHWITZ (E.) Französische Studien. N.F. Heft 1. 12950. i.

BRUNET (H.) Difficultés de l'orthographie résolues par la traduction en l'idiome d'Auvergne. pp. 15. *Fontainebleau*, 1890. 8°.
12901. ccc. 12. (4.)

BIGARNE (C.) Patois et locutions du Pays de Beaune. pp. 250. 21. *Beaune*, 1891. 8°.
12953. cc. 14.

COLINGE (J.) Encore 1000 Expressions vicieuses belges. pp. 30. *Namur*, 1892. 8°. Pam. 47.

LA LOJE (P. de) Glossaire du Bas Bèri, Indre. *Paris*, 1891, *etc.* 8°. 12954. g.

DUPLAN (A. P.) Patois de Bigorre. pp. 129. *Turbes*, 1891. 4°. 12952. i. 9.

THIBAULT (A.) Glossaire du Pays b'aisois. pp. 355. *Blois*, 1892. 8°. 12954. ff. 29.

KERBEUZEC (H. de) Locutions populaires du pays de Dol-en-Bretagne. 2 pt. *Rennes*, 1894. 8°. 12954. d. 49.

ROUSSEY (C.) Glossaire du parler de Bournois. pp. 415. *Paris*, 1894. 8°. 12953. h. 22.

LOGIE (T.) Phonology of the patois of Cachy. pp. 73. *Baltimore*, 1892. 8°. 12952. ee. 31.

DEVAUX (A.) De l'étude des patois du Haut-Dauphiné. 1890. 8°. Ac. Grenoble. *Académie Delphinale.* Bulletin. Sér. 4. Tom. 3. Ac. 340.

—— Essai sur la langue vulgaire du Haut-Dauphiné au moyen âge. 1892. 8°. Ac. Grenoble. *Académie Delphinale.* Bulletin. Sér. 4. Tom. 5. Ac. 340.

—— Essai sur la langue vulgaire du Dauphiné septentrional au moyen âge. pp. 520. *Paris*, 1892. 8°. 12950. d. 2.

LANUSSE (M.) De l'Influence du dialecte gascon sur la langue française xvᵉ. à xviiᵉ. siècles. pp. 470. *Paris*, 1893. 8°. 11852. h. 26.

PHILIPON (È.) Patois de la commune de Jujurieux. pp. 80. *Paris*, 1892. 8°.
12901. d. 35. (10.)

NIZIER DU PUITSPELU ( ) Essai de phonétique lyonnaise. pp. 144. *Lyon*, 1885. fol.
12953. i. 18.

—— Académie du Gourguillon. Le Littré de la Grand Côte. pp. 341. *Lyon*, 1895. 8°.
12953. g. 29.

VILLEFRANCHE (J. M.) Essai de grammaire du patois lyonnais. pp. 309. *Bourg*, 1891. 8°.
12950. e. 39.

DAGNET (A.) Le Patois manceau tel qu'il se parle entre Le Mans et Laval. pp. 180. *Laval*, 1891. 8°. 12953. g. 26.

PELLEGRINI (J.) Essai d'un dictionnaire niçois, français, italien. *Nice*, 1894, *etc.* 8°. 12942. cc.

MOISY (H.) Glossaire comparatif anglo-normand. *Caen*, 1889, *etc.* 8°. 12954. e.

PIAT (L.) Dictionnaire français-occitanien. *Montpellier*, 1893, *etc.* 8°. 12953. h. 18.

ÉVEILLÉ (A.) Glossaire saintongeais. pp. 408. *Paris*, 1887. 8°. 12954. ff. 30.

DURET (V.) Grammaire savoyarde. pp. 91. *Berl.* 1893. 8°. 12950. f. 36.

Ac. Le Puy. *Société d'Agriculture.* VINOLS DE MONTFLEURY (de) *Baron.* Vocabulaires patois vellavien-français. pp. 207. *Le Puy*, 1891. 8°. 12950. f. 34.

MARTELLIÈRE (P.) Glossaire du Vendômois. pp. 366. *Orléans*, 1893. 8°. 12953. f. 26.

See also CANADIAN DIALECT. *Infra: History, Old French :* PROVENÇAL LANGUAGE: WALLOONS.

FRENCH—*continued*.

Dictionaries.

Bos (A.) Glossaire de la Langue d'Oïl xiᵉ-xivᵉ siècles. pp. 466. *Paris*, 1891. 8°. 12954. g. 16.

Ac. Paris. *Société Philologique*. Dictionnaire de la Société filologique française. pp. 64.
Paris, 1894. 8°.   12953. h. 21.

Bescherelle (L. N.) Nouveau Dictionnaire de la langue française. pp. 1415.
Paris, 1891-94. 8°.   12952. f. 11.

Hatzfeld (A.) and Darmesteter (A.) Dictionnaire de la langue française du commencement du xviiᵉ siècle jusqu'à nos jours.
Paris, 1890, etc. 8°.   12953. i.

Littré (M. P. É.) Dictionnaire de la langue française. Supplément. pp. 375. 84.
Paris, 1892. 4°.   12952. i. 10.

Stappers (H.) Dictionnaire d'Etymologie française. pp. 959. *Paris*, 1893. 12°. 12950. df. 48.

Vincent (P.) Dictionnaire illustré; langue française. *Paris*, 1893. 8°. 12950. de. 14.

Ibrāhīm Jād. Dictionnaire français-arabe des termes judiciaires, et commerciaux. pp. 1589.
Alexandrie, 1894. 8°.   12903. f. 29.

Marcel (J. J.) Dictionnaire français-arabe des dialectes vulgaires. pp. 572. *Paris*, 1885. 8°.
012904. g. 6.

Yūsuf Ya'kūb Hubaish. Dictionnaire français-arabe. *Le Caire*, 1890, etc. 4°. 012904. k. 1.

Bailly ( ) Dictionnaire chinois-françois.
2 tom. *Saigon*, 1889. 4°. 12910. h. 20.

Dictionaries. Dictionnaire phonétique chinois-français. pp. 623. *Peking*, 1893. 4°.
12910. i. 23.

Billequin (A.) Dictionnaire français-chinois.
pp. 830. *Peking*, 1891. 4°. 12910. k. 15.

Dictionaries. Dictionnaire chinois-français de la langue mandarine. pp. 736. *Hongkong*, 1893. 8°.
12910. dd. 24.

Calisch (I. M.) and (N. S.) Nieuw fransch Woordenboek. 2 pt. *Arnhem*, 1893. 8°.
12950. e. 37.

Delinotte (L. P.) and Nolen (T.) Dictionnaire des idiotismes de la langue hollandaise et de la langue française. pp. 312. *Amsterd*. 1891. 8°.
12972. ccc. 1.

Gasc (F. E. A) Dictionary of the French and English Languages. pp. 1214. *Lond*. 1892. 8°.
2272. d. 2.

Jaeschke (R,) Nutt's conversation Dictionaries. English-French. pp. 490. *Lond*. 1892. 16°.
12953. b. 57.

Lallemand (H.) and Ludwig (A.) English and French Vocabulary. pp. 670. *Lond*. 1894. 16°.
12950. a. 53.

Spiers (A.) Nouveau Dictionnaire général anglais-français, etc. 2 pt. *Paris*, 1889. 4°.
12950. l. 1.

Davis (J. F.) French-English Vocabulary of less familiar words in E. Souvestre's Un Philosophe sous les Toits. pp. 75.
Lond. 1893, 8°.   12954. bb. 43.

Barrère (A. M. V.) Dictionary of English and French military terms. *Lond*. 1895, etc. 8°.
8823. h. 49.

Fletcher (J. J.) Pocket glossary of Technical Terms. French-English. pp. 203.
Lond. 1893, obl. 32°.   12954. a. 54.

Pirrie (W.) Technical Dictionary, French-English, of Sea Terms. pp. 354. *Lond*. 1895. 8°.
8806. a. 66.

Romagné (E.) Dictionnaire militaire français-allemand. pp. 176. *Paris*, 1894. 8°.
12962. f. 34.

FRENCH.—Dictionaries—*continued*.

Bailly (A.) Dictionnaire grec-français. pp 2227.
Paris, 1895. 8°.   12923. d. 31.

Kontopoulos (N.) Λεξικον Ἑλληνογαλλικον, etc.
pp. 1107. ἐν 'Αθηναις, 1889. 8°. 12924. cc. 20.

Benoist (L. E.) and Goelzer (H.) Nouveau Dictionnaire latin-français. pp. 1713.
Paris, 1893. 8°.   12933. i. 11.

Dictionaries. Magyar-Franczia és Franczia-Magyar Szótár. *Budapest*, 1890, etc. 8°.
12975. m. 1.

Könnye (N.) Dictionnaire français-hongrois et hongrois-français. 2 pt. *Budapest*, 1891. 16°.
12976. aa. 20.

Sarda (P.) Dictionnaire français-malgache.
pp. 226. *Paris*, 1895. 8°. 12910. a. 53.

Soler y Arqués (C.) Diccionario manual franco-español ó hispano-francés. pp. 802.
Madrid, 1893. 8°.   12950. e. 38.

Klint (A.) Fransk-svensk Ordbok. pp. 678.
Stockholm, 1893. 8°.   12972. c. 47.

Etymology.

Gutheim (F.) Über Konsonanten-Assimilation im Französischen. pp. 98. *Heidelberg*, 1891. 8°.
12954. f. 41.

Koerting (G.) Formenlehre der französischen Sprache. *Paderborn*, 1893, etc. 8°. 12954. ff.

Lammens (H.) Remarques sur les mots français dérivés de l'Arabe. pp. 314. *Beyrouth*, 1890. 8°.
012904. cc. 1.

Pavot (T.) Étymologies dites inconnues.
pp. 309. *Paris*, 1891. 8°. 12954. ff. 25.

Stappers (H.) Dictionnaire synoptique d'Étymologie française. pp. 959. *Paris*, 1893. 12°.
12950. df. 48.

Examination Papers.

Ac. Oxford. *University*. Oxford and Cambridge Local Examination questions on French.
pp. 157. *Lond*. 1893. 8°. 12950. bb. 53.

Stiévenard (L.) Key to the Local Exam. questions. pp. 176. *Lond*. 1893. 8°. 12953. de. 24.

Ac. Cambridge. *University of Cambridge*. Cambridge Local Examinations. French examination papers. pp. 93. *Lond*. 1891. 8°. 12952. a. 50.

Millar (E.) French examiner. For the use of candidates for the Cambridge Local Examinations. pp. 44. *Lond*. 1891. 8°. 12950. bbb. 41.

Ac. London. *University*. Matriculation French papers. 1894. 8°. Tutorial Series. 12205. c. 235.

Just (H. E.) and Lhuissier (L. J.) Matriculation Model answers: French. London University Matriculation. 1891, 8°. Tutorial Series.
12205. c. 56.

Lhuissier (L. J.) and Wyatt (A. J.) Intermediate and B.A. French papers, London.
pp. 88. 1892. 8°. Tutorial Series. 12205. c. 97.

Ac. London. *College of Preceptors*. Examination papers in French. pp. 74. *Lond*. 1890. 8°.
12953. cc. 12.

G. B. & I. *Civil Service Commissioners*. Army examination papers in French. pp. 141.
Lond. 1891. 8°.   12954. cc. 47.

Vecqueray (J. W. J.) French papers. pp. 215.
Lond. 1890. 8°.   12954. d. 8.

Grammars: Methods of Learning French: Exercises.

Augé (C.) Troisième livre de Grammaire. pp. 886.
Paris, 1895. 12°.   12952. df. 34.

Ayer (N. L. C.) Grammaire comparée de la langue française. pp. 709. *Bâle*, 1885. 8°.
12950. h. 43.

Chot (J.) Grammaire française. pp. 144.
Tongres, 1890. 8°.   12950. c. 32.

2 B

FRENCH.—Grammars—*continued.*

DARMESTETER (A.) Cours de Grammaire de la langue française. *Paris,* 1891, *etc.* 12°. 12954. d.

LARIVE ( ) and FLEURY ( ) La première (-troisième) année de Grammaire. 6 pt. *Paris,* 1895. 12°.   12950. cc. 32.

RALU (A.) Étude satirique de la Grammaire française. pp. 299. *Paris,* 1893. 12°.
12315. dd. 10.

VESSOIT (A.) Nouvelle Méthode inductive d'enseignement grammatical. pp. 312. *Paris,* 1893. 12°.   12950. cc. 20.

ARMITAGE (G. F.) Second Year French for higher grade schools. pp. 159. *Leeds,* 1895. 8°.
12954. cc. 53.

BARBIER (P. E. E.) Graduated French examination course. pp. 137. *Lond.* 1891. 8°.
12954. cc. 48.

BARLET (S.) Preceptor's junior French course. pp. 176. *Lond.* 1895. 8°.   12950. df. 53.

BELFOND (J.) A French primer. pp. 67. *Lond.* 1892. 8°.   12954. d. 27.

BELL (*Mrs.* H.) French without Tears. pp. 62. *Lond.* 1895. 8°.   12952. df. 35.

BERTENSHAW (T. H.) Longman's French course. pp. 208. *Lond.* 1891. 8°.   12954. e. 28.

—— Key and supplement. pp. 186. *Lond.* 1891. 8°.   12954. d. 13.

BLOUET (H.) Elementary French. pp. 151. *Lond.* 1895. 8°.   12950. df. 50.

BOCHER (L.) Rational method of learning French. 7 pt. *Lond.* 1891. 8°.   12954. d. 15.

BOÏELLE (J.) First French course. pp. 172 *Lond.* 1892. 8°.   12954. d. 31.

BRACHET (A.) Public School elementary French Grammar. pp. 371. *Lond.* 1892. 8°.
12953. de. 22.

BUÉ (B.) First French book. pp. 172. *Lond.* 1894. 8°.   12950. de. 16.

CHARDENAL (C. A.) Standard French primer. *Lond.* 1892. 8°.   12954. ccc.

DORET (G. H.) Easy French Grammar. pp. 76. *Lond.* 1892. 8°.   12954. d. 24.

DUBOURG (A. J.) French Course. Second year. pp. 106. 1885. 8°. Chambers's Educational Course.   1158. b.

EVE (H. W.) and BAUDISS (F. de) Wellington College French Grammar. pp. 368. *Lond.* 1894. 8°.   12953. de. 25.

CALAIS (A. I.) Wellington College French Exercise book. pp. 213. *Lond.* 1889. 8°.
12950. df. 44.

FASNACHT (G. E.) Supplementary exercises to Macmillan's Progressive French course. pp. 80. *Lond.* 1894. 8°.   12950. de. 17.

FRENCH GRAMMAR. Epitome of French Grammar. pp. 39. *Plymouth,* 1893. 16°.
12901. de. 12. (4.)

—— Colloquial exercises in French Grammar. pp. 183. 16. *Lond.* 1895. 8°.   12953. de. 29.

FRENCH RULES. French Rules in rhyme. pp. 8. *Lond.* 1893. 12°.   Pam. 47.

GAILLARD (J. D.) and (A.) French for young folks. pp. 188. *Lond.* 1892. 8°. 12953. e. 29.

GOLDSMID (E.) Collection of French exercises. pp. 130. *Lond.* 1891. 8°.   12954. e. 27.

GOUIN (F.) First lesson in French. pp. 83. *Lond.* 1893. 8°.   12950. cc. 27.

GUILGAULT (L.) The French handbook. pp. 300. 1892. 8°. CRAWLEY (W. J. C.) Open Competition Handbooks.   12200. d.

HALL (J. P.) and (T.) First French course. pp. 260. *Lond.* 1891. 8°.   12954. bb. 41.

FRENCH.—Grammars—*continued.*

HALL (J. P.) and (T.) Key to exercises in Hall's French courses. 2 pt. *Lond.* 1892. 8°.
12954. ccc. 3.

HUGO ( ) Hugo's simplified system. French. 14 pts. *Lond.* 1890. 8°.   12902. ccc. 22.

JANTON (L.) Elementary course of French Grammar. pp. 202. *Paisley,* 1891. 8°.
12954. d. 12.

KROEH (C. F.) Living method for learning how to think in French. pp. 140. *Hoboken,* 1892. 8°.   12950. cc. 18.

LALLEMAND (H.) and ANTOINE (A.) Hossfeld's advanced French Grammar. pp. 96. *Lond.* 1891. 8°.   12954. d. 10.

LARMOYER (M. de) Practical French Grammar. *Lond.* 1892, *etc.* 8°.   12950. c. 36.

MORAN (J. A.) French Grammar and composition. pp. 126. *Dublin,* 1891. 8°. 12954. cc. 45.

MORIARTY (L. M.) French Grammar. 2 pt. 1890. 8°. SONNENSCHEIN (E. A.) Parallel Grammar Series.   12902. aa.

PELLISSIER (E.) Junior French Grammar. pp. 186. *Lond.* 1891. 8°.   12954. d. 16.

—— Junior French exercises with vocabulary. pp. 168. *Lond.* 1894. 8°.   12954. d. 47.

ROGET (F. F.) First Steps in French history and philology. pp. 328. *Lond.* 1892. 8°.
9200. c. 9.

ROSENTHAL (R. S.) The Meisterschafts-system. *Lond.* 1891. 8°.   12902. cc. 46.

SCHNEIDER (C. H.) First Year's French course. pp. 223. *Edinb.* 1891. 8°.   12953. c. 43.

SHARP (G.) Elementary French exercises. pp. 131. *Lond.* 1890. 8°.   12954. d. 6.

SISSISON (E. M.) Oxford and Cambridge French primer. 2 pt. 1889. 12°. Gill's School Series.   12202. c.

—— Gill's Imperial French primer. pp. 288. *Lond.* 1889. 8°.   12954. d. 9.

SMITH (*Sir* W.) Key to the French Principia. 4 pt. *Lond.* 1888-91. 8°.   12954. d. 33.

SOMERVILLE (A. A.) Primer of French Grammar. pp. 151. *Lond.* 1894. 8°.   12954. d. 46.

—— Primary French exercises. pp. 123. *Lond.* 1895. 8°.   12953. de. 28.

SPIERS (V. J. T.) Rapid exercises on French Grammar. pp. 182. *Lond.* 1893. 8°.
12954. e. 40.

STARCK (A.) French by easy stages. pp. 100. *Lond.* 1889. 8°.   12950. df. 46.

STEDMAN (A. M. M.) First French lessons. pp. 99. *Lond.* 1891. 8°.   12952. df. 33.

—— Steps to French. pp. 79. *Lond.* 1894. 8°.
12954. a. 57.

STIER (G.) Lehrbuch der französischen Sprache. 2 Th. *Leipz.* 1895. 8°.   12950. bbb. 45.

THOMAS (T. E.) Simplified French accidence. *Lond.* 1895. 8°.   12950. c. 41.

CRAPP (C. F.) French Genders. pp. 15. *Manch.* 1891. 8°.   12901. ccc. 12. (8.)

DICKINSON (B. B.) French Genders. pp. 19. *Rugby,* 1894. 8°.   12950. g. 4.

READINGENSIS. Gender of French nouns seen at a glance. *Lond.* 1894. *s. sh.* 8°. 12950. c. 39.

BLOUET (H.) Terminations of the regular French verbs. *Lond.* 1894. 8°.   12954. a. 56.

BREYMANN (H.) Die Lehre vom französischen Verb. pp. 136. *München,* 1882. 8°. 12954. f. 39.

BREWER (J. J.) Conjugations of irregular and defective French verbs. pp. 102. *Lond.* 1891. 8°.   12954. cc. 44.

ESCLANGON (A.) The French Verb newly treated. pp. 205. *Lond.* 1895. 8°.   12953. g. 28.

FRENCH.—Grammars—*continued*.

GOULD (C. A.) The French Verb on the historical or derivative system. pp. 41.
Lond. 1893. 4°.   12950. c. 35.

JACQUET (A. M.) French Conjugations at a glance. pp. 8. *Lond.* 1892. *obl.* 8°. 12954. c. 29.

—— Junior Student's French Verb exercise book. pp. 44. *Lond.* 1892. *obl.* fol. 12950. g. 3.

—— Senior Student's French Verb exercise book. pp. 44. *Lond.* 1892. *obl.* fol.   Pam. 47.

THOMSON (J. G.) French irregular Verbs. pp. 73. *Paisley*, 1895. 8°.   12950. bbb. 42.

WAKEFORD (W.) French Verbs classified and arranged. *Brighton*, 1891. 12°. 1865. c. 1. (8.)

WILLIAMSON (E. D.) French irregular Verbs with their inflexions. pp. 112. *Lond.* 1893. 8°.
12954. bb. 42.

SHARP (G.) Exercises in French syntax. pp. 138. *Lond.* 1890. 8°.   12954. d. 7.

STEDMAN (A. M. M.) French Exercises on elementary syntax. pp. 103. *Lond.* 1891. 8°.
12954. cc. 43.

STORR (F.) Hints on French syntax. pp. 48. *Lond.* 1891. 8°.   12954. cc. 49.

TRÜE (E. T.) and HAY (E. H.) Elements of French syntax. pp. 124. *Lond.* 1894. 8°.
12950. a. 40.

History : Old French.

BRUNOT (F.) Précis de Grammaire historique de la langue française. pp. 698. *Paris*, 1894. 8°.
12950. cc. 33.

DARMESTETER (A.) Cours de Grammaire historique de la langue française.
Paris, 1895, *etc.* 12°.   12950. cc. 34.

ÉTIENNE (E.) La Langue française depuis les origines jusqu'à la fin du XI° siècle.
Paris, 1890, *etc.* 8°.   12950. d.

—— Essai de grammaire de l'ancien Français, IX°-XIV° siècles. pp. 521. *Paris*, 1895. 8°.
12952. e. 18.

FAUCHER DE SAINT-MAURICE (N. H. E.) Notes sur la formation du franco-normand. pp. 85.
Montréal, 1892. 8°.   Pam. 47.

MARIAL (W.) Essai sur les Strates de la langue française. pp. 57. *Paris*, 1890. 8°. 12950. l. 2.

BOS (A.) Glossaire de la Langue d'Oïl. pp. 466. *Paris*, 1891. 8°.   12954. g. 16.

PARIS (G.) Manuel d'ancien français. *Paris*, 1888, *etc.* 8°.   011840. k. 45.

ROGET (F. F.) Introduction to old French. pp. 390. *Lond.* 1894. 8°.   12950. ec. 28.

TOYNBEE (P. J.) Specimens of old French, IX–XV centuries. pp. 492. 205. 1892. 8°.
Clarendon Press Series.   2319. b. 1.

DARMESTETER (A.) and HATZFELD (A.) Le seizième Siècle en France. pp. 384.
Paris, 1889. 12°.   011840. g. 69.

COHN (G.) Die Suffixwandlungen im Vulgärlatein und im vorlitterarischen Französisch. pp. 322. *Halle*, 1891. 8°.   12933. f. 35.

DUBISLAV (G.) Satzbeiordnung für Satzunterordnung im Altfranzösischen. pp. 31.
Berl. 1888. 4°.   Pam. 47.

MATZKE (J. E.) Dialektische Eigenthümlichkeiten in der Entwickelung des mouillierten l im Altfranzösischen. 1890. 8°. Ac. Baltimore.
Modern Language Association. Publications. Vol. 5. No. 2.   Ac. 2683/2.

NASTASI (J.) Die Lehre der Nebensätze im Cligés von Chrestien de Troyes. pp. 52.
Linz, 1894. 8°.   11840. i. 47. (5.)

RISOP (A.) Studien zur Geschichte der französischen Konjugation auf -ir. pp. 132.
Halle, 1891. 8°.   12954. f. 40.

FRENCH.—History : Old French—*cont*.

HUGUET (E.) Étude sur la syntaxe de Rabelais. pp. 458. *Paris*, 1894. 8°.   12954. ff. 32.

WAGNER (R.) Stellung des attributiven adjektivs in altfranzösischen Prosatexten.
Greifswald, 1890, *etc.* 8°.   12984. c.

SCHARSCHMIDT (E.) E. Pasquiers Thätigkeit auf dem Gebiete der französischen Sprachgeschichte. pp. 34. *Bautzen*, 1892. 4°.   12902. h. 17. (5.)

See also supra: *Grammars*: PROVENÇAL LANGUAGE : ROMANCE LANGUAGES.

Idioms.

DELINOTTE (L. P.) and NOLEN (Th.) Dictionnaire des Idiotismes de la langue néerlandaise et de la langue française. pp. 312.
Gand, 1891. 8°.   12950. cc. 8.

DESHUMBERT (M.) Dictionary of difficulties in French. pp. 132. *Lond.* 1894. 8°. 12954. d. 45.

HOFMAN (C. A.) Formes idiomatiques comparées. Fransch-nederlandsche. pp. 161.
Amsterd. 1890. 8°.   12902. ccc. 21.

MAYER (A. v.) Manual of English-French-German Idioms. pp. 326. *Lond.* 1895. 8°.
12950. df. 51.

PAYNE (J. B. de V. P.) French Idioms and proverbs. pp. 162. *Lond.* 1893. 8°.
12950. cc. 24.

See also supra: GRAMMARS.

Orthography.

BAILLAIRGÉ (C. P. F.) Vocabulaire des homonymes de la Langue française. pp. 212.
Joliette, 1891. 16°.   12950. df 47.

BLOCH (G.) Die Reform der französischen Orthographie. pp. 234. *Aarau*, 1894. 8°. 12953. h. 20.

BRUNET (H.) Les difficultés de l'Orthographie résolues par la traduction en l'idiome d'Auvergne. pp. 15. *Fontainebleau*, 1890. 8°.   Pam. 47.

COTY (A.) La Revision de l'Orthographe et l'Académie. pp. 134. *Paris*, 1892. 12°.
12950. df. 49

DURAND (A.) Nouvelle Orthographe française. pp. 36. *Paris*, 1891. 8°.   12901. de. 17. (6.)

HAVET (L.) La simplification de l'Orthographie. pp. 60. *Paris*, 1890. 8°.   12954. c. 28.

PARIS. *Société des Correcteurs.* Changements orthographiques introduits dans le Dictionnaire de l'Académie, 1877. pp. 72. 1892. 12.
12901. ccc. 16. (6.)

Pronunciation : Phonetics.

CHRISTEN (A.) Vade-mecum of French pronunciation. pp. 133. *Lond.* 1893. 8°.
12954. bb. 10.

FAURE (H.) Quelques bizarreries de la Langue française. pp. 30. *Moulins*, 1891. 8°.
12903. dd. 34. (8.)

GIRARDOT (C. E.) Guide to French Pronunciation. pp. 21. *Lond.* 1891. 16°. 12901. c. 44. (4.)

LESAINT (M. A.) Traité de la Pronunciation française. pp. 502. *Halle*, 1890. 8°. 12954. e. 25.

SICARD (G.) Guide de la Pronunciation française. pp. 125. *Paris*, 1893. 8°.   12950. c. 37.

BEYER (F.) Das Lautsystem des Neufranzösischen. pp. 104. *Cöthen*, 1887. 8°. 12953. f. 24.

BLONDEL (J. E.) Phonologie mécanique de la langue française. pp. 407. *Paris*, 1895. 8°.
12953. f. 28.

PASSY (P.) Les sons du Français. pp. 139. *Paris*, 1892. 12°.   12954. d. 41.

Patois. *See supra*: DIALECTS.

Translation from and into French.

BARBIER (P. E. E.) Second French Reader and writer. pp. 135. 1892. 8°. SONNENSCHEIN (E. A.) Parallel Grammar Series. 12902 aa.

2 B 2

FRENCH LITERATURE.

Bibliography.

Académie Française. *See* FRANCE.

FRENCH LITERATURE.—*continued.*
History and Criticism.
General.

Ac. Paris. *Société d'Histoire littéraire.* Revue d'histoire littéraire de la France. *Paris*, 1894, etc. 8°.   P.P. 4331. abb.

ALBERT (P.) La littérature française des origines au XVIII° siècle. pp. 477. *Paris*, 1891. 4°.
11840. m. 37.

ALQ (L. d') Anthologie des femmes écrivains poètes et prosateurs. pp. 412. *Paris*, 1893. 8°.
12238. aa. 21.

ANSPACH (A.) Résumé de l'histoire de la littérature française. pp. 392. *Heidelberg*, 1892. 8°.
011840. k. 66.

BANDERET (P.) Histoire résumée de la littérature française. pp. 272. *Berne*, 1894. 8°.
011850. h. 47.

BASTIT (G.) La Gascogne littéraire. pp. 356. *Bordeaux*, 1894. 12°.   011850. eee. 42.

BRUNETIÈRE (F.) L'Évolution des Genres dans l'histoire de la littérature. *Paris*, 1890, etc. 8°.
011824. de. 3.

—— Nouvelles Questions de critique. pp. 386. *Paris*, 1890. 18°.   011840. g. 70.

CHAUVIN ( ) and LE BIDOIS (G.) La Littérature française par les critiques contemporains. pp. 620. *Paris*, 1895. 8°.   011850. eee. 36.

COLOMBEY (É) Ruelles, Salons et cabarets. Histoire anecdotique de la littérature française. 2 tom. *Paris*, 1892. 8°.   011850. g. 3.

DOUMIC (R.) and LEVRAULT (L.) Études sur les auteurs prescrits pour l'examen du brevet supérieur. pp. 350. *Paris*, 1893. 12°.
011850. f. 49.

ÉDOUARD (E. J. E.) Biographical Notes of standard French authors of the 17th, 18th and 19th centuries. pp. 32. *Portsmouth*, 1893. 16°.
10662. a. 16.

FORTIER (A.) Histoire de la littérature française. pp. 351. *N.Y.* 1893. 8°.   011850. eee. 7.

HALLARD (J. H.) Gallica and other essays. pp. 157. *Lond.* 1895. 4°.   12354. dd. 9.

JEANROY-FÉLIX (V.) Histoire de la littérature française jusqu'à Malherbe. pp. 650. *Paris*, 1892. 8°.   11850. f. 36.

JUNKER (H. P.) Grundriss der Geschichte der französischen Litteratur. pp. 498. 1894. 8°. Sammlung von Kompendien. Ser. 1. No. 2.
12205. k.

KEENE (H. G.) Literature of France. pp. 219. 1892. 8°. KNIGHT (W.) University Extension Manuals.   12204. f.

MAGER (A.) Geschichte der französischen Literatur. pp. 199. *Wien*, 1890. 8°. 011840. h. 49.

PERGAMENI (H.) La littérature française dans son développement. pp. 234. *Brux.* 1893. 12°.
011850. f. 31.

RAHSTEDE (H. G.) Wanderungen durch die französische Litteratur. *Oppeln*, 1891, etc. 8°.
011824. f. 8.

RAJNA (P.) Le Origini dell' epopea francese. pp. 550. *Firenze*, 1884. 8°.   011850. k. 3.

ROGET (F. F.) First Steps in French history, etc. pp. 328. *Lond.* 1892, 8°.   9200. c. 9.

ROSSEL (V.) Histoire de la littérature française hors de France. pp. 531. *Lausanne*, 1895. 8°.
11825. p. 26.

SAINTE-BEUVE (C. A.) Galerie de portraits littéraires. pp. 517. *Paris*, 1893. 8°. 10659. f. 16.

SAINTSBURY (G. E. B.) Primer of French literature. pp. 144. 1891. 8°. Clarendon Press Series.   2320. b. 31.

—— Miscellaneous Essays. pp. 429. *Lond.* 1895. 8°.   012357. h. 68.

FRENCH LITERATURE. — History, etc.—*continued.*

SPIERS (V. J. T.) History and literature of France in tables and essays. pp. 364. *Lond.* 1894. 8°.
9210. cc. 28.

TARSOT (L.) and CHARLOT (M.) Études sur les textes d'explication du brevet supérieur. pp. 774. *Paris*, 1891. 8°.   011824. e. 33.

ULRICH (W.) Tafeln der französischen Litteratur. pp. 48. *Leipz.* 1891. 8°.   011824. i. 17. (13.)

WEISS (J. J.) Essais sur l'histoire de la littérature française. pp. 384. *Paris*, 1891. 12°.
011824. de. 10.

Various Periods.

CLÉDAT (L.) La Poésie en France au moyen âge. pp. 240. *Paris*, 1893. 12°.   011850. h. 31.

JEANROY (A.) Les origines de la Poésie lyrique en France au moyen-âge. pp. 523. *Paris*, 1889. 8°.
011840. m. 38.

LENIENT (C.) La Poésie patriotique au moyen âge. pp. 459. *Paris*, 1891. 8°. 011824. de. 38.

PARIS (G.) La Littérature française au moyen âge. pp. 316. *Paris*, 1890. 8°.   011824. f. 12.

—— Les origines de la Poésie lyrique en France au moyen âge. pp. 63. *Paris*, 1892. 4°.
Pam. 15.

VORETZSCH (C.) Die französische Heldensage. pp. 32. *Heidelberg*, 1894. 8°.   Pam. 15.

OWEN (J.) Skeptics of the French Renaissance. pp. 830. *Lond.* 1893. 8°.   2217. e. 2

FAGUET (É.) Seizième Siècle. Études littéraires. pp. 425. *Paris*, 1894, 8°.   011850. f. 58.

HAUSER (H.) La Poésie populaire en France au XVI° siècle. pp. 26. *Clermont-Ferrand*, 1894. 8°.
11840. i. 47. (3.)

LENIENT (C.) La Poésie patriotique, XVI° et XVII° siècles. *Paris*, 1894, etc. 8°.
011850. eee. 18.

PATARD (V.) La vérité dans la question O. Basselin et J. Le Houx à propos du Vau-de-vire. pp. 136. *Paris*, 1891. 12°.   011824. e. 20.

ALLAIS (G.) Malherbe et la Poésie française, 1585-1600. pp. 424. *Paris*, 1892. 8°.
011824. h. 64.

DELAPORTE (P. V.) Du Merveilleux dans la littérature sous le règne de Louis XIV. pp. 424. *Paris*, 1891. 8°.   011824. i. 9.

DUPUY (A.) Histoire de la littérature française au XVII° siècle. pp. 641. *Paris*, 1892. 8°.
11824. i. 39.

FAGUET (É.) Les grands maîtres du XVII° siècle, etc. pp. 317. *Paris*, 1892. 8°.   11850. m. 18.

JANET (P.) Les Passions et les caractères dans la littérature du XVII° siècle. pp. 389. *Paris*, 1888. 18°.   011824. e. 15.

KOERTING (H.) Geschichte des französischen Romans im XVII. Jahrhundert. 2 Bde. *Oppeln*, 1891. 8°.   011824. h. 4.

LE BRETON (A.) Le Roman au XVII° siècle. pp. 322. *Paris*, 1890. 8°.   011824. de. 8.

LONGHAYE (G.) Histoire de la littérature française au XVII° siècle. *Paris*, 1895, etc. 8°.
011850. g.

MORILLOT (P) Le Roman en France depuis 1610. pp. 611. *Paris*, 1893, 8°. 011850. f. 2.

SATIRES. Satires et portraits au XVII° siècle. pp. 144. *Paris*, 1891. 12°.   12238. cc. 10.

FAGUET (É.) Dix-huitième siècle. Études littéraires. pp. 537. *Paris*, 1890. 18°.
011840. g. 79.

ROCAFORT (J.) Les Doctrines littéraires de l'Encyclopédie. pp. 338. 1890, 8°. 011824. i. 3.

COLLIGNON (A.) Diderot. pp. 304. *Paris*, 1895. 8°.   010663. f. 45.

FRENCH LITERATURE. — History, etc.—*continued.*

Ducros (L.) Diderot. pp. 344. *Paris*, 1894. 8°.
010663. f. 6.

Chuquet (A.) J. J. Rousseau. pp. 201. 1893. 8°. Grands Écrivains. 10664. e.

Grand Carteret (J.) J. J. Rousseau jugé par les Français d'aujourd'hui. pp. 575.
Paris, 1890, 8°. 010661. i. 17.

Marmontel (J. F.) Memoirs of Marmontel. 2 vols. *Lond.* 1895. 8°. 010663. i. 23.

Brunetière (F.) L'Évolution de la Poésie lyrique en France au xix° siècle.
Paris, 1894, etc. 8°. 011850. eee. 19.

Grenier (É.) Souvenirs littéraires. pp. 347.
Paris, 1894, 12°. 011850. f. 67.

Meissner (F.) Der Einfluss deutschen Geistes auf die französischen Litteratur des 19. Jahrhunderts. pp. 249. *Leipz.* 1893. 8°.
011850. i. 29.

Meunier (G.) Les grands Historiens du xix° siècle. pp. 430. *Paris*, 1894. 12°. 011850. f. 72.

Monod (G.) Les Maîtres de l'histoire. pp. 312.
Paris, 1894. 12°. 010663. f. 23.

Montégut (É.) Dramaturges et romanciers.
pp. 419. *Paris*, 1890. 8°. 011840. g. 68.

Pellissier (G.) Le Mouvement littéraire au xix° siècle. pp. 382. *Paris*, 1890. 8°.
011842. de. 4.

Nisard (J. M. N. D.) Essais sur l'école romantique. pp. 357. *Paris*, 1891. 12°. 11851. b. 25.

Brunetière (F.) Le Roman naturaliste.
pp. 370. *Paris*, 1883. 12°. 11840. aa. 7.

Klincksieck (F.) Zur Entwicklungsgeschichte des Realismus. pp. 56. *Marburg*, 1891. 8°.
Pam. 15.

Saintsbury (G. E. B.) Essays on French novelists. pp. 460. *Lond.* 1891. 8°. 011850. g. 9.

Velde (M. S. v. d.) French fiction of to-day, etc. 2 vol. *Lond.* 1891. 8°. 011840. h. 63.

Flat (P.) Essais sur Balzac. pp. 323.
Paris, 1893. 12°. 011850. g. 21.

Lemer (J.) Balzac. pp. 348. *Paris*, 1892. 12°.
010662. ff. 12.

Baju (A.) L'Anarchie littéraire. Les différentes écoles. pp. 35. *Paris*, 1892. 8°. Pam. 15.

Biré (E.) Études et portraits. pp. 380.
Lyon, 1893. 8°. 010663. i. 19.

Brunetière (F.) Essais sur la littérature contemporaine. pp. 356. *Paris*, 1892. 12°.
011824. de. 48.

—— Nouveaux Essais sur la littérature contemporaine. pp. 335. *Paris*, 1895. 12°.
11851. b. 27.

Bunand (A.) Petits Lundis. Notes de critique. pp. 243. *Paris*, 1890. 18°. 011840. g. 82.

Cornut (É.) Les Malfaiteurs littéraires
pp. 347. *Paris*, 1892. 12°. 8409. e. 26.

Doumic (R.) Portraits d'écrivains. pp. 330.
Paris, 1892. 12°. 010662. g. 8.

—— Écrivains d'aujourd'hui. pp. 318.
Paris, 1894. 8°. 011850. f. 76.

Ferraud de Pontmartin (A. A. J. M.) Count. Épisodes littéraires. pp. 325. *Paris*, 1890. 8°.
011840. i. 58.

Fouquier (M.) Profils et portraits. pp. 310.
Paris, 1891. 8°. 011824. e. 19.

Frary (R.) Essais de critique. pp. 344.
Paris, 1891. 12°. 011824. e. 32.

Frommel (G.) Esquisses contemporaines.
pp. 286. *Lausanne*, 1891. 8°. 011824. e. 40.

Gaucher (M.) Causeries littéraires. 1872-88.
pp. 357. *Paris*, 1890. 12°. 011840. f. 73.

FRENCH LITERATURE. — History, etc.—*continued.*

Gille (P. H.) Les Mercredis d'un Critique.
pp. 386. *Paris*, 1895. 18°. 011850. g. 66.

Hennequin (É.) Études de critique scientifique. pp. 235. *Paris*, 1890. 8°. 011840. e. 69.

Huret (J.) Enquête sur l'évolution littéraire. pp. 455. *Paris*, 1891. 12°. 011824. de. 43.

Jourdain (F.) Les Décorés, ceux qui ne le sont pas. pp. 278. *Paris*, 1895. 12°. 010663. f. 58.

Klein (F.) Le Mouvement néo-chrétien.
pp. 63. *Paris*, 1892. 8°. 3900. bb. 43. (9.)

Larroumet (G.) Nouvelles études de littérature. pp. 344. *Paris*, 1894. 8°. 012356. ee. 21.

Lazare (B.) Figures contemporaines. pp. 281.
Paris, 1895. 8°. 010663. f. 39.

Montégut (É.) Esquisses littéraires. pp. 311.
Paris, 1893. 8°. 011850. f. 28.

Pellissier (G.) Essais de littérature contemporaine. pp. 391. *Paris*, 1893. 12°.
011850. f. 19.

—— Nouveaux essais de littérature contemporaine. pp. 382. *Paris*, 1895. 8°. 011850. eee. 62.

P.P. *Paris*. Le Livre moderne, publiée par O. Uzanne. Tom. 1-4. *Paris*, 1890, 91. 8°.
P.P. 6475. ba.

—— Revue des Livres nouveaux. 1888, 1895, *Paris*, 1888-95. 8°. P.P. 6541. ba.

Prat (P.) Littérature contemporaine. pp. 156.
Paris, 1892. 8°. 011824. de. 46.

Renard (G.) Les Princes de la jeune critique. pp. 299. *Paris*, 1890. 12°. 011840. f. 72.

—— Critique de combat. pp. 350.
Paris, 1894. 12°. 011850. g. 68.

Rouque-Ferrier (A.) Le Midi; ses poètes et ses lettrés, 1874-90. pp. 534.
Paris, 1892. 8°. 011824. h. 58.

Sprigge (S. S.) The Society of French Authors. pp. 49. *Lond.* 1889. 8°. 11899. e. 27.

Tissot (E.) Les évolutions de la critique française. pp. 373. *Genève*, 1890. 8°. 011840. f. 77.

Wyzewa (T. de) Nos Maîtres. pp. 363.
Paris, 1895. 8°. 011850. eee. 76.

See also Biography, *Literary:* Drama: Fiction: Poetry.

Selections.

French Classics. Examination series of French classics. *Lond.* 1894, etc. 8°. 12238. aa.

Merlet (G.) Extraits des Classiques français. pp. 640. *Paris*, 1892. 12°. 12238. b. 18.

Saintsbury (G. E. B.) Specimens of French literature. pp. 559. 1892. 8°. Clarendon Press Series. 2320. h. 20.

Darmesteter (A.) and Hatzfeld (A.) Morceaux choisis des principaux écrivains du xvi° siècle. pp. 384. *Paris*, 1891. 12°. 12238. bbb. 1.

Brachet (A.) Morceaux choisis des grands écrivains du xvi° siècle. pp. 318. *Paris*, 1894. 8°.
12239. b. 15.

Fasnacht (G. E.) Specimens of the great Writers in the 17th, 18th and 19th Centuries. pp. 592.
Lond. 1894. 8°. 12238. bb. 13.

Crane (T. F.) Le Romantisme français. Selection, 1824-48. pp. 362. *N.Y.* 1890. 16°.
12236. a. 25.

Belfond (J.) La France littéraire au xix° siècle.
Lond. 1891, etc. 8°. 12236. de.

Vecqueray (J. W. J.) Morceaux détachés d'auteurs contemporains. pp. 284. *Lond.* 1895. 8°.
12238. aa. 27.

See also Poetry.

FRESHWATER. Walker (R.) Phœnicia in Freshwater. pp. 20. *Freshwater*, 1892. 8°.
07703. i. 1. (14.)

FRESSIN. FROMENTIN ( ) Fressin. Histoire, *etc.* pp. 668. *Lille, 1892. 8°.* 010171. f. 37.

FRIBOURG. Ac. Fribourg. *Université.* Collectanea Friburgensia. *Friburgi, 1894, etc. 4°.*
Ac. 607/2.

DAGUET (A.) Histoire de Fribourg des temps anciens jusqu'à 1481. pp. 187. 1889. 8°. Ac. Fribourg. *Société d'Histoire.* Archives. Tom. 5. Livr. 1. Ac. 6938.

REICHLEN (F.) Archéologie fribourgeoise. *Fribourg, 1894, etc. 8°.* 07708. g.

FRIENDLY ISLANDS. *See* TONGA.

FRIENDLY SOCIETIES. ENGLAND. *Friendly Societies.* Memorandum on valuations of Friendly Societies. pp. 8. *Lond. 1891. 8°.*
08227. e. 46. (7.)

FOWKE (V. de S.) Industrial and Provident Societies Act, 1893. pp. 188. *Lond. 1894. 8°.*
6345. aa. 11.

FOWLE (T. W.) The Poor Law, Friendly Societies and old age destitution. pp. 23. *Oxf. 1892. 8°.*
Pam. 82.

HARDWICK (C.) History of Friendly Societies. pp. 170. *Manch. 1893. 8°.* 8225. aa. 44.

HEWAT (A.) Friendly Societies. 1886. 8°. Glasgow. *Insurance and Actuarial Society.* Transactions. Ser. 2. No. 4. 08227. e.

HIJMANS (I. H.) De Verjaringsinstituten. *'s Gravenh. 1892, etc. 8°.* 6005. h.

MARTINET (A.) Les Sociétés de Secours mutuels et les assurances ouvrières. pp. 312. *Paris, 1891. 8°.* 8282. f. 27.

PETIT (E.) Les Sociétés de Secours mutuels en France. pp. 180. *Paris, 1893. 8°.* 8827. de. 45.

PRATT (W. T.) Law of Friendly Societies. pp. 352. *Lond. 1894. 8°.* 2232. a. 13.

SÉRULLAZ (G.) Les Sociétés de Secours mutuels et la question des retraites, *etc.* pp. 44. *Lyon, 1890. 8°.* 8276. g. 42.

THRIFT. Useless Thrift, or, How the poor are robbed. pp. 64. *Lond. 1895. 12°.* Pam. 82.

WILKINSON (J. F.) Mutual Thrift. pp. 324. 1891. 8°. Social Questions of to-day. 08276. e.

BUFFALOES, *Order of.* The R.A.O.B. Buffalo Directory. *Lond. 1893, etc. 16°.* 04785. de.

MONTAGUE (W.) Buffaloism as a registered society. pp. 30. *Lond. 1890. 8°.* Pam. 25.

COLOMBO. *Ceylon Mutual Provident Association.* Rules. pp. 4. *Colombo, 1893. 4°.* Pam. 82.

DRUIDS, *Order of.* Introductory Book. pp. 20. *Lond. 1889. 8°.* 4785. bb. 57. (8.)
—— Order of Druids' quarterly report and journal. *Manch. 1892, etc. 8°.* 4782. aa. & 2114.

SHEFFIELD. *Equalized Independent Druids.* Quarterly Journal. *Sheffield, 1893, etc. 8°.*
08275. m.

FORESTERS, *Order of.* Constitutions and laws of the Order. pp. 270. 1893. 16°. 4785. a. 29.
—— Quarterly Report. Jan. 1891, *etc.* *Leeds, 1891, etc. 8°.* 08275. m.

LONDON. *Friendly Society of Iron Founders.* Annual Report. *Lond. 1890, etc. 8°.* 8276. e. 68.
—— Monthly Report. *Lond. 1894, etc. 8°.*
8282. ff.

See also BUILDING SOCIETIES.

FRIENDS, *Society of.* BALTIMORE, *Society of Friends.* Minutes of proceedings. pp. 133. *Baltimore, 1892. 8°.* 4152. e. 19.

BECK (W.) The Friends, who they are. pp. 277. *Lond. 1893. 4°.* 4715. cc. 18.

FRITH (F.) The Quaker ideal. pp. 102. *Lond. 1894. 8°.* 4152. de. 17.

FRIENDS, *Society of.* Conference of Friends on the Home Rule question. pp. 70. *Lond. 1893. 16°.* 8146. cc. 4.

FRIENDS, Society of—continued.

JENKINS (C. F.) Quaker Poems. A collection of verse. pp. 269. *Phila. 1893. 8°.* 11688. i. 1.

LAND (W.) Testimony concerning the Principles and Practices of truth as held by Friends. pp. 387. *Newport, 1885. 8°.* 4139. bbb. 22. (3.)

NEWMAN (H. S.) The Friends. pp. 15. *Leominster, 1890. 8°.* 4139. aa. 23. (4.)

THOMSON (C. W.) Reflections on the Faith and Practice of the Friends. pp. 32. *Lond. 1892. 8°.* 4139. aaa. 25. (4.)

History.

BENNETT (A. W.) Pre-Foxite Quakerism. pp. 44. *Lond. 1894. 8°.* 4705. cc. 14. (12.)

FOX (G.) Journal. 2 vol. *Lond. 1891. 8°.*
4903. f. 59.

BUDGE (J.) Glimpses of G. Fox and his Friends. pp. 232. *Lond. 1892. 8°.* 4905. de. 39.

FRIENDS, *Society of.* Shilling biographical Series. *Lond. 1892, etc. 8°.* 4906. de.

FRIENDS' QUARTO SERIES. Friends' Quarto Series. *Lond. 1892, etc. 4°.* 4715. g.

P.P. *London.* Quakeriana. Books, antiquities, prints. *Lond. 1894, etc. 8°.* P.P. 6481. l.

R., J. M. Six Generations of Friends in Ireland. 1655–1890. pp. 239. *Lond. 1893. 8°.*
4955. g. 8.

WHITE (W.) Friends in Warwickshire in the 17th and 18th centuries. pp. 161. *Lond. 1894. 8°.* 4715. bb. 30.

ELIOT PAPERS. The Eliot Papers. *Gloucester, 1893, etc. 4°.* 9906. g.

HARE (A. J. C.) The Gurneys of Earlham. 2 vol. *Lond. 1895. 8°.* 9903. bb. 19.

ROBINSON (W.) Friends of a half century. 1840–90. pp. 330. *Lond. 1891. 8°.* 4905. g. 5.

THOMAS (A. C.) and (R. H.) History of the Society of Friends in America. 1894. 8°. American Church History Series. Vol. 12.
4744. g.

CARROLL (H. K.) Report of statistics of Churches in the U.S. pp. 812. 1894. 8°. Eleventh Census of the U.S. 1882. c. 1.

APPLEGARTH (A. C.) Quakers in Pennsylvania. pp. 84. 1892. 8°. Johns Hopkins University Studies. Ser. 10. No. 8. Ac. 2689.

FRIENDSHIP. TRUMBULL (H. C.) Friendship the master-passion. pp. 413. *Phila. 1892. 4°.* 8409. l. 9.

FRIESLAND. Ac. Leeuwarden. *Provinciaal Friesch Genootschap.* ANDREÆ (A. J.) Nalezing op de nieuwe Naamlijst van Grietmannen. pp. 171. *Leeuwarden, 1893. 8°.* Ac. 965/17.
—— ROMEIN (T. A.) Naamlijst der Predikanten in de Hervormde Gemeenten van Friesland. 2 dln. *Leeuwarden, 1886–92. 8°.* Ac. 965/16.

BLOK (P. J.) Friesland in Mittelalter. pp. 49. *Leer, 1891. 8°.* 9007. ff. 5. (5.)

BROUGHAM (Hon. R.) Cruise on Friesland "Broads." pp. 207. *Lond. 1891. 8°.*
010271. f. 7.

DOUGHTY (H. M.) Friesland Meres. pp. 457. *Lond. 1890. 8°.* 10271. e. 1.

DYKSTRA (W.) Uit Friesland volksleven van vroeger en later. *Leeuwarden, 1892, etc. 8°.*
10270. ff. 22.

HECK (P.) Die altfriesische Gerichtsverfassung. pp. 499. *Weimar, 1894. 8°.* 5307. b. 23.

SUFFLING (E. R.) Cruise on the Friesland Meres. pp. 50. *Lond. 1894. 8°.* 10271. bb. 25.

FRIESLAND, East. MANNINGA (U.) Ostfriesische Volks- und Rittertrachten. pp. 82. 1893. 8°. Ac. Emden. *Gesellschaft für bildende Kunst.* Jahrbuch. Bd. 10. Ac. 5378.

FUNGI—*continued.*

COSTANTIN (J.) and DUFOUR (L.) Nouvelle flore des Champignons. pp. 291. *Paris*, 1895. 8°.
07028. e. 58.

DE BARY (A.) Comparative morphology and biology of the Fungi. pp. 525. *Oxf.* 1887. 8°.
2252. f.

ELLIS (J. B.) and OVERHART (B. M.) North American Pyrenomycetes. pp. 793.
Newfield, 1892. 8°.   07028. l. 10.

FEUILLEAUBOIS ( ) Les Champignons de la France. pp. 10. *Toulouse*, 1893. 8°. Pam. 1.

HESSE (R.) Die Hypogaeen Deutschlands.
Halle, 1890, etc. fol.   7028. h. 15.

KIRCHNER (O.) and EICHLER (J.) Beiträge zur Pilzflora von Württemberg. 1894, *etc.* 8°. Ac. Stuttgard. *Verein für vaterländische Natur-kunde.* Jahreshefte. Jahrg. 50.   Ac. 2893.

LAPLANCHE (M. C. de) Dictionnaire icono-graphique des Champignons supérieurs.
pp. 542. *Paris*, 1894. 8°.   7029. a. 21.

LUCAND (J.) Figures peintes de Champignons de la France. *Autun*, 1889, *etc.* fol.   7074. m.

MASSEE (G.) British Fungus Flora.
Lond. 1892. *etc.* 8°.   7054. df. 9.

—— British Fungi. pp. 232. *Lond.* 1891. 8°.
07028. f. 35.

MOELLER (A.) Die Pilzgärten einiger südameri-kanischer Ameisen. pp. 127. 1893. 8°.
SCHIMPER (A. F. W.) Botanische Mittheilungen.
Hft. 6.   7029. k.

NEW SOUTH WALES. *Department of Agriculture.* Host and habitat index of Australian Fungi.
pp. 44. *Sydney*, 1893. 8°.   Pam. 1.

OUDEMANS (C. A. J. A.) Révision des Cham-pignons dans les Pays-Bas. 1892, *etc.* 8°. Ac. Amsterdam. *Akademie van Wetenschappen.* Ver-handelingen. Sectie 2. Deel 2.   Ac. 944/2.

QUÉLET (L.) Flore mycologique de la France.
pp. 492. *Paris*, 1888. 12°.   7054. df. 7.

PATOUILLARD (N.) Énumération des Cham-pignons en Tunisie. pp. 19. 1892. 8°. Ex-ploration scientifique de la Tunisie. 10105. ff.

SACCARDO (P. A.) Synopsis Pyrenomycetum.
Lond. 1891, *etc.* 8°.   07076. f. 11.

SCHWALB (C.) Das Buch der Pilze. pp. 218.
Wien, 1891. 8°.   07028. g. 18.

—— Die naturgemässe Conservierung der Pilze.
pp. 114. *Wien*, 1889. 8°.   7075. f. 1. (5.)

TAVEL (F. v.) Vergleichende Morphologie der Pilze. pp. 208. *Jena*, 1892. 8°. 7054. h. 21.

U.S. *Dept. of Agriculture.* Journal of Mycology.
Wash. 1889, *etc.* 8°.   7053. e. 31.

WEED (C. M.) Fungi and fungicides. pp. 228.
N.Y. 1894. 8°.   7028. a. 4.

See also BACTERIOLOGY: BOTANY, *General* and *Cryptogamia :* LICHENS : MYCETOZOA.

FUR. LACROIX-DANLIARD ( ) Le Poil des Animaux et les Fourrures. pp. 419.
Paris, 1892. 12°.   7206. b. 21.

POLAND (H.) Fur-bearing Animals in nature and commerce. pp. 392. *Lond.* 1892. 8°. 7208. ee. 12.

FURNACES. *See* HEATING.

FURNESS. BARBER (H.) Furness and Cart-mel notes. pp. 391. *Ulverston*, 1894. 8°.
010358. f. 55.

FURNITURE. Ac. Paris. *Société des Bibliophiles.* Inventaire des Meubles du Château de Pau. pp. 235. *Paris*, 1892. 4°.
Ac. 8933/13.

GARDINER (F. M.) Furnishing for every home.
pp. 130. *Lond.* 1894. 8°.   7820. bb. 23.

HAVARD (H.) Les arts de l'Ameublement.
pp. 162. *Paris*, 1892. 8°.   7817. f. 28.

FURNITURE.—*continued.*

HASLUCK (P. N.) House Decoration. pp. 160.
Lond. 1894. 8°.   7943. aa. 61.

HIRTH (G.) Das deutsche Zimmer der Gothik und Renaissance, des Barock-, Rococo- und Zopfstils. pp. 448. *München*, 1886. 4°.
7814. f. 16.

LAFOND (P.) Une Famille d'Ébénistes français. Les Jacob. pp. 35. *Paris*, 1894. 8°. Pam. 94.

LESSING (J.) Moebel des XVII. Jahrhunderts. 1895. 8°. Berlin. *K. Museen.* Vorbilder-Hefte. Hft. 17.   1756. b.

LITCHFIELD (F.) Illustrated history of Furniture.
pp. 280. *Lond.* 1893. 8°.   7805. e. 9.

PRATT (C.) and SONS. Hints on Furnishing.
pp. 85. *Bradford*, 1893. 8°.   7820. aa. 29.

RIS-PAQUOT (O. E.) Le Mobilier et les objets qui s'y rattachent. pp. 122. *Paris*, 1893. 8°.
07944. e. 24.

See also ART, *Decorative :* CARPENTRY: COL-LECTIONS AND COLLECTORS ; WOODWORK.

FÜRSTENFELD. LANGE (H.) Eine steier-ische Stadt im 17. Jahrhunderte. pp. 139.
Graz, 1890. 8°.   10215. c. 2.

FÜRTH. LOTTER (H.) Gross-Industrie und Gross-Handel von Nürnberg-Fürth. pp. 180.
Nürnberg, 1894. fol.   8245. g. 36.

GABOON. DOMERGUE (A.) Notes de voyages. Gabon. pp. 210. *Paris*, 1893, 8°. 010096. f. 33.

FRANCE. *Ministère de Commerce.* Bulletin ad-ministratif du Gabon-Congo. 1849–1887.
Paris, 1889, *etc.* 8°.   08227. f.

PAYEUR-DIDELOT ( ) Notes et mémoires sur le Gabon-Congo. 1894, *etc.* 8°. Ac. Nancy. *Société de Géographie.* Bulletin. 1894. Ac. 6034.

See also AFRICA, *French Possessions* and *West :* FRANCE, *Colonies.*

GAELIC LANGUAGE AND LITERA-TURE. MACBEAN (L.) Elementary lessons in Gaelic. pp. 64. *Inverness*, 1893. 8.
12978. b. 46.

—— Guide to Gaelic conversation and pro-nunciation. pp. 119. *Inverness*, 1884. 8°.
12978. b. 47.

MAC FARLANE (M.) Phonetics of the Gaelic Language. pp. 95. *Paisley*, 1889. 8°.
12978. b. 49.

REID (D.) Course of Gaelic Grammar. pp. 148.
Glasg. 1895. 8°.   12978. b. 50.

GRAY (J.) Personal and place names in the Book of Deer. pp. 30. *Peterhead*, 1894. 4°.
Pam. 47.

DUNOON. Gaelic topography of the Dunoon district. pp. 47. *Kirkintilloch*, 1892. 8°. Pam. 47.

CAMERON (A.) Reliquiæ Celticæ. Texts, papers and studies. *Inverness*, 1892, *etc.* 8°.
11595. g. 16.

MACLEAN (H.) Ultonian Hero-ballads. Col-lected in the Highlands from 1516 till 1870.
pp. 184. *Glasg.* 1892. 8°.   11595. c. 34.

MACDONALD (A.) The Uist Collection. Poems and songs. pp. 220. *Glasg.* 1894. 8°.
11595. c. 46.

MAC NEILL (N.) Literature of the Highlanders.
pp. 350. *Inverness*, 1892. 8°.   2308. b. 27.

SAUNDERS (T. B.) Life and letters of J. Mac-pherson. pp. 327. *Lond.* 1895. 8°. 10856. g. 5.

ROGER (J. O.) Celtic MSS. in relation to the Macpherson fraud. pp. 56. *Lond.* 1890. 8°.
011840. f. 80.

GAMES—*continued.*

WHITNEY (C. W.) A Sporting Pilgrimage.
pp. 397. *Lond.* 1895. 8°. 07905. i. 6.
See also ANELLETTO : BASEBALL : BETTING :
BILLIARDS : BOWLS : CARDS : CHESS : CRICKET :
CROQUET : DRAUGHTS : FIVES : FLIPPERS : FOOT-
BALL : GAMBLING : GOLF : HALMA : HOCKEY :
KHANHOO : LACROSSE : MARO : POLO : QUOITS :
RACKETS : ROUNDERS : SALOMO : SKAT : TENNIS :
WHIST.

History, etc.

FALKENER (E.) Games ancient and oriental.
pp. 366. *Lond.* 1892. 8°. 7913. e. 13.
BUEDINGER (M.) Die römischen Spiele und der
Patriciat. pp. 74. 1891. 8°. Ac. Vienna.
Akademie. Sitzungsberichte. Phil.-hist. Classe.
Bd. 123. Ac. 810/6.
DITCHFIELD (P. H.) Old English Sports and
pastimes. pp. 132. *Lond.* 1891. 8°. 7912. aa. 6.
GOMME (A. B.) Traditional Games of England,
Scotland and Ireland. 1894, *etc.* 8°. GOMME
(G. L.) Dictionary of British Folk-lore.
2348. d. 1.
—— Children's Singing Games.
Lond. 1894, *etc.* obl. 4°. M.D. 780.
YEATMAN (E. F. E.) and HALL (M. R.) "On
the Green." Village games. pp. 47.
Lond. 1894. 16°. 7912. a. 32.
SPITZER (R.) Beiträge zur Geschichte des Spieles
in alt Frankreich. pp. 54.
Heidelberg, 1891. 8°. 011824. h.
NEWELL (W. W.) Games of American Children.
pp. 242. *N.Y.* 1884. 4°. 7908. d. 35.
IM THURN (E. F.) Primitive Games of the
natives of Guiana. pp. 37.
Georgetown, 1890. 8°. 7912. ee. 2. (3.)
See also FOLK LORE.

GANDU LANGUAGE.
See AFRICAN LANGUAGES.

GARD, Department.
LOMBARD-DUMAS (A.)
Catalogue des monuments mégalithiques du
Gard. 1894. 8°. Ac. Nîmes. *Académie.* Mé-
moires. Sér. 7. Tom. 16. Ac. 330/2.
See also LANGUEDOC.

GARDENING.

General.

ALLEN (C. L.) Bulbs and tuberous-rooted Plants.
pp. 311. *N.Y.* 1893. 8°. 07028. k. 16.
AMATEUR. Amateur's handbook on Gardening.
pp. 194. *Liverp.* 1894. 8°. 07076. i. 20.
AMHERST (*Hon.* A. M.) History of gardening
in England. pp. 398. *Lond.* 1895. 8°.
7030. dd. 5.
AUSTIN (A.) In Veronica's Garden. pp. 167.
Lond. 1895. 8°. 012356. ff. 5.
BADGER (E. W.) Cottage Gardening. pp. 36.
Lond. 1893. 8°. 7074. e. 10. (8.)
BAILEY (L. H.) Horticulturists' blue-book.
pp. 302. *N.Y.* 1895. 8°. 07077. e. 1.
BALTET (C.) L'Horticulture française. pp. 62.
Paris, 1890. 8°. 7073. e. (4.)
BARNARD (A.) Orchards and Gardens ancient
and modern. pp. 260. *Lond.* 1895. obl. 8°.
7078. dc. 28.
BEETON (S. O.) Gardening Book. pp. 456.
Lond. 1895. 8°. 7077. bbb. 2.
—— All about Gardening. pp. 576.
Lond. 1895. 8°. 07028. k. 23.
BELLAIR (G. A.) Traité d'Horticulture.
pp. 738. *Paris,* 1892. 8°. 07076. e. 35.
BLOMFIELD (R.) and THOMAS (F. I.) The Formal
Garden in England. pp. 249. *Lond.* 1892. 8°.
07028. k. 17.

GARDENING.—General—*continued.*

BOIS (D.) Dictionnaire d'Horticulture.
Paris, 1893, *etc.* 8°. 07076. m.
BRIGHT (H. A.) Year in a Lancashire Garden.
pp. 124. *Lond.* 1891. 8°. 7055. aaa. 5.
CHAMBERLAIN (E. L.) and DOUGLAS (F.) Gentle-
woman's Book of gardening. pp. 218. 1892. 8°.
ADAMS (W. H. D.) Victoria Library. 012208. f.
DENY (E.) Jardins et parcs publics. pp. 134.
Paris, 1893. 4°. 7054. g. 19.
ELLACOMBE (H. N.) In a Gloucestershire Garden.
pp. 302. *Lond.* 1895. 8°. 07028. k. 25.
ENCYCLOPÆDIAS. Dictionnaire d'Horticulture et
de jardinage. *Paris,* 1892, *etc.* 8°. 367.
FISCHER-BENZON (R. v.) Altdeutsche-Garten-
flora. pp. 254 *Kiel,* 1894. 8°. 7054. h. 28.
FISH (D. T.) Cassell's popular Gardening. 4 vol.
Lond. 1893, *etc.* 8°. 07076. l. 1.
GILLOT (X.) Herborisations dans le Jura Central.
1891. 8°. Ac. Lyons. *Société Botanique.* An-
nales. Année 17. Ac. 3250.
GUEIDAN ( ) Manuel des cultures pour la
Provence. pp. 405. *Marseille,* 1895. 8°.
07028. e. 53.
HOLE (S. R.) A Book about the Garden.
pp. 259. *Lond.* 1892. 8°. 07076. f. 3.
JOHNSON (G. W.) Gardener's Dictionary.
pp. 1072. *Lond.* 1894. 8°. 7054. ee. 20.
LONDON. *Horticultural Exhibition.* Catalogue
and Guide. pp. 94. *Lond.* 1892. 8°.
7959. aaa. 55.
MOTTET (S.) La Mosaïculture. pp. 94.
Paris, 1891. 8°. 07076. e. 27.
MUELLER (F. v.) *Baron.* Select extra-tropical
Plants. pp. 594. *Melbourne,* 1891. 8°.
07028. l. 2.
NICHOLSON (G.) Illustrated dictionary of Gar-
dening. 4 vol. *Lond.* 1885–89. 4°. 2029. d.
PAUL (W.) Contributions to horticultural Litera-
ture. pp. 565. *Waltham Cross,* 1892. 8°.
07076. k. 4.
P.P. *London.* The Garden Annual.
Lond. 1891, *etc.* 8°. P.P. 2488. eca.
—— Cottage Gardening. *Lond.* 1892, *etc.* 4°.
P.P. 2248. bab.
POTTER ( ) Popular Gardening, *etc.* pp. 105.
Lond. 1894. 16°. 7054. aa. 32.
ROBBINS (M. C.) Rescue of an old Place.
pp. 289. *Bost.* 1892. 8°. 7054. df. 8.
ROBINSON (W.) Garden Design and architects'
gardens. pp. 73. *Lond.* 1892. 8°. 7054. f. 25.
—— The Wild Garden. pp. 304.
Lond. 1894. 8°. 7054. cc. 26.
RODA (M.) and (G.) Manuale del Giardiniere,
fioricoltore e decoratore di giardini. pp. 411.
Torino, 1891. 8°. 07028. e. 38.
SEDDING (J. D.) Garden-Craft old and new.
pp. 215. *Lond..* 1895. 8°. 07028. f. 65.
SLADE (D. D.) Evolution of Horticulture in New
England. *N.Y.* 1895. 8°. 7075. a. 6.
THAXTER (C.) An Island Garden. pp. 126.
Bost. 1894. 8°. K.T.C. 11. a. 8.
VAN RENSSELAER (M. G.) Art Out-of-doors.
pp. 399. *Lond.* 1893. 8°. 7054. df. 11.
WATTS (E.) Modern practical Gardening.
pp. 564. *Lond.* 1890. 8°. 7073. dc. 11.
WEBSTER (A. D.) Hardy ornamental Flowering
Trees and shrubs. pp. 140. *Lond.* 1893. 8°.
07028. f. 51.
WILLIAMSON (W.) Horticultural Handbook.
pp. 248. *Edinb.* 1895. 8°. 07023. c. 47.
WRIGHT (J.) Horticulture. Ten lectures.
pp. 154. *Lond.* 1893. 8°. 7077. aaa. 14.

GARDENING.—General—*continued.*

WRIGHT (J.) Garden Flowers and plants.
pp. 144. *Lond.* 1895. 8°.   7077. aaa. 19.
YRIARTE (C.) Les Fleurs et les jardins de Paris.
pp. 277. *Paris,* 1893. 12°.   07076. c. 50.

BELLAIR (G. A.) Les Plantes pour apartements
et fenêtres. pp. 144. *Paris,* 1893. 12°.
7029. aa. 38.
BOIS (D.) Les Plantes d'appartement et les
plantes de fenêtres. pp. 388. *Paris,* 1891. 12°.
7077. de. 33.
CHAMBERLAIN (E. L.) Town and home Gardening. pp. 160. *Lond.* 1893. 8°.   7054. df. 12.
COLLINS (C.) Greenhouse and window Plants.
pp. 160. *Lond.* 1895. 8°.   7054. a. 13.

GOWIE (W.) Gardening in South Africa. pp. 47.
Grahamstown, 1887. 8°.   7073. de. 13. (5.)
MAC DONALD (D.) "My African Garden."
pp. 72. *Lond.* 1892. 8°.   7028. aaa. 5.
ROTH (J.) Manual of South African gardening.
pp. 292. *Cape Town,* 1894. 8°.   07028. e. 49.
SPECK (W.) Guide on gardening in Jamaica.
pp. 47. *Kingston,* 1891. 8°.   7074. e. 11. (6.)
See also ALLOTMENTS: BOTANY.

Botanical Gardens. *See* BOTANY.

Flowers and Flower Gardening. *See* FLOWERS.

Fruit and Vegetable Culture.

BELLAIR (G. A.) Les Arbres fruitiers. pp. 318.
Paris, 1891. 8°.   7078. c. 39..
BREVANS (J. de) Les Légumes et les fruits.
pp. 324. *Paris,* 1893. 12°.   7030. aa. 9.
BUNYARD (G.) Fruit Farming for profit.
pp. 157. *Maidstone,* 1890. 8°.   07076. f. 9.
—— Modern Fruit culture, 2 pt.
Maidstone, 1892. 8°.   07076. g. 7.
CHEAL (J.) Practical Fruit culture. pp. 194.
1892. 8°. Bell's Agricultural Series. 7075. de.
CONWENTZ (H.) Monographie der baltischen
Bernsteinbäume. pp. 151. *Danzig,* 1890. 4°.
7202. g. 7.
DE SALIS (H. A.) Gardening à la mode. Fruits:
vegetables. *Lond.* 1895. 8°.   7077. b. 21.
FISH (D. T.) Vegetables and flowers. pp. 19.
Lond. 1887. 8°.   7073. de. 13. (3.)
GARNER (G.) How to Grow Vegetables and
fruit. pp. 113. *Liverpool,* 1894. 8°. 7078. b. 60.
HARRIMAN (G.) Tomato and Fruit growing for
women. pp. 55. *Lond.* 1894. 8°. 07077. g. 3.
HEUZÉ (G.) La Petite Culture, agricole, légu-
mière et fruitière. pp. 401. *Paris,* 1891. 8°.
07076. c. 23.
HIBBERD (S.) Amateur's Kitchen Garden.
pp. 306. *Lond.* 1893. 8°.   2252. b. 13.
—— Profitable Gardening. pp. 328.
Lond. 1893. 8°.   2252. a. 11.
HILLS (A. F.) Fruit Culture and flower farm-
ing. pp. 15. *Lond.* 1892. 8°. 8435. bb. 62. (2.)
HOOPER (C. H.) Fruit-farming. pp. 26.
Edinb. 1890. 8°.   07076. h. 38.
LINDGREN (E.) Handbok i svenska trägårds-
skötseln. 9 pts. *Stockholm,* 1886–90. 8°.
07028. g. 15.
MANNING (W. S.) Hints for profitable Fruit-
growing. pp. 111. *Lond.* 1891. 8°. 7029. b. 27.
P P. *London.* Fruit Trade Journal.
Lond. 1890, *etc.* 8°.   N.R.
RIVERS (T.) The Miniature Fruit Garden and
modern orchard. pp. 208. *Lond.* 1891. 8°.
07076. c. 31.
SIRODOT (E.) Maladies des Arbres fruitiers.
pp. 166. *Paris,* 1894. 12°.   7077. de. 41.

GARDENING.—Fruit Culture, etc.—*cont.*

SMITH (J.) Encyclopædia of new methods for
bottling Fruits, *etc.* pp. 45. *Lewes,* 1891. 8°.
07914. ee. 2. (6.)
SUTTON AND SONS. Culture of Vegetables from
seeds and roots. pp. 425. *Lond.* 1895. 8°.
07028. f. 54.
VILMORIN-ANDRIEUX ET CIE. Les Légumes usuels.
2 tom. *Paris,* 1890. 8°.   07076 c. 22.
WATKINS (A.) Amateur's Guide. Directions for
Vegetables. pp. 24. *Lond.* 1891. 8°.
7074. e. 12. (5.)
WHITEHEAD (C.) Hints on Vegetable and fruit-
farming. pp. 53. *Lond.* 1893. 8°.
7075. f. 1. (10.)
WRIGHT (J.) The Fruit-Grower's guide. 3 vol.
Lond. 1891–95. 8°.   7073. ee. 29.

ENGLISHMAN. The Fruit industry of California.
Lond. 1895. 8°.   Pam. 1.
WHITING (D.) Fruit-farming in California.
pp. 111. *Lond.* 1893. 8°.   07076. e. 40.
WILLIAMS (F. H.) Florida for Fruit-farming.
Lond. 1890. 8°.   Pam. 86.
ILLINOIS. Illinois; summary of its advantages as
a fruit-growing section. pp. 30. *Chicago,* 1893. 8°.
Pam. 1.
See also APPLE: BOTANY, *Economic*: ONION:
ORANGE: POTATO: TOMATO.

Horticultural Buildings.

TAFT (L. R.) Greenhouse Construction.
pp. 210. *N.Y.* 1894. 8°.   7054. df. 21.
YOUNG (F. C.) Mechanical work in Garden and
Greenhouse. pp. 105. 1893. 8°. Ward & Lock's
Amateurs' Practical Aid Series.   07944. ee.

Market Gardening. *See supra*: FRUIT.

Trees and Tree-growing. *See* FORESTRY.

GARONNE, River. BARRON (L.) La Garonne.
pp. 407. *Paris,* 1891. 8°.   10169. d. 4.
GARSDALE. THOMPSON (W.) Sedbergh,
Garsdale and Dent. pp. 280. *Leeds,* 1892. 8°.
10360. k. 12.
GAS AND GASES. BRANNT (W. T.) Pe-
troleum and the occurrence of natural gas.
pp. 715. *Phila.* 1895. 8°.   7105. dd. 2.
DAVIS (F.) Practical Volumetric analysis.
pp. 35. *Lond.* 1894. 8°.   8909. f. 12.
HEMPEL (W.) Methods of Gas analysis.
pp. 384. *Lond.* 1892. 8°.   8909. bb. 9.
KIMBALL (A. L.) Physical properties of Gases.
pp. 238. 1890. 8°. Heinemann's Scientific
Handbooks.   8708. f.
LINDNER (G.) Theorie der Gasbewegung.
pp. 150. *Berl.* 1890. 4°.   8755. m. 11.
OSTWALD (W.) Das Ausdehnungsgesetz der Gase.
pp. 211. 1894. 8°. Ostwald's Klassiker. Nr. 44.
8706. de.
PHILLIPS (F. C.) Researches on the chemical pro-
perties of Gases. 1893. 4°. Ac. Philadelphia.
Philosophical Society. Transactions. N.S.
Vol. XVII. Pt. 3.   Ac. 1830/3.
SUTTON (F.) Systematic handbook of Volumetric
analysis. pp. 554. *Lond.* 1890. 8°. 8908. k. 12.
WATSON (H. W.) Treatise on the kinetic theory
of Gases. pp. 87. 1893. 8°. Clarendon Press.
Series.   2319. b. 10.
WILLS (G. S. V.) Volumetric analysis. pp. 89.
Lond. 1892. 8°.   8909. aa. 22.
See also CHEMISTRY: NITROGEN: OXYGEN.

GAS LIGHTING AND GAS MA-CHINERY. CHESTER (W. R.) Bibliography
of Coal Gas. pp. 250. *Nottingham,* 1892. 8°.
011900. i. 6.

GAS LIGHTING, etc.—*continued*.

Ac. Chatham. *Royal Engineers' Institute.* Notes on the manufacture and distribution of Coal Gas. pp. 211. *Chatham*, 1894. 8°.
8716. bb. 52.

BELLAMY (C. R.) Best way to burn Gas for lighting purposes. pp. 16. *Liverp.* 1895. 8°.
Pam. 79.

BEZANT (A. F.) Oil or Gas for lighting our homes? pp. 4. *Lond.* 1891. 8°.   Pam. 13.

BRANNT (W. T.) Petroleum : with the occurrence and uses of natural gas. pp. 715.
Phila. 1895. 8°.   7105. dd. 2.

CONSTANT (T. E.) How to give Gas. pp. 36.
Lond. 1894. 8°.   7306. e. 25. (4.)

CRIPPS (F. S.) Guide-framing of Gas-holders. pp. 119. *Lond.* 1889. 4°.   8768. cc. 21.

—— Flow of Gases and proportioning gas mains. pp. 15. *Bolton*, 1892. 4°.   8706. f. 23. (9.)

FLETCHER (T.) Coal Gas as a fuel. pp. 8. 71.
Warrington, 1890. 8°.   8715. c. 50.

GALINE (L.) Traité général d'Éclairage. pp. 412. *Paris*, 1894. 8°.   8715. dd. 30.

GENTSCH (W.) Gasglühlicht. pp. 130.
Stuttgart, 1895. 8°.   8716. aaa. 48.

HERRING (W. R.) Construction of Gas works described. pp. 458. *Lond.* 1892. 8°.
8767. f. 14.

HUGHES (S.) Gas Works. pp. 416.
Lond. 1892. 8°.   8716. b. 49.

HUMPHREYS ( ) Universal Gas register.
Lond. 1891. 12°.   8715. ee. 46.

LONDON. *Institution of Gas Engineers.* Transactions, 1891, *etc.* 8°. *Lond.* 1892, *etc.* 8°. 8716. d.

MONT-SERRAT (E. de) and BRISAC (E.) Le Gaz et ses applications. pp. 366. *Paris*, 1892. 12°.
8716. b. 48.

ROSENBOOM (E.) Die Gasbeleuchtung. 1895. 8°.
WEYL (T.) Handbuch der Hygiene. Bd. 4.
7391. dd.

SCHILLING (E.) Neuerungen auf dem Gebiete der Erzeugung des Steinkohlen-Leuchtgases. pp. 259. *München*, 1892. 4°.   8715. g. 29.

SLABY (A.) Calorimetrische Untersuchungen über den Kreisprozess der Gasmaschine. 1890–92. 4°. Ac. Berlin. *Verein zur Beförderung des Gewerbfleisses.* Verhandlungen.
Ac. 4435.

STOTT (J.) Architect's and surveyor's handbook of Gasfitting. pp. 40. *Lond.* 1895. 12°.
8716. a. 17.

SUGG (M. J.) Art of cooking by Gas. pp. 287.
Lond. 1890. 8°.   7945. e. 1.

HORNBY (J.) The Gas Engineer's laboratory handbook. pp. 304. *Lond.* 1894. 8°.
8715. b. 71.

LEDEBUR (A.) Die Gasfeuerungen für metallurgische Zwecke. pp. 126. *Leipz.* 1891. 8°.
8715. h. 21.

VERMAND (P.) Les Moteurs à Gaz et à pétrole. pp. 176. 1893. 8°. Encyclopédie des aide-mémoire.   8709. g.

WITZ (A.) Traité des moteurs à Gaz. pp. 435.
Paris, 1892. 8°.   8768. m. 2.

MURDOCK (W.) Letter to a Member of Parliament from Mr. W. Murdock in vindication of his claims for incorporating a Gas-light and Coke Company, 1809. pp. 15. *Lond.* 1892. 8°.
8715. ee. 47.

CROWTHER (F. J.) Provisional orders of the Board of Trade in reference to Gas Undertakings.
pp. 48. *Lond.* 1893. 8°.   6126. aaaa. 18.

GAS LIGHTING, etc.—*continued*.

MICHAEL (W. H.) and WILL (J. S.) Law relating to Gas lighting. pp. 834. *Lond.* 1894. 8°.
2230. c. 15.

NEWBIGGING (T.) Valuation of Gas-works for assessment. pp. 72. *Lond.* 1891. 8°.
08227. ee. 18.

BEMIS (E. W.) Municipal ownership of Gas in the U.S. pp. 185. 1891. 8°. Ac. Saratoga. *Economic Association.* Publications. Vol. 6. Nos. 4 & 5.   Ac. 2388.

DELAHAYE (P.) L'Abaissement du prix du Gaz à Paris. pp. 31. *Paris*, 1890. 8°.
8226. f. 59. (7.)

SERF (A.) Les Grands Fiefs modernes. Le monopole du gaz. pp. 64. *Paris*, 1892. 8°.
8277. ee. 31. (14.)

See also MACHINERY, *Gas Engines*.

GASCONY. CHAMBRELENT (J.) Les Landes de Gascogne. pp. 111. *Paris*, 1887. 8°.
10173. ee. 4.

LANUSSE (M.) De l'Influence du dialecte gascon sur la langue française. pp. 470. *Paris*, 1893. 8°.
11852. h. 26.

BASTIT (G.) La Gascogne littéraire. pp. 356.
Bordeaux, 1894. 12°.   011850. cee. 42.

See also ARMAGNAC : BIGORRE : GERS : HAUTES PYRÉNÉES : LANDES : PROVENÇAL LANGUAGE AND LITERATURE.

GASTEROPODA. *See* MOLLUSCA.

GÂTINAIS. THOISON (E.) Petites notes d'Histoire gâtinaise. pp. 152. *Paris*, 1891. 8°.
10168. e. 3.

See also FONTAINEBLEAU : NIÈVRE, YONNE, *Departments*.

GAU-ALGESHEIM. BRILMAYER (C. J.) Geschichte der Stadt Gau-Algesheim. pp. 127.
Mainz, 1883. 8°.   10255. aa. 8.

GAUGING. MANT (J. B.) Pocket Book of Mensuration and Gauging. pp. 249.
Lond. 1891. *obl.* 8°.   8548. aa. 26.

O'REILLY (T. E.) Practical Gauging. pp. 172.
Lond. 1891. 8°.   7942. a. 56.

GAUL. *See* FRANCE, *Antiquities and History :* NUMISMATICS.

GAZETTEERS. BARBIER (J. V.) Lexique géographique du monde entier.
Paris, 1894, *etc.* 4°.   10005. h.

CHAMBERS (W.) and (R.) Concise Gazetteer of the world. pp. 768. *Lond.* 1895. 8°.
10004. ccc. 4.

CHISHOLM (G. G.) Longman's Gazetteer of the world. pp. 1788. *Lond.* 1895. 4°.   2059. c.

COAN (T. M.) Pronouncing Gazetteer of the world. 1890. 4°. Webster's International Dictionary.   2112. g.

EGLI (J. J.) Nomina geographica.
Leipz. 1892, *etc.* 8°.   10002. h. 11.

MURRAY (J. H.) Routledge's Gazetteer of the world. pp. 238. *Lond.* 1891. 8°. 10005. c. 3.

SMITH (B. E.) Cyclopædia of Names. pp. 1085.
Lond. 1894. fol.   2112. g.

RITTER (C.) Geographisch-statistisches Lexikon.
Leipz. 1894, *etc.* 8°.   10002. i.

GELATINE. *See* GLUE.

GEMMI PASS. *See* ALPS.

GEMS: JEWELLERY.
General.

BAUER (M.) Edelsteinkunde.
Leipz. 1895, *etc.* 8°.   7108. gg.

BLOCHI (A.) La vente des Diamants de la couronne. pp. 108. *Paris*, 1888. 8°.
7805. de. 16.

GEMS.—General—_continued._

Doelter (C.) Edelsteinkunde. pp. 260.
Leipz. 1893. 8°.   07109. g. 38.

Fremy (E.) Synthèse du Rubis. pp. 58.
Paris, 1891. 4°.   7107. g. 4.

Kunz (G. F.) Gems and precious stones of
North America. pp. 367. _N.Y._ 1892. 4°.
     7105. h. 5.

Orpen (_Mrs._ G.) Stories about famous precious
stones. pp. 286. _Bost._ 1890. 8°. 7742. bb. 27.

Streeter (E. W.) Precious Stones and gems.
pp. 355. _Lond._ 1892. 8°.   2248. d. 17.

See also Diamonds : Mineralogy : Pearls.

Engraved Gems and Jewellery.

Ac. London. _British Museum._ Description of
casts from ancient engraved Gems. pp. 15.
Lond. 1891. 8°.   7702. de. 10. (4.)

Babelon (E.) La Gravure en pierres fines.
pp. 320. _Paris._ 1894. 8°.   2261. cc. 4.

Bequet (A.) Les Bagues franques et mérovingiennes. 1893. 8°. Ac. Namur. _Société archéo-
logique._ Annales. Tom. 20.   Ac. 5531.

France. _M. de l'Instruction._ Inventaires relatifs
aux joyaux des Princes d'Orléans-Valois 1389–
1481. pp. 221. _Paris,_ 1894. 8°. 7709. bbb. 41.

Middleton (J. H.) Lewis Collection of gems and
rings in Corpus Christi College, Cambridge.
pp. 93. _Lond._ 1892. 8°.   7805. de. 20.

Morgan (J. de) Liste des Bijoux de la XII°
dynastie découverts dans la pyramide de
Dahchour. pp. 11. _Cairo,_ 1894. 8°. Pam. 3.

Sommerville (M.) Engraved Gems. Their
history, _etc._ pp. 783. _Phila._ 1889. 4°.
     7705. ee. 30.

Evans (_Sir_ John) Posy-rings. pp. 30.
Lond. 1892. 8°.   07703. f. 3. (14.)

Fourdrignier (É.) Étude sur les Bracelets et
Colliers gaulois. pp. 28. _Paris,_ 1893. 8°.
     Pam. 3.

Lanza di Scalea (P.) Donne e Gioielli in
Sicilia nel medio evo e nel rinascimento.
pp. 350. _Palermo,_ 1892. 8°. 7742. ee. 15.

Melani (A.) Svaghi artistici femminili. pp. 348.
Milano. 1891. 4°.   K.T.C. 5. b. 19.

Molinier (É.) Dessins et modèles. Les arts du
métal. pp. 144. _Paris,_ 1892. 8°. 7808. f. 6.

Ondes Reggio (G. d') Sopra tre Anelli greco-
siculi. pp. 11. _Palermo,_ 1891. 8°.
     7704. k. 11. (.5)

Roger-Miles (L.) La Bijouterie. pp. 278.
Paris, 1895. 8°.   07807. ee. 1.

Szendrei (J.) Catalogue de la collection de
Bagues de Madame G. de Tarnoczy. pp.384.
Paris, 1889. 8°.   7708. aa. 55.

P.P. _Birmingham._ Manufacturing Jewellers'
trade advertiser. _Birmingham,_ 1892–94. 8°.
     N.R.

_See also supra : General : Gold and Silver
Work._

GENABUM. _See_ Orleans.

GENEVA, City and Canton. Mayor (J.)
Fragments d'Archéologie génevoise. 2 sér.
Genève, 1892–94. 8°.   07708. g. 41.

Reber (B.) Recherches dans le territoire de
l'ancien évêché de Genève. 1892. 8°. Ac.
Geneva. _Société d'Histoire._ Mémoires. N.S.
Tom. 3.   Ac. 6941.

Fazy (H.) Les constitutions de Genève. pp.335.
Genève, 1890. 8°.   9304. c. 7.

Mugnier (F.) Répertoire de titres et documents
relatifs à l'ancien comté de Genève. 1891. 8°.
Ac. Chambéry. _Société Savoisienne._ Mémoires. Sér. 2. Tom. 5.   Ac. 5240.

GENEVA—_continued._

Borel (F.) Les Foires de Genève au 15° siècle.
pp. 256. _Genève,_ 1892. 4°.   7709. g. 32.

Dunant (É.) Les Relations politiques de Genève
avec Berne, 1536–1654. pp. 222.
Genève, 1894. 8°.   9304. f. 16.

Foss (R.) Zur Reformationsgeschichte von Genf.
pp. 26. _Berl._ 1893. 4°.   4532. g. 10. (5.)

Golay (É.) Étude sur le vieux Droit génevois,
1576. 1889. 8°. Ac. Geneva. _Institut Na-
tional._ Bulletin. Tom. 29.   Ac. 610.

Fazy (H.) L'alliance de 1584 entre Berne,
Zurich et Genève. pp. 127. _Genève,_ 1891. 8°.
     9305. b. 12.

Leti (G.) Genève à la fin du XVII° siècle.
1892. 8°. Ac. Geneva. _Institut National._
Bulletin. Tom. 31.   Ac. 610.

Du Bois-Melly (C.) Relations de la cour de
Sardaigne et de Genève, 1754–92. pp. 349.
Genève, 1891. 8°.   9080. c. 30.

Lavanchy (J. M.) Le diocèse de Genève pendant
la Révolution. 2 tom. _Annecy,_ 1894. 8°.
     4629. dd.

Favre (É.) Mémorial des 50 années de la Société
d'Histoire de Genève. pp. 438. _Genève,_ 1889. 8°.
     07708. f. 16.

Curchod (F.) Description des cathédrales de
Lausanne et de Genève. pp. 114.
Lausanne, 1891. 8°.   7817. f. 23.

Geneva. _Association pour la Restauration de la
Cathédrale._ Saint-Pierre. Publication de l'Association. pp. 118. _Genève,_ 1891. 4°.
     7817. k. 6.

Mercier (J) Le chapitre de Saint-Pierre de
Genève. pp. 398. _Annecy,_ 1890. 8°. 4661. f. 24.

Maury (L.) Le Réveil religieux dans l'église
réformée à Genève, 1810–50. 2 pt.
Paris, 1892. 8°.   4660. de. 1.

Choisy (E.) Genève centre protestant international? pp. 16. _Genève,_ 1892. 8°.
     3900. g. 12. (9.)

Rod (É.) Genève. 1892. 4°. Les Capitales du
monde. No. 11.   10025. g.

Geneva. _Conseil Municipal._ Communication
relative au procès intenté à la ville de Genève
par les consorts de Civry. pp. 19.
Genève, 1892. 4°.   5551. i. 3.

Ritter (E.) Glossaires et lexicographes génevois. pp. 19. _Genève,_ 1893. 8°.
     12903. c. 52. (8.)

See also Switzerland.

Lake.

Bourdon (G.) Le cañon du Rhône et le lac de
Genève. 1894. 8°. Ac. Paris. _Société de
Géographie._ Bulletin. Sér. 7. Tom. 15.
     Ac. 6035.

Fatio (G.) Le yachting sur le Lac Leman.
pp. 202. _Genève,_ 1894. 8°.   8806. b. 51.

Forel (F. A.) Le Léman. Monographie lim-
nologique. _Lausanne,_ 1892, _etc._ 8°. 10195. ee. 8.

Geneva. _Conseil Administratif._ Utilisation des
forces motrices du Rhône et régularisation du
Lac Leman. pp. 279. _Genève,_ 1890. 4°. 1807. b. 11.
—— Atlas. fol.   1807. d. 1.

GENITO-URINARY-ORGANS. Anderson (W.) Urinary and reproductive Organs.
1893. 8°. Morris (H.) Treatise on Anatomy.
     7419. l. 10.

Bastianelli (R.) Studio sulle infezioni delle
vie urinarie. 1895. 8°. Ac. Rome. _Accademia
Medica._ Atti. Ann. 21.   Ac. 3707.

Bazy (P.) Maladies des voies urinaires.
pp. 187. 1892. 8°. Encyclopédie des aide-
mémoire.   8079. g.

GEODESY—*continued.*

SCHÖTZ (O. E.) Die norwegische Commission der Europäischen Gradmessung. pp. 42. *Kristiania*, 1894. 8°. Pam. 4.

U.S. *Coast Survey.* Laws relating to the Geodetic Survey. pp. 59. *Wash.* 1887. 8°. 10497. ee. 36.

VOGLER (C. A.) Abbildungen geodätischer Instrumente. pp. 77, *Berl.* 1892. 4°. 8560. i. 24.

WITKOVSKY (B.) Des travaux géodésiques en Angleterre et aux Etats-Unis. pp. 30. 1893. 8°. Ac. Helsingfors. *Suomen Maantieteellinen Seura. Fennia.* VIII. Ac. 6113.

See also CARTOGRAPHY : LATITUDE AND LONGITUDE : SURVEYING.

GEOGRAPHY.

Bibliography.

Ac. London. *Royal Geographical Society.* Catalogue of the Library. pp. 833. *Lond.* 1895. 8°. BB.I. c. 22.

—— Florence. *Società Geografica.* CARDON (F.) Pubblicazioni geografiche stampate in Italia, 1800–90. pp. 310. *Roma*, 1892. 8°. Ac. 6010/7.

General.

ANTHONISZ (J. E.) The Standard Geography. *Galle*, 1889, *etc.* 16°. 10003. b. 4.

ARNOLD-FOSTER (H. O.) This World of Ours. pp. 312. *Lond.* 1891. 8°. 10003. cc. 3.

BOS (P. R.) Beknopt leerboek der land- en volkenkunde. pp. 223. *Groningen*, 1892. 8°. 10005. bbb. 6.

BROOK (S.) Descriptive Geography. pp. 624. *Lond.* 1891. 8°. 10002. c. 4.

BROWN (R.) Countries of the World. *Lond.* 1894, *etc.* 8°. 10025. ee.

BURGER (C. P.) Gronden der wiskundige Aardrijkskunde. pp. 99. *Leiden*, 1894. 8°. 10005. bb. 30.

CASSELL (J.) New Geographical readers. *Lond.* 1895, *etc.* 8°. 10004. aa. 10.

CENTURY GEOGRAPHICAL READERS. Century Geographical readers. *Lond.* 1890, *etc.* 8°. 10004. aa.

CHAIRGRASSE (J. B.) Cours de Géographie contemporaine. 1889, *etc* 8°. LACROIX (D.) Encyclopédie des connaissances civiles et militaires. 8708. n.

CHAMBERS (W.) and (R.) Geographical readers. *Edinb.* 1892, *etc.* 8°. 10005. aa.

CHIKHACHEV (P.) Études de Géographie. pp. 263. *Florence*, 1890. 8°. 10002. ee. 18.

CHISHOLM (G. G.) Longmans' junior school Geography. pp. 96. *Lond.* 1891. 8°. 10002. ee. 22.

—— Longmans' school Geography for S. Africa. pp. 365. *Lond.* 1891. 8°. 10004. c. 3.

CLARKE (C. B.) Geographic reader. pp. 149. *Lond.* 1894. 8°. 10005. aa. 22.

—— Reader in general Geography. pp. 82. *Lond.* 1894. 8°. 10004. aa. 9.

CLYDE (J.) Elementary Geography. pp. 195. *Edinb.* 1892. 8°. 10005. aaa. 25.

—— School Geography. pp. 551. *Edinb.* 1895. 8°. 2252. b. 1.

COLES (J.) Geography for candidates. 3 pt. *Lond.* 1891. 8°. 12200. ee. 5.

DAHLBERG (P.) Større lærebog i Geografi. pp. 151. *Kjøbenh.* 1893. 8°. 10004. ccc. 3.

DELON (C.) Cent tableaux de Géographie pittoresque. *Paris*, 1889. 4°. 10001. f. 20.

DOUGLAS (J.) Introductory Geography. pp. 88. *Edinb.* 1892. 8°. 10005. aa. 18.

—— Progressive Geography. pp. 160. *Edinb.* 1892. 8°. 10005. aa. 17

GEOGRAPHY.—General—*continued.*

ERSLEV (E.) Geografi med billeder. pp. 104. *Kjøbenh.* 1889. 8°. 10003. aaaa. 41.

FRYE (A. E.) Primary Geography. pp. 127. *Lond.* 1894. 4°. 10004. l. 4.

—— Complete Geography. pp. 184. *Bost.* 1895. 4°. 10001. g. 12.

GEOGRAPHY. Elementary Geography. pp. 25. *Singapore*, 1893. 8°. 10003. b. 6.

—— Synoptical Geography of the world. pp. 192. *Lond.* 1892. 8°. 10005. aa. 19.

GIBSON (J.) Geography made easy. pp. 187. *Lond.* 1890. 8°. 10005. bb. 28.

GILL (G.) Student's Geography. pp. 1000. *Lond.* 1890. 8°. 10004. dd. 5.

GIRARD (J.) La Géographie littorale. pp. 231. *Paris*, 1895. 8°. 10002. h. 17.

GUENTHER (S.) Handbuch der mathematischen Geographie. pp. 793. 1890. 8°. RATZEL (F.) Bibliothek geographischer Handbücher. 10005. dd.

HIGH SCHOOL MANUAL. High school manual of Geography. pp. 394. *Lond.* 1893. 8°. 10004. c. 9.

HORN (J. S.) Scholar's Geography. pp. 179. *Manch.* 1893. 8°. 10003. aaa. 23.

HUDSON (A.) Guide to the study of Geography. pp. 24. *Lond.* 1895. 8°. 10002. c. 1.

HUGHES (W.) Introduction to Geography. pp. 100. 1893. 8°. Philip's Geographical Manuals. 10006. de.

—— Compendium of modern Geography. pp. 866. *Liverp.* 1893. 8°. 10003. c. 5.

—— Elementary class-book of modern Geography. pp. 252. *Lond.* 1892. 8°. 10002. aa. 23.

—— Class-book of modern Geography. pp. 446. *Lond.* 1892. 8°. 10005. bbb. 5.

—— Advanced Class-book of modern Geography. pp. 818. *Lond.* 1892. 8°. 10002. e. 5.

HUGUES (L.) Scritti geografici. *Torino*, 1894, *etc.* 12°. 10003. cc.

JAGER (C. C.) Leerboek der Aardsrijkskunde. pp. 219. *Purmerend*, 1893. 8°. 10004. i. 6.

JOHNS (B. G.) Elements of Geography. pp. 186. *Lond.* 1892. 12°. 10003. aaa. 20.

JOHNSTON (A. K.) School physical and descriptive Geography. pp. 408. 1892. 8°. London Geographical Series. 10001. bbb.

JOHNSTON (R.) Competitive Geography. pp. 522. *Lond.* 1894. 8°. 10005. bbb. 7.

KELTIE (J. S.) Applied Geography. pp. 169. *Lond.* 1890. 8°. 10001. aaa. 32.

KETTLER (J. I.) Beiträge zur Geographie. *Weimar*, 1894, *etc.* 8°. 10003. de.

KIRCHHOFF (A.) and SONNENSCHEIN (A.) School Geography. *Lond.* 1891, *etc.* 8°. 10004. h. 5.

KRAUSE (C. C. F.) Aphorismen zur geschichtswissenschaftlichen Erdkunde. pp. 80. *Berl.* 1894. 8°. 10002. ee. 29.

LANGLER (J. R.) Hughes's picturesque Geographical Readers. *Lond.* 1887, *etc.* 8°. 10005. aa.

LAWSON (W.) Geographical Primer. pp. 36. *Edinb.* 1891. 12°. 10004. aa. 6.

—— Junior class Geography. pp. 108. *Edinb.* 1891. 8°. 10003. aaa. 17.

LÖFFLER (E.) Omrids af Geographien. *Kjøbenh.* 1893, *etc.* 8°. 10002. i.

LONGMANS, GREEN AND Co. Handbooks of Geography. *Lond.* 1886, *etc.* 8°. 10004. dd. 6.

LYDE (L. W.) Man on the Earth. Course in geography. pp. 192. *Lond.* 1895. 8°. 10003. bb. 9.

GEOGRAPHY.—General—*continued.*

MACKAY (A.) Intermediate Geography.
Edinb. 1894. 8°.   10004. bb. 32.

MORRISON (C.) Shilling Geography. pp. 150.
Lond. 1893. 8°.   10003. aaa. 24.

PLATT (A. W.) Geographical Terms. pp. 19.
Lond. 1895. 8°.   Pam. 90.

PRINS (A. W.) Geillustreerde Aardrijksbe-
schrijving. *Amsterd.* 1890, *etc.* 8°.   10005. f.

PUPIL TEACHER. Pupil teacher's Geographical
Year-books. pp. 76. *Edinb.* 1887. 8°.
     10002. aa. 36.

READER. Graphic Geographical reader. Collins'
School Series.   12204. cc.

RECLUS (J. J. É.) Leçon d'ouverture du cours de
Géographie comparée. pp. 16.
Brux. 1894. 8°.   10105. ee. 10. (14.)

REGINA GEOGRAPHICAL READER. The "Regina"
Geographical reader. *Lond.* 1891, *etc.* 8°.
     10004. aaa.

REID (A.) First book of Geography. pp. 72.
Edinb. 1890. 16°.   10003. aa. 18.

—— Rudiments of modern Geography. pp. 184.
Edinb. 1893. 16°.   10003. aaaa. 49.

RICHTHOFEN (F. v.) Festschrift Freiherrn von
Richthofen zum sechzigsten Geburtstag.
pp. 418. *Berl.* 1893. 4°.   12252. k. 6.

SEELEY (A.) This great Globe. pp. 231.
1894. 8°. Seeley's First Lesson Books. 012202. ff.

SOMERVILLE (A. A.) and THOMSON (R. W. W.)
Outlines of Geography. pp. 119.
Lond. 1895. 4°.   10002. c. 2.

SPENCE (L. M. D.) Civil Service Geography.
pp. 168. 1890. 8°. Civil Service Series.
     2238. a. 12.

SUTHERLAND (A.) Class book of Geography, *etc.*
pp. 270. *Lond.* 1894. 8°.   10003. aaaa. 50.

TEACHER. The Teacher's Geography. pp. 39.
Lond. 1892. 8°.   10001. aaa. 33.

WARD (M. J. B.) The Round World. pp. 123.
Lond. 1890. 8°.   10004. f. 7.

WETHEY (E. R.) New manual of Geography.
Lond. 1893, *etc.* 8°.   10004. c. 7.

—— School headings in Geography.
Lond. 1893, *etc.* 8°.   10004. c. 6.

WHITE (J.) Abstract of general Geography.
pp. 96. *Edinb.* 1890. 12°.   10005. aaa. 22.

YOXALL (J. H.) Pupil-teacher's Geography.
pp. 295. 1891. 8°. Jarrold's Pupil-teacher's
Series.   12200. d.

See also EARTH : GAZETTEERS.

Ancient and Historical Geography.

ALEXIS, *Frère.* Histoire de la Géographie.
1892. 8°. Ac. Antwerp. *Société de Géographie.*
Bulletin. Tom. 16.   Ac. 6096.

LUCA (G. de) Storia della geografia. pp. 104.
Napoli, 1881. 8°.   10002. h. 15.

MORRISON (C.) Historical school Geography.
pp. 388. *Lond.* 1893. 8°.   10005. aaa. 26.

FILLION (L. C.) Atlas géographique de la Bible.
pp. 58. *Lyon,* 1890. 4°.   10076. i. 8.

HAUG (H) Vergleichende Erdkunde und alttestamentliche geographische Weltgeschichte.
2 Hefte. *Gotha,* 1894. 4°.   10003. e. 1.

HOMMEL (F.) Geographie der klassischen Altertums. pp. 923. 1889. 8°. MUELLER (I. E. P. v.)
Handbuch der klassischen Altertums-Wissenschaft. Bd. 3.   2259. g. 6.

COLUMBA (G. M.) Gli Studi geografici nel I.
secolo dell' Impero romano,
Torino, 1893. *etc.* 8°.   10002. dd.

STRABO. Selections from Strabo. pp. 376.
Oxf. 1893. 8°.   10002. e. 7.

GEOGRAPHY.—Ancient, etc.—*continued.*

STRABO. Géographie de Strabon. 4 tom.
Paris, 1886–90. 8°.   10001. aa. 25.

DUBOIS (M.) Examen de la Géographie de
Strabon. pp. 390. *Paris,* 1891. 8°. 10001. k. 6.

RYLANDS (T. G.) Geography of Ptolemy eluci-
dated. pp. 97. *Dublin,* 1893. 4°. 10001. h. 4.

YA'ḲUB, *Mar, Saint.* Études sur l'Hexaméron de
Jacques d'Édesse. pp. 45.
Helsingfors, 1892. 8°.   753. h, 6.

AVEZAC-MACAYA (M. A. P. d') Le Ravennate et
son exposé cosmographique. pp. 117.
Rouen, 1888. 4°.   10002. ee. 28.

GALLOIS (L.) Les géographes allemands de la
Renaissance. pp. 266. 1890. 8°. Ac. Lyons.
Faculté des Lettres. Bibliothèque. Tom. 13.
     Ac. 8922/2.

LOEWENBERG (J.) Das Weltbuch Sebastian
Francks. pp. 37. 1893. 8°. Sammlung wissenschaftlicher Vorträge. N.F. Ser. 8. Hft. 177.
     12249. l.

OPPEL (A.) Terra incognita. Eine Darstellung
der Entwickelung der Erdkenntnis von Ausgange des Mittelalters. pp. 68.
Bremen, 1891. 8°.   10001. f. 21.

MAC CLYMONT (J. R.) Theory of an antipodal
Southern Continent during the 16th century.
pp. 23. *Hobart,* 1892. 8°.   Pam. 87.

MARKHAM (C. R.) Major Rennell and the rise of
modern English Geography. pp. 232. 1895. 8°.
Century Science Series.   8709. f.

Commercial Geography.

CHISHOLM (G. G.) Handbook of commercial
Geography. pp. 515. *Lond.* 1892. 8°.
     10004. h. 9.

—— Smaller commercial Geography. pp. 208.
Lond. 1892. 8°.   10004. h. 7.

DEVILLE (V.) Manuel de Géographie commerciale. 2 tom. *Paris,* 1893. 8°.   10004. i. 5.

DUBOIS (M.) Géographie économique de l'Afrique,
l'Asie, l'Océanie et l'Amérique. pp. 732.
Paris, 1889. 8°.   10002. aa. 34.

GANEVAL (J. A.) Dictionnaire de Géographie
commerciale. *Lyon,* 1890, *etc.* 4°.   708.

GONNER (E. C. K.) Commercial Geography.
pp. 205. *Lond.* 1894. 8°.   10004. aaa. 7.

MILL (H. R.) Elementary commercial Geography. pp. 195. 1894. 8°. Pitt Press Series.
     2322. c. 45.

YEATS (J.) Commercial Instruction. pp. 354.
Lond. 1890. 8°.   8229. aaa. 45.

—— Map Studies of the mercantile World.
pp. 336. *Lond.* 1890. 8°.   8229. aaa. 46.

Examination Papers, etc.

EVANS (T.) Midland hand-book of Geography
questions. pp. 96. *Lond.* 1891. 8°. 10002. b. 2.

PREMIER TEST CARDS. New Premier test cards
in geography, *etc.* 5 pt. *Lond.* 1888. 8°.
     12210. bb.

RICHARDSON (J. L.) Watson's Department Examination questions. Geography, *etc.* 6 pt.
Lond. 1887, 88. 8°.   12204. bbbb. 15.

SKERRY (G. E.) Practical papers in Civil Service
Geography. pp. 142. *Lond.* 1894. 8°.
     10003. b. 7.

Geographical Education.

ALLARD (L. J.) Manière d'enseigner la Géographie. pp. 95. *Parthenay,* 1888. 8°.
     10003. bbb. 34.

TROMNAU (A.) Zur Reform des Lehrverfahrens
im geographischen Unterricht. pp. 46. 1891. 8°.
Pädagogische Zeit- und Streitfragen. Hft. 21.
     8310. c.

GEOGRAPHY.—Educational—continued.

VIGUIER (M.) La Géographie dans les chaires de l'Université. pp. 32. Avignon, 1893. 8°.
8304. e. 24. (9.)

Geographical Societies and Periodicals.

CLAPARÈDE (A. de) Annuaire des Sociétés de Géographie. Genève, 1892, etc. 8°. 10004. dd.

P.P. Halle. Beiträge zur Methodik der Erdkunde. Halle, 1894, etc. 8°. P.P. 3954. b.

Ac. London. Royal Geographical Society. Review of British Geographical Work, 1789–1889. pp. 257. Lond. 1893. 8°. BB.I. a. 11.

P.P. New York. Goldthwaite's Geographical Magazine. N.Y. 1891, etc. 8°. P.P. 3904. ma.

Ac. Paris. Société de Géographie. Rapports annuels sur les progrès de la Géographie. Paris, 1895, etc. 8°. Ac. 6035/6.

P.P. Paris. Revue française de l'étranger et des colonies. Paris, 1888, etc. 8°. P.P. 3807. afa.

—— L'Année cartographique. Paris, 1891, etc. fol. 263.

—— Annales de Géographie. Paris, 1891, etc. 8°. P.P. 3937. ba.

—— Rome. Rivista geografica italiana. Roma, 1893, etc. 8°. P.P. 3911. b.

Physical Geography. See EARTH: PHYSIOGRAPHY.

GEOLOGY.

Bibliography.

KLOOS (J. H.) Repertorium der auf die Geologie Braunschweigs und der angrenzenden Landestheile bezüglichen Litteratur. pp. 204. Braunschweig, 1892. 8°. 07109. g. 31.

P.P. London. Annals of British Geology. Lond. 1891, etc. 8°. P.P. 2122. ga.

WHITNEY (J. D.) List of American authors in Geology. pp. 11. 1882. 8°. Ac. Cambridge. Harvard University. Bibliographical Contributions. No. 15. 11905. i.

General.

Ac. Congrès Géologique. Compte rendu. 1878, etc. Londres, 1880, etc. 8°. Ac. 3101.

—— Londres, 1888. Catalogue de l'exposition géologique. 2 pt. Londres, 1888. 8°. 07109. c. 21. (7.)

—— Berkeley. University of California. Bulletin of the Department of Geology. Berkeley, 1893, etc. 8°. Ac. 3186.

—— Konigsberg. Physikalisch - Oekonomische Gesellschaft. Führer durch die geologischen Sammlungen des Provinzialmuseums. pp. 104. Königsberg, 1892. 8°. 7106. b. 45.

—— Paris. Société Géologique. Mémoires. Paris, 1890, etc. 4°. Ac. 3115/3.

—— U.S. Geological Society. Bulletin. Wash. 1890, etc. 8°. Ac. 3187.

AVELING (E. B.) Introduction to the study of Geology. pp. 354. Lond. 1893. 8°. 7106. a. 44.

BIRD (C.) Elementary Geology. pp. 248. Lond. 1891. 8°. 07109. e. 12.

—— Geology. Manual for students in advanced classes. pp. 429. 1894. 8°. Longman's Advanced Science Manuals. 8709. k.

BONNEY (T. G.) C. Lyell and modern Geology. pp. 224. 1895. 8°. Century Science Series. 8709. f.

BROWNE (A. J. J.) Geology. pp. 248. 1893. 8°. Whittaker's Library of Popular Science. 8709. aa.

—— Student's Handbook of Physical Geology. pp. 666. Lond. 1892. 8°. 7202. aaa. 33.

COLE (G. A. J.) Aids to practical Geology. pp. 402. Lond. 1893. 8°. 7108. de. 25.

—— Open-Air Studies. Introduction to Geology. pp. 322. Lond. 1895. 8°. 7106. ff. 28.

GEOLOGY.—General.—continued.

DAWSON (Sir J. W.) Meeting-place of Geology and History. pp. 223. Lond. 1894. 8°.
4429. ccc. 24.

—— Some salient points in the Science of the Earth. pp. 499. N.Y. 1894. 8°. 07109. f. 4.

F., A. A Fanciful View of Geology. pp. 8. Lisburn, 1893. 8°. 07109. f. 5. (7.)

GEIKIE (Sir A.) Outlines of Field-Geology. pp. 252. Lond. 1891. 8°. 2248. a. 4.

—— Text-Book of Geology. pp. 147. Lond. 1893. 8°. 2248. f. 6.

GEIKIE (J.) Fragments of Earth Lore. pp. 428. Edinb. 1893. 8°. 07109. h. 28.

GIRARD (R. de) Études de Géologie biblique. Fribourg, 1893, etc. 8°. 3107. bb.

HOWORTH (Sir H. H.) The Glacial Nightmare and the Flood. 2 vol. Lond. 1893. 8°.
7106. c. 14.

JUKES (J. B.) School manual of Geology. pp. 430. Lond. 1892. 8°. 7109. a. 11.

KAYSER (E.) Lehrbuch der geologischen Formationskunde. pp. 386. Stuttg. 1891. 8°.
07109. g. 26.

—— Text Book of comparative Geology. pp. 426. Lond. 1893. 8°. 07109. g. 37.

KUNTZE (O.) Geogenetische Beiträge. pp. 77. Leipz. 1895. 8°. Pam. 27.

LEWIS (W. S.) The two Geologies. pp. 41. 1890. 8°. Present Day Tracts. No. 63. 4018. aa.

MEUNIER (S.) La Géologie comparée. pp. 296. Paris, 1895. 8°. 8708. cc.

MILLER (H.) Landscape Geology. pp. 63. Edinb. 1891. 8°. 7857. b. 40.

MUNICH. K. B. Oberbergamt. Geognostische Jahreshefte. Cassel, 1888, etc. 8°. 07109. l.

PENNING (W. H.) Text book of Field Geology, etc. pp. 325. Lond. 1894. 8°. 07109. i. 3.

P.P. Rome. Rassegna delle Scienze geologiche. Roma, 1891, etc. 8°. P.P. 2083.

PRESTWICH (J.) Collected papers on controverted questions of Geology. pp. 279. Lond. 1895. 8°.
07108. g. 14.

—— On underground Temperatures. pp. 116. Lond. 1886. 8°. 8756. de. 41.

ROBERTS (R. R.) Introduction to modern Geology. pp. 270. 1893. 8°. University Extension Manuals. 12204. f.

ROTHPLETZ (A.) Geotektonische Probleme. pp. 175. Stuttg. 1894. 8°. 07108. h. 1.

WALTHER (J.) Einleitung in die Geologie als historische Wissenschaft. Jena, 1893, etc. 8°.
7108. ee.

WILSON (J. S.) Geological Mechanism. pp. 138. Lond. 1889. 8°. 7107. b. 1.

YOUNG (J.) Geological Chronology. pp. 32. Glasg. 1892. 8°. Pam. 27.

See also EARTH: EARTHQUAKES: GLACIERS: PHYSIOGRAPHY : VOLCANOES.

Mineralogy. See MINERALOGY.

Palaeontology. See PALAEONTOLOGY.

Petrography.

Ac. London. British Museum. Department of Mineralogy. Introduction to the study of Rocks. pp. 118. Lond. 1895. 8°. 7108. de. 29.

BAYLEY (W. S.) Summary of progress in Petrography, 1886–91. 6 pt. Madison, 1887–92. 8°.
7108. b. 17.

CANADA. Geological Survey. Catalogue of a stratigraphical collection of Canadian Rocks. pp. 128. Ottawa, 1893. 8°. 7109. g. 38.

HATCH (F. H.) Introduction to the study of Petrology. pp. 128. Lond. 1891. 8°. 7108. de. 22.

GEOLOGY.—Petrography—*continued*.

HATCH (F. H.) Text-book of Petrology. pp. 222. *Lond.* 1892. 8°.   07109. e. 13.

HUNT (A. R.) Examination of evidence advanced by T. G. Bonney in support of the Archæan Age of the Devonshire Schists. pp. 17. *Hertford*, 1893. 8°.   Pam. 27.

KEYES (C. R.) Classification of lower Carboniferous Rocks of the Mississippi Valley. pp. 24. *Wash.* 1892. 8°.   Pam. 3.

LACROIX (A.) Étude sur le Métamorphisme de contact des Roches volcaniques. pp. 88. 1894. 4°. Ac. *Paris. Académie des Sciences.* Mémoires. Tom. 31.   2098. g.

LÉVY (A. M.) Les Minéraux des Roches. pp. 334. *Paris*, 1888. 8°.   7104. de. 19.

—— Structures des Roches éruptives. pp. 93. *Paris*, 1889. 8°.   7108. ee. 9.

—— Étude sur la détermination des feldspaths. pp. 70. *Paris*, 1894. 8°.   7108. ee. 13.

LOEWL (F.) Die gebirgbildenden Felsarten. pp. 159. *Stuttg.* 1893. 8°.   07108. g. 5.

MELBOURNE. *Industrial Museum.* Catalogue of specimens of Rocks of Victoria. pp. 127. *Melbourne*, 1894. 8°.   7108. de. 27.

ROBERTS (T.) Jurassic Rocks of the neighbourhood of Cambridge. pp. 96. *Camb.* 1892. 8°.   07109. g. 32.

STRANGWAYS (C. E. F.) Jurassic Rocks of Britain. 3 vols. 1892, 93. 8°. G. B. & I. *Geological Survey.* Memoirs.   S. 218. (21.) *See also* MINERALOGY : MOUNTAINS.

Local Geology.

Africa.

POMEL (A.) Carte géologique de l'Algérie. 2 pt. *Alger*, 1890. 4°.   7105. g. 12.

FICHEUR (E.) Description géologique de la Kabylie du Djurjura. pp. 474. *Alger*, 1890. 8°.   07109. g. 18.

HOEHNEL (L. v.) Orographisch-hydrographische Skizze des Forschungsgebietes der Teleki'schen Expedition. 1891. fol. Ac. Vienna. *K. Akad. der Wissenschaften.* Denkschriften. Math.-naturwissenschaftliche Classe. Bd. 58.   Ac. 810/13.

ROSIWAL (A.) Über Gesteine aus dem Gebiete zwischen Usambara und dem Stefanie-See. 1891. fol. Ac. Vienna. *K. Akad. der Wissenschaften.* Denkschriften. Math.-naturwissenschaftliche Classe. Bd. 58.   Ac. 810/13.

CORNET (J.) Les formations post-primaires du bassin du Congo. 1894. 8°. Ac. Liège. *Société géologique.* Annales. Tom. 21.   Ac. 3146.

ALFORD (C. J.) Geological features of the Transvaal. pp. 69. *Lond.* 1891. 8°.   07109. g. 19.

America and the West Indies.

TARR (R. S.) Economic geology of the United States. pp. 509. *N.Y.* 1894. 8°. 07109. g. 41.

DARTON (N. H.) Record of N. American Geology, 1891. pp. 73. 1892. 8°. United States. *Geological Survey.* Bulletin. No. 99. 1829. a. 7.

U.S. *Geological Survey.* Regulations of the U.S. Geological Survey. pp. 105. *Wash.* 1893. 8°.   7109. g. 36.

BRANNER (J. C.) Relations of the State and National Geological Surveys to each other. pp. 21. *Salem*, 1890. 8°.   Pam. 27.

ALABAMA. *Geological Survey.* Bulletin. *Montgomery*, 1892, *etc.* 8°.   07108. g.

PUMPELLEY (R.) Geology of the Green Mountains in Massachusetts. pp. 206. 1894. 4°. U.S. *Geological Survey.* Monographs. Vol. 23. 1828. b.

GEOLOGY.—America, etc.—*continued*.

MISSOURI. *Geological Survey.* Bulletin. *Jefferson City*, 1891, etc. 8°.   07109. l.

—— Reports of the Survey of 1889, *etc.* pp. 226. *Jefferson City*, 1891, *etc.* 8°   07109. l.

—— Biennial Report of the State Geologist. *Jefferson City*, 1893, 8°.   07109. g.

HAWORTH (E.) Contribution to the Archæan Geology of Missouri. pp. 40. *Minneapolis*, 1888. 8°.   Pam. 27.

FONCK (F.) Introducion á la Jeolojía de la rejion austral de sud-América. *Valparaiso*, 1893, etc. 8°.   7106. i.

BRANNER (J. C.) Geology of the Sergipe-Alagôas Basin of Brazil. 1890. 4°. Ac. Phila. *American Philosophical Society.* Transactions. Vol. 16. Pt. 3.   Ac. 1830/3.

SCOTLAND (H.) On the Geology of Jamaica. On Mining in Jamaica. 2 pt. *Jamaica*, 1890. 8°.   07109. h. 13.

See also supra : Petrography.

Asia.

INDIA. *Geological Survey.* Manual of the Geology of India. pp. 543. *Calcutta*, 1893. 8°.   7109. dd. 14.

—— Contents and Index of vol. 1 to 20 of the Records of the Geological Survey of India. pp. 118. *Calcutta*, 1890. 8°.   7107. de.

MEDLICOTT (H. B.) Sketch of the Geology of the Punjab. pp. 58. *Calcutta*. 1888. 8°. Pam. 27.

NAUMANN (E.) and NEUMAYR (M.) Zur Geologie von Japan. pp. 42. 1890. fol. Ac. Vienna. *K. Akad. der Wissenschaften.* Denkschriften. Math.-naturwissenschaftliche Classe. Bd. 57.   Ac. 810/13.

NAUMANN (E.) Neue Beiträge zur Geologie Japans, *etc.* pp. 45. 1893. 4°. Petermanns Mitteilungen aus J. Perthes' geographischer Anstalt. Ergänzungsheft Nr. 108. P.P. 3946.

BLANCKENHORN (M.) Beiträge zur Geologie Syriens. pp. 135. *Cassel*, 1890. 4°. 7107. e. 12.

Australasia.

CHEWINGS (C.) Beiträge zur Kenntniss der Geologie Süd- und Central-Australiens. pp. 41. *Heidelberg*, 1894. 8°.   07109. e. 19. (8.)

CURRAN (J. M.) Contribution to the Geology of Bathurst, New South Wales. 1891. 8°. Ac. Sydney. *Linnæan Society.* Proceedings. Vol. 6. Pt. 2.   Ac. 3100.

QUEENSLAND. Geology of Queensland and New Guinea. 3 pts. *Brisbane*, 1892. 8°. 7109. g. 33. *See also supra, Petrography.*

Europe.

Ac. *Congrès géologique.* Livret-guide géologique dans le Jura et les Alpes. pp. 306. *Paris*, 1894. 8°.   07109. g. 45.

BOEHM (A.) Steiner Alpen. pp. 91. *Wien*, 1893. 8°.   7106. i. 18.

GRAEFF (F.) Geologische und petrographische Studien in der Montblanc Gruppe. pp. 40. 1894. 8°. Ac. Freiburg. *Naturforschende Gesellschaft.* Berichte. Bd. 9.   Ac. 2880.

ROTHPLETZ (A.) Ein geologischer Querschnitt durch die Ost-Alpen. pp. 268. *Stuttgart*, 1894. 8°.   07109. h. 41.

KINKELIN (F.) Eine geologische Studienreise durch Österreich-Ungarn. 1890. 8°. Ac. Frankfort. *Senckenbergische Gesellschaft.* Bericht.   Ac. 2878/3.

DIMITROV (L.) Beiträge zur geologischen Kenntniss des Vitosa-Gebietes in Bulgarien 1893. fol. Ac. Vienna. *K. Akad. der Wissenschaften.* Denkschriften. Math.-wissenschaftliche Classe. Bd. 60.   Ac. 810/13.

GEOLOGY.—Europe—*continued.*

ROUMANIA. *Ministerulŭ Lucrărilorŭ.* Annaiulŭ Biurouluĭ Geologicŭ. *Bucuresci,* 1893, *etc.* 8°.
　　　　　　　　　　　　　　　07109. l.

ROSIWAL (A.) Geologische Untersuchungen im centralen Balkan. 1890. fol. Ac. Vienna. *K. Akad. der Wissenschaften.* Denkschriften. Math.-wissenschaftliche Classe. Bd. 57.
　　　　　　　　　　　　　　　Ac. 810/13.

TOULA (F.) Geologische Untersuchungen in östlichen Balkan. 1890. fol. Ac. Vienna. *K. Akad. der Wissenschaften.* Denkschriften. Math.-wissenschaftliche Classe. Bd, 57.
　　　　　　　　　　　　　　　Ac. 810/13.

RÖRDAM (K.) Danmarks geologisk Undersøgelse. pp. 109. *Kjøbenh.* 1890. 8°.　07109. k. 21.

MEUNIER (S.) Géologie régionale de la France. pp. 789. *Paris,* 1889. 8°.　07108. h. 2.

GRAND' EURY (C.) Géologie du bassin houiller du Gard. pp. 354. *Saint-Étienne,* 1890. 4°.
　　　　　　　　　　　　　　　7109. k. 16.
—— Atlas. fol.　　　　　　　1824. e. 10.

LAPPARENT (A. de) La Géologie en chemin de fer. Description du Bassin parisien. pp. 608. *Paris,* 1888. 12°.　　　　07109. i. 1.

FOURNIER (A.) Études géologiques des chemins de fer du Poitou. 1891, *etc.* 8°. Ac. Niort. *Société de Statistique.* Mémoires. Sér. 3. Tom. 8.
　　　　　　　　　　　　　　　Ac. 316.

LAROQUE (H.) Géologie descriptive du Bassin de la Voulzie. pp. 332. *Provins,* 1891. 8°.
　　　　　　　　　　　　　　　7109. aa. 25.

TROUESSART (É. L.) Au Bord de la Mer. Géologie des côtes de France. pp. 344. *Paris,* 1893. 8°..　　　　7002. aa. 2.

Ac. Heidelberg. *Geologische Landesanstalt.* Mitteilungen. *Heidelberg,* 1890, *etc.* 8°. Ac. 3141.

BRUNSWICK. *Cammer-Direction der Bergwerke.* Beiträge zur Geologie Braunschweigs. *Braunschweig,* 1894, *etc.* 8°.　07188. g.

STEINMANN (G.) and GRAEFF (F.) Géologischer Führer der Umgebung von Freiburg. pp. 141. *Freiburg,* 1895. 8°.　　7109. a. 10.

BEHME (F.) Geologischer Führer durch die Umgebung der Stadt Goslar. pp. 64. *Goslar,* 1894. 8°.　　07108. ee. 1. (8.)

DEECKE (W.) Die mesozoischen Formationen der Provinz Pommern. pp. 115. 1895. 8°. Ac. Greifswald. *Naturwissenschaftlicher Verein.* Mittheilungen. Jhrg. 26.　Ac. 2940.

Ac. London. *Geologists' Association.* Record of Excursions, 1860–90. pp. 571. *Lond.* 1891. 8°.
　　　　　　　　　　　　　　　Ac. 3172/5.

HUME (W. F.) Researches on the Upper Cretaceous Zones of the South of England. pp. 103. *Lond.* 1893. 8°.　　　　7109. e. 21.

LEWIS (H. C.) Papers on the Glacial Geology of Great Britain and Ireland. pp. 469. *Lond.* 1894. 8°.　　　　07109. g. 43.

MEESON (F.) Table of Oligocene, Eocene and Cretaceous Strata, pp. 6. *Woking,* 1895. 8°.
　　　　　　　　　　　　　　　7108. b. 15.

RAMSAY (*Sir* A. C.) Physical Geology of Great Britain. pp. 421. *Lond.* 1894. 8°.　2030. d.

WALFORD (E. A.) Making of the Dasset and Edge Hills of S. Warwickshire. 1895. 8°.
　　　　　　　　　　　　　　　Pam. 27.

MELLO (J. M.) Hand-book to the Geology of Derbyshire. pp. 89. *Lond.* 1891. 8°.
　　　　　　　　　　　　　　　7109. aa. 22.

FOWLER (J. B.) Local Geology for amateurs and beginners. pp. 22. *Lond.* 1895. 8°.
　　　　　　　　　　　　　　　07109. m. 7. (14.)

MORTON (G. H.) Geology of the country around Liverpool. pp. 287. *Lond.* 1891. 8°.
　　　　　　　　　　　　　　　07109. g. 20.

GEOLOGY.—Europe—*continued.*

LONDON. *Geological Field Class.* Lectures on the Geology of the London District. pp. 216. *Lond.* 1891. 8°.　　　　7108. a. 21.

Ac. G. B. & I. *British Association.* Contribution to the Geology of Nottinghamshire. pp. 90. *Nottingham,* 1893. 8°.
　　　　　　　　　　　　　　　7003. a. 11

HULL (E.) Physical Geology of Ireland. pp. 328. *Lond.* 1891. 8°.　10390. cc. 4.

EVANS (J. W.) Geology of the North-east of Caithness. pp. 48. *Lond.* 1891. 8°. Pam. 27.

RICHARDSON (R.) County of Edinburgh. Geology. pp. 40. *Edinb.* 1895. 8°. 10369. dd. 5.

LEPSIUS (G. R.) Geologie von Attika. pp. 196. *Berl.* 1893. 4°.　　　　7105. f. 1.

SALOMON (W.) Geologische Studien am Monte Aviólo. 1890. 4°. Ac. Berlin. *Deutsche geologische Gesellschaft.* Zeitschrift. Bd. 42.
　　　　　　　　　　　　　　　Ac. 3137.

PORTIS (A.) Contribuzioni alla storia fisica del bacino di Roma. pp. 293. *Torino,* 1893. 8°.
　　　　　　　　　　　　　　　7105. f. 3.

TALOTTI (G. B.) Cenni su di alcuni studi geologici nella Provincia di Trapani. pp. 54. *Trapani,* 1881. 8°.　7462. e. 2. (9.)

NICKLÈS (R.) Recherches géologiques sur les terrains secondaires et tertiaires d'Alicante. pp. 219. *Lille,* 1891. 8°.　7107. c. 3.

NATHORST (A. G.) Sveriges Geologi. *Stockh.* 1892, *etc.* 8°.　　07109. l.

See also supra : Petrography.

GEOMETRY.

General.

Ac. G. B. & I., *Association for the Improvement of Geometrical Teaching.* Graphic demonstrations of Geometric Problems. ff. 8. *Lond.* 1891. 8°.　　　　8535. cc. 33.

BARLOW (C. W. C.) Geometry of the similar figures. pp. 123. 1895. 8°. TUTORIAL SERIES. Tutorial Series.　　　12205. c. 245.

BIOCHE (C.) Introduction à l'etude de la géometrie moderne. pp. 95. *Paris,* 1891. 8°.
　　　　　　　　　　　　　　　8535. df. 15.

BLAIKIE (J.) and THOMSON (W.) Text-book of geometrical Deductions. *Lond.* 1891, *etc.* 8°.
　　　　　　　　　　　　　　　8534. aa. 31.

BRIGGS (W.) and EDMONDSON (T. W.) Geometrical properties of the Sphere. pp. 47. 1893. 8°. Tutorial Series.　12205. c. 162.

CARROLL (J.) Key to Carroll's Geometry. pp. 48. *Lond.* 1893. 8°.　　8507. b. 60.

CHAVE Y CASTILLA (J.) Ensayo de una nueva teoria de la Proporcionalidad de las líneas rectas. pp. 91. *Madrid.* 1891. 8°. 8533. i. 33.

CRANZ (H.) Das apollonische Berührungsproblem und verwandte Aufgaben. pp. 232. 1891. 8°. Kleyer's Encyclopädie.　8705. g.

CZUBER (E) Theorie der Beobachtungsfehler. pp. 418. *Leipz.* 1891. 8°.　8548. de. 22.

DAY (A. G.) Practical Plane & Solid Geometry. 2 pt. 1891. 8°. Cox (E. J.) Revision Sheets.
　　　　　　　　　　　　　　　8530. g. 41.

DIXON (E. T.) Foundations of Geometry. pp. 143. *Camb.* 1891. 8°.　　8535. d. 4.

DOBBIE (A. B.) Text-book of Solid Geometry. pp. 222. 1894. 8°. Blackie's Science Text-Books.　　　　　　　　8703. bb.

DUPUIS (N. F.) Elements of synthetic Solid Geometry. pp. 239. *N.Y.* 1893. 8°. 8530. aa. 47.

EAGLES (T. H.) Descriptive Geometry. pp. 319. *Lond.* 1891. 8°.　　　　8535. ccc. 34.

EBERHARD (V.) Zur Morphologie der Polyeder. pp. 245. *Leipz.* 1891. 8°.　　8535. d. 9.

GEOMETRY.—General—continued.

EBERHARD (V.) Die Grundgebilde der ebenen Geom trie. *Leipz.* 1895, *etc.* 8°.   8535. i.

EDWARDS (G. C.) Elements of Geometry. pp. 293. *N.Y.* 1895. 8°.   08533. f. 1.

FÜHRMANN (W.) Synthetische Beweise plani-metrischer Sätze. pp. 190. *Berl.* 1890. 8°.   8535. e. 37.

GOOD (T. W.) Science and Art Geometry. pp. 143. *Lond.* 1888. 8°.   8533. d. 12.

GOODMAN (W.) Bacon's excelsior chart of Geo-metrical Figures. *Lond.* 1893. fol.   Tab. 11747. a. (56.)

GOY (P. de) Usage de l'Imaginaire en Géo-metrie. 1889. 8°. Ac. Metz. *Société des Lettres.* Mémoir s. Sér. 3. An. 15. Ac. 370.

GRAHAM (R. H.) Geometry of Position. pp. 192. *Lond.* 1891. 8°.   8535. aaa. 48.

GRASSMANN (R.) Die Ausdehnungslehre. pp. 132. *Stettin,* 1891. 8°.   8535. ccc. 35.

GRIFFITHS (J.) Notes on the application of the Theory of Elliptic Transformation to the forma-tion of Semi-Covariants. pp. 18. *Oxf.* 1890. 8°.   Pam. 38.

—— Notes on the recent Geometry of the Triangle. pp. 39. *Oxf.* 1891. 8°.   8533. d. 27. (6.)

HALSTED (G. B.) Elementary Synthetic Geo-metry. pp. 164. *N.Y.* 1893. 8°.   08533. h. 3.

HEATH (R. S.) Solid Geometry. pp. 106. *Lond.* 1891. 8°.   8535. aa. 20.

HILLIER (D. E.) Illustrated geometrical Defini-tions. *Leeds,* 1894. fol.   Tab. 11747. b. (48.)

JONES (T.) Descriptive Geometry. 2 ser. *Manch.* 1893. 8°.   8534. cc. 34.

—— Practical Geometry. pp. 79. *Manch.* 1893. 8°.   8535. de. 12.

JONSON (B.) The New School of Art Geometry. pp. 192. *Lond.* 1890. 8°.   8535. ccc. 29.

KILLING (W.) Einführung in die Grundlagen der Geometrie. *Paderborn,* 1893, *etc.* 8°. 8535. dd.

KRAFT (F.) Abriss des geometrischen Kalküls. pp. 255. *Leipz.* 1893. 8°.   8535. dd. 18.

KUMPA (J.) Anschauung und Darstellung. 2 pt. *Darmstadt,* 1890. 8°. & fol.   14001. a. 30.

LACHLAN (R.) Elementary treatise on modern Pure Geometry. pp. 288. *Lond.* 1893. 8°.   8535. d. 16.

LINSENBARTH (H.) Untersuchungen über Uni-kursalkurven dritter Ordnung. pp. 35. *Berl.* 1895. 4°.   Pam. 38.

LOBACHEVSKY (N.) Geometrische Untersuchun-gen zur Theorie der Parallellinien. pp. 61. *Berl.* 1887. 8°.   Pam. 38.

—— Geometrical researches on the theory of Parallels. pp. 50. *Austin,* 1891. 8°. 8535. d. 15.

MARIE (M.) Réalisation des formes imaginaires en Géométrie. pp. 179. *Paris,* 1891. 8°.   8535. df. 19.

MOLENBROEK (P.) Anwendung der Quater-nionen auf die Geometrie. pp. 257. 8. *Leiden,* 1893. 8°.   8535. c. 13.

MORRIS (I. H.) Practical Plane and Solid Geo-metry. pp. 260. *Lond.* 1890. 8°. 8535. b. 35.

ORIO Y RUBIO (M.) Libro de problemas geomé-tricos, *etc. Palencia,* 1894, *etc.* 4°.   8531. df.

PETERSEN (J.) Text-book of elementary Plane Geometry. *Lond.* 1880. 8°.   8507. b. 32.

RAWLE (J. S.) Practical Plane and Solid Geo-metry. pp. 127. *Lond.* 1891. 8°. 8534. aa. 33.

RESAL (H.) Exposition de la Théorie des sur-faces. pp. 171. *Paris,* 1891. 8°.   8533. cc. 40.

RICHARDSON (G.) and RAMSEY (A. S.) Modern Plane Geometry. pp. 199. *Lond.* 1894. 8°.   8533. b. 41.

GEOMETRY.—General—continued.

ROHN (C.) and PAPPERITZ (E.) Lehrbuch der darstellenden Geometrie. *Leipz.* 1893, *etc.* 8°.   8535. d.

RUCHONNET (C.) Exposition géométrique des propriétés des courbes. pp. 180. *Lausanne,* 1887. 8°.   8533. d. 23.

RUSSELL (J. W.) Elementary treatise on Pure Geometry. pp. 323. 1893. 8°. Clarendon Press Series.   2319. b. 9.

SAUVAGE (P.) Les Lieux géométriques. pp. 113. *Paris,* 1893. 8°.   8535. d. 20.

SCABANO (A.) I Cinque Poliedri regolari. pp. 24. *Napoli,* 1891. 8°.   Pam. 38.

SCHROETER (H.) Grundzüge einer reingeome-trischen Theorie der Raumkurve vierter Ord-nung. pp. 100. *Leipz.* 1890. 8°.   8535. f. 31.

SEIPP (H.) Lehrbuch der räumlichen Elementar-Geometrie. 1892, *etc.* 8°. Kleyer's Encyklo-pädie.   8705. g.

SHAW (E. R.) Inventional Geometry. pp. 11. *N.Y.* 1895. 8°.   8533. dd. 11. (9.)

SMITH (W. B.) Introductory modern Geometry of point, ray and circle. pp. 297. *Lond.* 1893. 8°.   8535. de. 11.

SPENCER (W. G.) Inventional Geometry. pp. 47. *Lond.* 1892. 8°.   8535. b. 47.

STAHL (H.) and KOMMERELL (V.) Die Grund-formeln der allgemeinen Flächentheorie. pp. 114. *Leipz.* 1893. 8°.   8535. dd. 19.

STEWART (S. T.) Plane and Solid Geometry. pp. 406. *N.Y.* 1891. 8°.   8535. df. 16.

THIRY (C.) Applications remarquables du théo-rème de Stewart. pp. 94. *Gand,* 1891. 8°.   Pam. 38.

ZANTEN (L. v.) and SCHOLTEN (G. A.) Leerboek der Meetkunde. pp. 144. *Groningen,* 1894. 8°.   8533. c. 40.

———

ANDERSON (R. E.) The Plane Triangle A B C. pp. 14. *Edinb.* 1892. 8°.   8531. cc. 28. (6.)

DOUGLAS (W. D.) How to trisect any angle. pp. 22. *Cardiff,* 1892. 8°.   8534. aa. 36.

EMMERICH (A.) Die brocardschen Gebilde, *etc.* pp. 153. *Berl.* 1891. 8°.   8535. d. 8.

FIALKOWSKY (N.) Die vollständige Tri-section des Winkels. pp. 25. *Wien,* 1893. 8°. Pam. 38.

GRIFFITHS (J.) Notes on recent Geometry of the Triangle. pp. 39. *Oxf.* 1891. 8°.   Pam. 38.

KOENIG (M.) Die geometrische Theilung des Winkels. pp. 32. *Berl.* 1894. 8°.   Pam. 38.

LANIGAN (J. A.) The Trisection of the Angle. pp. 15. *Hyde Park, Mass.* 1890. 8°.   Pam. 38.

———

KARAGIANNIDES (A.) Die nichteuklidische Geo-metrie. pp. 44. *Berl.* 1893. 8°.   Pam. 38.

LORIA (G.) Il Periodo aureo della Geometria greca. 1890. 4°. Ac. *Accademia delle Scienze.* Memorie. Ser. 2. Tom. 40.   Ac. 2816.

See also CIRCLE : MATHEMATICS.

Analytical Geometry.

BIANCHI (L.) Lezioni di Geometria differenziale. pp. 541. *Pisa,* 1894. 8°.   8533. i. 11.

BRIGGS (W.) and BRYAN (G. H.) Elements of Co-ordinate Geometry. pp. 220. 1891. 8°. Tutorial Series.   12205. c. 34.

EDMONDSON (T. W.) Key to Briggs and Bryan's Co-ordinate Geometry. pp. 191. 1892. 8°. Tutorial Series.   12205. c. 96.

BRIGGS (W.) and BRYAN (G. H.) Worked examples in Co-ordinate Geometry. pp. 61. 1891. 8°. Tutorial Series.   12205. cc. 41.

CASEY (J.) Treatise on Analytical Geometry. pp. 564. 1893. 8°. Dublin University Press Series.   2322. e.

GEORGIA, Asia. AURIAC (E. d') Thamar, Reine de Géorgie 1184–1212. *Angers*, 1892. 8°.
10601. ff. 11. (3.)

STANLEY (H. M) My early Travels. 2 vol. *Lond.* 1895. 8°. 10027. ce. 4.

GEORGIAN FOLK TALES. Georgian Folk Tales. pp. 175. 1894. 8°. Grimm Library. No. 1.
12431. ee.

See also CAUCASUS : RUSSIA.

GEORGIA, United States. BROWN (J. M.) Mountain campaigns in Georgia. pp. 72. *Buffalo*, 1890. 4°. 9605. f. 11.

JONES (C. C.) Military operations in Georgia during the war. pp. 32. *Augusta*, 1893. 8°.
9551. k. 8. (8.)

—— Biographical sketches of delegates from Georgia to the Continental Congress. pp. 211. *Bost.* 1891. 8°. 010882. l. 2.

FOLSOM (M. M.) Scraps of Song and Southern Scenes. pp. 199. *Atlanta*, 1889. 8°. 12356. m. 11.

HAMMOND (N. J.) The University of Georgia. pp. 173. *Atlanta*, 1893. 8°. 8366. bb. 42.

GERA. MEISSNER (H.) Die Stadt Gera und das fürstliche Haus Reuss i. L. *Gera*, 1893, *etc.* 8°. 10255. cc.

GERMAN-FRENCH WAR, 1870-71.
AC, *etc.* Chatham. *Royal Engineers' Institute.* The Franco-German War, 1870-71. pp. 294. *Chatham*, 1894. 8°. 9135. dd. 8.

ALMIRANTE (J.) Estudio sobre la Guerra franco-germana, 1870. pp. 495. *Madrid*, 1891, 8°.
9079. m. 2.

BAUER (M.) Unter rothgekreuzten Standarten, *etc.* pp. 113. *Berl.* 1895. 8°. 9080. f. 7.

BERG (M v.) Ulanen-Briefe von der 1. Armee. pp. 253. *Bielefeld*, 1893. 8°. 9078. g. 14.

BONDOIS (P.) Histoire de la Guerre de 1870-71. pp. 460. *Paris*, 1888. 4°. 9080. m. 2.

BRIEFE. Briefe aus dem Kriege 1870-71. pp. 327. *Mannheim*, 1890. 8°. 9080. d. 35.

CARDINAL VON WIDDERN (G.) Deutschfranzösischer Krieg 1870-71. *Berl.* 1893, *etc.* 8°.
9080. f.

CHUQUET (A.) La Guerre 1870-71. pp. 310. *Paris*, 1895. 8°. 9079. k. 9.

EHRENBERG (F.) Kleine Erlebnisse in grosser Zeit. pp. 162. *Strassburg*, 1890. 8°. 9080. cc. 9.

EHRENBERG (H.) Feldzugs-Erinnerungen. pp. 224. *Rathenow*, 1891. 8°. 9080. cc. 29.

ELFONS (P. v.) Tagebuch des deutsch-französischen Krieges, 1870-71. *Saarbrücken*, 1893, *etc.* 8°. 304.

ERNST (W.) Vom Rhein bis zum Kanal. pp. 158. *Rathenow*, 1893. 8°. 9080. ee. 5.

FEHLEISEN (E.) Der deutsch-französische Krieg 1870-71. pp. 432. *Reutlingen*, 1893, 8°.
9080. m. 4.

FORBES (A.) Memories and Studies of War. pp. 368. *Lond.* 1895. 8°. 12354. dd. 10.

GERMAN-FRENCH WAR. Erinnerungen eines ehemaligen pfälzischen Reservelieutenants. pp. 283. *Kaiserslautern*, 1891. 8°. 9080. c. 32.

GERMANS. Ruses de guerre des Allemands. pp. 32. *Nancy*, 1891. 8°. 9004. gg. 24. (8.)

GUNTERMANN (A.) Mit Badens Wehr für deutsche Ehr. *Freiburg*, 1895, *etc.* 8°. 9335. bb.

HARTMANN (J. v.) Briefe aus dem deutsch-französischen Kriege. pp. 180. *Kassel*, 1893. 8°.
9080. e. 8.

HEROS VON BORCKE (J. H.) Mit Prinz Friedrich Karl. pp. 319. *Berl.* 1893. 8°. 10704. g. 42.

HOENIG (F.) Gefechtsbilder aus dem Kriege 1870, 71. *Berl.* 1891, *etc.* 8°. 9080. e.

GERMAN-FRENCH WAR—*continued.*
HORST VON GERSDORFF ( ) Vor zwanzig Jahren. *Rathenow*, 1893, 8°. 9080. c. 37.

KANAPPE ( ) Sans Armée, 1870-71. pp. 335. *Paris*, 1893. 8°. 9080. e. 5.

KNECHTEL (O.) Erinnerungen eines 75ers aus dem Feldzuge 1870-71. pp. 206. *Bremen*, 1895. 8°. 9080. cc. 13.

KOCH-BREUBERG (F.) Drei Jahre in Frankreich. pp. 172. *München*, 1891. 8°. 9080. bbb. 31.

KUNZ (H.) Die deutsche Reiterei in den Schlachten des Krieges 1870-71. pp. 423. *Berl.* 1895. 8°. 9080. dd. 24.

LANUSSE (E.) Vingt Minutes dans la Vie d'un Peuple. pp. 377. *Paris*, 1893. 12°. 9080. e. 4.

MANGEOT (H.) Des Causes de nos revers de 1870-71. pp. 39. *Nancy*, 1895. 8°.
8830. bbb. 13. (8.)

MAZADE (A. de) Lettres et notes intimes, 1870-71. pp. 738. *Beaumont*, 1891. 8°.
9080. k. 8.

MOLTKE (H. C. B. v.) *Count.* Gesammelte Schriften und Denkwürdigkeiten. 7 Bde. *Berl.* 1891, 92. 8°. 12252. i. 4.

—— Essays, Speeches and Memoirs. 2 vol. *Lond.* 1893. 8°. 12354. k. 16.

—— The Franco-German War of 1870-71. pp. 447. *Lond.* 1893. 8°. 9080. cc. 21.

JUNG (H. F. J.) M. de Moltke et ses Mémoires. pp. 32. *Paris*, 1892, 8°. 9004. c. 16. (8.)

NEBE (H.) Erlebnisse eines badischen Feld-artilleristen, 1870-71. pp. 159. *Karlsruhe*, 1893. 8°. 9080. c. 38.

PONCHALON (H. de) Souvenirs de Guerre, 1870-71. pp. 305. *Paris*, 1893, 8°. 9080. c. 6.

POULLIN (M.) Les forteresses françaises en 1870-71. pp. 312. *Paris*, 1893. 8°. 9080. i. 17.

ROBOLSKY (H.) Die 25-jährigen Gedenktage des Krieges von 1870-71. pp. 223. *Leipz.* 1895. 8°.
9080. ee. 12.

ROMAGNY (C. M.) Guerre franco-allemande, 1870-71, *etc.* pp. 385. *Paris*, 1891. 8°.

—— Atlas. 1891. 4°. 9079. l. 7.

ROUSSET (C. F. M.) Histoire de la Guerre Franco-Allemande, 1870, 71. *Paris*, 1895, *etc.* 8°.
9080. f.

ROUSSET (L.) Les Combattants de 1870-71. pp. 368. *Paris*, 1891. 8°. 9080. ee. 2.

SCHEIBERT (J.) Der Krieg, 1870-71. pp. 168. *Berl.* 1895. 8°. 9080. m. 5.

SIEBENUNDSECHZIGER. Bis in die Kriegsgefangenschaft. pp. 136. *Berl.* 1893. 8°. 9080. g. 3.

SELBITZ (H. v.) Aus grosser Zeit! Kleine Erinnerungen aus dem Feldzuge 1870/71. *Ansbach*, 1895, *etc.* 8°. 9079. f.

SOUS-OFFICIER. Journal d'un Sous-Officier, 1870. pp. 331. *Paris*, 1891. 8°. 9080. aaa. 41.

TIEMANN (H.) Feldzugserinnerungen eines Kriegsfreiwilligen. pp. 119. *Braunschweig*, 1895. 8°. 9080. c. 16.

WAGNER (F. B.) 300 Tage im Sattel. pp. 183. *Dresden*, 1892. 8°. 9080. c. 36.

WALKER (*Sir* C. P. B.) Days of a Soldier's Life. pp. 411. *Lond.* 1894 8°. 9078. dd. 19.

WARMENG (C.) Erlebnisse eines Arztes aus der französischen Kriegs Zeit. 1870-71. pp. 311. *Berl.* 1892. 8°. 9080. cc. 3.

WITT (P. de) Six mois de Guerre, 1870-71. pp. 111. *Paris*, 1894. 8°. 9080. aa. 17.

WOLOWSKI (A. L.) Campagnes de 1870-71. pp. 278. *Paris*, 1893. 12°. 9080. e. 9.

YVERT (L) Les vaillantes chevauchées de la cavalerie française, 1870-71. pp. 222. *Paris*, 1895. 8°. 8830. f. 39.

GERMAN-FRENCH WAR—*continued.*

GENEVOIS (H.) Carnot et la défense nationale. pp. 31. *Paris*, 1894. 8°. Pam. 69.

GRANDIN (L.) Le dernier Maréchal de France. Canrobert. pp. 343. *Paris*, 1895. 8°. 010662. i. 35.

BRUNEL (I. M.) Le général Faidherbe. pp. 316. *Paris*, 1892. 12°. 010662. g. 11.

JARRAS (L.) Souvenirs du Général Jarras, 1870. pp. 403. *Paris*, 1892. 8°. 010662. h. 13.

DUMAS (N. J. B. H. A.) La Guerre, 1870. Première campagne de l'Est. pp. 335. *Paris*, 1891. 8°. 9080. ec. 1.

EUVRARD (X.) Guerre de 1870. La première armée de l'Est. pp. 268. *Paris*, 1895. 8°. 9080. dd. 25.

GRATIOLET (L.) Souvenirs d'un artilleur de l'armée du Rhin. pp. 265. *Paris*, 1892. 12°. 9080. aaa. 43.

SEUBERT (A.) Translation of the story of the Flying Column for the protection of right shore of the Rhine. pp. 32. *N.Y.* 1891. 8°. 9008. g. 7. (6.)

YVERT (L.) Combats de l'armée du Rhin, 1870. pp. 261. *Paris*, 1893. 8°. 9079. i. 20.

MARTIN (P.) Wissembourg, Reichsoffen, Forbach. pp. 290. *Paris*, 1891. 8°. 9079. h. 12.

MATTHAEI (W.) Ein Gang über das Schlachtfeld von Wörth. pp. 115. *Strassb.* 1895. 8°. 10235. b. 31.

FROESCHWILLER. Relation de la bataille de Froeschwiller. pp. 300. *Paris*, 1890. 8°. 9080. aaa. 34.

BADEL (É.) Mars-la-Tour et son monument. pp. 106. *Mars-la-Tour*, 1893. 8°. 9080. k. 4.

MALO (C.) La Question de Nancy et la défense nationale. pp. 54. *Paris*, 1894. 8°. 8830. f. 38. (10.)

ZAISS (J.) Aus dem Tagebuch eines bad. Pioniers. Schilderung der Belagerungen von Strassburg und Belfort. pp. 157. *Karlsruhe*, 1894. 8°. 9080. c. 39.

BOUCHARD (L.) Mémoires d'un Soldat de l'Armée de Metz. pp. 247. *Saint-Amand*, 1894. 8°. 9078. ccc. 36.

BRANCHARD (E. L. R.) Les trois batailles sous Metz. pp. 190. *Briey*, 1894. 8°. 9079. h. 22.

FIRCKS (A. R. G. H. T. v.) Die Vertheidigung von Metz. pp. 477. *Leipz.* 1893. 8°. 9080. g.

G., A. Fallait-il quitter Metz en 1870? pp. 24. *Paris*, 1893. 8°. 9078. ff. 17. (6.)

MARCHAL (G.) Le Drame de Metz. pp. 384. *Paris*, 1890. 8°. 9080. dd. 17.

METZ. Metz. 1870. Kriegsgeschichtliche Studie. pp. 132. *Weisbaden*, 1893. 8°. 9080. cc. 30.

NATZMER (G. E. v.) Bei der Landwehr, vor Metz. pp. 168. *Gotha*, 1894. 8°. 9080. cc. 32.

HOENIG (F.) 24 Stunden Moltkescher Strategie entwickelt an den Schlachten von Gravelotte und St. Privat. pp. 247. *Berl.* 1891. 8°. 8823. n. 15.

KUNZ (H.) Die Schlacht von Noisseville. pp. 130. *Berl.* 1892. 8°. 9079. i. 15.

LEBRUN (B. L. J.) Bazeilles-Sedan. pp. 336. *Paris*, 1891. 12°. 9080. bbb. 37.

PLANÇON (A.) Sedan—Bazeilles. pp. 92. *Paris*, 1891. 8°. 012803. f. 46.

ZOLA (É.) La Débâcle. pp. 636. *Paris*, 1892. 8°. 12517. e. 38.

—— The Downfall. pp. 534. *Lond.* 1892. 8°. 012548. eeee. 1.

ARNAUD (J.) La Débâcle de M. Zola. pp. 20. *Paris*, 1892. 8°. 11825. q. 21. (2.)

LANUSSE (E.) L'Heure suprême à Sedan. pp. 381. *Paris*, 1892. 12°. 9080. aaa. 42.

GERMAN-FRENCH WAR.—*continued.*

DESCHAUMES (E.) L'Armée du Nord, 1870-71. Campagne du Général Faidherbe. pp. 293. *Paris*, 1895. 4°. 9080. l. 9.

HUPIN (E.) Les Moblots sédanais à Givet. pp. 44. *Sedan*, 1893. 8°. 9078. cc. 27. (8.)

LEHAUTCOURT (P.) Campagne de la Loire. Coulmiers et Orléans. pp. 474. *Paris*, 1893. 8°. 9079. f. 11.

—— Campagne de la Loire. Josnes, Vendôme, Le Mans. pp. 444. *Paris*, 1895. 8°. 9080. f. 9.

FÉLIX (G.) Le Général Chanzy. pp. 239. *Tours*, 1895. 8°. 9080. g. 9.

GRANDIN (L.) Chanzy. pp. 364. *Paris*, 1895. 8°. 010662. k. 18.

HOENIG (F.) Der Volkskrieg an der Loire. *Berl.* 1893, etc. 8°. 9079. f.

KORTZFLEISCH (G. F. A. v.) Der Feldzug gegen den Loir und die Einnahme von Vendôme. pp. 165. *Berl.* 1892. 8°. 9079. i. 13.

COLTELLONI (P.) Combat et incendie de Châteaudun. pp. 32. *Paris*, 1892. 8°. 9004. gg. 31. (6.)

CLARIN DE LA RIVE (A.) Il Condottiere G. Garibaldi 1870-71 pp. 375 *Paris*, 1892. 8°. 10629. c. 34.

ADAMISTRE (G.) Le Pont de Fontenoy. Épisodes de la guerre de partisans dans les Vosges. pp. 80. *Paris*, 1890. 12°. 9080. cc. 21.

BOURRAS (M. A.) Rapport du Colonel B. sur les opérations du Corps Franc des Vosges. pp. 71. *Paris*, 1892. 8°. 010662. ff. 30.

WOLLOWSKI (A. L.) Le Colonel Bourras et le Corps Franc des Vosges. pp. 321. *Paris*, 1892. 12°. 9080. bb. 32.

DORMOY (P. A.) Les trois batailles de Dijon, 30 Oct., 26 Nov., 21 Jan. 1870-71. pp. 600. *Paris*, 1894. 8°. 9079. k. 7.

JALNY (P.) La Bataille de Nuits, 18 déc. 1870. pp. 92. *Beaune*, 1894. 8°. 9080. aaa. 45.

LEGRIS (F.) Les Prussiens à Lagny. *Paris*, 1891, etc. 8°. 9080. ee.

K., Y. Le combat de Châtillon et l'investissement de Paris au Sud. pp. 80. *Paris*, 1893. 8°. 9080. cc. 28.

AUBOURG (L.) Siège de Paris 1870-71. Souvenirs intimes. pp. 86. *Caen*, 1894. 16°. Pam. 28.

DUQUET (A.) Paris, Thiers, le plan Trochu et l'Haÿ, 2-29 Nov. pp. 368. *Paris*, 1895. 8°. 9080. e. 15.

—— Paris, la Malmaison, le Bourget et le 31 octobre. pp. 345. *Paris*, 1893. 12°. 9080. bb. 34.

—— Paris. Les Batailles de la Marne, 30 Nov.—8 Déc. pp. 374. *Paris*, 1893. 12°. 9080. aa. 22.

G., A. Le Blocus de Paris et la première armée de la Loire. 2 pt. *Paris*, 1889, 90. 8°. 9080. c. 23.

GILBERT (J.) Siège de Paris. Notes d'un mobile breton. pp. 156. *Saint Brieuc*, 1894. 8°. 9080. e. 14.

ROUVET (M.) Viollet-le-Duc et Alphand au siège de Paris. pp. 349. *Paris*, 1892. 8°. 9079. l. 9.

THOUMAS (C. A.) Paris, Tours, Bordeaux. pp. 292. *Paris*, 1893. 8°. 9231. g. 21.

VALLETTE (R.) Les Mobiles de la Vendée au siège de Paris, 1870-1871. pp. 27. *Vannes*, 1888. 8°. Pam. 28.

WERNERSDORF (C. T.) Fünf Monate vor Paris. pp. 215. *Altenburg*, 1894. 8°. 10169. bbb. 23.

KUNZ (H.) Der grosse Durchbruchsversuch der zweiten Pariser Armee, 29. Nov.—3. Dez. pp. 127. *Berl.* 1891. 8°. 9080. dd. 16.

GERMAN-FRENCH WAR — *continued.*

FRANCE. *Army.* Betrachtungen über die Operationen der französischen Ost-, West- und Nord-Armee, Januar 1871. pp. 103. *Wien,* 1890. 8°.
8831. c. 20.

GENEVOIS (H.) Les dernières cartouches, janvier 1871. pp. 410. *Paris,* 1893. 8°. 9080. d. 38.

VORMENG (C.) Bilder aus der französischen Okkupationszeit. pp. 293. *Berl.* 1893. 8°.
9080. cc. 31.

LACROIX (C. de) Les morts pour la patrie. Tombes militaires à la mémoire des soldats tués pendant la guerre. pp. 64. *Paris,* 1891. 4°.
10662. i. 31.

FONTANE (T.) Souvenirs d'un prisonnier de guerre allemand en 1870. pp. 270.
Paris, 1892. 8°. 9078. ccc. 16.

GUERS (É.) Les soldats français dans les prisons d'Allemagne. pp. 378. *Paris,* 1890. 8°.
9080. c. 25.

—— How French Soldiers fared in German Prisons. pp. 388. *Lond.* 1891. 8°. 9080. cc. 6.

QUESNAY DE BEAUREPAIRE (A.) De Wissembourg à Ingolstadt. Souvenirs d'un capitaine prisonnier en Bavière. pp. 309,
Paris, 1891. 8°. 9079. l. 6.

BOURNAND (F.) Le Clergé pendant la Guerre 1870–1871. pp. 366. *Paris,* 1891. 8°.
9080. cc. 20.

ARSAC (J. d') Les Frères des Écoles chrétiennes pendant la guerre. pp. 430. *Paris,* 1892. 8°.
9080. cc. 22.

TURQUAN (J.) Les Femmes de France pendant l'Invasion. pp. 445. *Paris,* 1893. 8°. 9080. e. 3.
See also FRANCE, *History :* GERMANY, *History.*

GERMAN LANGUAGE.

Bibliography.

BREUL (C. H.) Bibliographical Guide to the study of the German Language. pp. 144.
Lond. 1895. 8°. 11901. aaa. 42.

General.

EBERING (E.) Berliner Beiträge zur germanischen Philologie. *Berl.* 1893, *etc.* 8°. 12901. d.

HILDEBRAND (H. R.) Gesammelte Aufsätze zur deutschen Philologie. pp. 335.
Leipz. 1890. 8°. 12962. f. 31.

—— Vom deutschen Sprachunterricht in der Schule. pp. 278. *Leipz.* 1890. 8°. 8357. cc. 46.

MOLEE (E.) Germanik English. Scheme for uniting the English and German languages. pp. 64. *Bristol, Dak,* 1889. 8°. 12901. e. 38.

MUSGRAVE (C. A.) The Caricature of German in English Schools. pp. 32. *Lond.* 1894. 8°.
12901. bbb. 45. (6.)

Commercial German.

EITZEN (F. W.) Wörterbuch der Handelsprache, Deutsch-englisch. pp. 915. *Leipz.* 1893. 8°.
12962. o. 4.

HOSSFELD (C.) Deutsch - spanischer Handels-Correspondent. pp. 400. *Lond.* 1891. 16°.
10920. aa. 25.

PREISINGER (H.) German Commercial Reader. pp. 196. *Lond.* 1893. 8°. 8228. aaaa. 16.

SMITH (F. C.) Introduction to Commercial German. pp. 192. 1892. 8°. Macmillan's Commercial Class-books. 012202. h.

Conversation.

CHARLIN (A.) Constant-Speaking System. German Text. pp. 136. *Lond.* 1894. 8°. 12963. c. 36.

LANGE (F. K. W.) Easy German Dialogues, *etc.* pp. 79. *Lond.* 1893. 8°. 12962. ccc. 18.

SWAN (H.) Travellers' Colloquial German. pp. 142. *Lond.* 1891. 8°. 12962. aa. 26.
See also supra: Commercial.

GERMAN — *continued.*

Dialects.

MENTZ (F.) Bibliographie der deutschen Mundartenforschung. pp. 181. 1893. 8° BREMER (O.) Sammlung kurzer Grammatiken. Bd. 2. 12962 q.

BREMER (O.) Sammlung kurzer Grammatiken deutscher Mundarten. *Leipz.* 1893, *etc.* 8°.
12962. q.

SCHMITZ (W.) Die Misch-Mundart in den Kreisen Geldern, Aachen, *etc.* pp. 211. *Dülken,* 1893. 8°. 12962. p. 6.

JARDON (A.) Grammatik der achener Mundart. *Aachen,* 1891, *etc.* 8°. 12962. q.

KAHL (W.) Mundart und Schriftsprache im Elsass. pp. 62. *Zabern,* 1893. 8°. 12962. o. 2.

ALSATIAN STUDIES. Alsatische Studien. *Strassb.* 1891, *etc.* 8°. 12962. k.

BRENNER (G.) Mundarten und Schriftsprache in Bayern. pp. 83. 1890. 8°. Bayerische Bibliothek. Bd. 18. 12253. g.

DREYER (A.) Aus mein' Hoamatland. Gedichte in altbayerischer Mundart. pp. 82.
Passau, 1891. 8°. Pam. 61.

BRENNER (O.) and HARTMANN (A.) Bayerns Mundarten. *München,* 1891, *etc.* 8°. 12963. k. 33.

BRENDICKE (H.) Der berliner Volksdialekt. 1892. 8°. Ac. Berlin. *Verein für die Geschichte Berlins.* Schriften. Hft. 29. Ac. 7328.

HECKING ( ) Die Eifel in ihrer Mundart. pp. 112. *Prüm,* 1890. 8°. 12962. aaa. 37.

LUMTZER (V.) Die leibitzer Mundart. 1894. 8°. PAUL (H.) Beiträge zur Geschichte der deutschen Sprache. Bd. 19. Hft. 1, 2. 12962. o.

HOFFMANN (E.) Die Vocale der lippischen Mundart. pp. 69. *Hannover,* 1887. 8°. Pam. 47.

SCHOEPPE (C.) Naumburgs Mundart. pp. 58. *Naumburg,* 1893. 8°. Pam. 47.

BORNEMANN (J. W. J.) Plattdeutsche Gedichte. pp. 344. *Berl.* 1891. 8°. 11528. ee.

Ac. Hamburg. *Verein für Niederdeutsche Sprachforschung.* Forschungen. *Norden,* 1886, *etc.* 8°.
Ac. 9822/5.

KNOOP (O.) Plattdeutsches aus Hinterpommern. 2 pt. *Posen,* 1890. 4°. Pam. 47.

FRISCHBIER (H.) Preussiches Wörterbuch. 2 Bde. *Berl.* 1882, 83. 8°. 12962. s. 3.

LEITHAEUSER (J.) Gallicismen in niederrheinischen Mundarten. *Barmen,* 1891, *etc.* 4°.
12962. s. 2.

GALLÉE (J. H.) Altsächsische Grammatik. 1891. 8°. BRAUNE (W.) Sammlung kurzer Grammatiken. No. VI. 12962. q.

SCHLUETER (W.) Untersuchungen zur Geschichte der altsächsischen Sprache.
Göttingen, 1892, *etc.* 8°. 12962. o.

ECKART (R.) Niedersächsische Sprachdenkmäler. pp. 68. *Osterwieck,* 1893. 8°.
011902. m. 20. (21.)

HERTEL (D.) Die salzunger Mundart. pp. 150. 1888. 8°. Ac. Meiningen. *Hennebergischer Verein.* Neue Beiträge. Lief. 5. 9325. d.

FISCHER (H.) Geographie der schwäbischen Mundart. pp. 88. *Tübingen,* 1895. 4°.

—— Atlas. 1895. *obl.* fol. 14001. d. 25.

BOHNENBERGER (C.) Geschichte der schwäbischen Mundart im XV. Jahrhundert. *Tübingen,* 1892, *etc.* 8°. 12962. o.

FISCHER (H.) Beiträge zur Litteraturgeschichte Schwabens. pp. 246. *Tübingen,* 1891. 8°.
011824. f. 48.

HEINZERLING (J.) Probe eines Wörterbuches der siegerländer Mundart. pp. 39.
Leipz. 1891. 8°. 12901. d. 34. (5.)

GERMAN.—Dialects—*continued.*

SCHMIDT (B.) Der Vocalismus der siegerländer Mundart. pp. 139. *Halle,* 1894. 8°.
12962. g. 34.

KNOTHE (F.) Wörterbuch der schlesischen Mundart in Nordböhmen. pp. 583.
Hohenelbe, 1888. 8°.   12963. d. 53.

WERCHOTA (A.) G'schichtn aus n Grobn aussa. pp. 184. *Graz,* 1890. 8°.   12331. i. 35.

HERWIG (M.) Idiotismen aus Thüringen. pp. 32.
Eisleben, 1893. 4°.   12902. h. 19. (3.)

WINDER (E.) Die vorarlberger Dialectdichtung. pp. 172. *Innsbruck,* 1890. 8°.   011824. i. 6.

REICHARDT (E.) Die wasunger Mundart.
1895, *etc.* 8°. Ac. Meiningen. *Verein für meiningische Geschichte. Schriften.* Hft. 17.
Ac. 7114.

BACCIOCCO (F. A.) Der wiener Dialect. pp. 62.
Wien, 1890. 8°.   12901. d. 32. (6.)

HOFFMAN (W. J.) Notes and vocabulary of the Pennsylvania German dialect. 1889. 8°. Ac. Philadelphia. *American Philosophical Society. Proceedings.* Vol. 26. No. 129.   Ac. 1830.

LEARNED (M. D.) Pennsylvania German dialect. pp. 114. *Baltimore,* 1889. 8°.   12972. o. 2.
See also infra : History : SWISS DIALECTS, YIDDISH.

Dictionaries.

FAULMANN (C.) Etymologisches Wörterbuch der deutschen Sprache. pp. 421.
Halle, 1891, 92. 8°.   12962. l. 16.

BRYNILDSEN (J.) Tysk-norsk, dansk Ordbog.
Kristiania, 1895, *etc.* 8°.   12972. dd.

ADLER (G. J.) Dictionary of the German and English languages, *etc,* 2 pt. *N.Y.* 1890. 8°.
Cat. Desk.

EITZEN (F. W.) Wörterbuch der Handelsprache, Deutsch-englisch. pp. 915. *Leipz.* 1893. 8°.
12962. o. 4.

FLUEGEL (J. G.) English-German and German-English Dictionary. 3 vol. *Lond.* 1891. 8°.
2116. f.

—— Praktisches Wörterbuch der englischen und deutschen Sprache. 2 Thle. *Leipz.* 1891. 8°.
12962. k. 18.

JAESCHKE (R.) Nutt's Conversation Dictionaries. English-German. pp. 570. *Lond.* 1893. 16°.
12962. a. 28.

KLUGE (F.) Etymological Dictionary of the German Language. pp. 446. *Lond.* 1891. 8°.
2272. c. 20.

KRUMMACHER (M.) Wörterbuch der englischen und deutschen Umgangesprache. 3 pt.
Lond. 1892. 8°.   12962. ccc. 17.

MURET (E.) Encyclopædic English-German and German-English Dictionary.
Berl. 1891, *etc.* 8°.   12962. m. 8.

WALLER (J. R.) English-German and German-English Medical Dictionary. *Leipz.* 1891. 8°.
7321. aaa. 20.

WEIR (F.) Cassell's German Dictionary. 2 pts.
Lond. 1891. 8°   12963. bbb. 46.

WIEDEMANN (F. J.) Ehstnisch-deutsches Wörterbuch. pp. 1406. 2 vol.
St. Petersburg, 1893. 8°.   12963. m. 9.

ROMAGNÉ (E.) Dictionnaire militaire français-allemand. pp. 176. *Paris,* 1894. 8°.
12962. f. 34.

GIANNARES (A. N.) Wörterbuch der deutschen und griechischen Sprache. pp. 1146.
Athen, 1888. 8°.   12924. cc. 21.

—— Deutsch-neugriechisches Handwörterbuch. 2 Abth. *Hannover,* 1883. 8°.   12923. bbb. 20.

SIEGFRIED (C.) and STADE (B.) Hebräisches Wörterbuch zum Alten Testamente.
Leipz. 1892, *etc.* 8°.   012904. h.

GERMAN.—Dictionaries—*continued*

KÖNNYE (N.) Deutsch-ungarisches und unga-risch-deutsches Taschenwörterbuch. 2 Thle.
Wien, 1890. 8°.   12976. a. 20.

BOOCH-ÁRKOSSY (F.) Polnisch-deutsches and deutsch-polnisches Taschenwörterbuch. 2 pt.
Leipz. 1890. 8°.   12975. b. 1.

ENENKEL (A.) and SOUZA PINTO ( ) Novo Diccionario portuguez-allemão e allemão-portuguez. 2 pt. *Paris,* 1894. 8°.   12943. a. 50.

ALEXI (T.) Dicţionar romăno-german.
pp. 337. *Kronstadt,* 1894. 8°.   12943. cc. 9.

GROSSMANN (S. J.) Dicţionar german-romîn.
Iasi, 1890, *etc.* 4°.   273.

KOIRANSKY (Z.) Russisch-deutsches militärisches Wörterbuch. *Berl.* 1892, *etc.* 8°.
8825. bbb. 34.

JANEŽIČ (A.) Deutsch-slovenisches Hand-Wörterbuch. pp. 841. *Klagenfurt,* 1889. 8°.
12975. i. 15.

HOPPE (O.) Schwedisch-deutsches Wörterbuch. pp. 400. *Stockholm,* 1892. 8°.   12972. f. 22.

Etymology.

HEYSE (J. C. A.) 14,000 Fremdwörter nach ihrer Abstammung erklärt und verdeutscht.
pp. 448. *Hannover,* 1895. 8°.   12962. b. 60.

MAY (M.) Beiträge zur Stammkunde der deutschen Sprache. pp. 299. *Leipz.* 1893. 8°.
12962. s. 4.

RUMPELT (H. B.) Die deutschen Zahlwörter historisch dargestellt. pp. 48. *Oxf.* 1893. 8°.
12962. g. 30.

SEILER (F.) Die Entwicklung der deutschen Kultur im Spiegel des deutschen Lehnworts.
Halle, 1885, *etc.* 8°.   12963. e. 16.

SPOETTEL (A.) Zur Sprachreinigung. Eine Sammlung der gebräuchlichsten Fremdwörter.
pp. 39. *München,* 1891. 8°.   12901. d. 37. (9.)
See also supra : Dictionaries. Infra : History.

Examination Papers and Exercises.

JUST (H. E.) and LHUISSIER (L. J.) Matriculation Model Answers : French and German. 1891. 8°. Tutorial Series.   12205. c. 56.

EVE (H. W.) and BAUDISS (F. de) First German Exercises. pp. 95. *Lond.* 1895. 8°. 12963. e. 17.

HAPPÉ (L. A.) Questions and Exercises on the grammar and idioms of German. pp. 143.
Lond. 1892. 8°.   12962. g. 20.

HORNING (L. E.) Material for exercises in German Composition. pp. 175. *Toronto,* 1895. 8°.
12962. ccc. 28.

MULLINS (W. E.) Elementary German Exercises. pp. 255. *Lond.* 1894. 8°.   12963. c. 38.

SOMERVILLE (A. A.) and BYRNE (L. S. R.) Primary German Exercises. pp. 191.
Lond. 1894. 8°.   12962. c. 34.

Grammars, etc.

BACON (E. F.) Guide for learning the German Language. pp. 272. *Lond.* 1891. 8°.
12962. dd. 24.

BECKER (H. B.) Oxford and Cambridge German Primer. 3 pt. 1890. 12°. Gill's School Series.
12202. e.

BEHAGHEL (O.) Historical Grammar of the German language. pp. 194. *Lond.* 1891. 8°.
12954. d. 21.

EVE (H. W.) School German Grammar.
pp. 369. *Lond.* 1890. 8°.   12963. cc. 46.

—— Short German Accidence. pp. 106.
Lond. 1893. 8°.   12963. f. 35.

EYSENBACH (W.) Practical Grammar of the German Language. pp. 346. *Lond.* 1887. 8°.
12963. cc. 47.

GERMAN.—Grammars—*continued.*

GIBBINS (H. de B.) Companion German Grammar.
pp. 58. *Lond.* 1891. 8°.   12963. cc. 45.

HARCOURT (L.) German for beginners.
pp. 200. *Marburg,* 1895. 8°.   12962. g. 35.

HEINTZE (A.) Gut Deutsch. Eine Anleitung
zur Vermeidung der häufigsten Verstösse gegen
den guten Sprachgebrauch. pp. 180.
Berl. 1894. 8°.   12963. c. 15.

HENRY (V.) Précis de grammaire comparée de
l'anglais et de l'allemand. pp. 418.
Paris, 1893. 8°.   12901. d. 41.

—— Short Comparative Grammar of English
and German. pp 391. *Lond.* 1894. 8°.
      12962. cc. 48.

HUGO ( ) Simplified System. French. German.
Spanish. 14 pts. *Lond.* 1890. 8°. 12902. ccc. 22.

KROCH (C. F.) Living Method for learning how
to think in German. pp. 272. *Lond.* 1893. 8°.
      12963. f. 36.

KUPHAL (O.) Idiomatic Study of German.
N.Y. 1895, *etc.* 8°.   12963. bbb. 47.

LARSSEN (C.) Kortfattet Lærebog i det tyske
Forretningsprog. pp. 176.
Christiania, 1892. 8°.   12963. d. 50.

LUMSDEN (L. I.) Lessons in German. pp. 280.
Lond. 1895. 8°.   12962. c. 36.

MEISSNER (A. L.) Public School German Grammar. *Lond.* 1892, *etc.* 8°.   12962. ccc. 13.

PEARSON (J. Y.) and STRANGWAYS (A. H. F.)
Elementary German Grammar for Wellington
College. pp. 138. *Lond.* 1895. 8°. 12963. e. 18.

RANSOM (J. U.) Longmans' German Course.
Lond. 1892, *etc.* 8°.   12962. ccc.

—— Key and Supplement. pp. 88.
Lond. 1893. 8°.   12962. cc. 47.

ROSENTHAL (R. S.) The Meisterschaftssystem.
French and German Languages, *etc.*
Lond. 1891. 8°.   12902. cc. 46.

SACHS (H.) German Conversational Grammar.
pp. 288. *Lond.* 1894. 8°.   12962. b. 59.

SANDERS (D. H.) Lehrbuch der deutschen
Sprache für Schulen. 3 pt. *Berl.* 1888, 89. 8°.
      12962. cc. 39.

—— Leitfaden zur Grundlage der deutschen
Grammatik. pp. 157. *Berl.* 1884. 8°.
      12963. bbb. 45.

SCHUENEMANN (H.) Oral Lessons in German.
Lond. 1894, *etc.* 8°.   12962. ccc. 27.

SOMERVILLE (A. A.) and BYRNE (L. S. R.) Primer
of German Grammar. pp. 111. *Lond.* 1894. 8°.
Lond. 1894. 8°.   12962. cc. 33.

SOSNOSKY (T. v.) Der Sprachwort, Sprachregeln
und Sprachsünden. pp. 231. *Breslau,* 1894. 8°.
      12962. cec. 25.

VALENTINE (W. W.) New High German. 2 vol.
Lond. 1894. 8°.   12962. p. 5.

VALKHOFF (J. N.) Volledige leercursus des
duitsche taal. 3 stk. *Groningen,* 1891. 8°.
      12963. cc. 48.

VECQUERAY (J. W. J.) German Accidence for
schools. pp. 40. *Lond.* 1894. 4°. 12962. i. 29.

WEBB (H. S. B.) First German Book. pp. 210.
Lond. 1894. 8°.   12963. c. 37.

WEISSE (T. H) Elements of German. pp. 220.
Lond. 1893. 8°.   12962. c. 31.

WILLIAMS (G. H.) German Course. pp. 193.
Lond. 1892. 8°.   12962. aaa. 39.

WILMANNS (W.) Deutsche Grammatik.
Strassb. 1893, *etc.* 8°.   12962. o.

C., S. Aids to the Mastery of German Declensions. pp. 37. *Lond.* 1891. 16°.   Pam. 47.

JACKSON (S.) German Declensions. pp. 14.
Lond. 1891. 12°.   12962. ccc. 12.

GERMAN.—Grammars—*continued.*

PLOETZ (R. A.) Table of German Declension.
Lond. 1890. 4°.   1865. c. 1. (4.)

STORR (F.) German Declensions and Conjugations. pp. 28. *Lond.* 1891. 8°. 12962. c. 29.

WHEATLEY (W. A.) German Declensions simplified and symbolized. pp. 53. *Syracuse,* 1895. 8°.
      12963. aaa. 32.

GOUIN (F.) Traité des verbes irréguliers allemands. pp. 48. *Paris,* 1892. 4°. 12962. ccc. 19.

LORENTZ (F.) Über das schwache Präteritum
des Germanischen. pp. 79. *Leipz.* 1894. 8°.
      12962. g. 33.

See also infra : History.

History: Old and Middle German.

BILTZ (C.) Neue Beiträge zur Geschichte der
deutschen Sprache. pp. 250. *Berl.* 1891. 8°.
      12962. p. 3.

SANDERS (D. H.) Geschichte der deutschen
Sprache. pp. 142. *Berl.* 1887. 8°. 11851. f. 33.

STREITBERG (W.) Zur germanischen Sprachgeschichte. pp. 116. *Strassb.* 1892. 8°. 12962. h. 43.

NABERT (H.) Das deutsche Sprachgebiet in
Europa. pp. 133. *Stuttg.* 1893. 8°. 12963. d. 49.

JELLINEK (M. H.) Beiträge zur Erklärung der
germanischen Flexion. pp. 107. *Berl.* 1891. 8°.
      12962. h. 42.

NOREEN (A. G.) Abriss der urgermanischen
Lautlehre. pp. 278. *Strassb.* 1894. 8°.
      12962. g. 32.

WILMANNS (W.) Deutsche Grammatik. Götisch,
Alt- und Mittelhochdeutsch.
Strassb. 1893, *etc.* 8°.   12962. o.

PIPER (P.) Die Sprache Deutschlands bis zum
12en Jahrhundert. 2 Thle. *Paderborn,* 1880. 8°.
      011850. h. 27.

BRAUNE (W.) Abriss der althochdeutschen Grammatik. pp. 62. 1895. 8°. Sammlung kurzer
Grammatiken. Nr. 1.   12901. e. 33.

HOLZ (G.) Urgermanisches geschlossenes é und
verwandtes. pp. 49. *Leipz.* 1890. 8°. Pam. 47.

LICHTENBERGER (H.) De Verbis quæ in vetustis-
sima Germanorum lingua reduplicatum præ-
teritum exhibebant. pp. 103. *Nanceii,* 1891. 8°.
      12962. l. 15.

WILKENS (F.) Zum hochalemannischen Kon-
sonantismus der althochdeutschen Zeit. pp. 91.
Leipz. 1891. 8°.   12903. dd. 33. (6.)

BACHMANN (A.) Mittelhochdeutsches Lesebuch.
pp. 279. *Zürich,* 1892. 8°.   12962. g. 29.

KAINZ (C.) Grammatik der mittelhochdeutschen
Sprache. pp. 174. 1894. 8°. Kunst der Polyglottie. Thl. 43.   12902. c.

KHULL (F.) Beiträge zum mittelhochdeutschen
Wörterbuche. pp. 40. *Graz,* 1884. 8°.
      12903. dd. 37. (2.)

LEGERLOTZ (G.) Mittelhochdeutschen Lesebuch.
pp. 134. *Bielefeld,* 1892. 8°. 11511. aaa. 2.

Idioms.

BECKER (A. L.) First steps in German idioms.
pp. 189. *Lond.* 1891. 8°.   12962. aa. 27.

KAPHAL (O.) Idiomatic Study of German.
N.Y. 1895, *etc.* 8°.   12963. bbb. 47.

MAYER (A. v.) Manual of English-French-German idioms. pp. 326. *Lond.* 1895. 8°.
      12950. df. 51

WEISSE (T. H.) Short guide to German idioms.
pp. 156. *Lond.* 1892. 8°.   12962. aa. 28.
See also supra : Grammars.

Old and Middle High German.

See supra : History.

Orthography.

ALBRECHT (A.) Ein Mahnwort an die Recht-
schreibungsneuerer in deutschen Sprache.
pp. 41. *Halle,* 1893. 8°. 12902. de. 1. (7.)

GERMAN.—Orthography—_continued._

B\x (R.) Vorschläge zur Reform der deutschen Orthographie. pp. 134. _Leipz._ 1891. 8°.
12962. i. 28.

BAUSE (J.) Wie kann unsere Schrift vereinfacht und vervolkommnet werden? pp. 144. _Paderborn_, 1893. 8°.   12962. e. 31.

LEFMANN (S.) Ueber deutsche Rechtschreibung. 1894. 8°. Sammlung wissenschaftlicher Vorträge. Ser. VI. Heft. 129.   12249. l.

LINHOFF (M.) Zur deutschen Richtigschreibung. pp. 40. _Westfalen_, 1891. 8°. 12901. ccc. 14. (7.)

MIEHLKE (A.) Die Geschichte unserer Sprachlaute und Orthographie. pp. 39. _Graudenz_, 1891. 4°.   12902. i. 2. (10.)

S., F. Eine Sprachpauke oder kein Dogma der Ortografi-entwiklungsfreiheit. pp. 41. _Bonn_, 1894. 8°.   12902. bb. 40. (10.)

SCHREIBER (J. M.) Regelung der deutschen Orthographie. pp. 104. _Wien_, 1883. 8°. 12962. g. 31.

Platt-Deutsch. _See supra : Dialects._

Pronunciation : Phonetics.

BREMER (O.) Deutsche Phonetik. pp. 208. 1893. 8°. Sammlung kurzer Grammatiken. Bd. 1.   12962. q.

MIEHLKE (A.) Die Geschichte unserer Sprachlaute. pp. 39. _Graudenz_, 1891. 4°.
12902. i. 2. (10.)

NOREEN (A. G.) Abriss der urgermanischen Lautlehre. pp. 278. _Strassb._ 1894. 8°.
12962. g. 32.

VIETOR (W.) Die Aussprache des Schriftdeutschen. pp. 101. _Leipz._ 1890. 8°.
011824. e. 59.

—— German Pronunciation. pp. 133. _Leipz._ 1890. 8°.   12963. f. 38.

Slang.

GENTHE (A.) Deutsches Slang. pp. 73. _Strassb._ 1892. 8°.   12901. ccc. 16. (5.)

KLUGE (F.) Deutsche Studentensprache. pp. 136. _Strassb._ 1895. 8°.   12963. bbb. 48.

KOKES ( ) Schlagworte des Humors. pp. 182. _Leipz._ 1891. 8°.   12316. ce. 7.

MEIER (J.) Hallische Studentensprache. pp. 97. _Halle_, 1894. 8°.   12962. q. 6.

Translation from and into German.

BUCHHEIM (C. A.) Modern German Reader. 1892, _etc._ 8°. Clarendon Press Series.
2320. b. 12.

BULL (H. A.) German Selections for translation at sight. pp. 126. _Lond._ 1890. 8°. 12252. aaa. 7.

DAVID (A. A.) Stories and Exercises in German. pp. 65. _Lond._ 1892. 8°.   12962. ccc. 15.

HAPPÉ (L. A.) Practical German Readings. pp. 162. _Lond._ 1894. 8°.   12963. e. 14.

HONIGH (C.) Hoogduitsch Leesboek. 3 dltj. _Groningen_, 1891. 8°.   12962. cc. 45.

JONES (F.) German Science Reader. pp. 147. _Lond._ 1892. 8°.   8703. aa. 28.

LAUNY (L.) and PIO (J.) Tysk Læsebog. pp. 227. _Kjøbenh._ 1890. 8°.   12250. g. 13.

LECHNER (A. R.) Easy Readings in German. pp. 199. _Lond._ 1895. 8°.   12962. aaa. 40.

MORICH (R. J.) Advanced German Texts. _Lond._ 1893, _etc._ 8°.   12253. c.

RENNARD (D. S.) German Unseens. _Lond._ 1895, _etc._ 8°.   12962. aaa.

SONNENSCHEIN (A.) German through English. pp. 204. _Lond._ 1895. 8°.   12962. bbb. 34.

STRANGWAYS (A. H. F.) Advanced Passages for German unseen translation. pp. 192. _Lond._ 1895. 8°.   12962. bbb. 51.

GERMAN.—Translation—_continued._

VIERHOUT (C. J.) Deutsche Sprech- und Schreibübungen für die Mittelklassen. pp. 126. _Gorcum_, 1893. 8°.   12963. d. 51.

WEBB (H. S. B.) Primary German Translation book. pp. 231. _Lond._ 1894. 8°. 12963. bbb. 3.

WEBB (H. S. B.) German Historical Reading book. pp. 302. _Lond._ 1892. 8°. 9326. aaa. 15.

—— German Military and Naval Reading book. pp. 315. _Lond._ 1891. 8°.   12253. b. 10.

BUCHHEIM (C. A.) First Book of German Prose. pp. 156. _Lond._ 1894. 8°.   12963. aaa. 33.

BUCHHEIM (E. S.) Elementary German Prose Composition. pp. 108. 1894. 8°. Clarendon Press Series.   2319. aa. 4.

BUCHMANN (L.) Army Examinations Composition book. pp. 151. 1890. 8°.   12272. bbb. 16.

HAPPÉ (L. A.) Passages for Translation at sight into German. _Lond._ 1892, _etc._ 8°.   12950. cc.

HORNING (L. E.) Material for exercises in German composition. pp. 175. _Toronto_, 1895. 8°.
12962. ccc. 28.

JOERG (J. A.) German Test Papers, pieces for prose composition. pp. 86. _Lond._ 1894. 8°.
12962. ccc. 26.

MEISSNER (A. L.) Primer of German Composition. pp. 77. _Lond._ 1894. 8°.   12962. aa. 30.

RANSOM (J. U.) Longman's German Composition. (Key.) 2 pt. _Lond._ 1894, 8°. 12963. cc. 49.

ULRICH (A. J.) Ulrich's German Prose. 2 pt. pp. 123. _Lond._ 1893. 8°.   12962. bbb. 30.

WEBB (H. S. B.) Manual of German Composition. pp. 199. _Lond._ 1892. 8°.   12962. cc. 46.

GERMAN LITERATURE.

Bibliography.

BREUL (C. H.) Bibliographical Guide to the study of German Literature. pp. 144. _Lond._ 1895. 8°.
11901. aaa. 42.

P.P. _Leipsic._ Verzeichnis der neu erschienenen Bücher. _Leipz._ 1894, _etc._ 8°.   BB.R. c. 9.

THELERT (G.) Supplement zu Heinsius', Hinrichs' u. Kaysers Bücher-Lexikon. pp. 405. _Grossenhain_, 1893. 8°.   2048. c.

HAYN (H.) Bibliotheca Germanorum Nuptialis. Verzeichniss von Einzeldrucken deutscher Hochzeitgedichte und Hochzeitscherze. pp. 89. _Köln_, 1890. 8°.   11901. aa. 32.

FOCK (G.) Catalogus' Dissertationum classicarum. Verzeichnis von etwa 18300 Abhandlungen aus dem Gesamtgebiete der klassischen Philologie u. Altertumskunde. 3 pt. _Leipz._ 1893. 8°.
011900. ee. 31.

P.P. _Berlin._ Jahres-Verzeichniss der an den deutschen Schulanstalten erschienenen Abhandlungen. _Berl._ 1890, _etc._ 8°.   P.P. 6513. lc

History and Criticism.

ALTMUELLER (H.) Deutsche Klassiker und Romantiker. pp. 155. _Kassel_, 1892. 8°.
11824. e. 45.

BILTZ (C.) Neue Beiträge zur Geschichte der deutschen Litteratur. pp. 250. _Berl._ 1891. 8°.
12962. p. 3.

BOCK (A.) Deutsche Dichter in ihren Beziehungen zur Musik. pp. 264. _Leipz._ 1893. 8°.
7898. g. 51.

BOYESEN (H. H.) Essays on German Literature. pp. 359. _Lond._ 1892. 8°.   011824. g. 5.

BREUL (C. H.) Biographical Guide to the study of German Literature. pp. 144. _Lond._ 1895. 8°.
11901. aaa. 42.

BRUGIER (G.) Abriss der deutschen National-Litteratur. pp. 286. _Freiburg_, 1895. 8°.
11825. p. 19.

GERMAN LITERATURE—continued.

Selections.

Morich (R. J.) Modern German Series of school
texts. Lond. 1892, etc. 8°.   12253. c.

Muellenhoff (C. V.) and Scherer (W.) Denkmäler deutscher Poesie und Prosa aus dem
VIII.-XII. Jahrhundert. 2 Bde. Berl. 1892. 8°.
                                        11517. h. 2.

Ulrich (A. J.) Ulrich's German Classics.
Lond. 1894, etc. 8°.   12253. c.
See also Poetry.

GERMANS, in Foreign Countries. Bark
(E.) Deutschlands Weltstellung und Aufgabe
der Deutschen im Auslande. pp. 94.
Zürich, 1890. 8°.   8154. aa. 13.

Neumann (L.) Die deutschen Gemeinden in
Piemont. pp. 40. Freiburg, 1891. 8°. Pam. 91.

Chmerkin (X.) Les Juifs et les Allemands en
Russie. pp. 39. Paris, 1893. 8°.   Pam. 31.

Sartorius von Waltershausen (F. H. W. A. v.)
Die Zukunft des Deutschthums in den Vereinigten Staaten. pp. 40. 1885. 8°. Deutsche Zeit-
und Streit-Fragen. Jhrg. XIV.   12209. f.
See also Germany, Colonies.

GERMANY. [See note on page 1.]
See also under each of the Countries, etc., forming the German Empire.

Antiquities.

Ac. etc. Halle. Provinzial-Museum der Provinz
Sachsen. Mittheilungen aus dem Provinzial-
Museum. Halle, 1891, etc. 8°.   Ac. 5470.

—— Stuttgard. Württembergischer Anthropologischer Verein. Fundberichte aus Schwaben.
Stuttgart, 1893, etc. 8°.   Ac. 6229. c.

Hartung (O.) Die deutschen Altertümer des
Nibelungenliedes. pp. 551. Cöthen, 1894. 8°.
                                     07708. g. 39.

Hoff (L.) Die Kenntnis Germaniens im Altertum. pp. 86. Coesfeld, 1890. 8°. Pam. 28.

Holz (G.) Beiträge zur deutschen Altertumskunde. Halle, 1894, etc. 8°.   9327. dd.

Muellenhoff (C. V.) Deutsche Altertumskunde. Berl. 1890, etc. 8°.   9325. ff. 3.

Moravičansky (F. S. P.) Das slavische Altgermanien. pp. 125. Brünn, 1882. 8°. 9325. aaa. 12.

Kirchmayr (H.) Der Volkstamm der Quaden.
2 Bde. Brünn, 1888-93. 8°.   9325. ff. 5.

Holub (J.) Der Name Germani in Tacitus Germania. pp. 25. Freiwalden, 1891. 8°.
                                     9008. g. 8. (6.)

Lueckenbach (A.) De Germaniae quae vocatur
Tacitae fontibus. pp. 69. Marpurgi, 1891. 8°.
                                     Pam. 14.

Caraccio (M.) I Germani e la loro coltura.
pp. 176. Padova, 1890. 8°.   9327. e. 12.
See also infra, History : Teutonic Mythology :
Rome, Antiquities, in Germany.

Army.
General.

Boguslawski (A. v.) Die Nothwendigkeit der
zweijährigen Dienstzeit. pp. 47. Berl. 1891. 8°.
                                     8831. c. 24. (6.)

—— Die Parteien und die Heeresreform. pp. 61.
Berl. 1892. 8°.   8830. c. 43. (12.)

Buhrke ( ) Bestimmungen über die Versorgung der Hinterbliebenen von Angehörigen des
Reichsheeres. pp. 212. Berl. 1891. 8°.
                                     8830. h. 27.

Drygalski (A. v.) Kaleidoskop aus der militärischen Welt. pp. 192. Berl. 1891. 8°. 8828. b. 3.

Erdmann (W.) Handbuch für die Gemeinde-
Verwaltungen des Reiches in Militär-Angele-
genheiten. pp. 260. Berl. 1893. 8°. 8830. h. 21.

GERMANY.—Army—continued.

Exner ( ) The German Army. 1893. 8°.
Armies of to-day.   8829. i. 9.

Gneist (H. R. v.) Die Militärvorlage von 1892
und der preussiche Verfassungskonflikt.
pp. 144. Berl. 1893. 8°.   8828. ff. 27.

Gallus. Coup d'œil sur les forces militaires de
l'Allemagne. pp. 220. Paris, 1888. 8°.
                                     8074. ee. 33.

Germany. Army. Schriften zur deutschen
Heeresreform. Stuttg. 1890, etc. 8°. 8831. l.

—— Die Soldatenmisshandlungen vor dem
deutschen Reichstag. pp. 26. Berl. 1891. 8°.
                                     8277. ee. 33. (7.)

Heumann (A.) L'Armée allemande. pp. 204.
Paris, 1895. 8°.   8831. bbb. 38.

Klaussmann (A. O.) Der Humor im deutschen
Heere. 2 vol. Berl. 1895. 8°.   012314. f. 63.

Krebs (G.) Militärische Sprichwörter und Redensarten. pp. 213. Wien, 1895. 8°.
                                     8824. bbb. 34.

Kretschman (v.) Rekruten-Briefe des
deutschen Soldatenhorst. pp. 197.
Berl. 1894. 16°.   8823. a. 16.

Manché ( ) Ansichten über die deutsche
Reiterei. pp. 37. Rathenow, 1891. 8°.
                                     8830. k. 33. (8.)

Moltke (H. C. B. v.) Count. Gesammelte
Schriften und Denkwürdigkeiten. 7 Bde.
Berl. 1891-92. 8°.   12252. i. 4.

—— Essays, Speeches and Memoirs. 2 vol.
Lond 1893. 8°.   12354. k. 16.

Otto (A.) Dienst bei den Bezirks-kommandos
der deutschen Armee. pp. 227. Berl. 1894. 8°.
                                     8828. b. 62.

Pardiellan (P. de) L'Armée allemande.
pp. 266. Paris, 1892. 8°.   8823. aaa. 49.

—— Aide-Mémoire de l'Officier français en Allemagne. [With coloured plates of German
uniforms.] pp. 141. Paris, 1890. 16°. 8823. a. 10.

Rijn (R. v.) Individualismus und Schablone im
deutschen Heere. pp. 59. Berl. 1892. 8°.
                                     8830. k. 32. (5.)

Roche (J.) L'Armée française et l'armée allemande. pp. 57. Paris, 1895. 8°.   Pam. 2.

Roy (P. R.) Répertoire des termes militaires
allemands. pp. 178. Paris, 1891. 8°. 8823. g. 21.

Saxonicus. Die Umbildung des Heeres zum
zweitenmal das Schicksal Deutschlands. pp. 32.
Leipz. 1893. 8°.   Pam. 67.

Schurig (E.) Der Humor in der sächsischen
Armee. pp. 140. Dresden, 1893. 8°.
                                     012314. g. 9.

Selbach (E. A.) Der Einjährige muss bleiben!
pp. 16. Düsseldorf, 1893. 8°. 8830. c. 43. (13.)

Weigelt (G) Handbuch für die Einjährig-
Freiwilligen. pp. 296. Berl. 1893, etc. 8°.
                                     8830. bbb.

Whitman (S.) Psychologie der deutschen Armee.
Berl. 1889. 8°.   8831. l. 9. (4.)

Germany. Army. German Field Exercise, 1888.
Part II. The Fight. pp. 80. Lond. 1886. 8°.
                                     8823. aa. 25.

Manchester. Tactical Society. Order of Field
Service of the German Army. 2 pt.
Lond. 1893, 94. 8°.   8829. a. 38.

History.

Elster (D.) Bilder aus der Kulturgeschichte
des deutschen Heeres. pp. 304. Leipz. 1892. 8°.
                                     8825. cc. 31.

Kleist (B. v.) Die Generale der königlich
preussischen Armee von 1840-90. pp. 1106.
Hannover, 1891. 8°.   10706. l. 50.

Sproesser ( ) Deutschlands Heerführer 1640-
1894. Leipz. 1895, etc. 8°.   8830. h.

GERMANY.—Army—*continued*.

GERMANY, *Empire of.* La Cavalerie allemande. Histoire, *etc.* pp. 782. *Paris*, 1892. 8°. 8828. ff. 24.

KRIPPENSTAPEL (F.) Die preussischen Husaren von den ältesten Zeiten. pp. 197.
　Berl. 1893. 4°.　　　　　　　8824. k. 30.

KUNZ (H.) Die deutsche Reiterei in den Schlachten des Krieges von 1870-71. pp. 423.
　Berl. 1895. 8°.　　　　　　9080. dd. 24.

VOGT (H.) Geschichte der deutschen Reiterei in Einzelbildern. *Rathenau*, 1891, *etc.* 8°. 8823. n.

KNOETEL (R.) Uniformenkunde. Blätter zur Geschichte der Entwickelung der militärischen Tracht. *Rathenow*, 1890, *etc.* 8°.　8827. dd. 9.

P.P. *Berlin.* Anciennetäts-Liste der Offiziere des deutschen Heeres. *Berl.* 1890, *etc.* 8°.
　　　　　　　　　　　　P.P. 2444. aa.

Regimental Histories etc.

HEYM (O.) Die Geschichte des reitenden Feld-jäger-Corps. 2 pt. *Berl.* 1890. 8°. 8830. l. 13.

HAERING (O.) Geschichte der preussichen Garde. pp. 359. *Berl.* 1891. 8°.　　8824. ccc. 12.

SCHEVEN (P. v.) Offizier-Stammrollen des Garde-Grenadier-Regiments, Nr. 2. pp. 457.
　Berl. 1894. 8°.　　　　　8828. g. 40.

KATHEN (H. v.) Das 3. Garde-Regiment. pp. 444. 134. *Berl.* 1891. 8°.　8831. k. 25.

BAGENSKY (B. v.) Regiments-Buch des Grenadier-Regiments 1. Pommerschen, Nr. 2. pp. 466.
　Berl. 1892. 8°.　　　　　8828. g. 37.

PETERMANN ( ) Geschichte des colbergschen Grenadier-Regiments. pp. 267. *Berl.* 1889. 8°.
　　　　　　　　　　　8831. k. 18.

SCHREIBER (G.) Geschichte des Infanterie-Regiments 4. Pommerschen, Nr. 21. pp. 476. 78.
　Berl. 1889. 8°.　　　　　8831. k. 16.

JAGWITZ (F. v.) Geschichte des Lützowschen Freikorps. pp. 313. *Berl.* 1892. 8°. 8831. i. 28.

GOLTZ ( ) Abriss der Geschichte des Infanterie-Regiments 6. Ostpreussisches, Nr. 43. pp. 64.
　Berl. 1892. 8°.　　　　8823. aaa. 48.

BREYDING (E. E. C. J.) Geschichte des Füsilier-Regiments, Nr. 73. pp. 487. *Berl.* 1891. 8°.
　　　　　　　　　　8823. n. 20.

LIVONIUS (W.) Chronik des Füsilier-Bataillons 2. Hanseatischen Inf.-Reg., No. 76. pp. 76.
　Lübeck, 1891. 8°.　　　8830. c. 43. (11.)

MEMERKY (v.) Das Offizier-Korps des Füsilier-Regiments, Nr. 80. pp. 213. *Berl.* 1891. 8°.
　　　　　　　　　　8830. d. 4.

KOENEMANN ( ) Geschichte des Infanterie-Regiments 3. Hessischen, Nr. 83. pp. 149.
　Berl. 1891. 8°.　　　　　8824. ccc. 29.

WAGNER ( ) Geschichte des Regiments "Prinz Johann Georg," Nr. 107. pp. 326.
　Leipz. 1893. 8°.　　　　8829. i. 15.

SCHEMPP ( ) Geschichte des 3. Würth. Infanterie-Regiments, N°. 121. pp. 512.
　Stuttg. 1891. 8°.　　　8823. ddd. 18.

GERMANY. *Army.* Rang-Liste des Offizier-Corps der Inspection der Jäger und Schützen. pp. 37.
　Berl. 1885. 8°.　　　　8830. f. 34.

STAPP ( ) Geschichte des K. bayerischen 6. Infanterie-Regiments. pp. 171. *Berl.* 1891. 8°.
　　　　　　　　　　8824. c. 16.

BRUEHL (F. v.) Uebersicht der Geschichte des königlichen Regiments der Gardes du Corps. pp. 175. 71. *Berl.* 1890. 8°.　8823. aaa. 39.

MINCKWITZ (A. v.) Die ersten kursächsischen Leibwachen zu Ross und zu Fuss. pp. 125.
　Dresden, 1894. 8°.　　　8828. ff. 32.

CRAMON (A. v.) Geschichte des Leib Kürassier-Regiments, Nr. 1. pp. 240. *Berl.* 1893. 8°.
　　　　　　　　　　8830. l. 28.

GERMANY.—Army—*continued*.

BOJANOWSKI (P. v.) Carl August als Chief des 6. P. Kürassier-Regiments. pp. 147.
　Weimar, 1894. 8°.　　　10708. cc. 53.

GERMANY. *Army.* Geschichte des 2. badischen Dragoner-Regiments, Nr. 21. pp. 282.
　Berl. 1893. 8°.　　　　8829. e. 43.

MACKENSEN ( ) Schwarze Husaren. Geschichte des Leib-Husaren-Regiments, Nr. 1. 2 Bde.
　Berl. 1892. 4°.　　　　8824. k. 27.

GERMANY. *Army.* Geschichte des Zieten-Husaren-Regiments. pp. 64. *Rathenow*, 1892. 8°.
　　　　　　　　　　8823. h. 29.

ECK (v.) Geschichte des 2. westfälischen-Husaren-Regiments, Nr. 11. pp. 433.
　Mainz, 1893. 8°.　　　　8828. h. 44.

KOSSECKI (C. v.) Geschichte des 2. hessischen Husaren-Regiments, Nr. 14. pp. 511.
　Leipz. 1887-91. 8°.　　　8824. k. 13.

BREDAU (H. C. C. W. v.) Geschichte des Ulanen-Regiments, Nr. 4. pp. 148. 80.
　Berl. 1890. 8°.　　　　8825. ee. 6.

—— Atlas. *Leipz.* 1890. fol.　8825. h. 8.

FOERSTER (H. H. F. C. v.) Geschichte des Ulanen-Regiments, Nr. 8. pp. 526. 233.
　Berl. 1890. 8°.　　　　8827. k. 2.

GLASENAPP (G. v.) Geschichte des Ulanen-Regiments, Nr. 15. pp. 232. *Berl.* 1894. 8°.
　　　　　　　　　　8827. h. 30.

SCHMALTZ ( ) Aufzeichnungen über das 1. Ulanen-Regiment, Nr. 17. pp. 272.
　Berl. 1891. 8°.　　　　8823. n. 6.

PFETTEN-ARNBACH (T. v.) Das bayerische 1. schwere Reiter-Regiment.
　München, 1890, *etc.* 8°.　8830. k. 16.

ULRICH (M.) Gedenkblätter aus der Geschichte des k. bayerischen 4. Chevaulegers-Regimentes. pp. 537. *Wien*, 1892. 8°.　8824. k. 26.

W., G. Anciennetäts-Liste der Artillerie-Offiziere des deutschen Reichs-Heeres. pp. 57.
　Burg, 1891. 4°.　　　8829. h. 37. (1.)

SPROTTE ( ) Geschichte des Feld Artillerie-Regiments Nr. 9. pp. 311. *Berl.* 1891. 8°.
　　　　　　　　　　8823. n. 23.

COLDITZ (v.) Geschichte des Feld-Artillerie-Regiments Nr. 10. pp. 274. *Berl.* 1891. 8°.
　　　　　　　　　　8823. n. 16.

BAUMANN (J.) Geschichte des k. b. 1. Feld-Artillerie-Regiments. pp. 184.
　Ingolstadt, 1892. 8°.　　8824. c. 36.

PRUSSIA. *Army.* Das k. preuss. Kadettencorps. pp. 138. *Berl.* 1892. 8°.　8824. i. 38.

BOGUSLAWSKI (A. v.) Die Landwehr, 1813-93. pp 28. *Berl.* 1893. 8°.　8829. l. 24. (4.)

Colonies.

BROSE (M.) Repertorium der deutsch-kolonialen Litteratur. pp. 113. *Berl.* 1891. 8°.
　　　　　　　　　　11902. aa. 13.

BENETE (M. P.) Die Ausbildung der Kolonial-beamten. pp. 90. *Berl.* 1894. 8°. 8154. d. 23.

HESSLER (C.) Kurze Landeskunde der deutschen Kolonieen. pp. 48. *Leipz.* 1891. 8°. 10498. c. 25.

P.P. *Berlin.* Koloniales Jahrbuch.
　Berl. 1889, *etc.* 8°.　　P.P. 3806. f.

RIEBOW ( ) Die deutsche Kolonial-Gesetzgebung. pp. 706. *Berl.* 1893. 8°. 05604. k. 5.

SCHMIDT (R.) Deutschlands Kolonien.
　Berl. 1895, *etc.* 8°.　　10095. d.

STOECKLIN (J.) Les Colonies et l'émigration allemandes. pp. 2. 5. *Paris*, 1888. 12°. 10024. cc. 13.

VOLZ (B.) Unsere Kolonien. pp. 369.
　Leipz. 1891. 8°.　　　10028. f. 20.

See also AFRICA, *German Possessions:* CAMEROON: DAMARALAND.

GERMANY—*continued.*

Constitution and Government.

ALTMANN (W.) Urkunden zur Erläuterung der Verfassungsgeschichte Deutschlands im Mittelalter. pp. 270. *Berl.* 1891. 8°. 6005. ee. 27.

LEHMANN (H. O.) Quellen zur deutschen Reichsgeschichte. pp. 309. *Berl.* 1891. 8°. 9325. ee. 22.

TURNER (S. E.) Sketch of the Germanic Constitution to the dissolution of the Empire. pp. 185. *N.Y.* 1888. 8°. 9325. c. 9.

MOLLAT (G.) Lesebuch zur Geschichte der deutschen Staatswissenschaft, 1250-1807. pp. 131. *Tübingen,* 1891. 8°. 8009. h. 1.

RODENBERG (C.) Zur Geschichte der Idee eines deutschen Erbreiches im 13. Jahrhundert. 1895. 8°. Ac. Vienna. *Universitas.* Mittheilungen des Instituts für Geschichtsforschung. Bd. 16. Ac. 803.

SICKEL (W.) Beiträge zur deutschen Verfassungsgeschichte des Mittelalters. 1894. 8°. Ac. Vienna. *Universitas.* Mittheilungen des Instituts für Geschichtsforschung. Ergänzungsband 3. Ac. 803.

MOLLAT (G.) Geschichte der Staatswissenschaft von Kant bis Bluntschli. *Cassel,* 1890, *etc.* 8°. 8074. ee. 35.

RIETSCHEL (S.) Die Civitas auf deutschen Boden bis zum Ausgange der Karolingerzeit. pp. 102. *Leipz.* 1894. 8°. 5206. c. 1.

SCHMIDT (W. A.) Geschichte der deutschen Verfassungsfrage, 1812-15. pp. 497. *Stuttg.* 1890. 8°. 9326. df. 8.

FISCHER (R.) Das Recht des deutschen Kaisers. pp. 195. *Berl.* 1895. 8°. 8072. eee. 14.

GERMANY, *Empire of.* Verfassung des deutschen Reichs. pp. 64. *Berl.* 1891. 16°. 5606. a. 13.

—— The Federal Constitution of Germany. pp. 43. 1890. 8°. Ac. Philadelphia. *University.* Publications. Pol. Econ. Series. No. 7. Ac. 2692.

HAENEL (A.) Deutsches Staatsrecht. 1892, *etc.* 8°. BINDING (C.) Systematisches Handbuch, *etc.* Abt. 5. Tl. 1, *etc.* 5605. ff.

GIESE (A.) Deutsche Bürgerkunde. pp. 127. *Leipz.* 1894. 8°. 8009. b. 33.

HEGEL (G. W. F.) Kritik der Verfassung Deutschlands. pp. 143. *Kassel,* 1893. 8°. 8074. bb. 38.

RITTER ( ) Das deutsche Reich als Staat. *Dessau,* 1891, *etc,* 8°. 8074. f. 30.

RUVILLE (A. v.) Das deutsche Reich ein monarchischer Einheitsstaat. pp. 294. *Berl.* 1894. 8°. 8072. df. 13.

STENGEL (C. v.) Wörterbuch des deutschen Verwaltungsrechts. 4 Bde. *Freiburg,* 1889-93. 8°. 5605. f. 14.

TRIEPS (A.) Das deutsche Reich und die Bundesstaaten in ihren rechtlichen Beziehungen. pp. 232. *Berl.* 1890. 8°. 8072. eee. 6.

WENZEL (J.) Comparative view of the Executive and Legislative departments of Germany, *etc.* pp. 22. *Bost.* 1891. 8°. 8010. a. 3.

PISTORIUS (T.) Die Staatsgerichtshöfe und die Ministerverantwortlichkeit. pp. 209. *Tübingen,* 1891, 8°. 8009. f. 16.

PERELS (F.) and SPILLING ( ) Das Reichsbeamtengesetz. pp. 283. *Berl.* 1890. 8°. 5605. f. 20.

KOELLER (L. v.) Anleitung zur zweiten Prüfung der höheren Verwaltungs-Beamten. *Hannover,* 1893, *etc.* 8°. 05604. h.

BRAATZ (J.) Der deutsche Reichstag in Wort und Bild. pp. 57. *Berl.* 1892. 8°. 010707. f. 21.

ROBINSON (J. H.) German Bundesrath. pp. 68. 1891. 8°. Ac. Philadelphia. *University.* Publications. Pol. Econ. Series. Vol. III. No. 1. Ac. 2692. p.

ROBOLSKY (H.) Der deutsche Reichstag. 1867-92. pp. 480. *Berl.* 1893. 8°. 8074. f. 34.

BENING (H.) Das deutsche Reichswahlgesetz. pp. 46. *Leipz.* 1892. 8°. 8074. f. 37. (6.)

EISENHART (W.) Gegen das allgemeine gleiche Wahlrecht. pp. 28. *Halle,* 1890. 8°. 8074. f. 37. (3.)

See also infra: History: Law: Politics: ELECTIONS: HOLY ROMAN EMPIRE.

Empire of, to A.D. 1806.

See HOLY ROMAN EMPIRE.

Evangelical Church.

See EVANGELICAL CHURCH.

Finance. *See infra:* TRADE.

History.

Bibliography.

DAHLMANN (F. C.) Quellenkunde der deutschen Geschichte. pp. 341. *Göttingen,* 1883. 8°. •B.B.M. c. 19.

LOEHER (F. v.) Grundzüge der Geschichte unserer Archive. pp. 490. *Paderborn,* 1890. 8°. 11899. g. 41.

DAHLMANN (F. C.) Quellenkunde der deutschen Geschichte. pp. 730. *Göttingen,* 1894. 8°. 9326. cc. 42.

General.

DAWSON (W. H.) Germany and the Germans. 2 vol. *Lond.* 1894. 8°. 10240. cc. 4.

DITTMAR (G.) Geschichte des deutschen Volkes. *Heidelberg,* 1891, *etc.* 8°. 9327. dd. 6.

DULLER (E.) Geschichte des deutschen Volkes. 2 Bde. *Berl.* 1891, 8°. 9325. ff. 4.

GERLACH (G. T.) 2000 Jahre deutscher Geschichte. pp. 32. *Köln,* 1894. 8°. 8074. h. 3. (13.)

GEBHARDT (B.) Deutscher Kaiser-Saal. pp. 787. *Stuttgart,* 1894. 8°. 9327. h. 1.

KLUCKHOHN (A.) Vorträge und Aufsätze. pp. 509. *München,* 1894. 8°. 010707. g. 46.

LAMPRECHT (C.) Deutsche Geschichte. *Berl.* 1891, *etc.* 8°. 9326. df.

LINDNER (T.) Geschichte des deutschen Volkes. 2 Bde. *Stuttgart,* 1894. 8°. 09325. i. 1.

MEYER (J.) Bilder aus der Geschichte des deutschen Volkes. *Gera,* 1894, *etc.* 8°. 9427. ee.

MŒSER (J.) Deutsche Geschichte. 1892. 8°. Deutsche Litteraturdenkmale. Heft 40. 12253. bbb.

MUSGRAVE (C. A.) German History. pp. 98. 1894. 8°. Examination Series. 12202. eee.

P.P. *Breslau.* Zeitschrift für deutsche Kulturgeschichte. *Breslau,* 1890, *etc.* 8°. P.P. 4748. md.

—— *Leipsic.* Germania. Illustrierte Monatsschrift. *Leipz.* 1894, *etc.* 8°. P.P. 1898. bd.

TAYLOR (B.) History of Germany from the earliest times. pp. 476. *N.Y.* 1894. 8°. 09325. g. 10.

WIDMANN (S.) Geschichte des deutschen Volkes. pp. 908. *Paderborn,* 1894. 8°. 09325. h. 13.

WOERLE (C.) Deutscher Geschichtskalender. pp. 726. *Leipz.* 1891. 8°. 9327. dd. 7.

Various Periods.

Earliest Period to the 19th Century.

HODGKIN (T.) Italy and her Invaders. *Oxf.* 1892, *etc.* 8°. 2068. c.

KIRCHMAYR (H.) Die altdeutsche Volkstamm der Quaden. 2 Bde. *Brünn,* 1888, 93. 8°. 9325. ff. 5.

GERMANY.—History—*continued.*

KLEE (G. L.) Bilder aus der älteren deutschen Geschichte. 3 pt. *Gütersloh,* 1890-92. 8°.
9327. bb. 22.

MALZACHER (A.) Geschichte der Alamannen. *Stuttgart,* 1894, *etc.* 8°. 09325. g.

TACITUS (C. C.) Romania e Germania, secondo le relazioni di Tacito. pp. 278. *Trieste,* 1892. 8°.
9041. g. 4.

—— Tacitus' Germania. Erklärt von U. Zernial. pp. 101. *Berl.* 1890. 8°. Pam. 28.

KEMMER (O.) Arminius. pp. 71. *Leipz.* 1893. 8°.
9327. dd. 12. (3.)

TARAMELLI (A.) Le Campagne di Germanico nella Germania. pp. 188. *Pavia,* 1891. 8°.
9041. m. 2.

MEYER (E.) Untersuchungen über die Schlacht im Teutoburger Walde. pp. 232. *Berl.* 1893. 8°.
9040. f. 24.

STAMFORD (T. v.) Das Schlachtfeld im Teutoburger Walde. pp. 330. *Cassel,* 1892. 8°.
9041. g. 14.

TIEFFENBACH (R.) Über die Örtlichkeit der Varus-Schlacht. pp. 31. *Berl.* 1891. 8°.
9008. l. 1. (7.)

HOLUB (J.) 1. Der Name 'Germani' in Tacitus Germania 2. pp. 25. *Freiwaldau,* 1891. 8°.
9008. g. 8. (6.)

LUECKENBACH (A.) De Germaniae quae vocatur Taciteae fontibus. pp. 69. *Marpurgi,* 1891. 8°.
Pam. 14.

JOUVENCEL (P. de) L'Indépendance des Gaules et l'Allemagne. pp. 134. *Paris,* 1890. 12°.
9200. b. 3.

KOENNECKE (M.) Das alte thüringische Königreich und sein Untergang 531 n. C. pp. 54. *Querfurt,* 1893. 8°. 9327. dd. 12. (4.)

WATTENBACH (W.) Deutschlands Geschichtsquellen im Mittelalter. 2 Bde. *Berl.* 1893. 8°.
09325. h. 11.

HENDERSON (E. F.) History of Germany in the Middle Ages. pp. 437. *Lond.* 1894. 8°.
09325. g. 9.

MENZEL (V.) Deutsches Gesandschaftswesen im Mittelalter. pp. 259. *Hannover,* 1892. 8°.
8026. f. 21.

PRIERATSCH (F.) Die deutschen Städte im Kampfe mit der Fürstengewalt. *Berl.* 1892, *etc.* 8°. 9326. df.

ROTH VON SCHRECKENSTEIN (C. H.) Die Ritterwürde und der Ritterstand. pp. 735. *Freiburg,* 1886. 8°. 9914. h. 25.

HENNEBERG (H.) Die politischen Beziehungen zwischen Deutschland und Frankreich, 1289-1308. pp. 164. *Strassb.* 1891. 8°. 9073. cc. 5.

LEROUX (A.) Nouvelles Recherches sur les Relations de la France avec l'Allemagne, 1378-1461. pp. 367. *Paris,* 1892. 8°. 9079. h. 16.

JANSSEN (J.) Geschichte des deutschen Volkes seit dem Ausgang des Mittelalters. *Freiburg,* 1890, *etc.* 8°. 9327. e.

LINDNER (T.) Zur deutschen Geschichte im 15 Jahrhundert. 1892. 8°. Ac. Vienna. *Universitas.* Mittheilungen des Instituts für Geschichtsforschung. Bd 13, Heft 3. Ac. 803.

P.P. *Berlin.* Hohenzollerische Forschungen. *Berl.* 1891, *etc.* 8°. P.P. 3545. h.

NEUMANN-STRELA (C.) Das Haus Hohenzollern und das deutsche Reich. *Berl.* 1890, *etc.* 8°.
9327. d.

BEHRENS (F. W.) Deutsches Ehr- und Nationalgefühl, 1600-1815. pp. 150. *Leipz.* 1891. 8°.
011840. i. 74.

BAUMGARTEN (H.) Gustav Adolf und die deutschen Protestanten. pp. 19. *Coburg,* 1893. 8°.
Pam. 8.

GERMANY.—History—*continued.*

ERDMANNSDOERFFER (B.) Deutsche Geschichte. 1648-1740. 1892, *etc.* 8°. ONCKEN (W.) Allgemeine Geschichte. Hauptabth. III. Th. 7.
2068. (22.)

TANERA (C.) Deutschlands Kriege von Fehrbellin bis Königgrätz, *etc.* *München,* 1891, *etc.* 8°. 9076. ccc. 9.

BIEDERMANN (F. C.) Deutschland im achtzehnten Jahrhundert. 2 Bde. *Leipz.* 1880. 8°.
09325. h. 3.

See also EUROPE : HOLY ROMAN EMPIRE : THIRTY YEARS WAR, *etc.*

Nineteenth Century.

GUENTHER (R.) Geschichte des Feldzuges von 1800 in Ober-Deutschland. pp. 210. *Frauenfeld,* 1893. 8°. 9080. i. 13.

MEINECKE (F.) Die deutschen Gesellschaften und der Hoffmannsche Bund. pp. 79. *Stuttgart,* 1891. 8°. 9007. ff. 6. (10.)

PETERSDORFF (H. v.) General von Thielmann. pp. 352. *Leipz.* 1894. 8°. 10708. g. 36.

LETTOW-VORBECK (O. v.) Der Krieg von 1806 und 1807. 2. Bde. *Berl.* 1891. 8°. 9079. k. 1.

SAUER (W.) Blüchers Übergang über den Rhein bei Caub. pp. 88. *Wiesbaden,* 1892. 8°.
9079. h. 18.

BIEDERMANN (F. C.) 1815-40. Fünfundzwanzig Jahre deutscher Geschichte. *Breslau,* 1890, *etc.* 8°. 9326. aaa. 11.

FLATHE (T.) Quellen zur vaterländischen Geschichte des 19 Jahrhunderts. *Leipz.* 1893, *etc.* 8°. 9326. de.

MOLLATT (G.) Quellenbuch zur Geschichte der deutschen Politik im 19 Jahrhundert. pp. 293. *Leipz.* 1892. 8°. 8073. d. 18.

PROELSS (J.) Das junge Deutschland. pp. 814. *Stuttgart,* 1892. 8°. 8186. f. 19.

SALOMON (L.) Deutschlands Leben und Streben im 19 Jahrhundert. pp. 326. *Stuttgart,* 1893. 8°. 9325. c. 10.

WENCK (W. B.) Deutschland vor hundert Jahren. 2 vol. *Leipz.* 1887, 90. 8°. 8073. bbb. 17.

BLUM (H.) Auf dem Wege zur deutschen Einheit. 2 Bde. *Jena,* 1893. 8°. 09325. g. 7.

HENNE-AM-RHYN (O.) Die nationale Einigung der Deutschen. pp. 92. *Hannover,* 1891. 8°.
9326. ee. 5.

GOETTE (R.) Geschichte der deutschen Einheitsbewegung im 19 Jahrhundert. *Gotha,* 1891, *etc.* 8°. 09325. g. 1.

KRAUSE (G.) Growth of German Unity. pp. 206. *Lond.* 1892. 8°. 9326. aaa. 13.

MECKLENBURGER. Die Einigung Deutschlands. pp. 131. *Dresd.* 1894. 8°. 9327. d. 12.

SCHULTHEISS (F. G.) Geschichte des deutschen Nationalgefühles. *München,* 1893, *etc.* 8°.
09325. h.

BIEDERMANN (F. C.) Fünfzig Jahre im Dienste des nationalen Gedankens. pp. 232. *Breslau,* 1892. 8°. 8072. de. 28.

BLOS (W.) Die deutsche Revolution. 1848 und 1849. pp. 670. *Stuttgart,* 1893. 8°. 9327. dd. 9.

MALLESON (G. B.) Refounding of the German Empire, 1848-71. pp. 326. *Lond.* 1893. 8°.
9326. de. 10.

WILLIAM I., *Emperor.* Politische Correspondenz Kaiser Wilhelms I. pp. 412. *Berl.* 1890. 8°.
8074. e. 32.

MARQUARDT (L.) Charakterzüge aus dem Leben Kaiser Wilhelms I. pp. 249. *Leipz.* 1890. 8°.
10704. g. 41.

SCHMITZ (M.) Kaiser Wilhelm I. pp. 85. *Neuwied,* 1892. 8°. 10704. i. 19.

GERMANY.—History—*continued.*

ONCKEN (W.) Das Zeitalter des Kaisers Wilhelm.
2 Bde. 1888, 90. 8°. Allgemeine Geschichte.
Hauptabth. IV. Th. 6.   2068. (31.)

THOMM (A.) Das Zeitalter Kaiser Wilhelm I.
Striegau, 1892. 8°.   09325. g. 3.

ERNEST II, *Duke of Saxe Coburg.* Aus meinem
Leben und aus meiner Zeit. *Berl.* 1892, *etc.* 8°.
10703. h. 39.

GARLEPP (B.) Die Paladine Kaiser Wilhelms I.
Breslau, 1890, *etc.* 8°.   010707. e.

SCHULZE (P.) and KOLLER (O.) Bismarck-Litera-
tur. Bibliographische Zusammenstellung.
pp. 70. *Leipz.* 1895. 8°.   011900. i. 11.

BISMARCK-SCHOENHAUSEN (O. E. L. v.) *Prince.*
Fürst Bismarcks gesammelte Reden. 3 Bde.
Berl. 1894. 8°.   8074. c. 14.

—— Die politischen Reden des Fürsten Bismarck. *Stuttgart,* 1892, *etc.* 8°.   8026. dd.

—— Sammlung der parlamentarischen Reden
Bismarcks seit dem Jahre 1847. 16 Bde.
Berl. 1890. 8°.   8074. aaaa. 8.

—— Die Ansprachen des Fürsten Bismarck,
1848-94. pp. 358. *Stuttgart,* 1895. 8°.
8072. dd. 4.

—— Fürst Bismarcks Briefe. pp. 376.
Berl. 1892. 8°.   10920. ccc. 37.

—— Aus Bismarcks politischen Briefwechsel.
pp. 243. *Berl.* 1893. 8°.   8072. c. 1.

—— Die schönsten Bismarckbriefe. pp. 69.
Dresd. 1892. 8°.   Pam. 35.

—— Lichtstrahlen aus Bismarcks Reden, Briefen
und Gesprächen. pp. 181. *Berl.* 1890. 8°.
12301. e. 33.

—— Neue Tischgespräche und Interviews.
pp. 427. *Stuttgart,* 1895. 8°.   10705. gg. 35.

—— Denkwürdigkeiten aus dem Leben des
Fursten Bismarck. *Leipz.* 1890, *etc.* 8°.
10704. i. 11.

—— Bismarcks Leben und Wirken. pp. 486.
Leipz. 1894. 8°.   010707. ee. 26.

BLUM (H.) Fürst Bismarck und seine Zeit.
München, 1894, *etc.* 8°.   10703. ff.

BUELOW (W. v.) Neue Bismarck-Erinnerungen.
pp. 311. *Berl.* 1895. 8°.   10703. ff. 14.

DAHN (F.) Fürst Bismarck. pp. 59.
Leipz. 1892. 8°.   8074. aaaa. 15. (3.)

HERMANN (P.) Das Leben des Fürsten Bismarck.
pp. 382. *Chicago,* 1894. 8°.   10703. ff. 15.

KOEHLER (W.) Fürst Bismarck. Sein Leben
und sein Wirken. pp. 122. *Minden,* 1890. 8°.
10601. e. 5. (4.)

KOHL (H.) Fürst Bismarck. Regesten zu einer
wissenschaftlichen Biographie.
Leipz. 1891, *etc.* 8°.   10703. h. 37.

—— Bismarck-Jahrbuch. *Berl.* 1894, *etc.* 8°.
10704. k.

KOSER (R.) Fürst Bismarck. Festrede zur Feier
des 77. Geburtstages. pp. 24. *Bonn,* 1892. 8°.
10601. ff. 7. (7.)

KRAEMER (H.) Unser Bismarck.
Stuttgart, 1894, *etc.* fol.   129.

LOWE (C.) Prince Bismarck. pp. 330.
Lond. 1892. 8°.   10703. e. 25.

MUELLER (W.) Fürst Bismarck. pp. 288.
Stuttgart, 1890. 8°.   10703. de. 24.

SONNENBURG (F.) Fürst Bismarck. pp. 185.
Berl. 1895. 8°.   10704. f. 35.

POSCHINGER (H. v.) Fürst Bismarck und die
Parlamentarier. *Breslau,* 1894, *etc.* 8°. 8074. h.

BISMARCK-SCHOENHAUSEN (O. E. L. v.) *Prince.*
Reden und Vorträge gehalten bei der Vorfeier
des 77. Geburtstages. pp. 54.
Dresd. 1892. 8°.   Pam. 8.

GERMANY.—History—*continued.*

DAHN (F.) Zum 80. Geburtstage des Fürsten
Bismarck. pp. 84. *Breslau,* 1895. 8°.
10707. aaa. 45.

PENZLER (J.) Marksteine von Bismarcks Lebens-
weg. pp. 154. *Leipz.* 1895. 8°. 10704. cc. 45.

PFLEIDERER (E.) Festrede zur Vorfeier von
Bismarcks 80sten Geburtstag. pp. 17.
Tübingen, 1895. 8°.   Pam. 8.

SCHIEMANN (T.) Bismarck. Festrede zu seinem
80sten Geburtstage. pp. 16. *Berl.* 1895. 8°.
Pam. 3.

STEGMANN (R.) Fürst Bismarck und seine Zeit.
pp. 164. *Wolfenbüttel,* 1895. 8°. 10707. cc. 44.

STRECKER (C.) Otto von Bismarck. Ein Lebensbild, *etc.* pp. 157. *Berl.* 1895. 8°. 10704. g. 44.

WIPPERMANN (C.) Fürst Bismarcks 80. Geburtstag. pp. 298. *München,* 1895. 8°.
10705. aaa. 44.

MOLTKE (H. C. B. v.) *Count.* Gesammelte
Schriften und Denkwürdigkeiten. 7 Bde.
Berl. 1891-92. 8°.   12252. i. 4.

—— Essays, Speeches and memoirs. 2 vol.
Lond. 1893. 8°.   12354. k. 16.

BUCHNER (W.) Feldmarschall von Mo'tke.
pp. 407. *Lahr,* 1895. 8°.   010707. ff. 10.

LOCKROY (E.) M. de Moltke; ses mémoires et la
guerre future. pp. 258. *Paris,* 1892. 8°.
010707. e. 30.

MOLTKE (H. C. B. v.) *Count.* Moltke, his Life
and Character. pp. 315. *Lond.* 1892. 8°.
10704. f. 34.

MORRIS (W. O'C.) Moltke. Biographical study.
pp. 419. *Lond.* 1893. 8°.   010707. ee. 16.

MUELLER-BOHN (H.) Graf Moltke. pp. 550.
Berl. 1891. 8°.   10704. i.

SCHRECK (E.) Generalfeldmarschall von Moltke.
pp. 108. *Düsseldorf,* 1890. 8°.   010707. e. 8.

ROON (W. v.) *Count.* Denkwürdigkeiten aus dem
Leben des Grafen von Roon. 2 Bde.
Breslau, 1892. 8°.   010707. e. 38.

HEITZ (E.) Die sozialpolitische Bewegung in
Deutschland, 1863-90. pp. 45.
Stuttgart, 1891. 8°.   8277. ee. 1. (10.)

DENMARK. *Army.* Den dansk-tydske Krig, 1864.
Kjøbenh. 1890, *etc.* 8°.   9424. i. 12.

THORSANDER (G.) Dansk-Tyska Kriget 1864.
pp. 111. *Stockholm,* 1890. 8°.   9080. c. 27.

WILLE (R.) Lose Tagebuchblätter aus dem
Feldzug gegen Dänemark. pp. 283.
Berl. 1895. 8°.   9080. ee. 11.

MOLTKE (H. C. B. v.) *Count.* Moltkes Feldzugs-
Entwurf 1866. pp. 41. *Berl.* 1892. 8°. Pam. 2.

KUNZ (H.) Der Feldzug der Mainarmee im
Jahre 1866. pp. 230. *Berl.* 1890. 8°. 9079. h. 13.

SCHMIDT (J. v.) Die kurhessische Armeedivision,
1866. pp. 255. *Kassel,* 1892. 8°. 9326. aaa. 14.

GERMANY. Die nationalliberale Partei, 1867-92.
pp. 161. *Leipz.* 1892. 8°.   8072. dd. 3.

MAURENBRECHER (W.) Gründung des deutschen
Reiches, 1859-71. pp. 262. *Leipz.* 1892. 8°.
9327. d. 11.

SYBEL (H. C. L. v.) The Founding of the
German Empire by William I. 3 vol.
N.Y. 1890, 91. 8°.   9326. df. 11.

EBERSTEIN (A. v.) Kritische Bemerkungen über
von Sybel's Begründung des deutschen Reiches
durch Wilhelm I. 2 Thle.
Wiesbaden, 1890. 8°.   9327. d. 9.

BENEDETTI (V.) *Count.* Studies in Diplomacy.
pp. 323. *Lond.* 1895. 8°.   8026. e. 10.

BLUM (H.) Das deutsche Reich zur Zeit Bismarcks. 1871-96. pp. 708. *Leipz.* 1893. 8°.
8074. g. 4.

GERMANY.—History—*continued.*

WHITMAN (S.) Imperial Germany. pp. 304.
Lond. 1891. 8°. 10256. aa. 37.

A., B. v. Fürst Bismarcks deutsche Politik seit
der Begründung des neuen Reiches. pp. 126.
Leipz. 1895. 8°. 8074. ee. 49.

MOLLAT (G.) Reden des ersten deutschen Parla-
ments. pp. 832. *Osterwieck,* 1895. 8°. 9327. g. 2.

RICHTER (E.) Im alten Reichstag. Erinnerungen. *Berl.* 1894, *etc.* 8°. 8072. eec.

SABIN (J.) Zwölf Jahre deutscher Parteikämpfe,
1881–92. pp. 67. 1892. 8°. WOLFF (E.)
Deutsche Schriften. Reihe 2. Heft. 5. 12250. i.

MENZENBACH (J.) L. Windthorst in sein Leben
und Wirken. *Trier,* 1891, *etc.* 8°.
010707. e. 34.

PHILIPPSON (M.) Friedrich III. pp. 310.
Berl. 1893. 8°. 10704. i. 21.

SCHRADER (C.) Der deutsche Kaiser Friedrich.
pp. 14. *Berl.* 1889. 8°. 10601. ee. 5. (14.)

TAYLOR (L.) "Fritz" of Prussia. pp. 612.
Lond. 1891. 8°. 10703. ee. 26.

WILLIAM II., *Emperor.* Ansprachen und Erlasse,
1888–90. pp. 117. *Leipz.* 1891. 8°. 12301. m. 25.

FREDERIC (H.) The Young Emperor, William II.
pp. 251. *Lond.* 1892. 8°. 10703. de. 29.

GAGLIARDI (E.) Guglielmo II. pp. 456.
Torino, 1893. 8°. 10705. bb. 53.

HECKEDORN ( ) *Baron.* Guillaume II. pp. 347.
Paris, 1892. 8°. 8072. ee. 27.

HENGST (H.) Unser Kaiser Wilhelm. pp. 79.
Berl. 1894. 8°. 10703. ff. 9.

LOWE (C.) The German Emperor William II.
pp. 274. 1895. 8°. Public Men of To-day.
10600. e.

MEISTER (F.) Kaiser Wilhelm II. pp. 398.
Berl. 1894. 8°. 10703. f. 25.

MUECKE (A.) Kaiser Wilhelm II. pp. 111.
Berl. 1892. 8°. 8074. ee. 42.

REDERN (E. v.) Kaiser Wilhelm II. und seine
Leute. pp. 274. *Berl.* 1891. 8°. 10703. de. 31.

REIMANN (C.) Kaiser Wilhelm II. pp. 56.
Minden, 1891. 8°. 8074. ee. 47. (6.)

TERBISSE (A.) Kaiser Wilhelm II. pp. 27.
Paderborn, 1891. 8°. 10601. f. 9. (16.)

WIERMANN (H.) Kaiser Wilhelm II. als Soldat.
pp. 145. *Berl.* 1892. 8°. 10703. de. 32.

GERMAN. Wilhelm II. als Erzieher. pp. 27.
Berl. 1895. 8°. Pam. 72.

WILLIAM II., *Emperor.* L'Empereur allemand.
pp. 95. *Paris,* 1893. 8°. 10703. de 37.

—— Kaiser Wilhelm II. pp. 44.
Stuttgart, 1893. 8°. 8074. aaaa. 6.

WIERMANN (H.) Deutsche Politik seit Bismarcks
Entlassung, 1890–92. pp. 333. *Berl.* 1893. 8°.
8073. d. 16.

CAPRIVI (G. L. v.) *Count.* Die Reden des Grafen
von Caprivi 1883–93. pp. 424. *Berl.* 1894. 8°.
8074. bb. 42.

WIPPERMANN (C.) Deutscher Geschichtskalender
für 1890, *etc. Leipz.* 1890, *etc.* 8°. 9326. de. 9.

ST . . . . R ( ) *Baron.* Hof und Gesellschaft
in deutschen Residenzen. pp. 392.
Berl. 1890. 8°. 10256. c. 5.

See also EUROPE : FRANCE, *Military History of
the Revolution, etc.:* GERMAN FRENCH WAR :
infra : Politics.

History, *Ecclesiastical.*

GOULD (S. B.) The Church in Germany. pp. 400.
1891. 8°. DITCHFIELD (P. H.) National Churches.
8534. de.

HAUCK (A.) Kirchengeschichte Deutschlands.
2 Thle. *Leipz.* 1887, 90. 8°. 4662. c. 5.

GERMANY.—History—*continued.*

HOPE (A.) The Conversion of the Teutonic Race.
pp. 313. *Lond.* 1892. 8°. 4535. b. 13.

KUHLMANN (B.) Der heilige Bonifatius.
pp. 504. *Paderborn,* 1895. 8°. 4823. d. 11.

KUMMER (F.) Die Bischofswahlen in Deutschland, 1378–1418. pp. 183. *Jena,* 1892. 8°.
4662. c. 14.

Ac. Rome. *K. preuss. historisches Institut.*
Nuntiaturberichte aus Deutschland.
Gotha, 1892, *etc.* 8°. Ac. 6515.

KREBS (K.) Beiträge und Urkunden zur deutschen Geschichte im Zeitalter der Reformation.
Leipz. 1895, *etc.* 8°. 4662. d.

BAX (E. B.) The Social Side of the Reformation
in Germany. *Lond.* 1894, *etc.* 8°. 4660. de.

LEONROD (F. L. v.) *Baron.* Die Hirtenschreiben
des Bischofes von Eichstätt. pp. 464.
Ingolstadt, 1892. 4°. 4887. ee. 6.

See also CHURCH HISTORY: EVANGELICAL
CHURCH : ROMAN CATHOLIC CHURCH, in Germany :
for works on Luther and the other German
Reformers, see CHURCH HISTORY, *Reformation.*

Law.

BRUNNER (H.) Forschungen zur Geschichte des
deutschen Rechtes. pp. 750. *Stuttgart,* 1894. 8°.
6005. h. 22.

BURCHARD (K.) Die Hegung der deutschen Ge-
richte im Mittelalter. pp. 315. *Leipz.* 1893. 8°.
6005. h. 15.

FROMMHOLD (G.) Deutsche Rechtsgeschichte.
pp. 224. *Berl.* 1894. 8°. 05604. g. 7.

HUEBNER (R.) J. Grimm und das deutsche Recht.
pp. 187. *Göttingen,* 1895. 8°. 5604. e. 3.

ALTMANN (P. A.) Der Erlassvertrag und der
Entwurf eines bürgerlichen Gesetzbuchs.
Leipz. 1891, *etc.* 8°. 05604. h. 13.

JAKUBEZKY (C.) Bemerkungen zu dem Entwurfe
eines bürgerlichen Gesetzbuches. pp. 358.
München, 1892. 8°. 5604. d. 2.

KINDEL (W.) Das Rechts-geschäft und sein
Rechtsgrund. pp. 264. *Berl.* 1892. 8°.
05604. h. 18.

LIEBE (V. v.) Sachenrechtliche Erörterungen zu
dem Entwurfe eines bürgerl.chen Gesetzbuches.
pp. 159. *Leipz.* 1891. 8°. 5604. bb. 4.

REATZ (C. F.) Die zweite Lesung des Entwurfs
eines bürgerlichen Gesetzbuchs. 1892, *etc.* 8°.
P.P. *Leipsic.* Archiv für Theorie des deutschen
Handelsrechts. P.P. 1385. d.

BALTZ-BALZBERG (H. v.) Muster Processe.
Wien, 1894, *etc.* 8°. 8831. cc.

BIRKMEYER (C.) Die Lehre von der Teilnahme
des deutschen Reichsgerichts. pp. 305.
Berl. 1890. 8°. 05604. h. 2.

BRAUN (A.) Traité de droit civil allemand.
pp. 564. *Brux.* 1893. 8°. 05604. h. 36.

CHAISEMARTIN (A.) Proverbes et maximes du
Droit germanique. pp. 585. *Paris,* 1891. 8°.
05604. h. 17.

FIORETTI (G.) Le leggi civili della Germania.
Napoli, 1888, *etc.* 8°. 6005. h. 1.

GIERKE (O.) Deutsches Privatrecht. 1895, *etc.* 8°.
BINDING (C.) Systematisches Handbuch, *etc.*
5605. ff.

GROTEFEND (G. A.) Das gesammte preussisch-
deutsche Gesetzgebungs-Material.
Düsseldorf, 1890, *etc.* 8°. 5605. ff.

HEILFRON (E.) Das gemeine Privatrecht des
deutschen Reichs. *Berl.* 1893, *etc.* 8°. 5606. de.

HERGENHAHN (T.) Rechtsprechung der deutschen
Gerichtshöfe über Prozessbevollmächtigte und
Rechtsanwälte. *Hannover,* 1894, *etc.* 8°. 05604. k.

GERMANY.—Law—*continued.*

Hess (A.) Abhandlungen aus dem Gebiete des Civil- und Strafrechts. pp. 62.
Hamb. 1892. 8°. 05604. i. 6.

Horn (A.) Zur Reform des deutschen Civilprozesses. pp. 128. *Leipz.* 1893. 8°.
05604. i. 19.

Kleinfeller (G.) Die geschichtliche Entwicklung des Thatsachen-ides in Deutschland.
pp. 320. *Berl.* 1891. 8°. 5604. ee. 11.

Kohler (J.) Gesammelte Beiträge zum Civilprocess. pp. 604. *Berl.* 1894. 8°. 05604. i. 36.

Kolligs (R.) Die wichtigsten civilrechtlichen Entscheidungen des Reichsgerichts. pp. 152.
Berl. 1893. 8°. 5606. bb. 11.

Kraut (W. T.) Grundriss zu Vorlesungen über das deutsche Privatrecht. pp. 608.
Berl. 1886. 8°. 05604. h. 26.

Lehr (P. E.) Traité de droit civil germanique. 2 tom. *Paris,* 1892. 8°. 05604. h. 25.

Leuss (H.) Was ist von unsern Magistrat zu halten? pp. 74. *Hannover,* 1892. 8°. Pam. 72.

Maass (C.) 55 Jahre deutscher Reichs-Gesetzgebung. pp. 561. *Leipz.* 1892. 8°. 05604. g. 1.

Opet (O.) Geschichte der Prozesseinleitungsformen. *Breslau,* 1891, *etc.* 8°. 6005. cc. 1.

Pfaff (F.) Sachregister zu dem Bundes-bezw. Reichs-Gesetzblatt, 1867–90. pp. 268.
Mainz, 1891. 4°. 5605. h. 19.

Pfizer (G.) Wort und That. Ein Nothruf für deutsches Recht. pp. 120. *Leipz.* 1892. 8°.
5604. ccc. 25.

Pollak (R.) Gerichtliches Geständniss im Civilprozesse. pp. 178. *Berl.* 1893. 8°.
05604. i. 20.

Scherer (M.) Die Entscheidungen des Reichsgerichts. *Leipz.* 1892, *etc.* 8°. 05604. i.

Skedl (A.) Das Mahnverfahren. pp. 180. *Leipz.* 1891. 8°. 05604. h. 11.

Trutter (J.) Bona fides im civil Prozesse. pp. 297. *München,* 1892. 8°. 05604. i. 14.

Zenthoefer (P.) Das subjective Recht nach allgemeinen Grundsätzen. pp. 400.
Berl. 1881. 8°. 5656. g. 15.

See also Law, *Commercial: Criminal: Ecclesiastical:* Law Reports.

Local Government. *See* Local Government.

Navy.

Batsch ( ) Deutsch' See-Gras. pp. 448.
Berl. 1892. 8°. 8807. c. 51.

Germany. *Navy.* Unsere Marine in der elften Stunde. pp. 262. *Berl.* 1891. 8°. 8807. cc. 32.

Reichsfreund. Fort mit unserer Marine?
pp. 16. *Berl.* 1895. 8°. Pam. 43.

Uhl ( ) Deutschlands Seemacht. pp. 152.
Bamberg, 1895. 8°. 8806. ccc. 20.

Werner (B. v.) Die Kriegsmarine. pp. 225.
Leipz. 1894. 8°. 8806. de. 47.

—— Deutsches Kriegschiffsleben und Seefahrkunst. pp. 450. *Leipz.* 1891. 8°. 8807. d. 21.

Heye (A.) Die Marine-Infanterie. pp. 201.
Berl. 1891. 8°. 8823. ddd. 20.

Politics.

General and Domestic.
1890.

Bismarck-Schoenhausen (O. E. L. v.) *Prince.* Bismarck und die deutsche Nation. pp. 66.
Leipz. 1890. 8°. 8074. h. 13. (1.)

—— Offener Brief an Fürsten Bismarck von einem Nihilisten. pp. 60. *Berl.* 1890. 8°.
Pam. 72.

—— Fürst Bismarck's Selbstvertheidigung.
pp. 78. *Leipz.* 1890. 8°. 8074. c. 26. (3.)

GERMANY.—Politics—*continued.*

Breslau (K. v.) Er geht! Was nun? pp. 51.
Berl. 1890. 8°. 8074. f. 37. (2.)

Conrad (M. G.) Deutsche Weckrufe. pp. 178.
Leipz. 1890. 8°. 8074. bb. 34.

Germany. *Sozialdemokratische Partei.* Protokoll über die Verhandlungen des Parteitages.
pp. 320. *Berl.* 1890. 8°. 8073. d. 15.

Hildebrandt (M.) Ohne Bismarck. pp. 47.
Berl. 1890. 8°. 8074. g. 5. (1.)

Kuerschner (J.) Der neue Reichstag, 1890.
pp. 432. *Stuttgart,* 1890. 32°. 8073. aa. 3.

Morre (C.) Die Arbeiter-Partei und der Bauernstand. pp. 75. *Graz,* 1890. 8°. Pam. 83.

Nerrlich (P.) Herr von Treitschke und das junge Deutschland. pp. 84. *Berl.* 1890. 8°.
8074. ee. 47. (2.)

Richter (E.) Die Irrlehren der Sozialdemokratie. pp. 48. *Berl.* 1890. 8°. Pam. 82.

Schultze (F. W.) Ne quid nimis. Offener Brief. pp. 92. *Berl.* 1890. 8°. 8831. l. 9. (7.)

1891.

Bauer (F.) Kaiser und Arbeiter. pp. 158.
Bonn, 1891. 8°. 08276. g. 8.

Bewer (M.) Bei Bismarck. pp. 72.
Dresd. 1891. 8°. 10704. h. 30.

—— Bismarck im Reichstage. pp. 64.
Dresd. 1891. 8°. 8074. h. 3. (2.)

—— Bismarck und Rothschild. pp. 43.
Dresd. 1891. 8°. Pam. 72.

Bismarck (O. E. L. v.) *Prince.* Ueber die Erfolge und Folgen der Bismarck'schen Politik. pp. 42.
Berl. 1891. 8°. 8074. h. 3. (9.)

—— 101 Kukukseier seit Bismarcks Rücktritt ins Reichnest gelegt. pp. 64. *Berl.* 1891. 8°.
8074. f. 26.

—— Das Ende des Fürsten von Bismarck.
pp. 46. *Berl.* 1891. 8°. 8074. h. 3. (4.)

Blum (H.) Die Lügen unserer Sozialdemokratie. pp. 422. *Wismar,* 1891. 8°. 8072. de. 26.

Fortschritt. Der Fortschritt der Sozialdemokratie. pp. 23. *Leipz.* 1891. 8°. Pam. 82.

Germany. Grosspreussen oder die verfehlte Neugestaltung Deutschlands. pp. 58.
Berl. 1891. 8°. Pam. 72.

—— Programm der sozialdemokratischen Partei Deutschlands. pp. 8. *Berl.* 1891. 8°. Pam. 82.

—— *Sozialdemokratische Partei.* Protokoll über die Verhandlungen des Parteitages. 1891.
pp. 368. *Berl.* 1891. 8°. 8073. d. 14.

Geyer (F.) Die Bismarck-Hetze. pp. 43.
Berl. 1891. 8°. 8074. g. 5. (3.)

Ghibellinus. Kaiser, werde hart! Offener Brief. pp. 56. *Weimar,* 1891. 8°.
8074. f. 37. (5.)

Julius. Die nationalistische Partei in Deutschland. 1891. pp. 35. *Berl.* 1891. 8°.
8074. ee. 47. (4.)

Kunowski (L. v.) Wird die Socialdemokratie siegen? pp. 278. *Bielefeld,* 1891. 8°.
08276. g. 10.

Laicus (P.) Was will die Socialdemokratie.
pp. 35. *Crefeld,* 1891. 8°. 8277. a. 61. (3.)

Prussian. Was für einen Kurs haben wir?
pp. 76. *Gotha,* 1891. 8°. 8074. ee. 47. (5.)

Rudel (R.) Geschichte des Liberalismus und der deutschen Reichsverfassung. pp. 387.
Guben, 1891. 8°. 8072. e. 3.

Traub (T.) Warum gehen wir nicht mit der Sozialdemokratie? pp. 43. *Stuttgart,* 1891. 8°.
Pam. 82.

Wolff (E.) Deutsche Schriften für nationales Leben. *Kiel,* 1891, *etc.* 8°. 12250. l.

GERMANY.—Politics.—_continued._

1892.

ARNDT (A.) Festrede zur Bismarck-Feier in Halle. pp. 14. _Halle_, 1892. 8°.   Pam. 45.

BALDER. Die Wahrheit über Bismarck. pp. 164. _Leipz._ 1892. 8°.   8074. b. 46.

BAUER (E.) Caveat Populus! pp. 124. _Leipz._ 1892. 8°.   8074. ee. 38.

BISMARCK-SCHOENHAUSEN (O. E. L. v.) _Prince._ Bismarck und der Hof. pp. 33. _Dresd._ 1892. 8°.   8074. g. 5. (5.)

—— Bismarck. Ein politischer Nachruf. pp. 22. _Berl._ 1892. 8°.   8074. h. 3. (6.)

—— Fürst von Bismarck, der Herzog der Deutschen. pp. 13. _Berl._ 1892. 8°.   Pam. 46.

—— Fürst Bismarck und das deutsche Volk. pp. 14. _Strassb._ 1892. 8°.   8074. h. 3. (8.)

—— Wie Bismarck entlassen wurde! pp. 94. _Berl._ 1892. 8°.   8072. df. 12.

—— Bismarck und Caprivi. pp. 27. _Berl._ 1892. 8°.   8074. h. 3. (7.)

—— Ein wenig mehr Licht über Bismarck, Caprivi, _etc._ pp. 32. _Berl._ 1892. 8°.   8074. h. 3. (10.)

CAPRIVI (G. L. v.) _Count._ Darf Caprivi bleiben? pp. 25. _Berl._ 1892. 8°.   8074. g. 5. (6.)

F., G. v. Gegen die Caprivische Militärvorlage. pp. 16. _Berl._ 1892. 8°.   8830. h. 26. (5.)

GERMANY, _Empire of._ Konservatives Handbuch. pp. 383. _Berl._ 1892. 8°.   8074. c. 11.

KAISER. Der Kaiser in der Mitte. pp. 70. _Dresd._ 1892. 8°.   4034. m. 17. (5.)

KLEIN (E.) Der Socialdemokrat hat das Wort! pp. 198. _Freiburg_, 1892. 8°.   08276. g. 52.

KLESER (H.) Bismarck-Prometheus. pp. 32. _Köln_, 1892. 8°.   8074. h. 3. (11.)

LUCKO (H.) Ein Jahr im Centrum der deutsch-sozialer Partei. pp. 28. 1892. 8°.   8074. ff. 31. (9.)

NICHTBORUSSER. Das Ministerium Eulenburg-Caprivi. pp. 77. _Berl._ 1892. 8°. 8074. ee. 47. (7.)

PEINLICH (F.) Die Wahrheit über Bismarck. pp. 57. _Trier_, 1892, 8°.   8074. g. 5. (8.)

RICHTER (E.) Politisches A B C-Buch. pp. 444. _Berl._ 1892. 8°.   8074. bb. 37.

STUMM-HALBERG (v.) _Freiherr_ von Stumm und die Socialdemokratie. pp. 30. _Berl._ 1892. 8°.   Pam. 82.

WILLIAM II., _Emperor._ Wilhelm II., Romantiker oder Sozialist? pp. 33. _Zürich_, 1892. 8°.   8074. ee. 47. (9.)

1893.

BISMARCK-SCHOENHAUSEN (O. E. L. v.) _Prince._ Die Ächtung Bismarcks durch den "Neusten Kurs," _etc._ _Berl._ 1893. 8°.   8074. g. 5. (10.)

GERMAN. Mit dem Kaiser! pp. 30. _Leipz._ 1893. 8°.   8074. e. 24. (12.)

HAENTZSCHEL (W.) Beamtenthum und Socialdemokratie. pp. 56. _Leipz._ 1893. 8°.   Pam. 82.

HARTMANN (G. W.) Sensationelle Enthüllungen über die Führer der "Socialdemokratischen Partei." pp. 46. _Hamb._ 1893. 8°.   Pam. 82.

JASTROW (L.) "Sozialliberal." pp. 127. _Berl._ 1893. 8°.   8072. cee. 12.

KUERSCHNER (J.) Der neue Reichstag, 1893. _Stuttgart._ 1893. 24°.   8073. aa. 8.

LIEBERMANN VON SONNENBERG ( ) Herr Liebermann v. Sonnenberg als Parteiführer und Gesinnungsgenosse. pp. 139. _Leipz._ 1893. 8°.   8072. c. 2.

OERTEL (G.) Der Konservatismus als Weltanschauung. pp. 105. _Leipz._ 1893. 8°. 8074. ee. 43.

PATTAI (R.) Die neuesten politischen Ereignisse. pp. 33. _Wien_, 1893. 8°. 8074. ff. 32. (8.)

GERMANY.—Politics.—_continued._

PRENGEL (T.) Wahlkatechismus für die Wahlen zum Reichstage. pp. 145. _Berl._ 1893. 8°.   8074. c. 13.

SOZIALDEMOKRATIE. Nieder mit der Sozialdemokratie. pp. 40. _Berl._ 1893. 8°. Pam. 82.

WEBER ( ) Die Reichstagswahl von 1893. 1893. 8°. Sammlung theologischer und sozialer Reden. Ser. 4. Lief. 9–12.   4224. ff. 25.

WESTARP (A. v.) _Count._ Fürst Bismarck und das deutsche Volk. pp. 234. _München_, 1893. 8°.   8073. d. 17.

1894.

ANTI-LIBERAL. Wohin? Ein wort zur Warnung. pp. 25. _Leipz._ 1894. 8°. 8074. c. 26. (5.)

BAUMANN (J.) Preussisch? oder zugleich Deutsch und allgemeinmenschlich? pp. 181. _Frankfurt_, 1894. 8°.   8074. bb. 45.

GEHLSEN (H. J.) Aus dem Reiche Bismarck. pp. 80. _Berl._ 1894. 8°.   8074. bbb. 15.

HARTMUT (J.) 95 Sätze zur Reformierung des deutschen Reiches. pp. 47. _Leipz._ 1894. 8°.   8074. f. 37. (8.)

NEUMANN - HOFER (A.) Die Entwicklung der Socialdemokratie bei den Wahlen zur deutschen Reichstage. pp. 58. _Berl._ 1894. 8°. Pam. 82.

PHILIPPIKUS. Bismarck der Ganze! p. 62. _Leipz._ 1894. 8°.   Pam. 72.

SCHAEFFLE (A. E. F.) Deutsche Kern- und Zeitfragen. pp. 472. _Berl._ 1894. 8°. 8074. bb. 43.

SCHNEIDEWIN (M.) Das politische System des Reichskanzlers von Caprivi. pp. 158. _Danzig_, 1894. 8°.   8074. ee. 46.

THUENGEN-ROSSBACH (C. v.) _Baron._ Thüngen contra Caprivi. pp. 31. _Würzburg._ 1894. 8°.   Pam. 72.

1895.

BISMARCK-SCHOENHAUSEN (O. E. L. v.) _Prince._ Bismarck und die Socialdemokratie. pp. 38. _Dresd._ 1895. 8°.   Pam. 72.

BOGUSLAWSKI (A. v.) Vollkampfnicht Scheinkampf. pp. 88. _Berl._ 1895. 8°. 8074. ee. 50.

FABER (M.) Kaiser, Volk und Volksvertretung. pp. 33. _Leipz._ 1895. 8°.   Pam. 72.

KAISERLICHER. Fürst Bismarck und Herr von Bötticher. pp. 31. _Berl._ 1895. 8°.   Pam. 67.

WILLIAM II., _Emperor._ Der Kaiser und seine Rathgeber. pp. 51. _Berl._ 1895. 8°. Pam. 72.

WOLFF (A.) Vier Jahre nach Bismarck!? pp. 30. _Berl._ 1895. 8°.   Pam. 72.

_See also supra : Constitution : History : _SOCIALISM : SOCIAL SCIENCE.

Foreign.

GERMANY. Germania irredenta. pp. 52. _Dresd._ 1892. 8°.   8026. i. 5. (11.)

PEINLICH (F) Bismarck's Reise nach Wien und ihre Folgen. pp. 43. _Trier_, 1892. 8°.   8074. g. 5. (7.)

CONSULES. Videant Consules. La guerre est-elle inévitable? pp. 159. _Paris_, 1890. 12°.   8026. aaa. 38.

FIORE (P,) L'Empereur d'Allemagne, la France, _etc._ pp. 40. _Paris_, 1890. 8°. 8026. ee. 24. (7.)

GERMAN QUESTION. La Question allemande. pp. 62. _Paris_, 1888. 8°.   8026. i. 6. (4.)

GEFFCKEN (F. H.) Frankreich, Russland und der Dreibund. pp. 179. _Berl._ 1893. 8°.   8026. c. 7.

PARDIELLAN (P. de) Les Mœurs politiques des Allemands. pp. 221. _Paris_, 1894. 8°. 8074. dd. 1.

CENA (C.) La nostra alleanza colla Germania. pp. 13. _Roma_, 1893. 8°.   Pam. 67.

BIGELOW (P.) The German Emperor and his Eastern Neighbours. pp. 179. _Lond._ 1892. 8°.   10703. c. 36.

GERMANY.—Politics—*continued.*

BISMARCK-SCHOENHAUSEN (O. E. L. v.) *Prince.* Fürst Bismarck und Russlands Orientpolitik. pp. 55. *Berl.* 1892. 8°.　　8028. ff. 16. (11.)

BM. Wie der Herzog von Lauenburg, Fürst Bismarck, die russ.-französ. Freundschaft zu Stande brachte. pp. 54. *Leipz.* 1890. 8°.　　　　　　　　　　　　Pam. 72.

HELM (W. v.) Das russische Schreckgespenst und sein innerer Werth. pp. 54. *Hannover,* 1892. 8°.　　　　　Pam. 67.

STEIN (A.) Wer wird siegen? pp. 48. *Berl.* 1893. 8°.　　　3926. bb. 46. (7.)

WILLIAM II., *Emperor.* Wilhelm II. and Alexander III. pp. 32. *Dresden,* 1892. 8°.　　　　　　　　　8026. i. 5. (12.)

DOUGLAS (R. v. B.) *Baron.* Het Conflict tusschen Zwitserland en Deutschland in 1889. pp. 144. *Leiden,* 1891. 8°.　　5686. cc. 66.

RASCHÈR (J. M. v.) Der schweizer Staat und Preussen-Deutschland. pp. 188. *Berl.* 1893. 8°.　　　　　　　　8074. bb. 41.

See also EUROPE.

Reichstag. *See supra,* CONSTITUTION : POLITICS.

Roman Catholic Church.

See supra : HISTORY, *Ecclesiastical,* and ROMAN CATHOLIC CHURCH, *in Germany.*

Social Life.

HEGEL (C.) Städte der germanischen Völker im Mittelalter. 2 B.le. *Leipz.* 1891. 8°.　　　　　　　　8248. g. 13.

KALLSEN (O.) Die deutschen Städte im Mittelalter. *Halle,* 1891, *etc.* 8°.　　9326. df. 10.

LOEHER (F. v.) Kulturgeschichte der Deutschen im Mittelalter. *München,* 1891, *etc.* 8°.　　　　　　　　9327. dd. 8.

SASS (J.) Deutsches Leben zur Zeit der sächsischen Kaiser. pp. 81. *Berl.* 1892. 8°. 7709. f. 27.

SCHULTZ (A.) Deutsches Leben im XIV. und XV. Jahrhundert. *Wien,* 1892, *etc.* 8°.　　7709. i.

BAX (E. B.) Social Side of the Reformation in Germany. *Lond.* 1894, *etc.* 8°.　　4660. de.

HODERMANN (R.) Bilder aus dem deutschen Leben des 17. Jahrhunderts. *Paderborn,* 1890, *etc.* 8°.　　12357. dd. 3.

SCHULTZ (A.) Alltagsleben einer deutschen Frau zu Anfang des 18. Jahrhunderts. pp. 278. *Leipz.* 1890. 8°.　　7709. b. 42.

───────

BERLIN SOCIETY. Aus der berliner Gesellschaft unter Wilhelm II. pp. 297. *Berl.* 1892. 8°.　　　　　　　　10256. c. 10.

BRETON (J.) Notes d'un étudiant français en Allemagne. pp. 310. *Paris,* 1895. 12°.　　　　　　　　10240. b. 4.

DAWSON (W. H.) Germany and the Germans. 2 vol. *Lond.* 1894. 8°.　　10240. cc. 4.

FOURNIER DE FLAIX (E.) Pendant une mission en Russie. À travers l'Allemagne. 2 tom. *Paris,* 1894. 8°.　　08275. f. 8.

FREYBE (A.) Das deutsche Haus und seine Sitte. pp. 168. *Gütersloh,* 1892. 8°. 8409. e. 25.

JOZE (V.) La Ménagerie sociale. Babylone d'Allemagne. pp. 205. *Paris,* 1894. 12°.　　　　　　　　012330. g. 58.

LANO (P. de) La cour de Berlin. pp. 284. *Paris,* 1894. 12°.　　　10256. bb. 4.

LINDENBERG (P.) Am Kaiserhofe zu Berlin. pp. 151. *Berl.* 1894. 8°.　　10256. aaa. 35.

MITCHI ( ) Là-Bas et ailleurs. pp. 268. *Paris,* 1890. 8°.　　　10107. f. 14.

ST . . . R., *Baron.* Hof und Gesellschaft im deutschen Residenzen. pp. 392. *Berl.* 1890. 8°.　　　　　　　　10256. c. 5.

GERMANY.—Social Life—*continued.*

TISSOT (V.) L'Allemagne amoureuse. pp. 440. *Paris,* 1893. 12°.　　12354. cc. 4.

VILLERS (H. G. C. de) *Count.* En Allemagne. pp. 310. *Paris,* 1894. 12°.　　10256. bb. 3.

WHITMAN (S.) Teuton Studies. pp. 255. *Lond.* 1895. 8°.　　10235. bbb. 20.

WILLIAM II., *Emperor.* Hofleben unter Kaiser Wilhelm II. pp. 280. *Berl.* 1892. 8°.　　　　　　　　10256. aaa. 34.

WYZEWA (T. de) Chez les Allemands. L'art et les mœurs. pp. 242. *Paris,* 1895. 8°.　　　　　　　　10240. b. 3.

Topography.

BÆDEKER (C.) Allemagne du Nord. pp. 280. *Leipz.* 1893 8°.　　10108. d. 7.

── Southern Germany. pp. 266. *Leipz.* 1895. 8°.　　2352. a. 8.

BIGELOW (P.) The Borderland of Czar and Kaiser. pp. 343. *Lond.* 1895. 8°. 10024. aa. 29.

DAWSON (W. H.) Germany and the Germans. 2 vol. *Lond.* 1894. 8°.　　10240. cc. 4.

HAHN (F. G.) Topographischer Führer durch das nordwestliche Deutschland. pp. 322. *Leipz.* 1895. 8°.　　10256. bb. 6.

HEER (J. C.) Im deutschen Reich. pp. 296. *Zürich,* 1895. 8°.　　10256. bb. 5.

RICHTER (J. W. O.) Deutschland in der Kulturwelt. pp. 366. *Leipz.* 1891. 8°. 10240. cc. 3.

See also under each of the Countries forming the German Empire.

Trade : Finance : Tariffs : Taxation.

BRAUN (C.) Von Friedrich dem Grossen bis zum Fürsten Bismarck. Parallelen zur Geschichte der deutschen Wirthschaftspolitik. pp. 334. *Berl.* 1882. 8°.　　8074. f. 36.

KITTEL (J. B.) Die Frankenstein'sche Klausel und die deutsche Finanzreform. pp. 35. *Würzburg,* 1894. 8°.　　Pam. 23.

RESCH (P.) Geschichte der deutschen Nationalökonomie im 19. Jahrhunderte. pp. 46. *Graz,* 1888. 8°.　　Pam. 23.

PRUSSIA. Dokumente zur Geschichte der Wirthschaftspolitik. *Berl.* 1889, *etc.* 8°. 8074. ff.

THIELMANN-JACOBSDORFF (A. W. v.) Die Aera Caprivi-Heyden und die neudeutsche Wirthschaftspolitik. pp. 25. *Breslau,* 1893. 8°.　　8074. ee. 47. (11.)

WORMS (É.) La politique commerciale de l'Allemagne. pp. 305. *Paris,* 1895. 8°. 08226. i. 8.

───────

BONNENBERG (E.) Das Strafverfahren in Zoll- und Steuersachen. pp. 558. *Berl.* 1894. 8°.　　　　　　　　05604. h. 29.

BUERNER (R.) Zollhandbuch für die Hauptindustrien Deutschlands. *Zittau,* 1895, *etc.* 8°.　　　　　　　　08226. i.

GERMANY. Zur deutschrussischen Zollkonferenz. pp. 22. *Berl.* 1893. 8°.　　Pam. 23.

HAVENSTEIN (P.) Die Zollgesetzgebung des Reichs. pp. 264. *Berl.* 1892. 8°. 05604. i. 11.

MATLEKOVITS (S.) Die Zollpolitik der öst.-ung. Monarchie und des deutschen Reiches seit 1868. pp. 963. *Leipz.* 1891. 8°.　　　　　　　　08227. g. 28.

SCHAEFFLE (A. E. F.) Die Grundsätze der Steuerpolitik Deutschlands. pp. 658. *Tübingen,* 1880. 8°.　　08227. i. 26.

TRAUTVETTER ( ) Das Strafrecht der Zoll- und Verbrauchssteuergesetze. pp. 256. *Berl.* 1894. 8°.　　05605. b. 3.

HECKEL (M. v.) Die Einkommensteuer und die Schuldzinsen. pp. 187. *Leipz.* 1890. 8°.　　08227. g. 14.

GERMANY.—Trade, etc.—continued.

HAUSMANN (W.) Verkehrsteuern. pp. 99. Berl. 1894. 8°.   08227. f. 49.

NOELL (F.) Das Kommunalabgabengesetz vom 14. Juli 1893. pp. 405. Berl. 1894. 8°.   05604. h. 30.

OERTEL (O.) Das Kommunalabgabengesetz vom 14. Juli 1893. pp. 246. Liegnitz, 1894. 8°.   05604. i. 30.

ROHRSCHEIDT (K. v.) Die Polizeitaxen und ihre Stellung in der Reichs-Gewerbeordnung. pp. 127. Berl, 1893. 8°.   08227. i. 34.

KARSAI (S.) Das deutsche Tabaksteuer-Gesetz, 1879. pp. 120. Budapest, 1892. 8°. 08227. h. 25.

GERMANY. Die wirthschaftlichen Verträge Deutschlands. Berl. 1892, etc. 8°.   08227. i.

BORUSSEN. Ablehnen oder Annehmen. pp. 108. Gotha, 1891. 8°.   8072. df. 10.

COHN (G.) Beiträge zur deutschen Börsenreform. pp. 159. Leipz, 1895. 8°.   08226. h. 25.

FRIEDE. Der Friede auf dem Papier und der Friede eines thatsächlichen status quo. pp. 30. Berl. 1894. 8°.   Pam 67.

PFEFFER (C. E. M.) Pfeffers Handbuch des Verkehrswesens in Deutschland. 2 Tle. Leipz. 1894. 4°.   10256. h. 1.

EPHEMERIDES. Deutscher Schiffskalender, 1890, etc. Berl. 1890, etc. 16°.   P.P. 2444. aca.

RAINERI (S.) La Marina mercantile germanica. pp. 443. Roma, 1892. 8°.   8807. f. 40.

LOSCH (H.) Nationale Produktion und nationale Berufsgliederung. pp. 324. Leipz. 1892. 8°.   8228. f. 51.

SEIFARTH (F) Die Berufsstatistik des deutschen Reiches. Heidelberg, 1892, etc. 8°. 8206. bb. 30.

BARK (E.) Deutschlands Weltstellung. pp. 94. Zürich, 1890. 8°.   8154. aa. 13.

CHICAGO. Columbian Exposition. Amtlicher Katalog der Ausstellung des deutschen Reiches. pp. 256. Berl. 1893. 8°.   7958. h. 34.

HERBETTE (J) Les Conditions du Travail en Allemagne. pp. 384. 1890. 8°. FRANCE. M. des Affaires Étrangères. Recueil de Rapports.   08276. k.

See also CAPITAL AND LABOUR: LAW, Commercial.

GERM THEORY, of Disease. See BACTERIOLOGY.

GEROLZHOFEN: SIXT (F.) Chronik der Stadt Gerolzhofen. 1892, etc. 8°. Ac. Wurzburg. Historischer Verein. Archiv. Bd. 35, etc.   Ac. 7175.

GERONA. Ac. Barcelona. Associación de Arquitectos. BASSEGODA (J.) La Catedral de Gerona. pp. 83. Barcelona, 1889. 8°.   7817. g. 19.

GERPIUNES. QUENNE (C.) Gerpiunes et son pèlerinage. pp. 43. Mont-sur-Marchienne, 1890. 8°.   12410. ccc. 12 (2.)

GERS, Department. GERS. Archives civiles. pp. 355. 1892. 4°. Collection des inventaires-sommaires.   1814. b., etc.

BÉNÉTRIX (P.) Les Conventionnels du Gers. pp. 143. Auch, 1894. 8°.   10661. bbb. 53.

—— Changement de nom de communes du Gers sous la Terreur. pp. 15. Auch, 1891. 8°.   Pam. 28.

—— Le Vandalisme révolutionnaire dans le Gers. pp. 49. Bordeaux, 1891. 8°.   9004. c. 16. (6.)

TARBOURIECH (A.) Curiosités révolutionnaires du Gers. pp. 102. Auch, 1892. 8°. 9226. c. 25. See also ARMAGNAC: AUCH: GASCONY.

GERSAU. CAMENZIND (D.) Geschichte der Pfarrei Gersau. 1889. 8°. Ac. Einsiedeln. Historischer Verein. Mittheilungen. Hft. 6.   Ac. 6939.

GESEKE. GESEKE. Beiträge zur Geschichte der Stadt Geseke. Eberswalde, 1894, etc. 8°.   10261. e.

GHENT. VLAMINCK (A. L.) Les origines de la ville de Gand. pp. 127. 1891, 8°. Ac. Brussels. Académie. Mémoires couronnés. Tom. 45.   Ac. 985/4.

POTTER (F. de) Gent, van den oudsten tijd tot heden. 10 vol. 1882–89. 8°. POTTER (F. de) Geschiedenis van de Gemeenten, etc. 9414. d.

DUYSE (H. v.) Le Château des comtes de Gand. 1891. 8°. Ac. Antwerp. Académie d'Archéologie. Bulletin. Sér. 1. Tom. 7.   Ac. 5513.

HEINS (M.) Les ouvriers gantois. pp. 98. Gand, 1893. 8°.   Pam. 82.

CLAEYS (P.) Histoire du Théâtre à Gand. 3 tom. Gand. 1892. 8°.   011795. h. 3.

GHOSTS: APPARITIONS. DYER (T, F. T.) The Ghost World. pp. 447. Lond. 1893. 8°.   8632. ccc. 26.

GASPARIN (A. E. de) Du Surnaturel. 2 tom. Paris, 1892. 12°.   8632. ccc. 18.

LANG (A.) Cock Lane and common sense. pp. 357. Lond. 1894. 8°.   8632. h. 13.

LEE (F. G.) Sights and shadows. pp. 327. Lond. 1894. 8°.   8632. ccc. 29.

P.P. Paris. Annales des sciences psychiques. Paris, 1891, etc. 8°.   P.P. 597. gc.

PHILOSOPHUS. Ghosts and their modern worshippers. pp. 15. Lond. 1892. 8°.   Pam. 36.

PODMORE (F.) Apparitions and thought-transference. pp. 401. 1894. 8°. ELLIS (H. H.) Contemporary Science Series.   8709. i.

See also OCCULT SCIENCE: SPIRITUALISM.

GIANT'S CAUSEWAY. GIANT'S CAUSEWAY. Guide to the Giant's Causeway. pp. 104. Lond. 1893. 8°.   10347. aaa. 35.

GIBRALTAR. BENTABÓL Y URETA (H.) Presente y porvenir de Ceuta y Gibraltar. pp. 36. Madrid, 1894. 8°.   Pam. 67.

GIBRALTAR. Consolidated Laws of Gibraltar. pp. 788. Lond. 1890. 8°.   06605. g. 3.

GILBARD (G. J.) Popular history of Gibraltar. pp. 160. Gibraltar, 1881. 8°.   10161. cc. 13

STODDARD (C. A.) Spanish cities; with glimpses of Gibraltar. pp. 228. Lond. 1892. 8°.   10161. de. 26.

GIESSEN, University. STADE (B.) Reorganisation der Theologischen Fakultät zu Giessen, 1878. pp. 100. Giessen, 1894. 8°.   8357. ccc. 6

GILDING. See GOLD AND SILVER WORK.

GILGHIT. KNIGHT (E. F.) Where three Empires meet. pp. 528. Lond. 1893. 8°.   010057. e. 22.

GILSLAND. HEXHAM. Guide to Gilsland and the Borderland. pp. 224. Lond. 1895, 8°.   10347. aaa. 40.

GIPSIES. Ac. Edinburgh. Gypsy Lore Society, Journal, etc. Edinb. 1889, etc. 8°.   Ac. 9944.

—— Lisbon. Sociedade de Geographia. COELHO (F. A.) Os Ciganos de Portugal. pp. 302. Lisboa, 1892. 8°.   10007. i. 8.

AXON (W. E. A.) Romany Songs englished. pp. 3. 1890. 8°.   Pam. 58.

COLOCCI (A.) Gli Zingari. pp. 419. Torino, 1889. 8°.   10007. h. 43.

GROOME (F. H.) The Gypsies. 1891. 8°. MAGNÚSSON (E) National Life and Thought.   8186. g. 21.

GIPSIES—*continued.*

MACRITCHIE (D.) Scottish Gypsies under the Stewarts. pp. 123. *Edinb.* 1894. 8°.
　　　　　　　　　10007. cc. 16.

PENNELL (E. R.) To Gipsyland. pp. 240. *Lond.* 1893. 8°.　　　10007. bb. 16.

SIMSON (J.) Civilised Gipsies. pp. 24. *N.Y.* 1889. 8°.　　　　10007. h. 39.

—— Andrew Lang a gipsy. pp. 3. *N.Y.* 1892. 8°.　　　　　Pam. 7.

—— The Scottish People and press and the Gipsies. pp. 3. *N.Y.* 1891. 8°.　Pam. 90.

—— The Scottish press and the Gipsies. pp. 3. *N.Y.* 1893. 8°.　　Pam. 83.

—— Social emancipation of the Gipsies. pp. 24. *N.Y.* 1894. 8°.　8282. d. 51.

SMITH (G.) Gypsy Children. 2 pt. *Rugby,* 1893. 8°.　　　10007. aaa. 4.

WLISLOCKI (H. v.) Vom wandernden Zigeuner-volke. pp. 390. *Hamburg,* 1890. 8°.
　　　　　　　　　10007. f. 19.

—— Volksdichtungen der siebenbürgischen und südungarischen Zigeuner. pp. 431. *Wien,* 1890. 8°.　　　11527. dd. 24.

—— Volksglaube und religiöser Brauch der Zigeuner. pp. 184. 1891. 8°. Darstellungen aus dem Gebiete der nichtchristlichen Religionsgeschichte. Bd. 4.　　　4506. f.

—— Aus dem inneren Leben der Zigeuner. pp. 220. *Berl.* 1892, 8°.　10007. c. 42.

GIRGENTI. PIRANDELLO (L.) Laute der Mundart von Girgenti. pp. 52. *Halle,* 1891. 8°.
　　　　　　　　　12901. d. 36. (8.)

GIRLS' FRIENDLY SOCIETY. HILL (S. M.) Our Work and its fame. pp. 16. *Lond.* 1891. 8°.　　　08276. f. 21. (3.)

LONDON. *Girls' Friendly Society.* Handbook of elder members' Work. pp. 60. *Lond.* 1892. 16°.
　　　　　　　　　8277. a. 64.

—— Honorary Associates. pp. 7. *Lond.* 1890. 8°.
　　　　　　　　　08276. f. 21. (15.)

GIRONDE, Department. BERCHON (E.) Études paléo-archéologiques sur l'âge du bronze en Gironde. 1889. 8°. Ac. Bordeaux. *Société Archéologique.* [Transactions.] Tom. 14. Fasc. 3.　　　　　　Ac. 5297.

SOMMERVILLE (E. Œ.) and ROSS (M.) In the Vine Country. pp. 237. *Lond.* 1893. 8°.
　　　　　　　　　010171. e. 14.

See also AQUITAINE : BORDEAUX.

GIRYAMA LANGUAGE. *See* AFRICAN LANGUAGES.

GIZEH. *See* EGYPT, *Antiquities.*

GLACIERS : GLACIAL PERIOD. KEYES (C. R.) Glacial scorings in Iowa. 1895. 8°. Iowa. *Geological Survey.* Report. Vol. 3.　　　　　　　7106. i.

KILIAN (W.) Neige et glaciers. 1891, *etc.* 8°. Ac. Grenoble. *Société des Touristes.* Annuaire. No. 16.　　　　Ac. 6025.

PENCK (A.) Zur Vergletscherung der deutschen Alpen. pp. 15. *Halle,* 1885. 8°.　Pam. 27.

P.P. *London.* The Glacialist's Magazine. *Lond.* 1893, *etc.* 8°.　　P.P. 2122. f.

REID (H. F.) Studies of Muir Glacier, Alaska. 1892. 8°. National Geographic Magazine. Vol 4.　　　　　　　　Ac. 6192.

BALL (*Sir* R. S.) Cause of an Ice Age. 1892. 8°. LUBBOCK (*Sir* J.) Modern Science. Vol. 1.
　　　　　　　　　8709. f.

BELL (R.) Glacial phenomena in Canada. 1890. 8°. Ac. U.S. *Geological Society.* Bulletin. Vol. 1.　　　　　Ac. 3187.

GLACIERS—*continued.*

BRANNER (J. C.) Glaciation of the Wyoming and Lackawanna Valleys. pp. 20. 1886. 8°.
　　　　　　　　　Pam. 27.

CAPPELLE (H. v.) Einige medeelingen over de glaciale vormingen in Twente. pp. 20. 1894. 8°. Ac. Amsterdam. *K. Akademie.* Verhandelingen. Sectie 2. Del III.　Ac. 944/2.

DAWSON (*Sir* J. W.) The Canadian Ice Age. pp. 301. *Montreal.* 1894. 8°.　07109. f. 1.

GEIKIE (J.) The great Ice Age. pp. 850. *Lond.* 1894. 8°.　　　　2030. e.

LEWIS (H. C.) Papers on the glacial Geology of Great Britain and Ireland. pp. 469. *Lond.* 1894. 8°.　　　07109. g. 43.

LINDVALL (C. A.) Glacialperioden. pp. 45. *Stockholm,* 1891. 8°.　07109. h. 23.

PARTSCH (J.) Die Vergletscherung des Riesengebirges zur Eiszeit. 1894. 8°. LEHMANN (R.) Forschungen zur deutschen Landes- und Volkskunde. Bd. 8.　　10235. i. 10.

PENCK (A.) Die Eiszeit in den Pyrenäen. pp. 69. *Leipz.* 1884. 8°.　Pam. 27.

TRISSL (A.) Sündflut oder Gletscher? pp. 122. *Regensburg,* 1894. 8°.　　4017. h. 9.

WRIGHT (G. F.) Glacial boundary in Western Pennsylvania, Ohio, Kentucky. 1890. 8°. U.S. *Geological Society.* Bulletin. No. 58.
　　　　　　　　　7109. cc.

GLADBACH, Abbey. ECKERTZ (G.) Das Verbrüderungs- und Todtenbuch der Abtei Gladbach. 1880. 8°. Ac. Aix-le-Chapelle. *Geschichtsverein.* Zeitschrift. Bd. 2. Ac. 7008.

GLAMIS CASTLE. LYON (P.) *Earl of Strathmore.* The book of Record. Diary by Patrick, first Earl of Strathmore, 1684–89. pp. 194. 1890. 8°. Ac. Edinburgh. *Scottish History Society.* Publications. Vol. 9. Ac. 8256.

GLAMORGAN. CLARK (G. T.) Cartæ quæ ad Dominium de Glamorgan pertinent. 2 vol. *Dowlais,* 1885–90. 4°.　　10369. i. 10.

THOMAS (T. H.) Inscribed Stones of Glamorganshire. pp. 13. *Cardiff,* 1893. 8°.
　　　　　　　　　07703. f. 3. (17.)

GLARUS. SCHINDLER (F.) Die Sammlungen des histor. Vereins des Kantons Glarus. 1890. 8°. Ac. Zurich. *Historischer Verein.* Jahrbuch. Hft. 25.　　　　Ac. 6997.

SCHULTE (A.) Gilg Tschudi, Glarus und Säckingen. 1893. 8°. Ac. Zurich. *Allgemeine Geschichtforschende Gesellschaft.* Archiv. Bd. 18.
　　　　　　　　　Ac. 6995/2.

GLASGOW. Ac. Glasgow. *University.* University of Glasgow, old and new. pp. 146. *Glasg.* 1891. fol.　　K.T.C. 2. a. 3.

BARR ( ) and BROWN (J.) Biographical sketches of the Lord Provosts of Glasgow. pp. 381. 52. *Glasg.* 1883. 8°.　　10816. g. 15.

BAYNHAM (W.) The Glasgow Stage. pp. 221. *Glasg.* 1892. 8°.　　11795. df. 21.

CLERCQ (D. de) Glasgow en hare gemeente-organisatie. pp. 35. *Amsterdam,* 1891. 8°.
　　　　　　　　　8277. h. 18. (5.)

GLASGOW. Glasgow and its Environs. pp. 358. *Lond.* 1891. 4°.　　10369. i. 11.

—— A B C Guide to Glasgow. pp. 31. *Glasg.* 1891. 8°.　10352. ee. 16. (3.)

—— Graphic Guide to Glasgow. pp. 82. *Glasg.* 1893. 32°.　10349. a. 35. (2.)

—— *Magistrates.* Case for the Town Council of Glasgow setting forth the grounds on which they urge that the boundaries of the city should be extended. pp. 52. *Edinb.* 1887. 8°.
　　　　　　　　　10369. i. 18.

GLASGOW—*continued.*

GLASGOW. Acts of Parliament relating to the Glasgow Police. pp. 556. *Glasg.* 1893. 8°.
6583. g. 15.

—— *Social Union.* The Glasgow Sanitary Summary. pp. 15. *Glasg.* 1891. 8°.   Pam. 32.

MACKENZIE (P.) Curious Glasgow characters. pp. 115. *Glasg.* 1891. 8°.   012330. f. 62.

MAC LELLAN (D.) Glasgow Public Parks. pp. 159. *Glasg.* 1894. 4°.   010370. ff. 4.

CRAIG (A.) The Elder Park, Govan. pp. 207. *Glasg.* 1891. 4°.   10369. l. 9.

LANG (J. M.) Glasgow and the Barony thereof. pp. 126. *Glasg.* 1895. 4°.   10370. dd. 23.

MITCHELL (J. O.) Two Glasgow Firms: W. Connel & Co. and the Crums of Thornliebank. pp. 23. 14. *Glasg.* 1894. 8°.   08227. i. 29. (18.)

NICOL (J.) Statistics of the City of Glasgow. 1885–91. pp. 447. *Glasg.* 1891. 8°. 8223. dh. 6.

SOMERVILLE (T.) George Square, Glasgow. pp. 304. *Glasg.* 1891. 8°.   10370. d. 33.

YOUNG (W.) Municipal Buildings, Glasgow. pp. 35. *Glasg.* 1890. 4°.   1732. c. 3.

See also EXHIBITIONS.

GLASS MANUFACTURE AND PAINTING.

Ac. Breslau. *Museum Schlesischer Altertümer.* CZIHAK (E. v.) Schlesische Gläser. pp. 288. *Breslau,* 1891. 8°.
07945. n. 24.

APPERT (L.) and HENRIVAUX (J.) Verre et Verrerie. pp. 460. 1894. 4°. LECHALAS (M. C.) Encyclopédie des travaux publics.   012216. i.

HALLEN (A. W. C.) French 'Gentlemen Glassmakers,' in England and Scotland. pp. 16. *Edinb.* 1893. 4°.   Pam. 26.

HARRISON (J. P.) On a Glass Necklace from Africa in the Pitt-Rivers Museum. pp. 15. *Lond.* 1893. 8°.   Pam. 3.

HAVARD (H.) Les Arts de l'Ameublement. La Verrerie. pp. 314. *Paris,* 1894. 8°.
07944. g. 10.

HONDT (P. d') Venise. L'Art de la verrerie. pp. 155. *Paris,* 1893. 8°.   7805. d. 2.

LIÉGE GLASSES. Verres liégeoises "façon de Venise." 1886. 8°. Ac. Liége. *Institut Archéologique.* Bulletin. Tom. 18. Livr. 3.
Ac. 5527.

WYZEWA (T. de) Les Arts du feu. pp. 143. *Paris,* 1892. 8°.   7944. h. 32.

Ac., *etc.* Nuremberg. *Germanisches National-museum.* Katalog der im germanischen Museum befindlichen Glasgemälde. pp. 52. 1884. 4°.

P.P. *Munich.* Anzeiger für Kunde des deutschen Mittelalters. Bd. 17.   P.P. 3542. aa.

CAUWENBERGHS (C. v.) Notice historique sur les peintres-verriers d'Anvers. pp. 82. *Anvers,* 1891. 8°.   7808. bbb. 29. (2.)

DESPIERRES (G.) Portail et vitraux de l'Église Notre-Dame d'Alençon. pp. 24. *Paris,* 1891. 8°.
10105. ee. 11. (6.)

DUFOUR (A.) and MUGNIER (F.) Notes pour servir à l'histoire des Savoyards. Les verriers-vitriers du xive au xixe siècle. 1894. 8°. Ac. Chambéry. *Société Savoisienne.* Mémoires. Tom. 33.   Ac. 5240.

ANDREE (J.) Handbuch der Mosaik- und Glasmalerei. 1891. 8°. Seemann's Kunsthandbücher. No. 8.   7805. de.

GULLICK (T. J.) Oil painting on Glass. pp. 84. *Lond.* 1892. 8°.   7854. bb. 58.

JAENNICKE (F.) Handbuch der Glas-Malerei. pp. 299. *Stuttgart,* 1890. 8°.   7808. aaa. 47.

GLASS—*continued.*

MERSON (O.) Les Vitraux. pp. 314. *Paris,* 1895. 8°.   2261. cc. 7.

MESNAGE (V.) Les Vitraux de l'Église Saint-Saturnin de Tours. pp. 46. *Tours,* 1890. 4°.
7805. eee. 28.

RAHN (J. R.) Ausstellung von Glasgemälden aus dem Nachlasse des Dichters J. M. Usteri, 1763–1827. pp. 30. *Zürich,* 1894. 4°.
7808. f. 21. (9.)

STYGER (C.) Glasmaler und Glasgemälde im Lande Schwyz 1465–1680. pp. 62. 1885. 8°. Ac. Einsiedeln. *Historischer Verein.* Mittheilungen. Hft 4.   Ac. 6939.

SUFFLING (E. R.) Handbook on Glass Painting. pp. 102. *Lond.* 1890. 8°.   7854. ccc. 45.

See also ART, *Decorative :* ENAMELS.

GLASTONBURY, Abbey and Town.

Ac. Somerset. *Record Society.* Rentalia et Custumaria Abbatum Monasterii Glastoniae, 1235–61. pp. 312. *Lond.* 1891. 4°.   Ac. 8133/5.

GLASTONBURY. Legend of the Holy Thorn. pp. 24. *Glastonbury,* 1880. 8°. 10358. aaa. 58.

GASQUET (F. A.) The last abbot of Glastonbury and his companions. pp. 195. *Lond.* 1895. 8°.
4902. f. 31.

GLASTONBURY. Where to buy at Glastonbury. *Brighton,* 1891. 4°.   10361. k. 28.

GLATZ.

VOLKMER (F.) and HOHAUS ( ) Geschichtsquellen der Graffschaft Glatz. 5 Bde. *Habelschwerdt,* 1883–91. 8°.   10255. g. 22.

GLAUCHAU.

KUUTH (G.) Geschichte der Kirchengemeinde von St. Georgen zu Glaucha. pp. 252. *Halle a. S.,* 1891. 8°.   4662. c. 21.

GLENALMOND, Trinity College.

See TRINITY COLLEGE.

GLENESK.

EDWARDS (D. H.) Historical guide to Glenesk district, *etc.* pp. 135. *Brechin,* 1893. 8°.   10369. aaa. 49.

GLOBES.

FIORINI (M.) Erd- und Himmelsgloben. pp. 137. *Leipz.* 1895. 8°. 8561. l. 1.

GLOGAU.

BELOW (H. v.) Glogaus Belagerung und Vertheidigung. 1806. pp. 67. *Berl.* 1893. 8°.   9327. dd. 12. (2.)

GLOUCESTER, City and Cathedral.

BAZELEY (W.) The Guilds of Gloucester. pp. 11. *Bristol,* 1888. 8°.   Pam. 3.

HYETT (F. A.) Gloucester and her Governor during the Civil War. pp. 45. *Gloucester,* 1891. 8°.   9008. g. 10. (3.)

JENNINGS (J.) History and guide to Gloucester. pp. 66. *Gloucester,* 1888. 8°. 10348. ccc. 58. (7.)

SPENCE (H. D. M.) Dreamland in history. pp. 228. *Lond.* 1891. 8°.   9225. l. 15.

BAZELEY (W.) The early Days of the Abbey of Gloucester. pp. 7. *Gloucester,* 1890. 8°.
10348. d. 19. (2.)

CLARK (F. H.) Memories of the College School, Gloucester, 1859–67. pp. 124. *Gloucester,* 1890. 8°.   8364. aaa. 39.

GLOUCESTERSHIRE.

HYETT (F. A.) and BAZELEY (W.) Bibliographer's Manual of Gloucestershire Literature. *Gloucester,* 1894, *etc.* 8°.   11900. ee. 35.

GLOUCESTER, *County.* Murray's handbook for Gloucestershire. pp. 17. 185. *Lond.* 1895. 8°.
2364. a. 17.

SCOTT (C. W.) Among the Apple Orchards. pp. 138. *Lond.* 1895. 8°.   10350. aaa. 53.

STRATFORD (J.) Gloucestershire biographical notes. pp. 360. *Gloucester,* 1887. 8°.
10803. g. 12.

GLOUCESTERSHIRE—*continued.*

WITCHELL (C. A.) and STRUGNELL (W. B.) Fauna and Flora of Gloucestershire. pp. 301. *Stroud*, 1892. 8°.   7003. e. 3.

Ac. London. *English Dialect Society.* NORTHALL (G. F.) Folk-phrases of four counties. pp. 43. *Lond.* 1894. 8°.   Ac. 9934/36.

GLUE: GELATINE. DAWIDOWSKY (F.) Treatise on the raw materials and fabrication of Glue, gelatine, *etc.* pp. 297. *Phila.* 1884. 12°.   07945. f. 21.

GLYCERINE. JOHNSTONE (J.) Action of Glycerine on the brain. pp. 16. *Edinb.* 1891. 16°.   Pam. 39.
See also FATS AND OILS.

GNOSTICISM. HARNACK (A.) Über das gnostische Buch Pistis Sophia. 1891. 8°.

GEBHARDT (O. v.) and HARNACK (A.) Texte und Untersuchungen. Bd. 7. Hft. 2.   3623. b.

HESS (J. J.) Der gnostische Papyrus von London. pp. 17. *Freiburg*, 1892. fol. 1705. b. 18.

KUNZE (J.) Die Historiae Gnosticismi fontibus quaestiones. pp. 78. *Lipsiae*, 1894. 8°.   4535. cc. 2. (8.)

SCHMIDT (C.) Gnostische Schriften in koptischer Sprache aus dem Codex Brucianus. pp. 692. 1892. 8°.   GEBHART (O. v.) and HARNACK (A.) Texte und Untersuchungen. Bd. 8.   3623. b.

—— De Codice Bruciano. *Lipsiae*, 1892, *etc.* 8°.   4999. c.

See also CHURCH HISTORY.

GOA. CUNHA RIVARA (J. H. da) Inscripções lapidares da India portugueza. 1894. 8°. Ac. Lisbon. *Sociedade de Geographia.* Boletim. Sér. 13. No. 8.   Ac. 6020.

MENDES PINTO (F.) Voyages of F. Mendez Pinto. pp. 464. 1891. 8°. Adventure Series.   012207. k.

BURTON (*Sir* R. F.) First four chapters of Goa and the Blue Mountains. pp. 117. *Madras*, 1890. 12°.   10058. aa. 40.
See also PORTUGAL, *Colonies :* ROMAN CATHOLIC CHURCH, *in Portugal.*

GOAT. DUURLOO (B. A.) and LARSEN (A. P.) Om Gedehold i Danmark. pp. 47. *Kjøbenh.* 1892. 8°.   Pam. 42.
See also ANIMALS, *Domestic.*

GOITRE. BLAKE (E. T.) Myxœdema, Cretinism and the Goitres. pp. 89. *Bristol*, 1894. 8°.   7616. dd. 1.

MACNAMARA (F. N.) Goitre. 1893. 8°.

DAVIDSON (A.) Hygiene of Warm Climates.   7686. dd. 2.

MITROVICH (P.) Contribution à l'étude de l'énucléation et de l'extirpation du Goitre. pp. 153. *Genève*, 1894. 8°.   7616. i. 18.

TURRELL (W. J.) Operative treatment of Bronchocele. pp. 63. *Oxf.* 1892. 8°. 7616. h. 27.
See also BASEDOW'S DISEASE : CRETINISM.

GOLD AND SILVER.

Metallurgy of Gold and Silver : Mining and Milling Processes.

BROWN (W. L.) Manual of assaying Gold and Silver ores. pp. 333. 1890. 8°. Heinemann's Scientific Handbooks.   8708. f.

EISSLER (M.) Metallurgy of Gold. pp. 678. *Lond.* 1895. 8°.   7106. bb. 35.

——Cyanide Process for the extraction of Gold and its application on the Witwatersrand Gold Fields. pp. 93. *Lond.* 1895. 8°. 7106. ff. 26.

FUCHS (E.) L'Or. Traitement des Minéraux auro-argentifères. 1892. 8°. Encyclopédie chimique. Tom. 5. Pt. 2.   8907. h. i.

GOLD AND SILVER—*continued.*

HOEMAN (H. O.) Gold milling in the Black Hills. pp. 46. *Chicago*, 1893. 8°.   Pam. 27.

KIRKPATRICK (T. S. G.) Hydraulic Gold Miner's manual. pp. 31. *Lond.* 1890. 8°. 7106. a. 30.

LOBLEY (J. L.) The genesis of Gold. pp. 14. *Lond.* 1893. 8°.   Pam. 27.

LOUIS (H.) Handbook of Gold milling. pp. 504. *Lond.* 1894. 8°.   7106. ff. 24.

MIDDLETON (R. J.) Gold mining. pp. 28. *Lond.* 1885. 8°.   Pam. 27.

NEW YORK. *Mechanical Gold Extractor Co.* Mechanical reduction of Gold ores by the Crawford Mill. pp. 32. *N.Y.* 1893. 8°.   Pam. 27.

ROSE (T. K.) Metallurgy of Gold. pp. 462. 1894. 8°. ROBERTS-AUSTEN (W. C.) New Metallurgical Series. Vol. 2.   07108. g.

SULMAN (H. L.) The Sulman "Float" and "Fine" Gold and "Slimes" recovery process. pp. 60. *Lond.* 1894. 8°.   7109. e. 23.

—— Bromo-cyanide process for the treatment of Gold ores. pp. 99. *Lond.* 1895. 8°. 7108. b. 16.

TRENT (L. C.) Combination process for working silicious and semi-base ores containing Gold and Silver. pp. 24. *Chicago*, 1892. 8°.   07109. e. 23. (7.)

See also MINERALOGY.

Gold Mines, etc.

AFRICA, *South.* Gold Fields of South Africa. pp. 915. *Cape Town*, 1890. 8°.   07109. h. 3.

FULTERER (C.) Afrika in seiner Bedeutung für die Goldproduktion. pp. 191. *Berl.* 1895. 8°.   7107. e. 14.

MATHERS (E. P.) Zambesia, England's El Dorado in Africa. pp. 480. *Lond.* 1891. 8°.   010096. ee. 21.

REUNERT (T.) Diamonds and Gold in South Africa. pp. 242. *Cape Town*, 1893. 8°.   7106. ff. 22.

SMITH (R. M.) Great Gold lands of South Africa. pp. 296. *Lond.* 1891. 8°. 10097. ccc. 11.

RUGG (R.) Gold Fields and mineral resources of Mashonaland. pp. 42. *Lond.* 1891. 8°.   Pam. 27.

SAWYER (A. R.) Goldfields of Mashonaland. pp. 99. *Manch.* 1894. 8°.   07108. g. 2.

ABRAHAM (F.) Aufrichtige Geschichte der Goldminen des Witwatersrands. pp. 51. *Berl.* 1892. 8°.   7106. ff. 23.

—— New era of the Goldmining Industry in the Witwatersrand. pp. 47. *Lond.* 1894. 8°.   07108. g. 6.

GOLDMANN (C. S.) History of the Gold and other companies of Witwatersrand. 2 pt. *Lond.* 1892. 8°.   08225. l. 14.

HATCH (F. H.) and CHALMERS (J. A.) Gold Mines of the Rand. pp. 306. *Lond.* 1895. 8°.   07109. k. 24.

SOUTH AFRICAN REPUBLIC. Laws having special reference to Gold Fields. pp. 233. *Johannesburg*, 1892. 16°.   6606. a. 6.

—— *Witwatersrand.* Monthly return of Gold. *Johannesburg*, 1894, *etc.* fol.   1826. d.

SPIEGEL (E.) Die Südafrikanische Republik und ihre Goldproduktion. pp. 31. *Berl.* 1893. 8°.   Pam. 27.

TRANSVAAL. South African Goldfields. pp. 20. *Lond.* 1893. 8°.   Pam. 27.

WASHINGTON. *Inter-State Land Bureau.* Facts about the Gold fields of the Southern States. pp. 21. *Wash.* 1893. 12°.   Pam. 27.

SYMONS (B.) Gold Fields of Nova Scotia. 1892. 8°.   Pam. 27.

GOLD AND SILVER—*continued.*

IRONBARKS. Golden Gully Gold Mining Company. pp. 16. *Sydney*, 1888. 8°.   Pam. 27.

BARKER (W. H.) The Croydon Gold Field, North Queensland. pp 87. *Lond.* 1892. 8°.
         7108. b. 14.

CHARTERS TOWERS. History of the "Brilliant" Gold Mine, Charters Towers. pp. 5.
Charters Towers, 1890. 8°.   07109. m. 4. (4.)

LONDON. *Exhibition of Mining and Metallurgy*, 1890. Catalogue of the minerals exhibited by the Local Committee, Charters Towers, North Queensland. pp. 24. *Lond.* 1890. 8°.   Pam. 27.

MARSLAND (L. W.) Charters Towers Gold Mines. pp. 214. *Lond.* 1892. 8°.   07109. h. 20.

BARKER (W. H.) The Gold Fields of Western Australia. pp. 86. *Lond.* 1894. 8°. 07108. g. 10.

CALVERT (A. F.) Western Australia and its Gold fields. pp. 61. *Lond.* 1893. 8°.
         10491. cc. 10.

—— Coolgardie Goldfield : W. Australia. pp. 114. *Lond.* 1894. 8°.   7106. e. 11.

LONDON. *Exhibition of Mining and Metallurgy.* Catalogue of specimens of Gold, etc., exhibited by the New Zealand Government. pp. 39. *Lond.* 1890. 8°.   Pam. 27.

MAC KAY (A.) Older auriferous drifts of Central Otago. pp 48. *Wellington*, 1894. fol. Pam. 27.

———

KING (W.) and POPE (T. A.) Gold, copper and lead in Chota Nagpore. pp. 176.
Calcutta, 1891. 8°.   7105. aa. 3.

SMITH (P. B.) Report on the Kolar Gold Field. pp. 52. *Madras*, 1889. fol.   7105. g. 11.
See also MINERALOGY.

Gold and Silver Coinage. *See* MONEY.

Silver.

EISSLER (M.) Metallurgy of Silver. pp. 362. *Lond.* 1891. 8°.   7106. a. 40.

FRAENKEL (J. E.) Die Zukunft des Silbers. pp. 30. 1894. 8°. Sammlung wissenschaftlicher Vorträge. N.F. Ser. 8. Hft. 191.
        12249. l., *etc.*

GASKELL (W. H.) Silver Tables. *Lond.* 1894. 8°.
        8548. df. 42.

HALHED (W. B.) Silver production. pp. 11. *Lond.* 1895. 8°.   08226. h. 15. (15.)

NEEDHAM (S. G.) Silver. Equivalents of New York with standard in London. ff. 51. *Lond.* 1890. 4°.   8548. g. 23.

PARACELSUS ( ) Die Zukunft des Silbers. pp. 16. *Kassel*, 1894. 8°.   Pam. 23.

STETEFELDT (C. A.) The Lixiviation of Silver-Ores with hyposulphite solutions. pp. 233. *N.Y.* 1888. 8°.   7106. cc. 20.

SUESS (E.) Die Zukunft des Silbers. pp. 227. *Wien*, 1892. 8°.   08227. i. 5.
See also supra : Metallurgy of Gold and Silver : GOLD AND SILVER WORK : MINERALOGY : MONEY.

GOLD AND SILVER WORK. Ac. Riga. *Gesellschaft für Geschichte der russischen Ost-See Provinzen.* Goldschmiedearbeiten in Livland, Estland und Kurland. pp. 24. *Lübeck*, 1892. fol.   1811. a. 8.

CHAOURCE. Catalogue du trésor d'Argenterie gallo-romaine à Chaource. pp. 19. *Paris*, 1886. 8°.   7706. ee. 18. (10.)

DUTCH GOLDSMITH'S WORK. Reproductions d'anciennes gravures d'Orfèvrerie hollandaise. *La Haye*, 1892, *etc.* fol.   7805. g.

GARNIER (J.) Les anciens Orfèvres de Dijon. pp. 47. *Dijon*, 1889. 8°.   7913. i. 43. (8.)

GOLD AND SILVER WORK—*cont.*

GEE (G. E.) Jeweller's assistant in the Art of working in Gold, *etc.* pp. 238. *Lond.* 1892. 8°.
        7106. a. 42.

GMELIN (L.) L'Oreficeria medioevale negli Abruzzi. pp. 74. *Teramo*, 1891. 8°. 7807. c. 25.

GUASTI (G.) Del Crocefisso d'Argento attribuito a Benvenuto Cellini. pp. xli. *Firenze*, 1893. 8°.
        7808. bbb. 28. (8.)

HAVARD (H.) Les Arts de l'ameublement. L'Orfévrerie. pp. 170. *Paris*, 1892. 8°.   7942. f.

MAIGNE (W.) and MATHEY (O.) Nouveau Manuel de Dorure, argenture, *etc.* pp. 416. 1891. 18°. Encyclopédie Roret.   12208. b.

STEWART (H.) History of the Company of Gold and Silver Wyre-Drawers. pp. 140. *Lond.* 1891. 4°.   8248. f. 22.

WRIGHT (B. M.) Description of the collection of Gold Ornaments from the "huacas" of aboriginal races of the north-western provinces of South America. pp. 49. *Lond.* 1885. 8°.
        7708. aaa. 57.
See also ART, *Decorative* : GEMS AND JEWELLERY : PLATE.

GOLD COAST. BELL (H. H. J.) History, trade, resources and condition of the Gold Coast. pp. 46. *Liverp.* 1893. 8°.   Pam. 89.

EILOART (E.) The Land of Death. pp. 65. *Lond.* 1890. 8°.   Pam. 66.

ELLIS (A. B.) History of the Gold Coast. pp. 400. *Lond.* 1893. 8°.   9061. dd. 12.

GRIFFITH (W. B.) Ordinances of the Gold Coast Colony. pp. 777. *Lond.* 1887. 8°.
        06606. h. 4.

REINDORF (C. C.) History of the Gold Coast. pp. 356. *Basel*, 1895. 8°.   9061. d. 27.

STRÖMBERG (C. F. L. W.) Minnen och bilder från Guldkusten. pp. 252. *Lund.* 1890. 8°.
        010096. ee. 25.
See also AFRICA, *West* : ENGLAND, *Colonies.*

GOLDEN ROSE.
See CHURCH HISTORY, *Papacy.*

GOLD FISH. *See* CYPRINIDAE.

GOLDSBOROUGH. BAILDON (W. P.) Chapter in the history of Goldsborough. 2 pt. *Bingley*, 1894. 8°.   10348. d. 20. (8.)

GOLF. CLARK (R.) Golf. pp. 304. *Lond.* 1893. 8°.   07905. h. 11.

COLOMBO. *Golf Club.* Constitution and rules, 1893. pp. 56. *Galle*, 1893. obl. 24°. 7908. de. 11.

COMPTON (C. H.) The antiquity of Golf. pp. 13. *Lond.* 1881. 8°.   Pam. 83.

DALRYMPLE (W.) Handbook to Golf. pp. 116. *Edinb.* 1895. 8°.   7912. aa. 44.

DIRECTORIES. Stanley Froy's Golfer's pocket Directory. *Lond.* 1894, *etc.* 16°.   7912. a.

GOLF. A Golf Score-book. *Lond.* 1890. 32°.
        7915. de. 13. (3.)

HALF HOURS. Half Hours with an old Golfer. pp. 184. *Lond.* 1895. 8°.   7906. c. 38.

HUTCHINSON (H.) Golfing. pp. 120. 1893. 8°. ALCOCK (C. W.) "Oval" Series of Games.
        07905. f.

—— Hints on Golf. pp. 75. *Edinb.* 1891. 8°.
        7907. aaa. 61.

—— Famous Golf Links. pp. 201. *Lond.* 1891. 8°.   7908. ee. 12.

—— Golf. pp. 480. 1895. 8°. Badminton Library.   2264. aa. 7.

IRWIN (J. F.) Golf Sketches. *Lond.* 1892. 8°.
        12315. i. 57.

KNIGHT (W.) and OLIPHANT (T. T.) Stories of Golf, with rhymes on Golf. pp. 146. *Lond.* 1894. 8°.   7912. aaa. 8.

GOLF—*continued.*

LANG (A.) Batch of Golfing papers. pp. 123. *Lond.* 1892. 8°.　　　　　7907. aa. 65.

LEE (J. P.) Golf in America. pp. 194. *N.Y.* 1895. 8°.　　　　　7912. de. 2.

MAC PHERSON (J. G.) Golf and golfers. pp. 100. *Edinb.* 1891. 8°.　　　　7906. de. 35.

MARIASSY (　) Le Golf en Angleterre. Les Golf Clubs de France. pp. 46. *Cannes*, 1894. 8°.　　　　　　　　　7907. df. 17. (8.)

RALSTON (W.) Golfing according to the Badminton Library and W. Ralston. pp. 25. *Lond.* 1894. *obl.* 8°　　　12316. i. 60.

SAINT ANDREWS, *Golf Club.* Laws of Golf. pp. 40. *Lond.* 1895. 8°.　　　7912. de. 1. (9.)

SIMPSON (*Sir* W. G.) The Art of Golf. pp. 186. *Edinb.* 1892. 8°.　　　　7908. dd. 20.

SMART (J.) A Round of the Links : views of Golf Greens of Scotland. *Edinb.* 1893. *obl.* fol.　　　　　　　　K.T.C. 7. b. 7.

W., G. B. The phraseology of Golf. *Lond.* 1893. *obl.* 12°.　　　　7908. de. 9.

GONDAL. HARIKRISHNA LĀLAṢAṄKARA DAVE. History of Gondal. pp. 202. *Bombay*, 1889. 8°.　　　　　　　　　9057. a. 35.

GONORRHŒA. *See* VENEREAL DISEASES.

GOOD FRIDAY. *See* LENT.

GOODRICH CASTLE. SEATON (D.) Goodrich Castle. pp. 12. *Ross*, 1895. 12°. Pam. 3.

GOOD TEMPLARS. *See* TEMPERANCE.

GOODWIN SANDS. TREANOR (T. S.) Heroes of the Goodwin Sands. pp. 255. *Lond.* 1892. 8°.　　　4429. ee. 35.

GOOSE. COOK (W.) Pheasants, Turkeys and Geese. pp. 69. *Lond.* 1894. 8°. 7294. bbb. 16.

See also ANIMALS, *Domestic* : POULTRY.

GORILLA. EISLER (P.) Das Gefäss- und periphere Nervensystem des Gorilla. pp. 78. *Halle*, 1890. 4°.　　　　　7208. h. 29.

WALDEYER (W.) Das Gorilla-Rückenmark. pp. 147. 1889. 4°. Ac. Berlin. *Societas Regia.* Abhandlungen, 1888.　　　　Ac. 855/6.

GORING. STONE (P. G.) Account of the Church and Priory at Goring. pp. 54. *Goring*, 1893. 8°.　　　　4707. dd. 3.

TAUNT (H. W.) Goring and the neighbourhood. pp. 122. *Oxf.* 1894. 8°.　　10350. aaa. 52.

GÖRLITZ. FRISCH (　) Alte görlitzer Geschlechter und die Wappen derselben. pp. 60. *Görlitz*, 1891. 8°. 9916. b. 28. (4.)

JECHT (R.) Über das älteste görlitzische Stadtbuch von 1305 ff. pp. 19. *Görlitz*, 1891. 8°.　　　　　　　9009. m. 8. (3.)

GORTYNA. *See* CRETE.

GÖRZ-GRADISCA. HOCHEGGER (A.) Gemeinde-Ordnung der Kronländer, Görz-Gradisca. 2 Bde. *Trieste*, 1893, 94. 8°.　　05549. k.

GOSLAR. ASCHE (T.) Die Kaiserpfalz zu Goslar. pp. 215. *Goslar*, 1892, 8°. 10235. aa. 33.

ERDMANN (T.) Die alte Kaiserstadt Goslar. pp. 237. *Goslar*, 1892. 8°.　　10256. c. 11.

GOSLAR. Urkundenbuch. *Goslar*, 1893, *etc.* 8°.　　　　　　　　　Ac. 7161.

MUELLER-GROTE (G.) Die Malereien des Huldigungssaales im Rathause zu Goslar. pp. 111. *Berl.* 1892. 8°.　　　　7858. gg. 15.

GOTHA. *See* SAXE COBURG GOTHA.

GOTHENBURG. HAGSTRÖM (K.) Kort beskrifning öfver Bohuslän jämte Göteborg. pp. 64. *Stockholm*, 1890. 8°.　　Pam. 91.

For the Gothenburg System of Licensing Public Houses, *see* LICENSING LAWS.

GOTHLAND, West. GOTHLAND, *West.* Loi de Vestrogothie. pp. 464. *Paris*, 1894. 8°.　　　　　　　　　5307. bb. 2.

GOTHS AND GOTHIC LANGUAGE. HODGKIN (T.) Italy and her Invaders. Vol. 1, 2, 3. *Oxf.* 1892, *etc.* 8°.　　　　2068. c.

—— Theodoric the Goth. pp. 442. 1891, 8°. ABBOTT (E.) Heroes of the Nations. Vol. 4.　　　　　　　　　10603. dd.

HOLLANDER (A. G.) Om gotiska Folkstammens. pp. 110. *Stockholm*, 1889. 8°.　10007. cc. 10.

BRAITMAIER (F.) Göthekult und Göthephilologie. pp. 118. *Tübingen*, 1892. 8°. 011824. h. 66.

EDGREN (H.) Jämförande Grammatik. *Göteborg*, 1893, *etc.* 8°.　　　12901. c.

FEIST (S.) Grundriss der gotischen Etymologie. pp. 167. 1888. 8°. Sammlung indogermanischer Wörterbücher. Vol. 2.　　12902. dd.

MAROLD (C.) Stichometrie und Leseabschnitte in den gotischen Episteltexten. pp. 18. *Königsberg*, 1890. 4°.　　　Pam. 47.

PRIESE (O.) Deutsche-gotisches Wörterbuch, *etc.* pp. 64. *Leipz.* 1890. 8°. 12901. d. 30. (13.)

WILMANNS (W.) Deutsche Grammatik. Gotisch, *etc. Strassb.* 1893, *etc.* 8°. 12962. o.

WREDE (F.) Über die Sprache der Ostgoten in Italien. pp. 208. 1891. 8°. BRINK (B. ten) and SCHERER (W.) Quellen und Forschungen, *etc.* Hft. 68.　　　　　　　2338. h.

WRIGHT (J.) Primer of the Gothic Language. pp. 247. 1892. 8°. Clarendon Press Series.　　　　　　　　　2319. a. 38

See also GERMAN LANGUAGE : GERMANY, *Antiquities and History* : TEUTONIC MYTHOLOGY.

GOTTINGEN, University. Ac. Gottingen. *Academia Georgia Augusta*, Verzeichniss der Vorlesungen auf der Georg-Augusts-Universität. *Gottingen*, 1893, *etc.* 8°.　　8385. f.

—— Index Scholarum publice et privatim MDCCCLXXXXIII habendarum. *Gottingæ*, 1893, *etc.* 8°.　　　　8385. f.

GOUT. DUTTON (T.) Indigestion, Gout, *etc.* pp. 220. *Lond.* 1893. 8°.　7616. aaa. 10.

GRANVILLE (J. M.) Notes and conjectures on Gout. pp. 84. *Lond.* 1894. 8°. 7630. aaa. 39.

MAYER (　) Effects of the Kronenquelle Water in the treatment of Gout. pp. 11. *Breslau*, 1891. 8°.　　07305. e. 23. (13.)

ROBERTS (*Sir* W.) Chemistry and therapeutics of Uric Acid and Gout. pp. 136. *Lond.* 1892. 8°.　　　7630. bbb. 16.

ROOSE (E. C. R.) Gout and its relations to diseases of the liver and kidneys. pp. 229. *Lond.* 1894. 8°.　　　　7620. a. 19.

WADE (W. F.) On Gout as a peripheral neurosis. pp. 59. *Lond.* 1893. 8°.　7620. de. 25.

See also RHEUMATISM : URIC ACID.

GOVAN. *See* GLASGOW.

GOVERNMENT : POLITICS.

Bibliography.

MAEHLBRECHT (O.) Wegweiser durch die neue Litteratur der Rechts- und Staatswissenschaften. pp. 748. *Berl.* 1893. 8°.　　BB.C. d. 6.

General.

Ac. New York. *Columbia College.* Political Science Quarterly. *N.Y.* 1886, *etc.* 8°.　　　　　　　　　P.P. 3639. ab.

—— Philadelphia. *American Academy of Political and Social Science.* Annals. *Phila.* 1890, *etc.* 8°.　　　　Ac. 2383.

ANTONIADES (B.) Die Staatslehre des Thomas ab Aquino. pp. 127. *Leipz.* 1890. 8°.　8009. f. 10.

GOVERNMENT.—General—*continued.*

BACKHAUS (W. E.) Vom rechten Staate.
pp. 152. *Braunschweig*, 1894. 8°.   8009. f. 19.

BAIN (F. W.) Body and Soul. pp. 466.
Lond. 1894. 8°.   8468. k. 24.

BENTHAM (J.) Fragment on Government.
pp. 241. *Oxf.* 1891. 8°.   8007. ee. 4.

BERNATZIK (E.) Republik und Monarchie.
pp. 52. *Freib.* 1892. 8°.   Pam. 64.

BLUNTSCHLI (J. C.) Theory of the State.
pp. 550. *Oxf.* 1892. 8°.   2016. b.

BOURINOT (J. G.) Canadian studies in Comparative Politics. pp. 92. *Montreal*, 1890. 4°.
8007. g. 8.

BRUDER (A.) Staatslexikon. *Freib.* 1889, *etc.* 8°.
012216. i.

BUIJS (J. T.) Studien over Staatkunde en Staatsrecht. *Arnhem*, 1894, *etc.* 8°.   8010. g.

BURGESS (J. W.) Political Science and comparative constitutional Law. 2 vol.
Bost. 1890–91. 8°.   8039. f. 12.

CAGGIANO (G.) Libertà e progresso. Anarchia e socialismo. pp. 16. *Napoli*, 1890. 16°. Pam. 8.

CENNI (E.) Della Libertà considerata in sè stessa, *etc.* pp. 589. *Napoli*, 1891. 8°. 8009. i. 31.

CIMBALI (G.) Il Diritto del più forte. pp. 215.
Roma, 1892. 8°.   8275. i. 1.

COHN (M. M.) Study showing the play of physical and social factors in the creation of Institutional Law. pp. 235. 1892. 8°. Johns Hopkins University Studies.   Ac. 2689.

CROZIER (J. B.) Civilization and progress.
pp. 464. *Lond.* 1892. 8°.   8469. dd. 30.

DELORY (M.) La Politique et ses principes.
pp. 484. *Saint-Omer*, 1890. 8°.   8009. f. 13.

DESJARDINS (A.) De la Liberté politique.
pp. 365. *Paris*, 1894. 8°.   8010. ee. 6.

DONNAT (L.) La Politique expérimentale.
pp. 588. 1891. 8°. Bibliothèque des sciences contemporaines. Vol. 12.   8709. b.

FIELD (D. D.) The duties of the State. pp. 37.
Lond. 1890. 8°.   8277. ee. 30. (6.)

FRANKENSTEIN (K.) Hand- und Lehrbuch der Staatswissenschaften. *Leipz.* 1893, *etc.* 8°.
8009. k.

FUNCK-BRENTANO (T.) La Politique. pp. 430.
Paris, 1892. 8°.   8007. e. 4.

GENNRICH (P.) Die Staats- und Kirchenlehre Johanns von Salisbury. pp. 171.
Gotha, 1894. 8°.   4535. c. 8.

GIESE (A.) Einführung in die allgemeine Lehre vom Staate. pp. 127. *Leipz.* 1894. 8°.
8009. b. 33.

GIL FORTOUL (J.) Filosofía constitucional.
pp. 424. *Paris*, 1890. 18°.   8009. aaa. 27.

GÓMES PALACIOS (J.) La Escuela de la Libertad. pp. 320. *Buenos A.* 1889. 8°. 8006. cc. 5.

GRABSCHEIDT (F. v.) Der moderne Staat und seine Aufgaben. pp. 77. *Wien*, 1894. 8°.
8008. dd. 9.

GREEF (G. de) L'Évolution des Croyances et des doctrines politiques. pp. 330.
Bruxelles, 1895. 8°.   8008. aaa. 9.

GREEN (T. H.) Lectures on the principles of Political Obligation. pp. 252. *Lond.*, 1895. 8°.
8010. ee. 8.

GUMPLOWICZ (L.) Die sociologische Staatsidee.
pp. 134. *Graz*, 1892. 8°.   08276. h. 51.

HAUKE (F.) Die geschichtlichen Grundlagen des Monarchenrechts. pp. 146. *Wien*, 1894. 8°.
5549. df. 12.

HERRIOTT (F. I.) Sir W. Temple on the origin and nature of Government, *etc. Phila.* 1893. 8°.
11826. d. 46. (6.)

GOVERNMENT.—General—*continued.*

HEWINS (W. A. S.) Studies in Political Science.
Lond. 1895, *etc.* 8°.   08207. f.

HOFFMAN (F. S.) The sphere of the State.
pp. 275. *N.Y.* 1894. 8°.   8009. bbb. 11.

JONA (G.) Studi costituzionali. Diritto costituzionale e diritto amministrativo. pp. 147.
Modena, 1889. 8°.   8010. f. 2.

KANT (I.) Principles of Politics. Edited by W. Hastie. pp. 148. *Edinb.* 1891. 8°. 8009. e. 12.

KATÔ (H.) Der Kampf ums Recht des Stärkeren.
pp. 154. *Berl.* 1894. 8°.   08276. k. 25.

KENT (C. B. R.) Essays in Politics, *etc.*
pp. 190. *Lond.* 1891. 8°.   8009. aaa. 28.

KOCH (G.) Beiträge zur Geschichte der politischen Ideen. *Berl.* 1892. *etc.* 8°. 8009. h. 20.

KRAUSE (C. C. F.) Der Erdrechtsbund.
pp. 149. *Leipz.* 1893. 8°.   8008. dd. 5.

LALOR (J. J.) Cyclopædia of Political Science, *etc.* 3 vol. *Chicago*, 1881–88. 8°. 8716. ee. 1.

LEROY-BEAULIEU (P. P.) L'État moderne et ses fonctions. pp. 463. *Paris*, 1890. 8°.
8009. f. 7.

—— The Modern State in relation to Society.
pp. 215. *Lond.* 1891. 8°.   08276. e. 14.

LILLY (W. S.) On Shibboleths. pp. 261.
Lond. 1892. 8°.   8009. i. 26.

LINGG (E.) Empirische Untersuchungen zur allgemeinen Staatslehre. pp. 235.
Wien, 1890. 8°.   8009. f. 9.

LOMBROSO (C.) and LASCHI (R.) Il Delitto politico e le Rivoluzioni. pp. 555.
Torino, 1890. 8°.   7004. df. 17.

MAC ARTHUR (J. N.) Government. pp. 120.
Lond. 1892. 8°.   8009. aaa. 34.

MACCHIAVELLI (N.) Il Principe. Edited by L. G. Burd. pp. 402. *Oxf.* 1891. 8°.   8008. ee. 11.

MACCUNN (J.) Ethics of citizenship. pp. 223.
Glasg. 1894. 8°.   8005. ccc. 19.

MACKAY (T.) A Plea for liberty. pp. 414.
Lond. 1891. 8°.   8276. g. 44.

MARQFOY (G.) La République. *Paris*, 1891, *etc.* 8°.
8010. g.

MERX (E. O. A.) Die Ideen von Staat und Staatsmann. pp. 46. *Heidelberg*, 1892. 8°.
Pam. 64.

MICELI (V.) Lo Stato e la nazione nei rapporti fra il diritto costituzionale e il diritto internazionale. pp. 289. *Firenze*, 1890. 8°.
8033. h. 17.

MOLLAT (G.) Lesebuch zur Geschichte der Staatswissenschaft des Auslandes. pp. 191.
Osterwieck, 1891. 8°.   8007. ee. 6.

MOWRY (W. A.) Elements of civil Government.
pp. 211. *Bost.* 1892. 8°.   8175. ee. 1. (1.)

NORDAU (M. S.) Conventional lies of our civilization. pp. 346. *Lond.* 1895. 8°.   8409. l. 25.

NOVICOU (J.) Les Luttes entre Sociétés humaines. pp. 752. *Paris*, 1893. 8°. 8277. d. 37.

O'BRIEN (M. D.) The natural rights to Freedom.
pp. 388. *Lond.* 1893. 8°.   08276. h. 40.

OPPENHEIM (J.) De Theorie van den organischen staat. pp. 34. *Groningen*, 1893. 8°. Pam. 64.

PEARSON (C. H.) National Life and character.
pp. 381. *Lond.* 1894. 8°.   08275. ee. 6.

P.P. *Florence.* Rassegna di Scienza politiche.
Firenze, 1883, *etc.* 8°.   P.P. 3566. m.

—— *Leipsic.* Zeitschrift für Litteratur und Geschichte der Staatswissenschaften.
Leipz. 1893, *etc.*. 8°.   P.P. 1423. hcb.

—— *Paris.* Revue de Droit Public et de la science politique. *Paris*, 1894, *etc.* 8°.
P.P. 1370. gn.

GOVERNMENT.—General—*continued.*

Pí y Margall (F.) La Luchas de nuestros días. pp. 441. *Madrid, 1890. 8°.* 8042. aa. 23.

Pollock (*Sir* F.) Introduction to the history of the Science of Politics. pp. 128. *Lond. 1895. 8°.* 8005. bb. 15.

Posada (A.) Tratado de Derecho político. *Madrid, 1893, etc. 8°.* 8007. e. 5.

Proal (L.) La Criminalité politique. pp. 307. *Paris, 1895. 8°.* 8010. ee. 10.

Ratkowsky (M. G.) Encyklopädie der Rechts- und Staatswissenschaften. pp. 102. *Wien, 1890. 8°.* 6005. e. 2.

Ratzenhofer (G.) Wesen und Zweck der Politik. 3 Bde. *Leipz. 1893. 8°.* 8009. i. 33.

Ritchie (D. G.) Principles of State Interference. pp. 172. *Lond. 1891. 8°.* 08276. e. 1.

—— Natural Rights. pp. 304. 1895. 8°. Muirhead (J. H.) Library of Philosophy. 2023. f.

Robert (P.) König Lear's Geist im modernen Staatswesen. pp. 67. *Leipz. 1895, 8°.* 8074. ee. 48.

Robertson (A.) Lectures on the science and study of Politics. pp. 78. *Dundee, 1888. 8°.* 6006. c. 36.

Roscher (W.) Politik : geschichtliche Natur- lehre der Monarchie, Aristokratie und Demo- kratie. pp. 722. *Stuttgart, 1893. 8°.* 8008. f. 6.

Rousseau (J. J.) The Social Contract. Trans- lated by R. M. Harrington. pp. 227. *N.Y. 1893. 8°.* 8009. aa. 22.

—— The Social Contract. Translated by H. J. Tozer. pp. 247. *Lond. 1895. 8°.* 08276. ee. 7.

Sanz y Escartin (E.) De la Autoridad política en la sociedad contemporánea. 1894. 8°. Ac. Madrid. *R. Academia.* Discursos de recepcion. Tom. 6. Ac. 142/2.

Schvarcz (G.) Montesquieu und die Verant- wortlichkeit der Räthe des Monarchen in Eng- land, Aragonien, Ungarn, Siebenbürgen und Schweden. pp. 168. *Leipz. 1892. 8°.* 8009. i. 27.

Secondat (C. de) *Baron de Montesquieu.* Esprit des Lois. Livres i.–v. pp. 328. *Paris, 1892. 8°.* 8008. aaa. 7.

Selby (F. G.) Politics, ancient and modern. pp. 28. *Bombay, 1892. 8°.* 8009. c. 29.

Seydel (M.) Staatsrechtliche und politische Abhandlungen. pp. 217. *Freiburg. 1893. 8°.* 8008. f. 8.

Shebbeare (C. J.) The Greek theory of the State and the Nonconformist conscience. pp. 116. *Lond. 1895. 8°.* 08275. ee. 38.

Sidgwick (H.) The elements of Politics. pp. 632. *Lond. 1891. 8°.* 2020. d.

Seal (H.) On the nature of State Interference. pp. 96. *Lond. 1893. 8°.* 8277. ee. 42.

Van Ornum (W. H.) Why Government at all? pp. 368. *Chicago, 1892. 8°.* 8008. b. 2.

Vincent (A.) Lex Mundi. pp. 121. *Lond. 1892. 8°.* 8006. c. 4.

Walcker (C.) Politik der konstitutionellen Staaten. pp. 301. *Karlsruhe, 1890. 8°.* 8009. f. 8.

Worthington (S.) Politics and Property. pp. 334. *N.Y. 1891. 8°.* 08276. f. 7.

See also Anarchism : Constitutions : Elec- tions : Local Government : Parliaments : Referendum : Social Science, and for the constitution and politics of each country under the country required.

Administration : Ministers of State, etc.

Goodnow (F. J.) Comparative Administrative Law. 2 vol. *N.Y. 1893. 8°.* 6005. h. 10.

GOVERNMENT.—Administration, etc. —*continued.*

Idsinga (J. W. H. M. v.) De administratieve Rechtspraak en de constitutioneele monarchie. *'s Gravenhage, 1893, etc. 8°.* 8009. k.

Jona (G.) Studi costituzionale e diritto am- ministrativo. pp. 147. *Modena, 1889. 8°.* 8010. f. 2.

Triepel (H.) Das Interregnum. pp. 117. *Leipz. 1892. 8°.* 8009. g. 23.

Waltrain Cavagnari (V.) Elementi di scienza dell' Amministrazione. pp. 306. *Firenze, 1890. 8°.* 8207. aa. 29.

Crayssac (A.) De la Responsabilité des minis- tres. pp. 187. *Bordeaux, 1890. 8°.* 8009. g. 21.

Dupriez (L.) Les Ministres dans les principaux pays d'Europe et d'Amérique. 2 tom. *Paris, 1892–93. 8°.* 8010. ee. 4.

Hervieu (H.) Les Ministres, leur rôle et leurs attributions. pp. 782. *Paris, 1893. 8°.* 8051. g. 19.

See also supra : General : and under the Sub- heading Constitution of each country.

Democracy : Universal Suffrage.

B. The Truth about Democracy. pp. 92. *Lond. 1890. 8°.* 8009. e. 11.

Correa y Zafrilla (P.) Democracia, federación y socialismo. pp. 280. *Madrid, 1891. 8°.* 08276. h. 37.

Cree (N.) Direct Legislation by the people. pp. 194. *Chicago, 1892. 8°.* 8009. aa. 19.

Eichthal (E. d') Souveraineté du Peuple et gouvernement. pp. 264. *Paris, 1895. 8°.* 8008. aaa. 8.

Government. Government by the People. pp. 159. *Lond. 1895. 8°.* 8005. c. 2.

Laveleye (É de) *Baron.* Le Gouvernement dans la Démocratie. 2 tom. *Paris, 1891. 8°.* 8009. f. 17.

Vibert (C. T.) Le Droit divin de la Démocratie. pp. 432. *Paris, 1881. 8°.* 8009. b. 36.

Nyssens (A.) Le Suffrage universel tempéré. pp. 12. *Brux. 1890. 8°.* Pam. 73.

Onclair (A.) Le Suffrage universel. pp. 39. *Brux. 1893. 8°.* Pam. 64.

Paepe (C. de) Le Suffrage universel et la capacité politique de la classe ouvrière. pp. 16. *Gand. 1890. 8°.* Pam. 73.

See also supra : General.

Federal Government.

Hart (A. B.) Introduction to the study of Federal Government. pp. 200. *1891. 8°. Har- vard University.* Harvard Historical Mon- graphs. No. 2. Ac. 2692/6.

Trinchant (J.) Unitarismo y federalismo. pp. 219. *Madrid, 1890. 8°.* 8042. aaa. 30.

Westerkamp (J. B.) Staatenbund und Bundes- staat. pp. 549. *Leipz. 1892. 8°.* 8008. f. 7.

Referendum.

Deploige (S.) Le Referendum en Suisse. pp. 190. *Brux. 1892. 8°.* 8072. f. 2.

Lorand (G.) Le Referendum. pp. 36. *Brux. 1890. 8°.* Pam. 64.

See also Belgium : Switzerland, *Constitution, etc.*

GRÄFENTONNA. Reinhardt (G.) Ge- schichte des Marktes Gräfentonna. pp. 384. *Langensalza, 1892. 8°.* 10256. bb. 1.

GRAHAMSTOWN. Grahamstown. Souve- nir of Grahamstown. pp. 51. *Grahamstown, 1887. 4°.* 10095. ee. 15.

—— Guide to Grahamstown. pp. 48. *Cape Town, 1893. 8°.* Pam. 89.

See also Cape of Good Hope.

GRAN. Györffy (L.) Geschichte und Beschreibung der graner Basilika. pp. 55.
Gran, 1890. 8°   4535. b. 15. (6.)

GRANADA. Province and City. Almagro Cárdenas (A.) Museo granadino de Antigüedades árabes. pp. 190. *Granada,* 1886–93. fol.
                                    7709. l. 22.

Contreras (R.) Estudio descriptivo de los monumentos árabes de Granada. pp. 378.
Madrid, 1885. 8°.   7706. b. 35.

Durán y Lerchundi (J.) La Toma de Granada. 2 tom. *Madrid,* 1893. 8°.   10631. dd. 23.

Gómez Moreno (M.) Guía de Granada. pp. 530.
Granada, 1892. 8°.   10160. aaa. 21.

Pi y Margall (F.) Granada. pp. 576. 1885. 8°.
España. Sus Monumentos.   2060. c.

See also Alhambra : Arabs : Spain.

GRAN CHACO. Baldrich (J. A.) El Chaco central norte. pp. 292.
Buenos A. 1889. 8°.   10481. i. 16.

Boggiani (G.) Viaggi d'un artista nell' America Meridionale. pp. 335. *Roma,* 1895. 4°.
                                    10480. h. 26.

Gonzalez (M.) El Gran Chaco Argentino.
pp. 214. *Buenos A.* 1890. 8°.   10480. h. 17.

Mallat de Bassilan (M. J. S. A.) L'Amérique inconnue. pp. 280. *Paris,* 1892. 8°.
                                    10481. d. 31.

Paz Guillen (J.) A través del Gran Chaco.
pp. 85. *Buenos A.* 1886. 8°.   Pam. 86.

See also Argentine Republic.

GRANDE CHARTREUSE. Boutrais (C.) The Monastery of the Grande Chartreuse.
pp. 234. *Lond.* 1893. 12°.   4629. bb. 8.

Roux (X.) La Grand Chartreuse avant la Révolution. pp. 104. *Grenoble,* 1892. 8°.
                                    4629. c. 12.

GRAND TRUNK RAILWAY, Canada. *See* Railways.

GRANVILLE. Launay (J.) Histoire du siége de Granville. pp. 171. *Granville,* 1893. 8°.
                                    9231. g. 22.

Trebuchet (L.) La Baie de Cancale, Granville, *etc.* pp. 160. *Paris,* 1888. 8°.   010171. e. 12.

GRAPE. *See* Vine.

GRAPHOLOGY. Aruss (A.) La Graphologie simplifiée. pp. 286. *Paris,* 1892. 12°.
                                    7942. e. 40.

Barter (J.) How to tell Character from handwriting. pp. 38. *Lond.* 1891. 8°.
                                    7942. aaa. 52.

Crépieux-Jamin (J.) Traité pratique de Graphologie. pp. 268. *Paris,* 1890. 12°. 7942. bb. 58.

—— Handwriting and Expression. pp. 242.
Lond. 1892. 8°.   7942. i. 38.

Deschamps (L.) La Philosophie de l'écriture.
pp. 160. *Paris,* 1892. 8°.   7942. i. 42.

Frith (H.) How to read Character in handwriting. pp. 138. *Lond.* 1890. 8°.
                                    7942. cc. 33.

Graphologie. Graphologie. pp. 47.
Paris, 1891. 8°.   7943. aa. 59.

Hardy (W. J.) Handwriting of Kings and Queens of England. pp. 176. *Lond.* 1893. 8°.
                                    7709. k. 21.

Michon (J. H.) Système de Graphologie.
pp. 323. 33. *Paris,* 1888. 12°.   7942. e. 36.

—— Méthode pratique de Graphologie. pp. 214.
Paris, 1888. 12°.   7942. e. 35.

Miracle y Carbonnell (F.) Napoleon I. y su escritura. pp. 258. *Barcelona,* 1892. 8°.
                                    7942. h. 32.

See also Handwriting.

GRASSE. B. Guide to Grasse. pp. 121.
Lond. 1891. 8°.   10168. cc. 31.
See also Riviera.

GRASSES: PASTURES. Bailey (F. M.) and Gordon (P. R.) Plants reputed poisonous and injurious to Stock. pp. 112.
Brisbane, 1887. 8°.   07028. l. 14.

Hackel (E.) The true Grasses. pp. 228.
N.Y. 1890. 8°.   07028. g. 12.

Hutchinson (W.) Handbook of Grasses.
pp. 92. *Lond.* 1895. 8°.   07076. e. 60.

Johns (C. H.) Grasses. pp. 96. *Lond.* 1892. 8°.
                                    4419. f. 32.

Lamson-Scribner (F.) Hungarian Brome Grass. pp. 4. 1894. 8°. U.S. *Department of Agriculture.* Publications.   7053. e. 48.

Mackay (T.) Manual of Grasses useful to New Zealand. *Wellington,* 1887, *etc.* 8°. 07076. l. 2.

New South Wales. *Department of Agriculture.* Forage Plants of Australia. pp. 94.
Sydney, 1891. 8°.   07076. k. 6.

Pérez (V.) and Sagot (P. A.) Le Tagasaste, cytisus proliferus varietas, fourrage important. pp. 38. *Paris,* 1892. 8°.   7074. l. 10. (10.)

Sutton and Sons. Formation of Lawn tennis and Cricket grounds from seed. pp. 19.
Lond. 1892. 8°.   Pam. 1.

U.S. *Department of Agriculture.* Illustrations of N. American Grasses. *Wash.* 1891, *etc.* 4°.
                                    7053. e. 47.

Wolff (E. T.) Farm Foods. pp. 365.
Lond. 1895. 8°.   07293. g. 22.
See also Agriculture : Botany, *Economic.*

GRASSINGTON. Harker (B. J.) "The Buxton of Yorkshire." pp. 130.
Manch. 1890. 8°.   10358. cc. 52.

GRAUDENZ. Froelich (X.) Chronik der Stadt Graudenz. pp. 92. *Graudenz,* 1891. 8°.
                                    10255. ee. 4.

GRAVESEND. Ridgway (A.) Penny guide to Gravesend. *Gravesend,* 1891. 8°.
                                    10347. d. 10. (7.)

GRAVITATION. Carruthers (G. T.) The cause of Gravity. pp. 33. *Inverness,* 1892. 8°.
                                    8767. cc. 30. (9.)

Hafner (E.) Die Anziehungs- und Abstossungskräfte in der Natur. pp. 119. *Glarus,* 1891. 8°.
                                    8704. e. 28.

Schlichting (C.) Die Gravitation ist eine Folge der Bewegung des Aethers. pp. 15.
Lüben, 1892. 8°.   8777. bbb. 30. (7.)
See also Earth.

GREAT BEAR LAKE. Petitot (É. F. S.) Exploration de la région du grand Lac des Ours. pp. 469. *Paris,* 1893. 8°. 10460. aaa. 29.

GREAT BRITAIN AND IRELAND. For all works relating to the United Kingdom *see* England.

GREAT EASTERN RAILWAY. *See* Railways.

GREAT GRANSDEN. Edmonds (A. J.) History of Great Gransden.
St. Neots, 1892–95. 8°.   10352. dd. 16.

GREAT HAMPDEN. Great Hampden. Parish Registers of Great Hampden. pp. 199.
Lond. 1888. 4°.   9917. i. 13.

GREAT NORTHERN RAILWAY. *See* Railways.

GREAT SLAVE LAKE. Petitot (É.) Autour du grand lac des Esclaves. pp. 369.
Paris, 1892. 12°.   10470. dd. 27.

GREAT WESTERN RAILWAY. *See* Railways.

GREECE.
Antiquities: Social Life of Ancient Greece.
Bibliography.

FOCK (G.) Catalogus Dissertationum philologicarum classicarum. 4 pt. *Leipz.* 1893. 8°.
011900. cc. 45.

VALMAGGI (L.) Manuale di Filologia classica. pp. 336. *Torino,* 1894. 8°. 12933. i. 12.

General.

AC., etc. Boston, Mass. *Archaeological Institute. School of Classical Studies at Athens.* Bulletin. *Bost.* 1893, etc. 8°. Ac. 5790/5.

—— Papers of the School. *Bost.* 1885, etc. 8°.
Ac. 5790/9.

—— London. *British Museum.* Photographic reproductions of Greek and Roman Antiquities. *Lond.* 1891, etc. fol. Tab. 1226. c.

—— *Society for the Promotion of Hellenic Studies.* Supplementary Papers. *Lond.* 1892, etc. fol.
1711. a.

ASCHERSON (C. E. F.) Berliner Studien, *etc. Berl.* 1884, etc. 8°. P.P. 4991. e.

BERLIN DISSERTATIONS. Berliner Abhandlungen zur klassichen Altertumswissenschaft. *Berl.* 1894, etc. 8°. 11312. dd.

BONNET (M.) La Philologie classique. Six conférences sur les études relatives à l'antiquité grecque et romaine. pp. 224. *Paris,* 1892, 8°.
8311. b. 5.

BRUNN (H. v.) Archäologische Studien dargebracht von A. Furtwängler, *etc.* pp. 91. *Berl.* 1893. 4°. 7706. h. 24.

DUMONT (A.) Mélanges d'archéologie et d'épigraphie. pp. 666. *Paris,* 1892. 8°. 7704. d. 15.

DRISLER (H.) Classical Studies in honour of H. Drisler. pp. 310. *N.Y.* 1894. 8°. 11312. o. 9.

ENGELMANN (R.) Pictorial Atlas to the Iliad and Odyssey. pp. 35. *Lond.* 1892. fol.
1702. a. 7.

GARDNER (P.) Manual of Greek Antiquities. pp. 736. *Lond.* 1895. 8°. 2259. b. 18.

HAAS (G. E.) Der Geist der Antike. pp. 575. *Graz,* 1894. 8°. 11312. e. 39.

HERMANN (C. F.) Lehrbuch der griechischen Antiquitäten. *Freiburg,* 1889, etc. 8°.
07707. i.

LIPSIUS (H.) Griechische Studien H. Lipsius zum sechzigsten Geburtstag dargebracht. pp. 187. *Leipz.* 1894. 8°. 11812. q. 9.

MUELLER (I. E. P. v.) Handbuch der klassischen Altertums-Wissenschaft. *München,* 1891, etc. 8°. 2259. g.

OEHLER (R.) Klassisches Bilderbuch. pp. 105. *Leipz.* 1892. 8°. 7706. ee. 36.

PASDERA (A.) Dizionario di Antichità classica. *Torino,* 1891, etc. 8°. 7706. d.

PATER (W. H.) Greek Studies. pp. 315. *Lond.* 1895. 8°. 11312. d. 60.

PAULY (A. F. v.) Real-Encyclopädie der classischen Altertumswissenschaft. *Stuttg.* 1893, etc. 8°. 2282. f. 2.

ROBERT (C.) Aus der Anomia. Archaeologische Beitraege. pp. 214. *Berl.* 1890. 8°. 7708. dd. 15.

ROSSBACH (O.) Griechische Antiken des archaeologische Museums in Breslau. pp. 43. *Breslau,* 1889. 4°. 7875. e. 27.

SCHLIMMER (J. G.) and BOER (Z. C. de) Woordenboek der Grieksche en Romeinsche Oudheid. pp. 588. *Haarlem,* 1890. 8°. 7706. f. 15.

SCHREIBER (T.) Atlas of classified Antiquities. pp. 202. *Lond.* 1895. obl. 8°. 1702. b. 4.

SEYFFERT (A. O.) Dictionary of classified Antiquities. pp. 716. *Lond.* 1895. 8°. 2051. c.

GREECE.—Antiquities, etc.—*continued.*

VALMAGGI (L.) Manuale di filologia classica. pp. 336. *Torino,* 1894. 8°. 12933. i. 12.

VIENNA ERANOS. Eranos Vindobonensis. pp. 385. *Wien,* 1893. 8°. 7706. ee. 39.

WAGNER (J.) Realien des griechischen Alterthums. pp. 124. *Brunn,* 1892. 8°. 7708. cc. 51.

See also ART, *Ancient:* INSCRIPTIONS: NUMISMATICS: SCULPTURE: TERRA COTTA: VASES.

Recent Excavations, etc.

DIEHL (C.) Excursions archéologiques en Grèce. pp. 388. *Paris,* 1890. 8°. 7705. a. 31.

—— Excursions in Greece to recently explored sites. pp. 408. *Lond.* 1893. 8°. 7705. aaa. 41.

GARDNER (P.) New chapters in Greek history. Historical results of recent excavations. pp. 459. *Lond.* 1892. 8°. 9026. f. 9.

REINACH (S.) Documents sur les fouilles et découvertes dans l'Orient hellénique 1883-90. pp. 786. *Paris,* 1891. 8°. 7704. cc. 22.

SCHUCKHARDT (C.) Schliemann's Ausgrabungen im Lichte der heutigen Wissenschaft. pp. 405. *Leipz.* 1891. 8°. 7706. f. 22.

—— Schliemann's Excavations. pp. 363. *Lond.* 1891. 8°. 2259. d. 11.

JOSEPH (D.) Die Paläste des homerischen Epos, mit Rucksicht auf die Ausgrabungen H. Schliemanns. pp. 81. *Berl.* 1893. 8°.
7705. aaaa. 39.

WALDSTEIN (C.) Excavations at the Heraion of Argos. *Lond.* 1892, etc. 4°. 7705. h. 31.

AC. Boston, Mass. *Archaeological Institute.* CLARKE (J. T.) Doric Shaft and Base found at Assos. pp. 21. *Baltimore,* 1886. 8°. Ac. 5790/12.

HOMOLLE (T.) Les Travaux de l'École française dans l'Ile de Délos. *Paris,* 1890. 8°.
7705. ee. 25. (4.)

WARSBERG (A. v.) *Baron.* Eine Wallfahrt nach Dodona. pp. 149. *Graz,* 1893. 8°.
10125. ccc. 7.

PARIS (P.) Platée. pp. 320. 1891. 8°. Ac. *Athens.* École française. Bibliothèque.
Ac. 5206/2.

BAUNACK (J. F.) Aus Epidauros. pp. 104. *Leipz.* 1890. 4°. 7705. ee. 23.

KABBADIAS (T.) Fouilles d'Épidaure. *Athènes,* 1891, *etc.* fol. 1704. c.

LACHAT (H.) Épidaure. Restauration des monuments. pp. 249. *Paris,* 1895. fol.
K.T.C. 13. b. 7.

KABBADIAS (P.) Fouilles de Lycosoura. *Athènes,* 1893, etc. 4°. 7706. h.

GARDNER (E. A.) Excavations at Megalopolis. pp. 141. 1892. fol. Ac. London. *Society for the Promotion of Hellenic Studies.* Supplementary Papers. No. 1. 1711. a.

BELGER (C.) Die mykenische Lokalsage von den Gräbern Agamemnons. pp. 41. *Berl.* 1893. 4°.
7704. k. 10. (2.)

PARIS. *Louvre.* Terres cuites et autres antiquités trouvées dans la Nécropole de Myrina. pp. 348. *Paris,* 1886. 8°. 7706. e. 23.

—— Proto-Ionic Capital from the Site of Neandreia. pp. 35. *Baltimore,* 1886. 8°.
Ac. 5790/11.

CURTIUS (E.) and ADLER (F.) Olympia. *Berl.* 1890, etc. 8°. 1703. b. 6.

—— [Plates.] fol. 1703. c. 10.

RHOMAÏDES (C.) Olympia. pp. 33. *Athens,* 1890. fol. K.T.C. 4. a. 1.

BERLIN. *Königliche Museen.* Beschreibung der antiken Skulpturen mit Ausschluss der pergamenischen Fundstücke. pp. 554. *Berl.* 1891. 8°.
7875. cc. 2.

GREECE.—Antiquities, etc.—*continued.*
Social Life, etc.

BLUEMNER (H.) Home Life of the ancient Greeks. pp. 548. *Lond.* 1895. 8°. 　　7705. aa. 40.

BUSOLT (G.) Die griechischen Staats- und Rechtsaltertümer. pp. 384. 1892. 8°. MUELLER (I. E. P. v.) Handbuch der klassischen Altertums-Wissenschaft. Bde. 4. Abt. 1. Hälfte 1. 　　2259. g.

FOWLER (W. W.) The City-state of the Greeks. pp. 332. *Lond.* 1893. 8°. 　　8009. aaa. 31.

GILBERT (G.) Handbuch der griechischen Staatsalterthümer. *Leipz.* 1893, *etc.* 8°. 　　7706. c. 50.

HAMMOND (B. E.) Political Institutions of the ancient Greeks. pp. 122. *Lond.* 1895. 8°. 　　9026. ff. 40.

REICH (E.) Græco-Roman Institutions. pp. 100. *Oxf.* 1890. 8°. 　　5205. aa. 22.

SEEBOHM (H. E.) On the structure of Greek Tribal Society. pp. 147. *Lond.* 1895. 8°. 　　9026. ff. 41.

BÉNARD (L.) Les Courses de Chars aux Jeux publics de la Grèce. 1891. 8°. Ac. Nantes. *Société Archéologique.* Bulletin. Tom. 30. 　　Ac. 5319.

BLUEMNER (H.) Home life of the ancient Greeks. pp. 548. *Lond.* 1893. 8°. 7705. aa. 38.

CHURCH (A. J.) Pictures of Greek life. pp. 320. *Lond.* 1893. 8°. 　　9026. b. 32.

DAVIDSON (T.) Education of the Greek people. pp. 229. *Lond.* 1895. 8°. 　　8311. aa. 36.

EVANS (M. M.) *Lady.* Chapters on Greek dress. pp. 84. *Lond.* 1893. 8°. 　　7705. aaa. 42.

FOUGÈRES (G.) La Vie publique et privée des Grecs. pp. 116. *Paris,* 1894. 4°. 7701. k. 4.

FALKENER (E.) The Grecian house as described by Vitruvius. pp. 21. *Lond.* 1893. 4°. 　　7706. ee. 40.

GUHL (E.) and KONER (W.) Leben der Griechen. *Berl.* 1893, *etc.* 8°. 　　7704. cc.

MILHAUD (G.) Leçons sur les origines de la Science grecque. pp. 306. *Paris,* 1893. 8°. 　　8486. e. 9.

MOMMSEN (A.) Über bie Zeit der Olympien. pp. 102. *Leipz.* 1891. 8°. 　　9026. g. 15.

MONCEAUX (P.) La Grèce avant Alexandre. pp. 320. *Paris,* 1892. 8°. 　　7705. b. 50.

OPITZ (C. R.) Das häusliche Leben der Griechen. pp. 302. 1894. 8°. Kulturbilder aus dem klassischen Altertume. 6. 　　7709. aaa.

POMERANZ (B.) La Grèce et la Judée dans l'antiquité. *Paris,* 1891, *etc.* 8°. 　　9009. d.

SARTORI (C.) Studien aus dem Gebiete der griechischen Privataltertümer. *München,* 1893, *etc.* 8°. 　　7706. g.

SITTL (C.) Die Gebärden der Griechen. pp. 386. *Leipz.* 1890. 8°. 　　7706. f. 16.

LA CHAUVELAYS (J. de) Les Armes et la tactique des Grecs devant Troie. pp. 120. *Paris,* 1891. 8°. 　　8823. n. 11.

PERNICE (E.) Griechische Gewichte. pp. 215. *Berl.* 1894. 8°. 　　07708. i. 1.

See also ART, *Ancient :* ATHENS: DRAMA : GREEK LITERATURE: INSCRIPTIONS: MUSIC: PELOPONNESUS : SPARTA.

Army, *of Modern Greece.*

G. B. & I. *War Office.* Handbook of the armies of the minor Balkan States. pp. 61. *Lond.* 1891. 8°. 　　8823. g. 20.

History, *General and Ancient.*

ABBOTT (E.) History of Greece. *Lond.* 1893, *etc.* 8°. 　　2382. b.

GREECE.—History—*continued.*

ALLCROFT (A. H.) and MASOM (W. F.) Early Grecian history to 495 B.C. pp. 156. 1891. 8°. Tutorial Series. 1887, *etc.* 8°. 　　12205. c. 53.

—— Synopsis of Grecian history to 495 B.C. pp. 24. 1891. 8°. Tutorial Series. 12205. c. 67.

BELOCH (J.) Griechische Geschichte. *Strassb.* 1893, *etc.* 8°. 　　9026. i. 7.

—— Storia greca. *Roma,* 1891, *etc.* 8°. 9026. d. 2.

BUSOLT (G.) Griechische Geschichte bis zur Schlacht bei Chaeroneia. 1893, *etc.* 8°. Handbücher der alten Geschichte. Bd. 1. 9009. l. 1.

DURUY (V.) History of Greece. 4 vol. *Lond.* 1892. 8°. 　　2382. f.

FREEMAN (E. A.) History of Federal Government in Greece. pp. 692. *Lond.* 1893. 8°. 　　2238. e. 8.

FUSTEL DE COULANGES (N. D.) Nouvelles recherches sur quelques problèmes d'histoire. pp. 482. *Paris,* 1891. 8°. 　　9009. l. 3.

GARDNER (P.) Historical Results of recent excavations in Greece, *etc.* pp. 459. *Lond.* 1892. 8°. 　　9026. f. 9.

HOLM (A.) The History of Greece. *Lond.* 1894, *etc.* 8°. 　　9026. e. 22.

MACDERMOT (T. B.) Outlines of Grecian history. *Dublin,* 1889. 12°. 　　9026. de. 3.

MAHAFFY (J. P.) Problems in Greek history. pp. 240. *Lond.* 1892. 8°. 　　2382. b. 1.

MYERS (P. v. N.) History of Greece for colleges. pp. 577. *Bost.* 1895. 8°. 　　9026. aa. 34.

OMAN (C. W. C.) History of Greece to the death of Alexander the Great. pp. 560. *Lond.* 1891. 8°. 　　9026. aa. 22.

POLLARD (A.) True stories from Greek history. pp. 318. *Lond.* 1892. 8°. 　　9026. aaa. 19.

ROBINSON (W. S.) Short history of Greece. pp. 392. *Lond.* 1895. 8°. 　　9026. a. 15.

TONIAZZO (G.) La Grecia. Prospetto storico. pp. 226. *Milano,* 1891. 8°. 　　012200. h. 12.

FOWLER (W. W.) The City-state of the Greeks. pp. 332. *Lond.* 1893. 8°. 　　8009. aaa. 31.

GILBERT (G.) Handbuch der griechischen Staatsalterthümer. *Leipz.* 1893, *etc.* 8°. 　　7706. c. 50.

HAMMOND (B. E.) Greek Constitutions. pp. 68. *Camb.* 1891. 8°. 　　8007. ee. 5.

—— Political Institutions of the ancient Greeks. pp. 122. *Lond.* 1895. 8°. 　　9026. ff. 40.

SEEBOHM (H. E.) On the structure of Greek Tribal Society. pp. 147. *Lond.* 1895. 8°. 　　9026. ff. 41.

SCHNEIDER (É.) Les Pélasges et leurs descendants. pp. 289. *Paris,* 1894. 12°. 10125. a. 4.

DELBRUECK (H.) Die Perserkriege und die Burgunderkriege. pp. 314. *Berl.* 1887. 8°. 　　9041. i. 17.

GRUNDY (G. B.) Topography of the Battle of Platæa. pp. 76. *Lond.* 1894. 8°. 9026. ff. 39.

GRANT (A. J.) Greece in the age of Pericles. pp. 325. 1893. 8°. KNIGHT (W.) University Extension Manuals. 　　12204. f.

WITT (C.) The Retreat of the Ten Thousand. pp. 191. *Lond.* 1891. 8°. 　　9026. aaa. 18.

ALLCROFT (A. H.) Decline of Hellas. pp. 371. 323 B.C. pp. 176. 1894. 8°. Tutorial Series. 　　12205. c. 230.

BOUGOT (A.) Rivalité d'Eschine et Démosthène. pp. 197. *Paris,* 1891. 8°. 　　9026. ff. 31.

CARRAROLI (D.) La leggenda di Allessandro Magno. pp. 375. *Mondovi,* 1892. 8°. 10606. b. 48.

KOLSTER (W. H.) Alexander der Grosse. pp. 39. 1890. 8°. Sammlung wissenschaftlicher Vorträge. No. 99. 　　12249. m.

2 R

GREECE.—History—continued.

MAAS (O.) Kleitarch und Diodor. Eine Quellen-untersuchung. *St. Petersburg, 1894, etc.* 8°.
　11312. q.

SCHWARZ (F. v.) Alexander des Grossen Feldzüge in Turkestan. pp. 103. *München, 1893.* 8°.
　9026. h. 20.

WEINERT (A.) Die achäische Bundesverfassung. *Demmin, 1881, etc.* 4°.　9026. i.

HERTZBERG (G. F.) Histoire de la Grèce sous la domination des Romains. 3 tom.
Paris, 1887–90. 8°.　9026. h. 7.

See also ATHENS : HISTORY, *Ancient* : SPARTA.
For the history from A.D. 330–1453, *see* BYZANTINE EMPIRE.

Mediæval and Modern.

BIKÉLAS (D.) La Grèce byzantine et moderne. pp. 435. *Paris, 1893.* 8°.　9136. f. 22.

—— Seven essays on Christian Greece. pp. 298. *Paisley, 1890.* 8?.　9136. f. 18.

BLANCARD (T.) Les Mavroyéni. Essai d'étude additionnelle à l'histoire moderne de la Grèce. pp. 916. *Paris, 1893.* 8°.　9916. aaa. 26.

PHANARIOT. Livre d'Or de la Noblesse phanariote en Grèce. pp. 160. *Athènes, 1892.* 4°.
　9904. m. 25.

DRAGOUMES (N.) Souvenirs historiques. pp. 400. *Paris, 1890.* 18°.　9136. bb. 15.

CHURCH (E. M.) Sir R. Church in Italy and Greece. pp. 356. *Edinb. 1895.* 8°.　010817. g. 1.

SKORDELES (B. G.) and KOURTIDES (A. P.) Σκηνογραφίαι ἐκ τῆς Ἑλληνικῆς Ἐπαναστάσεως. pp. 61. *ἐν Ἀθηναις, 1889.* 8°.　Pam. 28.

THOUVENEL (E. A.) La Grèce du roi Othon. pp. 465. *Paris, 1890.* 8°.　8028. de. 25.

BÉRARD (V.) La Turquie et l'Hellénisme contemporain. pp. 352. *Paris, 1893.* 12°.
　8028. aaa. 11.

COUITÉAS (B.) La Grèce après la faillite. pp. 316. *Paris, 1895.* 12°.　9026. aa. 32.

P.P. *Paris.* L'Orient. *Paris, 1889, etc.* fol.
　P.P. 9455.

SAMUELSON (J.) Greece ; her present condition. pp. 102. *Lond. 1894.* 8°.　10125. aaa. 22.

Law, Ancient.

CATELLANI (E.) Il Diritto internazionale nell' antica Grecia. *1892.* 8°. AC. *Rome. Accademia di Conferenze.* Studi. Anno 13.
　Ac. 6541.

DARESTE (R.) La science du Droit en Grèce. pp. 319. *Paris, 1893.* 8°.　5254. c. 15.

HRUZA (E.) Beiträge zur Geschichte des griechischen Familienrechtes. *Erlangen, 1892, etc.* 8°.
　5254. cc. 17.

HITZIG (H. F.) Das griechische Pfandrecht. pp. 148. *München, 1895.* 8°.　5206. cc. 21.

LIPSIUS (J. H.) Von der Bedeutung des griechischen Rechts. pp. 32. *Leipz. 1893.* 8°.
　6005. g. 18. (11.)

SZÁNTÓ (E.) Das griechische Bürgerrecht. pp. 165. *Freib. 1892.* 8°.　5206. d. 15.

Naval Antiquities. *See* NAVAL SCIENCE, *History.*

Philosophy. *See* PHILOSOPHY.

Religion and Mythology.

BROWN (J. B.) Stoics and Saints : Lectures on later heathen Moralists. pp. 296.
Glasg. 1893. 8°.　4534. ee. 14.

DICTIONARIES. Pronouncing dictionary of Mythology. pp. 163. *Lond. 1892.* 16°. 7706. a. 42.

ELY (T.) Olympos : tales of the Gods of Greece. pp. 298. *Lond. 1891.* 8°.　4503. de. 1.

GREECE.—Religion, etc.—continued.

DYER (L.) Studies of the Gods in Greece at certain sanctuaries. pp. 457. *Lond. 1891.* 8°.
　4506. bb. 25.

ELSER (C.) Die Lehre des Aristoteles über das Wirken Gottes. pp. 228. *Münster, 1893.* 8°.
　8460. f. 25.

FARRER (J. A.) Paganism and Christianity. pp. 256. *Lond. 1891.* 8°.　4503. bb. 31.

FORESTI (A.) Mitologia greca. 2 vol. *Milano, 1892.* 8°.　012200. h. 65.

FRANCILLON (R. E.) Gods and Heroes. pp. 292. *Edinburgh, 1892.* 8°.　4503. aaa. 3.

GAYLEY (C. M.) The Classic Myths in English literature. pp. 539. *Bost. 1893.* 8°.
　4503. bb. 39.

MUELLER (H. D.) Historisch - mythologische Untersuchungen. pp. 134. *Göttingen, 1892.* 8°.
　4503. c. 8.

MUIRHEAD (J. H.) The Greek Ideal and modern life. *1890.* 8°. LONDON. *South Place Society.* Publications. No. 27.　4109. f.

MURR (J.) Die Gottheit der Griechen als Naturmacht. pp. 80. *Innsbruck, 1892.* 8°. Pam. 41.

—— Die Pflanzenwelt in der griechischen Mythologie. pp. 323. *Innsbruck, 1890.* 8°.
　4503. e. 22.

—— Die Parusie der Gottheit in vegetativer Substanz. pp. 23. *Innsbruck, 1892.* 8°.
　Pam. 41.

NIEBUHR (B. G.) Stories of the Greek heroes. pp. 151. *Lond. 1892.* 8°.　4503. a. 43.

OTTEN (A.) Die Gottesidee, die leitende Idee in der Entwickelung des griechischen Philosophie. pp. 288. *1895.* 8°. Wissenschaftliche Handbibliothek. Reihe 2. No. 3.　3558. e.

PLOIX (C.) La Nature des Dieux. pp. 474. *Paris, 1888.* 8°.　4503. ee. 33.

PURFER (L.) La Résurrection de la Mythologie. pp. 248. *Paris, 1894.* 12°.　4503. aaa. 23.

PUSCH (L.) Katechismus der Religion des Sokrates. pp. 47. *Leipz. 1893.* 8°.　Pam. 41.

REICHENBERGER (S.) Die Entwicklung des metonymischen Gebrauchs von Götternamen in der griechischen Poesie. pp. 118.
Karlsruhe, 1891. 8°.　12923. de. 6.

SCHRAMMEN (J.) Tales of the Gods of ancient Greece. pp. 188. *Ger. Lond. 1894.* 8°.
　4503. a. 12.

SMITH (*Sir* W.) Classical Dictionary of Greek Biography, Mythology, *etc.* pp. 1018.
Lond. 1894. 8°.　2259. b. 16.

STEUER (W.) Die Gottes- und Logoslehre des Tatian. pp. 113. *Leipz. 1893.* 8°. 3623. b. 17.

TUEMPEL (C.) Bemerkungen zu einigen Fragen der griechischen Religionsgeschichte. pp. 23. *Neustettin, 1887.* 4°.　Pam. 41.

WESTCOTT (B. F.) *Bp. of Durham.* Essays in the history of Religious Thought in the West. pp. 397. *Lond. 1891.* 8°.　8486. aaa. 1.

BEER (R.) Heilige Höhen der alten Griechen. pp. 86. *Wien, 1891.* 8°.　4503. cc. 17.

HOLLAND (R.) Heroenvögel in der griechischen Mythologie. pp. 37. *Leipz. 1895.* 4°. Pam. 41.

STUETZLE ( ) Das griechische Orakelwesen. 2 Abth. *Ellwangen, 1887, 91.* 4°. 4506. dd. 1.

FOUCART (P.) Recherches sur les mystères d'Éleusis. pp. 84. *Paris, 1895.* 4°. 4503. h. 3.

RUBENSOHN (O.) Die Mysterienheiligtümer in Eleusis und Samothrake. pp. 240. *Berl. 1892.* 8°.　4503. ee. 20.

TAYLOR (T.) The Eleusinian and Bacchic Mysteries. pp. 258. *N.Y. 1891.* 8°. 4503. g. 2.

GREECE.—Religion, etc.—continued.

WALTON (A.) The Cult of Asklepios. pp. 136. 1894. 8°. Cornell Studies in Classical Philology. No. 3. Ac. 2692. g./3.

BAND (O.) Das attische Demeter-Kore-Fest der Epikleidia. Berl. 1887, etc. 4°. 4503. g.

HOFFMANN (O. A.) Hermes und Kerykeion. pp. 52. Marburg, 1890. 8°. Pam. 41.

DRESSLER (F. R.) Triton und die Tritonen in der Litteratur und Kunst der Griechen. Wurzen, 1892, etc. 4°. 4503. g.

ESCHER (J,) Triton und seine Bekämpfung durch Herakles. pp. 139. Leipz. 1890. 8°. 4504. g. 24.

ALLÈGRE (F.) Étude sur la Déesse grecque Tyche. pp. 243. 1889. 8°. Ac. Lyons. Faculté des Lettres. Bibliothèque. Tom. 14. Ac. 8922/2.

See also PHILOSOPHY, History: RELIGION.

Topography and Modern Social Life.

BENT (J. T.) Modern Life and thought amongst the Greeks. 1891. 8°. MAGNÚSSON (E.) National Life and Thought. 8486. g. 21.

MELINGO (P. v.) Griechenland in unseren Tagen. pp. 223. Wien, 1892. 8°. 10125. cc. 31.

RODD (J. R.) Customs and lore of Modern Greece. pp. 294. Lond. 1892. 8°. 12431. ee. 6.

SMITH (R. A. H. B.) Greece under King George. pp. 350. Lond. 1893. 8°. 10125. dd. 2.

SMITH (Sir W.) Classical Dict. of Geography, etc. Lond. 1894. 8°. 2259. b. 16.

HAUSSOULLIER (B.) Grèce. Guide Joanne. 2 vol. Paris, 1890-91. 8°. 10125. aa. 17.

BAEDEKER (C.) Greece. pp. 376. Leipsic, 1894. 8°. 2352. a.

ARMSTRONG (I. J.) Two roving Englishwomen in Greece. pp. 300. Lond. 1893. 8°. 10125. aaa. 21.

BOROTRA (H.) Lettres orientales. Paris, 1893, etc. 8°. 10126. df.

CABROL (É.) Voyage en Grèce, 1889. pp. 156. Paris, 1890. 4°. 10125. h. 2.

FREEMAN (E. A.) Studies of Travel. 2 vol. N.Y. 1893. 12°. 10026. aa.

HARDWICKE (H. J.) From Alps to Orient. pp. 246. Sheffield, 1891. 8°. 10106. aa. 4.

HARTUNG (B.) Sommertage in Egypten und Griechenland. pp. 150. Leipz. 1895. 8°. 10078. bb. 1.

LÜTKEN (A.) Fra Adria til Bosporus. Kjøbenh. 1892, etc. 8°. 10126. f. 19.

PHILIPPSON (A.) Bericht über eine Reise durch Griechenland. 1890. 8°. Ac. Berlin. Gesellschaft für Erdkunde. Zeitschrift. Bd. 25. Ac. 6075/2.

—— Reisen in Nord-Griechenland. 1895. 8°. Ac. Berlin. Gesellschaft für Erdkunde. Zeitschrift. Bd. 30. Ac. 6075/2.

PSICHARES (I.) Autour de la Grèce. pp. 352. Paris, 1895. 12°. 10125. aa. 24.

Trade, Finance, etc.

TRIKOUPES (C.) The Finances of Greece. Speech, 1886. pp. 56. Lond. 1886. 8°. 8248. e. 12. (8.)

—— The Finances of Greece. Speech, 1888. pp. 63. Lond. 1887. 8°. 08229. f. 1. (8.)

GUIRAUD (P.) La propriété foncière en Grèce. pp. 654. Paris, 1893. 8°. 5206. ee. 24.

COUITÉAS (B.) La Grèce après la faillite. pp. 316. Paris, 1895. 12°. 9026. aa. 32.

GEORGIADES (D.) La Grèce économique et financière en 1893. pp. 144. Paris, 1893. 8°. 8227. i. 38.

GREECE.—Trade, etc.—continued.

NIKOLAIDES (N. S.) AND Co. Guide des chemins de fer et navigation en Grèce. Athens, 1891, etc 16°. 8235. aa.

GREEK CHURCH. ACHELIS (H.) Die ältesten Quellen des orientalischen Kirchenrechtes. 1891. 8°. GEBHARDT (O. v.) Texte für Geschichte der altchristlichen Literatur. Bd. 6. 3623. b.

BERNARDAKES (D. N.) The mother of all Churches. pp. 48. Lond. 1891, 8°. Pam. 11.

BOIS (H.) Le Dogme grec. pp. 299. Paris, 1893. 12°. 3900. b. 54.

EROERTERUNGEN. Erörterungen zur Einführung in das Verständniss der orthodox-katholischen Auffassung in ihrem Verhältniss zur römischen und protestantischen. pp. 40. Berl. 1893. 8°. 3926. cc. 18. (3.)

LITURGIES. Greek Church. Euchologium. Euchology: a manual of prayers. pp. 524. Kidderminster, 1891. 8°. 3395. d. 24.

MEMOR. Khalifat, Patriarcat et Papauté. pp. 231. Paris, 1893. 8°. 4570. aa. 16.

MICHEL (P.) L'Orient et Rome: étude sur l'union. pp. 378. Saint-Amand, 1895. 8°. 3926. aaa. 41.

MISSIONNAIRE. La Question religieuse en Orient et l'Union des Églises. pp. 92. Paris, 1893. 12°. 3926. aa. 24.

MOSCHAKES (I.) Catechism of the Orthodox Eastern Church. pp. 63. Lond. 1894. 8°. 4429. a. 90.

SAREPTA (J. de) L'Église Catholique-Grecque en Galilée. pp. 56. Paris, 1890. 8°. 3926. g. 37. (10.)

SCHWARZLOSE (C.) Der Bilderstreit, ein Kampf der griechischen Kirche um ihre Eigenart. pp. 266. Gotha, 1890. 8°. 4535. c. 4.

SILVESTER, Archb. of Czernowitz. Apologie der orthodoxen Kirche der Bukowina. pp. 60. Czernowitz, 1889. 4°. Pam. 93.

SOKOLOV (D.) Darstellung des Gottesdienstes der orthodox-katholischen Kirche des Morgenlandes. pp. 171. Berl. 1893. 8°. 3475. de. 18.

See also ATHOS, Mount: CHURCH HISTORY: RUSSIA, Church of.

GREEK LANGUAGE, Ancient.

General: History and Study of.

Ac. Ithaca, N.Y. Cornell University. Studies in classical Philology. Ithaca, 1887, etc. 8°. Ac. 2692. g./3.

ASCHERSON (C. E. F.) Berliner Studien für classische Philologie. Berl. 1884, etc. 8°. P.P. 4991. e.

BOLTZ (A.) Hellenisch, die internationale Gelehrtensprache der Zukunft. pp. 328. Leipz. 1890. 8°. 12923. eee. 21.

ITALIAN STUDIES. Studi italiani di Filologia Classica. Firenze, 1893, etc. 8°. 11312. p.

MULLER (H. C.) and FLAMENT (A. J.) Hellenische Bibliothek. Leiden, 1891, etc. 8°. 12923. de.

—— Alt- und neugriechisch Studien. Leiden, 1895, etc. 8°. 12924 g.

P.P. Berlin. Wochenschrift für klassische Philologie. Berl. 1884, etc. 8°. P.P. 4991. ea.

—— Turin. Bollettino di filologia classica. Torino, 1894, etc. 8°. 95.

PRAGUE STUDIES. Prager Studien aus dem Gebiete der classischen Alterthumswissenschaft. Prag, 1894, etc. 8°. 12933. h.

SCERBO (F.) Caratteristiche del greco. pp. 139. Firenze, 1893. 8°. 12924. ff. 46.

2 E 2

GREEK LANGUAGE—*continued.*

SEYMOUR (T. D.) Introduction to the language and verse of Homer. pp. 104. 1889. 8°.

WHITE (J. W.) and SEYMOUR (T. D.) College Series, *etc.* 11305. ee.

VALMAGGI (L.) Manuale di filologia classica. pp. 336. *Torino*, 1894. 8°. 12933. i. 12.

STOKES (G. T.) Greek in Gaul and western Europe down to A.D. 700. *Dublin*, 1892. 8°. 12901. d. 36. (14.)

HESSELING (D. C.) Over het Grieksch der Middeleeuwen. pp. 23. *Leiden*, 1893. 8°. 12903. dd. 37. (11.)

OMONT (H.) Essai sur les débuts de la Typographie grecque à Paris, 1507–16. pp. 72. 1891. 8°. Ac. *Paris. Société de l'Histoire.* Mémoires. Tom. 18. Ac. 6883/2.

BAHNSCH (F.) Die Zukunft des griechischen Sprachunterrichts auf den Gymnasien. pp. 23. *Konitz*, 1891. 8°. 8304. bb. 7. (4.)

CLARK (E. C.) Greek and other studies at Cambridge. pp. 15. *Camb.* 1891. 8°. 8304. aa. 16. (11.)

LYTTELTON (*Hon.* E.) Compulsory Greek. 1891. 8°. Thirteen Essays on Education, *etc.* 8311. e. 2.

MAYOR (J. E. B.) Mutato nomine. [An argument for the retention of Greek at Cambridge.] pp. 4. *Camb.* 1891. 8°. 8304. e. 20. (14.)

STEPHEN (J. K.) The living Languages. Defence of the Study of Greek at Cambridge. pp. 52. *Camb.* 1891. 8°. 8304. e. 16. (15.)

VOGELREUTER (O.) Geschichte des griechischen Unterrichts in deutschen Schulen. pp. 67. *Hannover*, 1891. 8°. 8304. bb. 10. (5.)

WALTERS (J. R.) The Place of Greek in culture. pp. 8. *Lond.* 1891. 8°. 8304. a. 8. (11.)

See also EDUCATION, *Classical.*

Biblical Greek.

ROBERTS (A.) Short proof that Greek was the language of Christ. pp. 116. *Paisley*, 1893. 8°. 4808. bbb. 29.

BURTON (E. de W.) Syntax of moods and tenses in New Testament Greek. pp. 215. *Lond.* 1893. 8°. 12923. de. 18.

GREEN (S. G.) Brief introduction to New Testament Greek. pp. 128. 1894. 8°. Present Day Primers. 4429. eee.

—— Handbook to the grammar of the Greek Testament. pp. 564. *Lond.* 1892. 8°. 4429. f. 1.

HUDDILSTON (J. H.) Essentials of New Testament Greek. pp. 233. *N.Y.* 1895. 8°. 12924. cc. 33.

KENNEDY (H. A. A.) Sources of New Testament Greek. pp. 172. *Edinb.* 1895. 8°. 3155. f. 41.

MOULTON (J. H.) Introduction to the study of New Testament Greek. pp. 252. 1895. 8°.

GREGORY (A. E.) Books for Bible Students. 3125. dd.

VITEAU (J.) Étude sur le grec du Nouveau Testament. pp. 240. *Paris*, 1893. 8°. 3205. e. 29.

WINER (G. B.) Grammatik des neutestamentlichen Sprachidioms. *Göttingen*, 1894, *etc.* 8°. 12923. d.

Composition. *See infra: Translation,*

Dialects.

AUDOUIN (E.) Étude des Dialectes grecs littéraires. pp. 11. 304. *Paris*, 1891. 8°. 12924. cc. 26.

HOFFMANN (H.) Die griechischen Dialekte. *Göttingen*, 1891, *etc.* 8°. 12923. de.

ZURETTI (C. O.) Sui Dialetti letterari greci. pp. 33. *Torino*, 1892. 8°. 11312. p. 2. (9.)

GREEK LANGUAGE.—Dialects—*cont.*

SMYTH (H. W.) Sounds and inflections of the Greek Dialects. Ionic. pp. 668. *Oxf.* 1894. 8°. 12923. de. 22.

PRELLWITZ (W.) De Dialecto Thessalica. pp. 63. *Gottingæ*, 1895. 8°. 12901. g. 30. (4.)

Dictionaries: Etymology.

BRANDT (A. v.) Lexigraphie grecque. pp. 105. *Brux.* 1895. 8°. 12923. d. 33.

GIANNARES (A. N.) Ἐπίτομον Ἑλληνικον Λεξικον. 2 tom. Ἐν Ἀθηναις, 1891. 8°. 12923. cc. 8.

SOPHOCLES (E. A.) Greek Lexicon of the Roman and Byzantine Periods. pp. 1188. *N.Y.* 1893. 8°. 2113. c.

C., W. Index of noteworthy words and phrases found in the Clementine Writings. pp. 105. *Lond.* 1893. 8°. 3623. aa. 38.

DU FRESNE (C.) *Seigneur de Cange.* Glossarium ad scriptores mediae et infimae Graecitatis. *Vratislaviae*, 1890, *etc.* fol. 12924. k.

MAUNOURY (A. F.) Dictionnaire de Racines grecques et de leurs principaux dérivés. *Paris*, 188-. 8°. 12923. b. 49.

WAGENINGEN (J. v.) Vocabularium bij de opstellen ter oefening in de grieksche Vormleer. te *Groningen*, 1892, *etc.* 8°. 12923. de.

MEHLER (E.) Woordenboek op de gedichten van Homerus. pp. 528. *Sneek*, 1892. 8°. 11335. d. 2.

COHEN DE BOER (Z.) Woordenboek op Xenophon's Anabasis. pp. 203. *Tiel*, 1893. 8°. 12923. de. 21.

WHITE (J. W.) and MORGAN (M. H.) Dictionary to Xenophon's Anabasis. pp. 290. *Bost.* 1892. 8°. 12923. de. 9.

BAILLY (A.) Dictionnaire grec-français. pp. 2227. *Paris*, 1895. 8°. 12923. d. 31.

KONTOPOULOS (N.) Λεξικον Ἑλληνογαλλικον, *etc.* pp. 1107. ἐν Ἀθηναις, 1889. 8°. 12924. cc. 20.

GIANNARES (A. N.) Wörterbuch der deutschen und griechischen Sprache. pp. 1146. *Athen*, 1888. 8°. 12924. cc. 21.

PRELLWITZ (W.) Etymologisches Wörterbuch der griechischen Sprache. pp. 382. *Göttingen*, 1892. 8°. 12923. dd. 32.

FUERST (J.) Glossarium Graeco-Hebraeum. *Strassb.* 1890, *etc.* 8°. 012904. h. 2.

LEWY (H.) Die semitischen Fremdwörter im Griechischen. pp. 266. *Berl.* 1895. 8°. 12924. f. 41.

BRENOUS (J.) Étude sur les Hellénismes dans la syntaxe latine. pp. 445. *Paris*, 1895. 8°. 12934. f. 23.

Examination Papers.

BELTON (R. C.) Digest of Greek Grammar examination questions. pp. 120. *Lond.* 1891. 8°. 12924. f. 19.

HEBBLETHWAITE (P.) Key to Greek examination papers. pp. 204. 1891. 8°. STEDMAN (A. M. M.) School Examination Series. 12205. f.

HAYES (B. J.) and MASOM (W. F.) Greek. London University matriculation papers. 1888–91. 2 pt. 1891. 8°. Tutorial Series. 12205. c. 25.

—— Matriculation and intermediate Greek. pp. 103. 1891. 8°. Tutorial Series. 12205. c. 221.

Exercises. *See infra: Translation.*

Grammars, etc.

ABBOTT (E.) and MANSFIELD (E. D.) Primer of Greek Grammar. *Lond.* 1895, *etc.* 8°. 12924. cc. 32.

BLACKIE (J. S.) Greek Primer, colloquial and constructive. pp. 64. *Lond.* 1891. 8°. 12923. e. 20.

GREEK.— Grammars, etc.—*continued.*

CHASSANG (A.) Grammaire grecque. pp. 372. *Paris*, 1890. 8°.   12923. e. 19.

CROISET (A.) and PETITJEAN (J.) Grammaire grecque. pp. 613. *Paris*, 1892. 8°.   12923. cc. 15.

EDGREN (H.) Jämförande grammatik, omfattande Sanskrit, Grekiska, Latin och Gotiska. *Göteborg*, 1893, *etc.* 8°.   12901. cc.

GEDDES (*Sir* W. D.) Compendious Greek Grammar. *Edinb.* 1893, *etc.* 8°.   12923. cc. 16.

GOODWIN (W. W.) Greek Grammar. pp. 451. *Lond.* 1894. 8°.   12923. cc. 19.

HARDER (F.) Griechische Schulgrammatik. 2 Tle. *Dresd.* 1892. 8°.   12923. c. 33.

HIME (M. C.) Introduction to the Greek Language. pp. 330. *Lond.* 1891. 8°. 12924. e. 27.

KAEGI (A.) Kaegi's Grieksche Grammatica. pp. 284. *Groningen*, 1893. 8°.   12924. h. 20.

KUEHNER (R.) Ausführliche Grammatik der griechischen Sprache. *Hannover*, 1890, *etc.* 8°.   12923. de.

LA ROCHE (J.) Beiträge zur griechischen Grammatik. *Leipz.* 1893, *etc.* 8°.   12923. de.

MONRO (D. B.) Grammar of the Homeric Dialect. pp. 436. 1891. 8°. Clarendon Press Series.   2320. h. 12.

MULLER (H. C.) Historische Grammatik der hellenischen Sprache. 1891, *etc.* 8°.

MULLER (H. C.) and FLAMENT (A. J.) Hellenische Bibliothek.   12923. de.

RITCHIE (F.) First steps in Greek. pp. 106. *Lond.* 1891. 8°.   12923. cc. 6.

SCHREIBER (W.) Praktische Grammatik der altgriechischen Sprache. pp. 186. 1890. 8°. Die Kunst der Polyglottie. Th. 25. 12902. c.

SONNENSCHEIN (E. A.) Greek Grammar for schools. 1892, *etc.* 8°. Parallel Grammar Series.   12902. aa.

STEWART (T. A.) New first Greek course. pp. 176. *Edinb.* 1891. 8°.   12924. cc. 27.

VOLLBRECHT (W.) Griechische Schulgrammatik. pp. 267. *Leipz.* 1892. 8°.   12923. c. 32.

KALLENBERG (H.) Studien über den griechischen Artikel. pp. 26. *Berl.* 1891. 4°.   12902. h. 19. (2.)

PARMENTIER (L.) Les Substantifs et les adjectifs en -ες- dans la langue d'Homère et d'Hésiode. pp. 192. *Gand*, 1889. 8°.   12924. g. 21.

KOHN (M.) De usu Adjectivorum et participiorum pro substantivis, apud Thucydidem. pp. 33. *Berolini*, 1891. 8°. 12901. d. 35. (7.)

BARON (C.) Le Pronom relatif et la conjonction en grec. pp. 188. *Paris*, 1891. 8°. 12923. de. 2.

FLENSBURG (N.) Über Ursprung des Pronomens Αὐτος pp. 69. *Lund*, 1893. 8°. 12903. e. 29. (3.)

GREEK VERBS. Greek verbs conjugated at a glance. *Manch.* 1891. obl. 4°.   12923. a. 50.

HAMILTON (G.) Classic Moods. pp. 93. *Edinb.* 1894. 4°.   12902. dd. 42.

HOLMES (D. H.) Die mit Präpositionen zusammengesetzten Verben bei Thukydides. pp. 47. *Berl.* 1895. 8°.   Pam. 47.

MUTZBAUER (C.) Die Grundlagen der griechischen Tempuslehre. pp. 402. *Strassb.* 1893. 8°.   11315. dd. 31.

NALL (G. H.) and GRENFELL (A. G.) Card of regular and irregular Greek Verbs. pp. 36. *Lond.* 1895. 8°.   12923. c. 35.

REINHARDT (R.) De Infinitivi cum articulo conjuncti usu Thucydideo. pp. 22. *Oldenburg*, 1891. 4°.   12902. h. 17. (4.)

GREEK.—Grammars, etc.—*continued.*

BÉNARD (L.) Essai sur la signification des formes verbales en Grec d'après le texte d'Hérodote. pp. 285. *Paris*, 1890. 8°.   12923. ccc. 22.

SUETTERLIN (L.) Zur Geschichte der Verba denominativa im Altgriechischen. *Strassb.* 1891, *etc.* 8°.   12923. de.

WEYMOUTH (R. F.) On the rendering into English of the Greek Aorist and Perfect. pp. 55. *Lond.* 1894. 8°.   12902. ccc. 35. (4.)

COURTOY (A.) Les Préfixes en grec. pp. 123. *Brux.* 1894. 8°.   12901. b. 49.

LUTZ (L.) Die Casus-Adverbien bei den attischen Rednern. pp. 40. *Würzb.* 1891. 8°.   Pam. 47.

PITMAN (H.) Greek Conjunctions. pp. 54. *Lond.* 1895. 8°.   12924. aaa. 57.

JOOST (A.) Was ergiebt sich aus dem Sprachgebrauch Xenophons für die Behandlung der griechischen Syntax in der Schule? pp. 340. *Berl.* 1892. 8°.   12923. de. 10.

MIDDLETON (G.) Essay on analogy in Syntax. pp. 95. *Lond.* 1892. 8°.   12901. f. 41.

MILES (E. H.) Comparative Syntax of Greek and Latin. *Camb.* 1893. 8°.   12932. dd. 15.

ROWE (T. B.) Greek Syntax and note-book. pp. 190. *Lond.* 1891. 8°.   12924. d. 21.

SCHANZ (M.) Beiträge zur historischen Syntax der griechischen Sprache. *Wurzb.* 1882, *etc.* 8°.   12902. i.

THOMPSON (F. E) Elementary Greek Syntax. pp. 81. *Lond.* 1892. 8°.   12924. bb. 41.

FARNELL (G. S.) Rules and exercises on Greek Sentences. pp. 63. *Lond.* 1892. 8°.   12923. bbb. 28 .

SIDGWICK (A.) Greek Sentence construction. pp. 16. *Lond.* 1890. 8°.   12924. cc. 19.

SMITH (R. H.) Theory of conditional sentences in Greek. pp. 694. *Lond.* 1894. 8°.   12923. dc. 23

See also supra : Biblical Greek.

Pronunciation : Phonetics.

ARNOLD (E V.) and CONWAY (R. S.) Restored pronunciation of Greek. pp. 19. *Camb.* 1895. 8°.   Pam. 47.

DAWES (E. A. S.) Pronunciation of the Greek aspirates. pp. 103. *Lond.* 1894. 8°.   12923. bb. 44.

SMYTH (H. W.) Sounds and inflections of the Greek Dialects. Ionic. pp. 668. *Oxf.* 1894. 8°.   12923. dc. 22.

TÉLFY (I.) Chronologie und Topographie der griechischen Aussprache. pp. 86. *Leipz.* 1893. 8°.   12923. bb. 43.

Prosody. *See* POETRY.

Translation : Exercises.

BENDALL (H.) and LAURENCE (C. E.) Graduated passages from Greek authors for first-sight translation. *Camb.* 1891, *etc.* 8°.   12935. f.

COBET (C. B.) Grieksch Leesboek. pp. 117. *Haarlem*, 1888. 8°.   12923. dc. 3.

GREENSTOCK (W.) Primer of Greek exercises. pp. 267. *Lond.* 1895. 8°.   12923. cc. 21.

—— Key. pp. 175. *Lond.* 1895. 8°.   12923. cc. 22.

KAEGI (A.) Griechisches Übungsbuch. *Berl.* 1894, *etc.* 8°.   12923. d.

MORICE (F. D.) Stories in Attic Greek. pp. 192. *Lond.* 1894. 8°.   12924. cc. 31.

NALL (G. H.) Exercises on the first Greek syntax of W. G. Rutherford. pp. 214. 1892. 8°.

RUTHERFORD (W. G.) Macmillan's Greek Course.   12924. cc.

GREEK.—Translation, etc.—continued.

SORMANI (P. V.) and VERSMEETEN (P.) Grieksche Oefeningen. *Groningen*, 1893, *etc.* 8°.
12924. h.

STEDMAN (A. M. M.) Easy Greek Passages for unseen translation. pp. 56. *Lond.* 1892. 8°.
12923. cc. 10.

WELLS (E. A.) Crustula. pp. 137. *Lond.* 1890. 8°.
12923. cc. 5.

YOUNG (A. W.) Tutorial Greek reader. pp. 125. 1894. 8°. Tutorial Series.
12205. c. 229.

See also supra: Grammars.

Modern Greek.

AC, *etc.* Athens. Συλλογος "Κοραη." 'Αθηνησιν, 1892, *etc.* 8°.
Ac. 9760.

GIANNARES (A. N.) Concise Dictionary of English and modern Greek Languages. pp. 436. *Lond.* 1895. 8°.
12923. bbb. 46.

—— Deutsch-neugriechisches Handwörterbuch. 2 Abth. *Hannover*, 1883. 8°.
12923. bbb. 20.

CHATZIDAKES (G. N.) Einleitung in die neugriechische Grammatik. pp. 464. 1892. 8°. Bibliothek indogermanischer Grammatiken. Bd. 5.
2272. f. 10.

GIANNARES (A. N.) 'Ηχω 'Αθηνων ητοι 'Εγχειριδιον της λαλουμενης 'Ελληνικης γλωσσης. pp. 178. *Leipz.* 1893. 8°.
12923. cc. 18.

KONSTANTINIDES (M.) Neohellenica. Introduction to modern Greek. pp. 470. *Lond.* 1892. 8°.
12923. cc. 11.

MEYER (G.) Neugriechische Studien. 2 pt. 1894. 8°. Ac. Vienna. *K. Akademie der Wissenschaften.* Sitzungsberichte. Phil.-hist. Classe. Bd. 130.
Ac. 810/6.

MITSOTAKIS (J. K.) Praktische Grammatik der neugriechischen Schrift- und Umgangssprache. pp. 260. 1891. 8°. SACHAU (C. E.) Lehrbucher. Bd. 5.
12906. h.

—— Neugriechischer Sprachführer. pp. 385. *Leipz.* 1892. 16°.
12924. a. 53.

MULLER (H. C.) and FLAMENT (A. J.) Hellenische Bibliothek, *etc. Leiden*, 1891, *etc.* 8°. 12923. de.

—— Alt- und Neugriechisch. Studien. *Leiden*, 1895, *etc.* 8°.
12924. g.

PAVOLINI (P. E.) Über Dvandva-Composita im Neugriechischen. pp. 5. *Berl.* 1891. 8°.
12903. dd. 33. (5.)

PETRARIS (K.) Neugriechische Konversations-Grammatik. pp. 476. *Heidelberg*, 1895. 8°.
12923. bb. 45.

PSYCHARES (I.) Essais de grammaire historique néo-grecque. 2 pt. *Paris*, 1886–89. 8°.
12924. h. 14.

SPYRIDIS (G.) Langue grecque actuelle ou moderne. pp. 504. *Paris*, 1895. 8°.
12923. d. 32.

THUMB (A.) Die neugriechische Sprache. pp. 36. *Freiburg*, 1892. 8°. 12901. d. 36. (15.)

GREEK LITERATURE.

Bibliography.

FOCK (G.) Catalogus Dissertationum philologicarum classicarum. 3 pt. *Leipz.* 1893. 8°.
011900. ee. 31.

LEGRAND (É.) Bibliographie Hellénique, description des ouvrages publiés par des Grecs au dix-septième siècle. *Paris*, 1894, *etc.* 8°.
011900. k.

VALMAGGI (L.) Manuale di Filologia classica. pp. 336. *Torino*, 1894. 8°.
12933. i. 12.

History and Criticism.

AC. Ithaca, N.Y. *Cornell University.* Studies in classical Philology. *Ithaca*, 1887, *etc.* 8°.
Ac. 2692. g. 3.

GREEK LITERATURE—continued.

ASCHERSON (C. E. F.) Berliner Studien, *etc. Berl.* 1884, *etc.* 8°.
P.P. 4991. e.

BERNHARDY (G.) Grundriss der griechischen Litteratur. *Halle*, 1892. *etc.* 8°.
11312. s.

BLAYDES (F. H. M.) Adversaria in comicorum graecorum fragmenta. *Halis S.*, 1890, *etc.* 8°.
11312. dd. 23.

BUTCHER (S. H.) Some Aspects of the Greek genius. pp. 321. *Lond.* 1893. 8°.
012357. h. 53.

CHRIST (W. v.) Geschichte der griechischen Litteratur bis auf die Zeit Justinians. 1890. 8°. MUELLER (I. E. P. v.) Handbuch der klassischen Altertums-Wissenschaft. Vol. 7. 2259. g.

CINQUINI (A.) Note di letteratura greco-latina. pp. 60. *Milano*, 1893. 8°.
Pam. 14.

EGGER (A. É.) La Littérature grecque. pp. 419. *Paris*, 1890. 8°.
11315. h. 31.

—— Essai sur l'histoire de la critique chez les Grecs. pp. 587. *Paris*, 1887. 8°.
11312. bbbb. 22.

EGGER (M.) Histoire de la littérature grecque. pp. 396. *Paris*, 1892. 12°. 11312. aaa. 34.

GEIST (H.) Was bieten die antiken Schriftsteller der modernen Jugend? *Posen*, 1894, *etc.* 8°.
011850. g.

HERWERDEN (H. v.) Studia critica in epigrammata graeca. pp. 157. *Leiden*, 1891. 8°.
11312. m. 36.

ITALIAN STUDIES. Studi italiani di Filologia classica. *Firenze*, 1893, *etc.* 8°. 11312. p.

JEBB (R. C.) Growth and influence of classical Greek Poetry. pp. 290. *Lond.* 1893. 8°.
11312. e. 30.

—— Influence of the Greek Mind on modern life. 1894. 8°. LONDON. *Society for the Extension of University Teaching.* Aspects of Modern Study.
8367. aa. 19.

JEVONS (F. B.) History of Greek Literature. pp. 525. *Lond.* 1894. 8°.
2051. a.

MAHAFFY (J. P.) History of classical Greek. *Lond.* 1895, *etc.* 8°.
2280. a. 1.

MULLER (H. C.) and FLAMENT (A. J.) Hellenische Bibliothek. *Leiden*, 1891, *etc.* 8°.
12923. de.

PANDIANI (G. B. L.) Carattere della Lirica greca e della Tragedia di Eschilo. pp. 114. *Milano*, 1891. 8°.
11312. dd. 31.

P.P. *Berlin.* Wochenschrift für klassische Philologie. *Berl.* 1884, *etc.* 8°.
P.P. 4991. ea.

—— *Turin.* Bolletino di Filologia classica. *Torino*, 1894, *etc.* 8°.
95.

PERRY (T. S.) History of Greek Literature. pp. 877. *N.Y.* 1890. 8°.
11312. m. 35.

PRAGUE STUDIES. Prager Studien, *etc. Prag*, 1894, *etc..* 8°.
12933. h.

SALVERTE (F. de) Le Roman dans la Grèce ancienne. pp. 403. *Paris*, 1894. 12°. 11312. n. 2.

SCHVELL (R.) Die Anfänge einer politischen Literatur bei den Griechen. pp. 37. *München*, 1890. 4°.
Pam. 14.

SECHER (J. M.) Hovedpunkter af den græske Literaturhistorie. pp. 105. *Kjøbenh.* 1890. 8°.
11312. d. 50.

SEYFFERT (A. O.) Dictionary of classical Antiquities, Literature, *etc.* pp. 706. *Lond.* 1891. 4°.
7706. ee. 31.

SOLDINI (E.) Breve storia della Satira in Grecia. pp. 140. *Cremona*, 1891. 8°.
11312. d. 55.

SYMONDS (J. A.) Studies of the Greek Poets. 2 vol. *Lond.* 1893. 8°.
2282. c. 2.

VALMAGGI (L.) Manuale di Filologia classica. pp. 336. *Torino*, 1894. 8°.
12933. i. 12.

GREEK LITERATURE—*continued.*

Susemihl (F. F. C. E.) Geschichte der griechischen Litteratur in der Alexandrinerzeit. *Leipz.* 1891, *etc.* 8°. 　　　　11312. p.

Reitzenstein (R.) Epigramm und Skolion. pp. 288. *Giessen,* 1893. 8°. 　　11312. e. 32.

Krumbacher (C.) Geschichte der byzantinischen Litteratur. pp. 494. 1891. 8°. Mueller's Handbuch. Bd. 9. 　　　　　　2259. g. 6.

─────

Homer. Index Homericus. pp. 874. *Lipsiæ,* 1891. 8°. 　　　　11335 i. 24.

Acqua Giusti (A. dall') Sopra i Poemi omerici. pp. 109. *Venezia,* 1890. 8°. 　11315. h. 33.

Bergstedt (H.) Striden om Homer. pp. 163. *Norrköping,* 1893. 8°. 　　11315. g. 43.

Butler (S.) Lecture on the humour of Homer. pp. 43. *Camb.* 1892. 8°. 　11315. d. 30. (5.)

—— On the Trapanese origin of the Odyssey. pp. 24. 13. *Camb.* 1893. 8°. 11315. d. 30. (7.)

Cauer (P.) Grundfragen der Homerkritik. pp. 321. *Leipz.* 1895. 8°. 　11315. h. 34.

Clerke (A. M.) Familiar studies in Homer. pp. 302. *Lond.* 1892. 8°. 　11315. dd. 27.

Engelmann (R.) Pictorial Atlas to Homer's Iliad and Odyssey. pp. 35. *Lond.* 1892. *obl. fol.* 　　　　　　　　　　1702. a. 7.

Erhardt (L.) Die Entstehung der homerischen Gedichte. pp. 546. *Leipz.* 1894. 8°. 　　　　　　　　　11335. d. 3.

Gladstone (*Right Hon.* W. E.) Landmarks of Homeric study. pp. 160. *Lond.* 1890. 8°. 　　　　　　　　　2282. b. 1.

Knoetel (A. F. R.) Homeros und seine Werke. *Leipz.* 1894, *etc.* 8°. 　　11315. df. 21.

Lang (A.) Homer and the Epic. pp. 424. *Lond.* 1893. 8°. 　　　　11335. i. 26.

Leaf (W.) Companion to the Iliad for English readers. pp. 411. *Lond.* 1892. 8°. 2280. b. 1.

Nilsson (J. O.) Den homeriska hjeltesagans. pp. 116. *Göteborg,* 1889. 8°. 　11315. c. 43.

Dieterich (A.) De Hymnis Orphicis capitula quinque. pp. 56. *Marpurgi C.* 1891. 8°. 　　　　　　　　　　Pam. 14.

See also Drama : Greece, *Antiquities :* Philosophy, *History of :* Poetry.

GREENFORD PARVA. Brown (J. A.) Chronicles of Greenford Parva. pp. 154. *Lond.* 1891. 8°. 　　　010358. f. 23.

GREENHOUSES. *See* Gardening, *Horticultural Buildings.*

GREENLAND. Lauridsen (P.) Bibliographia groenlandica. pp. 247. 1890. 8°. Denmark. *Commission for Ledelsen af de geologiske Undersøgelser i Grønland.* Meddelelser. Hft. 13. 　　　10460. dd.

Drygalski (E. v.) Grönlands Gletscher und Inlandeis. pp. 62. 1892. 8°. Ac. Berlin. *Gesellschaft für Erdkunde.* Zeitschrift. Bd. 27. No. 1. 　　　　　　　　　　Ac. 6075/2.

Holm (G. F.) Den danske Konebaads-Expedition til Grønlands Østkyst. pp. 379. *Kjøbenh.* 1887. 8°. 　　10460. e. 27.

Nansen (F.) Paa ski over Grønland. pp. 704. *Kristiania,* 1890. 8°. 　10460. ff. 27.

—— The first crossing of Greenland. pp. 452. *Lond.* 1892. 8°. 　　10460. bbb. 25.

Peary (J. D.) My Arctic journal. A year among ice-fields and Eskimos. pp. 240. *Lond.* 1893. 8°. 　　10460. e. 32.

Ryder (C. H.) Forslag og Plan til en Undersøgelse af Grønlands Østkyst. pp. 24. *Kjøbenh.* 1890. 8°. 　　　Pam. 86.

GREENLAND—*continued.*

Warming (J. E. B.) Om Grønlands Vegetation. 1888. 8°. Denmark. *Commission for Ledelsen af de geologiske Undersøgeler om Grønland.* Meddelelser om Grønland. Hft. 12. 10460. dd. *See also* Eskimos.

GREEN MOUNTAINS, Massachusetts. *See* Geology, *Local.*

GREENOCK. Greenock. Views and reminiscences. *Greenock,* 1891. 4°. 　10370. i. 3

GREENSTED. Greensted. Parish Registers of Greensted. pp. 89. 1892. *fol.* 9916. f. 39.

GREGORIAN MUSIC. *See* Music, *Ecclesiastical.*

GREIFSWALD, University. Ac. Greifswald. *Alberts-Universität.* Aeltere Universitäts-Matrikeln, Universität Greifswald. 1893, *etc.* 8°. Prussia. *Staatsarchive.* Publicationen. Bd. 25, *etc.* 　　　　　　　　　9386. ee.

GRENADA, Island of. Wells (S.) Sketch of the Island of Grenada. pp. 37. *Kingston,* 1890. 8°. 　　　　Pam. 86. *See also* West Indies.

GRENOBLE. Franclieu (A. M. de) Les martyrs de l'Église de Grenoble, 1794. pp. 262. *Lyon,* 1890. 8°. 　　　　4867. c. 4.

Prudhomme (A.) Inventaire des archives antérieures à 1790. Ville de Grenoble. 1886, *etc.* 4°. Collection des inventaires-sommaires. 1815. b.

Rousset (H.) and Brichet (É.) Histoire des rues de Grenoble. pp. 228. *Grenoble,* 1893. 8°. 　　　　　　　　　10170. e. 1.

—— Le Théâtre à Grenoble. pp. 172. *Grenoble,* 1891. 8°. 　　011795. f. 53.

—— Les Jeux olympiques au Rondeau 1832-92. pp. 159. *Grenoble,* 1894. 8°. 　7907. dd. 22. *See also* Dauphiny.

GRESSONEY. Sella (V.) and Vallino (D.) Monte Rosa e Gressoney. *Biella,* 1890, *etc. obl.* 4°. 　　　1783. a. 20.

GREYSTOCK. Hudleston (L.) Sketch of the history of St. Andrew's Church, Greystock. pp. 17. *Penrith,* 1894. 8°. 　4707. d. 6.

GRIMSBY. Bates (A.) Gossip about old Grimsby. pp. 133. *Grimsby,* 1893. 8°. 　　　　　　　　010358. f. 38.

Saint James, *Parish of, Great Grimsby.* Register Book. pp. 435. *Great Grimsby,* 1889. 8°. 　　　　　　　　9916. ee. 8.

GRINSTEAD, West. *See* West Grinstead.

GRIQUALAND, West. Cape of Good Hope. *Parliament.* Report of the Committee on Griqualand West land tenure. pp. 25. *Cape Town,* 1882. 8°. 　　　　Pam. 66. *See also* Africa, *South :* Cape of Good Hope : Kimberley.

GRISONS, Canton. Planta (P. C. v.) Geschichte von Graubünden. pp. 440. *Bern,* 1892. 8°. 　　　　9304. de. 3.

Tollemache (*Hon.* B. L. C.) Grisons Incidents in olden times. pp. 79. *Lond.* 1891. 8°. 9305. aa. 7.

Planta (P. v.) Chronik der Familie von Planta. pp. 397. *Zürich,* 1892. 8°. 　9902. f. 31.

Salis-Soglio (N. v.) Die Familie von Salis. pp. 368. *Lindau,* 1891. 8°. 　9916. b. 26.

Berchter (J. L. F.) Das berchter'sche Tagebuch. Beitrag zur Geschichte der französischen Invasion in Graubünden, 1799. pp. 24. *Luzern,* 1882. 8°. 　　　　Pam. 28.

Grisons. Code civil du Canton des Grisons. pp. 169. *Paris,* 1893. 8°. 　05551. f. 7. *See also* Davos : Engadine : Romansch Language : Switzerland : Watering-Places.

GRONINGEN. Ephem. Groningsche Volks-almanak voor het jaar 1893. pp. 234.
Groningen, 1892. 8°.   P.P. 4549. bb.
Schepers (J. B.) Groningen als Hanzestad. pp. 107. *Groningen,* 1891. 8°.   010271. f. 10.

GROSSENHAIN. Schuberth (G. W.) Chronik der Stadt Grossenhain. pp. 426.
Grossenhain, 1887–92. 4°.   10250. l. 1.

GROTON, Mass. Boutwell (F. M.) People and their homes in Groton. pp. 18.
Groton, 1890. 8°.   Pam. 86.
Green (S. A.) Account of Physicians and dentists of Groton. pp. 90. *Groton,* 1890. 8°.
010882. h. 19.

GROUSE: TETRAONIDAE. Grant (W. R. O.) Handbook to Game Birds.
1895, *etc.* 8°. Allen's Naturalist's Library.
7001. eee.
Klein (E. E.) Etiology and pathology of Grouse Disease. pp. 130. *Lond.* 1892. 8°. 07293. k. 4.
Macpherson (H. A.) The Grouse. pp. 293. 1894. 8°. Watson (A. E. T.) Fur and Feather Series.   7906. dd.
Millais (J. G.) Game Birds and shooting sketches. pp. 72. *Lond.* 1892. 4°. 7285. k. 10.
Schaeck (F. de) Monographie des Francolins. 1891. 8°. Ac. Paris. *Société Zoologique.* Mémoires. Tom. 4. Pts. 3 & 4.   Ac. 3556/3.
Valentinitsch (F.) Das Haselhuhn, Tetrao bonasia. pp. 288. *Wien,* 1892. 8°. 7285. g. 17.

GROWTH. *See* Children.

GUADELOUPE. Vauchelet (P.) La Guadeloupe : ses enfants célèbres. pp. 130.
Paris, 1894. 12°.   9771. b. 2.
See also France, *Colonies :* West Indies.

GUANABACOA. Vidal y Cireral (F.) Historia de la villa de Guanabacoa. pp. 117.
Habana, 1887. 8°.   10481. dd. 23.

GUARANI LANGUAGE. *See* Indian Languages.

GUARDIANS, of the Poor. *See* Local Government : Pauperism.

GUATEMALA. Guatemala. Commercial Directory of Guatemala, *etc.* 1891. 8°. U.S. *Bureau of American Republics.* Bulletin. No. 28.   08225. k. 1.
Lemale (C.) Guia geográfica de los centros de poblacion de Guatemala. pp. 421.
Guatemala, 1881. 4°.   10480. dd. 32.
Paris. *Exposition,* 1889. Introducción al catálogo de los objetos procedentes de Guatemala. pp. 26. *Guatemala,* 1890. 8°.   Pam. 18.
Sapper (C.) Grundzüge der physikalischen Geographie von Guatemala. pp. 59. 1894. 4°. P.P. *Gotha.* Mittheilungen aus Perthes' Geographischer Anstalt. Ergänzungsheft, Nr. 113.
P.P. 3946.
Stoll (O.) Die Ethnologie der Indianerstämme von Guatemala. pp. 112. 1889. 4°. P.P. *Leyden.* Archiv für Ethnographie. P.P. 3863. h.
See also America, *Central and South.*

GUÉRANDE. Boceret (E. de) Guérande pendant la période révolutionnaire. pp. 32.
Vannes. 1895. 8°.   Pam. 91.

GUIANA. Friederichsen (L.) Ralegh's Karte von Guayana um 1595. pp. 9.
Hamburg, 1892. 8°.   10481. h. 27.
Coudreau (H.) Vocabulaires des langues Ouayana, Aparai Oyampi, Émérillon. pp. 144. Bibliothèque linguistique américaine. Tom. xv.
12907. dd. 17.

GUIANA—*continued.*
British.
Ac. Demerara. *Royal Agricultural Society.* Handbook of British Guiana, by J. Rodway. pp. 93. *Georgetown,* 1893. 4°.   10480. d 27.
Bronkhurst (H. V. P.) Geography of British Guiana. pp. 140. *Demerara,* 1890. 8°.
10470. aa. 40.
Chicago. *World's Exposition.* Catalogue of the exhibits of British Guiana. pp. 44.
Chicago, 1893. 8°.   Pam. 18.
Davis (N. D.) Records of British Guiana.
Demerara, 1888. 8°.   9004. l. 34. (5.)
Farrar (T.) Notes on the history of the Church in Guiana. pp. 226. *Berbice,* 1892. 8°.
4745. bbb. 41.
Guiana. British Guiana and its resources. pp. 104. *Lond.* 1895. 8°.   10480. b. 38.
Pearson (J. G.) New Overseer's manual. pp. 74. *Georgetown,* 1890. 8°.   10480. aaa. 43.
Rodway (J.) History of British Guiana. *Georgetown,* 1891, *etc.* 8°.   10481. ff. 35.
—— and Watt (T.) Chronological History of Guiana. 1493-1668. pp. 240.
Georgetown, 1888. 8°.   9772. b. 16.
—— In the Guiana Forest. pp. 242.
Lond. 1894. 8°.   7002. aaa. 4.

Guiana. Laws of British Guiana. 5 vol.
Oxf. 1895. 8°.   06606. k. 2.
Cox (C. T.) Index to the Laws of British Guiana, 1870-90. pp. 13. *Demerara,* 1890. fol.
6784. g. 16.
Belmonte (B. E. C.) The Administrator General's Department and Ordinances 15, 16, and 17 of 1887. pp. 94. *Demerara,* 1889. 8°.
8154. bbb. 28.
Grose (C. B.) Labour Ordinances. With notes and forms. pp. 250. *Demerara,* 1889. 8°.
06606. g. 9.

Venezuela. *M. de Relaciones Exteriores.* Correspondence between the Venezuelan Government and H.B.M.'s Government, about the frontier, *etc.* 3 pt. *Caracas,* 1887. fol.
8179. i. 20.
—— Latest Correspondence on the limits of Guiana. pp. 66. *Caracas,* 1887. fol. 8179. i. 19.
Seijas (R. F.) Límites británicos de Guayana. pp. 661. *Carácas,* 1888. 4°.   8179. k. 3.
Guzman Blanco (A.) Límites guayaneses Epístola del Presidente. pp. 8.
Paris, 1890. 8°.   Pam. 65.
—— Una palabra más sobre Límites guayeneses. pp. 8. *Paris,* 1890. 8°.   Pam. 65.
—— Límites guayaneses entre Venezuela y la Gran Bretaña. p. 11. *Paris,* 1890. 8°. Pam. 65.
Rojas (J. M.) Las Fronteras de Venezuela. *Paris,* 1891. 8°.   8180. dd. 10.
Dutch.
Fontaine (O.) La Guyane néerlandaise. 1891. 8°. Ac. Brussels. *Société de Géographie.* Bulletin. Année 15. No. 6.   Ac. 6098.
French.
Coudreau (H. A.) Chez nos Indiens. Quatre années dans la Guyane française. pp. 614. *Paris,* 1893. 8°.   10480. g. 18.
—— Dix Ans de Guyane. 1892. 8°. Ac. Paris. *Société de Géographie.* Bulletin. 1891. Ac. 6035.
Domergue (A.) Simples notes de voyages. pp. 210. *Paris,* 1893. 8°.   010096. f. 33.
Mury (P.) Les Jésuites à Cayenne. pp. 283. *Strassb.* 1895. 8°.   4765. ee. 31.

GUIENNE. *See* AQUITAINE.

GUILDS. GLOTIN (H.) Étude sur les syndicats professionnels. pp. 438. *Paris*, 1892. 8°.
    5406. de. 10.

CAUWENBERGHS (C. v.) La Corporation des Quatre Couronnés d'Anvers. pp. 53. *Anvers*, 1889. 8°.
    Pam. 23.

WINS (P. A.) La Connétablie des boulangers de Mons. 1894. 8°. Ac. Mons. *Société des Sciences.* Mémoires. Sér. 5. Tom. 7.   Ac. 1013.

HIBBERT (F. A.) Influence and development of English Gilds, as illustrated by the craft gilds of Shrewsbury. pp. 168. 1891. 8°. Cambridge Historical Essays. No. 5.   9009. c.

LAMBERT (J. M.) Two thousand years of Gild life. pp. 414. *Hull*, 1891. 4°.   8245. gg. 18.

PRING (J. H.) On the Origin of Gilds. pp. 24. *Taunton*, 1883. 8°.   07703. f. 3. (7.)

Ac. Birmingham. *Birmingham Institute.* Register of the Guild of Knowle, Warwick. pp. 272. *Walsall*, 1894. 4°.   4705. f. 20.

COLSTON (J.) Incorporated trades of Edinburgh. pp. 237. *Edinb.* 1891. 4°.   8248. f. 23.

TRÉVÉDY (J.) Les anciennes Corporations brestoises. 1894. 8°. Ac. Quimper. *Société Archéologique.* Bulletin. Tom. 21.   Ac. 5306.

MORAND (L.) Les anciennes Corporations de Chambéry. pp. 338. *Chambéry*, 1892. 8°.
    8248. f. 27.

MOUSSAC (de) *Marquis.* La Corporation des bouchers de Limoges. pp. 116. *Paris*, 1892. 8°.
    8247. ff. 38.

MARTIN (A.) La Communauté des boulangers du Mans. pp. 125. *Mamers*, 1891. 8°.
    08229. g. 43.

CAPPLIEZ ( ) Histoire des métiers de Valenciennes et de leurs saints patrons. pp. 380. *Valenciennes*, 1893. 8°.   8248. h. 5.

MOISET (C.) Les Corporations d'arts et de métiers dans le département de l'Yonne 1891. 8°. Ac. Auxerre. *Société des Sciences.* Bulletin. Vol. 44.
    Ac. 2860.

HEGEL (C.) Städte und Gilden der germanischen Völker im Mittelalter. 2 Bde. *Leipz.* 1891. 8°.
    8248. g. 13.

SCHMIDT (F. G. A.) Handelsgesellschaften in den deutschen Stadtrechtquellen des Mittelalters. pp. 96. 1883. 8°. GIERKE (O.) Untersuchungen zur deutschen Staatsgeschichte. No. 15.
    6025. e. 9.

OSNABURG. Die ältesten osnabrückischen Gildeurkunden bis 1500. pp. 92. *Osnabrück*, 1890. 8°.
    Pam. 23.

GONETTA (G.) Bibliografia delle Corporazioni d'arti e mestieri d'Italia. pp. 99. *Roma*, 1891. 8°.   011900. f. 4.

MONZA. *Società dei Mercanti.* Statuti della Società dei mercanti di Monza. pp. 243. *Monza*, 1891. 4°.   8248. f. 28.

RODOCANACHI (E. P.) Les Corporations à Rome depuis la chute de l'Empire romain. 2 tom. *Paris*, 1894. 4°.   8248. k. 2.
—— Les statuts de la Corporation des Cochers de Rome. pp. 18. *Paris*, 1891. 4°. 8248. f. 24.

BRUNNER (C.) Die Zunft der Schärer unter den schweizerischen Wundärzten des XVI. Jahrhunderts. pp. 24. *Zürich*, 1891. 8°. Pam. 39.

DAVIS (A. M.) Corporations in the days of the Colony. pp. 34. *Camb., Mass.* 1894. 8°.
    Pam. 33.

See also LONDON, *Corporation, etc.*

GUINEA. *See* AFRICA, *West.*

GUÎNES. GUÎNES. Transcript of the Registers of the Protestant Church at Guisnes, 1668–85. pp. 329. 1891. 4°. Ac. London. *Huguenot Society.* Publications. Vol. 3.
    Ac. 2073/4.

GUIPÚZCOA. ECHEGARAY (C. de) Investigaciones referentes á Guipúzcoa, *etc.* pp. 372. *San Sebastián*, 1893. 8°.   10161. dd. 11.
See also BASQUE LANGUAGE AND RACE.

GUISBOROUGH. Ac. Durham. *Surtees Society.* Publications. Vol. 86. Cartularium Prioratus De Gyseburne. *Durham*, 1889, *etc.*
    Ac. 8045/66.

GUISE, Familistère de. BERNARDOT (F.) Le familistère de Guise, France, et son fondateur J. B. A. Godin. pp. 40. *Nîmes*, 1893. 8°.
    8282. g. 27. (8·)

FISCHER (M.) Das Familistère Godins. pp. 40. 1890. 8°. Deutsche Zeit- und Streitfragen. No. 68.   12209. f.

GUITAR. MORALES (J. de J.) Manual de Guitarra. pp. 14. *Mexico*, 1890. obl. 4°.
    7896. dd. 7.

RAM (A.) Simple Method of arranging accompaniments for the Guitar. pp. 12. *Lond.* 1890. 16°.   7897. a. 74.
See also MUSICAL INSTRUMENTS.

GUJARAT. EDALJĪ DOSĀBHĀĪ. History of Gujarat. pp. 345. *Ahmedabad*, 1894. 8°.
    9056. d. 27.

GUJRÁT. Gazetteer of the Gujrat District. pp. 170. *Lahore*, 1894. 8°.   10056. k. 39.

GUJARATI LANGUAGE AND LITERATURE. Ac. London. *British Museum.* Catalogue of Marathi and Gujarati books. pp. 195. *Lond.* 1892. 8°. Cat. Desk B.

ARDSHER FRĀMJĪ MUS and NĀNĀBHĀĪ RUSTAMJĪ RĀNĪNĀ. Dictionary of English and Gujarati. 1891, *etc.* 4°.   12907. g.

BENGALI (L. M.) and MERCHANT (H. G.) New pocket Gujarati into English Dictionary. pp. 812. *Lond.* 1893. 32°.   12907. a. 57.

DOSĀBHĀĪ HORMASJĪ BĀMJĪ. Sansár Kosh, vocabulary of articles of commerce in English and Gujaráti. pp. 89. *Bombay*, 1894. 8°.
    14150. b. 29.

JAYASIMHA RATNACHANDRA PĀNDE and MAHĀSUKHA CHUNILĀLA JAVERI SHAH. Pocket Dictionary of Gujarati & English. 2 pt. *Ahmedabad*, 1892. 8°.   12906. a. 53.

LALUBHĀĪ GOKALADĀSA PATEL. Pocket Gujarati-English Dictionary. pp. 1040. *Ahmedabad*, 1892. 8°.   12907. a. 56.

MĀNEKJĪ PESTANJĪ RĀNDERIĀ and NĀTHUBHĀĪ HĪRĀCHAND PATEL. English-Gujarati Dictionary. pp. 272. *Ahmedabad*, 1892. 8°.
    12906. a. 36.

MOTIRĀMA TRIKAMDĀSA. Pronouncing pocket English and Gujarati Dictionary. pp. 1186. *Bombay*, 1891. 16°.   12907. a. 53.

ARDSHER NASARVĀNJĪ MEHETĀ. The Daily Companion. English idiomatic sentences with Gujarati translations. pp. 178. *Bombay*, 1893. 12°.
    14150. a. 46.

DĀHYĀBHĀĪ DALPATBHĀĪ DALĀL. Manual of Gujarati Grammar. pp. 78. 28. *Surat*, 1889. 8°.
    12906. cc. 31.

MANCHERSHĀH PĀLANJĪ KAIKUBĀD. Principles of Gujarati Grammar in English. pp. 207. *Surat*, 1895. 12°.   14150. a. 48.

NAUROZJĪ DOSĀBHĀĪ KĀSĪNĀTH. Colloquial phrases in Gujerati and English. 2 pt. *Bombay*, 1894, 95. 12°.   14150. a. 47.

PŪRṆĀNANDA MAHĀNANDA BHAṬṬA. Hand book of Gujarati Grammar. 4 pt. *Bombay*, 1889. 12°.
    12906. aaa. 51.

GUJARATI LANGUAGE—*continued.*

TAYLOR (G. P.) Student's Gujārāti Grammar. pp. 228. *Surat*, 1893. 8°.   12907. ff. 18.

TISDALL (W. St. C.) Simplified Grammar of Gujarāti. pp. 189. 1892. 8°. Trübner's Simplified Grammars.   2268. a.

SENTENCES. Short Sentences, English and Gujarati. pp. 67. *Bombay*, 1881. 16°.
    14150. a. 19.

DĀHYĀBHĀĪ DALPATBHĀĪ DALĀL. Gujarati proverbs with their English equivalents. pp. 21. *Surat*, 1889. 8°.   14146. e.

MAHĀSUKHA CHUNĪLĀLA SHĀH. Proverbs, Gujarati and English. pp. 40. *Ahmedabad*, 1892. 16°.   14146. e. 29.

GULF STREAM. REDWAY (J. W.) Climate and the Gulf Stream. pp. 5. 1890. 8°. Pam. 79.

GULVAL. GULVAL. Parish Registers of Gulval. pp. 172. *Penzance*, 1893. 4°.
    9902. f. 37.

GUNNERY: FIRE ARMS: MILITARY SHOOTING. BIRNIE (R.) Gun making in the United States. 1891. 8°. Ac. New York. *Military Service Institution.* Journal. Vol. 12.
    Ac. 4358.

P.P. *London.* Arms and explosives. *Lond.* 1892, *etc.* 4°.   N.R.

POLAIN (J.) Des bancs d'épreuves des Armes à feu. 4 pt. *Liège*, 1892–93. 8°.   8824. d. 51.

POLAIN (A.) Recherches sur l'épreuve des Armes à feu au pays de Liège. pp. 368. *Liège*, 1891. 8°.   8828. i. 36.

BÉTHUYS (G.) and MANCEAU (C.) L'Outillage d'une Armée, canons et forteresses. pp. 320. *Paris*, 1892. 8°.   8824. k. 16.

CALORI STREMITI (P.) *Marquis.* Il Cannoniere pratico, 1795. pp. 78. *Modena*, 1894. 8°.
    8828. ff. 31.

CRONEAU (A.) Canon, torpilles et cuirasse, leur installation à bord des bâtiments. pp. 202. 1892. 8°. Encyclopédie des aide-mémoire.
    8709. g.

DOLLECZEK (A.) Artilleristisches Taschenbuch. pp. 191. 1895. 8°. Braumüller's militarische Taschenbücher. Bd. 3.   8829. aa.

DREDGE (J.) Modern French Artillery with illustrations of French war-ships. pp. 458. 1892. 8°. Engineering Series.   8755. m.

G. B. & I. *Admiralty.* Courses of instruction in Gunnery Ships. pp. 59. *Lond.* 1891. 8°.
    Pam. 43.

—— *Royal Artillery.* Treatise on service ordnance. 1893. pp. 691. *Lond.* 1893. 8°.
    8830. k. 29.

—— Handbook for Gardner and Nordenfelt rifle calibre machine guns. pp. 52. *Lond.* 1891. 8°.
    8831. c. 22. (4.)

—— Handbook for the 0·45″ Gardner Gun. pp. 11. *Lond.* 1893. 8°.   8830. h. 26. (7.)

—— Handbook for the 0·303″ Maxim Magazine rifle-chamber machine Gun. pp. 27. *Lond.* 1893. 8°.   8831. c. 27. (7.)

—— Handbook of the 0·45-Inch Maxim Gun. pp. 16. *Lond.* 1892. 8°.   8831. bbb. 36. (12.)

—— Handbook of the 0·45″ Maxim M. H. chamber machine Gun. pp. 29. *Lond.* 1893. 8°.
    8831. c. 27. (8.)

LUKIN (H. T.) Questions and Answers on Maxim machine Gun. pp. 32. 1895. 8°. Gale and Polden's Military Series.   8830. a. 94.

G. B. & I. Handbook of the 3-pounder Nordenfelt quick-firing Gun. 1891. pp. 18. *Lond.* 1891. 8°.   8831. c. 22. (3.)

GUNNERY—*continued.*

G. B. & I. Handbook for the Nordenfelt 6-Pr. quick firing Guns. pp. 21. *Lond.* 1893. 8°.
    8830. h. 26. (8.)

—— Handbook of the 0·45-inch 5-barrel Nordenfelt Guns. pp. 23. *Lond.* 1893. 8°.
    8831. c. 27. (10.)

—— Handbook of the 3-pounder Hotchkiss quick-firing Gun. pp. 20. *Lond.* 1892. 8°.
    8831. bbb. 36. (1.)

—— Handbook of the 6-pounder Hotchkiss quick-firing Gun. pp. 17. *Lond.* 1892. 8°.
    8831. bbb. 36. (2.)

—— Handbook of 7-pr. steel rifled M.L. Guns of 150 lb. pp. 56. *Lond.* 1893. 8°.
    8831. c. 27. (5.)

—— Handbook for 9-pr. R. M. L. Guns of 6 cwt. & 8 cwt. pp. 34. *Lond.* 1892. 8°.
    8831. bbb. 36. (4.)

—— Handbook for the 12-pr. B.L. Gun. pp. 61. *Lond.* 1893. 8°.   8831. c. 27. (6.)

—— Handbook for the 13 pr. rifled M.L. gun of 8 cwt. pp. 37. *Lond.* 1892. 8°.
    8831. bbb. 36. (7.)

—— Handbook for the 16-pr. rifled M. L. Gun of 12 cwt. 1891. pp. 33. *Lond.* 1891. 8°.
    8831. c. 22. (7.)

—— Handbook for the 20-pr. R.B.L. Gun of 16 cwt. pp. 31. *Lond.* 1892. 8°.   8823. o. 14.

GRIFFIN (H. L.) Notes on the 64-pr. R. M. L. converted Gun, the 40-pr. R. B. L., and the 16-pr. R. M. L. Guns. pp. 71. *Hull*, 1894. 16°.
    8829. a. 37.

G. B. & I. Handbook for the 64-pr. rifled M.L. converted Guns of 58 and 71 Cwt. pp. 45. *Lond.* 1892. 8°.   8831. bbb. 36. (8.)

—— Handbook of the 64-pr. R.M.L. Gun of 64 Cwt. pp. 36. *Lond.* 1893. 8°. 8831. c. 27. (3.)

—— Handbook for 4-inch R.M.L. jointed Howitzer. pp. 24. *Lond.* 1890. 8°.
    8831. c. 23. (7.)

—— Handbook for 4-inch B.L. gun. pp. 34. *Lond.* 1890. 8°.   8831. c. 23. (6.)

—— Handbook of the 4·7 inch quick-firing gun. pp. 26. *Lond.* 1892. 8°.   8831. bbb. 36. (10.)

—— Handbook of the 5-inch B.L. Gun. pp. 35. *Lond.* 1890. 8°.   8831. c. 23. (8.)

—— Handbook for the 6-inch B.L. Guns. pp. 83. *Lond.* 1892. 8°.   8823. n. 18.

—— Handbook for the 6·6 Inch R.M.L. Howitzer. pp. 41. *Lond.* 1893. 8°.
    8831. c. 27. (1.)

—— Handbook for the 7-inch rifled breech-loading Guns of 72 cwt. and 82 cwt. pp. 39. *Lond.* 1892. 8°.   8831. bbb. 36. (9.)

—— Handbook for the 7-inch rifled muzzle-loading Guns of 6½ and 7 tons. pp. 66. *Lond.* 1892. 8°.   8831. bbb. 36. (5.)

—— Handbook for the 8-in. R.M.L. Howitzer of 46 cwt. pp. 38. *Lond.* 1890. 8°.
    8831. c. 22. (2.)

—— Handbook for the 9·2-inch B.L. Gun. pp. 98. *Lond.* 1892. 8°.   8323. n. 17.

—— Handbook for the 10-inch B.L. Gun. pp. 100. *Lond.* 1892. 8°.   8824. ff. 42.

—— Handbook for the 11-inch rifled muzzle-loading Gun of 25 tons. pp. 50. *Lond.* 1892. 8°.   8831. bbb. 36. (6.)

—— Handbook for the 12-inch rifled muzzle-loading Gun of 25 Tons. pp. 50. *Lond.* 1893. 8°.   8831. c. 27. (4.)

—— Handbook for the R.M L. 12·5-inch 38-ton Gun. pp. 81. *Lond.* 1893. 8°. 8831. c. 27. (2.)

—— Handbook for the 12-inch B.L. 47 ton gun. pp. 44. *Lond.* 1891. 8°. 8831. c. 22. (6.)

GUNNERY—*continued.*

HENRARD (P. J. J.) Les Fondeurs d'Artillerie. 1889. 8°. Ac. Antwerp. *Académie d'Archéologie.* Annales. Sér. 4. Tom. 5.   Ac. 5513.

HERMIDA Y ÁLVAREZ (G.) Nuevo material de Artilleria. 2 pt. *Madrid*, 1894. 8°. 8827. cc. 45.

LONGRIDGE (J. A.) Field Gun of the future. pp. 28. *Lond.* 1892. 8°.   8830. h. 26. (6.)

LUKOUDES (P. S.) Mémoire sur un nouveau système de Bouches-à-feu démontables. pp. 48. *Athènes*, 1891. 4°.   Pam. 2.

MALENGREAU (J.) L'Artillerie Canet à l Exposition d'Anvers. pp. 92 *Brux.* 1894. 8°.   8827. h. 29.

NICOL (E.) Traité d'Artillerie à l'usage des officiers de marine. pp. 349. *Paris*, 1894. 8°.   8758. ccc. 3.

PANZERA (F. W.) Questions and answers on Gunnery. pp. 146. *Lond.* 1892. 8°. 8831. f. 40.

SCHROEDER (S.) The U.S.S. Vesuvius, with special reference to her pneumatic battery. pp. 65. 1894. Ac. Annapolis. *Naval Institute.* Papers, *etc.* Vol. 20.   Ac. 4398.

WILLE (R.) Das Feldgeschütz der Zukunft. pp. 324. *Berl.* 1891. 8°.   8823. n. 22.

—— Projectiles en tungstène. pp. 107. *Berl.* 1891. 8°.   8823. dd. 19.

WUICH (N.) Vorträge über die Wirkungsfähigkeit der Geschütze. pp. 232. *Wien*, 1891. 8°.   8829. l. 15.

———

G. B. & I. *Army.* Manual of Field range-finding. 1890. pp. 80. *Lond.* 1890. 8°. 8831. c. 25. (5.)

—— Handbook for the depression range-finder for elevated batteries. pp. 15. *Lond.* 1893. 8°.   8831. bbb. 36. (11.)

WHISH (J. T.) The "Aide-Tireur" range finder. pp. 12. *Lond.* 1891. 8°. 8831. ee. 16. (6.)

See also BALLISTICS : FORTIFICATION : MILITARY SCIENCE : WEAPONS.

Ammunition. *See* GUNPOWDER.

Rifles and other Small Arms: Musketry Instruction.

ARMES. Les Armes à feu portatives des armées actuelles. pp. 251. *Paris*, 1894. 8°. 8830. h. 25.

BIHÁLY (J.) Die Schiess-Vorschriften der fünf bedeutendsten Heere Europas. pp. 348. *Wien*, 1893. 8°.   8826. h. 27.

BRUNS (P.) Effets du projectile du nouveau Fusil de petit calibre. pp. 57. *Brux.* 1891. 4°.   8826. i. 18.

DEMA SOLER (A.) and MORALES AGUILERA (J.) Descripción del Fusil Mauser español, modelo 1893. pp. 130. *Toledo*, 1895. 8°. 8832. bb. 5.

ENGH ( ) Le Fusil à répétition du système Engh admis aux épreuves du Gouvernement belge. pp. 29. *Liège*, 1889. 8°. 8831. l. 8. (2.)

EXPERT. Notes on Shooting. pp. 67. *Lond.* 1894. 8°.   Pam. 83.

FOULKES (A. G.) Theory and practice of target Shooting. pp. 228. *Lond.* 1895. 8°.   8828. bbb. 31.

FULTON (G. E.) Gregory's Score Register. pp. 44. *Lond.* 1895. obl. 8°. 8831. a. 89.

GERMANY. *Army.* Règlement sur le tir de l'infanterie. pp. 174. *Paris*, 1894. 8°. 8823. g. 29.

G. B. & I. *Army.* Text book for Military Small Arms and ammunition. pp. 157. *Lond.* 1895. 8°.   8829. bbb. 49.

—— Modern military Rifles and Carbines. 1891. fol.   1865. c. 4. (4.)

—— Regulations for Musketry Instruction. Lee-Metford Rifle and Carbine. pp. 225. *Lond.* 1894. 16°.   8831. e. 25.

GUNNERY—*continued.*

G. B. & I. *Army.* Martini-Henry Rifle and Carbine. pp. 53. *Lond.* 1891. 8°. 8831. e. 1. (5.)

—— Regulations for Musketry Instruction for the Martini-Henry Rifle and Carbine. pp. 261. *Lond.* 1892. 8°.   8829. a. 22.

—— Manual and firing exercises for the Snider Artillery Carbine. pp. 67. *Lond.* 1890. 16°.   8831. e. 1. (3.)

—— *Navy.* Magazine Rifle. Firing Exercise. Aiming Drill. pp. 56. *Lond.* 1891. 8°.   8831. e. 1. (4.)

—— Magazine Rifle. Rifle exercises for her Majesty's Fleet. pp. 52. *Lond.* 1893. 16°.   8831. a. 88. (7.)

GOULD (A. C.) Modern American Rifles. pp. 338. *Bost.* 1892. 8°.   8828. bbb. 28.

GREENER (W. W.) The Gun and its development. pp. 742. *Lond.* 1892. 8°.   2264. d. 10.

—— Modern shot Guns. pp. 202. *Lond.* 1891. 8°.   7908. ee. 13.

—— The Breech-loader. pp. 386. *Lond.* 1895. 8°.   07905. f. 36.

HABART (J.) Die Geschosswirkung der 8-Millimeter-Handfeuerwaffen an Menschen und Pferden. pp. 114. *Wien*, 1892. 8°.   6095. f. 29.

KINDER (C. W.) Sham Fighting with the rifle. pp. 30. *Lond.* 1890. 8°.   8831. ee. 16. (5.)

LEMMI (S.) Il Tiro a segno nazionale. pp. 80. *Firenze*, 1892. 8°.   8823. dd. 25.

MARKSMAN. Modern Rifle shooting. pp. 174. *Lond.* 1895. 16°.   8826. aa. 27.

MAYNE (C. B.) Infantry Fire tactics for Canadian Militia. pp. 16. *Toronto*, 1890. 8°.   8830. k. 33 (6.)

MILLER (W. S.) School of Musketry at Hythe. pp. 41. *Lond.* 1892. obl. 4°.   8830. g. 34.

ORTUS (J.) Lebel contre Manlicher et Vetterli. pp. 84. *Paris*, 1891. 8°.   8830. g 33. (3.)

PARIS. *Union des Sociétés de Tir.* Biographie des Sociétés de Tir. *Paris*, 1892, *etc.* 8°.   7907. dd.

PIEPER ( ) Le fusil Pieper à répétition. pp. 43. *Liége*, 1888. 8°.   8830. bbb 13. (5.)

SCIENCES. Fusils à répétition, poudre sans fumée. pp. 128. *Brux.* 1892. 8°.   8824. k. 21.

See also MILITARY SCIENCE.

For works on shooting game, *etc.* and sporting guns, *see* SPORT.

GUNPOWDER: GUNCOTTON: AMMUNITION.

ALLASON (U.) La Polvere senza fumo, *etc.* pp. 110. *Torino*, 1893. 8°.   8828. aaa. 26.

CLÉMENT ( ) Lettres sur la Poudre sans fumée. pp. 100. *Paris*, 1891. 8°.   8830. g. 30.

FRANCE. *M. de la Guerre.* Mémorial des Poudres et salpêtres. *Paris*, 1882, *etc.* 8°.   8909. ccc.

G. B. & I. *Army.* Treatise on Ammunition. pp. 582. *Lond.* 1892. 8°.   8831. k. 29.

LONGRIDGE (J. A.) Smokeless Powder and its influence on gun construction. pp. 49. *Lond.* 1890. 8°.   8831. l. 10. (8.)

PLACH (F.) Die gepresste Schiesswolle. pp. 133. *Pola*, 1891. 8°.   8807. cc. 36.

POUTEAUX (A.) La Poudre sans fumée et les poudres anciennes. pp. 156. *Dijon*, 1892. 8°.   8830. k. 20.

RIGG (A.) and GARVIE (J.) Modern Guns and smokeless Powder. pp. 83. *Lond.* 1892. 8°.   8830. bbb. 5.

SCIENCES. Fusils à répétition, Poudre sans fumée. pp. 128. *Brux.* 1892. 8°.   8824. k. 21.

TECHTERMANN (de) La Poudre sans fumée et la Tactique. pp. 32. *Berne*, 1891. 8°. Pam. 2.   8830. g. 33. (5.)

See also GUNNERY : MILITARY SCIENCE.

GÜNZBURG. EDLHARD (F. X.) Chronik der Stadt Günzburg. pp. 163. *Günzburg,* 1894. 8°.
10255. h. 9.

GURDASPUR. GURDÁSPUR. Gazetteer of the Gurdaspur District. pp. 2. 197.
Lahore, 1892. 8°.   10056. k. 35.

GUTTA PERCHA AND CAOUT-CHOUC. CHAPEL (E.) Le Caoutchouc et la gutta-percha. pp. 601. *Paris,* 1892. 8°.
7075. k. 5.

HEINZERLING (C.) Grundzüge der Lederberei-tung. 2 pt. 1882, 83. 8°. BOLLEY (P. A.) Handbuch der chemischen Technologie. Bd. 6. Gruppe 4. Abt. 1, 2.   8905. eee.

GWALIOR. GWALIOR. History of the fortress of Gwalior. pp. 55. *Bombay,* 1892. 8°.
757. e. 40.

GYMNASTICS : ATHLETICS.
General.

ALEXANDER (A.) New Sports for schools, clubs and gymnasia. pp. 80. *Lond.* 1895. 8°.
07905. h. 24.

DIMMOCK (A.) Tricks and exercises on the horizontal bar. pp. 36. *Chatham,* 1890. 8°.
7912. aaa. 7.

DISSE (J. S. G.) and LABBERTÉ (L. D.) Hand-leiding voor het onderwijs in de vrije en orde-oefeningen der Gymnastik. pp. 316.
Rotterdam, 1891. 8°.   7908. eee. 6.

DUSTOUR (J.) Notice sur la section de Genève de la Société de Gymnastique. pp. 173.
Genève, 1893. 8°.   07905. f. 23.

EDELMAN (H.) Geneeskundige kamergymnastiek. pp. 80. *Deventer,* 1893. 8°.   7912. aaa. 15.

G. B. &. I. *Navy.* Handbook of Gymnastic Exercises. pp. 113. *Lond.* 1893. 8°.
8807. aa. 47.

GRIFFIN (H. H.) Athletics. pp. 119. 1891. 8°. All England Series.   7908. df.

GUTSMUTHS (J. C. F.) Gymnastik für die Jugend. pp. 258. *Wien,* 1893. 8°.
07905. h. 15.

HOFFMANN (L.) Home Gymnastics. pp. 186. *Lond.* 1892. 8°.   7907. de. 45.

HOOLE (H.) Relation of athletic Sports to public health, *etc.* pp. 40. *Lond.* 1891. 8°. Pam. 39.

KNAUFF (T. C.) Athletics for physical culture. pp. 422. *N.Y.* 1894. 8°.   07905. f. 27.

KOEHLER (H. J.) Manual of Calisthenic exer-cises. *Wash.* 1892. 16°.   Pam. 83.

MAMOZ (D.) De la Gymnastique en France. pp. 289. *Angoulême,* 1891. 8°.   7908. c. 37.

MANUEL. Manuel de Gymnastique.
Paris, 1893, *etc.* 8°.   7912. a. 29.

MULLERS (G. J.) Vrije Oefeningen, Orde-oefe-ningen en Spelen. 2 deel. *Zutphen,* 1891. 8°.
7907. dd. 13.

NOAKES (S. G.) System of free Gymnastics as practised in Military Gymnasia. pp. 76.
1893. 8°. Gale and Polden's Military Series.
8830. a. 82.

PARANT (L.) Les sociétés de Gymnastique dans l'Ain. pp. 152. *Bourg,* 1893. 8°.   07905. h. 7.

P.P. *London,* Athletes' record.
Lond. 1894, *etc.* 8°.   P.P. 2489. fdb.

—— The Gymnast. *Lond.* 1890, *etc.* 4°.
P.P. 1832. i.

SAMPSON (C. A.) Strength, a treatise on develop-ment and use of muscle. pp. 240.
Lond. 1895. 8°.   7404. aaaa. 5.

SCHERSTÉN (O. E.) Gymnastik. 1889. 8°.
BALCK (V.) Illustreradt Bibliothek. No. 4.
7908. d. 22.

SHEARMAN (M.) Athletics. pp. 464. 1894. 4°.
Badminton Library.   2261. aa. 1.

SMITH (W. M.) Athletics and athletic sports of Scotland. pp. 138. *Paisley,* 1891. 8°.
7906. de. 36.

U.S. *Amateur Athletic Union.* Constitution, by-laws, *etc.* pp. 138. *N.Y.* 1890. 8°. 7908. c. 35.

BISHOP (E. M.) Americanized Delsarte Culture. pp. 202. *Wash.* 1892. 8°.   7404. df. 8.

HUGHES (H.) Lehrbuch der Atmungsgymnastik. pp. 166. *Wiesbaden,* 1893. 8°.   07905. i. 5.

LAGRANGE (F.) De Exercice chez les adultes. pp. 367. *Paris,* 1891. 8°.   7912. aa. 10.

MASON (M.) Miss Mason on the utility of Exercise. pp. 32. *Heidelberg,* 1890. 8°.
7305. ee. 21. (3.)

MAGENDIE (A.) Les Effets moraux de l'Exercice physique. pp. 224. *Paris,* 1893. 8°. 8411. e. 6.

STEBBINS (G.) Dynamic breathing and harmonic gymnastics. pp. 155. *N.Y.* 1893. 8°.
7907. d. 40.

Physical Education, Drill, etc.

ALEXANDER (A.) Physical Drill of all nations. pp. 165. *Lond.* 1894. 8°,   07905. h. 12.

—— Drill for the standards. pp. 199.
Lond. 1895. 8°.   7912. aaa. 18.

BERTONI (G.) Educazione fisica. pp. 242.
Modena, 1891. 8°.   07905. h. 2.

CHESTERTON (T.) Manual of Drill and physical exercises. pp. 170. *Lond.* 1893. 8°.
8830. aaa. 60.

DUPUY (L. E.) Le Mouvement et les Exercices physiques. pp. 344. *Paris,* 1893. 8°.
7907. d. 39.

FARRINGTON (F. W.) Medburn Bar-Bell exer-cises. pp. 28. *Lond.* 1894. 8°.   07905. h. 16.

—— Medburn Dumb-Bell exercises. pp. 46.
Lond. 1894. 8°.   07905. h. 17.

HARVEY (F. J.) Teacher's Manual of physical exercises. pp. 166. *Lond.* 1894. *obl.* 8°.
7907. df. 15.

LATOUR (L.) L'Éducation physique en Angle-terre et en France. pp. 51. *Paris,* 1891. 8°.
8304. a. 7. (4.)

MAAZEN (P.) and HAGE (J.) Vak j. Tachtig methodische lessen in de vrije- en ordevefenin-gen. *Tiel,* 1893, *etc.* 8°.   07905. g.

MACLAREN (A.) Physical Education. pp. 462. 1895. 8°. Clarendon Press Series.   2320. c. 4.

MOSSO (A.) L' Educazione fisica della gioventù. pp. 235. *Milano,* 1894. 8°.   8311. aaa. 18.

OXLEY (C.) Manual of Drill and physical exer-cises. pp. 203. *Lond.* 1895. 8°.   7907. e. 32.

PELLIZZARI (P.) La Scienza in relazione con la scuola. pp. 34. *Arezzo,* 1895. 8°.   Pam. 17.

P.P. *London.* Physique. Nos. 1–8.
Lond. 1891. 8°.   1866. b. 9.

POSSE (N.) *Baron.* Special Kinesiology of edu-cational Gymnastics. pp. 380. *Bost.* 1894. 8°.
7905. cc. 29.

ROOK (E. C.) and (L. J.) Drills and Marches. pp. 128. *Phila.* 1890. 8°.   7913. ee. 29.

SANCHEZ SOMOANO (J.) Gimnástica escolar.
Madrid, 1890, *etc.* 8°.   7906. ccc. 30.

TREVES (F.) Physical Education. pp. 75.
Lond. 1892. 8°.   7908. dd. 28.

U.S. *Department of War.* Manual of calisthenic exercises. pp. 54. *Wash.* 1892. 16°.
7913. de. 17. (4.)

WESTWELL (J. W.) Instructions for the new Musical Drill. *Redditch,* 1894. 8°.
1865. c. 1. (21.)

Swedish Drill.

BROMAN (A.) School Gymnastics on the Swedish system. pp. 105. *Lond.* 1895. 8°. 7912. aaa. 20.

GYMNASTICS.—Swedish Drill—cont.

KELLGREN (H.) Zur Technik der schwedischen manuellen Behandlung. pp. 189.
Berl. 1895. 8°. 　　　　　　　7461. dd. 4.

MÉLIO (G. L.) Manual of Swedish Drill. pp. 81.
Lond. 1894. 8°. 　　　　　　　7912. aa. 1.

NISSEN (H.) A. B. C. of the Swedish system of educational Gymnastics. pp. 107.
Phila. 1891. 8°. 　　　　　　　7908. df. 13.

POSSE (N.) *Baron.* Handbook of school-gymnastics of the Swedish System. pp. 192.
Bost. 1892. 8°. 　　　　　　　7912. a. 25.

TANNER (A. E.) Physical Culture for men, women and children. pp. 29. *Lond.* 1894. 4°.
　　　　　　　　　　　　　　　7906. h. 22.

Training.

ADAM (G. M.) Sandow on physical Training. pp. 244. *Lond.* 1894. 8°. 　　7908. f. 28.

BARTER (S.) Barter's Manual Training diagrams. *Lond.* 1889. fol. 　　　1810. d. 1. (12.)

CHECKLEY (E.) National method of Physical Training. pp. 152. *Lond.* 1892. 8°. 7012. aa. 9.

CONNORS (T.) On modern Training. pp. 20. *Manch.* 1895. 8°. 　　7907. df. 18. (10.)

CORTIS (H. L.) Principles of Training for amateur Athletes. pp. 46. *Lond.* 1887. 8°. 7912. df. 3. (1.)

DUNCAN (H. O.) and SUBERBIE (L.) L'Entraînement à l'usage des vélocipédistes, coureurs et touristes. pp. 200. *Paris,* 1890. 8°.
　　　　　　　　　　　　　　　7908. eee. 12.

HOOLE (H.) Science and art of Training. pp. 124. *Lond.* 1895. 8°. 　　7908. e. 35.

THORNTON (J. P.) Training for health, strength, speed and agility. pp. 260. *N.Y.* 1890. 8°.
　　　　　　　　　　　　　　　7404. cc. 14.

GYNECOLOGY. *See* WOMEN, *Diseases, etc.*

GYPRIPEDIUM. *See* ORCHIDS.

HACHENBURG. HACHENBURG. Catalog der sayn'schen und wittgenstein'schen Sammlung auf Schloss Hachenburg. pp. 91.
Minden, 1891. 8°. 　　　　　7807. aa. 4.

HADDINGTON. ROBB (J.) History of Haddington. pp. 66. *Haddington,* 1891. 8°.
　　　　　　　　　　　　　10348. ccc. 60. (7.)

SINCLAIR (W.) Pictorial guide to Haddington. pp. 64. *Haddington,* 1891. 8°.
　　　　　　　　　　　　　10348. ccc. 60. (8.)

HADDINGTONSHIRE. BELL (J. M.) Castles of the Lothians. pp. 97.
Edinb. 1893. 4°. 　　　　　　10370. i. 4.

BLACKLOCK (T. B.) Sketches in East Lothian. *Edinb.* 1892. fol. 　　　　1785. b. 13.

MARTINE (J.) Reminiscences and notices of parishes of Haddington. pp. 221.
Haddington, 1894. 8°. 　　　10369. ccc. 30.

HADDLESEY. WORSFOLD (J. N.) History of Haddlesey. pp. 254. *Lond.* 1894. 8°.
　　　　　　　　　　　　　010358. h. 18.

HADDON HALL. CARRINGTON (W. A.) Selections from Stewards' accounts at Haddon Hall. pp. 56. *Derby,* 1894. 8°. 07703. f. 3. (18.)

COOKE (W. E.) Haddon Hall. *Lond.* 1892. fol.
　　　　　　　　　　　　　10352. m. 8.

MANNERS (J.) *Duchess of Rutland.* Haddon Hall, notes on its history. *Bakewell,* 1893. 8°.
　　　　　　　　　　　　　10347. cc. 26. (5.)

HADLEIGH. SPOONER (E.) Almshouse Chapel, Hadleigh. pp. 3.
Bury-St.-Edmunds, 1891. 8°. 10348. d. 19. (16.)

HAEMORRHOIDS. *See* RECTUM.

HAGUE, The. BOURLIER (E.) Souvenir du troisième centenaire de l'Église wallonne de La Haye. pp. 105. *La Haye,* 1891. 8°. 4685. g. 15.

GRAM (J.) 's Gravenhage in onzen tijd. pp. 285. *Amsterd.* 1893. 8°. 　10271. h. 11.

KRUL (R.) Haagsche Doctoren, chirurgen en apothekers. pp. 220. *'s Gravenh.* 1891. 8°.
　　　　　　　　　　　　　7679. de. 13.

See also EXHIBITIONS.

HAIDARABAD. HUSAIN, *Balgrāmi Saiyid,* and WILLMOTT (C.) Sketch of the Nizam's Dominions. *Bombay,* 1883, *etc.* 8°.
　　　　　　　　　　　　　010057. l. 10.

HAIL. *See* INSURANCE: METEOROLOGY.

HAILEYBURY COLLEGE. DANVERS (F. C.) Memorials of old Haileybury College. pp. 668. *Westminster,* 1894. 4°. 8364. de. 36.

HAILEYBURY COLLEGE. Haileybury Register, 1862-91. pp. 388. *Hertford,* 1891. 8°.
　　　　　　　　　　　　　8364. e. 44.

HAIN, Monastery. FABER (H.) Eine Beschreibung der Karthause Hain. pp. 83.
M. Gladbach, 1892. 8°. 　　　4662. c. 22.

HAINAULT. PRUD'HOMME (É.) Les échevins dans la province de Hainaut. pp. 483. 1890. 8°. Ac. Mons. *Société des Sciences.* Mémoires. Sér. 5. Tom. 2. 　　Ac. 1013.

HAIR: HAIRDRESSING. PARKER (H.) The Human Hair. pp. 51. *Lond.* 1894. 8°.
　　　　　　　　　　　　　07305. i. 11. (6.)

PATTESON (R. G.) Synopsis of diseases of the Hair. pp. 15. *Lond.* 1891. 16°. 　7640. a. 5.

ROBINSON (T.) Baldness and greyness. pp. 135. *Lond.* 1891. 8°. 　　　　7630. aaa. 33.

CHILD (T.) Wimples and crisping-pins, *etc.* pp. 209. *Lond.* 1895. 8°. 　7743. c. 25.

COCHERIS (P. W.) Les Parures primitives. pp. 266. *Paris,* 1894. 4°. 　7743. g. 19.

VILLERMONT (M. de) *Countess.* Histoire de la Coiffure féminine. pp. 822. *Brux.* 1891. 8°.
　　　　　　　　　　　　　7742. ee. 13.

PRICE (G.) Ancient and modern Beards. pp. 8. 1893. 8°. 　　　　　　Pam. 24.

MORTON (J.) Mysteries and art of an easy Shave. pp. 56. *Lond.* 1893. 8°. 　07944. e. 28.

SQUIRE (A. B.) Superfluous Hair and the means of removing it. pp. 64. *Lond.* 1893. 8°.
　　　　　　　　　　　　　7641. a. 36.

See also COSTUME.

HAITI. *See* HAYTI.

HALLAMSHIRE. *See* SHEFFIELD.

HALLAND. HAGSTRÖM (K.) Kort beskrifning öfver Halland. pp. 47. *Stockholm,* 1891. 8°.
　　　　　　　　　　　　　10106. de. 5. (5.)

LARSSON (H.) Halland vid midten af det 17de århundradet. pp. 115. *Halmstad,* 1891. 8°.
　　　　　　　　　　　　　10281. c. 5.

HALLE, an der Saale. BEYSCHLAG (D. W.) Das zweihundertjährige Jubiläum der Universität. pp. 64. *Halle,* 1895. 8°. 8357. l. 23.

HERTZBERG (G. F.) Übersicht über die Geschichte der Universität. pp. 78. *Halle,* 1894. 8°.
　　　　　　　　　　　　　8357. bb. 36.

—— Die Stadt und Universität Halle, 1794. pp. 65. 1894. 8°. Ac. Halle. *Thüringisch-Sächsischer Verein.* Neue Mittheilungen. Bd. 18. 　　　　　　　　　　　Ac. 7345.

MEIER (J.) Hallische Studentensprache. pp. 97. *Halle,* 1894. 8°. 　　12962. q. 6.

SCHRADER (W.) Geschichte der Friedrichs-Universität. 2 Thle. *Berl.* 1894. 8°.
　　　　　　　　　　　　　8357. f. 28.

HALLE, an der Saale—*continued.*

SARAN (G.) Die Kirchenordnungsversuch des Rates zu Halle, 1677–79. 1891. 8°. Ac. Halle. *Thuringisch-Sächsischer Verein.* Neue Mitteilungen. Bd. 18. Ac. 7345.

HALLUCINATIONS. FRIEDMANN (M.) Ueber den Wahn. pp. 196. *Wiesbaden, 1894.* 8°. 7660. g. 33.

IRELAND (W. W.) The Blot upon the Brain. pp. 388. *Edinb.* 1893. 8°. 7660. g. 15.

SULLY (J.) Illusions. pp. 390. 1895. 8°. International Scientific Series. Vol. 34. 2324. b. 1.

See also INSANITY.

HALMA. HINTS. Hints on Halma. pp. 17. *Reading,* 1894. 8°. 7912. ee. 3. (8.)

RULES. Rules of the game of Halma. pp. 6. *Lond.* 1891. 32°. 7915. de. 19. (1.)

HAM, Surrey. CHANCELLOR (E. B.) History of Ham, etc. *Richmond,* 1894. 8°. 10349. k. 3.

HARLAND (W. H.) Ham Common and the Dysarts. pp. 77. *Kingston,* 1894. 8°. 6426. aaaa. 30

See also LONDON, *Environs.*

HAMBURG. BALLHEIMER (R.) Zeittafeln zur hamburgischen Geschichte. pp. 20. *Hamb.* 1895. 8°. Pam. 28.

HALLE (E. L. v.) Studien zur hamburgischen Handelsgeschichte. *Berl.* 1891, *etc.* 8°. 08227. h. 18.

MEYEY (E. L.) Hamburgische Wappen- und Genealogien. pp. 496. *Hamb.* 1890. 8°. 9904. m. 24.

TEGELER (L.) Die Kriegsfahrten der Hamburger zu Wasser und zu Lande. pp. 344. *Hamb.* 1894. 8°. 09325. h. 14.

NIRRNHEIM (H.) Hamburg in der ersten Hälfte des 15. Jahrhunderts. pp. 157. *Hamb.* 1890. 8°. 9124. b. 4.

SCHRADER (T.) Hamburg vor 200 Jahren. pp. 367. *Hamb.* 1892. 8°. 10261. h. 18.

HEITMUELLER (F.) Hamburgische Dramatiker zu Zeit Gottscheds. pp. 101. *Dresd.* 1891. 8°. 011824. h. 7.

DAVOUT (L. N.) Davout in Hamburg, 1813–14. pp. 196. *Mülheim,* 1892. 8°. 9079. g. 20.

—— Le Maréchal Davout à Hambourg. pp. 123. *Nancy,* 1890. 8°. 9080. c. 28.

HEYDEN (W.) Die Entwicklung des politischen Wahlrechts in Hamburg. pp. 96. *Hamb.* 1894. 8°. 9366. f. 3.

—— Die hamburger Sparkasse von 1827. pp. 247. *Hamb.* 1893. 4°. 8225. ff. 37.

MEYER (F. A.) Das Wasserwerk Hamburg's. pp. 36. *Hamb.* 1894. fol. 8776. h. 33.

MELLE (W. v.) Das hamburgische Staatsrecht. pp. 295. *Hamb.* 1891. 8°. 05604. h. 1.

NIEMEYER (L.) Hamburger Privatrecht. *Hamb.* 1892, *etc.* 8°. 5604. aa.

SCHROEDER (O.) Sea-going Vessels in the harbour of Hamburg. pp. 34. *Hamb.* 1891. 8°. 6005. de. 4. (5.)

See also EXHIBITIONS : HANSE TOWNS.

For the Cholera Epidemic of 1892–93, *see* CHOLERA.

HAMBYE, Abbey. LE CONTE (R.) Études sur les abbayes des Bénédictins et sur celle de Hambye en particulier. pp. 556. *Bernay,* 1890. 8°. 4629. bb. 6.

HAMMERSHUS. MÖLLER (J. P.) Vejviser for Bεsøgende ved Hammershus Ruiner. pp. 23. *Nexø,* 1893. 16°. Pam. 91.

HAMPSHIRE. GILBERT (H. M.) and GODWIN (G. N.) Bibliotheca Hantoniensis. Books relating to Hampshire. pp. 80. *Southampton,* 1891. 8°. B.B.K. a. 1.

HAMPSHIRE—*continued.*

Ac. London. *Harleian Society.* Publications. Vol. XXXV. Hampshire Allegations for marriage licenses, 1680–1837. *Lond.* 1893, *etc.* 8°. 2118. e.

BEVAN (G. P.) Tourist's guide to Hampshire. pp. 120. *Lond.* 1891. 8°. 10352. a. 56.

BRUCE (J. M.) Climate of Somerset and Hampshire. 1895, *etc.* 8°. Ac., *etc.* London. *Medical and Chirurgical Society.* Vol. 1. 7462. g.

CARTWRIGHT (J.) The Pilgrim's Way from Winchester to Canterbury. pp. 157. *Lond.* 1893. 8°. 10349. h. 32.

COWPER (F.) Sailing Tours. Pt. ii. Coasts of Hants. *Lond.* 1892, *etc.* 8°. 10360. e.

DE CRESPIGNY (R. C.) and HUTCHINSON (H. G.) The New Forest. pp. 293. *Lond.* 1895. 8°. 010350. g. 2.

GASQUET (F. A.) Hampshire Recusants in the reign of Queen Elizabeth. pp. 58. *Lond.* 1895. 8°. 4705. bbb. 32.

HAMPSHIRE. Apartment, hotel and trade guide for Hampshire. pp. 168. *Southampton,* 1891. 8°. 010358. e. 25.

HARPER (C. G.) The Portsmouth Road and its tributaries. pp. 372. *Lond.* 1895. 8°. 010358. h. 24.

P.P. *Southampton.* The Hampshire Independent, Antiquary and Naturalist. *Southampton,* 1891, *etc.* 4°. P.P. 1925. egb.

SHORE (T. W.) History of Hampshire. pp. 286. 1892. 8°. Popular County Histories. 2368. e.

HAMPTON COURT. HAMPTON COURT. Hampton Court Palace. 1892. 8°. Victorian Series. 10348. ccc.

LOGAN (M.) Guide to Italian pictures at Hampton Court. pp. 48. 1894. 8°. Kyrle Pamphlets. 7808. c.

HAMYRITIC LANGUAGE.
See SABAEANS.

HAND : FINGERS. ADAMS (W.) On Contractions of the Fingers. pp. 154. *Lond.* 1892. 8°. 7482. g. 18.

BIRKNER (F.) Zur Anthropologie der Hand. 1895. 8°. Ac. Munich. *Gesellschaft für Anthropologie.* Beiträge zur Anthropologie Bayerns. Bd. 11. Ac. 6229.

ERNST (F. G.) Application of suitable mechanism to a case of Amputation of both Hands. pp. 15. *Lond.* 1893. 8°. 07482. ee. 8.

GALTON (F.) Finger-prints. pp. 216. *Lond.* 1892. 8°. 7419. i. 26.

—— Decipherment of blurred Finger-prints. pp. 18. *Lond.* 1893. 8°. 7419. i. 31.

—— Finger-print Directories. pp. 127. *Lond.* 1895. 8°. 7419. i. 33.

GUERMONPREZ (F. J. O.) Autoplastie de la Main par désossement d'un doigt. *Lille,* 1891. 8°. 7306. e. 23. (2.)

LEDDERHOSE (G.) Über Folgen und Behandlung von Fingerverletzungen. 1895. 8°. VOLKMANN (R. v.) Sammlung klinischer Vorträge. N.F. Nr. 121. 7441. g.

LIERSCH (L. W.) Die linke Hand. *Berl.* 1893. 8°. 7305. f. 5. (9.)

HANDWRITING. MAURY (A.) La Invención de la Escritura. pp. 146. *Madrid,* 1891. 8°. 7706. a. 44.

BERGER (P.) Histoire de l'Écriture dans l'antiquité. pp. 389. *Paris,* 1891. 8°. 2268. f. 21.

HARDY (W. J.) Handwriting of Kings and Queens of England. pp. 176. *Lond.* 1893. 8°. 7709. k. 21.

MIRACLE Y CARBONELL (F.) Napoleon I. y su escritura. pp. 258. *Barcelona,* 1892. 8°. 7942. h. 32.

HANDWRITING—*continued.*

HAZLEHURST (H.) Handwriting of the insane. *Phila.* 1887. 8°.   7660. bb. 3

FRAZER (P.) Manual of the study of Documents to establish the individual character of Handwriting and to detect fraud. pp. 218. *Phila.* 1894. 8°.   7942. g. 31.

HAGAN (W. E.) Treatise on disputed Handwriting. pp. 289. *N. Y.* 1894. 8°. 7942. k. 43.

PREYER (W.) Zur Psychologie des Schreibens. pp. 230. *Hamb.* 1895. 8°.   7944. dd. 6.

BACON (G. W.) Bacon's reform in Handwriting. pp. 15. 16. *Lond.* 1895. 4°.   Pam. 94.

BRUCE (J.) Teacher's guide to the system of Penmanship taught by J. Bruce. *Lond.* 1894. obl. 4°.   7942. g. 27.

COPY BOOKS. Royal Copy books. 16 pt. *Lond.* 1893. 8°.   1879. a. 1.

DARNELL (G.) New Series of penny Copy books. *Lond.* 1892. 4°.   1267. d. 9.

ENGLISH HANDWRITING. Curso de Escritura inglesa. 8 pt. *Lond.* 1891. obl. 8°. 1269. a. 40.

HUGHES AND Co. Examination Copy-books. Nos. 1–7. *Lond.* 1890. 4°.   1880. a. 66.

—— Art of handwriting. pp. 72. *Lond.* 1891. 8°.   7942. cc. 32.

JACKSON (J.) Jackson's Compendium for use in the teaching of Handwriting. pp. 60. *Lond.* 1895. 8°.   7942. aaa. 57.

—— Theory and practice of Handwriting. pp. 170. *Lond.* 1894. 8°.   07944. g. 13.

—— Upright versus sloping Writing. pp. 14. *N. Y.* 1894. 12°.   Pam. 94.

KEEFE (J.) Copying Manuscript. pp. 40. *Liverp.* 1893. fol.   1880. b. 24.

KING (C. F.) University College writing models. *Lond.* 1890. obl. 8°.   7942. a. 50.

METHOD. Method of Teaching civil service writing. pp. 20. *Lond.* 1895. 8°. 7942. g. 29.

MEYRAT (P.) L'Écriture raisonnée. Nos. 1–3. *Limoges,* 1895. 4°.   7953. l. 22.

PÅHLMAN (O.) and (J.) Skriftkonstens historia. pp. 66. *Stockholm,* 1892. 8°. 12901. ccc. 23.

PURON (J. G.) El Calígrafo moderno de Appleton. 6 num. *Nueva York,* 1892. obl. 4°. 1890. a. 22.

Q. Revolution in Penmanship. pp. 8. *Burgess Hill,* 1893. 16°.   Pam. 94.

STOKES (W.) Rapid Writing, for rapidly teaching to write, pp. 288. *Lond.* 1884. 12°. 7942. a. 73.

STOLZE (E.) Von der Bilderschrift zur Stenographie. *Berl.* 1891, *etc.*   12991. d.

STRANGE (E. F.) Alphabets. A handbook of lettering. pp. 294. 1895. 8°. WHITE (J. W. G.) Ex-Libris Series.   K.T.C. 42 a. 1.

GERMAN MANUSCRIPTS. Choix de Manuscrits allemands, pour se familiariser avec l'écriture. pp. 60. *Paris,* 1893. 8°. 12963. dd. 36. (11.)

LÉVY (B.) Briefsammlung. Recueil de lettres allemandes reproduites en écritures autographiques. pp. 295. *Paris,* 1881. 8°. 010920. f. 30.

See also CRYPTOGRAPHY : GRAPHOLOGY : PALAEOGRAPHY : SHORTHAND.

HANOVER. Ac. Hanover. *Architecten- und Ingenieur-Verein.* Hannoverland in Wort und Bild. pp. 63. *Hannover,* 1892. fol.   1786. c. 18.

ULRICH (A.) Bilder aus Hannovers Vergangenheit. pp. 132. *Hannover-Linden,* 1891. 8°.   10240. f. 3.

BAHRDT (W.) Geschichte der Reformation der Stadt Hannover. pp. 142. *Hannover,* 1891. 8°.   4662. e. 9.

HANOVER—*continued.*

ULRICH (O.) Die Stadt Hannover im siebenjährigen Kriege. 1894. 8°. Ac. Luneberg. *Historischer Verein.* Zeitschrift. Jahrg. 1894.   Ac. 7085.

HASSELL (W. von) Das Kurfürstentum Hannover vom baseler Frieden bis 1806. pp. 455. *Hannover,* 1894. 8°.   9386. dd. 3.

THIMME (F.) Die inneren Zustände des Kurfürstentums Hannover, 1806–13. *Hannover,* 1893, *etc.* 8°.   9366. h.

JAENECKE (M.) Die Gewerbe-Politik des ehemaligen Königreichs Hannover, 1815–66, *etc.* pp. 66. *Marburg,* 1892. 8°.   8072. f. 3.

LUNEBURG. Von Lüneburg bis Langensalza. pp. 152. *Bremen,* 1894. 8°.   9080. d. 40.

GUTBIER (H.) Der Kampf bei Langensalza 27. Juni 1866. pp. 275. *Langensalza,* 1891. 8°.   9366. bbb.

PLINKE (A. H.) Stadthannoversche Fragen und Klagen. pp. 79. *Hannover,* 1895. 8°. Pam. 91.

HANOVER, New Hampshire. CHASE (F.) History of Dartmouth College and the town of Hanover. *Camb.* 1891, *etc.* 8°. 10412. i. 10.

HANSE TOWNS. STIEDA (W.) Hansischvenetianische Handelsbeziehungen in 15. Jahrhundert. pp. 191. *Rostock,* 1894. 4°. 8245. ff. 37. *See also* BREMEN : HAMBURG : LUBECK.

HARBOURS. *See* PORTS.

HARDCASTLE CRAGS. HARDCASTLE CRAGS. Guide to Hardcastle Crags. pp. 51. *Hebden Bridge,* 1894. 8°.   10348. c. 26. (5.)

HARE. TANTARA. Hare Hunting. pp. 66. *Lond.* 1893. 8°.   7908. bb. 49. *See also* SPORT.

HARE AND HOUNDS. BENSON (R. S.) Rugby School Hare and Hounds. pp. 50. *Rugby,* 1894. 8°.   7906. de. 39.

HARMONY. *See* MUSIC, General.

HARROGATE. LAVIS (H. J. J.) Prescriber's guide to the Harrogate Waters. pp. 48. *Lond.* 1892. 8°.   7462. aa. 37.

LIDDELL (J.) Mineral Waters of Harrogate. pp. 62. *Edinb.* 1893. 8°.   7462. bb. 35.

ROBERTS (A.) Harrogate Mineral Waters and homœopathy. pp. 16. *Lond.* 1893. 8°.   07305. h. 16. (15.)

WARD, LOCK AND Co. Pictorial guide to Harrogate. pp. 223. *Lond.* 1892. 8°. 10351. cc. 62.

HARROW-ON-THE-HILL. BUSHELL (W. D.) Harrow Octocentenary Tracts. 5 no. *Camb.* 1893, 94. 8°.   010358. g.

GARDNER (S.) Architectural history of Harrow Church. pp. 95. *Harrow.* 1895. 8°. 7817. i. 9.

HARROW SCHOOL. Harrow School Register. 1801–93. pp. 784. *Lond.* 1894. 8°. 8364. f. 24.

—— The Harrovian. *Harrow,* 1888, *etc.* 4°.   P.P. 6144. ba.

HARVARD COLLEGE. Ac. Cambridge. *Harvard University.* List of Publications of Harvard University and its officers. 1881, *etc.* 8°. Library of Harvard. Bibliographical Contributions. Nos. 12, 21, 23, 28, 33, 38.   11905. i.

—— Report of a special Committee on changes in the Academic Department. pp. 18. *Camb.* 1890. 8°.   8304. e. 19. (9.)

BOLTON (C. K.) Gossiping guide to Harvard. pp. 94. *Camb.* 1895. 8°.   10412. aaa. 45.

DAVIS (A. M.) Notes concerning the Records of Harvard College. pp. 14. 1888. 8°. Library of Harvard. Bibliographical Contributions. No. 27.   11905. i.

HARVARD COLLEGE—*continued.*

GREEN (S. A.) List of Commencement Days at Harvard College, 1642–1700. pp. 12. 1895. 8°.
8366. de. 45. (11.)

—— Harvard College in early times. 1672–77. pp. 7. *Bost.* 1894. 8°. 8366. de. 45. (9.)

HILL (G. B.) Harvard College, by an Oxonian. pp. 329. *N.Y.* 1894. 8°. 8364. cc. 67.

NORTON (C. E.) Harvard University. 1895. 4°. Four American Universities. 8364. i. 9.

PIERCE (J.) Some notes on Harvard Commencements, 1803–48. 1890. 8°. Ac. Boston. *Massachusetts Historical Society.* Proceedings. Ser. 2. Vol. 5. Ac. 8400/2.

WINSOR (J.) Archives of Harvard College. pp. 4. *Worcester,* 1894. 8°. Pam. 17.

HARWICH. BLOOM (J. H.) Heraldry and monumental Inscriptions in the Churches, and Burial Grounds of Harwich. pp. 127. *Hemsworth,* 1893. 4°. 9902. g. 24.

HARZ MOUNTAINS. Ac. Wernigerode. *Harz-Verein für Geschichte.* Festschrift zur 25-jährigen Gedenkfeier des Harzvereins.| pp. 155. *Wernigerode,* 1893. 4°. 7701. i. 2.

BAHLSEN (O.) Touren-Buch vom Harzgebirge. pp. 41. *Leipz.* 1891. 16°. 10256. a. 14.

HARTZ. Geschichte der Burgen und Klöster des Harzes. *Leipz.* 1895, *etc.* 8°. 10256. b.

HASNON, Abbey. DEWEZ (J.) Histoire de l'Abbaye d'Hasnon. pp. 582. *Lille,* 1890. 8°. 4629. k. 12.

HASTINGS AND ST. LEONARDS. APEL (H.) Album of photographs of Hastings and St. Leonards. *Hastings,* 1895. obl. 8°. 10360. aa. 36.

ELWORTHY (T.) Hastings Water supply. pp. 8. *St. Leonards,* 1894. 8°. Pam. 79.

HOWARD (M. M.) Handbook to Hastings and St. Leonard's. pp. 191. *Lond.* 1893. 8°. 10351. aa. 60.

PARSONS (F. J.) Illustrated guide to Hastings and St. Leonards. pp. 133. *Hastings,* 1881. 8°. 10350. bbb. 35.

PASCOE (C. E.) Eastbourne, Hastings and St. Leonard's. pp. 86. *Lond.* 1891. 8°. 10360. a. 14.

PIKE (W. T.) Guide to Hastings and St. Leonards. pp. 96. *Hastings,* 1888. 8°. 10358. cc. 47.

HATS. BRIGHAM (W. T.) Baltimore Hats past and present. pp. 142. *Baltimore,* 1890. 8°. 7942. e. 37.

RIPERT (A.) Ministère du Commerce. Etude sur la chapellerie anglaise. pp. 12. *Paris,* 1890. 8°. Pam. 23.

HAUBOURDIN. SPRIET (C. S.) Haubourdin. pp. 304. *Lille,* 1891. 8°. 10172. ee. 2.

HAUSSA. *See* SOUDAN.

HAUTE-FONTAINE, Abbey. GILARDONI (C.) L'Abbaye de Haute-Fontaine et le Jansénisme. pp. 241. *Vitry-le-F.* 1894. 8°. 4630. df. 4.

HAUTEFORT. CHAMPEVAL (J. B.) Le Château d'Hautefort au XVIIᵉ siècle. 1893, 94. 8°. Ac. Périgueux. *Société Historique.* Bulletin. Tom. 20, 21. Ac. 6886.

HAUTE LOIRE, Department. FRANCUS, *Le Docteur.* Voyage à travers la Haute-Loire. *Le Puy,* 1894, *etc.* 8°. 10174. bb.
See also VELAY.

HAUTE MARNE, Department. MARTIN (A.) Petite histoire de la Haute-Marne. pp. 264. *Chaumont,* 1892. 12°. 10109. aaa. 4.
See also CHAMPAGNE.

HAUTE PYRÉNÉES, Department.
PYRENEES, *Upper, Department.* Archives ecclésiastiques. pp. 265. 1892. 4°. Collection des inventaires-sommaires. 1814 b., *etc.*

RICARD (L.) La Bigorre et les Hautes-Pyrénées pendant la Révolution. pp. 302. *Paris,* 1894. 8°. 9231. l. 8.

See also BIGORRE : GASCONY.

HAUTE-VIENNE, Department. BOSREDON (P. de). Notes pour servir à la sigillographie de la Haute-Vienne. pp. 268. *Limoges,* 1892. 8°. 7757. e. 28.
See also LIMOUSIN : MARCHE.

HAVANNA. *Cámara oficial de Comercio.* Memoria que presenta la Junta Directiva de sus trabajos, 1889–90. pp. 37. *Habana,* 1890. 8°. 8225. ee. 40.
See also CUBA.

HAVEL, River. WEISKER (G.) Slavische Sprachreste aus dem Havellande. *Rathenow,* 1890, *etc.* 8°. 12975. m.

HAVERFORD COLLEGE. GARRETT (P. C.) History of Haverford College. pp. 732. *Phila.* 1892. 8°. 8366. f. 31.

HAVRE. GARSAULT (T.) Histoire de la ville du Havre. pp. 275. *Havre,* 1893. 8°. 10171. bb. 2.

MACK (J.) Notice sur les archives historiques du Havre. 1890. 8°. Ac. Havre. *Société Havraise.* Recueil. 1890. Ac. 2612.

AMPHOUX (H.) Essai sur l'histoire du Protestantisme au Havre. pp. 463. *Havre,* 1894. 8°. 4629. e. 39.

DUVAL (T.) Bp. of Soissons. Les Ursulines du Havre. pp. 226. *Rouen,* 1890. 8°. 4629. i. 8.

FLOUR DE SAINT-GENIS ( ) L'esprit public et les élections au Havre de 1787–90. 1889. 8°. Ac. Havre. *Société Havraise.* Recueil. 1889. Ac. 2612.

HAWAIIAN ISLANDS. ALEXANDER (W. D.) Brief history of the Hawaiian People. pp. 341. *N.Y.* 1891. 8°. 9781. cc. 4.

DAVIES (T. H.) Letters upon the political crisis in Hawaii, 1893–94. pp. 68. *Honolulu,* 1894. 8°. Pam. 65.

HAWAIIAN HISTORY. Two Weeks of Hawaiian history. The revolution of 1893. pp. 44. *Honolulu,* 1893. 8°. 9008. l. 2. (9.)

DANA (J. D.) Characteristics of Volcanoes, with contributions of facts from the Hawaiian Islands. pp. 399. *N.Y.* 1890. 8°. 07109. k. 13.

GOWEN (H. H.) The Paradise of the Pacific. pp. 180. *Lond.* 1892. 8°. 10491. de. 13.

HAWAII. Hawaii, the paradise and inferno of the Pacific. pp. 20. *Honolulu,* 1892. obl. 8°. 10491. de. 17.

KIRCHOFF (T.) Eine Reise nach Hawaii. pp. 199. *Altona,* 1890. 8°. 10491. f. 32.

MARCUSE (A.) Die hawaiischen Inseln. pp. 186. *Berl.* 1894. 8°. 10492. ff. 15.

NOTTAGE (C. G.) In Search of a Climate. *Lond.* 1894. 8°. 10492. ff. 14.

PALMER (J. A.) Memories of Hawaii. pp. 139. *Bost.* 1894. 8°. 10491. ff. 18.

REMY (J.) Ascension de MM. Brenchley et Remy au Maunaloa, Polynésie. pp. 45. *Châlons-sur-Marne,* 1892. 8°. Pam. 87.

SAUVIN (G.) Une Royaume polynésien. Îles Hawaï. pp. 321. *Paris,* 1893. 12°. 10491. bbb. 51.

STEVENS (J. L.) and OLESON (W. B.) Picturesque Hawaii. pp. 126. *Honolulu,* 1894. obl. fol. 1789. a. 35.

HAWAIIAN ISLANDS—continued.

STODDARD (C. W.) A trip to Hawaii. pp. 46.
San Francisco, 1892. 8°.   10491. d. 32.

—— Hawaiian Life. pp. 288. *Chicago*, 1894. 8°.
    10491. b. 38.

WHITNEY (H. M.) Tourists' guide through the
Hawaiian Islands. pp. 176. *Honolulu*, 1890. 8°.
    10492. d. 29.

See also PACIFIC OCEAN AND ISLANDS.

HAWKING. *See* FALCONRY.

HAWKSHEAD. COWPER (H. S.) Monumental Inscriptions in the church and churchyard of Hawkshead, *etc.* pp. 84.
Kendal, 1892. 8°.   9905. aaa. 27.

HAWORTH. FORSHAW (C. F.) Poets of Haworth and district. pp. 196.
Bradford, 1891. 8°.   11601. ff. 20.

HAYNES. HAYNES. Parish Registers of Haynes, 1596–1812. pp. 141. *Leeds*, 1891. 8°.
    9906. f. 16.

HAYTI AND SANTO DOMINGO.

History, Constitution, Law and Politics.

CASTONNET DES FOSSES (H.) La révolution de
Saint Domingue. pp. 380. *Paris*, 1893. 8°.
    9771. aaa. 2.

SUCHET (J. M.) Toussaint Louverture, prisonnier au fort de Joux. pp. 14.
Besançon, 1892. 8°.   Pam. 8.

ÉDOUARD (E.) Le Panthéon haïtien. pp. 76.
Paris, 1885. 8°.   10601. b. 26. (4.)

BOUZON (J.) Études sur la présidence de Faustin
Souloucque, 1847–49. pp. 208.
Port-au-Prince, 1894. 8°.   9771. c. 2.

LÉGITIME (F. D.) Histoire du governement du
général Légitime. pp. 422. *Paris*, 1890. 8°.
    9772. e. 7.

ROCHE-GRELLIER ( ) Quatre Mois de Ministère
sous général Légitime. pp. 44.
Paris, 1890. 8°.   Pam. 66.

MATHON (E.) Documents pour l'histoire d'Haïti.
1888–89, *etc.* pp. 260. *Paris*, 1890. 8°.
    9772. ee. 17.

NAYSER (S.) Les Filibustiers de la Tortue et la
France en 1890. pp. 70. *Paris*, 1891. 8°.
    8179. e. 2.

AUGUSTE (J.) Quelques vérités à propos des
récents évènements de la République d'Haïti.
pp. 59. *Paris*, 1891. 8°.   Pam. 46.

ANGULO GURIDI (A.) Examen de las Constituciones de Hispano-América, el Brasil y Haïtí.
2 tom. *Santiago*, 1891. 8°.   8180. k. 7.

DÉVOT (J.) La Nationalité et son influence.
Examen de la loi no. 2 du code civil d'Haïti.
pp. 171. *Paris*, 1893. 8°.   5424. dd. 12.

HAYTI. Les Codes haïtiens. 2 tom.
Port-au-Prince, 1890. 8°.   6735. f. 1.

JUSTIN (J.) Étude sur les Institutions haïtiennes.
Paris, 1894, *etc.* 8°.   8179. c.

BOUZON (J.) De l'esprit d'association en Haïti.
Conférence. pp. 31. *Port-au-Prince*, 1893. 12°.
    Pam. 65.

ÉDOUARD (E.) Essai sur la politique intérieure
d'Haïti. pp. 143. *Paris*, 1890. 12°.
    8180. aaa. 9.

FIRMIN (A.) Haïti au point de vue politique,
administratif et économique. pp. 48.
Paris, 1891. 8°.   Pam. 65.

JANVIER (L. J.) La République d'Haïti et ses
visiteurs 1840–82. pp. 636. *Paris*, 1883. 8°.
    8179. d. 2.

—— Haïti aux Haïtiens. pp. 43.
Paris, 1884. 12°.   Pam. 65.

HAYTI AND SANTO DOMINGO.—
History, etc.—continued.

JANVIER (L. J.) Les Antinationaux. Actes et
principes. pp. 101. *Paris*, 1884. 8°. 8180. aa. 15.

MARCELIN (F.) Questions haïtiennes. pp. 176.
Paris, 1891. 8°.   8179. a. 10.

MARCELIN (L. J.) Haïti. Ses guerres civiles.
3 pt. *Paris*, 1892–93. 8°.   8180. g. 20.

ROCHE-GRELLIER ( ) Haïti, son passé, son
avenir. pp. 152. *Paris*, 1891. 8°. 8156. df. 13.

Topography.

FERRET (A.) La République dominicaine.
pp. 216. *Brux.* 1894. 8°.   10481. aa. 42.

FORTUNAT (D.) Abrégé de la géographie de l'Ile
d'Haïti. pp. 166. *Paris*, 1890. 18°.
    10480. aa. 20.

ROUZIER (S.) Dictionnaire géographique d'Haïti
illustré. *Paris*, 1892, *etc.* 8°.   10470. h. 32.

TIPPENHAUER (L. G.) Die Insel Haiti. pp. 693.
Leipz. 1893. 8°.   10480. g. 17.

TEXIER (C.) Au Pays des généraux, Haïti.
pp. 306. *Paris*, 1891. 18°.   10480. aaa. 42.

Trade and Finance.

FIRMIN (A.) Haïti et ses relations économiques
avec la France. pp. 16. *Paris*, 1892. 8°.
    8226. g. 40. (10.)

HAYTI. Commercial directory of Haiti and Santo
Domingo. pp. 11. 1891. 8°. U.S. *Bureau of
American Republics.* Bulletin. No. 29.
    08225. k. 1.

—— Les Adversaires des chemins de fer d'Haïti.
Paris, 1895. *etc.* 8°.   8235. bb.

MARCELIN (F.) Le département des Finances
d'Haïti, 1892–94. *Paris*, 1895, *etc.* 8°. 08226. g.

ROCHE-GRELLIER ( ) Études économiques sur
Haïti. pp. 120. *Paris*, 1891. 8°. 08207. h. 2.

ST. DOMINGO, *Republic of.* Import duties of
Santo Domingo. *Eng. & Spain.* pp. 87. 1891. 8°.
U.S. *Bureau of American Republics.* Bulletin.
No. 12.   08225. k. 1.

HAZEBROUCK. FINOT (J.) Ville d'Hazebrouck. Inventaire sommaire des archives.
1886. 4°. France. *M. de l'Intérieur.* Collection des inventaires-sommaires. 1814–15. b., *etc.*

HEAD : NECK : HEADACHE. FROHSE
(F.) Die oberflächlichen Nerven des Kopfes.
pp. 23. *Berl.* 1895. fol.   1832. c. 21.

KUPFFER (C. v.) Studien zur vergleichenden
Entwicklungsgeschichte des Kopfes der Kranioten. *München*, 1893, *etc.* 8°.   7406. dd.

SCHMIDT (E. O.) Anatomy of the human Head.
pp. 16. *Lond.* 1895. 8°.   7419. l. 13.

CAMPBELL (H.) Headache, *etc.* pp. 410.
Lond. 1894. 8°.   7616. i. 10.

JONES (H. M.) Subjective noises in the Head.
pp. 152. *Lond.* 1891. 8°.   7611. c. 1.

SMITH (E. N.) Spasmodic Wry-neck and other
movements of the head. pp. 55. *Lond.* 1891. 8°.
    Pam. 39.

See also BRAIN : SKULL.

HEART. BALFOUR (G. W.) The senile Heart.
pp. 300. *Lond.* 1894. 8°.   7616. f. 10.

BROADBENT (J. F. H.) Adherent Pericardium.
pp. 126. *Lond.* 1895. 8°.   7616. aaaa. 5.

BURNETT (J. C.) On Neuralgia, with a chapter
on Angina Pectoris. pp. 172. *Lond.* 1894. 8°.
    7630. aa. 27.

CLARKE (J. H.) Diseases of the Heart and
arteries. pp. 195. *Lond.* 1895. 8°. 7616. aaaa. 1.

COLSON ( ) Recherches physiologiques sur l'occlusion de l'Aorte thoracique. pp. 57. 1891. 8°.
Ac. Brussels. *Académie des Sciences.* Mémoires. Tom. 44.   Ac. 985/4.

HEAT—continued.

WARREN (I.) Elementary treatise on Heat. pp. 426. *Dublin*, 1895. 8°.   8768. bb. 15.

WITZ (A.) Thermodynamique à l'usage des ingénieurs. pp. 215. 1892. 8°. Encyclopédie des aide-mémoire.   8709. g.

WOOLLCOMBE (W. G.) Practical work in Heat. pp. 61. *Oxf.* 1893. 8°.   8715. b. 68.

WORMELL (R.) Lectures on Heat. pp. 95. *Lond.* 1891. 8°.   8715. aa. 55.

WRIGHT (M. B.) Heat. pp. 336. *Lond.* 1893. 8°.   8716. aaa. 40.

BERTHELOT (M. P. E.) Traité pratique de Calorimétrie chimique. pp. 192. 1893. 8°. Encyclopédie des aide-mémoire.   8709. g.

LAAR (J. J. v.) Die Thermodynamik in der Chemie. pp. 196. *Amsterd.* 1893. 8°. 8908. d. 4. *See also* PHYSICS.

HEATING.

BALDWIN (W. J.) Hot-water Heating. pp. 392. *Lond.* 1892. 8°. 8776. ee. 53.

BILLINGS (J. S.) Ventilation and Heating. pp. 500. *N.Y.* 1893. 8°.   8777. h. 23.

DIESEL (R.) Theory and construction of a rational Heat Motor. pp. 88. *Lond.* 1894. 8°.   8768. cc. 29.

GRAHAM (M.) Hints on the construction and working of Regenerator Furnaces. pp. 131. *Lond.* 1894. 8°.   8767. g. 8.

HOOD (C.) Treatise upon Warming buildings by hot water. pp. 512. *Lond.* 1891. 8°. 2249. g. 7.

JACOB (E. H.) Notes on the Warming of houses, churches and schools. pp. 124. 1894. 8°. Manuals of Health.   7404. a.

JONES (W.) Heating by hot water. pp. 220. *Lond.* 1894. 8°.   8715. b. 70.

KEITH (J.) Houses of Parliament. Report on heating, *etc.* pp. 18. *Lond.* 1894. 8°. Pam. 79.

SHAW (W. N.) Warming. 1892. 8°. STEVENSON (T.) Treatise on Hygiene.   7391. g. 18.

WILLETT (J. R.) Heating of residences. pp. 34. *Chicago*, 1893. 8°.   8777. bbb. 28. (10.)

WITZ (A.) Les Machines thermiques. pp. 186. 1894. 8°. Encyclopédie des aide-mémoire.
   8709. g.

HEAVEN. *See* ESCHATOLOGY.

HEBÉCOURT.

JOSSE (H.) Notice historique sur les communes de Vers et d'Hébécourt. pp. 186. 1891. 8°. Ac. Amiens. *Société d'Archéologie.* Mémoires. Sér. 4. Tom. 1.
   Ac. 5343.

HEBREW LANGUAGE.

General: Miscellaneous.

HALL (A.) Who hath believed our Report? On some affinities of the Hebrew language. pp. 47. *Lond.* 1891. 8°.   12901. d. 36. (7.)

—— Hebrew unveiled. Affinities of the Hebrew Language. pp. 40. *Lond.* 1894. 8°. 012904. g. 3.

BERGER (S.) Quam notitiam linguae Hebraicae habuerint Christiani medii aevi temporibus. pp. 60. *Parisiis*, 1893. 8°.   012904. h. 12.

DINGLE (E.) Typal use of the Letters of the Hebrew alphabet. pp. 15. *Plymouth*, 1893. 8°.
   3019. e. 16.

MAGGS (J. T. L.) Introduction to the study of Hebrew. pp. 190. 1894. 8°. GREGORY (A. E.) Books for Bible Students.   3125. dd.

POZNAŃSKI (S.) Beiträge zur Geschichte der hebr. Sprachwissenschaft. *Berl.* 1894, *etc.* 8°.
   012904. h.

RODOSI (C.) Origin of modern Culture. Languages and their derivation from the Hebraica. pp. 182. *Chicago*, 1892. 8°.   12901. d. 38.

SCHACH (F.) Eine auferstandene Sprache. pp. 20. *Berl.* 1892. 8°.   12903. e. 28. (9.)

HEBREW—continued.

Accents: Orthography: Vowel Points.

ACKERMANN (A.) Geschichte des Verständnisses der hebräischen Accentuation. pp. 44. *Berl.* 1893. 8°.   12903. df. 28. (6.)

—— Das hermeneutische Element der biblischen Accentuation. pp. 88. *Berl.* 1893. 8°.
   12904. df. 51.

BUECHLER (A.) Untersuchungen zur Entstehung der hebräischen Accente. pp. 182. 1891. 8°. Ac. Vienna. *K. Akademie der Wissenschaften.* Sitzungsberichte. Phil.-hist. Classe. Bd. 124.
   Ac. 810/6.

DAVIS (A.) Hebrew Accents of the Books of the Bible. pp. 70. *Lond.* 1892. 8°. 012204. ee. 3.

BARDOWICZ (L.) Studien zur Geschichte der Orthographie des Althebräischen. pp. 112. *Frankfurt*, 1894. 8°.   012904. h. 23.

MARGOLIOUTH (G.) The superlinear Punctuation. pp. 42. *Lond.* 1893. 8°.   Pam. 47.

Dictionaries.

GESENIUS (F. H. W.) Hebrew and English Lexicon of the Old Testament. *Oxf.* 1892, *etc.* 4°.
   012904. k. 2.

—— Hebräisches und aramäisches Handwörterbuch über das Alte Testament. pp. 931. *Leipz.* 1890. 8°.   012904. h. 5.

SIEGFRIED (C.) and STADE (B.) Hebräisches Wörterbuch zum Alten Testamente. *Leipz.* 1892, *etc.* 8°.   012904. h.

FUERST (J.) Glossarium Graeco-Hebraeum der griechische Wörterschatz der judischen Midraschwerke. *Strassb.* 1890, *etc.* 8°. 012904. h. 2.

DICTIONARIES. Maqré Dardeqé. Dictionnaire hébreu-italien de la fin du XIV° siècle. pp. 56. *Paris*, 1889. 8°.   12902. f. 35. (6.)

Exercises.

GEDEN (A. S.) Exercises to accompany the Hebrew Grammar of Gesenius-Kautzsch. pp. 83. *Lond.* 1894. 8°.   012904. e. 3.

MASON (P. M.) 'Hebrew' Exercise Book. pp. 450. *Camb.* 1894. 8°.   012904. h. 15.

ROBERTSON (J.) Hebrew Exercises. pp. 38. *Glasg.* 1893. 8°.   12901. d. 36. (17.)

Grammar.

BACHER (W.) Die Anfänge der hebräischen Grammatik. 1895, *etc.* 8°. Ac. Germany. *Deutsche Morgenländische Gesellschaft.* Zeitschrift. Bd. 49.   Ac. 8815/2.

ITALIE (H.) Leercursus der Hebreeuwsche Tal. *Amsterdam*, 1892, *etc.* 8°.   012904. g.

NYLANDER (C. U.) Lärobok i hebräiska Språket. pp. 217. *Upsala*, 1887. 8°.   012904. h. 6.

STRACK (H. L.) Hebräische Grammatik. 2 pt. 1891. 8°. PETERMANN (J. H.) Porta linguarum orientalium. Pt. 1.   12904. de.

CARRIER (A. S.) The Hebrew Verb. pp. 33. *Chicago*, 1891. 8°.   012904. h. 8.

DRIVER (S. R.) Treatise on the use of the tenses in Hebrew. pp. 306. 1892. 8°. Clarendon Press Series.   2320. b. 36.

ZERWECK (N.) Die hebräische Präposition Min. pp. 60. *Leipz.* 1894. 8°.   12903. e. 29. (7.)

KNUDTZON (J. A.) Om det saakaldte perfektum og imperfektum i Hebraisk. pp. 152. *Kristiania*, 1889. 8°.   12904. df. 49.

HERNER (S.) Syntax der Zahlwörter im Alten Testament. pp. 148. *Lund*, 1893. 8°.
   012904. g. 4.

Synonyms.

LEVIN (S.) Versuch einer hebräischen Synonymik. *Berl.* 1894, *etc.* 8°.   012904. h.

HANDS (A. W.) Introduction to the study of Hebrew Synonyms for words expressing Fear. pp. 31. *Gloucester*, 1891. 8°. 12901. d. 30. (15.)
See also SEMITIC LANGUAGES.

HEBREW LITERATURE. Ac. London. *British Museum.* Catalogue of Hebrew Books acquired, 1868–1892. pp. 532. *Lond.* 1894. 4°.
                                                    Cat. Desk. B.
STEINSCHNEIDER (M.) Supplementum catalogi Librorum Hebraeorum in Bibliotheca Bodleiana. pp. 24. *Leipzig,* 1894. 8°.   1939. f. 22.
LONDON. *Library of the Corporation.* Catalogue of Hebraica and Judaica in the Library. pp. 231. *Lond.* 1891. 8°.   11899. ff. 51.
ZEITLIN (W.) Bibliographisches Handbuch der neuhebräischen Litteratur. *Leipz.* 1891, *etc.* 8°.
                                                    011902. m.
HERDER (J. G. v.) Vom Geist der ebräischen Poesie. 2 Tle. 1890. 8°. Bibliothek theologischer Klassiker. Bde. 30, 31.   3605. l.
KARPELES (G.) Jewish Literature. pp. 404. *Phila.* 1895. 8°.   4034. i. 48.
LENZ (H. K.) Judenliteratur und Literaturjuden. pp. 67. *Münster,* 1893. 8°.   Pam. 31.
P.P. *Vienna.* Monatsschrift für die Literatur des Judenthums. *Wien,* 1889, *etc.* 8°.
                                                    P.P. 17. h.
STEINSCHNEIDER (M.) Die hebraischen Uebersetzungen des Mittelalters. pp. 1077. *Berl.* 1893. 8°.   4999. f. 9.
KOHUT (G. A.) Early Jewish literature in America. pp. 44. *N.Y.* 1895. 8°. 11852. gg. 34.

HEBRIDES. BICKERDYKE (J.) Days in Thule. pp. 180. *Westminster,* 1894. 8°.
                                                    7907. ff. 5.
BROWN (J. A. H.) and BUCKLEY (T. E.) Vertebrate fauna of the Inner Hebrides. pp. 262. *Edinb.* 1892. 8°.   7208. d. 7.
—— Vertebrate fauna of the outer Hebrides. pp. 279. *Edinb.* 1888. 8°.   7206. i. 10.
GRAHAM (H. D.) The Birds of Iona and Mull. pp. 279. *Edinb.* 1890. 8°.   7285. aa. 16.
JAMIESON (J.) Historical account of the Culdees of Iona. pp. 257. *Glasg.* 1890. 8°. 4735. c. 30.
ILAY. Stent Book and acts of the Balliary of Islay 1718–1843. pp. 292. *Edinb.* 1890. 4°.
                                                    10370. h. 16.
GRAHAM (R. C.) Carved stones of Islay. pp. 119. *Glasg.* 1895. 4°.   7709. k. 31.
MACKENZIE (A.) The Isle of Skye in 1882–83. pp. 203. *Inverness,* 1883. 8°.   8142. b. 24.
MACKENZIE (W.) Gaelic Incantations, charms, *etc.* pp. 86. *Inverness,* 1895. 8°. 8631. f. 48.
See also SCOTLAND, *Highlands.*

HEDDERNHEIM. Ac. Frankfort. *Gesellschaft für Frankfurts Geschichte.* Mittheilungen über römische Funde in Heddernheim. *Frankfurt,* 1894. 4°.   7706. h. 29.

HEDON. BOYLE (J. R.) Early history of the town and port of Hedon. pp. 227. *Hull,* 1895. 4°.   10358. i. 16.

HEDONISM. WATSON (J.) Hedonistic Theories. pp. 248. *Glasg.* 1895. 8°. 8409. d. 14. *See also* PHILOSOPHY.

HEIDELBERG. Ac. Carlsruhe. *Badische Historische Commission.* Statuten und Reformationen der Universität Heidelberg. pp. 383. *Leipz.* 1891. 4°.   8357. l. 19.
—— Heidelberg. *Historisch-Philosophischer Verein.* Neue heidelberger Jahrbücher. *Heidelberg,* 1891, *etc.* 8°.   Ac. 890.
DIETZ (E.) Die deutsche Burschenschaft in Heidelberg. pp. 162. *Heidelberg,* 1894. 8°.
                                                    8357. cc. 51.
HOLSTEIN (H.) Zur Gelehrtengeschichte Heidelbergs beim Ausgang des Mittelalters. pp. 26. *Wilhelmshaven,* 1893. 4°.   Pam. 17.

HELENSBURGH. HELENSBURGH. Helensburgh and the Gareloch. *Helensburgh,* 1894. 16°.
                                          10369. a. 47.
—— *U.P. Church.* Helensburgh U. P. Church Jubilee, 1894. pp. 48. *Helensburgh,* 1894. 4°.
                                          4735. e. 24.

HELIGOLAND. DANCKWERTH (C.) Helgoland einst und jezt. pp. 22. *Berl.* 1891. 8°.
                                          10107. ff. 27. (6.)
DIERCKS (G.) Helgoland. pp. 33. 1891. 8°. Sammlung gemeinverständlicher Vorträge. N.F. No. 121.   12249. m.
HALLIER (E.) Helgoland unter deutscher Flagge. pp. 336. *Hamb.* 1892. 8°.   10256. b. 45.
LOUIS SALVATOR, *Archduke of Austria.* Helgoland, eine Reise-Skizze. pp. 31. *Würzburg,* 1890. 8°.   Pam. 91.
SEELIG (R.) Helgoland. Führer und Rathgeber. pp. 44. *Hamb.* 1883. 8°. 10106. de. 9. (4.)
STENZEL ( ) Helgoland und die deutsche Flotte. pp. 48. *Berl.* 1891. 8°.   Pam. 43.
HERON-FERMOR (R. M.) Speech in condemnation of the Cession of Heligoland. pp. 16. *Brighton,* 1890. 8°.   8026. ee. 24. (8.)
WALLER (H.) Heligoland for Zanzibar. pp. 51. *Lond.* 1893. 8°.   Pam. 81.
GAETKE (H.) Die Vogelwarte Helgoland. pp. 609. *Braunschweig,* 1891. 8°. 7285. g. 15.
—— Heligoland as an Ornithological Observatory. pp. 599. *Edinb.* 1895. 8°.   7285. g. 20.

HELIOGRAPH. LOHSE (O.) Beschreibung des Heliographen. 1889. 4°. Ac. Potsdam. *Astrophysikalisches Observatorium.* Publicationen. Bd. 4.   8752. i. 6.

HELIOPOLIS. *See* BAALBEC.

HELL. *See* ESCHATOLOGY.

HELLUM. Ac. Aalborg. *Jydsk Historisk-Topografisk Selskab.* Bidrag til Hellum Herreds Beskrivelse. pp. 293. *Aalborg,* 1890–92. 8°.
                                          Ac. 7621/2.

HELSINGBORG. LILLIESTRÅLE (N. F.) Magnus Stenbock och slaget vid Helsingborg. pp. 15. *Helsingborg,* 1890. 8°.   Pam. 28.

HELSINGFORS. Ac. Helsingfors. *Finska Universitet.* Commentationes in memoriam actorum CCL. annorum. *Helsingfors,* 1890, *etc* 4°. & 8°.   Ac. 1095.
EHRSTRÖM (E.) Helsingfors Stads Historia. pp. 171. 1890. 8°. Ac. Helsingfors. *Svenska Literatur sällskapet.* Skrifter. No. 15. Ac. 9082.
HELSINGFORS. [Circulars, *etc.* issued by manufacturers at Helsingfors, *Helsingfors,* 1891, 92.
                                          1880. c. 13. (23.)

HELVELLYN. *See* ENGLAND, *Lake District.*

HEMIPTERA. Ac. *etc.* Brussels. *Musée Royal d'Histoire naturelle.* Catalogue des Hémiptères. *Brux.* 1893, *etc.* 8°.   Ac. 2959/3.
ANTESSANTY (G. d') Hémiptères hétéroptères de l'Aube. 1890. 8°. Ac. Troyes. *Société d'Agriculture.* Mémoires. Tom. 54. Ac. 260.
EDWARDS (J.) Hemiptera Homoptera of the British Islands. *Lond.* 1894, *etc.* 8°. 7297. cc.
SAUNDERS (E.) Hemiptera Heteroptera of the British Islands. *Lond.* 1892, *etc.* 8°.
                                          7298. ee. 26.
HUEBER (T.) Fauna Germanica. Hemiptera heteroptera. pp. 143. *Ulm,* 1891. 8°.
                                          7297. e. 32.
UHLER (P. R.) Observations upon the Heteropterous Hemiptera of California. 1894. 8°. Ac. San Francisco. *California Academy.* Proceedings. Ser. 2. Vol. 4.   Ac. 3037.
See also INSECTS.

HEMPSTEAD. HEMPSTEAD. *Parish Church.*
Inscriptions in Hempstead Church. pp. 14.
Lond. 1886. 4°.   Pam. 26.

HEPATICAE. BREIDLER (J.) Die Leber-
moose Steiermarks. 1894. 8°. Ac. Gratz. *Naturwissenschaftlicher Verein.* Mittheilungen.
Jahrg. 1893.   Ac. 2905.

COOKE (M. C.) Handbook of British Hepaticae.
pp. 310. *Lond.* 1894. 8°.   07028. k. 11.

PEARSON (W. H.) List of Canadian Hepaticæ.
pp. 31. *Montreal,* 1890. 8°.   7074. k. 11. (8.)

—— Hepaticæ Madagascarienses. pp. 11. 1893. 8°.
Ac. Christiania. *Videnskabs-Selskab.* Forhandlinger. aar 1892. No. 14.   Ac. 1054.

LONDON. *Botanical Record Club.* London Catalogue of British Mosses and Hepatics. pp. 32.
Lond. 1881. 8°.   7031. e. 25. (6.)

See also MOSSES.

HERACLEOPOLIS MAGNA.
See EGYPT, *Antiquities.*

HERALDRY AND GENEALOGY.

Bibliography.

GATFIELD (G.) Guide to books and MSS. relating to Heraldry and Genealogy. pp. 646.
Lond. 1892. 8°.   BB.T. d. 15.

MARSHALL (E. W.) Genealogists' Guide.
pp. 884. *Guildford,* 1893. 8°.   Cat. Desk A.

General Works on Heraldry and Genea-
logy. BRETT (E. J.) Record of the origin
and development of Arms and Armour.
pp. 120. 8. *Lond.* 1894. 4°.   K.T.C. 24. b. 7.

BRITISH HERALDRY. Glossary of terms used in
Heraldry. pp. 659. *Oxf.* 1894. 8°. 9906. aa. 1.

CHAMPEAUX (J. de) Devises : Cris de guerre ;
légendes ; dictons. pp. 288. *Dijon,* 1890. 8°.
     9916. c. 9.

CROLLALANZA (G. de) Araldica Ufficiale.
pp. 131. *Pisa,* 1891. 8°.   9904. aaa. 3.

CUSSANS (J. E.) Handbook of Heraldry.
pp. 353. *Lond.* 1893. 8°.   2119. a.

DIELITZ (J.) Die Wahl- und Denksprüche, *etc.*
pp. 476. *Frankf. a. M.* 1888. 4°. 9916. dd. 10.

GHEUSI (P. B.) Le Blason héraldique. pp. 373.
Paris, 1892. 8°.   9903. f. 14.

GOURDON DE GENOUILLAC (N. J. H.) L'Art
héraldique. pp. 290. *Paris,* 1889. 8°. 2261. c.

GRAZEBROOK (G.) Attempt to classify and date
the Shapes found in heraldic Shields. 1890. 8°.
Ac. Liverpool. *Historic Society.* Proceedings.
Vol. 41.   Ac. 8100.

GRELLET (J.) L'Art héraldique. pp. 15.
Neuchatel, 1892. 8°.   Pam. 26.

GUIGARD (J.) Nouvel Armorial du bibliophile.
2 tom. *Paris,* 1890. 8°.   2400. g.

HULME (F. E.) History and practice of Heraldry.
pp. 281. *Lond.* 1892. 8°.   9904. ccc. 3.

JOUFFROY D'ESCHAVANNES ( ) Traité de la
science du Blason. pp. 280. *Paris,* 1891. 8°.
     9905. bb. 26.

JUNIUS (J. H.) Heraldick. pp. 369.
Amsterd. 1894. 8°.   9906. ee. 23.

LABITTE (A.) Traité du Blason. pp 279.
Paris, 1892. 12°.   9902. ccc. 11.

MOENS (J. B.) Armoiries des principaux états
du globe. *Brux.* 1890. 8. *sh.* fol. 1856. d. 1. (76.)

NISBET (A.) A. Nisbet's heraldic Plates origin-
ally intended for his "System of Heraldry."
pp. 192. *Edinb.* 1892. fol.   9915. i. 8.

TRIBOLATI (F.) Grammatica araldica. pp. 116.
Milano, 1892. 12°.   9905. a. 12.

WARNECKE (F.) Heraldische Meister. Hundert
heraldische Kunstblätter. *Berl.* 1894. fol.
     K.T.C. 29. b. 5.

HERALDRY.—General Works on—*cont.*

WOODWARD (J.) and BURNETT (G.) Treatise on
Heraldry British and Foreign. 2 vol.
Edinb. 1892. 8°.   2400. d. 13.

—— Treatise on ecclesiastical Heraldry.
pp. 580. *Edinb.* 1894. 8°.   2400. d. 14.

ADLERSFELD (E. v.) Das goldene Buch. Verzeichniss der regierenden Fürstenhäuser Europas.
pp. 564. *Breslau,* 1892. 16°.   9905. a. 13.

LORENZ (O.) Genealogischer Hand- und Schul-
Atlas. pp. 43. *Berl.* 1892. 8°.   9914. bb. 12.

See also KNIGHTHOOD, *Orders of.*

Austria.

STYRIA. Steiermärkisches Wappen-Buch, 1567.
pp. 16. 180. *Graz,* 1893. 8°.   9906. ee. 3.
Ac. Vienna. *Verein "Adler."* HOHENBUEHEL
(L. v.) *Baron.* Beiträge zur Geschichte des
tiroler Adels. pp. 130. *Wien,* 1891. 8°.
     9902. g. 22.

Baltic Provinces, of Russia.

GERNET (A. v.) Forschungen zur Geschichte des
baltischen Adels. *Reval,* 1893, *etc.* 8°. 9906. ee.

Belgium.

BOSMANS (J.) Armorial de la Belgique.
Brux. 1889. 8°.   9916. a. 22.

—— Traité d'Héraldique belge. pp. 255.
Brux. 1890. 8°.   9903. d. 5.

RIDDER (A. de) Devises et Cris de guerre de la
Noblesse belge. pp. 82. *Brux.* 1894. 16°.
     9905. a. 16.

Denmark.

ELVIUS (S.) and HIORT-LORENZEN (H. R.) Danske
patriciske Slægter. *Kjøbenh.* 1891, *etc.* 8°.
     9904. e.

France.

RENAUD ( ) De l'origine des Fleurs de Lis
dans les Armoiries royales. pp. 12.
Château-Thierry, 1891. 8°.   9916. b. 28. (7.)

DELATHEURATTE (A. D.) and BARDIES (C.) Lettres
sur les Armoiries, les particules et la noblesse.
pp. 137. *Paris,* 1891. 12°.   9905. bb. 27.

GUIGARD (J.) Nouvel Armorial du bibliophile.
2 tom. *Paris,* 1890. 8°.   2400. g.

HALLEZ D'ARROS ( ) *Count.* L'Armorial général
de France de C. R. d'Hozier. Notice historique.
pp. 42. *Paris,* 1891. 8°.   9906. b. 9. (13.)

HOZIER (C. R. d') Collège héraldique de France.
Armorial général. pp. 252. *Dijon,* 1895. 8°.
     9906. bb. 9.

MAILHOL (D de) Dictionnaire historique et
héraldique de la Noblesse française.
Paris, 1895, *etc.* 8°.   9906. i.

MAUROY (A. de) De la Noblesse maternelle.
1891. 8°. Ac. Paris. *Conseil Héraldique.* Annuaire. Année 4.   Ac. 5912.

VIAN (L.) La Particule nobiliaire. pp. 196.
Paris, 1891. 8°.   9905. aaa. 26.

Ac. Paris. *Société de l'histoire de la Révolution.*
Liste des membres de la Noblesse impériale.
pp. 189. *Paris,* 1889. 8°.   Ac. 6885. b/3.

RÉVÉREND (A.) *Viscount.* Armorial du premier
Empire. *Paris,* 1894, *etc.* 8°.   9906. i.

MAGNY (L. de) Armorial des Princes, ducs, marquis, barons et comtes romains en France, créés
de 1815 à 1890. pp. 93. *Paris,* 1891. 8°.
     9914. bb.

SOULTRAIT (G. de) *Count.* Armorial du Bourbonnais. 2 tom. *Moulins,* 1890. 4°. 9915. bb. 9.

POTIER DE COURCY (P.) Nobiliaire et armorial
de Bretagne. 3 tom. *Rennes,* 1890. 4°.
     9915. dd. 5.

HERALDRY.—France—*continued.*

Régis de l'Estourbeillon ( ) *Count.* La noblesse de Bretagne. *Vannes,* 1891, *etc.* 4°. 9906. f.

Colonna de Cesari Rocca ( ) Armorial corse. pp. 64. *Paris,* 1892. 8°. 9903. bb. 17.

Avril de Burey (R. A. L.) *Viscount.* Les Archives héraldiques d'Évreux. pp. 376. *Évreux,* 1890. 4°. 9902. i. 30.

Steyert (A.) Armorial de Lyonnais, Forez, Beaujolais, Franc-Lyonnais et Dombes. *Lyon,* 1892, *etc.* 4°. 9915. d.

Cumont (M. P. T. de) *Marchioness.* Recherches sur la noblesse du Périgord. pp. 376. *Paris,* 1890. 8°. 9916. b. 22.

Froidefond de Boulazac (A. de) Armorial de la noblesse du Périgord. 2 tom. *Périgueux,* 1891. 8°. 9916. ee. 7.

Beauchet-Filleau (E. H. E.) and Chergé (C. de) Dictionnaire des familles du Poitou. *Poitiers,* 1891, *etc.* 8°. 9916. dd.

Figuères (R. de) and Armand (A.) Armorial du Département de la Somme. *Abbeville,* 1895. 8°. 9906. bb. 8.

Gigord (R. de) La Noblesse de Villeneuve de Berg en 1789. pp. 777. *Lyon,* 1894. 4°. 9906. h. 3.

Germany.

Adlersfeld (E. v.) Das goldene Buch. Verzeichniss der deutschen Standesherren. pp. 564. *Breslau,* 1892. 16°. 9905. a. 13.

Bry (T. de) Emblemata Nobilitatis. Stamm- und Wappenbuch. *Berl.* 1894. fol. K.T.C. 40. b. 2.

—— Emblemata Saecularia. Kulturgeschichtliches Stamm- und Wappenbuch. *Berl.* 1894. fol. K.T.C. 40. b. 1.

Dachenhausen (A. v.) *Baron.* Genealogisches Taschenbuch des Uradels. *Brünn,* 1891, *etc.* 8°. 9905. bb. 28.

Gundlach (O.) Bibliotheca familiarum nobilium. Repertorium gedruckter Familien-Geschichten. pp. 332. *Neustrelitz,* 1886. 8°. 9916. b. 25.

Keil (R.) and (R.) Die deutschen Stammbücher des 16ten bis 19ten Jahrhunderts. pp. 337. *Berl.* 1893. 8°. 011901 e. 22.

Roth von Schreckenstein (C. H.) Die Ritterwürde und der Ritterstand. pp. 735. *Freiburg,* 1886. 8°. 9914. h. 25.

Sibmacher (J.) Johan Sibmacher's Wappen-Büchlein. pp. 5. *Berl.* 1893. obl. 4°. 9904. aaa. 5.

Wurmann (F.) Sammlung aller Amts, Siegel und Wappen der Magistrate, Bürgermeistereien und Polizei-behörden der deutschen Städte. *Kaufbeuren,* 1894, *etc.* 4°. 9906. i.

Ac. Carlsruhe. *Historische Kommission.* Kindler von Knobloch (J.) Oberbadisches Geschlechterbuch. *Heidelberg,* 1894, *etc.* 4°. Ac. 7066/8.

Zangemeister (C.) Die Wappen, und Standarten der grossen heidelberger Liederhandschrift, Manesse Codex. *Heidelberg,* 1892, *etc.* fol. 9902. l.

Meyer (E. L.) Hamburgische Wappen und Genealogien. pp. 496. *Hamb.* 1890. 8°. 9904. m. 24.

Kissel (C.) Hessisches Wappenbuch. pp. 77. *Giessen,* 1893. 8°. 9914. ff. 7.

Gritzner (A. M. F.) Das Wappen der Kurfürsten zu Brandenburg, 1417–1701. 1894. 4°. Ac. Berlin. *Verein "Herold."* Festschrift. 9914. d. 17.

HERALDRY.—Germany—*continued.*

Gritzner (A. M. F.) Landes- und Wappenkunde der brandenburgisch-preussischen Monarchie. pp. 310. *Berl.* 1894. 8°. 9906. g. 15.

Janecki (M.) Handbuch des preussischen Adels. *Berl.* 1892, *etc.* 8°. 9914. ff. 4.

Germany. Bauernwappen der deutschen Nordsee-Marschen. *Bremerhafen,* 1892, *etc.* 8°. 9914. g.

Great Britain and Ireland and Colonies.

Gatfield (G.) Guide to books and manuscripts relating to English and Foreign Heraldry and Genealogy. pp. 646. *Lond.* 1892. 8°. BB.T. d. 15.

Marshall (G. W.) The Genealogist's guide. pp. 884. *Guildford,* 1893. 8°. Cat. Desk A.

Scrutton (G.) Queen Victoria's Ancestors to the middle ages. pp. 28. *Lond.* 1887. 8°. 1860. d. 1. (41.)

Fox-Davies (A. C.) and Crookes (M. E. B.) Book of Public Arms. Armorial Bearings of counties, cities, towns and universities of the United Kingdom. pp. 57. *Edinb.* 1894. 4°. 2400. h. 7.

Johnston (W.) and (A. K.) Illustrations of flags and arms of the United Kingdom. *Edinb.* 1893, *etc.* fol. Tab. 11747. a. (90.)

Burke (*Sir* J. B.) History of the landed gentry of Great Britain and Ireland. 2 vol. *Lond.* 1894. 8°. 2119. c.

England and Wales. Alphabetical account of the Nobility and Gentry, 1673. pp. 124. *Lond.* 1892. fol. 9906. f. 12.

Fox-Davies (A. C.) Armorial Families. Peerage, Baronetage and Knightage, and directory of some Gentlemen of coat-armour. pp. 1086. *Edinb.* 1895. 4°. 2400. h.

Howard (J. J.) and Crisp (F. A.) Visitation of England and Wales. *Lond.* 1893, *etc.* 8°. K.T.C. 32. b. 2.

Ac. London. *Harleian Society.* Publications. Vol. xxxvii. Familiae minorum Gentium. Diligentia Josephi Hunter. *Lond.* 1894, *etc.* 4°. 2118. e.

Crisp (F. A.) Fragmenta Genealogica. *Lond.* 1889, *etc.* fol. 9916. f. 9.

Blaydes (F. A.) Genealogia Bedfordiensis: Landed Gentry of Bedfordshire, 1538–1700. pp. 507. *Lond.* 1890. 4°. 9916. c. 21.

Ac. Cumberland. *Antiquarian Society.* Jackson (W.) Papers and pedigrees relating to Cumberland and Westmoreland. 2 vol. *Lond.* 1892. 8°. Ac. 5630/7.

Cumberland. Pedigrees recorded at the Heralds' Visitations of Cumberland and Westmorland. 1615–66. pp. 172. *Carlisle,* 1891. 8°. 9914. cc. 1.

Durham. Pedigrees recorded at the Visitations of Durham. 1575–1615–66. *Lond.* 1887. 8°. 9904. cc. 2.

Fletcher (W. G. D.) Leicestershire Pedigrees. pp. 207. *Lond.* 1887. 4°. 9906. g. 21.

Ryley (W.) and Dethick (H) Visitation of Middlesex, 1663. pp. 101. *Lond.* 1887. 8°. 9902. g. 26.

Ac., *etc.* London. *Harleian Society.* Publications. Vol. 32. Visitacion of Norffolk, 1563. pp. 375. *Lond.* 1891. 8°. 2118. d.

Northumberland. Pedigrees recorded at the Visitations of Northumberland, 1615–66. pp. 139. *Newcastle,* 1891. 8°. 9914. cc. 2.

Cole (H. D.) Heraldic Bearings of families of the Isle of Wight. *Lond.* 1891, *etc.* 4°. 9902. i. 7.

Ross (F.) Yorkshire Family romance. pp. 254. *Hull,* 1891. 8°. 9903. bb. 16.

HERALDRY.—Great Britain, etc.—*cont.*

BLOOM (J. H.) Heraldry in Churches of the W. Riding of Yorkshire. 6 pt. *Hamsworth*, 1892–95. 8°. 9904. e. 6.

COLLIER (C. V.) Notes on the Heraldry in the Church of Bridlington. pp. 9. *Bridlington*, 1893. 8°. Pam. 26.

ANDERSON (J. M.) Heraldry of St. Andrews University. pp. 24. *Edinb.* 1895. 8°. 9905. b. 31.

MACCALL (H. B.) Some old Families of Scotland. pp. 290. *Birmingham*, 1890. 4°. K.T.C. 5. b. 9.

PAUL (J. B.) An Ordinary of Arms contained in the Public Register of Scotland. pp. 263. *Edinb.* 1893. 8°. 9906. ee. 1.

TAYLOR (J.) Great historic Families of Scotland. 2 vol. *Lond.* 1891–94. 4°. 9906. i. 20.

O'HART (J.) Irish Pedigrees. 2 vol. *Dublin*, 1887. 8°. 2400. d. 8.

—— Irish Landed Gentry, when Cromwell came to Ireland. pp. 773. *Dublin*, 1887. 8°. 2400. d. 9.

Ac. etc. Welshpool. *Powysland Club.* Pedigrees of Montgomeryshire Families. pp. 167. 1888. *Lond.* 1888. 8°. Ac. 8225/2.

BURKE (*Sir* J. B.) Genealogical and heraldic history of the Colonial Gentry. *Lond.* 1891, *etc.* 8°. 2120. c.

G. B. & I. *Colonies.* Arms and Badges of the several Colonies. *Lond.* 1881. fol. 1861. d. 23.

Greece.

PHANARIOT. Livre d'Or de la Noblesse Phanariote. pp. 160. *Athènes*, 1892. 4°. 9904. m. 25.

India.

LETHBRIDGE (*Sir* R.) The Golden book of India. pp. 584. *Lond.* 1893. 8°. 2119. d.

Italy.

CROLLALANZA (G. di) Araldica Ufficiale. pp. 131. *Pisa*, 1891. 8°. 9904. aaa. 3.

ITALIAN ILLUSTRIOUS FAMILIES. Storia genealogica delle Famiglie italiane. *Firenze*, 1891, *etc.* 4°. 9915. i.

MELONI-SATTA (P.) L' Arma di Sardegna. pp. 16. *Cagliari*, 1892. 8°. 9905. aaa. 31. (3.)

PADIGLIONE (C.) Le Massime della Commissione regionale napoletana per gli elenchi nobiliari. pp. 78. *Napoli*, 1893. 8°. 9906. g. 10.

Jews.

WOLF (L.) Jewish Coats of Arms. pp. 10. *Lond.* 1889. 8°. 9916. bb. 17. (6.)

Netherlands.

RIETSTAP (J. B.) De wapens van den Nederlandschen Adel. pp. 552. *Groningen*, 1890. 8°. 9916. c. 5.

Spain.

CUATRO TORRES (de las) *Baron.* El Blasón de Tarragona. pp. 30. *Barcelona*, 1891. 8°. 9903. b. 10.

VIGIL (C. M.) Heraldica asturiana y catálogo armorial de España. pp. 396. *Oviedo*, 1892. 8°. 9904. f. 9.

Sweden.

KINBERG (A.) Gotländska slägter. *Visby*, 1889, *etc.* 4°. 9902. dd.

Tyrol. *See supra : Austria.*

United States of America.

BROWNING (C. H.) Americans of Royal Descent. pp. 732. *Phila.* 1891. 8°. 9916. cc. 9.

HERALDRY.—United States—*continued.*

APPLETON (W. S.) Pedigrees and arms of New England. pp. 10. *Bost. Mass.* 1891. 8°. 9916. b. 29. (8.)

BECKWITH (P.) Creoles of St. Louis. pp. 169. *St. Louis*, 1893. 8°. 9902. e. 29.

ZIEBER (E.) Heraldry in America. pp. 427. *Phila.* 1895. 8°. 9916. d. 24.

HÉRAULT, Department. Ac. Montpellier. *Société de Géographie.* Géographie du Département de l'Hérault. *Montpellier*, 1891, *etc.* 8°. 010171. k.

SAUREL (F.) Histoire religieuse de l'Hérault pendant la Révolution. *Paris*, 1894, *etc.* 8°. 4629. d.

See also CEVENNES : MONTPELLIER.

HERBALS. *See* BOTANY, *Medical.*

HERBITZHEIM. LEVY (J.) Geschichte des Klosters und Pfarrei Herbitzheim. pp. 288. *Strassb.* 1892. 8°. 4662. c. 17.

HEREDITY. CLOUSTON (T. S.) The Neuroses of development pp. 138. *Edinb.* 1891. 8°. 7660. g. 19.

GUYAU (J. M.) Education and Heredity. pp. 306. 1891. 8°. ELLIS (H. H.) Contemporary Science Series. 8709. i.

HECKSCHER (A.) Bidrag til Grundlæggelse af en afstemningslære. pp. 204. *Kjøbenh.* 1892. 8°. 8006. c. 5.

KAUFMANN (M.) Heredity and personal Responsibility. pp. 63. 1895. 8°. Present Day Tracts. Vol. 13. 2210. a.

LEMOIGNE (A.) Ipotesi sulla causa dell' eredità negli animali superiori. pp. 77. *Milano*, 1894. 8°. 7406. g. 23.

ORR (H. B.) Theory of Development and Heredity. pp. 255. *N.Y.* 1893. 8°. 7006. c. 14.

SANSON (A.) L'Hérédité normale et pathologique. pp. 430. *Paris*, 1893. 8°. 7410. ee. 41.

STRAHAN (S. A. K.) Marriage and disease. Study of Heredity. pp. 326. *Lond.* 1892. 8°. 7641. aaa. 28.

VALLET (P.) La Vie et l'Hérédité. pp. 388. *Paris*, 1891. 12°. 8470. ccc. 15.

WEISMANN (A.) Amphimixis oder die Vermischung der Individuen. pp. 176. *Jena*, 1891. 8°. 7405. e. 2.

—— Aufsätze über Vererbung und verwandte biologische Fragen. pp. 848. *Jena*, 1892. 8°. 7002. f. 12.

—— Essays on Heredity. 1891, *etc.* 8°. Clarendon Press Series. 2319. b. 4.

—— The Germ-plasm : a theory of heredity. pp. 477. 1893. 8°. ELLIS (H. H.) Contemporary Science Series. 8709. i.

ROMANES (G. J.) Examination of Weismannism. pp. 221. *Lond.* 1893. 8°. 7006. c. 13.

See also EVOLUTION.

HEREFORD. BREWER (H.) Series of Photographic views of Hereford. *Hereford*, 1895. obl. 4°. 10360. aa. 37.

HEREFORD. Catalogue of documents, selected from the municipal archives of the City of Hereford. ff. 40. *Hereford*, 1894. fol. 11900. k. 29.

WARD, LOCK AND CO. Handbook to Hereford Cathedral. *Lond.* 1890. 8°. 010358. l. 20

HEREFORDSHIRE. TIMMINS (H. T.) Nooks and corners of Herefordshire. pp. 160. 3. *Lond.* 1892. 4°. 10351. k. 19.

WORCESTER. Murray's Handbook for Worcestershire and Herefordshire. pp. 16. 168. *Lond.* 1894. 8°. 2364. a. 17.

HERESIES. ALEXANDER, *Bishop of Lycopolis.* Alexandri Lycopolitani contra Manichae opiniones disputatio, etc. pp. 50. *Lips.* 1895. 8°.
　　　　　　　　2278. i. 10.
HENNER (C.) Beiträge zur Organisation der päpstlichen Ketzergerichte. pp. 383. *Leipz.* 1890. 8°. 4061. dd. 9.
MENENDEZ Y PELAYO (M.) Historia de los heterodoxos Españoles. 3 vol. *Madrid,* 1880, 81. 8°. 4625. d. 1.
THUEMMEL (W.) Zum Beurtheilung des Donatismus. pp. 104. *Halle,* 1893. 8°. 4534. ee. 16. *See also* CHURCH HISTORY: GNOSTICISM: INQUISITION.

HERIOTS. BROUGHTON-ROUSE (E. B.) The Law of Heriots. pp. 46. *Lond.* 1892. 8°.
　　　　　　　　6306. h. 10.

HERNE BAY. HERNE BAY. Rambler's Guide to Herne Bay. pp. 108. *Herne Bay,* 1892. 8°.
　　　　　　　　10351. b. 69.
WATKINSON (J.) Herne Bay illustrated. *Herne Bay,* 1889. fol. 10351. h. 34.

HERNIA. BENNETT (W. H.) Lectures on abdominal Hernia. pp. 225. *Lond.* 1893. 8°.
　　　　　　　　7620. de. 22.
BROESIKE (G.) Ueber intraabdominale, retroperitoneale, Hernien. pp. 206. *Berl.* 1891. 8°.
　　　　　　　　7620. e. 21.
ENGLISCH (J.) Über Hernia obturatoria. pp. 160. *Leipz.* 1891. 4°. 7620. df. 25.
LUCAS-CHAMPIONNIÈRE (J.) Cure radicale des hernies. pp. 724. *Paris,* 1892. 8°. 7620. df. 29.
MACREADY (J. F. C. H.) Treatise on Ruptures. pp. 442. *Lond.* 1893. 8°. 7630. f. 24.
MANLEY (T. H.) Hernia. pp. 231. *Phila.* 1893. 8°. 7641. f. 29.
REMEDI (V.) Sulla patogenesi dell' Ernie.↑ 1890. 8°. Ac. Sienna. *Accademia delle Scienze.* Atti. Ser. 4. Vol. 2. Ac. 3703.

HERRING FISHERIES. *See* FISH.

HERSTMONCEUX. VENABLES (E.) Handbook to Herstmonceux Castle and Church. pp. 64. *Battle,* 1884. 8°. 10348. c. 26. (3.)

HERTFELD. DEMME (L.) Nachrichten und Urkunden zur Chronik von Hertfeld. *Hertfeld,* 1891, *etc.* 8°. 10255. f. 22.

HERTFORDSHIRE. FOSTER (A. J.) Guide to Hertfordshire. pp. 119. *Lond.* 1891. 8°.
　　　　　　　　10352. a. 61.
HERTFORD. Murray's handbook for Hertfordshire. pp. 260. *Lond.* 1895. 8°. 2364. b. 31.
KINGSTON (A.) Hertfordshire during the Civil War. pp. 212. *Lond.* 1894. 4°. 10358. dd. 26.
P.P. *London.* Middlesex and Hertfordshire notes and queries. *Lond.* 1895, *etc.* 8°.
　　　　　　　　P.P. 6033. g.

HERZGOVINA. *See* BOSNIA.

HESPERIDAE. *See* LEPIDOPTERA.

HESSE, Grand Duchy; Cassel: Nassau. HESSLER (C.) Geschichte von Hessen. pp. 228. *Cassel,* 1891. 8°. 9385. f. 8.
—— Bilder aus der hessischen Geschichte und Sage. pp. 110. *Cassel,* 1892. 8°. 012330. e. 7.
MUENSCHER (F.) Geschichte von Hessen. pp. 550. *Marburg,* 1894. 8°. 9385. e.
KOEHLER (W.) Hessische Kirchenverfassung im Zeitalter der Reformation. pp. 97. *Giessen,* 1894. 8°. 4662. f. 12.

KUENZEL (H.) Das Grossherzogtum Hessen. pp. 786. *Giessen,* 1893. 8°. 9365. eee. 4.
SCHMIDT (A. B.) Kirchenrechtliche Quellen des Grossherzogthums Hessen. pp. 239. *Giessen,* 1891. 8°. 05107. ee. 18.

HESSE.—Grand Duchy, etc.—*continued.*
REIMER (H.) Hessisches Urkundenbuch. 1891, *etc.* 8°. PRUSSIA. *Staatsarchive.* Publicationen. Bd. 48. 9386. eee.
KUECH (F.) Geschichte des Landgrafen Hermann II. von Hessen. pp. 216. 1894. 8°. Ac. Cassel. *Verein für hessische Geschichte.* Zeitschrift. N. F. Bd. 19. Ac. 7025.
WERTHERN (v.) *Baron.* Die hessischen Hülfstruppen in nordamerikanischen Unabhängigkeitskriege. pp. 47. *Cassel,* 1895. 8°. Pam 2.
GERLAND (O.) 1810--1860. Zwei Menschenalter kurhessischer Geschichte. pp. 191. *Kassel,* 1892. 8°. 9365. bb. 4.
BAEHR (O.) Das frühere Kurhessen. pp. 140. *Kassel,* 1895. 8°. 9365. bbb. 21.
SCHMIDT (J. v.) Die vormals kurhessische Armeedivision, 1866. pp. 255. *Kassel,* 1892. 8°.
　　　　　　　　9326. aaa. 14.

See also NASSAU.

HETEROCERA. *See* LEPIDOPTERA.

HEUSTRICH. NEUKOMM (M.) Bad Heustrich. pp. 55. *Bern,* 1888. 8°. 7462. ee. 4. (21.)

HEXHAM, Abbey. HODGES (C. C.) Abbey of St. Andrew, Hexham. pp. 62. *Lond.* 1888. fol.
　　　　　　　　1730. d. 16.
WARD, LOCK, AND CO. Gossiping guide to Hexham and the Borderland. pp. 224. *Lond.* 1895. 8°. 10347. aaa. 40.

HIDDENSOE. GUENTHER (A.) Die Dislokationen auf Hiddensoe. pp. 64. *Berl.* 1892. 8°.
　　　　　　　　07109. g. 29.

HIGHAM. FIELDING (C. H.) Handbook of Higham. pp. 66. *Rochester,* 1882. 8°.
　　　　　　　　10360. ee. 35.

HIGH HALDEN. HIGH HALDEN. Collection of Inscriptions in the parish church of High Halden. pp. 76. *Tenterden,* 1895. 8°.
　　　　　　　　9905. bbb. 47.

HIGHWAYS: STREETS. CODRINGTON (T.) Maintenance of macadamized Roads. pp. 186. *Lond.* 1892. 8°. 8768. cc. 14.
DUPIN (E.) Guide pour l'extension du système des rechargements généraux cylindrés des chaussées. pp. 253. *Paris,* 1895. 8°. 8767. g. 33.
DYKES (J. E.) and STUART (D.) Manual of the Roads and Bridges, Scotland, Act, 1878. pp. 238. *Edinb.* 1890. 8°. 6573. cc. 2.
ENGLAND AND WALES. *Local Government Board.* Report on Road maintenance. pp. 21. *Lond.* 1889. 8°. Pam. 79.
FLETCHER (W.) History of steam locomotion on common roads. pp. 288. *Lond.* 1891. 8°.
　　　　　　　　8767. g. 1.
HAMMERICH (E.) Land- og Købstadkommunernes Vejvæsen. pp. 355. *Kjøbenh.* 1892. 8°.
　　　　　　　　5725. aaa. 11.
HARCOURT (E. W.) Maintenance of main Roads. pp. 13. *Lond.* 1882. 8°. Pam. 23.
PHILADELPHIA. *Committee on Better Roads.* Essays on Road-making and Maintenance. pp. 319. *Phila.* 1891. 8°. 8768. e. 19.
PRATT (J. T.) Law of Highways and main roads. pp. 1016. *Lond.* 1893. 8°. 2232. b. 23.
SOIGNIE (J. de) Plantations le long des Voies de Communication. pp. 75. *Brux.* 1894. 8°.
　　　　　　　　0702N. h. 35.
U.S. *Road Inquiry, Office of.* Bulletin. *Wash.* 1894, *etc.* 8°. 7053. e. 52.
BURKE (M. D.) Brick for Street pavements. pp. 108. *Cincinnati,* 1894. 8°. 8768. cc. 39.
SPINKS (W.) Law and practice as to Paving private streets. pp. 171. *Lond.* 1892. 8°.
　　　　　　　　6126. cc. 28.

HILDESHEIM. BAUER (C.) Geschichte von Hildesheim. *Hildesheim,* 1891, *etc.* 8°.
10255. h. 3.

CUNO (H.) Mittelalterliche Kloster-Anlagen unter Bezugnahme auf die hildesheimer Beispiele. pp. 16. *Hildesheim,* 1886. 8°. Pam. 25.

—— Hildesheims Künstler im Mittelalter. pp. 20. *Hildesheim,* 1886. 8°. 7807. k. 18. (2.)

—— Die chernen Thürflügel am Dom zu Hildesheim. pp. 20. *Hildesheim,* 1888. 8°.
7807. k. 18. (5.)

EULING (C.) Hildesheimer Land und Leute des 16ten Jahrhunderts. pp. 99.
Hildesheim, 1892. 8°. 10235. aaa. 32.

HIMALAYAS. A., F. E. S. Sport in Ladakh. pp. 32. *Lond.* 1895. 8°. 7905. i. 30.

CONWAY (W. M.) Climbing and exploration in the Karakoram Himalayas. 3 vol. *Lond.* 1894. 8°. K.T.C. 19. a. 15.

HOOKER (*Sir* J. D.) Himalayan Journals. pp. 574. 1891. 8°. BETTANY (G. T.) The Minerva Library. 012207. h.

J., K. C. A. Sportsman's vade-mecum for the Himalayas. pp. 120. *Lond.* 1891. 8°.
7908. dd. 13.

MAC CORMICK (A. D.) An artist in the Himalayas. pp. 306. *Lond.* 1895. 8°. 010057. i. 3.

NEWALL (D. J. F.) Highlands of India strategically considered. 2 vol. *Lond.* 1882–87. 8°.
10058. bbb. 14.

See also DARJEELING: HINDU KUSH: MOUNTAINS.

HINDI LANGUAGE. Ac. London. *British Museum.* Catalogues of the Hindi printed books in the British Museum. 4 pt. *Lond.* 1893. 4°. Cat. Desk. B.

ĀRYĀ. Hindi Grammar. *Benares,* 1888. 8°
14160. e. 25. (2.)

DĪNANĀTHA DEVA. Sikshámani. Anglo-Hindi Manual. pp. 419. *Calcutta,* 1891. 8°.
14160. c. 29.

KELLOGG (S. H.) Grammar of the Hindi language. pp. 584. *Lond.* 1893. 8°. 2268. f. 20.

SYĀMALĀLA. Anglo-Oriental primer for beginners. pp. 26. *Allahabad,* 1889. 16°. 14160. a.

HINDUISM. VEDAS. Rig-Veda-Samhitâ: sacred hymns of the Brâhmans. Edited by F. Max Müller. *Lond.* 1890, *etc.* 4°. 14010. e. 13.

MUELLER (F. M.) Vedic Hymns. Translated by F. M. Müller. 1891, *etc.* 8°. Sacred Books of the East. Vol. 32. 2003. b.

HILLEBRANDT (A.) Vedainterpretation. pp. 21. *Breslau,* 1895. 8°. Pam. 47.

—— Vedische Mythologie. *Breslau,* 1891, *etc.* 8°.
4503. c.

LUDWIG (A.) Ueber Methode bei Interpretation des Rgveda. pp. 72. *Prag,* 1890. 4°.
14010. e. 14.

MUELLER (F. M.) Lectures on the Vedânta philosophy. pp. 173. *Lond.* 1894. 8°.
4506. cc. 2.

NĀRĀYANA HEMACHANDRA. Sayings of sages from Hindu Sacred books. pp. 118. *Ahmedabad,* 1895. 8°. 14085. a. 10.

OLDENBERG (H.) Die Religion des Veda. pp. 620. *Berl.* 1894. 8°. 4503. cc. 31.

PHILLIPS (M.) The Teaching of the Vedas. pp. 240. *Lond.* 1895. 8°. 4503. aaa. 12.

REED (E. A.) Hindu Literature. pp. 410. *Chicago,* 1891. 8°. 011824. f. 2.

MONIER-WILLIAMS (*Sir* M.) Indian Wisdom. pp. 576. *Lond.* 1893. 8°. 4506. dd. 3.

HINDUISM—*continued.*

DURGĀPRASĀDA. Who wrote the Puranas? pp. 7. *Lahore,* 1891. 8°. Pam. 41.

ARUNDALE (F.) The Idea of Re-birth. pp. 155. *Lond.* 1890. 8°. 4503. a. 37.

BALARĀMA MALLIKA. Jagannatha worship at Puri. pp. 85. *Calcutta,* 1892. 8°. 4503. b. 9.

BETTANY (G. T.) The Great Indian Religions. pp. 291. 1892. 8°. World's Religions Series.
4503. aaa.

BOHNENBERGER (C.) Der altindische Gott Varuna nach den Liedern des Rgveda. pp. 127. *Tübingen,* 1893. 8°. 4503. c. 9.

CALAND (W.) Altindischer Ahnencult. pp. 266. *Leiden,* 1893. 8°. 4503. ee. 29.

CHINTĀMANA VINĀYAKA VAĪDYA. History of Hindu Social Reform-agitation. pp. 77. *Poona,* 1890. 12°. 14139. c. 32.

CROOKE (W.) Introduction to the Folklore of Northern India. pp. 420. *Allahabad,* 1894. 8°.
4503. ee. 31.

DURGĀPRASĀDA. The Doctrine of Re-incarnations. pp. 17. *Lahore,* 1891. 8°. Pam. 41.

HINDU YOUNG MEN. Treatise for the use of Hindu young men containing the esoteric explanations for Maha Linga, *etc.* pp. 24. *Madras,* 1891. 8°. Pam. 41.

INDIA. Mythology of India illustrated. Vol. I. Pts. 1–3. *Lond.* 1893, 94. fol. 4504. l. 2.

MAC DONALD (K. S.) Is Hinduism a religion? pp. 8. *Calcutta,* 1890. 8°. 4503. b. 4. (4.)

MILLOUÉ (L. de) Religions de l'Inde. pp. 335. 1890. 8°. Annales du Musée Guimet.
7704. a. 37.

MONIER-WILLIAMS (*Sir* M.) Hinduism. pp. 238. 1894. 8°. Non-Christian Religious Systems.
2212. a.

—— Indian Wisdom. pp. 576. *Lond.* 1893. 8°.
4506. dd. 3.

MUELLER (F. M.) India, what can it teach us? pp. 315. *Lond.* 1892. 8°. 2386. a. 1.

PATNA. Patna, Gaya and Benares. Buddhism and Hinduism. pp. 135. *Calcutta,* 1890. 8°.
4503. b. 4. (1.)

P.P. *Calcutta.* The Hindoo Magazine. *Calcutta,* 1891, *etc.* 8°. P.P. 3800. ad.

RAGUNATHA RĀU. Comparison of the different Sects of Hinduism. *Madras,* 1890. 16°.
Pam. 41.

SCHULTZE (T.) Vedanta und Buddhismus als Fermente für eine künftige Regeneration des religiösen Bewusstseins. 2 pt. *Leipz.* 1893. 8°.
4503. ee. 26.

SIVAṢANKARA PANDYA. Lectures on subjects connected with Hindu religion. 3 pt. *Madras,* 1888, 89. 8°. 759. b. 5.

SRĪNIVĀSA RĀU. Three Brahmanical sects. pp. 11. *Bellary,* 1894. 8°. Pam. 41.

SUNDARARĀMA AIYAR. The Hindu ideal and practice of Duty. pp. 49. *Madras,* 1892. 8°.
Pam. 41.

THOMAS (F. W.) Mutual influence of Muhammadans and Hindus. pp. 117. *Camb.* 1892. 8°.
8022. cc. 9.

UPENDRANĀTHA MUKHOPĀDHYĀYA. Refutation of Non-Hindu assertions regarding certain current topics. pp. 23. *Calcutta,* 1887. 8°.
Pam. 41.

WILKINS (W. J.) Hindu Mythology. pp. 411. *Calcutta,* 1882. 8°. 2212. a.

BANESS (T.) An Essay on Cows' Protection. pp. 5. *Amritsar,* 1893. 8°. Pam. 41.

INDIA. The Cow question in India. pp. 54. *Madras,* 1894. 8°. Pam. 41.

HINDUISM—*continued.*

ROGERS (A.) To the Secretary of State for India. Letter on the " Cow-killing question." ff. 4. *Lond.* 1894. fol.   8009. m. 3.

See also ARYA SAMAJ, INDIA, *Native Races:* MARRIAGE, *Law of :* RELIGION. *History, etc.*

Hinduism and Christianity.

BĀBĀ PADAMANAJĪ. Once Hindu: now Christian. pp. 155. *Lond.* 1890. 8°.   4920. aaaa. 52.

DURGĀPRASĀDA. Defence of Manu, against the calumny of Christian Priests. pp. 65. *Lahore,* 1891. 8°.   Pam. 41.

HARLEZ (C. de) La Bible dans l'Inde et la vie de Jezeus Christna d'après M. Jacolliot. pp. 304. *Paris,* 1891. 12°.   4504. a. 4.

INDIA. India Hindu, and India Christian. pp. 63. *Madras,* 1893. 8°.   4503. b. 8.

JESUS CHRIST. Jesus in the Vedas. pp. 61. *N.Y.* 1892. 8°.   4506. aa. 18.

PARANI-ĀNDI, S. Are not Hindus Christians? pp. 12. *Madras,* 1888. 8°.   Pam. 41.

PHILLIPS (M.) Bhagavad-Gita. Its doctrines stated and refuted. pp. 34. *Madras,* 1893. 12°.   Pam. 41.

ROBERTSON (J. M.) Christ and Krishna. pp. 156. *Lond.* 1889. 8°.   4017. e. 14.

ROBSON (J.) Hinduism and its relation to Christianity. pp. 269. *Edinb.* 1893. 8°.   4503. aa. 48.

Hindu Law.

AVINĀSACHANDRA MITRA. Hindu Law of Adoption. pp. 77. *Calcutta,* 1890. 8°.   5319. de. 24. (5.)

COWELL (H.) Treatise on Hindu Law. pp. 175. *Calcutta,* 1895. 8°.   5319. b. 24.

GOLĀPCHANDRA SARKĀR. Hindu Law of Adoption. pp. 485. 1891. 8°. Tagore Law Lectures.   5318. aaa.

KOHLER (J.) Altindisches Prozessrecht. pp. 56. *Stuttgart,* 1891. 8°.   Pam. 34.

KRISHNAKAMALA BATTACHĀRYA. Law relating to the joint Hindu Family. pp. 741. 1885. 8°. Tagore Law Lectures.   5318. aaa.

NAVĪNACHANDRA DE. Notes on Hindu Law. 2 pt. *Dinapore,* 1893, 94. 8°.   5319. aaa. 37.

RAMACHANDRA AIYAR. Collection of Decisions of the High Courts of the Hindu law of Adoption, Debt and Survivorship. pp. 73. 2. *Nellore,* 1893. 8°.   05319. i. 8.

V., F. R. Hindu Law in Bombay. pp. 49. *Bombay,* 1892. 8°.   5319. bb. 9.

See also MARRIAGE, *Law of.*

HINDU-KUSH. MACINTYRE (D.) Hindu-Koh. pp. 362. *Edinb.* 1891. 8°. 7907. dd. 14. *See also* HIMALAYAS.

HINDUSTANI LANGUAGE. ADĀLAT KHAN. Vocabulary of words in Hindūstānī, Persian and Bengalī. pp. 67. *Calcutta,* 1890. 8°.   12907. b. 39.

BLUMHARDT (J. F.) English Hindustani Vocabulary. pp. 23. 1892. 8°. DICTIONARIES. Military vocabularies.   12902. ccc.

CRAVEN (T.) Popular Dictionary, English-Hindustani and Hindustani-English. 2 pt. *Lucknow,* 1889. 8°.   12906. aaa. 52.

RĀJĀRĀMĀ. Manual of English and Hindustanī terms in the Roman character. pp. 101. *Lahore,* 1889. 16°.   14117. a. 27. (3.)

AḤMAD 'ALĪ, *Saiyid.* Manual, comprising meanings and derivations of important words, explanations, notes, translations into Hindustani, *etc.* pp. 134. *Patna,* 1890. 8°. 14117. a. 27. (4.)

HINDUSTANI—*continued.*

CURTOIS (A.) Manual of the Hindustani language. pp. 146. *Madras,* 1887. 12°.   12906. b. 45.

—— Hints to candidates for examination in Hindustani. pp. 48, 17. *Madras,* 1888. 8°.   14117. b. 48.

GREEN (A. O.) Hindūstānī Grammar. 2 pt. *Oxf.* 1895. 8°.   12906. de. 11.

HINDUSTANI LANGUAGE. Hindustani without a master. *Bombay,* 1892, *etc.* 8°.   12910. a. 40.

KĀDIR. Easy guide to Hindustani, for military officers and others. pp. 60. *Madras,* 1888. 8°.   14117. b 46.

P.P. *Bombay.* The Urdu Instructor. 2 vol. *Bombay,* 1882–83. 8°.   14117. b. 50.

PHILLIPS (A. N.) Hindustani Idioms. pp. 228. *Lond.* 1892. 8°.   12907. bb. 42.

SCHULTZE (M.) Grammatik der hindustanischen Sprache. pp. 56. *Leipz.* 1894. 8°.   Pam. 47.

SEIDEL (A.) Grammatik der Hindustani-Sprache. pp. 194. 1893. 8°. Die Kunst der Polyglottie. Tl. 40.   12902. c.

SMALL (G.) Grammar of the Urdū Language in Romanized character. pp. 205. *Calcutta,* 1895. 8°.   12907. aaa. 57.

—— Anglo-Urdū Medical handbook. pp. 199. *Calcutta,* 1895. 8°.   7383. c. 23.

TAGLIABUE (C.) Grammatica della Lingua Indostana. pp. 258. 1892. 8°. NAPLES. *R. Istituto Orientale.* Collezione Scolastica. Vol. 1.   012904. g.

ADĀLAT KHAN. Book of Exercises. pp. 325. *Calcutta,* 1890. 8°.   12907. bbb. 42.

PYĀRE LĀL AGNIHOTRĪ. Translation Exercise book. pp. 67. *Lahore,* 1890. 8°.   14117. b. 39. (4.)

THWAYTES (E. C.) Dakani Manuscripts. Specimens of Hindustani handwriting. *Madras,* 1892. 4°.   14117. b. 57.

URDU CHARACTERS. Evils of the Urdu characters. pp. 22. *Shahjahanpur,* 1883. 8°.   14160. c. 11. (3.)

HINDUSTANI CONVERSATION. Handbook to Hindoostanee Conversation. pp. 56. *Calcutta,* 1890. 12°.   14117. aa. 14. (1.)

TWEEDIE (J.) Hindústáni as it ought to be spoken. pp. 350. *Calcutta,* 1893. 8°.   12907. bb. 27.

—— Supplement. Translations of the exercises, *etc.* pp. 39. *Calcutta,* 1893. 12°. 14117. aa. 25.

WILMOT (H. E.) One thousand Hindustani idiomatic sentences. pp. 96. *Madras,* 1887. 8°.   14117. b. 47.

MĀLEM SĀHĪB. Lascari-Bât. Sentences used in the daily routine of a modern passenger steamer. pp. 110. *Lond.* 1892. 16°.   12907. a. 51.

HIP. BRODHURST (B. E.) Observations on Congenital Dislocation of the Hip. pp. 19. *Lond.* 1895. 8°.   Pam. 38.

JUDSON (A. B.) Notes on the Question of the Value of Traction in the Treatment of Hip disease. pp. 40. *N.Y.* 1893. 8°.   07305. f. 17. (9.)

—— Practical Points in the treatment of Hip disease. pp. 15. *N.Y.* 1893, 8°.   07305. f. 17. (10.)

WILLARD (De F.) Operative treatment of Hip-disease. pp. 30. *Phila.* 1890. 8°.   Pam. 39.

HIRE PURCHASE SYSTEM. *See* SALE, *Law of.*

HIRUDINEA. BOLSIUS (H.) Recherches sur la structure des organes segmentaires des Hirudinées. 1889. 8°. CARNOY (J. B.) La Cellule. Tom. 5.   7421. i

HIRUDINEA—continued.

BOLSIUS (H.) Nouvelles Recherches. pp. 77. 1891. 8°. CARNOY (J. B.) La Cellule. Tom. 7. Fasc. 1.   7421. i.

—— Les Organes ciliés des Hirudinées. 1891, etc. 8°. CARNOY (J. B.) La Cellule. Tom. 7. Fasc. 2.   7421. i.
See also VERMES.

HISTOLOGY.
BOEHM (A. A.) and DAVIDOFF (M. v.) Lehrbuch der Histologie des Menschen. pp. 404. Wiesbaden, 1895. 8°.   7419. dd. 1.
BOYCE (R.) Textbook of morbid Histology. pp. 477. Lond. 1892. 8°.   7441. h. 9.
CARNOY (J. B.) Cellule : recueil de cytologie et d'histologie. Lierre, 1885, etc. 8°.   7421. i.
ISRAEL (O.) Traité pratique d'Histologie pathologique. pp. 312. Paris, 1891. 8°. 7442. g. 22.
KAHLDEN (C. v.) Methods of pathological Histology. pp. 171. Lond. 1894. 8°.   7441. e. 8.
LAUNOIS (P. E.) and MORAU (H.) Manuel d'Histologie. pp. 513. Paris, 1892. 12°. 7419. a. 2.
RAWITZ (B.) Grundriss der Histologie. pp. 284. Berl. 1894. 8°.   7419. bb. 3.
REMY (C.) Manuel des travaux pratiques d'Histologie. pp. 421. Paris, 1889. 8°. 7420. aa. 17.
ROMMELAERE (G. A. V.) Programme du cours d'Histologie à l'Université de Bruxelles. pp. 567. Brux. 1894. 8°.   7404. e. 5.
SCHAEFER (E. A.) Essentials of Histology. pp. 302. Lond. 1892. 8°.   2254. d. 16.
SCHUMANN (K.) Morphologische Studien. Leipz. 1892, etc. 8°.   7029. dd.
SCHWALBE (G.) Morphologische Arbeiten. Jena, 1891, etc. 8°.   7419. i. 21.
STIRLING (W.) Outlines of practical Histology. pp. 419. Lond. 1893, 8°.   7420. de. 7.
STOEHR (F.) Lehrbuch der Histologie. pp. 303. Jena, 1891. 8°.   7419. i. 13.
WALKHOFF (O.) Mikrophotographischer Atlas der normalen Histologie menschlicher Zähne. pp. 23. Hagen, 1894. fol.   1833. a. 23.
WEICHSELBAUM (A.) Grundriss der pathologischen Histologie. pp. 500. Leipz. 1892. 8°.   7441. h. 12.

—— Elements of pathological Histology. pp. 456. Lond. 1895. 8°.   7442. dd. 2.
See also ANATOMY : CELLS.

HISTORY, General.

For the History of each country, see under the country required.

Bibliography.

ADAMS (C. K.) Manual of Historical Literature. pp. 720. N.Y. 1888. 8°.   BB.M. a. 9.
JASTROW (I.) Handbuch zu Litteraturberichten. pp. 235. Berl. 1891. 8°.   11899. f. 47.

Universal and Miscellaneous.

B., F. Kort Udtog af Verdenshistorien. pp. 190. Kjøbenh. 1890. 8°.   9425. bb. 7.
BERTOLINI (F.) Compendio di Storia. 3 vol. Bologna, 1892. 8°.   9008. b. 10.
DOEDES (N. D.) Kort overzicht der algemeene Geschiedenis. pp. 206. Groningen, 1894. 8°.   9008. bbb. 21.
FISHER (G. P.) Outlines of universal History. pp. 674. N.Y. 1892. 8°.   9009. d. 12.
GONZALEZ (E. M.) Lecciones orales de Historia. 2 tom. Carácas, 1891. 8°.   9097. g. 1.
HENDRIKS (J. V.) Handboek der algemeene Geschiedenis. pp. 302. Alkmaar, 1891. 8°. 9009. i. 19.
HUBERTS (W. J. A.) Korte handleiding tot de Kennis der algemeene Geschiedenis. 3 stkj. Zwolle, 1888. 8°.   9009. aaa. 17.

IBO ALFARO (M.) Compendio de la Historia universal. pp. 518. Madrid, 1885. 8°.   9009. c. 16.
MARTENS (W.) Lehrbuch der Geschichte. Hannover, 1892, etc. 8°.   9004. m. 10.
MÉNARD (L.) Cours d'Histoire universelle. pp. 39. Paris, 1892. 8°.   9007. ff. 5. (9.)
NANSEN (M. M.) Kortfattet Lærebog i verdenshistorien for Ungdommen. pp. 182. Kjøbenh. 1890. 8°.   9009 aa. 19.
NIKEL (J.) Allgemeine Kulturgeschichte. pp. 505. 1895. 8°. Wissenschaftliche Handbibliothek. Reihe 3. No. 2.   3558. c.
OLLIER (E.) Cassell's Universal History. 4 vol. Lond. etc., 1888–90. 8°.   9004. n. 12..
RANKE (L. v.) Weltgeschichte. 2 Bde. Leipz. 1895. 8°.   9007. g. 25.
REICH (E.) History of Civilization. pp. 554. Cincinnati, 1887. 8°.   9009. bb. 23.
THRIGE (S. B.) Verdenshistoriske Smaaskrifter. Kjøbenh. 1892, etc. 8°.   9007. ee.
WALCKER (C.) Grundriss der Weltgeschichte. pp. 315. Karlsruhe, 1892. 8°.   9007. ff. 3.
WEBER (G.) Lehrbuch der Weltgeschichte. 2 Bde. Leipz. 1888. 8°.   9009. l. 6.
WEBER (L.) Mehr Licht in der Weltgeschichte. pp. 247. Bruschsal, 1894. 8°.   9007. g. 24.
WEITEMEYER (H.) Haandbog i Verdenshistorien Kjøbenh. 1890, 92. 8°.   9009. h. 18.

———

ADAMS (H.) Historical Essays. pp. 422. Lond. 1891. 8°.   9009. d. 10.
ADAMS (W. M.) The Drama of Empire. pp. 192. Lond. 1891. 8°.   9009. cc. 2.
ARNAUD-JEANTI (L.) L'Esprit classique, son rôle dans l'histoire des sociétés. pp. 426. Paris, 1891. 8°.   9009. aaa. 16.
BAUMGARTEN (H.) Historische und politische Aufsätze und Reden. pp. 528. Strassb. 1894. 8°.   9009. d. 19.
BELOW (G. v.) Beiträge zur Geschichtsforschung. Paderborn, 1893, etc. 8°.   9008. de.
GREGOROVIUS (F.) Die grossen Monarchien in der Geschichte. pp. 26. München, 1890. 4°.   9009. m. 9. (2.)
GRUPP (G.) System und Geschichte der Kultur. 2 Bde. Paderborn, 1891, 92. 8°.   9007. ff. 2.
KERR (R. P.) The Voice of God in History. pp. 283. Richmond, 1890. 8°.   4534. bbb. 4.
LUEDECKE (F.) Die Ironie in der Geschichte. pp. 46. Gotha, 1891. 8°.   9004. c. 14.
STIRLING (A. H.) Torch-bearers of History. pp. 277. Lond. 1895. 8°.   10001. bbb. 18.
See also infra: Dictionaries, Philosophy: CALENDARS.

Ancient.

BELOCH (J.) Studi di Storia antica. Roma, 1891, etc. 8°.   9009. l.
BUDD (T.) From the Deluge to the Christian Era. 2 pt. Norwich, 1890. 8°.   Pam. 5.
BUEDINGER (M.) Die Universalhistorie im Alterthume. pp. 222. Wien, 1895. 8°. 9008. cc. 17.
CABALLERO Y ESTEVAN (T. T.) De Oriente á Occidente. pp. 522. San Sebastian, 1891. 8°.   9008. bbb. 2.
CASAGRANDI (V.) Raccolta di Studi di Storia antica. Catania, 1893, etc. 8°.   9007. g.
HITTELL (J. S.) History of the mental growth of Mankind in ancient Times. 4 vol. N.Y. 1893. 8°.   9008. de. 6.
KOCH (J. B.) Lærebog i Oldtidens Historie. pp. 228. Kjøbenh. 1893. 8°.   9009. c. 12.

HISTORY.—Ancient—*continued.*

LINCKE (A.) Forschungen zur alten Geschichte. *Leipz.* 1891, *etc.* 8°.   9026. cc.

MEYER (E.) Forschungen zur alten Geschichte. *Halle,* 1892, *etc.* 8°.   9009. l.

REICHE. Reiche der alten Welt. *Calw,* 1891, *etc.* 8°.   9008. aaa. 5.

STOW (E.) Stories from Ancient History. pp. 161. *Lond.* 1892. 8°.   9009. aaa. 20.

STUDIEN. Studien zur alten Geschichte. *Tübingen,* 1890, *etc.* 8°.   9009. l.

BARBERIS (T. G.) Storia antica dell' Oriente. pp. 325. *Torino,* 1890. 8°.   9055. aaa. 21.

GENTILE (I.) L'Oriente antico. pp. 231. *Milano,* 1890. 8°.   012200. h 20.

LANDAU (W. v.) *Baron.* Beiträge zur Altertumskunde des Orients. *Leipz.* 1893, *etc.* 8°.   754. b. 22.

MAC CURDY (J. F.) History, Prophecy and the Monuments. *N. Y.* 1894, *etc.* 8°.   4516. d.

MASPERO (G.) Histoire ancienne des peuples de l'Orient classique. *Paris,* 1895, *etc.* 8°.   7704. k.

MELIN ( ) Histoire ancienne des peuples de l'Orient. pp. 359. *Moulins,* 1893. 8°.   9009. aaa. 22.

MONTELIUS (O.) Orienten och Europa. 1895, *etc.* 8°. Ac. Stockholm. *Vitterhets och Antiqvitets Akademien.* Antiqvarisk Tidskrift. Del 13.   Ac. 7800/4.

NIEBUHR (C.) Studien zur Geschichte des alten Orients. *Leipz.* 1894, *etc.* 8°.   9055. dd.

P.P. *Paris.* Revue Sémitique d'histoire ancienne. *Paris,* 1893, *etc.* 8°.   P.P. 37. cf.

SAYCE (A. H.) The Higher Criticism and the verdict of the Monuments. pp. 575. *Lond.* 1894. 8°.   4429. d. 2.

VALETON (M.) Handboek der oude Geschiedenis. 2 Dl. *Groningen,* 1881–83. 8°.   9008. l. 5.

WACHSMUTH (C.) Einleitung in das Studium der alten Geschichte. pp. 717. *Leipz.* 1895. 8°.   9008. l. 4.

WINCKER (H.) Altorientalische Forschungen. *Leipz.* 1893, *etc.* 8°.   7704. bb.

See also ASSYRIA : ATHENS : CARTHAGE : CHALDEA : EGYPT : GREECE: HITTITES : PHŒNICIA : ROME.

Ecclesiastical. *See* CHURCH HISTORY.

Mediæval and Modern.

ADAMS (G. B.) Civilization during the middle ages. pp. 463. *Lond.* 1894. 8°.   9073. c. 2.

CHURCH (R. W.) Beginning of the middle ages. pp. 269. *Lond.* 1895. 8°.   9073. a. 22.

ERSLEV (K. S. A.) Oversigt over middelalderens Historie. 2 pt. *Kjøbenh.* 1891–93. 8°.   9008. bbb. 19.

GRUPP (G.) Kulturgeschichte des Mittelalters. *Stuttg.* 1894, *etc.* 8°.   9008. i.

LAVISSE (E.) and RAMBAUD (A.) Histoire générale du iv° siècle à nos jours. *Paris,* 1893, *etc.* 8°.   9004. m.

P.P. *Paris.* Le Moyen Âge : Bulletin mensuel. *Paris,* 1888, *etc.* 8°.   P.P. 4331. abc. and 950.

SEIGNOBOS (C.) Histoire de la Civilisation au moyen âge et dans les temps modernes. pp. 575. *Paris,* 1893. 8°.   9076. ccc. 13.

DUCOUDRAY (G.) History of modern Civilization. pp. 585. *Lond.* 1891. 8°.   9009. d. 6.

HEIGEL (C. T.) Essays aus neuerer Geschichte. pp. 347. *München,* 1892. 8°.   9009. d. 18.

JACKSON (L.) Ten centuries of European Progress. pp. 364. *Lond.* 1891. 8°. 9080. bbb. 22.

HISTORY.—Mediæval, etc.—*continued.*

JORISSEN (T. T. H.) Historische Studiën. pp. 538. *Haarlem,* 1891. 8°.   9009. i. 18.

LACOUR-GAYET (G.) Histoire des temps modernes, 1610–1789. pp. 600. *Paris,* 1892. 8°.   9008. aaa. 18.

MAISCH (G.) Religion und Revolution nach ihrem gegenseitigen Verhältnis. pp. 215. *Leipz.* 1892. 8°.   4650. e. 26.

MUELLER (W.) Bilder aus der neuern Geschichte. pp. 350. *Stuttg.* 1893. 8°. 9080. bb. 35.

RANKE (L. v.) Ueber die Epochen der neueren Geschichte. pp. 238. *Leipz.* 1888. 8°. :   09325. g. 2.

FRANCK (A.) Réformateurs et publicistes de l'Europe, 18me siècle. pp. 382. *Paris,* 1893. 8°.   011850. i. 12.

DICKIE (J.) Sketch of human Progress during the 19th Century. pp. 56. *Glasg.* 1894. 16°.   8276. aa. 67.

JAEGER (O.) and MOLDENHAUER (F.) Auswahl wichtiger Aktenstücke zur Geschichte des 19. Jahrhunderts. pp. 606. *Berl.* 1893. 8°. 9079. f. 10.

LILLY (W. S.) A Century of Revolution. pp. 239. *Lond.* 1890. 8°.   8009. g. 20.

MONCRIEFF (A. R. H.) Scenes from our Century. pp. 442. *Lond.* 1887. 8°.   9080. cc. 14.

VOGT (W.) Welt- und Zeitgeschichte, 1862–90. pp. 559. *Heidelberg,* 1892. 8°.   9009. i. 21.

P.P. *London.* The Times Annual. 1890, *etc.* *Lond.* 1891, *etc.* 8°.   P.P. 3435. dda.

—— *Paris.* L'Annuaire Universel illustré. *Paris,* 1893, *etc.* 4°.   P.P. 2416. ab.

—— La Vie politique à l'Étranger. *Paris,* 1890, *etc.* 12°.   P.P. 3612. cba.

See also infra : Dictionaries: CRUSADES: EUROPE: HOLY ROMAN EMPIRE, and under the subheading *History* of each country.

Dictionaries, Tables, etc.

BABO (M. v.) Synchronistic wall-charts for the teaching of history. *Berl.* 1886, *etc.* fol.

—— Explanatory notes. 8°. Tab. 11747. a. (42.)

BICKERSTETH (A.) The Harmony of History. Tables from 1209 B.C. to 322 B.C. *Lond.* 1893. fol.   9006. h. 10.

BREWER (E. C.) The historic Note-Book. pp. 997. *Lond.* 1891. 8°.   9009. d. 9.

BRINCKMEIER (E.) Praktisches Handbuch der historischen Chronologie. pp. 504. *Berl.* 1882. 8°.   9008. cc. 15.

BRUDER (A.) Staatslexikon. *Freiburg,* 1889, *etc.* 8°.   012216. i.

GIRY (A.) Manuel de Diplomatique. pp. 944. *Paris,* 1894. 8°.   2050. c.

HAYDN (J.) Haydn's dictionary of Dates. pp. 1216. *Lond.* 1895. 8°.   2085. f.

HERBST (W.) Encyklopädie der neueren Geschichte. Bde. 5. *Gotha,* 1880–90. 8°.   012215. k. 1.

PUTNAM (G. P.) Tabular views of universal History. pp. 211. *N.Y.* 1890. 8°. 9009. cc. 6.

SCAIFE (A. H.) Synoptical Chart of History. *Canada,* 1894, *s. sh.* fol.   Tab. 1700. d.

THOMS (P. E.) Important events in the World's History. pp. 124. *Cincinnati,* 1892. 8°.   9009. aa. 24.

WAGNER (L.) Book of Dates. pp. 236. *Lond.* 1892. 8°.   9025. bb. 14.

See also ENGLAND, *History, Chronological Tables.*

Philosophy, Study, Methods of Teaching.

ADAMS (B.) Law of Civilisation and Decay. pp. 302. *Lond.* 1895. 8°.   9008. k. 2.

BARTH (P.) Die Geschichtsphilosophie Hegels. pp. 148. *Leipz.* 1890. 8°.   8486. g. 17.

HISTORY.—Philosophy, etc.—*continued.*

BUSSE (K.) H. Spencers Philosophie der Geschichte. pp. 114. *Leipz.* 1894. 8°. 9008. dd. 12.

CHARAUX (C. C.) L'Histoire et la pensée. pp. 354. *Paris*, 1893. 8°. 9009. c. 13.

CHEVALIER (C. U. J.) Des Règles de la critique historique. pp. 20. *Lyon*, 1888. 8°. Pam. 28.

CRAWFORD (J. H.) The Brotherhood of mankind. pp. 379. *Edinb.* 1895. 8°. 08275. m. 5.

FLINT (R.) History of the Philosophy of History. *Edinb.* 1893, *etc.* 8°. 9007. g. 19.

GRAU (R. F.) The Goal of the human race. pp. 252. *Lond.* 1892. 8°. 4503. aaa. 9.

HARRISON (F.) The Meaning of History and other pieces. pp. 507. *Lond.* 1894. 8°. 9008. de. 7.

HARTUNG, afterwards PFLUGK-HARTUNG (J. v.) Geschichtsbetrachtungen. pp. 47. *Gotha*, 1890. 8°. 9004. m. 7. (14.)

JENTSCH (C.) Geschichtsphilosophische Gedanken. pp. 467. *Leipz.* 1892. 8°. 9008. aaa. 19.

KRÄMER (F, J. L.) De Wetenschap der historie. pp. 33. *Utrecht*, 1893. 8°. 9004. k. 15. (4.)

LACOMBE (P.) De l'Histoire considérée comme science. pp. 415. *Paris*, 1894. 8°. 9009. d. 21.

LAVOLLÉE (R.) La Morale dans l'Histoire. pp. 412. *Paris*, 1892. 8°. 9008. i. 14.

LE BON (G.) Les Lois psychologiques de l'évolution des peuples. pp. 176. *Paris*, 1894. 12°. 8462. aaa. 32.

LECKY (W. E. H.) The political value of History. pp. 57. *Lond.* 1892. 8°. 8009. aaa. 30.

POWELL (E. P.) The Philosophy of History. 1893. 8°. Ac. Brooklyn. *Ethical Association.* Evolution Series. No. 48. 7006. bbb.

SIMMEL (G.) Die Probleme der Geschichtsphilosophie. pp. 109. *Leipz.* 1892. 8°. 9009. d. 13.

STEFFENSEN (C.) Zur Philosophie der Geschichte. pp. 411. *Basel*, 1894. 8°. 9007. f. 23.

STRADA (J. de) Philosophie de l'impersonnalisme méthodique. pp. 246. *Paris*, 1894. 8°. 9009. d. 22.

WOLLNY (F.) Historisch-psychologischer Tractat. pp. 288. *Leipz.* 1892. 8°. 8486. c. 2.

CHEVALIER (C. U. J.) Des Règles de la critique historique. pp. 20. *Lyon*, 1888. 8°. 9004. m. 5. (3.)

JAMESON (J. F.) The History of historical writing in America. pp. 160. *Bost.* 1891. 8°. 011824. f. 26.

LORENZ (O.) Die Geschichtswissenschaft in Hauptrichtungen und Aufgaben kritisch erörtert. *Berl.* 1886, *etc.* 8°. 9009. l. 2.

MONOD (G.) Les Maîtres de l'histoire. pp. 312. *Paris*, 1894. 12°. 010663. f. 23.

ACTON (J. E. E. D.) *Baron Acton.* Lecture on the study of History. pp. 142. *Lond.* 1895. 8°. 2378. b. 7.

DEVÈZE (R.) De l'usage des documents originaux dans les études historiques. pp. 18. *Vitry-le-François*, 1894. 8°. 9004. gg. 29. (7.)

DIPPE (A.) Das Geschichtsstudium. pp. 132. *Berl.* 1891. 8°. 9009. d. 7.

FRÉDÉRICQ (P.) The study of History in Holland and Belgium. pp. 62. 1890. 8°. Johns Hopkins University Studies. Ser. 8. No. 10. Ac. 2689.

GUENTHER (A.) Vorschläge zu einer zeitgemassen Gestaltung des Geschichtsunterrichtes. pp. 48. 1887. 8°. Pädagogische Zeit- und Streitfragen. Heft. 17. 8310. c.

HISTORY.—Philosophy, etc.—*continued.*

HINSDALE (B. A.) How to study and teach History. pp. 346. *N.Y.* 1894. 8°. 8311. aa. 35.

HISTORIKER. Wie studiert man Geschichte? pp. 38. *Leipz.* 1894. 12°. 8304. aa. 18. (8.)

LODGE (R.) Study of History in a Scotch University. pp. 18. *Glasg.* 1894. 8°. Pam. 17.

MAHRENHOLTZ (R.) Wandlungen der Geschichtsauffassung und des Geschichtsunterrichtes. pp. 74. 1891. 8°. Deutsche Zeit- und Streit-Fragen. Hft. 84, 85. 12209. f.

RUDE (A.) Quellen im Geschichtsunterricht. pp. 24. 1892. 8°. Pädagogische Zeit- und Streitfragen. Hft. 27. 8310. c.

STEINER (C.) Zur Reform des Geschichtsunterrichts. pp. 189. 1891. 8°. Pädagogische Sammelmappe. Hft. 144. 8304. dd.

WILLIAMSON (G. C.) On learning and teaching History in Schools. *Lond.* 1891. 8°. Pam. 17.

See also ÉCOLE DES CHARTES : EDUCATION, *Methods of Teaching.*

HITTITES. CAMPBELL (J.) The Hittites. 2 vol. *Lond.* 1891. 8°. 7704. cc. 31.

HALÉVY (J.) Introduction au déchiffrement des inscriptions pseudo-hittites. pp. 20. *Paris*, 1893. 8°. 07703. i. 1. (18.)

LANTSHEERE (L. de) De la race et de la langue des Hittites. pp. 132. *Brux.* 1891. 8°. 7703. e. 28.

MENANT (J.) Éléments du Syllabaire hétéen. pp. 112. 1895. 4°. Ac. Paris. *Académie des Inscriptions.* Mémoires. Tom. 34. 2099. f.

PALESTINE. Exploration Fund. The Tell Amarna Tablets. pp. 212. *Lond.* 1893. 8°. 2356. b. 5.

PEISER (F. E.) Die hetitischen Inschriften. pp. 128. *Berl.* 1892. 4°. 7704. aa. 36.

PUCHSTEIN (O.) Pseudohethitische Kunst. pp. 22. *Berl.* 1890. 8°. 7706. g. 6. (11.)

SAYCE (A. H.) Les Hétéens. pp. 210. 1891. 8°. Annales du Musée Guimet. 7704. a. 37.

ZENJĪRLĪ. Inscriptions hétéennes de Zindjīrlī. pp. 123. *Paris*, 1894. 8°. 754. b. 25.

See also HISTORY, *Ancient.*

HOCHDORF. ESTERMANN (M.) Geschichte der alten Pfarrei Hochdorf. pp. 368. *Luzern*, 1891. 8°. 4662. c. 13.

—— Geschichte des Ruralkapitels Hochdorf. pp. 108. *Luzern*, 1892. 8°. 4662. e. 15.

HOCKEY. BATTERSBY (H. F.) Hockey. pp. 148. *Lond.* 1895. 8°. 7912. b. 3.

HOCKEY ASSOCIATION. Rules of the game of Hockey. pp. 31. *Lond.* 1892. 32°. 7908. de. 7. See also GAMES.

HOF. MEYER (C.) Quellen zur Geschichte der Stadt Hof. pp. 486. *Hof*, 1894. 8°. 10255. d. 3.

HOHENFELS. HUNDT (F.) Burg Hohenfels in Geschichte und Sage. pp. 29. *Wiesbaden*, 1894. 8°. Pam. 91.

HOHENZOLLERN, House of. HOHENZOLLERN, *House of.* Hohenzollerische Haus-Chronik. *Berl.* 1889. 4°. K.T.C. 3. b. 5.

NEUKOMM (E.) and ESTRÉE (P. d') Les Hohenzollern. pp. 347. *Paris*, 1892. 8°. 9903. bb. 18.

RICHTER (J. W. O.) Die Ahnen der preussischen Könige. pp. 350. *Hannover*, 1892. 8°. 9902. c. 25.

RULAND (C.) Die Hohenzollern. pp. 289. *Köln*, 1892. 8°. 9386. f. 28.

MEYER (J.) Erinnerungen an die Hohenzollernherrschaft in Franken. pp. 276. *Ansbach*, 1890. 8°. 10235. g. 8. See also GERMANY : PRUSSIA.

HOLBEACH. PEET (H.) Notes on Holbeach Church. pp. 24. *Holbeach*, 1890. 8°.
　　　　　　　　　　　　　　7706. g. 6. (10.)

—— The High Cross of Holbeach. pp. 5. *Horncastle*, 1894. 8°.　　　　Pam. 90.

HO-LIN. *See* KARAKARUM.

HOLLAND. *See* NETHERLANDS.

HOLOTHUROIDEA. *See* ECHINODERMATA.

HOLY ROMAN EMPIRE.

Constitution, etc.

ALTMANN (W.) Urkunden zur Erläuterung der Verfassungsgeschichte Deutschlands im Mittelalter. pp. 270. *Berl.* 1891. 8°.　6005. ee. 27.

KIRCHHOEFER (R.) Zur Entstehung des Kurcollegiums. pp. 190. *Halle*, 1893. 8°.
　　　　　　　　　　　　　　9325. ee. 23.

LINDNER (T.) Die deutschen Königswahlen. pp. 234. *Leipz.* 1893. 8°.　8074. ff. 28.

MOLLAT (G.) Geschichte der deutschen Staatswissenschaft von Kant bis Bluntschli. *Cassel*, 1890, *etc.* 8°.　8074. ee. 35.

—— Lesebuch zur Geschichte der deutschen Staatswissenschaft. pp. 131. *Tübingen*, 1891. 8°.
　　　　　　　　　　　　　　8009. h. 1.

RIETSCHEL (S.) Die Civitas auf deutschem Boden bis zum Ausgange der Karolingerzeit. pp. 102. *Leipz.* 1894. 8°.　5206. c. 1.

SICKEL (W.) Beiträge zur deutschen Verfassungsgeschichte des Mittelalters. 1894. 8°. Ac. Vienna. *Universitas*. Mittheilungen des Instituts für oesterreichische Geschichtsforschung. Ergänzungsband 3.　Ac. 803.

TURNER (S. E.) Sketch of the Germanic Constitution. pp. 185. *N.Y.* 1888. 8°. 9325. c. 9.

FUERSTENWERTH (L.) Die Verfassungsänderungen in den Reichsstädten zur Zeit Karls v. pp. 105. *Göttingen*, 1893. 8°. 09325. h. 7.

RODENBERG (C.) Zur Geschichte der Idee eines deutschen Erbreiches im 13. Jahrhundert. 1895. 8°. Ac. Vienna. *Universitas*. Mittheilungen des Instituts für oesterreichische Geschichtsforschung. Bd. 16.　Ac. 803.

VAHLEN (A.) Der deutsche Reichstag unter König Wenzel. pp. 188. *Leipz.* 1892. 8°.
　　　　　　　　　　　　　　09325. h. 4.

Ac. Munich. *K. Akademie der Wissenschaften*. Deutsche Reichstagsakten, *Gotha*, 1893, *etc.* 8°.
　　　　　　　　　　　　　　Ac. 714/11.

History.

GEBHARDT (B.) Deutscher Kaiser-Saal. pp. 787. *Stuttgart*, 1894. 8°.　9327. h. 1.

GUNDLACH (W.) Heldenlieder der deutschen Kaiserzeit. *Innsbruck*, 1894, *etc.* 8°. 11409. f.

HENDERSON (E. F.) Select documents of the Middle Ages. pp. 477. 1892. 8°. Bohn's Antiquarian Library.　2500. b.

HERRIG (H.) Das Kaiserbuch. Acht Jahrhunderte deutsche Geschichte. *Berl.* 1897, *etc.* 4°.
　　　　　　　　　　　　　　K.T.C. 5. b. 2.

LEHMANN (H. O.) Quellen zur deutschen Reichs- und Rechtsgeschichte. pp. 309. *Berl.* 1891. 8°.
　　　　　　　　　　　　　　9325. ee. 22.

PEUTZ (H. G.) Staatengeschichte des Abendlandes im Mittelalter. 2 Bde. 1885–87. 8°. ONCKEN (V.) Allgemeine Geschichte. Hauptabth. II. Th. 6.　2068. (12.)

DOELLINGER (J. J. I. v.) Addresses on historical and literary subjects. pp. 300. *Lond.* 1894. 8°.　2388. d. 4.

POUZET (P.) La Succession de Charlemagne et le Traité de Verdun. pp. 92. 1890. 8°. Ac. Lyons. *Faculté des Lettres. Bibliothèque.* Tom. 7.　Ac. 8922/2.

HOLY ROMAN EMPIRE.—History—
—continued.

BRUNENGO (G.) Il Patriziato romano di Carlomagno. pp. 416. *Prato*, 1893. 8°.
　　　　　　　　　　　　　　9166. dd. 17.

RITTER ( ) Karl der Grosse und die Sachsen. *Dessau*, 1894, *etc.* 8°.　9326. dd.

FREDERICK I. *Emperor.* Gesta Federici I. Imperatoris in Lombardio. pp.]110. 1892. 8°. PERTZ (G. H.) Scriptores Rerum Germanicarum.　9335. g.

BLOCH (H.) Forschungen zur Politik Kaiser Heinrichs VI., 1191–94. pp. 105. *Berl.* 1892. 8°.
　　　　　　　　　　　　　　9327. cc. 8.

BLONDEL (G.) Étude sur la politique de l'empereur Frédéric II. en Allemagne. pp 440. *Paris*, 1892. 8°.　9327. e. 14.

FREDERICK II. *Emperor.* Das Verhältnis Kaiser Friedrichs II. zu den Päpsten. 1888. 8°. GIERKE (O.) Untersuchungen zur deutschen Staatsgeschichte. No. 24.　6025. e. 9.

MITROVIĆ (B.) Federico II. e l'opera sua in Italia. pp. 127. *Trieste*, 1890. 8°.　9166. ee. 10.

KEMPF (J.) Geschichte des deutschen Reiches während des Interregnums. 1245–73. pp. 292. *Würzburg*, 1893. 8°.　09325. h. 6.

OTTO (H.) Die Beziehungen Rudolfs von Habsburg zu Papst Gregor x. pp. 99. *Innsbruck*, 1895. 8°.　4571. ee. 16.

ZISTERER (A.) Gregor x. und Rudolf von Habsburg. pp. 170. *Freiburg*, 1891. 8°.
　　　　　　　　　　　　　　4571. ee. 11.

HINNESCHIEDT (D.) Die Politik König Wenzels. *Darmstadt*, 1891, *etc.* 4°.　9325. ff

Ac. Munich. *K. Akademie der Wissenschaften*. Vatikanische Akten zur deutschen Geschichte in der Zeit Ludwigs des Bayern. pp. 926. *Innsbruck*, 1891. 8°.　Ac. 714/10.

PRIESACK (J.) Die Reichspolitik des erzbischofs Balduin von Trier, 1314–28. pp. 196. *Göttingen*, 1894. 8°.　4662. ee. 1.

BRANDENBURG (E.) König Sigmund und Kurfürst Friedrich I. von Brandenburg. pp. 220. *Berl.* 1891. 8°.　9326. dd. 4.

WINDECKE (E.) Denkwürdigkeiten zur Geschichte des Zeitalters Kaiser Sigmunds. pp. 591. *Berl.* 1893. 8°.　9327. ccc. 15.

GRUENBECK (J.) Die Geschichte Friedrichs III. und Maximilians I. pp. 72. 1891. 8°. PERTZ (G. H.) Die Geschichtschreiber der deutschen Vorzeit. Lief. 90.　9325. cc.

ARENBERGH (E. v.) Charles-Quint. 2 tom. *Lille*, 1890. 8°.　10658. f. 21.

NAMÈCHE (A. J.) L'Empereur Charles-Quint. 5 tom. *Louvain*, 1889. 8°.　9073. de. 20.

BAUMGARTEN (H.) Karl der Funfte und die deutsche Reformation. pp. 42. *Coburg*, 1893. 8°.
　　　　　　　　　　　　　　4662. c. 25. (7.)

SCHULZ (H.) Der Sacco di Roma, 1527–28. pp. 188. *Halle*, 1894. 8°.　9327. ccc.

KANNENGIESSER (P.) Der Reichstag zu Worms, 1545. pp. 131. *Strassb.* 1891. 8°.
　　　　　　　　　　　　　　4650. dd. 10.

Ac. Vienna. *K. Akademie der Wissenschaften*. Venetianische Depeschen vom Kaiserhofe. *Wien*, 1889, *etc.* 8°.　Ac. 810/7.

BARGE (H.) Die Verhandlungen zu Linz und Passau, *etc.* pp. 161. *Stralsund*, 1893. 8°.
　　　　　　　　　　　　　　09325. g. 6.

GOETZ (W.) Maximilians II. Wahl. pp. 207. *Würzburg*, 1891. 8°.　09325. g. 5.

HELING (J.) Die Wahl des Königs Matthias. *Belgard*, 1892, *etc.* 4°.　9327. e. 13.

HOLY ROMAN EMPIRE.—History—
continued.

PRIBRAM (A. F.) Die niederösterreichischen Stände in der Zeit Kaiser Leopold I. 1893. 8°. Ac. Vienna. *Universitas.* Mittheilungen des Instituts für oesterreichische Geschichtsforschung. Bd. 14. Ac. 803.

Ac. Carlsruhe. *Badische historische Commission.* Markgraf Ludwig Wilhelm von Baden und der Reichs-krieg gegen Frankreich. 1693–97. 2 Bde. *Karlsruhe*, 1892. 8°. Ac. 7066/5.

VILLERMONT (de) *Count.* Marie-Thérèse, 1717–80. 2 tom. *Paris*, 1895. 8°. 10704. k. 8.

SCHLITTER (H.) Pius VI. und Josef II. pp. 225. 1894. 8°. Ac. Vienna. *K. Akademie der Wissenschaften.* Fontes Rerum Austriacarum Abtheilung 2. Bd. 47. Ac. 810/9.
See also AUSTRIA: EUROPE: HISTORY, *Mediæval and Modern.*

HOLY SPIRIT. COULTAS (G.) Personal Pentecost. pp. 31. *Lond.* 1895. 16°.
4422. aa. 51. (10.)

CUMMING (J. E.) "Through the Eternal Spirit." pp. 384. *Stirling*, 1891. 8°. 4227. h. 21.

DIENEMANN (P.) Der heilige Geist als Inspirator. 1895. 8°. Sammlung theologischer Reden. Ser. 4. Lief. 7 & 8. 4224. ff. 25.

ELIOT (W. G.) The Holy Spirit. pp. 8. *Lond.* 1894. 8°. Pam. 92.

FULLER (M. J.) Temporal mission of the Holy Ghost. pp. 36. *Camb.* 1891. 8°. Pam. 95.

GORDON (A. J.) The Ministry of the Spirit. pp. 225. *Lond.* 1894. 8°. 4371. c. 28.

HUTCHINGS (W. H.) Person and work of the Holy Ghost. pp. 303. *Lond.* 1893. 8°.
4224. b. 85.

KOELLING (W.) Pneumatologie, oder die Lehre von der Person des heiligen Geistes. pp. 368. *Gutersloh*, 1894. 8°. 4227. h. 26.

LOWRY (S. C.) Work of the Holy Spirit. pp. 117. *Lond.* 1894. 8°. 4479. bb. 59.

MANNING (H. E.) *Cardinal.* Temporal mission of the Holy Ghost. pp. 260. *Lond.* 1892. 8°.
4014. dd. 4.

OBERDOERFFER (P.) De inhabitatione Spiritus Sancti in animabus justorum. pp. 131. *Tornaci*, 1890. 8°. 4227. h. 17.

PRATĀPACHANDRA MAJUMDĀR. The Spirit of God. pp. 323. *Bost.* 1894. 8°. 4371. c. 9.

ROBSON (J.) The Holy Spirit. pp. 248. *Edinb.* 1894. 8°. 4223. aa. 23.

ROTHERHAM (J. B.) The Greek article in relation to the Holy Spirit. pp. 56. *Newtown*, 1880. 8°. 4371. b. 25. (6.)

RYLE (J. C.) *Bp. of Liverpool.* About the Holy Ghost. pp. 24. *Lond.* 1894. 8°.
4422. ddd. 54. (9.)

SELBY (T. G.) The Holy Spirit and Christian privilege. pp. 272. 1894. 8°. WATKINSON (W. L.) "Life Indeed" Series. 3622. e.

SIMPSON (A. B.) The Holy Spirit. 2 vol. *N.Y.* 1895–96. 8°. 4371. ccc. 1.

HOLY SPIRIT, Order of the. BRUNE (P.) Histoire de l'Ordre du Saint-Esprit. pp. 451. *Paris*, 1892. 8°. 4784. h. 8.

HOLY WEEK. *See* LENT.

HOMBURG v. d. Höhe. HEYD (H. S. C. W.) Homburg vor der Höhe. pp. 61. *Homburg*, 1884. 8°. 10235. aaa. 16.

SCHETELIG (A.) Homburg-Spa. pp. 106. *Lond.* 1893. 8°. 7462. aaa. 46.
See also WATERING-PLACES, *etc.*

HOMESTEAD, Law of. *See* LAND, *Tenures, United States.*

HOMICIDE. AUBRY (P.) La contagion du Meutre. pp. 308. *Paris*, 1894. 8°. 6095. e. 1.

KLEINPAUL (R.) Menschenopfer und Ritualmorde. pp. 80. *Leipz*, 1892. 8°. Pam. 41.

THIÉNARD (A.) L'Assassinat. pp. 215. *Paris*, 1892. 12°. 6057. aa. 38.

WACHENFELD (F.) Die Begriffe von Mord und Totschlag. pp. 296. *Marburg*, 1890. 8°.
5606. e. 9.

RÉGIS (E.) Les Régicides dans l'histoire et dans le présent. pp. 97. *Lyon*, 1890. 8°. 6057. e. 18.

VIKTOR (C.) Fürstenmorde. pp. 130. *Hamburg*, 1894. 8°. 9007. cc. 38.
See also CRIME: LAW, *Criminal:* PUNISHMENT, *Capital:* SUICIDE.

HOMILETICS.

General.

CARPENTER (W. B.) *Bp. of Ripon.* Lectures on Preaching. pp. 254. *Lond.* 1895. 8°. 4498. bb. 2.

CUYLER (T. L.) The young Preacher. pp. 111. *Edinb.* 1893. 8°. 4499. cc. 26.

DAWSON (J.) The Soul of the Sermon. Personality of the preacher. pp. 87. *Lond.* 1895. 8°.
4499. b. 24.

DECLINE. Decline of the Pulpit and its causes. pp. 208. *Lond.* 1892. 8°. 4175. de. 36.

ELDRIDGE (C. O.) The Lay Preacher's handbook. pp. 179. *Lond.* 1894. 8°. 4499. aaa. 35.

HORTON (R. F.) Verbum Dei. Yale lectures on preaching. pp. 279. *Lond.* 1893. 8°. 4499. c. 28.

MAGEE (W. C.) *Archbp. of York.* Art of Preaching and extempore speaking. pp. 24. *Lond.* 1894. 8°. 4429. c. 21. (17.)

MOMERIE (A. W.) Preaching and Hearing and other sermons. pp. 327. *Edinb.* 1890. 8°.
4479. dd. 11.

OLIVER (A.) What and how to Preach. pp. 189. *Edinb.* 1892. 8°. 4499. cc. 25.

PIERSON (A. T.) Divine art of Preaching. pp. 147. *Lond.* 1892. 8°. 4499. aa. 18.

PREACHING. Preaching: the matter and the manner. pp. 32. *Lond.* 1893. 8°. 4499. b. 23.

STALKER (J.) The Preacher and his models. Yale Lectures on Preaching. pp. 284. *Lond.* 1891. 8°. 4499. cc. 22.

STORRS (R. S.) Conditions of success in Preaching without notes. pp. 182. *Lond.* 1892. 8°.
4499. b. 19.

See also THEOLOGY, *Pastoral.*

History.

BOUCHER (É.) L'Éloquence de la chaire. Histoire littéraire. pp. 472. *Lille*, 1894. 8°.
4498. dd. 1.

ARMITAGE (F.) Sermons du XIIᵉ siècle en vieux Provençal. pp. 121. *Heilbronn*, 1884. 8°.
4426. df. 13.

LECOY DE LA MARCHE (A.) La Chaire française au moyen âge. pp. 547. *Paris*, 1886. 8°. 4498.f 21.

FREPPEL (C. É.) *Bp. of Angers.* Bossuet et l'éloquence sacrée au XVIIᵉ siècle. 2 tom. *Paris*, 1893. 8°. 4498. e. 2.

LEBARQ (J.) Histoire de la Prédication de Bossuet. pp. 471. *Lille*, 1891. 8°. 4999. dd. 14.

ALBERT (F. R.) Die Geschichte der Predigt in Deutschland bis Luther. *Gütersloh*, 1892, *etc.* 8°.
4062. e.

GAUDEAU (B.) Les Prêcheurs burlesques en Espagne au XVIIIᵉ siècle. pp. 568. *Paris*, 1891. 8°. 4867. gg. 9.

CAMERA OBSCURA. Modern Anglican Preachers. pp. 197. *Lond.* 1892. 8°. 4906. aaa. 66.

Selected Sermons: Sermon Notes, etc.

ANDERSON (J. W. D.) Kansas Methodist Pulpit. pp. 297. *Topeka*, 1890. 8°. 4487. o. 21.

HOMILETICS—*continued.*

ANGLICAN PULPIT LIBRARY. Sermons: outlines: illustrations. *Lond.* 1894, *etc.* 8°.   4498. g.

BAGSHAWE (J. B.) Skeleton Sermons for Sundays and holidays. pp. 226. *Lond.* 1893. 8°.
    4499. cc. 28.

BOWDISH (W. W.) Inter-Denominational Sermons. pp. 325. *N.Y.* 1891. 8°.   4487. b. 30.

CORBETT (F. St. J.) The Preacher's Year. pp. 179. *Lond.* 1894. 8°.   4499. bb. 18.

EICHBAUM (F. A. G.) The Preacher's Scrapbook. pp. 224. *West Malvern,* 1892. 8°. 4499. cc. 31.

ENCYCLOPÆDIAS. Cyclopædia of Nature teachings. pp. 552. *Lond.* 1892. 8°.   4372. ee. 19.

GREGORY (J. R.) Harvest and Thanksgiving Services. Sermons. pp. 228. *Lond.* 1890. 8°.
    4462. aaa. 2.

HYDE (T. D.) Sermon-pictures for busy preachers. 2 vol. *Lond.* 1892. 8°.   4499. b. 22.

—— Sermon-pictures for children's services. pp. 216. *Lond.* 1892. 8°.   4499. b. 20.

LISTS. Lists of subjects for courses of Sermons. 2 series. *West Malvern,* 1891. 8°. 4499. cc. 32.

MORTIMER (A. G.) Sermons in Miniature. pp. 209. *Lond.* 1891. 8°.   4498. e. 1.

P.P. *Liverpool.* The Liverpool Pulpit. *Liverpool,* 1892, *etc.* 4°.   P.P. 793. and 1607.

—— *London.* The Preacher's Magazine. *Lond.* 1890, *etc.* 8°.   P.P. 437. c.

—— Pulpit Quarterly Review. *Lond.* 1894, *etc.* 8°.   P.P. 790. dm.

—— Sermon Year-book. *Lond.* 1891, *etc.* 8°.   P.P. 790. dha.

PENTECOST (G. F.) Marylebone Presbyterian Pulpit. *Lond.* 1895, *etc.* 8°.   4462. bb.

RAND (E. H.) Sermon Register and ready reference. *Lond.* 1890. 8°.   1880. a. 63.

RÉPERTOIRE. Répertoire de la Prédication protestante au XIX° siècle. pp. 200. *Vals,* 1895. 8°.
    4999. bbb. 29.

SADLER (M. F.) Sermon outlines. pp. 321. *Lond.* 1892. 8°.   4499. b. 21.

WESLEYAN PREACHERS. Outlines and Sketches of sermons. pp. 268. *Lond.* 1887. 8°.
    4499. c. 17.

HOMOEOPATHY. BRADFORD (T. L.) Homœopathic Bibliography of the U.S. pp. 596. *Phila.* 1892. 8°.   011901. g. 7.

Ac. *Congrès d'Homœopathie.* Comtes rendus du Congrès. pp. 256. *Paris,* 1889. 8°. Ac. 3698. b.

—— *London. British Homœopathic Society.* Journal of the British Homœopathic Society. *Lond.* 1893, *etc.* 8°.   Ac. 3843.

—— *U.S. Institute of Homœopathy.* Drug Attenuation; its objects, modes, means and limits. pp. 18. *Phila.* 1880. 8°.
    07509. e. 15. (5.)

ASHWELL (L. T.) Companion to the British and American Homœopathic Pharmacopœias. pp. 200. *Lond.* 1890. 8°.   07509. de. 9.

BAKODY (T.) Scientific medicine in its relation to Homœopathy. pp. 60. *Phila.* 1891. 8°.
    07305. h. 11.

BRADFORD (T. L.) Life and letters of Dr. Hahnemann. pp. 513. *Phila.* 1895. 8°.
    010707. g. 47.

CLARKE (J. H.) Bird's eye view of Hahnemann's Organon of Medicine. pp. 19. *Lond.* 1893. 8°.
    7306. e. 22. (4.)

—— Homœopathy. pp. 98. *Lond.* 1894. 8°.
    7321. aa. 27.

COMPLAINTS. Common Complaints and Materia-Medica of homœopathic Remedies. pp. 69. 1895. 16°.   7509. de. 85.

HOMOEOPATHY—*continued.*

DRUMMOND (J.) Popular Guide to Homœopathy. pp. 364. *Lond.* 1890. 8°.   7321. aaa. 15.

GUIDE. Concise guide to Health. pp. 44. *Glasg.* 1891. 16°.   7321. aa. 22. (3.)

HAHNEMANN (S. C. F.) Therapeutic Hints. pp. 59. *Lond.* 1894. 8°.   7442. c. 14.

HARRIS (H.) After Twenty Years and twenty years after. pp. 30. *Lond.* 1891. 8°.
    07305. h. 6. (5.)

JONES (S. A.) Grounds of a Homœopath's faith. pp. 92. *N.Y.* 1880. 8°.   7321. bbb. 22.

LAURIE (J.) Homœopathic Guide for family use. pp. 128. *Lond.* 1895. 8°.   7321. a. 17.

LONDON. *Homœopathic League.* Annual Report. *Lond.* 1892, *etc.* 8°.   7680. aaa.

—— Homœopathic League tracts. *Lond.* 1888, *etc.* 8°.   7383. dd.

MACK (C. S.) Philosophy in Homœopathy. pp. 174. *Chicago,* 1890. 8°.   7410. c. 24.

MOORE (J. M.) Common-sense Homœopathy. pp. 104. *Liverpool,* 1894. 8°.   7321. aa. 26.

P.P. *London.* The Homœopath. *Lond.* 1891, *etc.* 4°.   P.P. 3311. ba.

POTTER (S. O. L.) Index of comparative Therapeutics. pp. 279. *Chicago,* 1882. 8°. 7460. a. 2.

—— Signs of the Times. pp. 5. 1880. 8°.
    07305. h. 4. (8.)

PUHLMANN (C. G.) Handbuch der homöopathischen Praxis. pp. 670. *Leipz.* 1894. 8°.
    07305. h. 27.

ROBERTS (A.) Harrogate Mineral Waters and homœopathy. pp. 16. *Lond.* 1893. 8°.
    07305. h. 16. (15.)

RUDDOCK (E. H.) Text book of Medicine and Surgery on homœopathic principles. pp. 1082. *Lond.* 1893. 8°.   7383. h. 10.

RUSSELL (J. H.) Hints on Diet, with reference to Homœopathy. pp. 70. *Lond.* 1890. 8°.
    07305. e. 17. (1.)

SCHLEGEL (E.) Homöopathic und Cholera. pp. 30. *Tübingen,* 1892. 8°.   Pam. 39.

SCHUESSLER (W. H.) Die nieuwe Homeopathie. pp. 53. *Paarl,* 1891. 8°.   07305. i. 13. (11.)

SHULDHAM (E. B.) The family Homœopathist. pp. 152. *Lond.* 1890. 8°.   7321. a. 6.

For Electro-homœopathy (Count Mattei's system), *see* ELECTRICITY, *Medical :* for Homœopathic Hospitals, *see* HOSPITALS; and for Veterinary Homœopathy, *see* VETERINARY MEDICINE.

HOMOPTERA. *See* HEMIPTERA.

HONDURAS. CHARLES (C.) Honduras. pp. 216. *Chicago,* 1890. 8°.   10481. cc. 29.

HONDURAS. Commercial Directory. 1891. U.S. *Bureau of American Republics.* Bulletin. No. 28.   08225. k. 1.

—— Import duties of Honduras. pp. 42. 1891. 8°. U.S. *Bureau of American Republics.* Bulletin. No. 24.   08225. k. 1.

P.P. *Edinburgh.* Handbook of British Honduras. *Edinb.* 1890, *etc.* 8°.   P.P. 2587. dd.

See also AMERICA, *Central and South :* ENGLAND, *Colonies.*

HONG-KONG. CHAILLEY-BERT (J.) La Colonisation de l'Indo-Chine. L'expérience anglaise. pp. 398. *Paris,* 1892. 12°.
    10058 cc. 32.

F., F. Account of the visit of the Duke and Duchess of Connaught to Hongkong. pp. 36. *Hongkong,* 1890. 4°.   9930. gg. 20.

HONGKONG. Handbook to Hongkong. pp. 136. *Hongkong,* 1893. 8°.   10057. aa. 12.

LEGGE (W.) Guide to Hongkong. pp. 77. *Hongkong,* 1893. 8°.   010057. o. 19.

HONG-KONG—*continued.*

SHEPHERD (B.) Index to the streets, houses, and leased lots in Victoria. pp. 135.
Hongkong, 1894. 8°.   10058. g. 27.

SKERTCHLY (S. B. J.) Our Island. Naturalist's description of Hongkong. pp. 56.
Hongkong, 1893. 8°.   10058. aaa. 40.

HONGKONG. *Legislative Council.* Reports of meetings of the Legislative Council.
Hongkong, 1893, *etc.* 8°.   8022. e.

—— Ordinances of the legislative Council. 1844–90. 2 vol. *Hongkong*, 1891, 92. 8°.   06606. g. 10.

LEACH (A. J.) "Magistrates' Ordinance, 1890." pp. 166. *Hongkong*, 1891. 8°.   06606. f. 6.

SHEPHERD (B.) Companies' Ordinances of Hongkong. pp. 110. *Hongkong*, 1891. 8°.   06606. f. 8.

See also ENGLAND, *Colonies.*

HOORN. KROON (H.) and KAPTEIJN (F.) Nieuwe Kroniek van Hoorn. pp. 199.
Hoorn, 1891. fol.   10270. g. 6.

HOOSAC MOUNTAINS. WOLFF (J. E.) Geology of Hoosac Mountain. 1894. 4°. U.S. *Geological Survey.* Monographs. Vol. 23.   1828. b.

HOPS. DAVIS (G. W.) Hand book on the chemistry of Hops. pp. 118. *Lond.* 1895. 8°.   7073. aa. 2.

P.P. *London.* Hop and Malt Trades' Journal. *Lond.* 1891, *etc.* 4°.   1996.

WHITEHEAD (C.) Hop Cultivation. pp. 46. *Lond.* 1893. 8°.   Pam. 1.

See also BEER.

HORBLING. HORBLING. Baptismal, Marriage and Burial Registers of Horbling. pp. 203. *Liverp.* 1895. 8°.   9906. b. 7.

HORSE.

General.

ARMATAGE (G.) The Horse, its varieties and management. pp. 272. *Lond.* 1893. 8°.   7291. aa. 20.

BOUSSON (M. A. E.) Étude de la représentation du Cheval. pp. 90. *Paris*, 1892. 8°.   7291. ccc. 2.

CONSTABLE (H. S.) Something about Horses. pp. 293. *Lond.* 1891. 8°.   012357. f. 10.

EERELMAN (O.) Horses and Dogs. pp. 39. *Lond.* 1895. 4°.   7295. k. 4.

FITZWYGRAM (*Sir* F. W. J.) Horses and Stables. pp. 560. *Lond.* 1894. 8°.   07293. i. 25.

FLOWER (*Sir* W. H.) The Horse. pp. 196. 1891. 8°. LUBBOCK (*Rt. Hon. Sir* J.) Modern Science.   8709. f.

GORDON (W. J.) Horse-world of London. pp. 190. *Lond.* 1893. 8°.   4429. f. 13.

GOUBAUX (A.) and BARRIER (G.) The exterior of the Horse. pp. 916. *Lond.* 1892. 8°.   7291. ee. 4.

HAYES (M. H.) Among Men and Horses. pp. 358. *Lond.* 1894. 8°.   07905. i. 10.

—— Points of the Horse. pp. 379. *Lond.* 1893. 8°.   7291. aaa. 32.

JACOULET (J.) and CHOMEL (C.) Traité d'Hippologie. *Saumur*, 1894, *etc.* 8°.   07293. m.

LUPTON (J. I.) Horses, sound and unsound. pp. 211. *Lond.* 1893. 8°.   07293. i. 19.

NAVAROJĪ DORABJĪ DHĀKMĀRVĀLĀ. Demonstrations in the modes of handling and examining the Horse. pp. 154. *Bombay*, 1894. 8°.   07293. l. 3.

PELAGIUS. How to buy a horse. pp. 132. *Lond.* 1893. 8°.   7291. aa. 22.

HORSE—*continued.*

SIDNEY (S.) The Book of the Horse. pp. 630. *Lond.* 1892–93. 8°.   7293. l. 20.

TEGETMEIER (W. B.) and SUTHERLAND (C. L.) Horses, *etc.* pp. 166. *Lond.* 1895. 8°.   07293. i. 27.

VAN BUSKIRK (S.) The latest Work on the Horse. pp. 52. *Auckland*, 1895. 8°. 7291. aa. 34.

See also ANIMALS, *Domestic.*

Anatomy, Physiology and Methods of Testing Age. *See* VETERINARY MEDICINE.

Breeds: Breeding and Stud Books.

BLEW (W. C. A.) Light Horses, breeds, *etc.* pp. 226. 1894. 8°. SINCLAIR (J.) Live Stock Handbooks. No. 2.   7291. c.

LOWE (C. B.) Breeding Racehorses by the figure system. pp. 262. *Lond.* 1895. 8°. 07905. l. 6.

OSBORNE (J.) Horse-Breeders' handbook. 2 pt. *Lond.* 1895. 8°.   07291. k. 1.

PEASE (A. E.) Horse-breeding for farmers. pp. 133. *Lond.* 1894. 8°.   7291. aa. 29.

SIMONOV (L. N.) and MOERDER (J. v.) Les Races chevalines. pp. 316. *Paris*, 1894. 4°.   7291. d. 15.

UNDERWOOD (W. C.) The British War Horse. pp. 16. *Lond.* 1893. 8°.   8830. d. 11. (16.)

WARBURTON (F. T.) The Race Horse. pp. 270. *Lond.* 1892. 8°.   7906. d. 34.

GASSEBNER (H.) Die Pferdezucht im Österreich. *Wien*, 1893, *etc.* 8°.   7293. l.

G. B. & I. *War Office.* Report on Horse Breeding in Hungary, 1894. pp. 12. *Lond.* 1895. fol.   8826. i. 31. (3.)

—— Report on Horse Breeding in France. pp. 35. *Lond.* 1893. 8°.   7204. c. 16. (10.)

WRANGEL (C. G.) Ungarns Pferdezucht. *Stuttg.* 1891, *etc.* 8°.   7295. i. 17.

HUMFREY (J.) Horse-Breeding and rearing in India. pp. 147. *Calcutta*, 1887. 8°. 07293. g. 19.

TWEEDIE (W.) The Arabian Horse. pp. 411. *Edinb.* 1894. 4°.   7294. h. 5.

AUREGGIO (E.) Les Chevaux du Nord de l'Afrique. pp. 512. *Alger*, 1893. 4°. 7293. l. 21.

ALGIERS. *Bureau de l'Agriculture.* Stud-Book de la race barbe. pp. 518. *Alger*, 1892. 8°.   7295. ee. 3.

BURDETT-COUTTS (W. L. A. B.) Brookfield Stud of old English breeds of horses. pp. 178. *Lond.* 1891. 4°.   7295. i. 16.

NORWICH. *Hackney Stud Book Society.* Report of the Hackney Horse Society's fourth show. pp. 30. *Norwich*, 1888, 8°.   7293. d. 28.

G. B. & I. *Yorkshire Coach Horse Society.* Yorkshire Coach Horse Stud book. *York*, 1887, *etc.* 8°.   07293. i.

FRENCH STUD BOOK. Stud book français. *Paris*, 1891, *etc.* 8°.   7291. e.

PALACHE (J. T.) The Jamaica Stud book. pp. 236. *Jamaica*, 1892. 8°.   7291. aa. 17.

LUEBBEN (E.) Oldenburger Gestütbuch. pp. 664. *Bremen*, 1891. 8°.   07293. k. 1.

INSTERBURG. *Landwirthschaftlicher Central-Verein für Litauen.* Ostpreussisches Stutbuch. *Berl.* 1890, *etc.* 8°.   7291. o.

ABERDEEN. *Shetland Pony Stud Book Society.* Shetland Pony Stud book. *Aberd.* 1891, *etc.* 8°.   07293. i. 6.

BOURNEMOUTH. *Pony Stud Book Society.* Pony Stud book. *Bournemouth*, 1891, *etc.* 8°.   7291. aaa.

G. B. & I. *Polo Pony Society.* Polo Pony Society Stud book. *Ludlow*, 1894, *etc.* 8°.   07291. g.

See also RACING.

HORSE—*continued*.

Breaking and Training.

ANDERSON (E. I.) Curb, Snaffle and Spur. pp. 132. *Edinb.* 1894. 8°.   07293. i. 26.

BOYSE ( ) How to tame and train your Horses. pp. 15. *Cape Town*, 1894. 8°.   Pam. 42.

CROCKER (E. K.) The education of the Horse. pp. 374. *Glasg.* 1894. 8°.   07293. g. 16.

HUTCHISON (W. M.) Hints on Colt-breaking. pp. 117. *Lond.* 1892. 8°.   07293. g. 1.

See also HORSEMANSHIP.

Law relating to the Horse.

LUPTON (J. I.) Horses, with the law relating to sales, *etc.* pp. 211. *Lond.* 1893. 8°.   07293. i. 19.

STEWART (D. R.) The Law of Horses. pp. 280. *Edinb.* 1892. 8°.   6376. e. 32.

CHARTON DE MEUR (M.) Dictionnaire de Jurisprudence hippique. pp. 345. *Paris*, 1891. 12°.   7912. aa. 14.

Stables : Stabling : Saddlery, etc.

BIRCH (J.) Examples of Stables, *etc.* pp. 64. *Edinb.* 1892. 8°.   7817. k. 9.

GIRAUD (B.) Stable Building and fitting. pp. 103. *Lond.* 1891. 8°.   7293. bbb. 32.

COMMINGES (M. A. de) *Count.* Le Cheval. Soins pratiques. pp. 462. *Paris*, 1893. 8°.   07293. g. 13.

FISHER (A. T.) Through the Stable and saddle-room. pp. 342. *Lond.* 1891. 8°.   7291. aa. 12.

FITZWYGRAM (*Sir* F. W. J.) Horses and Stables. pp. 560. *Lond.* 1894. 8°.   07293. i. 25.

FISHER (A. T.) The Farrier; or, "No foot, no horse." pp. 170. *Lond.* 1893. 8°. 07293. g. 7.

HUNTING (W.) Art of Horse-shoeing. pp. 115. *Lond.* 1895. 8°.   07293. i. 31.

PADER (J.) Précis théorique et pratique de Maréchalerie. pp. 393. *Paris*, 1892. 8°.   7291. aa. 15.

P.P. *Carlisle.* The Horse Shoe. *Carlisle*, 1893, *etc.* 8°.   P.P. 6077. ab. and 2208.

G. B. & I. *Army.* Manual of Saddles and collars. pp. 71. *Lond.* 1894. 8°. 8830. aaa. 61.

SMITH (F.) Manual of Saddles and sore backs. pp. 50. *Lond.* 1891. 8°.   8831. f. 31.

LONDON. *Saddlers' Company.* Catalogue of an exhibition of Saddlery and harness. pp. 90. *Lond.* 1892. 8°.   7958. e. 10.

P.P. *Walsall.* Saddlery and harness. *Walsall*, 1891, *etc.* 4°.   N.R.

WALLACE, BAILEY AND WILKINS. Saddlers' and harness makers' book of lengths. pp. 20. *Chatteris*, 1886. 8°.   07944. ee. 4. (5.)

ZSCHILLE (R.) and FORRER (R.) Die Pferdetrense in ihrer Formen-Entwicklung. pp. 16. *Berl.* 1893. fol.   1706. b. 10.

—— Der Sporn in seiner Formen-Entwicklung. pp. 24. *Berl.* 1891. fol.   1706. b. 9.

See also HORSEMANSHIP : VETERINARY MEDICINE.

HORSEMANSHIP. ALLBUTT (A.) Hints to Horsewomen. pp. 81. *Lond.* 1893, 8°.   07905. f. 9.

ANDERSON (E. L.) Modern Horsemanship. pp. 207. *Edinb.* 1895. 8°.   07905. i. 14.

AURE (d.) *Viscount.* Traité d'Équitation. pp. 193. *Paris*, 1893. 8°.   7906. h. 21.

BAUCHER (F.) Dressage méthodique du Cheval de selle. pp. 204. *Paris*, 1891. 8°. 7906. g. 39.

CHÉZELLES (H. de) *Viscount.* L'Homme de Cheval. pp. 227. *Paris*, 1893. 8°. 07293. g. 18.

CONSTABLE (H. S.) Something about Horses. pp. 293. *Lond.* 1891. 8°.   7908. ee. 21.

DODGE (T. A.) Riders of many lands. pp. 486. *Lond.* 1894. 8°.   7907. dd. 20.

DUPLESSIS (C.) L'Équitation en France. pp. 640. *Paris*, 1892. 8°.   7906. h. 20.

ENGLISH (H. G.) The art of riding. pp. 132. *Lond.* 1891. 8°.   7912. aa. 8.

FILLIS (J.) Principes d'équitation. pp. 425. *Paris*, 1892. 8°.   07905. l. 1.

FITZ-JAMES (de) *Duchess.* Principes d'Équitation. pp. 110. *Paris*, 1893. 4°.   1818. a. 8.

HAYES (A. M.) The Horsewoman. pp. 272. *Lond.* 1893. 8°.   07905. f. 1.

HAYES (M. H.) Riding. pp. 285. *Lond.* 1891. 8°.   7908. eee. 2.

HEYDEBRAND UND DER LASA (L. v.) Illustrirte Geschichte der Reiterei. pp. 188. *Wien*, 1892. 8°.   7908. dd. 26.

HORSEMAN. Riding. pp. 12. *Lond.* 1891. 8°.   7912. ee. 2. (7.)

HOWARD (H. C.) *Earl of Suffolk.* Racing and steeplechasing. pp. 439. 1893. 4°. Badminton Library.   2264. aa.

KERR (W. A.) Practical Horsemanship. pp. 222. 1891. 8°. All England Series.   7908. df.

—— Riding for Ladies. pp. 91. 1891. 8°. All England Series.   7908. df.

LE BON (G.) L'Équitation actuelle et ses principes. pp. 439. *Paris*, 1892, 12°. 7907. d. 38.

MARTINENGO-CESARESCO (E.) *Count.* L'arte di Cavalcare. 4 vol. *Salo*, 1894. 8°. 07905. h. 20.

MUSANY (F.) Conseils pour le Dressage des chevaux difficiles. pp, 277. *Paris*, 1880. 8°.   7907. i. 20.

O'DONOGHUE (N. P.) Ladies on Horseback. pp. 284. *Lond.* 1891. 8°.   7908. ee. 9.

PICARD (L.) and BOUCHARD (G.) Album d'Hippiatrique. *Paris*, 1892. fol.   1818. d. 2.

SCHOENBECK (B.) Die Widersetzlichkeit des Pferdes. pp. 179. 1893. 8°. Thaer-Bibliothek.   7078. d.

SUDBURY (M. W.) Hints to Horsemen. pp. 83. *Norwich*, 1893. 8°.   7912. aa. 31.

VALLET (L.) Le Chic à Cheval. pp. 274. *Paris*, 1891. 4°.   7905. k. 18.

VAUX (C. M. de.) Écuyers et Écuyères. Cirques d'Europe. pp. 368. *Paris*, 1893. 8°.   7907. dd. 18.

WEIR (R. W.) Riding. pp. 448. 1895. 8°. Badminton Library.   2264. aa. 14.

YATES (M. T.) Famous Rides in all ages. pp. 318. *Lond.* 1892. 8°.   9004. g. 22.

———

EULE (O. F.) Meine Erlebnisse auf dem Distance-Ritt, Berlin-Wien. pp. 29, *Leipz.* 1892. 8°.   7912. f. 2. (6.)

FREYTAG (F.) Der Distanzritt und das Pferd. pp. 14. *Flensburg*, 1893. 8°. 7204. a. 31. (6.)

MAYERHOFFER (R.) Ein Distanzritt Agram-Wien. pp. 61. *Wien*, 1894. 8°. 7906. df. 27.

PEITZ (O.) Mein Distanzmarsch von Berlin nach Wien. pp. 46. *Flöha*, 1893. 12°. Pam. 83.

PIRQUET VON CESENATICO (P.) *Baron.* Der grosse Distanzritt zwischen Wien und Berlin. pp. 29. *Wien*, 1892. 8°.   7912. f. 2. (7.)

VIENNA. Wien-Berlin—Berlin-Wien. pp. 230. *Wien*, 1892. 8°.   7912. aa. 28.

—— Distanzritt Wien-Berlin, October 1892. pp. 24. *Wien*, 1893. 8°.   7907. dd. 19.

WILCKENS (M.) Der Distanzritt und die Vollbluttfrage. pp. 48. *Wien*, 1893. 8°.   7004. df. 20. (8.)

HORSEMANSHIP—*continued.*

HANDS. Hands and Mouths. Driving and Bitting. pp. 46. *Lond.* 1894. 8°. 7912. df. 4. (5.)

KNIGHT (C. L. W. M.) Hints on driving. pp. 180. *Lond.* 1894. 8°. 07905. f. 19.

SAINT MAUR (A. P. B.) *Duke of Somerset.* Driving. 1889. 4°. Badminton Library. 7905. f.

THOMSON (R. A.) Team and tandem Driving. 1894. 8°. GREVILLE (B. V.) *Baroness Greville.* Ladies in the Field, *etc.* 07905. f. 15.

See also COACHING : HORSE : HUNTING : RACING : SPORT : TROTTING.

HORTICULTURE. *See* FLOWERS : GARDENING.

HOSPITALS.

General.

BURDETT (H. C.) Hospitals of the world. *Lond.* 1891–93. 8°. 2024. e.

—— Portfolio of Plans. 1893. fol. 1832. e. 9.

BURDETT (H. C.) Helps in Sickness and to health. pp. 484. *Lond.* 1894. 8°. 7404. cc. 23.

—— Uniform system of accounts and tenders for Hospitals. pp. 76. *Lond.* 1893. *etc.* 08227. e. 48.

CHOAY (E.) Centres universitaires et établissements hospitaliers à l'étranger. pp. 146. *Paris,* 1892. 8°. 7679. df. 36.

DOLAN (T. M.) Our state Hospitals. pp. 66. *Leicester,* 1894. 8°. 7687. ee. 21.

ERICHSEN (J. E.) Hospital Federation for clinical purposes. pp. 23. *Lond.* 1892. 8°. 07305. h. 16 (10.)

FAURE (H.) Étude sur les œuvres hospitalières à Narbonne, en Angleterre, en Ecosse. pp. 219. *Narbonne,* 1890. *etc.* 7688. g. 8.

—— Étude de la situation hospitalière à Narbonne et dans le nord de la France. pp. 106. *Narbonne,* 1891. 8°. 7688. h. 1.

—— Les Revenus des Hospices et les subventions municipales. pp. 26. *Narbonne,* 1892. 8°. 8277. h. 19. (11.)

GALTON (*Sir* D.) Healthy Hospitals. pp. 287. *Oxf.* 1893. 8°. 7687. ee. 13.

HAKE (A. E.) Suffering London; relation of voluntary hospitals to society. pp. 179. *Lond.* 1892. 8°. 7687. c. 16.

LÉPREVOST (A.) Hôpitaux. 1889. 8°. Ac. Havre-de-Grâce. *Société d'Études Diverses.* Recueil. 1889. Ac. 2612.

P.P. *London.* Burdett's Hospital annual. *Lond.* 1890, *etc.* 8°. P.P. 2487. feg.

PINZI (C.) Gli Ospizi medioevali e l'Ospedal-Grande di Viterbo. pp. 430. *Viterbo,* 1893. 8°. 7688. g. 12.

ROTHSCHILD (H. de) Etablissements hospitaliers dans l'antiquité. pp. 69. *Macon,* 189 . 8°. 7680. a. 17.

ROGER-MILÈS (L.) La Cité de Misère. pp. 334. *Paris,* 1891. 8°. 7688. aa. 47.

SOUTHAM (G. A.) and (E. A.) "Hors de Combat"; three weeks in a hospital. pp. 106. *Lond.* 1891. 8°. 7688. g. 10.

TOLLET (C.) Les Hôpitaux modernes au XIX° siècle. pp. 334. *Paris,* 1894. 4°. 7687. i. 9.

BAXTER (C. P.) Hospital Service book. pp. 185. 73. *Lond.* 1895. 8°. 3408. b. 51.

See also CHARITIES : EDUCATION, *Medical* : MEDICINE.

Hospitals for Infectious Diseases.

ABBOTT (S. W.) Isolation Hospitals for infectious diseases. pp. 46. 1894. 8°. 7561. k. 26. (6.)

CURGENVEN (J. B.) Protest against the sums spent yearly upon the maintenance of Fever Hospitals in London. *Lond.* 1891. 8°. 7561. k. 26.(8.)

HOSPITALS—*continued.*

ENGLAND AND WALES. *Local Government Board.* Annual Report, 1880–81. Supplement on Hospitals for infectious diseases. pp. 361. *Lond.* 1894. 8°. 7561. i. 40.

MAC NEILL (R.) The Prevention of Epidemics, and construction of isolation hospitals. pp. 247. *Lond.* 1894. 8°. 7687. ee. 22.

Pharmacopoeias. *See* PHARMACOPOEIAS.

Reports and Accounts of Hospitals.

BALTIMORE. *Johns Hopkins Hospital.* Description of Johns Hopkins Hospital. pp. 116. *Baltimore,* 1890. 4°. 7686. k. 3.

—— Bulletin. *Baltimore,* 1892, *etc.* 4°. 7687. i.

HAGEMEYER (A.) Das neue Krankenhaus der Stadt Berlin am Urban. pp. 152. *Berl.* 1894. 8°. 7688. g. 13.

BIRMINGHAM. *Hospital Reform Enquiry Committee.* Report of the Committee. pp. 36. *Birmingham,* 1891. 8°. Pam. 39.

BOSTON. *City Hospital.* Report of Trustees of the Boston City Hospital on establishing cottage hospitals. pp. 43. *Bost.* 1893. 8°. Pam. 39.

—— *Homoeopathic Hospital.* Fifteenth Annual Report. pp. 44. *Bost.* 1883. 8°. 7688. c. 15.

JARMAN (S. G.) The Bridgwater Infirmary. pp. 77. *Saint Ives,* 1890. 8°. Pam. 39.

WOODROFFE (W. H.) Hospital for infectious diseases for Canterbury. Report. pp. 6. *Lond.* 1891. fol. Pam. 39.

EDINBURGH. *Hospitals.* Edinburgh Hospital Reports. *Edinb.* 1893, *etc.* 8°. 07686. h.

WIMBERLEY (D.) The Hospital of Inverness and Dunbar's Hospital. pp. 136. *Inverness,* 1893. 8°. 8277. cc. 45.

LONDON. *Medical Institutions.* Medical institutions of London. pp. 60. *Lond.* 1895. 8°. Pam. 39.

CLARKE ( ) *Mrs.* Helpless; history of the British Home for Incurables. pp. 37. *Lond.* 1894. 8°. Pam. 39.

WILKS (S.) and BETTANY (G. T.) Biographical history of Guy's Hospital. pp. 500. *Lond.* 1892. 8°. 7687. ecc. 36.

LONDON. *Great Northern Central Hospital.* Annual Report. *Lond.* 1895, *etc.* 8°. 7688. b.

KING'S COLLEGE HOSPITAL, *London.* Reports. *Lond.* 1895, *etc.* 8°. 07686. i.

LONDON. *London Homoeopathic Hospital.* Reports. *Lond.* 1891, *etc.* 8°. 7688. f.

—— *Magdalen Hospital.* Origin of the London Magdalen Hospital, *etc.* pp. 8. *Wellington,* 189 . 8°. 8282. ff. 9. (15.)

MOORE (N.) Brief Relation of the state of St. Bartholomew's Hospital. pp. 60. *Lond.* 1895. 8°. 7688. aa. 59.

CANO Y DE LEÓN (M.) El nuevo Hospital militar de Madrid. pp. 212. 1891. 8°. P.P. *Madrid.* Memorial de Ingenieros del Ejército. Tom. 46. P.P. 4025. aa.

BEU (P.) Histoire de Bicêtre. pp. 480. *Paris,* 1890. 4°. 10172. f. 21.

Ac. Paris. *Société de l'Histoire de Paris.* COYECQUE (E.) L'Hôtel-Dieu de Paris au moyen-âge. 2 tom. *Paris,* 1891. 8°. Ac. 6883/10.

COCHIN (A.) L'Hôpital Cochin. La Laicisation 1780–1885. pp. 202. *Paris,* 1890. 8°. 7688. g. 6.

MORTON (T. G.) and WOODBURY (F.) History of the Pennsylvania Hospital. pp. 575. *Phila.* 1895. 8°. 7687. f. 17.

PHILADELPHIA. *Hospital.* Reports. *Phila.* 1891, *etc.* 8°. 7688. g.

HOSPITALS—continued.

DELMAS (L.) Histoire de l'Hôtel-Dieu de Poitiers. pp. 94. *Poitiers*, 1894. 8°. 7687. eee. 39.

P.P. *Vienna.* Jahrbuch der wiener Kranken-Anstalten. *Wien*, 1893, etc. 8°. P.P. 2440. l. For Hospital Medical Schools. *See* MEDICINE, *Education.*

HOTELS. LIEBENAU (T. v.) Das Gasthof-und Wirthshauswesen der Schweiz in aelterer Zeit. pp. 347. *Zürich*, 1891. 8°. 7709. f. 23.

ROBINSON (E. F.) Early history of Coffee Houses in England. pp. 240. *Lond.* 1893. 8°. 7709. b. 46.

KEMPT (R.) Convivial Caledonia. Inns and taverns of Scotland. pp. 157. *Lond.* 1893. 8°. 10369. ccc. 26.

REVENDICATIONS. Les Revendications des garçons de café. pp. 14. *Paris*, 1894. 8°. Pam. 82.

ALEXANDER (G.) "Simplex" system of Hotel book-keeping. pp. 8. *Lond.* 1895. 8°. 8531. cc. 28. (7.)

HOTELS REGISTER. The Hotels Register. *Congleton*, 1895. fol. 1881. a. 54.

WHATLEY (G. E. S.) Companion to Hotel book-keeping. pp. 12. *Lond.* 1893. 8°. 8531. dd. 28. (9.)

See also LICENSING LAWS.

HOUGHTON, Hants. BOYCE (E. J.) History of Parochial Registers. Illustrations from those of Houghton. pp. 57. *Winchester*, 1895. 8°. 9904. i. 42.

HOUR, Universal. *See* TIME.

HOUSEHOLD MANAGEMENT.

B., A. R. The "Colonial Household Guide." pp. 223. *Capetown*, 1890. 8°. 07945. f. 27.

BARNETT (E. A.) and O'NIEL (H. C.) Primer of Domestic Economy. pp. 130. *Lond.* 1892. 8°. 7942. a. 61.

BEACH (*Mrs.* K.) Girls' Domestic Economy. pp. 46. *Lond.* 1891. 8°. 07945. e. 61.

BEETON (I. M.) Book of Household Management. pp. 1308. *Lond.* 1892. 8°. 7942. dd. 9.

—— Family Cookery and Housekeeping book. pp. 640. *Lond.* 1893. 8°. 07945. h. 39.

—— Every-day Cookery and Housekeeping book. pp. 568. *Lond.* 1890. 8°. 07945. h. 24.

BLACKIE (W. G.) and SON. Domestic Economy readers. *Lond.* 1895, etc. 8°. 07944. df.

BORGHINI (L.) Manual de Economía Doméstica. pp. 98. *Paris*, 1895. 8°. 7945. a. 54.

CASSELL (J.) Book of the Household. 4 vol. *Lond.* 1893, 94. 8°. 7944. d. 17.

COLLEY (A.) Domestic Economy for students and teachers. pp. 202. *Hull*, 1895. 8°. 7942. bbb. 54.

COOLEY (A. J.) Cyclopædia of practical Receipts. 2 vol. *Lond.* 1892. 8°. 2022. c.

DE SALIS (H. A.) Wrinkles and notions for every household. pp. 139. *Lond.* 1892. 8°. 7944. d. 14.

HANDY BOOK. Handy book of the Household. pp. 188. *Lond.* 1892. 8°. 7942. de. 7.

HANSEN-TAYLOR (M.) Letters to a young housekeeper. pp. 219. *Lond.* 1892. 8°. 07944. e. 9.

HASSELL (J.) Lessons in Domestic Economy. pp. 192. 1893. 8°. Collins' School Series. 12204. cc.

HEADDON (M. E.) Housework and Domestic Economy. pp. 102. *Lond.* 1893. 8°. 7942. k. 42.

HINTS. Hints for housewives. *Lond.* 1892, etc. 8°. 2147.

HOUSEHOLD GUIDE. Household Guide of useful receipts. pp. 51. *Lond.* 1891. 8°. Pam. 94.

HOUSEHOLD MANAGEMENT—cont.

HOUSEKEEPING. Economical Housekeeping. pp. 27. *Lond.* 1891. 8°. 7942. h. 31. (5.)

HOUSEWIFE. Housewife's cheque-book. *Lond.* 1895, etc. obl. 8°. 7943. de.

HUGHES (J.) Domestic Economy. pp. 448. *Lond.* 1891. 8°. 07945. e. 46.

HUMPHRY (C. E.) Housekeeping. pp. 308. *Lond.* 1893. 8°. 07944. e. 4.

LANGLET (M.) Husmoderen i staden och på landet. pp. 1122. *Stockholm*, 1892. 8°. 07945. h. 41.

LOFTIE (M. J.) Comfort in the home. pp. 102. *Lond.* 1895. 8°. 07944. e. 46.

MAJOR (H.) Teacher's manual of lessons on Domestic Economy. pp. 436. *Lond.* 1893. 8°. 7309. de. 16.

MEN. Men, and how to manage them. Book for Australian wives. pp. 121. *Melbourne*, 1885. 8°. 7942. a. 60.

MUSKETT (P. E.) Art of living in Australia. pp. 431. *Lond.* 1894. 8°. 07944. e. 23.

NEWSHOLME (A.) and SCOTT (M. E.) Domestic Economy. pp. 340. *Lond.* 1894. 8°. 07944. e. 41.

PAUL (F. T.) Text-book of Domestic Economy. *Lond.* 1893, etc. 8°. 7404. df.

P.P. *Dublin.* The Lady of the house. *Dublin*, 1890, etc. fol. 1827.

—— *London.* Housewifery. *Lond.* 1892, etc. 4°. 1577.

—— Lett's Ladies' year book and Housekeeper's diary. *Lond.* 1894, etc. 8°. P.P. 2501. pba.

—— Practical Housekeeping. *Lond.* 1891, etc. 8°. 819.

RECIPES. Recipes. pp. 212. *Lond.* 1891. 8°. 07945. h. 20.

RIGG ( ) Domestic Economy for the new code. 3 pt. *Lond.* 1893. 8°. 07944. e. 12.

ROWE (J. R.) Housekeeper's Account book. *Leicester*, 1895. 8°. 8518. de. 34.

SENN (C. H.) Practical Household recipes. *Lond.* 1892, etc. 8°. 07945. f.

SHARMAN (E. A.) Common-sense Lessons in housework. pp. 60. *Lond.* 1894. 8°. 07944. e. 35.

SIMON (G.) L'Art de vivre. pp. 390. *Paris*, 1892. 12°. 7404. e. 1.

SMITH (J.) Domestic Encyclopædia. pp. 191. *Lewes*, 1891. 4°. 7944. de. 44.

SPON (E.) and (F. N.) Household Manual. pp. 1013. *Lond.* 1891. 8°. 2027. c.

WINSNES (H. O.) Husholdningsbog for tarvelige Familier i By og Bygd. pp. 140. *Kristiania*, 1892. 8°. 07944. e. 20.

DUTIES. Duties of servants. pp. 119. *Lond.* 1894. 8°. 07944. e. 47.

GALLAHER (F. M.) Lessons in domestic service. pp. 324. *Dublin*, 1894. 8°. 07944. ee. 42.

LEWIS, afterwards HAMMICK (E.) *Lady.* Domestic Service in the present day. pp. 87. *Lond.* 1889. 8°. 8416. aaa. 47.

SERVANT. The Servants' Question. pp. 17. *Lond.* 1894. 8°. Pam. 82.

See also COOKERY.

HOUSE-PAINTING. *See* ART, *Decorative.*

HOUSES. BALCH (E.) Glimpse of old English Homes. pp. 223. *Lond.* 1890. 8°. 010358 g. 10.

HODGES (E.) Some ancient English homes. pp. 280. *Lond.* 1895. 4°. 10348. d. 21.

DOWELL (S.) Acts relating to the Tax on inhabited Dwelling-houses. pp. 39. *Lond.* 1893. 8°. 6425. df. 22.

HOUSES—*continued.*

FRANCE. *Ministère de l'Instruction.* Enquête sur les conditions de l'Habitation en France. Les maison-types. pp. 381. *Paris,* 1894 8°.
             7817. i. 8.

GARDINER (F. M.) Furnishing and fittings for every Home. pp. 130. *Lond.* 1894. 8°.
             7820. bb. 23.

GOETZ (W.) Das nordische Wohnhaus während des 16. Jahrhunderts. pp. 31. 1891. 8°. Sammlung wissenschaftlicher Vorträge. Hft. 131.
             12249. m.

HOFFMEYER (S.) Almindelige Betingelser for Overtagelse af Husbygningsarbejder. pp. 18. *Aalborg,* 1890. fol.   Pam. 34.

NIMBEAU (F.) L'Entrepreneur de peinture en bâtiment. pp. 372. *Paris,* 1894. 8°. 7858. gg. 30.

REID (*Sir* H. G.) Housing the people. pp. 69. *Paisley,* 1895. 8°.   08275. e. 28.

RIS-PAQUOT (O. E.) L'Habitation. pp. 120. *Paris,* 1894. 12°.   7817. bb. 2.

SCHNEIDER (K.) Das Wohnungsmietrecht und seine sociale Reform. pp. 170. 1893. 8°. SCHMOLLER (G.) Staat-wissenschaftliche Forschungen. Bd. 12.   8205. dd.

TARBUCH (E. L.) Handbook of House property. pp. 299. *Lond.* 1892. 8°.   2230. a. 13.

WILLIAMS (R.) The People the Nation's Wealth. pp. 16. *Lond.* 1895. 8°.   Pam. 82.

YALSDUAM (L.) An Order to view. pp. 320. *Lond.* 1892. 8°.   012330. f. 41.

See also ARCHITECTURE, *Pt. I. Domestic,* and *Pt. II. England:* ART, *Decorative:* CAPITAL AND LABOUR, *Pt. I. Housing of the Working Classes:* DRAINAGE : LAND TENURES : SANITATION.

HOWLEY. BAILDON (W. P.) Early history of Howley. pp. 16. *Bradford,* 1893. 8°.
             10348. d. 20. (5.)

HOZÉMONT. VANDRIKEN (L.) L'ancien Comté de Hozémont. pp. 321. *Liége,* 1895. 8°.
             10170. ccc. 7.

HUDDERSFIELD. ADHEM (A. B.) In darkest Huddersfield, why have we no Public Library? pp. 31. *Huddersfield,* 1891. 8°. Pam. 6.

HUDSON RIVER. INGERSOLL (E.) Illustrated guide to the Hudson River. pp. 243. *Chicago,* 1893. 8°.   10413. bbb. 31.

HUDSON'S BAY. AILLAIRGÉ (G. F.) Le Détroit et la baie Hudson. pp. 54. *Joliette,* 1888. 8°.   10411. aa. 50. (2.)

HUGUENOTS. *See* FRANCE, *Protestants.*

HULL. *See* KINGSTON-ON-HULL.

HUMANITY, Religion of. *See* POSITIVISM.

HUNGARIAN LANGUAGE AND LITERATURE. DICTIONARIES. Magyar-franczia és Franczia-magyar Szótár. *Budapest,* 1890, *etc.* 8°.   12975. m. 1.

KÖNNYE (N.) Dictionnaire français-hongrois et hongrois-français. 2 pt. *Budapest,* 1891. 16°.
             12976. aa. 29.

—— Deutsch-ungarisches und ungarisch-deutsches Taschenwörterbuch. 2 Thle. *Wien,* 1890. 8°.   12976. a. 20.

DONÁTH (I.) Grammatica ungherese. pp. 143. *Fiume,* 1892. 8°.   12975. h. 20.

DUKA (T.) Essay on Ugor Languages. pp. 67. *Lond.* 1889. 8°.   12976. dd. 28.

HORNYÁNSZKY (G.) Grammatik der ungarischen Sprache. pp. 167. *Budapest,* 1894. 8°.
             12975. ccc. 1.

KOVÁCS (K.) Beszél ön magyarul?—Sprechen Sie ungarisch? pp. 135. *Brünn,* 1882. 8°.
             12976. aa. 26.

HUNGARIAN—*continued.*

ZIGÁNY (G. A.) Letteratura ungherese. pp. 295. *Milano,* 1892. 8°.   012200. h. 103.

HUNGARY. [*See note on page* 1.] For all Works relating to Austria-Hungary, *see* AUSTRIA.

Antiquities and History.

KUBINYI (F.) Nomenclator Hungarorum Antiquorum. *Budapestini,* 1891, *etc.* fol.   6.

CSERGHEŐ (G.) and CSOMA (J.) Alte Grabdenkmäler aus Ungarn. pp. 122. *Budapest,* 1890. 8°.
             7875. de. 26.

KAINDL (R. F.) Beiträge zur älteren ungarischen Geschichte. pp. 86. *Wien,* 1893. 8°.
             9007. g. 22. (7.)

FRANKL, *afterwards* FRAKNÓI (V.) Mathias Corvinus, König von Ungarn. 1458-90. pp. 316. *Freiburg,* 1891. 8°.   10790. h. 1.

PISKO (J.) Skanderbeg. pp. 162. *Wein,* 1894. 8°.   10606. h. 21.

KRONES VON MARCHLAND (F. X.) Zur Geschichte Ungarns, 1671-83. 1894. 8°. Archiv für österreichische Geschichte. Bd. 80.   Ac. 810/8.

WEISER (F.) Die marianischen Congregationen in Ungarn und die Rettung Ungarns, 1686-99. pp. 160. *Regensburg,* 1891. 8°.   4662. e. 11.

SOMOGYI (E.) Ludwig Kossuth. pp. 214. *Leipz.* 1894. 8°.   010795. h. 3.

See also AUSTRIA : HOLY ROMAN EMPIRE.

Constitution.

STEINBACH (G.) Die ungarischen Verfassungsgesetze. pp. 127. *Wien,* 1891. 8°.   5511. a. 9.

See also AUSTRIA.

Ethnology : Topography, etc.

P.P.   *Pest.* Ethnologische Mitteilungen aus Ungarn. *Budapest,* 1887, *etc.* 4°. P.P. 3863. i.

PLUSZKY (Á.) Hungary. 1891. 8°. MAGNÚSSON (E.) National Life and Thought. 8486. g. 21.

WLISLOCKI (H. v.) Volksglaube und religiöser Brauch der Magyaren. pp. 171. 1893. 8°. Darstellungen aus dem Gebiete der nichtchristlichen Religionsgeschichte. Bd. 8.   4506. f.

—— Aus dem Volksleben der Magyaren. pp. 183. *München,* 1893. 8°.   10215. e. 16.

BUOTE (E.) Die rumänische Frage in Ungarn. pp. 432. *Berl.* 1895. 8°.   8074. h. 4.

GAIDOZ (H.) Les Roumains de Hongrie. pp. 30. *Paris,* 1894. 8°.   10105. ee. 12. (11.)

TRANSYLVANIA. The Roumanian Question in Hungary. pp. 151. *Vienna,* 1892. 8°. 8074. h. 1.

—— La Quistione romena nella Ungheria. pp. 139. *Vienna,* 1893. 8°.   8028. ff. 20.

X. Roumains et Hongrois. Leurs rapports envisagés aux points de vue des intérêts roumains. pp. 32. *Budapest,* 1891. 8°.
             8026. aaa. 41. (5.)

BELL (F. A.) Ungarn in Wort und Bild. pp. 534. *Zürich,* 1890. 8°.   10215. b. 4.

CHÉLARD (R.) La Hongrie contemporaine. pp. 382. *Paris,* 1891. 8°.   10215. aaa. 31.

COLE (G. A. J.) The Gypsy Road : journey from Krakow to Coblentz. pp. 166. *Lond.* 1894. 8°.
             10108. de. 12.

FELBERMANN (L.) Hungary and its people. pp. 390. *Lond.* 1892. 8°.   10201. c. 6.

FLETCHER (M.) Sketches of Life and character in Hungary. pp. 248. *Lond.* 1892. 8°.
             10215. c. 3.

HUNGARY. Guide-book. pp. 548. *Zurich,* 1890. 8°.   10215. b. 5.

See also AUSTRIA.

HUNGARY—*continued.*

Trade and Finance.

DEUTSCH (A.) 25 Jahre ungarischer Finanz- und
Volkswirthschaft. pp. 95. *Berl.* 1892. 8°.
       8225. eee. 47.

HUNGARY. Les Fabricants-exportateurs de Hongrie. pp. 160. *Budapest,* 1894. 8°. 08227. ee. 60.

VAUTIER (G.) La Hongrie économique. pp. 486.
Paris, 1893. 8°.   08225. k. 4.

HUNGERFORD. MONEY (W.) Historical
sketch of Hungerford. pp. 73.
Newbury, 1894. 8°.   010358. f. 52.

HUNS. HODGKIN (T.) Italy and her Invaders.
Vol. 2. *Oxf.* 1892, *etc.* 8°.   2068. c.

HUNTING. BABDASTRANDARSYSLA. Reglugjörð fyrir Barðastrandarsyslu um grenjaleitir.,
pp. 16. *Reykjavík,* 1886. 8°.   867. i. 42. (6.)

CASTOR. Century of Foxhunting with the
Warwickshire hounds. pp. 206.
Banbury, 1891. 8°.   7908. ee. 17.

CHARLTON (J.) Twelve Packs of honnds.
ff. 104. *Lond.* 1891. obl. fol.   1818. a. 4.

CHÉZELLES (H. de) *Viscount.* Vieille Vénerie.
pp. 184. *Paris,* 1894. 8°.   07905. f. 21.

COLLYER (M. A.) Incidents with the Warnham
Stag hounds. *Lond.* 1894. obl. fol. 1870. b. 26.

DIXON (H. H.) Druid Sporting Library. 5 vol.
Lond. 1895. 8°.   07905. f. 29.

ELMHIRST (E. P.) Fox-hound, forest and
prairie. pp. 584. *Lond.* 1892. 8°. 7908. dd. 17.

GREVILLE (B. V.) *Baroness Greville.* Ladies
in the Field. pp. 287. *Lond.* 1894. 8°.
      07905. f. 15.

HALL (F.) "Hoick For'ard." pp. 31.
Lond. 1895. obl. 8°.   12316. i. 64.

HORE (J. P.) History of the Royal Buckhounds.
pp. 400. *Lond.* 1893, 8°.   07905. h. 14.

LIGNIVILLE (J. de) *Count de Bey.* Miettes et
véneries. 2 pt. *Paris,* 1892. 4°. 7108. dd. 23.

ONSENBRAY (H. d') L'École du Piquer. pp. 117.
Paris, 1894. 12°.   07905. f. 25.

OSMOND (R. E. d') *Count.* Les Hommes des Bois.
pp. 272. *Paris,* 1892. 8°.   07905. h. 3.

PULESTON (T. H. G.) History of Fox-hunting in
the Wynnstay country. pp. 196. *Lond.* 1893. 4°.
      7908. f. 26.

RADCLIFFE (F. P. D.) The Noble Science.
pp. 331. *Lond.* 1893. 8°.   7908. f. 23.

RUSSELL (F.) In Scarlet and Silk, Recollections of hunting. pp. 294. *Lond.* 1895, 8°.
      07905. g. 9.

SAHLENDER (P. M.) Englische Jagdlitteratur im
14. 15. und 16. Jahrhundert. pp. 31.
Leipz. 1895. 8°.   7912. f. 2. (8.)

—— Der Jagdtraktat Twici's, des Hofjägers bei
Edward II. von England. pp. 60. *Lond.* 1894. 8°.
      7912. f. 2. (9.)

SCHWAPPACH (A.) Jagd- und Fischereipolitik.
pp. 306. 1894. 8°. FRANKENSTEIN (K.) Handbuch der Staatswissenschaften. Bd. 10.
      8009. k.

SOMEREST (H. C. F.) *Duke of Beaufort.*
Hunting. pp. 385. 1894. 8°. Badminton
Library.   2264. aa.

TANTARA. Hare Hunting. pp. 66. *Lond.* 1893. 8°.
      7908. bb. 49.

VYNER (R. T.) Notitia Venatica. pp. 406.
Lond. 1892, 8°.   7905. i. 16.

See also DOG : HORSEMANSHIP : SPORT.

HUNTINGDONSHIRE. HERTFORD. Murray's Handbook for Hertfordshire and Huntingdonshire. pp. 260. *Lond.* 1895. 8°.
      2364. b. 31.

HURIEL. BOURGOUGNON (G.) Monographie
du Canton d'Huriel. pp. 144.
Montluçon, 1895. 8°.   010171. k. 16.

HURON, Lake. DAY ( ) Trip among the
islands of Lake Huron. pp. 12. *Lond.* 1890. 8°,
      Pam. 40.

HUSBAND AND WIFE, Law of.
See MARRIAGE.

HUSSITES. *See* BOHEMIA.

HUYSBURG, Monastery. ECKART (T.)
Geschichte des Klosters Huysburg. pp. 47.
Braunschweig, 1892. 8°.   4662. c. 25. (6.)

HWANG-HO, River. *See* YELLOW RIVER.

HYDERABAD. *See* HAIDERABAD.

HYDRAULICS : HYDROMECHANICS.
BERTHOT (P.) Traité de l'élévation des Eaux.
pp. 384. *Paris,* 1893. 8°.   8777. g. 7.

BJÖRLING (P. R.) Water or Hydraulic motors.
pp. 287. *Lond.* 1894. 8°.   8777. b. 48.

BLOCH (F.) Eau sous pression. pp. 180.
1894. 8°. Encyclopédie des aide-mémoire.
      8709. g.

BODMER (G. R.) Hydraulic Motors. pp. 551.
1895. 8°. Specialist's Series.   8708. k.

BUCHETTI (J.) Les Moteurs hydrauliques actuels.
3 pt. *Paris,* 1892. 4°.   8776. h. 32.

COLYER (F.) Hydraulic, lifting and pressing
Machinery. pp. 197. *Lond.* 1892. 8°.
      8768. f. 7.

JHERING (A. v.) Amerikanische Wasserhebemaschinen. pp. 55. *Berl.* 1894. 8°.
      8777. k. 11.

MARKS (G. C.) Hydraulic Machinery employed
in concentration and transmission of power.
pp. 120. *Manch.* 1891. 8°.   8767. cc. 17.

OLIVE (J.) Traité d'Hydraulique. pp. 684.
1891. 8°. LACROIX (D.) Encyclopédie des
connaissances.   8708. n.

ROBINSON (H.) Hydraulic Power and machinery.
pp. 226. *Lond.* 1893. 8°.   8776. bb. 65.

SCHEFFLER (H.) Die Hydraulik auf neuen
Grundlagen. pp. 225. *Leipz.* 1891. 8°.
      8776. b. 62.

SLAGG (C.) Water Engineering. pp. 309.
Lond. 1895. 8°.   8776. aaaa. 25.

HETT (C. L.) Turbine manual and Millwrights'
handbook. pp. 62. *Lond.* 1892. 8°.
      8777. b. 41.

INNES (C. H.) The Centrifugal Pump. Turbines
and water motors. pp. 178. *Manch.* 1893. 8°.
      8777. aaa. 31.

LAVERGNE (G.) Les Turbines. pp. 235. 1893. 8°.
Encyclopédie des aide-mémoire.   8709. g.

LUDEWIG (H.) Allgemeine Theorie der
Turbinen. pp. 194. *Berl.* 1890. 4°.
      8776. g. 43.

POINCARÉ (H.) Théorie des Tourbillons.
pp. 211. *Paris,* 1893. 8°.   8768. l. 22.

See also ENGINEERING : HYDRODYNAMICS : IRRIGATION : MACHINERY : MECHANICS : PUMPS :
RIVERS : For Waterworks, *see* WATER.

**HYDRODYNAMICS : HYDROSTA-
TICS.** BASSER (A. B.) Elementary treatise
on Hydrodynamics. pp. 187. *Camb.* 1890. 8°.
      8768. d. 32.

DUHEM (P.) Hydrodynamique.
Paris, 1891, *etc.* 4°.   8767. l. 24.

KLIMPERT (R.) Hydrodynamik. 1892, *etc.* 8°.
KLEYER (A.) Naturwissenschaftliche Encyklopädie.   8705. g.

LAMB (H.) Hydrodynamics. pp. 604.
Camb. 1895. 8°.   8776. d. 29.

HYDRODYNAMICS, etc.—*continued.*

BRIGGS (W.) and BRYAN (G. H.) Text-book of Hydrostatics. pp. 208. 1895. 8°. Tutorial Series.   12205. c. 244.

GREAVES (J.) Treatise on elementary Hydrostatics. pp. 204. *Camb.* 1894. 8°.   8777. aaa. 38.

GREENHILL (A. G.) Treatise on Hydrostatics. pp. 536. *Lond.* 1894. 8°.   8767. cc. 26.

LONEY (S. L.) Hydrostatics for beginners. pp. 304. 1893. 8°. Pitt Press Mathematical Series.   2322. cc. 35.

MINCHIN (G. M.) Hydrostatics and elementary Hydrokinetics. pp. 424. 1892. 8°. Clarendon Press Series.   2319. b. 5.

PINKERTON (H.) Hydrostatics and Pneumatics. pp. 344. 1893. 8°. Blackie's Science Text books.   8703. bb.

ZEUTHEN (H. G.) Forelæsning over Hydrostatik. pp. 32. *Kjöbenh.* 1893. 8°.   8777. bbb. 30. (9.)

See also DYNAMICS: HYDRAULICS: PHYSICS: STATICS.

HYDROGRAPHY. *See* SEA.

HYDROMETER. CASELLA (L.) Direct reading Hydrometer scales. *Lond.* 1892. fol.   1801. d. 1. (130.)

HYDROPATHY. ALLSOP (R. O.) The „Hydropathic establishment and its Baths. pp. 107. *Lond.* 1891. 8°.   7470. ee. 2.

DOUDNEY (G. H.) The Water cure in the bedroom. pp. 46. *Bristol,* 1891. 8°. 7461. c. 19.

KNEIPP (S.) My Water Cure. pp. 282. *Edinb.* 1893. 8°.   7461. c. 21.

—— Thus shalt thou live. Hints and advice. pp. 389. *Lond.* 1894. 8°.   7461. e. 8.

C., H. F. Guide du Kneippiste. pp. 17. *Brux.* 1893. 12°.   07305. f. 20. (9.)

CLIFFORD (M.) The Kneipp Water-cure. pp. 16. *Lond.* 1894. 8°.   07305. f. 19. (3.)

NIEMANN (C.) Kneipp und seine ärztlichen Jünger. pp. 79. *Frankfurt,* 1894. 8°.   7462. i. 3.

PAUL (E.) Gegen Kneipp. pp. 52. *Leipz.* 1894. 16°.   07305. i. 12. (5.)

SUESSBACH ( ) Kneipp-Priessnitz. pp. 37. *Berl.* 1894. 8°.   7306. df. 25. (9.)

WORMSER (M.) Pfarrer Kneipp im Lichte der Wissenschaft. pp. 29. *Berl.* 1894. 8°.   7306. h. 15. (10.)

See also WATERING-PLACES, *etc.*

HYDROPHOBIA. DIERCKX (F.) Une visite à l'Institut Pasteur. pp. 84. *Louvain,* 1890. 8°.   7306. df. 15. (9.)

DUPRÉ (V.) Intorno all'antidoto del Dottor Dupré. pp. 60. *Genova,* 1890. 8°.   07305. e. 23. (2.)

HARVEY (R.) The Pasteur Institute and vivisection. pp. 24. *Calcutta,* 1895. 8°. Pam. 85.

ILLINGWORTH (C. R.) Address upon Hydrophobia. pp. 32. *Lond.* 1895. 8°.   7306. e. 26. (11.)

KAIKHUSRAU NASARVĀNJĪ BAHĀDURJI. Hydrophobia. Examination of Pasteur's treatment. pp. 23. *Bombay,* 1893. 8°.   7306. e. 26. (5.)

SUZOR (J. R.) Exposé du traitement de la Rage par la méthode Pasteur. pp. 272. *Paris,* 1888. 8°.   7561. bb. 11.

HYDROSTATICS. *See* HYDRODYNAMICS.

HYGIENE.

General.

AC. *Congrès International des Sciences Médicales.* Deutsches Gesundheitswesen. pp. 309. *Berl.* 1890. 8°.   Ac. 3699/3.

HYGIENE.—General—*continued.*

AC. Rome. *R. Università di Roma.* Annali d'Igiene sperimentale della Università di Roma. *Roma,* 1891, *etc.* 8°.   Ac. 104. b.

ADLER (M. N.) Health laws of the Bible. pp. 11. *Lond.* 1892. 8°.   Pam. 31.

ARLIDGE (J. T.) Hygiene and mortality of Occupations. pp. 568. *Lond.* 1892. 8°. 7404. de. 7.

BALLIN (A. S.) Personal Hygiene. pp. 227. *Lond.* 1894. 8°.   7404. d. 13.

—— Health and beauty in Dress. pp. 244. *Lond.* 1893. 8°.   7404. df. 7.

BLACK (G.) The Family Health-book. pp. 469. *Lond.* 1892. 8°.   7383. dd. 4.

BLACKWELL (E.) Why Hygienic Congresses fail. pp. 40. *Lond.* 1892. 8°.   7306. df. 20. (5.)

BOCCI (B.) Guida tecnica del Medico igienista. pp. 315. *Milano,* 1892. 8°.   7404. cc. 20.

BREMOND (F.) Les Préjugés en hygiène. pp. 159. *Paris,* 1892. 8°.   7404. cc. 17.

BUECHNER (F. C. C. L.) Das Buch vom langen Leben. pp. 288. *Leipz.* 1892. 8°. 7390. ee. 19.

BURDETT (H. C.) Helps in Sickness and to health. pp. 484. *Lond.* 1894. 8°. 7404. cc. 23.

BURGESS (A. T.) Classified Series of Science and Art questions in Hygiene. pp. 16. *Lond.* 1894. 8°.   7306. e. 22. (12.)

CLUTTERBUCK (J. B.) Stray notes on Hygiene. pp. 69. *Lond.* 1892. 8°.   7404. de. 8.

CORNARO (L.) How to regain Health and live a hundred years. pp. 38. *Lond.* 1894. 16°.   7404. a. 46.

COSGRAVE (E. M.) Hints and helps for Home Hygiene. pp. 143. *Lond.* 1893. 16°. 7688. a. 46.

CURRIER (C. G.) Art of preserving Health. pp. 468. *N.Y.* 1893. 8°.   7390. ee. 20.

DAVIES (A. M.) Handbook of Hygiene. pp. 590. *Lond.* 1895. 8°.   7404. aaaa. 2.

DAVIES, afterwards YORKE-DAVIES (N. E.) Health in the active and sedentary. pp. 256. *Lond.* 1894. 8°.   7620. de. 32.

DENMARK. Denmark; its hygiene, *etc.* pp. 474. *Copenhagen,* 1891. 8°.   7680. e. 9.

DESROCHES (J. J.) Catéchisme d'hygiène privée. pp. 64. *Montréal,* 1889. 8°. 7306. de. 41. (2.)

DEWEY (E. H.) True science of Living. pp. 323. *Norwich, Conn.* 1895. 8°. 7391. f. 31.

DUTTON (T.) Domestic Hygiene. pp. 199. *Lond.* 1894. 8°.   7404. c. 39.

ELLIS (H. H.) Nationalisation of Health. pp. 244. *Lond.* 1892. 8°.   7404. df. 3.

FERGUSON (R. B.) Aids to the mathematics of Hygiene. pp. 89. *Lond.* 1894. 8°. 8777. a. 5.

GILLET DE GRANDMONT ( ) Berlin au point de vue de l'hygiène. pp. 152. *Paris,* 1891. 8°.   7391. g. 14.

GRADUATE. Lecture to young men on the preservation of Health. *Lond.* 1892. 8°. Pam. 39.

HALL (W. W.) Popular Cyclopædia of Health maxims. pp. 248. *Lond.* 1892. 8°. 7383. h. 9.

HEALTH RULES. Elementary Health rules. pp. 8. *Durham,* 1892. 16°.   Pam. 39.

HELPS. Helps to Health and beauty. pp. 117. *Lond.* 1895. 8°.   07944. df. 2.

JAEGER (G.) Health Culture. pp. 188. *Lond.* 1892. 8°.   7404. c. 37.

KELLOGG (J. H.) Second Book in Hygiene. pp. 291. *N.Y.* 1894. 8°.   7404. df. 9.

KESTEVEN (W. H.) Health and hurry. pp. 66. *Lond.* 1891. 8°.   7404. aaa. 48.

KIMMINS (C. W.) Chemistry of life and health. pp. 167. 1892. 8°. SYMES (J. E.) University Extension Series.   012202. g.

HYGIENE.—General—*continued.*

KINGZETT (C. T.) Nature's Hygiene. pp. 502.
Lond. 1894. 8°. 7391. ee. 5.

KNEIPP (S.) Thus Shalt Thou Live. Hints and advice. pp. 389. *Lond.* 1894. 8°. 7461. e. 8.

KOTELMANN (L.) Gesundheitspflege im Mittelalter. pp. 276. *Hamburg*, 1890. 8°. 7679. f. 22.

LEI MANN (C. B.) Methods of practical Hygiene. 2 vol. *Lond.* 1893. 8°. 7404. de. 9.

MAC CALLUM (H.) Lectures on Hygiene. pp. 90. *Hongkong*, 1891. 8°. 7391. f. 27.

MEDICUS. How to improve the Physique. pp. 51. *Lond.* 1893. 8°. 7912. aa. 21.

MIERS (H. A.) and CROSSKEY (R.) The Soil in relation to Health. pp. 135. *Lond.* 1893. 8°. 7109. a. 12.

MITCHELL (K.) Gentlewoman's book of Hygiene. pp. 256. 1892. 8°. ADAMS (W. H. D.) Victoria Library. 012208. f.

MONIN (E.) L'Hygiène des riches. pp. 360. *Paris*, 1891. 8°. 7404. a. 43.

—— The Hygiene of beauty. pp. 171. *Lond.* 1893. 8°. 7404. bb. 46.

MOFFITT (E. J.) Domestic Hygiene. 1891. 8°. Hughes's Domestic Economy. 07945. e. 46.

MORRIS (M.) The Book of Health. *Lond.* 1892, *etc.* 8°. 7383. k. 3.

NEWSHOLME (A.) Hygiene. pp. 448. *Lond.* 1892. 8°. 7404. df. 2.

—— Elementary Hygiene. pp. 187. *Lond.* 1893. 8°. 7404. aaa. 52.

NIGHTINGALE (F.) Health Teaching in towns and villages. pp. 27. *Lond.* 1894. 8°. 7306. e. 22. (17.)

NOEL (H. A.) Moral value of Health. 1887. 8°. MANCHESTER. *Sanitary Association.* Health Lectures. Ser. 11. 7404. bbb.

NOTTER (J. L.) and FIRTH (R. H.) Hygiene. pp. 433. *Lond.* 1895. 8°. 7404. aaaa. 10.

OSBORN (S.) Ambulance Lectures on Hygiene. pp. 158. *Lond.* 1891. 8°. 7688. a. 34.

PARIS. *Congrès International d'Hygiène.* Compte rendu des séances, 1889. pp. 128. *Paris*, 1889. 8°. 7404. d. 3.

PARKES (E. A.) Manual of practical Hygiene. pp. 769. *Lond.* 1891. 8°. 7404. de. 5.

PARKES (L. C.) Hygiene and public health. pp. 531. 1895. 8°. Lewis's Practical Series. 7482. a.

—— The elements of Health. pp. 246. *Lond.* 1895. 8°. 7404. aaaa. 4.

P.P. *London.* The Hygienic Advertiser. *Lond.* 1891, *etc.* 8°. 25.

—— *London.* Lancet. Lancet Reports on the International Congresses of Hygiene from 1876 to 1889. pp. 81. *Lond.* 1891. 8°. 7404. d. 7.

PISTOR (M.) Deutsches Gesundheitswesen. pp. 309. *Berl.* 1890. 8°. 7688. g. 5.

POORE (G. V.) Essays on rural Hygiene. pp. 372. *Lond.* 1894. 8°. 8776. a. 69.

POPE (J. J.) Number One, and how to take care of him. pp. 188. *Lond.* 1883. 8°. 7404. a. 34.

PRIESTLEY (E.) Hygiene under difficulties. pp. 130. *Lond.* 1891. 8°. 8777. aaa. 36.

"RED CROSS" SERIES. Health Hand-books. *Lond.* 1890, *etc.* 8°. 7404. d.

REYNOLDS (E. S.) Primer of Hygiene. pp. 164. *Lond.* 1894. 8°. 7404. a. 44.

RICHARD (E.) Précis d'Hygiène appliquée. pp. 779. *Paris*, 1891. 8°. 7404. cc. 12.

ROAD. The royal road to beauty. pp. 87. *Bombay*, 1894. 8°. Pam. 39.

HYGIENE.—General—*continued.*

ROBERTS (R. L.) Illustrated lectures on Hygiene. pp. 213. *Lond.* 1892. 8°. 7688. aa. 46.

ROHÉ (G. H.) Text-book of Hygiene. pp. 553. *Phila.* 1894. 8°. 7390. g. 26.

RUFF (J.) Illustriertes Gesundheits-Lexikon. pp. 804. *Strassb.* 1894. 8°. 7390. g. 27.

SCHOFIELD (A. T.) Manual of personal and domestic Hygiene. pp. 278. *Lond.* 1894. 8°. 7404. bb. 47.

—— How to keep healthy. pp. 224. *Lond.* 1891. 8°. 7404. c. 34.

SCIENCES. Les Sciences biologiques, *etc.* pp. 800. *Paris*, 1893. 8°. 7001. g. 7.

STABLES (W. G.) Mother's book of Health. pp. 233. *Lond.* 1894. 8°. 07581. f. 4.

—— Boy's own book of Health. pp. 238. *Lond.* 1892. 8°. 7404. df. 4.

STACPOLE (F.) The Reason Why; an explanation of the true principles of healthy clothing. pp. 133. 1891. 8°. 7391. f. 28.

STEVENSON (T.) and MURPHY (S. F.) Treatise on Hygiene. *Lond.* 1892, *etc.* 8°. 7391. g. 18.

THOMPSON (C. J. S.) Cult of beauty: handbook of personal hygiene. pp. 191. *Lond.* 1894. 8°. 7404. e. 3.

WAGER (H.) and HERBERT (*Hon.* A. E. W. M.) Bad Air and bad Health. pp. 98. *Lond.* 1894. 8°. 7405. aaa. 27.

WAKEFIELD (H. R.) Elementary text-book of Hygiene. pp. 212. 1892. 8°. Blackie's Science Text Books. 8703. bb.

WALLIS (I. W.) Manual of Hygiene. pp. 150. *Lond.* 1894. 8°. 7404. cc. 21.

WEYL (T.) Handbuch der Hygiene. *Jena*, 1893, *etc.* 8°. 7391. dd.

WHITELEGGE (B. A.) Hygiene and public health. pp. 586. 1894. 8°. Manuals for Students. 2255. a. 34.

WILSON (G.) Handbook of Hygiene. pp. 751. *Lond.* 1892. 8°. 2254. c. 20.

YOUNG (H. M.) Health without medicine. pp. 47. *Chester*, 1894. 8°. 7461. aaa. 21.
See also CHILDREN : SANITATION : WOMEN.

Hygiene of Schools.

JANKE (O.) Die Litteratur der Schulhygiene. pp. 54. 1892. 8°. MEYER (J.) Pädagogische Zeit- und Streitfragen. Bd. 4. Hft. 6. 8310. c.

BURGERSTEIN (L.) and NETOLITZKY (A.) Handbuch der Schulhygiene. pp. 429. 1895. 8°. WEYL (T.) Handbuch der Hygiene. Bd. 7. 7391. dd.

DÖDERLEIN (C.) Om vore Skolebørns Hygiene, *etc.* pp. 171. *Christiania*, 1890. 8°. 7404. b. 48.

DUKES (C.) Health at School. pp. 498. *Lond.* 1894. 8°. 8311. c. 10.

—— Work and overwork in relation to Health in schools. pp. 69. *Lond.* 1893. 8°. Pam. 17.

KOEZLE (J. F. G.) Die pädagogische Pathologie in der Erziehungskunde. pp. 494. *Gütersloh*, 1893. 8°. 07581. e. 24.
See also CHILDREN.

Hygiene of Tropical Countries.

DAVIDSON (A.) Hygiene and diseases of warm Climates. pp. 1016. *Edinb.* 1893. 8°. 7686. dd. 2.

SCHELLONG (O.) Die Klimatologie der Tropen. pp. 48. *Berl.* 1891. 8°. Pam. 39.

—— Akklimatisation und Tropen-hygiene. 1894. 8°. WEYL (T.) Handbuch der Hygiene. Bd. 1. 7391 dd.

GRANT (C. S.) West African Hygiene. pp. 51. *Lond.* 1884. 8°. 7688. aa. 14.

HYGIENE of Tropical Countries—*cont.*

KOHLSTOCK (P.) Ärztlicher Ratgeber für Ostafrika. pp. 344. *Berl.* 1891. 8°. 7390. de. 13.

MURRAY (J.) How to live in tropical Africa. pp. 252. *Lond.* 1895. 8°. 7687. a. 15.

PARKE (T. H.) Guide to Health in Africa. pp. 175. *Lond.* 1893. 8°. 07686. e. 8.

WALLER (H.) Health hints for Central Africa. pp. 61. *Lond.* 1893. 8°. 7306. de. 42. (7.)

FAYRER (*Sir* J.) On Preservation of health in India. pp. 51. *Lond.* 1894. 8°. 7687. a. 14.

MOORE (*Sir* W. J.) Manual of Hygiene for India. pp. 764. *Lond.* 1893. 8°. 7383. dd. 5.

SCHARLIEB (M.) A Woman's word to women on the care of their health in India. pp. 240. *Lond.* 1895. 8°. 8415. de. 45.

See also DISEASES, *Tropical.*

Military Hygiene. *See* MEDICINE, *Military.*

Public Health. *See* SANITATION.

HYMENOPTERA. DALLA TORRE (C. W. v.) Catalogus Hymenopterorum. *Lipsiae*, 1894, *etc.* 8°. 7298. dd.

AC. London. *British Museum.* Catalogue of British Hymenoptera. pp. 236. *Lond.* 1891. 8°. 7207. e. 17.

SAUNDERS (E.) Hymenoptera Aculeata of the British Islands. *Lond.* 1893, *etc.* 8°. 7297. h.

BATH (W. H.) Young Collector's Handbook of Ants, Bees, Flies, *etc.* pp. 108. 1888. 8°. Young Collector Series. 7001. aaa.

ADLER (H.) Alternating Generations. Biological study of oak galls and gall flies. pp. 198. *Oxf.* 1894. 8°. 7297. aa. 36.

See also ANT: BEES.

HYMNOLOGY. BÄCK (A.) Huru hafva våra förfäder sjungit sina psalmer. pp. 28. *Stockholm*, 1891. obl. 8°. 7898. e. 27.

BAILEY (M. B.) Guide to Church Hymnals. *Lond.* 1890. obl. 8°. 4999. aaa. 15.

BIBLE. *Psalms.* The .True Psalmody: the Psalms the Church's only manual of praise. pp. 212. *Edinb.* 1888. 8°. 3090. de 37.

BURRAGE (H. S.) Baptist Hymn Writers. pp. 682. *Portland*, 1888. 8°. 4999. d. 15.

CHEVALIER (C. U. J.) Poésie liturgique du moyen âge. pp. 232. *Paris*, 1893. 8°. 3477. e. 8.

DECHEVRENS (A.) Du Rythme dans l'Hymnographie latine. pp. 159. *Paris*, 1895. 8°. 7899. bb. 2.

DEVAUX (A.) De l'Hymnologie latine. pp. 25. *Lyon*, 1890. 8°. 011824. i. 17. (5.)

DORRICOTT (I.) and COLLINS (T.) Lyric Studies: Methodist hymnal guide. pp. 328. *Lond.* 1891. 8°. 4999. b. 18.

GREEN (S. G.) Hymnody in our Churches. pp. 20. *Lond.* 1895. 8°. Pam. 30.

HILL (F. C.) Tables to aid the selection of hymns for use in connection with Hymns Ancient and Modern. *Lond.* 1891. 8°. Pam. 75.

JULIAN (J.) Dictionary of Hymnology. pp. 1616. *Lond.* 1892. 8°. 2002. d.

MANITIUS (M.) Geschichte der christlich-lateinischen Poesie bis zur Mitte des 8. Jahrhunderts. pp. 518. *Stuttg.* 1891. 8°. 011840. h. 67.

MORRISON (D.) Great Hymns of the Church. pp. 250. *Lond.* 1890. 8°. 3435. g. 23.

NELLE (W.) Das neue evangelische Gesangbuch für Rheinland und Westfalen. pp. 39. *Dortmund*, 1890. 8°. Pam. 75.

ONUFRIO (F. d') Gl' Inni sacri di A. Manzoni. pp. 384. *Palermo*, 1894. 8°. 4999. df. 1.

HYMNOLOGY—*continued.*

PALMER (R.) *Earl of Selborne.* Hymns, their history and development. pp. 216. *Lond.* 1892. 8°. 4999. aa. 13.

PARKER (W. H.) The Psalmody of the Church. pp. 269. *N.Y.* 1889. 8°. 4999. ee. 4.

PITMAN (E. R.) Lady Hymn writers. pp. 369. *Lond.* 1892. 8°. 4999. bb. 35.

TUCKER (W. H.) Hymns Ancient and Modern, tested by Holy Scripture. pp. 57. *Lond.* 1891. 8°. Pam. 92.

WETZSTEIN (O.) Die religiöse Lyrik der Deutschen im 19. Jahrhundert. pp. 336. *Neustrelitz*, 1891. 8°. 4999. e. 21.

WOLFRUM (P.) Die Entstehung des deutschen evangelischen Kirchenliedes in musikalischer Beziehung. pp. 250. *Leipz.* 1890. 8°. 7897. i. 39.

WIRTH (C. V.) Der evangelische Liederschatz. *Nurnberg*, 1893, *etc.* 8°. 4999. cc.

WOLKAN (R.) Das Kirchenlied der Böhmischen Brüder im xvi. Jahrhunderte. pp. 178. *Prag*, 1891. 8°. 4999. b. 20.

HYMNS.

English.

B, A. H. Hymns for Special Services. pp. 64. *Lond.* 1893. 16°. Pam. 30.

BELL (C. D.) and Fox (H. E.) The Church of England Hymnal. pp. 490. *Lond.* 1894. 8°. 3433. de. 74.

BROOKE (S. A.) Christian Hymns. pp. 358. *Lond.* 1891. 8°. 3438. ff. 36.

CARTER (F. E.) Truro Mission Hymn book. pp. 128. *Lond.* 1892. 8°. 3433. de. 71.

CENTENARY MISSIONARY HYMNAL. Centenary Missionary Hymnal. pp. 60. *Lond.* 1895. 16°. 3435. b. 55.

D., E. R., and KEYMER (N.) The People's Service book, for congregational worship at the Holy Eucharist. pp. 20. *West Malvern*, 1894. 16°. Pam. 30.

ESSEX HALL HYMNAL. Essex Hall Hymnal, *etc.* pp. 431. *Lond.* 1891. 8°. 3434. bb. 56.

FARMER (J.) Hymns and Chorales for schools. pp. 180. *Oxf.* 1893. 8°. 3438. e. 50.

FRY (J. S.) Selection of Hymns. pp. 260. *Lond* 1894. 8°. 3435. b. 5.

HOLLAND (W. L.) The Bible Hymnal. pp. 372. *Edinb.* 1894. 8°. 3435. g. 33.

HYMNS. Hymns for the opening services of new chapels and schools. pp. 31. *Lond.* 1891. 8°. Pam. 30.

HORDER (W. G.) Hymns: supplemental to existing collections. *Lond.* 1894. 8°. 3434. de. 59.

JONES (N.) Hymn book for young people's Mission Services. pp. 32. *Lond.* 1890. 8°. Pam. 30.

KEATINGE (C.) The Army Catholic Hymn book. pp. 48. *Lond.* 1893. 16°. 3435. a. 59.

LITURGIES. England, *Church of.* S. John's Cathedral, Hongkong. Anthem book. pp. 66. *Hongkong*, 1892. 8°. 3125. cc. 39.

—— Rome, *Church of.* Cecilian Anthology for the Roman Catholic congregation in Hong-Kong. pp. 168 *Hong-Kong*, 1894. 12°. 3436. ee. 12.

—— U.S. *Evangelical Lutheran Churches.* Church Book, for Evangelical Lutheran Congregations. pp. 498. *Phila.* 1893. 8°. M.D. 898.

LORETTO HYMN BOOK. Loreto Hymn book. *Manch.* 1895. 16°. Pam. 30.

PECULIAR PEOPLE. Peculiar People's Hymn book. pp. 660. *Thundersley*, 1880. 16°. 3435. ccc. 44.

HYMNS.—English—continued.

PSALMS. Psalms and Hymns for school and home. pp. 427. *Lond.* 1892, 8°. 3435. ff. 45.

REEKS (J.) St. George's Hymn book. pp. 92. *Lond.* 1895. 16°. Pam. 30.

SCOTLAND, *Free Church of.* Home and School Hymnal. pp. 367. *Edinb.* 1892. 8°. 3438. e. 48.

SONGS. Sacred Songs for School use. pp. 20. *Singapore,* 1893. 16°. Pam. 30.

SUNDAY AFTERNOON SONG BOOK. Sunday Afternoon Song book. pp. 112. *Lond.* 1892. 16°. 3437. ff. 46.

UNION MISSION HYMNAL. Union Mission Hymnal. pp. 64. *Lond.* 1894. 16°. Pam. 30.

WHITTEMORE (W. M.) Our Children's Hymnal. pp. 96. *Lond.* 1894. 16°. 3434. a. 61.

WILEMAN (W.) Protestant Hymn book. pp. 32. *Lond.* 1894. 8°. Pam. 30.

WINTERS (W.) Sunday School Hymnal. pp. 256. *Lond* 1892. 8°. 3433. a. 50.

WOODS (M. A.) Hymns for School Worship. pp. 110. *Lond.* 1890. 8°. 3434. de. 42.

Latin.

CARLONI (L.) L'Arpa Liturgica, ossia gl' inni della Chiesa Cattolica. 2 vol. *Forlì,* 1891. 8°. 3435. g. 29.

CHEVALIER (C. U. J.) Poésie liturgique de l'Église catholique en Occident. pp. 288. *Tournai,* 1894. 8°. 3435. k. 2.

COLES (A.) Latin Hymns with translations. pp. 77. *N.Y.* 1892. 8°. 3436. l. 1.

DREVES (G. M.) Hymnodia Hiberica. Spanische Hymnen des Mittelalters. pp. 290. 1894. 8°. Analecta Hymnica. Bd. 16. 3435. f. 31.

HYMNI. Hymni usitati Latine redditi. *Eng. & Lat.* pp 23. *Dublin,* 1880. 12°. 3435. ccc. 39.

RAND (S. T.) Hymni recentes Latini. *Halifax,* 1888. 8°. 3435. ccc. 38.

RANKIN (J.) Exposition of the Apostles' Creed. With a catena of ancient Latin hymns. pp. 366. *Edinb.* 1890. 8°. 3504. f. 24.

THOMAS, *de Celano.* Dies Iræ. Latin text, with a prose translation. pp. 52. *Chicago,* 1892. 8°. 3435. ff. 44.

WERNER (J.) Die ältesten Hymnensammlungen von Rheinau. pp. 123. 1891. 4°. Ac. Zurich. *Gesellschaft für Erforschung vaterländischer Alterthümer.* Mittheilungen. Bd. 23. Hft. 3. Ac. 5367.

German, Dutch, Icelandic.

LITURGIES. Old Catholics. *Hymns.* Godsdienstig gezangboek voor Oud-Katholieken. pp. 176. *Rotterdam,* 1890. 8°. 3434. de. 56.

VERZAMELING. Verzameling van geestelijke liederen. pp. 58. *Kaapstad,* 1893. 16°. 3425. aa. 43.

EVANGELICAL CHURCH HYMNBOOK. Gesangbuch der evangelischen Brüdergemeine. pp. 700. 8. *Gnadau,* 1893. 8°. 3425. h. 33.

ZAHN (J.) Die Melodien der deutschen evangelischen Kirchenlieder. *Gutersloh,* 1889, *etc.* 8°. M.E. 590. a.

SÁLMABÓK. Sálmabók til Kirkju- og Heimasöngs. pp. 596. *Reykjavik,* 1892. 12°. 3425. e 19.

HYPERION, Satellite of Saturn.

See SATURN.

HYPNOTISM. ANGLEMONT (A. d') L'Hypnotisme scientifiquement démontré, *etc.* pp. 98. *Paris* 1891. 8°. 7410. ee. 35.

ARNOLD (H.) Die Heilkräfte des Hypnotismus. pp. 95. *Leipz.* 1892. 8°. 7410. cc. 41.

HYPNOTISM—continued.

ARNOLD (H.) Schulmedizin und Wunderkuren. pp. 70. *Leipz.* 1892. 8°. 7410. cc. 42.

AZAM (E. A.) Hypnotisme et double conscience. pp. 375. *Paris,* 1893. 8°. 7410. ee. 42.

BARETY (A.) Le Magnétisme animal étudié sous le nom de force neurique. pp. 662. *Paris,* 1887. 8°. 7410. f. 1.

BENEDIKT (M.) Hypnotismus und Suggestion. pp. 90. *Leipz.* 1894. 8°. 7410. f. 3.

BERNHEIM (H.) De la Suggestion et de ses applications à la thérapeutique. pp. 608. *Paris,* 1891. 12°. 7410. df. 31.

—— Hypnotisme, suggestion, psychothérapie. pp. 518. *Paris,* 1891. 8°. 7410. e. 31.

—— Neue Studien ueber Hypnotismus. pp. 380. *Leipz.* 1892. 8°. 7410. e. 37.

BONJEAN (A.) L'Hypnotisme, ses rapports avec le droit et la thérapeutique. pp. 316. *Paris,* 1892. 8°. 7410. df. 47.

BRUNNBERG (T.) Hypnotismen bedömb af fackmän. pp. 79. *Upsala,* 1893. 8°. 7410. ee. 44.

BUÉ (A.) Le Magnétisme curatif. pp. 430. *Paris,* 1894. 8°. 7410. f.

COATES (J.) How to Mesmerise. pp. 120. *Lond.* 1893. 8°. 7410. aaaa. 7.

CRISFIELD (T.) Value of Hypnotism. pp. 39. *Lond.* 1893. 8°. 7410. bb. 33. (13.)

CULLERRE (A.) La Thérapeutique suggestive et ses applications. pp. 318. *Paris,* 1893. 8°. 7410. df. 49.

DARBY (J.) Memoirs of the Marvellous and mysteries unveiled. *Lond.* 1892, *etc.* 8°. 7410. ee. 34.

DELBŒUF (J. R. L.) Magnétiseurs et médecins. pp. 115. *Paris,* 1890. 8°. 7410. dh. 61.

—— L'Affaire des Magnétiseurs de Braine-le-Château. pp. 8. *Liège,* 1891. 8°. 7410. bb. 33. (1.)

—— L'Hypnotisme devant les Chambres belges. pp. 80. *Paris,* 1892. 8°. 6095. g. 4.

DREHER (E.) Drei psycho-physiologische Studien. pp. 108. *Leipz.* 1891. 8°. 7410. dh. 62.

EFFERTZ (O.) Studien über Hypnotismus, Suggestion. pp. 102. *Bonn,* 1894. 8°. 7410. d. 40.

FIGUIER (L.) Les Mystères de la science. pp. 725. *Paris,* 1893. 4°. 8630. i. 20.

FOREL (A.) Der Hypnotismus. pp. 172. *Stuttg.* 1891. 8°. 7410. e. 33.

FOVEAU DE COURMELLES ( ) Hypnotism. pp. 321. *Lond.* 1891. 8°. 7410. df. 32.

FRANCO (G. G.) L'Hypnotisme revenu à la mode. pp. 379. *St. Amand,* 1890. 8°. 7410. de. 49.

FRANZOS (C. E.) Die Suggestion und die Dichtung. pp. 129. *Berl.* 1892. 8°. 7410. bb. 43.

FRONTAURA (J. M.) Historias de espiritismo e hypnotismo. *Santiago,* 1887. 8°. 8631. ee. 38.

FUNCK (H.) Der Magnetismus in der badischen Markgraffschaft. pp. 76. *Freib.* 1894. 8°. 7410. dg. 48.

GEIJERSTAM (C. AF) Hypnotism och religion. pp. 189. *Stockholm,* 1890. 8°. 7410. df. 37.

GROSSMANN (J.) Die Erfolge der Suggestionstherapie, Hypnose, bei Influenza. pp. 38. *Berl.* 1892. 8°. 07305. h. 18. (9.)

HAAS (L.) Ueber Hypnotismus und Suggestion. pp. 92. *Augsburg,* 1893. 8°. 7306. e. 23. (15.)

HART (E. A.) Hypnotism. pp. 15. *Lond.* 1893. 8°. Pam. 39.

—— Hypnotism and the new Witchcraft. pp. 182. *Lond.* 1893. 8°. 7410. df. 48.

HYPNOTISM—continued.

HEBERLE (M. A.) Hypnose und Suggestion im deutschen Strafrecht. pp. 88.
München, 1883. 8°.   7305. f. 6. (6.)

HECKER (E.) Hypnose und Suggestion im Dienste der Heilkunde. pp. 38.
Wiesbaden, 1893. 8°.   7305. f. 5. (8.)

HILLER (H. C.) Rhythmic Heredity, *etc.*
pp. 355. *Lond.* 1894. 8°.   7006. e. 26.

HIRSCH (M.) Suggestion und Hypnose.
pp. 209. *Leipz.* 1893. 8°.   7410. ccc. 4.

HÖFELT (I. A.) Het Hypnotisme in verband met het strafrecht. pp. 87. *Leiden*, 1889. 8°.
    5686. cc. 51.

HUDSON (T. J.) Law of psychic Phenomena.
pp. 409. *Lond.* 1893. 8°.   7410. dg. 46.

JOIRE (P.) Précis de Neurohypnologie. pp. 327.
Paris, 1892. 8°.   7410. df. 41.

KIESEWETTER (C.) Mesmer's Leben und Lehre.
pp. 180. *Leipz.* 1893. 8°.   10708. ee. 32.

KINGSBURY (G. C.) Practice of hypnotic suggestion. pp. 206. *Bristol*, 1891. 8°.
    7410. ee. 11.

LAURENT (É.) Les Suggestions criminelles.
pp. 56. *Lyon*, 1891. 8°.   6095. f. 25.

LEHMANN (A.) Die Hypnose und die damit verwandten normalen Zustände. pp. 194.
Leipz. 1890. 8°.   7410. ee. 30.

LIÉBEAULT (A. A.) Thérapeutique suggestive.
pp. 308. *Paris*, 1891. 12°.   7410. df. 36.

LOBET (L.) L'hypnotisme devant les Chambres belges. pp. 20. *Verviers*, 1891. 12°.
    7410. bb. 33. (5.)

—— L'Hypnotisme en Belgique. pp. 42.
Verviers, 1891. 8°.   7410. bb. 33. (4.)

LUYS (J. B.) Les émotions chez les hypnotiques étudiées. pp. 164. *Paris*, 1886. 16°.
    7410. df. 42.

MINDE (J. R.) Ueber Hypnotismus. pp. 88.
München, 1891. 8°.   07305. k. 13. (5.)

MOESSMER (F.) Die mittelbare Thäterschaft in Berücksichtigung des Hypnotismus im Strafrecht. pp. 109. *München*, 1892. 8°.
    6095. e. 35.

MOLL (A.) Der Rapport in der Hypnose. pp. 242.
1892. 8°. Ac. Germany. *Gesellschaft für psychologische Forschung.* Schriften. Hft. 3.
    Ac. 3782.

MOREAU (P. G.) L'Hypnotisme. pp. 611.
Paris, 1891. 12°.   7410. df. 33.

NICOLL (A.) Hypnotic Suggestion. pp. 48.
Lond. 1891. 8°.   7410. de. 50.

NIZET (H.) L'Hypnotisme. pp. 304.
Brux. 1893. 8°.   7410. de. 58.

P.P. *Berlin.* Zeitschrift für Hypnotismus.
Berl. 1892. *etc.* 8°.   P.P. 3237. ab.

—— *London.* Borderland. Telepathy, Hypnotism,
etc. Lond. 1893. *etc.* 4°.   P.P. 636. cl.

PITRES (A.) Leçons cliniques sur l'Hystérie et l'hypnotisme. 2 tom. *Paris*, 1891. 8°.
    7410. e. 34.

POST (C. W.) I am well. Practice of natural Suggestion as distinct from hypnotic influence.
pp. 148. *Bost.* 1895. 8°.   7410. de. 60.

PREYER (W.) Ein merkwürdiger Fall von Fascination. pp. 55. *Stuttgart*, 1895. 8°.
    7410. c. 47.

RAINALDI (R.) Le Localizzazioni cerebrali studiate in un caso d' Ipnotismo. pp. 332.
Foligno, 1891. 4°.   7107. i. 2.

REGNIER ( ) and GRANDCHAMPS (de) Histoire de l'Hypnotisme. pp. 298. 1890. 8°. Ac.
Milan. Fondazione Scientifica. Atti. Vol. 10.
    Ac. 2810.

HYPNOTISM—continued.

RINGIER (G.) Erfolge des therapeutischen Hypnotismus in der Landpraxis. pp. 204.
München, 1891. 8°.   7410. d. 36.

ROUXEL ( ) Histoire et philosophie du magnétisme. 2 tom. *Paris*, 1895. 12°.
    8758. aa. 3.

SCHAFFER (C.) Suggestion und Reflex.
pp. 113. *Jena*, 1895. 8°.   7410. f. 5.

SCHMICK (J. H.) Die nachirdische Fortdauer der Persönlichkeit. pp. 149. *Leipz.* 1891. 8°.
    7410. ee. 33.

SCHMIDKUNZ (H.) Der Hypnotismus in gemeinfasslicher Darstellung. pp. 266.
Stuttgart, 1892. 8°.   7410. bb. 45.

—— Psychologie der Suggestion. pp. 425.
Stuttgart, 1892. 8°.   8469. f. 34.

SCHNEIDER (J. P. F.) L'Hypnotisme. pp. 391.
Paris, 1894. 12°.   7410. bb. 48.

SCHRENCK-NOTZING (A. v.) *Baron.* Die Suggestions-Therapie bei krankhaften Erscheinungen des Geschlechtssinnes. pp. 314.
Stuttgart, 1892. 8°.   7410. ee. 37.

—— Der Hypnotismus im münchener Krankenhause. pp. 39. *Leipz.* 1894. 8°. 7305. f. 5. (11).

SCHULTZE (F.) Ueber den Hypnotismus. pp. 34.
1892. 8°. Deutsche Zeit- und Streit-Fragen.
Hft. 105.   12209. f.

SIMONIN (A. H.) Solution du problème de la Suggestion hypnotique. pp. 133.
Paris, 1889. 12°.   7410. df. 44.

SINNETT (A. P.) The rationale of Mesmerism.
pp. 163. *Lond.* 1892. 8°.   7410. dg. 43.

STOLL (O.) Suggestion und Hypnotismus in der Völkerpsychologie. pp. 523. *Leipz.* 1894. 8°.
    7410. dh. 63.

TARCHANOFF (I.) Hypnotisme, suggestion et lecture des pensées. pp. 163. *Paris*, 1891. 12°.
    7410. df. 34.

TRICHT (V. v.) L'Hypnotisme. pp. 67.
Namur, 1892. 8°.   7410. bbb. 33. (12.)

TUCKEY (C. L.) Psycho-Therapeutics. pp. 321.
Lond. 1891. 8°.   7410. ee. 32.

—— Value of Hypnotism in chronic alcoholism.
pp. 57. *Lond.* 1892. 8°.   7410. cc. 39.

VINCENT (R. H.) The elements of Hypnotism.
pp. 270. *Lond.* 1893. 8°.   7410. df. 51.

WETTERSTRAND (O. G.) Der Hypnotismus und seine Anwendung in der praktischen Medicin.
pp. 122. *Wien*, 1891. 8°.   7410. e. 32.

WOLLNY (F.) Ueber den Hypnotismus. pp. 35.
Leipz. 1891. 8°.   07305. h. 17. (6.)

—— Eine Appellation an die deutsche Ehrlichkeit in Sachen der Hypnose und Suggestion.
pp. 39. *Leipz.* 1894. 8°.   Pam. 39.

WOOD (H.) Ideal Suggestion through mental photography. pp. 163. *Bost.* 1893. 8°.
    7410. cc. 43.

YOUNGER (D.) Full instructions in Mesmerism.
pp. 158. *Lond.* 1890. 8°.   7410. ee. 28.

HYPOGAMIA. *See* FUNGI.

HYSTERIA. BASTIAN (H. C.) Various forms of hysterical Paralysis. pp. 199.
Lond. 1893. 8°.   7620. df. 32.

BOURNEVILLE (M. D.) Recherches sur l'Épilepsie, l'Hystérie, et l'idiotie. pp. 263.
Paris, 1888. 8°.   7660. df. 21.

BREUER (J.) and FREUD (S.) Studien über Hysterie. pp. 269. *Leipz.* 1895. 8°. 7630. dd. 8.

BUZZARD (T.) On Simulation of Hysteria by disease of the nervous system. pp. 113.
Lond. 1891. 8°.   7630. de. 15.

EFFERTZ (O.) Studien über Hysterie. pp. 102.
Bonn, 1894. 8°.   7410. d. 40.

HYSTERIA—*continued.*

FEINKIND (S.) Du Somnambulisme, ses rapports avec l'hystérie. pp. 155. *Paris*, 1893. 8°.
7410. f. 2.

GILLES DE LA TOURETTE (G.) Traité de l'Hystérie d'après l'enseignement de la Saltpêtrière. pp. 582. *Paris*, 1891. 8°. 7660. h. 2.

HART (E. A.) Hypnotism and Hysteria. pp. 15. *Lond.* 1893. 8°. 7306. e. 22. (9.)

JANET (P.) État mental des Hystériques. pp. 304. *Paris*, 1894. 8°. 7660. de. 19.

PANSIER (P.) Les manifestations oculaires de l'Hystérie. pp. 171. *Paris*, 1892. 8°.
7410. d. 32.

PITRES (A.) Leçons sur l'Hystérie. 2 tom. *Paris*, 1891. 8°. 7410. e. 34

HYTHE. BIRCH (W. P.) and Co. Pocket guide to Folkestone, Hythe, *etc.* *Folkestone*, 1891. 32°. Pam. 90.

FOLKESTONE. English's handbook of Folkestone, Hythe, *etc.* pp. 166. *Folkestone*, 1894. 8°.
10350. aaa. 55.

HALL (T. G.) St. Leonard's Church, Hythe. pp. 48. *Folkestone*, 1890. 8°. 10352. e. 4.

MILLER (W. S.) The School of Musketry at Hythe. pp. 41. *Lond.* 1892. obl. 4°.
8830. g. 34.

WILKS (G.) Barons of the Cinque Ports and parliamentary representation of Hythe. pp. 126. *Folkestone*, 1892. 4°. 8133. h. 7.

IBERIANS. *See* SPAIN, *Antiquities.*

IBURG, Monastery. STUEVE (C.) Beitrag zur Geschichte der Leben des Klosters Iburg. 1893. 8°. Ac. Osnaburg. *Historischer Verein.* Mittheilungen. Bd. 18. Ac. 7145.

ICE AGE. *See* GLACIERS, *etc.*

ICELAND.

Antiquities and History.

Ac. REYKJAVÍK. *Íslenzka Fornleifafélag. Árbók.* *Reykjavík*, 1881, *etc.* 8°. Ac. 5552.

EGILL, *Skallagrímsson.* Story of Egil Skallagrímsson. pp. 222. *Lond.* 1893. 8°.
12410. ee. 22.

STORM (G.) Islandske Annaler indtil 1578. pp. 667. *Christiania*, 1888. 8°. 9424. i. 11.

THORGILSSON (A.) Íslendingabók, er skrifað hefir Ari Þorgilsson, og Landnámabók. pp. 556. *Reykjavík*, 1891. 8°. 867. i. 49.

CLAUSEN (J.) and LEVIN (P.) Island i Fristatstiden. pp. 45. *Kjøbenh.* 1890. 8°.
9004. gg. 26. (2.)

THORKELSSON (J.) Saga Jörunder Hundadagakóngs. pp. 215. *Kaupmannahöfn*, 1892. 8°.
10761. dd. 3.

SIGURÐSSON (J.) Jón Sigurðsson the Icelandic Patriot. pp. 63. 16. *Reykjavík*, 1887. 8°.
867. k. 4.

P.P. *Reykjavík.* Aldamót. *Reykjavík*, 1891, *etc.* 8°. P.P. 165. k.

ICELAND. *Bishops.* Stories of the Bishops of Iceland. pp. 126. *Lond.* 1895. 8°. 4888. ee. 2. *See also* ICELANDIC LITERATURE.

Fisheries. *See* FISH.

Icelandic Discovery of America. *See* AMERICA.

Law.

DRECHSEL (C. F.) Samling af Islandske Love. pp. 40. *Kjøbenh.* 1892. 8°. 5725. bb. 19. (7.)

ELLWOOD (T,) Landnama Book of Iceland, *etc.* *Kendal*, 1894. 8°. 10280. e. 16.

ICELAND.—Law—*continued.*

STEPHENSON (M.) *the Younger*, and SVEINBJÖRNSSON (L. E.) Lögfræðisleg formálabok. pp. 343. *Reykjavík*, 1886. 8°. 868. h. 35.

Mythology. *See* ICELANDIC LITERATURE.

Topography, etc.

ARGONAUTS. Narrative of the voyage of the Argonauts in 1880. pp. 134. *Edinb.* 1881. 8°.
10281. f. 10.

FRANCE. *Navy.* Instructions nautiques sur les Fœroe, l'Islande, *etc.* pp. 172. *Paris*, 1894. 8°.
10497. cc. 7.

HOWELL (F. W. W.) Icelandic Pictures with pen and pencil. pp. 176. *Lond.* 1893. 8°.
10281. k. 3.

JOHNSTRUP (J. F.) Om de vulkanske Udbrud of Solfatarerne i den nordøstlige Del of Island. *Kjøbenh.* 1890. 8°. Ac. 2969.

MAC CORMICK (W. T.) A Ride across Iceland. pp. 103. *Lond.* 1892. 8°. 10281. aaa. 17.

RABOT (C.) Explorations dans l'Océan glacial arctique. pp. 69. 1894. 8°. Ac. Paris. *Société de Géographie.* Bulletin. Sér. 7. Tom. 15.
Ac. 6035.

TWEEDIE (E. B.) A Girl's ride in Iceland. pp. 180. *Lond.* 1895. 8°. 10280. aa. 26.

G.B. & I. *Hydrographic Office.* Information relating to currents, ice, and magnetism on the coast of Iceland. ff. 34. *Lond.* 1891. 8°. 10496. g. 26.

ICELANDIC LANGUAGE.

FALK (H. S.) Oldnorsk Læsebog. pp. 170. *Kristiania*, 1889. 8°. 12972. ee. 43.

HOLTHAUSEN (F.) Lehrbuch der altisländischen Sprache. *Weimar*, 1895, *etc.* 8°. 12972. l.

KAHLE (B.) Die altnordische Sprache im Dienste des Christentums. 1890, *etc.* 8°. HENNING (R.) Acta Germanica. Bd. 1. 12963. dd. 40.

—— Die Sprache der Skalden auf Grund der Binnen- und Endreime. pp. 303. *Strassb.* 1892. 8°. 12972. f. 21.

LARSSON (L.) Ordförrådet de älsta isländska handskrifterna. pp. 438. *Lund*, 1891. 4°.
12976. m. 15.

NYGAARD (M.) Oldnorsk Læsebog. pp. 35. *Bergen*, 1891. 8°. 12972. ce. 46.

PASSY (P.) De Nordica Lingua quantum in Islandia ab antiquissimis temporibus mutata sit. pp. 63. *Lutetiae*, 1891. 8°. 12901. d. 33. (10.)

THORKELSSON (J.) Beygning sterkra sagnorða í Íslensku. pp. 576. *Reykjavík*, 1888–94. 8°.
867. l. 1.

—— Breytingar á myndum viðtengingurháttar í Fornnorsku og Forníslensku. pp. 67. *Reykjavík*, 1887. 8°. 867. k. 5. (14.)

THORKELSSON (P.) Samtalsbók Íslenzk-Frönsk. pp. 100. *Kaupmannahöfn*, 1893. 12°.
12972. c. 46.

ICELANDIC LITERATURE. JÓNSSON (F.) Ágrip af bókmenntasögu Íslands. 2 pt. *Reykjavík*, 1891–2. 8°. 867. i. 61.

—— Den oldnorske og oldislandske Litteraturs Historie. *Kjøbenh.* 1893, *etc.* 8°. 011850. k.

NYGAARD (M.) Udvalg af den norrøne litteratur. 3 del. *Bergen*, 1889. 8°. 12260. f. 9.

Eddas.

Ac. Copenhagen. *Samfund til Udgivelse af gammel nordisk Litteratur.* Codex regius af den ældre Edda. pp. 193. *Kjøbenh.* 1891. 4°.
Ac. 9057/6.

EDDA. *Poetic.* Harbardssången [the text of the Hárbarðsljóð, with a Swedish translation.] pp. 72. *Stockholm*, 1891. 8°. 11565. h. 10.

—— Die Lieder der sogenannten älteren Edda. pp. 17. 401. *Leipz.* 1892. 8°. 11565. de. 58.

ICELANDIC LITERATURE—continued.

MEYER (E. H.) Die Eddische Kosmogonie.
pp. 118. *Freiburg*, 1891. 8°.   4503. ee. 4.

SANDER (N. F.) Rigveda und Edda. pp. 71.
Stockholm, 1893. 8°.   4503. ee. 27.

SIJMONS (B.) Die Lieder der Edda. 1888, *etc.* 8°.
ZACHER (J.) Germanistische Handbibliothek.
No. 7.   2286. e.

PITT (R. J.) The Tragedy of the Norse Gods.
pp. 256. *Lond.* 1893. 8°.   4503. b. 3.

Sagas.

BÓSI. Die Bósa-Rímur. pp. 100. 1894. 8°.
WEINHOLD (C.) Germanistische Abhandlungen.
Heft x.   12208. gg.

CEDERSCHIÖLD (G. J. C.) Altnordische Saga-
Bibliothek. *Halle*, 1892, *etc.* 8°. 12403. f. 21.

—— Kalfdrâpet och vänpröfningen. pp. 41.
Lund, 1890. 8°.   011824. f. 67. (3.)

KUECHLER (C.) Nordische Heldensagen.
pp. 264. *Bremen*, 1892. 8°. 12410. ccc. 8.

MAJOR (A. F.) Sagas and Songs of the Norsemen. pp. 134. *Lond.* 1894. 8°. 011652. l. 20.

MORRIS (W.) and MAGNÚSSON (E.) The Saga
Library. *Lond.* 1891, *etc.* 8°.   2324. h. 1.

NORTHERN LIBRARY. Translations of Icelandic
Sagas. *Lond.* 1895, *etc.* 8°.   12203. ff.

ATLI. Atla Saga Ótryggssonar. pp. 24.
Seyðisfirði, 1886. 8°.   867. i. 46. (10.)

Ac. Copenhagen. *Samfund til Udgivelse af
gammel nordisk Litteratur.* Egils Saga Skalla-
grímssonar tilligemed Egils større kvad.
pp. 465. *Kjøbenh.* 1886–88. 8°.   Ac. 9057.

—— FRIÐTHJÓFR. Sagan ock Rimorna om
Friðþiófr hinn Frækni. pp. 158.
Kjøbenh. 1893. 8°.   Ac. 9057.

JÓNSSON (T.) Saga Þingeyinga.
Akreyri, 1887, *etc.* 18°.   867. k. 3.

VOLSUNGS. Die Völsungasaga. pp. 216.
Berl. 1891. 8°.   11557. h. 23.

For the "Heimskringla," *see* NORWAY, *History.*

ICHTHYOL. PHYSIOLOGY. Physiology and
therapy of Ichthyol. pp. 62. *Lond.* 1895. 8°.
    7306. e. 27. (11.)

ICKWORTH. ICKWORTH. Ickworth Survey
Boocke. Año 1665°. pp. 97. *Ipswich*, 1893. fol.
    10368. l. 5.

—— Ickworth Parish Registers. pp. 109.
Wells, 1894. 4°.   9906. b. 3.

IDAHO. IDAHO. Resources and attractions
of Idaho. pp. 132. *St Louis*, 1893. 10411. d. 30.

—— Southern Idaho. pp. 16.
Seattle, 1893. 8°.   Pam. 86.

IDEALISM. BOEHRINGER (A.) Kant's er-
kenntnis-theoretischer Idealismus. pp. 86.
Leipz. 1890. 4°.   Pam. 49.

RICARDOU (A.) De l'Idéal. pp. 356.
Paris, 1890. 8°.   8469. k. 7.

WILLMANN (O.) Geschichte des Idealismus.
Braunschweig, 1894, *etc.* 8°.   8486. d.

IDENTIFICATION. *See* ANTHROPOMETRY :
EVIDENCE.

IDIOCY. *See* INSANITY.

IGLAU. PRUSIK (E.) Die Gemeinde Iglau.
pp. 305. *Iglau*, 1890. 8°.   10210. f. 4.

ILE-BARBE. NIEPCE (L.) Les Environs de
l'Ile-Barbe. pp. 479. *Lyon*, 1892. 8°.
    10171. d. 10.

ILE-BOUCHARD. GRIMAUD (H.) Notice
sur la ville de l'Île Bouchard. pp. 29.
Tours, 1895. 8°.   Pam. 91.

ILE DE RÉ. *See* LA ROCHELLE.

ILFRACOMBE. CATFORD ( ) Eclipse
album of Ilfracombe. *Lond.* 1892. 8°.
    10352. l. 27.

FOSTER (W. R.) Bijou guide to Ilfracombe.
pp. 47. *Ilfracombe*, 1894. 24°. 10349. a. 35. (4.)

WADE (Z. E. A.) The ancient Church of Ilfracombe. pp. 124. *Ilfracombe*, 1891. 8°.
    10350. de. 22.

ILKLEY. COLLYER (R.) and TURNER (J. H.)
Ilkley, ancient and modern. pp. 282.
Otley, 1885. 4°.   10358. l. 8.

VICKERS (T. R.) and (E.) Album of Ilkley.
Ilkley, 1895. *obl.* 8°.   10360. aa. 34.

WADDINGTON (T. A. J.) Guide to Ilkley.
pp. 40. *York*, 1895. 8°.   Pam. 90.

WARD, LOCK AND Co. Guide to Ilkley. pp. 124.
Lond. 1892. 8°.   10368. aaa. 58.

ILLAHUN. *See* EGYPT, *Antiquities.*

ILLEGITIMACY. AURITI (G.) La Ricerca
della paternità naturale. pp. 97.
Lanciano, 1894. 8°.   5357. d. 3.

BOTT (W. H.) Manual of the law in Affiliation
Proceedings. pp. 158. *Lond.* 1894. 8°.
    6325. de. 38.

CRAMOND (W.) Illegitimacy in Banffshire.
pp. 24. 1892. 12°.   Pam. 82.

FISHER (J. G.) Illegitimate Children. Inquiry
into their native rights. pp. 41. *Lond.* 1893. 8°.
    08275. ee. 21. (9.)

LA GRASSERIE (R. de) De la Recherche et des
effets de la paternité naturelle. pp. 238.
Paris, 1893. 8°.   5408. aaa. 7.

LEFFINGWELL (A.) Illegitimacy; and the influence of seasons upon conduct. pp. 160.
Lond. 1892, 8°.   08276. e. 33.

LONDON. *Legitimation League.* Rights of natural
children. pp. 85. *Lond.* 1893. 8°. 8285. aa. 62.

POLLACZEK (F.) Die unverehelichten Mütter
und der Code civil in Deutschland. pp. 38.
Neuwied, 1893. 8°.   5604. e. 1. (7.)

ILLINOIS. BARTON (H. J.) Elements of
civil Government of Illinois. pp. 63.
Bost. 1892. 8°.   8175. ee. 1. (2.)

BLANCHARD (R.) History of Illinois. pp. 128.
Chicago, 1883. 8°.   9615. dd. 3.

ILLINOIS. Illinois: its advantages as a fruit-
growing section. pp. 30. *Chicago*, 1893. 8°.
    Pam. 1.

—— Statistics of Coal in Illinois, 1893. pp. 162.
Springfield, 1894. 8°.   07108. g. 11.

MOSES (J.) Illinois, historical and statistical.
2 vol. *Chicago*, 1889, 92. 8°. 9605. dd. 11.

WALLACE (J.) History of Illinois under the
French rule. pp. 433. *Cincinnati*, 1893. 8°.
    9605. dd. 12.

ILLUMINATION AND MINIA-
TURES. Ac. London. *British Museum.*
Guide to the MSS. exhibited. pp. 140.
Lond. 1895. 8°.   11903. b. 42.

—— Miniatures and borders from the Book of
Hours of Bona Sforza. pp. xliii.
Lond. 1894. 4°.   K.T.C. 28. a. 1.

BEISSEL (S.) Vaticanische Miniaturen. pp. 59.
Freiburg, 1893. fol.   1705. a. 17.

BRADLEY (J. W.) Life and works of G. G.
Clovio, miniaturist. pp. 400. *Lond.* 1891. 8°.
    7857. dd. 7.

CELTIC ORNAMENT. Examples from the Books
of Kells and Durrow. pp. 30. *Dubl.* 1892. 4°.
    7709. c. 10.

CLAUDIN (A.) Les Enlumineurs de Toulouse
aux XV° et XVI° siècles. pp. 67. *Paris*, 1893. 8°.-
    011902. m. 21. (12.)

ILLUMINATION AND MINIATURES
—*continued.*

DELISLE (L. V.)   Un feuillet des Heures de Charles, frère de Louis XI.   pp. 6. *Nogent*, 1894. 8°.   11903. aa. 24.

DURRIEU (P.)   Manuscrits d'Espagne remarquables par leurs peintures.   1893. 8°.   Ac.   *Paris. École des Chartes.*   Bibliothèque.   Vol. 54.
                                                                         Ac. 8930.

—— Les Manuscrits à miniatures des Héroïdes d'Ovide.   pp. 36.   *Paris*, 1894. 8°.   7708. a. 49.

GUILLOT (E.)   L'Ornamentation des manuscrits au Moyen Âge.   [Series of plates.]   3 pt. *Paris*, 1892. 4°.   7854. aa. 12.

—— L'Ornamentation des manuscrits au Moyen Âge.   3 pt.   *Paris*, 1892. 4°.   7854. aa. 12.

—— Elements d'ornamentation du XVIᵉ au XVIIIᵉ siècle.   *Paris*, 1892. 4°.   7854. aa. 13.

LABITTE (A.)   Les Manuscrits, et l'art de les orner.   pp. 398.   *Paris*, 1893. 8°.   7709. h. 32.

—— L'Art de l'Enluminure.   pp. 76. *Paris*, 1893. 8°.   7808. bbb. 27. (5.)

LEITSCHUH (F. F.)   Geschichte der karolingischen Malerei.   pp. 471.   *Berl.* 1894. 8°.
                                                              7858. gg. 26.

LITURGIES.   *Hours.*   Account of an illuminated Manuscript of the Hours of the B.V.M.   Executed about A.D. 1450.   pp. 7.   *Lond.* 1894. 4°.
                                                              7709. g. 34.

MARCEL (L.)   La Miniature à Langres, 15ᵉ siècle.   pp. 44.   *Paris*, 1892. 4°.   7709. l. 17.

MIDDLETON (J. H.)   Illuminated Manuscripts in classical and mediaeval times.   pp. 270. *Camb.* 1892. 8°.   2262. f.

MOLINIER (A.)   Les Manuscrits et les miniatures. pp. 333.   *Paris*, 1892. 8°.   7807. e. 27.

MONTE CASSINO.   La Paleografia artistica nel Codici cassinesi.   20 tav.   *Montecas*, 1888. 4°.
                                                              7743. i. 4.

PISCICELLI TAEGGI (O.)   Le Miniature nei codici cassinesi.   *Monte Cassino*, 1887, *etc.* fol.
                                                              1705. b. 15.

QUARITCH (B.)   Palæography.   Notes upon the medieval art of Illumination.   pp. 96. *Lond.* 1894. 8°.   7709. h. 37.

REISS (H.)   Collection of Miniatures reproduced in facsimile.   *Wien*, 1890. 8°.   K.T.C. 15. a. 8.

SWOBODA (H.)   Die griechischen Volksbeschlüsse. pp. 320.   *Leipz.* 1890. 8°.   7706. g. 1.

THOMPSON (*Sir* E. M.)   English illustrated Manuscripts.   pp. 67.   *Lond.* 1895. 8°.
                                                              K.T.C. 42. b. 1.

VARNHAGEN (H.)   Über die Miniaturen in vier französischen Handschriften des 15. Jahrhunderts.   pp. 40.   *Erlangen*, 1894. 4°.   7858. c. 27.

WEALE (W. H. J.)   Gerard David, Illuminator. pp. 72.   1895. 8°.   Portfolio Monographs. No. 24.   P.P. 1931. pcd.

See also ALPHABETS : MANUSCRIPTS : PALAEOGRAPHY.

ILLUSIONS.   *See* HALLUCINATIONS.

ILLUSTRATION.   *See* ENGRAVING.

ILSENBURG.   HERRE (H.)   Ilsenburger Annalen.   pp. 107.   *Leipz.* 1890. 8°.
                                                              9327. d. 10.

IMBECILITY.   *See* INSANITY.

IMITATION.   TARDE (G.)   Les Lois de l'Imitation.   pp. 431.   *Paris*, 1890. 8°.
                                                              8462. e. 26.

IMMORTALITY.   *See* ESCHATOLOGY.

INCARNATION, Doctrine of the.
See CHRISTIANITY, *Atonement, etc.*

INCUNABULA.   *See* BIBLIOGRAPHY.

INDEPENDENTS.   *See* CONGREGATIONALISM.

INDEX EXPURGATORIUS.   CATALOGUES.
Index librorum prohibitorum Leonis XIII. jussu editus.   pp. 414.   *Augustae T.*, 1894, 8°.
                                                              011902. e. 23.

ARNDT (A.)   De Libris prohibitis commentarii. pp. 316.   *Ratisbonae*, 1895. 8°.   4999. dd. 16.

MEYER (F. H.)   Der Index librorum prohibitorum.   1890. 8°.   Ac.   Leipsic.   *Verein für Erforschung vaterländischer Alterthümer.*   Mittheilungen.   Bd. 8.   Ac. 7073.

INDIA.   [*See note on page* 1.]
See also BENGAL : BOMBAY : ENGLAND, *Colonies, etc.* : MADRAS, *etc.*

Bibliography.

Ac.   Calcutta.   *Indian Museum.*   Catalogue of books in the Library of the Indian Museum. pp. 332. 109.   *Calcutta*, 1889. 8°.   011903. e. 20.

G. B. & I.   *India Office.*   Press list of India Office Records to 1630.   pp. 54.   *Lond.* 1891. fol.
                                                              11901. i. 23.

—— Report on the old Records of the India Office, by Sir G. Birdwood.   pp. 316. *Lond.* 1891. 8°.   011902. f. 30.

INDIA.   Catalogue of official Reports relating to India, 1892, *etc.*   Compiled by F. Campbell. *Lond.* 1893, *etc.* 8°.   011900. ee.

MADRAS.   Press list of ancient Records in Fort St. George.   *Madras*, 1891, *etc.* fol.   11906. l.

See also infra : History, British Rule.

Antiquities.

CTESIAS.   Ancient India as described by Ktesias. pp. 104.   *Calcutta*, 1882. 8°.   010057. e. 13.

FUEHRER (A. A.)   Monumental antiquities and inscriptions in the N.W. Provinces and Oudh. pp. 425.   1891. 8°.   INDIA.   *Archæological Survey.*   Reports, New Series.   Vol. 2.   2354. g.

GRIFFIN (*Sir* L. H.)   Famous monuments of Central India.   *Lond.* 1886. 4°.   1730. a. 3.

HEWITT (J. F.)   Ruling Races of prehistoric times in India.   pp. 627.   *Westminster*, 1894. 8°.
                                                              9056. ee. 19.

INDIA.   Great Temples of India.   pp. 96. *Madras*, 1894. 8°.   7814. e. 44.

—— *Archæological Survey.*   Epigraphia Indica, *etc.*   *Calcutta*, 1888, *etc.* fol.   7708. f.

LE BON (G.)   Les Monuments de l'Inde. pp. 254.   *Paris*, 1893. 4°.   K.T.C. 1. b. 12.

OPPERT (G.)   On the original Inhabitants of Bharatavarsa.   pp. 711.   *Westminster*, 1893, 8°.
                                                              10007. cc. 15.

REA (A.)   Archæological survey of Southern India.   pp. 28.   *Madras*, 1891. fol.
                                                              7706. h. 26.

Army.   *See* ENGLAND, *Army.*

Castes.   *See infra* : NATIVE RACES.

Christianity in.   *See* MISSIONS.

Crime.   *See* CRIME : LAW, *Criminal.*

Ethnology.   *See infra* : Native Races.

Gold Production.   *See* GOLD

Government : Administration : Civil Service.

AITCHISON (*Sir* C. U.)   Collection of Treaties, relating to India and neighbouring countries. 11 vols.   *Calcutta*, 1892. 8°.   2386. g.

BIRKMYRE (W.)   The Secretary of State for India in council.   pp. 40.   *Lond.* 1886. 8°.   8228. bb.

INDIA.—Government, etc.—*continued.*

BHUJAṄGARĀYA NAYUDU, *K.* Manual of the Civil Account code. pp. 28. *Madras*, 1890. 8°. 08227. ee. 46. (1.)

CARSTAIRS (R.) British work in India. pp. 302. *Edinb.* 1891. 8°. 8022. de. 19.

GLADSTONE (C. E.) Civil employ in India. pp. 84. *Bedford*, 1894. 8°. 8023. a. 3.

GURUPRASĀDA SENA. Notes on some questions of Administration in India. pp. 358. *Bankipore*, 1893. 8°. 8022. aa. 3.

HUNTER (*Sir* W. W.) The Indian Empire. pp. 852. *Lond.* 1893. 8°. 2318. h. 3.

—— England's Work in India. pp. 148. *Madras*, 1890. 8°. 8022. a. 3.

INDIA. Public Service Commission and its result. pp. 43. *Lucknow*, 1890. 8°. 8023. g. 32. (6.)

NANDAKRISHṆA VASU. Statutory Civil Service, and the Public Service Commission. pp. 98. *Calcutta*, 1888. 12°. 8023. cc. 25.

POWELL (B. H. B.) Account of the Land Revenue and its administration. pp. 260. *Oxf.* 1894. 8°. 8023. b. 12.

SAMPSON (C. H,) Manual of rules applicable to Members of the Indian Civil Service. pp. 254. *Calcutta*, 1891. 8°. 8022. f. 8.

STRACHEY (*Sir* J.) India. pp. 411. *Lond.* 1894. 8°. 2370. c. 1.

TUPPER (C. L.) Our Indian Protectorate. pp. 426. *Lond.* 1893. 8°. 8022. f. 9.

UPENDRANĀTHA MUKHOPĀDHYĀYA. Man of business. A book on official works. pp. 216. *Calcutta*, 1891. 12°. 08227. de. 16.

WHISH (C. W.) A District Office in Northern India. pp. 352. *Calcutta*, 1892. 8°. 8023. f. 33.

See also EXAMINATIONS. *Infra: Politics.*

History.

Bibliography. See supra : BIBLIOGRAPHY.

General, and to the 17th Century.

ADAM (J.) Epochs of Indian history. *Lond.* 1893, *etc.* 8°. 9056. a.

BHOJĀJĪ VADHĀJĪ DAIYĀ. Bird's-Eye View of the history of India. pp. 4. *Surat*, 1890. fol. Pam. 28.

INDIA. Hand-book of Indian history. *Madras*, 1887, *etc.* 8°. 9056. a. 8.

HUNTER (*Sir* W. W.) The Indian Empire. pp. 852. *Lond.* 1893. 8°. 2318. h. 3.

—— Brief history of the Indian peoples. pp. 254. *Oxf.* 1892. 8°. 9057. a. 38.

—— School history of Northern India. pp. 154. *Calcutta*, 1891. 8°. 9056. aaa. 29.

KANHAIYĀ LĀL, and KĀLĪCHARANA. Epitome of the history of Hindustan. *Cawnpore*, 1890, *etc.* 8°. 9056. a. 7.

KEENE (H. G.) History of India. 2 vol. *Lond.* 1893. 8°. 9057. bb. 5.

LETHBRIDGE (*Sir* R.) History of India. pp. 207. *Lond.* 1893. 8°. 9057. a. 42.

MARSHMAN (J. C.) Abridgment of the history of India. pp. 569. *Edinb.* 1893. 8°. 9057. a. 40.

MUELLER (F. M.) India. What can it teach us? pp. 315. *Lond.* 1892. 8°. 2386. a. 1.

MUTCHMORE (S. A.) The Moghul, Mongol, Mikado and missionary. 2 vol. *N.Y.* 1891. 8°. 10058. de. 4.

POPE (G. U.) Longman's school history of India. pp. 303. *Lond.* 1892. 8°. 9056. aaa. 31.

—— Little Raja's primer of Indian history. pp. 128. *Lond.* 1893. 8°. 9057. a. 41.

RAMEŚACHANDRA DATTA. Brief history of India. pp. 261. *Calcutta*, 1891. 8°. 9056. e. 20.

INDIA.—History——*continued.*

SELL (E.) and LAWRENCE (J. T.) Story of India to the death of Aurangzeb. pp. 26. *Madras*, 1890. 12°. 9004. bbb. 14. (7.)

SIVAPRASĀDA, *Raja.* History of Hindustan. pp. 91. *Lucknow*, 1890. 8°. 14156. g. 36.

—— History of India. pp. 68. *Agra*, 1890. 8°. 9004. bbb. 14. (8.)

—— The Historian, an epitome of Indian history. pp. 52. *Lucknow*, 1890. 8°. 9004. gg. 25. (6.)

WHEELER (J. T.) Epitome of Wheeler's Tales from Indian history. pp. 107. *Allahabad*, 1890. 8°. 9057. aaaa. 1.

HEWITT (J. F.) Ruling races of prehistoric Times in India. pp. 627. *Westminster*, 1894. 8°. 9056. ee. 19.

INDIA. India in Vedic Times. pp. 44. *Madras*, 1893. 8°. 9004. bbb. 16. (5.)

RAGOZIN (Z. A.) Vedic India as embodied in the Rig-Veda. pp. 457. 1895. 8°. Story of the Nations. 9004. ccc. 16.

MAC CRINDLE (J. W.) The Invasion of India by Alexander the Great. pp. 432. *Westminster*, 1893. 8°. 9026. ff. 32.

MUHAMMAD HAIDAR. The Tarikh-i-Rashidi. History of the Moghuls of Central Asia. pp. 535. *Lond.* 1895. 8°. 757. ff. 1.

POOLE (S. L.) The Mohammadan Dynasties. pp. 361. *Westminster*, 1894. 8°. 9055. aaa. 38.

HOLDEN (E. S.) The Mogul Emperors of Hindustan, 1398–1707. pp. 365. *Westminster*, 1895. 8°. 10606. c. 32.

HORN (P.) Das Heer- und Kriegswesen der Grossmoghuls. pp. 160. *Leiden*, 1894. 8°. 8823. dd. 44.

ADAMS (W. H. D.) Warriors of the Crescent. pp. 317. *Lond.* 1892. 8°. 10606. bbb. 8.

NOER (F. A. v.) *Count.* Kaiser Akbar. 2 pt. *Leiden*, 1880, 85. 8°. 10606. h. 23.

STEPHENS (H. M.) Albuquerque. pp. 222. 1892. 8°.

HUNTER (*Sir* W. W.) Rulers of India. 10603. d.

French in India.

HAURIGOT (G.) Les Établissements français dans l'Inde. pp. 237. *Paris*, 1891. 8°. 010057. ee. 30.

MALLESON (G. B.) History of the French in India from 1674 to 1761. pp. 614. *Lond.* 1893. 8°. 2386. g.

BARBÉ (É) Le nabab René Madec. Histoire des projets de la France sur le Bengale et le Pendjab, 1772–1808. pp. 291. *Paris*, 1894. 8°. 010663. i. 9.

Ac. Paris. *École des Langues Orientales Vivantes.* ĀNANDARAṄGA PIḶḶAI. Les Français dans l'Inde. Dupleix et Labourdonnais. *Paris*, 1894. 8°. 752. f. 33.

CASTONNET DES FOSSES (H.) La Chute de Dupleix. *Angers*, 1888. 8°. 9007. ff. 6. (4.)

POULAIN (C.) Notes sur l'Inde française. *Châlon-sur-S.* 1892, *etc.* 8°. 10058. d.

LAOUENAN (F. J. M.) *Archbp. of Pondicherry.* Lettres sur l'Inde. pp. 296. *Paris*, 1893. 8°. 010057. f. 17.

British Rule.

Ac. Madras. *Historical Society.* Proceedings. *Madras*, 1890, *etc.* 4°. Ac. 8601.

ADAMS (W. H. D.) The makers of British India. pp. 489. *Lond.* 1895. 8°. 9057. bb. 6.

BOMBAY. Selections from the State papers, preserved in the Bombay Secretariat. Home Series. *Bombay*, 1887, *etc.* 4°. 8022. g.

—— Marátha Series. *Bombay*, 1885, *etc.* 4°. 8022. h.

INDIA.—History—*continued.*

EAST INDIES. Charters relating to the East India Company, 1600–1761. pp. 310.
Madras, 1887. 4°.   8023. l. 9.

—— Register of Letters, etc., of the Governour and Company of Merchants trading into the East Indies, 1600–19. pp. 530. *Lond.* 1893. 8°.
9057. c. 8.

JÑĀNENDRACHANDRA VASU. Synopsis of Cox's history of British rule in India. pp. 120.
Calcutta, 1889. 12°.   Pam. 28.

LYALL (*Sir* A. C.) Rise and expansion of the British Dominion in India. pp. 355.
Lond. 1894. 8°.   9057. b. 24.

MAHENDRANĀTHA DATTA. Sketch of the history of the establishment of British Rule in India. pp. 92. *Benares*, 1888. 12°.   9004. c. 16. (2.)

HOLMES (F. M.) Four heroes of India,—Clive, Warren Hastings, Havelock, Lawrence. pp. 176.
Lond. 1892. 8°.   10803. bb. 24.

PIMBLETT (W. M.) How the British won India. pp. 244. *Lond.* 1893. 8°.   9057. a. 39.

FORREST (G. W.) Administration of Warren Hastings, 1772–85. pp. 317. *Calcutta*, 1892. 8°.
9057. b. 20.

LAWSON (*Sir* C. A.) Private life of Warren Hastings. pp. 254. *Lond.* 1895. 8°.
10815. d 18.

MALLESON (G. B.) Life of Warren Hastings. pp. 563. *Lond.* 1894. 8°.   10815. e. 16.

STRACHEY (*Sir* J.) Hastings and the Rohilla War. pp. 324. *Oxf.* 1892. 8°.   9057. aaa. 34.

RICAUD (H.) Warren Hastings et son procès. pp. 32. *Paris*, 1892. 8°.   10803. f. 3. (8.)

COMPTON (H.) Account of the European military adventurers of Hindustan, 1784–1803. pp. 419.
Lond. 1892. 8°.   9057. b. 19.

KARR (W. S. S.) The Marquess Cornwallis. pp. 202. 1890. 8°. HUNTER (*Sir* W. W.) Rulers of India.   10603. dd.

MALLESON (G. B.) Life of the Marquess Wellesley. pp. 239. 1895. 8°. Statesmen Series. 10602. e.

BELL (J. H.) British Folks & British India fifty years ago. pp. 207. *Manch.* 1891. 8°.
10826. ff. 19.

MARTINEAU (J.) Life and correspondence of Sir Bartle Frere. 2 vol. *Lond.* 1895. 8°.
10816. cc. 27.

TEMPLE (*Sir* R.) James Thomason. pp. 215.
Oxf. 1893. 8°.   10815. bb. 30.

CAMPBELL (*Sir* G.) Memoirs of my Indian career. 2 vol. *Lond.* 1893. 8°.   10815. eee. 16.

THORNTON (J. H.) Memories of seven Campaigns. 1856–91. pp. 359. *Westminster*, 1895. 8°.
9057. c. 11.

ADYE (*Sir* J. M.) Recollections of a military Life. pp. 382. *Lond.* 1895. 8°.   10815. ee. 21.

BROWNE (J.) Cawnpore and the Nana of Bithoor. pp. 27. *Cawnpore*, 1890. 8°.   Pam. 88.

BURNE (*Sir* O. T.) Clyde and Strathnairn. 1891. 8°. HUNTER (*Sir* W. W.) Rulers of India.
10603. dd.

D'OYLY (*Sir* C.) Eight months' experience of the Sepoy Revolt, 1857. pp. 55.
Blandford, 1891. 8°.   9005. d. 26. (6.)

FORBES-MITCHELL (W.) Reminiscences of the Mutiny, 1857–59. pp. 295. *Lond.* 1893. 8°.
9057. aa. 22.

GRANT (*Sir* J. H.) Life of General Sir Hope Grant. 2 vol. *Edinb.* 1894. 8°. 10817. dd. 16.

GROOM (W. T.) With Havelock from Allahabad to Lucknow, 1857. pp. 110. *Lond.* 1894. 8°.
9056. e. 21.

HALLS (J. J.) Arrah in 1857. Defence of Arrah House. pp. 137. *Dover*, 1893. 8°. 9057. aa. 19.

INDIA.—History—*continued.*

INGLIS (*Hon.* J. S.) *Lady.* The Siege of Lucknow. pp. 240. *Lond.* 1892. 8°.   9057. b. 18.

INNES (J. J. M.) Lucknow and Oude in the Mutiny. pp. 340. *Lond.* 1895. 8°. 9057. aaa. 37.

MAUDE (F. C.) Memories of the Mutiny. 2 vol. *Lond.* 1894. 8°.   9057. b. 23.

MILES (A. H.) and PATTLE (A. J.) Stories of the Indian Mutiny. pp. 440. *Lond.* 1895. 8°.
9057. aa. 24.

NASH (J. T.) Volunteering in India. Military services of the Bengal Yeomanry Cavalry during the Mutiny. pp. 136. *Lond.* 1893. 8°.
9057. bb. 3.

OUVRY (M. H.) Lady's Diary before and during the Mutiny, 1854–58. pp. 166.
Lymington, 1892. 8°.   9057. b. 25.

OWEN (W.) The Martyrs of the Indian Rebellion. pp. 144. *Lond.* 1891. 8°. 4804. aa. 22.

WILBERFORCE (R. G.) An unrecorded chapter of the Indian Mutiny. pp. 240. *Lond.* 1895. 8°.
9057. aa. 23.

SATYACHANDRA MUKHOPĀDHYĀYA. Indian History of our own times, 1859–88. 3 pt.
Calcutta, 1891. 8°.   9056. c. 2.

THORNTON (T. H.) Colonel Sir R. Sandeman: his life on our Indian frontier. pp. 392.
Lond. 1895. 8°.   10817. ee. 17.

FORREST (G. W.) The administration of the Marquis of Lansdowne, 1888–94. pp. 72.
Calcutta, 1894. 8°.   9057. c. 10.

See also infra: Politics: BOMBAY: CHITRAL. MADRAS: MANIPUR.

Hygiene. *See* HYGIENE.

Indian National Congress and National Social Conference.

INDIA. *Indian National Congress.* Report.
Lucknow, 1886, *etc.* 8°.   8022. g.

—— Fourth Indian National Congress. Allahabad, 1888. Account of proceedings. pp. 48.
Allahabad, 1888. fol.   1852. d. 5.

B. Congress Sketches: review of speeches and speakers at the fourth Congress. pp. 55.
Lucknow, 1889. 8°.   Pam. 67.

INDIA. *Indian National Congress.* Indian National Congress: Allahabad, 1888. Impressions of two English visitors. pp. 34.
Lond. 1889. 8°.   8023. ee. 26. (8.)

—— Report of Proceedings of the fifth Congress. pp. 42. *Bombay.* 1890. 4°.   8022. f. 12.

—— *National Social Conference.* Report of the fourth National Social Conference, Calcutta, 1890. pp. 62. *Poona*, 1891. 8°.   8022. b. 4.

—— Report of the sixth National Social Conference. pp. 82. *Poona*, 1893. 8°. 8022. bbb. 13.

COLVIN (*Sir* A.) Audi alteram partem: two letters on certain aspects of the Indian National Congress movement. *Simla*, 1888. 8°.
8023. ee. 26. (4.)

HUME (A. O.) Speech on the Indian National Congress. pp. 18. *Calcutta*, 1888. 8°.
8023. ee. 26. (6.)

INDIA. India in England. Speeches on the Indian National Congress in England in 1889. 2 vol. *Lucknow*, 1889. 9°.   8023. g. 31.

—— *Indian National Congress.* The Indian National Congress, its origin, history and objects. pp. 112. *Madras*, 1888. 8°.   8023. g. 32. (1.)

INDIAN MUTINY. The Mutiny and the Congress. pp. 10. *Serampore*, 1891 8°.   Pam. 67.

NORTON (E.) The National Congress vindicated. pp. 28. *Lucknow*, 1889. 8°.   8023. g. 32. (4.)

ŚIVASANKARA PANDYA. Indian National Congress series. *Madras*, 1888, *etc.* 8°.   8022. aaa.

INDIA.—National Congress, etc.—*cont.*

TĀRĀPADA VANDYOPĀDHYĀYA. Indian National Congress. pp. 40. *Calcutta*, 1888. 8°.
8023. ee. 26. (6.)

VIRESVARA MITRA. View of the Indian National Congress. pp. 37. *Benares*, 1889. 8°.
8022. de. 24. (10.)

See also infra: Native Races : Politics.

Land Tenures. *See* LAND.

Languages and Literature. *See* BENGALI: GUJARATI: HINDI: HINDUSTANI: MALAYALAM: MARATHI: SANSKRIT, TAMIL, *etc.*

Law.

INDIA. *Legislative Council.* Code of Civil Procedure. pp. 174. 118. *Poona*, 1889. 8°.
5319. aa. 11.

——— The New Code of Civil Procedure. pp. 304. *Calcutta*, 1889. 8°. 5319. b. 16.

STOKES (W.) Second Supplement to the Anglo-Indian Codes. pp. 115. *Oxf.* 1891. 8°. 5318. c. 23.

DRAPES (G. F. T.) Definition and Construction of the Indian Statute book. pp. 178. *Bangalore*, 1891. 8°. 5319. b. 18.

MANUEL (R. A.) Guide to Indian Statutes 1834-84. pp. 112. *Rangoon*, 1884. 8°.
8023. ee. 22.

COWELL (H.) History and constitution of the Courts in India. pp. 214. *Calcutta*, 1894. 8°.
05319. i. 5.

OZZARD (H. H.) Cantonment Magistrate's manual. pp. 93. *Calcutta*, 1890. 8°. 5319. a. 10.

PLEADER. Guide to the study of Law: questions and answers to the N.W.P. Law Examination Papers, 1874-83. pp. 223. *Lucknow*, 1890. 8°.
5318. aaa. 4.

REMFREY (H. H.) Codification and improvement of Law in India. pp. 18. *Calcutta*, 1891. 8°.
Pam. 33.

P.P. *Madras.* Madras Law Journal. *Madras*, 1891, *etc.* 8°. P.P. 1351. agb.

TĀRĀPRASANNA DĀSA. Judicial service in the Lower Provinces. pp. 40. *Dacca*, 1889. 8°.
Pam. 34.

WILSON (*Sir* R. K.) Digest of Anglo-Muhammadan Law. pp. 500. *Lond.* 1895. 8°.
05319. g. 2.

——— Tables showing differences between English and Indian Law. pp. 20. *Camb.* 1890. 4°.
5319. g. 19.

RUSSELL (L. P.) Indian Companies Acts, 1887. pp. 434. *Bombay*, 1888. 8°. 5318. c. 20.

GRIFFITH (W.) Commentaries on the Indian Easements Act. pp. 114. *Madras*, 1886. 8°.
5319. aaa. 32.

BROUGHTON (L. P. D.) Estoppel by matter of record in civil Suits in India. pp. 168. *Lond.* 1893. 8°. 5318. bb. 30.

NARASIMHA RĀU. Law Student's companion. Indian Evidence Act. Examination questions. pp. 44. *Madras*, 1890. 8°. Pam. 33.

LALUBHĀĪ PRĀNAVALLABHADĀSA PARIKH. Hand Book of Giras and guarantee. pp. 401. *Bombay*, 1889. 8°. 5318. d. 21.

INDIA. *Legislative Council.* Guardians and wards Act. pp. 98. *Calcutta*, 1891. 8°. 5319. c. 15.

KEDĀRANATHA RĀYA. Indian Limitation Act. pp. 215. *Calcutta*, 1891. 8°. 5319. cc. 4.

UPENDRANĀTHA MITRA. Commentaries on the Indian Limitation Act. pp. 290. 48. *Calcutta*, 1891. 8°. 05319. i. 7.

GRIFFITH (W.) The Indian Transfer Acts. pp. 293. *Madras*, 1892. 8°. 5319. b. 21.

MITRA (A. C.) Transfer of Property Act, 1882. pp. 85. *Calcutta*, 1891. 8°. 6306. e. 7.

INDIA.—Law—*continued.*

DRAPES (G. F. T.) Provincial Small Cause Court Act. pp. 161. *Madras*, 1891. 8°. 05319. i. 1.

GRIFFITH (W.) Indian Trusts Act. pp. 265. *Madras*, 1888. 8°. 5319. aaa. 33.

See also HINDUISM : LAW, *Criminal :* MOHAMMEDANISM.

Local Government. *See* LOCAL GOVERNMENT.

Missions. *See* MISSIONS.

Native Races : Ethnology : Caste : Religion, *etc.*

CALAND (W.) Altindischer Ahnencult. pp. 266. *Leiden*, 1893. 8°. 4503. ee. 29.

HEWITT (I. F.) Ruling Races of prehistoric times in India. pp. 627. *Westminster*, 1894. 8°.
9056. ee. 19.

INDIA. The Principal Nations of India. pp. 156. *Madras*, 1892. 8°. 10058. a. 24.

LAMAIRESSE (E.) L'Inde avant le Bouddha. pp. 328. *Paris*, 1891. 12°. 4503. bb. 35.

——— L'Inde après le Bouddha. pp. 464. *Paris*, 1892. 12°. 4503. de. 5.

PRAMATHANĀTHA VASU. History of Hindu civilisation during British rule. *Calcutta*, 1894, *etc.* 8°. 8022. bb. 28.

RAMACHANDRA GHOSHA. History of Hindu civilisation, as illustrated in the Vedas. pp. 223. *Calcutta*, 1889. 8°. 9057. aaa. 31.

RAMESACHANDRA DATTA. History of civilisation in Ancient India. 2 vol. 1893. 8°. Trübner's Oriental Series. 2318. h. 8.

NAVĪNACHANDRA RĀYA. History of Caste distinctions among the Hindus. pp. 78. *Allahabad*, 1890. 8°. Pam. 41.

RAGUNATHA RĀU, R. Lecture on the Arayan system of Caste. pp. 47. *Madras*, 1890. 16°.
Pam. 41.

RISLEY (H. H.) Tribes and castes of Bengal. Anthropometric data. 2 vol. *Calcutta*, 1891. 8°.
010057. k. 1.

——— Tribes and castes of Bengal. Ethnographic glossary. 2 vol. *Calcutta*, 1891. 8°.
010057. k. 2.

CHAITANYA KRISHŅA NĀGA. Criticisms on Mr. Risley's articles on Brahmans, Kayasthas and Vaidyas in his "Tribes and castes of Bengal." *Calcutta*, 1893, *etc.* 8°. 4503. b.

SCHOEBEL (C.) L'Histoire des castes de l'Inde. 2 pt. 1883-90. Ac. *Paris. Société Académique.* Bulletin. Deuxième série. Tom. 2, 3.
Ac. 8812/3.

VISHŅUNĀRĀYANA DHAR. Caste system in India. pp. 23. *Lond.* 1888. 8°. 8023. ee. 26. (7.)

INDIA. Ways and means for the amelioration of the condition of Non-Brahmin Races. pp. 80. *Madras*, 1893. 8°. Pam. 67.

FAIR PLAY. Non-Brahmin races and the Indian public service. pp. 13. *Madras*, 1892. 8°.
Pam. 67.

GREEVEN (R.) Knights of the Broom. Attempt to collect some of the ceremonies of sweepers in the Benares division. pp. 85. *Benares*, 1894. 8°.
4503. c. 10.

PĀNDIYAN (T. B.) Slaves of the soil in Southern India. pp. 52. *Madras*, 1893. 8°. 8277. c. 55.

CARSTAIRS (R.) Human nature in rural India. pp. 344. *Edinb.* 1895. 8°. 010057. c. 38.

CROOKE (W.) Introduction to the popular Religion of Northern India. pp. 420. *Allahabad*, 1894. 8°. 4503. ee. 31.

KIPLING (J. L.) Beast and man in India. pp. 401. *Lond.* 1891. 8°. 7002. f. 6

2 H

INDIA.—Topography, etc.—*continued.*

HUNTER (*Sir* W. W.) The Indian Empire.
pp. 852. *Lond.* 1893. 8°.   2318. h. 3.

JÑĀNĀRJITAM PILLAI. How to master the geography of India. pp. 48. *Madras,* 1889. 8°.
Pam. 88.

LYDE (L. W.) Elementary geography of India.
pp. 99. *Lond.* 1893. 16°.   9056. a. 10.

NEWALL (D. J. F.) The Highlands of India strategically considered. 2 vol.
Lond. 1882–87. 8°.   10058. bbb. 14.

COOK (T.) India. Information for travellers.
pp. 104. *Lond.* 1891. 8°.   10058. a. 15.

INDIA. Murray's Handbook for India. pp. 484.
Lond. 1894. 8°.   2364. b. 24.

LYTTELTON (*Hon.* K. S.) How to pack, how to dress, how to keep well, on a winter tour in India. pp. 30. *Lond.* 1892. 8°.   Pam. 88.

PRIESTLEY (N. G.) Distance and route Tables. India. pp. 169. *Bombay,* 1892. 4°.
8235. i. 52.

ARNOLD (E. L. L.) On the Indian hills. pp. 350.
Lond. 1893. 8°.   010057. e. 25.

BALLOU (M. M.) The Pearl of India. pp. 335.
Lond. 1894. 8°.   010057. e. 35

BLAVATSKY (H. P.) From the Caves and jungles of Hindostan. pp. 318. *Lond.* 1892. 8°.
010057. f. 11.

BREMNER (C. S.) A Month in a Dandi. pp. 214.
Lond. 1891. 8°.   010057. e. 9.

BURRELL (W. S.) and CUTHILL (E. E.) Indian Memories. pp. 304. *Lond.* 1893. 8°.
010057. e. 23.

CAINE (W. S.) India as seen by W. S. C.
pp. 7. 76. *Lucknow,* 1889. 8°. 8023. g. 32. (3.)

CARPENTER (E.) From Adam's Peak to Elephanta. pp. 363. *Lond.* 1892. 8°. 010057. f. 10.

CHEVRILLON (A.) Dans l'Inde. pp. 334.
Paris, 1891. 8°.   10056. aaa. 23.

CLÉRY (L.) De Paris à Lahore. pp. 366.
Paris, 1893. 12°.   10057. aa. 15.

DE WINDT (H.) A Ride to India across Persia and Baluchistán. pp. 340. *Lond.* 1891. 8°.
10075. ff. 19.

DOUGHERTY (J. A.) The East Indies Station; cruise of H.M.S. "Garnet." pp. 237.
Malta, 1892. 8°.   10058. cc. 31.

GORDON (J. D.) Work and play in India.
pp. 293. *Lond.* 1895. 8°.   010057. e. 16.

HURST (J. F.) Indika. Country and people of India. pp. 794. *N.Y.* 1891. 8°. 010057. l. 9.

KLEIN (A.) Among the Gods. Scenes of India.
pp. 355. *Edinb.* 1895. 8°.   010057. h. 5.

KNOX (M. V. B.) A Winter in India. pp. 306.
N.Y. 1891. 8°.   10058. cc. 33.

MACLEOD, *afterwards* WILSON (A. C.) After five years in India. pp. 312. *Lond.* 1895. 8°.
010057. e. 36.

MARRAT (J.) The Land of the Ganges. pp. 212.
Lond. 1892. 8°.   10058. a. 22.

MAYER (J. E.) Humour and pathos of Anglo-Indian life. pp. 277. *Lond.* 1895. 8°.
12330. ccc. 43.

MILN (L. J.) When we were strolling Players in the East. pp. 354. *Lond.* 1894. 8°.
010057. f. 29.

MURDOCH (J.) Pictorial Tour round India.
pp. 65. *Madras,* 1890. 4°   10058. l. 9.

P.P. *Allahabad.* North Indian notes and queries.
Allahabad, 1891, *etc.* 4°.   P.P. 3798. aa.

REES (J. D.) H.R.H. the Duke of Clarence in Southern India. pp. 213. *Lond.* 1891. 8°.
010057. l. 6.

INDIA.—Topography, etc.—*continued.*

REES (J. D.) Lord Connemara's Tours in India.
pp. 381. *Lond.* 1892. 8°.   010057. f. 1.

S., F. A. and G., G. Complete Indian housekeeper. pp. 330. *Edinb.* 1890. 8°. 07915. e. 59.

THOBURN (J. M.) India and Malaysia. pp. 562.
Cincinnati, 1892. 8°.   4766. ee. 21.

UKHTOMSKY (E. E.) *Prince.* Voyage en Orient de son A.I. le Césarevitch. pp. 392.
Paris, 1893. 4°.   1789. d. 1.

WILKINS (W. J.) Harry's Trip to India.
pp. 128. *Lond.* 1894. 8°.   4429. eee. 29.

ZALESKI ( ) Ceylon et les Indes. pp. 411.
Paris, 1891. 8°.   10058. aa. 35.

Ac. *London. Hakluyt Society.* VALLE (P. d.) Travels of P. della Valle in India. 2 vol.
Lond. 1892. 8°.   Ac. 6172/67.

CASTONNET DES FOSSES (H.) Bernier, ses voyages dans l'Inde. pp. 78. *Angers,* 1888. 8°.
10057. k. 3.

MACMILLAN (M.) The Globe Trotter in India two hundred years ago. pp. 214. *Lond.* 1895. 8°.
10058. df. 6.

TWINING (T.) Travels in India a hundred years ago. pp. 529. *Lond.* 1893. 8°.   010057. i. 1.

Trade, Finance, etc.

BROWN (R.) The Opium revenue and Indian finance. pp. 24. *Glasg.* 1891. 8°.
08227. ee. 46. (5.)

CALCUTTA. *Society for the Promotion of Indian Industries.* Journal of the Society.
Calcutta, 1892, *etc.* 8°.   08276. i. 19.

CHICAGO. *Columbian Exposition.* Industrial art manufactures of the Indian Empire. pp. 36.
1893. 8°.   7808. bbb. 29. (7.)

HUNTER (*Sir* W. W.) The Indian Empire.
pp. 852. *Lond.* 1893. 8°.   2318. h. 3.

KAILĀSACHANDRA. Essay on the poverty of India.
pp. 34. *Hugli,* 1893. 8°.   08226. h. 14. (13.)

LĀLA-CHANDA. Essay on the decline of Native Industries. pp. 31. *Lahore,* 1894. 8°. Pam. 82.

LONDON. *Imperial Institute.* Year book of the Imperial Institute. *Lond.* 1892, *etc.* 8°. 2121. d.
—— Hand-books of commercial products. Indian Section. *Calcutta,* 1891, *etc.* 8°.   08226. l.

MACGEORGE (G. W.) Ways and works in India. Public works in that country. pp. 565.
Westminster, 1894. 8°.   08235. f. 40.

OMAN (J. C.) Industrial development of India.
pp. 25. *Lahore,* 1891. 8°.   8277. h. 20. (8.)

POONA. *Industrial Association.* Industrial Quarterly Review of Western India.
Poona, 1892, *etc.* 8°.   P.P. 3800. fdb.

TOWNSEND (C. C.) Mineral wealth of India.
pp. 61. *Bombay,* 1891. 8°.   7108. de. 26.

VARADĀCHĀRIYAR. Indian Arts and industries, *etc.* pp. 24. *Madras,* 1894. 8°.   Pam. 94.

WATT (G.) Memorandum on resources of British India. pp. 79. *Calcutta,* 1894. 8°.
08226. k. 6. (16.)

See also MONEY: RAILWAYS.

INDIANA. CONNER (J. B.) Indiana Agriculture. pp. 24. *Indianapolis,* 1893. 8°. Pam. 1.

PHINNEY (A. J.) Natural Gas field of Indiana. 1891. 4°. U.S. *Geological Survey.* Annual Report. No. 11, pt. 1.   1828. aa.

INDIAN CLUBS. COBBETT (G. T. B.) and JENKIN (A. F.) Indian Clubs. pp. 113.
1893. 8°. All England Series.   7908. df.

INDIAN CORN. *See* MAIZE.

2 H 2

INDIAN LANGUAGES, American.

North America: Canada and United States.

BRINTON (D. G.) The American Race. A linguistic classification of the tribes of N. and S. America. pp. 392. *N.Y*, 1891. 8°. 10408. bb. 35.

—— Characteristics of American Languages. pp. 8. *Cleveland*, 1894. 8°. 12910. d. 31. (11.)

FERNÁNDEZ Y GONZÁLEZ (F.) Los Lenguajes hablados por los indígenas del norte y centro de América. pp. 112. *Madrid*, 1893. 8°.
12910. g. 33.

Ac. Washington. *Smithsonian Institution.*
PILLING (J. C.) Bibliography of the Algonquian Languages. pp. 614. *Wash.* 1891. 8°.
BB.R. c. 7.

CUOQ (J. A.) Grammaire de la Langue algonquine. 1893. 4°. Ac. Ottawa. *Royal Society.* Proceedings. Vol. 10. Ac. 1883.

ELIOT (J.) Bibliographic notes on Eliot's Indian Bible and on his other translations. pp. 58. *Wash.* 1890. 8°. 4999. k. 5.

HECKEWAELDER (J. G. E.) Comparative vocabulary of Algonquin Dialects. pp. 7. *Camb.* 1887. 4°. 12902. i. 2. (2.)

TOOKER (W. W.) Algonquian terms Patawomeke and Massawomeke. pp. 11. *Wash.* 1894. 8°.
12910. d. 31. (13.)

BIBLE. *Selections.* Readings from Holy Scripture in the language of the Blackfoot Indians. pp. 47. *Lond.* 1890. 8°. 4429. aa. 77.

FOSTER (G. E.) Literature of the Cherokees. pp. 109. *Ithaca*, 1889. 12°. 011850. f. 44.

LITURGIES. England, *Church of. Common Prayer.* Part of the Book of Common Prayer, translated into the language of the Chipewyan Indians. pp. 276. *Lond.* 1891. 8°. 3408. bbb. 30.

CREE PRIMER. Cree Primer. pp. 39. *Lond.* 1893. 8°. 4429. a. 62.

HORDEN (J.) *Bp. of Moosonee.* Grammar of the Cree Language. pp. 238. *Lond.* 1881. 8°.
12910. a. 36.

—— Bible and Gospel history in the language of the Cree Indians. pp. 64. *Lond.* 1892. 8°.
4429. b. 5.

ENGLAND, *Church of. Catechism.* The Catechism in the language of the Cree Indians. pp. 14. *Lond.* 1892. 8°. 4429. b. 6.

MACKAY (J. A.) Psalms and Hymns in the language of the Cree Indians. pp. 111. *Lond.* 1891. 8°. 4429. aaa. 38.

RIGGS (S. R.) Dakota-English dictionary. pp. 665. 1890. 4°. U.S. *Geographical Survey of the Rocky Mountains.* Contributions. Vol. 7.
1828. e.

—— Dakota grammar. pp. 239. 1893. 4°. U.S. *Geographical Survey of the Rocky Mountains.* Contributions to Ethnology. Vol. 9. 1828. e.

Ac. Washington. *Smithsonian Institution.*
PILLING (J. C.) Bibliography of the Iroquoian Languages. pp. 208. *Wash.* 1888. 8°.
011902. f. 10.

—— Philadelphia. *Historical Society.* Lenâpé-English Dictionary. pp. 236. *Phila.* 1888. 4°.
12910. bb. 48.

CHRISTIAN DOCTRINE. Catechism of Christian Doctrine translated into Flat-head. pp. 102. *Woodstock College*, 1891. 16°. 3504. dg. 3.

ILLINOIS VOCABULARY. Illinois and Miami vocabulary and Lord's Prayer. pp. 9. *N.Y.* 1891. 8°. 12903. dd. 34. (9.)

Ac. Washington. *Smithsonian Institution.*
PILLING (J. C.) Bibliography of the Muskhogean Languages. pp. 114. *Wash.* 1889. 8°.
011902. f. 11

BEAUCHAMP (W. M.) Indian Names in New York. pp. 148. *Fayetteville*, 1893. 8°.
12910. aaa. 76.

Ac. Washington. *Smithsonian Institution.*
PILLING (J. C.) Bibliography of the Salishan Languages. pp. 86. *Wash.* 1893. 8°.
11904. l. 15. (3.)

—— Bibliography of the Siouan Languages. pp. 87. *Wash.* 1887. 8°. 011903. m. 11. (6.)

BOMPAS (W. C.) *Bp. of Selkirk.* Lessons and prayers in the Tenni or Slavi language. pp. 126. *Lond.* 1892. 8°. 4376. de. 6

HYMNS. Hymns in the Tenni or Slavi language. pp. 118. *Lond.* 1889. 8°. 4420. aaa. 73.

SCHULENBURG (A. C. v. d.) *Count.* Die Sprache der Zimshian-Indianer. pp. 372. *Braunschweig*, 1894. 4°. 12910. h. 18.

Ac. Washington. *Smithsonian Institution.*
MALLERY (G.) Introduction to the study of Sign Language among N. American Indians. pp. 72. *Wash.* 1880. 4°. 12901. l. 20.

MALLERY (G.) Sign Language among North American Indians. pp. 287. *Wash.* 1881. 8°.
12910. i. 30.

Central and South America: Mexico.

BRINTON (D. G.) The American Race. pp. 392. *N.Y.* 1891. 8°. 10408. bb. 35.

—— Characteristics of American Languages. pp. 8. *Cleveland*, 1894. 8°. 12910. d. 31. (11.)

—— Studies in the South American native Languages. 2 pt. *Phila.* 1892. 8°. 12910. e. 42.

—— Notes on Fuegian Languages. 1892. 8°.
12910. d. 31. (3.)

FERNÁNDEZ Y GONZÁLEZ (F.) Los lenguajes hablados por los indígenas del centro de América. pp. 112. *Madrid*, 1893. 8°. 12910. g. 33.

MITRE (B.) Lenguas americanas. Estudio bibliográfico de las obras del P. L. de Valdivia. pp. 153. *La Plata*, 1894. 8°. 12910. aa. 71.

VINAZA (de la) *Count.* Bibliografía española de Lenguas indígenas de América. pp. 427. *Madrid*, 1892. 8°. 11900. i. 36.

AIMARA. Catálogo de las voces usuales de Aimará. pp. 35. *Paris*, 1894. 8°. 12901. de. 16. (7.)

STEINEN (C. v. d.) Zweite Schingú-Expedition 1887-88. Die Bakaïri-Sprache. pp. 403. *Leipz.* 1892. 8°. 12910. d. 24.

CAHITA LANGUAGE. Arte de la Lengua cahita. pp. 264. *Mexico*, 1890. 8°. 12910. b. 39.

BRETON (R.) Dictionnaire caraibe-français. pp. 480. *Leipz.* 1892. 8°. 12907. aa. 69.

CHAÑABAL LANGUAGE. Fragments sur la Langue chañabal. pp. 4. *Louvain*, 1892. 8°.
12901. d. 34. (9.)

PLATZMANN (J.) Algunas obras raras sobre la Lengua cumanagota. *Leipz.* 1888, etc. 8°.
12910. d.

BARBOSA RODRIGUES (J.) Vocabulario indigena comparado. pp. 83. *Rio de Janeiro*, 1892. 8°.
12907. f. 21.

RUIZ DE MONTOYA (A.) Lexicon Hispano-Guaranicum. pp. 545. *Stuttgardiae*, 1893. 8°.
12910. cc. 16.

—— Linguæ Guaraní grammatica Hispanice edita. pp. 330. *Stuttgardiæ*, 1892. 8°.
12910. cc. 12.

ROSA (A. de la) Estudio de la filosofia de la Lengua mexicana. pp. 115. *Guadalajara*, 1889. 8°. 12901. d. 37. (4.)

BOBAN (E.) Catalogue de la Collection de M. Goupil. Manuscrits figuratifs et autres. 3 pt. *Paris*, 1891. fol. 1707. c. 11.

INDIAN LANGUAGES.—Central and South America—*continued.*

BRINTON (D. G.) Native Calendar of Central America and Mexico. pp. 59. *Phila.* 1893. 8°. 8563. e. 5.

CHARENCEY (H. de) *Count.* Vocabulaire français maya. pp. 87. *Alençon,* 1884. 8°. 12901. d. 35. (2.)

—— Chrestomathie Maya. pp. 301. 1891. 8°. Ac. Paris. *Société Philologique.* Actes. Tom. 19. Ac. 9808.

—— De la Formation des mots en Langue maya. *Copenhague,* 1884. 8°. 12901. d. 32. (2.)

FOERSTEMANN (E. W.) Erläuterungen zur Mayahandschrift der K. Bibliothek zu Dresden. pp. 80. *Dresd.* 1886. 4°. 7708. dd. 15.

—— Zur Entzifferung der Mayahandschriften. 2 pt. *Dresd.* 1887–91. 8°. Pam. 47,

ADAM (L.) Langue mosquito. pp. 134. 1891. 8°. Coleccion lingüística americana. Tom. 14. 12907. dd. 17.

MARBAN (P.) Arte de la Lengua moxa. pp. 664. 202. *Leipz.* 1894. 8°. 2910. c. 7.

FERNÁNDEZ FERRAZ (J.) Nahuatlismos de Costa Rica. pp. 148. *San José,* 1892. 8°. 12910. bb. 42.

CONDREAN (H.) Vocabulaires des langues du Guyane, Ouayana, Aparaï, etc. pp. 144. 1892. 8°. Bibliothèque linguistique américaine. Tom. xv. 12907. dd. 17.

LITURGIES. Rome, Ch. of. Textes puquina contenus dans le Rituale Peruanum de Geronimo de Ore, 1607. pp. 67. *Leipz.* 1894. 8°. 12910. dd. 35.

DOMINGO, *de S. Thomas.* Arte de la Lengua quichua. pp. 96. *Leipz.* 1891. 8°. 12910. aa. 38.

CHARENCEY (H. de) *Count.* Textes en Langue tarasque. pp. 6. *Louvain,* 1890. 8°. 12902. d. 32. (7.)

PAREJA (F.) Arte de la Lengua timuquana. pp. 132. 1886. 8°. Coleccion lingüística americana. Tom. 77. 12907. dd. 17.

BÁRCENA (A.) Arte de la Lengua toba. 1894. 8°. Ac. La Plata. *Museo.* Revista. Tom. 5. Ac. 3091.

DICTIONARIES. Vocabulario castellano-zapoteco. pp. 222. *Mexico,* 1893. fol. 12907. h. 12.

BELMAR (F.) Cartilla del Idioma zapoteco serrano. pp. 30. *Oaxaca,* 1890. 12°. Pam. 45.

REYES (G. de los) Gramatica de las Lenguas zapoteca-serrana y zapoteca del valle. pp. 100. *Oaxaca,* 1891. 8°. 12910. bb. 40.

INDIAN OCEAN, DOUGHERTY (J. A.) The East Indies Station: cruise of H.M.S. Garnet. pp. 237. *Malta,* 1892. 8°. 10058. cc. 31.

G. B. & I. *Hydrographic Office.* West coast of Hindostan Pilot. pp. 414. *Lond.* 1891. 8°. 10496. g. 38.

—— Islands in the Southern Indian Ocean. pp. 480. *Lond.* 1891. 8°. 10496. g. 39.

IMRAY (J. F.) and JENKINS (H. D.) Indian Ocean Pilot. pp. 1296. 32. *Lond.* 1886. 8°. 10496. d. 13.

TAYLOR (A. D.) India directory for steamers and sailing-vessels. 2 pt. *Lond.* 1891. 8°. 10496. d. 11.

INDIANS, American.

North America.

BANDELIER (A. F.) Report of investigations among the Indians of the South-western United States. 1890, *etc.* 8°. Ac. Boston. *Archæological Institute.* Papers. American Ser. III., *etc.* Ac. 5790/8.

BETTANY (G. T.) Red, brown and black Men of America, *etc.* pp. 289. *Lond.* 1890. 8°. 10007. f. 20.

INDIANS.—North America—*continued.*

BRINTON (D. G.) The American Race. pp. 392. *N.Y.* 1891. 8°. 10408. bb. 35.

—— On various relations between the American and Asian Races. *Chicago,* 1894. 8°. Pam. 86.

COLLIER (P.) Mr. Picket-Pin and his friends. pp. 157. *Lond.* 1894. 8°. 10410. aaa. 46.

DEMANCHE (G.) Au Canada et chèz les Peauxrouges. pp. 192. *Paris,* 1890. 8°. 10460. ff. 16.

DORMAN (R. M.) Origin of primitive Superstitions among the aborigines of America. pp. 398. *Phila.* 1881. 8°. 4505. e. 4.

GRINNELL (G. B.) Story of the Indian. pp. 270. 1895. 8°. HITCHCOCK (R.) Story of the West Series, *etc.* 10408. de.

HAMMERER (J. D.) Account of a plan for civilizing the N. American Indians, proposed in the 18th Century. pp. 28. 1890. 12°. Winnowings in American History. Indian Tracts. No. 1. 9551. aaa.

HORDEN (J.) *Bp. of Moosonee.* Forty-two years amongst the Indians. pp. 223. *Lond.* 1893. 8°. 4429. eee. 6.

LAKE MOHONK. Proceedings of the eighth meeting of the Lake Mohonk Conference of Friends of the Indian, 1890. pp. 159. *Lake Mohonk,* 1890. 8°. 8156. ee. 12.

MAC LEAN (J.) Indians of Canada. pp. 351. *Lond.* 1892. 8°. 10470. f. 29.

MALLERY (G.) Pictographs of the N. American Indians. pp. 256. *Wash.* 1886. 8°. 12910. i. 31.

MORICE (A. G.) Notes on the Western Dénés. pp. 222. 1894. 8°. Ac. Toronto. *Canadian Institute.* Transactions. Vol. 4. Ac. 1885/3.

NORDENSKIÖLD (G.) Ruiner af Klippboningar i Mesa Verdes Cañons. pp. 193. *Stockholm,* 1895. fol. 7701. i. 6.

PAGE (J.) D. Brainerd: the Apostle to the N. American Indians. pp. 160. *Lond.* 1891, 8°. 4985. dd. 19.

PARRY (F.) Sacred Symbols and numbers of aboriginal America. pp. 45. *N.Y.* 1894. 8°. 07703. h. 1. (17.)

STRONG (J. C.) Wah-Kee-Nah and her people. Customs and legends of the N. American Indians. pp. 275. *N.Y.* 1893. 8°. 10413. bbb. 33.

TURNER (F. J.) Character of the Indian trade in Wisconsin. pp. 75. 1891. 8°. Johns Hopkins University Studies. Ser. 9. No. 11–12. Ac. 2689.

ATKINS (T. A.) Indian Wars and the uprising of 1655. pp. 14. *Yonkers,* 1892. 8°. 9555. f. 4. (5.)

ELLIS (E. S.) Indian Wars of the United States, 1607—1890-91. pp. 516. *N.Y.* 1892. 8°. 9005. ff. 6.

BOURKE (J. G.) On the Border with Crook. pp. 491. *Lond.* 1892. 8°. 10412. ee. 29.

DUNN (J. P.) Massacres of the mountains. History of Indian wars of the Far West. pp. 784. *N.Y.* 1886. 8°. 9503. dd. 17.

HOPE (A. R.) The Wigwam and the war-path. pp. 352. *Lond.* 1892. 8°. 10409. d. 22.

—— The Men of the backwoods. pp. 488. *Lond.* 1893. 8°. 9555. aaa. 28.

LEWIS (M.) History of the expedition under the command of Lewis and Clark. 4 vol. *Lond.* 1893. 8°. 10412. i. 11.

YAWGER (R. N.) The Indian and the pioneer. *Syracuse,* 1893, *etc.* 8°. 9615. df. 6.

YOUNG (E. R.) Stories from Indian wigwams. pp. 293. *Lond.* 1893. 8°. 4765. de. 15.

INDIANS.—North America—*continued.*

BOURKE (J. G.) Notes upon the gentile organization of the Apaches of Arizona. pp. 14. 1890. 8°.   10412. dd. 25. (2.)

—— The Medicine-men of the Apache. 1892. 4°. Ac. Washington. *Smithsonian Institute.* Report. No. 9.   Ac. 1875/8.

PATTERSON (G.) Beothiks or Indians of Newfoundland. 1892. 4°. Ac. Ottawa. *Royal Society.* Proceedings. Vol. ix.   Ac. 1883.

FOSTER (G. E.) Literature of the Cherokees. pp. 109. *Ithaca*, 1889. 12°.   011850. f. 44.

BECKWOURTH (J. B.) Life and adventures of J. P. Beckwourth, chief of the Crow nation of Indians. pp. 440. 1892. 8°. Adventure Series.   012207. k.

THOMAS (C) The Cherokees in Pre-Columbian Times. pp. 97. *N.Y.* 1890. 8°.   7708. a. 68.

CASWELL (H. S.) Our life among the Iroquois Indians. pp. 321. *Bost.* 1892. 8°. 4767. ccc. 17.

RAND (S. T.) Legends of the Micmacs. pp. 452. 1894. 8°. Wellesley Philological Publications.   12430. l.

STEVENSON (J.) Ceremonial of Hasjelti Dailjis and mythical sand painting of the Navajo Indians. 1891. 4°. Ac. Washington. *Smithsonian Institute.* Report, etc. 8th report.   Ac. 1875/8.

BANDELIER (A. F.) Historical introduction to studies among the Sedentary Indians of New Mexico. 1893, *etc.* 8°. Ac. Boston. *Archæological Institute.* Papers. American series. I., *etc.*   Ac. 5790/8.

WARREN (W. W.) History of the Ojibways. 1885. 8°. Ac. Saint Paul. *Minnesota Historical Society.* Collections. Vol. 5.   Ac. 8405.

Ac. Washington. *Smithsonian Institution.* DORSEY (J. O.) Omaha and Ponka Letters. pp. 127. *Wash.* 1891. 8°.   10905. g. 26.

THOMAS (C.) The Story of a Mound: Shawnees in the Pre-Columbian Times. 1891. 8°. American Anthropologist. Vol. 4. Ac. 6239/2.

DORSEY (J. O.) Study of Siouan cults. 1894. 4°. Ac. Washington. *Smithsonian Institution.* Annual Report. 11th report.   Ac. 1875/8.

FINERTY (J. F.) War-path and bivouac, conquest of the Sioux. pp. 460. *Chicago*, 1890. 8°.   9605. cc. 15.

SIOUX. Memoir of the Sioux. 1890. 8°. Ac. Saint Paul. *Macalester College.* Contributions. Department of History. No. 10.   Ac. 2692. s.

KRAUSE (A.) Die Tlinkit-Indianer. pp. 420. *Jena*, 1885. 8°.   10460. f. 31. *See also* CANADA and UNITED STATES, *History.*

Central and South America and Mexico.

BETTANY (G. T.) Red Men of America, *etc.* pp. 289. *Lond.* 1890. 8°.   10007. f. 20.

BRINTON (D. G.) The American Race. pp. 392. *N.Y.* 1891. 8°.   10408. bb. 35.

—— Nagualism. Study in native American folk-lore and history. pp. 65. *Phila.* 1894. 8°.   12430. k. 38.

—— The native Calendar of Central America and Mexico. pp. 59. *Phila.* 1893. 8°.   8563. c. 5.

—— On various relations between American and Asian Races. *Chicago*, 1894. 8°. Pam. 86.

BOURKE (J. G.) Laws of Spain in their application to the American Indians. pp. 8. *Wash. D.C.*, 1894, 8°.   Pam. 34.

BRINE (L.) Travels amongst American Indians. pp. 422. *Lond.* 1894. 8°.   07708. g. 33.

DELORME SALTO (R.) Los Aborígenes de América. pp. 230. *Madrid*, 1894. 8°.   10408. cc. 35.

INDIANS.—Central America, etc.—*cont.*

PARRY (F.) Sacred Symbols and numbers of Aboriginal America. pp. 45. *N.Y.* 1894. 8°.   07703. h. 1. (17.)

UHLE (F. M.) Kultur und Industrie südamerikanischer Völker. 2 Bde. *Berl.* 1889, 90. fol.   1705. b. 13.

STEINEN (C. v. d.) Unter den Naturvölkern Zentral-Brasiliens. pp. 570. *Berl.* 1894. 8°.   10481. i. 29.

BOGGIANI (G.) Viaggi nell' America Meridionale. I Caduvei. pp. 335. *Roma*, 1895. 4°.   10480. h. 26.

RESTREPO TIRADO (E.) Estudios sobre los aborigines de Colombia. *Bogotá*, 1892, *etc.* 8°.   10481. ee.

CANDELIER (H.) Rio-Hacha et les Indiens Goajires. pp. 282. *Paris*, 1893. 8°.   10481. c. 34.

STOLL (O.) Die Ethnologie der Indianerstämme von Guatemala. pp. 112. 1889. 4°. P.P. *Leyden.* Internationales Archiv für Ethnographie. Band I. Suppl.   P.P. 3863. h.

COUDREAU (H. A.) Chez nos Indiens. Quatre années dans la Guyane française, 1887-91. pp. 614. *Paris*, 1893. 8°.   10480. g. 18.

BUELNA (E.) Peregrinacion de los Aztecas, *etc.* pp. 152. *Mexico*, 1892. 8°.   10481. de. 6.

GIMENO DE FLAQUER (C.) Civilization de los antiguos pueblos mexicanos. pp. 108. *Madrid*, 1890. 8°.   7706. aa. 51.

LE PLONGEON (A.) Sacred mysteries among the Mayas and the Quiches, 11500 years ago. pp. 163. *N.Y.* 1886. 8°.   7706. c. 44.

MEXICO. Histoire de la nation mexicaine. pp. 158. *Paris*, 1893. 8°.   9771. e. 1.

PARRY (F.) The Sacred Maya Stone. pp. 70. *Lond.* 1893. fol.   7705. i. 20.

OLIVEIRA CEZAR (F. de) Leyendas de los Indios Quichuas. pp. 108. *Buenos A.* 1892. 8°.   12430. cc. 32.

ROCHA (D. A.) Tratado del origen de los Indios del Perú, Méjico, Santa Fe y Chile. 2 vol. 1891. 8°. Coleccion de libros, *etc.* Tom. 3 & 4.   9551. bbb.

CASAS (B. de las) Bp. *of Chiapa.* De las antiguas gentes del Perú. pp. 290. 1892. 8°. Colección de libros españoles raros. Tom. 21. 12230. aa.

LISTA (R.) Los Indios Tehuelches. pp. 125. *Buenos A.* 1894. 8°.   10481. aa. 41.

MARCANO (G.) Ethnographie précolombienne de Venezuela. 2 pt. 1889, 90. 8°. Ac. Paris. *Société d'Anthropologie.* Mémoires. Sér. 2. Tom. 4.   Ac. 6227/2. *See also* ARAUCANIA: COSTA RICA: MEXICO: PERU.

INDIA RUBBER. ROSE (H.) Vulcanite Work. pp. 63. *Lond.* 1895. 8°. 7611. cc. 10.

SLOANE (T. O.) Rubber hand-stamps and the manipulation of Rubber. pp. 146. *N.Y.* 1891. 8°.   7942. cc. 34.

INDIES, Dutch.

History : Administration : Military Affairs : Law.

KLOOT (M. A. v. R. v. d.) De Gouverneurs-Generaal van Nederlandsche-Indië 1610-1888. pp. 355. *'s Gravenh.* 1891. 8°.   10759. k. 29.

MENDELS (I.) H. W. Daendels Gouverneur-Generaal van Oost-Indië, 1762-1807. pp. 301. 209. *'s Gravenh.* 1890. 8°. 10759. k. 25.

BROEK (J. A. v. d.) Oud Oost-Indië. *Haarlem*, 1893, *etc.* 8°.   8022. dd.

CHILLEY-BERT (J.) Le Recrutement des fonctionnaires coloniaux. pp. 87. *Paris*, 1893, 8°.   Pam. 66.

INDUSTRIES—*continued.*

ENGLAND. Industries of the South and West of England. pp. 312. *Lond.* 1891. 8°. 8226. i. 12.

GREEN (J. L.) Rural Industries of England. pp. 205. *Lond.* 1895. 8°. 08276. g. 73.

GREGORJ (G.) Le piccole Industrie fra i contadini, *etc.* pp. 228. *Treviso,* 1891. 8°. 08276. h. 19.

MASSACHUSETTS. *Bureau of Statistics of Labour.* Annual statistics of Manufactures. *Bost.* 1890, *etc.* 8°. 8275. l.

BIRCH (J.) AND Co. Guide book to Technical Literature. pp. 230. *Lond.* 1891. 8°. 011903. e. 25.

HAFERKORN (H. E.) and HEISE (P.) Handy lists of Technical Literature. 6 pt. *Milwaukee,* 1889, 90. 8°. 011902. f. 17.

AMATEUR WORK. Amateur work illustrated. *Lond.* 1891–96. 8°. 7944. dd. 8.

ARTS AND CRAFTS ESSAYS. Arts and Crafts essays. pp. 420. *Lond.* 1893. 8°. 7808. df. 2.

BITHELL (R.) A Counting-house Dictionary. pp. 326 *Lond.* 1893. 8°. 08227. de. 19.

BOWER (J. A.) How to Make common things. For Boys. pp. 240. *Lond.* 1892. 8°. 7820. bbb. 35.

CARUS (P.) The Philosophy of the tool. pp. 24. *Chicago,* 1893. 8°. Pam. 49.

CHEMIST. Some splendid trade Secrets. *Dublin,* 1894. 8°. Pam. 94.

COOLEY (A. J.) Cyclopædia of practical receipts. 2 vol. *Lond.* 1892. 8°. 2022. c.

ENCYCLOPÆDIAS. "Scientific American" Cyclopedia of receipts. pp. 675. *N.Y.* 1892. 8°. 07945. g. 5.

HASSELL (J.) Technology for schools. pp. 192. *Lond.* 1893. 8°. 07944. e. 7.

LECHALAS (M. C.) Encyclopédie industrielle. *Paris,* 1894, *etc.* 8°. 8709. c.
—— Atlas. 4°. 14001. c. 25.

LUEGER (O.) Lexikon der gesamten Technik. *Stuttgart,* 1895, *etc.* 8°. 07944. k.

MACKMURDO (A. H.) Plain Handicrafts. pp. 63. *Lond.* 1892. 8°. 7944. cc. 39.

RASMUSSEN (C. V.) Vare-Leksikon. pp. 486. *Kjøbenh.* 1893. 8°. 12972. aa. 23.

RIDER (W.) Technical Series. *Lond.* 1893, *etc.* 8°. 7078. e.

RIS-PAQUOT (O. E.) Les petites Occupations manuelles et artistiques. pp. 160. *Paris,* 1894. 12°. 07944. e. 36.

SIMMONDS (P. L.) Commercial Dictionary of trade products. pp. 510. *Lond.* 1892. 8°. 8245. e. 70.

YOUNG (F.) Every man his own Mechanic. pp. 924. *Lond.* 1890. 8°. 7817. g. 24.

See also ART, *Decorative* : EDUCATION, *Technical* : FACTORIES : INVENTIONS : MACHINERY.

INEBRIETY. *See* ALCOHOLISM.

INFLAMMATION. KRONACHER (A.) Die Aetiologie und das Wesen der akuten eitrigen Entzündung. pp. 108. *Jena,* 1890. 8°. 7419. i. 14.

LEBER (T.) Die Entstehung der Entzündung, *etc.* pp. 535. *Leipz.* 1891. 4°. 7611. g. 34.

MECHNIKOV (I.) Leçons sur la pathologie comparée de l'Inflammation. pp. 239. *Paris,* 1892. 8°. 7630. h. 27.
—— Lectures on comparative pathology of Inflammation. pp. 218. *Lond.* 1893. 8°. 7616. h. 19.

See also SUPPURATION.

INFLUENZA. Ac. Berlin. *Verein für Innere Medicin.* Die Influenza-Epidemie 1889/90. pp. 194. *Wiesbaden,* 1892. 4°. 7560. k. 6.

INFLUENZA—*continued.*

ALTHAUS (J.) Influenza. pp. 407. *Lond.* 1892. 8°. 7616. aa. 40.

CLUTTERBUCK (J. B.) Stray notes on Hygiene and on Influenza. pp. 69. *Lond.* 1892. 8°. 7404. de. 8.

CREIGHTON (C.) History of Epidemics in Britain. 2 vol. *Camb.* 1891–94. 8°. 2255. f. 8.

DIXEY (F. A.) Epidemic Influenza. pp. 29. *Oxf.* 1892. 8°. 7561. k. 9.

DOWSE (T. S.) Brain and nerve exhaustion and the nervous sequelæ of Influenza. pp. 140. *Lond.* 1894. 8°. 7630. e. 20.

EBSON (C.) La Grippe and its treatment. pp. 46. *N.Y.* 1891. 16°. 07305. i. 12. (2.)

ENGEL (F.) Die Influenza-Epidemie in Egypten 1889/90. pp. 48. *Berl.* 1893. 4°. 7560. i. 16.

FRIEDRICH (P. L.) Die Influenza-Epidemie 1889/90. 1894. 8°. GERMANY. *Kaiserliches Gesundheitsamt.* Arbeiten. Bd. 9. 7440. h.

GRANVILLE (J. M.) Note on the nature and treatment of "Influenza." pp. 8. *Lond.* 1893. 8°. 07305. f. 17. (8.)

GOSLETT (C.) Influenza and how to go through it. pp. 16. *Lond.* 1892. 8°. 7306. df. 19. (11.)

GRASSET (J.) Leçons sur la Grippe, 1889–90. pp. 98. *Montpellier,* 1890. 8°. 7616. h. 9.

GROSSMANN (J.) Die Erfolge der Suggestionstherapie bei Influenza. pp. 38. *Berl.* 1892. 8°. 07305. h. 18. (9.)

HESSE-DARMSTADT. Die Influenza-Epidemie 1891/92 in Hessen. pp. 68. *Darmstadt,* 1893. 8°. 7305. f. 5. (7.)

HULMANN (M.) Contribution à l'étude de la nature de la Grippe. pp. 106. *Paris,* 1894. 8°. 7560. d. 5.

INFLUENZA. Influenza : history, nature and cure. pp. 26. *Lond.* 1892. 8°. 07305. h. 16. (11.)

JANKOWSKI (J.) Das Denguefieber. pp. 32. *St. Gallen,* 1890. 8°. 07305. f. 14. (5.)

KIRN (L.) Die nervösen Störungen der Influenza. 1891. 8°. VOLKMANN (R. v.) Sammlung klinischer Vorträge. N. F. Nr. 23. 7441. g.

KRANNHALS (H.) Die Influenza-Epidemie 1889–90 in Riga. pp. 62. *St. Petersburg,* 1891. 8°. 07305. k. 13. (4.)

OLDFIELD (J.) The Influenza. pp. 6. *Lond.* 1892. 8°. 8435. bb. 62. (10.)

RIPPERGER (A.) Die Influenza. Ihre Geschichte, Epidemiologie. *etc.* pp. 338. *München,* 1892. 8°. 7561. k. 8.

RUHEMANN (J.) Die Influenza, 1889/90. pp. 188. *Leipz.* 1891. 8°. 7615. e. 8.

RUSSELL (*Hon.* F. A. R.) The spread of Influenza. pp. 58. *Lond.* 1891. 8°. 07305. h. 6. (11.)

SISLEY (R.) Epidemic Influenza. pp. 150. *Lond.* 1891. 8°. 7561. i. 37.
—— Study of Influenza and the laws concerning infectious diseases. pp. 119. *Lond.* 1892. 8°. 6426. e. 9.

TEISSIER (J.) L'Influenza de 1889–90 en Russie. pp. 78. *Paris,* 1891. 4°. 7560. h. 13.

VIREY (É.) Étude sur quelques formes nerveuses de la Grippe. pp. 80. *Paris,* 1893. 4°. 7383. ddd. 2. (4.)

ULRIK (A.) Den danske Fællesforskning angaaende Influenza-Epidemien. pp. 58. *Københ.* 1890. 8°. 7305. de. 27. (5.)

WOLFF (J.) Die Influenza-Epidemie, 1889–92. pp. 167. *Stuttg.* 1892. 8°. 7560. e. 18.

WUTZDORFF ( ) Die Influenza-Epidemie 1891/92. 1894. 8°. GERMANY. *K. Gesundheitsamt.* Arbeiten. Bd. 9. 7440. h.

See also DISEASE, *Infectious.*

INFUSORIA. *See* PROTOZOA.

INGOLSTADT. FISCHER (J.) Die Stadt-pfarrkirche in Ingolstadt. pp. 29.
Ingoldstadt, 1892. 8°. 7808. bbb. 29. (3.)

INISHOWEN. *See* DONEGAL.

INITIAL LETTERS. *See* ALPHABETS : IL-LUMINATION.

INJUNCTIONS, Law of. BEACH (C. F.)
Commentaries on the Law of Injunctions. 2 vol.
Albany, 1895. 8°. 06617. e. 4.

INK. BLONDEL (S.) Les outils de l'Écrivain.
pp. 232. *Paris*, 1890. 18°. 7942. cc. 30.
DESMAREST (L.) Fabrication des Encres et cirages. pp. 345. *Paris*, 1895. 8°
07944. ee. 21.

See also PENS.

INKERMANN, Battle of. *See* CRIMEAN WAR.

INQUESTS. *See* CORONERS.

INQUISITION. HENNER (A.) Beiträge zur Organisation der päpstlichen Ketzerge-richte. pp. 383. *Leipz*, 1890. 8°. 4061. dd. 9.
TANON (L.) Histoire de l'Inquisition en France.
pp 567. *Paris*, 1893. 8°. 4629. i. 27.
AMABILE (L.) Il Santo Officio della Inquisi-zione in Napoli. 2 vol. *Città di C.* 1892. 8°.
4071. l. 12.
FOERSTER (P.) Der Einfluss der Inquisition auf das geistige Leben der Spanier. pp. 24.
Berl. 1890. 4°. 11850. m. 14. (6.)
LEA (H. C.) Chapters from the history of Spain connected with the Inquisition. pp. 522.
Phila. 1890. 8°. 4625. aaa. 3.
MENENDEZ Y PELAYO (M.) Historia de los heterodoxos Españoles. 3 vol.
Madrid, 1880. 8°. 4625. d. 1.
MENEZES (C. J. de) A Inquisição em Portugal.
2 tom. *Porto*, 1893. 8°. 4625. a. 35.
MEDINA (J. T.) Historia de la Inquisición en Chile. 2 tom. *Santiago de C.* 1890. 8°.
4745. ee. 11.

INSANITY : PSYCHIATRY.
General.

AC. *Congrès international de Médecine mentale.*
Comptes rendus. pp. 602. *Paris*, 1890. 8°.
Ac. 3701.
BAILLARGER (J. G. F.) Recherches sur les Maladies mentales. 2 tom. *Paris*, 1890. 8°.
7660. g. 16.
BALL (B.) Du Délire des persécutions. pp. 107.
Paris, 1890. 8°. 7660. df. 22.
BEACH (F.) Psychological Medicine in J. Hun-ter's time, and the progress it has made. pp. 35.
Lond. 1891. 8°. 7660. a. 13.
BLANDFORD (G. F.) Insanity and its treatment.
pp. 508. *Edinb.* 1892. 8° 7660. de. 9.
BLIN (E. É. E.) De l'idée de Persécution.
pp. 109. *Paris*, 1890. 8°. 7760. dd. 12.
BRUSHFIELD (T. N.) Notes on the symptoms and medico-legal aspects of Insanity. pp. 25.
1890. 8°. Pam. 39.
CHARUEL (L.) De la simulation de la Folie chez les aliénés. pp. 81. *Paris*, 1893. 8°. 7660. g. 25.
CLOUSTON (T. S.) Clinical lectures on Mental Diseases. pp. 708. *Lond.* 1892. 8°. 7660. h. 3.
COTARD (J.) Études sur les Maladies cérébrales et mentales. pp. 443. *Paris*, 1891. 8°.
7660. c. 4.
DUMAS (G.) Les états intellectuelles dans la Mélancolie. pp. 142. *Paris*, 1895. 8°.
8162. aa. 25.
DUPAIN (J. M.) Étude sur le Délire religieux.
pp. 307. *Paris*, 1888. 8°. 7660. g. 18.

INSANITY.—General—*continued.*
FÉRÉ (C.) La pathologie des émotions. pp. 605.
Paris, 1892. 8°. 7660. g. 1.
FROMENT ( ) Étude sur la Simulation des maladies mentales. 1890. 8°. Ac. Amiens.
Académie des Sciences. Mémoires. Tom 37.
Ac. 540.
GRAY (L. C.) Treatise on nervous and mental Diseases. pp. 687. *Lond.* 1893. 8°. 7660. g. 24.
HAZLEHURST (H.) Handwriting of the Insane.
Phila. 1887. 8°. 7660. bb. 3.
HYSLOP (T. B.) Mental Physiology in its relations to mental disorders. pp. 552. *Lond.* 1895. 8°.
7660. g. 34.
IRELAND (W. W.) The Blot upon the Brain.
pp. 388. *Edinb.* 1893. 8°. 7660. g. 15.
KIRCHHOFF (T.) Lehrbuch der Psychiatrie.
pp. 552. *Leipz.* 1892. 8°. 7660. g. 23.
KOCH (J. L. A.) Die psychopathischen Minder-wertigkeiten. *Ravensburg*, 1891, *etc.* 8°.
7660. cc. 22.
KRAEPELIN (E.) Der psychologische Versuch in der Psychiatrie. pp. 91. 1895. 8°. Psycho-logische Arbeiten. Bd. 1. 8463. g.
KRETZSCHMAR (F.) Die Unvollkommenheit der heutigen Psychiatrie. pp. 93. *Leipz.* 1891. 8°.
07305. h. 18. (4.)
LAEHR (H.) Die Literatur der Psychiatrie im XVIII. Jahrhundert. pp. 53. *Berl.* 1892. 4°.
11902. l. 21.
LARROUSSINIE (P.) De la Dissimulation chez les aliénés. pp.132. *Paris*, 1893. 4°. 7383. ddd. 2. (2.)
LOEHR (H.) Gedenktage der Psychiatrie und ihrer Hülfsdisciplinen in allen Ländern.
pp. 478. *Berl.* 1893. 8°. 7660. g. 28.
LOMBROSO (C.) Nouvelles recherches de Psychia-trie. pp. 180. *Paris*, 1892. 12°. 7660. aa. 37.
MABILLE (H.) and LALLEMANT (E.) Des Folies diathésiques. pp. 151. 1891. 4°. Ac. Paris.
Académie de Médecine. Mémoires. Tom. 36.
fasc. 2. Ac. 3725.
MAGNAN (V.) Leçons sur les Maladies mentales.
Paris, 1890. 8°. 7660. df. 31.
MAUDSLEY (H.) The pathology of Mind.
pp. 571. *Lond.* 1895. 8°. 2254. c. 14.
NISBET (J. F.) The insanity of Genius.
pp. 340. *Lond.* 1891. 8°. 8463. i. 25.
P.P. *New York.* Journal of nervous and mental Disease. Vol. XVI., *etc.* *N.Y.* 1891, *etc.* 8°.
P.P. 3232. he.
PICHON (G.) Folies passionelles. pp. 378.
Paris, 1891. 12°. 7660. a. 14.
PONTOPPIDAN (K.) Psychiatriske Forelæsninger.
pp. 176. *Kjøbenh.* 1892. 8°. 7660. aa. 39.
POWELL (H. A.) Surgical aspect of Traumatic Insanity, *etc.* pp. 49. *Oxf.* 1893. 8°.
7305. f. 6. (7.)
PRONIER (E.) Étude sur la contagion de la folie.
pp. 91. *Lausanne*, 1892. 8°. 07305. h. 20. (2.)
RICOTTI (G.) La Pazzia e la sua influenza nel secolo XIX. *Chieti*, 1894. fol. 7660. i. 1.
ROTHE (A. v.) Geschichte der Psychiatrie in Russland. pp. 104. *Leipz.* 1895. 8°. 7660. g. 35.
SÉGLAS (J.) Leçons cliniques sur les Maladies mentales, Salpêtrière, 1887–94. pp. 835.
Paris, 1895. 8°. 7660. d. 3.
—— Le Délire des négations. pp. 234. 1894. 8°.
Encyclopédie des aide-mémoire. 8709. g.
SEMELAIGNE (R.) Les grands Aliénistes français.
Paris, 1894, *etc.* 8°. 010662. i.
SHAW (J.) Epitome of mental Diseases. pp. 345.
Bristol, 1892. 8°. 7660. de. 8.
SPECHT (G.) Die Mystik im Irrsinn. pp. 127.
Wiesbaden, 1891. 8°. 7660. g. 20.

INSANITY.—General—*continued.*

SOMMER (R.) Diagnostik der Geisteskrankheiten. pp. 302. *Wien*, 1894. 8°.   7660. g. 31.

SUTHERLAND (H.) Difficulties of prognosis in Insanity. pp. 31. *Lond.* 1895, 8°. 7660. df. 35.

TUKE (D. H.) Dictionary of psychological Medicine. 2 vol. *Lond.* 1892. 8°.   7660. dd. 5.

—— Prichard and Symonds in especial relation to Mental science. pp. 116. *Lond.* 1891. 8°.
          7660. df. 27.

—— Insanity of over-exertion of the Brain. pp. 66. *Edinb.* 1894. 8°.   7660. g. 30.

WALMSLEY (F. H.) Outlines of Insanity. pp. 154. *Lond.* 1892. 8°.   7660. df. 29.

WIJSMAN (J. W. H.) Diagnostiek der Zielsziekten. pp. 247. *Amsterd.* 1892. 8°. 7660. cc. 26.

ZIEHEN (T.) Psychiatrie. pp. 470. 1894. 8°. Wredens Sammlung medizinischer Lehrbücher. Bd. 17.   7321. h.

See also HALLUCINATIONS.

Care of the Insane : Asylums, etc.

AC. London. *Medico-Psychological Association.* Handbook for attendants on the Insane. pp. 122. *Lond.* 1893. 8°.   7660. de. 14.

BIBBY (G. H.) Asylum Construction and arrangement. pp. 77. *Lond.* 1894. 8°.   7817. aaa. 1.

BOTHE (A.) Die familiale Verpflegung Geisteskranker der Irren-Anstalt der Stadt Berlin. pp. 154. *Berl.* 1893. 8°.   7660. g. 27.

BURDETT (H. C.) Hospitals and asylums of the World. 4 vol. *Lond.* 1891–93. 8°.   2024. e.

—— Portfolio of Plans. 1893. fol.   1832. e. 9.

FIELD (R.) Practical suggestions as to the water supply and drainage for Lunatic Asylums. pp. 17. *Lond.* 1892. 8°.   Pam. 79.

GARSTIN (J. R.) Memorandum as to the terms on which Government Loans are made for public works in Ireland, particularly for Lunatic Asylums. pp. 12. *Dublin*, 1895. 8°. Pam. 23.

HARDING (W.) Mental Nursing. pp. 156. *Lond.* 1894. 8°.   7660. df. 34.

KIRCHHOFF (T.) Grundriss einer Geschichte der deutschen Irrenpflege. pp. 192. *Berl.* 1890. 8°.
          7660. dd. 11.

LAEHR (H.) Die Heil- und Pflegeanstalten für Psychisch-Kranke des deutschen Sprachgebietes. pp. 229. *Berl.* 1891. 8°. 7660. df. 28.

LATHROP (C. C.) A Secret Institution. pp. 339. *N.Y.* 1890. 8°.   7660. a. 12.

LONDON. *British Hospital for Mental Disorders.* Report. *Lond.* 1892, etc. 8°.   7660. cc.

MERCIER (C.) Lunatic Asylums, organisation and management. pp. 300. *Lond.* 1894. 8°.
          7660. g. 26.

—— The Attendant's companion. Duties of attendants in Lunatic Asylums. pp. 128. *Lond.* 1892.   7660. a. 15.

TUKE (D. H.) Reform in the treatment of the Insane. Early history of the Retreat, York. pp. 96. *Lond.* 1892. 8°.   7660. c. 6.

VALLÉE (A.) Insane in the Province of Quebec. pp. 72. *Quebec*, 1890. 8°.   7660. df. 36.

WILLIAMS (C.) New method of treating the Insane. pp. 8. *Liverp.* 1893. 8°.
          07305. f. 17. (11.)

MACDONALD (C. F.) Practical workings of the new Laws for the State Care of the Insane. pp. 43. *N.Y.* 1894. 8°.   Pam. 23.

NEW YORK. *State Charities Aid Association.* Proceedings of Public Meeting to commemorate the completion of State Care Legislation for the Insane. No. 53. pp. 52. *N.Y.* 1891. 8°.
          8282. ff. 8. (13.)

INSANITY.—Care of the Insane—*cont.*

PENNSYLVANIA. Compendium of the laws of Pennsylvania, relating to the supervision of the Insane in State Hospitals, *etc.* pp. 224. *Harrisburg*, 1889. 8°.   06616. g. 18.

Idiocy : Imbecility.

CARLSEN (J.) Statistiske undersøgelser angaaende Aandssvage i Danmark 1888–89, *etc.* pp. 77. *Dan.* and *Eng.* *Kjøbenh.* 1891. 8°. 7660. f. 38.

CHASLIN (P.) La Confusion mentale primitive. pp. 264. *Paris*, 1895. 8°.   7660. de. 24.

LOBB (J.) Pauper Idiots and imbeciles. pp. 12. *Lond.* 1895. 8°.   Pam. 39.

SHUTTLEWORTH (G. E.) Mentally-deficient Children. pp. 140. *Lond.* 1895. 8°. 7660. de. 21.

SOLLIER (P.) Psychologie de l'Idiote et de l'imbécile. pp. 276. *Paris*, 1891. 8°. 7660. e. 5.

VOISIN (J.) L'Idiotie hérédité et dégénérescence mentale. pp. 295. *Paris*, 1893. 12°.
          7660. de. 16.

BEACH (F.) Treatment and education of mentally feeble children. pp. 32. *Lond.* 1895. 8°.
          7660. de. 20.

Insanity and Crime.

GUENTHER (R.) Über Behandlung der irren Verbrecher. pp. 132. *Leipz.* 1893. 8°.
          6056. e. 25.

STRAHAN (S. A. K.) Suicide and Insanity. pp. 228. *Lond.* 1893. 8°.   8425. e. 18.

WINSLOW (L. S. F.) Eccentricity of youth leading to crime. pp. 54. *Lond.* 1895. 8°. Pam. 39.

See also CRIME : MEDICINE, *Legal.*

Lunacy Laws.

ARCHBOLD (J. F.) Archbold's Lunacy. pp. 905. *Lond.* 1895. 8°.   2232. d. 3.

CHAMIER (D.) Lunacy Law. pp. 104. 1892. 12°. Wilson's Legal Handy Books. |6426. aaa. 39.

ELMER (J.) Practice in Lunacy under Commissions and Inquisitions. pp. 481. *Lond.* 1892. 8°.   2232. c. 1.

G. B. & I. Victoria, *Queen.* Rules in Lunacy. 1893. pp. 5. *Lond.* 1893. 8°. 6190. cc. 4. (10.)

HUGGARD (W. R.) The Lunacy Law : its defects. pp. 7. *Lond.* 1885. 8°.   Pam. 32.

LEWIS (G. P.) The Insane and the Law. pp. 432. *Lond.* 1895. 8°.   6095. c. 27.

MERCIER (C.) Lunacy Law for medical men. pp. 148. *Lond.* 1894. 8°.   6426. aaa. 25.

POPE (H. M. R.) Treatise on the Law and practice of Lunacy. pp. 573. *Lond.* 1890. 8°.
          2018. c.

SEMELAIGNE (R.) De la Législation sur les Aliénés dans les Iles Britanniques. pp. 136. *Paris*, 1892. 8°.   6426. e. 11.

MORIN (G.) Les Interdits devant la loi. pp. 29. *Paris*, 1891. 8°.   Pam. 34.

THIERRY (H.) De la Responsabilité atténuée. pp. 240. *Paris*, 1891. 8°.   6095. d. 34.

LEPPMANN (A.) Die Sachverständigen-Thätigkeit bei Seelenstörungen. pp. 273. *Berl.* 1890. 8°.   5604. g. 15.

See also MEDICINE, *Legal.*

INSCRIPTIONS.

Assyrian and Babylonian.

See ASSYRIA, *Antiquities.*

Egyptian. *See* EGYPT, *Antiquities.*

English. *See* EPITAPHS.

Etruscan.

PAULI (C.) Corpus Inscriptionum Etruscarum. *Lipsiæ*, 1893, *etc.* fol.   7701. k.

INSCRIPTIONS.—Oriental—*continued.*

WRIGHT (W.) Phœnician and Cypriote Inscriptions. pp. 8. *Lond.* 1887. 8°. 7704. e. 17. (15.)

EUTING (J.) Sinaïtische Inschriften. pp. 92. *Berl.* 1891. 4°. 7703. g. 27.

HOUDAS (O.) and BASSET (R.) Épigraphie tunisienne. pp. 40. *Alger*, 1882. 4°. 7707. aaa. 49.

INDIA. *Archæological Survey.* Epigraphia Indica. *Calcutta*, 1888, *etc.* fol. 7708. f.

BHAVNAGAR. *Archæological Department.* Collection of Prakrit and Sanskrit Inscriptions. pp. 233. *Bhavnagar*, 1894. fol. 14058. d. 6.

RICE (B. L.) Epigraphia Carnataca. Inscriptions in Mysore. *Bangalore*, 1894, *etc.* 4°. 14058. c. 8.

CUNHA RIVARA (J. H. da) Inscripções lapidares da India portugueza. 1894. 8°. Ac. Lisbon. *Sociedade de Geographia.* Boletim. Ser. 13. No. 8. Ac. 6020.

BERGAIGNE (A.) Inscriptions sanscrites de Campa. 1893. 4°. Notices et extraits des Manuscrits. Tom. 27. Bar. T. u.

RADLOV (V.) Die alttürkischen Inschriften der Mongolei. *St. Petersburg*, 1894, *etc.* 8°. 758. h. 40.

Ac. Helsingfors. *Suomen Muinaismuisto-Yhtiö.* Inscriptions de l'Iénissei. pp. 17. *Helsingfors*, 1889. fol. † 7701. k. 3.

—— Inscriptions de l'Orkhon. pp. 48. *Helsingfors*, 1892. fol. 7705. i. 18.

Roman. *See supra :* LATIN.

Runic. *See* RUNIC INSCRIPTIONS.

Semitic. *See supra :* Oriental.

INSECTS.

General.

Ac. London. *Entomological Society.* Catalogue of the Library. pp. 312. *Lond.* 1893. 8°. 011902. h. 45.

—— London. *City of London Entomological Society.* Transactions, *etc.* *Lond.* 1891, *etc.* 8°. Ac. 3652.

—— Paris. *Société Entomologique.* Bulletin des séances. *Paris*, 1891, *etc.* 8°. Ac. 3609/3.

—— Philadelphia. *Academy of Natural Sciences.* Entomological News. *Phila.* 1890, *etc.* 8°. Ac. 3051/6.

—— Stockholm. *Entomologiska Föreningen.* Uppsatser i praktisk Entomologi. *Stockholm*, 1891, *etc.* 8°. Ac. 3647/2.

—— Toronto. *Entomological Society.* Annual Report. *Toronto*, 1892, *etc.* 8°. Ac. 3690/2.

ADLERZ (G.) Om digestionssekretionen hos Insekter. pp. 51. 1890. 8°. Stockholm. *Vetenskaps Academien.* Bihang till Handlingar. Bd. 16. Afd. 4. Ac. 1070/7.

BADENOCH (L. N.) Romance of the Insect world. pp. 298. *Lond.* 1893. 8°. 7297. aaa. 39.

COMSTOCK (J. H.) and (A. B.) Manual for the study of Insects. pp. 701. *Ithaca*, 1895. 8°. 7296. cc. 3.

DIBDIN (E.) Some common Insects. pp. 148. *Lond.* 1895. 8°. 7296. b. 8.

GRABER (V.) Vergleichende Studien am Keimstreif der Insecten. 1890. fol. Ac. Vienna. *K. Akademie der Wissenschaften.* Denkschriften. Math.-naturwissenschaftliche Classe. Bd. 57. Ac. 810/13.

KIRBY (W. F.) Elementary text-book of Entomology. pp. 281. *Lond.* 1892. 8°. 2251. i. 5.

MIALL (L. C.) Natural history of aquatic Insects. pp. 395. *Lond.* 1895. 8°. 7298. aaa. 26.

NAGEL (W.) Die niederen Sinne der Insekten. pp. 67. *Tübingen*, 1892. 8°. 7297. c. 18. (12.)

INSECTS.—General—*continued.*

SCHROEDER (C.) Entwickelung der Raupenzeichnung. pp. 67. *Berl.* 1894. 8°. Pam. 42.

XAMBEU (P. J. V.) Mœurs et métamorphoses d'Insectes. 1891. 8°. Ac. Lyons. *Société Linnéenne.* Annales. N.S. Tom. 38. Ac. 2817/2.

PIGOTT (T. D.) London Birds and Insects. pp. 168. *Lond.* 1892. 8°. 7206. cc. 6.

KARSCH (F.) Die Insecten der Berglandschaft Adeli im Hinterlande von Togo. 1893, *etc.* 8°. Ac. Berlin. *Entomologischer Verein.* Zeitschrift. Bd. 38. Ac. 3625.

SCHÖTT (H.) Beiträge zur Kenntniss der Insektenfauna von Kamerun. 1894, *etc.* 8°. Ac. Stockholm. *K. Vetenskaps-Akademien.* Bihang till handlingar. Bd. 19. Ac. 1070/7.

Ac. Prague. *Gesellschaft für Physiokratie.* Catalogus Insectorum faunae bohemicae. *Prag.* 1892, *etc.* 8°. 7298. ccc.

TWAMLEY, afterwards MEREDITH (L. A.) Bush Friends in Tasmania: native Insects, *etc.* pp. 76. *Lond.* 1891. fol. 7028. h. 14.

HUDSON (G. V.) Elementary Manual of New Zealand Entomology. pp. 128. *Lond.* 1892. 8°. 7297. b. 23.

See also PALAEONTOLOGY : ZOOLOGY ; and for each Order, Genus or Species under the name required.

Economic Entomology : Noxious Insects.

U.S. *Department of Agriculture.* Bibliography of contributions to American economic Entomology. *Wash.* 1889, *etc.* 8°. 7053. c. 38.

Ac. Calcutta. *Indian Museum.* Notes on economic Entomology. *Calcutta*, 1888, *etc.* 8°. 7297. h. 13.

AUSTRALIA. Destructive Insects of Australia. pp. 27. *Melbourne*, 1890. 8°. Pam. 42.

BOS (J. R.) Zoologie für Landwirte. pp. 182. 1892. 8°. Thaer Bibliothek. Bd. 78. 7078. d.

—— Agricultural Zoology. pp. 256. *Lond.* 1894. 8°. 7204. a. 30.

BUTLER (E. A.) Our household Insects. pp. 344. *Lond.* 1893. 8°. 7298. aaa. 22.

FRITZ (N.) De danske skadelige Naaletræinsekter. pp. 84. *Kjøbenh.* 1892. 8°. 7297. f. 19.

FRENCH (C.) Handbook of the destructive Insects of Victoria. *Melbourne*, 1891, *etc.* 8°. 7298. c.

G. B. & I. *Board of Agriculture.* Report of the Intelligence Department on injurious Insects. *Lond.* 1891, *etc.* 8°. Ac. 3484/2.

—— Special Report on the Diamond-back moth caterpillar. pp. 30. *Lond.* 1891. 8°. 7297. c. 18. (4.)

HAGEMANN (A. O. C.) Vore norske Forstinsekter eller de for Skovene skadelige Insekter i Norge. pp. 144. *Christiania*, 1891. 8°. 7297. a. 49.

HENSCHEL (G.) Die Insecten-Schädlinge in Ackerland und Küchengarten. pp. 232. *Leipz.* 1890. 8°. 7297. a. 41.

METZGER (A.) and MUELLER (N. J. C.) Die Nonnenraupe und ihre Bakterien. pp. 160. 1895. 8°. WEISE (W.) Mündener forstliche Hefte. Beiheft I. 7078. dd.

MONTILLOT (L.) Les Insectes nuisibles. pp. 360. *Paris*, 1891. 8°. 7297. a. 44.

ORMEROD (E. A.) Text-book of agricultural Entomology. pp. 238. *Lond.* 1892. 8°. 7297. aa. 35.

—— Paris-Green as a means of destruction of orchard moth caterpillars. pp. 8. *Lond.* 1891. 8°. 7298. d. 3. (7.)

—— Preliminary observations on the Sugar-cane Shot-borer Beetle (Xyleborus perforans). pp. 24 *Lond.* 1892. 8° Pam. 42.

INSURANCE.—General and Life—_cont._

LIFE ASSURANCE BONDAGE.   Life Assurance
bondage. pp. 176. 1892. 8°.   Common Sense
Series.   8277. a

LINDSAY (C. S.)   Negotiable Bond policy.
pp. 29. _Lond._ 1895. 16°.   8228. aa. 63.

LIVERPOOL   _Pioneer Life Assurance Company._
Prospectus. pp. 42. _Liverp._ 1891. 8°. Pam. 23.

MAC CLINTOCK (E.)   On the effects of Selection.
pp. 87. _N.Y._ 1892. 8°.   08227. g. 35.

MACLEAN (J. G.)   Prices of Insurance Companies'
shares, 1891. _Stirling,_ 1892. fol.
                                          1882. d. 2. (68.)

MEMORANDA.   Memoranda for Life Assurance
agents. pp. 37. _Lond._ 1891. 8°.
                                          8228. aaaa. 17. (10.)

MONILAWS (W. M.)   Surplus Funds of Life
Assurance Offices. _Leeds,_ 1887. 4°. 8225. g. 28.

—— Companion to "Surplus Funds": analysis
of reports of Life offices for the last three years.
pp. 105. _Edinb._ 1894. 8°.   8225. aa. 45.

MORRELL (C. F.)   Insurance.   Manual of law.
pp. 284. _Lond._ 1892. 8°.   6375. aaa. 52.

NEW YORK.   Insurance laws of the State of New
York. pp. 162. _N.Y._ 1892. 8°.   06616 k. 5.

PAXTON (R. L.)   Catchpenny Assurance. pp. 10.
Lond. 1894. 16°.   Pam. 23.

P.P. _London._   The Insurance File.   Reproductions of annual reports and balance sheets of
Insurance offices. _Lond._ 1892, _etc._ obl. 8°.
                                          8206. f. 29.

—— Equitable Record.   Equitable Life Assurance society of the U.S.   _Lond._ 1894, _etc._ 4°.
                                          N.R.

ROSE (T. G.)   Costless Life Assurance.   Guide
to offices yielding 2 and 4 per cent. compound
interest on policies. pp. 20. _Lond._ 1893. 8°.
                                          08226. h. 14. (14.)

ROTHERY (H. J.) and RYAN (G. H.)   Premium
Conversion tables. pp. 199. _Lond._ 1893. 8°.
                                          8548. df. 35.

SPENSLEY (C.)   Thousand tips about Life Assurance offices. _Sheffield,_ 1893. 8°. 1882. d. 2. (80.)

STOLK (R. W. v.)   Onderlinge Assurantie.
pp. 87. _Leiden,_ 1891. 8°.   5685. aa. 3.

TATHAM (J.)   Manchester Life Table.   pp. 33.
Manch. 1892. 8°.   08227. k. 31. (9.)

TYPALDO-BASSIA (A.)   Les Assurances sur la vie.
pp. 279. _Paris,_ 1892. 8°.   08227. f. 36.

WAGNER (A.)   Le Assicurazioni.   1889. 8°.
Biblioteca dell' economista.   Ser. 3.   Vol. 13.
                                          8205. k.

WEILL-MANTOU (J.)   Assurances sur la Vie.
pp. 197.   1893. 8°.   Encyclopédie des aide-
mémoire.   8709. g.

WILKIE (J.)   Life Assurance agent's vade-mecum.
pp. 65. _Edinb._ 1894. 8°.   8548. b. 36.

_____

MÂREAU (E.)   Dictionnaire de Médecine à l'usage
des Assurances sur la vie.   pp. 435.
Paris, 1890. 12°.   7321. b. 22

POLLOCK (J. F.) and CHISHOLM (J.)   Medical
handbook of Life Assurance.   pp. 214.
Lond. 1895. 8°.   7390. f. 9.

_Working Classes' Insurance, Accident,
Sickness, etc._

ADLER (G.)   Die Versicherung der Arbeiter
gegen Arbeitslosigkeit in Basel. pp. 72.
Basel, 1895. 8°.   8275. f. 29.

BELLOM (M.)   Les Lois d'Assurance ouvrière à
l'Étranger. _Paris,_ 1892, _etc._ 8°.   6005. h. 4.

DREXLER (A.)   Das Recht auf Arbeit und die
Arbeiterversicherung. pp. 36. _Basel,_ 1894. 8°.
                                          Pam. 82.

INSURANCE.—General and Life—_cont._

GIGOT (A.)   Les Assurances ouvrières et le
Socialisme d'état. pp. 27. _Paris,_ 1895. 8°.
                                          Pam. 82.

GRENTHE (L.)   Prévoyance et mutualité.   Essai
d'un projet, _etc._ pp. 155. _Pontoise,_ 1894. 8°.
                                          08275. f. 28.

LUDWIG (F.)   Der industrielle Lebensversicher-
ungs. pp. 48. _Hagen,_ 1892. 8°.
                                          08227. g. 47. (10.)

MACKAY (T.)   Insurance and Saving.   1892. 8°.
Charity Organisation Series.   08276. f

MANDL (M.)   Oesterreichische Gesetze über Arbeiterversicherung. 1893, _etc._ 16°. GELLER (L.)
Oesterreichische Gesetze.   Hft. 38. 5511. aaa.

MARTINET (A.)   Les Sociétés de secours mutuels
et les Assurances ouvrières.   pp. 312.
Paris, 1891. 8°.   8282. f. 27

MENZEL (A.)   Die Arbeiterversicherung nach
österreichischen Rechte. pp. 504.
Leipz. 1893. 8°.   05549. h. 1

P.P. _London._   Insurance Industrial pocket chart.
Lond. 1894, _etc._ 8°.   P.P. 2501. fad.

ROSENBERG (G. J.)   Zur Arbeiterschutzgesetz-
gebung in Russland. pp. 156. _Leipz._ 1895. 8°.
                                          5756. d. 9.

SCHMIEGEL (A.)   Die Organe der sozialpolitischen
Gesetzgebung in Sachsen. pp. 57.
Dresden, 1890. 8°.   08276. f. 20. (12.)

SMITH (J.)   More light; secret of Industrial Life
Assurance. pp. 51. _Glasg._ 1892. 8°.
                                          8228. aaaa. 19. (9.)

VILLETARD DE PRUNIÈRES (M.)   De l'Assurance
contre les Accidents du travail, _etc._ pp. 458.
Paris, 1892. 8°.   08227. i. 10.

_____

ARBEITERFREUND.   Die Arbeiterfrage **und die**
Arbeiter-Versicherungsgesetze. pp. 50.
Pilsen, 1893. 8°.   Pam. 82.

BLASIUS (H.)   Unfallversicherungsgesetz und
Arzt. pp. 150. _Berl._ 1892. 8°.   6095. f. 28.

GEBHARD (H.)   Die nach dem Invaliditäts- und
Altersversicherungsgesetze versicherten Personen. pp. 328. _Berl._ 1893. 8°.   08225. k. 7.

GERMANY.   Die Invaliditäts- und Altersversicherung der Arbeiter nach dem Reichsgesetz 1889.
pp. 67. _Berl._ 1891. 8°.   8277. ee. 33. (6.)

HABRICH (L.)   Die Arbeiterversicherungen des
deutschen Reiches.   pp. 162.
Düsseldorf, 1893. 8°.   8277. ee 47.

JUST (   )   Das Reichsgesetz betreffend die In-
validitäts- und Altersversicherung, 1889.
pp. 564. _Berl._ 1892. 8°.   05604. i. 10.

RIESENFELD (C. E.)   Das besondere Haftpflicht-
recht der deutschen Arbeiter-Versicherungs-
Gesetze. pp. 313. _Berl._ 1894. 8°. 05604. i. 28.

WOEDTKE (E. v.)   Unfallversicherungsgesetz
und Gesetz über die Ausdehnung der Unfall- und
Krankenversicherung. pp. 328. _Berl._ 1890. 8°.
                                          5606. a. 9.

—— Das Reichsgesetz betreffend die Invalidi-
täts- und Altersversicherung. pp. 201.
Berl. 1889. 8°.   5606. a. 10.

See also infra : Pensions.

For the Insurance of seamen, _see infra : Marine._

Agricultural.

ARENTS (C. R.)   Tree Insurance.   _N.Y._ 1894. 8°.
                                          08226. k. 4. (7.)

MAVET (P.)   Agricultural Insurance. pp. 388.
Lond. 1893. 8°.   08227. g. 44.

SARRAZIN (F.)   Die Naturgesetze des Hagels und
die Hagelversicherung. pp. 50.
Lichterfelde, 1890. 8°.   Pam 79.

INSURANCE.—Agricultural—*continued*

SUCHSLAND (H.) Die Hagelversicherungsfrage in Deutschland. pp. 170. 1890. 8°. Ac. Halle. *Academia Fridericiana.* CONRAD (J.) Sammlung nationalökonomischer Abhandlungen. Bd. 7.   Ac. 2320.

Fire Insurance.

CLEMENT (G. A.) Digest of Fire Insurance decisions. pp. 690. *N.Y.* 1893. 8°. 06616. k. 13.

FIRE INSURANCE CHART. Fire Insurance chart, 1891. *Lond.* 1892. *etc. obl.* 8°. 1882. d. 2. (104.)

GEMMELL (J.) Economical aspects of Fire Insurance. 1884. 8°. Glasgow. *Insurance Society.* Transactions. No. 12. 08227. e.

LANE (J. N.) Practice of Fire Insurance in the U.S. 1893. 8°. Glasgow. *Insurance Society.* Transactions. 3rd series. No. 7. 08227. e.

MALLETT (R. F.) Classification of Fire risks. pp. 66. 254. *Norwich,* 1894. 4°. 8228. k. 35.

OSTRANDER (D.) Law of Fire Insurance. pp. 670. *Chicago,* 1892. 8°. 6615. h. 14.

P.P. *London.* Insurance Fire pocket chart. *Lond.* 1894, *etc.* 4°. P.P. 2501. fad.

RASCH (W.) Zur Frage des Versicherungswertes in der Feuerversicherung. pp. 100. 1892. 8°. Ac. Halle. *Academia Fridericiana.* CONRAD (J.) Sammlung statistischer Abhandlungen. Bd. 8. Hft. 2. Ac. 2320.

RELTON (F. B.) Account of Fire Insurance Companies during the 17th and 18th centuries. pp. 562. *Lond.* 1893. 8°. 8248. f. 21. *See also supra: General.*

Marine.

AUKLAND (T. F.) Marine Insurance. pp. 47. 1893. 8°. London. *Shipmasters' Society.* Papers. Session 4. 1890, *etc.* 8°. 8806. cc.

BENEKE (M. P.) Die geschichtliche Entwicklung des Ristorno in der Seeversicherung. pp. 41. *Berl.* 1891. 8°. Pam. 32.

D., J. T. Our next War. A word on War Premiums. pp. 62. *Lond.* 1893. 8°.
    08227. g. 47. (15.)

GOW (W.) Marine Insurance. pp. 401. 1895. 8°. Macmillan's Commercial class-books.
    012202. h.

GREY (H. M.) Lloyd's yesterday and to-day. pp. 96. *Lond.* 1893. 8°. 08227. f. 44.

TYSER (C. R.) Law relating to losses under a policy of Marine Insurance. pp, 232. *Lond.* 1894. 8°. 6835. c. 12.

UNDERWRITING. On Underwriting. pp. 47. *Lond.* 1890. 8°. 8228. aa. 48.

GEBHARD (H.) Die Versicherung der Seeleute. *Berl.* 1892, *etc.* 8°. 08227. ee.

LANNA (A. v.) Die Unfallversicherung österreichischen Seeleute. pp. 62. *Leipz.* 1894. 8°.
    8277. dd. 13.

Pensions for Old Age.

ATKINSON (A.) National Insurance and Pension scheme. pp. 16. *Bradford,* 1894. 8°.
    8282. cc. 47. (12.)

BRAMSEN (L.) Sur quelle base pourrait-on créer une Caisse nationale de Retraite. pp. 68. *Copenhague,* 1891. 8°. 8277. de. 28. (7.)

DRAGE (G.) Problem of the aged Poor. pp. 375. *Lond.* 1895. 8°. 08275. f. 30.

EATON (D. C.) Pensions. pp. 97. *New Haven,* 1893. 8°. 08227. h. 34.

FOWLE (V. de S.) The Poor Law, Friendly Societies and old age destitution. pp. 23. *Oxf.* 1892. 8°. Pam. 82.

GIRARD (P.) La Caisse nationale des Retraites. pp. 23. *Angers,* 1891. 8°. 8228. aaaa. 17. (20.)

INSURANCE.—Pensions, Old Age—*cont.*

JACKSON (R.) How to obtain an old age Pension. pp. 16. *Lond.* 1895. 8°. Pam. 82.

"M." A Prosperous kingdom. Problem of pensions for old age. pp. 53. *Lond.* 1892. 8°.
    Pam. 82.

ORMEROD (J. R.) Scheme for the formation of Pension Assurance societies. pp. 16. *Warrington,* 1893. 8°. 8228. aaaa. 17. (20.)

PENSIONS. Pensions for all at sixty and an eight hours day. pp. 45. *Lond.* 1892. 8°. 8257. aa. 61

ROBERTSON (J.) New light on the question of old age Pensions by proposed formation of the Glasgow Mutual Aid Association. pp. 6. *Glasg.* 1893. 8°. 08227. g. 47. (14.)

SÉRULLAZ (G.) Les sociétés de Secours mutuels et la question des Retraites. pp. 44. *Lyon,* 1890. 8°. 8276. g. 42.

SHARP (D.) Scheme for a national System of Rest-Funds or Pensions. pp. 16. *Lond.* 1892. 8°. 8277. ee. 28. (17.)

SINCOCK (J. B.) Old Age Pensions and life insurance tables. pp. 7. *Bridgwater,* 1892. 8°.
    08227. g. 47. (13.)

SPENDER (J. A.) The State and Pensions in old age. pp. 165. *Lond.* 1892. 8°. 08276. e. 34.

TAYLOR (W.) State Pensions. *Bristol,* 1892. 8°.
    8277. ee. 28. (19.)

TULLIS (J.) Old Age Pensions. A scheme for the formation of a Citizens' National Union. pp. 39. *Glasg.* 1892. 8°. 8282. g. 24. (6.)

WECKESSER (F. J. G.) Guerre au paupérisme, ou tous rentiers par l'affiliation à la Caisse de Retraite. pp. 23. *Brux.* 1894. 8°. Pam. 82.

WILKINSON (J. F.) Pensions and pauperism. pp. 127. *Lond.* 1892. 8°. 8277. a. 62. *See also supra: Working Classes.*

INTEREST AND DISCOUNT TABLES.
See READY RECKONERS: TABLES.

INTESTINES. JESSETT (F. B.) Surgical diseases of the Intestines. pp. 327. *Lond.* 1892. 8°. 7480. de. 10.

NOTHNAGEL (H.) Die Erkrankungen des Darms und des Peritoneum. 1895, *etc.* 8°. Specielle Pathologie, *etc.* Bd. 11. 7441. d.

PICK (A.) Vorlesungen über Magen- und Darmkrankheiten. *Leipz.* 1895. 8°. 7630. ddd.

BARLING (G.) On Appendicitis. pp. 92. *Birmingham,* 1895. 8°. 7482. g. 19.

BERTHELIN (L.) Complications hépatiques de l'Appendicite. pp. 140. *Paris,* 1895. 4°.
    7620. ee. 38.

DAMAYE (L.) Du traitement chirurgical de l'Appendicite. pp. 107. *Paris,* 1895. 4°.
    7481. k. 3.

HAWKINS (H. P.) Diseases of the Vermiform Appendix. pp. 139. *Lond.* 1895. 8°.
    7630. h. 34.

JONNESCO (T.) and JUVARA (E.) Anatomie des ligaments de l'Appendice vermiculaire. pp. 57. *Paris,* 1895. 8°. 7419. f. 11.

KELYNACK (T. N.) Contribution to the pathology of the Vermiform Appendix. pp. 223. *Lond.* 1893. 8°. 7620. df. 34.

LENNANDER (K. G.) Über Appendicitis. pp. 24. 1893. 8°. VOLKMANN (R. v.) Sammlung klinischer Vorträge. N.F. Nr. 75. 7441. g.

TALAMON (C.) Appendicitis and perityphlitis. pp. 239. *Edinb.* 1893. 8°. 7630. aaa. 35. *See also* HERNIA.

INVENTIONS. BAYLY (J. P.) Universal information for Inventors. pp. 20. *Lond.* 1892. 8°. 6145. aa. 37. (3.)

INVENTIONS—*continued.*

HUBERT (P. G.) Inventors. pp. 299. 1894. 8°.
Men of achievement. 10601. df.

KENYON (E. C.) T. A. Edison, the telegraph-boy
who became a great Inventor. pp. 128.
Lond. 1895. 8°. 10882. aa. 48.

MARTIN (J.) Chats on Invention. pp. 142.
Lond. 1894. 8°. 8768. cc. 31.

P.P. *Liverpool.* Discovery. Devoted to invention. 2 vol. *Liverp.* 1891–92. 4°.
P.P. 1678.

PLESSNER (M.) Ein Blick auf die grossen Erfindungen des 20. Jahrhunderts. *Berl.* 1892, *etc.* 8°.
8709. k.

REULING (W.) Die Anrechte der Auftraggeber
an den Erfindungen ihrer Beauftragten. pp. 28.
Berl. 1892. 8°. Pam. 34.

ROUTLEDGE (R.) Discoveries and Inventions of
the 19th century. pp. 681. *Lond.* 1891. 8°.
8768. c. 22.

SAMTER (H.) Buch der Erfindungen. pp. 1027.
Berl. 1893. 8°. 8705. cc. 32.

TEMPLE (R.) and (C.) Invention and Discovery.
pp. 442. *Lond.* 1892. 8°. 7942. f. 29.

THWAITE (B. H.) Cultivation of the Inventive
Faculty. pp. 16. *Lond.* 1894. 8°.
08275. ee. 21. (15.)

See also INDUSTRIES : PATENTS.

INVENTORIES. MÉLY (F. de) and BISHOP
(E.) Bibliographie des Inventaires imprimés.
Paris, 1892, *etc.* 8°. 011900. f.

Ac. Paris. *Société des Bibliophiles.* Inventaire
des meubles du Château de Pau, 1561–62, *etc.*
pp. 235. *Paris,* 1892. 4°. Ac. 8933/13.

—— Rambouillet. *Société Archéologique.* Inventaires de l'Hôtel de Rambouillet en 1652–71.
pp. 191. *Tours,* 1894. 8°. Ac. 5340/5.

—— Rouen. *Société de l'histoire de Normandie.*
FÉLIX (J.) Inventaire de P. Surreau, Receveur
Général de Normandie. pp. 444.
Rouen, 1892. 8°. Ac. 6890/28.

ANNE, *of Austria, Queen of France.* Inventaire
après décès de la reine Anne. pp. 37.
Paris, 1892. 8°. 07703. h. 1. (4.)

GUIFFREY (J. J.) Inventaires de Jean Duc de
Berry, 1401–16. *Paris,* 1894, *etc.* 8°. 07708. k.

LA TRÉMOILLE (F. de) Inventaire de F. de La
Trémoille, 1542. pp. 214. *Nantes,* 1887. 4°.
7709. k. 32.

TAILLEBOURG. Inventaires du Château de Taillebourg. pp. 51. *La Rochelle,* 1890. 8°. Pam. 3.

INVERESK. *See* MUSSELBURGH.

INVERNESS. INVERNESS. Handbook to Inverness. pp. 66. *Inverness,* 1891. 8°.
10348. ccc. 60. (4.)

MACBAIN (A) Personal and surnames of Inverness. pp. 105. *Inverness,* 1895. 8°. 9904. bb. 9.

MACKENZIE (A.) Guide to Inverness. pp. 118.
Inverness, 1893. 8°. 10369. cc. 29.

OBAN. The Royal route, Oban to Inverness.
2 pt. *Lond.* 1887. 8°. 10369. a. 44.

WIMBERLEY (D.) The Hospital of Inverness and
Dunbar's Hospital. pp. 136.
Inverness, 1893. 8°. 8277. cc. 45.

See also MORAY : SCOTLAND, *Highlands.*

INVERTEBRATA. *See* ZOOLOGY, and under
each Family, Genus or Species.

IONA. *See* HEBRIDES.

IOWA. HARSHA (W. J.) The Story of Iowa.
pp. 341. *Omaha,* 1890. 8°. 9602. d. 1.

PERRY (W. S.) *Bp. of Iowa.* Iowa as a mission
field. pp. 10. *Davenport,* 1891. 12°. Pam. 40.

IOWA—*continued.*

RICHMAN (I. B.) J. Brown among the Quakers,
etc. pp. 239. *Des Moines,* 1894. 8°.
10882. aa. 47.

IPECACUANHA. JACQUEMET (É.) Étude
des Ipécacuanhas. pp. 326. *Paris,* 1889. 8°.
7510. dd. 13.

IPSWICH. CRISP (F. A.) Calendar of Wills
at Ipswich, 1444–1600. pp. 524. 1895. 4°.
9906. i. 15.

GLYDE (J.) Illustrations of old Ipswich. pp. 84.
Ipswich, 1889. fol. 10352. m. 9.

GRIMSEY (B. P.) Members of the Council since
1835. pp. 76. *Ipswich,* 1892. 8°. 8139. aaa. 12.

—— Freemen of the borough of Ipswich. Pt. 1.
Ipswich, 1892. 8°. 10352. c. 31.

—— Monograph on the parish of St. Nicholas,
Ipswich. pp. 136. *Ipswich,* 1891. 8°.
010358. e. 15.

IQUIQUE. CASTLE (W. M. F.) Sketch of
Iquique. pp. 54. *Plymouth,* 1887. 8°.
10480. df. 1. (3.)

IRBY. IRBY-UPON-HUMBER. Parish Register
of Irby-upon-Humber. pp. 128.
Lond. 1890. fol. 9916. f. 37.

IRELAND. [*See note on page* 1.]
For works on the United Kingdom, *see* ENG-
LAND.

Antiquities.

BONWICK (J.) Irish Druids. pp. 328.
Lond. 1894. 8°. 4503. bb. 40.

BOURKE (U. J.) Pre-Christian Ireland. pp. 235.
Dublin, 1887. 8°. 7707. aa. 41.

KNOWLES (W. J.) Irish Stone Axes and Chisels.
pp. 23. 1893. 8°. Pam. 3.

MARTIN (W. G. W.) Pagan Ireland : an archæological sketch. pp. 689. *Lond.* 1895. 8°.
7708. aa. 67.

STOKES (G. T.) Antiquities from Kingstown to
Dublin. 1893, *etc.* 8°. 7709. c.

—— Island Monasteries of Ireland. 1891. 8°.
4705. e. 34. (2.)

WAKEMAN (W. F.) Archaeologica Hibernica.
pp. 322. *Dublin,* 1891. 8°. 2258. a. 18.

WESTROPP (T. J.) Prehistoric stone Forts of
central Clare. *Dublin,* 1893. 8°. Pam. 3.

Army in.

P.P. *Dublin.* The Irish Military guide.
Dublin, 1891, *etc.* 8°. N.R.

WHITE (J. G.) Account of the Yeomanry of Ireland, 1796 to 1834. pp. 33. *Cork,* 1893. 4°.
8830. k. 26.

Church of.

FALLOW (T. M.) Cathedral Churches of Ireland.
pp. 99. *Lond.* 1894. 8°. 10390. f. 13.

IRELAND. *Church of.* Annual Conference, Belfast, 1893. Report. pp. 80. *Belfast,* 1893. 4°.
4165. g. 1.

WARREN (*Right Hon.* R. R.) The Kingdom of
Christ and the Church of Ireland. pp. 197.
Lond. 1891. 8°. 4165. c. 11.

See also infra : HISTORY, *Ecclesiastical.*

Emigration : Irish in Various Countries.

DAVIN (N. F.) The Irishman in Canada.
pp. 692. *Lond.* 1887. 8°. 9555. eee. 14.

PERRY (A. L.) Scotch Irish in New England.
pp. 55. *Bost.* 1891. 8°. 9008. g. 11. (6.)

MAC MICKEN (G.) The abortive Fenian Raid on
Manitoba. pp. 11. *Winnipeg,* 1888. 8°.
9007. ff. 5. (2.)

LE CARON (H.) Twenty-five Years in the Secret
Service. pp. 311. *Lond.* 1892. 8°. 10825. g. 2.

TYNAN (P. J. P.) Irish National Invincibles.
pp. 660. *N.Y.* 1894. 8°. 9509. c. 8.

2 I

IRELAND.—History, *Ecclesiastical—cont.*

O'ROURKE (J.) Battle of the faith in Ireland. pp. 599. *Dublin*, 1887. 8°.   4735. cc. 12.

PIKE (C.) The Story of religion in Ireland. pp. 176. *Lond.* 1895, 8°.   4735. aa. 32.

SMEDT (C. de) Acta Sanctorum Hiberniae. pp. 975. *Edinburgi*, 1888. 4°.   4828. f. 6.

STOKES (M. M.) Six Months in the Apennines; pilgrimage in search of vestiges of Irish Saints in Italy. pp. 313. *Lond.* 1892. 8°. 10136. f. 12.

—— Three Months in the Forests of France: pilgrimage in search of vestiges of Irish Saints in France. pp. 291. *Lond.* 1895. 8°.
    10171. ee. 19.

PATRICK, *Saint.* Epistles and Hymns of Saint Patrick. pp. 128. *Lond.* 1894. 8°. 4429. c. 18.

MALONE (S.) Chapters towards a life of St. Patrick. pp. 226. *Dublin*, 1892. 12°. 4824. aa. 14.

MORRIS (W. B.) Life of Saint Patrick. pp. 303. *Lond.* 1890. 8°.   4829. b. 8.

—— Ireland and Saint Patrick. pp. 307. *Lond.* 1891. 8°.   3940. cc. 9.

NEWELL (E. J.) Saint Patrick. pp. 237. 1890. 8°. Fathers for English Readers. 4421. a.

O'DONOGHUE (D.) Saint Brendan in story and legend. pp. 399. *Dublin*, 1893. 8°. 4829. bb. 9.

ADAMNAN, *Saint.* Adamnani Vita S. Columbae. Edited by J. T. Fowler. pp. 201. *Oxf.* 1894. 8°.   4829. cc. 1.

ZIMMER (H.) The Irish Element in mediæval culture. pp. 139. *N.Y.* 1891. 12°. 4535. bb. 13.

CHARLES (E.) Early Christian missions of Ireland. pp. 425. *Lond.* 1893. 8°.   4429. c. 1.

ROTH (D.) *R.C. Bp. of Ossory.* The Analecta. pp. 608. *Dublin*, 1884. 8°.   4735. bb. 29.

IRELAND. Les Martyrs de la province dominicaine d'Irlande. pp. 107. *Paris*, 1890. 8°.
    4829. c. 4.

CARR (J. A.) Life and times of J. Ussher, Archbp. of Armagh. pp. 398. *Lond.* 1895. 8°.
    4955. ee. 28.

O'REILLY (B.) J. MacHale, Archbp. of Tuam. 2 vol. *N.Y.* 1890. 8°.   4956. h. 3.

See also PRESBYTERIANISM : ROMAN CATHOLIC CHURCH, *in Ireland.*

Land Tenure, etc. *See* LAND TENURE.

Law.

DRUMMOND (M.) and SMITH (P. L.) Rules of the Supreme Court, Ireland, 1891. pp. 628. *Dublin*, 1891. 8°.   6503. e. 2.

IRELAND. Supreme Court. Crown Office rules. 1891. pp. 98. *Dublin*, 1891. 8°. 6503. bb. 14.

RHADAMANTHUS. Our Judges. pp. 132. *Dublin*, 1890. 8°.   6503. aa. 11.

See also COUNTY COURTS : LAW, *Criminal.*

Parliament. *See supra :* History.

Politics.
1886–89.

ASHBURNHAM (B.) *Earl of Ashburnham.* English Catholics and home rule. pp. 8. *Lond.* 1886. 8°.
    8146. bb. 33. (3.)

BAGSHAWE (E. G.) *R.C. Bp. of Nottingham.* Monstrous Evils of English rule in Ireland. pp. 23. *Nottingham*, 1886. 8°.   Pam. 68.

LONDON. *British Home Rule Association.* British Home Rule Association publications. *Lond.* 1886, *etc.* 8°.   8146. aaa.

—— *Liberal Unionist Association.* The Case for the Union. *Westminster*, 1886–90. 8°.
    8146. bb. 32.

O'BRIEN (R. B.) Articles on Ireland. 1886. 8°. P.P. Dublin. *Freeman's Journal.* Freeman Pamphlets. No. 8.   8145. f. 9.

IRELAND.—Politics—*continued.*

KINGSLEY (J.) Irish Nationalism. pp. 52. *Lond.* 1887. 8°.   8146. bb. 33. (6.)

BALFOUR (*Right Hon.* A. [J.) Mr. Balfour's coercion record in Ireland, 1887–88. pp. 23. 1888. 8°. P.P. Dublin. *Freeman's Journal.* Freeman Pamphlets. No. 17.   8145. f. 9.

GLADSTONE (*Right Hon.* W. E.) Coercion in Ireland. Speech, Feb. 17, 1888. pp. 31. *Lond.* 1888. 8°.   Pam. 68.

—— Treatment of the Irish Members. Speech, Aug. 20, 1888. pp. 20. *Lond.* 1888. 8°.
    8146. cc. 5. (6.)

IRELAND. Scenes from the triumph of "Law and Order" in Ireland under the last Coercion Act. *Dublin*, 1889. fol.   1852. c. 4.

1890,

G. B. & I. *Special Commission to inquire into charges against certain Members of Parliament.* The Special Commission Act, 1888. Report of Proceedings. 4 vol. *Lond.* 1890. 4°. 8145. g. 2.

—— Handbook to the report of the Commission. pp. 116. *Lond.* 1890. 8°.   8146. c. 14.

—— Collection of newspaper cuttings upon the Special Commission. 6 vol. 1889–90. fol.
    1887. d. 6.

GLADSTONE (*Right Hon.* W. E) The Parnell Commission. Speech, March 24, 1890. pp. 23. *Lond.* 1890. 8°.   8146. cc. 5. (2.)

BALFOUR (*Right Hon.* A. J.) Mr. Balfour's tours in Connemara and Donegal. pp. 99. *Dublin*, 1890. 8°.   8146. aaa. 39.

BEESLY (E. S.) Mind your own business. Words to Gladstonians about Mr. Parnell. pp. 7. *Lond.* 1890. 8°.   8146. bb. 33. (8.)

CECIL (R. A. T. G.) *Marquis of Salisbury.* Mr. Parnell and the Irish Question. Speech, Dec. 3, 1890. pp. 15. *Lond.* 1890. 8°. 8146. cc. 6. (7.)

IRELAND. *National League.* Irish National league leaflets. *Dublin*, 1890, *etc.* 8°. 8146. d.

—— National Fidelity ; a home rule plea. pp. 4. *Lond.* 1890. 8°.   8146. cc. 6. (8.)

—— More thoughts about Ireland. pp. 17. *Lond.* 1890. 8°.   8146. cc. 5. (7.)

O'CONNELL (J. R.) Plea for a peasant proprietary for Ireland. pp. 28. *Dublin*, 1890. 8°. 8146. c. 15.

ODWYER (E. T.) *R.C. Bp. of Limerick.* Mgr. O'Dwyer et les Nationalistes irlandais. pp. 63. *Lond.* 1890. 8°.   Pam. 68.

RUSSELL (T. W.) How the Irish members got into gaol. pp. 64. *Westminster*, 1890. 8°.
    8146. cc. 5. (10.)

SMITH (S.) Speech on the difficulties of the Irish Question. pp. 24. *Liverp.* 1890. 8°.
    8146. cc. 5. (11.)

TYNDALL (J.) Mr. Gladstone's sudden reversal of Polarity. pp. 8. *Dublin*, 1890. 8°.
    8146. bbb. 51. (3.)

WANLISS (T. D.) Colonial view of home rule. pp. 31. *Dundee*, 1890. 8°.   8146. cc. 6. (9.)

1891.

ARNOLD (M.) On home rule for Ireland. pp. 14. *Lond.* 1891. 8°.   8146. bb. 33. (9.)

BECKLEY (F. J.) Surveying in the west of Ireland. pp. 62. *Lond.* 1891. 8°.
    8146. bbb. 43.

DEAN (G. A.) Irish separatists, their English and Scotch supporters. pp. 5. 122. *Towcester*, 1891. 8°.   8146. aa. 32.

KERVYN DE VOLKAERSBEKE (P. A. C.) La Lutte de l'Irlande. pp. 384. *Lille*, 1891. 8°.
    9509. bbb. 16.

LANCASTER (G.) The Landlord and home rule questions considered. pp. 26. *Glasg.* 1891. 8°.
    Pam. 82.

IRELAND.—Politics—*continued.*

MAC CARTHY (M. J. F.) Mr. Balfour's rule in Ireland. pp. 84. *Dublin.* 1891. 8°.
　　　　　　　　　　　　　8146. aaa. 40.
PARNELLITE SPLIT. The Parnellite split. pp. 196. *Lond.* 1891. 8°. 　　8146. c. 16.

1892.

BELFAST. *Ulster Unionist Convention.* Ulster Unionist Convention, June 1892. pp. 120. *Belfast,* 1892. 8°. 　　8146. bbb. 44.
CLANCHY (T. J.) Ireland in the twentieth century. pp. 44. *Dublin,* 1892. 8°.
　　　　　　　　　　　　　8146. aa. 33.
GLADSTONE (*Right Hon.* W. E.) Special aspects of the Irish Question. pp. 372. *Lond.* 1892. 8°.
　　　　　　　　　　　　　8146. aaa. 41.
—— Gladstone, Ireland, Rome. pp. 259. *Lond.* 1892. 8°. 　　3940. cc. 11.
—— Mr. Gladstone on Ulster. Speech, June 18, 1892. pp. 16. *Westminster,* 1892. 8°.
　　　　　　　　　　　　　8146. cc. 6. (11.)
GREAT BRITAIN. The Union and the unionists. *Reading,* 1892. 8°. 　　8146. cc. 6. (12.)
GREGORY (W.) John Bull and the Philistines : short history of ancient Home Rule movements. pp. 39. *Lond.* 1892. 8°. 　　Pam. 78.
IRELAND. Ireland's woes from a foreigner's point of view. pp. 22. *Lond.* 1892. 8°.
　　　　　　　　　　　　　8146. cc. 5. (13.)
—— Irish home rule and British industry. pp. 16. *Leicester,* 1892. 8°. 　8146. cc. 6. (13.)
IRISHMAN. "Hear the Right." Irishman's appeal to the British working man. pp. 10. *Armagh,* 1892. 8° 　　8146. cc. 6. (14.)
JENKINS (R. C.) Revival of the exploded doctrine of "Passive Obedience" in its recent application to the Province of Ulster. pp. 9. *Folkestone,* 1892. 8°. 　　8138. aa. 20. (5.)
LLOYD (C. D. C.) Ireland under the Land League. pp. 243. *Edinb.* 1892. 8°. 8146. cc. 1.
S., R. J. Does home rule mean Rome rule? pp. 15. *Lond.* 1892. 8°. 　8146. bb. 33. (11.)
THYNNE (R.) Plain words from Ireland. pp. 47. *Lond.* 1892. 8°. 　　8146. cc. 5. (14.)

1893.

BAGENAL (P. H. D.) The Priest in politics. pp. 212. *Lond.* 1893. 8°. 　8146. aaa. 45.
BARNABY (*Sir* N.) Christmas 1892 in Connaught. pp. 35. *Lond.* 1893. 8°. 　　Pam. 68.
BARTLETT (*Sir* E. A.) Union or separation. pp. 417. *Lond.* 1893. 8°. 　8146. b. 26.
BRYCE (*Right Hon.* J.) Home Rule Bill of 1893. Speech, Feb. 14, 1893. pp. 15. *Westminster,* 1893. 8°. 　8146. cc. 6. (17.)
BULL (J.) John Bull's Divorce suit. pp. 16. *Lond.* 1893. 8°. 　　Pam. 22.
CIVIS. The new Tyranny. Study in present day politics. pp. 24. *Lond.* 1893. 8°.
　　　　　　　　　　　　　8146. cc. 5. (16.)
DAVIN (N. F.) Home Rule. Speech. pp. 15. *Toronto,* 1893. 8°. 　8146. bbb. 51. (5.)
DAVITT (M.) Settlement of the Irish Question. Speech, April 11, 1893. pp. 20. *Westminster,* 1893. 8°. 　8146. cc. 6. (18.)
DICEY (A. V.) A Leap in the dark. pp. 239. *Lond.* 1893. 8°. 　　8145. de. 7.
DONOVAN (A.) The Irish rebellion of 1898. pp. 12. *Dublin,* 1893. 8°. 　　Pam. 6.
FILLEUL (P. V. M.) Mr. Gladstone's Home Rule bill. pp. 24. *Weston-s.-M.* 1893. 8°.
　　　　　　　　　　　　　8146. bb. 33. (13.)
FRIENDS, *Society of.* Conference of Friends upon the home rule question, April 21, 1893. pp. 70. *Lond.* 1893. 16°. 　　8146. cc. 4.

IRELAND.—Politics—*continued.*

WATSON (R. S.) Reply by a member of the Society of Friends to R. S. Watson's pamphlet, "Home Rule for Ireland." pp. 47. *Gloucester,* 1893. 8°. 　8146. bbb. 57. (9.)
GLADSTONE (*Right Hon.* W. E.) The Home Rule Bill. Speech, Feb. 13th, 1893. pp. 27. *Westminster,* 1893. 8°. 　8146. cc. 6. (19.)
G. B. & I. Victoria, *Queen.* The Home Rule Bill. Summary, 1893. pp. 12. *Westminster,* 1893. 8°. 　8146. cc. 6. (20.)
—— Outline of the Home Rule Bill. pp. 14. *Westminster,* 1893. 8°. 　8146. cc. 6. (21.)
—— The Home Rule pill. pp. 64. *Lond.* 1893. *obl.* 8°. 　　12331. ee. 29.
HIBERNICUS. New "Hibernia Pacata," or "The message of peace." pp. 35. *Dublin,* 1893. 8°.
　　　　　　　　　　　　　8146. bbb. 51. (6.)
IRELAND. The new Home Rule Policy. pp. 112. *Dublin,* 1893. 8°. 　　8146. cc. 3.
—— Lights on home rule. pp. 16. *Lond.* 1893. 8°. 　8146. cc. 6. (22.)
IRWIN (*Mrs.* E. W.) Home Rule for Ireland. pp. 104. *Wiarton,* 1893. 8°. 　8154. a. 14.
MEATH ELECTION PETITIONS. The Meath Election petitions. pp. 24. *Southwark,* 1893. 8°.
　　　　　　　　　　　　　Pam. 68.
MORTON (J.) Gladstone answered and the Irish Question solved. pp. 117. *Lond.* 1893. 8°.
　　　　　　　　　　　　　8146. cc. 2.
O'BRIEN (W.) Irish Ideas. pp. 167. *Lond.* 1893. 8°. 　　8146. bbb. 49.
O'FLANNAGAN (P.) Ireland a nation! Diary of an Irish Cabinet Minister. pp. 37. *Belfast,* 1893. 8°. 　　12315. i. 67.
REDMOND (J. E.) The Case for amnesty. pp. 16. *Dublin,* 1893. 8°. 　8146. cc. 5. (18.)
TRISTRAM (J. W.) The Home Rule Bill as it would affect Irish Protestants. *Brigg,* 1893. 8°.
　　　　　　　　　　　　　8138. aa. 20. (8.)
WILEMAN (W.) Rome Rule in Ireland and civil war. pp. 31. *Lond.* 1893. 8°. 8146. bb. 33. (14.)
WILLIAMS (A.) Home Rule. pp. 12. *Lond.* 1893. 8°. 　　8146 cc. 6. (24.)
WOLSEY-SEAMAN (W.) England's Rights and demands before home rule. pp. 42. *Lond.* 1893. 8°. 　　　　Pam. 68.

1894-95.

B., R. J. Ireland as it is and as it would be under home rule. pp. 415. *Birmingham,* 1894. 8°.
　　　　　　　　　　　　　8145. d. 1.
HAMILTON (J.) Sixty Years' experience as an Irish landlord. pp. 429. *Lond.* 1894. 8°.
　　　　　　　　　　　　　8146. b. 27.
IRISH CHARACTER. Irish Character: Mr. Gladstone's character. pp. 27. *Lond.* 1894. 8°.
　　　　　　　　　　　　　8146. bbb. 51. (10.)
LECKY (W.) Green graves in Ireland. pp. 136. *Baltimore,* 1894. 8°. 　　10390. de. 8.
HALLETT (T. G. P.) Union versus home rule. pp. 68. *Lond.* 1895. 8°. 　　8146. cc. 7.

Presbyterianism. *See* PRESBYTERIANISM.

Roman Catholic Church.

See supra: History, Ecclesiastical : ROMAN CATHOLIC CHURCH, *in Ireland.*

Topography and Social Life.

FRENCH (H. W.) Our boys in Ireland. pp. 331. *N.Y.* 1891. 8°. 　　10390. g. 19.
IRELAND. Report of the administration of the Irish Distress Fund. pp. 6. *Dublin,* 1892. 8°.
　　　　　　　　　　　　　8277. h. 19. (12.)
IRISH PEASANT. The Irish Peasant. Sociological study. pp. 164. *Lond.* 1892, 8°.
　　　　　　　　　　　　　08276. c. 38.

IRELAND.—Topography, etc.—_continued._

LE FANU (W. R.) Seventy years of Irish Life. pp. 306. _Lond._ 1893. 8°.   012330. k. 2.

MAXWELL (W. H.) Wild sports of the West of Ireland. pp. 337. _Lond._ 1892. 8°.   012634. k. 39.

BAEDEKER (C.) Great Britain. Handbook. pp. 547. _Leipz._ 1894, 8°.   2353. a.

BANIM (M.) Here and there through Ireland. 2 pt. _Dublin_, 1891, 92. 8°.   10390. de. 7.

BLACK (A.) and (C.) Guide to Ireland. pp. 369. _Lond._ 1895, 8°.   10390. aaaa. 25.

BOVET (M. A. de) Trois mois en Irlande. pp. 481. _Paris_, 1891. 8°.   10390. bb. 40.

—— Three months' tour in Ireland. pp. 7. 312. _Lond._ 1891. 8°.   10390. cc. 3.

C., J. B. Ireland in the Magic Lantern. pp. 47. _Dublin_, 1894. 8°.   10348. d. 20. (10.)

CROSSLEY (F. W.) Irish Tourist development. pp. 16. _Dublin_, 1892. 8°.   10390. f. 9.

DAGG (G. A. de M. E.) "Devia Hibernica." Road and route guide of the Royal Irish Constabulary. pp. 354. _Dublin_, 1893. 8°.   10390. bb. 44.

DOMENECH (E.) Voyages légendaires in Ireland. pp. 400. _Lyon_, 1894. 8°.   10390. g. 21.

FALLOW (T. M.) Cathedral Churches of Ireland. pp. 99. _Lond._ 1894. 8°.   10390. f. 13.

G. B. & I. Round the Coast. Album of pictures. _Lond._ 1895, _etc._ obl. fol.   1558.

—— _Hydrographic Office._ The Irish Coast pilot. pp. 520. _Lond._ 1893. 8°. 10496. g. 23.

GUY ( ) South of Ireland pictorial guide. pp. 151. _Cork._ 1891. 8°.   10390. f. 6.

HALL (M.) Notes on the geography of the British Isles. pp. 110. _Dublin_, 1895. 8°.   10348. b. 27.

HARTLAND (W. B.) Wayside Ireland. pp. 70. _Cork_, 1895. 8°.   Pam. 90.

HOLE (S. R.) A little tour in Ireland. pp. 240. _Lond._ 1892. 4°.   10390. g. 17.

HULL (E.) Physical geology and geography of Ireland. pp. 328. _Lond._ 1891. 8°.   10390. cc. 4.

P.P. _Dublin._ The Irish Tourist. _Dublin_, 1894, _etc._ 8°.   P.P. 3904. g. and 232.

—— Dublin. _Irish Times._ "Irish Times" tours in Ireland. pp. 225. _Dublin_, 1888. 8°.   10390. bb. 42.

SPURRIER (W. J.) Cyclists' Route book for Great Britain and Ireland. pp. 188. _Lond._ 1893. 8°.   10348. cc. 24.

SUMMER RESORTS. Summer Resorts. pp. 64. _Lond._ 1895. 8°.   10348. d. 22.

WAKEMAN (W. F.) Tourists' picturesque guide to Ireland. pp. 416. _Dublin_, 1890. 8°.   10390. cc. 2.

WARD (C. S.) Ireland. East, West and South. pp. 221. 1895. 8°. Thorough Guide Series. Vol. 13.   10347. aaa.

WARD, LOCK AND Co. Guide to Connemara and the western highlands of Ireland. pp. 158. _Lond._ 1891. 8°.   10390. bb. 13.

WHERE. Where shall we go? Guide to the Watering-places, _etc._ Edited by A. R. Hope Moncrieff. pp. 348. _Lond._ 1892. 8°.   10347. c. 33.

For Travels in the Eighteenth Century, _see supra_ : History ; for the Topography of the United Kingdom, _see_ ENGLAND.

Trade, etc.

GRIMSHAW (T. G.) Facts and figures about Ireland. _Dublin_, 1893, _etc._ 8°.   8223. dh. 15.

IRELAND.—Trade, etc.—_continued._

KELLER (J. B.) Industrial Ireland. pp. 48. _Lond._ 1891. 8°.   8146. cc. 5. (12.)

Irish, in Foreign Countries.

See supra : Emigration, etc.

IRIDEAE. Ac. etc. London. _Horticultural Society._ FOSTER (M.) Bulbous Irises. pp. 85. _Lond._ 1893. 8°.   7028. aaa. 4.

BALICKA-IWANOWSKA (G.) Contribution à l'étude du genre Iris, et des genres voisins. pp. 56. _Genève_, 1893. 8°.   07028. f. 53.

BAKER (J. G.) Handbook of the Irideæ. pp. 247. _Lond._ 1892. 8°.   07028. l. 6.
See also FLOWERS.

IRISH LANGUAGE AND LITERATURE. Ac. Dublin. _Gaelic Union._ The Gaelic Journal. _Dublin_, 1882, _etc._ 8°.   Ac. 9954. & 79.

—— London. _Henry Bradshaw Society._ Vol. IV. Antiphonary of Bangor ; early Irish manuscript in the Ambrosian library at Milan. Edited by F. E. Warren. _Lond._ 1893. etc. 4°.   Ac. 9929/4.

ARBOIS DE JUBAINVILLE (M. H. de) L'Épopée celtique en Irlande. 1892. etc. 8°. Cours de littérature celtique. Tom. 5, _etc._   2308. g.

BROOKE (S. A.) The need of getting Irish Literature into the English tongue. pp. 66. _Lond._ 1893. 4°.   11840. bbb. 50.

DONLEVY (A.) Introduction to the study of the Irish Language. pp. 69. _Dublin_, 1891. 8°.   12978. ee. 8.

HOGAN (E.) Latin lives of the Saints as aids towards the translation of Irish texts. pp. 140. 1894. 8°. Ac. Dublin. _Royal Irish Academy._ Todd Lecture Series. Vol. 5.   Ac. 1540/7.

HYDE (D.) Story of early Gaelic Literature. pp. 174. 1895. 8°. DUFFY (_Sir_ C. G.) New Irish Library. Vol. 6.   012208. df.

HYDE (D.) Beside the Fire. Irish folk stories [with Irish text.] pp. 203. _Lond._ 1890. 8°.   12431. k. 16.

LOTH (J.) Essai sur le Verbe néo-celtique en Irlandais. pp. 92. _Paris_, 1882. 8°.   12978. h. 9.

MAC CARTHY (B.) Codex Palatino-Vaticanus. No. 830. pp. 450. 1892. 8°. Ac. Dublin. _Royal Irish Academy._ Todd Lecture Series. Vol. 3.   Ac. 1540/7.

MAC CONGLINNE. The Vision of MacConglinne ; middle-Irish wonder tale. Edited by K. Meyer. pp. 212. _Lond._ 1892. 4°.   12411. ee. 19.

MEYER (K.) Hibernica Minora. Fragment of an old-Irish treatise on the Psalter. pp. 101. 1894. 4°. Anecdota Oxoniensia. Pt. VIII.   12204. f.

MONTGOMERY (H. R.) Specimens of early native poetry of Ireland in English metrical translations. pp. 311. _Dublin_, 1892. 8°. 11595. c. 35.

O'DONOGHUE (D. J.) The Poets of Ireland. 2 pt. _Lond._ 1892. 8°.   10803. f. 18.

O'GRADY (S. H.) Silva Gadelica : collection of tales in Irish. 2 vol. _Ir._ and _Eng._ _Lond._ 1892. 8°.   12430. l. 8.

ROSNAREE. Cath Ruis na Rig for Bóinn ; with preface and translation. By E. Hogan. pp. 282. 1892. 8°. Ac. Dublin. _Royal Irish Academy._ Todd Lecture Series. Vol. 4.   Ac. 1540/7.

DUFFY (_Sir_ C. G.) The revival of Irish Literature. pp. 161. _Lond._ 1894. 8°. 011850. eee. 4.

—— Prospects of Irish Literature for the people. pp. 12. _Lond._ 1893. 4°.   11840. m. 39. (5.)

IRISH LANGUAGE, etc.—*continued*

O'DONOGHUE (D. J.) The Poets of Ireland. 3 pt.
Lond. 1892. 8°.   10804. f. 18.

—— The humour of Ireland. pp. 434. 1894. 8°.

DIRCKS (H. H.) International Humour.
                                                     012314. g.

RYAN (W. P.) The Irish Literary revival.
pp. 184. *Lond.* 1894. 8°.   011850. f. 51.
See also BALLADS : CELTIC LANGUAGES : ENGLISH
LITERATURE : POETRY.

IRISH SEA. *See* SAINT GEORGE'S CHANNEL.

IRON AND STEEL. Ac. G. B. & I. *Iron
and Steel Institute.* The Iron and Steel Institute in America, in 1890. pp. 508.
Lond. 1892. 8°.   Ac. 4460/2.

BIRKINBINE (J.) Production of Iron Ores in
1891. 1892. 8°. U.S. *Geological Survey.*
Publications.   Pam. 27.

HOWE (H. M.) Metallurgy of Steel.
N.Y. 1891, *etc.* fol.   7107. g. 5.

KENDALL (J. D.) Iron Ores of Great Britain and
Ireland. pp. 430. *Lond.* 1893. 8°. 7106. ff. 18.

TURNER (T.) Metallurgy of Iron and Steel.
1895, *etc.* 8°. ROBERTS-AUSTEN (W. C.) New
Metallurgical Series.   07108. g.

WINCHELL (N. H.) Iron Ores of Minnesota.
pp. 430. 1891. 8°. MINNESOTA. *Geological and
Natural History Survey.* Bulletin. No. 6. 7002. i.

———

ARNOLD (J. O.) Steel Works Analysis. pp. 350.
1895. 8°. Specialist's Series.   8708. k.

CAMPREDON (L.) L'Acier : historique, fabrication, *etc.* pp. 344. *Paris*, 1890. 8°. 7104. aa. 2.

BARTLETT (J. H.) Manufacture, consumption
and production of Iron and Steel in Canada.
pp. 167. *Montreal*, 1885. 8°.   07109. e. 10.

BILLY (E. de) Fabrication de la Fonte. pp. 211.
1894. 8°. Encyclopédie des aide-mémoire.
                                                     8709. g.

COPE (G. W.) Iron and Steel interests of Chicago.
pp. 97. *Chicago*, 1890. 8°.   8829. a. 20.

EHRENWERTH (J. v.) Steiermarks Eisenindus-
trie. 1890. 8°. Culturbilder aus Steiermark.
                                                     08225. l. 4.

EWING (J. A.) Magnetic induction in Iron.
pp. 351. *Lond.* 1891. 8°.   8757. f. 23.

GUBBINS (R. R.) New system of Hot Charging
and Hot Piling Puddle Bars. pp. 8.
Erith, 1891. fol.   7943. k. 30. (5.)

HELSON (C.) La Sidérurgie en France et à
l'étranger. 2 vol. *Paris*, 1894. 8°.   7105. h. 6.

—— Plates. 1894. fol.   7105. i. 8.

HIORNS (A. H.) Iron and Steel manufacture.
pp. 180. *Lond.* 1893. 8°.   7108. a. 25.

HUNTSMAN (B.) Historique de l'invention de
l'Acier fondu, *etc.* pp. 15. *Paris*, 1888. 8°.
                                              07944. ee. 4. (6.)

JENKINS (W.) Consett Iron Company. Description of the works. pp. 96. *Newcastle*, 1893. 8°.
                                                     07944. g. 4.

JOYNSON (F. H.) Iron and Steel maker. pp. 447.
Lond. 1892. 8°.   7106. a. 43.

JUEPTER VAN JONSTORFF (H.) *Baron.* Fortschritte im Eisenhütten-Laboratorium in den
letzten 10. Jahren. *Leipz.* 1895, *etc.* 8°. 8909. dd.

LARKIN (J.) Practical Brass and Iron founder's
guide. pp. 394. *Phila.* 1892. 8°.   7106. ff. 15.

LEDEBUR (A.) Handbuch der Eisen- und Stahl-
giesserei. pp. 460. *Weimar*, 1892. 8°. 7105. bb. 2.

LUNGE (G.) Das Zeitalter des Stahles. pp. 34.
1894. 8°. Sammlung wissenschaftlicher Vorträge. N.F. Hft. 202.   12249. m.

SKELTON (H. J.) Economics of Iron and Steel.
pp 314. *Lond.* 1892. 8°.   7106. aa. 35.

SPENCER (A.) Roll-turning for sections in Steel
and Iron. pp. 11. 56 plates. *Lond.* 1891. 4°.
                                              8767. l. 25.

IRON—*continued.*

STEAD (J. E.) Report on Aluminium in Steel.
pp. 33. *Lond.* 1890. 8°.   7912. i. 43. (11.)

SWANK (J. M.) History of the manufacture of
Iron in all ages. pp. 884. *Phila.* 1892. 8°.
                                                     7109. c. 16.

TAMM (A.) Analyser å järnmalmer utförda åren
1871–90. pp. 31. *Stockholm*, 1890. 4°.
                                                     7106. i. 15.

U. S. A. *Bureau of Labour.* Cost of Production : Iron. Steel, *etc.* pp. 1404. 1891. 8°. Report of Bureau of Labour, VI.   8275. k.

VIAL (É.) Rôle du Fer dans l'organisation.
pp. 110. *Paris*, 1891. 8°.   7442. c. 27.

VOSMAER (A.) Mechanical and other properties
of Iron and Steel. pp. 203. *Lond.* 1891. 8°.
                                                     7106. b. 44.

WEDDING (H.) Basic Bessemer process. pp. 224.
N.Y. 1891. 8°.   7107. d. 2.

—— Die Eisenprobirkunst. pp. 305.
Braunschweig, 1894. 8°.   7106. bb. 34.

WILLIAMS (W. M.) Chemistry of Iron and Steel
making. pp. 420. *Lond.* 1890. 8°. 7106. a. 31.
See also METALLURGY.

IRON AND STEEL WORK. ADAMS (H.)
Practical Designing of structural Ironwork.
Lond. 1894, *etc.* 8°.   8768. ccc.

ERSKINE (F. J.) Bent Iron work. pp. 54.
Lond. 1892. 8°.   7817. e. 16.

GARDENGHI (C.) Trattato di moderne costruzioni
in Ferro. pp. 126. *Bologna*, 1889, 90. 8°.
                                                     8765. g. 19.

GARDNER (J. S.) Ironwork. pp. 152. 1893. 8°.
Ac. London. *S.K. Museum.* Art Handbooks.
                                                     2266. b. 39.

HARDY (G. A.) Complete Ironmonger. pp. 258.
Lond. 1895. 8°.   08226. h. 6.

HAVARD (H.) Les Arts de l'Ameublement. La
Serrurerie. pp. 174. *Paris*, 1893. 8°.
                                                     7808. c. 19.

HENDLEY (T. H.) Damascening on Steel or Iron.
Lond. 1892. fol.   K.T.C. 9. b. 11.

OSLET (G.) Traité de Charpente en fer. pp. 830.
1891. 8°. LACROIX (D.) Encyclopédie, *etc.*
                                                     8708. n.

PURDY (C. T.) Steel construction of Buildings.
1894. 8°. Ac. Madison. *University.* Bulletin.
Engineering Series. Vol. 1. No. 3. Ac. 1792.
See also ART, *Decorative :* METAL WORK.

IROQUOIS. *See* INDIANS.

IRRIGATION. ASSMANN (G.) Die Bewässer-
ung und Entwässerung. pp. 326.
München, 1893. 8°.   8777. d. 35.

BARKER (T. H.) Bickford system of Irrigation.
pp. 20. *Lond.* 1893. 8°.   8777. bbb. 29. (5.)

NEWELL (F. H.) Water supply for Irrigation.
1893. 4°. U.S. *Geological Survey.* Annual
Report, *etc.* No. 13. Pt. 3.   1828. aa.

SCOTT (J.) Irrigation and Water-Supply.
pp. 149. *Lond.* 1889. 8°.   8703. ccc. 45.

SUBBA RÂVA, C.K. Utilization of Irrigation
Water. 1883. 8°. MADRAS. *Agricultural Exhibition.* Report.   7959. bb. 34.

———

HANRIC (M. A.) Irrigations de la partie est de la
plaine de la Mitidja, Alger. pp. 271.
Alger, 1894. 8°.   8777. d. 36.

MYERS (F.) Irrigation : or the New Australia.
pp. 64. *Lond.* 1893. 8°.   Pam. 1.

VICTORIA. *Royal Commission on Water Supply.*
Progress reports. Irrigation in Western America,
Egypt and Italy. pp. 213. *Melbourne*, 1887. 8°.
                                                     8776. cc. 13.

IRRIGATION—continued.

EGYPT. *Ministry of Public Works.* Report on perennial Irrigation. pp. 53. 46.
Cairo, 1894. 4°.   8777. 7. 10.

—— Plans. 1894. fol.   14001. k. 23·

WHITEHOUSE (F. C.) How to save Egypt, *etc.*
pp. 12. *Lond.* 1893. 8°.   Pam. 67.

DIENNE (de) *Count.* Histoire du Desséche-
ment des lacs en France avant 1789. pp. 570.
Paris, 1891. 8°.   8777. h. 21.

BUCKLEY (R. B.) Irrigation works in India and
Egypt. pp. 348. *Paris,* 1893. 8°. 8777. h. 25.

WILSON (H. M.) Irrigation in India. 1891. 4°.
U.S. *Geological Survey.* Annual Report.
No. 12. Pt. 2.   1828. aa.

U.S. *Department of Agriculture. Irrigation
Inquiry, Office of.* Bulletin. *Wash.* 1893, *etc.* 8°.
    7053. e. 42.

WILSON (H. M.) American Irrigation engineering. 1893. 4°. U.S. *Geological Survey.* Annual Report. No. 13. Pt. 3.   1828. aa.

BILLINGHURST (G. E.) La Irrigación en Tarapacá.
pp. 193. *Santiago,* 1893. 8°.   8776. f. 28.

VIÑAS (M. A.) Estudios de la Irrigacion del
valle de la Chira. pp. 15. *Lima,* 1894. fol.
    8777. i. 8.

IRVINE. Ac. Ayr. *Archæological Association.*

DOBIE (J. S.) Muniments of the Royal Burgh
of Irvine. *Edinb.* 1890, *etc.* 8°.   Ac. 5766/3.

IRWELL, River. DAVIS (G. E) and (A. R.)

The Irwell and its tributaries. pp. 96.
Manch. 1890. 8°.   8777. aaa. 21.

ISCHIA. MATTEUCCI (D.) Una gita alle

isole d'Ischia e di Capri. pp. 30. *Jesi,* 1894. 8°.
    Pam. 91.

ISENBURG, Principality. MAYER (M.)

Geschichte der Mediatisirung des Fürsten-
thumes Isenburg. pp. 267. *München,* 1891, 8°.
    9335. l. 4.

ISÈRE, Department. BRICHET (E.) Le

Conseil Général de l'Isère, 1790–1890. pp. 95.
Grenoble, 1890. 8°.   9226. bbb. 25.
See also DAUPHINÉ.

ISLAY. *See* HEBRIDES.

ISOPODA. *See* CRUSTACEA.

ISSOIRE. LONGY (A.) Histoire d'Issoire.

pp.506. *Clermont-Ferrand,* 1890. 4°. 10172. f. 10.

ISTRIA. BELLO (N. del) La Provincia dell'

Istria. pp. 195. *Capodistria,* 1890. 8°.
    08227. ee. 37.

HOCHEGGER (A.) Gemeinde-Ordnung der Kronländer, Istrien, *etc.* 2 Bde. *Trieste,* 1893, 94. 8°.
    05549. k.

TOMASIN (P.) Die Volksstämme im Gebiete von
Triest und in Istrien. pp. 107. *Trieste,* 1890. 8°.
    10215. bb. 24.

TAMARO (M.) Le Città dell' Istria.
Parenzo, 1892, *etc.* 8°.   10125. de. 24.
See also AUSTRIA-HUNGARY.

ITALIAN LANGUAGE.
Conversation.

FIELD (M.) Travel talk in Italy. pp. 150.
Naples, 1890. 8°.   12941. aaa. 43.

LETARD (G. N.) Guida alla Conversazione
italiana. inglese e maltese.
Malta, 1891, *etc.* obl. 16°.   12902. a.

RICCARDO (F.) Dialoghi inglesi-italiani.
pp. 225. *Lond.* 1891. 16°.   12941. dc. 9.

SWAN (H.) Travellers' colloquial Italian.
pp. 107. *Lond.* 1892. 8°.   12941. aaa. 41.

Dialects.

MICHELANGELI (A.) Il Dialetto nella Lingua.
pp. 23. *Palermo,* 1892. 8°   Pam. 47.

ITALIAN.—Dialects—*continued.*

FINAMORE (G.) Vocabolario dell' Uso abruzzese. pp. 321. *Città di C.* 1892. 8°.
    12942. cc. 24.

GAUDENZI (A.) I suoni e le parole dell' odierno
Dialetto della città di Bologna. pp. 292.
Torino, 1889. 8°·   12942. bb. 37.

PIRANDELLO (L.) Laute und Lautentwickelung
der Mundart von Girgenti. pp. 52.
Halle, 1891. 8°.   12901. d. 36. (8.)

ARRIVABENE (F.) Vocabolario italiano-mantovano. pp. 110. *Mantova,* 1892. 4°. 12941. h. 31.

MARANESI (E.) Vocabolario modenese-italiano.
Modena, 1892, *etc.* 8°.   1114.

PELLEGRINI (J.) Essai d'un dictionnaire niçois,
français, italien. *Nice,* 1894, *etc.* 8°. 12942. cc.

FORTI-CASTELLI (G.) Saggio sui provincialismi
del Piemonte. pp. 84. *Mondovi,* 1892. 8°.
    12903. e. 26. (13.)

ROCCO (E.) Vocabolario del Dialetto napolitano.
Napoli, 1890 *etc.* 8°.   928.

NINNI (A. P.) *Count.* Materiali per un Vocabolario della Lingua del contado di Treviso.
2 pt. *Venezia,* 1891. 8°.   12942. bbb. 32.

ULRICH (J.) Trattati religiosi in antico Dialetto
veneziano. pp. 181. *Bologna,* 1891. 8°. 12226. cc.
See also OSCAN DIALECT.

Dictionaries.

AMBRA (F. d') Vocabolario della Lingua
italiana. pp. 1372. *Firenze,* 1891. 8°.
    12943. c. 25.

RIGUTINI (G.) and FANFANI (P.) Vocabolario
italiano della lingua parlata. pp. 1296.
Firenze, 1893. 8°.   12942. l. 4.

JAESCHKE (R.) Nutt's conversation Dictionaries.
English-Italian. pp. 424. *Lond.* 1894. 16°.
    12942. a. 50.

MELZI (B.) Nuovo Dizionario inglese-italiano e
italiano-inglese. 2 pt. *Milano,* 1892. 8°.
    12943. bb. 41.

ROBERTS (J. P.) Dizionario italiano-inglese e
inglese-italiano. 2 pt. *Firenze,* 1891. 8°.
    12942. cc. 20.

ANSTRUTHER (R. H.) and SETTEMBRINI (R.) Sea-
faring phrases, English and Italian. pp. 134.
Portsmouth, 1894. 8°.   8806. bb. 31.

For Dictionaries *etc.* of Italian Dialects, *see
supra:* Dialects.

Grammars, etc.

FERRIS (A.) Primi elementi di Grammatica
italiana. *Malta,* 1890, *etc.* 8°.   12941. aa. 47.

HUGO (C.) Simplified system. Italian.
Lond. 1890. 8°.   12902. ccc. 22.

ITALIAN LESSONS. Italian Lessons. pp. 201.
Lond. 1894. 8°.   12942. aa. 31.

PARATO (G.) and MOTTURA (C.) Nuova Grammatica della lingua italiana. pp. 148.
Torino, 1893. 8°.   12942. cc. 25.

ROSENTHAL (R. S.) Meisterschaft System.
Italian language. pp. 470. *Lond.* 1892. 8°.
    12941. b. 44.

SCARTAZZINI (G. A.) Grammaire italienne.
pp. 185. *Davos,* 1895. 8°.   12943. aaa. 34.

MENGER (L. E.) Historical development of
possessive pronouns in Italian. pp. 69.
Baltimore, 1893. 8°.   12941. h. 33.

FRANCESCHINI (G.) La Correzione delle sen-
tenze. pp. 413. *Bologna,* 1894. 8°. 5357. bb. 1.

Synonyms.

ORLANDO (G.) Dizzionario dei Sinonimi italiani.
pp. 435. *Torino,* 1892. 8°.   12932. aaa. 51.

ZECCHINI (S. P.) Dizionario delle Frasi sino-
nime. pp. 405. *Torino,* 1891. 8°. 12941. cc. 4.

ITALIAN LANGUAGE—continued.

Translation from and into Italian.

BEVIR (J. L.) Italian Passages for translation. pp. 212. *Lond.* 1891. 8°.   12227. bbb. 3.

SCOTTI (C.) Italian Composition. pp. 164. *Lond.* 1892. 8°.   12942. aaa. 43.

—— Hossfeld's Italian Prose reader. pp. 352. *Lond.* 1891. 16°.   12941. de. 10.

ITALIAN LITERATURE. ITALIAN

BOOKS. I migliori Libri italiani. pp. 434. *Milano,* 1892. 8°.   011902. i. 9.

P.P. *Pisa.* Rassegna bibliografica della Letteratura italiana. *Pisa,* 1893, *etc.* 8°.   75.

ANCONA (A. d') and BACCI (O.) Manuale della Letteratura italiana. *Firenze,* 1892, 8°.   011850. f.

BORGOGIONI (A.) Studi di Letteratura storica. pp. 376. *Bologna,* 1891. 8°.   011824. f. 43.

CANTÙ (C.) Della Letteratura italiana esempj e guidizj. *Torino,* 1891, *etc.* 8°.   2310. g.

FLAMINI (F.) Studi di storia letteraria. pp. 453. *Livorno,* 1895. 8°.   011824. e. 67.

PICCARDO-BIASCI (O.) I grandi Poeti italiani. pp. 92. *Torino,* 1893. 8°.   011824. k. 21.

SNELL (F. J.) Primer of Italian Litterature. pp. 184. 1893. 8°. Clarendon Press Series.   2320. b. 45.

SOLDINI (E.) Storia della Satira in Italia. pp. 140. *Cremona,* 1891. 8°.   11312. d. 55.

ZUMBINI (B.) Studi di Letteratura italiana. pp. 358. *Firenze,* 1894. 8°.   011850. eee. 70.

RONCA (U.) Cultura medioevale e Poesia latina d' Italia nei Secoli XI e XII. 2 vol. *Roma,* 1892. 8°.   011850. g. 26.

Ac. Florence. *Società Dantesca.* Bullettino. *Firenze,* 1890, *etc.* 8°.   Ac. 9386.

—— New York. *American Dante Society.* Year Book. *N.Y.* 1891, *etc.* 8°.   Ac. 9507.

AUVRAY (L.) Les Manuscrits de Dante des Bibliothèques de France, pp. 195. 1892. 8°. Ac. Athens. *École Française.* Bibliothèque. Fasc. 56.   Ac. 5206/2.

BARTOLINI (A.) Studi danteschi. *Siena,* 1889, *etc.* 8°.   11420. cc. 4.

BAYNES (H.) Dante and his ideal. pp. 108. *Lond.* 1891. 8°.   11420. b. 11.

BLACK (J. S.) Dante illustrations and notes. pp. 83. *Edinb.* 1890. 8°.   11420. d. 5.

BROWNING (O.) Dante; his life and writings. pp. 104. *Lond.* 1891. 8°.   11420. b. 14.

BUSCAINO-CAMPO (A.) Studii Danteschi. pp. 189. *Trapani,* 1892. 8°.   11420. d. 11.

BUTLER (A. J.) Dante; his times and work. pp. 201. *Lond.* 1895. 8°.   11420. ccc. 15.

CARBONARA-TORTONA (M. da) Studi Danteschi. *Tortona,* 1890, *etc.* 8°.   11420. cc

CRESCIMANNO (G.) Figure Dantesche. pp. 229. *Venezia,* 1893. 8°.   11420. dd. 6.

CROSS (J. W.) Impressions of Dante. pp. 314. *Edinb.* 1893. 8°.   11420. e. 20.

HENSMAN (M.) Dante Map. (Places visited or mentioned by him.) *Lond.* 1892. 16°.   11420. cc. 14.

LAJOLO (G.) Indagini sulla vita di Dante. pp. 210. *Torino,* 1893. 8°.   11421. d. 20.

LAMARTINE DE PRAT (M. L. A. de) Dante, Pétrarque, le Tasse. pp. 373. *Paris,* 1893. 12°.   11420. ccc. 10.

LUNGO (I. d.) La figurazione storica del medio evo nel poema di Dante. 2 pt. *Firenze,* 1891. 8°.   11420. e. 22.

MOORE (E.) Dante and his early biographers. pp. 181. *Lond.* 1890. 8°.   11420. c. 22.

ITALIAN LITERATURE—continued.

NATOLI (L.) Gli Studi Danteschi in Sicilia. pp. 138. *Palermo,* 1893. 8°.   11420. gg. 12.

NOBILI (E.) Dante e l'avvenire. pp. 45. *Firenze,* 1891. 8°.   11420. i. 8. (11.)

OELSNER (H.) Influence of Dante on modern thought. pp. 120. *Lond.* 1895. 8°.   11420. bb. 11.

PASSERINI (G. L.) Collezione di Opusculi danteschi. *Città di Castello,* 1893, *etc.* 8°.   11420. cc.

P.P. *Venice.* Giornale Dantesco. *Roma,* 1893, *etc.* 8°.   P.P. 4234. ba.

POLETTO (G.) Alcuni Studi su Dante. pp. 345. *Siena,* 1892. 8°.   11420. cc. 21.

PONTA (M. G.) Due Studi Danteschi. pp. 57. *Roma,* 1890. 8°.   11420. e. 23. (5.)

ROD (E.) Dante. pp. 237. *Paris,* 1891. 12°.   11420. e. 21.

SCARTAZZINI (G. A.) Dantologia. pp. 408. *Milano,* 1894. 8°.   012200. i. 7.

—— Dante-Handbuch. pp. 511. *Leipz.* 1892. 8°.   11420. e. 25.

VEDEL (V.) Dante. En Studie. pp. 301. *Kjøbenh.* 1892. 8°.   10132. aaa. 9.

VITTI (T.) Studi su Dante. pp. 63. *Napoli,* 1891. 8°.   11422. cc. 23. (8.)

WICKSTEED (P. H.) Dante. Sermons. pp. 122. *Lond.* 1890. 8°.   11421. ccc. 14.

OWEN (J.) Skeptics of the Italian renais-ance. pp. 419. *Lond.* 1893. 8°.   2217. e. 2.

SYMONDS (J. A.) Short history of the Renaissance in Italy. pp. 354. *Lond.* 1893. 8°.   9167. h. 10.

RASI (L.) I Comici italiani. *Firenze,* 1894, *etc.* 8°.   10629. h.

WERNER (A.) The Humour of Italy. pp. 315. 1892. 8°. DIRCKS (W. H.) International Humour Series.   012314. g.

KOEPPEL (E.) Studien zur Geschichte der italienischen Novelle in der englischen Litteratur des 16. Jahrhunderts. pp. 100. 1892. 8°. BRINK (B. ten) Quellen und Forschungen. Hft. 70.   2338. h.

VANZETTI (A.) Carattere della Epopea romanzesca in Italia. pp. 83. *Firenze,* 1890. 8°.   011824. f. 28. (7.)

KIENERK (G.) I Promessi Sposi e il romanzo storico in Italia. pp. 54. *Firenze,* 1893. 8°.   11825. q. 23. (4.)

SANCTIS (F. de) Studio su G. Leopardi. pp. 349. *Napoli,* 1894. 8°.   011850. eee. 69.

GUARDIONE (F.) La Letteratura contemporanea in Italia. pp. 192. *Palermo,* 1890. 8°.   011824. e. 29.

MORANDI (L.) Antologia della nostra critica Letteraria moderna. pp. 756. *Città di C.* 1893. 8°.   011850. f. 47.

ITALY. [See note on page 1.]

See also under each of the States forming the present Kingdom of Italy.

Antiquities.

PAULI (C.) Altitalische Forschungen. *Leipz.* 1885, *etc.* 8°.   7706. de.

—— Altitalische Studien. *Hannover,* 1883, *etc.* 8°.   7706. e. 16.

SANTAMARIA SCALARICCI (G.) Del sacro nome d'Italia, *etc. Bologna,* 1889. 8°.   9166. k. 8.

BONI (G.) Il Catasto dei monumenti in Italia. pp. 10. *Roma,* 1892. fol.   7705. h. 34. (7.)

See also ETRUSCANS ; OSCAN LANGUAGE : ROME : UMBRIAN LANGUAGE.

ITALY—*continued.*

Army.

AVERESCŮ (A.) Conférence sur l'organisation de l'Armée italienne. pp. 24. *Bucarest,* 1890. 8°.
8831. c. 24. (2.)

CAMOUS (E.) L'Esercito ed il problema economico-sociale in Italia. pp. 31.
Firenze, 1892. 8°.   8830. k. 32. (2.)

COLAJANNI (N.) La Difesa nazionale e le economie nelle spese militari. pp. 88.
Catania, 1892. 8°.   8823. aaa. 50.

DUPAIN (L.) L'Administration militaire italienne. pp. 284. *Paris,* 1892. 8°. 8828. ee. 33.

GOIRAN (G.) The Italian Army. 1893. 8°.
Armies of to-day.   8829. i. 9.

PARENTI (D.) Disposizioni vigenti sulle Pensioni militari. pp. 304. *Livorno,* 1892. 8°.
8826. ff. 33.

SLADE (J. R.) Handbook of the Italian Army.
pp. 86. *Lond.* 1891. 8°.   8831. ee. 15.

Z., F. P. Il Matrimonio degli ufficiali dell' esercito e la nuova legge sulle pensioni. pp. 26.
Catania, 1893. 8°.   Pam. 37.

BOSI (P.) Il Reggimento di cavalleria nizza (1°.)
pp. 302. *Milano,* 1890. 4°.   8825. g. 23.

G. B. & I. *War Office.* Cavalry manœuvres in Italy, 1890. pp. 23. *Lond.* 1891. 8°. Pam. 2.

HUMBERT I., *King of Italy.* Le grandi manovre dell' anno 1892. pp. 166. *Roma,* 1892. 8°.
8829. dd. 24.

Colonies and Emigration.

MACOLA (F.) L'Europa alla conquista dell' America latina. pp. 437. *Venezia,* 1894. 8°.
8180. f. 40.

PEZZINI (A.) L' Emigrazione nazionale. pp. 51.
Parma, 1890. 8°.   08276. k. 4. (12.)

JANNONE (G.) L' Emigrazione italiana nell' Argentina. pp. 215. *Napoli,* 1891. 8°. 7462. de. 28.

See also AFRICA, *Colonisation :* ASSAB : ERITREA.

Constitution, Government and Parliament.

RIVERA (G.) Le Istituzioni sociali italiane nella Dominazione Barbarica. pp. 248.
Lanciano 1892. 8°.   9167. i. 23.

SARDINIA AND PIEDMONT. Constitution of the Kingdom of Italy, March 4th, 1848. pp. 44.
1894. 8°. Ac. Philadelphia. *American Academy.*
Annals. Vol. 5. No. 3.   Ac. 2383.

ITALY. Leggi sulla publica sicurezza. 1865, 89.
4 pt. *Torino,* 1890. 8°.   5361. a. 4.

EPHEM. L' Almanacco dell' Italiano, contenente i nomi dei membri del governo e delle due camere, *etc.* *Roma,* 1893, *etc.* 8°. P.P. 2384. t.

GIULINI (G.) Il Decentramento dello Stato e la dislocazione delle imposte. pp. 78.
Milano, 1892. 8°.   08227. i. 30. (8.)

MICELI (V.) Carattere giuridico del governo constituzionale. *Perugia,* 1894, *etc.* 8°. 8033. h.

ORLANDO (V. E.) Principii di diritto amministrativo. pp. 376. *Firenze,* 1891. 8°. 6006. e. 16.

PALMA (L.) Corso di diritto costituzionale. 3 vol.
Firenze, 1883–85. 8°.   8010. b. 2.

PEVERELLI (E.) Il Consiglio di Stato. pp. 64.
Torino, 1891. 8°.   Pam. 70.

PUNTURO (B.) Diritto amministrativo.
Caltanissetto, 1891, *etc.* 8°.   5359. cc.

ZANICHELLI (D.) Studi politici e storici.
pp. 715. *Bologna,* 1893. 8°.   8009. bbb. 10.

COSTABILE VERRONE (   ) La Decadenza parlamentare in Italia. pp. 19. *Roma,* 1889. 8°.
8033. g. 34. (6.)

ITALY.—Constitution, etc.—*continued.*

JONA (G.) La Rappresentanza politici. pp. 339.
Modena, 1892. 8°.   8007. e. 3.

MORINI (C.) Corruzione elettorale. pp. 207.
Milano, 1894. 8°.   8032. b 40.

SARTI (T.) Il Parlamento subalpino e nazionale.
pp. 977. *Terni,* 1890. 8°.   10630. g. 23.

CORNETTE (C.) L'État civil des italiens en France.
pp. 244. *Paris,* 1889. 8°.   5424. aa. 17.

See also infra : History : Politics.

History.

General and to the Nineteenth Century.

AC. Rome. *Istituto Storico.* Bullettino.
Roma, 1886, *etc.* 8°.   Ac. 6513/2.

CHIESI (G.) Italiani illustri nella storia.
pp. 334. *Milano,* 1890. fol.   10630. h. 21.

GHISLERI (A.) Atlantino storico d' Italia. 3 pt.
Bergamo, 1891. 8°.   9166. bbb. 42.

HARRISON (F. B.) True stories from Italian History. pp. 278. *Lond.* 1891. 8°. 9166. ccc. 6.

ITALIAN LIFE. Gli Albori della vita italiana.
pp. 398. *Milano,* 1895. 8°.   9166. ccc. 23.

REINACH (J.) La France et l'Italie devant l'histoire. pp. 244. *Paris,* 1893. 8°. 9079. h. 20.

SEWELL (E. M.) Outline history of Italy.
pp. 283. *Lond.* 1895. 8°.   9167. b. 3.

VILLARI (P.) Storia politica d' Italia. 11 pt.
Milano, 1881. 4°.   9167. l. 1.

ZALLA (A.) Studi storici. pp. 328.
Firenze, 1890. 8°.   9166. ccc. 7.

HODGKIN (T.) Italy and her Invaders.
Oxf. 1892, *etc.* 8°.   2068. c.
—— Theodoric the Goth. pp. 442. 1891. 8°.
ABBOTT (E.) Heroes of the nations. Vol. 4.
10603. dd.

PROCOPIUS, *of Cæsarea.* La Guerra gotica.
1895, *etc.* 8°. Ac. Rome. *Istituto Storico.*
Fonti per la storia d' Italia. No. 23. Ac. 6543.

CARLONI (F. F.) Gl' Italiani all' Estero.
Città di C. 1888, *etc.* 8°.   10629. a.

FREEMAN (E. A.) History of federal government in Italy. pp. 692. *Lond.* 1893. 8°. 2238. e. 8.

CIPOLLA (C.) Pubblicazioni sulla Storia medioevale italiana. 1892. 8°. P.P. *Venice.* Nuovo Archivio veneto. Tom. 6.   P.P. 3556. v.

SICHIROLLO (G.) Compendio della storia d' Italia nel medio evo. pp. 440. *Lendinara,* 1890. 8°.
9165. ccc. 11.

ITALY. La Vita Italiana nel trecento. pp. 592.
Milano, 1892. 8°.   9166. ccc. 19.

BROWNING (O.) Guelphs and Ghibellines. 1256–1409. pp. 213. *Lond.* 1893. 8°. 9165. bb. 5.
—— Age of the Condottieri, 1409–1530.
pp. 275. *Lond.* 1895. 8°.   9166. ccc. 21.

BERTOLINI (F.) Storia d' Italia, 1300–1530.
Milano, 1894, *etc.* fol.   660.

VILLARI (P.) Niccolò Machiavelli e i suoi tempi.
Milano, 1895, *etc.* 8°.   10630. dd. 32.

SYMONDS (J. A.) Short history of the Renaissance in Italy. pp. 354. *Lond.* 1893. 8°. 9167. h. 10.

PICCIONE (E.) La Rinascenza greco-latina ed il risorgimento politico italiano. pp. 39.
Bologna, 1888. 8°.   8033. g. 34. (5.)

VOIGT (G.) Die Wiederbelebung des classischen Alterthums. 2 Bde. *Berl.* 1893. 8°. 11312. p. 10.

CARDUCCI (G.) La Vita italiana nel cinque-cento.
3 vol. *Milano,* 1894. 8°.   9167. c. 5.

NOLHAC (P. de) and SOLERTI (A.) Il viaggio in Italia di Enrico III., Ré di Francia. pp. 343.
Torino, 1890. 8°.   010661. f. 44.

GAFFAREL (P.) Bonaparte et les républiques italiennes, 1796–99. pp. 303. *Paris,* 1895. 8°.
9079. f. 14.

ITALY.—History—*continued.*

TROLARD (E.) Pèlerinage aux champs de bataille françuis d'Italie. De Montenotte au Pont d'Arcole. pp. 510. *Paris*, 1893. 12°. 9080. b. 48.

—— De Rivoli à Solferino. pp. 410.
Paris, 1893. 8°. 10136. bbb. 29.

GUENTHER (R.) Geschichte des Feldzuges von 1800 in Ober-Italien. pp. 210.
Frauenfeld, 1893. 8°. 9080. i. 13.

DEJOB (C.) Madame de Staël et l'Italie.
pp. 267. *Paris*, 1890. 8°. 010661. f. 16.

See also ROME, *History*, and under the history of each State forming the Kingdom of Italy.

Nineteenth Century.

BLASI (R.) La nuova Italia. pp. 156.
Torino, 1891. 8°. 8033. f. 16.

BONETTI (A. M.) I Martiri italiani. 3 tom.
Modena, 1891. 8°. 10629. cc. 32.

BULLE (C.) Geschichte des Königreiches Italien. pp. 652. 1890. 8°. ONCKEN (W.) Allgemeine Geschichte. Hauptabth. 4. Theil 3. 2068.](28.)

BULLE (O.) Die italienische Einheitsidee in ihrer litterarischen Entwicklung. pp. 345.
Berl. 1893. 8°. 8033. g. 42.

GIACOMETTI (G.) La Question italienne, 1814–60. pp. 394. *Paris*, 1893. 12°. 9166. ccc. 18.

LUISE (G. de) Storia critica delle Rivoluzioni italiane. *Napoli*, 1887, *etc.* 4°. 9167. ccc.

MARTINENGO CESARESCO (E.) *Countess.* The Liberation of Italy 1815–70. pp. 420.
Lond. 1895. 8°. 9167. e. 5.

O'CLERY (P. K.) The Making of Italy. pp. 552. *Lond.* 1892. 8°. 9167. ccc. 37.

ORSI (P.) Come fu fatta l' Italia. pp. 204.
Torino, 1891. 8°. 9166. ccc. 9.

PROBYN (J. W.) Italy : from the fall of Napoleon I. to 1890. pp. 312. *Lond.* 1891. 8°.
9166. ccc. 12.

RORAI (S. di) Il Genio della Rivoluzione. Periodo I. 1789–1848. pp. 375.
Venezia, 1890. 8°. 9166. d. 19.

THAYER (W. R.) Dawn of Italian independence : Italy from 1814 to 1849. 2 vol. *Bost.* 1893. 8°.
9166. d. 22.

BERTOLINI (F.) Letture di storia del Risorgimento italiano. pp. 402. *Milano*, 1895. 8°.
9167. c. 7.

TIVARONI (C.) L' Italia durante il dominio austriaco, 1815–49. *Torino*, 1892, *etc.* 8°. 9166. ccc.

CAPPELLETTI (L.) Storia di Carlo Alberto.
pp. 616. *Roma*, 1891. 8°. 10630. dd. 24.

CHIERICI (L.) Carlo Alberto, e il suo ideale.
pp. 62. *Roma*, 1892. 8°. 9004. bbb. 16. (2.)

MASI (E.) Il Segreto del Re Carlo Alberto.
pp. 277. *Bologna*, 1890. 8°. 9166. ccc. 10.

PERRERO (D.) Gli ultimi reali di Savoia ed il principe Carlo Alberto di Carignano. pp. 463.
Torino, 1889. 8°. 10629. d. 17.

COSTA DE BEAUREGARD (A.) *Marquis.* Les dernières années du roi Charles-Albert. pp. 587.
Paris, 1890. 8°. 10629. dd. 21.

CAPPELLETTI (L.) Storia di Vittorio Emanuele II. 3 vol. *Roma*, 1892, 93. 8°. 9165. cc. 10.

RODOCANACHI (E. P.) Le Comte de Cavour. 1833–35. pp. 13. *Paris*, 1891. 8°.
10601. ff. 4. (9.)

MANNCARDI (F.) Reminiscenze storiche.
Torino, 1890, *etc.* 8°. 9167. h. 7.

REVEL (G. de) Dal 1847 al 1855. La spedizione di Crimea. pp. 191. *Milano*, 1891. 8°.
9079. g. 15.

GIACOMELLI (A.) Reminiscenze della mia vita politica, 1818–53. pp. 350. *Firenze*, 1893. 8°.
9166. ccc. 20.

ITALY.—History—*continued.*

HUEBNER (J. A. v.) Une Année de ma vie. 1848–49. pp. 574. *Paris*, 1891. 8°. 010707. ce. 1.

TULLIOLI ( ) Reminiscenze di un Bersagliere, 1848–90. pp. 295. *Milano*, 1893. 8°. 9167. f. 2.

SCHACK (A. F. von) *Count.* J. Mazzini und die italienische Einheit. pp. 185. *Stuttg.* 1891. 8°.
9166. d. 20.

—— Mazzini e l' Unità italiana. pp. 320.
Roma, 1892. 8°. 9167. h. 8.

MAZZINI (G.) Essays. pp. 263. *Lond.* 1894. 8°.
8032. bb. 39.

VISMARA (A.) Materiali per una bibliografia del Generale G. Garibaldi. pp. 100.
Como, 1891. 8°. 10631. f. 43.

BORDONE (J. P. T.) Garibaldi. 1807–82. pp. 464.
Paris, 1891. 12°. 10630. cc. 27.

SELLA (Q.) Discorsi parlamentari. 5 vol.
Roma, 1887–9?. 8°. 8032. k. 3.

BREGANZE (L.) A. Depretis ed i suoi tempi.
pp. 298. *Verona*, 1894. 8°. 10630. cc. 37.

MINGHETTI (M.) M. Minghetti, uomo di stato.
pp. 212. *Torino*, 1894. 8°. 8010. de. 16.

—— Discorsi parlamentari. Vol. 1, 3–8.
Roma, 1888–90. 8°. 8032. l. 5.

MANCINI (P. S.) Discorsi parlamentari. 2 vol.
Roma, 1893. 8°. 8033. l. 1.

BARTH (H.) Crispi. pp. 268. *Leipz.* 1893. 8°.
10630. d. 49.

CRISPI (F.) Scritti e discorsi politici. 1849–90.
pp. 765. *Roma*, 1890. 8°. 8033. h. 16.

—— Crispi. pp. 240. *Roma*, 1890. 8°.
10629. d. 15.

NARJOUX (F.) Crispi. pp. 333. *Paris*, 1890. 12°.
010661. e. 57.

BAILLIENCOURT (de) Italie. 1852–62. Feuillets militaires. pp. 403. *Paris*, 1894. 12°.
9167. c. 1.

LEBRUN (B. L. J.) Souvenirs des guerres de Crimée et d'Italie. pp. 336. *Paris*, 1889. 18°.
9080. aaa. 28.

WIMPFFEN (E. F. de) Crimée—Italie. pp. 180.
Paris, 1892. 8°. 9079. i. 8.

GRANDIN (L.) Campagne de 1859. Les Français en Italie. pp. 449. *Paris*, 1891. 8°. 9080. g. 1.

MASSUERO (L.) A San Martino della Battaglia.
pp. 134. *Como*, 1894. 8°. 9167. b. 2.

CECCONI (G.) Il 27 Aprile 1859. Narrazione.
pp. 63. *Firenze*, 1891. 8°. 9007. ff. 5. (8.)

ADAMOLI (G.) Da San Martino a Mentana.
pp. 422. *Milano*, 1892. 8°. 9166. ccc. 17.

ITALY. Politica segreta italiana. 1863–70.
pp. 452. *Torino*, 1891. 8°. 9166. d. 32.

REVEL (G. di) Da Ancona a Napoli. pp. 216.
Milano, 1892. 8°. 10132. f. 14.

SCUDIER (A. von) *Baron.* Betrachtungen über den Feldzug 1866 in Italien.
Wien, 1894, *etc.* 8°. 9167. i.

MATHES VON BILABRUCK (C.) Taktische Studie über die Schlacht von Custoza. pp. 145.
Wien, 1891. 8°. 9080. d. 36.

VERDY DU VERNOIS (J. von) Tactical Study, based on the battle of Custozza. pp. 112. 9.
1894. 8°. Gale and Polden's Military Series.
8830. b. 50.

WALDSTAETTEN (J. von) Strategische Grundsätze in ihrer Anwendung auf den Feldzug in Italien 1866. pp. 122. *Wien*, 1895. 8°.
9080. dd. 23.

See also EUROPE.

History, *Ecclesiastical.*

PENNINGTON (A. R.) The Church in Italy.
pp. 499. 1895. 8°. DITCHFIELD (P. H.) The National Churches. 4534. de.

ITALY.—History.—*Ecclesiastical—continued.*

DRESDNER (A.) Sittengeschichte der italienischen Geistlichkeit im 10. und 11. Jahrhundert. pp. 392. *Breslau*, 1890. 8°.   4605. ee. 5.

GEBHARDT (É.) L'Italie mystique, histoire de la renaissance religieuse au moyen âge. pp. 326. *Lond.* 1890. 8°.   4605. aaa. 22.

See also CHURCH HISTORY, *General* and *Papacy:* ROMAN CATHOLIC CHURCH: WALDENSES.

Law.

ABIGNENTE (G.) Elementi della storia del diritto in Italia. 2 pt. *Napoli*, 1884, 87. 8°.   5359. aaa. 4.

PERTILE (A.) Storia del Diritto italiano. *Torino*, 1891, etc. 8°.   6005. i.

SCHUPFER (F.) Manuale di storia del Diritto italiano. pp. 491. *Città di C.* 1892. 8°.   5384. aaa. 25.

ARMANNI (L.) Il Tempo immemorabile e la cessazione della demanialità. pp. 307. *Roma*, 1889. 8°.   5359. ee. 22.

CAVAGNARI (C.) Nuovi orizzonti del Diritto civile in rapporto colle istituzioni pupillari. pp. 451. *Milano*, 1891. 8°.   5359. ee. 27.

COLAMARINO (D.) Il Diritto civile italiano. *Napoli*, 1886, etc. 8°.   5359. eeee.

DUTHOIT (E.) L'Enseignement du Droit dans les Universités d'Italie. pp. 185. *Paris*, 1894. 12°.   8356. aa. 26.

FALCONE (G.) La Giuria in Italia. pp. 38. *Palermo*, 1891. 8°.   Pam. 70.

GIURIATI (D.) Gli Errori giudiziari. pp. 544. *Milano*, 1893. 8°.   6006. e. 20.

GUARIGLIA (A.) Il Concordato nel Diritto italiano e straniero. pp. 348. *Napoli*, 1892. 8°.   8026. d. 3.

LATTES (A.) Studii di Diritto statutario. pp. 108. *Milano*, 1886. 8°.   5359. aaa. 10.

LOMONACO (G.) Istituzioni di Diritto civile italiano. *Napoli*, 1894, etc. 8°.   5373. e.

MORTARA (L.) Istituzioni di Ordinamento giudizario. pp. 271. *Firenze*, 1890. 8°.   6006. e. 14.

—— Principii di Procedura civile. pp. 348. *Firenze*, 1890. 8°.   5359. a. 3.

PASSARO (S.) La Rivoluzione della magistratura. pp. 32. *Napoli*, 1893. 8°.   Pam. 34.

P P. *Palermo.* Archivio di Diritto. *Palermo*, 1891, etc. 8°.   P.P. 1379. f.

RAMPONI (L.) La Teoria delle presunzioni nel diritto civile. pp. 355. *Torino*, 1890. 8°.   5359. ee. 20.

RIVALTA (V.) Dispute celebri di diritto civile. pp. 244. *Bologna*, 1895. 8°.   5206. c. 4.

ROSA (S. la) La rivocazione della sentenza civile. pp. 301. *Catania*, 1893. 8°.   5359. ee. 34.

RUSSO TRAVALI (G.) Dell' Azione revocatoria. pp. 123. *Palermo*, 1890. 8°.   5359. ee. 26.

See also supra, CONSTITUTION : LAW, *Commercial, Criminal* and *Ecclesiastical.*

Politics, *Domestic.*

ANTINORI (G.) Le Elezioni politiche in Italia. pp. 67. *Napoli*, 1890. 8°.   Pam. 70.

GALLETTI (B.) L' Attualità e l' onorevole F. Crispi. pp. 60. *Palermo*, 1890. 8°.   Pam. 70.

LAMPERTICO (F.) L' Italia e la Chiesa. pp. 108. *Firenze*, 1890. 8°.   8033. g. 36.

SANCTIS (F. de) Scritti politici. pp. 268. *Napoli*, 1890. 8°.   8032. aaa. 14.

BALAN (P.) La vera realtà delle cose in Roma ed in Italie. pp. 247. *Modena*, 1891. 8°.   8033. f. 17.

ITALY.—Politics—*continued.*

JACINI (S.) *Count.* Le Forze conservative nella nuova Italia. pp. 53. *Firenze*, 1891. 8°. Pam. 70.

MURRI (A.) La vera e la falsa Grandezza dell' Italia nuova. pp. 16. 1891. 8°. BOLOGNA. *Associazione radicale.* Scritti politici. i. 8033. i.

SIGNORINI (G.) La repubblica in Italia. pp. 13. *Parma*, 1891. 8°.   Pam. 70.

BACCELLI (C.) Unione del popolo in Roma ed in Italia. pp. 8. *Roma*, 1893. 8°. 8033. g. 43.

CHIESA (E.) L' Idea politica di C. Cattaneo ricordata al popolo. pp. 23. *Milano*, 1893. 8°.   Pam. 70.

CINCINNATO. La Rivoluzione unica salvezza d' Italia. pp. 31. *Alessandria*, 1893. 12°. Pam. 70.

NORSA (G.) I Radicali alla camera. pp. 29. *Roma*, 1892. 8°.   Pam. 70.

SENATORE. 24 Novembre 1893. Che farà ora l' Italia? pp. 15. *Roma*, 1893. 8°. Pam. 70.

AMICIS (F. de) La mia cara Italia. pp. 139. *Milano*, 1894. 8°.   8050. h. 10.

GIAMPIETRO (E.) L'Italia al bivio. pp. 133. *Roma*, 1894. 8°.   8032. cc. 16.

GRABINSKI (G.) Le Mouvement révolutionnaire en Italie. pp. 130. *Paris*, 1894. 8°. 9167. k. 22.

GUIDOTTI (G.) Un anno di Dittatura in Italia. pp. 222. *Palermo*, 1894. 8°.   8032. b. 41.

MASSARANTI (T.) Come la pensava il Dottor Lorenzi. pp. 358. *Roma*, 1894. 8°. 8276. ff. 41.

NICOLETTI (M.) I nostri tempi. pp. 90. *Ariano*, 1894. 8°.   8032. cc. 18.

PISACANE (C.) Saggio sulla rivoluzione. pp. 269. *Bologna*, 1894. 8°.   08275. f. 17.

SIOTTO-PINTÓR (M.) Lo Riforma sociale in Italia. pp. 450. *Firenze*, 1894. 8°.   08277. ff. 9.

TURIELLO (P.) Politica contemporanea. pp. 107. *Napoli*, 1894. 8°.   8033. h. 19.

See also supra, CONSTITUTION : ROMAN CATHOLIC CHURCH, *in Italy.*

Foreign.

CASTONNET DES FOSSES (H.) La France et l'Italie dans la Mer Rouge. pp. 24. *Lille*, 1889. 8°.   8026. i. 6. (6.)

CENA (C.) La nostra Alleanza colla Germania. pp. 13. *Roma*, 1893. 8°.   Pam. 67.

CHANNEBOT (A.) L'Empire ottomane, l'Italie et la France. pp. 24. *Paris*, 1891. 12°.   8028. f. 32. (4.)

CIFARELLI (M.) Italia deplomatica tra i mari ed i monti. pp. 78. *Bari*, 1888. 8°. 8033. g. 34. (2.)

CRISPI (F.) Crispi bei Bismarck. pp. 238. *Stuttgart*, 1894. 8°.   8032. b. 42.

M., R. de. La France et l'Italie. pp. 13. 1891. 8°.   Pam. 67.

MAZZOLENI (A.) L' Italia nel movimento per la pace. pp. 73. *Milano*, 1891. 8°. 8026. i. 5. (7.)

MORDACQ (C.) Influence italienne à Tunis et dans la Tripolitaine. pp. 11. *Paris*, 1891. 8°.   8028. de. 30. (12.)

MUSSET (E. S. B.) Union helléno-latine. pp. 32. *Paris*, 1890. 8°.   8026. ee. 24. (10.)

NEGRO (M.) Quelles sont les causes de la Haine française contre l'Italie? *Lond.* 1893. 8°.   Pam. 67.

TORRACA (M.) Neutralità o alleanze. pp. 38. *Roma*, 1891. 8°.   8026. i. 5. (9.)

See also EUROPE.

Roman Catholic Church.

See supra, History, *Ecclesiastical:* CHURCH HISTORY : ROMAN CATHOLIC CHURCH, *in Italy.*

Topography : Social Life.

MARINELLI (G.) Saggio di cartografia italiana. pp. 29. *Firenze*, 1894. 8°.   Pam. 91.

ITALY.—Topography, etc.—*continued.*

BAEDEKER (C.) Italie septentrionale.
Leipz. 1895. 8°. 10108. d. 22.

—— Central Italy and Rome. pp. 410. 14.
Leipz. 1893. 8°. 2352. a.

COOK (T.) Tourist's handbook for Southern Italy. pp. 398. 8. Lond. 1892. 8°.
10136. bbb. 28.

ITALY. Murray's handbook for Northern Italy. pp. 541. Lond. 1891. 8°. 2364. a. 21.

JOANNE (P.) Italie. pp. 444. Paris, 1893. 8°.
10135. aa. 19.

—— Italie du Centre. pp. 579.
Paris, 1893. 8°. 10136. b. 1.

PÈLERIN. Guide du pèlerin en Italie. pp. 707.
Nice, 1894. 12°. 10136. b. 2.

BARBIER (P.) Italie : souvenirs et impressions. pp. 321. Paris, 1893. 8°. 10131. f. 1.

BAZIN (R.) Les Italiens d'aujourd'hui. pp. 315. Paris, 1894. 12°. 10136. bbb. 31.

BEELI (P.) Souvenirs de voyage en Italie.
pp. 189. Bordeaux, 1893. 12°. 10130. aa. 8.

BORIONI (L.) La vita della Provincia italiana. pp. 39. Roma, 1893. 8°. Pam. 82.

BOSCH (F. v.) Sous le bleu. pp. 79.
Gand, 1893. 4°. 10135. b. 1.

BOURGET (P.) Sensations d'Italie. pp. 342.
Paris, 1891. 12°. 10131. cc. 7.

BUATHIER (J. M.) À Rome et en Italie.
pp. 166. Paris, 1892. 8°. 10129. a. 5.

FLOERKE (G.) Italisches Leben. pp. 441.
Stuttg. 1890. 8°. 10129. bbb. 27.

FREEMAN (E. A.) Studies of Travel. 2 vol.
N.Y. 1893. 12°. 10026. aa.

GERMAN. Unsere Bundesgenossen und Bundesgenossinnen in Italien. pp. 287.
Kassel, 1895. 8°. 8026. aa. 36.

HARDWICKE (H. J.) From Alps to Orient.
pp. 246. Sheffield, 1891. 8°. 10106. aa. 4.

HOLDER-EGGER (O.) Bericht über eine Reise nach Italien. 1892. 8°. Ac. Germany. Gesellschaft für ältere deutsche Geschichtskunde. Neues Archiv. Bd. 17. Hft. 3. Ac. 7003.

HUOT DE GONCOURT (E. L. A.) and (J. A.) L'Italie d'hier. pp. 287. Paris, 1894. 8°.
10132. b. 1.

IGNORANTE. Six mois en Italie. pp. 337.
Paris, 1893. 12°. 10132. aaa. 12.

JACOBSON (J.) Reisebriefe aus Italien. pp. 327.
Königsberg, 1893. 8°. 10107. cc. 13.

LABAT (A.) Voyage en Italie. pp. 79.
Paris, 1894. 8°. 10129. d. 7.

LERIS (G. de) L' Italia Superiore. pp. 350.
Milano, 1892. 4°. 10151. ff. 2.

M., D. R. Art Note Book for Northern Italy. pp. 115. Lond. 1894. 12°. 7854. aaa. 41.

MAZINI, afterwards VILLARI (I.) Here and there in Italy. pp. 269. Lond. 1893. 8°. 10131. c. 2.

MONTET (C. É.) Choses de Rome et d'Italie.
pp. 344. Paris, 1892. 12°. 10130. aa. 7.

NEUKOMM (E.) Voyage au Pays du déficit. pp. 298. Paris, 1890. 12°. 8032. aaa. 11.

NIELSEN (F.) Dagbogsblade fra Italien. pp. 90. 1890. 8°. Smaaskrifter til Oplysning for Kristne. Vol. 5. 3605. i.

NYBLOM (C. R.) Ett år i Södern. Bilder från Italien. pp. 254. Upsala, 1883. 8°.
10129. dd. 3.

ORGELS (L.) Une exploration en Italie. pp. 63. Gand, 1890. 8°. 10107. e. 13. (4.)

PAULUCCI DI CALBOLI (R.) Marquis. L'Italie vagabonde. pp. 35. Paris, 1895. 8°. 8282. de. 49.

ITALY.—Topography, etc.—*continued.*

PELLECHET (J.) Lettres d'Italie, 1856-57.
pp. 202. Paris, 1894. 12°. 10135. bbb. 13.

PENNELL (J.) and (E. R.) Our sentimental Journey through Italy. Lond. 1893. 8°.
010168. e. 1.

POISSON ( ) Italie-Rome.
Orléans, 1893, etc. 8°. 10131. cc.

THOLIN (G.) Impressions, études et souvenirs. pp. 391. Lyon, 1890. 8°. 12355. i. 32.

THOMPSON (G. E.) Spring at the Italian Lakes. pp. 151. Lond. 1892. 8°. 10130. bbb. 20.

ULLRICH (T.) Reise-Studien aus Italien. pp. 417. Berl. 1893. 8°. 12249. ccc. 2.

VEDEL (V.) Fra Italien. pp. 208.
Kjøbenh. 1892. 8°. 10132. aaa. 9.

HENSMAN (M.) Dante Map. [Map of Italy on which are marked places mentioned in Dante's writings, etc.] Lond. 1892. 16°. 11420. cc. 14.

LE HIRBEC (D.) Voyages aux Antilles, et en Italie, 1642-44. pp. 92. Laval, 1890. 8°.
10028. g. 12.

BERGERET DE GRANCOURT (P. J. O.) Bergeret et Fragonard. Journal d'un voyage en Italie 1773-74. pp. 431. 1895. 8°. Ac. Poitiers. Société des Antiquaires. Mémoires. Sér. 2. Tom. 17. Ac. 5326.

THRALE, afterwards PIOZZI (H. L.) Glimpses of Italian Society. pp. 327. Lond. 1892. 8°.
10129. bbb. 32.

For the Italian Alps, see ALPS.

Trade and Finance.

AZZONI (F.) Il Debito pubblico italiano.
pp. 375. Milano, 1891. 8°. 012200. h. 2.

BRUNI (E.) Contabilità generale dello Stato. pp. 421. Milano, 1892. 8°. 012200. h. 51.

BRUSCHETTI (V.) Count. Sul modo di restaurare le Finanze italiane. pp. 22. Roma, 1894. 8°.
Pam. 23.

GRABINSKI (G.) Count. Il Pagamento e l' insequestrabilità dei Salarii. pp. 28.
Bologna, 1894. 8°. 08226. k. 5. (10.)

MAGLIANO (A.) La Situazione finanziaria, 1858. pp. 29. Roma, 1890. 8°. 8226. f. 59. (8).

MUZII (A.) Trattato sulla stima dei fondi. pp. 559. Napoli, 1891. 8°. 8229. f. 41.

PICCINELLI (F.) Apprezzamento dei valori pubblici e delle operazioni di Borsa. pp. 236.
Milano, 1891. 8°. 12206. b. 54.

PISANI (E.) Il Problema finanziario in Italia. pp. 43. Roma, 1894. 8°. Pam. 23.

SCHULLERN-SCHRATTENHOFEN (H. v.) Die theoretische Nationalökonomie Italiens. pp. 214.
Leipz. 1891. 8°. 08207. g. 14.

BRUNI (E.) Il nuovo Catasto italiano. pp. 346.
Milano, 1893. 8°. 012200. h. 52.

—— L' Imposta sui redditi di ricchezza mobile . pp. 218. Milano, 1894. 8°. 012200. h. 113.

—— La Riscossione delle imposte dirette.
pp. 158. Milano, 1892. 8°. 012200. h. 50.

CANNADA-BARTOLI (G.) Il Catasto della Imposta fondiaria. pp. 308. Napoli, 1890. 8°.
08227. h. 11.

LUZZATI (I.) Disegno di legge sugli effetti giuridici del catasto. pp. 141. Torino, 1891. 8°.
5359. cc. 28.

OBERTI (E.) Imposta progressiva. pp. 171.
Torino, 1894. 8°. 08226. h. 18.

PISTONO (A.) L' Imposta di ricchezza mobile. pp. 56. Torino, 1891. 8°. 8228. aaaa. 17. (11.)

ITALY. Codice doganale italiano. pp. 1078.
Milano, 1894. 8°. 012200. h. 119.

ITALY.—Trade, etc.—_continued._

PARETO (V.) Le Protectionnisme en Italie, ses résultats. pp. 16. _Paris_, 1891. 8°.
08227. ee. 46. (11.)

SALOMON (L.) Deux années de Protectionnisme en Italie. pp. 58. _Milan_, 1890. fol. 8228. l. 6.

VIVANTE (F.) Le Commerce spécial de l'Italie et le tarif minimum. pp. 59. _Paris_, 1894. 8°.
Pam. 23.

BILLOT (A.) Les Conditions du travail en Italie. pp. 51. 1891. 8°. FRANCE. _M. des Affaires Étrangères._ Recueil de rapports. 08276. k.

CAREGA DI MURICCE (F.) Estimo rurale. pp. 161. _Milano_, 1890. 8°. 12206. b. 66.

ROSTAND (E.) Une Visite à quelques institutions de prévoyance en Italie. pp. 292. _Paris_, 1891. 8°. 08227. f. 26.

SANTANGELO SPOTO (I.) L'Homestead e le condizioni della proprietà in Italia. pp. 30. _Palermo_, 1890. 8°. 08267. k. 4. (14.)

See also BANKING : CAPITAL AND LABOUR.

ITHACA. SEILLIÈRE (E.) Une excursion à Ithaque. pp. 76. _Paris_, 1892. 4°. 10125. g. 4.

IVORY COAST. _See_ AFRICA, _West._

IVY. HIBBERD (S.) The Ivy. pp. 115. _Lond._ 1893. 4°. 7054. c. 37.

JACKAL. MIVART (S. G.) Dogs, Jackals, etc. pp. 216. _Lond._ 1890. 4°. 7206. dd. 7.

JACOBITE CHURCH. RAE (G. M.) Syrian Church in India. pp. 388. _Edinb._ 1892. 8°. 4534. ee. 5.

PARRY (O. H.) Six months in a Syrian Monastery. pp. 400. _Lond._ 1895. 8°. 10077. g. 38.

CEYLON. Jacobites of Ceylon. By a Missionary Apostolic. pp. 54. _Colombo_, 1889. 8°. Pam. 93.

JACQUES CARTIER, Quebec. DIONNE (N. E.) Le Fort Jacques-Cartier. pp. 34. _Montréal_, 1891. 8°. Pam. 3.

JADE. HILTON (J.) Remarks on Jade. pp. 21. 4. _Exeter_, 1888, 91. 8°. Pam. 27.

—— Further remarks on Jade. pp. 13. 1891. 8°. Pam. 27.

See also MINERALOGY.

JAÉN. PI Y MARGALL (F.) Granada, Jaén, etc. pp. 576. 1885. 8°. España. Sus Monumentos. 2060. c.

JAINS. BASTIAN (A.) Ideale Welten, etc. 3 Bde. _Berl._ 1892. 8°. 4503. h. 1.

PULLÉ (F. L.) Catalogo dei Manoscritti giainici della Biblioteca Nazionale di Firenze. _Firenze_, 1894, etc. 8°. 14096. dd. 2.

WEBER (A.) Sacred literature of the Jains. pp. 143. _Bombay_, 1893. 4°. 4506. g. 2.

JAIPUR. JACOB (S. S.) Jeypore Portfolio of architectural details. 6 pt. _Lond._ 1890. fol. 1736. c. 1.

JAMAICA.
General : History : Topography.

CUNDALL (F.) Bibliotheca Jamaicensis. pp. 38. _Kingston_, 1895. 8°. Pam. 6.

Ac., etc. Kingston. _Institute of Jamaica._ Bulletin. _Kingston_, 1892, etc. fol. Ac. 1958/4.

—— Journal. _Kingston_, 1891, etc. 8°. Ac. 1958.

—— Jamaica in 1895. Handbook of information. pp. 77. _Kingston_, 1895. 8°. 10480. b. 25.

JAMAICA.—General, etc.—_continued._

BACON (E. M.) and AARON (E. M.) The new Jamaica. pp. 243. _N.Y._ 1890. 8°.
10480. b. 36.

JAMAICA. Tourist Guide. pp. 102. _Kingston_, 1893. 4°. 10480. bbb. 39.

M., M. Port Royal and its harbour. pp. 56. _Port Royal_, 1893. 8°. 10481. bbb. 47.

PARKHURST (V. P.) Picturesque Jamaica. Pt. 1–5. _Kingston_, 1887. fol. 1790. b. 8.

SAINT MARY, _Jamaica, Parish of._ Handbook. 3 pt. _Jamaica_, 1894. 8°. 10481. bbb. 50.

SPECK (W.) Guide on gardening in Jamaica. pp. 47. _Kingston_, 1891. 8°. 7074. e. 11. (6.)

STUART (H. W. V.) Adventures amidst equatorial Forests. To which is added " Jamaica revisited." pp. 268. _Lond._ 1891. 8°. 10481. i. 23.

THOMAS (H. T.) Untrodden Jamaica. pp. 90. _Kingston_, 1890. 8°. 10480. cc. 30.

WARD (C. J.) World's Fair. Jamaica at Chicago. pp. 95. _N.Y._ 1893. 8°. 7956. f. 4.

See also ENGLAND, _Colonies :_ WEST INDIES.

Church of England.

ELLIS (J. B.) History of the Church of England in Jamaica. pp. 136. _Kingston_, 1891. 8°.
4745. c. 36.

NUTTALL (E.) _Bp. of Jamaica._ The Churchman's Manual. pp. 295. _Jamaica_, 1893. 8°.
3456. df. 25.

Law.

FEURTADO (W. A.) Index to the Laws of Jamaica, 1892. pp. 158. _Jamaica_, 1892. 8°.
06606. f. 10.

SAMUEL (L. L.) Index to the Resident Magistrates' Law. pp. 36. _Jamaica_, 1889. 4°.
6606. dd. 1.

—— Justice's pocket guide. pp. 115. _Jamaica_, 1894. 16°. 6606. a. 9.

Medical Works.

PHILLIPPO (J. C.) Cholera in Jamaica in 1850–54. pp. 33. _Kingston_, 1892. 8°. Pam. 39.

MAUNSELL (S. E.) Contribution to the medico-military history of Jamaica. pp. 61. _Kingston_, 1891. fol. 7687. i. 6.

See also HYGIENE, _of Tropical Countries._

Stud Book. _See_ HORSE.

JAN MAYEN ISLAND. BIENAIMÉ (A. P. L.) Voyage de "La Manche" à l'île Jan-Mayen. pp. 268. _Paris_, 1894. 8°.
10460. ff. 22.

RABOT (C.) Explorations dans l'Océan glacial arctique. pp. 69. 1894. 8°. Ac. Paris. _Société de Géographie._ Bulletin. Sér. 7. Tom. 15.
Ac. 6035.

JANSENISTS. _See_ FRANCE, _History, Ecclesiastical :_ UTRECHT, _Jansenist Church._

JAPAN. [_See note on page_ 1.]

Bibliography.

WENCKSTERN (F. v.) Bibliography of the Japanese Empire. Books, essays and maps in European languages relating to Japan, 1859–93 A.D. pp. 338. 68. _Leiden_, 1895. 8°.
BB.I. a. 13.

Ainos. _See_ AINOS.

Army and Navy.

LEHAUTCOURT (P.) L'Armée et la Marine japonaises. pp. 51. _Paris_, 1892. 8°. Pam. 2.

Christianity in. _See_ MISSIONS.

Constitution and Government.

HARTOG (L. de) Over de Grondwet van Japan. 1892. 8°. Ac. Amsterdam. _K. Akademie._ Verslagen, etc. Reeks 3. Deel. 9. Ac. 914.

JAPAN.—Constitution, etc.—*continued*.

IYENAGA (T.) Constitutional Development of Japan, 1853–81. pp. 56. 1891. 8°. Johns Hopkins University Studies. Ser. 9. No. 9.
Ac. 2689.

MUTCHMORE (S. A.) Moghul, Mongol, Mikado and Missionary. 2 vol. *N.Y.* 1891. 8°.
10058. de. 4.

NORMAN (H.) The Real Japan, *etc.* pp. 364. *Lond.* 1892. 8°. K.T.C. 6. a. 1.

POLDER (L. v. de) La Pairie japonaise. pp. 64. *Yokohama,* 1885. 8°. Pam. 67.

SIMMONS (D. B.) Notes on Land Tenure and local institutions in old Japan. 1891. 8°. Ac. Yokohama. *Asiatic Society.* Transactions. Vol. 19. Ac. 8828/6.

SINKITI ARIMORI. Das Staatsrecht von Japan. pp. 111. *Strassb.* 1892. 8°. 05319. i. 3.

Earthquakes. *See* EARTHQUAKES.

History and Politics.

Ac. London. *Japan Society.* Transactions. *Lond.* 1893, *etc.* 8°. Ac. 8821.

CHAMBERLAIN (B. H.) Things Japanese. pp. 503. *Lond.* 1891. 8°. 010057. e. 14.

GRIFFIS (W. E.) Japan in history. pp. 230. *Bost.* 1892. 8°. 10058. a. 23.

LAMAIRESSE (E.) Le Japon. Histoire, *etc.* *Paris,* 1892. 8°. 010057. f. 5.

MURRAY (D.) Japan. pp. 431. 1894. 8°. Story of the Nations. 9004. ccc. 12.

MUTCHMORE (S. A.) The Moghul, Mongol, Mikado, *etc.* 2 vol. *N.Y.* 1891. 8°. 10058. de. 4,

NORMAN (H.) The Real Japan. pp. 364. *Lond.* 1892, 8°. K.T.C. 6. a. 1.

SCHLEGEL (G.) and CORDIER (H.) Archives pour servir à l'étude de l'histoire, *etc.*, de l'Asie Orientale. *Leide,* 1890, *etc.* 8°. 10058. h.

ASSO (T. H.) Pictures of ancient Japanese history. *Tōkyō,* 1890. 4°. 11100. f. 9.

BERTIN (L. E.) Les grandes Guerres civiles du Japon. pp. 422. *Paris,* 1894. 8°. 9055. h. 1.

DENING (W.) Life of Toyotomi Hideyoshi. pp. 417. *Tokio,* 1890. 8°. 11099. b. 29.

POOLE (S. L.) Life of Sir H. Parkes. 2 vol. *Lond.* 1894. 8°. 10817. dd. 15.

HARRIS (T.) T. Harris, first American Envoy in Japan. pp. 351. *Bost.* 1895. 8°. 10883. d. 7.

LAYRLE (J.) La Restauration impériale au Japon. pp. 387. *Paris,* 1893. 12°. 9055. aaa. 27.

INOUYE (J.) The Japan-China War: Kinchow, Port Arthur and Taiienwan. pp. 37. *Yokohama,* 1895. 8°. 9055. ee. 33.

—— The Fall of Wei-hai-wei. pp. 31. *Yokohama,* 1895. 8°. 9055. ee. 32.

MORRIS (J.) War in Korea. pp. 108. *Lond.* 1894. 8°. 8023. aaa. 10.

VLADIMIR. The China-Japan War. pp. 449. *Lond.* 1895. 8°. 9055. d. 32.

VILLENOISY (F. de) La Guerre sino-japonaise et ses conséquences pour l'Europe. pp. 48. *Paris,* 1895. 8°. Pam. 67.

CURZON (*Hon.* G. N.) Problems of the Far East. *Lond.* 1894, *etc.* 8°. 8023. dd. 26.

DIÓSY (A.) "Yamato Damashi-ī," The Spirit of old Japan. pp. 8. *Woking,* 1893. 8°.
Pam. 67.

INAGAKI (M.) Japan and the Pacific. pp. 265. *Lond.* 1890. 8°. 8022. de. 18.

MORRIS (J.) Advance Japan. pp. 433. *Lond.* 1895. 8°. 010057. h. 6.

JAPAN.—History, etc.—*continued*.

NITOBE (I.) Intercourse between the United States and Japan. pp. 198. Johns Hopkins University Studies. Extra vol. 8. Ac. 2689.

Law.

JAPAN. Projet de Code civil. 4 tom. *Tokio,* 1890, 91. 8°. 05319. f. 1.

WIGMORE (J. H.) Materials for the study of private Law in Old Japan. 1892, *etc.* 8°. Ac. Yokohama. *Asiatic Society.* Transactions. Vol. 20, *etc.* Ac. 8828/6.

KWAMPORITSU. Kamporitsu oder Hiakkajo, ein japanisches Rechtbuch. pp. 45. *Berl.* 1888. 4°. 11099. g. 8.

See also supra : Constitution : LAW, *Commercial.*

Navy. *See supra :* Army.

Religious.

COBBOLD (G. A.) Religion in Japan. pp. 113. *Lond.* 1894. 8°. 4429. c. 35.

GRIFFIS (W. E.) Religions of Japan. pp. 457. *Lond.* 1895. 8°. 4503. b. 14.

LAMAIRESSE (E.) Le Japon. Histoire, religion, *etc.* pp. 275. *Paris,* 1892, 8°. 010057. f. 5.

LOWELL (P.) Occult Japan; or, the way of the Gods. pp. 379. *Bost.* 1895. 8°. 4503. b. 15.

See also BUDDHISM : MISSIONS.

Statistics. *See infra :* TRADE.

Topography and Social Life,

CANADIAN PACIFIC RAILWAY. Japan and China. Handbook of information. pp. 19. *Liverp.* 1893. 8°. Pam. 86.

KEELING ( ) Guide to Japan. pp. 164. *Yokohama,* 1890. 8°. 10058. a. 19.

SATOW (E. M.) and HAWES (A. G. S.) Murray's handbook for Japan. pp. 459. *Lond.* 1891. 8°. 2364. a. 23.

SCIDMORE (E. R.) Westward to the Far East. pp. 51. *Montreal,* 1892. 8°. 010057. f. 21.

Ac. London. *Japan Society.* Transactions and Proceedings. *Lond.* 1893, *etc.* 8°. Ac. 8821.

ARNOLD (*Sir* E.) Seas and Lands. pp. 535. *Lond.* 1891. 8°. 010057. ee. 17.

—— Japonica. pp. 128. *Lond.* 1892. 8°. 010057. l. 7.

BACON (A. M.) Japanese Girls and Women. pp. 333. *Bost.* 1891. 8°. 10058. aa. 34.

—— A Japanese Interior. pp. 267. *Bost.* 1893. 8°. 10058. de. 7

BICKERSTETH (M. J.) Japan as we saw it. pp. 354. *Lond.* 1893. 8°. 010057. f. 15.

BIGOT (G.) Croquis japonais. *Tokio,* 1886. fol. 1784. b. 4.

CARMICHAEL (A. W.) From Sunrise Land. pp. 180. *Lond.* 1895. 8°. 4765. ee. 29.

CHAMBERLAIN (B. H.) Things Japanese. pp. 503. *Lond.* 1891. 8°. 010057. e. 14.

CORDIER (H.) Notice sur le Japon. pp. 83. *Paris,* 1894. 8°. Pam. 88.

DHASP (J.) Le Japon contemporain. pp. 344. *Paris,* 1893. 12° 010057. e. 30.

EXNER (A. H.) Japan. Skizzen von Land und Leuten. pp. 208. *Leipz.* 1891. 8°. 010057. l. 4.

FERGUSON (J.) From Ceylon to England by the way of China, Japan, *etc.* pp. 111. *Colombo,* 1891. 4°. 10026. k. 13.

GARDINER (R. S.) Japan as we saw it. pp. 135. *Bost.* 1892. 4°. 10057. c. 3.

JAPAN.—Topography, etc.—continued.

GRENON. Verdant Simple's views of Japan. pp. 125. *Yokohama*, 1890. 8°.   010057. f. 20.

HARADA (T.) Die japanischen Inseln. *Berl.* 1890, *etc.* 8°.   07109. h. 17.

HEARN (L.) Glimpses of unfamiliar Japan. 2 vol. *Lond.* 1894. 8°.   010057. e. 29.

——— "Out of the East." pp. 341. *Lond.* 1895. 8°.   10058. de. 10.

GOH (D.) The Family relations in Japan. pp. 45. *Lond.* 1893. 8°.   8282. g. 27. (12.)

KONOW (H.) I. Asiens Furvande. *Kjøbenh.* 1892–94. 8°.   010057. f.

LANDOR (A. H. S.) Alone with the hairy Ainu. pp. 325. *Lond.* 1893. 8°.   010057. f. 23.

LECOMTE (F. D.) Voyage pratique au Japon. pp. 368. *Paris*, 1893. 12°.   10058. de. 6.

LOWELL (P.) Noto, an unexplored corner of Japan. pp. 261. *Bost.* 1891. 8°. 10058. b. 36.

MARISCHAL (A.) Le Japon. Ac. Brussels. *Société de Géographie*. Bulletin. Année 17, *etc.* Ac. 6098.

MILN (L. J.) When we were Strolling Players in the East. pp. 354. *Lond.* 1894. 8°.   010057. f. 29.

MORRIS (J.) Advance Japan. pp. 433. *Lond.* 1895. 8°.   010057. h. 6.

NAUMANN (E.) Beiträge zur Geographie Japans, *etc.* pp. 45. 1893. 4°. Petermanns Mitteilungen. Ergänzungsheft Nr. 108.   P.P. 3946.

NIPPOLD (O.) Wanderungen durch Japan. pp. 220. *Jena*, 1893. 8°.   10058. cc. 37.

NORMAN (H.) The real Japan. pp. 364. *Lond.* 1892. 8°.   K.T.C. 6. a. 1.

OGAWA (K.) Costumes and customs in Japan. *Tokyo.* 1892. fol.   K.T.C. 3. b. 19.

PAGE (J.) Japan: its people and missions. pp. 160. *Lond.* 1895. 8°.   4767. bb. 25.

PARSONS (A.) Notes in Japan. pp. 226. *Lond.* 1895. 8°.   010057. g. 1.

SCHLEGEL (G.) and CORDIER (H.) Archives pour servir à l'étude de la géographie de l'Asie Orientale. *Leide*, 1890, *etc.* 8°.   10058. h.

SLADEN (D. B. W.) The Japs at home. pp. 354. *Lond.* 1895. 8°.   10058. df. 8.

SUENSON (E.) Skizzer från Japan. pp. 211. *Stockholm*, 1890. 8°.   10058. a. 16.

TAMURA (N.) The Japanese Bride. pp. 92. *N.Y.* 1893. 8°.   8416. de. 41.

THWING (E. P.) Ex Oriente: Studies. ff. 119. *N.Y.* 1891. 8°.   12352. dd. 2.

TRACY (A.) Rambles through Japan without a guide. pp. 287. *Lond.* 1892. 8°. 10058. de. 5.

TRISTRAM (H. B.) Rambles in Japan. pp. 304. *Lond.* 1895. 8°.   4430. f. 4.

TSURAYUKI. Log of a Japanese journey from the Province of Tosa to the Capital. *Meadville*, 1891. 8°.   11099. a. 11.

USSÈLE (L.) À travers le Japon. pp. 172. *Paris*, 1891. 8°.   010057. ee. 11.

VINCENT (E. G.) Newfoundland to Cochin China. pp. 374. *Lond.* 1892. 8°.   10024. e. 23.

WINKLER (H.) Japaner und Altaier. pp. 24. *Berl.* 1894. 8°.   Pam. 88.

YOUNGHUSBAND (G. J.) On short Leave to Japan. pp. 233. *Lond.* 1894. 8°.   010057. e. 28.

See also AINUS.

Trade: Finance: Statistics.

JAPAN. *Department of Statistics*. Résumé statistique de l'Empire du Japon. *Tokio*, 1887, *etc.* 4°.   11099. d. 22.

CASTONNET DES FOSSES (H.) Le Commerce du Japon. pp. 28. *Angers*, 1889. 8°.   08227. i. 29. (3.)

JAPAN.—Trade, etc.—continued.

CHAMBERLAIN (B. H.) Things Japanese. *Lond.* 1891. 8°.   010057. e. 14.

JAPAN. *Imperial Mint.* Report of the Commissioner. pp. 40. *Hiogo*, 1887. 8°.   11099. d. 21.

KUSSÁKA (J. T.) Das japanische Geldwesen. pp. 100. *Berl.* 1890. 8°.   08227. ee. 48. (2.)

MARISCHAL (A.) Le Japon, ses produits, *etc.* 1893, *etc.* 8°. Ac. Brussels. *Soc. de Géographie*. Bulletin. Année 17, *etc.*   Ac. 6098.

NIEUWENHUYSE (L. v.) Le Japon matériel. pp. 326. *Brux.* 1890. 8°.   010057. f. 3.

RATHGEN (C.) Japans Volkswirtschaft und Staatshaushalt. pp. 785. 1891. 8°. SCHMOLLER (G.) Staatswissenschaftliche Forschungen. Bd. 10. Hft. 4.   8205. dd.

ROESLER (C. F. H.) Entwurf eines Handels-Gesetzbuches für Japan. 3 Bde. *Tokio*, 1884. 8°.   5318. dd. 4.

T., W. H. The Currency of Japan. pp. 331. *Yokohama*, 1882. 8°.   8246. cc. 44.

VINCENT (E. G.) Newfoundland to Cochin China. With reports on British trade, *etc.* pp. 374. *Lond.* 1892. 8°.   10024. e. 23.

See also LAW, *Commercial.*

JAPANESE LANGUAGE. VIÑAZA (de la) *Count*. Escritos de los Portugueses y Castellanos referentes á las lenguas de China y el Japón. pp. 139. *Lisbon*, 1892. 8°. 011901. ee. 20.

SCHLEGEL (G.) and CORDIER (H.) T'ung pao. Archives pour servir à l'étude de l'Asie Orientale. *Leide*, 1890, *etc.* 8°.   10058. h.

NEMOTO SHO. Vocabulary and conversations of the English, French, German and Japanese languages. pp. 73. *Tōkyō*, 1889. *obl.* 4°.   12901. de. 14.

ROUX (L.) Dictionnaire de poche français-japonais. pp. 218. 1894. 16°.   12910. a. 45.

FARSARI (A.) Pocket-Book of Japanese Words and Phrases. pp. 49. 18. *Yokohama*, 1890. 8°.   12910. a. 27.

KOMOR (S.) Hand-Buechlein japanischer Worte und Phrasen. pp. 34. *Yokohama*, 1894. 8°.   12910. a. 48.

SCHILS (G. H.) Elementa linguae Yaponicae classicae. pp. 68. *Leodii*, 1884. 8°.   12910. bb. 47. (5.)

GATTINONI (G.) Grammatica giapponese della lingua parlata. pp. 168. *Venezia*, 1890. 8°.   12910. f. 37.

LYMAN (B. S.) Change from surd to sonant in Japanese compounds. pp. 17. *Phila.* 1894. 8°.   12910. d. 31. (12.)

LLOYD (A.) Japanese colloquial texts with translations. pp. 95. *Lond.* 1890. 8°.   12910. aaa. 60.

PLAUT (H.) Japanisches Lesebuch. pp. 428. 1891. 8°. SACHAU (C. E.) Lehrbücher. Bd. 4.   12906. h.

CONINGHAM (C. G.) and KONDO (M. T.) Practical business conversation for Japanese merchants dealing with foreigners. pp. 155. *Yokohama*, 1894. 8°.   12910. a. 47.

INOUYE (T.) Modern linguist, conversations in English, French, German, Japanese. pp. 165. *Tokio*, 1886. *obl.* 8°.   12901. aaa. 24.

LANGE (R.) Lehrbuch der japanischen Umgangsprache. pp. 512. 1890. 8°. SACHAU (C. E.) Lehrbücher des Seminars. Bd. 1.   12906. h.

MATSUMOTO (K.) Conversations in English and Japanese. pp. 225. *Tokyo*, 1886. 8°.   12910. aa. 37.

MUTSU (H.) Japanese Conversation course. pp. 58. *Tokio*, 1894. 8°.   12910. aaa. 75.

JAPANESE LANGUAGE—*continued.*

NISHIMURA (S.)   English-Japanese mercantile conversations. pp. 147. *Yokohama,* 1888. 8°.
12910. a. 46.

OI (K.) English-Japanese conversations.
pp. 360. *Tokyo,* 1891. 8°.   12910. a. 49.

WALTER (E. T.) Lehrbuch der modernen japanischen Umgangssprache. pp. 213.
Leipz. 1891. 8°.   12910. cc. 4.

JAVA. Ac. Batavia. *Genootschap van Kunsten.* LOUW (P. J. F.) De Java-Oorlog. 1825-30. *Batavia,* 1894, *etc.* 8° & 4°.   9057. d.

DEVENTER (M. L. v.) Het nederlandsch Gezag over Java en onderhoorigheden sedert 1811.
's Gravenhage, 1891, *etc.* 8°.   9055. dd.

COBLIJN (W. A.) De Verdediging van Java.
pp. 185. *'s Gravenhage,* 1890. 8°.   8831. k. 24.

SCHOCH (C. F.) De Heerendiensten op Java.
pp. 280. *'s Gravenhage,* 1891. 8°.   9055. df. 24

VEER (J. P. de) Souvenir aan de groote Manoeuvres op Java, 1888. *s' Gravenhage,* 1890. fol.
1857. c. 11.

———

Ac. Batavia. *Genootschap van Kunsten.* IJZERMAN (J. W.) Beschrijving der oudheden nabij de grens des Residentie's Soerakarta. 2 pt.
Batavia, 1891. 4° & fol.   Ac. 975/13.

BOYS (H. S.) Some notes on Java and its administration by the Dutch. pp. 92.
Allahabad, 1892. 8°.   10055. aaaa. 33.

KLEYN (R. H.) Het gewestelijk Bestuur op Java.
pp. 280. *Leiden,* 1889. 8°.   8023. ee. 39.

MALJER (L. T.) De Javaan, als mensch en als lid. pp. 262. *Batavia,* 1894. 8°.   10055. c. 6.

NEDERBURGH (I. A.) Het Staatsdomein op Java, *etc.* pp. 131. *Leiden,* 1882. 8°.   8023. ee. 28.

WORSFOLD (W. B.) A visit to Java. pp. 283.
Lond. 1893. 8°.   010055. e. 13.

———

ARNTZENIUS (G.) Beschouwingen over de gouvernementskoffiecultuur op Java. pp. 158.
's Gravenhage, 1890. 8°.   07076. i. 2.

WESSELS (L.) De opheffing van het monopolie van de geelwongen Koffiecultuur op Java.
pp. 72. *'s Gravenhage,* 1890. 8°. 8226. ff. 33. (4.)

—— De voorstellen van de Indische Regeering omtrent de gouvernements-koffiecultur op Java.
pp. 55. *'s Gravenhage,* 1892. 8°.   Pam. 23.

ANDRÉ (A. T.) Cultuur en bereiding van Indigo op Java. pp. 316. *Amsterd.* 1891. 8°.
7077. i. 9.

GRONEMAN (I.) Uit en over Midden-Java.
pp. 319. *Zutphen,* 1891. 8°.   010055. ee. 8.

ROO (L. W. G. de) De verkoop van Opium op Java. pp. 32. *Nijmegen,* 1892. 8°. 8409. l. 24. (8.)

SOETERWOUDE (W. E. v.) De Opium-vloek op Java, *etc.* *'s Gravenh.* 1890. 4°.   8435. i. 10.

ZEGERS (J. L.) Het Opium-Vraagstuk. pp. 523.
Nijmegen, 1890. 8°.   8226. h. 39.

BASSET (N.) De Kultuur van Suikerriet op Java door F. J. Potter. pp. 70.
Arnhem, 1890. 8°.   Pam. 1.

KRUEGER (P. W.) Mededeelingen van het proefstation voor Suikerriet in West-Java.
Dresd. 1890, *etc.* 8°.   07076. g. 22.
See also BANTAM : BATAVIA : BUITENZORG : INDIES, *Dutch :* MALAYSIA : NETHERLANDS, *Colonies.*

JAVAN LANGUAGE. BOHATTA (H.) Grammatik der javanischen Sprache. pp. 192.
1892. 8°. Die Kunst der Polyglottie. Tl. 39.
12902. c.

FOKKER (A. A.) Leercursus in brieven om zonder onderwijzer de Javaansche Taal te leeren.
Zutphen, 1891, *etc.* 8°.   12910. dd. 16.

JAVAN LANGUAGE—*continued.*

ROORDA (T.) Beknopte javaansche Grammatika.
pp. 342. *Zwolle,* 1893. 8°.   12972. dd. 27.

VALK (J. W. v. d.) Handleiding om de Javaansche Taal te leeren spreken. pp. 80.
Leiden, 1892. 8°.   12903. c. 52. (6.)

Ac. Leyden. *Academia Lugduno-Batava.* Catalogus van de javaansche Handschriften der Universiteits-Bibliotheek. pp. 434.
Leiden, 1892. 8°.   Ac. 940/7.
See also MALAY LANGUAGE.

JAW. COLLINS (F. H.) Diminution of the Jaw in the civilized races an effect of disuse.
pp. 16. *Lond.* 1891. 8°.   Pam. 39.

HEATH (C.) Injuries and diseases of the Jaws.
pp. 428. *Lond.* 1894. 8°.   7616. h. 21.
See also TEETH.

JEANNETTE, Ship. *See* ARCTIC REGIONS.

JEDBURGH ABBEY. WATSON (J.) Jedburgh Abbey. pp. 190. *Edinb.* 1894. 4°.
4735. eee. 12.

JEHLUM. INCE (J.) Appendix to Ince's guide to Kashmir. Account of the Jhelum Valley Road. pp. 84. *Calcutta,* 1892. 8°.
10058. a. 28.

JELLING. KRISTJANSEN (K. M.) Jelling Seminarium, 1841-91, *etc.* pp. 108.
Odense, 1892. 8°.   8357. f. 21.

JEMAPPES, Battle of. *See* FRANCE, *Military History of the Revolution.*

JEMTLAND. HÖGBOM (A. G.) Jemtland, med infartsvägar. pp. 73. *Stockholm,* 1891. 8°.
10280. aa. 23.

JENA. ZACHAU (O.) Die Stadtschule in Jena.
pp. 40. *Jena,* 1892. 8°.   8304. aa. 19. (5.)
For the Battle of Jena, *see* under the History of FRANCE and PRUSSIA.

JERSEY. *See* CHANNEL ISLANDS.

JERUSALEM. Ac. London. *Palestine Pilgrims' Text Society.* Publications.
Lond. 1887, *etc.* 8°.   Ac. 6171.

DODU (G.) Histoire des Institutions dans le royaume latin de Jérusalem, 1099-1291.
pp. 381. *Paris,* 1894. 8°.   9055. dd. 25.

ROEHRICHT (R.) Der Untergang des Königreichs Jerusalem. pp. 58. 1894. 8°. Ac. Vienna. *Universitas.* Mittheilungen des Instituts für oesterreichische Geschichtsforschung.
Bd. 15.   Ac. 803.

—— Die Jerusalemfahrten der Grafen Philipp Ludwig, 1484, und Reinhard von Hanau, 1550.
1891. 8°. Ac. Cassel. *Verein für hessische Geschichte.* Zeitschrift. N.F. Bd. 16.   Ac. 7025.

ALBOUY (A.) Jérusalem et les Sanctuaires de la Judée. pp. 276. *Paris,* 1894. 8°.. 10077. l. 12.

COURET (A.) Les légendes du Saint-Sépulcre.
pp. 148. *Paris,* 1894. 8°.   4535. bb. 16.

CONIL (F.) Histoire du mouvement catholique dans la Ville Sainte. pp. 554.
Paris, 1894. 8°.   4534. d. 4.

FORBES (S. R.) The Holy City : Jerusalem.
pp. 82. *Chelmsford,* 1892. 8°.   10078. aaa. 36.

LEES (G. R.) Jerusalem illustrated. pp. 163.
Newcastle, 1893. 8°.   10078. c. 37.

LAGRANGE (M. J.) Saint Étienne et son sanctuaire à Jérusalem. pp. 188. *Paris,* 1894. 8°.
4829. c. 34.

LOTI (P.) Jérusalem. pp. 221. *Paris,* 1895. 12°.
10078. b. 22.

MORTAIS-AVRIL (*Mme.* J.) Pèlerinage 1893-94.
Jérusalem. pp. 456. *Angers,* 1895. 8°.
10078. cc. 4.

JERUSALEM—*continued.*

OLIPHANT (F. R.) Notes of a pilgrimage to Jerusalem. pp. 161. *Edinb.* 1891. 8°.
10078. aa. 18.

OLIPHANT (M. O.) Jerusalem, its history and hope. pp. 515. *Lond.* 1891. 8°. 4516. e. 13.

PÉCHENARD (P. L.) De Reims à Jérusalem. pp. 319. *Reims,* 1893. 8°. 10078. c. 38.

RONCHETTI (C. M.) Jerusalem. pp. 410. *Milano,* 1891. 8°. 10075. f. 12.

ROOKER (J.) Modern pilgrim in Jerusalem. pp. 120. *Lond.* 1895. 8°. 10078. bbb. 1.

SAINT CLAIR (G.) Buried cities and Bible countries. pp. 378. *Lond.* 1891. 8°.
10078. c. 29.

SCHIFFERS (M. J.) Amwâs, das Emmaus des hl. Lucas. pp. 236. *Freiburg* 1890. 12°.
10078. c. 26.

STANLEY (H. M.) My early Travels. 2 vol. *Lond.* 1895. 8°. 10027. ee. 4.

TENZ (J. M.) Description of ancient Jerusalem. *Lond.* 1894. 8°. 4516. b. 38.

WHITTY (J. I.) Discovery of Whitty's Wall at Jerusalem. pp. 18. *Lond.* 1895. 8°. Pam. 88.

See also CRUSADES : JEWS, *History* : PALESTINE.

JESI. COLINI (F.) Memorie storiche jesine. *Jesi,* 1890, *etc* fol. 10135. i.

JESTERS. GABOTTO (F.) La Epopea del Buffone. pp. 94. *Bra,* 1893. 12°. 11429. f. 26.

RODOCANACHI (E.) Courtisanes et Bouffons. pp. 199. *Paris,* 1894. 12°. 12331. ee. 39.

JESUITS.

Bibliography.

BACKER (A. de) Bibliothèque de la Compagnie de Jésus. Nouvelle édition par C. Sommervogel. *Brux.* 1890. *etc.* 4°. 2008. g.

DELISLE (L. V.) Bibliothèque de la Compagnie de Jésus. [Review of Sommervogel's edition.] pp. 10. *Paris,* 1895. 4°. Pam. 6.

SIMONIN (J.) Bibliothèque douaisienne de la Compagnie de Jésus. pp. 338. *Douai,* 1890. 8°. 4999. e 20.

Controversy, etc.

ASCHENFELDT-HANSEN (C.) Jesuiterne og Nutidens Pavedømme. *Kjøbenh.* 1891. 8°. Pam. 25.

BERGGREN (J. E.) Om A. Arnaulds och B. Pascals moralteologiska strid med Jesuiterna. *Upsala,* 1890, *etc.* 8°. 4092. f. 18.

DUHR (B.) Jesuiten Fabeln. pp. 104. *Freiburg,* 1891. 8°. 4091. cc. 8.

EISELE (E.) Wir lassen sie nicht herein ! pp. 24. *Leipz.* 1891. 8°. 3910. ee. 41. (16.)

FANNIUS (C.) Die Quintessenz des modernen Jesuitismus. pp. 113. *Zürich,* 1892. 8°. 4091. f. 4.

FRANKE (C.) Jesu Moral und der Jesuiten Moral. pp. 16. *Leipz.* 1891. 8°. 3914. b. 3. (6.)

GLEIZE (L.) Chez les Jésuites. pp. 276. *Paris,* 1894. 12°. 4091. aaa. 8.

GUILLAUME (L.) Les Jésuites et les classiques chrétiens. pp. 184. *Gand,* 1894. 8°. 4092. e. 2.

HOENSBROECH (P. v.) P. Tschackert und die authentischen Gesetze des Jesuitenordens. pp. 48. *Berl.* 1891. 8°. 4092. f. 19.

—— Die " Preussischen Jahrbücher," Prof. Harnack und die Jesuiten. pp. 110. *Berl.* 1891. 8°. 4091. cc. 9.

—— Warum sollen die Jesuiten nicht nach Deutschland zurück? pp. 152. *Freiburg,* 1891. 8°. 4091. bbb. 22.

JESUITS.—**Controversy, etc.**—*continued.*

HUBER (F. P.) Mein letztes Wort über den Jesuitenorden. pp. 99. *Leipz.* 1895. 8°.
4092. cc. 8.

JESUITS. The Jesuits. pp. 32. *Lond.* 1894. 8°.
Pam. 78.

—— Der Jesuitenstreit in Erfurt. pp. 43. *Leipz.* 1891. 8°. 3911. ee. 51. (9.)

KUNTZEMUELLER (O.) Darf das Jesuitengesetz aufgehoben werden? pp. 106. *Graudenz,* 1893. 8°. 4092. f. 20.

NIPPOLD (F.) Der Jesuitenstreit in Wiesbaden, *etc.* pp. 80. *Halle,* 1891. 8°. Pam. 25.

—— Die jesuitischen Schriftsteller der Gegenwart in Deutschland. pp. 76. *Leipz.* 1895. 8°.
4999. bbb. 28.

OBERBREYER (M.) Für und gegen die Jesuiten. pp. 47. *Düsseldorf,* 1892. 8°. Pam. 93.

QUADT-WYKRADT-ISNY (F.) *Count.* Offener Brief in der Jesuiten-Frage. pp. 20. *Kempten,* 1891. 8°. 3914. b. 3. (10.)

SULLIVAN (E.) *Bp. of Algoma.* The Jesuits and their system. ff. 5. 1890. fol.
1897. c. 8. (100.)

THOEMES (N.) Die Dankesschuld des preussischen Staates und Volkes gegen die Jesuiten. pp. 76. *Frankf.* 1894. 8°. 4091. cc. 12.

History of the Order and of Jesuit Missions.

ROSE (S.) Loyola and the early Jesuits. pp. 632. *Lond.* 1891. 8°. 4829. ee. 9.

PEREZ (R.) La santa Casa de Loyola. pp. 183. *Bilbao,* 1891. 8°. 10160. dd. 2.

HAMY (A.) Galerie illustrée de la Compagnie de Jésus. *Paris,* 1893, *etc.* fol. 4783. h.

—— Documents pour servir à l'histoire des domiciles de la Compagnie de Jésus, 1540-1773. pp. 96. *Paris,* 1892. fol. 4784. h. 7.

REUSCH (F. H.) Beiträge zur Geschichte des Jesuitenordens. pp. 266. *München,* 1894. 8°.
04785. i. 1.

SOMMERVOGEL (C.) Les Jésuites de Rome et de Vienne en MDLXI. pp. 34. *Brux.* 1892. 8°.
4091. bbb. 24.

KREBS (R.) Die Publizistik der Jesuiten und ihrer Gegner in den letzten Jahrzehnten vor Ausbruch des dreissigjährigen Krieges. pp. 248. *Halle,* 1890. 8°. 4091. g. 4.

JESUITS. Die Jahrbücher der Jesuiten zu Schlettstadt, 1615-1765. 1895, *etc.* 8°. Quellenschriften der elsässischen Kirchengeschichte. Bd. 2.
4662. f.

FEY (C.) Der Anteil der Jesuiten an der preussischen Königskrone von 1701. pp. 46. *Leipz.* 1892. 8°. 9008. g. 10. (7.)

THOEMES (N.) Der Anteil der Jesuiten an der preussischen Königskrone von 1701. pp. 112. *Berl.* 1892. 8°. 9008. g. 12. (8.)

WITTE (L.) Friedrich der Grosse und die Jesuiten. pp. 114. *Bremen,* 1892. 8°.
9008. g. 11. (8.)

SCHOLL (C.) Die Jesuiten in Baiern. pp. 71. *Würzburg,* 1892. 8°. 4662. d. 18. (5.)

RICHTER (W.) Geschichte der Paderborner Jesuiten. *Paderborn,* 1892, *etc.* 8°. 4662. d.

POLLARD (A. F.) The Jesuits in Poland. pp. 98. *Oxf.* 1892. 8°. 4785. cc. 29.

MENEZES (C. J. de) Os Jesuitas e o Marquez de Pombal. 2 vol. *Porto,* 1893. 8°. 4625. a. 36.

JESUITS. Ménologe de la Compagnie de Jésus. Missions de l'Archipel, de l'Arménie, de la Syrie, de l'Égypte, du Canada, des Indes Orientales et de la Chine. 2 pt. *Paris,* 1892. 4°. 4092. i. 1.

JESUITS.—History, etc.—*continued.*

EHRENBERG (R.) Die Jesuiten-Mission in Altona. pp. 70. 1893. 8°. Altona unter Schauenburgischer Herrschaft. No. 7.   10250. g. 2.

MURY (P.) Les Jésuites à Cayenne. pp. 283. *Strasbourg*, 1895. 8°.   4765. ee. 31.

SANTIAGO. *Biblioteca Nacional.* Catálogo de los manuscritos relativos á los antiguos Jesuítas de Chile. pp. 543. *Santiago*, 1891. 8°. 4999. f. 11.

ENRICH (F.) Historia de la Compañia de Jesús en Chile. *Barcelona*, 1891, *etc.* 8°. 04785. m. 3.

GUZMAN (L. de) Historia de las misiones de la Compañía de Jesus en la India oriental. pp. 674. *Bilbao*, 1891. 4°.   4766. h. 3.

JENKINS (R. C.) The Jesuits in China. pp. 165. *Lond.* 1894. 8°.   4765. ee. 28.

See also RELIGIOUS ORDERS.

JEVINGTON. FOLEY (E. W.) Reminiscences of Jevington. pp. 25. *Lond.* 1891. 12°.   10347. aa. 37. (3.)

JEWELLERY. *See* GEMS.

JEWS.

General: Social: Anti-Semitic Movement.

AHLWARDT (H.) Die Judenfrage. pp. 26. *Leipz.* 1892. 8°.   4034. l. 43. (6.)

—— Schwerin und Bleichröder. Edelmann und Jude. pp. 95. *Dresden*, 1893. 8°. 4034. l. 42.

ALBERT (J.) H. Heine und der Antisemitismus. pp. 45. *Nossen*, 1892. 8°.   4034. m. 16. (5.)

ALSBERG (M.) Rassenmischung im Judenthum. pp. 40. 1891. 8°. Sammlung wissenschaftlicher Vorträge. N.F. Ser. 5.   12249. m.

ANTISEMITIC MIRROR. Die Antisemiten im Lichte des Christenthums, des Rechtes und der Moral. *Danzig*, 1890, *etc.* 8°.   4034. de. 39.

ANTISEMITISM. Der Antisemitismus und die ethische Bewegung. pp. 59. *Berl.* 1893. 8°.   4034. m. 17. (9.)

ASTFALCK (C.) Ein Beitrag zur Lösung der Judenfrage. pp. 46. *Cöln*, 1892, 8°.   4034. m. 16. (6.)

AUDIFFRENT (J. B. G.) Le seconde à M. Drumont. pp. 33. *Marseille*, 1892. 8°. 4034. k. 34. (10.)

AUERBACH (F.) Der Antisemitismus und das freisinnige Judentum. pp. 21. *Frankfurt*, 1893. 8°.   4034. m. 17. (10.)

BAHR (H.) Interviews. Der Antisemitismus. pp. 215. *Berl.* 1894. 8°.   4034. i. 40.

BARON (D.) The Jewish problem. pp. 70. *Lond.* 1894. 8°.   4034. i. 41.

BERG (A.) Judentum und Sozialdemokratie. pp. 61. *Berl.* 1891. 8°.   4034. m. 17. (3.)

BIRNBAUM (N.) Die nationale Wiedergeburt des jüdischen Volkes in seinem Lande. pp. 44. *Wien*, 1893. 8°.   4034. h. 50. (5.)

BISMARCK-SCHOENHAUSEN (O. E. L. v.) *Prince.* Die Antisemiten und Bismarck. pp. 50. *Leipz.* 1892. 8°.   4034. l. 43. (5.)

CAILLEUX (T.) La Judée en Europe. pp. 221. *Paris*, 1894. 8°.   4516. aa. 17.

CALTHROP (G.) The Jewish question. 1891. 8°. STUART (E. A.) City Pulpit. No. 182. 4478. k.

DARMESTETER (J.) Selected Essays. pp. 310. *Lond.* 1895. 8°.   012356. k. 3.

DIMIDOW (P.) Wo hinaus? Mahnwort an die westeuropäischen Juden. pp. 77. *Charlottenburg*, 1891. 8°.   4034. m. 15. (4.)

DOLFE (A.) Der ewige Jude. pp. 32. *Trier*, 1891. 8°.   4034. i. 46. (4.)

DOMINICUS (J.) Lessings Stellung zum Judenthum. pp. 39. *Dresden*, 1893. 8°.   4034. m. 15. (9.)

DRUMONT (É. A.) Gambetta et sa cour. Barons juifs. pp. 36. *Paris*, 1892. 8°. 4034. m. 15. (9.)

JEWS.—General, etc.—*continued.*

DRUMONT (E. A.) Le Testament d'un Antisémite. pp. 456. *Paris*, 1894. 12°.   4034. de. 46.

DUPONT (E.) La République universelle, gouvernée par les Juifs. pp. 68. *Paris*, 1893. 8°.   4034. f. 38. (4.)

EBERSTEIN (A. v.) *Baron.* 1892. pp. 79. *Wiesbaden*, 1893. 8°.   4034. m. 17. (11.)

ERDMANSDOERFFER (H. G.) Die Juden und die Cholera. pp. 32. *Leipz.* 1892. 8°.   Pam. 11.

FORE-FAURÉ. Face aux Juifs! pp. 317. *Paris*, 1891. 8°.   4034. de. 34.

GERECKE (A.) Die Verdienste der Juden um die Erhaltung der Wissenschaften. pp. 47. *Zürich*, 1893. 8°.   4034. h. 51. (9.)

GERMAN ANTISEMITIC CHRONICLE. Deutsche antisemiten Chronik, 1888–94. pp. 205. *Zürich*, 1894. 8°.   4034. m. 19.

GERMAN CITIZEN. Civis Germanus sum. Von einem Juden. *Berl.* 1891, *etc.* 8°.   4034. l.

HAMON (A. F.) and BACHOT (G.) L'Agonie d'une société. pp. 346. *Paris*, 1894. 12°.   8228. aaaa. 13.

HODENBERG (B. v.) *Baron.* Die Stellung der deutschen Rechtspartei zum Antisemitismus. pp. 37. *Leipz.* 1894. 8°.   Pam. 31.

JACOBS (J.) Studies in Jewish statistics. pp. 59. 88. *Lond.* 1891. 8°.   4034. k. 24.

JEWS. Die Aufhebung der Juden-Emanzipation. pp. 116. *Leipz.* 1895. 8°.   Pam. 31.

—— Ist die Judenfrage eine Culturfrage? pp. 29. *Berl.* 1890. 8°.   4034. m. 17. (2.)

—— Die Judenfrage u. der Antisemitismus vor dem Richterstuhl der Menschlichkeit. *Hamb.* 1890, *etc.* 4°.   4033. k.

—— The Jewish question. From the German. pp. 23. *Lond.* 1891. 8°.   4034. g. 45. (8.)

—— Della Questione giudaica in Europa. pp. 90. *Prato*, 1891. 8°.   4033. de. 10.

—— Der Jude. Zeitgemässe Betrachtung von einem katholischen Geistlichen. pp. 20. *Posen*, 1892. 8°.   Pam. 13.

—— Ernste Plaudereien über die Judenfrage. pp. 80. *Berl.* 1893. 8°.   4034. h. 51. (10.)

—— The Jewish question and the mission of the Jews. pp. 335. *Lond.* 1894. 8°.   4034. i. 37.

JOSAPHET, *Don.* Bibel und Judenthum. pp. 155. *Passau*, 1893. 8°.   4034. m. 6.

KAHN (Z.) Religion et patrie. pp. 32. *Paris*, 1892. 8°.   4034. g. 45. (10.)

KAYSER (F.) Die Ausbeutung der christlichen Konfessionen durch die Juden. pp. 41. *Münster*, 1895. 8°.   Pam. 31.

KOHN (J.) Assimilation, Antisemitismus und Nationaljudenthum. pp. 32. *Wien*, 1894. 8°.   Pam. 31.

KONIECKI (H.) Wustan. Die Götterdämmerung unserer Zeit. pp. 112. *Berl.* 1892. 8°.   4034. de. 42.

—— Die antisemitische " Canaille " vor Gericht. pp. 32. *Berl.* 1893. 8°.   4034. m. 17. (12.)

KOSMOPOLITUS (E.) Die Lösung der Judenfrage in humanitärster Weise. pp 82. *Leipz.* 1892. 8°.   4034. m.

KR., W. Die Fraction der Antisemiten im Reichstage. pp. 59. *Berl.* 1890. 8°.   4034. m. 16. (3.)

LAIE. Der Antisemitismus in seinen Ursachen und Wirkungen. pp. 15. *München*, 1892. 8°.   4034. m. 16. (7.)

LENZ (H. K.) A. Stolz und die Juden. pp. 80. *Münster*, 1893. 8°.   4034. i. 46. (8.)

LEON (S.) Unser heutiges Judenthum. pp. 40. *Berl.* 1890. 8°.   4034. m. 16. (1.)

JEWS.—History—continued.

BIBLE. Old Testament History. By T. H. Stokoe. Oxf. 1895, etc. 8°.   3149. aa.

BLAIKIE (W. G.) Heroes of Israel. pp. 480. Lond. 1894. 8°.   4805. f. 6.

BOSCAWEN (W. St. C.) The Bible and the Monuments. pp. 177. Lond. 1895. 8°.   7704. aaa. 55.

BRUGSCH (H.) Steininschrift und Bibelwort. pp. 344. Berl. 1891. 8°.   12249. cc. 37.

DRIVER (S. R.) Introduction to the Literature of the Old Testament. pp. 565. 1894. 8°. SALMOND (S. D. F.) International Theological Library. I.   3605. k.

FOX (A.) Patriarchs and leaders of Israel. pp. 230. Lond. 1890. 8°.   3155. k. 35.

GORDON (R. A.) The Old Testament History. Lond. 1890, etc. 8°.   4129. aa. 2.

GRUENBAUM (M.) Neue Beiträge zur semitischen Sagenkunde. pp. 291. Leiden, 1893. 8°.   4516. ee. 27.

JACOBS (J.) Studies in Biblical Archæology. pp. 148. Lond. 1894. 8°.   3129. dd. 27.

JOHNSON (J.) Stories of Jewish Heroes. pp. 288. 1891. 8°. Stepping Stones to Bible History. 5.   4420. g. 4.

LORIMER (G. C.) The People's Bible History. pp. 1241. Chicago, 1895. 4°.   3107. e. 5.

MACDONALD (M.) Harmony of ancient History of the Jews. pp. 301. Phila. 1891. 12°. 9009. cc. 4.

MAC CURDY (J. F.) History, Prophecy, and the monuments. N.Y. 1894, etc. 8°.   4516. d.

MALLY (J.) Historia sacra Antiqui Testamenti. pp. 293. Strigonii, 1890. 8°.   3149. g. 18.

MASPERO (G.) Histoire de l'Orient. pp. 240. Paris, 1891. 8°.   9055. aa. 10.

NIEBUHR (C.) Geschichte des ebräischen Zeitalters. Berl. 1894, etc. 8°.   4516. e.

PALUDAN-MÜLLER (B.) Bibelhistorien og den gammeltestamentlige Kritik. pp. 72. Kjøbenh. 1893. 8°.   3105. de. 3. (9.)

POMERANZ (B.) La Grèce et la Judée dans l'antiquité. Paris, 1891, etc. 8°.   9009. d.

RENDU (A.) The Jewish race in ancient and Roman history. pp. 439. Lond. 1895. 8°.   9009. c. 14.

RIEHM (E. C. A.) Handwörterbuch des biblischen Altertums. 2 Bde. Bielefeld, 1893. 8°.   3149. i. 15.

SAYCE (A. H.) The Higher Criticism and the verdict of the monuments. pp. 575. Lond. 1894. 8°.   4429. d. 1.

SCHOEPFER (A.) Geschichte des Alten Testaments. Brixen, 1893, etc. 8°.   3155. l.

SMITH (Sir W.) Dictionary of the Bible. Lond. 1893, etc. 8°.   2000. d.

SMITH (W. R.) The Old Testament in the Jewish church. pp. 458. Lond. 1892. 8°.   2202. b. 1.

GREEN (W. H.) Moses and the Prophets. Works of Robertson-Smith and a Kuenen reviewed by W. H. Green. pp. 369. N.Y. 1891. 8°. 3155. de. 27.

STANLEY (A. P.) Lectures on the history of the Jewish Church. 3 vol. Lond. 1883. 8°. 2212. h.

VERNES (M.) Essais bibliques. pp. 372. Paris, 1891. 8°.   3127. dd. 4.

VISSER (J. T. de) Hebreeuwsche Archaeologie. Utrecht, 1891, etc. 8°.   7705. b. 48.

WEDGWOOD (J.) The Message of Israel in the light of modern criticism. pp. 316. Lond. 1894. 8°.   4034. k. 28.

WILDEBOER (G.) Die Litteratur des Alten Testaments nach der Zeitfolge ihrer Entstehung. pp. 464. Göttingen, 1895. 8°.   3149. i. 16.

ZUNZ (L.) Die gottesdienstlichen Vorträge de Juden, historisch entwickelt. pp. 516. Frankfurt, 1892. 8°.   4034. l. 35.

HARRIS (M. H.) The People of the Book. Bible history to the death of Moses. pp. 184. N.Y. 1890. 16°.   3129. b. 2.

SAYCE (A. H.) Patriarchal Palestine. pp. 277. Lond. 1895. 8°.   4429. d. 3.

HARPER (H. A.) From Abraham to David. pp. 235. Lond. 1892. 8°.   3149. b. 6.

WILLIAMSON (A.) Light from Eastern lands on Abraham, Joseph and Moses. pp. 242. Edinb. 1892. 8°.   3155. de. 24.

TOMKINS (H. G.) Life of Joseph in the light of Egyptian lore. pp. 192. 1891. 8°. By-Paths of Bible Knowledge.   2202. a.

BRUGSCH (H.) Die biblischen sieben Jahre der Hungersnoth nach dem Wortlaut einer altägyptischen Felsen-Inschrift. pp. 162. Leipz. 1891. 8°.   7702. bb. 39.

CAVAGNARO (C.) Gli Ebrei in Egitto. Genova, 1890, etc. 8°.   4516. e.

WRIGHT (G. H. B.) Was Israel ever in Egypt? pp. 382. Lond. 1895. 8°.   4516. e. 23.

BACON (B. W.) The triple Tradition of the Exodus. pp. 382. Hartford, 1894. 8°.   3155. l. 17.

BOYD (T. H.) A crisis in Egypt? What happened on the day of the Exodus. pp. 36. Dublin, 1893. 8°.   Pam. 5.

LAROCHE (E.) Chronologie des Israélites; l'Exode. pp. 176. Angers, 1892. 8°.   7703. f. 25.

MAGNIN (P. de) Le Passage de la Mer Rouge. pp. 8. Nimes, 1891. 8°.   3103. df. 2. (6.)

NETELER (B.) Die Zeitstellung des israelitischen Auszugs in der ägyptischen Geschichte. pp. 16. Münster, 1895. 8°.   Pam. 3.

YOUNGHUSBAND (F.) The Story of the Exodus. pp. 148. Lond. 1891. 8°.   3149. df. 40.

ALBERS (E.) Die Quellenberichte in Josua I.-XII. pp. 150. Bonn, 1891. 8°.   3155. k. 36.

OLIPHANT (M. O.) Jerusalem, its history and hope. pp. 515. Lond. 1891. 8°   4516. e. 13.

KENNARD (H. M.) Philistines and Israelites. pp. 254. Lond. 1893. 8°.   4516. e. 16.

BUDDE (C.) Die Bücher Richter und Samuel. pp. 276. Giessen, 1890. 8°.   3166. ee. 35.

GEIKIE (J. C.) Landmarks of Old Testament history. Samuel to Malachi. pp. 525. Lond. 1894. 8°.   3155. l. 13.

BIBLE. Old Testament. Story of the kings of Israel and Judah. pp. 255. Lond. 1895. 8°.   3165. ccc. 42.

FOX (A.) The Judges and kings of Israel. pp. 266. Lond. 1891. 8°.   4516. de. 1.

HERVEY (Lord A. C.) Bp. of Bath and Wells. Books of Chronicles in relation to the Pentateuch and the Higher Criticism. pp. 175. Lond. 1892. 8°.   4429. aa. 64.

DARMESTETER (J.) Les Prophètes d'Israël. pp. 386. Paris, 1895. 12°.   3187. aaa. 9.

KIRKPATRICK (A. F.) The doctrine of the Prophets. pp. 540. Lond. 1892. 8°. 4456. de. 2.

LEATHES (S.) The Law in the Prophets. pp. 312. Lond. 1891. 8°.   3185. g. 32.

MEIGNAN (G.) Archbp. of Tours. Les Prophètes d'Israël. pp. 756. Paris, 1892. 8°.   3166. ee. 45.

SMITH (W. R.) The Prophets of Israel and their place in History. pp. 446. Lond. 1895. 8°.   2202. b. 3.

JEWS.—History—_continued._

CHEYNE (T. K.) Introduction to the Book of Isaiah. pp. 448. _Lond._ 1895. 8°.   3187. e. 11.

GAUTIER (L.) La Mission du prophète Ézéchiel. pp. 376. _Lausanne_, 1891. 8°.   3185. df. 36.

KOSTERS (W. H.) Het herstel van Israël in het Perzische tijdvak. pp. 152. _Leiden_, 1893. 8°.   4516. cc. 7.

HOONACKER (A. v.) Néhémie en l'an 20 d'Artaxerxès I. ; Esdras en l'an 7 d'Artaxerxès II. pp. 90. _Gand_, 1892. 8°.   3166. ee. 46.

AMITAÏ (L. K.) Étude sur les rapports qui ont existé entre les Romains et les Juifs jusqu'à la prise de Jérusalem par Titus. pp. 136. _Paris_, 1894. 8°.   4516. cc. 6.

BERLINER (A.) Geschichte der Juden in Rom. 2 Bde. _Frankfurt_, 1893. 8°.   4516. e. 21.

SCHUERER (E.) History of the Jewish people in the time of Christ. 1890-91. 8°. Clark's Foreign Theological Library. Ser. 5. Vol. 23-25, 41, 43, 2015. (23.)

DEISSMANN (G. A.) Beiträge zur Geschichte der Sprache, des Schrifttums und der Religion des hellenistischen Judentums. pp. 297. _Marburg_, 1895. 8°.   3126. g. 17.

JOSEPH _ben_ JOSHUA. La Vallée des Pleurs. Chronique des souffrances d'Israel jusqu'à nos jours. 1575. pp. 262. _Paris_, 1881. 8°.   4516. cc. 3.

NEUBAUER (A.) and STERN (M.) Hebräische Berichte über die Judenverfolgungen während der Kreuzzüge. pp. 224. 1892. 8°. Germany. Historische Commission fur Geschichte der Juden. Bd. 2.   4516. ccc. 1.

STEINSCHNEIDER (M.) Die hebraischen Ubersetzungen des Mittelalters. pp. 1077. _Berl._ 1893, 8°.   4999. f. 9.

LANDAU (A.) Geschichte der jüdischen Ärzte. pp. 144. _Berl._ 1895. 8°.   7680. df. 4.

PHILIPSON (D.) Old European Jewries. pp. 281. _Phila._ 1894. 8°.   4034. i. 44.

JEWS. The Jewish Question and the mission of the Jews. pp. 332. _Lond._ 1894. 8°.   4034. i. 39.

KAYSERLING (M.) Gedenkblätter. Hevorragende jüdische Persönlichkeiten des 19. Jahrhunderts. pp. 92. _Leipz._ 1892. 8°.   10606. c. 25.

See also HISTORY, _Ancient._

History, _etc._, of the Jews in various Countries.
Algeria.

AUMERAT ( ) L'Anti-sémitisme à Alger. pp. 224. _Alger_, 1885. 8°.   4034. i. 42.

GOURGEOT (F.) La Domination juive en Algérie. pp. 178. _Alger_, 1894. 8°.   4034. m. 7.

Alsace. See infra : Germany.

Austria : Bohemia.

GREFE (C.) Beiträge zur Geschichte der Israeliten in Wien. _Wien_, 1891. _etc._ 8°.   1852. a. 9,

PENNELL (J.) The Jew at Home. Impressions of a summer in Austria. pp. 130. _Lond._ 1892. 8°.   10292. e. 6.

SAITSCHIK (R.) Beiträge zur Geschichte der rechtlichen Stellung der Juden in Oesterreich-Ungarn vom 10. bis 16. Jahrhundert. pp. 59. _Frankfurt_, 1890. 8°.   4034. m. 14. (3)

EMIL (E.) Erinnerungen eines alten Pragers. Ghettogeschichten. pp. 251. _Leipz._ 1893. 8°.   4516. e. 19.

PRAGUE. Die Inschriften des alten prager Judenfriedhofes. _Braunschweig_, 1893, _etc._ 8°.   10215. e.

See also supra : General, Anti-Semitic Movement.

JEWS.—History—_continued._
China.

CORDIER (H.) Les Juifs en Chine. pp. 14. _Paris_, 1891. 8°.   4516. de. 6. (4.)

GLOVER (A. K.) Jewish-Chinese Papers. 5 pt. 1894. 8°.   4034. k. 29.

England.

Ac. London. _Jewish Historical Society._ Transactions. _Lond._ 1895, _etc._ 8°.   Ac. 8106.

RYE (W.) Persecutions of the Jews in England. pp. 36. _Lond._ 1887. 8°.   Pam. 31.

JACOBS (J.) The Jews of Angevin England. pp. 425. 1893. 8°.   POWELL (F. Y.) English History from Contemporary Writers. 9503. aaa.

—— Little St. Hugh of Lincoln : researches in history. pp. 18. _Lond._ 1894. 8°.   4516. f. 9. (11.)

—— The London Jewry, 1290. pp. 35. _Lond._ 1887. 8°.   Pam. 31.

ABRAHAMS (B. L.) Expulsion of the Jews from England in 1290. pp. 83. _Oxf._ 1895. 8°.   4516. bbb. 3.

WOLF (L.) Crypto-Jews under the Commonwealth. pp. 16. _Lond._ 1894. 8°.   4516. f. 9. (13.)

—— Jewish Coats of Arms. pp. 10. _Lond._ 1889. 8°.   9916. bb. 17. (6.)

LONDON. _Russo-Jewish Committee._ Statistics of Jewish population in London, 1873-93. _Lond._ 1894. 4°.   Pam. 31.

See also ANGLO-ISRAELISM.

France.

LÉVY (.É.) Un document sur les Juifs du Barrois en 1321-23. pp. 15. _Paris_, 1890. 8°.   4516. f. 9. (5.)

GERSON (M. A.) Essai sur les Juifs de la Bourgogne au moyen-âge. pp. 68. _Dijon_, 1893. 8°.   4516. e. 18.

GUIDONIS (B.) _Bp. of Lodève._ Les Juifs et l'Inquisition dans la France méridionale. pp. 20. _Paris_, 1891. 8°.   4516. de. 6. (5.)

LÉON (H.) Histoire des Juifs de Bayonne. pp. 436. _Paris_, 1893. 4°.   4515. f. 2.

LEGEAY (F.) Note sur les Juifs au Mans. pp. 16. _Le Mans_, 1890. 8°.   4516. f. 9. (4.)

KAHN (L.) Histoire de la Communauté israélite de Paris. pp. 144. _Paris_, 1894. 12°.   4516. aa. 18.

MOSSÉ (B.) La Révolution française et le Rabbinat. pp. 283. _Avignon_, 1890. 8°. 4034. l. 24.

See also supra : General, Anti-Semitic Movement.

Germany.

Ac. Berlin. _Institutum Judaicum._ Schriften. _Berl._, _etc._, 1886, _etc._ 8°.   Ac. 2031.

STERN (M.) Die israelitische Bevölkerung der deutschen Städte. _Frankfurt_, 1890, _etc._ 8°.   4516. bb. 24.

LEWIN (A.) Juden in Freiburg i. B. pp. 110. _Trier_, 1890. 8°.   4034. h. 47.

LOEWENSTEIN (L.) Beiträge zur Geschichte der Juden in Deutschland. _Frankfurt_, 1895. _etc._ 8°.   4516. 6.

NUREMBERG JEWS. Memorbook of Nürnberg, the names of the Jews martyred in that city, 5109= 1349 A.D. pp. 29. _Lond._ 1881. 8°.   Pam. 31.

KRACAUER (J.) Die Schicksale der frankfurter Juden, 1612-16. pp. 27. _Frankfurt_, 1892. 4°.   Pam. 31.

GLASER (A.) Geschichte der Juden in Strassburg. pp. 88. _Strassb._ 1894. 8°.   Pam. 31.

GIESE (W.) Die Juden und die deutsche Kriminal-statistik. pp. 107. _Leipz._ 1893. 8°.   4034. f. 38. (5.)

JEWS.—Judaism and Christianity—*cont.*

Priluker (J.) Zwischen Judenthum und Christenthum. pp. 32. *Hamb.* 1891. 8°.
4034. m. 14. (6.)

Quilliam (W. H.) The Religion of the Sword. *Liverp.* 1891, *etc.* 8°. 4503. dc.

Regnard (A.) Le bilan du Judaïsme et du Christianisme. *Paris*, 1890, *etc.* 8°. 4033. dc. 14.

Réthoré (F.) Du passé et de l'avenir du judaïsme et du christianisme. pp. 363. *Paris*, 1894. 8°. 4503. cc. 27.

Reynolds (J. W.) Reasoning with the Jews. pp. 23. *Lond.* 1891. 8°. 4034. c. 51. (5.)

Steinmeyer (F. L.) Der Apostel Paulus und das Judenthum. 1894. 8°. Studien über den Brief an die Römer. 3267. f.

Toy (C. H.) Judaism and Christianity. pp. 456. *Bost.* 1891. 8°. 4376. gg. 11.

Wilkinson (S.) Modern Judaism versus the Bible. pp. 40. *Lond.* 1893. 8°. 4034. g. 45. (12.)

Language and Literature.

See Hebrew Language, *etc.*

Music. *See* Music, *History.*

Prophets. *See supra:* History.

Religion, Ritual, Law, etc.

Abrahams (I.) and Montefiore (C. G.) Aspects of Judaism. pp. 290. *Lond.* 1895. 8°.
4034. d. 69.

Ac. Berlin. *Institutum Judaicum.* Schriften. *Berl. etc.*, 1886, *etc.* 8°. Ac. 2031.

Adler (H. N.) The ideal Jewish Pastor: a sermon. pp. 19. *Lond.* 1891. 8°.
4034. k. 34. (6.)

Benzinger (J.) Hebräische Archaeologie. pp. 515. 1894. 8°. Achelis (E. C.) Grundriss, *etc.* Abt. 6. 3622. e.

Bruce (W. S.) Ethics of the Old Testament pp. 292. *Edinb.* 1895. 8°. 3128. c. 3.

Chicago. *Columbian Exposition.* Judaism at the World's Parliament of Religions. pp. 418. *Cincinnati*, 1894. 8°. 4033. g. 43.

Cobb (W. F.) Origines Judaicæ. Inquiry into heathen faiths as affecting Judaism. pp. 283. *Lond.* 1895. 8°. 4516. c. 24.

Duff (A.) Old Testament theology. *Lond.* 1891, *etc.* 8°. 3149. i.

French (R. V.) Lex Mosaica: or the Law of Moses and the Higher Criticism. pp. 652. *Lond.* 1894. 8°. 2202. d. 1.

Friedlaender (M.) The Jewish Religion. pp. 528. *Lond.* 1891. 8°. 4034. de. 38.

—— Text-book of the Jewish Religion. pp. 98. *Lond.* 1891. 8°. 4033. df. 52.

Gilbert (J.) Nature, the supernatural, and the religion of Israel. pp. 438. *Lond.* 1893. 8°.
4371. e. 12.

Goldstein (M. A.) Gebet und Glaube. Ein Beitrag zur Erklärung und Erläuterung des Gottesdienstes und dessen Gebräuche. pp. 125. *Budapest*, 1890. 8°. 4033. g. 40.

Higgens (E.) Hebrew Idolatry and superstition. pp. 80. *Lond.* 1895. 8°. 4503. aaa. 25.

Jacobs (J.) Studies in Biblical archæology. pp. 148. *Lond.* 1894. 8°. 3129. dd. 27.

Joseph (M.) The Ideal in Judaism and other sermons. pp. 207. *Lond.* 1893. 8°. 4034. i. 27.

Kirkpatrick (A. F.) The Doctrine of the Prophets. pp. 540. *Lond.* 1892. 8°. 4456. de. 2.

Leathes (S.) The Law in the Prophets. pp. 312. *Lond.* 1891. 8°. 3185. g. 32.

Loewy (A.) Half a century of progress, *etc.* pp. 17. *Lond.* 1893. 8°. 4034. k. 34. (11.)

JEWS.—Religion, etc.—*continued.*

Montefiore (C. G.) Hibbert Lectures on the religion of the ancient Hebrews. pp. 576. *Lond.* 1892. 8°. 2212. e.

Moses (A.) The Religion of Moses. pp 138. *Louisville*, 1894. 8°. 4034. b. 54.

Naville (T.) Les Sacrifices lévitiques et l'expiation. pp. 147, *Lausanne*, 1891. 8°.
3155. f. 44.

Paetsch (A.) Skizzen aus der jüdischen Priestergeschichte. pp. 50. 1890. 8°. Pädagogische Sammelmappe. Reih. 12. 8304. dd.

Philippson (L.) Die Rhetorik und jüdische Homiletik. pp. 118. *Leipz.* 1890. 8°.
4034. de. 25.

Quilliam (W. H.) The Religion of the Sword. *Liverp.* 1891, *etc.* 8°. 4503. de.

Riehm (E. C. A.) Handwörterbuch des biblischen Altertums. 2 Bde. *Bielefeld*, 1893. 8°.
3149. i. 15.

Robertson (J.) The early Religion of Israel. pp. 524. *Edinb.* 1892. 8°. 4516. de. 5.

Rubin (S.) Kabbala und Agada in mythologischer Personification der Fruchtbarkeit in der Natur. pp. 58. *Wien*, 1895. 8°. Pam. 31.

Sack (I.) Die Religion Altisraels. pp. 178. *Leipz.* 1885. 8°. 4034. de. 29.

Sayce (A. H.) The Higher Criticism and the verdict of the Monuments. pp. 575. *Lond.* 1894. 8°. 4429. d. 2.

Schultz (H.) Old Testament theology. *Edinb.* 1892. 8°. 3149. i. 11.

Smith (*Sir* W.) Dictionary of the Bible. *Lond.* 1893, *etc.* 8°. 2000. d.

Smith (W. R.) Lectures on the Religion of the Semites. pp. 507. *Lond.* 1894. 8°. 2212. e. 3.

Vaconius (F.) Die messianische Idee der Hebräer geschichtlich entwickelt. *Kirchhain*, 1892, *etc.* 8°. 4034. i.

Vernes (M.) Du prétendu Polythéisme des Hébreux. 1891, *etc.* 8°. Ac. Paris. *École Pratique.* Bibliothèque. Sciences religieuses. Vol. 2. Ac. 8929/7.

Visser (J. T. de) Hebreeuwsche Archaeologie. *Utrecht*, 1891, *etc.* 8°. 7705. b. 48.

Whitehouse (O. C.) Primer of Hebrew antiquities. pp. 159. 1895. 8°. Present Day Primers. 4429. eee.

Zunz (L.) Die gottesdienstlichen Vorträge der Juden. pp. 516. *Frankf.* 1892. 8°. 4034. l. 35.

Bullinger (E. W.) Name of Jehovah in the Book of Esther. pp. 7. *Lond.* 1889. 8°.
3149. g. 23. (4.)

Hopps (J. P.) Who was Jehovah? pp. 24. *Lond.* 1891. 8°. 4227. f. 37.

Norland (R.) Rev. A. Löwy on Elohistic and Jehovistic Proper Names. pp. 16. *Lond.* 1890. 8°. 12901. d. 36. (4.)

Newberry (T.) The Tabernacle and the Temple. pp. 115. 1887. 8°. The Englishman's Bible.
3053. g. 12.

Paine (T. O.) Solomon's Temple and Capitol, Ark of the Flood and Tabernacle. pp. 198. *Lond.* 1886. 4°. 1896. b. 7.

Jelski (I.) Die innere Einrichtung des grossen Synedrions zu Jerusalem. pp. 99. *Breslau*, 1894. 8°. 4034. l. 44.

Wright (C. H. H.) The Synagogue and its lessons. pp. 16. *Lond.* 1893. 16°.
3939. cc. 25. (2.)

Wutzdorff ( ) Der Zukunftstempel des Volkes Israel. pp. 51. *Leipz.* 1893. 8°.
4034. m. 16. (13.)

JEWS.—Religion, etc.—*continued*.

SINGER (J.) Die Tonarten des traditionellen Synagogengesanges. pp. 19. 11. *Wien*, 1886. 8°.   7895. e. 29.

TALMUD. Moëd. *Chagigah*. Translation of the treatise Chagigah. pp. 166. *Camb.* 1891. 8°.   4034. l. 28.

—— Wozu der Lärm? Talmud-Auszüge in philosemitischer und in antisemitischer Beleuchtung. pp. 47. *Leipz.* 1892. 8°.   4034. l. 43. (7.)

—— Der wahre Talmudjude. Geordnet von A. Katz. pp. 165. *Berl.* 1893. 8°. 4034. i. 33.

—— Talmudic Sayings. Selected by H. Cohen. *Cincinnati*, 1894. 8°.   4034. g. 54.

BACHER (W.) Die Agada der palästinensischen Amoräer. *Strassb.* 1892, *etc.* 8°. 4034. l. 34.

BLOCH (M.) Der Vertrag nach mosaisch-talmudischem Rechte. pp. 108. *Budapest*, 1893. 8°.   4034. h. 48.

DEUTSCH (E. O. M.) The Talmud. pp. 107. *Phila.* 1895, 8°.   4034. i. 47.

EISENMENGER (J. A.) J. A. Eisenmenger's Entdecktes Judentum. *Dresden*, 1892, *etc.* 8°.   4034. m.

EISENSTADT (M.) Ueber Bibelkritik in der talmudischen Literatur. pp. 54. *Berl.* 1894. 8°.   Pam. 31.

ESCHELBACKER (J.) Zwei Reden über den Talmud. pp. 47. *Trier*, 1892. 8°.   4034. m. 15. (7.)

IMBER (N. H.) Topics of to-day in the Talmud. pp. 31. *Lond.* 1889. *obl.* 16°. 4034. a. 19.

ISAACS (A. S.) Stories from the Rabbis. pp. 201. *Lond.* 1893. 8°.   4034. i. 29.

LAIBLE (H.) Jesus Christ in the Talmud. pp. 108. *Camb.* 1893. 8°.   4034. k. 32.

PRESSEL (W.) Der Thalmud vor dem Schwurgericht. pp. 68. *Leipz.* 1893. 8°. 4034. i. 32.

REICH (H. L.) Zur Genesis des Talmud. *Wien*, 1892, *etc.* 8°.   4034. m.

ROHLING (A.) A. Rohling's Talmud-Jude. pp. 144. *Leipz.* 1891. 8°.   4034. k. 19.

ROTHENBUECHER (A.) Sohar, Talmud und Antisemiten. pp. 91. *Berl.* 1895. 8°.   4034. f. 39.

STEIN (S.) Materialien zur Ethik des Talmud. *Frankfurt*, 1894, *etc.* 8°.   4034. g.

EURINGER (M.) Der Masorahtext das Koheleth kritisch untersucht. pp. 136. 48. *Leipz.* 1890. 8°.   3166. ee. 36.

KOENIGSBERGER (B.) Aus Massorah und Talmudkritik. *Berl.* 1892, *etc.* 8°. 4034. k. 21.

GELBHAUS (S.) Die Targumliteratur. *Frankfurt*, 1893, *etc.* 8°.   01901. e. 2.

GRUENHUT (L.) Kritische Untersuchung des Midrasch Kohelet Rabba. *Frankfurt*, 1893, *etc.* 8°.   4034. i.

ROSENTHAL (L. A.) Über den Zusammenhang der Mischna, *etc. Strassb.* 1890, *etc.* 8°. 4034. l.

BOIS (H.) Essai sur les origines de la Philosophie judéo-alexandrine. pp. 414. *Paris*, 1890. 8°.   8486. bbb. 28.

DEANE (W. J.) Pseudepigrapha: account of apocryphal sacred writings of the Jews. pp. 348. *Edinb.* 1891. 8°.   3166. ee. 32.

THOMSON (J. E. H.) Books which influenced our Lord and his Apostles. pp. 497. *Edinb.* 1891. 8°.   3186. i. 25.

BACHER (W.) Die Bibelexegese der jüdischen Religionsphilosophen des Mittelalters. pp. 155. *Strassb.* 1892. 8°.   3149. g. 21.

NARBEL (J. L.) Étude sur le Parti pharisien. pp. 257. *Paris*, 1891. 8°.   4516. c. 15.

JEWS.—Religion, etc.—*continued*.

DEDIE (M.) Les Esséniens. pp. 50. *Montauban*, 1895. 8°.   Pam. 31.

WEINSTEIN (N. I.) Beiträge zur Geschichte der Essäen. pp. 92. *Wien*, 1892. 8°.   4516. cc. 4.

SCHWARZ (A.) Die Controversen der Schammaiten und Hilleliten. *Karlsruhe*, 1893, *etc.* 8°.   4034. m.

ARK (B.) Historische Enthuellungen ueber die Juden Moral und das Blutgeheimniss. pp. 42. *Rom*, 1894. 8°.   4034. l. 43. (9.)

DESPORTES (H.) Tué par les Juifs. Avril 1890. pp. 60. *Paris*, 1890. 18°.   4034. f. 38. (2.)

FERN (A.) Die jüdische Moral und das Blut-Mysterium. pp. 47. *Leipz.* 1893. 8°.   4034. m. 16. (9.)

FREIMUT (B.) Die jüdischen Blutmorde. pp. 187. *Münster*, 1895. 8°.   4034. i. 49.

NATHAN (P.) Der Prozess von Tisza-Eszlár. pp. 416. *Berl.* 1892. 8°.   4033. g. 41.

REINACH (S.) L'accusation du Meurtre rituel. pp. 22. *Paris*, 1893. 8°.   4034. h. 51. (11.)

FABIUS (D. P. D.) Mozaïsch en romeinsch Recht. pp. 87. *Amsterd.* 1890. 8°.   Pam. 32.

MENDELSOHN (S.) Criminal jurisdiction of the ancient Hebrews. pp. 270. *Baltimore*, 1891. 8°.   5125. e. 10.

OORT (H.) Oud-Israëls rechtswezen. *Leiden*, 1892. 8°.   Pam. 31.

POHLMANN (W.) Das Judentum und sein Recht. pp. 43. *Neuwied*, 1893. 8°.   4034. l. 43. (8.)

POLACCO (V.) La Questione del divorzio e gli Israeliti in Italia. pp. 75. *Padova*, 1894. 8°.   5176. aaa. 34.

ADLER (M. N.) The Health laws of the Bible. pp. 11. *Lond.* 1892. 8°.   Pam. 31.

ADLER (H. N.) Sanitation as taught by the Mosaic Law. pp. 12. *Lond.* 1893. 8°. Pam. 31.

DEMBO (J. A.) The Jewish method of Slaughter. pp. 111. *Lond.* 1894, 8°.   7291. i. 17.

See also CIRCUMCISION : LAW, *Criminal* : RELIGIONS, *History of.*

JOHANNESBURG. CAPE TOWN. Cape Town illustrated. With information concerning Johannesburg. pp. 131. *Cape Town*, 1891. 8°.   10097. a. 33.

See also GOLD : TRANSVAAL.

JOHNS HOPKINS UNIVERSITY. GILMAN (D. C.) Johns Hopkins University, 1873-93. pp. 15. *Baltimore*, 1893. 8°.   8366. d. 23. (5.)

JOHNSTOWN. Pennsylvania. MACLAURIN (J. J.) Story of Johnstown. pp. 380. *Harrisburg*, 1890. 8°.   10410. g. 20.

JOINERY. See CARPENTRY.

JOINTS. FESSLER (J.) Festigkeit der menschlichen Gelenke. pp. 180. *München*, 1891. 8°.   7182. k. 18.

GUYOT (T.) L'Arthritis, maladie constitutionnelle. pp. 160. *Paris*, 1890. 8°. 7620. df. 22.

MARSH (H.) Diseases of the Joints. pp. 532. *Lond.* 1895, 8°.   7620. de. 34.

PREINDLSBERGER (J.) Die Behandlung der Gelenktuberculose aus der Klinik Albert. pp. 258. *Wien*, 1894. 8°.   7616. dd. 2.

WILLARD (De F.) Erasion in diseases of the Joints. pp. 10. *Phila.* 1890. 8°.   Pam. 39.

See also SPRAINS : SURGERY.

JOLIETTE. JOLIETTE, *Canada* Joliette illustré. pp. 64. *Joliette*, 1893. 4°. 10470. i. 17.

JOURNALISM: NEWSPAPERS.

Bibliography.

Ac. Aberdeen. *University of Aberdeen.* List of Periodicals in the Library.
Aberdeen, 1895, etc. 8°.   011899. i.

Berlin. *K. Bibliothek.* Verzeichniss der Zeit- und Vereinsschriften der Bibliothek.
Berl. 1892, etc. 8°.   011901. f.

Huch (R.) Die Wick'sche Sammlung von Flugblättern in der Stadtbibliothek Zürich.
pp. 26. 1895. 8°. P.P. *Zurich.* Neujahrs-blatt, 1895.   P.P. 4731. b.

Poole (W. F.) and Fletcher (W. I.) Poole's Index to Periodical Literature. First Supplement, 1882–87. pp. 483. *Lond.* 1888. 8°.
Cat. Desk B.

—— Second Supplement, 1887–92. pp. 476.
Lond. 1893. 8°.   Cat. Desk B.

P.P. *New York.* The Annual Literary Index.
1892, etc. *N.Y.* 1893, etc. 8°. Cat. Desk B.

—— *London.* Index to periodical literature of the World, Edited by W. T. Stead.
Lond. 1891, etc. 8°.   P.P. 6483. c.

General.

Bulthaupt (H. A.) Ueber den Einfluss des Zeitungswesens auf Litteratur und Leben.
pp. 56. 1891. 8°. Wolff (E.) Deutsche Schriften. Hft. 3.   12250. i.

Dana (C. A.) The Art of Newspaper making.
pp. 114. *Lond.* 1895. 8°.   011899. g. 2.

Dubief (E.) Le Journalisme. pp. 313.
Paris, 1892. 8°.   11852. df. 17.

Mackie (J. B.) Modern Journalism. pp. 144.
Lond. 1894. 8°.   11852. df. 24.

Norton (B. T.) and Feasey (G. T.) Newspaper Accounts pp. 230. *Lond.* 1895. 8°, 8548. df. 46.

Pen. The Pen as a means of earning a livelihood. pp. 24. *Manch.* 1894. 12°.
011850. eee. 56. (6.)

Philips (M.) The making of a Newspaper.
pp. 322. *N.Y.* 1893. 8°.   11899. bb. 24.

Phillips (E.) How to become a Journalist.
pp. 150. *Lond.* 1895. 8°.   011824. f. 71.

Stead (W. T.) A Journalist on journalism.
Lond. 1892. 8°.   11852. bb. 21.

Yeo (H.) Newspaper Management. pp. 112.
Manch. 1891. 8°.   08225. df. 1.

See also Advertisements : Press, *Laws, etc.*

Austria.

Zenker (E. V.) Geschichte der wiener Journalistik bis zum Jahre 1848. pp. 159.
Wien, 1892. 8°.   11852. e. 24.

France.

Bonjean (F.) Treize ans de Journalisme dans la presse républicaine. pp. 71.
Annecy, 1895. 8°.   11852. e. 31.

Lajeune Vilar (A.) Les coulisses de la Presse, *etc.* *Paris*, 1895, *etc.* 12°.   011850. eee. 50.

Ollivier (O. É.) Du régime de la presse. pp. 39.
Paris, 1892. 8°.   Pam. 69.

Roulet (L.) Trente mois de gérance au journal L'Union Républicaine de Fontainebleau.
pp. 115. *Fontainebleau*, 1895. 8°.   8050. h. 9.

Paris. *Association des Journalistes.* Catalogue de l'Exposition des portraits des journalistes, 1793–1893. pp. 267. *Paris*, 1893. 12°.
7851. aaa. 40.

P.P. *Paris*, Annuaire de la Presse française des colonies et de l'étranger.
Paris, 1891, *etc.* 8°.   P.P. 2404. k.

See also supra : General: Press, Laws.

Germany.

Koch (L.) Die Schattenseiten unserer Tagespresse. pp. 58. 1892. 8°. Bode (W.) Tages- und Lebensfragen. Nr. 9.   8277. de.

Oetker (F.) Die strafrechtliche Haftung des verantwortlichen Redakteurs. pp. 120.
Stuttg. 1893. 8°.   6055. df. 23.

Weigelt (C.) 150 Jahre—Schlessische Zeitung, 1742–1892. pp. 316. *Breslau*, 1892. 8°.
9385. i. 2.

Zangemeister (C.) Verzeichniss der Zeitschriften welche von der Universitätsbibliothek Heidelberg gehalten werden. pp. 99.
Heidelberg, 1893. 8°.   11901. cc. 31.

See also supra : General.

Great Britain and Ireland.

Browne (T. B.) Geographical arrangement of the country press of the United Kingdom.
Lond. 1891. 4°.   11901. d. 27. (3.)

Fisher (J. R.) and Strahan (J. A.) The Law of the Press. pp. 297. *Lond.* 1891. 8°.
6375. h. 25.

Massingham (H. W.) The London daily Press.
pp. 192. *Lond.* 1892. 8°.   4429. df. 30.

Pendleton (J.) Newspaper Reporting. pp. 245.
1890. 8°. Wheatley (H. B.) Book-Lover's Library.   11900. aa.

Reader. The Newspaper Reader: selections from the Journals of the 19th Century. pp. 255.
Lond. 1891. 8°.   12273. aaa. 18.

Wellsman (W. H.) Provincial Press with offices in London. pp. 72. *Lond.* 1893. 8°.
11852. e. 27.

Mayhew (A.) A Jorum of "Punch." pp. 150.
Lond. 1895. 8°.   11852. df. 26.

Spielmann (M. H.) The history of "Punch."
pp. 592. *Lond.* 1895. 8°.   11840. m. 40.

P.P. *Sheffield.* History of the Sheffield Independent, 1819–92. *Sheffield*, 1892. 8°.
11903. bb. 54. (7.)

P.P. *Worcester.* *Berrow's Worcester Journal.* The oldest English Newspaper. pp. 17.
Worcester, 1890. 8°.   011902. m. 20. (9.)

Norrie (W.) Edinburgh Newspapers. pp. 48.
Earlston, 1891. 8°.   011902. m. 19. (12.)

See also supra : General.

India.

Wright (A.) Baboo English: curiosities of Indian Journalism. pp. 108. *Lond.* 1891. 8°.
012314. e. 45.

Italy.

Bernardini (N.) Guida della Stampa periodico italiana. pp. 744. *Lecce*, 1890. 8°.
11899. ff. 49.

Italy. *M. di Agricultura.* Elenco dei Periodici del Regno d' Italia. pp. 80. *Milano*, 1891. 8°.
11899. i. 39.

Luciani (V.) Le Pubblicazioni periodiche nel diritto privato. pp. 166. *Roma*, 1895. 8°.
5373. ee. 33.

Piccioni (L.) Il Giornalismo letterario in Italia.
Torino, 1894, etc. 8°.   11852. e.

Spain.

Criado y Dominguez (J. P.) Antigüedad é importancia del Periodismo español. pp. 93.
Madrid, 1892. 8°.   11852. e. 28.

Hartzenbusch (E.) Apuntes para un catálogo de Periodicos madrileños, 1661–1870. pp. 421.
Madrid, 1894. 8°.   11906. c. 2.

United States of America.

Smyth (A. H.) Philadelphia Magazines, 1741–1850. pp. 264. *Phila.* 1892. 8°. 11852. df. 18.

Weeks (S. B.) Press of North Carolina in the Eighteenth Century. pp. 80. *Brooklyn*, 1891. 8°.
11902. f. 43.

See also supra : General.

JOYENVAL, Abbey. Dutilleux (A.)
Notice sur l'Abbaye de Joyenval. pp. 35.
Versailles, 1891. 8°. 4629. bbb. 17. (3.)

JUBA, River. *See* Africa, *Central and East.*

JÜLICH. Korth (L.) Volksthümliches aus
dem Kreise Jülich. 1892. 8°. Ac. Aix-la-
Chapelle. *Aachener Geschichtsverein.* Zeitschrift. Bd. 14. Ac. 7008.

JUPITER, Planet. Clerke (E. M.) Jupiter
and his System. pp. 44. *Lond.* 1892. 8°.
Pam. 4.
Plassmann (J.) Der Planet Jupiter. pp. 105.
1892. 8°. Ac. Bonn. *Görres Gesellschaft.*
Vereinschrift, 1892. Ac. 2026. (2.)
See also Astronomy : Sun and Solar System.

JURA, Mountains and Department.
Brune (P.) Les Églises romanes dans le Jura.
pp. 46. *Caen*, 1894. 8°. 7808. bbb. 27. (6.)
Gillot (X.) Herborisations dans le Jura central.
pp. 83. *Lyon*, 1891. 8°. 07028. h. 31.
C., E. Histoire de la persécution révolutionnaire
dans le Jura, 1789–1800. pp. 357.
Lons-le-S. 1893. 8°. 4630. df. 3.
Stocker (F. A.) Vom Jura zum Schwarzwald.
Aarau, 1884, *etc.* 8°. 12431. i.
See also Franche-Comté : Geology : Switzer-
land.

JURISPRUDENCE. *See* Law.

JURISPRUDENCE, Medical.
See Medicine, *Legal.*

JURY. Brett (J. P.) Grand Jury Law.
pp. 119. *Dublin*, 1894. 8°. 6146. f. 29.
Brun (P. M.) En engelsk Jurysag. pp. 79.
Kjøbenh. 1892. 8°. 6005. de. 4. (6.)
Huband (W. G.) Treatise on the law relating
to the Grand Jury, Coroner's Jury and Petty
Jury, in Ireland. pp. 1176. *Dublin.* 1895. 8°.
6503. dd. 12.
Lesser (M. A.) Historical development of the
Jury System. pp. 274. *Rochester, N.Y.* 1894. 8°.
6005. aa. 9.
Upward (A.) Trial by Jury and the labour
movement. pp. 24. *Manch.* 1891. 8°. Pam. 82.
Möller (E. J.) Nævninger. pp. 90.
Kjøbenh. 1892. 8° 5725. bb. 11.
Arbinet (S.) Le Jury criminel. pp. 143.
Paris, 1891. 8°. 5103. de. 5.
Durante (S.) Il Giurato italiano. pp. 432.
Torino, 1890. 8°. 5359. cc. 21.
Falcone (G.) La Giuria in Italia. pp. 38.
Palermo, 1891. 8°. Pam. 70.
La Scola (F.) Sul Giuri penale. pp. 92.
Palermo, 1890. 8°. 6055. aa. 11.
Martinez Ibañez (E.) El Jurado ante la razon
y la practica. pp. 235. *Madrid*, 1891. 8°.
6005. a. 5.

JUTE. *See* Textile Fabrics.

JUTLAND. South. *See* Schleswig-Holstein.

KABYLES. *See* Berbers.

KAFFRARIA. *See* Missions.

KAFIR LANGUAGE.
See African Languages.

KAISERLAUTERN. *See* France, *Military
History of the Revolution.*

KAISER WILHELM'S LAND.
See New Guinea.

KALAHASTI. Raghunātha Rāu. Brief
history of Kalahasti. 2 vol. *Madras*, 1891. 8°.
10058. a. 25.

KALEVALA. *See* Finnish Literature.

KALMAR. Baehrendtz (F. J.) Kalmar
slott. pp. 52. *Kalmar*, 1889. 8°. 10105. e. 4. (2.)
See also Småland.

KANDY. Burrows (S. M.) Visitor's guide
to Kandy. pp. 62. *Colombo*, 1894. 8°.
10057. aaa. 8.
Siebel (J. B.) Notes on Kandy. pp. 44.
Colombo, 1894. 8°. Pam. 88.
Kandy. *Queen's College.* Calendar. pp. 28.
Colombo, 1893. 8°. P.P. 2575. w.

KANNADA LANGUAGE. *See* Canarese.

KANSAS. Admire (W. W.) Poetical and legis-
lative Hand-book for Kansas. pp. 459. 71.
Topeka, 1891. 8°. 8156. aa. 6.
Hay (R.) Geology and mineral resources of
Kansas. pp. 66. *Topeka*, 1893. 8°. 07109. h. 43.
Kansas, *State of.* History of the State of Kansas.
pp. 1616. *Chicago*, 1883. 4°. 9603. g. 12.
—— Populist Hand-book for Kansas. pp. 290.
Indianapolis, 1891. 8°.. 8157. bb. 8.
—— Mineral resources of Kansas. pp. 23.
Chicago, 1893. 8°. 07109. e. 19. (7.)
Prentis (N. L.) Kansas Miscellanies. pp. 218.
Topeka, 1889. 8°. 10413. f. 7.
Robinson (C.) The Kansas Conflict. pp. 487.
N.Y. 1892. 8°. 9604. c. 1.

KAPPEL. Rahn (J. R.) Ballinger's Beschrei-
bung des Klosters Kappel. 1892. 4°. Ac. Zurich.
*Gesellschaft für Erforschung Vaterländischer
Alterthümer.* Mittheilungen. Bd. 23. Hft. 4.
Ac. 5367.

KARACHI. Watson (W.) Guide to Karachi.
pp. 115. *Karachi*, 1891. 8°. 010057. e. 20.

KARAKORUM. Gaubil (A.) Situation
de Ho-Lin en Tartarie. pp. 50.
Leide, 1893. 8°. 010055. f. 2.

KARNUL. Karnál. Gazetteer. pp. 322.
Lahore, 1892. 8°. 10056. k. 38.

KASHMIR. Digby (W.) Condemned un-
heard. The Government of India and the
Maharaja of Kashmir. pp. 226. *Lond.* 1890. 8°.
8022. f. 6.
Gordon (J. D.) Work and play in India and
Kashmir. pp. 293. *Lond.* 1893. 8°.
010057. e. 16.
Ince (J.) Appendix to Ince's guide to Kashmir.
Rawal Pindi to Srinagar. pp. 84.
Calcutta, 1892. 8°. 10058. a. 28.
Kashmir Conspiracy. The Kashmir Conspiracy,
or the truth of the Maharaja's case. pp. 92.
Lahore, 1890. 8°. Pam. 67.
Knight (E. F.) Where three Empires meet.
pp. 528. *Lond.* 1893. 8°. 010057. e. 22.
Lawrence (W. R.) The Valley of Kashmir.
pp. 478. *Lond.* 1895. 4°. 10057. df. 18.
Murray (C. A.) *Earl of Dunmore.* The Pamirs.
2 vol. *Lond.* 1893. 8°. 10076. e. 4.
Newall (D. J. F.) The Highlands of India
strategically considered. 2 vol.
Lond. 1882–87. 8°. 10058. bbb. 14.

Avināsachandra Mitra. Medical practice in
Kashmir. 1889. pp. 25. *Lahore*, 1890. 8°.
7306. e. 23. (I.)

KASSAI RIVER. *See* Africa, *Eastern and
Central.*

KATANGA. *See* Africa, *Central, etc.*

KEIGHLEY. Forshaw (C. F.) The Poets
of Keighley. pp. 196. *Bradford*, 1891. 8°.
11601. ff. 20.

KEMPEN. VELTEN (G.) Geschichte des Lehrerseminars zu Kempen. pp. 167.
Düsseldorf, 1890. 8°.   8357. cc. 45.
KENDAL. Ac. Cumberland. *Antiquarian and Archæological Society.* KENDAL. Boke off Recorde containing the acts in or concerning the Corporation of Kirkbiekendall. pp 438.
Kendal, 1892. 8°.   Ac. 5630/8.
KENT.
History and Antiquities.
ABELL (H. F.) Short History of Kent. pp. 95.
Ashford, 1895. 8°.   10352. bb. 61.
CARTWRIGHT, afterwards ADY (J.) The Pilgrim's way from Winchester to Canterbury. pp. 157. *Lond.* 1893. 8°.   10349. h. 32.
FRAMPTON (T. S.) Early presentations to Kentish Benefices. pp. 7. *Lond.* 1892. 8°.   Pam. 29.
GREENSTREET (J. H.) Abstracts of the feet of Fines for Kent, temp. Edward III.
Lond. 1889, etc. 8°.   010358. f. 13.
HARPER (C. G.) The Dover Road. pp. 363.
Lond. 1895. 8°.   010350. i. 9.
HUTCHINSON (J.) Men of Kent and Kentishmen. pp. 160. *Canterbury*, 1892. 8°.   10803. bb. 26.
PAYNE (G.) Collectanea Cantiana; archæological researches in the neighbourhood of Sittingbourne. pp. 218. *Lond.* 1893. 8°.
                                         7709. aa. 30.
STEAD (R.) Bygone Kent. pp. 267.
Canterbury, 1892. 8°.   010358. i. 9.
WILKS (G.) Barons of the Cinque Ports and parliamentary representation of Hythe.
pp. 126. *Folkestone*, 1892. 4°.   8133. h. 7.
Topography.
BEVAN (G. P.) Tourist's Guide to Kent.
pp. 151. *Lond.* 1891. 8°.   10352. a. 59.
BLACK (A.) Guide to Kent. pp. 342.
Lond. 1893. 8°.   10347. bb. 7.
COWPER (F.) Sailing Tours. Pt. II. Coasts of Kent. *Lond.* 1892, etc. 8°.   10360. c.
EWART (W.) Climate of the south eastern counties. 1895. 8°. Ac. London. *Medical and Chirurgical Society.* Climates of Great Britain. Vol. I.   7462. g.
KENT. Murray's handbook for Kent. pp. 22. 296.
Lond. 1892. 8°.   2364. a. 24.
MILES (W.) Field-Path rambles in West Kent.
Lond. 1893, etc. 8°.   10347. a.
VAUGHAN (H. S.) The way about Kent.
pp. 156. 1893. 8°. The Way-About Series.
No. 2.   010358. c.
KENTUCKY. GREEN (T. M.) Spanish Conspiracy. Containing the early struggles of Kentucky for autonomy. pp. 406.
Cincinnati, 1892. 8°.   9603. d. 1.
KERENZEN. GIRARD (T.) Kerenzen am Walensee. 1890. 8°. Ac. Zurich. *Historischer Verein.* Jahrbuch, etc. Hft. 25. Ac. 6997.
KERGUELEN'S LAND. BOSSIÈRE (R. E.) Notice sur les Iles Kerguelen. pp. 31.
Paris, 1893. 8°.   Pam. 87.
KERN DELTA, California. KERN DELTA. Location, resources and development of the Kern Delta. pp. 24. *Bakersfield*, 1893. 8°.
                                         Pam. 85.
KETTERING. BULL (F. W.) Sketch of the history of Kettering. pp. 202.
Kettering, 1891. 4°.   10360. k. 13.
KEW. GOLDNEY (S) Kew. pp. 30.
Richmond, 1892. 8°.   10348. d. 20. (1.)
CHANCELLOR (E. B.) History and antiquities of Kew, etc. pp. 410. *Richmond*, 1894. 4°.
                                         10349. k. 3.
See also LONDON, *Environs.*

KHANHOO. WILKINSON (W. H.) Game of Khanhoo. pp. 31. *Lond.* 1891. 32°.
                                         7915. de. 14. (4.)
KHARTOUM. BORELLI (O.) La chute de Khartoum, 26 jan., 1885. pp. 235.
Paris, 1893. 8°.   9061. c. 8.
See also EGYPT, *History, Modern.*
KHASI LANGUAGE. ROBERTS (H.) Sub-Himalayan. Grammar of the Khassi Language. pp. 209. 1891. 8°. PALMER (E. H.) Trübner's simplified grammars. XXI.   2268. a.
KHIVA. BURNABY (F. G.) A Ride to Khiva.
pp. 334. *Lond.* 1895. 8°.   10076. aa. 8.
Ac. Paris. *École des Langues Orientales.* MUHAMMAD IBN AHMAD, *al-Nasawi.* Histoire du Sultan Djelâl ed-Dîn Mankobirti, Prince du Kharezm. pp. 484. *Paris*, 1895. 8°.
                                         752. f. 35.
See also ASIA, *Central.*
KHORASSAN. HEDIN (S.) Genom Khorasan och Turkestan. 2 del. *Stockholm*, 1892, 93. 8°.
                                         10076. f. 10.
See also PERSIA.
KIDDERMINSTER. KNOX-FERGUSON (J.) Old Kidderminster. *Kidderminster*, 1894. fol.
                                         K.T.C. 25. b. 1.
KIDLINGTON. Ac. Oxford. *Historical Society.* STAPLETON (M. H. A.) Three Oxfordshire parishes. pp. 400. *Oxf.* 1893. 8°.
                                         Ac. 8126/15.
KIDNEYS. BENEKE (R.) Zur Lehre von der Versprengung von Nebennierenkeimen in die Niere. 1891. 8°. ZIEGLER (E.) Beiträge zur pathologischen Anatomie. Bd. 9.
                                         7441. eee. 18.
DAVIS (N. S.) Diseases of the Lungs and Kidneys. pp. 359. *Phila.* 1892. 8°. 7616. e. 11.
FUERBRINGER (P.) Text-Book of diseases of the Kidneys. *Lond.* 1895, etc. 8°.   7630. ff. 33.
KNIGHT (G. D.) Movable Kidney and intermitting hydronephrosis. pp. 129.
Lond. 1893. 8°.   7620. de. 26.
MARCHAL (P.) L'Acide urique et la fonction rénale chez les invertébrés. 1889. 8°. Ac. Paris. *Société Zoologique.* Mémoires. Tom. 3. Pt. 1.   Ac. 3556/3.
RIS (F.) Zur Nierenchirurgie. 1890. 8°. BRUNS (P.) Beiträge zur klinischen Chirurgie. Bd. 7.
                                         7481. ccc. 16.
ROCKWELL (A. D.) Diseases of the alimentary tract. 1894. 8°. BIGELOW (H. R.) International System of Electro-Therapeutics. 2024. e.
ROLLESTON (H. D.) The Coulstonian Lectures on the suprarenal bodies. pp. 45.
Lond. 1895. 8°.   Pam. 39.
ROOSE (E. C. R.) Gout, and its relations to diseases of the kidneys. pp. 229.
Lond. 1894. 8°.   7620. a. 19.
SENATOR (H.) Die Erkrankungen der Nieren. 1895, etc. 8°. NOTHNAGEL (H.) Specielle Pathologie, etc. Bd. 19.   7441. d.
See also DIABETES : GENITO-URINARY ORGANS.
KIEFF. MORRIS (I.) A Summer in Kieff.
pp. 205. *Lond.* 1891. 8°.   10292. h. 10.
KIEL. SARTORI (A.) Kiel und der Nord-Ostsee-Kanal. pp. 64. *Berl.* 1891. 8°.
                                         08235. f. 26.
KILIMA-NJARO. MEYER (H.) Across East African Glaciers. First ascent of Kilimanjaro. pp. 404. *Lond* 1891. 8°. 10097. m. 21.
LE ROY (A.) *Bp. of Alinda.* Au Kilima-Ndjaro.
Paris, 1893. 8°.   10097. i. 18.
See also AFRICA, *Eastern and Central.*

KILKENNY, City and County. HEALY (W.) History and antiquities of Kilkenny. *Kilkenny,* 1893, *etc.* 8°.   10390. f. 17.

KILLALOE. WESTROPP (T. J.) Killaloe: its ancient palaces and cathedral. *Dublin,* 1893, *etc.* 8°.   7709. bbb. 35.

KILLARNEY. FISHER (F. E.) Poems and notes descriptive of Killarney. pp. 68. *Lond.* 1890. 8°.   011653. f. 113.

WARD, LOCK AND Co. Guide to the Killarney Lakes. pp. 172. *Lond.* 1894. 8°. 10347. aaa. 41.

KILMACDUAGH. FAHEY (J.) History and antiquities of the Diocese of Kilmacduagh. pp. 480. *Dublin,* 1893. 8°.   10390. f. 12.

KILOLO LANGUAGE.
See AFRICAN LANGUAGES.

KILPATRICK. BRUCE (J.) History of the Parish of West or Old Kilpatrick. pp. 341. *Glasg.* 1893. 8°.   10370. e. 30.

KILSYTH. ANTON (P.) Kilsyth. pp. 320. *Glasg.* 1893. 8°.   10369. ccc. 25.

KIMBERLEY. CAPE TOWN. Guide to Cape Town. With information concerning Kimberley. pp. 131. *Cape Town,* 1891. 8°.   10097. a. 33.

STOW (F.) A Review of the Barkley Administration in relation to the South African Diamond Fields. pp. 38. *Southampton,* 1893. 8°. Pam. 66.
See also DIAMONDS : GRIQUALAND, *West.*

KINA BALU, Mount. *See* BORNEO.

KINDERGARTEN.
See EDUCATION, *Infants.*

KINEMATICS. *See* MECHANICS.

KINGS' CLIPSTONE. STAPLETON (A.) History of the Lordship of Kings' Clipstone. pp. 82. *Mansfield,* 1890. 8°.   10351. d. 39.

KINGSTON, Kent. KINGSTON. Parish Registers. pp. 189. *Brighton,* 1893. 8°. 9903. c. 14.

KINGSTON-ON-HULL. BOYLE (J. R.) Holy Trinity Church, Hull. pp. 99. *Hull,* 1890. 8°.   010358. e. 14.

LAMBERT (J. M.) Two thousand years of Gild Life. pp. 414. *Hull,* 1891. 4°.   8245. gg. 18.

KINGSTON - UPON - THAMES. KINGSTON, *upon Thames.* Kingston-upon-Thames in 1891. pp. 70. *Brighton,* 1891. 4°. 10368. k. 30.

KINGSWOOD, Gloucester. BRAINE (A.) History of Kingswood Forest. pp. 288. *Lond.* 1891. 8°.   010358. g. 19.

KINROSS. MACKAY (Æ. J. G.) Sketch of the history of Kinross. pp. 268. *Edinb.* 1890. 8°.   10369. f. 6.

KIRBY, West. IRVINE (W. F.) Village life in West Kirby three hundred years ago. pp. 32. *Liverp.* 1895. 8°.   Pam. 90.

KIRGHIZ. DINGELSTEDT (V.) Le régime patriarcal des Kirghiz. pp. 96. *Paris,* 1891. 8°.   5319. c. 10.
See also ASIA, *Central :* TURKISTAN.

KIRKCALDY. KIRKCALDY. Cabinet views of Kirkcaldy District. *Kirkcaldy,* 1891, 4°.   010370. ff. 3.

KIRKCUDBRIGHT. COLES (F. R.) Motes, Forts, and Doons of Kirkcudbrightshire. 2 pt. 1891, 92. 4°. Ac. Edinburgh. *Society of Antiquaries.* Proceedings. Vol. 25, 26.   Ac. 5770/2.

KITE, Ship. *See* ARCTIC REGIONS.

KLOSTERNEUBURG. DREXLER (C.) Das Stift Klosterneuburg. pp. 276. *Wien,* 1894. 8°.   7807. h. 35.

KNEE. JUDSON (A. B.) Contribution to the treatment of White Swelling of the Knee. pp. 7. *Chicago,* 1893. 8°.   7306. df. 22. (7.)

KNEIPP WATER CURE·
See HYDROPATHY.

KNIGHTHOOD. *See* FEUDALISM.

KNIGHTHOOD, Orders of. DAGUIN (A.) Ordres de Chevalerie autorisés en France. pp. 188. *Paris,* 1894. 8°.   9906. g. 16.

ELVIN (C. N.) Hand-book of Orders of Chivalry, War Medals and Crosses. *Lond.* 1894. 4°.   9906. g. 2.

GOURDON DE GENOUILLAC (N. J. H.) Nouveau dictionnaire des Ordres de Chevalerie. pp. 347. *Paris,* 1891. 8°.   9905. d. 34.

GRITZNER (A. M. F.) Handbuch der Ritter- und Verdienstorden aller Kulturstaaten. pp. 618. *Leipz.* 1893. 8°.   9905. aa. 23.

MANSFELD-BULLNER (H. V.) Vort Aarhundredes militaire Ordener og Hæderstegn. pp. 74. *Kjøbenh.* 1889. 8°.   9905. cc. 29.

ROTH VON SCHRECKENSTEIN (C. H.) *Baron.* Die Ritterwürde und der Ritterstand. pp. 735. *Freiburg,* 1886. 8°.   9914. h. 25.

BOSMANS (J.) Les Ordres italiens et leurs membres belges. pp. 62. *Brux.* 1892. 8°.   9902. dd. 12.

BOSSI (V.) Storia degli Ordini Equestri italiani. pp. 171. *Roma,* 1894. 8°.   9914. g. 9.

SCHOEPPL (F. H.) Die päpstl. Ritterorden der Gegenwart. pp. 31. *Graz,* 1893. 8°.   9914. bb. 13. (14.)

BOSMANS (J.) Les Ordres espagnols et leurs membres belges. pp. 99. *Brux.* 1892. 8°.   9902. dd. 10.

—— Les Ordres portugais et leurs membres belges. pp. 119. *Brux.* 1892. 8°. 9902. dd. 11.
See also HOLY SPIRIT, *Order of the :* MALTA, *Knights of :* TEMPLARS : TEUTONIC ORDER.

KNITTING. K., A. E. The Creevo Knitting card. *Kingstown,* 1895.   1810. d. 1. (54.)

LEWIS, *afterwards* HAMMICK (E.) *Lady.* Directions for Knitting socks and stockings. pp. 31. *Lond.* 1893. 8°.   7742. aaa. 8.

ROSEVEAR (E.) A Manual of Needlework and Knitting. pp. 136. *Lond.* 1894. 8°.   7743. bb. 69.

—— Needlework and Knitting for older girls, *etc.* 3 pt. *Lond.* 1894. 8°.   7742. bb. 66.

TRANTER ( ) and ADAMS ( ) Roumanian Knitting cards. 1891. 8°.   7742. aaa. 17.

WAITE (M.) Knitting cards for standards III. and IV. *Leeds,* 1891. 8°.   12210. cc. 2.

WARLEIGH (H. F. R. A.) Full directions for Knitting edgings. pp. 72. *Lond.* 1894, 8°.   7743. bb. 64.

—— Directions and scales for Knitting socks. pp. 96. *Lond.* 1894. 8°.   7743. bb. 63.
See also NEEDLEWORK.

KNOLE, Kent. KNOLE. Guide to Knole House. pp. 56. *Sevenoaks,* 1892. 8°.   10350. de. 25.

KNOWLE, Warwickshire. Ac. Birmingham. *Birmingham and Midland Institute.* Register of the Guild of Knowle. pp. 272. *Walsall,* 1894. 4°.   4705. f. 20.

KOLGUEV ISLAND. TREVOR-BATTYE (A. B. R.) Ice-Bound on Kolguev. pp. 458. *Lond.* 1895. 8°.   10170. f. 37.

KONGSBERG ALVER (J. L.) Kongsberg. pp. 59. *Kongsberg,* 1890. 8°.   10280. aa. 15.

KÖNIGGRÄTZ, Battle of.
See AUSTRIA : PRUSSIA.

KÖNIGSBERG. Krause (G.) Gottsched und Flottwell, die Begründer der deutschen Gesellschaft in Königsberg. pp. 292.
Leipz. 1893. 8°.   010707. f. 34.

Stettiner (P.) Aus der Geschichte der Albertina, 1544–1894. pp. 82. *Königsberg*, 1894. 8°.   8357. dd. 8.

Prutz (H. G.) Die Albertus-Universität zu Königsberg im 19. Jahrhundert. pp. 325.
Königsberg, 1894. 8°.   8357. dd. 7.

KONKANI LANGUAGE. Maffei (A. F. X.) Konkni ranantlo sobit sundor talo. [Konkani grammar.] *Mangalore*, 1892. 8°.   12907. b. 41.

KOREA. *See* Corea.

KORKUS. W., E. F. Brief sketch of the Korkus; hill tribe of Central India. 2 pt. *Bombay*, 1891. 8°.   10058. bbb. 34.

KOSSOVO. Novibazar. Novibazar und Kossovo. pp. 158. *Wien*, 1892. 8°. 10125. e. 12.

KRAKATOA. *See* Volcanoes.

KRIEGSPIEL. G. B. & I. *Army.* Rules for the conduct of the War-Game. pp. 33. *Lond.* 1884. 8°.   Pam. 2.

Rohr (F.) Taschenbuch zum Gebrauche bei taktischen Ausarbeitungen, Kriegspielen. pp. 237. *Wien*, 1894. 16°.   8823. h. 43.

KRONSTADT, Hungary. Zaminer (E.) Geschichte des Waldwesens der freien Stadt Kronstadt-Brassó. pp. 490. *Kronstadt*, 1891. 8°.   07076. m. 16.

KUFSTEIN. Prem (S. M.) Kufstein. pp. 76. *Kufstein*, 1893. fol.   10210. g. 3.

Maretich von Riv-Alpon (G.) *Baron.* Zur Geschichte Kufsteins. 1552–63. 1894. 8°. Ac. *Innspruck. Ferdinandeum.* Beiträge zur Geschichte von Tirol. Hft. 38.   Ac. 760.

KULMBACH. Meyer (C.) Quellen zur Geschichte der Stadt Kulmbach. pp. 314. *München*, 1895. 8°.   10235. k. 23.

Stein (F.) Kulmbach und die Plassenburg. *Kulmbach*, 1893, *etc.* 8°.   10255. h.

KULU. Tyacke (*Mrs.* R. H.) How I Shot my Bears. Tent Life in Kullu. pp. 318. *Lond.* 1893. 8°.   010057. e. 26.

KUMAUN. Gaṅgādatta Upreti. Proverbs and folklore of Kumaun. pp. 413. *Lodiana*, 1894. 8°.   14156. h. 51.

KÜNZELSAU. Ac. Stuttgard. *K. statistisch-topographisches Bureau.* Beschreibung des Oberamts Künzelsau. pp. 911. *Stuttgart*, 1883. 8°.   10256. cc. 10.

KURDISTAN. Bishop (I. L.) Journeys in Kurdistan. 2 vol. *Lond.* 1891. 8°. 10075. f. 5.

Mueller Simonis (P.) Relation des missions scientifiques de H. Hyvernat, *etc.* pp. 628. *Wash.* 1892. 8°.   10075. k. 7.

Nolde (E. F. v.) *Baron.* Reise nach Innerarabien und Kurdistan. pp. 272. *Braunschweig*, 1895. 8°.   10077. h. 18.

Parry (O. H.) Six months in a Syrian Monastery. pp. 400. *Lond.* 1895. 8°. 10077. g. 38.

Menant (J.) Les Yézidiz. pp. 232. 1892. 8°. *Annales du Musée Guimet.*   7704. a. 37.

KURILE ISLANDS. Landor (A. H. S.) Alone with the hairy Ainu. pp. 325. *Lond.* 1893. 8°.   010057. f. 23.

KURUNEGALA. Modder (F. H.) Handbook to Kurunegala. pp. 38. *Colombo*, 1894. 8°.   Pam. 88.

LAACH, Lake. Bruhns (W.) Die Auswürflinge des Laacher Sees. 1891. 8°. Ac. *Bonn. Naturhistorischer Verein.* Verhandlungen. Jahrg. 48. Hlfte. 2.   Ac. 2930.

LABRADOR. Canto (E. do) Quem deu o nome ao Labrador? pp. 23. *Ponta Delgada*, 1894. 8°.   10460. g. 13.

G. B. & I. *Hydrographic Office.* Newfoundland and Labrador pilot. pp. 532. 8. *Lond.* 1887–91. 8°.   10496. gg. 5.

Grenfell (W. T.) Vikings of to-day: Life among the Fishermen of Labrador. pp. 240. *Lond.* 1895. 8°.   10460. bb. 27.

Packard (A. S.) The Labrador Coast. pp. 6. 513. *N.Y.* 1891. 8°.   10470. h. 24.

LA BREA. *See* Trinidad.

LACE. Ac. London. *S. K. Museum.* Supplemental descriptive catalogue of specimens of Lace. pp. 46. *Lond.* 1891. 8°.   Pam. 18.

Brazzà Savorgnan (C. A. di) *Countess.* Guide to old and new Lace in Italy. pp. 189. *Venezia*, 1893. 4°.   7743. e. 10.

Champeaux (A. de) Les Arts du Tissu. pp. 144. *Paris*, 1892. 8°.   7944. h. 33.

Foillet (J.) Das Musterbuch des Jacques Foillet. 1598. *Berl.* 1891. 4°.   7743. c. 16.

Frauberger (T.) Handbuch der Spitzenkunde. pp. 272. 1894. 8°. Seemanns Kunsthandbücher. II.   7805. de. 3.

Hoffmann (W.) W. Hoffmann's Neues Modelbuch, 1604. *Berl.* 1891. obl. 8°.   1810. a. 28.

Melani (A.) Svaghi artistici femminili. pp. 348. *Milano*, 1891. 4°.   K.T.C. 5. b. 19.

Müntz (E.) Tapisseries, broderies et dentelles. pp. 43. *Paris*, 1890. 4°.   7743. g. 17.

Stringher (V.) L'industria dei Merletti nelle campagne. pp. 75. *Roma*, 1893. 8°. 7944. h. 34.

Vecelli (C.) Die Krone der kunstfertigen Frauen. 1691. *Berl.* 1891. obl. 8°. 7743. aa. 20.

Woodward (P.) Handbook to the law of copyright in registered Designs: with special application to class 9, lace. pp. 92. *Nottingham*, 1891. 8°.   6376. e. 30.

See also Needlework.

LACHISH. *See* Palestine, *Antiquities.*

LACHRYMAL PASSAGES. *See* Eye.

LA COUTURE. Boivin-Champeaux (L.) L'Église de la Couture au xviiiᵉ siècle. pp. 36. *Bernay*, 1887. 8°.   Pam. 29.

LACROSSE. Lacrosse. Laws of the game. pp. 28. *Manch.* 1893. 8°.   7912. de. 1. (5.)

See also Games.

LADAKH RANGE. *See* Himalayas.

LADRONES, Islands. Ibañez y García (L. de) Historia de las Islas Marianas. pp. 207. *Granada*, 1886. 8°.   9781. c. 2.

LAGOS. Lagos, *Colony of.* Ordinances and Orders in force, 1893. pp. 1011. *Lond.* 1894. 8°.   06606. h. 2.

Payne (J. A. O.) Table of events in Yoruba history, *etc.* pp. 111. *Lagos*, 1893. 8°.   9061. ee. 31.

See also Africa, *West:* England, *Colonies.*

LAGUNA, Brazil. Fonseca Galvão (M. do N. da) Notas sobre a Laguna. pp. 87. *Desterro*, 1884. 8°.   10480. e. 31. (2.)

LAGUY. *See* German-French War.

LAHNSTEIN, Ober and Nieder. Bodewig (R.) Lahnstein im dreissigjährigen Kriege. pp. 51. *Oberlahnstein*, 1894. 8°. 9004. h. 30. (5.)

LAHORE. Muḥammad Laṭīf, *Saiyad.*
pp. 426. *Lahore,* 1892. 8°.   010057. k. 7.
See also Punjab.

LAHUL. Tyacke (*Mrs.* R. H.) How I Shot
my Bears : Tent life in Lahoul. pp. 318.
Lond. 1893. 8°.   010057. e. 26.

LAIBACH. Hoernes (R.) Das Erdbeben
von Laibach. pp. 61. *Graz,* 1895. 8°. Pam. 27.

LAKES, English. *See* England, *Lake District.*

LAMBETH CONFERENCES. Perry
(W. S.) *Bp. of Iowa.* The third Lambeth Conference. pp. 98. 1891. 8°.   4705. bb. 37.

LAMBOURNE, Essex. Lambourne. The
Parish Register of Lambourne. pp. 76.
Lond. 1890. fol.   9916. f. 36.

LAMMERMUIR HILLS. Browne (J.
H.) Glimpses into the past in Lammermuir.
pp. 180. *Edinb.* 1892. 8°.   10370. dd. 18.

LAMPS. Allemagne (H. R. d') Histoire du
luminaire. pp. 702. *Paris,* 1891. 4°.
       K.T.C. 4. b. 2.
Cardaillac (F. de) Histoire de la Lampe antique en Afrique. pp. 92. *Paris,* 1891. 8°.
       7708. cc. 52.
Cudworth (W.) Antique Lamps. pp. 33.
Lond. 1893. 4°.   7708. aa. 61.
See also Lighting.

LANARK. Lanark. Extracts from the
Records of Lanark, 1150–1722. pp. 433.
Glasg. 1893. 4°.   10369. i. 19.

LANCASHIRE. Axon (E.) Bibliography
of Lancashire Antiquities. pp. 13.
Manch. 1892. 8°.   011902. m. 22. (1.)
Ao. Manchester. *Chetham Society.* Remains.
Vol. 27. N.S. Notes on Churches of Lancashire. pp. 127. *Manch.* 1893. 4°.   Ac. 8120.
—— Remains. Vol. 28. N.S. Lancashire and
Cheshire wills and inventories, 1572–1696.
pp. 252. *Manch.* 1893. 4°.   Ac. 8120.
Axon (E.) Bygone Lancashire. pp. 244.
Lond. 1892. 8°.   010358. i. 3.
Ellwood (T.) Landnama Book of Iceland as it
illustrates the dialect and antiquities of North
Lancashire. pp. 69. *Kendal,* 1894. 8°.
       10280. e. 16.
England. *Committee for the Relief of Plundered
Ministers.* Minutes relating to Lancashire. 1643–
60. 1893, *etc.* 8°. Ac. Manchester. *Record Society.*
Publications. Vol. 28.   Ac. 8121.
Grindon (L. H.) Lancashire. Historical and
descriptive notes. pp. 355. *Lond.* 1892. 8°.
       010358. e. 19.
Lancaster. Lancashire. Cities and towns. 2 pt.
Lond. 1890. 8°.   8225. ff. 1.
Mitchell (F. S.) Birds of Lancashire.
pp. 271. *Lond.* 1892. 8°.   7285. e. 28.
Newbigging (T.) Lancashire Characters and
places. pp. 153. *Manch.* 1891. 8°. 10360. d. 26.
Philips (N. G.) Views of old Halls in Lancashire, 1822–24. pp. 121. *Lond.* 1893. fol.
       1788. c. 28.
Roby (J.) Traditions of Lancashire. 2 vol.
Lond. 1892. 8°.   012330. h. 5.
Stanning (J. H.) Royalist Composition papers,
1643–60. 1891, *etc.* 8°. Ac. Manchester. *Record Society.* Publications. Vol. 24, *etc.* Ac. 8121.
Vincent (J. A. C.) Lancashire Lay subsidies :
Rolls from Henry III. to Charles II. 1893, *etc.* 8°.
Ac. Manchester. *Record Society.* Publications.
Vol. 27.   Ac. 8121.
Waugh (E.) Lancashire Sketches. 2 pt.
Manch. 1892. 8°.   010358. e. 20.

LANCASHIRE—*continued.*
Thornely (J. L.) Monumental Brasses of Lancashire. pp. 322. *Hull,* 1893. 8°. 7709. bb. 62.

Nightingale (B.) Lancashire Nonconformity.
Manch. 1890, *etc.* 8°.   4715. f. 4.
P.P. *Manchester.* Lancashire Congregational
calendar. *Manch.* 1887, *etc.* 8°. P.P. 2485. kf.
Shaw (W. A.) Materials for an account of the
Provincial Synod of Lancaster, 1646–60.
pp. 87. *Manch.* 1890. 8°.   4705. cc. 14. (4.)

LANCASTER. Ao. Manchester. *Chetham
Society.* Remains. N.S. Vol. 26, 31. Materials
for the history of the Church of Lancaster. 2 vol.
Manch. 1892–94. 4°.   Ac. 8120.
Cross Fleury. "Time-honoured Lancaster."
Historic notes. pp. 612. *Lancaster,* 1891. 8°.
       010358. g. 16.
—— Guide to Lancaster Castle. pp. 41.
York, 1895. 8°.   Pam. 90.
Waddington (T. A. J.) Guide to Morecambe
and Lancaster. pp. 35. *York,* 1894. 8°. Pam. 90.

LAND. Cultivation of. *See* Agriculture.

Estate Management.
Curtis (C. E) Estate Management. pp. 428.
Lond. 1895. 8°.   7078. df. 44.
Dowsett (C. F.) Land : its attractions and
riches. pp. 910. *Lond.* 1892. 8°. 08227. ee. 43.
Ephem. Diary and directory for the use of Surveyors, Land Agents, *etc.*   *Lond.* 1892. *etc.* 8°.
       P.P. 2491. u.
Garnier (R. M.) Land Agency. pp. 292.
Lond. 1891. 8°.   07076. g. 15.
See also Agriculture : Forestry : Gardening.

LAND SURVEYING. *See* Surveying.

LAND TENURES.

General.
Altamira y Crevea (R.) Historia de la propiedad comunal. pp. 366. *Madrid,* 1890. 8°.
       6005. aaa. 10.
Beaudouin (É.) La Limitation des Fonds de
terre. pp. 327. *Paris,* 1894. 8°. 5254. bb. 29.
Brickdale (C. F.) Notes on Land transfer in
various countries. pp. 66. *Lond.* 1894. 8°.
       6006. b. 25.
Bryan (E. A.) The Mark in Europe and America.
pp. 164. *Boston,* 1893. 8°.   08207. ee. 20.
Cecil (E.) Primogeniture. History of its development in various countries. pp. 16. 231.
Lond. 1895. 8°.   6005. e. 10.
Fluerscheim (M.) Rent, Interest and wages.
pp. 238. *Lond.* 1895. 8°.   08275. f. 25.
Fustel de Coulanges (N. D.) Origin of property in Land. pp. 153. *Lond.* 1891. 8°.
       08276. e. 9.
George (H.) A perplexed Philosopher : examination of Mr. H. Spencer's utterances on the
land question. pp. 319. *Lond.* 1893. 8°.
       8277. ee. 14.
Meagher (T.) Continental Law of Landlord
and Tenant. pp. 67. *Dublin,* 1883. 8°. Pam. 34.
Morris (R. B.) Summary of the Law of Land
Registration in the British Empire and foreign
countries. pp. 176. *Lond.* 1895. 8°. 6306. f. 12.
Ogilvie (W.) Birthright in Land. pp. 436.
Lond. 1891. 8°.   08276. g. 16.
Simon (G. E) Sur la Terre et par la Terre.
pp. 316. *Paris,* 1893. 12°.   08276. g. 63.
Spence (J. C,) Property in Land. pp. 16.
Lond. 1892. 8°.   8277. ee. 28. (18.)
Viollet (P.) Mémoire sur la tanistry. 1891. 4°.
Ac. Paris. *Académie des Inscriptions.* Histoire, *etc.* Tom. 32.   2099. f.

LAND TENURES.—General—_continued._

Cox (H.) Land Nationalization. pp. 189.
1892. 8°. GIBBINS (H. de B.) Social Questions.
08276. e.

WALLACE (A. R.) Land Nationalisation. pp. 252.
Lond. 1892. 8°. 08276. e. 42.

—— How to experiment in Land Nationalisation. pp. 3. _Lond._ 1892. 8°. 08275. ee. 22. (19.)

Australasia.

—— Land systems of Australasia. pp. 184.
Lond. 1894. 8°. 08276. e. 61.

EPPS (W.) The People and the Land. pp. 23.
Sydney, 1892. 8°. Pam. 82.

MIRAMS (J.) Land question in Victoria. Speech.
pp. 40. _Melbourne_, 1882. 8°. Pam. 66.

TASMANIA. _Ministry of Lands._ Crown Lands
guide. pp. 64. _Hobart_, 1891. 8°. Pam. 87.

Cape of Good Hope.

CAPE OF GOOD HOPE. _Parliament._ Report of
Select Committee on Griqualand West Land
Tenure. pp. 25. _Cape Town_, 1882. 8°. Pam. 66.

FOSTER (J.) Practice of the Deeds Registry
office of the Cape Colony. pp. 120.
Johannesburg, 1892. 8°. 06606. f. 11.

Denmark.

AUBERT (L. M. B.) Grundbøgernes. Historie i
Norge og Danmark. pp. 240.
Kristiania, 1892. 8°. 6955. ee. 12.

DENMARK. _Rigsarkivet._ Kronens Skøder paa
afhændet og erhvervet Jordegods i Danmark.
Kjøbenh. 1890, _etc._ 8°. 5705. h.
See also MORTGAGE.

England.
General.

ALIQUIS. How they got the Land : origin of the
Land-Tax. pp. 16. _Lond._ 1892. 8°. Pam. 82.

DAVIDSON (J. M.) Lay sermon on the Land.
pp. 13. 1887. 8°. 8277. aa. 69. (3.)

DAWSON (W. H.) The Unearned Increment.
pp. 156. _Lond._ 1890. 8°. 08276. e. 19.

DUDGEON (J. H.) The Land Question. pp. 85.
Glasg. 1886. 8°. Pam. 82.

DUMAS (J.) Le Problème foncier en Angleterre
mis en regard du problème agraire au IVᵉ siècle
de Rome. pp. 337. _Paris_, 1893. 8°. 08226. l. 1.

EDGCUMBE (E. R. P.) Village Reforms and the
Liberal Party. pp. 16. _Westminster_, 1892. 8°.
Pam. 68.

FLÜRSCHEIM (M.) Rent, Interest and wages.
pp. 238. _Lond._ 1895. 8°. 08275. f. 25.

HOBSON (J. A.) Co-operative labour upon the
Land. pp. 140. _Lond._ 1895. 8°. 08276. ee. 5.

JESSOPP (A.) Studies by a Recluse. pp. 281.
Lond. 1893. 8°. 012357. h. 2.

LONDON. _Land Restoration League._ Report.
Lond. 1891, _etc._ 8°. 8282. f. 24.

—— Special Report. _Lond._ 1891, _etc._ 8°.
8282. ff.

—— Leaflets, _etc._ _Lond._ 1891, _etc._ 8°.
1890. e. 4. (74.)

—— Among the Suffolk labourers with the
"Red Van." pp. 18. _Lond._ 1891. 8°. Pam. 82.

—— _Property Protection Society._ Leaflets.
Lond. 1892, _etc._ 8°. 08207. g.

REMEDY. United British Provinces. Sequel to
the remedy of Landlordism. pp. 15.
Lond. 1891. 8°. 8139. aa. 53. (10.)

STUBBS (C. W.) The Land and the Labourers.
pp. 228. _Lond._ 1891. 8°. 08276. e. 6.

WATSON (J.) Tenancy and Ownership. pp. 120.
Lond. 1891. 8°. 8228. bb

LAND TENURES.—England—_continued._

WICKSTEED (C.) Our Mother Earth. pp. 48.
Lond. 1892. 8°. 8277 ee. 3. (15.)

—— The Land for the People. pp. 107.
Lond. 1894. 8°. 08275. e. 22.

WILDMAN (J. R.) The Siding Rent question.
pp. 45. _Horsforth_, 1895. 8°. Pam. 23.

History.

ANDREWS (C. M.) The old English Manor.
pp. 291. _Baltimore_, 1892. 8°. 8275. g. 48.

ASHLEY (W. J.) The English Manor. 1891. 8°.
FUSTEL DE COULANGES (N. D.) The Origin of
Property in Land. 08276. e. 9.

—— Character of Villein Tenure. pp. 15.
Toronto, 1891. 8°. 6146. d. 22. (3.)

GARNIER (R. M.) History of the English Landed
Interest. pp. 406. _Lond._ 1892. 8°.
2238. cc. 14.

—— Annals of the British Peasantry. pp. 460.
Lond. 1895. 8°. 08277. g. 20.

GREEN (J. L.) Old Yeomen of England and
small holdings. pp. 43. _Lond._ 1892. 8°.
8277. ee. 1. (15.)

VINOGRADOV (P. G.) Villainage in England.
pp. 464. _Oxf._ 1892. 8°. 2240. d. 23.
See also FEUDALISM.

Law.

EDWARDS (W. D.) Compendium of the Law of
property in Land. pp. 558. _Lond._ 1891. 8°.
6306. f. 6.

GREENWOOD (H.) Our Land-Laws as they are.
pp. 135. _Lond._ 1891. 8°. 6306. a. 23.

LEFEVRE (_Right Hon._ G. J. S.) Agrarian Tenures.
pp. 313. _Lond._ 1893. 8°. 6306. bb. 16.

LIGHTWOOD (J. M.) Treatise on possession of
Land. pp. 342. _Lond._ 1894. 8°. 6306. f. 11.

POLLOCK (_Sir_ F.) The Land Laws. pp. 226.
1887. 8°. The English Citizen. 2238. bb.

SOLON (H.) The Land Laws. pp. 18.
Lond. 1890. 8°. 08276. f. 21. (10.)

CLERKE (A. S. J.) Law and practice under the
Settled Land Acts. pp. 256. _Lond._ 1891. 8°.
6305. df. 23.

HOOD (H. J.) and CHALLIS (H. W.) Conveyancing and Settled Land Acts. pp. 516.
Lond. 1895. 8°. 2232. e. 16.

Ao. London. _Cobden Club._ DILL (T. R. C.)
Transfer of Land by registration of Title.
pp. 58. _Lond._ 1893. 8°. 8228. bb.

BRICKDALE (C. F.) Law and practice respecting
the registration of Deeds in Middlesex.
pp. 82. _Lond._ 1892. 8°. 6306. bb. 14.

—— Notes on Land Transfer in various countries. pp. 66. _Lond._ 1894. 8°. 6006. b. 25.

COMYNS (W. H.) Exercises on Abstracts of Title.
pp. 315. _Lond._ 1895. 8°. 6306. f. 14.

EMMET (L. E.) Notes on perusing Titles.
pp. 240. _Lond._ 1895. 8°. 6305. a. 53.

ENGLAND. _Land Registry._ Examples of the
modes of Registration. pp. 24. _Lond._ 1893. fol.
6126. l. 1. (5.)

MORRIS (R. B.) Summary of the Law of Land
and Mortgage registration. pp. 176.
Lond. 1895. 8°. 6306. f. 12.

BROUGHTON-ROUSE (E. B.) The Law of Heriots.
pp. 46. _Lond._ 1892. 8°. 6306. h. 10.

BROWN (A.) Law and practice of Enfranchisement and Commutations. pp. 503.
Lond. 1895. 8°. 6306. aa. 44.

DANIELS (G. St. L.) Leases: principles and
points. pp. 195. _Lond._ 1895. 8°. 6306. a. 29.

LAND TENURES.—England—*continued.*

DANIELS (G. St. L.) Compendium of Commission cases. pp. 313. *Lond.* 1893. 8°.   6305. a. 52.

DAVISON (C. J.) Practical hints to Persons taking leases. pp. 23. *Lond.* 1894. 12°.   6145. aa. 36. (4.)

ELTON (C. I.) Treatise on the Law of Copyholds. pp. 660. *Lond.* 1893. 8°.   2230. b. 4.

RUDALL (A. R.) and GREIG (J. W.) The Law as to Copyhold enfranchisement. pp. 318. *Lond.* 1895. 8°.   6306. a. 27.

RYE (W.) "Leasehold Enfranchisement." pp. 16. *Norwich,* 1891. 8°.   Pam. 32.

TARN (A. W.) S. Brown Prize Essay on the enfranchisement of Leaseholds. pp. 83. *Lond.* 1893. 8°.   08227. i. 15.

TUNBRIDGE (W. S.) Law and Practice of Copyhold enfranchisement and commutation. pp. 100. *Lond.* 1888. 8°.   6306. aaa. 1.

WILLIAMS (J. H.) and YATES (W. B.) Law of Ejectment or recovery of possession of Land. pp. 404. *Lond.* 1894. 8°.   6306. e. 8.

BANKS (G.) Treatise on the Law of support for Land. pp. 177. *Lond.* 1894. 8°.   6306. h. 16.

See also CONVEYANCING : DISTRESS : EASEMENTS : LANDLORD AND TENANT : MORTGAGE : PROPERTY.

Small Holdings.

Ac. London. *Cobden Club.* BEAR (W. E.) Study of Small Holdings. pp. 98. *Lond.* 1893. 8°.   8228. bb.

DODD (J. T.) The Small Holdings Act, 1892. pp. 55. *Lond.* 1892. 8°.   6306. aa. 38.

FORSTER (C. D.) Manual of the Law relating to Small Agricultural Holdings. pp. 84. *Lond.* 1892. 12°.   6426. cc. 27.

GLADSTONE (*Right Hon.* W. E.) The Tory Small Holdings Bill. pp. 14. *Westminster,* 1892. 8°.   Pam. 68.

LEADAM (I. S.) Allotments and Small Holdings. pp. 8. *Altrincham,* 1890. 8°.   8282. g. 24. (4.)

MILLER (H. E.) Small Holdings Act, 1892. pp. 98. *Lond.* 1892. 8°.   6306. aa. 40.

SOULBY (A. E. B.) The Small Holdings Act, 1892. pp. 59. *Malton,* 1892. 8°.   6306. e. 6.

SPENCER (A. J.) The Small Holdings Act, 1892. pp. 56. *Lond.* 1892. 8°.   6306. bb. 15.

Taxation of Land.

BOURDIN (M. A.) Exposition of the Land Tax. pp. 228. *Lond.* 1894. 8°.   6426. df. 23.

JUSTITIA. Ought Landowners to bear a share of Local Taxation? pp. 31. *Edinb.* 1891. 8°.   08226. k. 14. (11.)

LAMOND (R. P.) The Taxation of Land. pp. 20. *Glasg.* 1894. 8°.   08226. k. 6. (14.)

BEKEN (G.) The Taxation of ground-rents. pp. 12. *Lond.* 1893. 8°.   8277. ee. 30. (18.)

DOWSETT (C. F.) Ground values Delusion. pp. 17. *Lond.* 1892. 8°.   08227. ee. 46. (16.)

MOULTON (J. F.) Taxation of Ground values. pp. 16. *Lond.* 1885. 8°.   8139. bbb. 48. (4.)

F., C. A. M. Rates and Ground-values. Review of the "Taxation of Ground-values, by J. F. Moulton." pp. 24. *Lond.* 1892. 8°.   Pam. 82.

WEBB (S.) Plea for the Taxation of Ground rents. pp. 15. *Lond.* 1887. 8°. 8282. ff. 11. (1.)

France.

BUREAU (P.) Le Homestead, ou l'insaisissabilité de la petite propriété foncière. pp. 391. *Paris,* 1895. 8°.   6616. cc. 6.

CHÉNON (E.) Les Démembrements de la propriété foncière en France. pp. 178. *Paris,* 1881. 8°.   5421. c. 3.

LAND TENURES.—France—*continued.*

LANÉRY D'ARC (P.) Du Franc aleu. pp. 455. *Paris,* 1888. 8°.   5403. ff. 25.

REROLLE (L.) Du Colonage partiaire et du métayage. pp. 674. *Paris,* 1888. 8°. 8282. f. 28.

VACHEZ (A.) Histoire de l'acquisition des terres nobles par les roturiers dans Lyonnais, Forez et Beaujolais du XIIIᵉ au XVIᵉ siècle. pp. 87. *Lyon,* 1891. 8°.   08276. k. 6.

See also FEUDALISM.

Germany.

AUBERT (L. M. B.) Grundbøgernes Historie i Tyskland. pp. 240. *Kristiania,* 1892, 8°.   6955. ee. 12.

BAVARIA. Das bayerische Landrecht, 1756. pp. 373. *München,* 1894. 8°.   5604. h. 22.

BRUENNECK (W. v.) Zur Geschichte des Grundeigenthums in Ost- und Westpreussen. *Berl.* 1891, *etc.* 8°.   5604. d. 1.

GERMANY. Entwurf einer Grundbuchordnung. 2 pt. *Berl.* 1889. 8°.   5604. g. 14.

LANDAGITATION. Zur Landagitation. pp. 16. *Berl.* 1891. 8°.   8277. ee. 33. (8.)

LEONI (A.) Die elsass-lothringischen Gesetze betreffend Grundeigenthum. pp. 248. *Strassb.* 1892. 8°.   5551. aa. 2.

MEYER (R.) Das Sinken der Grundrente. pp. 150. *Wien,* 1894. 8°.   08276. h. 55.

RABE (O.) Die volkswirtschaftliche bedeutung der Pacht. pp. 92. *Berl.* 1891. 8°. 08227. f. 27.

ROCKINGER (L. v.) Denkmäler des Baierischen Landesrechts vom 13. bis 16. Jahrhundert. *München,* 1891, *etc.* 4°.   5605. h. 20.

RUELF (J.) Das Erbrecht als Erbübel. pp. 216. *Leipz.* 1893. 8°.   6005. h. 20.

SCHULLERN-SCHRATTENHOFEN (H. v.) Untersuchungen über Begriff der Grundrente. pp. 168. *Leipz.* 1889. 8°.   08225. k. 8.

SCHWARTZ (E.) Das preussische Grundbuchrecht. *Berl.* 1892, *etc.* 8°.   05604. i. 3.

India.

AVINĀSACHANDRA MITRA. Transfer of Property Act, 1882. pp. 85. *Calcutta,* 1891. 8°. 6306. e. 7.

FRENCH (J.) Rent Recovery Act, Madras, 1865. pp. 108. *Madras,* 1894. 8°.   5319. aaa. 36.

MĀNEKJĪ BAHRĀMJĪ DADABHAI. Central Provinces Tenancy Act. pp. 534. *Bombay,* 1893. 8°.   05319. i. 9.

POWELL (B. H. B.) Land-systems of British India. 3 vol. *Oxf.* 1892. 8°.   2238. cc. 12.

—— Account of the Land Revenue and its administration in British India. pp. 260. *Oxf.* 1894. 8°.   8023. b. 12.

RAGUNATHA RAU. Letter on the Land tenure of Tanjore. pp. 21. *Madras,* 1890. 8°. Pam. 33.

See also MORTGAGE.

Ireland.

ACASON (W.) Land Purchase Hand-book. pp. 69. *Dublin,* 1891. 8°.   6503. a. 4.

CHERRY (R. R.) Irish Land Law and Land Purchase Acts, 1860 to 1891. pp. 769. *Dublin,* 1893. 8°.   6503. dd. 10.

G. B. & I. Record of Title, Ireland. General rules. pp. 104. *Dublin,* 1886. 8°. 6503. aaa. 18.

GREY (*Sir* G.) The Irish Land question. pp. 20. *Auckland,* 1889. 8°.   8146. cc. 5. (5.)

IRELAND. Present position and claims of Irish Landowners. pp. 16. *Dublin,* 1888. 8°.   8146. cc. 5. (3.)

JOHNSTON (H. A.) Irish Justice exhibited in the procedure of the Irish Land Commission. pp. 19. *Lond.* 1894. 8°. 8146. bbb. 51. (11.)

LAND TENURES.—Ireland—_continued._

LEECH (H. B.) Irish Landowners' Convention. Registration of title v. registration of assurances. pp. 156. _Lond._ 1891. 8°.　　6503. e. 3.

LEFEVRE (_Right. Hon._ G. J. S.) Agrarian Tenures. pp. 313. _Lond._ 1893. 8°. 6306. bb. 16.

NOLAN (F.) and KANE (R. R.) Statutes relating to the Law of Landlord and Tenant in Ireland. _Dublin_, 1892, _etc._ 8°.　　6503. bb. 12.

PEARSON (J.) Fair Rent: how found. pp. 36. _Dublin_, 1891. 8°.　　08227. ee. 46. (12.)

SULLIVAN (A. M.) New Land Bill explained. 2 pt. _Dublin_, 1881. 8°.　　8146. cc. 5. (1.)

See also supra: England : IRELAND, _Politics._

Italy.

CIANCI SANSEVERINO (N.) I Campi pubblici di alcuni Castelli del medio evo in Basilicata. pp. 176. _Napoli_, 1891. 8°.　　5359. ee. 31.

PIRRO (V. de) Della Enfiteusi. pp. 384. _Lanciano_, 1893. 8°.　　5373. ee. 31.

See also infra : Rome.

Japan.

SIMMONS (D. B.) Notes on Land Tenure in old Japan. 1891. 8°. Ac. Yokohama. _Asiatic Society._ Transactions. Vol. 19. Ac. 8828/6.

Netherlands.

GRATAMA (S.) Het Beklemrecht in zijne geschiedkundige ontwikkeling. _Groningen_, 1893, _etc._ 8°.　　5686. dd.

Norway.

AUBERT (L. M. B.) Grundbøgernes Historie i Norge. pp. 240. _Kristiania_, 1892. 8°.　　6955. ee. 12.

Palestine.

NEIL (J.) Land Tenure as preserved in the village-communities in Palestine. pp. 49. _Lond._ 1891, 8°.　　08276. g. 6.

Rome, Ancient.

BEAUDOUIN (É.) La Limitation des Fonds de terre. pp. 327. _Paris_, 1894. 8°. 5254. bb. 29.

DUMAS (J.) Le Problème foncier en Angleterre mis en regard du problème agraire au IV° siècle de Rome. pp. 337. _Paris_, 1893. 8°. 08226. l. 1.

STEPHENSON (A.) Public Lands and agrarian laws of the Republic. pp. 101. 1891, 8°. Johns Hopkins University Studies. Ser. 9. No. 7-8.　　Ac. 2689.

Scotland.

ARMOUR (S. B.) Valuation of property for rating in Scotland. pp. 380. _Edinb._ 1892. 8°.　　6583. c. 7.

ERSKINE (J.) Land Question : an enquiry into the ownership of land applicable to Scotland. pp. 131. _Glasg._ 1895. 8°.　　08275. f. 36.

LEFEVRE (_Right Hon._ G. J. S.) Agrarian Tenures. pp. 313. _Lond._ 1893. 8°. 6306. bb. 16.

RANKINE (J.) Treatise on the Law of Leases in Scotland. pp. 743. _Edinb._ 1893. 8°. 6573. h. 7.

—— Lecture on the Agricultural Holdings, Scotland, Act, 1883. pp. 72. _Edinb._ 1894. 8°.　　6583. a. 6.

MACKENZIE (A.) Analysis of the report of the Crofter Commission. pp. 79. _Inverness_, 1894. 8°.　　8142. d. 3.

MALCOLM (G.) Local migration of Crofters. pp. 95. _Edinb._ 1894. 8°.　　8142. d. 4.

See also supra : England : CONVEYANCING.

Spain.

GALLARDO Y MARTINEZ (A.) La movilización de la propiedad y el acta Torrens. pp. 197. _Barcelona_, 1893. 8°.　　6306. f. 10.

Tunis.

TUNIS. Loi foncière et règlements annexes. pp. 231. _Paris_, 1893. 8°.　　05319. k. 5.

LAND TENURES—_continued._

Turkey.

ARSLANIAN (D.) Das gesammte Recht des Grundeigenthums in der Türkei. pp. 48. _Wien_, 1894. 8°.　　5551. g. 20. (14.)

TURKEY. The Ottoman Land Code. pp. 396. _Lond._ 1892. 8°.　　758. d. 29.

United States.

ALLINSON (E. P.) Ground rents in Philadelphia. pp. 19. 1888. 8°. Ac. Philadelphia. _University._ Publications. Political Economy Series. No. 3.　　Ac. 2692. p.

ASHBY (N. B.) The Riddle of the sphinx. pp. 474. _Des Moines_, 1890. 8°.　　08207. g. 8.

MASON (O. T.) The Land Problem. 1897. 8°. Ac. Brooklyn. _Ethical Association._ Evolution Series. No. 22.　　7006. bbb.

PHILLIPS (W. A.) Labor, Land and law. pp. 471. _N.Y._ 1886. 12°.　　8277. ee. 23.

WAPLES (R.) A Treatise on Homestead and exemption. pp. 1027. _Chicago_, 1893. 8°.　　06616. k. 8.

See also MORTGAGE.

Wales.

RUTHIN. Court rolls of the Lordship of Ruthin or Dyffryn-Clwydd of the reign of Edward I. pp. 61. 1893. 8°. Cymmrodorion Record Series. No. 2.　　Ac. 8227/10.

WALES, _North._ Naturalisation of Land with reference to North Wales. pp. 16. _Lond._ 1892. 8°.　　8277. ee. 30. (17.)

LANDAU, HEUSER (E.) Die Belagerungen von Landau, 1702-03. pp. 208. _Lond._ 1894. 8°.　　9079. f. 13.

LANDES, Department and District.
DUFOURCET (J. E.) Les Landes et les Landais. pp. 496. 11. _Dax_, 1892. 8°.　　10169. dd. 16.

LANDE POPULAR POETRY. Poésie Populaire landaise. pp. 41. _Dax_, 1890. 8°.　　Pam. 59.

See also GASCONY.

LANDLORD AND TENANT, Law of.
FOA (E.) Relationship of Landlord and Tenant. pp. 765. _Lond._ 1895. 8°.　　6306. h. 18.

LAW. Law of Landlord and Tenant. pp. 255. _Lond._ 1891. 8°.　　6306. c. 4.

MEAGHER (T.) Continental law of Landlord and Tenant. pp. 67. _Dublin_, 1883. 8°.　　Pam. 34.

NOLAN (F.) and KANE (R. R.) Statutes relating to the law of Landlord and Tenant in Ireland. _Dublin_, 1892, _etc._ 8°.　　6503. bb. 12.

REDMAN (J. H.) and LYON (G. E.) Law of Landlord and Tenant. pp. 677. _Lond._ 1893. 8°.　　6325. cc. 25.

WETHERFIELD (F.) A B C of the law of Landlord, Tenant and Lodger. pp. 96. _Lond._ 1892. 8°.　　6325. a. 74.

WOODFALL (W.) Woodfall's Law of Landlord and Tenant. pp. 1118. _Lond._ 1893. 8°. 2017. f. _See also_ LAND TENURES.

LANDSBERG, Brandenburg. ECKERT (R.) Geschichte von Landsberg Warthe. _Landsberg_, 1890, _etc._ 8°.　　10235. k.

LANGENSALZA, Battle of.
See HANOVER : PRUSSIA.

LANGRES. Ac. Langres. _Société Historique._ VIGNIER (J.) Décade historique du diocèse de Langres. _Langres_, 1891, _etc._ 8°.　　Ac. 5310/3.

MARCEL (L.) Les Livres liturgiques de l'Église de Langres. pp. 88. _Paris_, 1890. 8°.　　4999. ee. 15.

LANGUAGE.—Phonetics—*continued.*

For the Phonetics of each language, *see* the Language required.

Sign Language.

See INDIAN LANGUAGES, *American.*

Speech of Monkeys. *See* MONKEYS.

Study and Teaching of Languages.

BREYMANN (H.) Die neusprachliche Reform-Literatur, 1876-93. pp. 155. *Leipz.* 1895. 8°.
011901. e. 30.

BREAL (M.) De l'Enseignement de Langues vivantes. pp. 147. *Paris,* 1893. 8°. 8355. de. 6.

ELLIOTT (A. M.) Methods of teaching modern Languages. pp. 185. *Bost.* 1893. 8°. 8311. b. 23.

GOUIN (F.) L'Art d'enseigner et d'étudier les Langues. pp. 95. *Paris,* 1886. 16°.
12902. bb. 38.

—— Art of teaching and studying Languages. pp. 407. *Lond.* 1892. 8°. 12902. cc. 48.

KLINGHARDT (H.) Drei weitere Jahre Erfahrungen mit der imitativen Methode. pp. 162. *Marburg,* 1892. 8°. 8310. d. 9.

LANGE (F. K. W.) Uniform series of graduated Language Courses. *Lond.* 1891, *etc.* 8°. 12901. ccc.

LAURIE (S. S.) Lectures on Language and linguistic method. pp. 197. *Edinb.* 1893. 8°.
12901. d. 39.

LENTZNER (C.) On the study of European Languages. pp. 20. *Lond.* 1892. 8°.
12901. ccc. 17. (10.)

LONDON. *Central School Association.* Systematic teaching of Languages on the "Series Method." pp. 60. *Lond.* 1894. 8°. 12903. e. 26. (10.)

MUELLER (F. M.) Lectures on the Science of Language and its place in education. pp. 112. *Lond.* 1891. 8°. 12902. cc. 45.

P.P. *Havre.* Revue de l'Enseignement des Langues vivantes. *Havre,* 1889, *etc.* 8°.
P.P. 1199. f.

—— *Leipsic.* Neuphilologische Blätter. *Leipz.* 1894, *etc.* 8°. P.P. 5044. cc.

—— *Paris.* Annuaire de l'Enseignement des Langues vivantes. *Paris,* 1891, *etc.* 8°.
P.P. 2404. i.

PHILOLOGIE. Wie studiert man neuere Philologie. pp. 43. *Leipz.* 1892. 8°. 12902. bb. 40. (9.)

POEHLMANN (L.) Die natürliche Methode Sprachen zu lernen. pp. 21. *Lond.* 1891. 8°.
Pam. 47.

—— The natural way of learning a Language. pp. 16. *Lond.* 1890. 8°. 12901. ccc. 13. (7.)

POIRÉ (A. C.) How to learn a Language. pp. 19. *Halifax,* 1894. 8°. 12903. e. 26. (11.)

SPINDLER (P.) Methode Schliemann zur Erlernung fremden Sprachen. *Leipz.* 1892, *etc.* 8°. 12901. k.

STENKULA (A. O.) Språkbildning i folkskolan. pp. 83. *Malmö,* 1890. 8°. Pam. 17.

STIEHLER (E. O.) Zur Methodik des neusprachlichen Unterrichts. pp. 54. *Marburg,* 1891. 8°. 8304. c. 19. (15.)

SYSTEM. The aural System for the mastery of a foreign Language, *etc.* pp. 16. *Bradford,* 1895. 8°. Pam. 47.

VERITAS ( ) Klassische Bildung. pp. 96. *Görlitz,* 1893. 8°. 8311. e. 4.

WHITFIELD (E. E.) Guide to the study of Languages for business purposes. pp. 32. *Lond.* 1892. 8°. 8304. aa. 19. (6.)

WIRTH (C.) 36 Gründe gegen das deutschfremdsprachliche Übersetzen an humanistischen Gymnasien. pp. 54. *Berl.* 1891. 8°.
12903. c. 28. (3.)

LANGUAGE.—Study, etc—*continued.*

WIRTH (C.) Zu den 36 Gründen gegen das deutschfremdsprachliche Übersetzen an humanistischen Gymnasien. Widerlegung. pp. 49. *Bayreuth,* 1892. 8°. 8311. g. 7.

JEKNAVORIAN (H.) Phrase-book for English-speaking people in eight languages. pp. 53. *Bost.* 1892. 8°. Pam. 47.

POUSSIÉ ( ) Manuel de Conversation en trente langues. pp. 204. *Paris,* 1890. obl. 8°.
12901. aa. 18.

VON NIEROTH (H. C.) The litt'e Talker in eight tongues. pp. 55. *Lond.* 1893. 4°.
12901. cc. 38.

Universal Language. *See* VOLAPÜK.

LANGUEDOC. GOULD (S. B.) In Troubadour-Land. pp. 339. *Lond.* 1891. 8°. 010171. h. 36.

JOURDANNE (G.) Étude sur les Littérateurs languedociens. pp. 30. *Carcassonne,* 1893. 8°.
11825. q. 21. (6.)

P.P. *Montpellier.* Le Felibrige Latin. *Montp.* 1890, *etc.* 8°. P.P. 4382. bca.

SPONT (A.) La gabelle du sel en Languedoc au 15ᵐᵒ siècle. pp. 57. *Toulouse,* 1891. 8°.
08226. k. 6. (7.)

See also ARDÈCHE : LOZÈRE : PROVENÇAL LANGUAGE : VELAY.

LANGUE d'OÏL. *See* FRENCH LANGUAGE.

LANNION. FRANCE ( ) Les Missionnaires du XVIIᵉ siècle au pays de Lannion. pp. 296. *Saint-Brieuc,* 1890. 12°. 4629. de. 7.

LAOS : SHANS. AYMONIER (É F.) Notes sur le Laos. pp. 298. *Saigon,* 1885. 8°.
010057. k. 4.

BRANDA (P.) Le Haut-Mékong, ou le Laos ouvert. pp. 64. *Paris,* 1887. 8°. Pam. 88.

HENRY (L.) Promenade au Cambodge et au Laos. pp. 99. *Paris,* 1894. 12°. 10055. aaaa. 38.

LEMIRE (C.) Affaires franco-siamoises. Le Laos Annamite. pp. 86. *Angers,* 1894. 8°.
10057. df. 17.

CUSHING (J. N.) Handbook of the Shan language. pp. 272. *Rangoon,* 1888. 8°. 12907. c. 31.

SHAN NAMES. Tables for the transliteration of Shan Names into English. pp. 12. *Rangoon,* 1891. 8°. 760. dd. 17.

See also INDO-CHINA : MALAYSIA.

LAPLAND. HAGEMANN (A. O. C.) Blandt-lapper of bumænd. pp. 124. *Kristiania,* 1889. 8°. 10280. cc. 8.

JACKSON (F. G.) The great Frozen Land. pp. 297. *Lond.* 1895. 8°. 10460. f. 30.

LINDÉN (J.) Beiträge zur Kenntniss des westlichen Theiles des russischen Lapplands pp. 24. 1894. 8°. Ac. Helsingfors. *Suomen Maantieteellinen Seura.* Fennia. Nr. 9. Ac. 6113.

RABOT (C.) Explorations dans la Laponie russe, 1889-91. Ac. Paris. *Société de Géographie.* Bulletin. Sér. 7. Tom, 10, 11, 12. Ac. 6035.

TENOW (C. L.) I Lappfrågan. pp. 136. *Stockholm,* 1893. 8°. 10281. b. 8.

Language.

WIKLUND (K. B.) Kleine lappische Chrestomathie. pp. 127. 1894. 8°. Ac. Helsingfors. *Suomalais Ugrilaisen Seura.* Apuneuvoja, *etc.* I. Ac. 9081/4.

—— Laut- und Formenlehre der lule-lappischen Dialekte. pp. 279. 1891. 8°. Ac. Gottenburg. *Götheborgska Wetenskaps.* Handlingar. Ny Följd. Häft. 25. Ac. 1063.

QUIGSTAD (J. K.) Nordische Lehnwörter im Lappischen. pp. 357. 1893. 8°. Ac. Christiania. *Videnskabs-Selskab.* Forhandlinger. aar 1893. No. I. Ac. 1054.

LA PLATA. Ac. La Plata. *Museo.* Revista del Museo. *La Plata,* 1890, *etc.* 8°.
Ac. 3091.

CARRASCO (G.) Del Atlántico al Pacífico. pp. 511. *Buenos A.* 1890. 8°. 10025. e. 3

DAIREAUX (É.) La Vie et les mœurs à La Plata. 2 tom. *Paris,* 1889. 8°. 10481. de. 9.

ERRERA (C.) La spedizione di S. Caboto al Rio della Plata. pp. 62. 1895. 8°. Archivio Storico Italiano. Ser. 5. Tom. 15.
P.P. 3557. a.

HUDSON (W. H.) The naturalist in La Plata. pp. 388. *Lond.* 1892. 8°. 7002. f. 8.

LEVEY (G. C.) Handy guide to the River Plate. pp. 214. *Lond.* 1890. 8°. 10481. aa. 35.

MULHALL (M. G.) and (E. T.) Handbook of the River Plate. pp. 686. *Buenos A.* 1892. 8°.
10481. b. 46.

MORANT (G. C.) Chili and the River Plate in 1891. pp. 268. *Lond.* 1891. 8°. 10481. aaa. 47.

QUESADA (E.) La Política chilena en el Plata. pp. 382. *Buenos A.* 1895. 8°. 8180. f. 41.

RESASCO (F.) Alle rive del Plata. pp. 483. *Milano,* 1890. 8°. 10481. c. 31.

—— En las riberas del Plata. 2 tom. *Madrid,* 1891. 8°. 10481. aa. 34.

SCALABRINI (A.) Sul Rio della Plata. pp. 483. *Como,* 1894. 8°. 10480. b. 37.

SCHUPP (A.) Ein Besuch am la Plata. pp. 248. *Freiburg,* 1891. 8°. 10481. e. 30.

VACA-GUZMAN (S.) Intereses comerciales entre Bolivia y el Plata. pp. 110. *Buenos A.* 1880. 8°. 8180. h. 27.

See also ARGENTINE REPUBLIC. For the dialect of La Plata, *see* AMERICAN DIALECTS, *Spanish.*

LA RABIDA, Franciscan Monastery. BECERRO DE BENGOA (R.) La Rábida. pp. 31. *Madrid,* 1892. 8°. 4532. 9. 11. (4.)

LA RÉOLE. CLAUDIN (A.) Les origines de l'Imprimerie à la Réole, 1517. *Paris.* 1894. 8°.
Pam. 6.

LARNE. BOYD (J.) Pictorial guide to Larne. pp. 98. *Larne,* 1891. 8°. 10390. aaaa. 19.

—— Popular album of Larne. *Larne,* 1892. 8°.
10390. cc. 5.

LA ROCHEFOUCAULD. BAUHAIN (E.) and GODEFROY (J.) Château de la Rochefoucauld en Angoumois. pp. xxi. *Paris,* 1893. 8°.
10173. eee. 9.

LA ROCHELLE AND SAINT MARTIN DE RÉ. MUSSET (G.) La Rochelle et ses ports. pp. 158. *La Rochelle,* 1890. 4°.
010171. f. 28.

JURIEN DE LA GRAVIÈRE (J. P. E.) Le Siège de La Rochelle. pp. 428. *Paris,* 1891. 12°.
9226. aaa. 39.

LARONZE (C.) Quas ob causas Rupellensis Republica perierit. pp. 116. *La Rochelle,* 1890. 8°.
010171. k. 3.

MERVAULT (P.) Saint-Martin de Ré et La Rochelle, 1627-28. pp. 76. *La Rochelle,* 1893. 8°. 9226. k. 23.

PHELIPPOT (R. T.) Lettre sur l'incendie de la mairie de la Ville de Saint Martin. pp. 24. *Saint-Martin,* 1891. 8°. 10106. i. 1. (11.)

LA ROCHETTE. HARENNE (J. B. de) Le Château de la Rochette. 1891. 8°. Ac. Liége. *Institut Archéologique.* Bulletin. Tom. 22. Livr. 1. Ac. 5527.

LAROQUE-DES-ALBÈRES. CARRÈRE (M. A. M.) Monographie de Laroque-des-Albères. pp. 186. *Céret,* 1894. 8°. 10169. aa. 1.

LARVIK. BONNEVIE (C. F.) Bad Larviks. pp. 63. *Larvik,* 1895. 12°. Pam. 39.

LARYNX. Ac. United States. *Laryngological Association.* Catalogue of the Library. pp. 19. *St. Louis,* 1885. 8°. 011903. l. 11.

AVELLIS (G.) Cursus der laryngoscopischen Technik. pp. 131. *Berl.* 1891. 8°. 7615. c. 9.

BALCOMB (J. T.) Diagrams of the Mouth and Larynx. *Lond.* 1891. 4°. 7616. a. 35.

BALL (J. B.) Intubation of the Larynx. pp. 54. *Lond.* 1891. 8°. 7616. h. 15.

COHEN (J. S.) Laryngology. *Phila.* 1891. 8°.
07305. k. 9. (9.)

CUTTER (E.) Some contributions to Laryngology. pp. 8. *Chicago,* 1890. 8°. 7306. df. 15. (8.)

GEGENBAUR (C.) Die Epiglottis. pp. 69. *Leipz.* 1892. 4°. 7421. i. 17.

GOUGENHEIM (A.) and GLOVER (J.) Atlas de laryngologie. pp. 48. *Paris,* 1894. fol.
1831. a. 2.

HERYNG (T.) La curabilité de la Phtisie du Larynx. pp. 191. *Paris,* 1888. 8°. 7615. f. 32.

KILLIAN (G.) Die Untersuchung der hinteren Larynxwand. pp. 77. *Jena,* 1890. 8°. Pam. 39.

KUTTNER (A.) Larynxödem und submucöse Laryngitis. pp. 82. *Berl.* 1895. 8°. 7615. c. 6.

MINICH (A.) Sulla Laringotomia inter-cricotiroidea. pp. 25. 1890. 8°. Ac. Venice. *Istituto di Scienze.* Atti. Tom. 38. Ac. 110.

PARIS. *Congrès d'Otologie et de Laryngologie,* 1889. Comptes rendus et mémoires. pp. 448. *Paris,* 1889. 8°. 7616. f. 28.

SAJOUS (C. E.) Diseases of the Nose and Larynx. 1894. 8°. BIGELOW (H. R.) System of Electro-Therapeutics. 2024. c.

SCHNITZLER (J.) Klinischer Atlas der Laryngologie. *Wien,* 1891, *etc.* 8°. 7615. f. 37,

SCHROETTER (L.) Vorlesungen über die Krankheiten des Kehlkopfes. *Wien,* 1892, *etc.* 8°.
7616. i.

THORNER (M.) Benign tumours of the Larynx. *Cincinnati.* 1892. 4°. Pam. 39

—— Intubation in an adult followed by a fatal edema of the Larynx after extraction of the tube. 1893. 8°. 7305. f. 6. (11.)

WILLIAMS (P. W.) Diseases of the upper Respiratory Tract. pp. 282. *Bristol,* 1894. 8°.
7816. f. **12.**

See also THROAT : VOICE.

LASCARI DIALECT.
See HINDUSTANI LANGUAGE.

LASSAY. GILLARD (J.) Lassay, ses écoles. pp. 45. *Laval,* 1890. 8°. 8305. f. 7. (8.)

LASSWADE. AITCHISON (C.) Lasswade Parish. pp. 31. *Edinb.* 1892. 8°. Pam. 90.

LAS VEGAS. LAS VEGAS. Souvenir of Las Vegas. *Chicago,* 1893. 12°. 10481. a. 27.

LATIN LANGUAGE.

Bibliography.

FOCK (G.) Catalogus Dissertationum classicarum. 3 pt. *Leipz.* 1893. 8°. 011900. cc. 31.

VALMAGGI (L.) Manuale di filologia classica. pp. 336. *Torino,* 1894. 8°. 12933. i. 12.

General : History.

Ac. Ithaca. *Cornell University.* Studies in classical Philology. *Ithaca,* 1887, *etc.* 8°.
Ac. 2692. g./3.

ASCHERSON (C. E. F.) Berliner Studien, *etc. Berl.* 1884, *etc.* 8°. P.P. 4991. c.

CONSTANS (L.) Étude sur la Langue de Tacite. pp. 154. *Paris,* 1893. 12°. 12933. c. 40.

ITALIAN STUDIES. Studi italiani di filologia classica. *Firenze,* 1893, *etc.* 8°. 11312. p.

LATIN.—General, etc.—continued.

KELLER (O.) Lateinische Volksetymologie. pp. 387. *Leipz.* 1891. 8°.   12933. f. 36.

LATIN LANGUAGE. Zur lateinischen Sprachgeschichte. *Leipz.* 1893, *etc.* 8°.   12933. h.

LINDSAY (W. M.) The Latin Language. pp. 659. *Oxf.* 1894. 8°.   12934. g. 32.

P.P. *Turin.* Bollettino di Filologia classica. *Torino*, 1894, *etc.* 8°.   95.

PRAGUE STUDIES. Prager Studien, *etc.* *Prague*, 1894, *etc.* 8°.   12933. h.

ROENSCH (H.) Collectanea philologa. pp. 325. *Bremen*, 1891. 8°.   12901. dd. 33.

SCERBO (F.) Caratteristiche del latino. pp. 139. *Firenze*, 1893. 8°.   12924. ff. 46.

WEISE (F. O.) Charakteristik der lateinischen Sprache. pp. 141. *Leipz.* 1891. 8°.   12934. d. 15.

REGNIER (A.) De la latinité de Saint Augustin. pp. 211. *Paris*, 1886. 8°.   12933. f. 37.

BONNET (M.) Le Latin de Grégoire de Tours. pp. 787. *Paris*, 1890. 8°.   12932. e. 22.

COHN (G.) Die Suffixwandlungen im Vulgärlatein. pp. 322. *Halle*, 1891. 8°. 12933. f. 35.

CORTESE (G.) La questione del Latino. pp. 34. *Torino*, 1894. 8°.   12903. dd. 36. (16.)

DUBOURGUIER ( ) Question du latin classique. pp. 64. *Amiens*, 1892. 8°.   8304. bb. 9. (9.)

FÉRON (P.) L'Enseignement du Latin d'après les vues de la pédagogie allemande. pp. 347. *Paris*, 1889. 8°.   8357. k. 11.

GUÉRIN (M.) La Question du Latin. pp. 328. *Paris*, 1890. 18°.   8356. aa. 13.

See also EDUCATION, *Classical :* OSCAN DIALECT.

Conversation.

D'OOGE (B. L.) Colloquia Latina. pp. 81. *Bost.* 1889. 8°.   12935. cc. 37.

Dictionaries and Vocabularies.

LEWIS (C. T.) Elementary Latin Dictionary. pp. 952. *Oxf.* 1891. 8°.   12935. c. 14.

MARCHANT (J. R. V.) and CHARLES (J. F.) Cassell's Latin Dictionary. pp. 927. *Lond.* 1892. 8°.   12935. c. 39.

STONE (E. D.) Latin Vocabularies. pp. 49. *Lond.* 1895. 8°.   12935. bbb. 56.

DAVIS (J. F.) Latin-English Vocabulary to Vergil's Aeneid, Book IX., *etc.* pp. 73. *Lond.* 1894. 8°.   12934. bb. 16.

—— Latin-English Vocabulary to Cæsar's Gallic War, Book VII. pp. 96. *Lond.* 1894. 8°.   12934. cc. 36.

SIHLER (E. G.) Complete Lexicon of the Latinity of Cæsar's Gallic War. pp. 188. *Bost.* 1891. 8°.   12935. c. 18.

STEDMAN (A. M. M.) Vocabulary of Latin idioms and phrases. pp. 40. *Lond.* 1894. 8°.   12924. cc. 30.

BENOIST (L. É.) and GOELZER (H.) Dictionnaire latin-français. pp. 1713. *Paris*, 1893. 8°.   12933. i. 11.

GALLÉE (J. H.) Uit bibliotheken en archieven. [List of Latin words from MSS. of the 8th to the 11th century.] pp. 46. *Leyden*, 1893. 8°.   12903. e. 28. (8.)

LOEWE (G.) Corpus Glossariorum Latinorum. *Lipsiae*, 1888, *etc.* 8°.   12934. k.

Examination Papers.

HAYES (B. J.) and MASOM (W. F.) London University Matriculation papers, 1888-91. 2 pt. 1891. 8°. Tutorial Series.   12205. c. 25.

PRUEN (G. G.) Latin Examination papers for army candidates. pp. 205. *Lond.* 1892. 8°.   12935. cc. 21.

LATIN—continued.

     Exercises. *See infra : Translation.*

     Grammars : Primers, etc.

BELCHER (R. H.) Elementary Latin Grammar. 2 pt. *Lond.* 1893, 94. 8°.   12935. cc. 4.

BLASE (H.) Historische Grammatik der lateinischen Sprache. *Leipz.* 1894, *etc.* 8°. 12934. k.

BOELTE ( ) Antike Tradition in der modernen lateinischen Schulgrammatik. *Frankf.* 1891. 8°.   12901. d. 35. (5.)

BORKING (L. H.) Latijnsche Spraakkunst. pp. 418. *Leiden*, 1893. 8°.   12934. k. 3.

BRÉAL (M.) and PERSON (L.) Grammaire latine. pp. 322. *Paris*, 1890. 8°.   12935. bb. 1.

CAPPELLE (F. v.) Latijnsche Grammatica. pp. 378. *Zaltbommel*, 1892. 8°.   12933. e. 21.

CONDER (R. F. R.) Primer of Church Latin. pp. 111. *Lond.* 1893. 8°.   12932. aaa. 50.

COOK (A. M.) Key to Macmillan's Shorter Latin course. pp. 75. *Lond.* 1891. 8°. 12935. de. 44.

DALGLEISH (W. K.) The Latin handbook. pp. 280. 1891. 8°. CRAWLEY (W. J. C.) Handbook of competitive examinations.   12200. d.

DEECKE (W.) Lateinische Schulgrammatik. 2 Bde. *Berl.* 1893. 8°.   12935. d. 3.

EDGREN (H.) Jämförande Grammatik. *Göteborg*, 1893, *etc.* 8°.   12901. cc.

FROST (P. H.) Handbook of Latin difficulties. pp. 179. *Lond.* 1892. 12°.   12935. df. 53.

GILDERSLEEVE (B. L.) Latin Grammar. pp. 550. *N.Y.* 1894. 8°.   12935. f. 9.

GILL (G.) "Imperial" Latin primer. pp. 408. *Lond.* 1889. 8°.   12934. e. 34.

GUTTERIDGE (M.) Young beginner's first Latin Book. pp. 104. 1891. 8°. SMITH (*Sir* W.) Beginner's Latin Course. Pt. I.   12934. f. 3.

HALLIDIE (A. R. S.) Latin Lessons for beginners. pp. 169. *Lond.* 1895. 8°.   12935. aa. 48.

HARPER (W. R.) and BURGESS (I. B.) Inductive Latin method. pp. 323. *N.Y.* 1888. 8°.   12935. cc. 35.

HAYES (B. J.) and MASOM (W. F.) Tutorial Latin Grammar. pp. 304. 1894. 8°. Tutorial Series.   12205. c. 234.

HUXLEY (L.) Elementary Latin course. pp. 204. *Lond.* 1891. 8°.   12935. e. 17.

INCE (J.) Latin Grammar of pharmacy. pp. 306. *Lond.* 1894. 8°.   12935. cc. 38.

JEEP (L.) Zur Geschichte der Lehre von den Redetheilen bei den lateinischen Grammatikern. pp. 316. *Leipz.* 1893. 8°.   12934. h. 19.

JUILLARD (A.) Cours de Langue latine. *Lausanne*, 1891, *etc.* 8°.   12934. d.

KINGDON (G. R.) Beaumont Latin Grammar. *Roehampton*, 1894. 8°.   12935. df. 54.

LATIN GRAMMAR. Elementary Latin Grammar. 1890, *etc.* 8°. Blackie's Elementary Text-Books.   12205. aa.

—— First steps in Latin Grammar. *Lond.* 1892, *etc.* 8°.   12935. cc. 18.

LINDSAY (W. M.) Short historical Latin Grammar. pp. 201. 1895. 8°. Clarendon Press Series.   2319. aa. 18.

MENDES DA COSTA (M. B.) and HARTMAN (J. J.) Beknopt leerboek der Latijnsche Spraakkunst. *Leiden*, 1895, *etc.* 8°.   12934. cc. 5.

OXFORD AND CAMBRIDGE LATIN PRIMER. Oxford and Cambridge Latin primer. 2 pt. 1890. 12°. Gill's School Series.   12200. ee.

RITCHIE (F.) Latin Grammar papers. pp. 84. *Lond.* 1895. 8°.   12933. cc. 39.

ROBY (H. J.) Grammar of the Latin language. 2 pt. *Lond.* 1887-92. 8°.   12934. cc. 39.

LATIN.—Grammars, etc.—*continued*.

SKUTSCH (F.) Forschungen zur lateinischen Grammatik. *Leipz.* 1892, *etc.* 8°.   12934. g.

SMITH (*Sir* WILLIAM) Principia Latina. *Lond.* 1893, *etc.* 8°.   12935. f. 7.

—— Key. 6 pt. *Lond.* 1892. 8°. 12935. cc. 24.

—— Principia Latina. Part v. pp. 176. *Lond.* 1892. 8°.   12935. cc. 20.

—— Young Beginner's Latin course. *Lond.* 1891, *etc.* 8°.   12934. f. 3.

—— Key. pp. 19. *Lond.* 1891. 8°. 12935. cc. 26.

STEDMAN (A. M. M.) First Latin lessons. pp. 162. *Lond.* 1891. 8°.   12934. e. 35.

WITHIEL (M.) Notae Latinae. pp. 18. *Lond.* 1892. 8°.   12932. cc. 24.

LUCHS (A.) Zur Lehre von der Genetivbildung der lateinischen Pronomina. 1890. 8°. STUDE-MUND (W.) Studia, *etc.* Bd. 1.   2270. d. 12.

HAMILTON (G.) Classic Moods. pp. 93. *Edinb.* 1894. 4°.   12902. dd. 42.

HOFFMANN (E.) Das Modus-Gesetz im lateinischen Zeitsatze. pp. 43. *Wien,* 1891. 8°.   12901. d. 34. (6)

LATTMANN (H.) Selbständiger und bezogener Gebrauch der Tempora im Lateinischen. pp. 150. *Göttingen,* 1890. 8°.   12933. f. 33.

WETZEL (M.) Eine Entgegnung auf die Schrift von Dr. H. Lattmann. pp. 106. *Paderborn,* 1890. 8°.   12935. e. 15.

—— Das Recht in dem Streite zwischen Hale und E. Hoffmann über die Tempora. pp. 47. *Paderborn,* 1892. 16°.   12901. ccc. 17. (12.)

BLASE (H.) Geschichte des Plusquamperfekts im Lateinischen. pp. 112. *Giessen,* 1894. 8°.   12935. e. 22.

JOB (L.) Le Présent et ses dérivés dans la conjugaison latine. pp. 664. *Paris,* 1893. 8°.   12934. h. 20.

WEISWEILER (J.) Das lateinische Participium futuri passivi. pp. 146. *Paderborn,* 1890. 8°.   12933. f. 32.

SJÖSTRAND (N.) De vi et usu supini secundi Latinorum. pp. 54. *Lundæ,* 1891. 8°.   12901. d. 36. (10.)

BAGBY (A.) Adverbs in Horace and Juvenal. pp. 37. *Baltimore,* 1891. 8°.   11312. g. 8. (1.)

ELMER (H. C.) Copulative conjunctions Que, Et, Atque. pp. 39. *Baltimore,* 1887. 8°.   12902. dd. 26. (3.)

BRENOUS (J.) Étude sur les Hellénismes dans la syntaxe latine. pp. 445. *Paris,* 1895. 8°.   12934. f. 23.

CARTER (G.) Rules of Latin syntax. pp. 23. *Lond.* 1894. 8°.   12933. f. 39.

LAPLANA (M.) Summa Syntaxica. 2 pt. *Friburgi,* 1894. 8°.   12934. aaa. 54.

MIDDLETON (G.) Essay on analogy in Syntax. pp. 95. *Lond.* 1892. 8°.   12901. f. 41.

MILES (E. H.) Comparative syntax of Greek and Latin. *Camb.* 1893. 8°.   12932. dd. 15.

RIEMANN (O.) Syntaxe latine. pp. 634. *Paris,* 1894. 12°.   12935. f. 10.

Idioms.

See supra : Dictionaries. Infra : Translation, etc.

Pronunciation: Phonetics.

Ac. Cambridge. *Philological Society.* Pronunciation of Latin in the Augustan period. pp. 8. *Lond.* 1889. 8°.   12901. d. 30. (9.)

ARNOLD (E. V.) and CONWAY (R. S.) Restored pronunciation of Greek and Latin. pp. 19. *Camb.* 1895. 8°.   Pam. 47.

KARSTEN (H. T.) De Uitspraak van het Latijn. pp. 166. *Amsterdam,* 1893. 8°.   12935. e. 21.

LATIN.—Pronunciation—*continued*.

PECK (H. T.) Latin Pronunciation. pp. 38. *N.Y.* 1890. 8°.   12935. c. 37.

SOLMSEN (F.) Studien zur lateinischen Lautgeschichte. pp. 208. *Strassb.* 1894. 8°.   12934. g. 33.

Prosody : Verse Composition.
See POETRY, *Latin.*

Translation from and into Latin: Exercises.

ABBOTT (E. A.) Dux Latinus : a first Latin construing book. pp. 187. *Lond.* 1893. 8°.   12935. bb. 57.

BENDALL (H.) and LAURENCE (C. E.) Graduated Passages for translation. *Camb.* 1891, *etc.* 8°.   12935. f.

BRACKENBURY (M. J. F.) Legenda Latina. Latin reading book. pp. 318. *Lond.* 1895. 8°.   11305. aa. 25.

DIX (C. M.) First Latin reader and writer. 2 pt. 1893. 8°. SONNENSCHEIN (E. A.) Parallel Grammar Series.   12902. aa.

—— Third Latin reader and writer. pp. 128. 1892. 8°. SONNENSCHEIN (E. A.) Parallel Grammar Series.   12902. aa.

DODDS (W.) Exercises on the Latin Syntax. pp. 104. 1891. 8°. SMITH (*Sir* W.) Young Beginner's Latin Course. Pt. 3.   12935. e.

DU PRÉ (A. M. D.) First Exercises on Latin construction. pp. 68. *Lond.* 1894. 8°.   12934. bb. 15.

EDGAR (J.) Latin Unseens. Hints on translation into English. pp. 118. *Edinb.* 1892. 8°.   12941. bb. 37.

FYFE (W. T.) Via Nova. New Latin reader. pp. 104. *Lond.* 1892. 8°.   12935. f. 3.

GARDINER (G. B.) and (A.) Latin Translation primer. pp. 113. *Lond.* 1894. 8°. 12935. aa. 46.

GODLEY (A. D.) Latin Stories. pp. 112. *Lond.* 1893. 8°.   12934. bb. 1.

HALL (T. D.) Translation at sight. pp. 115. *Lond.* 1895. 8°.   12935. cc. 48.

HEATLEY (H. R.) and KINGDON (H. N.) Excerpta Facilia. pp. 200. *Lond.* 1890. 8°.   12935. de. 34.

—— Gradatim. pp. 135. *Lond.* 1890. 8°.   12935. de. 35.

JOYCE (P. S. K.) Graduated selections for Latin unseen translation. pp. 82. *Lond.* 1893. 8°.   12935. cc. 32.

LATIN READER. Tutorial Latin reader. pp. 167. 1894. 8°. Tutorial Series.   12205. c. 251.

LATIN UNSEENS. Latin Unseens in prose and verse. *Lond.* 1894, *etc.* 8°.   12935. de.

LIVIUS (T.) Latin Prose exercises, based upon Livy, Book XXI. pp. 64. *Bost.* 1891. 8°.   9041. eee. 3.

MARSH (W.) and STEELE (R.) Flores historiarum. First Latin reader. pp. 144. *Lond.* 1894. 8°.   9503. bb. 43.

MEISSNER (C.) Latin Phrase-book. pp. 316. *Lond.* 1894. 8°.   12935. cc. 41.

MORICE (F. D.) Loculi : junior Latin reading book. pp. 200. *Lond.* 1892. 8°. 12933. cc. 36.

NIXON (J. E.) Latin Translations of selected pieces. pp. 88. *Camb.* 1890. 8°.   12935. c. 36.

PECK (H. T.) and ARROWSMITH (R.) Roman Life in Latin prose and verse. pp. 256. *Lond.* 1895. 8°.   11305. c. 13.

RAMSAY (G. G.) Latin Prose versions. pp. 381. *Oxf.* 1894. 8°.   12934. f. 20.

ROOPER (E. P.) and HERRING (F.) Primary Latin exercises. pp. 260. *Lond.* 1894. 8°.   12935. cc. 36.

LATIN.—Translation, etc.—*continued.*

STEDMAN (A. M. M.) First Latin reader. pp. 93. *Lond.* 1890. 8°.   12935. de. 36.

—— Exempla Latina. Exercises in Latin accidence. pp. 90. *Lond.* 1892. 8°.   12935. cc. 22.

—— Notanda Quaedam: miscellaneous Latin exercises. pp. 145. *Lond.* 1891. 8°.   12935. de. 42.

THOMAS (A. H.) Junior students' First Latin translation book. pp. 168. *Lond.* 1894. 8°.   12935. f. 8.

TURNER (J. A.) Easy Latin Passages for practice in unseen translation. pp. 201. *Lond.* 1891. 8°.   12933. cc. 32.

WALKER (W. A.) Beginner's Latin translation book. pp. 20. *Lond.* 1893. 8°. 12935. de. 46.

WELCH (W.) and DUFFIELD (C. G.) Exercises in unseen translation in Latin. pp. 115. 1893. 16°. Elementary Classics.   11305. bb.

WELLS (E. A.) Crustula. pp. 137. *Lond.* 1890. 8°.   12923. cc. 5.

WILMOT (D.) Sentences on Latin syntax. pp. 90. *Lond.* 1894. 8°.   12935. b. 6.

A., M. Latin Prose composition. pp. 53. 1889. 8°. Ars Grammatica Series. No. 2.   12935. e.

ALLCROFT (A. H.) and HAYDON (J. H.) Latin Composition. pp. 184. 1891. 8°. Tutorial Series.   12205. c. 33.

—— Key. pp. 32. 1890. 8°. Tutorial Series.   12205. c. 59.

CARTER (G.) Easy pieces for translation into Latin prose. pp. 98. *Lond.* 1895. 8°.   12935. aa. 47.

HARDIE (W. R.) Vetera recentia. Hints towards advanced composition in prose and verse. pp. 50. *Edinb.* 1895. 8°.   Pam. 47.

HIME (M. C.) Introduction to Latin prose composition. pp. 154. *Lond.* 1893. 8°. 12935. cc. 29.

—— Key. pp. 23. *Lond.* 1893. 8°. 12935. cc. 31.

HOLDEN (F. T.) Tripertita. pp. 123. *Lond.* 1894. 8°.   12933. cc. 37.

IVERSEN (C.) Latinske Stiløvelser. pp. 258. *Kjøbenhavn,* 1890. 8°.   12934. f. 19.

JOHANSSEN (J.) Latinske Stiløvelser. 2 pt. *Kristiania,* 1889. 8°.   12934. f. 18.

KENNEDY (B. H.) Exercises on the Shorter Latin primer. Key. 2 pt. *Lond.* 1891. 8°. 12935. e. 16.

LATIN LANGUAGE. Latine Vertenda. pp. 135. *Bedford,* 1894. 8°.   12935. de. 47.

LATIN PROSE CARD. Latin Prose card. pp. 4. 1891. 4°.   12934. i. 12.

LOWUM (A.) Latinske Stiløvelser. pp. 222. *Christiania,* 1890. 8°.   12935. f. 1.

MANSFIELD (E. D.) Exercises in Latin prose. pp. 255. *Lond.* 1895. 8°.   12935. cc. 44.

—— Key. pp. 112. *Lond.* 1891. 8°. 12935. cc. 30.

—— Outlines of Latin sentence construction. *Lond.* 1893. 8°.   12934. e. 15.

NORTH (M. A.) and HILLARD (A. E.) Latin Prose composition. pp. 282. *Lond.* 1895. 8°.   12935. cc. 47.

—— Key. pp. 108. *Lond.* 1895. 8°.   12935. b. 60.

RAMSAY (G. G.) Latin Prose composition. 1892, *etc.* 8°. Clarendon Press Series.   2320. aa. 1.

—— Latin Prose versions. pp. 381. *Oxf.* 1895. 8°.   12935. cc. 46.

RITCHIE (F.) Exercises in Latin Prose composition. pp. 216. *Lond.* 1893. 8°. 12935. cc. 33.

—— Key. pp. 82. *Lond.* 1894. 8°.   12935. cc. 39.

LATIN.—Translation, etc.—*continued.*

RITCHIE (F.) Latin Clause construction. pp. 39. *Lond.* 1892. 8°.   12935. f. 2.

STEDMAN (A. M. M.) The Latin Compound Sentence. pp. 120. *Lond.* 1892. 8°. 12935. cc. 23.

TURNER (B. D.) Advanced Manual of Latin Prose composition. pp. 400. *Lond.* 1893. 8°.   12935. f. 6.

WALTERS (W. C. F.) Hints in continuous Latin prose. pp. 84. *Lond.* 1895. 8°.   12934. bb. 32.

LATIN LITERATURE.

Bibliography.

VALMAGGI (L.) Manuale storico-bibliografico di filologia classica. pp. 336. *Torino,* 1894. 8°.   12933. i. 12.

History and Criticism.

ALY (F.) Geschichte der römischen Litteratur. pp. 355. *Berl.* 1894. 8°.   11312. p.

ASCHERSON (C. E. F.) Berliner Studien, *etc. Berl.* 1884, *etc.* 8°.   P.P. 4991. e.

BIRT (T.) Eine römische Litteraturgeschichte. pp. 210. *Marburg,* 1894. 8°. 11312. bbb. 25.

DUCASSE (F.) La Philosophie romaine d'après les poètes. pp. 177. *Lausanne,* 1892. 8°.   11312. e. 28.

GEIST (H.) Was bieten die antiken Schriftsteller der modernen Jugend? *Posen,* 1894, *etc.* 8°.   011850. g.

GOUMY (É.) Les Latins. pp. 267. *Paris,* 1892. 8°.   11312. d. 54.

NETTLESHIP (H.) Lectures and essays. Series 2. pp. 269. *Oxf.* 1895. 8°.   11312. d. 64.

OCCIONI (O.) Scritti di letteratura latina. pp. 332. *Torino,* 1891. 8°.   11312. c. 63.

P.P. *Turin.* Bollettino di filologia classica. *Torino,* 1894, *etc.* 8°.   95.

PRAGUE STUDIES. Prager Studien, *etc. Prag,* 1894, *etc.* 8°.   12933. h.

RAFN (C. H.) Hovedpunkter af den latinske Literaturs historie. pp. 80. *Kjøbenh.* 1890. 8°.   11312. d. 51.

REITZENSTEIN (R.) Drei Vermutungen zur Geschichte der römischen Litteratur. 1893. 8°. MOMMSEN (T.) Festschrift.   9040. f. 26.

RAMORINO (F.) Letteratura romana. pp. 340. *Milano,* 1894. 8°.   012200. i. 2.

REURE ( ) Les Gens de lettres et leurs protecteurs à Rome. pp. 470. *Paris,* 1891. 8°.   11312. e. 22.

TEUFFEL (W. S.) History of Roman literature. Revised by L. Schwabe. *Lond.* 1891, *etc.* 8°.   2051. a.

TRAUBE (L.) Untersuchungen zur Ueberlieferungsgeschichte römischer Schriftsteller. 1891. 8°. Ac. Munich. *K. Akademie.* Sitzungsberichte der phil.-philologischen Classe, 1891. Hft. 3.   Ac. 713/8.

TYRRELL (R. Y.) Latin Poetry. Lectures. pp. 323. *Lond.* 1895. 8°.   11312. d. 62.

ZOELLER (M.) Grundriss der Geschichte der römischen Litteratur. pp. 343. 1891. 8°. Sammlung von Kompendien. Ser. 1. 3.   12205. k.

BARILLARI (M.) Studî su la Satira latina. pp. 145. *Messina,* 1890. 8°.   11312. f. 51.

SOLDINI (E.) Breve storia della Satira in Roma e in Italia. pp. 140. *Cremona,* 1891. 8°.   11312. d. 55.

PROFESSEUR. Virgile et Horace, leur vie et leurs ouvrages. pp. 97. *Paris,* 1892. 8°.   11312. bbb. 22.

LEDERER (S.) Ist Vergil der Verfasser von "Culex" und "Ciris"? pp. 16. *Leipz.* 1890. 8°.   Pam. 14.

LATIN LITERATURE.—History—*cont.*

COMPARETTI (D.) Vergil in the middle ages.
pp. 376. *Lond.* 1895. 8°.   011824. e. 62.

DETTO (W. A.) Horaz und seine Zeit. pp. 186.
Berl. 1892. 8°.   11312. e. 23.

MANITIUS (M.) Analekten zur Geschichte des
Horaz im Mittelalter. pp. 127.
Göttingen, 1893. 8°.   11312. e. 35.

GREGORIO (G. de) Per la Storia comparata delle
Letterature neo-latine. pp. 65.
Palermo, 1893. 8°.   011824. k. 25.

DELISLE (L. V.) Littérature latine & histoire du
moyen âge. pp. 116. 1890. 8°. Ac. *Paris*.
Comité des Travaux historiques. Instructions.
   Ac. 437/5.

MANITIUS (M.) Geschichte der christlich-
lateinischen Poesie bis zur Mitte des 8. Jahrhunderts. pp. 518. *Stuttgart*, 1891. 8°.
   011840. h. 67.

RONCA (U.) Cultura medioevale e poesia latina
d' Italia nei Secoli XI. e XII. 2 vol.
Roma, 1892. 8°.   011850. g. 26.

Selections, etc.

BROWNRIGG (C. E.) Latin Prose of the silver
age. pp. 222. *Lond.* 1895. 8°.   11305. c. 14.

HERRMANN (M.) Lateinische Litteraturdenkmäler
des XV. u. XVI. Jhrhdts. *Berl.* 1891, *etc.* 8°.
   11305. d.

See also POETRY and for Selections for School
Use, *see* LATIN LANGUAGE, *Translation, etc.*

LATITUDE AND LONGITUDE. DINGLE

(E.) Study of Longitude as discovered by the
aid of the solar noontide altitude and declination only. pp. 24. *Plymouth*, 1892. 8°.
   8563. aaa. 31.

JOHNSON (A. C.) Brief methods of finding the
Latitude and Longitude. pp. 34.
Lond. 1889. 8°.   8807. d. 17.

MURRAY (J. B.) Simple Method of readily
finding the parallel of Latitude. pp. 14.
Glasg. 1893. 8°.   Pam. 4.
See also GEODESY : NAVIGATION : TIME.

LAUENBURG. HAUPT (R.) and WEYSSER

(F.) Die Bau- und Kunstdenkmäler im Kreise
Lauenburg. 2 pt. *Ratzeburg*, 1890. 8°. 7814. g. 1.

LAUNCESTON. ROBBINS (A. F.) Laun-

ceston, past and present. pp. 450.
Launceston, 1888. 8°.   10351. d. 37.

LAUNDRY WORK. *See* WASHING.

LAUSANNE. CURCHOD (F.) Description des

cathédrales de Lausanne et de Genève. pp. 114.
Lausanne, 1891. 8°.   7817. f. 23.

Ac. Lausanne. *Université.* Souvenir des Fêtes
inaugurales de l'Université, Mai 1891.
Lausanne, 1892. 4°.   8356. i. 13.

LAVAL, City and Diocese. ANGOT (A.)

Histoire de l'Imprimerie à Laval, jusqu'en 1789.
pp. 48. *Laval*, 1892. 8°.   11903. aa. 23. (7.)

COUANIER DE LAUNAY (E. L.) Légendaire du
diocèse de Laval. pp. 304. *Laval*, 1891. 8°.
   4829. c. 6.

JOUBERT (A.) Histoire de l'Église réformée de
Laval au XVIIe siècle. 1889. 8°. MAYENNE.
Commission historique. Procès-verbaux. Sér. 2.
Tom. 1.   010171. m. 18.

LA BEAULUÈRE (L. de) Comptes de l'Hôtel-
Dieu de Laval. 1685. 1890. 8°. MAYENNE.
Commission historique. Procès-verbaux. Sér. 2.
Tom. 1.   010171. m. 18.

LE BLANC DE LA VIGNOLLE (J.) Notes sur Laval.
pp. 40. *Paris*, 1894. 8°.   10105. ee. 11. (12.)

MORIN DE LA BEAULUÈRE (L. J.) Études sur les
communautés de Laval. pp. 391.
Laval, 1891. 8°.   4629. h. 17.

LAVAL—*continued.*

RICHARD (J. M.) Notes sur l'ancien Laval.
1889. 8°. MAYENNE. *Commission historique.*
Procès-verbaux. Sér. 2. Tom. 1. 010171. m. 18.

LAW.

For the Law of each country and subject other
than those given below, *see* the country or subject
required.

Bibliography.

CASPAR (C. N.) Catalogue of Law books.
pp. 100. *Milwaukee*, 1894. 8°. 011900. de. 8.

DRAMARD (E.) Bibliographie de la bibliographie
du Droit français et étranger. pp. 120.
Paris, 1893. 8°.   011900. ee. 17.

MAXWELL (W. H.) Catalogue of modern Law
books, British and Colonial. pp. 468.
Lond. 1895. 8°.   B.B.C. b. 20.

MUEHLBRECHT (O.) Wegweiser durch die neue
Litteratur der Rechtswissenschaften. pp. 748.
Berl. 1893. 8°.   011900. h. 15.

NEW YORK. *Association of the Bar.* Catalogue
of the Library. pp. 1135. *N.Y.* 1892. 8°.
   11905. e. 39

STEVENS (H. G.) and HAYNES (R. W.) Catalogue
of modern Law Works, 1865–94. pp. 249.
Lond. 1895. 8°.   11900. a. 51.

See also under the sub-heading LAW of each
country.

General Jurisprudence : History.

ANZILOTTI (D.) La Filosofia del Diritto.
pp. 220. *Firenze*, 1892. 8°.   8277. g. 50.

BEKKER (E. I.) Ernst und Scherz über unsere
Wissenschaft. pp. 250. *Leipz.* 1892. 8°.
   6006. b. 23.

BEMMELEN (P. v.) Les Notions fondamentales
du Droit civil. pp. 233. 1892. 8°. Ac. Amsterdam. *K. Akademie.* Verhandelingen. Afdeeling Letterkunde. Deel 1. No. 1. Ac. 944/3.

BERGBOHM (C.) Jurisprudenz und Rechtsphilosophie. *Leipz.* 1892, *etc.* 8°. 6005. cc.

BIANCO (P.) La filosofia del Diritto in Germania. pp. 158. *Salerno*, 1895. 8°. 6006. cc. 15.

BIERLING (E. R.) Juristische Prinzipienlehre.
Freiburg, 1894, *etc.* 8°.   6006. d.

BRUGI (B.) Introduzione enciclopedica alle
Scienze giuridiche. pp. 271.
Firenze, 1891. 8°.   6006. e. 15.

CARLE (G.) La vita del Diritto nei suoi rapporti
colla vita sociale. pp. 714. *Torino*, 1890. 8°.
   6025. f. 3.

FRENCH (F. C.) The concept of Law in Ethics.
pp. 51. *Providence*, 1892. 8°.   8409. l. 10.

HOLLAND (T. E.) Elements of Jurisprudence.
pp. 402. *Oxf.* 1895. 8°.   6005. e. 11.

HORTEN (H.) Die Personalexecution in Geschichte und Dogma. *Wien*, 1893, *etc.* 8°.
   6006. cc.

HOWARD (J. E.) Address on the functions of
Law. pp. 15. *Allahabad*, 1890. 8°.
   6190. aa. 31. (8.)

JHERING (R. v.) Scherz und Ernst in der Jurisprudenz. pp. 383. *Leipz.* 1885. 8°. 6005. b. 1.

KRAPT (A.) Rettens Forhold til den praktiske
Moral. pp. 254. *Københ.* 1892. 8°. 08275. m. 3.

KRAUSE (C. C. F.) Vorlesungen über Naturrecht.
pp. 288. *Leipz.* 1892. 8°.   8462. e. 33.

LA GRASSERIE (R. de) Étude des Législations
étrangères. *Paris*, 1895, *etc.* 8°.   6005. cc

LEITHNER ( ) Was ist Recht? pp. 160.
Leipz. 1893. 8°.   6005. ee. 28.

LORIMER (J.) Principes de Droit naturel. 2 tom.
Brux. 1890. 8°.   6005. c. 3.

MERRILL (J. H.) American and English Encyclopaedia of Law. *Northport*, 1887, *etc.* 8°.
   2016. a. & aa.

LAW.—General Jurisprudence, etc.—cont.

MIRAGLIA (L.) Filosofia del Diritto.
Napoli, 1893, etc. 8°. 6005. h.

NOLENS (W. H.) De Leer van Thomas van
Aquino over het Recht. pp. 181.
Utrecht, 1890. 8°. 6006. f. 25.

OCHOA (F.) Estudios Jurídicos. pp. 230.
Maracaibo, 1892. 8°. 6006. c. 37.

OFNER (J.) Studien sozialer Jurisprudenz.
pp. 86. Wien, 1894. 8°. 08276. h. 57.

ORBAN (O.) Cours d'Encyclopédie de Droit.
pp. 215. Liége, 1893. 8°. 5695. aa. 9.

P.P. Brussels. Sommaire des revues de Droit.
Table mensuelle de tous les articles.
Brux. 1891, etc. 8°. P.P. 6506. c.

—— Cambridge, Mass. Harvard Law review.
Camb. 1894, etc. 8°. P.P. 1352. m.

—— Naples. La Scuola positiva nella Giurisprudenza civile e penale. Napoli, 1891, etc. 8°.
P.P. 1379. g.

POLLOCK (Sir F.) Oxford Lectures. pp. 303.
Lond. 1890. 8°. 12355. i. 33.

POST (A. H.) Grundriss der ethnologischen
Jurisprudenz. Oldenburg, 1894, etc. 8°. 6006. cc.

PUGLIA (F.) Saggi di Filosofia giuridica.
pp. 271. Napoli, 1892. 8°. 6006. c. 35.

PUNTSCHART (V.) Die moderne Theorie des
Privatrechts. pp. 416. Leipz. 1893. 8°.
6005. h. 18.

RATKOWSKY (M. G.) Encyklopädie der Rechts-
und Staatswissenschaften. pp. 102.
Wien, 1890. 8°. 6005. e. 2.

RATTIGAN (W. H.) The science of Jurisprudence.
pp. 398. Lond. 1892. 8°. 6006. bb. 22.

RICHARD (G.) L'Origine de l'idée de Droit.
pp. 263. Paris, 1892. 8°. 6005. e. 7.

ROBERTSON (A.) Lectures on the Science and
study of Law. pp. 78. Dundee, 1888. 8°.
6006. c. 36.

ROTHE (T.) Traité de Droit naturel.
Paris, 1885, etc. 8°. 6005. de.

SALMOND (J. W.) Essays in Jurisprudence and
legal history. pp. 236. Lond. 1891. 8°.
6006. aa. 40.

—— First principles of Jurisprudence. pp. 264.
Lond. 1893. 8°. 6006. b. 24.

SCHROEDER (E. A.) Das Recht in der geschichtlichen Ordnung. pp. 390. Berl. 1893. 8°.
6005. h. 19.

STONE (J. H.) Notes on the history of ancient
Institutions, etc. pp. 88. 1890. 8°.
6146. d. 22. (2.)

THYRÉN (J. C. W.) Abhandlungen aus der
Rechtsphilosophie. Lund, 1894, etc. 8°.
6055. ee.

VACCARO (M. A.) Le basi del Diritto. pp. 388.
Torino, 1893. 8°. 8009. k. 5.

WATT (W. A.) Outline of legal Philosophy.
pp. 184. Edinb. 1893. 8°. 6006. aaa. 35.

HUGHES (W. T.) Technology of Law. Con-
densus of maxims, leading cases, etc. pp. 364.
Denver, 1893. 8°. 6145. i. 16.

SENIOR (W.) Tutor and Pupils: talks about law
maxims. pp. 52. Lond. 1891. 8°. 6006. ee. 7.

STROUD (F.) Judicial Dictionary of words and
phrases. pp. 916. Lond. 1890. 8°. 6190. h. 5.

WHARTON (G. F.) Legal Maxims. pp. 266.
Lond. 1892. 8°. 6145. h. 60.

AGUANNO (G. d') La Genesi e l'Evoluzione del
diritto civile. pp. 595. Torino, 1890. 8°.
6005. h. 2.

BURACCA (A.) Storia del Dritto. pp. 248.
Messina, 1889. 8°. 6005. cc. 24.

LAW.—General Jurisprudence, etc.—cont.

FICKER (J.) Untersuchungen zur Rechtsgeschichte. Innsbruck, 1891, etc. 8°. 05604. h. 15.

LEIST (B. W.) Alt-arisches Jus civile.
Jena, 1892, etc. 8°. 5254. cc.

LETOURNEAU (C. J. M.) L'Évolution juridique.
pp. 540. 1891. 8°. Bibliothèque anthropologique. No. 14. 7004. de.

NEUKAMP (E.) Entwicklungsgeschichte des
Rechts. Berl. 1895, etc. 8°. 6005. i.

SCAIFE (W. B.) Law and history. pp. 18.
1889. 8°. Johns Hopkins University Studies.
Notes, etc. 1889. No. 8. Ac. 2689.

STONE (J. H.) Notes on the History of ancient
institutions. pp. 88. 1890. 8°. Pam. 32.

TARDE (G.) Les Transformations du Droit.
pp. 208. Paris, 1894. 12°. 6006. a. 8.

See also infra : Mediaeval and Roman Law.

Commercial.

MEILI (F.) Die Kodifikation des internationalen
Civil- und Handelsrechts. pp. 151.
Leipz. 1891. 8°. 6955. bb. 8.

PERRONE (F.) L'idea sociale nel Diritto commerciale. pp. 52. Napoli, 1894. 8°. Pam. 32.

SALZEDO (N.) and CLOTET (L.) Le Droit commercial français et étranger. Paris, 1894, etc. 8°.
6825. de.

SPAEING (W.) Französisches, belgisches und
englisches Wechselrecht. pp. 323.
Berl. 1890. 8°. 6825. aa. 4.

Argentine Republic.

ARGENTINE REPUBLIC. Code de Commerce argentin. pp. 451. Paris, 1893. 8°. 6784. h. 6.

Austria-Hungary.

BAUSENWEIN (R.) Das österreichische und ungarische Handelsrecht. pp. 292.
Leipz. 1894. 8°. 5549. g. 42.

FRANKL (O.) Der Concurs der offenen Handels-
gesellschaft nach österreichischem Rechte.
pp. 78. Prag, 1891. 8°. Pam. 34.

HASENOEHRL (V.) Das oesterreichische Obliga-
tionenrecht. Wien, 1892, etc. 8°. 05549. k.

HEILINGER (A.) Oesterreichisches Gewerberecht.
Wien, 1894, etc. 8°. 05549. k.

HUNGARY. Code de Commerce hongrois, 1875.
pp. 376. Paris, 1894. 8°. 05551. f. 10.

Chili.

CHILI. Código de Comercio. pp. 507.
Santiago, 1889. 8°. 6784. h. 10.

—— Code de Commerce chilien. pp. 425.
Paris, 1892. 8°. 6825. de. 5.

ALFONSO J.) Comentario del título preliminar
y del título primero del Código de Comercio.
pp. 386. Santiago, 1886. 8°. 6784. g. 12.

Denmark.

HECKSCHER (I.) Kreditsalget og Sælgerens
Standsningsret. pp. 207. Kjøbenh. 1885. 8°.
5705. g. 3.

France.

ALLART (H.) Traité de la concurrence déloyale.
pp. 353. Paris, 1892. 8°. 5423. eee. 15.

BOUVIER BANGILLON (A.) La Législation nouvelle sur les Sociétés. pp. 203. Paris, 1894. 8°.
5423. e. 20.

CONSTANT (C.) Manuel de Droit commercial.
Paris, 1891, etc. 8°. 6825. eee.

CROME (C.) Die Grundlehren des französischen
Obligationenrechts. pp. 411.
Mannheim, 1894. 8°. 5406. de. 14.

DURAND-MORIMBEAU (E.) La Juridiction commerciale. Manuel formulaire. pp. 488.
Paris, 1894. 8°. 6825. eee. 10.

LAW.—Commercial—_continued._ '

HOUYVET (A.) Les Tribunaux de commerce. pp. 183. _Paris_, 1891. 8°.   5103. de. 8.

MUZARD (É.) Répertoire de jurisprudence commerciale. _Paris_, 1891, _etc._ 8°.   6825. de.

TOUSSAINT (G.) Parquet et coulisse. L'article 76. pp. 171. _Paris_, 1891. 8°.   5406. de. 3.

Germany.

FRIEDBERG (E.) Allgemeines deutsches Handelsgesetzbuch. pp. 548. _Leipz._ 1890. 8°.   5606. c. 4.

—— Formelbuch für Handels-, Wechsel- und Seerecht. pp. 390. _Leipz._ 1890. 8°. 6825. cc. 19.

FRIEDMANN (F.) Das Reichswuchergesetz in der Fassung der Wuchergesetznovelle, 1893. pp. 132. _Berl._ 1894. 8°.   5656. de. 9.

GERMANY. Gewerbe-Ordnung für das deutsche Reich. pp. 254. _Berl._ 1891. 16°. 5606. a. 11.

IMMERWAHR (P.) Der Minderkaufmann. pp. 74. _Breslau_, 1893. 8°.   05604. i. 26.

JACOBY (S.) Das Recht der Bank- und Warenkommission. pp. 202. _Erlangen_, 1891. 8°.   5606. de. 2.

KOCH (R.) Vorträge hauptsächlich aus dem Handels- und Wechselrecht. pp. 370. _Berl._ 1892. 8°.   08227. h. 12.

KOEHLER (L.) Das württembergische Gewerbe-Recht, 1805–70. pp. 292. _Tübingen_, 1891. 8°.   05604. h. 10.

LEHMANN (C.) Die geschichtliche Entwicklung des Aktienrechts. pp. 108. _Berl._ 1895. 8°.   05604. h. 33.

NEY (C.) Das deutsche Handels-, See- und Wechselrecht. pp. 341. _Berl._ 1890. 8°.   6835. aa. 19.

RIESSER (J.) Der Einfluss handelsrechtlicher Ideen auf den Entwurf eines bürgerlichen Gesetzbuchs. pp. 84. _Stuttg._ 1894. 8°.   05604. i. 35.

SILBERSCHMIDT (W.) Die Entstehung des deutschen Handelsgerichts. pp. 181. _Leipz._ 1894. 8°.   05604. i 33.

SPEIDEL (E.) Beiträge zu den Wuchsgesetzen des Hochwaldes. _Tübingen_, 1893, _etc._ 8°.   05605. i.

STAUB (H.) Kommentar zum deutschen Handelsgesetzbuch. _Berl._ 1891, _etc._ 8°.   05604. b. 4.

Great Britain and Ireland.

CLARK (S S.) Text-book on commercial Law. pp. 314. _N Y._ 1892. 8°.   6825. aa. 5.

CROWLEY (M.) Commercial Handbook. pp. 104. 1891. 12°. Wilson's Legal handy books.   6426. aaa. 39.

HURST (J.) and CECIL (_Lord_ E. A. R.) Principles of commercial Law. pp. 512. _Lond._ 1891. 8°.   6825. de. 3.

MATTHEWS (J. B.) Law relating to Covenants in restraint of trade. pp. 263. _Lond._ 1893. 8°.   6375. de. 7.

MUNRO (J. E. C.) Commercial Law. pp. 191. _Lond._ 1893. 8°.   6825. a. 10.

SCRUTTON (T. E.) Elements of mercantile Law. pp. 236. _Lond._ 1891. 8°.   6375. aa. 53.

Italy.

ITALY. Code de Commerce italien. pp. 306. _Paris_, 1892. 8°.   6825. de. 4.

FRANCHI (L.) Manuale del Diritto commerciale italiano. _Roma_, 1890, _etc._ 8°.   6825. d.

LATTES (A.) Il Diritto commerciale nella legislazione delle città italiane. pp. 379. _Milano_, 1884. 8°.   6825. aa. 7.

SRAFFA (A.) La Liquidazione delle Società commerciali. pp. 205. _Firenze_, 1891. 8°.   5359. aa. 10.

LAW.—Commercial—_continued._

VIDARI (E.) Corso di Diritto commerciale. _Milano_, 1893, _etc._ 8°.   5373. dd.

Japan.

LOENHOLM (L.) Japanese commercial Law. pp. 127. _Tokyo_, 1895. 8°.   5319. aa. 16.

—— Japanisches Handelsrecht. 1891. fol. Ac. Yedo. _Deutsche Gesellschaft._ Mittheilungen. Bd. 6.   Ac. 1944.

Mexico.

MEXICO. Código de Comercio. pp. 331. _México_, 1889. 8°.   6835. dd. 5.

—— Code de Commerce mexicain. pp. 435. _Paris_, 1894. 8°.   6784. f. 19.

Netherlands.

NETHERLANDS. Commercial code of the Netherlands. pp. 220. _Rotterdam_, 1893. 8°.   5685. a. 2.

Rome, Ancient. See infra: *Roman Law.*

Roumania.

ROUMANIA. Code de Commerce roumain. pp. 470. _Paris_, 1895. 8°.   5756. d. 7.

Spain.

SPAIN. Código de Commercio. pp. 707. _Madrid_, 1894. 8°.   5384. a. 2.

—— Code de Commerce espagnol. pp. 343. _Paris_, 1891. 8°.   5383. e. 4.

CARRERAS Y GONZALEZ (M.) Elementos del derecho mercantil de España. pp. 447. _Madrid_, 1893. 8°.   6825. aa. 6.

GALVEZ Y GONZALEZ (F.) and GUISADO (A.) Legislación de hacienda. pp. 189. _Madrid_, 1893. 8°.   5383. e. 8.

Switzerland.

SIEGMUND (L.) Handbuch für die schweizerischen Handelsregisterführer. pp. 627. _Basel_, 1892. 8°.   05551. f. 2.

United States. See supra: GREAT BRITAIN.

Venezuela.

DOMÉNICI (A.) Comentarios al Código de Comercio. pp. 746. _Carácas_, 1891. 8°.   6784. f. 18.

See also infra: International: Maritime: ARBITRATION: BANKING: BANKRUPCY: BILLS: COMPANIES: CONTRACT: SALE, _Law of._

Criminal.

Ac. Europe. *Union de Droit Pénal.* La Legislation pénale comparée. _Berl._ 1894, _etc._ 8°.   Ac. 2100.

COSTANZO PERATONER (C.) Dei Delitti contro la libertà. pp. 375. _Catania_, 1891. 8°.   5359. ee. 29.

ENGELMANN (W.) Die Schuldlehre der Postglossatoren und ihre Fortentwickelung, _etc._ pp. 342. _Leipz._ 1895. 8°.   5206. c. 3.

FABREGUETTES (M. P.) De la Complicité intellectuelle et des délits d'opinion. pp. 102. _Paris_, 1894–95. 8°.   5423. g. 3.

GOITEIN (E.) Das Vergeltungsprincip im biblischen und talmudischen Strafrecht. pp. 88. _Frankf._ 1893. 8°.   4034. k. 30.

HUTHER ( ) Der Kausalzusammenhang als Voraussetzung des Strafrechts. pp. 137. _Wismar_, 1893. 8°.   6055. df. 21.

LUCCHINI (L.) Le Droit pénal et les nouvelles théories. pp. 459. _Paris_, 1892. 8°. 6057. bb. 33.

MERKEL (A.) Vergeltungsidee und Zweckgedanke im Strafrecht. 1892. 8°. JHERING (R. v.) Festgabe.   6006. aa. 41.

ORTLOFF (H. F.) Staats- und Gesellschafts-Vertretung im Strafverfähren. pp. 114. _Tübingen_, 1892. 8°.   6055. f. 6.

LAW.—Criminal—_continued._

PFENNINGER (H.) Grenzbestimmungen zur criminalistischen Imputationslehre. pp. 103. _Zürich_, 1892. 8°.   6025. c. 1.

PFIZER ( ) Die Berufung in Straafsachen. pp. 40. 1891. 8°. Deutsche Zeit- und Streit-Fragen. Hft. 90.   12209. f.

PRUSSIA. Die preussischen Strafgesetze. _Berl._ 1894, _etc._ 8°.   05604. k.

RINTELEN (V.) Der Strafprozess. pp. 518. _Berl._ 1891. 8°.   5604. cee. 24.

SCHMIDT (R.) Staatsanwalt und Privatkläger. pp. 148. _Leipz._ 1891. 8°.   05604. h. 16.

—— Die Aufgaben der Strafrechtspflege. pp. 312. _Leipz._ 1895. 8°.   6055. df. 26.

SPOLER (C.) Das Beweisinteresse in Strafsachen, sog. Materielle Beweislast. _Giessen_, 1894, _etc._ 8°,   6055. cc.

TOBLER (H.) Die Grenzgebiete zwischen Notstand und Notwehr. pp. 159. _Zürich_, 1894. 8°.   6057. aaa. 39.

India.

NELSON (R. A.) The Indian penal Code. pp. 448. _Madras_, 1893. 8°.   5319. b. 23.

GRIFFITH (W.) Code of criminal Procedure. pp. 360. _Madras_, 1889. 8°.   5319. aaa. 31.

MAYNE (J. D.) Commentaries on the Indian penal code. pp. 682. _Madras_, 1890. 8°.   5318. b. 25.

STARLING (M. H.) Indian criminal Law. pp. 750. _Bombay_, 1890, 8°.   5319. aa. 12.

SUNDARA-SARMĀ. Catechetic Commentaires on the Indian penal code. pp. 90. _Madras_, 1893. 8°.   5319. bb. 10.

Ireland.

VANSTON (G. T. B.) Criminal Law and procedure, Ireland, Act. pp. 86. _Dublin_, 1887. 8°.   6503. aaa. 9.

Italy.

ARABIA (F. S.) I principii del Diritto penale applicati al codice italiano. pp. 502. _Napoli_, 1891. 8°.   5373. ee. 21.

—— Sull' applicazione del codice penale italiano. 1894. 8°. Ac. Naples. _R. Accademia di Scienze._ Atti. Vol. 26.   Ac. 96/2.

DESJARDINS (A.) La Méthode expérimentale appliquée au Droit criminel en Italie. pp. 183. _Paris_, 1892. 8°.   6055. f. 7.

LA SCOLA (F.) Sul Giuri penale. pp. 92. _Palermo_, 1890. 8°.   6055. aa. 11.

LECCI (A.) Il sistema delle pene nel Codice italiano. pp. 408. _Turin_, 1891. 8°.   5359. bb. 13.

MARCIANO (G.) Il Titolo decimo del Codice penale italiano. pp. 472. _Napoli_, 1890. 8°.   5373. ee. 22.

MASSE (É.) Le Code pénal italien. pp. 60. _Besançon_, 1890. 8°.   5423. g. 1. (2.)

SETTI (A.) Dell' Imputabilità secondo gli articoli 44–48 del Codice penale. pp. 445. _Torino_, 1892. 8°.   5359. ee. 32.

TRAVAGLIA (C.) Il nuovo Codice penale italiano. Commento. _Roma_, 1889, _etc._ 8°. 5358. bb. 12.

Jews.

MENDELSOHN (S.) Criminal Jurisprudence of the ancient Hebrews. pp. 270. _Baltimore_, 1891. 8°.   5125. e. 10.

Netherlands.

GANSOIJEN (A. P. tot) Iets over de kosten van het strafproces in Nederland. pp. 168. _Leiden_, 1891. 8°.   5686. cc. 69.

SIMONS (D.) Handleiding tot het Wetboek van Strafvordering. pp. 244. _Haarlem_, 1892. 8°.   5686. b. 9.

LAW.—Criminal—_continued._

ZILLESEN (H.) Het Wetboek van Strafvordering. _'s Gravenh._ 1887, _etc._ 16°.   5686. a. 24.

Scotland.

ANDERSON (A. M.) Criminal Law of Scotland. pp. 327. _Edinb._ 1892. 8°.   6583. aa. 11.

ANGUS (J. W.) Dictionary of Crimes according to the Law of Scotland. pp. 358. _Edinb._ 1895. 8°.   6485. b. 34.

BROWN (H. H.) Principles of summary criminal Jurisdiction. pp. 350. _Edinb._ 1895. 8°.   6583. cc. 11.

MACDONALD (J. H. A.) _Lord Kingsburgh._ Scottish Criminal Law System. pp. 31. _Glasg._ 1891. 4°.   6146. bbb. 27. (4.)

Sweden.

THYRÉN (J. C. W.) Abhandlungen aus dem Strafrechte. _Lund_, 1894, _etc._ 8°.   6055. ee.

Switzerland.

KOCHER (R.) Die Straf-Gerichtsorganisation und Straf-Prozessgesetzgebung der Schweiz. pp. 227. _Zürich_, 1894. 8°.   5510. a. 2.

STOOS (C.) Les Codes pénaux suisses. _Fr._ and _Germ._ pp. 867. _Bâle_, 1890. 4°.   6055. e. 3.

—— Die Grundzüge des schweizerischen Strafrechts. _Basel_, 1892, _etc._ 8°.   5551. g. 16.

United States.

FOURNIER (A.) Code de Procédure criminelle de l'état de New-York. pp. 478. _Paris_, 1893. 8°.   6617. l. 1.

See also infra: INTERNATIONAL: CRIME: EXTRADITION: INSANITY: MEDICINE, _Legal._ POLICE: PRISONS: PUNISHMENT.

Ecclesiastical.
General: Canon Law.

ANDRÉ (M.) Dictionnaire de Droit canonique. _Paris_, 1894, _etc._ 4°.   05107. l.

BARGILLIAT ( ) Prælectiones Juris Canonici. _Parisiis_, 1890, _etc._ 12°.   05107. e. 4.

BASSIBEY (R.) Des Sentences "ex informata conscientia." pp. 116. _Paris_, 1894. pp.   05107. f. 11.

BENDIX (L.) Kirche und Kirchenrecht. pp. 190. _Mainz_, 1895. 8°.   05107. g. 5.

DEMKO (G.) Jus Ecclesiasticum. 2 tom. _Agriae_, 1888. 8°.   05107. f. 10.

DROSTE (F.) Procedure in disciplinary and criminal cases of clerics. pp. 268. _N.Y._ 1887. 8°.   05107. ee. 11.

ERTEL (P.) Die Quellen des kirchlichen Rechtes. pp. 171. _Berl._ 1890. 8°.   6005. ee. 25.

GROSS (C.) Lehrbuch des katholischen Kirchenrechts. pp. 426. _Wien_, 1894. 8°. 05107. f. 1.

HEINER (F.) Katholisches Kirchenrecht. 1893, _etc._ 8°. Wissenschaftliche Handbibliothek. Reihe 1. Bd. 5, _etc._   3558. e.

KAHL (W.) Lehrsystem des Kirchenrechts. _Freiburg_, 1894, _etc._ 8°.   05107. f.

LAFARGE ( ) Le Gouvernement de l'Église; ou, principes du droit ecclésiastique. pp. 518. _Paris_, 1890. 8°.   05107. ee. 9.

MAHL-SCHEDL-ALPENBURG (F. J.) Grundriss des katholischen Kirchenrechtes. pp. 232. _Wien_, 1890. 8°.   5125. e. 11.

MELCHERS (P. L.) _Archbp. of Cologne._ De canonica Dioecesium Visitatione. pp. 180. _Coloniae ad R._ 1893. 8°.   05107. e. 6.

MIGNAULT (P. B.) Le Droit paroissial. pp. 690. _Montréal_, 1893. 8°.   5155. f. 11.

MIRBT (C.) Die Publizistik im Zeitalter Gregors VII. pp. 629. _Leipz._ 1894. 8°. 05107. g. 3.

LAW.—Ecclesiastical—*continued.*

ROME, *Ch. of. Curia Romana.* Formulary of the Papal Penitentiary in the 13th century. Edited by H. C. Lea. pp. 183. *Phila.* 1892. 8°.
    05107. f. 8.

SANGUINETI (S.) Juris ecclesiastici institutiones in usum prælectionum. pp. 587.
Romae, 1890. 8°.   05107. ee. 17.

SCHMIDT (A. B.) Der Austritt aus der Kirche. pp. 395. *Leipz.* 1893. 8°.   5125. e. 14.

SMITH (S. B.) Elements of ecclesiastical Law, *etc.* 3 vol. *N.Y.* 1889–90. 8°.   05107. ee. 10.

STANGL (J.) Konkordat und Religionsedikt.
München, 1895, *etc.* 8°.   5125. e.

TURINAZ (C. F.) *Bp. of Tarentaise.* De l'Etude et de la pratique du Droit canonique en France. pp. 49. *Paris,* 1891. 8°.   5063. bbb. 24. (7.)

Austria-Hungary.

DEMKO (G.) Jus ecclesiasticum respectu habito ad Hungariam. 2 tom. *Agriae,* 1888. 8°.
    05107. f. 10.

GROSS (C.) Lehrbuch des katholischen Kirchenrechts mit Berücksichtigung der Gestaltung d sselben in Oesterreich. pp. 426.
Wien, 1894. 8°.   05107. f. 1.

MAHL-SCHEDL-ALPENBURG (F. J.) Grundriss des kath. Kirchenrechtes, mit Berücksichtigung der österreich. Gesetzgebung. pp. 232.
Wien, 1890. 8°.   5125. e. 11.

WAHRMUND (L.) Das Kirchenpatronatrecht und seine Entwicklung in Oesterreich.
Wien, 1894, *etc.* 8°.   05107. i.
See also supra: General: Canon Law.

England.

BLUNT (J. H.) The Book of church law. pp. 546. *Lond.* 1894. 8°.   2228. b. 7.

BLYTH (T. A.) Handbook for the clergy. pp. 232. *Birmingham,* 1893. 8°.   5155. de. 26.

CHITTY (J.) Statutes relating to church and clergy. pp. 281. *Lond.* 1894. 8°. 5155. h. 12.

FOSTER (J. P.) Guide to all ecclesiastical fees. pp. 66. *Poulton,* 1893. 8°.   5155. b. 7. (6.)

HARDERN (T. B.) Church Discipline. pp. 100. *Camb.* 1892. 8°.   4109. c. 26.

LONDON, *Diocese.* Rules of the Consistory Court. pp. 18. *Lond.* 1893. 8°.   6190. cc. 4. (11.)

PHILLIMORE (*Right Hon. Sir* R. J.) Ecclesiastical Law of the Church of England. 2 vol.
Lond. 1895. 8°.   2016. d.

SMITH (T. E.) Summary of the Law and practice in the Ecclesiastical Courts. pp. 264.
Lond. 1895. 8°.   5155. b. 6.

TALBOT (G. J.) Modern decisions on Ritual. pp. 165. *Lond.* 1894. 8°.   5155. a. 32.

TRISTRAM (T. H.) Principal judgments delivered in the Consistory Courts. 1872–90. pp. 313.
Lond. 1893. 8°.   5155. cc. 29.

WHITEHEAD (B.) Church Law: concise dictionary. pp. 304. *Lond.* 1892. 8°. 5155. cc. 27.

READ (E. de L.) In the Court of the Archbishop of Canterbury. Read and others v. the Bishop of Lincoln. Judgment. pp. 123. *Lond.* 1894. 8°.
    5155. b. 4.

BENNETT (H. M.) The Lincoln Judgment. A word on its historical aspect. pp. 10.
Lond. 1890. 8°.   4108. de. 32. (3.)

ELWIN (W.) The Mixed Chalice and the Lincoln judgment. pp. 31. *Lond.* 1891. 8°.
    4109. c. 15. (3.)

FULLER (M. J.) The Throne of Canterbury; the Archbishop's jurisdiction. pp. 322.
Lond. 1891. 8°.   5155. e. 3.

JURISDICTION. Metropolitical Jurisdiction: so far as it relates to the trial of Bishops. pp. 39.
Lond. 1890. 8°.   4109. aaa. 21. (5.)

LAW.—Ecclesiastical—*continued.*

KING (E.) *Bp. of Lincoln.* Authority of the Archbishop in the Lincoln case. pp. 22.
Lond. 1891. 8°.   Pam. 32.

—— "Is there not a Cause?" Articles on the Lincoln case. pp. 24. *Lond.* 1890. 8°.
    4109. e. 20. (4.)

MONTAGU (*Lord* R.) The Lambeth Judgment. pp. 52. *Lond.* 1891. 8°.   4109. c. 15. (4.)

READ (E. de L.) Questions suggested by so much of the Lambeth Judgment as deals with the North Side Rubric. 2 pt.
Maidstone, 1891. fol.   Pam. 92.

TOMLINSON (J. T.) Historical grounds of the Lambeth Judgment examined. pp. 99.
Lond. 1892. 8°.   4109. c. 20.

PACIFICUS. Replies to Mr. Tomlinson's pamphlet. pp. 54. *Oxf.* 1891. 8°.   4109. c. 15. (7.)

WORDSWORTH (C.) Historical notes on the Archbishop's "Judgment," particularly in reference to Mr. J. T. Tomlinson's pamphlet. pp. 71.
Lond. 1891. 8°.   4109. c. 15. (8.)

ERRINGTON (F. H. L.) Clergy Discipline Act, 1892. pp. 96. *Lond.* 1892. 8°. 5155. h. 10.

G. B. & I. Rules under the Clergy Discipline Act, 1892. pp. 53. *Lond.* 1891. 8°.
    6146. k. 13. (3.)

—— Clergy Discipline Act, 1892. Scales of fees and costs. pp. 9. *Lond.* 1893. 8°.
    6190. cc. 4. (8).

ENGLAND. *English Church Union.* Clergy Discipline. Suggestions for legislation. pp. 45.
Lond. 1892. 8°.   4109. aaaa. 21. (8.)
See also CHURCHWARDENS: ENGLAND, *Church of:* TITHES.

France.

DUBIEF (A.) and GOTTOFREY (V.) Traité de l'administration des Cultes. *Paris,* 1891, *etc.* 8°.
    5406. de.

SCHIAPPOLI (D.) Diritto ecclesiastico vigente in Francia. *Torino,* 1892, *etc.* 8°.   5107. eee.

TARINAZ (C. F.) *Bp. of Tarentaise.* De l'Étude et de la pratique du Droit canonique en France. pp. 49. *Paris,* 1891. 8°.   5063. bbb. 24. (7.)
See also supra: General, Canon Law.

Germany.

MEJER (O.) Zum Kirchenrechte des Reformationsjahrhunderts. pp. 210. *Hannover,* 1891. 8°.
    05107. ee. 20.

CHRISTL (F.) Die Natur der Dotationen der Bischöfe und Domkapitel nach bayerischen Recht. pp. 40. *Regensburg,* 1895. 8°. Pam. 34.

SCHMIDT (A. B.) Kirchenrechtliche Quellen des Grossherzogthums Hessen. pp. 239.
Giessen, 1891. 8°.   05107. ee. 18.

SOHM (R.) Kirchenrecht. 1892, *etc.* 8°. BINDING (C.) Handbuch der deutschen Rechtswissenschaft. Abt. 8. Bd. 1, *etc.*   5605. ff.
See also supra: General: Canon Law: EVANGELICAL CHURCH.

Greek and other Oriental Churches.

ACHELIS (H.) Die ältesten Quellen des orientalischen Kirchenrechtes. 1891. 8°. GEBHARDT (O. v.) and HARNACK (A.) Texte. Bd. 6. 3623. b.

Iceland.

PJETURSSON (J.) Kirkjurjettur. pp. 256.
Reykjavík, 1890. 8°.   3925. aaa. 8.

Italy.

CADORNA (C.) Della condizione giuridica delle associazioni religiose negli stati civili. 2 vol.
Milano, 1893. 8°.   3900. i. 24.

FRIEDBERG (E.) Trattato del diritto ecclesiastico cattolico ed evangelico. pp. 864. *Torino,* 1893. 8°.
    05107. g. 1.

LAW.—Ecclesiastical—*continued.*

GALANTE (A.) Il Diritto di Placitazioue e l'economato dei benefici in Lombardia. pp. 128. *Milano*, 1894. 8°.   05107. h. 2.

See also supra: General: Canon Law.

Scotland.

BLACK (W. G.) Handbook of the parochial ecclesiastical Law of Scotland. pp. 236. *Edinb.* 1891. 8°.   5157. b. 11.

See also SCOTLAND, *Church of :* TITHES.

Spain.

GOMEZ SALAZAR (F.) Lecciones de disciplina eclesiastica de España. 2 tom. *Madrid*, 1894. 8°.   05107. ee. 24.

See also supra: General: Canon.

Education, Legal.

DÉVOT (J.) L'Enseignement du droit. pp. 230. *Paris*, 1893. 12°.   6784. a. 9

RUSSELL (C.) *Baron Russell of Killowen.* Legal Education. pp. 22. *Lond.* 1895. 8°. Pam. 32.

SAVIGNY (L. v.) Die französischen Rechtsfacultäten. pp. 223. *Berl.* 1891. 8°. 8355. eee. 15.

See also infra: Profession of : EXAMINATIONS.

Feudal.

See infra : Mediaeval : FEUDALISM.

Hindu. *See* HINDUISM.

International.

Bibliography.

U.S. *Department of State.* Index to the literature of International Law. *Wash.* 1887, *etc.* 4°.   11899. e. 30.

General : Public.

BONFILS (H.) Manuel de Droit international public. pp. 936. *Paris*, 1894. 12°.   6916. aa. 19.

BRY (G.) Précis de Droit international public. pp. 524. *Paris*, 1891. 12°.   6916. a. 5.

CHAUVEAU (M E.) Le Droit des Gens. pp. 187. *Paris*, 1891. 8°.   6915. df. 17.

CIMBALI (E.) Lo Stato secondo il Diritto internazionale universale. pp. 317. *Roma*, 1891. 8°.   6955. cc. 12.

COBBETT (P.) Leading Cases on International Law. pp. 385. *Lond.* 1892. 8°.   2228. c. 4.

DESJARDINS (A.) Le Congrès de Paris, 1856, et la Jurisprudence internationale. 1888. 4°. Ac. Paris. *Académie des Sciences Morales.* Mémoires. Tom. 16.   2098. f.

FALCKE ( ) Die Hauptperiode der sogenannten Friedensblokaden. 1827–1850. pp. 92. *Leipz.* 1891. 8°.   06955. ee. 3.

FÉRAUD-GIRAUD (L. J. D.) États et souverains, personnel diplomatique et consulaire, *etc.* devant les tribunaux étrangers. 2 tom. *Paris*, 1895. 8°.   06955. df. 25.

FUSINATO (G.) Introduzione a un corso di Diritto internazionale. 2 pt. *Macerata*, 1885. 8°.   06955. df. 16.

GEMMA (S.) E. Kant e gli utopisti del diritto internazionale. pp. 31. *Bologna*, 1893. 8°.   6005. g. 18. (10.)

GRIFFITH (W.) International Law. pp. 130. *Lond.* 1893. 8°.   06955. f. 2.

HALL (W. E.) Treatise on International Law. pp. 791. *Oxf.* 1895. 8°.   2228. c. 1.

—— Treatise on the Foreign Powers and jurisdiction of the British Crown. pp. 304. *Oxf.* 1894. 8°.   06955. df. 18.

HALLECK (H. W.) International Law. 2 vol. *Lond.* 1893. 8°.   2228. d. 10.

HEILBORN (P.) Das völkerrechtliche Protektorat. pp. 187. *Berl.* 1891. 8°.   06955. df. 6.

LAW.— International—*continued.*

HOLM (H.) Fordhandlingspolitiken og dens Resultater, *etc.* pp. 93. *Kjøbenh.* 1891. 8°.   Pam. 74.

JELLINEK (G.) System der subjectiven öffentlichen Rechte. pp. 318. *Freiburg*, 1892. 8°.   05604. i. 5.

KLEEN (R.) Neutralitetens lagar. *Stockholm*, 1889, *etc.* 8°.   06955. df. 5.

LABAND (P.) and STOERK (F.) Archiv für öffentliches Recht. *Freiburg*, 1886, *etc.* 8°.   P.P. 1403. k.

LABRA (R. M. de) El Instituto de Derecho internacional. pp. 42. *Madrid*, 1889. 8°.   6005. h. 26. (2.)

LA GRASSERIE (R. de) De l'unification des Législations de différents peuples. pp. 28. *Paris*, 1895. 8°.   Pam. 34.

LAWRENCE (T. J.) Handbook of public International Law. pp. 143. *Camb.* 1890. 8°.   6916. a. 4.

—— Principles of International Law. pp. 645. *Lond.* 1895. 8°.   06955. f. 4.

LEHR (P. E.) Tableau de l'organisation de l'Institut de Droit international, 1873–92. pp. 373. *Paris*, 1893. 8°.   06955. e. 1.

LESEUR (P.) Introduction à un cours de Droit international public. pp. 152. *Paris*, 1893. 8°.   06955. df. 19.

LÓPEZ (J. F.) Derecho y arbitraje internacional. pp. 200. *Paris*, 1891. 8°.   6915. eee. 22.

MEILI (F.) Die Kodifikation der internationalen Civil- und Handelsrechts. pp. 151. *Leipz.* 1891. 8°.   6955. bb. 8.

NIPPOLD (O.) Der völkerrechtliche Vertrag. pp. 285. *Bern*, 1894. 8°.   6955. f. 10.

NYS (E.) Les Origines du Droit international. pp. 414. *Brux.* 1894. 8°.   06955. ee. 17.

—— Les Initiateurs du Droit public moderne. pp. 62. *Brux.* 1890. 8°.   Pam. 32.

—— Le Droit international en France jusqu'au XVIII° siècle. pp. 208. *Brux.* 1891. 8°.   8009. f. 14.

—— Le Droit des gens dans les rapports des Arabes, *etc.* pp. 29. *Brux.* 1894. 8°.   6005. h. 26. (11.)

PIÉDELIÈVRE (R.) Précis de Droit international public. *Paris*, 1894, *etc.* 8°.   06955. df.

POINSARD (L.) Études de Droit international. *Paris*, 1894, *etc.* 8°.   6916. c.

PREUSS (H.) Das Völkerrecht im Dienste des Wirthschaftslebens. pp. 64 1891. 8°. Volkswirthschaftliche Zeitfragen. Hft. 99, 100.   8207. i.

RETORTILLO Y TORNOS (A.) Compendio de historia del Derecho internacional. pp. 285. *Madrid*, 1891. 8°.   6916. aa. 16.

—— Vocabulario del Derecho internacional público. pp. 179. *Madrid*, 1893. 8°.   6916. aa. 18.

SCHOPFER (S.) Le Principe juridique de la neutralité. pp. 306. *Lausanne*, 1894. 8°.   06955. ee. 15.

SNOW (F.) Cases and opinions on International Law. pp. 586. *Bost.* 1893. 8°.   06955. g. 2.

STEPHEN (J. K.) International Law and international relations. pp. 148. *Lond.* 1884. 8°.   6916. aa. 5.

TESTA (C.) Conflictos internacionaes. pp. 52. *Lisboa*, 1890. 8°.   Pam. 64.

VIARIS (de) *Marquis.* Les Dépêches secrètes et les conventions internationales. pp. 61. *Paris*, 1893. 8°.   8757. h. 25.

WALLGREN (H. G.) Den internationela Rättsordningens problem. pp. 212. *Upsala*, 1892. 8°.   06955. df. 23.

LAW.—International—*continued.*

WALKER (T. A.) Science of International Law. pp. 544. *Lond.* 1893. 8°.   06955. df. 13.

—— Manual of public International Law. pp. 244. *Camb.* 1895. 8°.   6955. e. 16.

WESTLAKE (J.) Chapters on the principles of International Law. pp. 275. *Camb.* 1894. 8°.   06955. df. 21.

—— Études sur les principes du Droit international. pp. 304. *Brux.* 1895. 8°.   06955. ee. 16.

WIESSE (C.) Reglas de Derecho internacional aplicables á las guerras civiles. pp. 372. *Lima*, 1893. 8°.   6915. df. 18.

WOOLSEY (T. D.) Introduction to the study of International Law. pp. 526. *Lond.* 1888. 8°.   06955. g. 4.

See also infra: Maritime: Military: Naval: ARBITRATION: CONSULS: DIPLOMACY.

Private.

BAR (L. v.) Lehrbuch des internationalen Privat- und Strafrechts. pp. 360. *Stuttgart*, 1892. 8°.   6916. aaa. 20.

—— Theory and practice of private International Law. pp. 1162. *Edinb.* 1892. 8°. 06955. ee. 10.

DURAND (L.) Essai de Droit international privé. pp. 820. *Paris*, 1884. 8°.   6955. ee. 10.

FUSINATO (G.) Introduzione a un corso di Diritto internazionale. 2 pt. *Macerata*, 1885. 8°.   06955. df. 16.

—— Questioni di Diritto internazionale privato. pp. 68. *Torino*, 1884. 8°.   Pam. 32.

—— Il Principio della scuola italiana nel Diritto privato internazionale. pp. 95. *Bologna*, 1885. 8°.   06955. df. 15.

FIORE (P.) Diritto internazionale privato. *Torino*, 1881. 8°.   06955. df.

GUILLAUME (J. J. G. P.) *Baron.* Le Mariage en droit international privé. pp. 549. *Brux.* 1894. 8°.   5176. ee. 2.

JETTEL (E.) Handbuch des internationalen Privat- und Strafrechtes. pp. 344. *Wien*, 1893. 8°.   5549. e. 31.

JITTA (D. J.) La méthode du Droit international privé. pp. 499. *La Haye*, 1890. 8°. 06955. ee. 4.

LA GRASSERIE (R. de) De l'unification des législations de différents peuples. pp. 28. *Paris*, 1895. 8°.   Pam. 34.

MEILI (F.) Geschichte und System des internationalen Privatrechts. pp. 209. *Leipz.* 1892. 8°.   06955. df. 9.

MONTEVIDEO. *Congreso de Derecho Internacional Privado.* Actas. pp. 650. *Buenos A.* 1889. 8°.   6915. f. 2.

NIEMEYER (T.) Positives internationales Privatrecht. *Leipz.* 1894, *etc.* 8°.   06955. ee.

—— Zur Methodik des internationalen Privatrechtes. pp. 39. *Leipz.* 1894. 8°.   Pam. 32.

P.P. *Erlangen.* Zeitschrift für internationales Privat- und Strafrecht. *Erlangen*, 1890, *etc.* 8°.   P.P. 1403. eb.

RATTIGAN (*Sir* W. H.) Private International Law. pp. 267. *Lond.* 1895. 8°.   06955. f. 3.

STORY (J.) Commentaries on the Conflict of Laws. pp. 901. *Bost.* 1883. 8°.   06955. ee. 13.

WHARTON (F.) Treatise on the Conflict of Laws. pp. 847. *Phila.* 1881. 8°.   06955. g. 1.

WEISS (A.) Traité de Droit international privé. *Paris*, 1892, *etc.* 8°.   06955. df.

CONSTANT (C.) De l'Exécution des jugements étrangers dans les divers pays. pp. 210. *Paris*, 1890. 8°.   6916. aaa. 19.

LAW.—International—*continued.*

HALL (W. E.) Treatise on the foreign Powers and Jurisdiction of the British Crown. pp. 304. *Oxf.* 1894. 8°.   06955. df. 18.

LACHAU (C.) De la Compétence des tribunaux français à l'égard des étrangers. pp. 468. *Paris*, 1893. 8°.   5423. e. 18.

PIGGOTT (F. T.) Service out of the Jurisdiction. pp. 262. *Lond.* 1892. 8°.   6281. g. 21.

Nationality : Naturalization.

PAGE (W.) Letters of Denization and acts of naturalization for aliens in England, 1509-1603. pp. 258. 1893. 4°. Ac. London. *Huguenot Society.* Publications. Vol. 8.   Ac. 2073/4.

DURAND (J.) Les Étrangers devant la Loi française. pp. 198. *Paris*, 1890. 8°.   5403. de. 2.

GEOUFFRE DE LAPRADELLE (A.) De la Nationalité d'origine. pp. 448. *Paris*, 1893. 8°.   06955. df. 14.

GRUFFY (G.) De l'unité de Nationalité dans la famille. pp. 210. *Paris*, 1893. 8°. 6955. f. 9.

PAVITT (A.) Guide to French Laws on Nationality and military service. pp. 42. *Lond.* 1893. 8°.   Pam. 34.

VACA-GUZMÁN (S.) La Naturalización de los extranjeros, *etc.* pp. 142. *Buenos A.* 1891. 8°.   6955. e. 15.

WEBSTER (P.) Treatise on the Law of citizenship in the United States, *etc.* pp. 338. *Albany*, 1891. 8°.   06616. f. 19.

See also CONSULS: EXTRADITION.

Jewish. *See JEWS.*

Maritime.

AUTRAN (F. C.) Code International de l'Abordage Maritime. pp. 208. *Paris*, 1890. 8°.   6916. aaa. 18.

GODCHOT (S.) Les Neutres. Étude de droit maritime. pp. 444. *Alger*, 1891. 8°. 06955. ee. 6.

LAFFLEUR DE KERMAINGANT (P. P.) Le Droit des gens maritime au commencement du XVII° siècle. *Paris*, 1892. 8°.   6005. de. 4. (7.)

P.P. *Paris.* Revue internationale du Droit maritime. *Paris*, 1885, *etc.* 8°.   P.P. 1275. d.

See also supra: International. Infra: Naval.

Denmark.

BENTZON (V.) Forelæsninger over den danske Søret. pp. 92. *Kjøbenh.* 1892. 8°. 5725. cc. 4.

—— Søloven og Lov om danske Skibes Registrering. pp. 188. *Kjøbenh.* 1892. 8°. 5725 .a. 10.

DENMARK. Forslag til Sølov. pp. 155. *Kjøbenh.* 1891. 8°.   5705. h. 10.

France.

CONSTANT (C.) Manuel de Droit commercial et maritime, *etc. Paris*, 1891, *etc.* 8°.   6825. eee.

DAVANSEAU ( ) Considérations sur les règlements d'Avaries. pp. 483. *Alger*, 1890. 8°.   6835. g. 3.

HAUMONT (A.) and LÉVAREY (A.) Les Transports maritimes. pp. 372. *Paris*, 1893. 8°.   6835. df. 16.

JOUËT-PASTRÉ (A.) Observations sur le projet de loi sur la marine marchande. pp. 10. *Paris*, 1892. 4°.   Pam. 43.

LYON-CAEN (C.) and RENAULT (L.) Traité de Droit maritime. *Paris*, 1894, *etc.* 8°. 6835. df.

SALANSON (U.) De la Contribution aux Avaries communes. pp. 171. *Paris*, 1893. 8°.   6835. ee. 11.

Germany.

FRIEDBERG (E.) Formelbuch für Handels- und Seerecht. pp. 390. *Leipz.* 1890. 8°.   6825. ee. 19.

LAW.—Maritime—_continued._

NEY (C.) Das deutsche See- und Wechselrecht. pp. 341. _Berl._ 1890. 8°.   6835. aa. 19.

Great Britain and Ireland.

ABBOTT (C.) _Baron Tenterden._ Treatise of the Law relative to Merchant Ships and seamen. pp. 1259. _Lond._ 1892. 8°.   2018. d.

BLACK (W. G.) Digest of Decisions in Scotch shipping cases, 1865–90. pp. 244. _Edinb._ 1891. 8°.   6583. g. 9.

CARVER (T. G.) Treatise on the Law relating to the Carriage of goods by sea. pp. 812. _Lond._ 1891. 8°.   6376. f. 19.

GIBSON (A.) and WELDON (A.) Student's Probate and Admiralty. pp. 359. _Lond._ 1895. 8°.   6355. ee. 12.

KAY (J.) Law relating to Shipmasters and seamen. pp. 825. _Lond._ 1894. 8°.   2232. e. 6.

KENNEDY (W. R.) Treatise on the Law of civil salvage. pp. 255. _Lond._ 1891. 8°. 6835. h. 4.

LEGGETT (E.) Treatise on the Law of charter-parties. pp. 662. _Lond._ 1894. 8°. 6835. cc. 8.

MACLACHLAN (D.) Treatise on the Law of merchant shipping. pp. 1075. _Lond._ 1892. 8°.   6835. h. 6.

MARSDEN (R. G.) Treatise on the law of Collisions at sea. pp. 644. _Lond._ 1891. 8°.   6835. aa. 18.

RAIKES (F. W.) "Both to blame." Conflict of law where two vessels are held jointly in fault for a collision. pp. 26. _Lond._ 1895. 8°. Pam. 32.

SCRUTTON (T. E.) Contract of Affreightment as expressed in charter-parties. pp. 370. _Lond._ 1893. 8°.   6375. de. 9.

SMITH (T. E.) Summary of Law and practice in Admiralty. pp. 216. _Lond._ 1892. 8°. 6835. df. 14.

MANSFIELD (_Hon._ J. W.) and DUNCAN (G. W.) Merchant Shipping Act, 1894. pp. 415. _Lond._ 1895. 8°.   6835. h. 7.

SCRUTTON (T. E.) Merchant Shipping Act, 1894. pp. 753. _Lond._ 1895. 8°.   6835. df. 19.

PULLING (A.) The Shipping Code. Merchant Shipping Act, 1894. pp. 414. _Lond._ 1894. 8°.   6835. dd. 8.

TEMPERLEY (R.) Merchant Shipping Act, 1894. pp. 714. _Lond._ 1895. 8°.   6835. h. 8.
See also BILLS OF LADING.

Italy.

VIDARI (E.) Il Diritto marittimo italiano. pp. 1102. _Milano_, 1892. 8°.   6835. bb. 11.

Sweden.

AFZELIUS (I.) Sjölagen med förklaringar ur autentika källor. pp. 263. _Stockholm_, 1891. 8°.   6835. hb. 15.

THURGREN (J. A.) Sveriges Rikes Sjölag tillika med tull-, skeppsmätnings- och Konsulat-författningarne. pp. 567. _Stockholm_, 1891. 8°.   5725. b. 17.
See also supra: _Commercial_: _International. Infra_: _Naval_: NAVAL SCIENCE: QUARANTINE.

Mediaeval.

HUBERTI (L.) Studien zur Rechtsgeschichte der Gottesfrieden und Landfrieden. _Ansbach_, 1892, _etc._ 8°.   06955. ce. 7.

FROIDEVAUX (H.) Étude sur la "Lex dicta Francorum Chamavorum." pp. 234. _Paris_, 1891. 8°.   5307. aaa. 9.

SÉE (H.) De Judiciariis Inquestis praesertim coram regiis jucibus XIII° seculo agente. pp. 105. _Carnuti_, 1890. 8°.   5403. eee. 14.

ADDOSIO (C. d') Bestie delinquenti. pp. 364. _Napoli_, 1892. 8°.   7709. aa. 31.
See also infra: _Roman_: FEUDALISM.

LAW—_continued._

Medical Jurisprudence.

See MEDICINE, _Legal._

Mercantile. _See supra_: _Commercial_: _Maritime._

Military.

LEVY (A.) Beiträge zum Kriegsrecht im Mittelalter. pp. 88. 1889. 8°. GIERKE (O.) Untersungen zur deutschen Rechtsgeschichte. No. 29.   6025. e. 9.

ROMBERG (E.) Des Belligérants et des prisonniers de guerre. pp. 308. _Brux._ 1894. 8°.   06955. df. 22.

SCHOPFER (S.) Le Principe de la neutralité dans l'histoire du droit de la guerre. pp. 306. _Lausanne_, 1894. 8°.   06955. ee. 15.

VASSAUX (E.) Prisonniers de guerre et otages. pp. 110. _Paris_, 1892. 8°.   06955. df. 10.

WEISL (E. F.) Das Militär-Strafverfahren in Russland, Frankreich und Deutschland. pp. 208. _Wien_, 1894. 8°.   6875. df. 10.

Austria.

DANGELMAIER (E.) Militär-rechtliche Abhandlungen. pp. 230. _Wien_, 1893. 8°. 6875. eee. 24.

WEISL (E. F.) Das Heeres-Strafrecht. _Wien_, 1892, _etc._ 8°.   6875. eee.

France.

FRANCE. Lois organiques militaires. _Paris_, 1895, _etc._ 8°.   6875. df.

CHAMPOUDRY (A.) Formules des questions à soumettre aux juges des Conseils du guerre. pp. 427. _Paris_, 1891. 8°.   6875. df. 7.

—— La Procédure militaire en campagne. pp. 365. _Paris_, 1893. 8°.   6875. df. 9.

—— La Justice prévotale aux armées. pp. 174. _Paris_, 1895. 8°.   6875. aa. 27.

DU CAZAL ( ) and CATRIN ( ) Médecine légale militaire. pp. 211. [1893.] 8°. Encyclopédie des aide-mémoire.   8709. g.

LASSALLE (C.) Code de Législation militaire en vue du temps de guerre. 2 tom. _Paris_, 1894, 8°.   6875. de. 11.

Germany.

MARCK (v.) Der Militär-Strafprozess in Deutschland. _Berl._ 1893, _etc._ 8°. 6875. eee.

WEIGEL (G.) Der bayerische Militär-Strafprozess. pp. 378. _Nurnberg_, 1889. 8°.   6875. eee. 19.

Great Britain and Ireland, etc.

G. B. & I. _Army._ Manual of Military Law. pp. 1158. _Lond._ 1894. 8°.   2230. a. 6.

—— Rules of Procedure in military trials. pp. 140. _Lond._ 1893. 8°.   8830. aaa. 59.

PRATT (S. C.) Military Law. pp. 247. 1895. 8°. BRACKENBURY (C. B.) Military handbooks. Vol. 5.   2249. a.

ANNA BHIMRÁVA. Handbook on Military Law for the Gaekwar's Army. ff. 91. _Bombay_, 1891. 8°.   6875. eee. 23.

Italy.

STELLA (S.) La Disciplina militare. pp. 45. _Torino_, 1890. 8°.   Pam. 2.
See also supra: _International_: MILITARY SCIENCE; and under the subheading _Army_ of each country.

Mohammedan. _See_ MOHAMMEDANISM.

Naval.

AUTRAN (F. C.) Code international de l'Abordage maritime. pp. 208. _Paris_, 1890. 8°.   6916. aaa. 18.

GODCHOT (S.) Les Neutres. Étude de droit maritime. pp. 444. _Alger_, 1891. 8°.   06955. ce. 6.

LAW.—Naval—*continued.*

LONDON. *Association for the Reform of the Law of Nations.* Territorial Waters. pp. 127. *Lond.* 1893. 8° 06955. de. 2.

WARAKER (T.) Naval Warfare of the future. pp. 213. *Lond.* 1892. 8°. 8806. cc. 18.

See also supra: International: Maritime; and under the subheading *Navy* of each country.

Profession of.

JAMES (C.) Curiosities of Law and lawyers. pp. 790. *Lond.* 1891. 8°. 6805. e. 1.

England.

A., M., and B., Ll. Guide to the Bar. pp. 215. *Lond.* 1893. 8°. 6190. aa. 30.

BALL (W. W. R.) Student's guide to the Bar. pp. 60. *Lond.* 1895. 8°. 6145. aa. 35.

HARRIS (R.) Hints on Advocacy. pp. 356. *Lond.* 1893. 8°. 2232. a. 11.

HERSCHELL (F.) *Baron Herschell.* Rights and duties of an Advocate. pp. 34. *Glasg.* 1890. 8°. 6146. bbb. 27. (3.)

ROBINSON (B. C.) Bench and Bar. pp. 336. *Lond.* 1891. 8°. 6006. aaa. 34.

LOFTIE (W. J.) Inns of Court and Chancery. pp. 88. *Lond.* 1895. 8°. 010350. f. 4.

MANSON (E.) Builders of our Law during the reign of Q. Victoria. pp. 236. *Lond.* 1895. 8°. 10825. bbb. 40.

THORPE (W. G.) Middle Temple table-talk. pp. 376. *Lond.* 1894. 8°. 12354. i. 37.

Ac. London. *Incorporated Law Society.* Solicitors' Act, 1888. pp. 15. 1889. 8°. 6190. cc. 3. (1.)

FOWKE (V. de S.) and HENDERSON (E. B.) Partnership between Solicitors. pp. 118. *Lond.* 1894. 8°. 6281. df. 9.

KAIN (G. J.) Solicitors' Bookkeeping by double entry. pp. 65. *Lond.* 1895. 8°. 8507. bb. 43.

ROUTLEDGE (J.) Relations of Client and Solicitor. pp. 127. *Gloucester,* 1886. 8°. 6190. aa. 29.

UTTLEY (T. F.) How to become a Solicitor. pp. 184. *Lond.* 1894. 8°. 6190. aa. 32.

WHITE (A. M.) Treatise on the constitution and government of Solicitors. pp. 495. *Lond.* 1894. 8°. 6146. d. 20.

JONES (C.) The Solicitor's Clerk. pp. 254. *Lond.* 1895. 8°. 6190. aa. 33.

SPRAY (H.) Lawyers' Clerks. pp. 15. *Lond.* 1894. 8°. 6190. aa. 31. (16.)

STIFF (H. W.) New Guide for Articled Clerks. pp. 239. *Lond.* 1895. 8°. 6190. a. 24.

See also EXAMINATIONS, *Legal.* BILLS, *of Costs.*

France.

ALLOU (R.) and CHENU (C.) Barreau de Paris. Grands Avocats du siècle. pp. 361. *Paris,* 1895. 8°. 010662. k. 14.

BAUBY (É.) Traité de la responsabilité civile des Notaires. pp. 765. *Paris.* 1894. 8°. 5408. e. 30.

FABRE (J.) Le Barreau de Paris 1810-70. pp. 483. *Paris,* 1895. 8°. 9231. g. 27.

FOUCHIER (C. de) Règles de la profession d'avocat dans l'ancienne législation française. pp. 346. *Paris,* 1895. 8°. 5206. dd. 2.

LEYMARIE (L. de) Les Avocats d'aujourd'hui. pp. 207. *Paris,* 1893. 8°. 5408. e. 15.

ROUXEL (J.) La Crise notariale. pp. 277. *Paris,* 1891. 8°. 5424. aa. 18.

SAVIGNY (L. v.) Die französischen Rechtsfakultäten. pp. 223. *Berl.* 1891. 8°. 8355. cccc. 15.

SIGNOREL (J.) La Femme-avocat. pp. 53. *Toulouse,* 1894. 8°. 6005. h. 26. (12.)

LAW.—Profession of—*continued.*

Rome. *See infra: Roman Law.*

Scotland.

EDINBURGH. *Society of Writers to the Signet.* History of the Society. pp. 494. *Edinb.* 1890. 4°. 6006. l. 2.

MURRAY (J. C.) Law of Scotland relating to Notaries Public, *etc.* pp. 354. *Edinb.* 1890. 8°. 6583. g. 6.

United States of America.

BENTON (J. H.) Influence of the Bar in our Government. pp. 63. *Bost.* 1894. 8°. Pam. 33.

DAVIS (W. T.) Bench and Bar of Massachusetts. 2 vol. *Bost.* 1895. 8°. 6005. k. 1.

DONOVAN (J. W.) Skill in Trials: civil and criminal cases won by the art of advocates. pp. 173. *Rochester,* 1891. 8°. 06616. de. 1.

WILLARD (J. A.) Half a century with Judges and Lawyers. pp. 371. *Bost.* 1895. 8°. 012330. e. 53.

WRIGHT (J. A.) How to get good Judges. pp. 85. *San Francisco,* 1892. 8°. 6616. aa. 1.

Roman.

AUDIBERT (A.) Études sur l'histoire du Droit romain. *Paris,* 1892, *etc.* 8°. 5254. cc.

BERLIN. *Savigny-Stiftung* Vocabularium Iurisprudentiae Romanae. *Berolini,* 1894, *etc.* 4°. 5206. f.

BLUME (W. v.) Novation, Delegation und Schuldübertragung. pp. 168. *Göttingen,* 1895. 8°. 5207. df. 22.

BRUNS (C. E. G.) Fontes Juris Romani Antiqui. 2 pt. *Friburgi,* 1893. 8°. 5254. cc. 22.

BRY (G.) Principes de Droit romain exposés dans leur développement historique. pp. 802. *Paris,* 1892. 12°. 5207. b. 3.

CAMPBELL (F. G. B.) Compendium of Roman Law. pp. 288. *Lond.* 1892. 8°. 2228. c. 3.

CARUSI (E.) L'Azione Publiciana in diritto romano. pp. 219. *Roma,* 1889. 8°. 5206. ee. 11.

CHAMIER (D.) Manual of Roman Law. pp. 233. *Lond.* 1893. 8°. 5254. aaa. 13.

COMBOTHECRA (X. S.) Les Actions pauliennes en droit romain. pp. 66. *Paris,* 1890. 8°. 5206. ee. 12.

COSTA (E.) Le Azioni exercitoria e institoria nel diritto romano. pp. 125. *Parma,* 1891. 8°. 5206. cc. 14.

COTTERELL (J. N.) Collection of Latin maxims and phrases translated. pp. 74. *Lond.* 1894. 8°. 6005. aaa. 12.

CUQ (É.) Les Institutions juridiques des Romains. pp. 768. *Paris,* 1891. 8°. 5254. c. 14.

ERTEL (P.) Die Quellen des römischen-gemeinen Rechtes. pp. 171. *Berl.* 1890. 8°. 6005. ee. 25.

FABIUS (D. P. D.) Mozaïsch en romeinsch Recht. pp. 87. *Amsterdam,* 1890. 8°. Pam. 32.

FOUCHIER (C. de) Règles de la profession d'avocat à Rome. pp. 346. *Paris,* 1895. 8°. 5206. dd. 2.

GOUDY (H.) Lecture on the fate of the Roman Law north and south of the Tweed. pp. 33. *Lond.* 1894. 8°. 5206. aaa. 3. (6.)

GRADENWITZ (O.) Vocabularium Jurisprudentiae Romanae. *Berolini,* 1894, *etc.* 4°. 5206. f.

GREENIDGE (A. H. J.) Infamia, its place in Roman law. pp. 219. *Oxf.* 1894. 8°. 5254. c. 17.

HEUMANN (H. G.) Handlexikon zu den Quellen des römischen Rechts. pp. 569. *Jena,* 1895. 8°. 5254. d. 5.

HITZIG (H. F.) Die Stellung Kaiser Hadrians in der römischen Rechtsgeschichte. pp. 24. *Zürich,* 1892. 8°. Pam. 32.

LAW.—Roman—*continued*.

HITZIG (H. F.) Die Assessoren der römischen Magistrate und Richter. pp. 214.
München, 1893. 8°.   5206. cc. 19.

JHERING (R. v.) Entwicklungsgeschichte des römischen Rechts. pp. 124. *Leiz*, 1894. 8°.   5207. df. 20.

KOSCHEMBAHR-LYSKOWSKI (J. v.) Die Theorie der Exceptionen nach römischen Recht. *Berl.* 1893, *etc.* 8°.   5206. dd.

KRUEGER (P.) Collectio Librorum Juris ante-Justiniani. *Berolini*, 1891, *etc.* 8°.   5254. aaa. 12.

—— Histoire des sources du Droit romain. pp. 552. 1894. 8°. MOMMSEN (T.) and MARQUARDT (J.) Manuel des Antiquités. Vol. 16.   9041. i. 2.

KUNTZE (J. E.) Der Parallelismus des Jus Publicum und Privatum bei den Römern. pp. 35. *Leipz.* 1889. 8°.   5206. aaa. 3. (I.)

LIEBENAM (W.) Zur Geschichte des römischen Vereinswesens. pp. 334. *Leipz.* 1890. 8°.   5206. ee. 13.

MACHELARD (E.) Dissertations de Droit romain. pp. 768. *Paris*, 1882. 8°.   5206. d. 12.

MITTEIS (L.) Reichsrecht und Volksrecht in den östlichen Provinzen des römischen Kaiserreichs. pp. 560. *Leipz.* 1891. 8°. 5606. d. 14.

NABER (J. C.) De verhouding van het Romeinsche Recht tot het hedendaagsche. pp. 24. *Utrecht*, 1889. 8°.   5206. bb. 2. (3.)

PALMIERI (G. B.) Appunti per la storia dei Glossatori. *Bologna*, 1892, *etc.* 8°.   5255. aa.

ROMAN LAW. Beiträge zur Lehre von den juristischen Personen nach römischem Recht. *Berl.* 1894, *etc.* 8°.   5206. dd.

SEELER (W. v.) Zur Lehre von der Conventionalstrafe nach römischem Recht. pp. 132. *Halle*, 1891. 8°.   5207. df. 15.

STOUFF (L.) De Formulis secundum legem romanam. Saec. VII.–XII. pp. 114. *Parisiis*, 1890. 8°.   5206. df. 6.

STURM (C. A. G.) Beiträge zum römischen Recht. pp. 115. *Naumburg*, 1891. 8°.   5206. aaa. 3. (4.)

VOIGT (M.) Römische Rechtsgeschichte. *Leipz.* 1892, *etc.* 8°.   5254. cc.

ROME. Corpus Juris Civilis. Recognovit P. Kruger et T. Mommsen. *Berolini*, 1888, *etc.* 8°.   5207. dg.

APPLETON (C.) Les sources des Institutes de Justinien. pp. 113. *Paris*, 1891. 8°.   5206. bb. 2. (5.)

DYDYŃSKI (T. v.) Beiträge zur handschriftlichen Überlieferung der justinianischen Rechtsquellen. *Berl.* 1891, *etc.* 8°.   5206. dd.

OERTMANN (P.) Die Volkswirtschaftslehre des Corpus Juris Civilis. pp. 154. *Berl.* 1891. 8°.   5206. ee. 19.

LEONHARD (R.) Institutionen des römischen Rechts. pp. 572. *Leipz.* 1894. 8°.   5207. df. 21.

NEY (C.) Institutionen und Pandekten für Studierende und Prüfungs-kandidaten. *Berl.* 1891, *etc.* 8°.   5606. aa. 14.

SOHM (R.) Institutes of Roman Law. pp. 520. *Oxf.* 1892. 8°.   5206. d. 13.

WILLIAMS (J.) Institutes of Justinian illustrated by English Law. pp. 351. *Lond.* 1893. 8°.   5254. aa. 29.

FITTING (H. H.) Die Institutionenglossen des Gualcausus, *etc.* pp. 140. *Berl.* 1891. 8°.   5206. cc. 15.

FERRINI (C.) Il Digesto. pp. 133. *Milano*, 1893. 8°.   012200. h. 64.

LAW.—Roman—*continued*.

GOUDSMIT (J. E.) The Pandects. pp. 368. *Madras*, 1891. 8°.   5206. b. 2.

HOELDER (E.) Pandekten. pp. 402. *Freiburg*, 1886–91. 8°.   5254. cc. 12.

STAMMLER (R.) Praktische Pandekten-übungen. pp. 533. *Leipz.* 1893. 8°.   5254. b. 30.

GRUEBER (E.) Roman law of Damage to property. pp. 288. *Oxf.* 1886. 8°.   5205. bb. 20.

ROME. Digest XLVII. 2. De Furtis. Translated by C. H. Monro. pp. 128. *Camb.* 1893. 8°.   5206. aa. 13.

—— Roman Law of Sale with modern illustrations. Translated by J. Mackintosh. pp. 272. *Edinb.* 1892. 8°.   5206. ee. 20.

—— Digest XIX. 2. "Locati Conducti." Translated by C. H. Monro. pp. 83. *Camb.* 1891. 8°.   5205. a. 3.

CARNAZZA (G.) Il Diritto commerciale dei Romani. pp. 199. *Catania*, 1891. 8°. 5206. ee. 23.

VOET (J.) Titles on Vindicationes and interdicta. Translated by J. J. C. Chitty. pp. 344. *Colombo*, 1893. 8°.   5254. aaa. 15.

GEIB (O.) Zur Dogmatik des römischen Bürgschaftsrechts. pp. 192. *Tübingen*, 1894. 8°.   5254. cc. 23.

HRUZA (E.) Beiträge zur Geschichte des römischen Familienrechtes. *Erlangen*, 1892, *etc.* 8°.   5254. cc. 17.

MAY (G.) and BECKER (H.) Précis des Institutions du droit privé de Rome. pp. 273. *Paris*, 1892. 12°.   5254. aa. 16.

MUIRHEAD (J.) Introduction au droit privé de Rome. pp. 618. *Paris*, 1889. 8°. 5206. df. 9.

LAW REPORTS : TRIALS : LEADING CASES.

Cape of Good Hope.

SEARLE (M. W.) Digest of cases in the courts of the Cape of Good Hope from 1850. 3 pt. *Cape Town*, 1885–93. 8°.   6606. bb. 11.

CAPE OF GOOD HOPE. Cases decided in the Supreme Court during the years 1850–65. *Cape Town*, 1884, *etc.* 8°.   6605. ee.

P.P. Cape Town. "Cape Times" Law reports. *Cape Town*, 1891, *etc.* 4°.   P.P. 1351. f.

Cyprus.

CYPRUS. Cyprus Law Reports. *Nicosia*, 1893, 8°.   06606. h.

England.

HAWARDE (J.) Les Reportes del cases in Camera Stellata, 1593–1609. pp. 502. *Lond.* 1894. 8°.   6125. l. 2.

POLLOCK (*Sir* F.) Revised Reports from 1785. *Lond.* 1891, *etc.* 8°.   Bar A. x.

—— Index of all reported Cases during the period covered by the Revised Reports, vol. I. to XV. 1785–1816. pp. 313. *Lond.* 1898. 8°.   Bar. A. x.

G. B. & I. *State Trials Committee.* Reports on State Trials (from 1820). *Lond.* 1888, *etc.* 8°.   Bar A. y.

AC. London. *Council of Law Reporting.* Digest of Cases from 1865–1890. 3 vol. *Lond.* 1892. 8°.   Bar. A. x.

TALBOT (G. J.) and FORT (H.) Index of cases judicially noticed, 1865–90. pp. 639. *Lond.* 1891. 8°.   6125. h. 6.

P.P. *London.* Reports, 1893, *etc.* Edited by J. Mews. *Lond.* 1894, *etc.* 8°.   P.P. 1345. ae.

—— London. *Law Journal.* Synopsis of contemporary Reports. *Lond.* 1895. *s. sh.* fol.   Tab. 11747. a. (80.)

RICKARDS (A. G.) and SAUNDERS (R. C.) Locus Standi Reports. *Lond.* 1892, *etc.* 8°.   6120. g.

LEAD—*continued.*

OLIVER (T.) Lead poisoning. pp. 121.
Edinb. 1891. 8°.   7620. df. 24.

PARMENTIER (F.) Plomb et ses composés.
pp. 140. 1892. 8°. FRÉMY (E.) Encyclopédie
chimique. Tom. 3. Cahier 13. Pt. 2. 8907. i.

LETHABY (W. R.) Leadwork, old and ornamental. pp. 148. *Lond.* 1893. 8°. 7808. df. 7.
See also METALS.

LEAMINGTON. GARROD (A. E.) Medical
springs of Leamington, *etc.* 1895. 8°. Ac.
London. *Medical and Chirurgical Society.* Climates of Great Britain. Vol. 1.   7462. g.

MANNING (J. C.) Glimpses of our local past.
pp. 181. *Leamington,* 1895. 8°. 10358. aa. 61.

LEASES. *See* LAND TENURES, *England.*

LEATHER : TANNING. BRIGGS (R.N.)
The American Tanner. pp. 38. *N.Y.* 1892. 12°.
Pam. 94.

GUÉRIN (U.) Tanneur de Nottingham. 1891. 8°.
Ac. Paris. *Société des études d'économie sociale.*
Les ouvriers des deux mondes. Sér. 2. fasc. 23.
8282. f. 18.

JEAN (F.) Industrie des Cuirs et des peaux.
pp. 195. 1892. 8°. Encyclopédie des aide-mémoire.   8709. g.

LELAND (C. G.) Leather Work. pp. 96.
Lond. 1892. 8°.   7817. f. 27.

STEVENS (J. W.) Leather Manufacture. pp. 240.
Lond. 1891. 8°.   07945. n. 23.

TAIRE (A.) Le Cuir et les peaux. pp. 287.
Paris, 1891. 12°.   7944. d. 12.

ZINN (M.) Anleitung zum Lederschnitt. pp. 32.
1893. 8°. Bossong's Kunsttechnische Bibliothek.
Bd. 9.   7858. f.

LEAU. WAUTERS (A.) Une ancienne description
de Léau. 1892. 8°. Ac. Brussels. *Commission
d'Histoire.* Compte rendu. Sér. 5. Tom. 2.
Ac. 986.

LEBANON, Ohio. Ac. Lebanon. *National
Normal University.* Catalogue of officers and
students 1891-92. pp. 240. *Lebanon,* 1892. 8°.
8367. aa. 17.

LEBUS. BREITENBACH ( ) Das Land Lebus
unter den Piasten. pp. 132.
Fürstenwalde Spree, 1890. 8°. 9004. m. (5.) 5.

LECCO. LECCO. Lecco e dintorni. Guida.
Lecco, 1893. 12°.   10136. bbb. 30.

LECTOURE. PLIEUX (A.) Étude sur l'instruction publique à Lectoure. pp. 246.
Agen, 1890. 8°.   8356. h. 12.

LEE, River. FLOWER (L.) The River Lee
up to date. pp. 39. *Lond.* 1893. 8°. Pam. 79.

LEEDS. Ac. Leeds. *Thoresby Society.* Publications. *Leeds,* 1889, *etc.* 8°.   Ac. 8092.

CURTIS (J. S.) Waddington's guide to Leeds.
pp. 99. *York,* 1894. 8°. 10360. bbb. 67.

RUSBY (J.) Leeds Parish Church antiquities.
Leeds, 1881-83. 8°.   4707. d. 4.

SPARK (F. R.) and BENNETT (J.) History of the
Leeds musical festivals, 1858-89. pp. 407.
Leeds, 1892. 8°.   7897. l. 19.

LEEK. MILLER (M. H.) Olde Leeke.
pp. 350. *Leek,* 1891. 4°.   10360. k. 11.

SMITH (T. J.) Banks and bankers of Leek.
pp. 38. *Leek,* 1891. 8°.   8248. d. 33.

LEGASPI. *See* PHILIPPINE ISLANDS.

LEGENDS AND TRADITIONS.
See FOLK LORE : SAINTS.

LEGERDEMAIN. Boys. Boys' Own Magic
and trick books. *Lond.* 1894, *etc.* 8°. 7913. h.

LEGERDEMAIN—*continued.*

BURLINGAME (H. J.) Leaves from Conjurers'
scrap books. pp. 274. *Chicago,* 1891. 8°.
7913. ee. 26.

DUCRET (É.) and BONNEFONT (G.) Le nouveau
Magicien prestidigitateur. pp. 389.
Paris, 1894. 8°.   7912. aaa. 19.

HOFFMANN (L.) Tricks with cards. pp. 145.
Lond. 1843. 8°.   7913. ee. 31.
—— Conjuring Tricks with dominoes, dice, balls,
etc. pp. 121. *Lond.* 1893. 8°. 7913. ee. 33.
—— Conjuring Tricks with coins, watches, rings,
etc. pp. 123. *Lond.* 1893. 8°. 7913. ee. 32.
—— Miscellaneous conjuring Tricks. pp. 124.
Lond. 1893. 8°.   7913. ee. 34.

MOON (G. P.) How to give a conjuring Entertainment. *Lond.* 1895. 16°. 7915. de. 20. (6.)

WEATHERLY (L. A.) The Supernatural ? With
chapter on oriental magic, by J. N. Maskelyne.
pp. 273. *Bristol,* 1891. 8°. 8632. ccc. 8.

LE HAVRE. *See* HAVRE.

LEHON. LE MOYNE DE LA BORDERIE (L. A. de)
Fondation du monastère de Lehon. 1891. 8°.
Ac. Saint Brieuc. *Société Archéologique.* Mé-
moires. Sér. 2. Tom. 4. Livr. 2. Ac. 5294/2.

LEIBITZ. LUMTZER (V.) Die leibitzer Mundart. 1891. 8°. PAUL (H.) Beiträge zur Geschichte der deutschen Sprache. Bd. 19. Hft. 1, 2.
12962. o.

LEICESTER. COWIE (G.) History of Wyg-
geston's Hospital, and The old Grammar School,
Leicester. pp. 127. *Leicester,* 1893. 8°.
8364. ee. 38.

EPHEM. Local Chronology. *Leicester,* 1888. 8°.
P.P. 2507. eeb.

HERNE (F. S.) History of the Town Library,
Town Hall, and permanent Library. pp. 28.
Leicester, 1891. 8°.   011900. ee. 3. (5.)

JOHNSON (A.) Glimpses of ancient Leicester.
pp. 306. *Lond.* 1891. 8°.   010358. h. 4.

MARTIN, *Saint.* Ch. of, at Leicester. Accounts
of churchwardens, 1489-1844. pp. 241.
Leicester, 1884. 4°.   010358. h. 3.

PALMER (C. F. R.) Friar-preachers of Leicester.
Leicester, 1884. 8°.   4705. e. 32. (2.)

STOREY (J.) Historical sketch of the principal
works of the Council of Leicester. pp. 268.
Leicester, 1895. 8°.   10358. dd. 28.

LEICESTERSHIRE. LEICESTER. *Public
Libraries.* Catalogue of books, maps, &c., re-
lating to Leicestershire. pp. 94.
Leicester, 1893. 8°.   011901. e. 18.

ANDREWS (W.) Bygone Leicestershire.
pp. 264. *Leicester,* 1892. 8°. 010358. i. 4.

DERBY. Murray's handbook for Derbyshire,
Leicestershire, *etc.* pp. 38. 229. *Lond.* 1892. 8°.
2364. a. 8.

HOLME (C.) History of the Midland Counties.
pp. 277. *Rugby,* 1891. 8°.   10360. d. 24.

P.P. Leicester. Leicestershire Notes and queries.
Leicester, 1891, *etc.* 8°.   P.P. 6636. bc.

LEININGEN. BRINCKMEIER (E.) Genea-
logische Geschichte des Hauses Leiningen.
Braunschweig, 1890, *etc.* 8°.   9905. dd.

LEIPSIC. LEHR (A.) Die Hausindustrie in
Leipzig. pp. 130. 1891. 8°. Ac. Leipsic
Verein für Socialpolitik. Schriften. No. 48.
Ac. 2322.

LEIPSIC. *Vereinigung Leipziger Architekten.*
Leipzig und seine Bauten. pp. 856.
Leipz. 1892. 8°.   10250. k. 3.

MOSER (O.) Reudnitz-Leipzig in seiner Vergangenheit und seiner Gegenwart. pp. 114.
Leipz. 1890. 8°.   10255. g. 20.

LEIPSIC—*continued.*

WUSTMANN (G.) Leipzig durch drei Jahrhunderte. 1 p. 24. *Leipz.* 1891. fol. 1787. d. 13.

Ac. Leipsic. *Academia.* Ordnung der Universitäts-Bibliothek. pp. 19. *Leipz.* 1894. 8°.
Pam. 6.

—— Ausgewählte Doktordissertationen der Juristenfakultät. *Leipz.* 1894, *etc.* 8°. Ac. 2122/7.

ULLRICH (P. W.) Die Anfänge der Universität Leipzig. *Leipz.* 1895, *etc.* 4°. 8357. l.

LEIPSIC. *Hochschule.* Beiträge zur Geschichte von Dozenten der Leipziger Hochschule. pp. 253. *Leipz.* 1894. 8°. 9007. g. 21.

LELANT. MATTHEWS (J. H.) History of the parish of Lelant. pp. 560. *Lond.* 1892. 4°.
10368. h. 30.

LE MANS. JOUBERT (A.) Les Réparations faites à divers édifices du Mans de 1368 a 1374. pp. 13. *Mamers,* 1889. 4°. 7706. f. 21. (5.)

LEDRU (A.) Asile à la cathédrale du Mans 1335–36. 1890. 8°. Ac. Le Mans. *Société Historique.* Revue. Tom. 28. Ac. 5321/3.

—— La nuit de Saint-Julien à la cathédrale du Mans, 1527. pp. 15. *Mamers,* 1890. 8°.
4629. ee. 7. (3.)

LEGEAY (F.) Note sur les Juifs au Mans. pp. 16. *Le Mans,* 1890. 8°. Pam. 31.

MARTIN (A.) La Communauté des boulangers du Mans. pp. 125. *Mamers,* 1891. 8°.
08229. g. 43.

DAGNET (A.) Le Patois manceau. pp. 180. *Laval,* 1891. 8°. 12953. g. 26.

LEMNOS. PAULI (C.) Eine vorgriechische Inschrift von Lemnos. pp. 81. *Leipz.* 1886. 8°.
7706. ee. 18. (12.)

LENNOX, The. *See* DUMBARTON.

LENSES. ORFORD (H.) Lens-Work for Amateurs. pp. 231. *Lond.* 1895. 8°.
8716. aa. 13.

See also EYE : OPTICS.

LENT, HOLY WEEK. BLACK (W.) Heads for mental prayer in Lent. pp. 55. *Lond.* 1893. 8°. 3456. df. 60. (4.)

DAVIES (J. P.) The comfortable season of Lent. Sermons. pp. 125. *Lond.* 1894. 8°.
4479. ee. 13.

GUERNSEY (L. E.) A Lent in earnest. pp. 198. *Lond.* 1892. 8°. 4401. p. 29.

HUNTINGTON (F. D.) *Bp. of Central New York.* Forty Days with the Master. pp. 319. *Lond.* 1891. 8°. 3457. g. 34.

KNOWLES (J. H.) Day-book for Lent. pp. 58. *Lond.* 1894. 12°. 3456. dd. 44.

LITTING (G.) Consider your Ways. Sermons. pp. 119. *Lond.* 1894. 8°. 4479. bb. 60.

MOTHER. Thoughts on the Epistles of Holy Week, for children. pp. 80. *Lond.* 1895. 16°.
3266. aa. 51.

MOSSE (W. G.) The Lenten Opportunity. pp. 119. *Lond.* 1893. 16°. 4429. bb. 1.

SABELA (P.) Course of Lenten sermons. pp. 107. *Lond.* 1893. 8°. 4479. aa. 63.

WILLIAMS (R.) On keeping Lent. pp. 14. *Lond.* 1891. 8°. 4371. de. 3. (4.)

WILSON (H.) Fifty-two meditations for Lent. pp. 148. *Lond.* 1894. 8°. 3456. dd. 41.

ADDERLEY (*Hon.* J. G.) The Legend of the way of grief. *Oxf.* 1894. 8°. 4422. d. 17. (5.)

CLARKE (R. F.) Little book for Holy Week. pp. 35. *Lond.* 1891. 8°. 3456. df. 59. (7.)

GALLWEY (P.) Watches of the sacred Passion. 2 vol. *Lond.* 1895. 8°. 4224. bbb. 28.

LENT—*continued.*

HARPER (F.) The first Good Friday. pp. 44. *Lond.* 1895. 8°. 4227. df. 2.

HOLY WEEK. Ceremonies of Holy Week explained. pp. 16. *Lond.* 1890. 8°.
3939. ccc. 2. (12.)

LIDDON (H. P.) Passiontide Sermons. pp. 299. *Lond.* 1891. 8°. 4466. d. 12.

PRIEST. Outlines for Holy Week. pp. 16. *Rugeley,* 1894. 8°. 3456. dd. 43.

See also CHRISTIANITY, *General, Atonement, Person and Teaching of Christ :* SEASONS, *Ecclesiastical.*

LENTON. GODFREY (J. T.) The Priory Fair at Lenton. pp. 4. *Nottingham,* 1893. 8°.
10348. ccc. 59. (8.)

LEOBSCHÜTZ. TROSKA (F.) Geschichte der Stadt Leobschütz. pp. 263. *Leobschütz,* 1892. 8°. 10215. e. 15.

LÉON, France. *See* FINISTÈRE.

LEPANTO. FAROCHON (P. A.) Chypre et Lépante. pp. 320. *Paris,* 1894. 8°.
9072. h. 9.

LEPIDOPTERA.

General.

HAASE (E.) Untersuchungen über die Mimicry auf Grundlagen eines Systems der Papilioniden. 2 pt. 1891. 4°. LEUCKART (R.) Bibliotheca Zoologica. Hft. 8. Lief. 3, 4. 7205. f.

KIRBY (W. F.) Hand-book to the Lepidoptera. 1894, *etc.* 8°. SHARPE (R. B.) Allen's Naturalist's Library. 7001. eee.

—— Synonymic catalogue of Lepidoptera Heterocera. *Lond.* 1892, *etc.* 8°. 7297. cc.

NICHOLAS MIKHAILOVICH, *Archduke of Russia.* Mémoires sur les Lépidoptères rédigés par N. M. Romanoff. *St. Petersbourg,* 1884, *etc.* 8°.
7297. dd.

See also INSECTS, *Noxious.*

European : Palaearctic.

KAPPEL (A. W.) and KIRBY (W. E.) British and European Butterflies and Moths. pp. 273. *Lond.* 1895. 8°. 7296. ee. 2.

KIRBY (W. F.) European Butterflies and Moths. *Lond.* 1894, *etc.* 4°. 7297. h.

RUEHL (F.) Die palaearktischen Grossschmetterlinge. *Leipz.* 1892, *etc.* 4°. 7297. c.

HOFMANN (E.) Die Raupen der Gross-Schmetterlinge Europas. pp. 318. *Stuttgart,* 1893. 4°.
7297. k. 9.

AUSTAUT (J. L.) Les Parnassiens. pp. 222. *Leipz.* 1889. 8°. 7297. aaa. 34.

Ac. London. *Ray Society.* BUCKLER (W.) Larvæ of British Butterflies and Moths. *Lond.* 1886, *etc.* 8°. 2027. f.

—— Winchester. *Natural History Society.* Macro-Lepidoptera of Winchester. pp. 31. *Lincoln,* 1891. 8°. 7004. de. 23. (10.)

BARRETT (C. G.) Lepidoptera of the British Islands. *Lond.* 1892, *etc.* 8°. 7298. e.

BLOOMFIELD (E. N.) Lepidoptera of Suffolk. pp. 60. *Lond.* 1890. 8°. 7298. d. 3. (4.)

DALE (C. W.) Lepidoptera of Dorsetshire. pp. 76. *Dorchester,* 1891. 8°. 7296. bb. 1.

FURNEAUX (W. S.) Butterflies and Moths (British). pp. 358. *Lond.* 1894. 8°. 7296. b. 7.

JOHNS (B. G.) Among the Butterflies. pp. 194. *Lond.* 1891. 8°. 7297. a. 43.

KIRBY (W. F.) British Butterflies and Moths. pp. 93. 1885. 8°. Young Collector Series.
7001. aaa.

LUCAS (W. J.) Book of British Butterflies. pp. 247. *Lond.* 1893. 8°. 7297. aaa. 38.

LEPIDOPTERA.—European, etc.—cont.

LUCAS (W. J.) Book of British Hawk-Moths.
pp. 157. Lond. 1895. 8°.   7297. aaa. 43.

MEYRICK (E.) Handbook of British Lepidoptera.
pp. 843. Lond. 1895. 8°.   7297. bb. 31.

MOSLEY (S. L.) Illustrations of varieties of British
Lepidoptera. Pt. 1–5. Huddersfield, 1883–85. 8°.
                                   7297. cc. 1.

PORRITT (G. T.) List of Yorkshire Lepidoptera.
1883. 8°. Ac. Huddersfield. Yorkshire Naturalists Union. Transactions. Pt. 5–7 & 9.
                                   Ac. 3016/2.

RYE (B. G.) Handbook of British Macro-Lepidoptera. Lond. 1895, etc. 8°.   500.

SAINT JOHN (J. S.) Larva Collecting and
breeding. pp. 165. Lond. 1890. 8°. 7297. a. 55.

SIMMS (G. E.) Butterfly and Moth collecting.
pp. 116. Lond. 1892. 8°.   7297. a. 52.

TUTT (J. W.) British Noctuæ.
Lond. 1891, etc. 8°.   7297. bb. 25.

—— Melanism and melanochroism in British Lepidoptera, etc. pp. 66. Lond. 1891. 8°. 7297. bb. 23.

G. B. & I. Board of Agriculture. Report on
the attack of the Diamond-back Moth Caterpillar. pp. 30. Lond. 1891. 8°.   Pam. 42.

JOURDHEUILLE (C.) Supplément au Catalogue
des Lépidoptères de l'Aube. 1890. 8°. Ac.
Troyes. Société d'Agriculture. Mémoires. Ser. 3.
Tom. 26.   Ac. 260.

GARBOWSKI (T.) Materialen zu einer Lepidopterenfauna Galiziens. 1892. 8°. Ac. Vienna.
K. Akademie. Sitzungsberichte. Math.-natur-
wissenschaftliche Classe. Bd. 101. Ac. 810/6.

HORMUZAKI (C. v.) Untersuchungen über die
Lepidopterenfauna der Bucovina. pp. 182.
Czernowitz, 1894. 8°.   7297. aa. 37.

KRIEGHOFF (E.) Die Gross-Schmetterlinge
Thüringens. 1884. 8°. Ac. Jena. Geo-
graphische Gesellschaft. Mitteilungen. Bd. 3.
Hft. 2 and 3.   Ac. 6086.

SCHØYEN (W. M.) Fortegnelse over Norges Lepi-
doptera. pp. 54. 1893. 8°. Ac. Christiania.
Videnskabs-Selskab. Forhandlinger. Aar 1893.
No. 13.   Ac. 1054.

SPARRE SCHNEIDER (H. J.) Lepidopterfauna'en
på Tromsøen. 1890. 8°. Ac. Tromsö. Museum.
Aarshefter. No. 15.   Ac. 2980.

PETERSEN (W.) Die Schmetterlinge der Ostsee-
provinzen Russlands, etc. Reval, 1890, etc. 8°.
                                   7206. k. 19.

Exotic.

HUEBNER (J.) Exotische Schmetterlinge. Exotic
butterflies. Brux. 1894, etc. 4°.   7296. h.

MABILLE (P.) and VUILLOT ( ) Novitates Lepi-
dopterologicæ. Paris, 1890, etc. 8°.   7297. i.

REBEL (H.) and ROGENHOFER (A. F.) Zur Lepi-
dopterenfauna der Canaren, etc. pp. 96. 1894. 8°.
Ac. Vienna. Naturhistorisches Hofmuseum.
Annalen. Bd. 9.   Ac. 2911.

WHITE (A. E. H.) Butterflies and Moths of
Teneriffe. pp. 107. Lond. 1894. 8°. 7297. bb. 30.

EDWARDS (H.) Bibliographical catalogue of the
transformation of North American Lepidoptera.
pp. 147. 1889. 8°. Ac. Washington. Smithsonian Institution. Bulletin of the National
Museum. No. 35.   Ac. 1875/13.

BALLARD (J. P.) Among the Moths and Butterflies. pp. 237. N.Y. 1891. 8°.   7297. bb. 28.

GROTE (A. R.) Hawk Moths of North America.
pp. 63. Bremen, 1886. 8°.   7297. e. 30.

KNOBEL (E.) Butterflies of New England.
pp. 40. Bost. 1895. obl. 8°.   7297. a. 63.

—— Night Moths of New England. pp. 63.
Bost. 1895. obl. 8°.   7298. a. 9.

LEPIDOPTERA.—Exotic—continued.

MAYNARD (C. J.) Manual of North American
Butterflies. pp. 226. Bost. 1891. 8°.
                                   7297. e. 33.

SCUDDER (S. H.) Guide to the commoner
Butterflies of the United States and Canada,
etc. pp. 206. N.Y. 1893. 8°.   7297. aaa. 40.

—— Frail Children of the air. pp. 279.
Bost. 1895. 8°.   7297. aa. 38.

SMITH (J. B.) Contribution toward a monograph
of the Noctuidæ of temperate North America.
pp. 237. 1890. 8°. Ac. Washington. Smithsonian Institution. Bulletin of the National
Museum. No. 38.   Ac. 1875/13.

MAASSEN (P.) Lepidopteren gesammelt in Colombia, Ecuador, Perú, Brasilien, Argentinien
und Bolivien. 1890. 8°. REISS (W.) Reisen
in Süd-Amerika.   60.

LUCAS (T. P.) Description of new Butterflies
and sphingidæ found in Queensland. 1891. 8°.
                                   7297. c. 18. (6.)

MEYRICK (E.) Descriptions of Australian Micro-
Lepidoptera. 1893. 8°. Ac. Sydney. Linnean
Society. Proceedings. Ser. 2. Vol. 7. Pt. 4.
                                   Ac. 3100.

SWINHOE (C.) Catalogue of Eastern and Australian Heterocera in the Oxford University
Museum. Oxf. 1892, etc. 8°.   7298. ccc. 2.

TEPPER (J. G. O.) Notes on South Australian
Rhopalocera. pp. 5. Adelaide, 1893. 8°.
                                   7298. d. 3. (14.)

LEECH (J. H.) Butterflies from China, Japan
and Corea. Lond. 1892, etc. 4°.   7297. k. 8.

SKERTCHLY (S. B. J.) Naturalist's description of
Hongkong. pp. 56. Hongkong, 1893. 8°.
                                   10058. aaa. 40.

HAMPSON (G. F.) Heterocera of Ceylon. pp. 182.
1893. 8°. Ac. London. British Museum.
Illustrations. Pt. 9.   7296. h.

RADLEY (P. E.) Label and exchange list of
Ceylon Lepidoptera. pp. 29. Colombo, 1891. 4°.
                                   Pam. 42.

HAMPSON (G. F.) Moths of British India.
1892, etc. 8°. BLANFORD (W. T.) Fauna of
British India.   7208. ee.

—— Heterocera of the Nilgiri District. pp. 144.
1891. 4°. Ac. London. British Museum. Illustrations of Heterocera.   7296. h.

WATSON (E. Y.) Hesperiidæ Indicæ. pp. 161.
Madras, 1891. 8°.   7297. f. 16.

PIEPERS (C.) Observations sur des vols de Lépidoptères aux Indes Orientales Néerlandaises.
1891. 8°. Ac. Batavia. Natuurkundige Vereeniging. Natuurkundig Tijdschrift. Deel 50.
                                   Ac. 3096.

SAALMUELLER (M.) Lepidopteren von Mada-
gascar. pp. 531. 1884–91. 4°. Ac. Frankfort.
Senckenberg'sche Naturforschende Gesellschaft.
Abhandlungen. Bd. 17.   Ac. 2878/2.

LEPROSY. BAILEY (W. C.) Lepers of our
Indian empire. pp. 252. Lond. 1892. 8°.
                                   4767. bbb. 5.

BROWN (A. M.) Comments on Leprosy.
Lond. 1888. 8°.   Pam. 39.

CRAVEN (P.) Le Père Damien. pp. 137.
Paris, 1890. 8°.   4886. aa. 40.

GUIDAULT (P.) La léproserie de Bourges.
pp. 79. Bourges, 1892. 8°.   07305. h. 17. (8.)

HANSEN (G. A.) and LOOFT (C.) Leprosy in its
clinical and pathological aspects. pp. 162.
Bristol, 1895. 8°.   7640. f. 3.

HAYES (A.) My Leper Friends. Account of
work among lepers in India. pp. 127.
Lond. 1891. 8°.   7640. aaa. 16.

LEPROSY—*continued.*

LÉTANCHE (J.) La Maladrerie d'Yenne, ancienne léprosie d'Entresaix. 1891. 8°. Ac. Chambéry. *Société d'histoire.* Mémoires. Sér. 2. Tom. 5.   Ac. 5240.

LONDON. *National Leprosy Fund.* Journal of the Leprosy investigation committee. *Lond.* 1890, *etc.* 8°.   7561. l. 2.

—— Essays on subjects connected with Leprosy. *Lond.* 1895, *etc.* 8°.   7561. d.

MACNAMARA (N. C.) Leprosy. 1893. 8°. DAVIDSON (A.) Hygiene of Warm Climates.   7686. dd. 2.

MÉNOS (W. C.) La Lèpre au point de vue de la contagion. pp. 82. *Paris,* 1890. 8°.   7620. ee. 28.

NASARVĀNĠĪ HORMASĴĪ CHAUKSĪ. Abstract of the Report of the Leprosy Commission in India. pp. 74. *Bombay,* 1893. 8°.   7630. ff. 32.

SENFT (E. A.) 75 années parmi les Lépreux. pp. 185. *Neuchâtel,* 1894. 8°.   7688. aa. 56.

TEBB (W.) Leprosy and vaccination. pp. 20. *Lond.* 1891. 8°.   07305. e. 23. (16.)

—— Recrudescence of Leprosy and its causation by vaccination. pp. 408. *Lond.* 1893. 8°.   7561. bb. 12.

THIN (G.) Leprosy. pp. 280. *Lond.* 1891. 8°.   7640. h. 24.

ZAMBACO (D. A.) Voyages chez les Lépreux. pp. 406. *Paris,* 1891. 8°.   7641. dd. 8.

LE PUY. ARSAC (G.) Prêtres et fidèles du diocèse mis à mort en 1794. 4 pt. *Le Puy,* 1894, *etc.* 16°.   4864. aaa.

BOUDON (A.) Les municipalités du Puy pendant la révolution. *Le Puy,* 1894, *etc.* 8°. 9231. dd.

—— Les municipalités du Puy, 1789–1889. 2 tom. *Le Puy,* 1892–93. 8°.   010171. f. 42.

P.P. Le Puy. Mélanges historiques publiés dans l'Écho de Velay. pp. 316. *Le Puy,* 1888. 8°.   10174. aa. 41.

VINOLS DE MONTFLEURY (J. G. de) Vocabulaires patois vellavien-français. 1890. 8°. Ac. Le Puy. *Société d'Agriculture.* Annales, *etc.* Tom. 34.   Ac. 353.
See also HAUTE-LOIRE.

LÉRINS, Abbey. HONORATUS, *Saint, Abbey of, at Lérins.* Lérins Abbey. pp. 32. *Lond.* 1891. 16°.   Pam. 29.

LES BAUX. BARTHÉLEMY (L.) La ville des Baux. pp. 28. *Marseille,* 1882. 8°.   10168. g. 17. (1.)

LESBOS. Ac. Berlin. *Archäologisches Institut.* KOLDEWEY (R.) Die antiken Baureste der Insel Lesbos. 2 pt. *Berl.* 1890. fol.   1706. b. 7.

GEORGEAKIS (G.) and PINEAU (L.) Le Folk-lore de Lesbos. pp. 372. 1894. 8°. Les Littératures populaires. Tom. 31.   2348. aa.

LESCURE, Cantal. PAUTARD (J. F.) Histoire de la paroisse de Lescure. pp. 156. *Saint-Flour,* 1893. 8°.   10171. aaa. 26.

LESSINES. GUIGNIES (V. J.) Histoire de la ville de Lessines. pp. 358. *Mons,* 1891. 8°.   010171. k. 11.

LETTERS: LETTER-WRITING.

CAHEN (A.) Lettres du XVIII° siècle. pp. 536. *Paris,* 1894. 12°.   10909. ccc. 31.

CALLAWAY (F. B.) Charm and courtesy in Letter-writing. pp. 250. *N.Y.* 1895. 8°. 10920. aaa. 43.

GIGAS (E.) Lettres inédites de divers savants du XVIIme et du XVIIIme siècle. *Copenhague,* 1890, *etc.* 8°.   010920. f.

JACQUINET (P.) Lettres choisies du dix-septième siècle. pp. 421. *Paris,* 1890. 12°.   10920. ccc. 35.

LETTERS—*continued.*

LANGLOIS (C. V.) Formulaires de lettres du XII°, du XIII°, et du XIV° siècle. pp. 32. *Paris,* 1890. 4°.   Pam. 35.

ORLANDO (F.) Carteggi italiani, inediti o rari. *Firenze,* 1892, *etc.* 8°.   010920. e.

RANNIE (D. W.) Letter writing as a form of literature. pp. 24. *Oxf.* 1895. 8°.   11826. d. 45. (17.)

ROQUES (M.) Choix de Lettres du XVII° siècle. pp. 518. *Paris,* 1890. 12°.   10909. e. 16.

BAYLES (W. E.) Anglo-Spanish Manual of commercial correspondence. pp. 222. *Lond.* 1891. 8°.   12941. de. 11.

BEETON (S. O.) Complete Letter-writer. pp. 258. *Lond.* 1895. 8°.   10921. aa. 39.

ELFFERS (H.) South African Letter-writer—bilingual correspondence. pp. 125. *Cape Town,* 1895. 8°.   10921. bbb. 40.

HOSSFELD (C.) Polyglot Correspondent in English, French, German and Spanish. pp. 444. *Lond.* 1891. 16°.   10920. aa. 24.

HOSSFELD (C.) and VATON (E.) Le Correspondant commercial français-allemand. pp. 400. *Paris,* 1892. 8°.   10921. a. 31.

HOSSFELD (C.) Deutsch-spanischer Handels-Correspondent. pp. 400. *Lond.* 1891. 16°.   10920. aa. 25.

LETTER-WRITER. Letter Writer's handbook. pp. 125. *Lond.* 1895. 8°.   10921. cc. 39.

RISSMANN (A.) Förmlichkeiten im schriftlichen Verkehr mit Behörden. pp. 64. 23. *Frankf.* 1894. 8°.   10921. aa. 37.

SCHOLL (C.) Phraseological Dictionary of commercial correspondence. pp. 898. *Liverp.* 1891. 8°.   12902. h. 16.

VATON (E.) and SANCHEZ (M.) Le Correspondant français-espagnol. pp. 400. *Paris,* 1892. 8°.   10921. a. 32.

VILLEHOUDET (O. de) Nouveau Secrétaire-guide des amoureux. pp. 398. *Paris,* 1894. 12°.   8416. de. 51.

LETTS: LITHUANIA. ALKSNIS (J.) Materialen zur lettischen Volks-Medicin. 1894. 8°. Ac. Dorpat. *Universität. Pharmakologisches Institut.* Historische Studien. No. 4. Ac. 3817/2.

AUNING (R.) Ueber den lettischen Drachen-Mythus, Puhkis. pp. 128. *Mitau,* 1892. 8°.   12431. c. 43.

BAYE (J. de) *Baron.* Compte-rendu des travaux du Congrès russe d'archéologie, 1893. Étude historique sur la Lithuanie. pp. 136. *Paris,* 1894. 8°.   7706. aaa. 51.

BIELENSTEIN (A.) Die Grenzen des lettischen Volksstammes. *St. Petersburg,* 1892. 4°.   10290. g. 11.

—— Atlas. 1892. fol.   1856. c. 6.

KEUSSLER (F. v.) Das livische und lettische Dünagebiet und die Fürsten von Polozk, Gercike und Kokenhusen. pp. 51. 1892. 8°. Ac. Riga. *Gesellschaft für Geschichte der Ostsee-Provinzen.* Mittheilungen. Bd. 15. Heft 1.   Ac. 7900.

WALDMANN (C.) Fahrten und Abenteuer im deutschen Elchlande. pp. 214. *Leipz.* 1891. 8°.   10256. cc. 14.

See also BALTIC PROVINCES.

Language and Literature.

FINCK (F. N.) Über das Verhältniss des baltisch-slavischen Nominalaccents zum Urindogermanischen. pp. 60. *Marburg,* 1895. 8°. 12975. h. 24.

LESKIEN (A.) Die Bildung der Nomina im Litauischen. 1891. 8°. Ac. Leipsic. *Gesellschaft der Wissenschaften.* Abhandlungen der phil.-hist. Classe.   Ac. 700/4.

LETTS.—Language, etc.—continued.

LETT. Leitfaden zur Erlernen der lettischen Sprache. pp. 52. Mitau, 1888. 8°.
        12901. d. 32. (4.)

PRELLWITZ (W.) Die deutschen Bestandteile in den Lettischen Sprachen.
Göttingen, 1891, etc. 8°. 12975. l. 23.

SAUSSURE (F. de) À propos de l'Accentuation lituanienne. 1894, etc. 8°. Ac. Paris. Société de Linguistique. Mémoires. Tom. 8, etc.
          Ac. 9810.

THOMSEN (V.) Berøringer mellem de finske og de baltiske, litauisk-lettiske, Sprog. pp. 308. 1890. 8°. Ac. Copenhagen. Kjøbenhavnsk Selskab. Skrifter. 6. Række. Bd. 1. Ac. 1023/2.

WIEDEMANN (O.) Das litauische Präteritum. pp. 230. Strassburg, 1891. 8°. 12975. l. 22.

See also BALTIC PROVINCES: FOLK LORE.

LEVELLING. HOLLOWAY (T.) Levelling, and its general application. pp. 147.
Lond. 1895. 8°.   8768. k. 17.

See also BUILDING: ENGINEERING.

LEWISHAM. Ac. Lewisham. Antiquarian Society. Register of the Church of Saint Mary, Lewisham. pp. 326. Lond. 1891. 8°.
        9916. ee. 1.

DUNCAN (L. L.) Parish Church of Saint Mary, Lewisham. pp. 73. Blackheath, 1892. 4°.
        4707. f. 17.

LEYLAND. WHITE (W. S.) Register book of Leyland. pp. 313. 1890. 8°. Ac. Manchester. Record Society. Publications. Vol. 21. Ac. 8121.

LEYTON. KENNEDY (J.) History of the Parish of Leyton. pp. 423. Leyton, 1894. 8°.
        10368. h. 35.

LHOTA NAGA LANGUAGE. WITTER (W. E.) Grammar of the Lhōtā Nāgā language. pp. 161. Calcutta, 1888. 8°. 12906. dd. 43.

LIANAS. SCHENCK (H.) Beiträge zur Biologie der Lianen. 2 Tl. 1892, 93. 8°. SCHIMPER (A. F. W.) Botanische Mittheilungen. Hft. 4.
        7029. k.

LIBARNA. IOZZI (O.) Cenno storico della antica Libarna. pp. 104. Pisa, 1890. 8°.
        07708. f. 23.

LIBEL AND SLANDER. COOPER (F. T.) Handbook of the Law of Defamation. pp. 319. Edinb. 1894. 8°.   6573. e. 2.

FRASER (H.) Principles and practice of the Law of Libel and Slander. pp. 284.
Lond. 1893. 8°.   6325. df. 21.

FROLA (P. E.) Delle Ingiurie e diffamazioni. pp. 495. Torino, 1890. 8°. 5359. c. 2.

STARKIE (T.) Law of Slander and Libel. pp. 1128. Lond. 1891. 8°. 2232. f. 6.

WORMS (E.) Les attentats à l'honneur. pp. 332. Paris, 1890. 8°. 5403. dd. 1.

LIBELLULIDAE. See DRAGON FLIES.

LIBERIA. BÜTTIKOFER (J.) Reisebilder aus Liberia. 2 Bde. Leiden, 1890. 8°. 10096. gg. 7.

CHICAGO. Columbian Exposition. Liberia. pp. 31. Chicago, 1893. 8°. 7958. bbb. 21.

DURHAM (F. A.) The Lone-star of Liberia. pp. 331. Lond. 1892. 8°. 8156. de. 7.

MAC PHERSON (J. H. T.) History of Liberia. pp. 61. 1891. 8°. Johns Hopkins University Studies. Series 9. No. 10. Ac. 2689.

SORELA (L.) Notas de una Misión en Liberia. pp. 39. Madrid, 1893. 8°. Pam. 89.

See also AFRICA, West: NEGROES.

LIBERTY, Religious, Political, etc.
CONSTANT (P.) La Révolution et la Liberté. pp. 305. Paris, 1895. 8°. 8050. g. 7.

LIBERTY—continued.

FUERSTENAU (H.) Das Grundrecht der Religionsfreiheit. pp. 342. Leipz. 1891. 8°.
        5604. ccc. 23.

GEORGES (H.) Étude sur la Liberté de conscience. pp. 11. Nancy, 1889. 8°. Pam. 49.

HÉMENT (F.) Entretiens sur la Liberté de conscience. pp. 146. Paris, 1890. 8°. 3900. aaa. 26.

LEFÈVRE (É.) La Liberté religieuse. pp. 51. Verviers, 1888. 8°. Pam. 93.

MARILLIER (L.) La Liberté de Conscience. pp. 280. Paris, 1890. 12°. 3900. c. 13.

MAYER (J. V.) Von der Freiheit. pp. 120. Freiburg, 1891. 8°. 8006. cc. 7.

SAUNOIS DE CHEVERT (G.) La Liberté de conscience en France et à l'Étranger. pp. 348. Paris, 1890. 8°. 3900. aaa. 25.

SIDEBOTHAM (E. W.) Religious Liberty, etc. pp. 20. Manch. 1893. 8°. 4139. dd. 2. (13.)

For works on Free-Will, see WILL.

LIBRARIES.

General.

Ac. G. B. & I. Library Association. Public Library manual. Lond. 1892, etc. 8°.
        011900. ee. 26.

—— Library Association series.
Lond. 1892, etc. 8°.   Ac. 9115/7.

—— Library Association year-book.
Lond. 1892, etc. 8°.   Ac. 9115/8.

ANTWERP. Conférence du Livre. Compte-rendu, etc. pp. 272. Anvers, 1891. 4°. 11900. k. 24.

CAMPBELL (F. B. F.) Remarks to the members of the Library Assistants' Association. pp. 23. Lond. 1895. 8°.   Pam. 6.

CHICAGO. Columbian Exposition. Deutsche Unterrichts-Ausstellung. Katalog der Bibliotheks-Ausstellung. pp. 44. Berl. 1893. 8°. Pam. 18.

CLARK (J. W.) Libraries in the Medieval and Renaissance periods. pp. 61. Camb. 1894. 8°.
        11900. bb. 55.

CRUNDEN (F. M.) The Free Public Library. Its uses and value. pp. 23. St. Louis, 1893. 8°.
        011902. m. 22. (11.)

FOVARGUE (H. W.) and OGLE (J. J.) Library Legislation, 1855-90. pp. 138. 1892. 8°. Ac. Great Britain and Ireland. Library Association. Public Library Manual. Pt. I. 011900. ee. 26.

GASQUET (F. A.) Notes on mediæval Monastic Libraries. pp. 20. Yeovil, 1891. 8°.
       011900. ee. 5. (11.)

GILMAN (D. C.) Development of the Public Library in America. pp. 13. Ithaca, 1891. 4°.
        11901. k. 37.

GOTTLIEB (T.) Ueber mittelalterliche Bibliotheken. pp. 520. Leipz. 1890. 8°. 011902. m. 9.

GRAESEL (A.) Grundzüge der Bibliothekslehre. pp. 424. Leipz. 1890. 8°. 11901. aa. 31.

GREENWOOD (T.) Public Libraries. pp. 598. Lond. 1894. 8°. 011902. c. 24.

—— Sunday-school and village Libraries. pp. 95. Lond. 1892. 8°. 011902. i. 16.

IRELAND (A.) Address on the moral influence of Free Libraries. pp. 13. Manchester, 1892. 8°.
       011902. m. 21. (10.)

—— Mr. Ireland's Address on "The moral Influence of Free Libraries." Comments.
Manch. 1892. 4°. 11903. bb. 54. (6.)

KAY (J. T.) Provision of novels in rate-supported Libraries. pp. 16. Lond. 1880. 12°. Pam. 6.

LANG (A.) The Library. pp. 192.
Lond. 1892. 8°.   11899. g. 45.

MATHEWS (E. R. N.) Birmingham and Bristol. Words about Public Libraries. pp. 16.
Bristol, 1892. 12°.   Pam. 6.

LIBRARIES.—General—_continued._

MILLAR (F.) "Thou shalt not steal." [Protest against the Free Libraries Act.] pp. 8.
Lond. 1890. 8°.　　08276. f. 20. (10.)

MONDY (M. C.) School Libraries and higher education. pp. 8. _Lond._ 1891. 8°. Pam. 17.

NOERRENBERG (C.) Congress der Bibliothekare in Chicago. pp. 33, _Leipz._ 1893. 8°. 11903. f. 35. (10.)

O'BRIEN (M. D.) Free Libraries. 1891. 8°,
MACKAY (T.) A Plea for Liberty. 8276. g. 44.

OGLE (J. J.) Place of the Free Public Library in popular education. pp. 8. _Lond._ 1891. 8°.
11903. f. 35. (5.)

P.P. _London._ The Library Review.
Lond. 1892, _etc._ 8°.　　P.P. 5939. k.

—— _Paris._ Revue des bibliothèques.
Paris, 1891, _etc._ 8°.　　P.P. 6475. i.

—— Revue des archives des bibliothèques, _etc._
Paris, 1895, _etc._ 8°.　　P.P. 6475. ia.

PETZHOLDT (J.) Manuale del Bibliotecario.
pp. 364. _Milano,_ 1894. 16°.　　012200. i. 4.

POOLE (W. F.) The University Library and the university curriculum. pp. 55.
Chicago, 1894. 8°.　　8364. aaa. 50.

REYER (E.) Entwicklung und Organisation der Volksbibliotheken. pp. 116. _Leipz._ 1893. 8°.
011901. ee. 23.

ROGERS (W. T.) Manual of Bibliography, Library Management, _etc._ pp. 172. _Lond._ 1891. 8°.
11899. e. 29.

ROUILLARD (E.) Les Bibliothèques populaires.
pp. 61. _Québec,_ 1890. 8°. 011902. e. 21. (4.)

SLATER (J. H.) The Library Manual. pp. 424.
Lond. 1892. 8°.　　011902. i. 8.

TEDDER (H. R.) Librarianship as a profession.
pp. 30. _Lond._ 1884. 12°.　　011902. e. 19. (2.)

TURNER (F. A.) Public Libraries and their relation to education. pp. 11. _Lond._ 1894. 8°.
11904. l. 14. (11.)

See also BIBLIOGRAPHY ; MANUSCRIPTS : TYPO-GRAPHY.

Cataloguing : Classification, Shelving, etc.

Ac. _Library Association._ Report of the Committee to revise the regulations for examining Library Assistants. pp. 6. _Lond._ 1891. 8°.
11904. l. 15. (2.)

Ac. Oxford. _Bodleian Library._ Rules for the Author Catalogue of the Bodleian. ff. 8.
1893. 8°.　　011902. m. 20. (20.)

AVETTA (A.) Indici e cataloghi. pp. 28.
Torino, 1891. 8°.　　Pam. 6.

BONAZZI (G.) Schema di Catalogo sistematico per le biblioteche. pp. 105. _Parma,_ 1890. 8°.
11899. f. 45.

CAMPBELL (F. B. F. P.) Introduction to the theory of a State-paper Catalogue. pp. 23.
Lond. 1891. 8°.　　11899. ee. 24.

CHANDLER (H. W.) Observations on the Bodleian classed catalogue. pp. 31. _Oxf._ 1888. 8°.
11900. c. 33. (1.)

NICHOLSON (E. W. B.) A Protest against 'The Bodleian Classed Catalogue' by H. W. Chandler.
pp. 4. _Oxf._ 1888. 4°.　　11900. c. 33. (2.)

COSENTINI (F.) Ordinamento sistematico nei cataloghi reali. pp. 60. _Pisa,_ 1893. 8°.
011901. f. 2.

COTGREAVE (A.) Cotgreave's Library Indicator.
Lond. 1887. 8°.　　Pam. 6.

—— Indicators versus Book-keeping. pp. 23.
Lond. 1885. 8°.　　Pam. 6.

CUTTER (C. A.) Rules for a Dictionary Catalogue. 1889. 8°. U. S. _Bureau of Education._
Report on Public Libraries. Part II. 011903. l. 14.

LIBRARIES.—Cataloguing, etc.—_cont._

CUTTER (C. A.) Alfabetic Order table. 1895. fol.
11905. c. 1.

DEWEY (M.) Decimal Classification and relatio index. pp. 593. _Bost._ 1894. 8°. 11903. d. 32.

—— Library School rules. pp. 72.
Bost. 1894. 8°.　　11899. h. 47.

FLETCHER (W. I.) Library Classification.
pp. 32. _Bost._ 1894. 8°.　　011901. c. 27.

FUMAGALLI (G.) Della Collocaz'one dei libri nelle pubbliche Biblioteche. pp. 165.
Firenze, 1890. 8°.　　011902. g. 39.

JAST (L. S.) Classification in Public Libraries.
pp. 10. _Lond._ 1895. 8°.　　11903. f. 35. (13.)

LINDERFELT (K. A.) Eclectic Card Catalog rules. pp. 104. _Bost._ 1890. 8°.　　11899. i. 41.

LONDON. _Sion College._ Order of classification of the Library. pp. 104. _Lond._ 1889. 8°.
011902. g. 41.

LUCCA. _R. Biblioteca._ Prospetto indicativo a sussidio del catalogo delle opere in libera consultazione. _Lucca,_ 1893. fol. 1890. e. 2. (102.)

NIZET (F.) Projet d'un Catalogue idéologique des périodiques. pp. 26. _Brux._ 1891. 8°.
011900. ee. 6. (2.)

SACCONI (G.) Un nuovo sistema di Legatura meccanica per cataloghi. pp. 11.
Firenze, 1891. 8°.　　11901. d. 26. (5.)

STAENDER (J.) Das Einheitsmass für die Raumberechnung von Büchermagazinen. pp. 11.
Berl. 1892. 8°.　　11901. d. 26. (7.)

STIKEMAN (G.) Adjustable Book shelving for Libraries. pp. 16. _N.Y._ 1895. fol. 1880. a. 4.

U.S. _Bureau of Education._ Catalog of "A.L.A." Library, 5000 volumes for a popular library.
pp. 592. _Wash._ 1893. 8°.　　011900. ee. 36.

WADDINGTON (G. W.) Indexing and arranging a reference library. pp. 8. _Whitby,_ 1894. 8°.
11903. b. 43. (8.)

ZANGEMEISTER (C) System der Realkatalogs des Univ.-Bibl. zu Heidelberg. _Heidelb._ 1893. fol.
1888. b. 5.

Reports and Accounts of Libraries.

CLEGG (J.) Directory of Booksellers, and list of Public Libraries. pp. 308. _Rochdale,_ 1891. 8°.
011902. e. 8.

WILSON (J. G.) The World's largest Libraries.
pp. 73. _N.Y._ 1894. 8°.　　011900. g. 2.

Algeria.

GAVAULT (P.) Notice sur la Bibliothèque d'Alger.
1894. 8°. Ac. Constantina. _Société Historique._
Revue Africaine. Ann. 38.　　Ac. 6915.

Austria-Hungary.

SACCONI RICCI (G.) Una Visita ad alcune biblioteche della Svizzera e dell' Austria. pp. 288.
Firenze, 1893. 8°.　　011901. e. 25.

GRATZ. _Landes-Bibliothek._ Bestimmungen für die Benützung der steiermärkischen Landes-Bibliothek. pp. 11. _Graz,_ 1893. 8°. 11904. c. 41. (7.)

ZWIEDINECK-SUEDENHORST (H. v.) Die steiermärkische Landes-Bibliothek. pp. 24.
Graz, 1893. 8°.　　011900. i. 5.

Belgium.

Ac. Brussels. _Bibliothèque Royale._ Rapport sur la situation de la Bibliothèque, 1890-91.
pp. 71. _Brux._ 1892. 8°.　　11903. f. 35. (6.)

—— Ghent. _Université de Gand._ Rapport sur la situation de la Bibliothèque de l'Université.
pp. 13. _Gand,_ 1894, _etc._ 8°.　　011900. e.

Canada. See infra : United States.

Egypt.

GRAND (P.) Rapport sur les Bibliothèques.
pp. 46. _Le Caire,_ 1894. 4°.　　11901. k. 18.

LIBRARIES.—Reports, etc.—*continued.*

France.

Ac. Paris. *Bibliothèque Nationale.* Notice des objets exposés. 3 pt. *Paris,* 1881. 8°.
11904. c. 18.

BÉRALDI (H.) Voyage d'un livre à travers la Bibliothèque Nationale. pp. 45. *Paris,* 1893. 4°.
011900. k. 7.

DELISLE (L. V.) Notes sur le Département des Imprimés de la Bibliothèque Nationale. pp. 61. *Paris,* 1891. 8°. 011900. f. 9. (7.)

JOURDAIN ( ) La Bibliothèque du Roi au début du règne de Louis xv., 1718–36. 1893. 8°.
Ac. Paris. *Société de l'Histoire de Paris.* Mémoires. Tom. 20. Ac. 6883/2.

OMONT (H.) Le Catalogue imprimé de la Bibliothèque du Roi au XVIIIe siècle. pp. 31.
Paris, 1895. 8°. Pam. 6.

VALLÉE (L.) La Bibliothèque Nationale. Documents pour servir à l'histoire de l'établissement. pp. 525. *Paris,* 1894. 8°. 011901. ee. 28.

PARIS. *Bibliothèque Cardinal.* La Bibliothèque Cardinal. *Paris,* 1891. 8°. 011902. e. 22. (6.)

BARBIER (V.) Monographie de la Bibliothèque de Chambéry. pp. 170. *Chambéry,* 1883. 8°.
11904. bbb. 34.

QUENTIN-BAUCHART (E.) La Bibliothèque de Fontainebleau. pp. 234. *Paris,* 1891. 4°.
11899. d. 16.

JADART (H.) Les anciennes bibliothèques de Reims, leur sort en 1790–91. pp. 39.
Reims, 1891. 8°. 011900. f. 10. (8.)

ANDREWS (W. L.) J. Grolier, Viscount d'Aguisy : account of his life and of his library. pp. 68.
N.Y. 1892. 8°. K.T.C. 6. a. 12.

Germany.

SACCONI RICCI (G.) Una visita ad alcune biblioteche della Svizzera e della Germania. pp. 288.
Firenze, 1893. 8°. 011901. c. 25.

SCHWENKE (P.) Adressbuch der deutschen Bibliotheken. pp. 411. *Leipz.* 1893. 8°.
011900. h. 13.

GROEPLER ( ) *Dr. Jur.* Bücherein mittelbarer Fürsten und Grafen Deutschlands. pp. 42.
Leipz. 1891. 8°. Pam. 6.

FROMM (E.) Die aachener Stadtbibliothek. pp. 12. *Aachen,* 1891. 8°. 011900. f. 8. (14.)

LEITSCHUH (E.) Geschichte der k. Bibliothek zu Bamberg nach der Säkularisation. pp. 34.
Bamberg, 1894. 8°. 11903. i. 35.

FRANKFORT ON THE MAIN. *Freiherrlich C. von Rothschild'sche Bibliothek.* Bibliotheksordnung vom 14. Juni 1893. pp. 4. *Frankfurt,* 1893. 8°.
11903. f. 34. (2.)

—— Benutzungsordnung vom 14. Juni 1893. pp. 8. *Frankfurt,* 1893. 8°. 11903. f. 34. (3.)

GRULICH (O.) Geschichte der Bibliothek der k. Leopoldinisch - Carolinischen deutschen Akademie der Naturforscher. pp. 300.
Halle, 1894. 8°. 11901. g. 44.

ZANGEMEISTER (C.) System des Realkatalogs des Universitäts-Bibliothek zu Heidelberg.
Heidelberg, 1893. fol. 1888. b. 5.

Ac. Cologne. *Hansische Geschichtsverein.* Das Archiv und die Bibliothek der Stadt Köln. pp. 26. *Köln,* 1894. 4°. 11899. k. 26.

—— Leipsic. *Academia Lipsiensis.* Ordnung der Universitäts-Bibliothek. pp. 19.
Leipz. 1894. 8°. 11903. f. 34. (5.)

RUEPPRECHT (C.) Münchens Bibliotheken. pp. 79. *München,* 1890. 8°. 011904. ee. 5. (10.)

LIBRARIES.—Reports, etc.—*continued.*

BEUCHER. Das Bedürfniss nach Reformen an der Staatsbibliothek in München. pp. 29.
München, 1894. 8°. 11903. f. 35. (9.)

RUEPPRECHT (C.) Die Büchersammlungen der Universität München. pp. 50.
Regensb. 1892. 8°. 011902. m. 22. (8.)

SCHMIDT (C.) Zur Geschichte der ältesten Bibliotheken zu Strassburg. pp. 200.
Strassb. 1882. 8°. 11899. g. 11.

THIAUCOURT (C.) La Bibliothèque de Strasbourg. pp. 117. *Paris,* 1893. 8°. 011901. g. 19.

WEIMAR. *Grossherzogliche Bibliothek.* Zuwachs der Bibliothek. 1889–92. pp. 88.
Weimar, 1893. 8°. 11903. f. 34. (4.)

HEINEMANN (O. v.) Die herzogliche Bibliothek zu Wolfenbüttel. pp. 345.
Wolfenbüttel, 1894. 8°. 011900. h. 10.

Great Britain and Ireland.

GREENWOOD (T.) Public Libraries. pp. 598.
Lond. 1894. 8°. 011903. e. 23.

SCHENKL (H.) Die Bibliotheken der Kathedralen von Salisbury, Exeter, Canterbury, *etc.* pp. 79. 1894. 8°. Ac. Vienna. *K. Akademie der Wissenschaften.* Sitzungsbericht. Phil.-hist. Classe. Bd. 131. Ac. 810/6.

WALLACE (E. D.) Memorial Institutions. Library of the British Museum. *N.Y.* 1887. 8°.
011902. g. 29.

BURBIDGE (E.) T. Cranmer, Archbishop of Canterbury. An account of his library. pp. 28.
1892. 8°. 011900. f. 6.

LONDON. *Bishopsgate Foundation.* History of the Foundation, with an account of the construction of the Library. pp. 15.
Lond. 1894. 8°. 011901. g. 30.

CLERKENWELL. *Public Library.* Librarian's Report on his visit to American Libraries. pp. 4.
1893. 8°. 11903. f. 34. (1.)

WELCH (C.) The Guildhall Library and its work. pp. 69. *Lond.* 1893. 8°. 11899. e. 41.

LONDON. *Holborn Public Library.* Report of the Commissioners, 1891–93. pp. 31.
Lond. 1893. 8°. 011901. i. 4.

LAMBETH. *Public Libraries.* Report, *etc.*
Lond. 1892, *etc.* 8°. 011901. g.

LONDON. *Minet Public Library.* Annual Report. *Lond.* 1893. *etc.* 8°. 011901. i.

PADDINGTON. *Public Library.* Annual Report. *Lond.* 1892, *etc.* 8°. 011901. e. 10.

PUTNEY. *Public Library.* Report.
Putney, 1890, *etc.* 8°. 011903. k. 34.

LONDON. *Sion College.* Order of classification of the Library. pp. 104. *Lond.* 1889. 8°.
011902. g. 41.

ROTHERHITHE. *Public Library.* Report. *etc.*
Rotherhithe, 1891, *etc.* 8°. 011901. e. 2.

SAINT GEORGE, *Hanover Square, Public Libraries.* Report. pp. 36. *Lond.* 1895. 8°. 11899. d. 19.

SAINT LEONARD, *Shoreditch, Public Libraries.* Report. pp. 26. *Lond.* 1894. 8°. 11901. h. 26.

SAINT MARTIN IN THE FIELDS. *Public Library.* Report. *Lond.* 1892, *etc.* 8°. 011901. e.

STOKE NEWINGTON. *Public Library.* Report. 2 pt. *Lond.* 1892–94. 8°. 011900. c. 13.

WEST HAM. *Public Libraries.* Special Report on organizing work in connection with the Public Libraries. pp. 35. *Stratford,* 1892. 8°.
011900. ee. 19.

BIRMINGHAM. *Birmingham Library.* Annual Meeting. Report and proceedings.
Birmingham, 1881, *etc.* 8°. 11902. h. 8.

BOOTLE. *Public Library,* Report, *etc.*
Liverp. 1888, *etc.* 8°. 011902. l. 8.

LIBRARIES.—Reports, etc.—_continued._

BRADFORD, _Yorkshire._ _Public Libraries._ Report. _Bradford_, 1882, etc. 8°.   11905. c. 29.

BRENTFORD. _Public Library._ Report. _Brentford_, 1890, etc. 8°.   011903. e.

JAMES (M. R.) Abbey of S. Edmund at Bury. The Library, etc. pp. 200. 1895. 8°. Ac. Cambridge. Antiquarian Society. Oct. Series. No. 28.   Ac. 5624.

SINKER (R.) The Library of Trinity College Cambridge. pp. 136. _Camb._ 1891. 8°.   11899. ee. 27.

LEAMINGTON. _Public Library._ Report. _Leamington_, 1884, etc. 4°.   011902. l.

PEET (H.) Inventory of the plate in the Parish Churches of Liverpool; with a catalogue of the ancient Library in St. Peter's Church. pp. 128. _Liverp._ 1893. 8°.   4707. cc. 13.

KAY (J. T.) The Owens College. Notes on the library. pp. 23. _Manch._ 1891. 8°.   Pam. 6.

EUREN (H. F.) Gleanings at the Norwich Free Library. pp. 206. _Norwich_, 1891. 8°.   11899. ee. 25.

Ac. Oxford. _Bodleian Library._ Compendious Cataloguing Rules for the Author Catalogue of the Bodleian Library. ff. 8. 1893. 8°.   011902. m. 20. (20.)

CHANDLER (H. W.) Observations on the Bodleian classed Catalogue. pp. 31. _Oxf._ 1888. 8°.   11900. c. 33. (1.)

NICHOLSON (E. W. B.) A Protest against 'The Observations on the Bodleian classed Catalogue,' by W. H. Chandler. pp. 4. _Oxf_ 1888. 4°.   11900. c. 33. (2.)

PORTSMOUTH. _Public Library._ Report, etc. _Portsea_, 1887, etc. 8°.   011902. g. 30.

TYNEMOUTH. _Public Library._ Report. _North Shields_, 1892, etc. 8°.   011901. e. 9.

MORRELL (W. W.) A Public Library for York. pp. 11. _York_, 1891. 8°.   011902. m. 19. (11.)

ABERDEEN. Proposals for a Public Library at Aberdeen. 1764. pp. 6. _Aberd._ 1893. 8°. Pam. 6.

ANDERSON (P. J.) Notes on the Libraries of the Universities of Aberdeen. pp. 27. _Aberd._ 1893. 8°.   011902. ee. 22. (8.)

ABERDEEN. _Public Library._ Manual for readers by A. W. Robertson. pp. 35. _Aberd._ 1892. 8°.   11903. b. 43. (6.)

ALLOA. _Public Library._ Report. 1890, etc. 8°.   011903. e.

LAW (T. G.) The Signet Library. pp. 20. _Edinb._ 1890. 4°.   11902. i. 23.

GLASGOW. _Mitchell Library._ Guide to the Mitchell Library, Glasgow. pp. 16. _Glasg._ 1892. 12°.   Pam. 6.

MURRAY (D.) Plea for Stirling's Library. pp. 18. _Glasg._ 1894. 8°.   011901. g. 28.

BELFAST. _Belfast Library._ History of the Belfast Library. pp. 128. _Belfast_, 1888. 8°.   11901. g. 42.

—— _Public Library._ Report. _Belfast_, 1889, etc. 8°.   011903. k. 37.

Italy.

GARBELLI (F.) Le Biblioteche in Italia all' época romana. pp. 232. _Milano_, 1894. 8°.   011901. h. 2.

CARINI (I.) La Biblioteca Vaticana. pp. 166. _Roma_, 1892. 8°.   011900. h. 11.

EHRLE (F.) Historia Bibliothecae Romanorum Pontificum. 1890, etc. 4°. Ac. Rome. _Academia di Conferenze._ Biblioteca, etc. Vol. 7, etc.   Ac. 6541/2.

GENNARI (A.) Monografia della Biblioteca di Ferrara. pp. 90. _Ferrara_, 1892. 8°.   011902. m. 22. (5.)

LIBRARIES.—Reports, etc.—_continued._

RAFFAELLI (F.) _Marquis._ La Biblioteca comunale di Fermo. pp. 200. _Recanati_, 1890. 12°.   011902. f. 44.

CHILOVI (D.) and PAPINI (A.) Il nuovo palazzo per la Biblioteca Nazionale Centrale di Firenze. pp. 8. _Firenze_, 1892. 8°.   11901. d. 25. (4.)

MODONA (L.) Topografia della Reale Biblioteca di Parma. pp. 16. _Parma_, 1894. 8°.   11904. l. 17. (7.)

Japan.

YEDO. _Tokyo Library._ Extract of Annual Report 1892. pp. 8. _Tokyo_, 1892. 8°.   11901. g. 35.

Sweden.

ANNERSTEDT (C.) Upsala Universitets biblioteks historia intill år 1702. pp. 119. _Stockholm_, 1894. 8°.   011899. k. 2.

Switzerland.

SACCONI RICCI (G.) Una visita ad alcune Biblioteche della Svizzera. pp. 288 _Firenze_, 1893. 8°.   011901. e. 25.

Ac. Basle. _Academia Basiliensis._ Bericht über die Verwaltung der Bibliothek der Universität Basel. _Basle_, 1893, etc. 8°.   011901. c.

—— Ordnung für die Benützung der Bibliothek der Universität Basel. pp. 7. _Basle_, 1892. 8°.   011903. e. 27. (5.)

United States and Canada.

FLETCHER (W. I.) Public Libraries in America. pp. 169. 1894. 8°. TODD (D. P.) Columbian Knowledge Series.   8709. e.

FLINT (W.) Statistics of Public Libraries in the U.S. and Canada. pp. 213. 1893. 8°. U.S. Bureau of Education. Circular of Information. No. 201.   8308. i.

UHLER (P. R.) Sketch of the history of Public Libraries in Baltimore. pp. 10. 1889. 8°. Johns Hopkins University Studies. Notes 1889. No. 5.   Ac. 2689.

BALTIMORE. _Mercantile Library Association._ Report, etc. _Baltimore_, 1889, etc. 8°. 011902. m. 7.

BOSTON. _Public Library._ Handbook for readers. pp. 138. _Bost._ 1890. 8°.   11899. aaa. 21.

GREEN (S. A.) Origin and growth of the Library of the Massachusetts Historical Society. pp. 35. _Camb. Mass._ 1893. 8°.   11904. l. 15. (5.)

BROOKLINE. _Brookline Library._ Bulletin. _Brookline_, 1894, etc. 8°.   011901. f.

Ac. Burlington. _University._ Views of the Billings Library. _Bost._ 1894. fol.   1887. b. 50.

H., G. W. Twenty-five years of the annals of Cornell University Library. pp. 12. _Ithaca_, 1893. 8°.   Pam. 6.

DENVER. _Public Library._ Handbook. pp. 182. _Denver_, 1895. 8°.   11900. a. 56.

BOLTON (C. K.) Harvard University Library. Sketch of its history, etc. pp. 17. _Camb._ 1894. 8°.   11904. l. 17. (5.)

JERSEY CITY. _Public Library._ Rules and Regulations. _Jersey City_, 1891. 16°.   Pam. 6.

Ac. New York. _Columbia College._ Report. _N.Y._ 1886, etc. 8°.   011903. f.

PHILADELPHIA. _Mercantile Library Company._ Charter, by-laws and rules. pp. 24. _Phila._ 1894. 8°.   11903. f. 35. (11.)

SALEM. _Public Library._ Report. _Salem_, 1890, etc. 8°.   011902. g. 31.

DU BOIS (H. P.) Four private Libraries of New York. _N.Y._ 1892. 8°.   K.T.C. 8. a. 3.

HALIFAX, _N.S._ _Library Commissioners._ Report. _Halifax_, 1890, etc. 8°.   011902. h.

HAMILTON, _Ontario._ _Public Library._ Report. _Hamilton_, 1890, etc. 8°.   11901. aaa. 53.

LICENSING LAWS. DAVIES (J. T.) Inn-keeper's handbook and Licensed Victualler's manual. pp. 120. *Lond.* 1893, 8°.
6146. e. 30.

DEWAR (D.) The Liquor Laws of Scotland. pp. 294. *Edinb.* 1894, 8°. 6583. cc. 6.

ENGLAND. *Church of England Temperance Society.* Offences against the Laws which concern the use of intoxicating liquors. *Lond.* 1890, *etc.* 8°.
8436. aa.

—— Licensing Laws. Recommendations to branches. pp. 4. *Lond.* 1890, 8°. Pam. 85.

HERSCHEL (*Sir* W. J.) The Licensing Laws. pp. 14. *Lond.* 1895. 8°. Pam. 85.

—— Breaches of the Licensing Laws. pp. 36. *Lond.* 1892. 8°. 8436. f. 3. (2.)

LATHOM (H. W. L. B.) Handy guide to the Licensing Acts. pp. 149. *Lond.* 1894. 12°.
6426. aaa. 22.

LEDLIE (W.) and GREED (H. L.) Wine and Spirit Merchants' guide and Licensed Vic-tuallers' manual. pp. 112. *Cape Town*, 1891. 8°.
6424. cc. 19.

LEWIS (D.) Civil Government and the drink trade. pp. 42. *Lond.* 1894. 8°. 8436. aaa. 58.

MONTGOMERY (R. M.) The Licensing Laws so far as they relate to the sale of intoxicating liquors. pp. 372. *Lond.* 1895. 8°. 6425. df. 26.

NORFOLK (E. W.) License Holders' guide. pp. 132. *Lond.* 1893. 8°. 6426. cc. 32.

O'BRIEN (J.) Licensing Laws. O'Brien v. the Justices of Manchester. Verbatim reports of the judgments of the Court of Quarter Sessions, the Queen's Bench Division, and the Court of Appeal. pp. 23. *Manch.* 1892. 8°.
6190. ccc. 3. (9.)

PATERSON (J.) Intoxicating Liquor Licensing Acts. pp. 427. *Lond.* 1894. 8°. 6425. de. 20.

REVIEW. Review of some points in the Licensing Laws. pp. 14. *Manch.* 1891. 8°.
8435. e. 24. (11.)

BLOGG (H. B.) What I saw of the Gothenburg system in Bergen. pp. 12. *Lond.* 1894. 8°.
8436. f. 3. (13.)

GOADBY (E.) The Gothenburg Licensing system. pp. 104. *Lond.* 1895. 8°. 8433. f. 8.

GOULD (E. R. L.) The Gothenburg system of liquor traffic. pp. 253. 1893. 8°. U.S. *Bureau of Labor.* Special Report. Report 5. 8275. k.

JOHNSON (J.) The Gothenburg system of Public-House Licensing. pp. 95. *Lond.* 1893. 8°.
8436. c. 7.

LARSSON (J.) Review of the working of the Gothenburg Public-House Licensing Co. *Göteborg*, 1890, fol. Pam. 85.

LEWIS (D.) The Gothenburg and Bergen schemes. pp. 71. *Lond.* 1895. 8°. 8436. f. 11.

MORTIMER (R.) Gothenburg Licensing system. pp. 8. *Lond.* 1892. 8°. 8435. e. 24. (24.)

WIESELGREN (S.) Gothenburg system. Its origin, object and effects. 2 pt. *Gothenburg*, 1886. 8°.
8435. c. 22.

WILSON (J. M.) The Scandinavian plan. A Sermon. pp. 16. *Lond.* 1894. 8°. 8436. f. 3. (7.)

WILSON (T. M.) Local option in Norway. pp. 96. *Lond.* 1891. 8°. 8436. aa. 42.

KRUSEMAN (J.) De Werking der Nederlandsche Trankwet. pp. 46. *Amsterd.* 1892. 8°.
8435. e. 21.

BUSH (R. E.) Legislation in California con-cerning Intoxicants. pp. 43. *Oakland*, 1890. 8°.
Pam. 85.

COPELAND (W. F.) Handbook of prohibition facts. pp. 128. *Lond.* 1892. 8°. 8436. a. 56.

LICENSING LAWS—*continued.*

DEWAR (T. R.) Experiences of prohibition in the United States, Canada, *etc.*, and of the Gothenburg system. pp. 15. *Lond.* 1895. 8°.
Pam. 85.

FANSHAWE (E. L.) Liquor Legislation in the U.S. and Canada. *Lond.* 1893. 8°. 8436. c. 13.

BENHAM (W. G.) Does a reduction in the number of Licensed Houses mean increased sobriety. pp. 4. *Colchester*, 1892. 8°. Pam. 85.

COVENTRY. *Coventry Licensed Victuallers' Associa-tion.* New phase of the Licensing Question, "One Man, One Licence." pp. 6.
Coventry, 1894. 8°. Pam. 85.

DALE (A. T.) The Licensed Trade. pp. 18. *Lond.* 1890. 8°. 8436. f. 1. (6.)

ENGLAND. *Church of England Temperance So-ciety.* The C.E.T.S. and the purchasing clauses of the Local Taxation Duties Bill. pp. 4. *Lond.* 1890. 8°. 8436. aa. 38. (10.)

—— Licensing Boards Bill of the Society. pp. 21. *Lond.* 1893. fol. Pam. 85.

—— Licensing Laws Amendment Act of the Society. pp. 15. *Lond.* 1894. fol. Pam. 85.

—— Licensing Boards Bill. pp. 8. *Lond.* 1894. fol. Pam. 85.

GOULD (E. R. L.) Popular Control of the Liquor Traffic. pp. 108. *Lond.* 1894. 8°.
8436. b. 43.

HARROP (H. B.) The Direct Veto. An exposure. pp. 16. *Lond.* 1893. 8°. Pam. 85.

JAYNE (F. J.) *Bp. of Chester.* Licensing pro-posals of the Bishop of Chester. pp. 23. *Lond.* 1892. 12°. 8436. f. 3. (4.)

KIRSOP (J.) Direct Veto Association. Prize essay. pp. 4. *Manch.* 1890. 8°. Pam. 85.

MACLAREN (A.) Rev. A. MacLaren on the Liquor traffic. pp. 7. *Manch.* 1889. 8°.
Pam. 85.

MACKENZIE (F. A.) Sober by Act of Parlia-ment. pp. 197. *Lond.* 1894. 8°. 8436. c. 15.

MANCESTRIAN. The Drink Trade: how to get rid of it, with compensation. pp. 15. *Manch.* 1893. 8°. 8436. f. 3. (10.)

MALINS (J.) Legislation on the Sunday closing of Public Houses. pp. 16. *Lond.* 1890. 8°.
8435. e. 24. (6.)

MARRIOTT (A. J.) The Public versus Publican and teetotal fanatic. pp. 12. *Lond.* 1892. 8°.
8436. f. 1. (10.)

MORGAN (P. C.) Handbook of statistics relating to the trade in Alcoholic Liquors. pp. 71. *Lond.* 1892. 8°. 8227. ee. 28.

NEWCASTLE-UPON-TYNE. The Licensed Trade and elections. Report of Meeting of the trade at Newcastle. *Newcastle*, 1891. 8°.
8139. bb. 48. (13.)

PEARSON (E.) Parliamentary precedents in regard to Compensation. pp. 22. *Lond.* 1888. 8°.
Pam. 85.

P.P. *London.* Licensed Victuallers' official annual. *Lond.* 1893, *etc.* 8°. P.P. 2493. eda.

WATSON (P.) Equitable Compensation. pp. 15. *Lond.* 1891. 8°. Pam. 85.

See also HOTELS : TEMPERANCE.

LICHENS. Ac. London. *British Museum.* Monograph of Lichens found in Britain. *Lond.* 1894, *etc.* 8°. 07028. l. 20.

ACLOQUE (A.) Les Lichens. pp. 376. *Paris*, 1893. 8°. 7054. df. 17.

DEICHMANN BRANTH (J. S.) Grønlands Lichen-Flora. 2 pt. 1887, 92. 8°. LANGE (J. M. C.) Conspectus Florae Groenlandicae. 10460. dd.

LICHENS—continued.

Dens (G.) and Pietquin (F.) Catalogue de Lichens observés en Belgique. 1891, etc. 8°. Brussels. *Société de Botanique.* Bulletin. Tom. 29, etc.　　　　　　　　　Ac. 3274.

Harmand (J.) Catalogue des Lichens observés, dans la Lorraine. 1895. 8°. Ac. Strasburg. *Société d'Histoire Naturelle.* Bulletin. Sér. 2. Tom. 13.　　　　　　　　　Ac. 2858/2.

Jatta (A.) Monografia Lichenum Italiae meridionalis. pp. 261. *Trano,* 1889. 8°. 7077. i. 7.

Nylander (W.) Lichenes Insularum Guineensium San Thomé. pp. 54. *Parisiis,* 1889. 8°.　　　　　　　　　07028. f. 44.

—— Lichenes exoticos a W. Nylander descriptos, in ordine systematico disposuit A. M. Hue. 1890, etc. 8°. Ac. Paris. *Muséum d'Histoire Naturelle.* Nouvelles Archives. Sér. 3. Tom. 2, etc.　　　　　　　　　Ac. 2855/4.

—— Enumeratio Lichenum Freti Behringii. pp. 91. *Caen,* 1888. 8°.　　　7030. g. 6. (3.)

—— Lichenes Japoniae. pp. 122. *Parisiis,* 1890. 8°.　　　　07028. f. 34.

—— Sertum Lichenæ æ tropicæ e Labuan et Singapore. pp. 48. *Parisiis,* 1891. 8°.　　　　　　　　　7030. g. 6. (9.)

Willey (H.) Enumeration of Lichens found in New Bedford, Mass. pp. 39. *New Bedford,* 1892. 8°.　　　　Pam. 1.

—— Synopsis of the Genus Arthonia. pp. 62. *New Bedford,* 1890. 8°.　　　7030. g. 1. (7.)

See also Algae : Botany, *Cryptogamia* : Fungi.

LICHFIELD.

Asher (H.) Guide to Lichfield city. pp. 33. *Lichfield,* 1892. 8°.　　　　　　　　10348. ccc. 59. (3.)

Harradine (C.) Guide to Lichfield Cathedral. pp. 24. *Lichfield,* 1891. 8°.　7808. aa. 44. (5.)

Ward, Lock and Co. Historical handbook to Lichfield Cathedral. *Lond.* 1890. 8°.　　　　　　　　010358. l. 21.

LIÈGE.

Daris (J.) Histoire de Liège pendant le XIIIᵉ et le XIVᵉ siècle. pp. 710. *Liège,* 1891. 8°.　　　　4685. e. 35.

Dejardin (A.) Supplément aux recherches sur les cartes de Liège. 1887. 8°. Ac. Liège. *Institut Archéologique.* Bulletin. Tom. 20. Livr. 2.　　　　　　　　　Ac. 5527.

Fréson (J.) La Justice criminelle dans l'ancien pays de Liège. pp. 204. *Liège,* 1889. 8°.　　　　　　　　6056. c. 2.

Lonchay (H.) La Principauté de Liège et la France au XVIIᵉ et au XVIIIᵉ siècle. pp. 190. 1891. 8°. Ac. Brussels. *Académie des Sciences.* Mémoires, in 8°. Tom. 44.　　Ac. 985/4.

Hock (A.) Liège sous le Régime hollandais, 1820-30. pp. 187. *Liège,* 1891. 8°. 10271. bh. 23.

Ac. Brussels. *Commission d'Histoire.* Cartulaire de l'église Saint-Lambert de Liège. *Brux.* 1893, etc. 4°.　　　　Ac. 986/26.

—— Liège. *Academia Leodiensis.* Esquisse historique sur les bâtiments universitaires. pp. 55. *Liège,* 1893. 8°.　　8357. b. 61.

LIFEBOATS. *See* Shipwrecks.

LIFU.

P., F. Notes grammaticales sur la langue de Lifu. pp. 72. *Paris,* 1882. 8°.　　　　　　　　12907. e. 28.

See also Pacific Ocean and Islands.

LIGHT.

Boltzman (L.) Vorlesungen über Maxwells Theorie der Elektricität und des Lichtes. *Leipz.* 1891, etc. 8°.　8757. g. 31.

Gaenge (C.) Die Polarisation des Lichtes. pp. 78. *Leipz.* 1894. 8°.　　8715. b. 72.

Gardiner (A.) Sound and Light. 1893, etc. 8°. Major (H.) Science Manuals.　　　　　　　　　8708. a.

LIGHT—continued.

Glazebrook (R. T.) Heat and Light. pp. 244. 207. 1894. 8°. Cambridge Natural Science Manuals. Physical Series.　8709. h.

Great Britain. *Department of Science and Art.* Outline of experiments and apparatus suitable for illustrating instruction in Light, etc. pp. 93. *Lond.* 1893. 8°.　　　Pam. 18.

Gruson (H.) Im Reiche des Lichtes. pp. 263. *Braunsch.* 1895. 8°.　　　8563. bb. 28.

Hammer (F.) Über den Einfluss des Lichtes auf die Haut. pp. 56. *Stuttg.* 1893. 8°.　　　　　　　　8708. l. 8. (5.)

Jones (D. E.) Elementary lessons in Heat and Light. pp. 282. *Lond.* 1891. 8°. 8715. aa. 53.

—— Lessons in Light and Heat. pp. 315, *Lond.* 1892. 8°.　　　　8715. aa. 56.

Le Dantec (L. M.) Nouvelle analyse des Vibrations lumineuses. pp. 156. *Paris,* 1892 8°.　　　　　8716. cc. 33.

Lommel (E.) Abhandlung über das Licht. 1890. 8°. Ostwald's Klassiker. No. 20.　　　　　　　　　8706. de.

Preston (T.) Theory of Light. pp. 574. *Lond.* 1895. 8°.　　　　8715. i. 2.

Spencer (J.) Sound, Light and Heat. pp. 223. *Lond.* 1890. 8°.　　　　8716. aaa. 32.

Steel (R. E.) Class-book on Light. pp. 184. *Lond.* 1891. 8°.　　　　8715. aa. 52.

Stewart (R. W.) Text-book of Light. pp. 210. 1894. 8°. Tutorial Series.　12205. c. 219.

Tarn (E. W.) Light. pp. 112. *Lond.* 1890. 12°.　　　　8703. bbb. 10.

Volkmann (P.) Vorlesungen über die Theorie des Lichtes. pp. 432. *Leipz.* 1891. 8°.　　　　　　　　8715. f. 41.

Wonders. Wonders of Light. pp. 124. *Lond.* 1890, 8°.　　　　8716. aaa. 34.

Wood (*Sir* H. T.) Light. pp. 143. 1891. 8°. Whittaker's Library of Science.　8709. aa.

Zwick (H.) Optical Experiments. pp. 54. *Lond.* 1893. 8°.　　　　8715. ee. 49.

Lambert (J. H.) Photometria, sive de mensura et gradibus luminis. 3 pt. 1892. 8°. Ostwald's Klassiker. Nr. 31-33.　　8706. de.

Langley (S. P.) Pritchard's Wedge Photometer. *Camb, Mass.* 1886. 4°.　Pam. 79.

Lindemann (E.) Photometrische Bestimmung der Grössenclassen der bonner Durchmusterung. pp. 162. *St Petersburg,* 1889. fol.　8562. h. 1.

Palaz (A.) Treatise on industrial Photometry. pp. 322. *N.Y.* 1894. 8°.　8716. dd. 11.

Pickering (E. C.) and Wendell (O. C.) Results of observations with the Meridian Photometer. pp. 266. 1890. 4°. Ac. Cambridge. *Harvard University. Astronomical Observatory.* Annals. Vol. 24.　　　　　　　　　8562. h.

See also Optics : Physics.

LIGHT HOUSES.

G. B. & I. *Hydrographic Office.* Admiralty list of Lights. *Lond.* 1892, etc. 8°.　　　　10497. ccc.

Hardy (W. J.) Lighthouses. pp. 224. *Lond.* 1895. 8°.　　　　4429. k. 15.

Heap (D. P.) Ancient and modern Light-Houses. pp. 220. *Bost.* 1889. 4°. 8806. ddd. 12.

LIGHTING.

Allemagne (H. R. d') Histoire du luminaire. pp. 702. *Paris,* 1891. 4°.　　　　　　　　K.T.C. 4. b. 2.

Beigel (R.) Entwickelungsgeschichte der öffentlichen Beleuchtung Strassburgs. pp. 85. *Strassb.* 1891. 8°.　　　8715. f. 40.

Bezant (A. F.) Oil or Gas for Lighting our homes ? pp. 4. *Lond.* 1891. 8°.　Pam. 13.

LINCOLN, City and Cathedral—cont.

WORDSWORTH (C.) Inventories of plate, vestments, &c., belonging to the Cathedral of Lincoln. pp. 82. 1892. 4°. Archaeologia. Vol. 53.
Cat. Desk I.

LINCOLNSHIRE. Ac. Lincoln. Record
Society. Publications. Horncastle, 1891, etc. 8°.
Ac. 8094.

ANDREWS (W.) Bygone Lincolnshire.
Hull, 1891, etc. 8°.   010358. h. 1.

CHURCH (A. J.) The Laureate's Country: places connected with the life of Lord Tennyson. pp. 111. Lond. 1891. fol.   Tab. 440. b.

GRANGE (E. L.) List of Civil War tracts relating to the County of Lincoln. pp. 20.
Horncastle, 1889. 4°.   011903. l. 15.

HALL (J. G.) Notices of Lincolnshire. pp. 200.
Hull, 1890. 8°.   010358. g. 26.

MADDISON (A. R.) Lincolnshire Wills. 2 pt.
Lincoln, 1888, 91. 8°.   9914. h. 20.

PADLEY (J. S.) Fens and floods of Mid-Lincolnshire. pp. 77. Lincoln, 1882. 4°. 10368. k. 15.

SYMPSON (E. M.) On Lincolnshire Rood-screens and Rood-lofts. pp. 29. Lincoln, 1891. 8°.
7820. cc. 12.

LINEN. IRISH LINEN. Hygienic excellence
of Irish Linen. pp. 24. Belfast, 1891. 8°.
07305. h. 6. (7.)

See also TEXTILE FABRICS.

LINIÈRES. BOUSSARD (J.) Canton de Linières. Illustré. 1890. 4°. BUHOT DE KERSERS
(A.) Histoire du Cher. Fasc. 20.   7815. de.

LINLITHGOWSHIRE. BELL (J. M.)
Castles of the Lothians. pp. 97.
Edinb. 1893. 4°.   10370. i. 4.

LINZ. BARGE (H.) Die Verhandlungen zu
Linz und Passau. pp. 161. Stralsund, 1893. 8°.
09325. g. 6.

GUTTENBERGER (L.) Bibliographie des Clerus der Diöcese Linz, 1785-1893. pp. 270.
Linz. 1893. 8°.   4999. f. 8.

LION. MELLISS (C. J.) Lion-hunting in Somali-
Land. pp. 186. Lond. 1895. 8°. 07905. i. 11.
See also SPORT.

LIPARI ISLANDS. LIPARI ISLANDS. Die
Liparischen Inseln. Prag, 1893, etc. 4°. 1789. d.

LIPPE. BORNHAK (C.) Die Thronfolge im
Fürstentum Lippe. pp. 64. Berl. 1895. 8°.
8074. c. 27.

LABAND (P.) Die Thronfolge im Fürstenthum Lippe. pp. 68. Freiburg, 1891. 8°.
8074. f. 38. (4.)

WEINGAERTNER (J.) Nachträge zur lippischen Münz-Geschichte. pp. 32. 1890. 8°. P.P.
Leipsic. Blätter für Münzkunde. P.P. 1339. c.

HOFFMANN (E.) Die Vocale der lippischen Mundart. pp. 69. Hannover, 1887. 8° Pam. 47.

LIPS. See MOUTH.

LISBON. CASTILHO (J. de) A. Ribeira de
Lisboa. pp. 750. Lisboa, 1893. 8°. 10162. i. 2.

CORREIA PAES (M. C.) Melhoramentos de Lisboa e seu porto. 2 vol. Lisboa, 1882-84. 8°.
10162. g. 13.

DAYOT (A.) Lisbonne. 1892. 4°. Les Capitales du Monde. No. 9.   10025. g.

EPHEM. Almanach commercial de Lisboa.
pp. 962. Lisboa, 1891. 8°.   P.P. 2387. f.

FREIRE DE OLIVEIRA (E.) Elementos para a historia do Municipio de Lisboa. 6 vol.
Lisboa, 1882-91. 8°.   9195. h. 4.

LISIEUX, Diocese of. VEUCLIN (E. V.)
Un Conflit clérical dans le diocèse de Lisieux en 1774. pp. 17. Bernay, 1890. 12°.   Pam. 93.

LITERATURE.

General Histories, Criticism, etc.

BAINTON (G.) The Art of Authorship. pp. 355.
Lond. 1890. 8°.   011840. i. 52.

BRANDES (G. M. C.) Menschen und Werke.
pp. 533. Frankf. 1894. 8°.   12354. dd. 3.

BRINK (B. ten) Über die Aufgabe der Litteraturgeschichte. pp. 28. Strassb. 1891. 8°.
011824. h. 27. (3.)

WETZ (W.) Ueber Litteraturgeschichte. Eine Kritik von ten Brink's Rede. pp. 82.
Worms, 1891. 8°.   011850. i. 5. (8.)

CARLYLE (T.) Lectures on the history of Literature. pp. 263. Lond. 1892. 8°.   2308. aa. 21.

CHAMBERS (E. K.) History and motives of Literary Forgeries. pp. 37. Oxf. 1891. 8°.
011824. h. 28. (10.)

CORSON (H.) The aims of Literary Study.
pp. 153. N.Y. 1895. 8°.   11850. ccc. 1.

DIETZ (H.) Les Littératures étrangères.
Paris, 1892, etc. 12°.   011824. de.

DOWDEN (E.) New studies in Literature.
pp. 451. Lond. 1895. 8°.   2308. d. 24.

ENCYCLOPEDIAS. Der gebildete Mann. Ein Welt-Lexikon der Litteratur. Berl. 1892, etc. 8°.
12209. dd.

GOMEZ CARRILLO (E.) Literatura extranjera. Estudios cosmopolitas. pp. 342.
Lond. 1895. 8°.   011850. ee. 9.

GOSSE (E. W.) Questions at issue. pp. 333.
Lond. 1893. 8°.   11840. aa. 13.

GUICCIARDI (G.) and SARLO (F. de) Fra i Libri : risultato di un' inchiesta biblio-psicologica.
pp. 259. Bologna, 1893. 8°.   011900. de. 4.

HOWELLS (W. D.) Criticism and Fiction. pp. 188.
Lond. 1891. 8°.   11851. aaa. 8.

HUNT (T. W.) Studies in Literature and style.
pp. 303. N.Y. 1890. 8°.   011840. f. 69.

JORDAN (A.) Literature in relation to Science.
pp. 31. Hull, 1892. 8°.   011850. h. 14. (4.)

KARPELES (G.) Allgemeine Geschichte der Litteratur. Berl. 1891. 8°.   011840. m. 44.

LETOURNEAU (C. J. M.) L'Évolution littéraire dans les diverses races. pp. 574.   1894. 8°.
Bibliothèque Anthropologique. Tom. 15.
7004. de.

LOTHAR (R.) Kritische Studien zur Psychologie der Litteratur. pp. 318. Breslau, 1895. 8°.
011824. f. 69.

MACLAUGHLIN (E. T.) Studies in mediæval Literature. pp. 188. N.Y, 1894. 8°.
12354. de. 13.

MATTHEWS (J. B.) With my Friends. With introductory essay on the art of collaboration.
pp. 284. Lond. 1891. 8°.   012631. k. 52.

MOELLENDORFF (P. G. v.) Die Weltliteratur.
pp. 70. Schanghai, 1892. 8°.   Pam. 15.

MORLEY (Right Hon. J.) The study of Literature. 1894. 8°. London. Society for the Extension of University Teaching. Aspects of Modern Study.   8367. aa. 19.

PONCELIS (M.) Historia de la Literatura.
pp. 478. Buenos A., 1891. 8°.   011824. i. 12.

PRAT (P.) Histoire de la Littérature. pp. 308.
Paris, 1891. 12°.   011824. e. 43.

PUTNAM (G. H.) Authors and their public in ancient Times. pp. 309. N.Y. 1894. 8°.
011850. h. 30.

ROBERTSON (J. M.) Essays towards a critical Method. pp. 287. Lond. 1889. 8°. 011840. i. 13.

ROD (É.) De la Littérature comparée. Discours d'inauguration. pp. 43. Genève, 1886. 8°.
Pam. 15.

RUSSELL (P.) The Authors' manual. pp. 292.
Lond. 1891. 8°.   011824. de. 5.

LITERATURE.—General, etc.—_continued._

SCHOPENHAUER (A.) The Art of Literature.
pp. 149. _Lond._ 1891. 8°.   011840. i. 64.

STAPFER (P.) Des Réputations littéraires.
Paris, 1893, _etc._ 8°.   011850. f.

TEJERA (F.) Manual de Literatura. pp. 384.
Carácas, 1891. 8°.   011824. h. 61.

TIVIER (H.) Histoire des Littératures étrangères.
pp. 662. _Paris_, 1891. 12°.   011824. e. 13.

VICKERS (R. H.) Martyrdoms of Literature.
pp. 456. _Chicago_, 1892. 8°.   011824. h. 69.

WALSH (W. S.) Hand-Book of literary Curiosities. pp. 1104. _Lond._ 1893. 8°. 011824. f. 58.

WHEATLEY (H. B.) Literary Blunders. pp. 226.
1893. 8°. Book-Lover's Library.   11900. aa.

BLIXÉN (S.) Estudio compendiado de la Literatura contemporanea, 1789–93.
Montevideo, 1894, _etc._ 8°.   011850. i.

DUEHRING (E. C.) Die Grössen der modernen Literatur. _Leipz._ 1893, _etc._ 8°.   011850. i.

ELLIS (H. H.) The New Spirit. pp. 250.
1892. 8°. The Scott Library.   012208. ce.

GENER (P.) Literaturas malsanas. pp. 405.
Madrid, 1894. 8°.   011850. g. 56.

LYNCH (A.) Modern Authors. pp. 189.
Lond. 1891. 8°.   011824. e. 30.

STERN (A.) Studien zu Litteratur der Gegenwart. pp. 449. _Dresden_, 1895. 8°.
    011824. i. 43.

LITHOGRAPHY. _See_ ENGRAVING.

LITHUANIA. _See_ LETTS.

LITTONDALE. BOYD (W.) Littondale: past and present. pp. 155. _Leeds_, 1891. 8°.
    10358. dd. 23.

LITURGIOLOGY. Ac. London. _Henry Bradshaw Society._ Publications.
Lond. 1891, _etc._ 8°.   Ac. 9929.

BARRAL (A. de) Autour du Clocher: coutumes et fêtes chrétiennes. pp. 300.
Paris, 1893. 8°.   3478. bb. 2.

BATIFFOL (P.) Histoire du Bréviaire romain.
pp. 356. _Paris_, 1893. 8°.   3477. cc. 4.

BENUSSI (B.) La Liturgia slava nell' Istria.
1893. 8°. Ac. Parenzo. _Società Istriana._
Atti. Vol. 9.   Ac. 5230.

BERNARD (T.) Cours de Liturgie romaine.
2 tom. _Paris_, 1895. 8°.   3477. df. 9.

DIEUSOITBÉNI (J. J.) Rubricarum Breviarii, Missalis et Ritualis explanatio triplex.
Hongkong, 1892, _etc._ 8°.   3477. df.

GELASIUS I., _Saint, Pope._ Gelasian Sacramentary. Edited by H. A. Wilson. pp. 400.
Oxf. 1894. 8°.   3395. c. 35.

GUNNING (J. H.) Opmerkingen over het liturgische element in den Gereformeerden Cultus.
pp. 169. _Groningen_, 1890. 8°.   3925. k. 34.

KLINDA (T. J.) Vademecum Liturgicum, _etc._
pp. 344. _Budapestini_, 1892. 8°.   3477. df. 2.

LEGG (J. W.) Sacring of the English Kings.
pp. 17. _Lond._ 1894. 8°.   3477. e. 10.

LITURGIES. _Greek Church._ La Liturgie grecque.
pp. 52. _Paris_, 1894. 12°.   Pam. 75.

LOCKHART (W.) The Chasuble: its form and size. pp. 20. _Lond._ 1891. 8°.   3478. bbb. 39.

MAL'TSEV (A.) Die göttlichen Liturgieen Johannes Chrysostomos, Basilios des Grossen und Gregorios Dialogos. _Ger._ and _Slav._ pp. 568.
Berl. 1890. 8°.   3356. g. 22.

—— Die Liturgien der orthodoxkatholischen Kirche des Morgenlandes. pp. 344.
Berl. 1894. 8°.   3476. h. 24.

LITURGIOLOGY—_continued_

MARCEL (L.) Les Livres liturgiques du diocèse de Langres. pp. 354. _Paris_, 1892. 8°.
    4999. e. 25.

PROBST (F.) Die ältesten römischen Sacramentarien. pp. 412. _Münster_, 1892. 8°.
    3475. dd. 14.

—— Liturgie des vierten Jahrhunderts und deren Reform. pp. 472. _Münster_, 1893. 8°.
    3476. i. 1.

QUARITCH (B.) Sketch of Liturgical History and literature. pp. 68. 1887. 16°. LONDON.
Sette of Odd Volumes. Opuscula. No. 14.
    012202. ff.

QUENSEL (J. O.) Bidrag till Svenska Liturgiens historia. _Upsala_, 1890, _etc._ 8°.   3478. g.

REICHEL (O. J.) English Liturgical Vestments in the 13th century. pp. 63. _Lond._ 1895. 8°.
    Pam. 75.

RINALDI-BUCCI (P. J.) De Insignibus Episcoporum commentaria. pp. 74.
Ratisbonæ, 1891. 8°.   Pam. 75.

ROCK (D.) Hierurgia; or the Holy Sacrifice of the Mass. 2 vol. 1892. 8°. Catholic Standard Library.   3605. i.

ROSSI (F.) Erudizioni liturgiche, sopra le città ed altri nomi che si leggono nella Santa Messa, nei Salmi e nelle lezioni del Breviario romano.
pp. 307. _Torino_, 1891. 8°.   3475. de. 15.

SCHOBER (G.) Explanatio editionis Breviarii Romani quæ a Rituum Congregatione uti typica declarata est. pp. 364. _Ratisbonæ_, 1891. 8°.
    3477. c. 2.

THALHOFER (V.) Handbuch der katholischen Liturgik. _Freiburg_, 1883, _etc._ 8°.   3475. ff. 2.

WILSON (H. A.) Index to the Leonine, Gelasian and Gregorian Sacramentaries. pp. 102.
Camb. 1892. 8°.   3477. d. 4.

See also EUCHARIST: HYMNOLOGY.

For the Liturgiology of the Church of England, _see_ ENGLAND, _Church of, Prayer Book._

LIVER. BRISSAUD (É.) and TOUPET ( ) Sur la tuberculose du Foie. 1887. 8°. VERNEUIL (A. A.) Études sur la tuberculose. Tom. 1.
    7561. k. 1.

BURNETT (J. C.) Greater diseases of the Liver.
pp. 186. _Lond._ 1891. 8°.   7620. a. 15.

CAYLEY (H.) Tropical diseases of the Liver.
1893. 8°. DAVIDSON (A.) Hygiene of Warm Climates, _etc._   7686. dd. 2.

FAYRER (_Sir_ J.) Tropical Liver abscess.
1893. 8°. DAVIDSON (A.) Hygiene of Warm Climates, _etc._   7686. dd. 2.

GASTON (P.) Du Foie infectieux. pp. 267.
Paris, 1893. 8°.   7620. df. 36.

GLÉNARD (F.) De l'exploration bimanuelle du Foie par le "procédé du pouce." pp. 47.
Paris, 1892. 8°.   07305. k. 14. (8.)

HOLBROOK (M. L.) Liver Complaint. pp. 152.
Lond. 1892. 8°.   7620. df. 28.

LANGENBUCH (C.) Chirurgie der Leber.
1894, _etc._ 8°. BILLROTH (C. A. T.) Deutsche Chirurgie. Lief. 29 b.   7482. cc.

ROCKWELL (A. D.) Diseases of the alimentary Tract. 1894. 8°. BIGELOW (H. R.) International System of Electro-Therapeutics.   2024. e.

ROGER (G. H.) Physiologie du Foie. pp. 198.
1893. 8°. Encyclopédie des aide-mémoire.
    8709. g.

ROOSE (E. C. R.) Gout, and its relations to diseases of the Liver. pp. 229. _Lond._ 1894. 8°.
    7620. a. 19.

THOMAS (J. D.) Operative treatment of Hydatid Cysts of the Liver. pp. 112.
Melbourne, 1889. 8°.   7630. e. 17.

LIVER—*continued.*

WIRSING (E.) Akute, gelbe Leber. 1892. 8°.
Ac. Vienna. *Physikalisch-medicinische Gesell-
schaft.* Verhandlungen. N.F. Bd. 26. Nr. 3,
Ac. 3763/3

See also ABDOMEN : BILE : DIGESTION.

LIVERDUN. LANG (G.) Liverdun. 1893, *etc.*
8°. Ac. Nancy. *Société de Géographie.* Bulletin. Tom. 15. Ac. 6034.

LIVERPOOL. FARRIE (H. C.) "Toiling
Liverpool." pp. 97. *Liverp.* 1886. 12°.
08276. df. 9. (2.)

PEET (H.) Inventory of the Plate and other
moveables in the Parish Churches of Liverpool, a transcript of the earliest register,
1660–72. pp. 128. *Liverp.* 1893. 8°.
4707. cc. 13.

THOMPSON (J.) Liverpool and Neighbourhood in
Ye Olden Time. pp. 126. *Liverp.* 1894. 4°.
10358. f. 36.

WARD, LOCK AND Co. Guide to and history
of Liverpool. pp. 187. *Lond.* 1892. 8°.
10351. cc. 61.

P.P. *Liverpool.* University College Magazine.
Liverp. 1892, *etc.* 4°. 1179.

**LIVERPOOL AND MANCHESTER
RAILWAY.** *See* RAILWAYS.

LIVERWORT. *See* HEPATICAE.

LIVONIA. Ac. Riga. *Gesellschaft für Geschichte der Ostsee Provinzen.* Goldschmiedearbeiten in Livland. pp. 24. *Lübeck,* 1892. fol.
1811. a. 8.

KEUSSLER (F. v.) Das livische Dünagebiet und
die Fürsten von Polozk, Gercike und Kokenhusen. pp. 51. 1892. 8°. Ac. Riga. *Gesellschaft für Geschichte der Ostsee Provinzen.*
Mittheilungen. Bd. 15. Heft. 1. Ac. 7900.

Ac. Riga. *Gesellschaft für Geschichte der
Ostsee Provinzen.* Bodeckers Chronik livländ-
ischer Ereignisse, 1593–1638. pp. 158.
Riga, 1890. 8°. 9456. g. 6.

BIENEMANN (F.) Gustav Adolf und Livland.
pp. 26. *Riga,* 1894. 8°. Pam. 28.

SCHIEMANN (T.) Russland und Livland bis ins
17. Jahrhundert. 2 Bde. 1885–87. 8°. ONCKEN
(W.) Allgemeine Geschichte. Hauptabth. II.
Th. 10. 2068. (16.)

SERAPHIM (E.) Geschichte Liv-, Est- und
Kurlands bis zur Einverleibung in das
russische Reich. 2 Bde. *Reval,* 1895. 8°.
9456. de. 2.

D., K. v. Die konfessionellen Wirren in Livland
vom 1865 bis zur Gegenwart. pp. 97.
Leipz. 1891. 8°. 4695. cc. 38.

HARNACK (O.) Livland als Glied des deutschen
Reichs vom 13. bis 16. Jahrhundert pp. 28.
Berl. 1891. 8°. 9004. gg. 27. (8.)

HAUPT (C.) Anleitung zum Verständnis der
livianischen Darstellungsform. pp. 86.
Leipz. 1892. 8°. Pam. 14.

KIPARSKI (W.) Zur Verfassungsreformfrage in
Livland. pp. 48. *Riga,* 1891, 8°.
5756. bbb. 27. (4.)

LIVONIA, Commentar zu dem vierten Buch des
livländischen Privatrechts. *Riga,* 1889, *etc.* 8°.
5756. bbb. 21.

See also BALTIC PROVINCES : RIGA.

LIVORNO. MARTINI (P.) Diario livornese,
1849. pp. 468. *Livorno,* 1892. 8°. 9166. d. 30.

LIZARDS. Ac. London. *British Museum.*
Catalogue of Lizards in the British Museum.
3 vol. *Lond.* 1885, 87. 8°. 7207. c. 9.

LIZARDS—*continued.*

RITTER (W. E.) Parietal eye in some Lizards
from the Western U.S. 1891. 8°. Ac. Cambridge. *Harvard University Museum.* Bulletin.
Vol. 20. No. 8. Ac. 1736/2.
See also REPTILES.

LIZY-SUR-OURCQ. BENOIST (L.) Notice
sur Lizy-sur-Ourcq. pp. 264. *Meaux,* 1889. 8°.
10172. f. 5.

LLANELLY. LLANELLY-SOUVENIR. Permanent photographs. *Llanelly,* 1895. 4°.
10369. ccc. 35.

LLANGOLLEN. JONES (H.) Handbook
to Llangollen. pp. 66. *Llangollen,* 1880. 8°.
10368. aa. 52.

LLANTWIT MAJOR. FRYER (A. C.)
Llantwit Major. pp. 125. *Lond.* 1893. 8°.
010358. f. 48.

LLOYD'S EXCHANGE.
See INSURANCE, *Marine.*

LÖBAU. LIEK (G.) Die Stadt Löbau. pp. 640.
Marienwerder, 1892. 8°. 10255. h. 4.

LOBSTER. *See* CRUSTACEA.

LOCAL GOVERNMENT. SHAW (A.)
Municipal Government in Continental Europe.
pp. 505. *N.Y.* 1895. 8°. 8010. bbb. 5.

England and Wales.
General.

ARMINJON (P.) L'Administration locale de
l'Angleterre. pp. 345. *Paris,* 1895. 8°.
8139. ee. 1.

BLUNDEN (G. H.) Local Taxation and finance.
pp. 136. *Lond.* 1895. 8°. 08276. ee. 3.

CHAMBERS (G. F.) Handy Digest of cases
relating to Local Government. pp. 222.
Lond. 1893. 8°. 6426. e. 12.

EPHEM. The Local Government annual.
Lond. 1892, *etc.* 8°. P.P. 2486. baa.

GLEN (W. C.) and (A.) Law relating to Local
Government. 2 vol. *Lond.* 1895. 8°.
6426. dc. 24.

GRAHAM (J. C.) Local and imperial Taxation
and Local Government. pp. 104.
Lond. 1894. 8°. 8228. c. 53.

JENKS (E.) Outline of English Local Government. pp. 236. *Lond.* 1894. 8°. 6426. aaa. 23.

KNIGHT AND Co. Model byelaws of the Local
Government Board. pp. 253. *Lond.* 1893. 8°.
6425. e. 29.

SHAW (A.) Municipal Government in Great
Britain. pp. 385. *Lond.* 1895. 8°. 8139. d. 2.

VAUTHIER (M.) Le Gouvernement local de
l'Angleterre. pp. 446. *Paris,* 1895. 8°.
6426. e. 25.

WRIGHT (R. S.) and HOBHOUSE (H.) Outline
of Local Government. pp. 152. *Lond.* 1894. 8°.
6426. f. 6.

County Councils. (Local Government Acts,
1888-1894.)

BLES (A. E.) De Local Government Act, 1888.
pp. 139. *Leiden,* 1889. 8°. 6425. cc. 16.

CHILTON (J.) Reading between the lines of
Ritchie's Bill, 1891. pp. 16. *Lond.* 1892. 8°.
8139. bb. 47. (3.)

ENGLAND AND WALES. *Assoc. of County Councils.*
Acts of the session 53 & 54 Vict. of interest to
County Councils. pp. 32. *Preston,* 1890. 8°.
6426. cc.

—— Acts of the session 54 & 55 Vict., of interest
to County Councils. pp. 77. *Lond.* 1891. 8°.
6426. cc. 23.

—— Cases of interest to County Councils
decided, 1890. pp. 45. *Preston,* 1890. 8°.
6246. cc.

LOCAL GOVERNMENT. — England and Wales—*continued.*

ENGLAND AND WALES. *Assoc. of County Councils.* County Business. Replies to questions, *etc.* pp. 84. *Lond.* 1892. 8°.   6426. cc. 24.
—— *Local Government Board.* Legislation of 1892 affecting County Councils. pp. 6. 1893. fol.   6126. l. 1. (6.)
LLOYD (J. B.) "County Councillors." Summary of their Duties and powers under the Act, 1888. *Lond.* 1888. 8°.   6190. cc. 4. (2.)
PARKER (F. R.) Duties of County Councils under the Local Government Act, 1894. pp. 132. *Lond.* 1894. 8°.   6425. df. 23.
POORE ( ) The tendency towards centralisation in County Management. pp. 22. *Lond.* 1894. 8°.   8139. bb. 51. (19.)
URLIN (R. D.) County Council guide. pp. 132. *Lond.* 1891. 8°.   6426. aaaa. 11.
See also infra : Elections.
For the County Council of London, *see* LONDON : *Local Government.*

District and Parish Councils. (*Local Government Act,* 1894.)

ACCOUNTS. How to keep the accounts of a Parish Council. pp. 90. *Lond.* 1895. 4°.   8548. f. 25.
AKERMAN (P. B.) and FORD (P. H.) Parish Councils. Handbook to the Local Government Act, 1894. pp. 251. *Lond.* 1894. 8°.   6425. aa. 52.
BAKER (A. S.) *Lady.* Parish Problems. pp. 116. *Lond.* 1895. 8°.   08275. g. 2.
BENHAM (W. G.) The "Parish Councils Act," 1894. pp. 63. *Colchester,* 1894. 8°.   6145. aa. 36. (3.)
BOSANQUET (S. R. C.) Parish Parliaments. pp. 30. *Lond.* 1894. 8°.   6145. aa. 37. (4.)
CHAMBERS (G. F.) Summary of the law relating to Parish Councils. pp. 64. *Lond.* 1895. 8°.   6425. c. 34.
—— Digest of the law relating to District Councils. pp. 283. *Lond.* 1895. 8°. 6426. f. 4.
DAVIES (J. W.) Parish Councils Act. pp. 236. *Bristol,* 1894. 8°.   6426. aaaa. 32.
—— Parish Councils Act. Model of standing orders, *etc.* for Parish Councils. pp. 35. *Lond.* 1895. 16°.   6426. a. 3.
—— Model of standing orders, *etc.* for Boards of Guardians. pp. 36. *Lond.* 1895. 16°.   6426. aaaa. 28.
—— Model of standing orders, *etc.* for Urban District Councils. pp. 37. *Lond.* 1895. 16°.   6426. a. 59.
—— Model of standing orders, *etc.* for Rural District Councils. pp. 36. *Lond.* 1895. 16°.   6426. aaaa. 27.
DODD (J. T.) Parish Councils Act explained. pp. 324. *Lond.* 1894. 8°.   6426. cc. 38.
—— The first Parish Meeting under the Parish Councils Act. pp. 78. *Lond.* 1894. 8°.   6425. de. 28.
—— Guide for rural District Councillors and Guardians. pp. 104. *Lond.* 1894. 8°.   6425. de. 29.
ELECTOR. Practical points on the future self-government of towns. pp. 16. *Lond.* 1894. 8°.   8282. ff. 12. (10.)
EMERY (G. F.) Guide to the Parish and District Councils Act. 2 pt. *Lond.* 1894. 8°. 6426. e. 22.
—— Handbook for Parish Councils. pp. 153. *Lond.* 1895. 8°.   6426. aaaa. 41.
—— People's guide for Urban Districts. pp. 32. *Lond.* 1894. 16°.   Pam. 32.
—— People's guide to the Parish Councils Act in Rural Parishes. pp. 31. *Lond.* 1895. 16°.   Pam. 32.

LOCAL GOVERNMENT. — England and Wales—*continued.*

ENGLAND. Re-making of rural England, and relation of Nonconformist churches to the Parish Councils Act, 1894. pp. 8. *Lond.* 1894. 8°.   4139. dd. 2. (14.)
FITZGERALD (J. V. V.) Local Government Act, 1894. pp. 320. *Lond.* 1894. 8°. 6426. de. 23.
FOWLER (*Right Hon.* H. H.) Parish and District Councils Bill. Speech. pp. 20. *Westminster,* 1893. 8°.   8139. bb. 47. (17.)
FREEMAN (A. C.) and (J. C.) Manual of the Local Government Act, 1894. pp. 93. *Lond.* 1894. 8°.   6426. ce. 2.
GLEN (W. C.) and (A.) Law relating to Local Government, including the Local Government Act, 1894. 2 vol. *Lond.* 1895. 8°. 6426. de. 24.
GOODSHIP (E.) Summary of the Local Government Act, 1894. pp. 8. *Lond.* 1894. 8°.   6146. bbb. 26 (6.)
GRAHAM (A. H.) and BRODHURST (S.) Guide to the Parish Councils Act, 1894. pp. 203. *Lond.* 1894. 8°.   6425. a. 58.
G. B. & I. Local Government Act, 1894. pp. 44. *Lond.* 1894. 8°. 6146. bbb. 26. (7.)
—— Parish Meetings. Parish Councils. District Councils. pp. 8. *Liverpool,* 1894. 8°.   6145. aa. 37. (6.)
—— Abstract of the Parish Councils Bill. pp. 32. *Manch.* 1894. 8°. 6145. aa. 37. (5.)
HADDEN ( ) Handbook on the Local Government Act, 1894. pp. 466. *Lond.* 1894. 8°.   6426. e. 15.
HUMPHREYS (G.) Law relating to Parish Councils. pp. 414. *Lond.* 1895. 8°.   6426. f. 2.
JENKIN (A. F.) Law relating to Parish Councils. pp. 636. *Lond.* 1895. 8°.   6425. aaaa. 15.
KENT (W. R.) Extracts from Local Government Act, 1894. pp. 8. *Frome,* 1894. 8°.   6146. bbb. 26. (8.)
KNIGHT (W. S. M.) Practical Parish Politics. pp. 16. *Lond.* 1894. 8°.   8282. ff. 12. (13.)
LEACH (C. H.) Parish Councils : paper on the provisions of the Act, 1894, affecting rural parishes. pp. 27. *Lond.* 1894. 8°.   6146. bbb. 26. (9.)
LITHIBY (J.) Law of District and Parish Councils. pp. 515. *Lond.* 1894. 8°.   6426. e. 16.
MACMORRAN (A.) and DILL (T. R. C.) Local Government Act, 1894. pp. 698. *Lond.* 1894. 8°.   6425. aaaa. 7.
MILLER (H. E.) Parish and District Councils and London vestries. pp. 27. *Lond.* 1894. fol.   6125. l. 3. (6.)
MOENS (W. J. C.) Guide to the Parish Councils Act. pp. 23. *Lymington,* 1894. 8°.   6146. bbb 26. (10.)
MORRISON (J. D.) The Villagers' Magna Charta. pp. 50. 1894. 16°. Bijou Library. No. 4.   12200. ee. 7.
MOTHERSOLE (H. B. N.) The Parish Councils guide. pp. 279. *Lond.* 1894. 8°. 6426. e. 19.
NASH (H. F.) and ALLPORT (J. S.) Parish Councils and Meetings. How to keep minutes, *etc.* pp. 120. *Lond.* 1895. 8°. 6426. aaaa. 31.
PARKER (F. R.) The Parish Councillor. pp. 236. *Lond.* 1895. 8°.   6425. aaaa. **12.**
RICHARDS (H. C.) Parish Councillor's guide to the Act, 1894. pp. 314. *Lond.* 1895. 8°.   6425. aaaa. **17.**
ROUNDELL (C. S.) Parish Councils. "The Villages for the Villagers." pp. 46. *Lond.* 1894. 8°.   6146. bbb. 26. (11.)
RYDE (W. C.) Local Government Act, 1894. pp. 288. *Lond.* 1894. 8°.   6126. cc. 36.

LOCAL GOVERNMENT. — England and Wales—*continued*.

SELLERS (W. E.) Our Village Parliament. Summary of the Act, and its relations to the Methodist people. pp. 32. *Lond.* 1894. 8°.
6145. aa. 37. (8.)

SMITH (R.) Making of the Parish and District Councils. pp. 31. *Haverhill*, 1894. 8°.
6145 aa. 37. (9.)

SOLICITOR. The Local Government Extension Bill. pp. 16. *Exeter*, 1893. 8°. 6190. cc. 3. (19.)

STEPHENS (H. C.) Parochial self-government in Rural Districts. pp. 270. *Lond.* 1893. 8°.
8277. de. 48.

STONE (J. H.) and PEASE (J. G.) Ready reference guide to Parish Councils and Meetings. pp. 201. *Lond.* 1894. 8°.   6426. aaaa. 21.

SYERS (H. S.) Local Government Act, 1894, as it affects the Church's interests. pp. 64. *Lond.* 1894. 8°.   6426. cc. 6.

See also PAUPERISM.

Elections, County, District and Parish Councils.

BLAIR (P. J.) A Manual for Parliamentary and County Council Elections. pp. 495. *Edinb.* 1893. 8°.   6583. f. 24.

LUSHINGTON (S. G.) County Council and Municipal Election manual. pp. 243. *Lond.* 1892. 12°.   6426. aaaa. 8.

NASH (H. F.) and ALLPORT (J. S.) Duties of Overseers and Agents and liabilities of Candidates under the Act, 1894. pp. 82 *Ipswich*, 1894. 8°.   6425. aaaa. 3.

PARKER (F. R.) Election of County Councils under the Act, 1888. pp. 422. *Lond.* 1892. 8°.   6325. df. 16.

DILL (T. R. C.) Guardians' and District Councillors' Election manual. pp. 306. *Lond.* 1894. 8°.   6425. aaaa. 8.

—— Parish Councils Election manual. pp. 189. *Lond.* 1894. 8°.   6425. de. 31.

PARKER (F. R.) Election of Guardians and District Councillors under the Act, 1894, *etc.* pp. 499. *Lond.* 1894. 8°.   6425. aaaa. 13

—— Election of Parish Councils under the Act, 1894. pp. 280. *Lond.* 1894. 8°.   6426. e. 18.

RYDE (W. C.) Election manual for Parish Councillors and Guardians. pp. 340. *Lond.* 1894. 8°.   6426. c. 20.

STONE (J. H.) and PEASE (J. G.) Ready reference guide to the Election of Parish and Rural District Councillors. pp. 84. *Lond.* 1894. 8°.
6426. aaaa. 23.

See also PARISHES : PAUPERISM : SANITATION : TOWNS.

France.

BABEAU (A.) La Province sous l'ancien Régime. 2 tom. *Paris*, 1894. 8°.   9231. g. 25.

CHARLES-ROUX (J.) Vingt Ans de vie publique. pp. 836. *Paris*, 1892. 8°.   9231. h. 13.

FRANCESCHI (G.) Manuel municipal. Commentaire de la Loi du 5 avril 1884. pp. 400. *Paris*, 1892. 8°.   5424. b. 16.

HENRIET (M.) Guide du Maire, officier de l'état civil. pp. 463. *Paris*, 1891. 8°.   5423. e. 17.

MONIO (D.) La République et ses représentants. Le Maire. pp. 81. *La Ferté-Macé*, 1893. 16°.
Pam. 69.

STRAUSS (R. R.) Administration départementale. Du Chef du Cabinet. pp. 98. *Valence*, 1891. 8°.
8006. aaa. 10.

THORLET (L.) Traité des Travaux communaux, à l'usage des maires. pp. 417. *Paris*, 1894. 8°.
5406. d. 1.

LOCAL GOVERNMENT—*continued*.

Germany.

BENZ (R. v.) Autonomie und Centralismus in der Gemeinde. pp. 56. *Innsbruck*, 1895. 8°.
Pam. 72.

BLODIG (H.) Die Selbstverwaltung als Rechtsbegriff. pp. 400. *Wien*, 1894. 8°.   6006. k. 4

PRUSSIA. Die Landgemeindeordnung für die östlichen Provinzen der Monarchie vom 3 Juli 1891. pp. 277. *Berl.* 1892. 8°.   5606. aaa. 15.

India.

NANDALĀLA SARKĀR. Extension of local Self-Government in Bengal. pp. 24. *Calcutta*, 1892. 8°.   Pam. 67.

WILSON (J.) Local Self-government in India. pp. 31. *Calcutta*, 1890. 8°.   8023. ee. 26. (10.)

Netherlands.

HARTMAN (H. G.) Bestuur en administratie der Gemeenten in Nederland. *'s Gravenh.* 1891, *etc.* 8°.   5685. f.

Scotland.

DONALDSON (J.) Local Government (Scotland) Act, 1894. pp. 95. *Glasg.* 1895. 8°.
6583. cc. 10.

MACDOUGALL (J. P.) and DODDS (J. M.) Parish Council guide for Scotland. pp. 174. *Edinb.* 1894. 8°.   6583. a. 7.

MUIRHEAD (J.) Byelaws and standing orders for Burghs in Scotland. pp. 284. *Glasg.* 1895. 8°.
6583. g. 17.

P.P. Edinburgh. Guide to Local Government in counties and burghs. *Edinb.* 1892, *etc.* 8°.
6583. aaa. 9.

SHENNAN (H.) Parish Councillor's Handbook. With the text of the Act, *etc.* pp. 66. *Edinb.* 1894 8°.   6425. de. 26.

United States of America. *See* TOWNS.

LOCAL OPTION.
See LICENSING LAWS : TEMPERANCE.

LOCARNO. RAHN (J. R.) Die Casa di ferro bei Locarno. pp. 26. 1891. 4°. Ac. Zurich. *Gesellschaft für Erforschung vaterländischer Alterthümer.* Mittheilungen. Bd. 23.   Ac. 5367.

LOCH LOMOND. LUMSDEN (J.) Guide to the natural history of Loch Lomond. pp. 103. *Glasg.* 1895. 8°.   7208. cc. 1.

LOCKJAW. *See* TETANUS.

LOCKSMITH'S WORK. *See* IRONWORK.

LOCOMOTION. *See* MOTION.

LOCOMOTIVE ENGINES.
See MACHINERY.

LOCOMOTOR ATAXIA. BLOCQ (P.) Les troubles de la Marche dans les maladies nerveuses. *Paris*, 1893. 8°.   7630. aaa. 37.

BURGER (H.) Die laryngealen Störungen der Tabes Dorsalis. pp. 166. *Leiden*, 1891. 8°.
7630. g. 20.

See also NERVES : SPINE.

LOCUST: LOCUSTIDAE.
See ORTHOPTERA.

LODGERS, Law of.
See LANDLORD AND TENANT.

LOFER. RESKA (L.) Führer durch Lofer. pp. 72. 1888. 8°. Wiener Touristen-Führer Hft. 24.   P.P. 2435. h.

LOGARITHMS. BORLETTI (F.) Celerimensura e tavole logaritmiche a 4 decimali. pp. 145. *Milano*, 1893. 8°.   8548. aaa. 36.

GONZAGA GASCÓ (L.) Tablas de Logaritmos. pp. 174. *Valencia*, 1890. 8°.   8548. b. 31.

LOGARITHMS—*continued.*

GUNDELFINGER (S.) and NELL (A. M.) Tafeln zur Berechnung neunstelliger Logarithmen. pp. 60. *Darmstadt*, 1891. 8°.　　Pam. 38.

HANNYNGTON (J. C.) Table of Logarithms and Anti-Logarithms. Four figures. pp. 41. *Lond.* 1880. 8°.　　8548. de. 14.

JONES (G. W.) Logarithmic Tables. pp. 160. *Lond.* 1893. 8°.　　8548. df. 29.

JORDAN (W.) Logarithmisch-trigonometrische Tafeln mit sechs Decimalstellen. pp. 420. *Stuttgart*, 1894. 8°.　　8535. h. 29.

KLEYER (A.) Fünfstellige korrekte logarithmische Tafeln. pp. 142. 1886. 8°. Kleyer's Encyklopädie.　　8705. g.

—— Lehrbuch der Logarithmen. 1884. 8°. Kleyer's Encyklopädie.　　8705. g.

LARSEN (S.) Trigonometrisk Logaritmetabel. pp. 64. *Kjøbenh.* 1891. g°.　　8548. cc. 3.

LONGE (A.) Bremiker's tables of Logarithms. *Lond.* 1887. 8°.　　8533. d. 27. (2.)

MACDONALD (W. R.) Notes on the theory of Logarithms. pp. 48. *Edinb.* 1885. 8°. 8535. d. 25.

MENDIZABAL TAMBORREL (J. de) Tables des Logarithmes à huit décimales. *Paris*, 1891. 4°.　　8548. h. 4.

MUELLER (E. R.) Vierstellige logarithmische Tafeln. pp. 32. 1892. 8°. Kleyers Encyclopädie.　　8705. g.

SEIFFERT (O.) Logarithmische Hilfstafel zur Berechnung der Fehlergleichungs-Koeffizienten. pp. 19. *Halle*, 1892. 8°.　　8548. e. 31.

WILSON (W. N.) Manual of Logarithms. pp. 120. *Lond.* 1894. 8°.　　8535. de. 14.

LOGIC. BAKER (A.) Outlines of Logic. pp. 161. *Lond.* 1891. 8°.　　8462. b. 21.

BENZONI (R.) L' Induzione. *Genova*, 1894, *etc.* 8°.　　8462. dd.

BOSANQUET (B.) Essentials of Logic. pp. 167. *Lond.* 1895. 8°.　　8462. bb. 42.

CALDI (G.) Metodologia della Interpretazione scientifica. *Torino*, 1893, *etc.* 8°. 8168. k. 22.

CARTWRIGHT (T.) Mental Science and Logic for teachers. pp. 194. *Lond.* 1892. 8°. 8462. b. 23.

CHAMORRO (E. R.) Psicologia y Logica. pp. 317. *Madrid*, 1890. 8°.　　8469. bbb. 50.

COPPENS (C.) Brief text-book of Logic. 2 pt. *N.Y.* 1892. 8°.　　8462. b. 28.

DIETZGEN (J.) Das Acquisit der Philosophie und Briefe über Logik. pp. 231. *Stuttgart*, 1895. 8°.　　8464. b. 40.

DIXON (E. T.) Essay on Reasoning. pp. 88. *Camb.* 1891. 8°.　　8470 f. 20.

ERDMANN (B.) Logik. *Halle*, 1892, *etc.* 8°.　　8470. g. 3.

FOWLER (T.) Logic, deductive and inductive. 2 pt. 1895. 8°. Clarendon Press Series.　　2319. aa. 19.

GIZZI (G. G.) La Logica negli uomini e negli animali. pp. 165. *Roma*, 1892. 8°. 8462. bb. 35.

GRASSMANN (R.) Die Denklehre oder die Lehre von den Arten der wissenschaftlichen Denkakte. pp. 531. *Stettin*, 1890. 8°.　　8533. i. 32.

—— Formelbuch der Denklehre. pp. 50. *Stettin*, 1890. 8?.　　8533. i. 31.

HAMILTON (E. J.) The Modalist, or, laws of rational conviction. pp. 331. *Bost.* 1891. 8°.　　8470. f. 19.

BOURDILLAT (F.) La Réforme logique de Hamilton. pp. 81. *Paris*, 1890. 8°. 8462. b. 20.

HEGEL (G. W. F.) The Logic of Hegel. Translated by W. Wallace. 2 vol. *Oxf.* 1892–94. 8°.　　2023. c.

LOGIC—*continued.*

HARRIS (W. T.) Hegel's Logic. A critical exposition. pp. 403. *Chicago*, 1890. 8°.　　8462. aaa. 24.

HILLEBRAND (F.) Die neuen Theorien der categorischen Schlüsse. pp. 102. *Wien*, 1891. 8°.　　8467. ff. 41.

HOLMAN (H.) Questions on Logic. 1891, *etc.* 8°. Tutorial Series.　　12205. c. 64.

HUGHES (H.) The Theory of Inference. pp. 256. *Lond.* 1894. 8°.　　8462. g. 30.

JONES (E. E. C.) Introduction to general Logic. pp. 283. *Lond.* 1892. 8°.　　8467. bb. 35.

JOUIN (L.) Compendium Logicae. pp. 302. *Neo-Eboraci*, 1884. 1°.　　8466. e. 25.

KANT (I.) Kants Kritik of Judgment. Translated by J. H. Bernard. pp. 429. *Lond.* 1892. 8°.　　8462. f. 6.

KEYNES (J. N.) Studies and exercises in formal Logic. pp. 476. *Lond.* 1894. 8°.　　2234. a. 20.

KROMAN (K.) Kurzgefasste Logik. pp. 389. *Kopenhagen*, 1890. 8°.　　8469. d. 29.

LANGE (F. A.) Logische Studien. pp. 149. *Leipz.* 1894. 8°.　　8462. e. 39.

LUTOSLAWSKI (W.) Logika Platona I.—Sur la logique de Platon. *Cracovie*, 1890. 8°. Pam. 49.

MAC LACHLAN (D. B.) Reformed Logic. pp. 233. *Lond.* 1892. 8°.　　8462. b. 25.

MILL (J. S.) System of Logic. pp. 671. 1892. 8°. Sir J. Lubbock's Hundred Books. No. 15.　　012207. l. 15.

MINTO (W.) Logic inductive and deductive. pp. 373. 1893. 8°. KNIGHT (W.) Dublin University Press Series.　　12204. f.

MONCK (W. H. S.) Introduction to Logic. pp. 258. 1890. 8°. Dublin University Press Series.　　2322. e.

NAGY (A.) Principi di Logica. pp 219. *Torino*, 1891. 8°.　　8464. b. 39.

OXFORD HANDBOOK. Oxford handbook of Logic. pp. 83. *Oxf.* 1893. 8°.　　8463. bb. 29.

PAGNANI (C.) *R.C. Bp. of Kandy.* First notions of Logic. pp. 272. *Colombo*, 1891. 8°.　　8470. ccc. 17.

POLAND (W.) Rational Philosophy. The laws of thought. pp. 104. *Bost.* 1892. 8°.　　8470. ccc. 14.

RAAB (F.) Wesen und Systematik der Schlussformen. pp. 52. *Wien*, 1891. 8°.　　Pam. 49.

SCHUPPE (W.) Grundriss der Erkenntnistheorie und Logik. pp. 186. *Berl.* 1894. 8°.　　8463. f. 34.

SIDGWICK (A.) The Process of argument. pp. 235. *Lond.* 1893. 8°.　　8462. b. 32.

SIGWART (C.) Logic. Translated by H. Dendy. 2 vol. 1895. 8°. MUIRHEAD (J. H.) Library of Philosophy.　　2023. f.

SPINOZA (B. de) Tractatus de Intellectus Emendatione. Translated by W. H. White. pp. 62. *Lond.* 1895. 8°.　　8462. h. 14.

WELTON (J) Manual of Logic. 1891, *etc.* 8°. Tutorial Series.　　12205. e.

VENN (J.) Symbolic Logic. pp. 540. *Lond.* 1894. 8°.　　8462. b. 39.

LOIRE, HAUTE, Department. *See* HAUTE LOIRE.

LOIRE, River. FRÉMY (L.) Société pour l'éxécution d'une voie entre Nantes et Orléans. Exposé de la situation de la Loire. pp. 12. *Nantes*, 1894. fol.　　Pam. 76.

JOANNE (P.) Itinéraire de la France. La Loire. pp. 39. 314. *Paris*, 1894. 8°.　　2362. a.

LOIRE, River—*continued.*

LEDIEU (A.) La vallée du Liger. 1887. 8°. Ac. Abbeville. *Société d'Émulation.* Mémoires Sér. 3. Vol. 4.   Ac. 230.

LOMBARDS: LOMBARDY. CALLIGARIS (G.) Di un nuovo manoscritto della Historia Langobardorum di Paolo Diacono. 1891. 8°. Ac. Rome. *Istituto Storico.* Bullettino. No. 10.   Ac. 6543/2.

HODGKIN (T.) Italy and her Invaders. Vols. 5 & 6. *Oxford*, 1895. 8°.   2068. c.

HORTZSCHANSKY (A.) and PERLBACH (M.) Lombardische Urkunden des elften Jahrhunderts. pp. 98. *Halle*, 1890. 8°.   9167. k. 20.

LOMBARDS. Consuetudines feudorum. Edidit C. Lehmann. *Gottingae*, 1892, *etc.* 4°.   5309. e.

SEREGNI (G.) La popolazione agricola della Lombardia nell' età barbarica. pp. 77. 1895. 8°. Ac. Milan. *Società Storica.* Archivio. Ser. 3. Vol. 3.   Ac. 6525.

BREYTON (A.) Remarques sur les causes qui ont facilité la Conquête franque en Lombardie. pp. 31. 1890. 8°. Ac. Lyons. *Faculté des Lettres.* Bibliothèque. Tom. 7.   Ac. 8922/2.

PITON (C.) Les Lombards en France. pp. 259. *Paris*, 1892. 8°.   8248. g. 14.

ROSA (G.) Tradizioni e costumi lombardi. pp. 107. *Bergamo*, 1891. 4°.   12431. l. 2. *See also* ITALY, *History.*

LONDON.

General: History: Guide-Books.

Ac. G. B. & I. *Archæological Institute.* Catalogue of drawings of Old London. pp. 44. *Lond.* 1893. 16°.   10350. aa. 45.

—— London. *Archæological Society.* OGILVY (J.) and MORGAN (W.) Map of the City of London, 1677. Edited by C. Welch. *Lond.* 1895. fol. & 8°.   S. 235. (13.)

ADAMS (W. H. D.) Book about London. pp. 350. *Lond.* 1890. 8°.   10349. d. 16.

—— Book about London : streets of London. pp. 224. *Lond.* 1890. 8°.   10349. d. 17.

AINSCOUGH (J. A.) London of the past. pp. 63. *Lond.* 1890. 8°.   10350. cc. 36.

ARABIA Y SOLANAS (R.) Una excursió á Londres. pp. 102. *Barcelona*, 1894. 4°.   10350. de. 31.

BANFIELD (F.) Great landlords of London. pp. 160. *Lond.* 1890. 8°.   08275. e. 11.

BECKER (C. J.) Souvenir of London. Facsimiles of water-colours. *Lond.* 1891. 8°. 10350. g. 10.

BESANT (*Sir* W.) History of London. pp. 256. *Lond.* 1893. 8°.   10350. aaa. 8.

—— London. pp. 343. *Lond.* 1894. 8°.   10348. ff. 37.

BOOTH (C.) Life and Labour of the people in London. 4 vol. *Lond.* 1889-93. 2240. bb. 22.

CHURCHER (J. G.) The old City Londiniensis. pp. 149. *Lond.* 1895. 8°.   10350. bb. 50.

CLODE (C. M.) London during the Great Rebellion. Memoir of Sir A. Reynardson. pp. 79. *Lond.* 1892. 8°.   10825. f. 31.

COMO. Midnight London ! pp. 61. *Lond.* 1894. 8°.   Pam. 82.

CONSTAPLE (H.) London after dark. pp. 80. *Lond.* 1894. 8°.   Pam. 82.

CORNMAN (F.) London shope signes, *etc.* of the XVI.-XVII. & XVIIIth centuries. 2 ser. *Lond.* 1891-94. 4°.   7709 e. 14.

DIBDIN (M. A.) Footprints of the past. Within a walk of the British Museum. pp. 127. *Lond.* 1892. 8°.   4429. de. 25.

DILKE (*Sir* C. W.) Londres. 1892. 8°. Les Capitales du Monde. No. 16.   10025. g.

LONDON.—General, etc.—*continued.*

DOWLING (R.) While London sleeps. pp. 188. *Lond.* 1895. 8°.   012330. f. 87.

DULCKEN (H. W.) Pictures of London. *Lond.* 1892. 8°.   10349. gg. 21.

HARE (A. J. C.) Walks in London. 2 vol. *Lond.* 1894. 8°.   2366. b. 3.

HENLEY (W. E.) A London Garland. English verse. pp. 203. *Lond.* 1895. 8°.   K.T.C. 11. b. 16.

HUTTON (L.) Literary landmarks of London. pp. 367. *Lond.* 1892. 8°.   10349. d. 23.

JOIN-LAMBERT (A.) Londres et les Anglais en 1771. pp. 50. *Paris*, 1890. 8°. 10349. gg. 20.

KEMMANN (G.) Der Verkehr Londons mit Berücksichtigung der Eisenbahnen. pp. 197. *Berl.* 1892. fol.   1802. b. 11.

KITTON (F. G.) Artistic London. pp. 19. *Lond.* 1891. 16°.   10348. aa. 9. (4.)

LOFTIE (W. J.) London City. pp. 377. *Lond.* 1891. 4°.   10350. h. 20.

LONDON. London past and present. pp. 274. *Lond.* 1894. 8°.   10350. bb. 42.

—— Photographic Views of London. pp. 142. *Lond.* 1895. *obl.* 8°.   10349. a. 37.

—— Social Centres of London. pp. 173. *Lond.* 1892. 8°.   08275. e. 14.

—— The Queen's London. Record of the great Metropolis in the fifty-ninth year of Queen Victoria. *Lond.* 1895, *etc.* obl. fol. 1787. aa. 16.

NORMAN (P.) London Signs and inscriptions. pp. 237. 1893. 8°. GOMME (G. L.) Camden Library.   7709. cc.

OLIVER (E.) The Romance of London. pp. 62. *Lond.* 1895. 8°.   10349. gg. 23.

PAUL (R. W.) Vanishing London : drawings of old houses, *etc.* pp. 24. *Lond.* 1894. 4°.   10349. k. 2.

P.P. *London.* London and Middlesex Notebook. *Lond.* 1891, *etc.* 8°.   P.P. 1925. dg.

ROSS (F.) Bygone London. pp. 292. *Lond.* 1892. 8°.   010358. i. 5.

SALA (G. A.) London up to date. pp. 378. *Lond.* 1894. 8°.   012330. g. 63.

STEFFEN (G. F.) In der Fünfmillionen-Stadt. pp. 387. *Leipz.* 1895. 8°.   010350. ee. 3.

STOW (J.) Survey of London. Edited by H. Morley. pp. 446. *Lond.* 1893. 8°.   10350. de 24.

THORNBURY (G. W.) Old and New London. 6 vol. *Lond.* 1887-93. 8°.   2065. d.

THORNTON (B.) Comparative climatology of London, *etc.* pp. 15. *Lond.* 1891. 8°.   7686. b. 7.

VALERA (P.) Londra sconosciuta. pp. 271. *Milano*, 1890. 8°.   10349. cc. 16.

VREDENBURG (E.) The sights of London. *Lond.* 1891. *obl.* fol.   1876. b. 12.

WILLIAMS (M. S.) Round London. pp. 387. *Lond.* 1892. 8°.   012357. l. 1.

PIGOTT (T. D.) London Birds and Insects. pp. 168. *Lond.* 1892. 8°.   7206. cc. 6.

SWANN (H. K.) The Birds of London. pp. 136. *Lond.* 1893. 8°.   7285. b. 5.

VALENTINE (J. T. T.) London Birds and Beasts. pp. 319. *Lond.* 1895. 8°.   7206. bb. 20.

BAEDEKER (C.) London and Environs. pp. 375. 44. *Leipsic*, 1894. 8°.   2352. a.

BLACK (A.) and (C.) Guide to London. pp. 372. *Lond.* 1891. 8°.   2366. a. 1.

COOK (T.) Handbook for London. pp. 118. *Lond.* 1895. 8°.   10350. bb. 51.

LONDON.—General, etc.—*continued.*

GOSDEN (W.) Langham Hotel Guide to London. pp. 31. 321. *Lond.* 1895. 8°.   10349. a. 30.

LONDON. Metropolitan London Guide. pp. 80. *Lond.* 1893. 24°.   10349. a. 35. (3.)

—— District Railway Guide to London. pp. 147. *Lond.* 1888. 4°.   10350. de. 19.

—— " Tit Bits " guide to London. pp. 140. *Lond.* 1895. 8°.   10350. aaa. 54.

—— Handbook to London, in English and French. pp. 243. *Lond.* 1891. 8°.   10349. d. 19.

—— Guide-Joanne. Londres. pp. 380. *Paris,* 1892. 8°.   10349. a. 23.

PASCOE (C. E.) London in little. pp. 90. *Lond.* 1891. 8°.   10360. a. 13.

LONDON. *Commissioners of Police.* Hackney Carriages. Tables of distances. pp. 727. *Lond.* 1888. *obl.* 8°.   10350. aa. 39.

—— Book of London Cab fares, *etc.* pp. 48. *Lond.* 1895. 24°.   Pam. 90.

Art Galleries. *See* EXHIBITIONS.

Bridges.

Ac. London. *New Shakspere Society.* Old London Bridge about 1600. *Lond.* 1881. 4°.   1757. d. (68.)

LONDON. The Tower Bridge. pp. 14. 1894. 8°. P.P. London. *Westminster Gazette.* Westminster " Populars."   N.R.

TUIT (J. E.) The Tower Bridge. pp. 106. *Lond.* 1894. 4°.   10349. i. 17.

WELCH (C.) History of the Tower Bridge and other bridges built by the Corporation. pp. 284. *Lond.* 1894. 4°.   10349. i. 18.

—— Short account of the Tower Bridge. pp. 61. *Lond.* 1894. 8°.   10350. bb. 44.

Building Laws of London. *See* BUILDING.

Churches.

GILBERTSON (L.) Notes on the fabric of the Cathedral of St. Paul, London. pp. 46. 1893. 8°. Kyrle Pamphlets. No. 1. 12204. f.

PAUL, *Saint, Cathedral of.* St. Paul's Cathedral in the time of Edward VI. Edited by J. O. Payne. pp. 30. *Lond.* 1893. 8°. 0002. ccc. 10.

—— Guide to St. Paul's Cathedral. pp. 63. *Lond.* 1892. 8°.   10349. aa. 37. (8.)

SIMPSON (W. S.) St. Paul's Cathedral from the 13th to the 16th centuries. pp. 312. *Lond.* 1894.. 8°.   4707. c. 27.

—— St. Paul's Cathedral. Views. With descriptive notes. *Lond.* 1895. *obl.* fol. 1732. a. 8.

—— Visitations of churches belonging to St. Paul's, 1249-1252. pp. 38. 1895. 4°. Ac. London. *Camden Society.* Camden Miscellany. Vol. 9.   Ac. 8113/39.

WELCH (C.) St. Paul's Cathedral and its literary associations. pp. 40. *Lond.* 1892. 8°.   011900. ee. 5. (17.)

MARSH (J. B.) St. Paul's Cross. pp. 103. *Lond.* 1892. 4°.   10349. f. 13.

BESANT (*Sir* W.) Westminster. pp. 312. *Lond.* 1895. 8°.   010350. i. 5.

BRADLEY, afterwards MURRAY SMITH (E. L.) Annals of Westminster Abbey. pp. 400. *Lond.* 1895. 4°.   K.T.C. 33. b. 2.

DOLAN (G.) Westminster Abbey. pp. 44. *Lond.* 1894. 8°.   10348. c. 25. (9.)

HARE (A. J. C.) Westminster. pp. 120. *Lond.* 1894. 8°.   10350. aa. 44.

KING (H. N.) A Walk through Westminster Abbey. [pp. 24. *Lond.* 1891. 8°.   10348. d. 19. (14.)

LONDON.—Churches—*continued.*

LOFTIE (W. J.) Brief account of Westminster Abbey. pp. 150. *Lond.* 1894. 8°. 4707. aaaa. 31.

LONDON. *Society for the Protection of Ancient Buildings.* Concerning Westminster Abbey. pp. 14. *Lond.* 1894. 8°.   7808. df. 16. (6.)

WESTMINSTER ABBEY. Inventory of the vestry in Westminster Abbey, 1388. pp. 92. *Westminster,* 1890. 4°   3477. e. 7.

DANIELL (A. E.) London City Churches. pp. 394. *Lond.* 1895. 8°.   07816. ee. 4.

UNDERHILL (J.) St. John's, Clerkenwell. pp. 12. *Lond* 1895. fol.   K.T.C. 16. a. 3.

WATNEY (J.) Account of the Hospital of St. Thomas of Acon, in the Cheap. pp. 308. *Lond.* 1892. 4°.   4705. g. 25.

HAWKINS (E. C.) The Church of St. Bride, Fleet St., *etc.* pp. 30. *Lond.* 1884. 8°. Pam. 90.

JOHN, *the Baptist, Saint, Priory of.* Guide to the Priory and Church of St. John, Clerkenwell. pp. 12. *Lond.* 1894. 8°.   Pam. 90.

CRICHTON (L.) and (P.) Antique church plate of St. Mary Abbots, Kensington. pp. 16. *Lond.* 1892. 8°.   Pam. 3.

BAYLIS (T. H.) The Temple Church. pp. 155. *Lond.* 1895. 16°.   4705. aa. 43.

WHITWORTH (W. A.) Quam Dilecta : description of All Saints' Margaret Street. pp. 198. *Lond.* 1891. 8°.   4707. aaa. 36.

THOMPSON (W.) History of the Church of St. Saviour, Southwark. pp. 152. *Lond.* 1894. 8°.   4707. cc. 14. (8.)

MARY, *the B.V., Church of, Newington.* Monumental inscriptions in the Churchyard of St. Mary, Newington. *Lond.* 1880, *etc.* 8°. 9906. b. 5.

CONWAY (M. D.) Centenary history of the South Place Society. pp. 186. *Lond.* 1894. 8°.   4715. b. 37.

THORPE (M.) and (C.) London Church staves. pp. 76. *Lond.* 1895. 8°.   3477. e. 11.

See also supra: General. Infra: Parishes: Parish Registers.

Clubs. *See* CLUBS.

Corporation : Livery Companies.

WELCH (C.) Notes on London Municipal Literature. pp. 32. *Lond.* 1895. 8°.   11899. f. 94.

ASHTON (J.) Lord Mayor's Show in the olden times. pp. 20. *Lond.* 1883. *obl.* 4°. 9930. h. 8.

LONDON. London and the Kingdom. History from the archives at Guildhall. By R. R. Sharpe. *Lond.* 1894, *etc.* 8°.   10349. d. 25.

—— Ten years' growth of the City of London. pp. 139. *Lond.* 1891. 8°.   8223. dh. 5.

—— City of London. " Strike, but hear." pp. 171. *Lond.* 1884. 8°.   10350. e. 40.

WOOLACOTT (J. E.) The Curse of Turtledom : exposé of the Livery Companies. pp. 111. *Lond.* 1894. 8°.   8248. b. 10.

HAZLITT (W. C.) Livery Companies of the City of London. pp. 692. *Lond.* 1892. 8°. 8248. f. 26.

STEWART (H.) History of the Company of Gold and Silver Wyre-Drawers. pp. 140. *Lond.* 1891. 4°.   8248. f. 22.

LONDON. Charters and bye-laws of the Mercers' Company. pp. 96. *Lond.* 1881. fol. 8245. g. 34.

WATNEY (J.) The Hospital of St. Thomas of Acon and the Plate of the Mercers' Company. pp. 308. *Lond.* 1892. 4°.   4705. g. 25

CHRISTIE (J.) Account of Parish Clerks, especially of the Fraternity of S. Nicholas. pp. 219. *Lond.* 1893. 4°.   9916. bb. 21.

SCOTT (J. B.) Account of the Wheelwrights' Company. pp. 72. *Lond.* 1884. 4°. 8248. h. 4.

LONDON—*continued.*

County Council. *See infra : Local Government.*

Environs.

BAEDEKER (C.) London and environs.
pp. 375. 44. *Leipsic*, 1894. 8°.　10108. d. 24.

DAVIDSON (J.) A Random Itinerary. pp. 204.
Lond. 1894. 8°.　10358. ccc. 44.

FITZGERALD (P.) London City suburbs as they
are to day. pp. 349. *Lond.* 1893. 4°.
10349. i. 16.

HOUNSELL (B.) Coach drives from London.
pp. 131. *Lond.* 1894. 8°.　10350. bb. 45.

LOFTIE (W. J.) Round about London. pp. 153.
Lond. 1893. 8°.　10352. a. 69.

LONDON. Photographic Views of London and
suburbs. pp. 142. *Lond.* 1895. *obl.* 8°.
10349. a. 37.

—— Within an Hour of London town. pp. 314.
Edinb. 1892. 8°.　7284. de. 4.

WALFORD (E.) Greater London. 2 vol.
Lond. 1893–95. 8°.　10348. h. 11.

See also BARNES : BARNET : BROCKLEY : BROM-
LEY : CROYDON : DULWICH : EPPING : KEW :
PLAISTOW : WIMBLEDON.

Inns of Court. *See* LAW, *Profession of.*

Livery Companies. *See supra : Corporation.*

Local Government.

WELCH (C.) Notes on London Municipal Literature. pp. 32. *Lond.* 1895. 8°.　11899. f. 94.

DE VESIAN (R. E.) Metropolitan Householder's
guide. pp. 144. *Lond.* 1895. 8°.　6425. de. 32.

EPHEM. Metropolitan Local Government annual.
Lond. 1891, *etc.* 8°.　P.P. 2486. baa.

LONDON. New London. Her Parliament and
its work. pp. 64. *Lond.* 1895. 4°. 10350. h. 22.

—— *County Council.* Annual report of Proceedings. *Lond.* 1891, *etc.* fol.　N.R.

—— London County Council Debates. Verbatim
report. *Lond.* 1893, *etc.* fol.　N.R.

—— A review of the work of the council 1892–93,
in an address by J. Hutton. pp. 29.
Lond. 1895. 8°.　N.R.

—— By-Laws and regulations, pp. 235.
Lond. 1894. 8°.　N.R.

DOUGLAS (T. H.) Dives and Lazarus : London
County Council's treatment of the poor in their
employ. pp. 20. *Lond.* 1890. 8°.　Pam. 82.

SAUNDERS (W.) History of the first London
County Council. 1889–91. pp. 63. 628.
Lond. 1892. 8°.　08276. i 6.

LONDON. *County Council.* Three Years' good
work for the people. 1889–92. pp. 32.
Lond. 1892. 8°.　Pam. 82.

STEAD (W. T.) London County Council Election 1892. Elector's Guide. pp. 100.
Lond. 1892. 4°.　8139. ff. 5.

HIGGINBOTTOM (F. J.) Guide to the third
London County Council. pp. 48.
Lond. 1895. 8°.　6426. ee. 7.

WEBB (S.) Economic heresies of the London
County Council. pp. 18. *Lond.* 1894. 8°.
8282. ff. 12. (18.)

—— Work of the London County Council.
pp. 31. *Deptford*, 1895. 8°.　Pam. 82.

EMMETT (J. T.) Basis of municipal Reform.
pp. 31. *Lond.* 1895. 8°.　Pam. 82.

LONDON. *London Reform Union.* List of officers,
rules, *etc.* 1893. 4°.　1890. e. 4. (78.)

—— Report and Balance sheet.
Lond. 1894, *etc.* 8°.　8277. dd.

—— Proceedings. *Lond.* 1892, *etc.* 4°.　2164.

WEBB (S.) Reform of London. 1894. 8°.
LONDON. *Eighty Club.* Report for 1893.
8139. aaa. 47.

—— Elections, Vestry, Guardians, *etc.* The
London Programme. pp. 218. *Lond.* 1895. 8°.
08275. e. 23.

CUTTER (T.) Metropolitan Valuation Act.
Model rules and regulations. pp. 31.
Lond. 1895. 8°.　6426. a. 60.

CLEMENTS (G. M.) Taxes on London land.
pp. 19. *Lond.* 1891. 8°.　8226. ff. 33. (6.)

See also supra : Corporation. For the law relating to building in London, *see* BUILDING.

Museums. *See* EXHIBITIONS.

Parishes : Districts : Buildings.

West and South-West.

BEAVER (A.) Memorials of old Chelsea.
pp. 428. *Lond.* 1892. 8°.　10349. i. 15.

ASHTON (J.) Hyde Park from Domesday-
Book to date. pp. 282. *Lond.* 1895. 8°.
010350. i. 7.

LANG (A.) Piccadilly. 1892. 8°. Great Streets
of the World.　10026. k. 16.

DASENT (A. I.) History of St. James's Square.
pp. 300. *Lond.* 1895. 8°.　10349. f. 14.

SHEPPARD (E.) Memorials of St. James's Palace.
2 vol. *Lond.* 1894. 8°.　010350. i. 1.

LOFTIE (W. J.) Whitehall. pp. 80. 1895. fol.
Portfolio Monographs. No. 16. P.P. 1931. pcd.

AC. London. *United Service Institution.* Story
of Whitehall Palace. By Viscount Dillon.
pp. 21. *Lond.* 1893. *obl.* 8°　10349. aa. 34.

BESANT (*Sir* W.) Westminster. pp. 312.
Lond. 1895. 8°.　010350. i. 5.

HARE (A. J. C.) Westminster. pp. 120.
Lond. 1894. 8°.　10350. aa. 44.

G. B. & I. *Commons, House of.* Select Committee
on Westminster Hall Restoration. 1884.
Papers. 3 pt. *Lond* 1884, 85. fol. 7815. d. 4.

CLINCH (G.) Mayfair and Belgravia. pp. 183.
Lond. 1892. 4°.　10350. h. 21.

BRIGDEN (T. E.) Eminent Men and women of
Marylebone and their homes. pp. 31.
Lond. 1891, 4°.　010358. f. 18.

Central.

HOLLINGSHEAD (J.) Story of Leicester Square.
pp. 76. *Lond.* 1892. 8°.　10349. ff. 4.

RIMBAULT (E. F.) Soho and its associations.
pp. 232. *Lond.* 1895. 8°.　010350. f. 6.

SOHO. Story of old Soho. pp. 59.
Lond. 1893. 4°.　10349. ff. 35.

BLOTT (W.) Chronicle of Blemundsbury. St.
Giles' in the Fields and Bloomsbury. pp. 426.
South Norwood, 1892. 4°.　10349. h. 31.

DEWE (J. A.) History of Ely Place. pp. 32.
Lond. 1895. 13°.　Pam. 29.

DAWSON (W.) A mid-London parish. S. John's,
Clerkenwell. pp. 88. *Lond.* 1885. 8°.
10350. bb. 39.

MAC CARTHY (J.) Charing Cross to St. Paul's.
pp. 59. *Lond.* 1891. fol.　Tab. 440. b.

ARCHER (T.) The Highway of letters (Fleet
Street). pp. 507. *Lond.* 1893. 8°.
10350. de. 27

HAWKINS (E. C.) Church and Parish of St.
Bride, Fleet Street. pp. 30. *Lond.* 1884. 8°.
Pam. 90.

MARSH (J. B.) St. Paul's Cross. pp. 103.
Lond. 1892. 4°.　10349. f. 13.

MARTIN (J. B.) " The Grasshopper " in Lombard
Street. Banking house of Martin and Co.
pp. 328. *Lond.* 1892. 8°.　8248. f. 25.

LONDON.—Parishes, etc.—*continued.*

POVAH (A.) Annals of the Parishes of St. Olave, Hart Street, and Allhallows Staining. pp. 429. *Lond.* 1894. 4°. 4705. g. 26.

DODD (J. A.) Troubles in a city parish, St. Botolph without Aldgate, under the Protectorate. pp. 14. *Lond.* 1895. 8°. 9004. l. 36. (7.)

LONDON. *City Lands Committee.* History of the Monument. pp. 119. *Lond.* 1893. 4°. 10350. dc. 29.

North and East.

GILTSPUR. Story of Church Street, Stoke Newington. pp. 92. *Stoke Newington,* 1893. 8°. 10350. aaa. 44.

HACKNEY MARSH. Story of Hackney Marsh. pp. 16. *Stoke Newington,* 1894. 8°. Pam. 90.

EHEM. Borough of West Ham and Stratford Almanack. *Stratford,* 1890, etc. 8°. P.P. 2508. pxb.

South.

BOGER (C. G.) Bygone Southwark. pp. 288. *Lond.* 1895. 8°. 010358. i. 14.

NORTH (C. N. M.) Archæology and architecture of Southwark. *Lond.* 188;. fol. 7815. df. 24.

SOUTHWARK. Rental and account of lands and tenements belonging to the Charities of St. Olave and St. John, Southwark. pp. 100. *Lond.* 1893. fol. 9903. k. 12.

SIMPKINSON (C. H.) A South London Parish. S. Paul's, Lorrimore Square, Walworth. pp. 78. *Lond.* 1894. 8°. 4429. c. 19.

See also supra: General: Churches; infra: Tower: CLUBS.

Parish Registers, etc.

SAINT BARTHOLOMEW EXCHANGE, *Parish.* Account books, 1596–1698. pp. 242. *Lond.* 1895. 4°. 10351. i. 16.

SAINT CHRISTOPHER LE STOCKS, *Parish.* Account Book, 1662–85. pp. 47. *Lond.* 1895. 4°. 9906. h. 5.

—— Wills, Leases and memoranda in the Book of Records. pp. 30. *Lond.* 1895. 4°. 9906. h. 6.

SAINT EDMUND, *the King, Parish.* Parish Registers, 1670–1812. pp. 151. *Leeds,* 1892. 8°. 9906. f. 18.

GEORGE, *Saint, Chapel of, Mayfair.* Register. 1889. 8°. Ac. London. *Harleian Society.* Publications. Registers. Vol. 15. 2118. e.

KENSINGTON, *Parish.* Parish Register. 1539–1675. pp. 179. 1890. 4°. Ac. London. *Harleian Society.* Publications. Registers. Vol. 16. 2118. c.

SAINT NICHOLAS ACONS, *Parish.* Register Book, 1539–1812. pp. 160. *Leeds,* 1890. 8°. 9906. f. 17.

HESSELS (J. H.) Archives of the London-Dutch Church. 1568–1872. pp. 296. *Lond.* 1892. 4°. 4705. f. 18.

Poor: Working Classes.

BOOTH (C.) Life and labour of the People in London. 4 vol. *Lond.* 1889–93. 8°. 2240. bb. 22.

CHIGNELL (R.) London Charities (unendowed). pp. 64. *Lond.* 1892. 8°. 08276. f. 43.

CLARKE (R. F.) Our Waifs and strays. pp. 24. *Lond.* 1889. 8°. 3939. ccc. 2. (2.)

HUNT (J.) Pioneer work in the Great City. pp. 231. *Lond.* 1895. 8°. 4192. bb. 48.

JAY (A. O. M.) Life in darkest London. pp. 146. *Lond.* 1891. 8°. 8276. aa. 51.

KNAPP (J. M.) The Universities and the social problem. University settlements in East London. pp. 235. *Lond.* 1895. 8°. 08275. i. 3.

LAZARUS (H.) Landlordism : illustration of the rise and spread of slumland. pp. 59. *Lond.* 1892. 8°. 8275. aaa. 56.

LONDON.—Poor, etc.—*continued.*

LONDON. *Saint Giles' Mission.* Story of thirty years in St. Giles. pp. 144. *Lond.* 1891. 8°. 4192. ee. 18.

—— A River of mercy and its first spring. Labour among the criminal classes. pp. 164. *Lond.* 1891. 8°. 4192. ee. 20.

SAUNDERS (G.) Stories of medical mission work in St. Giles. pp. 72. *Lond.* 1895. 16°. 4192. a. 33.

LONDON. *Mansion House Council on the Dwellings of the Poor.* Dwellings of the poor. Report. pp. 112. *Lond.* 1891. 8°. 08276. g. 4.

—— The Pinch of poverty. Sufferings of the London poor. pp. 352. *Lond.* 1892. 8°. 4192. ee. 22.

ROWE (J. T.) Town and gown. Work in St. George's, Camberwell. pp. 60. *Camb.* 1891. 4°. 4192. g. 2.

SELLERS (W. E.) Strange Scenes and strange experiences. pp. 190. *Lond.* 1894. 8°. 4399. l. 39.

SMILEY (F. E.) Evangelization of a great City. pp. 232. *Phila.* 1890. 8°. 4192. ee. 15.

TENNANT, *afterwards* STANLEY (D.) London street Arabs. Illustrations. pp. 67. *Lond.* 1890. 4°. 7854. ff. 41.

WILLIAMS (R.) London Rookeries and colliers' slums. pp. 82. *Lond.* 1893. 8°. 8282. ff. 5.

See also CAPITAL AND LABOUR, *Great Britain and Ireland :* CHARITIES.

Port of. *See* PORTS AND HARBOURS.

Sanitation : Public Health Act, 1891. *See* SANITATION.

Street Improvement.

CAWSTON (A.) Street improvements in London. pp. 136. *Lond.* 1893. 4°. 10349. h. 33.

—— Advantages of adopting a general scheme in making improvements to the London streets. pp. 21. *Lond.* 1893. 8°. 7808. bbb. 28. (7.)

See also BUILDING, *Laws, etc.*

Tower of London.

BARRETT (C. R. B.) The Tower : Etchings. *Lond.* 1889. fol. 10350. i. 13.

LOFTIE (W. J.) Authorised Guide to the Tower. pp. 152. *Lond.* 1888. 8°. 010350. f. 1.

—— Authorised guide to the Tower. Abridged. pp. 30. *Lond.* 1893. 8°. 10347. cc. 26. (2.)

LONDON. *Tower of London.* The Tower. Photographed by A. Mackie. 1894, 8°. Victorian Series. No. 4. 10348. ccc.

See also supra : General.

University : University College and School.

Ac. London. *University.* Guide. University Correspondence College. Calendar. *Lond.* 1891. etc. 8°. P.P. 2506. aca.

—— Matriculation Directory. 1887, etc. 8°. Tutorial Series.. 12205. c. 110.

—— Objections to the Gresham Commissioners' scheme. pp. 32. *Lond.* 1894. 8°. 8366. cc. 39. (11.)

—— *University College.* Regulations for Scholarships, Exhibitions, etc. *Lond.* 1891, etc. 8°. 8365. c.

ORME (T. A.) University College School. Register 1831–91. pp. 526. *Lond.* 1892. 8°. 8366. b. 45.

See also EXAMINATIONS.

Water Supply. *See* WATER.

LONDON AND NORTH-WESTERN AND LONDON AND SOUTH-WESTERN RAILWAYS. *See* RAILWAYS.

LONDONDERRY. WALKER (G.) Siege of Londonderry in 1689. pp. 225. *Lond.* 1893. 4°.
9509. c. 7.

LONGEVITY. *See* OLD AGE.

LONGFORGAN. PHILIP (A.) Parish of Longforgan. pp. 320. *Edinb.* 1895. 8°.
10369. ccc. 36.

LONG MELFORD. CONDER (E. L.) Church of Long Melford. pp. 95. *Lond.* 1887. fol.
7815. e. 15.

LONGUEMORT. HOIN (J.) Longuemort et ses seigneurs. 1890. 8°. Ac. Abbeville. *Société d'Émulation.* Mémoires. Sér. 4. Tom. 1.
Ac. 230.

LONGUEUIL. JODOIN (A.) and VINCENT (J. L.) Histoire de Longueuil. pp. 681. *Montréal,* 1889. 8°. 10470. f. 26.

LONLAY–L'ABBAYE. LE FAVERAIS (H.) Histoire de Lonlay-l'Abbaye. pp 308. *Mortain,* 1892. 8°. 4629. b. 33.

LORD HOWE ISLAND. *See* TAHITI.

LORD'S SUPPER. *See* EUCHARIST.

LORETTO. GARRATT (W. F. H.) Loreto, the New Nazareth and its jubilee. pp. 419. *Lond.* 1895. 8°. 10135. aaa. 15.

LORETTO. *Confraternity of the Holy House.* Let us love Mary by honoring her in her Holy House. pp. 55. *Recanati,* 1890. 16°. Pam. 77.

LORETTO MANUAL. The Loretto Manual. pp. 512. 152. *Dublin,* 1891. 8°. 3157. d. 20.

LORRAINE. *See* ALSACE-LORRAINE.

LOS ANGELES. P.P. *Los Angeles.* Illustrated Los Angeles Herald. July, 1893. *Los Angeles,* 1893. fol. P.P. 9098.

LOSTWITHIAL. H., F. M. Memorials of Lostwithiel. pp. 226. *Truro,* 1891. 8°.
010358. h. 20.

LOT, Department. GOULD (S. B.) The Deserts of southern France. 2 vol. *Lond.* 1894. 8°. 010171. h. 41.

LAPEYRE (E.) Les Insurrections du Lot en 1790. pp. 130. *Cahors,* 1892. 8°. 9231. g. 20. *See also* AQUITAINE.

LOTHIAN, East, *See* HADDINGTONSHIRE.

LOTHIAN, Mid. *See* EDINBURGH.

LOTTERIES. ASHTON (J.) History of English Lotteries. pp. 359. *Lond.* 1893. 8°.
012330. k. 1.

BRANDT (F.) Das Lotteriewesen unserer Zeit. pp. 100. *Hamb.* 1894. 8°. 08227. g. 51.

LASSON (A.) Lotterie und Volkswirthschaft. pp. 64. 1894. 8°. Volkswirthschaftliche Zeitfragen. Hft. 123, 124. 8207. i.

MARCINOWSKI (F.) Das Lotteriewesen in Preussen. pp. 214. *Berl.* 1892. 8°. 8226. cc. 53.

LOUGH DERG. O'CONNOR (D.) St. Patrick's Purgatory, Lough Derg. pp. 246. *Dublin,* 1895. 8°. 10390. bb. 46.

LOUGHTON HALL. WALLER (W. C.) Old Loughton Hall. pp. 7. 1893. 8°.
10384. e. 15. (8.)

LOUISBURG. DRAKE (S. A.) The taking of Louisburg, 1745. pp. 136. *Bost.* 1891. 8°.
9602. cc. 5.

LOUISIANA. FORTIER (A.) Louisiana studies. pp. 307. *New Orleans,* 1894. 8°.
10411. de. 18.

—— Bits of Louisiana Folk-lore. 1888. 8°. Ac. Baltimore. *Modern Language Association.* Translations, *etc.* Vol. III. Ac. 2683/2.

WALLACE (J.) History of Louisiana under the French rule. pp. 433. *Cincinnati,* 1893. 8°.
9605. dd. 12.

LOUISVILLE. DURRETT (R. T.) Centenary of Louisville. pp. 200. 1893. 4°. Filson Club Publications. No. 8. Ac. 8423.

LOURDES. AMORY DE LANGERACK (J.) La Grotte de Lourdes. pp. 168. *Lille,* 1884. 8°.
4808. g. 2.

AZEREDO TEIXEIRA D'AGUILAR (F. de) *Count de Samodães.* Uma visita a Lourdes. pp. 132. *Porto,* 1887. 8°. 10174. aa. 26.

BALLERINI (T.) Lourdes alla fine d'agosto del 1893. pp. 83. 4. *Roma,* 1894. 8°.
10169. de. 28.

BARBÉ (D.) Lourdes hier, aujourd'hui, demain. pp. 95. *Paris,* 1893. 8°. 4807. eee. 13.

—— Lourdes : yesterday, to-day, and to-morrow. Translated by A. Meynell. pp. 106. *Lond.* 1894. 8°. 4808. i. 23.

BOISSARIE ( ) Lourdes. Histoire médicale 1858–91. pp. 458. *Paris,* 1891. 12°. 4807. c. 1.

BOURNICHON (J.) Un des beaux faits de Lourdes. pp. 208. *St. Amand,* 1893. 8°. 4629. aa. 40.

BOYER D'AGEN (A.) Terre de Lourdes. pp. 354. *Paris,* 1894. 8°. 012550. f. 54.

CLARKE (R. F.) Medical testimony to the Miracles of Lourdes. pp. 24. *Lond.* 1892. 8°.
3939. ccc. 13.

CLÉMENT ( ) Les Miracles de Lourdes. pp. 125. *Lyon,* 1892. 8°. 4807. aaa. 5.

DAUZAT-DEMBARRÈRE (P.) Des origines politiques de la grotte de Lourdes. pp. 48. *Tarbes,* 1890. 8°. Pam. 46.

DOMENECH (E.) Lourdes. pp. 327. *Lyon,* 1894. 8°. 4808. d. 3.

LORRAINE. La Lorraine et l'Alsace à Lourdes, 1891. pp. 63. *St. Dié,* 1892. 8°. Pam. 10.

MARÈS (G.) Lourdes et ses environs. pp. 423. *Bordeaux.* 1894. 8°. 010168. e. 4.

MARTIN (P.) Skizze des bayerischen Pilger-Zuges nach Lourdes. 1894. pp. 75. *Augsburg,* 1894. 8°. 10171. a. 25.

MAZOYER (P.) Lourdes et Bétharram. pp. 312. *Paris,* 1895. 8°. 10174. aaa. 52.

RICARD (A.) Mes Pèlerinages. pp. 239. *Paris,* 1892. 12°. 10105. e. 3.

ZOLA (E. E. C. A.) Lourdes. pp. 598. *Paris,* 1894. 12°. 012550. g. 36.

—— Lourdes. Translated by E. A. Vizetelly. pp. 491. *Lond.* 1894. 8°. 012548. f. 48.

BOERI (A.) Lourdes e il romanzo di E. Zola. pp. 130. *Como,* 1894. 8°. 11825. o. 20.

LASSERRE (H.) Lettres à l'occasion du roman de M. Zola. pp. 121. *Paris,* 1895. 12°.
011850. eee. 49.

MONCOQ (D.) Réponse au Lourdes de M. Zola. pp. 53. *Caen,* 1894. 8°. 3900. i. 25. (4.)

MONIQUET (P.) Un mot à M. Zola et aux détracteurs de Lourdes. pp. 50. *Paris,* 1895. 12°. 3900. aaa. 36.

PIERRE, *l'Ermite.* Boissarie; Zola. Conférence. pp. 79. *Paris,* 1895. 8°. 011824. i. 38.

RICARD (A.) La vraie Bernadette de Lourdes. Lettres à M. Zola. pp. 280. *Paris,* 1894. 8°.
4864. ccc. 40.

LOUTH, Lincolnshire. GOULDING (R. W.) Louth old Corporation Records. pp. 202. *Louth,* 1891. 8°. 10351. l. h. 30.

LOUTH PARK ABBEY. Chronicon Abbatiæ de Parco Lude. Chronicle of Louth Park Abbey. pp. 85. 1891. 8°. Ac. Lincoln. *Record Society.* Publications. Vol. I. Ac. 8094.

LOUVAIN. EVEN (E. v.) Louvain dans le passé et dans le présent. *Louvain,* 1891, *etc.* 4°.
10270. h. 4.

LOUVAIN—*continued.*

LINDEN (H. v. d.) Histoire de la Constitution de Louvain au moyen âge. pp. 194. 1892. 8°. Ac. Ghent. *Université.* Recueil de travaux. Fasc. 7.   Ac. 2647/3.

Ac. Louvain. *Academia Lovianensis.* Bibliographie académique. pp. 311.
Louvain, 1880. 8°.   11902. bbb. 4.

REUSENS (E. H. J.) Documents relatifs à l'histoire de l'Université, 1425–1797.
Louvain, 1881, *etc.* 8°.   8355. df.

LOVE. I * * *, *M. le C. de.* Bibliographie des ouvrages relatifs à l'amour.
Paris, 1893, *etc.* 8°.   011902. l.

BEYLE (M. H.) De l'Amour. pp. 371.
Paris, 1882. 8°.   8416. cc. 33.

BOURGET (P.) Physiologie de l'amour moderne. pp. 435. *Paris,* 1891. 12°.   8416. dd. 37.

CORBIN (C. F.) A Woman's philosophy of Love. pp. 302. *Bost.* 1893. 8°.   8416. e. 32.

DANVILLE (G.) La Psychologie de l'amour. pp. 169. *Paris,* 1894. 12°.   8415. de. 41.

DARBLAY (P.) Physiologie de l'amour. pp. 253. *Pau,* 1889. 8°.   8416. de. 11.

DUMAS (G.) Tolstoy et la philosophie de l'amour. pp. 218. *Paris,* 1893. 8°.   011850. f. 32.

DUMONT (É.) Le Secrétaire des amoureux. pp. 192. *Paris,* 1893. 8°.   012330. g. 28.

FLEMING (T.) Love and courtship. pp. 14.
Malton, 1890. 8°.   Pam. 37.

GREENWOOD (F.) The Lover's Lexicon. pp. 319. *Lond.* 1893. 8°.   8415. de. 29.

MANTEGAZZA (P.) Gli Amori degli uomini. 2 vol.
Milano, 1892. 8°.   8416. df. 14.

MILLER (E.) The Evolution of Love. pp. 346.
Chicago, 1892. 8°.   4376. ee. 8.

SCHOPENHAUER (A.) Zur Metaphysik der Geschlechtsliebe. pp. 156. *Berl.* 1891. 8°.
                                      8416. dd. 42.

—— La Metafisica dell' amore. pp. 50.
Napoli, 1890. 8°.   8461. bbb. 48. (3.)

TAYLOR (J. W.) Love and marriage. pp. 61.
Carnforth, 1891. 8°.   7410. cc. 36.

See also MARRIAGE : SEX.

Courts of Love.

RAJNA (PIO) Le Corti d'Amore. pp. 100.
Milano, 1890. 8°.   7709. aa. 23.

ROWBOTHAM (J. F.) Troubadours and Courts of Love. pp. 324. 1895. 8°. Social England Series.
                                      9503. ccc.

LOVEDALE, South Africa. LOVEDALE. Lovedale. Illustrated. pp. 110.
Edinb. 1894. 8°.   4765. f. 18.

LOVISA. LOVISA. Vattenkuranstalten i Lovisa. pp. 18. *Lovisa,* 1895. 12°.   Pam. 39.

LÖWENSTEIN. ROMMEL (C.) Grundzüge einer Chronik der Stadt Löwenstein, pp. 245.
Löwenstein, 1893. 8°.   10235. g. 10.

LOWESTOFT. FLOOD (J.) Popular guide to Lowestoft. pp. 50. *Lowestoft,* 1895. 16°. Pam. 90.

LUBERTA. Summer sojourn on the East Coast. pp. 255. *Lowestoft,* 1892. 8°.   10360. e. 26.

STEBBINGS (F.) Guide to Lowestoft. pp. 96.
Lowestoft, 1894. 8°.   10352. f. 4.

LOYALTY ISLANDS. *See* UVEA.

LOZÈRE, Department. FALGAIROLLE (E.) Le Tribunal révolutionnaire de la Lozère, 1793. pp. 183. *Paris,* 1893. 8°.   9225. c. 21.
See also CEVENNES : LANGUEDOC.

LUBECK. Ac. Lubeck. *Geographische Gesellschaft.* Die Hansestadt Lübeck. pp. 347.
Lübeck, 1890. 8°.   10260. ff. 1.

—— Beilage enthaltend fünf Karten. fol.
                                      10260. h. 1.

LUBECK—*continued.*

FREDERICK I. Barbarossa, *Emperor.* Kaiser Friedrich I. Freibrief für Lübeck, 1188. pp. 19. *Lübeck,* 1893. 4°.   10260. g. 2.

GERMANY. *Reichsgericht,* Lübecks Hoheitsrecht über die Trave, *etc.* 1891. 8°. Ac. Lubeck. *Verein für Lübeckische Geschichte.* Zeitschrift. Bd. 6. Hft. 2.   Ac. 7078.

HACH (T.) Der Dom zu Lübeck. pp. 35.
Lübeck, 1891. fol.   1731. c. 5.

HASSE (P.) Die Anfänge Lübecks. pp. 23.
Lübeck, 1893. 8°.   10105. e. 4. (6.)

MOLLWO (C.) Die ältesten lübischen Zollrollen. pp. 27. *Lübeck,* 1894. 8°.   08226. h. 21.

SCHMIDT (G. H.) Statistik des Consums in Lübeck, 1836-68. 1891. 8°. Ac. Lübeck. *Verein für Lübeckische Geschichte.* Zeitschrift. Bd. 6. Hft. 2.   Ac. 7078.

STIEHL (C.) Musikgeschichte der Stadt Lübeck. pp. 116. *Lübeck,* 1891. 8°.   7898. l. 23.
See also HANSE TOWNS.

LUCCA. SIMONETTI (G.) I Duchi di Lucca durante la dominazione longobarda. pp. 34.
Rocca S. C. 1894. 8°.   Pam. 28.

LUCÉ. ALOUIS (V.) Lucé et ses environs aux XVIIᵉ et XVIIIᵉ siècles. pp. 112.
Mamers, 1891. 8°.   010171. k. 1.

LUCERNE. SCHWENDIMANN (J.) Der Bauernstand des Kantons Luzern. pp. 206.
Luzern, 1893. 8°.   8275. dd. 23.

SOWERBY (J.) Forest Cantons of Switzerland. pp. 288. *Lond.* 1892. 8°.   10136. cc. 11.

BRANDSTETTER (R.) Prolegomena zu einer Geschichte der Luzerner Mundart. pp. 88.
Einsiedeln, 1890. 8°.   011824. h. 31. (3.)

—— Die Reception der neuhochdeutschen Schriftsprache in Luzern, 1600-1830. pp. 90.
Einsiedeln, 1891. 8°.   Pam. 47.

LUCKNOW. INGLIS (*Hon.* J. S.) *Lady.* Siege of Lucknow. A diary. pp. 240.
Lond. 1892. 8°.   9057. b. 18.

INNES (J. J. M.) Lucknow and Oude in the Mutiny. pp. 340. *Lond.* 1895. 8°. 9057. aaa. 37.

MIRZĀ AMĪR BEG. Handbook of the sights of Lucknow. pp. 46. *Lucknow,* 1891. 8°. Pam. 88

MOORE (T.) Guide to the model of the Residency, Lucknow. pp. 26. *Lucknow,* 1885. 8°.
                                  9008. g. 11. (2.)

See also INDIA, *History.*

LUÇON. LACROIX (A.) Richelieu à Luçon. pp. 299. *Paris,* 1890. 8°.   4999. e. 21.

LUDLOW. WOOLLEY (G.) The Parish Church of Ludlow. pp. 52. *Ludlow,* 1893. 4°.
                                      7814. f. 18.

LUGANDA LANGUAGE.
See AFRICAN LANGUAGES.

LUGANO. PRENCIPE (G.) Guida commerciale della Città di Lugano. pp. 116.
Lugano, 1892. 8°.   10135. bb. 37.

LUGO. PEREIRA (A. J.) Romancero de la Ciudad de Lugo. pp. 221. *Lugo,* 1892. 8°.
                                      11450. g. 22.

LUMP-SUCKER, Fish. *See* DISCOBOLI.

LUNACY LAWS. *See* INSANITY.

LUNATIC ASYLUMS. *See* INSANITY.

LUNDA. DIAS DE CARVALHO (H. A.) A Lunda ou os estados do Muatiânvua. pp. 422.
Lisboa, 1890. 8°.   010096. g. 9.

DIAS DE CARVALHO (H. A.) Expedição portugueza do Muatiânvua. pp. 731.
Lisboa, 1890. 8°.   010096. h. 2.

LUNDA—*continued.*

MARQUES (A. S.) Expedição portugeza ao Muata-Ianvo. *Lisboa*, 1889, *etc.* 8°.   010096. ff. 12.
See also AFRICA, *West :* AFRICAN LANGUAGES.

LUNDY ISLAND. PAGE (J. L. W.) Coasts of Devon and Lundy Island. pp. 444.
Lond. 1895. 8°.   010358. e. 34.

LUNGS: RESPIRATORY ORGANS.

CLARK (*Sir* A.) Fibroid diseases of the Lung. pp. 199. *Lond.* 1894. 8°.   7616. h. 22.

DAVIS (N. S.) Diseases of the Lungs. pp. 359. *Phila.* 1892. 8°.   7616. e. 11.

FAISANS (L.) Maladies des Organes respiratoires. pp. 192. 1892. 8°. Encyclopédie des aide-mémoire.   8709. g.

FOX (W.) Treatise on diseases of the Lungs. pp. 1200. *Lond.* 1891. 8°.   7615. d. 5.

FOXWELL (A.) Essays in Heart and Lung disease. pp. 476. *Lond.* 1895. 8°. 7616. h 25.

GERHARDT (C. J.) Die Pleura-Erkrankungen. pp. 90. 1892. 8°. BILLROTH (T.) Deutsche Chirurgie. Lief. 43.   7482. cc.

GRANCHER (J.) Maladies de l'Appareil respiratoire. pp. 524. *Paris*, 1890. 8°. 7615. d. 3.

GRAWITZ (P.) Ueber die hämorrhagischen Infarkte der Lungen. pp. 69. 1891. 4°. VIRCHOW (R.) Festschrift.   7391. i. 1.

GUTTMANN (P.) Lehrbuch der klinischen Untersuchungs-Methoden für die Brust-Organe. pp. 518. *Berl.* 1892. 8°.   7620. df. 31.

HENSMAN (A.) The Thorax. 1893. 8°. MORRIS (H.) Treatise on Human Anatomy. 7419. l. 10.

NEATBY (E. A.) Pleural Effusions in children. pp. 20. 1892. 8°.   7305. de. 27. (9.)

POWELL (R. D.) On diseases of the Lungs. pp. 600. *Lond.* 1893. 8°.   7616. f. 9.

REIMARUS ( ) Die Rettung der Lungenkranken. pp. 20. *Leipz.* 1891. 8°.   Pam. 39.

SCHMIDT (M.) Die Krankheiten der oberen Luftwege. pp. 727. *Berl.* 1894. 8°. 7616. i. 11.

SPECK (C.) Physiologie des menschlichen Athmens. pp. 262. *Leipz.* 1892. 8°. 7460. ff. 26.

THOMAS (J. D.) Operative Treatment of Hydatid Cysts of the Lungs. pp. 112. *Melbourne*, 1889. 8°.   7630. e. 17.

WILLIAMS (C. T.) Aero-Therapeutics ; treatment of Lung diseases by climate. pp. 187.
Lond. 1894. 8°.   7461. g. 5.

DIXON (A. L. H.) Art of Breathing as applied to physical development. pp. 30.
Lond. 1895. 16°.   7616. a. 48.

GIBSON (G. A.) Cheyne-Stokes Respiration. pp. 133. *Edinb.* 1892. 8°.   7616. f. 8.

SMITH (F. A. A.) Keep your mouth shut. pp. 49. *Lond.* 1892. 8°.   7616. h. 20.

SNODIN (H.) Diaphragmatic Breathing ; beneficial effects upon the voice and health. pp. 8.
Lond. 1890. 8°.   Pam. 39.
See also ASTHMA : BRONCHITIS : CHEST : CONSUMPTION : PNEUMONIA.

LUNKUNDU LANGUAGE.
See AFRICAN LANGUAGES.

LUPUS. BERGMANN (E. v.) Die Behandlung des Lupus mit dem Koch'schen Mittel. 1891. 8°. VOLKMANN (R. v.) Sammlung klinischer Vorträge. N.F. No. 22.   7441. g.

BULKLEY (L. D.) Internal treatment of Lupus with phosphorus. pp. 6. *N.Y.* 1893. 8°.   7305. f. 6. (5.)

KAPOSI (M.) Ueber die Behandlung von Lupus mittels Koch'scher Lymphe. pp. 122.
Wien, 1891. 8°.   7640. g. 4.
See also SKIN.

LUSATIA. LIPPERT (W.) Wettiner und Wittelsbacher sowie die Niederlausitz im XIV. Jahrhundert. pp. 314. *Dresden*, 1894. 8°.   9340. f. 8.

GANDER (C.) Niederlausitzer Volksagen. pp. 197. *Berl.* 1894. 8°.   12430. l. 14.

LUSHAIS. REID (A. S.) Chin-Lushai Land. pp. 235. *Calcutta*, 1893, 8°.   010057. h. 10.

SOPPITT (C. A.) Account of the Kuki-Lushai Tribes on the North-East Frontier. pp. 88. *Shillong*, 1887. 8°.   12906. dd. 42.

LUTE. DOWLAND (J.) Douland's necessarie observations belonging to Lute-playing.
Leipz. 1891, 8°.   7806. de. 22. (10.)

RADECKE (E. L. S.) Das deutsche Lied in der Lautenmusik des 16. Jahrhunderts, *etc.* pp. 52.
Leipz. 1891. 8°.   Pam. 24.
See also MUSICAL INSTRUMENTS.

LUTHERAN CHURCH. FICKER (J.) Die Konfutation des Augsburgischen Bekenntnisses. pp. 194. *Leipz.* 1891. 8°.   4662. f. 4.

KOESTLIN (J.) Artiklerne om Troen i den Augsburgske Konfession. pp. 99. 1894. 8°. NIELSEN (F.) Smaaskrifter til Oplysning for Kristne. Bd. 9.   3605. i.

NYGÅRD (F. S. O. A. P.) Luthers Venner. Kirkehistoriske Nutids-Skizzer. pp. 437.
Odense, 1893. 8°.   4661. aa. 32.

JACOBS (H. E.) Lutheran movement in England. pp. 376. *Lond.* 1892. 8°.   4707. ee. 18.

LODS (A.) L'Église Luthérienne de Paris pendant la révolution. pp. 21. *Paris*, 1892. 8°.   4629. ee. 7. (9.)

CARROLL (H. K.) Report of statistics of Churches in the U.S. pp. 812. 1894. 8°. Eleventh Census of the U.S.   1882. c. I.

GRAEBNER (A. L.) Geschichte der Lutherischen Kirche in America. *St. Louis*, 1892, *etc.* 8°.   4745. dd.

JACOBS (H. E.) History of the Lutheran Churches in the U.S. pp. 539. 1893. 8°. American Church History Series. Vol. 4.   4744. g.
See also DENMARK, *Church of :* EVANGELICAL CHURCH : NORWAY, *History, Ecclesiastical.* For works on Luther and the Reformation, *see* CHURCH HISTORY.

LUXEMBURG, Grand Duchy and City.

BONNARDOT (F.) Les Archives de l'état de Luxembourg, 1890. 4°. Ac. Luxemburg. *Institut.* Publications de la Section historique. Vol. 41.   Ac. 5496/2.

ELTZ (J. v. d.) Aus Luxemburgs Vergangenheit und Gegenwart. pp. 198. *Trier*, 1891, 8°.   9327. bb. 20.

KELLEN (T.) Das Deutschthum in Luxemburg. pp. 50. 1892. 8°. Deutsche Zeit- und Streit-Fragen. N.F. Hft. 101.   12209. f.

TANDEL (É.) Les Communes luxembourgeoises. 2 tom. 1889. 8°. Ac. Arlon. *Société pour la Conservation des Monuments.* Annales. Tom. 21, 22.   Ac. 5514.

MOHR (M.) Die Finanzverwaltung der Grafschaft Luxemburg in 14. Jahrhunderts. pp. 62. 1892. 8°. ELSTER (L.) Staatswissenschaftliche Studien. Bd. 4.   8207. h.

RICHTER (F.) Der luxemburger Erbfolgestreit, 1438–43. pp. 73. 1889. 8°. P.P. *Treves.* Westdeutsche Zeitschrift. Ergänzungsheft 5.   P.P. 3533. b.

FELSENHART (J.) Études sur le Duché de Luxembourg, 1716–44. 4 pt. 1885–89. 4°. Ac. Arlon. *Société pour la Conservation des Monuments.* Annales. Tom. 17, 18, 19, 20.   Ac. 5514

LUXEMBURG—*continued.*

BAEDEKER (C.) Belgium and Holland, including Luxembourg. pp. 423. *Leipsic*, 1894. 8°. 2352. a.

PERK (M. A.) Schetsen uit Luxemburg. pp. 253. *Haarlem*, 1894, 8°. 10256. a. 24.

PFLIPS (H) Das luxemburger Land. pp. 158. *Aachen*, 1895. 8°. 10256. a. 23.

ROULLIER (G.) A travers le Grand-Duché. pp. 179. *Charleroi*, 1890. 8°. 10271. ff. 10.

MARCHOT (P.) Les patois du Luxembourg Central. pp. 16. *Paris*, 1891. 8°. 12902. i. 5. (4.)

LUXEUIL, Abbey. BEAUSÉJOUR (de) Le monastère de Luxeuil. pp. 104. *Besançon*, 1891. 8°. 4629. f. 31.

LUXOR. *See* EGYPT, *Antiquities.*

LUZON ISLAND. *See* PHILIPPINE ISLANDS.

LYCIA: LYDIA. BARBEY (W.) Lydie, Lycie. Études botaniques. Revues par W. Barbey. pp. 82. *Lausanne*, 1890. 4°. 7028. f. 1.

PERROT (G.) and CHIPIEZ (C.) History of Art in Lydia and Lycia, etc. pp. 405. *Lond.* 1892. 8°. 2259. f. 20.

LANCKOROŃSKI (C.) *Count.* Les villes de la Pamphylie et de la Lydie. *Paris*, 1890, etc. 4°. 7703. d.

RADET (G.) La Lydie au temps des mermnades, 687-546. pp. 325. 1893. 8°. Ac. Athens. *École Française.* Bibliothèque. Fasc. 63. Ac. 5206/2.

See also ASIA MINOR : GREECE.

LYCOSURA. *See* GREECE, *Antiquities.*

LYDD. OYLER (T. H.) Lydd, and its Church. pp. 52. *Ashford*, 1894. 8°. 10350. aaa. 48.

LYDIARD MANOR. MAC KNIGHT (W. H. E.) Lydiard Manor. pp. 112. *Lond.* 1892. 8°. 10360. d. 36.

LYING. TRUMBULL (H. C.) A Lie never Justifiable. Study in ethics. pp. 237. *Phila.* 1893. 8°. 8409. ccc. 23. *See also* ETHICS.

LYME REGIS. LYME REGIS. Guide book. 2 pt. *Lyme Regis*, 1894. 8°. 10360. aaa. 17.

LYMINGE. JENKINS (R. C.) Burial-place of St. Ethelburga the Queen in Lyminge. 633-643. pp. 27. *Folkestone*, 1890. 8°. Pam. 10.

—— Observations on the charter of the Duke Oswulf to the Monastery of Lyminge. pp. 19. *Folkestone*, 1892. 8°. 3940. bb. 31. (8.)

LYNTON. COLWILL (S.) English Switzerland. *Ilfracombe*, 1889. 32°. 10347. a. 14. (2.)

LYONS.

History, etc.

BAZIN (H.) Vienne et Lyon gallo-romains. pp. 407. *Paris*, 1891. 8°. 7708. cc. 53.

STEYERT (A.) Nouvelle histoire de Lyon. *Lyon*, 1895, etc. 8°. 10172. g.

MOLLIÈRE (H.) Recherches sur l'évaluation de la population de Lugdunum, du 1er au 1ve siècle. pp. 102. *Lyon*, 1892. 8°. 09200. e. 6.

Ac. Lyons. *Société des Bibliophiles.* Cartulaire das fiefs de l'Église de Lyon, 1173-1521. pp. 580. *Lyon*, 1893. 4°. 4630. e. 13.

GRISARD (J.J.) Notes sur les plans de Lyon du xve au xviiie siècle. pp. 216. *Lyon*, 1891. 8°. 10172. f. 20.

BLETON (A.) Tableau de Lyon avant 1789. pp. 108. *Lyon*, 1894. 4°. K.T.C. 33. b. 5.

WAHL (M.) Les premières années de la Révolution à Lyon, 1788-92. pp. 628. *Paris*, 1894. 8°. 9231. g. 26.

LYONS—*continued.*

CASTONNET DES FOSSES (H.) Le siège de Lyon en 1793. 1894. 8°. Ac. Angers. *Société d'Agriculture, etc.* Mémoires. Sér. 4. Tom. 6. Ac 245.

FOREST-FLEURY ( ) Le vieux Lyon qui s'en va. pp. 39. *Lyon*, 1890. 8°. 10172. f. 17.

VÉRICEL (G.) Vieux Usages lyonnais. pp. 72. *Lyon*, 1893. 12°. 12430. c. 36.

JOANNE (P.) Lyon. pp. 64. *Paris*, 1895. 8°. 10174. a. 30.

BAUDRIER (H.) Bibliographie lyonnaise. Imprimeurs, *etc.* au xvie siècle. *Lyon*, 1895, *etc.* 8°. 011901. ee.

VINGTRINIER (M. É. A.) Histoire de l'imprimerie à Lyon. pp. 440. *Lyon*, 1894. 8°. 011901. g. 27.

DUCOURTIEUX (P.) Les Barbou, imprimeurs : Lyon. pp. 30. *Limoges*, 1894. 8°. Pam. 6.

Trade.

BONZON (A.) Manuel des Sociétés par actions de la Région lyonnaise. pp. 784. *Lyon*, 1893. 8°. 08225. l. 19.

GENEVET (A.) Compagnie des Agents de change de Lyon. Histoire. pp. 311. *Lyon*, 1890. 4°. 8245. gg. 17.

PARISET ( ) La Chambre de Commerce de Lyon au xixe siècle. pp. 254. 1890. 8°. LYONS. *Académie des Sciences.* Mémoires. Classe des Sciences. Vol. 27. Ac. 364.

STORCK (A.) and MARTIN (H.) Lyon à l'Exposition Universelle, 1889. pp. 120. *Lyon*, 1891. 4°. 7743. g. 18.

Dialect.

NIZIER DU PUITSPELU ( ) Essai de phonétique lyonnaise. pp. 144. *Lyon*, 1885. fol. 12953. i. 18.

RAVERAT (A.) Encore Lugdunum. Recherches sur la véritable étymologie du nom de Corbeau. pp. 39. *Lyon*, 1890. 8°. 12902. g. 32. (4.)

VILLEFRANCHE (J. M.) Essai de grammaire du Patois lyonnais. pp. 309. *Bourg*, 1891. 8°. 12950. e. 39

MACAO. ACCACIO DA SILVEIRA PINTO (A.) Documentos de Macau. 1892. 8°. Ac. Lisbon. *Sociedade de Geographia.* Boletim. Ser. 11 a. Ac. 6020.

HONGKONG. *Hongkong, Canton and Macao Steamboat Company.* Information to travellers. pp. 21. *Hongkong*, 1893. 12°. Pam. 88.

HURLEY (R. C.) Tourists' guide to Canton and Macao. pp. 87. *Hongkong*, 1895. 8°. 10057. aaa. 9.

See also PORTUGAL, *Colonies.*

MACCLESFIELD. MACCLESFIELD. Walk through the public institutions of Macclesfield. pp. 190. *Macclesfield*, 1888. 4°. 10358. dd. 24.

MACEDONIA : MACEDO-ROUMANIANS. DONNER (E.) Compte rendu d'un voyage d'exploration dans la Macédoine. pp. 69. *Brux.* 1892. 8°. Pam. 88.

GLUECK (L.) Albanien und Macedonien. pp. 71. *Würzburg*, 1892. 8°. 10125. aa. 20.

GOLTZ (C. v. d.) *Baron.* Ein Ausflug nach Macedonien. pp. 154. *Berl.* 1894. 8°. 10125. aaa. 23.

MACEDONIA. Report on Macedonia since the Treaty of Berlin. pp. 54. *Lond.* 1880. 8°. Pam. 67.

NAUMANN (E.) Macedonien und seine neue Eisenbahn Salonik-Monastyr. pp. 58. *München*, 1894. 8°. 10125. cc. 35.

MACEDONIA—*continued.*

WEIGAND (G.) Die Aromunen. Untersuchungen über das Volk der sogenannten Makedo-Romanen. *Leipz.* 1894, *etc.* 8°.   012264. f. 17.

For the ancient history of Macedonia, *see* GREECE.

MAC GILL UNIVERSITY, Montreal. *See* MONTREAL.

MACHINERY: MECHANICAL EN-GINEERING.

General.

AC. London. *S.K. Museum.* List of books on Engineering and Machinery. pp. 68. *Lond.* 1889. 8°.   BB. E. a.

ADAMS (H.) Handbook for Mechanical Engineers. pp. 263. *Lond.* 1891. 8°. 8767. aa. 47.

APPLEBY (C. J.) Illustrated Handbook of Machinery. *Lond.* 1895, *etc.* 8°. 8766. de. 30.

BALE (M. P.) Modern Shafting and Gearing and economical transmission of power. pp. 102. 1893. 8°. Rider's Technical Series. No. 1. 7078. e.

BARBER (T. W.) Repair and maintenance of Machinery. pp. 466. *Lond.* 1895. 8°.
                    8767. k. 29.

BENJAMIN (P.) Modern Mechanism. pp. 924. *Lond.* 1892. 8°.   8768. f. 5.

BENTLEY (W.) Questions in Machine Construction and drawing. pp. 34. *Lond.* 1895. 8°.
                    Pam. 79.

BLAINE (R. G.) Elementary lessons in Machine design. pp. 208. *Lond.* 1893. 8°. 8767. g. 11.

BOLTON (R.) Motive Powers and their selection. pp. 257. *Lond.* 1895. 8°.   8767. cc. 31.

BROWNE AND SHARPE MANUFACTURING COMPANY. Treatise on the construction and use of Grinding Machines. pp. 147. *Providence,* 1891, 8°.
                    8768. i. 28.

—— A Treatise of the construction and use of Milling Machines. pp. 182. *Providence,* 1891. 8°·
                    07945. h. 31.

—— Treatise on Gearing. pp. 126. *Providence,* 1892. 8°.   8768. l. 14.

—— Formulas in Gearing. pp. 66. *Providence,* 1892. 8°.   8768. l. 10.

BUILDING DRAUGHTSMAN. Building and Machine Draughtsman. pp. 296. *Lond.* 1891. 8°.
                    8768. c. 29.

CHICAGO. *Columbian Exposition.* Official Catalogue. Machinery Hall and Annexes. pp. 48. *Chicago,* 1893. 8°.   7958. bb. 30.

CLARK (D. K.) Mechanical Engineer's Pocketbook. pp. 666. *Lond.* 1893. 8°. 8767. ee. 3.

CLERK (D.) Notes on Motive Power inventions. *Birmingham,* 1891, *etc.* 8°.   8767. f. 2.

CROWTHER (W. E.) Text-book of Machine construction and drawing. pp. 48. *Manch.* 1892. obl. 4°.   8767. cc. 23.

CRYER (T.) and JORDAN (H. G.) Machine construction and drawing. *Lond.* 1893. obl. 8°.
                    8768. bb. 5.

DAVY (W.) Machine Construction. Drawings. *Durham,* 1894, *etc.* 8°.   8768. m.

DREDGE (J.) Record of the Transportation exhibits at the Columbian Exposition. pp. 779. 1894. 4°. Engineering Series.   8755. m.

FLATHER (J. J.) Dynamometers and the Measurement of power. pp. 215. *N.Y.* 1892. 8°.
                    8768. bb. 4.

FOLEY (N.) Mechanical Engineer's reference book for machine construction. pp. 203. *Lond.* 1895. 4°.   8765. h. 27.

H., J. Helical Gears. pp. 127. 1893. 4°. Specialists' Series.   8708. k.

—— Toothed Gearing. pp. 208. *Lond.* 1892. 8°.   8767. f. 21.

MACHINERY.—General—*continued.*

H., J. Principles of Fitting. pp. 313. *Lond.* 1893. 8°.   8767. b. 49.

—— Pattern Making. pp. 336. *Lond.* 1894. 8°.   7817. bb. 4.

HALLIDAY (G.) Belt Driving. pp. 100. *Lond.* 1894. 8°.   8768. k. 16.

HOWARD AND BULLOUGH. Machinery Calculations and memoranda. pp. 123. *Accrington,* 1893. 8°.   8765. aa. 45.

HUTTON (W. S.) Practical Engineer's handbook. pp. 478. *Lond.* 1892. 8°.   8768. l. 9.

—— Works' Manager's hand-book. pp. 410. *Lond.* 1895. 8°.   8768. i. 30.

IMRAY (J.) and BIGGS (C. H. W.) First Principles of mechanical Engineering. pp. 368. *Lond.* 1893. 8°.   8767. f. 36.

INNES (C. H.) Problems in Machine design. pp. 187. *Manch.* 1894. 8°.   8767. g. 4.

JONES (T.) Engineering. [Sheets of diagrams, *etc.*] Nos. 1-32. 1888. 8°.   8767. cc. 12.

—— Machine Drawing. *Manch.* 1893, *etc.* 4°.
                    8768. g.

KIRKALDY (W. G.) Illustration of Kirkaldy's System of Mechanical Testing. pp. 302. *Lond.* 1891. 4°.   8765. g. 21.

LINEHAM (W. J.) Text-book of Mechanical Engineering. pp. 772. *Lond.* 1894. 4°.
                    8768. b. 1.

LOCKWOOD (C.) Dictionary of terms used in Mechanical Engineering. pp. 442. *Lond.* 1892. 8°.   8767. f. 22.

LOW (D. A.) and BEVIS (A. W.) Manual of Machine drawing and design. pp. 375. *Lond.* 1893. 8°.   8768. cc. 20.

MACHINIST. The General Machinist. pp. 204. *Lond.* 1891. 8°.   8768. cc. 13.

MARKS (E. C. R.) Mechanical Engineering materials. pp. 52. *Manch.* 1893. 8°.   8767. f. 35.

MOLESWORTH (*Sir* G. L.) Pocket book of formulae, *etc.,* for Mechanical Engineers. pp. 783. *Lond.* 1893. 8°.   8767. de. 1.

NICHOLSON (J. S.) Effects of Machinery on wages. pp. 143. *Lond.* 1892. 8°. 08276. e. 39.

REULEAUX (F.) The Constructor. Hand-book of machine design. pp. 312. *Lond.* 1893, 4°.
                    8767. l. 8.

RICHARD (G.) Le Mécanique générale à l'Exposition de Chicago. 1894. 8°. Ac. Paris. *Conservatoire des Arts.* Annales, *etc.* Sér. 2. Tom. 6.   Ac. 4415.

ROSE (J.) Complete practical Machinist. pp. 504. *Phila.* 1895. 8°.   8767. cc. 32.

SAMUELSON (J.) Labour-saving Machinery. pp. 94. *Lond.* 1893. 8°.   8277. de. 31.

SHELLEY (C. P B.) Workshop Appliances. pp. 377. 1894. 8°. GOODEVE (T. M.) Text-Books of Science.   2244. a. 21.

SPANGLER (H. W.) Valve-gears. pp. 175. *N.Y.* 1890. 8°.   8768. i. 29.

SPON (E.) Workshop Receipts. pp. 420. *Lond.* 1895. 8°.   2266. aa. 24.

TEMPLETON (W.) Modernised Templeton. Practical mechanic's workshop companion. pp. 474. *Lond.* 1895. 8°.   7820. aa. 32.

TROWBRIDGE (W. P.) Statistics of Power and Machinery. 1885-87. 4°. U.S. Tenth Census, *etc.* Vol. 16, 17.   1882. b. 16. 17.

USHER (J. T.) The modern Machinist. pp. 322. *Lond.* 1895. 8°.   8768. b. 4.

VAN CLEVE (B. F.) English and American Mechanic. pp. 476. *Phila.* 1890. 8°. 8768. cc. 9.

MACHINERY.—General—*continued.*

WILSON (W. H.) Manual of Pattern making and moulding. pp. 308. *Manch.* 1894. 8°.
8768. cc. 27.

See also ENGINEERING : INDUSTRIES.

Agricultural Machinery. *See* AGRICULTURE.

Electric Machinery.
See ELECTRICITY : RAILWAYS.

Gas and Oil Engines.

DONKIN (B.) Text-book on Gas, Oil, and Air Engines. pp. 419. *Lond.* 1894. 8°.
8768. bbb. 39.

LIECKFELD (G.) Die Petroleum- und Benzinmotoren. pp. 230 *München,* 1894. 8°. 8766. cc. 26.

RICHARD (G.) Les nouveaux Moteurs à gaz et à pétrole. 4 pt. *Paris,* 1892. 8° & 4°. 8768. f. 4.

VERMAND (P.) Les Moteurs à gaz et à pétrole. pp. 176. 1893. 8°. Encyclopédie des aide-mémoire.
8709. g.

WITZ (A.) Traité des Moteurs à gaz. pp. 435. *Paris,* 1892. 8°. 8768. m. 2.

Hydraulic Machinery. *See* HYDRAULICS.

Lifting Machinery, Cranes, etc.

COLYER (F.) Hydraulic, steam and hand-power Lifting Machinery. pp. 197. *Lond.* 1892. 8°.
8768. f. 7.

DELACHANAL (E.) Les grues électriques du port du Havre. 1895, *etc.* 8°. Ac. Paris. *Société des Ingénieurs.* Mémoires. Sér. 5. Ann. 48.
Ac. 4305.

G. B. & I. *Army.* Derricks, Sheers, and Holdfasts. pp. 139. *Lond.* 1893. 16°. 8831. e. 15.

JHERING (A. v.) Amerikanische Wasserhebemaschinen. 1893. 4°. Ac. Berlin. *Verein zur Beförderung das Gewerbfleisses.* Verhandlungen. 1893, 4.
Ac. 4435.

MARKS (E. C. R,) Notes on the construction of Cranes and lifting machinery. pp. 138. *Manch.* 1892. 8°. 8767. f. 18.

WEISBACH (J.) Mechanics of hoisting machinery. pp. 332. *Lond.* 1893. 8°. 8768. e. 25.

Mining Machinery. *See* MINERALOGY.

Steam Engines, *Locomotive and Stationary :* Railway Machinery,

ALEXANDER (J.) Model Engine construction. pp. 324. *Lond.* 1894. 8°. 8767. g. 29.

ALHEILIG (A.) and ROCHE (C.) Traité des Machines à vapeur. pp. 604. 1895. 8°. LECHALAS (M. C.) Encyclopédie industrielle.
8709. c.

—— Construction et résistance des Machines à vapeur. pp. 224. 1894. 8°. Encyclopédie des aide-mémoire.
8709. g.

BALE (M. P.) Handbook for Steam users. pp. 99. *Lond.* 1891. 8°. 8767. f. 11.

BRIGGS (C.) Simple and automatic Vacuum Brakes. pp. 48. *Leeds,* 1892. 8°. 8767. i. 4.

BROWN (A. G.) The Indicator for Steam Engines. pp. 265. *Manch.* 1894. 8°. 8767. g. 20.

BURN (R. S.) The Steam Engine. pp. 184. *Lond.* 1894. 8°. 8768. cc. 34.

—— The Steam Engine user. pp. 402. *Lond.* 1894. 8°. 8767. cc. 29.

CLARK (D. K.) The Steam Engine. 2 vol. *Lond.* 1890. 8°. 8768. f. 2.

COLYER (F.) Treatise on the working and management of Steam Engines. pp. 108. *Lond.* 1892. 8°. 8767. f. 10.

COOKE (C. J. B.) British Locomotives. pp. 381. *Lond.* 1893. 8°. 8767. g. 13.

COTTERILL (J. H.) The Steam Engine. pp. 426. *Lond.* 1890. 8°. 8768. cc. 10.

MACHINERY.—Steam, etc.—*continued.*

DAY (C.) Indicator Diagrams and engine testing. pp. 205. *Manch.* 1895. 8°. 8767. g. 27.

DEHARME (E.) and PULIN (A.) Chemins de fer. Matériel roulant. pp. 441. 1895. 8°. LECHALAS (M. C.) Encyclopédie industrielle. 8709. c.

DEMOULIN (M.) Traité de la construction des Machines à vapeur. pp. 430. *Paris,* 1895. 4°.
8767. dd. 19.

DYER (H.) The Steam Engine since the days of Watt. pp. 36. *Greenock,* 1889. 8°. Pam. 79.

ELLIS (W. I.) The Consumption of steam and water in Steam Engines. pp. 15. *Manch.* 1894. 8°. 8767. cc. 30. (17.)

EWING (J. A.) The Steam and other heat-Engines. pp. 400. *Camb.* 1894. 8°. 8768. k. 15.

FAY (P.) Guide du Traceur-Mécanicien. pp. 279. *Paris,* 1890. 8°. 8768. cc. 7.

FLETCHER (W.) History of Steam locomotion on roads. pp. 288. *Lond.* 1891. 8°. 8767. i. 30.

FREYTAG (F.) Die Dampfmaschinen der pariser Weltausstellung 1889. pp. 128. *Stuttgart,* 1891. 8°. 8768. l. 11.

FRYKHOLM (J. L.) Ångmaskinlära. pp. 366. *Stockholm,* 1890. 8°. 8807. e. 29.

GOODEVE (T. M.) Text-book on the Steam Engine. pp. 357. 48. *Lond.* 1891. 8°. 2249. b. 7.

G. B. & I. *Railways.* Round the Works of our great Railways. pp. 232. *Lond.* 1893. 8°.
8767. g. 12.

GRIMSHAW (R.) The Engine Runner's catechism. pp. 366. *N.Y.* 1891. 8°. 8767. a. 33.

—— The Locomotive catechism. pp. 362. *N.Y.* 1893. 8°. 8768. bb. 6.

HAEDER (H.) Handbook on the Steam Engine. pp. 440. *Lond.* 1893. 8°. 8767. f. 34.

HENTHORN (J. T.) The Corliss Engine and its management. pp. 96. *N.Y.* 1894. 8°. 8767. ee. 5.

HUGHES (G.) Construction of the modern Locomotive. pp. 261. *Lond.* 1894. 4°. 8767. k. 30.

JAMIESON (A,) Text-book on Steam-Engines. pp. 424. *Lond.* 1894. 8°. 8767. cc. 27.

JONES (H W.) Notes upon the management of Steam Engines. pp. 23. *Lond.* 1891. 8°.
8831. l. 12. (6.)

JONGKEES (A.) Beginselen der Stoomwerktuigkunde. pp. 699. *Hellevoetsluis,* 1891. 4°.
8767. f. 25.

KAHLBAUM (G. W. A.) Studien über Dampfspannkraftsmessungen. 2 pt. *Basel,* 1893. 8°.
8768. f. 12.

LANGMAID (J.) Elementary lessons in Steam machinery. pp. 197. *Torquay,* 1893. 8°. 8768. cc. 19.

LEASK (A. R.) Triple and quadruple expansion Engines. pp. 246. *Lond.* 1892. 8°. 8767. g. 9.

LELOUTRE (G.) Le fonctionnement des Machines à vapeur. pp. 223. 1894. 8°. Encyclopédie des aide-mémoire.
8709. g.

LE VAN (W. B.) Safety-valves. pp. 181. *Lond.* 1892. 12°. 8767. ee. 2.

LONDON. *Perkins Engine Company.* Official Reports of trial tests proving the advantages of the Perkins system of Engines. pp. 103. *Lond.* 1891. 8°. 8768. cc. 16.

LONDON. *Refuse Disposal Company.* Steam Power from house-dust. pp. 15. *Lond.* 1892. 8°. Pam. 79.

MAC DONNELL (R. W.) Elementary treatise on the Steam Engine. pp. 84. *Dublin,* 1895. 8°.
8767. g. 31.

—— Through Locomotive Works. pp. 66. *Dublin,* 1894. 8°. 8767. g. 21.

MADAMET (A.) Distribution de la Vapeur. pp. 152. 1893. 8°. Encyclopédie des aide-mémoire.
8709. g.

MACHINERY.—Steam, etc.—_continued._

MALLET (A.) Locomotives à adhérence totale pour courbes de petit rayon. 1894. 8°. Ac. Paris. _Société des Ingénieurs._ Mémoires. Sér. 5, ann. 47.   Ac. 4305.

MATHIEU (H.) L'A B C du Chauffeur. pp. 267. _Paris_, 1895. 16°.   8777. aa. 5.

MOREAU (A.) Traité des Chemins de fer. 1891, _etc._ 8°. LACROIX (D.) Encyclopédie des connaissances civiles.   8708. n.

MUSGRAVE (J.) Catalogue of vertical quadruple expansion Engines. pp. 283. _Bolton_, 1891. 8°.   8768. l. 8.

ORMEROD (C.) Driver's and Fireman's correspondent. pp. 71. _Plymouth_, 1895. 16°.   10920. a. 37.

PINCKNEY (P.) Summary of lecture : "Coming era of cheap Steam." pp. 18. _Portsmouth_, 1893. 24°.   Pam. 79.

POOL (C.) Working drawings of model Steam Engines. _Nottingham_, 1891. fol.   1802. d. 6.

PRAY (T.) Steam tables and Engine constants. pp. 85. _N.Y._ 1894. 8°.   8768. d. 34.

PORTER (C. T.) Treatise on the Richards Steam-Engine indicator. pp. 285. _Lond._ 1894. 8°.   8768. cc. 37.

PULLEN (W. W. F.) Injectors : their theory, construction and working. pp. 188. _Manch._ 1893. 8°.   8767. f. 40.

RANKINE (W. J. M.) Manual of the Steam Engine. pp. 615. _Lond._ 1891. 8°.   2249. b. 16.

RIGG (A.) Treatise on the Steam Engine, pp. 379. _Lond._ 1894. 4°.   8767. dd. 17.

SAUVAGE (É.) La Machine locomotive. pp. 327. _Paris_, 1894. 8°.   8767. g. 18.

SCHWEIGER-LERCHENFELD (A. v.) _Baron._ Vom rollenden Flügelrad. pp. 783. _Wien_, 1894. 8°.   8768. l. 24.

STACKHOUSE (J. F.) "Our Locomotives." _Lond._ 1895. obl. 4°.   8768. cc. 40.

STRETTON (C. E.) Locomotive Engine and its development. pp. 208. _Lond._ 1895, 8°. 8767. g. 22.

SUTCLIFFE (G. W.) Steam Power and mill-work. pp. 886. 1895. 8°. Specialist's Series. 8708. k.

VAUGHAN (M. G.) Locomotive Engineman's and Fireman's examination guide. pp. 80. _Plymouth_, 1895. 16°.   8767. a. 35.

WARREN (I.) Elementary treatise on Heat and the Steam Engine. pp. 426. _Dublin_ 1895. 8°.   8768. b. 3.

WEIR (J.) Steam Engine efficiency. pp. 75. _Glasg._ 1891. 8°.   8767. f. 3.

—— Steam Engine and energy conservation. pp. 148. _Glasg._ 1892. 8°.   8768. bb. 7.

WIDMANN (E.) Principes de la Machine à vapeur. pp. 156. 1893. 8°. Encyclopédie des aide-mémoire.   8709. g.

WITZ (A.) La Machine à vapeur. pp. 324. _Paris_, 1891. 12°.   8767. f. 12.

WRIGHT (J.) Indicator Diagram Record-book. _Westminster_, 1895. obl. 8°.   8767. de. 6.

WOOLWICH. _Artillery College._ Notes and memoranda on the Management of Steam Engines. pp. 23. _Lond._ 1891. 8°.   8830. d. 11. (7,)
See also BOILERS : RAILWAYS.

Marine Engines and Machinery.

See NAVAL SCIENCE, _Steamers, etc._

MÂCON. L'Architecture romane dans l'ancien diocèse de Mâcon. 1889, _etc._ 8°. Ac. Autun. _Société Éduenne._ Mémoires. Nouvelle sér. Tom. 17, _etc._   Ac. 5288/2.

MADAGASCAR. BENOÎT (F.) Madagascar. pp. 35. _Dijon_, 1895. 8°.   010095. l. 7.

MADAGASCAR—_continued._

BONNEMAISON (J.) Historique de Madagascar. pp. 180. _Tarbes_, 1894. 8°.   9061. d. 25.

BUNN (R. E.) Madagascar. pp. 24. _Lond._ 1895. 8°.   Pam. 89.

CHATEL (L.) Madagascar. pp. 44. _Lille_, 1895, 8°.   Pam. 89.

CATAT (L.) Voyage à Madagascar. 1889–90. pp. 436. _Paris_, 1895. 4°.   1787. aaa. 13.

COLSON (P. L.) Guide de Madagascar. pp. 220. _Paris_, 1895. 8°.   10097. c. 44.

COUSINS (W. E.) Madagascar of to-day. pp. 159. _Lond._ 1895. 8°.   4429. g. 6.

DAWSON (E. W.) Madagascar, past, present, and future. pp. 98. _Lond._ 1893. 8°.   010097. f. 2.

—— Madagascar : its capabilities and resources. pp. 83. _Lond._ 1895. 8°.   10096. b. 3.

DOMERGUE (A.) Simples notes de voyages. Madagascar. pp. 210. _Paris_, 1893. 8°.   010096. f. 33.

FERRAND (G.) Les Musulmans à Madagascar. 1891, _etc._ 8°. Ac. Algiers. _École Supérieure._ Publications, _etc._ pt. 9.   Ac. 5350/2.

GAUTIER (E) Guide du colon et du soldat à Madagascar. pp. 208. _Paris_, 1895. 8°.   10095. de. 23.

G. B. & I. _Hydrographic Office._ Islands in the Southern Indian Ocean, including Madagascar. pp. 480. _Lond._ 1891. 8°.   10496. g. 39.

LA VAISSIÈRE (P. C. M. L. de) Histoire de Madagascar, 2 tom. _Paris_, 1884. 8°. 4766. ff. 26.

LE CHARTIER (H.) and PELLERIN (G.) Madagascar depuis sa découverte jusqu'à nos jours. pp. 375. _Paris_, 1888. 8°.   10097. de. 19.

MAHY (F. de) Autour de Madagascar, _etc._ pp. 290. _Paris_, 1891. 8°.   010096. e. 45.

MANDAT GRANCEY (E. de) Souvenirs de la Côte d'Afrique, _etc._ _Paris_, 1892. 12°. 10097. ccc. 4.

MARTINEAU (A.) Madagascar. pp. 393. _Paris_, 1895. 8°.   010097. f. 4.

MAUDE (F. C.) Five years in Madagascar. pp. 285. _Lond._ 1895. 8°.   010096. e. 75.

MILHAUD (A.) Madagascar. pp. 192 _Paris_, 1894. 8°.   10096. a. 1.

PAISANT (M.) Madagascar. pp. 142. _Paris_, 1895. 8°.   010095. i. 8.

PIOLET (J. B.) Madagascar. pp. 587. _Paris_, 1895. 12°.   010097. e. 6.

TOWNSEND (W. J.) Madagascar : its missionaries and martyrs. pp. 160. _Lond._ 1892. 8°.   4767. ccc. 13.

ALLARD (L. E.) L'Immigration française à Madagascar. pp. 16. _Paris_, 1895. 8°. Pam. 66.

AUBANEL (N.) La France civilisatrice. Madagascar. pp. 278. _Paris_, 1895. 4°. 10096. i. 18.

BRUNET (L.) La France à Madagascar, 1815–95. pp. 367. _Paris_, 1895. 8°.   8027. b. 5.

CRESCENT (A.) Madagascar. Les droits de la France. 1895. 8°. Ac. Lyons. _Société de Géographie._ Bulletin. Tom. 13.   Ac. 6028.

DRUT (P.) Madagascar. Que sera l'Expédition ? pp. 64. _Paris_, 1894, 8°.   Pam. 67.

HUARD (L.) La Guerre illustrée. Madagascar. pp. 383. _Paris_, 1887. 4°.   9061. h. 7.

HUMBERT (G. L.) Madagascar. La dernière guerre franco-hova, 1883–85. pp. 166. _Paris_, 1895. 8°.   010096. ee. 48.

JOÛBERT (J.) La question de Madagascar. Les droits de la France. pp. 62. _Paris_, 1895. 8°.   8028. e. 33.

MARTINEAU (A.) Étude de politique. Madagascar en 1894. pp. 500. _Paris_, 1894. 8°.   8028. ff. 19.

MADAGASCAR—*continued.*

Moulin (J.) Madagascar et l'expédition française, 1883–86. pp. 71. *Cette*, 1886. 8°.
    Pam. 89.

Routier (G.) Les Droits de la France sur Madagascar. pp. 271. *Paris*, 1895. 12°.
    8027. b. 6.

See also Folk Lore: Malagasy Language: Nossi-Bé.

MADEIRA. Brown (A. S.) Madeira and the Canary Islands. pp. 267. *Lond.* 1894. 8°.
    10161. aaa. 19.

Ellerbeck (J. H. T.) Madeira and the Canary Islands. pp. 31. *Liverp.* 1891. 8°. Pam. 89.

Gale (B. T.) Visit to Madeira. pp. 19.
Lond. 1895. 8°.   Pam. 89.

Gordon (C. A.) The Flower of the ocean; Madeira. pp. 110. *Lond.* 1894. 8°.
    010096. ff. 28.

Lee (H.) Madeira and the Canary Islands. 2 pt. *Liverp.* 1888. 8°.   10095. bbb. 4.

Marsh (A. E. W.) Holiday wanderings in Madeira. pp. 180. *Lond.* 1892. 8°.
    10097. ccc. 12.

MADRAS, City and Presidency. Madras. Press list of ancient Records in Fort St. George, 1670, *etc. Madras*, 1891, *etc.* fol.   11906. l.

—— Diary and Consultation-book of the Agent Governor and Council 1682.
Madras, 1894, *etc.* 8°.   8022. f.

Bradshaw (J.) Sir T. Munro and the British Settlement of Madras. pp. 233. 1894, 8°.
Hunter (*Sir* W. W.) Rulers of India.
    10603. dd.

Madras. Collection of Letters between the Madras Government and Eyles Irwin, 1781–85. pp. 100. *Madras*, 1888. 8°.   8023. b. 14.

Srinivāsa Rāghavaiyaugār. Memorandum on the progress of the Madras Presidency during the last forty years. pp. 340. *Madras*, 1893. 8°.
    9056. dd. 24.

Madras. Charters of the High Court of Judicature at Madras, 1687–1865. pp. 160.
Madras, 1888. 4°.   8023. l. 10.

P.P. *Madras.* Madras Law Journal.
Madras, 1891, *etc.* 8°.   P.P. 1351. agb.

Annadurai Aiyar. Revenue Code, 1802–89. 2 vol. *Madras*, 1889. 8°.   5318. c. 21.

Madras. Guide to the city of Madras. pp. 199. *Madras*, 1889. 8°.   010057. c. 8.

Rea (A.) List of ancient Monuments selected for conservation in the Madras Presidency in 1891. pp. 28. *Madras*, 1891. fol. 7706. h. 26.
See also India: Malabar.

MADRID. Pérez Pastor (C.) Bibliografía madrileña, siglo xvi. pp. 431.
Madrid, 1891. 8°.   11899. h. 37.

Jorreto y Paniagua (M.) and Martínez Sanz (I.) Guia colombina. pp. 103. 102.
Madrid, 1892. 8°.   10160. cc. 8.

—— Las tres memorias sobre el Ayuntamiento de Madrid. pp. 70. *Madrid*, 1892. fol.
    8228. k. 34.

—— Biblioteca de la provincia de Madrid: crónica general de sus pueblos.
Madrid, 1889, *etc.* 8°.   10160. bbb.

Melgosa (M.) Los consumos en Madrid.
pp. 78. *Madrid*, 1892. 8°. 8228. aaaa. 19. (8.)

Peñasco de la Puente (H.) Páginas de la historia de Madrid. pp. 199. *Madrid*, 1891. 8°.
    10161. aaa. 17.

Sañudo Autrán (P.) Madrid fin de siglo.
pp. 113. *Madrid*, 1893. 8°. 10160. aaa. 20.

MADURA, India. *See* Missions.

MAESTRICHT. Habets (J.) De Fransche Emigranten te Maastricht. 1891. 8°. Ac.
Maestricht. *Société d'Archéologie.* Publications. Tom. 28.   Ac. 5500.

MAGDEBURG. Ac. Halle. *Historische Commission.* Urkundenbuch der Stadt Magdeburg. 1892, *etc.* 8°. Geschichtsquellen der Provinz Sachsen. Bd. 26, *etc.*   Ac. 7161.

Danneil (F. H. O.) Beitrag zur Geschichte des magdeburgischen Bauernstandes.
Halle, 1895, *etc.* 8°.   10240. i.

Leinung (W.) and Stumvoll (R.) Aus Magdeburgs Sage und Geschichte. pp. 237.
Magdeburg, 1894. 8°.   10256. c. 16.

Wolter (F. A.) Die staatsrechtliche Stellung Magdeburgs. pp. 68. 1893. 8°. Ac. Halle. *Thüringisch-sächsischer Verein.* Neue Mitteilungen. Bd. 18.   Ac. 7345.

Volkholz (R.) Die Zerstörung Magdeburgs, 1631. *Magdeburg*, 1892. 8°. 9079. f. 6.

Neubauer (E.) Wallenstein und die Stadt Magdeburg. pp. 246. *Magdeburg*, 1891. 8°.
    9326. dd. 5.

Wittich (C.) Pappenheim und Falkenberg. pp. 141. *Berl.* 1894. 8°. 09325. k. 12.

Holzapfel (R.) Forschungen zur Geschichte Magdeburgs aus der Zeit des Grossen Kurfürsten, *etc.* pp. 99. *Magdeburg*, 1892. 8°. 10240. c. 13.

MAGIC. *See* Legerdemain: Occult Science.

MAGIC LANTERN. Bolton (H. C.) Notes on the history of the Magic Lantern.
N.Y. 1889. 8°.   1810. d. 1. (4.)

Bothamley (C. H.) The Optical Lantern as an aid in teaching. pp. 48. *Lond.* 1892. 8°.
    8708. g. 27. (12.)

Hodges (J. A.) Lantern-slide Manual. pp. 142. *Lond.* 1892. 8°.   8909. bb. 37.

Pringle (A.) The Optical Lantern. pp. 99.
Lond. 1891. 8°.   8716. d. 6.

Transparencies. How to make Transparencies and Lantern slides. pp. 13. *Lond.* 1893. 8°. Pam. 13.

Wire (A. P.) and Day (G.) Knowledge through the Eye; how to illustrate lectures, *etc.* pp. 47.
Lond. 1894. 8°.   8716. aa. 12.

Wright (L.) Optical Projection: a treatise on the use of the lantern in exhibition. pp. 426.
Lond. 1891. 8°.   8716. aaa. 33.

MAGIC SQUARES. Barrett (T. S.) Magic Squares. pp. 32. *Berkhamsted*, 1894. 8°.
    7913. ee. 37.

Cavendish. Recreations with Magic Squares. pp. 84. *Lond.* 1894. 8°. 7913. c. 54.

Latoon (F.) On common and perfect Magic Squares. pp. 139. *Lond.* 1895. 4°. 8535. gg. 4.

Ozanam (J.) Magic Squares, and how to make them. pp. 32. *Berkhamsted*, 1893. 8°.
    8535. ccc. 48.

Portier (B.) Le Carré Diabolique de 9 et son dérivé le Carré Satanique de 9. pp. 31.
Alger, 1895. 8°.   Pam. 36.

Squares. Magic Squares: introduction to the study of their formation. pp. 32.
Berkhamsted, 1893. 8°.   8535. ccc. 43.

MAGNESIA, ad Meandrum. Kern (O.) Die Gründungsgeschichte von Magnesia am Maiandros. pp. 27. *Berl.* 1894. 4°. 9025. h. 17.
See also Ionia.

MAGNESIA, Mineral. Hanks (H. G.) History and description of Magnesia. pp. 27.
San Francisco, 1895. 8°.   Pam. 13.

MAGNETISM. *See* Electricity.

MAGNOLIA. King (G.) The Magnoliaceae of British India. 1891. fol. Calcutta. *Botanic Gardens.* Annals. Vol. 3.   1822. b.

MAHABALESHWAR. MAHABALESHWAR. Mahableshwar guide. pp. 91.
Bombay, 1890. 8°. 　　　　10057. aa. 10.

MAHÂBODHI. CUNNINGHAM (*Sir* A.) Mahâbodhi or the great Buddhist Temple at Buddha-Gaya. pp. 87. *Lond.* 1892. 4°. 　759. k. 7.

MAIN, River, Germany. FABER (E.) Zur Hydrographie des Maingebietes. pp. 185.
München, 1895. 8°. 　　　　8757. d. 40.

MAINE, France. CHARLES (R.) L'Invasion anglaise dans le Maine, 1417–28. 1889. 8°. Ac. Le Mans. *Société historique.* Revue, *etc.* Tom 25. 　　　　　Ac. 5321/3.

LE PAIGE (A. R.) Dictionnaire topographique du Maine. 2 tom. *Mayenne*, 1895. 8°. 4629. e. 37.

PIOLIN (P. L.) Le Théâtre chrétien dans le Maine au moyen-âge. 1891. 8°. Ac. Le Mans. *Société historique.* Revue. Tom. 29. Livr. 1. *See also* MAYENNE. 　　　　Ac. 5321/3.

MAINE, State of. U.S. GORGES (*Sir* F.) Sir F. Gorges and his Province of Maine. 3 vol. 1890. 4°. Ac. Albany. *Prince Society.* Publications. 　　　　　Ac. 9503.

FARRAR (C. A. J.) Through the Wilds. Sport and adventure in the forests of Maine. pp. 415. *Bost.* 1893. 8°. 　　　　10412. dd. 17.

HAYNES (G. H.) The State of Maine in 1893. pp. 98. *N.Y.* 1893. obl. 8°. 　10413. e. 7.

WALDRON (H. D.) The Summer State of Maine. pp. 24. *Bost.* 1893. 8°. 　10413. a. 18.

Ac. Portland. *Maine Genealogical Society.* Lincoln County Probate records.
Portland, 1893. *etc.* 8°. 　　　Ac. 5986/2.
See also NEW ENGLAND.

MAINZ. *See* MAYENCE.

MAISONS-LAFITTE. GALICHET (L.) Histoire de Maisons-Lafitte. pp. 400.
Maisons-Lafitte, 1893. 12°. 　10171. aaa. 25.

MAIZE. WILLIAMS (H.) AND Co. Fluctuations in price of maize. *Liverpool*, 1891. s. sh. fol.
　　　　　1882. d. 2. (72.)
See also CORN.

MAJORCA. *See* BALEARIC ISLES.

MALABAR. LOGAN (W.) Malabar. 3 vol. *Madras*, 1887–91. 8°. 　　10057. ee. 5.
See also MADRAS.

MALACODERMI. *See* COLEOPTERA.

MALACOSTRACA. *See* CRUSTACEA.

MALAGA. GUILLEN ROBLES (F.) Malaga musulmana. pp. 712. *Malaga*, 1880. 4°. 10161. f. 10
MALAGA. Relacion de la peste en Málaga, 1637. pp. 4. *Sevilla*, 1892. 8°. 　07305. h. 17. (9.)
PI Y MARGALL (F.) Granada, Málaga y Almería. pp. 576. 1885. 8°. España. Sus monumentos. 　　　　　2060. c.

MALAGASY LANGUAGE. SARDA (P.) Petit Dictionnaire français-malgache. pp. 226. *Paris*, 1895. 8°. 　　12910. a. 53.

COUSINS (W. E.) Concise Introduction to the study of the Malagasy Language. pp. 118. *Antananarivo*, 1894. 8°. 　12910. bb. 46.

DUBOIS (L. L.) Petit interprète du Soldat à Madagascar. pp. 26. *Paris*, 1895. 8°. Pam. 47.

MARRE DE MARIN (A.) Grammaire malgache. pp. 155. *Épinal*, 1894. 8°. 　12910. ccc. 3.

RAHIDY (P. B.) Cours pratique de Langue malgache. 3 pt. *Paris*, 1895. 8°. 12910. ccc. 2.

RICHARDSON (J.) Malagasy for beginners. pp. 120. *Antananarivo*, 1884. 8°. 12910. e. 30.

MALARIA. Ac. London. *New Sydenham Society.* MARCHIAFAVA (E.) Monographs on Malaria and the parasites of malarial fevers. pp. 428. *Lond.* 1894. 8°. 　Ac. 3838/61.

MALARIA—*continued.*

Ac. LONDON. *New Sydenham Society.* LAVERAN (A.) Paludism. pp. 197. *Lond.* 1893. 8°. 　　　　　　Ac. 3838/59.

BASTIANELLI (G.) and BIGNAMI (A.) Studi sulla infezione malarica. 1894. 8°. Ac. Rome. *Accademie Medica.* Atti. Vol. 15. Ac. 3707.

CROSSE (W. H.) Notes on Malarial Fevers on the River Niger. pp. 106. *Lond.* 1892. 8°. 　　　　　　7561. b. 32.

DAVIDSON (A.) Malarial diseases. 1893. 8°. Hygiene of Warm Climates. 　7686. dd. 2.

JOHNSTON (H. H.) Report on the relation between Malarial Fever at Mauritius and the meteorological elements. pp. 47.
Edinb. 1894. 8°. 　　　　Pam. 39.

LINDSAY (R.) Essay on Malaria and its Consequences. pp. 116. *Lond.* 1895. 8°. 07686. e. 11.

MANNABERG (J.) Die Malaria-Parasiten. pp. 195. *Wien*, 1893. 8°. 　7560. e. 19.

MARAGLIANO (E.) Behandlung der Malaria-krankheiten. 1894. 8°. PENZOLDT (F.) Handbuch der Therapie der Infektionskrankheiten. Bd. 1. 　　　　　7620. f.

MARCHIAFAVA (E.) and BIGNAMI (A.) Sulle Febbri malariche estivo-autunnali. 1892. 8°. Ac. Rome. *Accademia Medica.* Bullettino. Anno 18. 　　　　　Ac. 3707.

MATTEI (E. di) Contributo allo studio dell' Infezione malarica. pp. 102. 1895. 8°. Ac. Catania. *Accademia Gioenia.* Atti. Ser. 4. Vol. 8. 　　　　　Ac. 2805.

PEPPER (É.) De la Malaria. pp. 287.
· *Paris*, 1891. 8°. 　　　7686. aaa. 2.

PLEHN (F.) Ätiologische und klinische Malaria. pp. 47. *Berl.* 1890. 8°. 07305. k. 14. (3.)

SCHIAVUZZI (B.) La Malaria in Istria. 1890. 8°. Ac. Parenzo. *Società Istriana.* Atti. Vol. 5. 　　　　　Ac. 5230.

See also FEVERS.

MALAYALAM LANGUAGE. FOHNMEYER (L. J.) Grammar of the Malayalam language. *Mangalore*, 1889. 8°. 12906. dd. 37.

SUBBARĀYA AIYAR. Translation guide. English and Malayalam. *Cochin*, 1894, *etc.* 8°. 　　　　　14178. bb. 12.

MALAY LANGUAGE. BRANDSTETTER (R.) Malaio-polynesische Forschungen.
Luzern, 1893, *etc.* 4°. 　　　11825. q.

COWIE (A.) English-Sulu-Malay vocabulary. pp. 287. *Lond.* 1893. 8°. 　12907. bb. 4.

KEASBERRY (B. P.) English and Malay vocabulary. pp 88. *Singapore*, 1890. 12°. 12910. a. 26.

TOORN (J. L. v. d.) Minangkabausch-Maleisch-Nederlandsch Woordenboek. pp. 392.
's *Gravenhage*, 1891. 8°. 　12906. i. 21.

BRISSAUD (L.) Petit recueil malais-français. pp. 72. *Paris*, 1891. 12°. 12901. de. 17. (5.)

HINDORF (R.) Leitfaden zur Erlernung der malayischen Umgangssprache. pp. 72.
Berl. 1890. 8°. 　　　12910. aaa. 64.

HUDSON (H. H.) Malay Orthography. pp. 120. *Singapore*, 1892. 8°. 　12907. ee. 45.

MALAY PRONOUNCING HANDBOOK. Traveller's Malay Pronouncing handbook. pp. 299.
Lond. 1894. 16°. 　　　12910. a. 51.

MIDDEL (R. B.) De hoofdpunten der Maleische Grammatica toegelicht. pp. 57.
Amsterdam, 1893. 8°. 　　12910. b. 40.

ROST (R.) De la lengua y literatura Malayas. pp. 59. *Madrid*, 1895. 8°. 　12910. d. 36.

ROUVEROY VAN NIEUWAAL (M. C. v.) Het Maleisch in de Kazerne. pp. 96. *Breda*, 1891. 8°. 　　　　　12907. bb. 40.

MALAY LANGUAGE.—continued.

SEIDEL (A.) Grammatik der malayischen Sprache. pp. 176. 1891. 8°. Die Kunst der Polyglottie. Th. 34.   12902. c.

See also JAVAN LANGUAGE : MENANGKABO DIALECT.

MALAY PENINSULA AND MALAYSIA.

SHERBORN (C. D.) Bibliography of Malaya, 1888-90. 1890. 8°. Ac. Singapore. *Straits Asiatic Society.* Journal. No. 22.   Ac. 8828/4.

CLERCQ (F. S. A. de) Glimpses of the Eastern Archipelago. pp. 137. *Singapore,* 1894. 8°.   10491. dd. 10.

DENNYS (N. B.) Descriptive dictionary of British Malaya. pp. 423. *Lond.* 1894. 8°. 010057. l. 13.

KEANE (A. H.) Geography of the Malay Peninsula. pp. 192. *Lond.* 1892. 8°. 10055. aa. 3.

MAC LARTY (F. M.) Affairs of the Colony; history of the Straits Settlements and British Protected States of the Malay Peninsula. pp. 138. *Penang,* 1893. 8°. 9056. bb. 35.

MAC CALLUM (H. E.) A Trip across the Malay Peninsula. pp. 27. *Singapore,* 1894. 8°.   Pam. 88.

STRAITS SETTLEMENT. Précis concerning the Straits Settlements and the Native States of the Malay Peninsula. pp. 178. *Lond.* 1892. 8°.   010055. e. 12.

SWETTENHAM (F. A.) Malay Sketches. pp. 289. *Lond.* 1895. 8°.   010057. e. 37.

CARTHAUS (E.) Aus dem Reich von Insulinde. pp. 267. *Leipz.* 1891. 8°. 10470. g. 28.

G. B. & I. *Hydrographic Office.* Eastern Archipelago. 2 pt. *Lond.* 1890. 8°. 10496. ff. 20.

GUILLEMARD (F. H. H.) Stanford's Compend. of Geography. Australasia. Vol. 2. *Lond.* 1894. 8°.   2060. a.

HABERLANDT (G.) Indo-malayische Vegetationsbilder und Reiseskizzen. pp. 300. *Leipz.* 1893. 8°. 7054. h. 23.

HAGEN (B.) Anthropologische Studien aus Insulinde. pp. 149. 1890. 4°. Ac. Amsterdam. *K. Akademie van Wetenschappen.* Verhandelingen. Afdeeling Natuurskunde. Deel 28.   Ac. 944/2.

KNOX (M. V. B.) Winter in India and Malaysia. pp. 306. *N.Y.* 1891. 8°. 10058. cc. 33.

NIJLAND (E.) Schetsen uit Insulinde. pp. 411. *Utrecht,* 1892, 93. 8°. 10470. dd.

POWELL (B. F. S. B.) In Savage Isles and settled lands. pp. 438. *Lond.* 1892. 8°.   10026. g. 4.

SCHLEGEL (G.) Archives pour servir à l'étude de l'histoire, etc., de l'Asie Orientale. *Leide,* 1890, *etc.* 8°. 10058. h.

THOBURN (J. M.) India and Malaysia. pp. 562. *Cincinnati,* 1892. 8°. 4766. ee. 21.

See also BORNEO : CELEBES : INDIES, *Dutch* : JAVA : LAOS : MOLUCCAS : PENANG : PERAK : PHILIPPINE ISLANDS : STRAITS SETTLEMENTS : SUMATRA.

MALDON.

FITCH (E. A.) Maldon. pp. 12. *Colchester,* 1888. 12°. 10349. aa. 37. (4.)

MALINES.

CONINCKX (H.) Malines sous la République française. pp. 155. *Malines,* 1893. 8°. 10271. g. 6.

MALLING.

FIELDING (C. H.) Memories of Malling. pp. 291. *West Malling,* 1893. 8°. 010358. f. 36.

MALTA.

BALLOU (M. M.) Story of Malta. pp. 318. *Bost.* 1893. 8°. 10136. c. 24.

GAUCI (G.) Il grande assedio di Malta nel 1565. pp. 266. *Malta,* 1891. 8°. 9165. bb. 4.

MALTA —continued.

P.P. *Valetta.* Il Habbar Malti. *Malta,* 1889, *etc.* fol. 14599. f. 4.

PAGE (G. A.) Guide to Laws and Regulations of Malta. pp. 139. *Malta,* 1892. 8°. 6605. a. 4.

DINGLI (A.) Force and effects of Custom according to the Civil Law. With reference to the validity of marriages contracted in Malta. pp. 62. *Malta,* 1893. 8°.   Pam. 37.

BUSUTTIL (V.) Holiday customs in Malta. pp. 158. *Malta,* 1894. 8°. 12431. a. 36.

MALTA. Cost of living in Malta. pp. 23. *Malta,* 1895. 8°. 10136. aaa. 21.

BRUCE (D.) Malta Fever. 1893. 8°. DAVIDSON (A.) Hygiene of Warm Climates. 7686. dd. 2.

MALTA, Knights of.

BEDFORD (W. K. R.) Malta and the Knights Hospitallers. pp. 80. 1894. fol. The Portfolio. Monographs. No. 2.   P.P. 1931. pcd.

FAROCHON (P. A.) Les Chevaliers de Rhodes et de Malte. pp. 400. *Paris,* 1893. 4°. 4784. h. 10.

JOHN, *the Baptist, Saint. Knights Hospitallers.* Cartulaire général de l'Ordre des Hospitaliers, 1100-1310. *Paris,* 1894, *etc.* fol. 1896. b.

MUSCAT-FENECH (A.) Il Cavalieri ta Malta. pp. 61. *Malta,* 1882. 8°. 14599. b. 41. (2.)

CARRÉ DE BUSSEROLLE (J. X.) Catalogue des Chevaliers de Malte appartenant à des familles de la Touraine, de l'Anjou, *etc.* pp. 80. *Tours,* 1890. 8°. 9906. b. 9. (11.)

REID (H. J.) Ancient Religious Houses of Berks and Bucks. The Knights Hospitallers. pp. 15. *Reading,* 1890. 12°.   Pam. 25.

UNDERHILL (J.) St. John's, Clerkenwell. pp. 12. *Lond.* 1893. fol. K.T.C. 16. a. 3.

LA BRIÈRE (L. de) Souvenirs et vestiges de l'Ordre de Malte. pp. 43. *Évreux,* 1892. 8°.   Pam. 26.

—— L'Ordre de Malte en 1891. pp. 29. *Évreux,* 1891. 4°.   Pam. 26.

MONTAGNAC (de) *Baron.* L'Ordonnance des Chevaliers Hospitaliers. Description de l'uniforme. pp. 123. *Paris,* 1893. 4°. 4783. d. 19.

ROY (J. E.) L'Ordre de Malte en Amérique. pp. 68. *Québec,* 1888. 8°. 4784. cc. 47. (3.) *See also* MALTA.

MALTESE LANGUAGE.

CESAREO (P.) Rudimenti Grammaticali. pp. 39. *Malta,* 1891. 8°. 12901. ccc. 12. (6.)

FERRIS (A.) Primo Libro di Lettura Italo-maltese. pp. 46. *Malta,* 1891. 8°. 12903. aaa. 25.

—— Seguito al primo Libro di Lettura italo-maltese. pp. 84. *Malta,* 1893. 8°. 14599. b. 35. (2.)

LANZON (G. S.) Prose e Poesie in idioma maltese. pp. 34. *Malta,* 1889. 8°. 14599. b. 45. (6.)

LETARD (G. N.) Guida alla conversazione italiana, inglese e maltese. *Malta,* 1891, *etc.* obl. 16°.   12902. a.

PRECA (A.) Saggio intorno alla lingua maltese come affino dell' ebraico. pp. 115. *Malta,* 1880. 8°. 12904. c. 29.

MALVERN.

GRINDROD (C. F.) Malvern. pp. 221. *Malvern,* 1894. 8°. 10360. bbb. 6.

LINES (H. H.) Ancient camps on the Malvern Hills. pp. 16. *Worcester,* 1891. 8°. 7706. g. 4. (18.)

MAMMALIA.

Ac. Calcutta. *Indian Museum.* Catalogue of Mammalia. pt. 2. *Calcutta,* 1891. 8°. 7206. f. 9.

—— London. *British Museum.* Guide to the Galleries of Mammalia. pp. 126. *Lond.* 1894. 8°. 7206. f. 14.

MAMMALIA—*continued.*

FLOWER (W. H.) and LYDEKKER (R.) Introduction to the study of Mammals. pp. 763.
Lond. 1891. 8°.   7208. cc. 10.

HOSE (C.) Descriptive account of the Mammals of Borneo. pp. 78. *Diss,* 1893. 8°. 7206. cc. 7.

LYDEKKER (R.) Hand-book to the British Mammalia. pp. 339. 1895. 8°. SHARPE (R. B.) Allen's Naturalist's Library.   7001. eee.
See also ZOOLOGY, and under the name of each Order, Genus and Species.

MAMMOTH. DAWSON (G. M.) Notes on Mammoth-remains in the Yukon District of Canada and Alaska. pp. 9. *Lond.* 1894. 8°.
     07109. m. 7. (10.)
See also PALAEONTOLOGY.

MAN. ADONE (L.) Le origini dell' Uomo secondo i positivisti. pp. 222. *Napoli,* 1894. 8°.
     7005. aaa. 25.

ANDRESEN (C.) Die Entwickelung der Menschen. pp. 124. *Hamb.* 1891. 8°.   8467. f. 37.

AFPENT (J.) Die Geschichte des Menschen. pp. 96. *Leipz.* 1891. 8°.   8470. f. 17.

BELL (A. J.) Whence comes Man? 2 vol.
Lond. 1888–90. 8°.   4016. g. 10.

COMBE (G.) Constitution of Man in relation to natural laws. pp. 236. *Lond.* 1893. 8°.
     8462. bb. 29.

DRUMMOND (H.) Lowell Lectures on the Ascent of Man. pp. 444. *Lond.* 1894. 8°. 2236. cc. 22.

FUNCK-BRENTANO (T.) L'Homme et sa destinée. pp. 374. *Paris,* 1895. 8°.   9409. l. 32.

GORTON (D. A.) The Monism of Man. pp. 297. *N.Y.* 1893. 8°.   8470. f. 29.

HYDE (J.) Man : his nature, origin, and destiny. pp. 65. *Derby,* 1893, 8°.   Pam. 84.

KING (J. H.) Man an organic Community. 2 vol. *Lond.* 1893, 8°.   8462. f. 31.

LAIDLAW (J.) The Bible doctrine of Man. pp. 363. *Edinb.* 1895. 8°.   4465. i. 20.

LANG (C. R.) Son of Man. pp. 282.
Bost. 1892. 8°.   4018. bbb. 30.

LEE (J. W.) The making of a Man. pp. 372. *Lond.* 1893. 8°.   4371. aaa. 22.

MAC KINNEY (S. B. G.) Origin and nature of Man. pp. 95. *Lond.* 1895. 8°.   8466. c. 34.

MAN. Man in relation to Kosmos. pp. 45. *Lond.* 1890. 8°.   8463. d. 38. (12.)

PANAMA (M. de) *Viscountess.* Divine Problem of Man is a living Soul. pp. 111. *Lond.* 1894. 8°.
     4371. cc. 4.

S., J. The Great Problem ; Man's future place in the Universe. pp. 55. *Lond.* 1895. 8°.
     4257. bb. 21.

THORNTON (W.) Origin, purpose and destiny of Man. pp. 100. *Bost.* 1891. 8°.   8703. de. 41.
See also ANTHROPOLOGY : ETHNOLOGY.

MAN, Isle of. CAINE (T. H. H.) The little Manx Nation. pp. 159. *Lond.* 1891. 8°.
     10368. ccc. 37.

—— The little Man Island. pp. 50.
Douglas, 1894. 8°.   10368. cc. 51.

WALPOLE (S.) The Land of Home rule. pp. 287. *Lond.* 1893. 8°.   9509. k. 2.

MOORE (A. W.) Sodor and Man. pp. 276. 1893. 8°. Diocesan Histories.   4421. k.

KERMODE (P. M. C.) Catalogue of Manks Crosses. pp. 60. *Ramsay,* 1892. 8°. 7708. cc. 50.

MAN, *Isle of.* Statutes of the Isle of Man. *Lond.* 1883, *etc.* 8°.   6503. f.

MOORE (A. W.) Surnames and place-names of the Isle of Man. pp. 372. *Lond.* 1890. 8°.
     12978. f. 27.

MAN, Isle of—*continued.*

BOOTH (W.) The Isle of Man. pp. 103. 1892. 8°. Itinerary Series.   10368. aaa.

F., R. Beyond the silver streak in Manxland. pp. 72. *Manch.* 1894. 8°.   10348. c. 26. (7.)

ISLAND SCENERY. Island Scenery. pp. 144. *Lond.* 1893. 8°.   10368. e. 32.

MAHÉ DE LA BOURDONNAIS (A.) *Count.* Voyage dans l'Ile de Man. pp. 248. *Paris,* 1894. 8°.
     10368. f. 42.

MAN, *Isle of.* Guide to the Isle of Man. pp. 296. *Lond.* 1894. 8°.   10347. aaa. 39.

—— Brown's guide to the Isle of Man. pp. 401. *Douglas,* 1894. 8°.   10368. aa. 49.

SIMS (G. R.) Dagonet on our Islands. pp. 172. *Lond.* 1894. 8°.   10368. aa. 50.
See also MANX LANGUAGE.

MANCHESTER. Ac. Manchester. *Chetham Society.* Remains. N.S. Vol. 20, *etc.* Minutes of the Manchester Presbyterian Classes.
Manch. 1890, *etc.* 4°.   Ac. 8120.

—— Remains. N.S. Vol. 21, *etc.* Fellows of the Collegiate Church of Manchester.
Manch. 1891, *etc.* 4°.   Ac. 8120.

CROWTHER (J. S.) Architectural history of the Cathedral of Manchester. pp. 50.
Manch. 1893. fol.   7815. d. 7.

WARD, LOCK AND Co. Handbook to Manchester Cathedral. *Lond.* 1890. 8°.   010358. l. 14.

DIRECTORIES. *Manchester.* Manchester Directory for 1772. pp. 60. *Manch.* 1889. 8°.
     10352. cc. 39.

HORSFALL (T. C.) Government of Manchester. pp. 46. *Manch.* 1895. 8°.   Pam. 82.

MANCHESTER. Constable's accounts of the Manor of Manchester, 1612 to 1647, and 1743 to 1776. *Manch.* 1891, *etc.* 8°.   010358. l. 30.

—— Historical Record of recent enterprises of the Corporation of Manchester. pp. 192.
Manch. 1894. 8°.   10358. h. 26.

SIMPSON (J. H.) Law and Practice of the Court of Record for the Hundred of Salford. pp. 196. *Manch.* 1892. 8°.   6281. df. 8.

SINGTON (T.) Handbook of property values in Manchester, *etc. Manch.* 1889, *etc. obl.* 4°.
     1853. a. 15.

TATHAM (J.) Manchester Life Tables. New edition, 1893. pp. 57. *Manch.* 1893. 8°.
     08225. l. 22.

TOMLINSON (W.) Bye-ways of Manchester Life. pp. 286. *Manch.* 1887. 4°.   10368. g. 46.

Owens College.

Ac. Manchester. *Owens College.* Owens College. Descriptive sketch. pp. 24. *Manch.* 1891. 8°.
     8304. e. 20. (10.)

KAY (J. T.) Owens College. Notes on the Library. pp. 23. *Manch.* 1891. 8°.   Pam. 6.

MANCHESTER SHIP CANAL. HEYWOOD (J.) Guide to the Ship Canal. pp. 34.
Manch. 1894. 8°.   10348. ccc. 59. (10.)

MANCHESTER. Historical record of enterprises of the Corporation of Manchester. pp. 192.
Manch. 1894. 8°.   10358. h. 26.

PEMBER (E. H.) Manchester Ship Canal Bill. Reply of Mr. Pember on Behalf of the Promoters of the Bill. pp. 139. *Lond.* 1884. 8°.
     08235. e. 10.

MANCHESTER SHIP CANAL. Photogravure views. *Manch.* 1891. 16°.   10358 a. 47.

—— 12 "Photo Print" views. *Manch.* 1893. 16°.
     Pam. 76.

—— 18 Photo Print Views. *Manch.* 1894. *obl.* 8°.
     1701. b. 1. (120.)

MANCHESTER SHIP CANAL.—cont.

MANCHESTER SHIP CANAL. Panoramic views.
Manch. 1894. 8°.   10368. e. 33.

—— Handbook, schedule of rates and charges.
pp. 69. *Manch.* 1894. 8°.   08235. g. 16.

—— Illustrated history of the Canal. pp. 16.
Manch. 1894. 4°.   Pam. 90.

PULLIGNY (de) Canal maritime de Manchester. 1892. 8°. Ac. *Internationaler Binnenschifffahrts-Congress.* Quatrième Congrès, *etc.*
08235. h. 29.

MANCHU LANGUAGE. BANG (W.)
Uralaltaische Forschungen. pp. 44. 1890. 8°.
Einzelbeiträge zur Sprachwissenschaft. Hft. 10.
12902. g.

MOELLENDORFF (P. G. v.) Manchu Grammar.
pp. 52. *Shanghai*, 1892. 4°.   12910. g. 30.

MANCHURIA. CHRISTIE (D.) Ten years in
Manchuria. pp. 100. *Paisley*, 1895. 8°.
4767. bb. 23.

For Russian Manchuria, *see* SIBERIA.

MANDAEANS. ADAM. Mandäische Schriften aus der grossen Sammlung heiliger Bücher genannt Genzâ. pp. 232. *Göttingen*, 1893. 8°.
753. hh. 2.

MANDALAY. COLBECK (A. J.) Letters from
Mandalay. 1878–79 and 1885–88. pp. 113.
Knaresborough, 1892. 8°.   9056. aaa. 30.

See also BURMA.

MANICA. PAIVA DE ANDRADA (J. C.) Manica:
Report to the Minister of the Marine of Portugal.
pp. 63. *Lond.* 1891. 8°.   8022. bb. 27. (7.)

MANILA. BARRIE (A. D.) Away from ice to
Manilla in winter. pp. 70. *Dumfries*, 1890. 4°.
10470. g. 27.

FONSECA (J.) La Cathedral de Manila. pp. 82.
Manila, 1880. fol.   4745. f. 12.

See also PHILIPPINE ISLANDS.

MANIPUR. GRIMWOOD (E. St. C.) My Three
Years in Manipur. pp. 321. *Lond.* 1891. 8°.
9057. aaa. 33.

MANOMOHANA GHOSHA. Did the Manipur Princes obtain a fair trial? Arguments on behalf of Kula Chandra Sing, Maharaja of Manipur, and Tikendrajit Bir Sing, Jubraj of Manipur. pp. 121. *Lond.* 1891. 8°. 8023. cc. 27.

PRIMROSE (A. J.) Manipuri Grammar, vocabulary and phrase-book. pp. 100.
Shillong, 1888. 8°.   12906. dd. 41.

WRIGHT (M. J.) Three Years in Cachar. With an account of the Manipur massacre. pp. 188.
Lond. 1895. 8°.   10057. b. 9.

MANITOBA. CANADA. Manitoba and the
North-West territories, report by Mr. P. R. Ritchie. pp. 52. *Ottawa*, 1892. 8°.
10470. dd. 30. (6.)

DIONNE (N. E.) États-Unis, Manitoba et Nord-Ouest. pp. 184. *Quebec*, 1882. 8°. 10409. a. 20.

FOURSIN (P.) La Colonisation française au Canada, Manitoba. pp. 43. *Ottawa*, 1893. 8°.
Pam. 86.

LEGGE (A. O.) Sunny Manitoba. pp. 297.
Lond. 1893. 8°.   10470. f. 35.

MANITOBA. North-west farmer in Manitoba.
pp. 55. 1891. 8°.   10470. dd. 30. (3.)

—— Manitoba Official Handbook. pp. 64.
Liverpool, 1892. 8°.   Pam. 86.

—— Free homes in Manitoba. pp. 32.
Lond. 1892. 8°.   Pam. 86.

—— Manitoba. Opinions of eminent men.
pp. 15. *Liverpool*, 1892. 8°.   Pam. 86.

—— What Farmers say. pp. 16. *Lond.* 1892. 8°.
Pam. 86.

MANITOBA—continued.

MANITOBA. *Department of Agriculture.* Report on crops, live stock, etc., in Manitoba. pp. 14.
Winnipeg, 1892. 8°.   Pam. 1.

—— Report Delegates. Proceedings of a Delegation to report upon Manitoba, *etc.* pp. 24.
Lond. 1892. 8°.   Pam. 86.

—— Description of the Province. pp. 365.
Ottawa, 1893. 8°.   10470. h. 33.

—— Official information for investors and settlers.
pp. 32. *Liverpool*, 1893. 8°. 10470. dd. 30. (15.)

—— Why not go to Manitoba? pp. 8.
Liverpool, 1893. 16°.   Pam. 86.

MAC MICKEN (G.) The abortive Fenian Raid on Manitoba. pp. 11. *Winnipeg*, 1888. 8°.
9007. ff. 5. (2.)

PRENDERGAST (J. E. P.) The Manitoba School question. pp. 25. *Winnipeg*, 1893. 8°. Pam. 17.

TYRRELL (J. B.) Report on North-Western Manitoba. pp. 235. 1892. 8°. CANADA. *Geological Survey.* Report. N.S. Vol. 5, pt. 1. 7202. d.

MANNINGTON HALL. NEVILL (*Lady*
D. F.) Mannington and the Walpoles, Earls of Orford. pp. 42. *Lond.* 1894. obl. 8°. 1858. a. 4.

MANONVILLE. LEFEBVRE (H.) Manonville et ses Seigneurs. pp. 228. *Nancy*, 1891. 8°.
010171. f. 32.

MANORS. *See* LAND.

MANOSQUE. MANOSQUE. Livre des privilèges de Manosque, 1169–1315. pp. 6. 242.
Digne, 1894. 4°.   10172. i. 10.

MANSFIELD. GROVES (W. H.) History of
Mansfield. pp. 428. *Nottingham*, 1894. 8°.
10350. f. 34.

MANSFIELD. Ancient and modern Mansfield and report of Charter Day festivities. pp. 72.
Mansfield, 1891. 8°.   010358. g. 21.

MANTES. PERRIER DU CARNE ( ) L'Arrondissement de Mantes aux temps préhistoriques.
pp. 136. *Mantes*, 1894. 8°.   07708. k. 1.

MANTIDAE. *See* ORTHOPTERA.

MANTUA. BERTOLOTTI (A.) L'Archivio di
Stato in Mantova. pp. 61. *Montova*, 1892. 8°.
11901. g. 41.

—— I Comuni e le parrocchie della Provincia Mantovana. pp. 253. *Montova*, 1894. 8°.
10136. k. 8.

ARRIVABENE (F.) Vocabolario italiano-mantovano.
pp. 110. *Mantova*, 1892 4°.   12941. h. 31.

MANURES. ACLAND (*Sir* T. D.) Introduction to the Chemistry of Farming. pp. 222.
Lond. 1891. 8°.   07076. e. 29.

AIKMAN (C. M.) Farmyard Manure. pp. 65.
Edinb. 1892. 8°.   7077. de. 35.

—— Manures and the principles of manuring.
pp. 592. *Edinb.* 1894. 8°.   7078. e. 3.

BROWN (A.) Science of the Feeding stuffs and Manures of the farm. pp. 23. *Lewes*, 1894. 8°.
07031. de. 1. (10.)

CHRISTENSEN (C.) Gødnings læren. pp. 279.
Kjøbenh. 1893. 8°.   07028. g. 30.

DAVIS (G. W.) Hand Book on the chemistry of commercial Manures. pp. 118. *Lond.* 1895. 8°.
7073. aa. 2.

DYER (B.) Fertilisers and Feeding stuffs, their properties and uses. pp. 122. *Lond.* 1894. 8°.
7073. b. 61.

GRANDEAU (L. N.) Emploi du Nitrate de soude en agriculture. pp. 22. *Paris*, 1890. 8°.
7074. e. 9. (2.)

—— Instruction sur l'emploi du Nitrate de soude en agriculture. pp. 49. *Paris*, 1890. 8°.
7074. e. 9. (3.)

GRIFFITHS (A. B.) Treatise on Manures. pp. 447.
1892. 8°. Specialists' Series.   8708. k.

2 o 2

MANURES—*continued.*

LARBALETRIER (A.) Les Engrais et la fertilisation du sol. pp. 352. *Paris*, 1891. 12°. 7077. de. 34.

LLORENTE (A.) Teoria de los Abonos minerales aplicada á la nutrición de las plantas. pp. 76. *Zaragoza*, 1893. 8°.   Pam. 1.

LONDON. *Permanent Nitrate Company.* Nitrate in the garden. pp. 8. *Lond.* 1892. 8°. Pam. 1.

HARRIS (J.) Essay on Nitrate of soda as a Manure. pp. 96. *Lond.* 1890. 8°. 7073. de. 14. (9.)

MAERCKER (M.) Die Kalidüngung in ihrem Werte für die Erhöhung der landwirtschaftlichen Produktion. pp. 287. *Berl.* 1892. 8°.   7074. g. 2.

MUNRO (J. M. H.) Soils and Manures. pp. 275. 1892. 8°. Cassell's Agricultural Readers.   7077. de.

NITRATE. How to use Nitrate. pp. 63. *Lond.* 1892. 8°.   7073. de. 13. (11.)

SILZ (E.) De l'emploi du Sulfate de magnésie comme engrais. pp. 6. *Paris*, 1890. 8°. Pam. 13.

WAGNER (P.) The rational Manuring of Field Plants. pp. 32. *Lond.* 1891. 8°. 7074. l. 13. (9.) *See also* AGRICULTURE : PHOSPHATES.

MANUSCRIPTS.

Catalogues of Libraries and General Collections.

Ac. London. *British Museum.* Catalogue of additions to the Manuscripts, 1888–93. pp. 919. *Lond.* 1894. 8°.   Cat. Desk. A.

—— Guide to the Manuscripts, *etc.*, exhibited. pp. 140. *Lond.* 1895. 8°.   11903. b. 42.

—— Catalogue of the Stowe Manuscripts. *Lond.* 1895, *etc.* 8°.   Cat. Desk. A.

BIRD (S. R. S.) Guide to the classes of Documents preserved in the Public Record Office. pp. 355. *Lond.* 1891. 8°.   Cat. Desk. B.

Ac. Cambridge. *Fitzwilliam Museum.* Catalogue of the Manuscripts. pp. 472. *Camb.* 1895. 8°.   11903. k. 23.

JAMES (M. R.) Catalogue of Manuscripts in the Library of Jesus College, Cambridge. pp. 122. *Camb.* 1895. 8°.   011899. m. 4.

—— Catalogue of Manuscripts in the Library of Sidney Sussex College, Cambridge. pp. 132. *Camb.* 1895. 8°.   011901. f. 5.

—— A Descriptive Catalogue of the Manuscripts other than Oriental in the Library of King's College, Cambridge. pp. 87. *Camb.* 1895. 8°.   011899. m. 5.

—— A Descriptive Catalogue of the Manuscripts in the Library of Eton College. pp. 125. *Camb.* 1895. 8°.   011899. m. 2.

Ac. Oxford. *Bodleian Library.* Summary Catalogue of western Manuscripts not hitherto catalogued in the Quarto Series. *Oxf.* 1895, *etc.* 8°.   Cat. Desk. A.

—— Paris. *Bibliothèque Nationale.* Catalogue général des Manuscrits français. Par H. Omont. *Paris*, 1895, *etc.* 8°.   Bar. T. w.

—— Catalogus Codicum Hagiographicorum Latinorum, saeculo XVI. 4 tom. *Bruxellis*, 1889–93. 8°.   4999. ff. 2.

—— Manuscrits latins et français ajoutés aux fonds des nouvelles acquisitions, 1875–91. 2 pt. *Paris*, 1891. 8°.   011901. ee. 1.

DELISLE (L. V.) Manuscrits légués à la Bibliothèque Nationale par A. Durand. pp. 34. *Nogent-le-Rotrou*, 1894. 8°.   Pam. 6.

OMONT (H.) Nouvelles acquisitions du Département des Manuscrits pendant l'année 1891–92. *Paris*, 1892. 8°.   011900. h. 7.

—— Nouvelles acquisitions du Département des Manuscrits 1892–93. pp. 71. *Paris*, 1894. 8°.   011901. ee. 31.

OMONT (H.) Inventaire des Manuscrits de la collection Renaudot conservée à la Bibliothèque Nationale. pp. 30. *Paris*, 1890. 8°.   Pam. 6.

—— Inventaire de la collection Visconti conservée à la Bibliothèque Nationale. pp. 26. *Paris*, 1891. 8°.   Pam. 6.

Ac. Paris. *Musée des Archives.* Catalogue des Manuscrits conservés aux Archives Nationales. pp. 532. *Paris*, 1892. 8°.   011900. f. 20.

PARIS. *Bibliothèque Mazarine.* Catalogue des Manuscrits. 4 tom. 1885–91. 8°. FRANCE. *Ministère de l'instruction publique.* Catalogue des manuscrits des bibliothèques de France.   Bar. T. w.

OMONT (H.) Documents sur la vente des Manuscrits du Collège de Clermont à Paris, 1764. pp. 9. *Nogent-le-Rotrou*, 1891. 8°.   Pam. 6.

—— Inventaire des Manuscrits de la Collection Moreau. pp. 282. *Paris*, 1891. 8°. 11901. d. 20.

ABBEVILLE. Catalogue des Manuscrits de la Bibliothèque d'Abbeville. pp. 111. *Abbeville*, 1885. 8°.   011902. f. 42.

AVIGNON. Catalogue des Manuscrits de la Bibliothèque d'Avignon. pp. 433. *Avignon*, 1892. 8°.   011900. f. 18.

LABANDE (L. H.) Les Manuscrits de la Bibliothèque d'Avignon provenant de la librairie des Papes du XIV° siècle. pp. 16. *Paris*, 1895. 8°.   Pam. 6.

MANCEL (J. B. G.) Liste de Manuscrits de la collection Mancel à Caen. pp. 18. *Macon*, 1887. 8°.   011902. g. 2. (8.)

LAUZUN (P.) Les Manuscrits de la bibliothèque de Saint-Amans. pp. 52. *Agen*, 1889. 8°.   011900. ee. 5. (5.)

PRUSSIA. Verzeichniss der Handschriften im preussischen Staate. *Berl.* 1893, *etc.* 8°.   011901. g.

ROSE (V.) Verzeichniss der lateinischen Handschriften der K. Bibliothek zu Berlin. 1893, *etc.* 4°. BERLIN. *K. Bibliothek.* Die Handschriften-Verzeichnisse. Bd. 12, *etc.* 11905. m.

LEITSCHUH (F.) Katalog der Handschriften der K. Bibliothek zu Bamberg. *Bamberg*, 1895, *etc.* 8°.   11906. b.

NENTWIG (H.) Die mittelalterlichen Handschriften in der Stadtbibliothek zu Braunschweig. pp. 202. *Wolfenbüttel*, 1893. 8°.   011900. h. 20.

CARLSRUHE. *Hof- und Landesbibliothek.* Die Handschriften der Bibliothek. *Karlsruhe*, 1891, *etc.* 8°.   011903. h. 23.

EHWALD (R.) Beschreibung der Handschriften der Gymnasialbibliothek zu Gotha. pp. 34. *Gotha*, 1893. 4°.   11906. c. 4. (5.)

MELK, *Monastery of.* Catalogus Codicum qui in Bibliotheca Monasterii servantur. *Vindobonae*, 1889, *etc.* 8°.   011902. l.

HEYD (W. v.) Die historischen Handschriften der K. Bibliothek zu Stuttgart. 2 Bde. *Stuttgart*, 1889–91. 8°.   11899. i. 43.

P.P. *Forli.* Inventari dei Manoscritti delle biblioteche d'Italia. *Forli*, 1890, *etc.* 8°. 1065.

FLORENCE. *Biblioteca Nazionale Centrale.* Cataloghi dei Manoscritti della Biblioteca Nazionale di Firenze. 1889, *etc.* 8°. ITALY. *Ministero dell' Istruzione.* Indici. IV.   011903. k.

JORIO (G.) Codici ignorati nelle biblioteche di Napoli. *Lipsia*, 1892, *etc.* 8°.   011901. ee.

MARCHI (L. de) and BERTOLANI (G.) Inventario dei Manoscritti della Biblioteca Universitaria di Pavia. *Milano*, 1894, *etc.* 8°.   011900. e.

OTTINO (G.) I Codici bobbiesi nella Biblioteca Nazionale di Torino. pp. 72. *Torino*, 1890. 8°.   Pam. 6.

MANUSCRIPTS.—Catalogues, etc.—*cont.*

BIADEGO (G.) Catalogo dei Manoscritti della Biblioteca di Verona. pp. 664.
Verona, 1892. 8°.   011901. g. 11.

MARK, *Saint, Basilica of, Venice.* Inventaire des Manuscrits donnés à Saint-Marc par le cardinal Bessarion en 1468. pp. 59. *Paris*, 1894. 8°.   011901. g. 26.

NARDUCCI (E.) Catalogo di Manoscritti ora posseduti da D. B. Boncompagni. pp. 520.
Roma, 1892. 8°.   11901. g. 40.

LISBON. *Bibliotheca Nacional.* Manuscriptos, Collecção Pombalina. *Lisboa*, 1889. fol. 11900. k. 25.

OPORTO. *Bibliotheca Municipal.* Indice preparatorio do catalogo dos Manuscriptos. 3 fasc.
Porto, 1885, 88. 8°.   011902. f. 23.

GOTTWALD (B.) Catalogus Codicum manuscriptorum qui asservantur in Bibliotheca Monasterii Engelbergensis. pp. 327. *Friburgi*, 1891. 4°.   11900. i. 36.

See also AUTOGRAPHS : CARTULARIES : PALAEOGRAPHY.

     Armenian. See infra : Oriental.

     Celtic and Basque.

OMONT (H.) Catalogue des Manuscrits celtiques et basques de la Bibliothèque Nationale.
pp. 46. *Paris*, 1890. 8°.   Pam. 6.

     Coptic. See infra : Oriental.

     German.

Ac. Paris. *Bibliothèque Nationale.* Catalogue des Manuscrits allemands. pp. 176.
Paris, 1895. 8°.   11899. d. 20.

HELLER (H. A. v.) Verzeichnis altdeutscher Handschriften. pp. 178. *Tübingen*, 1890. 8°.   011902. g. 33.

     Greek.

Ac. London. *British Museum.* Greek Papyri in the British Museum. Edited by F. G. Kenyon. pp. 296. *Lond.* 1893. 4°.   1705. a. 16.
—— Facsimiles. fol.   1705. d. 6.

GRAUX (C.) Notices des Manuscrits grecs d'Espagne et de Portugal. pp. 321. *Paris*, 1892. 8°.   011901. g. 13.

MARTINI (E.) Catalogo di manoscritti greci nelle biblioteche italiane. *Milano*, 1893, *etc.* 8°.   011901. f.

MARK, *Saint, Basilica of, at Venice.* Inventaire des Manuscrits grecs donnés à Saint-Marc par le cardinal Bessarion en 1468. pp. 59.
Paris, 1894. 8°.   011901. g. 26.

NARDUCCI (E.) Catalogus Codicum manuscriptorum praeter Graecos et Orientales in Bibliotheca Angelica. *Romae*, 1893, *etc.* 4°.   11906. l.

MAES (C.) Saggio dell' intero catalogo di centosei Codici greci della Biblioteca Angelica.
Roma, 1894, *etc.* 8°.   11906. e.

OMONT (H.) Les Manuscrits grecs datés des xvᵉ et xviᵉ siècles de la Bibliothèque Nationale.
pp. 87. *Paris*, 1892. 8°.   11903. aa. 23. (9.)
—— Catalogue des Manuscrits grecs d'Antoine Éparque, 1538. pp. 18. *Paris*, 1892. 8°.   011900. f. 7. (8.)
—— Catalogue des Manuscrits grecs des bibliothèques des villes hanséatiques. pp. 29.
Leipz. 1890. 8°.   Pam. 6.
—— Les Manuscrits grecs de la Bibliothèque de Vérone. pp. 11. *Leipz.* 1891. 8°.   011900. ee. 3. (7.)

     Hebrew. See infra : Oriental.

     Latin. See supra : General.

     Slavonic.

CIÀMPOLI (D.) I Codici paleoslavi della R. Biblioteca Nazionale di San Marco. pp. 38.
Roma, 1894. fol.   11905. m. 4. (6.)

MANUSCRIPTS—*continued.*

     Spanish and Portuguese.

Ac. Paris. *Bibliothèque Nationale.* Catalogue des Manuscrits espagnols et portugais de la Bibliothèque Nationale. pp. 422.
Paris, 1881–92. 4°.   1888. a. 11.

     Oriental.

NARDUCCI (E.) Catalogus Codicum manuscriptorum praeter Orientales in Bibliotheca Angelica. *Romae*, 1893, *etc.* fol.   11901. i.

VIENNA. *Mechitarist Congregation.* Haupt-Catalog der armenischen Handschriften.
Wien, 1891, *etc.* 4°.   761. l. 1.

Ac. Oxford. *Bodleian Library.* Arabic Papyri of the Bodleian Library. pp. 7. *Lond.* 1893. 4°.   14542. e. 2.
—— London. *British Museum.* Supplement to the Catalogue of Arabic Manuscripts. By C. Rieu. pp. 935. *Lond.* 1894. 4°. Cat. Desk A.

HOUDAS (O.) and BASSET (R.) Mission scientifique en Tunisie. Pt. 2. *Alger*, 1884. 8°.   11901. bb. 48

RAINERUS, *Archduke of Austria.* Papyrus Erzherzog Rainer. *Wien*, 1892, *etc.* 8°. 754. c. 8.

CRUM (W. E.) Coptic Manuscripts brought from the Fayyum by W. M. Flinders Petri. pp. 92.
Lond. 1893. 4°.   7705. g. 41.

Ac. London. *British Museum.* Descriptive list of Hebrew and Samaritan MSS. pp. 134.
Lond. 1893. 8°.   Cat. Desk. A.
—— Leyden. *Academia Lugduno-Batava.* Catalogus van de Javaansche en Madureesche handschriften. pp. 434. *Leiden*, 1892. 8°. Ac. 940/7.

DE ZOYSA (L.) Catalogue of Pali, Sinhalese, and Sanskrit MSS. in temple libraries of Ceylon. pp. 31. *Colombo*, 1885. fol.   14096. f. 7.

Ac. London. *British Museum.* Supplement to the Catalogue of Persian Manuscripts. By C. Rieu. pp. 308. *Lond.* 1895. 4°. Cat. Desk. A.

JAMMU. *Raghunātha Temple Library.* Catalogue of the Sanskrit Manuscripts in the Raghunatha Temple Library. pp. 423. *Bombay*, 1894. 4°.   14096. f. 8.

MADRAS. *Oriental MSS. Library.* Alphabetical index of Manuscripts in the Library. 9 pt.
Madras, 1893. fol.   14096. f. 9.

RAMAKRISHNA GOPĀLA BHĀNPARAKARA. Lists of Sanskrit Manuscripts in private libraries in the Bombay Presidency. *Bombay*, 1893, *etc.* 8°.   14096. c. 12.

Ac. Paris. *Bibliothèque Nationale.* Manuscrits tamouls. ff. 49. *Paris*, 1880. fol.   761. i.

MANX LANGUAGE. Ac. Douglas, *Isle of Man. Manx Society.* Book of Common Prayer in Manx Gaelic. *Lond.* 1895, *etc.* 8°.   Ac. 8130/2.

MOORE (A. W.) Surnames and place-names of the Isle of Man. pp. 372. *Lond.* 1890. 8°.   12978. f. 27.

See also MAN, *Isle of.*

MANYDOWN. Ac. Hampshire. *Record Society.* Manor of Manydown. pp. 240.
Lond. 1895. 8°.   Ac. 8123/10.

MAORI RACE AND LANGUAGE. *See* NEW ZEALAND.

MAPS. *See* CARTOGRAPHY.

MARATHI LANGUAGE AND LITERATURE. APPĀJI KĀṢINĀTHA KHERA. Higher Anglo-Marathi grammar. pp. 528. 4.
Poona, 1895. 8°.   14140. g. 52.

BĀBĀ PADAMANAJĪ. Dictionary, English and Marathi. pp. 668. *Bombay*, 1889. 8°.   12906. dd. 29.

MARATHI—*continued.*

MOLESWORTH (J. T.) Compendium of Molesworth's Marathi and English dictionary. pp. 611. *Bombay*, 1890. 8°.   12907. cc. 33.

CANDY (T.) Idiomatic sentences, English and Maráthí. pp. 275. *Bombay*, 1888. 12°. 14140. g. 45.

MARATHI GRAMMAR. Marathi Grammar explained in English. pp. 119. *Bombay*, 1891. 8°.   12906. aaa. 56.

RĀMACHANDRA BHIKAJI JOSĪ. English companion to Joshi's Marathi Grammar. pp. 2. 133. *Poona*, 1892. 12°.   12907. b. 42.

Ac. London. *British Museum.* Catalogue of Marathi Printed Books. pp. 195. *Lond.* 1892. 4°.   Cat. Desk B.

GAṆAPATARĀVA RAGHUNĀTHA NAVALAKARA. Marathi Christian Literature. pp. 19. *Bombay*, 1890. 12°.   14137. a. 19.

MARBACH. GATRIS (A.) Die Abtei Marbach. 2 Bde. *Strassb.* 1895. 8°.   4782. h. 25.

MARBLE. *See* STONE.

MARBURG, University. Ac. Marburg. *Academia.* Das Universitätsgebäude zu Marburg. pp. 14. *Marburg*, 1891. 4°. 10250. i. 5.

WEBER (H.) Die Universität Marburg unter preussischen Herrschaft. pp. 22. *Marburg*, 1891. 8°.   8357. cc. 50. (3.)

MARCHE, Province. LA PORTE (A. de) Les Gens de qualité en Basse-Marche. Livr. 1–3. *Le Dorat*, 1886–89. 8°.   9916. c. 15.

TARDIEU (A.) Grand dictionnaire de la Haute-Marche. pp. 431. *Herment*, 1894. 4°. 9905. g. 4. *See also* CREUSE : HAUTE VIENNE : INDRE.

MAREDSOUS, Monastery. BENEDICT, *Saint, Monastery of.* Anecdota Maredsolana. *Maredsoli*, 1893, *etc.* 8°.   3605. k.

MARENGO. CIVALIERI-INVIZIATI (A.) La Colonna di Marengo. pp. 10. *Torino*, 1894. 8°.   Pam. 28.

MARENNES. LÉTELIÉ (J. A.) Une Plage sur l'océan. pp. 284. *Paris*, 1890. 12°. 10174. bb. 20.

MAREUIL-LES-MEAUX. PETITOT (E.) La Sépulture dolménique de Mareuil-les-Meaux. pp. 202. *Paris*, 1892. 12°.   7708. aa. 62.

MARGATE. CLARKE (W. J.) Photographic views of Margate. *Margate*, 1895. *obl.* 8°.   10360. aaa. 43.

MARIA ISLAND, Tasmania. *See* TASMANIA.

MARIASCHEIN. KROESS (A.) Die Residenz der Gesellschaft Jesu und der Wallfahrtsort Mariaschein. pp. 280. *Warnsdorf*, 1895. 12°.   4661. aaa. 33.

MARIAZELL. RABENLEHRER (M. M.) Mariazell, Oesterreichs Loreto. pp. 77. *Wien*, 1891. 16°.   10215. a. 2.

MARIGLIANO. RICCIARDI (R. A.) Marigliano ed i Comuni del suo mandamento. *Napoli*, 1891, *etc.* 8°.   10135. g.

MARIONNETTES. LEMERCIER DE NEUVILLE (L.) Histoire des Marionnettes modernes. pp. 306. *Paris*, 1892. 12°.   11794. b. 54.

MARKET HARBOROUGH. STOCKS (J. E.) and BRAGG (W. B.) Market Harborough Parish records to A.D. 1530. pp. 267. *Lond.* 1890. 8°.   010358. g. 8.

MARLBOROUGH. BENNETT (F. J.) Sketch history of Marlborough in Neolithic times. pp. 12. *Marlborough*, 1892. 8°. 07703. 3. 2. (12.)

—— Influence of Geology on settlement round Marlborough. pp. 17. *Marlborough*, 1891. 8°.   07109. m. 7. (2.)

MARLBOROUGH—*continued.*

BRADLEY (A. G.) History of Marlborough College. pp. 323. *Lond.* 1893. 8°.   8364. aaaa. 49.

LOCKWOOD (E.) Early days of Marlborough College. pp. 234. *Lond.* 1893. 4°. 8364. de. 33.

MARLBOROUGH COLLEGE. Papers relating to the Jubilee of Marlborough College, 1893. 1893. fol. and 8°.   8364. h. 15.

MARLIOZ. LEGRAND (M.) and JOANNE (P.) Aix-les-Bains et Marlioz. pp. 146. *Paris*, 1893. 16°.   10171. a. 19.

MARMORA. Sea of. *See* BOSPHORUS.

MARMOUTIER. MÉTAIS (C.) Cartulaire de Marmoutier. pp. 540. *Blois*, 1889–91. 8°.   4629. k. 14.

MARNE, Department. DICTIONARIES. Dictionnaire biographique des notabilités de la Marne. *Paris*, 1893. 8°.   010661. g. 48.

GALLI (H.) Les Représentants de la Marne aux assemblées de la Révolution. pp. 55. *Châlons*, 1894. 8°.   10661. c. 43. *See also* CHAMPAGNE.

MARO. RULES. Rules of the game of "Maro." pp. 10. *Lond.* 1891. 8°.   7912. df. 2. (8.)

MAROCCO.

Bibliography.

PLAYFAIR (*Sir* R. L.) and BROWN (R.) Bibliography of Morocco. pp. 262. 1892. 8°. BARBARY. Bibliography. Part 4.   BB.I. e. 15.

History, etc.

CAT (É.) Petite histoire de l'Algérie et Maroc. 2 tom. *Alger*, 1888, 91. 8°.   9061. de. 33.

CASTELLANOS (M. P.) Descripcion histórica de Marruecos. pp. 515. *Orihuela*, 1884. 8°.   010096. ee. 36.

ALVAREZ CABRERA (J.) Apuntes militares sobre el Imperio de Marruecos. pp. 189. *Madrid*, 1893. 8°.   8823. h. 45.

DIERCKS (G.) Materialien zur Kenntnis und Beurteilung des Scherifenreiches. pp. 228. *Berl.* 1894. 8°.   010096. e. 71.

OVILO Y CANALES (F.) Intimidades de Marruecos. pp. 70. *Madrid*, 1894. 8°.   8027. bbb. 21.

Topography.

BONSAL (S.) Morocco as it is. pp. 349. *Lond.* 1893. 8°.   010096. e. 50.

DESCLEZA (S.) A Marruecos. pp. 31. *Toledo*, 1893. 8°.   Pam. 67.

FINCK (H. T.) Spain and Morocco. pp. 182. *Lond.* 1891. 8°.   10160. bbb. 12.

FRANCE. *Dépôt des Cartes et Plans de la Marine.* Instructions nautiques sur la côte septentrionale du Maroc. pp. 196. *Lond.* 1893. 8°.   10497. bb. 36.

FRISCH (R. J.) Le Maroc. pp. 404. *Paris*, 1895. 8°.   10095. de. 25.

GANNIERS (A. de) Le Maroc d'aujourd'hui, d'hier et de demain. pp. 279. *Paris*, 1894. 8°.   010096. g. 20.

KERDEC CHÉNY (A. de) Guide du voyageur au Maroc. pp. 205. *Tanger*, 1888. 12°. 10097. a. 40.

LEARED (A.) Morocco and the Moors. pp. 354. *Lond.* 1891. 8°.   2358. d. 1.

MERRY̧ COLOM (F.) Mi Embajada extraordinaria á Marruecos en 1863. pp. 141. *Madrid*, 1894. 8°.   9061. ccc. 28.

MONTBARD (G.) À travers le Maroc. pp. 319. *Paris*, 1894. 8°.   10097. l. 13.

MONTBARD (G.) Among the Moors. pp. 281. *Lond.* 1894. 8°.   K.T.C. 30. b. 1.

PICARD (E.) El Moghreb al Aksa. pp. 427. *Brux.* 1893. 8°.   10095. de. 22.

MAROCCO—*continued.*

SESSIONS (F. C.) In Western Levant. pp. 252. *N.Y.* 1890. 8°.   10024. cc. 15.

SESTRI (J. A. de) Por todo Marruecos. pp. 409. *Barcelona,* 1885. 8°.   010096. i. 29.

STAEHELIN (A.) In Algerien, Marokko, *etc.* pp. 461. *Basel,* 1891, 8°.   10024. cc. 16. *See also* ARABIA : ARABS.

Tangier Dialect. *See* ARABIC LANGUAGE.

MARPLE. WAINWRIGHT (J.) Reminiscences of a lifetime in Marple. pp. 35. *Manch.* 1890. 8°.   10350. e. 37.

MARQUESAS ISLANDS. MARIN (A.) Au loin. Souvenirs des îles Marquises. pp. 384. *Paris,* 1891. 8°. .   10492. ff. 12.

MARQUESAS ISLANDS. E hamani pure no te Vikariato Apotoliko Marquises, me te Ui Katoliko. pp. 526. 79. *Paris,* 1892. 8°. 3456. e. 58. *See also* PACIFIC OCEAN AND ISLANDS.

MARRADI. MINI (G.) Marradi. Studio storico-araldico. pp. 108. *Castrocaro,* 1892. 8°.   9905. b. 30.

MARRIAGE.

General.

BAINTON (G.) The Wife as lover and friend. pp. 212. *Lond.* 1895. 8°.   8416. d. 41.

BALFOUR (J. A.) Marriage and parentage. pp. 135. *Bombay,* 1894. 12°.   7641. a. 41.

BLAKE (R. F.) The Greatest temptation in the world to Man. pp. 72. *Lond.* 1894. 8°.   8416. ccc. 49.

BOLO (H.) Du Mariage au divorce. pp. 265. *Paris,* 1891. 12°.   8416. dd. 40.

BUCKLER (H. R.) Holy Matrimony and single blessedness. pp. 16. *Lond.* 1894. 8°. Pam. 37.

BURGH (A.) and SPARK (J. J.) Marriage a success. pp. 72. *Lond.* 1891. 8°.   7410. cc. 37.

CORBIN (C. F.) Woman's philosophy of Love. pp. 302. *Bost.* 1893. 8°.   8416. e. 32.

DONISTHORPE (W.) Love and law. pp. 38. *Lond.* 1893. 8°.   Pam. 37.

ELLIS (E. L.) A Noviciate for Marriage. pp. 18. *Haslemere,* 1894. 8°.   Pam. 37.

GAUSSERON (B. H.) Doit-on se marier ? pp. 264. *Paris,* 1891. 12°.   8416. dd. 44.

HADDEN (J. C.) Are you Married ? pp. 160. *Glasg.* 1894, 8°.   8415. de. 32.

HARRISON (F.) Marriage ; discourse to the Positivist Society. pp. 29. *Lond.* 1887. 8°.   Pam. 37.

HAUSHOFER (M.) Die Ehefrage im Deutschen Reich. 1895. 8°. DAHMS (G.) Der Existenzkampf der Frau, *etc.* Hft. 3.   8416. g.

HUSBAND. The Husband that will suit you. pp. 215. *Calcutta,* 1890. 16°.   8416. de. 15.

ISOARD (L. R. E.) *Bp. of Annecy.* Le Mariage. Conférences. pp. 365. *Paris,* 1880. 12°.   8415. de. 21.

ISIDORE. Love, Marriage and happiness. pp. 96. *Lond.* 1894. 8°.   8416. df. 17.

JONES (H.) Courtship and Marriage. pp. 186. *Lond.* 1890. 8°.   8416. dd. 30.

LONGSHORE-POTTS (A. M.) Love, Courtship and Marriage. pp. 114. *Lond.* 1894. 8°.   8415. de. 35.

MANTEGAZZA (P.) L' arte di prender marito. pp. 263. *Milano,* 1894. 8°.   8416. de. 55.

—— Art of taking a Wife. pp. 310. *Lond.* 1894. 8°.   8416. de. 52.

MILL (S.) New Light on Love and Marriage. pp. 256. *Belfast,* 1894. 8°.   8415. de. 31.

MILLER (J. R.) Secrets of happy Home Life. pp. 32. *Lond.* 1894. 8°.   4399. aaaa. 15

MARRIAGE.—**General**—*continued.*

MILLER (J. R.) The perfect Home. pp. 206. *Lond.* 1895. 8°.   8416. de. 57.

MONSABRÉ (J. M. L.) Le Mariage. pp. 384. *Paris,* 1893. 8°.   8416. dd. 48.

OXONIENSIS. Early Marriage and late parentage. pp. 30. *Lond.* 1883. 8°.   08276. f. 21. (2.)

PETTITT (G.) Be Lovers still ! pp. 61. *Lond.* 1892. 16°.   8416. aa. 66.

RUBIN (M.) and WESTERGAARD (H.) Statistik der Ehen auf Grund der socialen Gliederung der Bevölkerung. pp. 132. *Jena,* 1890. 8°.   08276. h. 7.

SAINT-PAUL (A.) Du Célibat au Mariage. pp. 30. *Paris,* 1891. 8°.   Pam. 37.

SINCLAIR (B. D.) Crowning Sin of the age. pp. 70. *Bost.* 1892. 8°.   8416. df. 9.

SWAN, *afterwards* SMITH (A. S.) Courtship and Marriage. pp. 144. *Lond.* 1893. 8°. 8416. d. 39.

TALMAGE (T. de W.) The Marriage Ring. pp. 111. *Lond.* 1891. 8°.   8416. dd. 38.

TAYLOR (J. W.) Love and Mariage. pp. 61. *Carnforth,* 1891. 8°.   7410. cc. 36.

UNSWORTH (W.) Marriage-Knot wisely tied. pp. 286. *Lond.* 1892. 8°.   8416. df. 12.

ALLBUTT (H. A.) Disease and Marriage. pp. 82. *Lond.* 1891. 8°.   7641. b. 29.

STRAHAN (S. A. K.) Marriage and Disease. pp. 326. *Lond.* 1892. 8°.   7641. aaa. 28. *See also* FAMILY : LOVE : WOMEN.

History : Marriage Customs.

ACHELIS (T.) Die Entwicklung der Ehe. pp. 125. 1893. 8°. Beiträge zur Völkerkunde. II.   10007. f.

GIRAUD-TEULON (A.) Les Origines du mariage. pp 525. *Genève,* 1884. 12°.   8416. df. 22.

KAWERAU (W.) Die Reformation und die Ehe. pp. 104. 1892. 8°. Ac. Halle. *Verein für Reformationsgeschichte.* Schriften. Nr. 39.   Ac. 2027.

LUCKOCK (H. M.) The history of Marriage. pp. 359. *Lond.* 1895. 8°.   5176. aaa. 35.

LETOURNEAU (C. J. M.) Evolution of Marriage. pp. 373. 1891. 8°. ELLIS (H. H.) Contemporary Science Series.   8709. i.

MUḤAMMAD 'ABD AL-GHANĪ. Polygamy. pp. 19. *Lahore,* 1891. 8°.   Pam. 41.

WESTERMARCK (E.) History of human Marriage. pp. 644. *Lond.* 1894. 8°.   2236. f. 7.

PANNELLA (G.) Usi nuziali dell' Abruzzo Teramano. pp. 24. *Teramo,* 1894. 8°.   Pam. 37.

TAMURA (N.) The Japanese Bride. pp. 92. *N.Y.* 1893. 8°.   8416. dc. 41. *See also* WOMEN.

Law of Marriage and Divorce.

International and Ecclesiastical Law.

GARNIER (A.) Internationales Eheschliessungsrecht. pp. 239. *Bern,* 1884. 4°.   5176. f. 11.

GUILLAUME (J. J. G. P.) *Baron.* Le Mariage en droit international et la conférence de la Haye. pp. 549. *Brux.* 1894. 8°.   5176. ee. 2.

BRIDEL (L.) Le Droit des femmes et le marriage. pp. 167. *Paris,* 1893. 12°.   8416. df. 19.

CIGOI (A.) Die Unauflösbarkeit der christlichen Ehe und die Ehescheidung. pp. 248. *Paderborn,* 1895. 8°.   5176. e. 11.

GEFFCKEN (F. H.) Zur Geschichte der Ehescheidung vor Gratian. pp. 82. *Leipz.* 1894. 8°.   Pam. 32.

MARRIAGE, Law of—*continued.*

DESSAULLES (L. A.) Les erreurs de l'Église sur le mariage et le divorce. pp. 279.
Paris, 1894. 8°.   5176. aa. 14.

DINGLI (A.) Force and effects of Custom according to the Civil Law. With reference to the validity of marriages in Malta. pp. 62.
Malta, 1893. 8°.   Pam. 37.

GRECH (S.) Dove stà la ragione e il torto.
pp. 26. *Malta*, 1893. 8°.   Pam. 37.

ESMEIN (A.) Le Mariage en droit canonique.
2 tom. *Paris*, 1891. 8°.   5176. cc. 20.

FRÉMONT (J.) Le Divorce et la séparation de corps. pp. 191. *Québec*, 1886. 8°. 5176. cc. 21.

GASPARRI (P.) Tractatus canonicus de matrimonio. 2 vol. *Paris*, 1891. 8°.   5176. e. 5.

HASSAREK VON HEINLEIN (M.) Die bedingte Eheschliessung. pp. 264. *Wien*, 1892. 8°.
                                               5176. dd. 3.

HEINER (F.) Grundriss des katholischen Eherechts. pp. 281. 1892. 8°. Sammlung von Kompendien. Ser. II. No 1.   12205. k.

HOERMANN (W. v.) Die Desponsatio Impuberum.
pp. 269. *Innsbrück*, 1891. 8°.   5175. e. 22.

LAURENT (A.) De la validité du Mariage canonique contracté en France entre deux étrangers dont la loi reconnait ce mariage. pp. 64.
Paris, 1895. 8°.   Pam. 37.

MOEREN (A. B. v. der) Tractatus de Sponsalibus et matrimonio. pp. 196. *Gandavi*, 1889. 8°.
                                               5176. cc. 19.

ROSSET (M.) *Bp. of Maurienne.* De Sacramento Matrimonii tractatus canonicus.
Maurianæ, 1895, etc. 8°.   5176. d.

THEINER (J. A.) and (A.) Die Einführung der erzwungenen Ehelosigkeit bei den christlichen Geistlichen. *Barmen*, 1891, etc. 8°.   4530. cc.

WATKINS (O. D.) Holy Matrimony. Treatise on the divine law of marriage. pp. 717.
Lond. 1895. 8°.   5176. e. 9.

See also infra : England and Italy.

Austria-Hungary.

BUDAU (V.) Die Nothwendigkeit der Einführung der obligatorischen Civilehe in Oesterreich.
Wien, 1894. 8°.   Pam. 37.

Burma. See infra : India.

Chili.

LATORRE (E. C.) Estudio sobre la lei de Matrimonio civil. pp. 182. *Santiago*, 1887. 8°.
                                               5175. dd. 4.

Denmark.

WICKSELL (A. B.) Hustruens retslige Stilling.
pp. 58. *Kjøbenh.* 1891. 8°.   Pam. 37.

England.

ADVOCATE. Marriages, regular and irregular.
pp. 187. *Glasg.* 1893. 8°.   5176. aaa. 33.

GEARY (W. N. M.) Law of Marriage. pp. 637.
Lond. 1892. 8°.   5176. bb. 22.

WEDLOCK. Lawful Wedlock; or, How shall I make sure of a legal marriage? pp. 114.
Lond. 1892. 16°.   5176. a. 9.

CRAWLEY (C.) Law of Husband and Wife.
pp. 486. *Lond.* 1892. 8°.   6325. df. 17.

FOYSTER (J. A.) "New Matrimonial Code." Summary Jurisdiction, Married Women, Act, 1895. pp. 47. *Manch.* 1895. 8°. 6325. ccc. 1.

GRIFFITH (J. R.) Married Women's Property Acts 1870–84. pp. 259. *Lond.* 1891. 8°.
                                               6325. de. 30.

J., A. Summary Remedies of Wives. pp. 30.
Lond. 1892. 12°.   635. a. 75.

MARRIAGE.—Law of—*continued.*

MATTHEWS (J. B.) Manual of Law relating to married women. pp. 321. *Lond.* 1892. 8°.
                                               6325. de. 33.

SMITH (J. W.) Handy Book on the Law of Husband and Wife. pp. 258. 1892. 12°. Wilson's Legal Handy Books.   6426. aaa. 39.

DIXON (W. J.) Law and practice in Divorce, etc.
pp. 721. *Lond.* 1891. 8°.   2228. c. 6.

HARRISON (J. C.) Epitome of the Law of Divorce.
pp. 240. *Lond.* 1891. 8°.   6355. aaa. 31.

GIBSON (A.) and WELDON (A.) Student's Divorce.
pp. 359. *Lond.* 1895. 8°.   6355. ee. 12.

MANUAL. Manual of the chief rules and principles of Civil Marriage and Holy Matrimony. pp. 20.
Brighton, 1894. 8°.   Pam. 37.

BLACK (W.) Divorce. pp. 8. *Lond.* 1892. 8°.
                                               Pam. 37.

CHAPMAN (E. R.) Why we should oppose Divorce. *Lond.* 1890. 8°.   Pam. 37.

REYNOLDS (H. W.) Origen and the York report on Divorce. pp. 11. *Camb.* 1895. 8°.
                                               Pam. 37.

—— Examination of the York Report on Divorce.
pp. 26. *Camb.* 1895. 8°.   Pam. 7.

STUART (C.) Appeal to the Queen's Proctor in the case of Polygamy v. Polyandry. pp. 99.
Lewes, 1891. 8°.   8416. bbb. 55.

France.

GRUFFY (G.) Étude sur la naturalisation des femmes mariées. pp. 210. *Paris*, 1893. 8°.
                                               6955. f. 9.

ISAURE-TOULOUSE (J.) Manuel pratique du Mariage, du divorce, etc. pp. 200. *Paris*, 1891. 12°.
                                               5176. b. 15.

JOUITOU (J. B. L.) De la restriction de l'Hypothèque de la femme. pp. 195. *Paris*, 1892. 8°.
                                               5408. aa. 11.

COULON (H.) Le Divorce et l'adultère. pp. 76.
Paris, 1892, 8°.   5176. d. 3.

DENOS (G.) La Bigamie. Moyens de la prévenir.
pp. 52. *Chartres*, 1891. 8°.   Pam. 37.

FARINE (P.) Guide du Divorce et de la séparation. pp. 280. *Paris*, 1892. 8°. 5423. de. 12.

HITIER (J.) Le développement de la Jurisprudence en matière de Divorce depuis 1884.
pp. 121. *Paris*, 1895. 8°.   5176. ee. 3.

KELLY (E.) The French Law of Marriage.
pp. 280. *Lond.* 1895. 8°.   5176. ee. 1.

LECORNEC (G.) Le Divorce dans nos lois et dans nos mœurs. pp. 248. *Paris*, 1892. 12°.
                                               5176. aaa. 32.

WORMS (É.) Les Attentats à l'honneur; adultère, etc. pp. 332. *Paris*, 1890. 8°.   5403. dd. 1.

Germany.

ADLER (S.) Eheliches Güterrecht und Abschichtungsrecht. pp. 112. *Leipz.* 1893. 8°.
                                               5175. c. 5

BARAZETTI (C.) Das Eherecht. pp. 779.
Hannover, 1895. 8°.   5176. e. 12.

BARTSCH (H.) Das gerichtliche Verfahren in Ehesachen. pp. 477. *Wien*, 1894. 8°.
                                               5175. e. 23.

DARGUN (L.) Mutterrecht und Raubehe und ihre Reste. pp. 161. 1883. 8°. GIERKE (O.) Untersuchungen zur deutschen Rechtsgeschichte.
No. 16.   6025. e. 9.

HUBRICH (E.) Das Recht der Ehescheidung.
pp. 278. *Berl.* 1891. 8°.   5176. e. 7.

KUHLENBECK (L.) Reform der Ehe. pp. 136.
Leipz. 1891. 8°.   5176. bbb. 32.

STOELZEL (A.) Über das landesherrliche Ehescheidungsrecht. pp. 104. *Berl.* 1891. 8°.
                                               5175. e. 2.

MARRIAGE.—Law of—_continued._

WIEST (W.) Das Reichsgesetz über die Ehe-schliessung vom 6 Februar 1875. pp. 372.
Ellwangen, 1892. 8°.   05604. i. 12.

India and Burma (Buddhist, Hindu and Mohammedan Law).

ASSAM. Notes on the Marriage systems of Assam. pp. 56. *Calcutta,* 1892. 12°.   Pam. 37.

KARUṆĀKARA MENON. Observations on the Mala-bar Marriage bill. pp. 48. *Madras,* 1890. 8°.
          Pam. 37.

MANUEL (R. A.) Digest of Budhist law in matters relating to Marriage and divorce. pp. 188. *Rangoon,* 1885. 8°.   5319. c. 9.

MUḤAMMAD SAMĪ 'ALLĀH. Judgment containing an exposition of the Muhammadan Matrimonial Law. pp. 40, 32. *Allahabad,* 1891. 8°.
           14106. dd. 24.

ATULAKṚISHṆA NANDI. Thoughts on the Age of Consent bill. pp. 30. *Calcutta,* 1891. 12°.
          Pam. 37.

BALA GAṄGĀDHARA TILAKA. Texts of the Shas-tras against the Age of Consent bill. pp. 13. *Poona,* 1891. 12°.   Pam. 37.

BEHARĀMAJĪ MIHRLRANJĪ MALĀBARI. An Appeal from the daughters of India. pp. 20.
Lond. 1890. 8°.   Pam. 37.

CALCUTTA. Proceedings of a public Meeting at Calcutta to protest against the Age of Consent bill. pp. 58. *Calcutta,* 1891. 8°.   Pam. 37.

—— *Mahomedan Literary Society.* Practical View of the Age of Consent act. pp. 6. *Calcutta,* 1891. 8°.   Pam. 37.

CHHAJJŪ SIṂHA. Brahmacharya versus Child Marriage. pp. 29. *Lahore,* 1895. 8°. Pam. 85.

DĪNANĀTHA GAṄGULI. Essay on Age of Consent bill. pp. 9. *Halishahar,* 1891. 12°. Pam. 37.

INDIA. *Legislative Council.* Speeches at the time of passing the Age of Consent bill. pp. 72. *Bombay,* 1891. 8°.   Pam. 37.

—— No necessity for the Age of Consent bill. pp. 11. *Calcutta,* 1891. 8°.   Pam. 37.

KSHETRAMOHANA GAṄGOPĀDHYĀYA. Thoughts on Child Marriage in British India. pp. 24. *Calcutta,* 1891. 8°.   Pam. 37.

NANDALĀLA GHOSHA. O Empress! Pray do not interfere with religion. *Calcutta,* 1891. 8°.
          Pam. 37.

NĀRĀYAṆA BHAṬṬA. Vivahaprayoga or Marriage-Ritual for Brahmans of Riksakha. 3 pt. *Bangalore,* 1891. 8°.   14033. b. 58.

NĀRĀYAṆA GAṆEṢA CHĀNDAVAḌKAR. The British Government and Hindu religious customs. pp. 17. *Bombay,* 1891. 8°.   Pam. 37.

RAGHUNĀTHA RĀU. Hindu Shastrick aspect of the question of the Age of Consent. pp. 6, 7. *Madras,* 1891. 8°.   14039. b. 16. (2.)

RĀMANĀTHA TARKARATNA. "Garbhadhan Vya-vastha" opinion on the questions arising out of the Age of Consent bill. pp. 5. *Calcutta,* 1891. 8°.   Pam. 37.

SAṢADHARA TARKACHŪḌĀMAṆI. Second tract on the rites of Garvadhan. pp. 19. *Calcutta,* 1890. 8°.   Pam. 37.

T., K. T. Notes on the Age of Consent bill. pp. 30. *Bombay,* 1891. 8°.   Pam. 37.

YOGENDRACHANDRA GHOSHA. The Age of Con-sent. pp. 32. *Calcutta,* 1891. 8°.   Pam. 37.

Ireland.

IRELAND. Digest on the Irish Marriage Law. pp. 72. *Dublin,* 1888. 8°.   Pam. 37.

Italy.

BARTOLI (A.) Del Divorzio. pp. 63. *Firenze,* 1891. 8°.   Pam. 37.

MARRIAGE.—Law of—_continued._

BESIA (T.) Del Contratto di matrimonio. pp. 391. *Portici,* 1894. 8°.   5176. f. 12.

CALCHI-NOVATI (G.) Il Divorzio. pp. 46. *Milano,* 1892. 8°.   Pam. 37.

CAPPELLAZZI (A.) Il Divorzio. pp. 246. *Lodi,* 1893. 8°.   5176. a. 10.

DIENA (M.) Dei Figli di donna separata dal marito nati dopo la separazione. pp. 52. *Venezia,* 1891. 8°.   Pam. 34.

FARA MUSIO (F.) L'Adulterio è un reato. pp. 55. *Oristano,* 1891. 8°.   8408. h. 34. (4.)

FIORE (P.) Sulla controversia del Divorzio in Italia. pp. 64. *Torino,* 1891. 8°.   Pam. 37.

LEONARDI MURCURIO (G.) La precedenza obli-gatoria del Matrimonio. pp. 59. *Catania,* 1893. 8°.   Pam. 37.

MORONE (G.) Sul Divorzio. pp. 122. *Milano,* 1892. 8°.   5176. bbb. 33.

MOSCATELLI (A.) Appunti storici intorno al Divorzio. pp. 41. *Reggio-Emilia,* 1891. 8°.
          Pam. 37.

PREVITI (L.) Del Divorzio. pp. 93. *Roma,* 1891. 8°.   Pam. 37.

SERRELLI (N.) Pro Divortio. pp. 61. *Salerno,* 1891. 8°.   Pam. 85.

SOLE (B.) Il Divorzio. pp. 439. *Potenza,* 1894. 4°.   5176. i. 1.

TEMPIA (G. S.) La riforma del Matrimonio. pp. 86. *Roma,* 1890. 8°.   Pam. 37.

VILLANI (C.) La questione del Divorzio. pp. 50. *Napoli,* 1891. 8°.   Pam. 37.

Malta. See supra: Ecclesiastical and Inter-national Law.

Norway.

SCHEEL (H.) Om Ægtefællers Formuesforhold. pp. 304. *Kristiania,* 1892. 8°.   5725. d. 8.

Scotland.

MURRAY (D.) Law relating to the Property of married persons. pp. 249. *Glasg.* 1891. 8°.
          6325. e. 22.

WALTON (F. P.) Handbook of Husband and Wife. pp. 510. *Edinb.* 1893. 8°. 6583. cc. 4.

United States of America.

BISHOP (J. P.) Commentaries on Marriage, Divorce and Separation. 2 vol. *Chicago,* 1891. 8°.   5176. f. 10.

DURKS (M. P.) Notes on the Property Rights of married women in Virginia. pp. 87. *Lynchburg, Va.,* 1893. 8°.   06616. df. 19.

SMITH (S. B.) Marriage process in the United States. pp. 435. *N.Y.* 1893. 8°.   5176. e. 8.

WILLCOX (W. F.) The Divorce problem. pp. 74. 1891. 8°. Ac. New York. *Columbia College.* Studies in History, *etc.*   Ac. 2688/2.

Victoria, Australia.

VICTORIA. The Divorce Act, 1889. pp. 80. *Melbourne,* 1890. 8°.   6605. aa. 8.

See also WOMEN, *Laws relating to.*

MARS, Planet. FLAMMARION (C.) La Planète Mars et ses conditions d'habitabilité. pp. 608. *Paris,* 1892. 8°.   8562. ff. 32.

KEELER (J. E.) Physical observations of Mars. pp. 7. *Lond.* 1893. 4°.   8562. e. 31.

LOHSE (O.) Beobachtungen des Planeten Mars. pp. 42. 1891. 4°. Ac. Potsdam. *Astrophysi-kalisches Observatorium.* Publicationen. Nr. 28.
          8752. i. 6.

See also ASTRONOMY : SUN AND SOLAR SYSTEM.

MARSEILLES. TENOUGI (F.) Précis his-torique sur la ville de Marseille. pp. 37. *Marseille,* 1891. 8°.   Pam. 91.

MARSEILLES—*continued.*

TEISSIER (O.) Marseille au moyen âge, 1250–1480. pp. 201. *Marseille*, 1891. 8°. 010171. k. 4.

NICOLAS (C.) L'ancien couvent des Dominicains de Marseille. pp. 70. *Nîmes*, 1894. 8°.
4629. h. 19.

BLANCARD (L.) Inventaires des archives postérieures à 1789. Documents de la période révolutionnaire. 1889, *etc.* 4°. Collection des Inventaires, *etc.* 1814–15. b., *etc.*

MARSEILLES. *Chambre de Commerce.* Inventaire des archives modernes de la Chambre de Commerce. pp. 380. *Marseille*, 1882. 4°. 8245. h. 2.

TEISSIER (O.) La Chambre de Commerce de Marseille. pp. 411. *Marseille*, 1892. 8°.
08225. l. 21.

JOANNE (P.) Marseille et ses environs. pp. 55. *Paris*, 1894. 8°. 10168. aa. 34.

LAUGIER (L.) La Vérité sur les Docks. pp. 33. *Marseille*, 1891. 8°. 8277. ee. 30. (8.)

PALLIÈS (A.) Guide de l'étranger dans Marseille. pp. 278. *Paris*, 1895. 8°. 10174. de. 2.

ARNAVON (L. H.) L'Université de Marseille. pp. 26. *Marseille*, 1891. 8°. 8305. ff. 7. (10.)

MARSHAM. MARSHAM. Parish Register, 1538–1836. pp. 350. *Norwich*, 1889. 8°.
9905. c. 49.

MARSHFIELD. MARSHFIELD. Parish Registers of Marshfield. pp. 274. 1893. fol.
9916. f. 7.

MARSH WARBLER. FOWLER (W. W.) The Marsh Warbler in Oxfordshire and Switzerland. pp. 29. *Oxf.* 1893. 8°. 7285. de. 33. (8.)

MARS-LE-TOUR. *See* GERMAN-FRENCH WAR.

MARSTON MOOR, Battle of.
See ENGLAND, *History.*

MARSUPIALIA. LYDEKKER (R.) Handbook to the Marsupialia. pp. 302. 1894. 8°. SHARPE (R. B.) Naturalist's Library. 7001. eee.
See also MAMMALIA; ZOOLOGY.

MARTINIQUE. GARAUD (L.) Trois ans à la Martinique, *etc.* pp. 286. *Paris*, 1892. 8°.
10480. h. 20.

GUÈT (M. I.) Origines de la Martinique 1625–1720. pp. 406. *Vannes*, 1893. 8°. 9772. dd. 10.

MISMER (C.) Souvenirs de la Martinique. pp. 290. *Paris*, 1890. 12°. 10480. aa. 16.

FORTIER (É.) L'Ouragan de 1891 à la Martinique. pp. 100. *Paris*, 1892. 8°. 8755. cc. 59.

MONET (H.) La Martinique. [Hurricane of 18th Aug. 1891.] pp. 411. *Asnières*, 1891. 8°.
10470. h. 26.

See also FRANCE, *Colonies : WEST INDIES.*

MARVILLE. PIERROT (A.) Journal d'un habitant de Marville au XVIIᵉ siècle. pp. 83. *Montmédy*, 1894. 8°. 9004. h. 30. (8.)

MARY, the Blessed Virgin, Devotion to, etc. ALPHONSO MARIA, de' Liguori, *St.* Visits to the Holy Sacrament and to the B. Virgin. pp. 160. *Lond.* 1893. 8°. 3455. aaaa. 3.

BRIDGETT (T. E.) England for Our Lady. Sermon. pp. 32. *Lond.* 1893. 8°. Pam. 78.

CABRINI (F.) Saturday dedicated to Mary. pp. 458. 1893. 8°. Quarterly Series. Vol. 83.
3605. dd.

DROCHON (J. E. B.) Histoire illustrée des Pèlerinages français de la très Sainte Vierge. pp. 1272. *Paris*, 1890. 8°. 10172. f. 16.

DUMAX (V. A.) La généalogie de Notre-Seigneur Jésus-Christ et de la Très Sainte Vierge. pp. 401. 8°. *Paris*, 1890. 18°. 4226. g. 2.

FABER (F. W.) F. Faber's May-Book. pp. 108. *Lond.* 1894. 16°. 3456. df. 35.

Mary, the Blessed Virgin—*continued.*

FOUILLIT (J.) Notre-Dame de Pradelles. Centenaire de la délivrance de la statue miraculeuse. pp. 99. *Le Puy*, 1893. 8°. 4807. aaaa. 7.

FURNIVALL (F. J.) Early English Hymn to the Virgin. pp. 36. 1880. 8°. Ac. London. *English Dialect Society.* Miscellanies. Ac. 9935/3.

GALLWEY (P.) Devotion to the Mother of God in harmony with Scripture. Sermon. pp. 31. *Lond.* 1891. 8°. 4473. cc. 23. (13.)

HALL (A. C. A.) The Virgin Mother. Retreat addresses. pp. 233. *N.Y.* 1894. 8°. 4486. a. 69.

HOLWECK (F. G.) Fasti Mariani. pp. 378. *Friburgi*, 1892. 8°. 4808. c. 39.

JENKINS (R. C.) The worship of the Blessed Virgin Mary. pp. 24. *Folkestone*, 1890. 8°.
3940. bb. 31. (6.)

LEANTE Y GARCÍA (R.) Culto de María en la diócesis de Jaca. pp. 464. *Lerida*, 1889. 8°.
4625. aaa. 2.

LEE (F. G.) Sinless Conception of the Mother of God. pp. 168. *Lond.* 1891. 8°. 4227. h. 20.

LA MOYNE DE LA BORDERIE (L. A.) La Ceinture de la Sainte Vierge conservée à Quintin. pp. 114. *Saint-Brieuc*, 1890. 8°. 4807. eee. 12.

LIVIUS (T.) Mary in the Epistles : teaching of the Apostles concerning the Blessed Virgin. pp. 291. *Lond.* 1891. 8°. 3940. aaa. 20.

—— The Blessed Virgin in the Fathers of the first six centuries. pp. 481. *Lond.* 1893. 8°.
3940. h. 16.

MACKERETH (T.) Miraculous Conception evidences. pp. 8. *Lond.* 1892. 8°. Pam. 84.

MARY, *the B.V.* Mariolatry ; or, worship of the Virgin. pp. 56. *Lond.* 1892. 8°. 3940. bb. 30.

—— La Vierge Marie. Humilité et béatitudes. pp. 288. *Dijon*, 1892. 8°. 4224. a. 87.

—— Monte S. Giuliano, *Sicily.* L'Aurora consurgens della Cantica. pp. 15. *Trapani*, 1894. 8°. 9930. ccc. 27.

—— Manual for the use of Sodalities of our Lady. pp. 408. *Roehampton*, 1893. 8°.
3456. df. 1.

MORGOTT (F.) Maria nella dottrina di San Tommaso d'Aquino. pp. 207. *Piacenza*, 1891. 8°. 4224. bbb. 21.

MORTIER (D. A.) Le mouvement des yeux de l'image de Notre-Dame des Sept-Douleurs à Campocavallo. pp. 32. *Abbeville*, 1893. 8°.
4422. d. 18. (3.)

MUSSAFIA (A.) Studien zu den mittelalterlichen Marienlegenden. 1887–89. 8°. Ac. Vienna. *K. Akademie.* Sitzungsberichte. Phil.-historische Classe. Bd. 113, 115, 119. Ac. 810/6.

O'BRIEN (V.) Birthday book of the Madonna. pp. viii. *Dublin*, 1892. 8°. 4399. a. 2.

ORELLANA (B.) Recuerdos de mi Comision a Roma para gestionar la coronacion de la Virgen del valle de Catamarca. pp. 340. *Florencia*, 1893. 8°. 4808. dd. 2.

PALMER (J. R.) Immaculate Conception of the B.V. Mary. pp. 30. *Lond.* 1892. 8°. Pam. 78.

PEARSON (J.) *Bp. of Chester.* Views of Bishop Pearson and Fathers of the Reformation on the subject of the ever-virginity of S. Mary. pp. 18. *Lond.* 1889. 8°. 4109. c. 16. (7.)

PETITALOT (J. B.) The Virgin Mother, according to theology. pp. 490. *Lond.* 1889. 8°.
4808. g. 7.

PRESBYTER, *Anglicanus.* Woman, what have I to do with thee? pp. 147. *Lond.* 1895. 8°.
4224. bb. 49.

RICARD (A.) Saint Joseph, sa vie et son culte. pp. 394. *Lille*, 1892. 8°. 4808. i. 22.

MARY, the Blessed Virgin—*continued.*

SACERDOS. Divine Worship and devotion to the Blessed Virgin. pp. 63. *Lond.* 1894. 8°.
Pam. 78.

SERRANO Y ORTEGA (M.) Noticia de la devoción y culto que la ciudad de Sevilla ha profesado à la Immaculada Concepción de la Virgen Maria. pp. 920. *Sevilla,* 1893. 4°.   4625. cc. 6.

SHIPLEY (O.) Carmina Mariana. pp. 461. *Lond.* 1894. 8°.   11602. ccc. 25.

SIMPSON (W. J. S.) Lectures on S. Bernard of Clairvaux. With appendix on the Immaculate Conception. pp. 257. *Lond.* 1895. 8°.
4829. c. 19.

SOMMABÈRE ( ) Notre-Dame de Tudet ou de Protection dans l'ancienne Vicomté de Lomagne. pp. 218. *Toulouse,* 1894. 8°.   4629. aa. 41.

VAL D'EREMAO (J. P.) The Hail Mary; popular instructions. pp. 234. *Lond.* 1892. 8°.
3475. de 16.

VENTURI (J.) Notizie della apparizione della Gran Madre di Dio adorata in Monte Gridolfo. pp. 47. *Urbino,* 1890. 8°.   Pam. 10.

WELD (F. J.) Divine Love and the love of God's Mother. pp. 563. *Lond.* 1893. 8°. 4376. ee. 20.

WILPERT (J.) Die gottgeweihten Jungfrauen in den ersten Jahrhunderten der Kirche. pp. 105. *Freiburg,* 1892. 4°.   4783. f. 11.

WRIGHT (C. H. H.) The Church of Rome and Mariolatry. pp. 11. *Lond.* 1893. 16°.
3939. cc. 25. (4.)
See also LORETTO : LOURDES: MARIA-SCHEIN.

MARYLAND. BLACK (J. W.) Maryland's attitude in the struggle for Canada. pp. 73. 1892. 8°. Johns Hopkins University Studies. Ser. 10. No. 7.   Ac. 2689.

GAMBRALL (T. C.) Studies in the History of early Maryland. pp. 240. *N.Y.* 1893. 8°.
9605. d. 9.

MAC ILVAIN (J. W.) Early Presbyterianism in Maryland. pp. 33. 1890. 8°. Johns Hopkins University Studies. Notes. 1890. No. 3.
Ac. 2689.

PETRIE (G.) Church and State in Early Maryland. pp. 50. 1892. 8°. Johns Hopkins University Studies. Ser. 10. No. 4.   Ac. 2689.

SCHARF (J. T.) Resources of Maryland. pp. 240. *Annapolis,* 1892. 8°.   10411. cc. 38.

STEINER (B. C.) History of University education in Maryland. pp. 37. 1891. 8°. Johns Hopkins University Studies. Ser. 9. No. 3-4.
Ac. 2689.

U.S. *Department of Agriculture.* Climatology and physical features of Maryland. *Baltimore,* 1894, *etc.* 8°.   8757. dd.

MARYTON. FRASER (W. R.) Maryton Parish Church. pp. 24. *Lond.* 1892. 8°.
4705. b. 46. (4.)

MASAI LAND. BAUMANN (O.) Durch Massailand zur Nilquelle. pp. 385. *Berl.* 1894. 8°.
10097. l. 14.

KALLENBERG (F.) Auf dem Kriegspfad gegen die Massai. pp. 200. *München,* 1892. 8°.
010096. ff. 27.
See also AFRICA, *Central and East.*

MASHONALAND AND MATABELE-LAND. BALFOUR (A. B.) Twelve hundred miles in a wagon. pp. 265. *Lond.* 1895. 8°.
010097. g. 8.

BENT (J. T.) Ruined cities of Mashonaland. pp. 427. *Lond.* 1895. 8°.   010096. e. 73.

BLENNERHASSETT (R.) and SLEEMAN (L.) Adventures in Mashonaland. pp. 310. *Lond.* 1893. 8°.   010096. e. 62.

MASHONALAND, etc.—*continued.*

BRUCE (G. W. H. K.) *Bp. of Mashonaland.* Journals of the Mashonaland Mission, 1888–92. pp 99. *Lond.* 1893. 8°.   4767. dd. 5.

—— Memories of Mashonaland. pp. 242. *Lond.* 1895. 8°.   4765. ccc. 1.

CARNEGIE (D.) Among the Matabele. pp. 128. *Lond.* 1894. 8°.   4767. c. 37.

CHADWICK (J. C.) Three years with Lobengula. pp. 160. *Lond.* 1894. 8°.   10097. ccc. 18.

COLQUHOUN (A. R.) Matabeleland : the war, and our position. pp. 167. *Lond.* 1894. 8°.
8155. de. 14.

DONOVAN (C. H. W.) With Wilson in Matabeleland. pp. 322. *Lond.* 1894. 8°.   9061. d. 29.

DU POUGET (J. F. A) *Marquis de Nadaillac.* Le Mashonaland. pp. 42. *Paris,* 1894. 8°. Pam. 89.

EGLINTON AND Co. Handbook on Mashonaland. pp. 87. *Lond.* 1892. 8°.   10097. c. 38.

FINLASON (C. E.) A Nobody in Mashonaland. pp. 330. *Lond.* 1895. 8°.   010096. e. 74.

FITZ PATRICK (J. P.) Through Mashonaland with pick and pen. pp. 64. *Johannesburg,* 1892. 8°.   Pam. 89.

KNIGHT (E. F.) Rhodesia of to-day. pp. 151. *Lond.* 1895. 8°.   001096. e. 72.

MASHONALAND. With Mr. Rhodes through Mashonaland. pp. 13. *Lond.* 1892. 4°. Pam. 89.

MATABELE. The Matabele scandal and its consequences. pp. 46. *Camb.* 1894. 8°.   Pam. 66.

MATHERS (E. P.) Zambesi, England's El Dorado. pp. 480. *Lond.* 1891. 8°.   010096. ee. 21.

NEWMAN (C. L. N.) Matabeleland and how we got it. pp. 241. *Lond.* 1895. 8°. 9061. d. 26.

P.P. *Salisbury,* Mashonaland. The Rhodesia Herald. *Salisbury,* 1892, *etc.* fol. P.P.9637. ab.

RUGG (R.) Gold Fields and mineral resources of Mashonaland. pp. 42. *Lond.* 1891. 8°.
Pam. 27.

SAWYER (A. R.) The Goldfields of Mashonaland. pp. 99. *Manch.* 1894. 8°.   07108. g. 2.

SCHLICHTER (H. G.) The ruins in Mashonaland. pp. 4. *Lond.* 1893. 8°.   07708. g. 42. (2.)

—— Historical evidence as to the Zimbabwe Ruins. pp. 10. *Lond.* 1893. 8°. 07708. g. 42. (1.)

SELOUS (F. C.) Travel and adventure in S.E. Africa. pp. 503. *Lond.* 1893. 8°. 10096. ff. 12.

STUART (J. M.) The ancient gold fields of Africa. pp. 312. *Lond.* 1891. 8°.   07109. l. 3.

WOOD (J. G.) Through Matabeleland. pp. 198. *Lond.* 1893. 8°.   010096. c. 58.

WILLS (W. A.) and COLLINGRIDGE (L. J.) The downfall of Lobengula. pp. 335. *Lond.* 1894. 4°.   9061. ccc. 23.

WILLOUGHBY (*Sir* J. C.) Narrative of further excavations at Zimbabye. pp. 43. *Lond.* 1893. 8°.
7708. aa. 60.
See also AFRICA, *South :* MISSIONS. For the language, *see* AFRICAN LANGUAGES.

MASKS. EMERSON (E. R.) Masks, Heads and faces. pp. 312. *Lond.* 1892. 8°.   7808. e. 2.

HUTTON (L.) Portraits in Plaster. pp. 271. *N.Y.* 1894. 8°.   Banks. 2. f. 2.

MASS. *See* EUCHARIST.

MASSACHUSETTS. ADAMS (C. F.) Massachusetts. Its historians and its history. pp. 110. *Bost.* 1893. 8°.   9605. c. 16.

—— Three episodes of Massachusetts history. 2 vol. *Bost.* 1892. 8°.   9602. de. 13.

—— Antinomianism in Massachusetts Bay, 1636–38. pp. 415. 1894. 4°. Ac. Albany. *Prince Society.* Publications.   Ac. 9503.

MASSACHUSETTS—*continued.*

APPLETON (W. S.) The Loyal Petitions of 1666. pp. 10. *Camb.* 1891. 8°.   9555. f. 4. (1.)

BODGE (G. M.) Soldiers in King Philip's war. 1675–77. pp. 369. *Bost.* 1891. 8°. 9602. g. 2.

DAVIS (W. T.) Bench and Bar of Massachusetts. 2 vol. *Bost.* 1895. 8°.   6005. k. 1.

DAVIS (A. M.) Historical work of Massachusetts. pp 57. *Camb.* 1893. 8°.   9551. k. 8. (5.)

DOUGLAS (C. H. J.) Financial history of Massachusetts, to the American Revolution. pp. 148. 1892. 8°. Ac. New York. *Columbia College. Studies in History.* Vol. 1. No. 4.
    Ac. 2688/2.

GANNETT (H.) Geographic dictionary of Massachusetts. pp. 126. 1894. 8°. U.S. *Geological Survey.* Bulletin. No. 116.   1829. a. 7.

GREEN (S. A.) Northern boundary of Massachusetts in its relations to New Hampshire. pp. 24. *Worcester,* 1891. 8°.   Pam. 86.

—— Boundary line between Massachusetts and New Hampshire. pp. 30. *Lowell,* 1894. 8°.
    10412. dd. 25. (3.)

—— Remarks on the Waters-Winthrop Map. pp. 4. 1892. 8°.   10412. dd. 25. (7.)

—— First Census of Massachusetts. pp. 7. 1891. 8°.   08226. k. 6. (6.)

GRIFFIS (W. E.) Massachusetts. pp. 38. *Camb.* 1893. 4°.   10413. c. 43.

MASSACHUSETTS. *Militia.* Military types of the U.S. Militia and National Guard. *Bost.* 1893, *etc.* fol.   1861. e.

EMILIO (L. F.) History of the 54th Regiment of Massachusetts Volunteer Infantry, 1863–65. pp. 410. *Bost.* 1891. 8°.   9605. cc. 16.

MASSACHUSETTS. *Bureau of Statistics of Labour.* Annual statistics of Manufactures. *Bost.* 1888, *etc.* 8°.   1591. 25.

RAND (J. C.) One of a Thousand. Biographical sketches of representative men. pp. 707. *Bost.* 1890. 8°.   10880. i. 7.

See also BOSTON : CAPE COD : NEW ENGLAND.

MASSAGE. Dowse (T. S.) Primer of the art of Massage. pp. 151. *Bristol,* 1892. 8°.
    7461. a. 14.

ECCLES (A. S.) Practice of Massage. pp. 377. *Lond.* 1895. 8°.   7461. c. 9.

EWER (L.) Cursus der Massage. pp. 182. *Berl.* 1892. 8°.   7460. ee. 22.

FITCH (L.) Massage for beginners. pp. 31. 1891. 8°. RIDEAL (C. F.) *Nursing Record Series.*   7688. a.

GRAHAM (D.) A Treatise on Massage. pp. 342. *N.Y.* 1890. 8°.   07305. h. 7. (6.)

HALE (A. C.) The Art of Massage. pp. 144. *Lond.* 1893. 8°.   7461. f. 8.

HOFFA (A.) Technik der Massage. pp. 74. *Stuttgart,* 1893. 8°.   7461. i. 10.

HYDE (S.) Nurse's guide to Massage. pp. 62. *Manch.* 1894. 8°.   7461. c. 12.

KELLOGG (J. H.) The art of Massage. pp. 282. *Battle Creek,* 1895. 8°.   7461. i. 12.

KLEMM (C.) Die ärztliche Massage. pp. 72. *Riga,* 1883. 8°.   7305. de. 21. (7.)

OSTROM (K. W.) Massage and the original Swedish movements. pp. 143. *Lond.* 1892. 8°.
    7461. aa. 8.

MASSERANO. TEONESTUS, *Saint, Collegiate Church.* La chiesa collegiata di Masserano. pp. 85. *Torino,* 1894. 8°.   4605. f. 21.

MASTER AND SERVANT, Law of.
BARRISTER. Servants and Masters. pp. 36. *Lond.* 1894. 8°.   6325. de. 39.

See also CAPITAL AND LABOUR. Pt. I., *Law, etc.*

MATABELELAND. *See* MASHONALAND.

MATERIALISM. DREHER (E.) Der Materialismus. pp. 83. *Berl.* 1892. 8°. 8462. f. 29.

DREWS (A.) E. v. Hartmanns Philosophie und der Materialismus in der modernen Kultur. pp. 109. *Leipz.* 1889. 8°.   8464. cc. 44.

LETOURNEAU (C. J. M.) Science et Matérialisme. pp. 470. *Paris,* 1891. 8°.   4018. f. 19.

SCHMIDKUNZ (H.) Gegen den Materialismus. *Stuttgart,* 1892, *etc.* 8°.   4016. h. 13.

WOLLNY (F.) Apologie des Materialismus. pp. 38. *Leipz.* 1890. 8°.   4371. c. 1. (9.)

See also AGNOSTICISM.

MATERIALS, Strength and Resistance of. *See* ENGINEERING.

MATERIA MEDICA. BARTHOLOW (R.) Treatise of Materia Medica. pp. 820. *Lond.* 1893. 8°.   07509. i. 1.

BINZ (C.) Grundzüge der Arzneimittellehre. pp. 318. *Berl.* 1891. 8°.   7442. e. 6.

BOCQUILLON-LIMOUSIN (H.) Matière Médicale. *Paris,* 1891, *etc.* 8°.   7028. d.

BRUCE (J. M.) Materia Medica. pp. 582. *Lond.* 1891. 8°.   2255. a. 13.

D., M. Rhyming and mnemonic key to Materia Medica. pp. 48. *Lond.* 1891. 8°. 07305. h. 7. (8.)

DAKE (J. P.) Materia Medica as a science. pp. 24. *Phila.* 1881. 8°.   07509. c. 15. (4.)

HELBING (H.) Modern Materia Medica. pp. 295. *N.Y.* 1895. 8°.   07509. f. 12.

ISRAELSON (L.) Die Materia Medica des Klaudios Galenos. pp. 204. *Dorpat,* 1894. 8°.
    07509. f. 14.

JACKSON (R. E. S.) Note-book of Materia Medica. pp. 743. *Edinb.* 1895. 8°.   2256. b. 12.

LEONARD (C. H.) and CHRISTY (T.) Dictionary of Materia Medica. pp. 387. *Lond.* 1892. 8°.
    07509. de. 19.

MAISCH (J. M.) Manual of organic Materia Medica. pp. 539. *Phila.* 1890. 8°. 07509. de. 7.

MOELLER (J.) Lehrbuch der Arzneimittel-Lehre. pp. 544. *Wien,* 1893. 8°.   7509. f. 8.

MUHĪ AL-DĪN KHĀN. Materia Medica of Madras. *Madras,* 1891, *etc.* 8°.   7509. i.

PHILLIPS (C. D. F.) Materia Medica. *Lond.* 1894, *etc.* 8°.   07509. f. 10.

POTTER (S. O. L.) Handbook of Materia Medica. pp. 767. *Phila.* 1891. 8°.   07509. e. 14.

SEMPLE (C. E. A.) Elements of Materia Medica. pp. 480. *Lond.* 1892. 8°.   07509. de. 20.

SHEMTOB (M. H.) Abridged Materia Medica of the organic kingdom. 3 pt. *Bombay,* 1890, 16°.
    7509. de. 60.

SHOEMAKER (J. V.) Treatise on Materia Medica. pp. 1108. *Phila.* 1895. 8°.   07509. i. 6.

STIRLING (G.) Table of organic Materia Medica. pp. 44. *Lond.* 1893. *obl.* 16°.   7509. a. 11.

WHITE (W. H.) Materia Medica. pp. 614. *Lond.* 1892. 8°.   07509. de. 21.

WHITLA (W.) Elements of Materia Medica. pp. 646. *Lond.* 1892. 8°.   2256. a. 25.

See also BOTANY, *Medical* : PHARMACY : THERAPEUTICS.

MATHEMATICS.
General.

Ac. Berlin. *Societas Scientiarum.* KRONECKER (L.) Vorlesungen über Mathematik. *Leipz.* 1894, *etc.* 8°.   8535. i.

—— Edinburgh. *Mathematical Society.* Proceedings. *Lond.* 1894, *etc.* 8°.   Ac. 4278.

MATHEMATICS.—General—*continued.*

Ac. Palermo. *Circolo Matematico.* Rendiconti. *Palermo*, 1887, *etc.* 4°. 8535. gg.

BALL (W. W. R.) Mathematical recreations and problems. pp. 240. *Lond.* 1892. 8°. 8533. de. 19.

BERGBOHM (J.) Neue Rechnungsmethoden der höheren Mathematik. pp. 30. *Stuttgart*, 1891. 8°. 8533. dd. 12. (6.)

BIERMANN (O.) Elemente der höheren Mathematik. pp. 381. *Leipz.* 1895. 8°. 8534. dd. 13.

CAMPIN (F.) Treatise on Mathematics as applied to the constructive arts. pp. 326. *Lond.* 1893. 8°. 8531. aa. 48.

DAWBARN (A. Y.) Course of Mathematics. *Camb.* 1891, *etc.* 8°. 8535. de.

ENGEL (F.) Der Geschmack in der neueren Mathematik. pp. 21. *Leipz.* 1890. 8°. 8531. dd. 28. (4.)

GRASSMANN (H.) Grassmann's gesammelte mathematische Werke. *Leipz.* 1894, *etc.* 8°. 8535. h.

HAGEN (J. G.) Synopsis der hoeheren Mathematik. *Berl.* 1891, *etc.* 4°. 8534. g. 7.

HUDSON (W. H. H.) On the teaching of Mathematics. pp. 16. *Lond.* 1893. 8°. 8304. bb. 5. (17.)

KLEIN (F.) Lectures on Mathematics. pp. 109. *N.Y.* 1894. 8°. 8533. dd. 9.

LIE (M. S.) Vorlesungen über continuierliche Gruppen. pp. 810. *Leipz.* 1893. 8°. 8535. dd. 20.

LONGMANS, GREEN AND CO. Elementary Mathematics. *Lond.* 1892, *etc.* 8°. 8535. de.

LUNDBERG (E.) Den matematiska Undervisningen vid läroverk i Tyskland och Frankrike. pp. 136. *Stockholm*, 1889. 8°. 8310. e. 25.

MEYER (E.) Humes und Berkeleys Philosophie der Mathematik. pp. 57. 1894. 8°. ERDMANN (B.) Abhandlungen zur Philosophie. No. 3. 8462. g.

P.P. *Ghent.* Mathesis. Recueil mathématique. 10 tom. *Gand*, 1881, *etc.* 8°. P.P. 1546.

—— *London.* The Mathematical Gazette. *Lond.* 1894, *etc.* 4°. P.P. 1566. b.

—— *Paris.* L'Intermédiaire des Mathématiciens. *Paris*, 1894, *etc.* 8°. P.P. 1544. ab.

—— Revue de Mathématiques spéciales. *Paris*, 1890, *etc.* fol. P.P. 1575. ab. and 260.

PITT PRESS MATHEMATICAL SERIES. Mathematical Series. *Camb.* 1890, *etc.* 8°. 8535. aaa.

REPETITORIUM. Kurzes Repetitorium der höheren Mathematik. *Leipz.* 1893, *etc.* 8°. 8533. ee.

ROSSI (G.) La Matematica applicata alla teoria della ricchezza sociale. *Reggio-Emilia, etc.* 1889. 8°. 8276. i.

SAFFORD (T. H.) Mathematical Teaching and its modern methods. pp. 51. *Bost.* 1888. 8°. 8311. aaa. 22.

SMITH (H. J. S.) Collected Mathematical papers. 2 vol. *Oxf.* 1894. 8°. 8534. g. 10.

SMITH (J H.) Mathematical Series. *Lond.* 1894, *etc.* 8°. 8533. de.

SMITH (J. C.) Questions in Mathematics. pp. 157. *Brooklyn.* 1889. 8°. 8530. bb. 41.

SONNET (H.) Dictionnaire des Mathématiques appliquées. pp. 1474. *Paris*, 1895. 8°. 8768. f. 17.

STOFFAES ( ) Cours de Mathématiques supérieures. pp. 431. *Paris*, 1891. 8°. 8535. d. 6.

TANNENBERG (W. de) Thèses pour obtenir le grade de Docteur ès Sciences mathématiques. pp. 152. *Paris*, 1892. 4°. 8535. h. 25.

VIVANTI (G.) Il Concetto d'infinitesimo e la sua applicazione alla matematica. pp. 134. *Mantova*, 1894. 8°. 8534. d. 38.

MATHEMATICS.—General—*continued.*

WORMELL (R.) Plotting or Graphic Mathematics. pp. 88. *Lond.* 1892. 8°. 8533. de. 18.

See also ALGEBRA: ANALYSIS: ARITHMETIC: CALCULUS: CIRCLE: CONIC SECTIONS: DETERMINANTS: DYNAMICS: EQUATIONS: FUNCTIONS: GEOMETRY: HYDRODYNAMICS: LOGARITHMS: MAGIC SQUARES: MECHANICS: NUMBERS: PROBABILITIES: QUATERNIONS: STATICS: TRIGONOMETRY.

Examination Papers: Exercises.

BESANT (W. H.) The Mathematical Tripos. pp. 33. *Camb.* 1891. 8°. 8304. a. 8. (5.)

WOLSTENHOLME (J.) Mathematical Problems on the subjects for the Cambridge Tripos. pp. 499. *Lond.* 1891. 4°. 8531. df. 6.

BARLOW (C. W. C.) and BRYAN (G. H.) London University Matriculation Papers in Mathematics, 1888-91. 1891. 8°. Tutorial Series. 12205. c. 57.

Ac. London. *University.* Intermediate Mathematics. pp. 134. 1894. 8°. Tutorial Series. 12205. c. 222.

—— B.A. Pure Mathematics. Questions and solutions. 1891. 8°. Tutorial Series. 12205. c. 228.

G. B. & I. *Civil Service Commissioners.* Army examination papers in Mathematics, 1877-90. pp. 195. *Lond.* 1892. 8°. 8535. de. 8.

Ac. Woolwich. *Royal Military Academy.* Woolwich Mathematical papers, 1880-90. *Lond.* 1891. 8°. 8535. b. 44.

—— Woolwich Mathematical papers, 1885-94. *Lond.* 1895. 8°. 8533. e. 44.

G. B. *Committee on Education.* S. Kensington questions and solutions in first stage Mathematics, 1870-89. pp. 187. *Lond.* 1890. 8°. 8534. aa. 30.

RICHARDSON (A. T.) Progressive mathematical exercises. *Lond.* 1891, *etc.* 8°. 8534. aa. 35.

ROBERTS (R.) Test papers in Mathematics. 2 pt. *Lond.* 1893. 8°. 8533. aa. 27.

History.

BALL (W. W. R.) Short account of the history of Mathematics. pp. 520. *Lond.* 1893. 8°. 2242. cc. 1.

Primer of the history of Mathematics. pp. 146. *Lond.* 1895. 8°. 8532. aaa. 23.

CAJORI (F.) History of Mathematics. pp. 422. *N.Y.* 1894. 8°. 8533. d. 25.

CANTOR (M.) Vorlesungen über Geschichte der Mathematik. *Leipz.* 1894, *etc.* 8°. 8535. h.

DARSTELLUNG. Principielle Darstellung des Rechenunterrichtes auf historischer Grundlage. *München*, 1891, *etc.* 8°. 8533. d.

GUENTHER (S.) Abriss der Geschichte der Mathematik in Altertum. 1894. 8°. WINDELBAND (W.) Geschichte der alten Philosophie. 2259. g.

MUELLER (F.) Zeittafeln zur Geschichte der Mathematik, bis zum Jahre 1500. pp. 103. *Leipz.* 1892. 8°. 8704. e. 29.

POULAIN (A.) Coup d'œil sur l'histoire des Mathématiques. pp. 24. *Paris*, 1890. 8°. 8535. gg. 8. (5.)

STONE (O.) and THORNTON (W. M.) Annals of Mathematics. *Charlottesville*, 1884-87. 4°. 8535. h.

ZEUTHEN (H. G.) Forelæsning over Mathematikens Historie. pp. 292. *Kjøbenh.* 1893. 8°. 8535. d. 26.

AHMES. Ein mathematisches Handbuch der alten Aegypter, Papyrus-Rhind. pp. 278. *Leipz.* 1891. 4°. 7705. g. 39.

SUTER (H.) Die Mathematik auf den Universitäten des Mittelalters. 1887. 4°. ZURICH. *Kantonsschule.* Festschrift. 8385. i. 5.

MATHEMATICS.—History—*continued.*

RUDIO (F.) Ueber den Antheil der mathematischen Wissenschaften an die Kultur der Renaissance. pp. 33. 1892. 8°. Sammlung wissenschaftlicher Vorträge. N.F. Ser. 6. Hft. 142.
12249. m.

CAJORI (F.) History of Mathematics in the United States. pp. 400. 1890. 8°. U.S. *Bureau of Education.* Circular. No. 167.   8308. i.

MATHERAN. WILSON (F. H.) My trip to Matheran. pp. 41. *Madras,* 1888. 8°.
10057. aa. 9.

MATTO-GROSSO. TAUNAY (de) A Cidade de Matto-Grosso. pp. 116. *Rio de J.* 1891. 8°.
10481. d. 29.

MAURITIUS. DUPUY (R.) Geography of Mauritius. pp. 41. *Mauritius,* 1894. 8°.
Pam. 89.

G., A. Les courses à Maurice de 1812 à 1867. pp. 82. *Port-Louis,* 1894. 8°.   07905. i. 8.

JOURDAIN (H. J.) Mauritius. pp. 41. *Lond.* 1882. 8°.   010096. ee. 37.

MERVEN (T.) L'Ile Maurice depuis sa conquête par l'Angleterre. pp. 30. *Maurice,* 1895. 8°.
Pam. 28.

NAZ (*Sir* V.) Conférence sur l'Immigration indienne. pp. 34. *Port Louis,* 1891. 8°. Pam. 66.
—— Lettres sur le drainage de Port Louis. pp. 61. *Maurice,* 1895. 8°.   Pam. 79.

RAUVILLE (H. de) *Count.* Trois légendes de l'Ile de France. pp. 288. *Paris,* 1889. 12°.
10097. ccc. 2.

VIRIEUX (É.) Mille et une dates de l'histoire de l'Ile Maurice. pp. 79. *Port Louis,* 1894. 8°.
9061. ccc. 31.

See also ENGLAND, *Colonies.*

MAXEY. MAXEY. Register book of Maxey, 1538–1713. pp. 49. *Lond.* 1892. 8°. 9903. g. 8.

MAYA RACE AND LANGUAGE.
See INDIAN LANGUAGES, *American:* INDIANS, *American:* MEXICO, *Antiquities.*

MAYBOLE. LAWSON (R.) Places of interest about Maybole. pp. 102. *Paisley,* 1891. 8°.
10369. ccc. 14.

MAYENCE. HALLEIN (L.) Mainzer Civilrecht im 14. und 15. Jahrhundert. pp. 71. *Würzburg,* 1891. 8°.   5604. e. 1. (3.)
—— Mainzer Gerichtsformeln aus dem 15. Jahrhundert. pp. 122. *Würzburg,* 1891. 8°.
5604. e. 1. (4.)

JAEGER (J.) Beiträge zur Geschichte des Erzstifts Mainz unter Diether von Isenburg. pp. 42. *Osnabrück,* 1894. 4°.   4532. g. 10. (6.)

SCHAIBLE (C. H.) Die Einnahme von Mainz im Jahr 1792 und die Mainzer Jakobiner. pp. 87. *Karlsruhe,* 1892. 8°.   9327. bb. 21.

BOCKENHEIMER (C. G.) Die Einnahme von Mainz, 1792. pp. 37. *Mainz,* 1892. 4°.
9079. m. 3.

MENTZ. Der Zoll- und Binnenhafen zu Mainz. pp. 98. *Mainz,* 1887. 4°.   10250. i. 4.

MAYENNE, Department and Town.
GUERRIER ( ) Galerie française. Mayenne. pp. 88. *Paris,* 1895. 12°.   10174. aaa. 53.

LEBLANC (E.) Les Origines de la ville de Mayenne, et la croisade de 1158. pp. 41. *Mayenne,* 1891. 12°.   10107. c. 13. (5.)

LE COQ (F.) Documents pour servir à l'histoire de la constitution civile du Clergé dans la Mayenne. *Laval,* 1890, *etc.* 8°.   4629. d. 3.

MAYENNE. *Commission historique.* Procès-verbaux et documents. *Laval,* 1880, *etc.* 8°. 010171. m. 18.

MAYNOOTH COLLEGE. HEALY (J.) Maynooth College. pp. 774. *Dublin,* 1895. 4°.
8364. i. 8.

MEAT. *See* FOOD.

MEAUX. BÈGUE (J.) Notice historique sur Meaux sous la Révolution. pp. 39. *Argenteuil,* 1891. 8°.   9007. ff. 5. (3.)

GOUDEMETZ (H. J.) Voyage de Champeaux à Meaux en 1785. pp. 209. *Meaux,* 1892. 12°.
10170. bb. 6.

MOROT (G.) Histoire contemporaine de Meaux. pp. 216. *Meaux,* 1893. 8°.   10169. de 25.

MECCA AND MEDINA. ṢĀLIḤ ṢUBḤÎ. Pèlerinage à la Mecque et à Médine. pp. 129. *Le Caire,* 1894. 8°.   10077. g. 37.

See also MOHAMMEDANISM.

MECHANICS: KINEMATICS. APPELL (P.) Traité de Mécanique rationnelle. *Paris,* 1893, *etc.* 8°.   8535. dd.

ARNAL (L.) Traité de Mécanique. 1892, *etc.* 8°.
LACROIX (D.) Encyclopédie des connaissances civiles, *etc.*   8708. n.

BARBAT (C.) Petit dictionnaire de Mécanique. pp. 994. 234. *Paris,* 1894. 12°.   8768. bb. 12.

BARLOW (C. W. C.) and STEWART (R. W.) London Matriculation model answers in Mechanics, 1888–91. 1891. 8°. Tutorial Series. 12205. c. 58.

BENTLEY (W.) Questions in applied Mechanics. pp. 29. *Halifax,* 1895. 8°.   Pam. 79.

BOUASSE (H.) Introduction à l'étude de la Mécanique. pp. 301. *Paris,* 1895. 8°.
8768. f. 16.

BLAINE (R. G.) Elementary lessons in practical Mechanics. pp. 208. *Lond.* 1893. 8°. 8767. g. 11.

BRIGGS (W.) and BRYAN (G. H.) Elementary text-book of Mechanics. 1894, *etc.* 8°. Tutorial Series.   12205. c. 252.

BROWNE (W. J.) Mechanics for junior students. pp. 204. *Manch.* 1891. 8°.   8767. aa. 49.

BUDDE (E.) Allgemeine Mechanik der Punkte und starren Systeme. 2 Bde. *Berl.* 1890, 91. 8°.   8768. e. 20.

BURN (R. S.) Mechanics and Mechanism. pp. 141. *Lond.* 1892. 8°.   8767. c. 38.
—— Technical student's introduction to Mechanics. pp. 544. *Lond.* 1892. 8°. 8767. i. 23.

CALINON (A.) Étude de Cinématique. pp. 128. *Paris,* 1890. 8°.   8535. h. 15.

COTTERILL (J. H.) Applied Mechanics. pp. 630. *Lond.* 1895. 8°.   2249. f. 4.
—— and SLADE (J. H.) Lessons in applied Mechanics. pp. 512. *Lond.* 1891. 8° 8767. ee. 1.

CRYER (T.) and JORDAN (H. G.) Text-book of applied Mechanics. pp. 299. *Manch.* 1893. 8°.   8767. g. 1.

EASTON (J. G.) First Book of Mechanics. pp. 322. *Lond.* 1891. 8°.   8768. bb. 1.

GLAZEBROOK (R. T.) Mechanics. 3 vol. 1895. 8°. Cambridge Science Manuals. Physical Series.   8709. h.

GRAINDORGE (J.) Intégration des équations de la Mécanique. pp. 290. 1890. 8°. Ac. Liège. *Société des Sciences.* Mémoires. Sér. 2. Tom. 16.   Ac. 2961.

GRIEVE (W. H.) Elementary science reader. Mechanics. pp. 143. *Lond.* 1890. 8°. 8767. b. 46.

HAAG (P.) Cours de Mécanique rationnelle. pp. 549. *Paris,* 1894. 8°.   8768. e. 28.

HECHT (C.) Lehrbuch der reinen und angewandten Mechanik. *Dresd.* 1892, *etc.* 8°.
8768. f. 6.

HILLIER (D. E.) Mechanical Test Cards. *Leeds,* 1891, *etc.* 16°.   12210. d.

HOROBIN (J. C.) Elementary Mechanics. *Lond.* 1891, *etc.* 8°.   8768. bbb. 34.

MECHANICS—*continued.*

HOROBIN (J. C.) Theoretical Mechanics.
Lond. 1892, *etc.* 8°.   8768. bbb. 36.

HUGHES (W. G. C.) Condensed Mechanics.
pp. 116. *Lond.* 1891. 8°.   8767. cc. 22

JAMIESON (A.) Applied Mechanics. pp. 268.
Lond. 1892. 8°.   8768. bb. 2.

—— Text-book on applied Mechanics.
Lond. 1895, *etc.* 8°.   8768. b. 2.

JESSOP (C. M.) Elements of applied Mathematics. pp. 344. *Lond.* 1894. 8°. 8533. de. 28.

LOCK (J. B.) Mechanics for beginners.
Lond. 1891, *etc.* 8°.   8767. f. 5

LONEY (S. L.) Mechanics for beginners.
pp. 304. 1893. 8°. Pitt Press Mathematical
Series.   2322. cc. 35.

LOW (D. A.) Guide to examinations in applied
Mechanics of the Science and Art Department.
pp. 54. 1892. 8°. Blackie's Guides. 8703. aa.

MACH (E.) Science of Mechanics. pp. 534.
Lond. 1893. 8°.   8767. g. 10.

MAGNUS (*Sir* P.) Lessons in elementary Mechanics. pp. 371. *Lond.* 1892. 8°. 8767. f. 13.

—— Solutions of the Exercises. pp. 186.
Lond. 1892. 8°.   8767. f. 29.

MANNHEIM (A.) Principes et développements de
Géométrie cinématique. pp. 589.
Paris, 1894. 4°.   8535. i. 1.

PINKERTON (R. M.) Theoretical Mechanics.
pp. 186. 1890. 8°. Blackie's Science Text
Books.   8703. bb.

SELBY (A. L.) Elementary Mechanics of solids
and fluids. pp. 299. 1893. 8°. Clarendon
Press Series.   2319. b. 8.

SELLS (V. P.) Mechanics of daily life. pp. 181.
1893. 8°. SYMES (J. E.) University Extension
Series.   012202. g.

SPENCER (J.) Theoretical Mechanics. pp. 243.
Lond. 1892. 8°.   8766. a. 70.

THORNTON (A.) Theoretical Mechanics.
pp. 436. 1894. 8°. Longmans' advanced Science
Manuals.   8709. h.

WORMELL (R.) Elementary text-book of Mechanics. pp. 245. *Lond.* 1892. 8°. 8767. f. 6.

ZIWET (A.) Elementary treatise on theoretical
Mechanics. *Lond.* 1893, *etc.* 8°. 8768. l.

See also DYNAMICS: ELASTICITY: ENGINEERING:
HYDRAULICS: HYDROSTATICS, *etc.*: STATICS:
STRAINS AND STRESSES.

MECKLENBURG. LORENZ (C.) Der Anteil Mecklenburgs an der deutschen Nationallitteratur. pp. 64. *Rostock,* 1893. pp.
11826. d. 46. (7.)

LUNDIN (C. F.) Wismars pantsättande till Meklenburg-Schwerin. pp. 87. *Upsala,* 1892. 8°.
10256. d. 2.

MEDALS. *See* NUMISMATICS.

MEDIA. DELATTRE (A.) Le Peuple et
l'Empire des Mèdes. pp. 200. 1883. 4°. Ac.
Brussels. *Académie.* Mémoires couronnés, *etc.*
Tom. xlv.   Ac. 985/6.

HAUVETTE-BESNAULT (A.) Hérodote historien
des guerres médiques. pp. 512.
Paris, 1894. 8°.   9026. i. 8.

WIESBACH (F. H.) Die Achämenideninschriften.
pp. 126. *Leipz.* 1890. 8°.   7702. l. 28.
See also ASSYRIA: PERSIA.

MEDICINE.

See also ANATOMY: DIAGNOSIS: DISEASE:
HOMŒOPATHY: HYGIENE: PATHOLOGY: PHYSIOLOGY: THERAPEUTICS, *etc.*

MEDICINE—*continued.*

Bibliography.

AC., *etc.* London. *Pharmaceutical Society. North
British Branch.* Catalogue of the Library of
the Pharmaceutical Society. pp. 657.
Lond. 1894. 8°.   BB.C. c. 15.

GIACOSA (P.) Bibliografia medica italiana.
pp. 383. *Torino,* 1893. 8°.   011900. ce. 27.

NEALE (R.) The Medical Digest. pp. 794.
Lond. 1891. 8°.   BB.C. c. 11.

General: Handbooks: Systems of Medicine.

AC. Cincinnati. *College of Medicine.* Archives.
Cincinati, 1893, *etc.* 8°.   8366. g.

—— Edinburgh. *Royal Medical Society.* Dissertations. pp. 316. *Edinb.* 1892. 8°. Ac. 3850. b.

—— Gottenburg. *Läkaresällskap.* Göteborgs
Läkaresällskaps Förhandlingar.
Götborg, 1893, *etc.* 8°.   Ac. 3806.

—— Yedo. *Imperial University.* Mitteilungen
aus der medicinischen Falcutät.
Tokio, 1887, *etc.* 4°.   Ac. 2697/4.

AITCHISON (R. S.) Medical Handbook. pp. 347.
Lond. 1893. 8°.   7321. aa. 24.

ALLINSON (T. R.) Medical Essays.
Lond. 1891. *etc.* 8°.   7390. df

BEALE (L. S.) Lectures on the principles and
practice of Medicine. pp. 374. *Lond.* 1890. 8°.
7460. ff. 17.

BLACKWELL (E.) Christianity in Medicine.
pp. 24. *Lond.* 1891. 8°.   8409. ccc. 27. (2.)

BORN (G.) Bibliotheca Medica.
Cassel, 1893, *etc.* 4°.   7383. l.

BRAMWELL (J. B.) Atlas of clinical Medicine.
Edinb. 1891, *obl.* fol.   7440. k. 1.

BREMOND (F.) Les préjugés en Médecine.
pp. 159. *Paris,* 1892. 8°.   7404. cc. 17.

BUCK (A. H.) Reference Handbook of the
Medical Sciences. 8 vol. *Edinb.* 1888–98. 8°.
7383. k. 1.

BURGGRAEVE (A.) La Société de Médécine de
Gand et la médecine dosimétrique. pp. 312.
Brux. 1890. 4°.   7383. g. 6.

WESTWOOD-WILSON (C. W.) Key-notes of Dosimetric medical practice. pp. 59.
Cape Town, 1891. 12°.   7383. c. 21.

BURY (J. S.) Clinical Medicine. pp. 468.
Lond. 1894. 8°.   7442. i. 4.

CARTER (A. H.) Elements of practical Medicine.
pp. 552. *Lond.* 1895. 8°.   2255. b. 8.

CHARCOT (J. M.) Traité de Médecine.
Paris, 1891, *etc.* 8°.   7383. g.

CHARTERIS (M.) Practice of Medicine. pp. 712.
Lond. 1894. 8°.   7321. aa. 28.

COLLINS (W. J.) Rationalism and free thought
in Medicine. pp. 20. *Lond.* 1890. 8°. Pam. 39.

DORNBLUETH (O.) Kompendium der inneren
Medizin. pp. 388. *Leipz.* 1892. 8°.
7321. bbb. 21.

DRASCHE (A.) Gesammelte Abhandlungen.
pp. 710. *Wien,* 1893. 8°.   07305. l. 11.

DUSSELDORF. *Verein der Aerzte.* Fünfzig Beiträge
aus dem Gebiete der gesammten Medecin.
pp. 580. *Wiesbaden,* 1894. 8°.   7306. g. 17.

EWART (W.) Symptoms and physical signs. A
formulary. pp. 82. *Lond.* 1892. 8°. 7440. de. 7.

FAGGE (C. H.) Text-book of Medicine. 2 vol.
Lond. 1891. 8°.   2255. g. 8.

FENWICK (S.) Outlines of medical Treatment.
pp. 502. *Lond.* 1894. 8°.   2254. a. 8.

FINLAYSON (J.) Clinical Manual for the study
of medical cases. pp. 719. *Lond.* 1891. 8°.
2254. c. 9.

MEDICINE.—General, etc.—continued.

GARIEL (C. M.)　Cours de Physique médicale.
pp. 964.　Paris, 1892. 8°.　　　07305. h. 21.

GOIZET (L. H.)　La Vie prolongée au moyen de
la méthode Brown-Séquard.　pp. 359.
Paris, 1891. 12°.　　　　　7442. c. 12.

GRELLETY (J. L.)　Causeries.　pp. 287.
Macon, 1891. 8°.　　　　　7321. bb. 29.

GULL (Sir W. W.)　Collection of the writings of
W. W. Gull.　Lond. 1894, etc. 8°.　Ac. 3838/60.

HALL (W. W.)　Popular Cyclopædia of curative
maxims.　pp. 248.　Lond. 1892. 8°.　7383. h. 9.

HOBHOUSE (E.)　Scientific basis of Medicine.
pp. 55.　Oxf. 1895. 8°.　　7306. c. 26. (10.)

HUSBAND (H. A.)　Student's Hand-book of Medicine.　pp. 510.　Edinb. 1888. 8°.　2254. a. 18.

KEITH (G. S.)　Plea for a simpler life.　pp. 149.
Lond. 1895. 8°.　　　　7404. aaaa. 6.

KESWICK (J. B.)　Life and Living.　pp. 322.
Carlisle, 1895. 8°.　　　　7442. aa. 18.

KUHNE (L.)　Die neue Heilwissenschaft.
pp. 266.　Leipz. 1890. 8°.　　7460. ff. 18.

—— New science of Healing.　pp. 458.
Leipz. 1892. 8°.　　　　07305. h. 12.

LONDE (A.)　La Photographie médicale.
pp. 220.　Paris, 1893. 8°.　　8909. ccc. 3.

MACLEOD (Sir G. H. B.)　Note-book for Sir G.
Macleod's clinical class.　pp. 24.
Glasg. 1890. 8°.　　　　Pam. 39.

MOORE (N.)　Principles and practice of Medicine.
pp. 30.　Lond. 1893. 8°.　　7680. aa. 27.

MURRAY (W.)　Illustrations of the inductive
method in Medicine.　pp. 158.　Lond. 1891. 8°.
　　　　　　　　7320. aa. 2.

NATURE.　Nature's Remedy for the cure of
diseases and prolongation of life.　pp. 19.
Belfast, 1895. 12°.　　07305. i. 14. (5.)

OSLER (W.)　Principles and practice of Medicine.
pp. 1079.　Edinb. 1892. 8°.　　7383. h. 8.

P.P.　Bombay.　Indian Medico-chirurgical Review.　Bombay, 1893, etc. 8°.　P.P. 2889. da.

—— Doctor's Magazine.　A monthly journal.
Bombay, 1892, etc. 8°.　　P.P. 2889. d.

—— Calcutta.　Calcutta Journal of Medicine.
Calcutta, 1887, etc. 8°.　　P.P. 2888. ba.

—— Cape Town.　South African Medical Journal.
Cape Town, 1893, etc. 4°.　　P.P. 2881.

—— Copenhagen.　Medicinsk Aarskrift.
Kjøbenh. 1892, etc. 8°.　　P.P. 3080. d.

—— Edinburgh.　International Clinics.
Edinb. 1891, etc. 8°　　　P.P. 2857.

—— London.　Clinical Journal.
Lond. 1892, etc. 8°.　P.P. 2707. g. and 2152.

—— Medical Magazine.　Lond. 1892, etc. 8°.
　　　　　　　　P.P. 2707. f.

—— Monthly Medical Review.　Vol. I. Nos. 1-3.
Lond. 1891. 8°.　　　　1866. a. 17.

—— Popular Medical Monthly.
Lond. 1891, etc. 8°.　　　　2096.

—— Madras.　Madras Medical Record.
Madras, 1890, etc. 4°.　　P.P. 2888. d.

—— Paris.　Le Mercredi Médical.
Paris, 1890, etc. 8°.　P.P. 2907. ca. and 197.

—— La Semaine Médicale.　Paris, 1894, etc. fol.
　　　　　　P.P. 2907. lc. and 66.

—— Saint Louis.　Weekly Medical Review.
St. Louis, Mo., 1889, etc. 8°.　　　80.

—— Sheffield.　Quarterly Medical Journal.
Sheffield, 1893, etc. 8°.　　P.P. 2877. d.

POGGI (A.)　L'Unité des maladies et l'unité des
remèdes.　pp. 179.　Paris, 1890. 8°.　7461. e. 4.

PULIDO FERNANDEZ (A.)　Estudios médicos.
pp. 221.　Madrid, 1889. 8°.　　07305. c. 16.

MEDICINE.—General, etc.—continued.

PŪRNACHANDRA SENA.　Medical Science advanced.　pp. 180.　Calcutta, 1893. 8°.
　　　　　　　　7383. aa. 2.

REICH (E.)　Immaterielle Ursachen der Krankheiten.　Gr.-Lichterfelde, 1894, etc. 8°.　7410. d.

ROBERTS (F. T.)　Theory and practice of medicine.　pp. 1168.　Lond. 1894. 8°.　　2024. c.

SAWYER (Sir J.)　Contributions to practical
medicine.　pp. 201.　Birmingham, 1891. 8°.
　　　　　　　　7442. aaa. 19.

SILVERLOCK (H.)　Medical and surgical emergency reference book.　pp. 120.　Lond. 1890. 12°.
　　　　　　　　7321. aaa. 18.

SOARES (F. P.)　Resumo de tratamento medico.
pp. 84.　Hongkong, 1893. 8°.　07305. i. 11. (3.)

STEWART (T. G.)　Clinical Lectures on important
symptoms.　Edinb. 1888, etc. 8°.　　7442. i.

STRUEMPELL (A.)　Text-book of Medicine.
pp. 1043.　Lond. 1893. 8°.　　07305. k. 12.

TAYLOR (F.)　Manual of the practice of Medicine.
pp. 950.　Lond. 1895. 8°.　　07305. i. 16.

THIERFELDER (T.)　Beiträge zur wissenschaftlichen Medizin.　pp. 253.　Leipz. 1895. 8°.
　　　　　　　　7383. k. 4.

VIRCHOW (R. L. C.)　Internationale Beiträge zur
wissenschaftlichen Medicin.　3 Bde.
Berl. 1891. 8°.　　　　7383. g. 7.

WHEELER (A.)　Student's Hand-book of Medicine.
pp. 396.　Edinb. 1894. 8°.　　7460. aa. 5.

WHIPPLE (L. E.)　Philosophy of Mental Healing.
pp. 234.　N.Y. 1893. 8°.　　7410. cc. 44.

YEO (I. B.)　Manual of medical Treatment.
2 vol.　Lond. 1895. 8°.　　　7440. de. 11.

See also infra: Dictionaries.

Chemistry, Medical.

See CHEMISTRY: CHEMISTS AND DRUGGISTS.

Dictionaries of Medicine and Medical Terms.

BILLINGS (J. S.)　National medical Dictionary,
English, French, German, Italian and Latin.
2 vol.　Edinb. 1890. 8°.　　07305. k. 4.

CARPENTER (W. M.)　Index of the practice
of Medicine.　pp. 304.　N.Y. 1884. 8°.
　　　　　　　　7321. bbb. 24.

CHITTENDEN (J. F.)　Medical Phrase Book in
Hindustānī, English, French and Spanish.
pp. 74.　Port-of-Spain, 1893, 8°.　12901. cc. 36.

DUANE (A.)　Student's Dictionary of Medicine.
pp. 650.　Lond. 1894. 8°.　　07305. h. 24.

DUNGLISON (R.)　Dictionary of Medical Science.
pp. 1181.　Lond. 1893. 8°.　　2024. c.

GAD (J.)　Real Lexikon der medicinischen
Propädeutik.　Wien, 1893, etc. 8°.　7383. i.

GOULD (G. M.)　Illustrated Dictionary of
Medicine.　pp. 1633.　Lond. 1894. 8°.
　　　　　　　　07305. h. 12.

—— Pocket Medical Dictionary.　pp. 317.
Lond. 1892. 8°.　　　　7321. aaa. 26.

HOBLYN (R. D.)　Dictionary of terms used
in Medicine.　pp. 822.　Lond. 1892. 8°.
　　　　　　　　2254. a. 15.

KEATING (J. M.) and HAMILTON (H.)　New pronouncing Dictionary of Medicine.　pp. 818.
Edinb. 1892. 8°.　　　　7320. dd. 8.

—— Pocket Medical Lexicon.　pp. 280.
Lond. 1891. 24°.　　　　7321. a. 10.

LEWIS (H. K.)　Pocket medical Vocabulary.
pp. 314.　Lond. 1891. 16°.　　7321. a. 11.

MÂREAU (E.)　Dictionnaire de Médicine à l'usage
des Assurances.　pp. 435.　Paris, 1890. 12°.
　　　　　　　　7321. b. 22.

MAYNE (R. G.)　Short Dictionary of medical
terms.　pp. 160.　Lond. 1891. 8°.　7321. a. 12.

MEDICINE.—Dictionaries, etc.—cont.

QUAIN (Sir R.) Dictionary of Medicine. 2 vol. Lond. 1894. 8°. 2024. e.

TAYLOR (S.) Index of Medicine. pp. 794. Lond. 1894. 8°. 07305. f. 18.

THOMSON (S.) Dictionary of domestic Medicine. pp. 736. Lond. 1894. 8°. 2255. g. 14.

WALLER (J. R.) English-German and German-English Medical Dictionary. Leipz. 1891, 90. 8°. 7321. aaa. 20.

WALTERS (F. R.) Household Dictionary of Medicine. pp. 379. Lond. 1895. 8°. 07305. h. 31.

Education.

BERGÉ (A.) Guide de l'étudiant à l'hôpital. pp. 209. 1892. 8°. Encyclopédie des aide-mémoire. 8709. g.

BILLINGS (J. S.) Ideals of medical Education. pp. 22. Yale, 1891. 8°. 07305. h. 19. (6.)

CHOAY (E.) Centres universitaires et établissements hospitaliers à l'étranger. pp. 146. Paris, 1892. 8°. 7679. df. 36.

EDINBURGH. Medical School. Edinburgh Medical School Calendar. Lond. 1884, etc. 8°. 7679. de.

FAULKNER (A. S.) Guide to the public Medical Services. pp. 72. Lond. 1893. 8°. 7306. e. 22. (5.)

G. B. & I. General Council of Medical Education. Minutes of the General Medical Council. Lond. 1894, etc. 8°. 7688. dd.

GUY'S HOSPITAL. Guy's Hospital Medical School. Lond. 1895, etc. 8°. 7688. b.

HARTMANN (A.) Die Reform des medicinischen Unterrichtes. pp. 88. Berl. 1894. 8°. 7679. bb. 4.

HUMPHRY (Sir G. M.) Degrees in Medicine at Cambridge. pp. 27. Camb. 1891. 8°. 8304. a. 8. (8.)

HUN (H.) Guide to American medical students in Europe. pp. 151. N.Y. 1883. 8°. 7688. aa. 49.

ITALY. Medical Schools. Le Scuole Italiane di Clinica Medica. 2 vol. Milano, 1894. 8°. 7680. df. 3.

LONDON. Saint Mary's Hospital. St. Mary's Hospital Medical School. Lond. 1895, etc. 8°. 7688. c.

NEVINS (W. P.) Oxford, Natural Science and the Faculty of Medicine. pp. 32. Oxf. 1890. 8°. Pam. 17.

NICAISE (E.) Les Écoles de Médecine au Moyen Âge. pp. 9. Paris, 1891. 8°. 07305. h. 7. (9.)

POTTER (S. O. L.) American versus European medical education. pp. 31. Chicago, 1890. 8°. 07305. h. 4. (13.)

PUSCHMANN (T.) History of medical education. pp. 650. Lond. 1891, 8°. 7679. f. 24.

See also EXAMINATIONS.

Electricity, Medical. See ELECTRCITY.

History.

BAAS (J. H.) Outlines of the history of medicine. pp. 1173. N.Y. 1889. 8°. 7679. e. 22.

BERDOE (E.) Origin and growth of the Healing Art. pp. 509. Lond. 1893. 8°. 7679. b. 8.

ECCLES (R. G.) Evolution of medical science. pp. 23. Bost. 1890. 8°. 7006. e. 12. (2.)

HEGEWALD (L.) Vergangenheit und Gegenwart der Heilkunde. München, 1892, etc. 8°. 7679. aaa.

HARTMANN (F.) Occult Science in medicine. pp. 100. Lond. 1893. 8°. 8632. e. 30.

KATSCH (J. F.) Entwickelungsgang des Aehnlichkeitsaxioms von Empedokles bis auf Hahnemann. pp. 133. Stuttgart, 1891. 8°. 7679. f. 23.

MEDICINE.—History—continued.

MITCHELL (S. W.) Early History of instrumental precision in medicine. pp. 42. New Haven, 1892. 8°. 7679. e. 20.

POTTER (S. O. L.) Progress of Medicine, measured by the progress of therapeutics. pp. 76. San Fran. 1888. 8°. 07305. h. 4 (9.)

REPETITORIUM. Kurzes Repetitorium der Geschichte der Medicin. pp. 93. Leipz. 1893, etc. 8°. 7679. ff.

SOZINSKEY (T. S.) Medical Symbolism in connection with historical studies in the arts of healing. pp. 171. Phila. 1891. 8°. 7679. de. 12.

STOKES (Sir W.) Altered relations of surgery to medicine. pp. 40. Lond. 1888. 8°. 07305. g. 6. (11.)

VIERORDT (H.) Medizinisches aus der Weltgeschichte. pp. 80. Tübingen, 1893. 8°. 7680. de. 5.

WINTERBOTTOM (A.) Evolution of medicine and surgery. pp. 32. Lond. 1890. 8°. Pam. 39.

BARTELS (M.) Die Medicin der Naturvölker. Leipz. 1893, etc. 8°. 7680. e.

BOUCHINET (A.) Des états primitifs de la Médecine. pp. 88. Paris, 1891. 8°. 07305. h. 7. (7.)

DENEFFE (V.) Des Ventouses et de la révulsion chez les anciens. pp. 15. Gand, 1895. 8°. Pam. 39.

PETERSEN (J.) Hauptmomente in der älteren Geschichte der medicinischen Klinik. Kopenhagen, 1890. 8°. 7679. ee. 2.

FINLAYSON (J.) Ancient Egyptian Medicine. pp. 55. Glasg. 1893. 8°. Pam. 39.

ALBERT (M.) Les Médecins grecs à Rome. pp. 323. Paris, 1894. 8°. 7679. ff. 1.

KOSTOMOIRES (G. A.) Études sur les Écrits inédits des anciens médecins grecs. pp. 76. Paris, 1890. 8°. 7679. e. 18.

BURGGRAEVE (A.) Études sur Hippocrate au point de vue de la méthode dosimétrique. pp. 765. Paris, 1893. 8°. 7383. h. 14.

SOURLANGAS (M.) Étude sur Hippocrate. pp. 83. Paris, 1894. 8°. 7679. e. 23

DUPOUY (E.) Médecine et mœurs de l'ancienne Rome d'après les poètes. pp. 439. Paris, 1892. 12°. 7679. a. 1.

LANDAU (R.) Geschichte der jüdischen Ärzte. pp. 144. Berl. 1895. 8°. 7680. df. 4.

RIEUNIER (A.) Quelques mots sur la Médecine au moyen âge. pp. 59. Paris, 1892. 8°. 67305. k. 13. (10.)

DICKINSON (W. H.) Harveian Oration on Harvey. pp. 34. Lond. 1891. 8°. 7679. de. 14.

SCIENCES. Les Sciences biologiques à la fin du XIXᵉ siècle. pp. 800. Paris, 1893. 8°. 7001. g. 7.

DENMARK. Denmark, its medical organization. pp. 474. Copenhagen, 1891. 8°. 7680. e. 9.

HIRSCH (A.) Geschichte der medicinischen Wissenschaften in Deutschland. pp. 739. 1893. 8°. Ac. Munich. K. Akademie. Geschichte der Wissenschaften. Bd. 22. Ac. 714/4.

AVINĀSACHANDRA MITRA. Medical practice in Kashmir, 1889. pp. 25. Lahore, 1890. 8°. Pam. 39.

ALKSNIS (J.) Materialen zur lettischen Volksmedicin. 1894, 8°. Ac. Dorpat. Pharmakologisches Institut. Historische Studien. No. 4. Ac. 3817/2.

Ac. Mexico. Instituto Medico. Instituto Medico Nacional. Eng. & Span. pp. 14. México, 1892. 8°. Pam. 39.

VULLIET ( ) Quinze jours à St. Pétersbourg. Notes sur les institutions médicales. pp. 23. Paris, 1891. 8°. Pam. 39.

MEDICINE.—History—continued.

HJELT (O. E. A.) Svenska och finska medicinal-verkets historia. *Helsingfors*, 1891, *etc.* 8°.
7680. e.

RUSSELL (G. W.) Early Medicine and medical men in Connecticut. pp. 158. 1892. 4°.
7680. e. 10.

See also infra : Profession of Medicine.

Household and Domestic Medicine.

BARTON (E. A.) Colonist's medical Handbook. pp. 158. *Lond.* 1890. 8°. 7321. aa. 17.

BELL (R.) Home book of medical Treatment. pp. 460. *Glasg.* 1895. 8°. 07305. i. 15.

BLACK (G.) The Doctor at Home. pp. 894. *Lond.* 1891. 8°. 7321. e. 13.

—— Family Health-Book. pp. 469. *Lond.* 1892. 8°. 7383. dd. 4.

—— Every-day Ailments and Accidents. pp. 426. *Lond.* 1892. 8°. 7383. dd. 3.

FAMILY PHYSICIAN. The Family Physician, *etc. Lond.* 1893, *etc.* 8°. 7391. ee.

FLEURY (C. R.) Modern Household Medicine. pp. 712. *Lond.* 1893. 8°. 7383. c. 22.

ROBERTSON (J. M.) The Household Physician. pp. 1104. *Lond.* 1890. 8°. 07305. k. 8.

STACPOOLE (F.) The Home Doctor. pp. 104. *Paisley*, 1895. 8°. 7321. e. 15.

THOMSON (S.) Dictionary of Domestic Medicine. pp. 736. *Lond.* 1894. 8°. 2255. g. 14.

Legal Medicine.

BRISTOWE (L. S.) Legal hand-book for Hospital Authorities. pp. 151. *Lond.* 1894. 8°.
6425. aaa. 36.

CHAPMAN (H. C.) Manual of Medical Juris-prudence. pp. 237. *Phila.* 1892. 8°.
6095. aaa. 33.

DUCAZAL ( ) and CATRIN ( ) Médecine legale militaire. pp. 211. 1893. 8°. Encyclopédie des aide-mémoire. 8709. g.

GOTTSCHALK (R.) Grundriss der gerichtlichen Medicin. pp. 322. *Leipz.* 1894. 8°.
6095. de. 13.

GRIBBLE (J. D. B.) and HEHIR (P.) Outlines of Medical Jurisprudence. *Madras*, 1891. 8°.
6095. cc. 18.

GUEORGUIEFF (S. G.) Quelques notions sur l'Histoire de la Médecine légale en Russie. pp. 59. *Genève*, 1890. 8°. 6005. g. 18. (4.)

GUY (W. A.) and FERRIER (D.) Principles of Forensic Medicine. pp. 832. *Lond.* 1895. 8°.
6095. bb. 26.

LECHOPIÉ (A.) and FLOQUET (C.) Droit médical. pp. 350. *Paris*, 1890. 12°. 6095. de. 11.

LUFF (A. P.) Text-Book of Forensic Medicine. 2 vol. *Lond.* 1895. 8°. 6095. df. 1.

MANN (J. D.) Forensic Medicine. pp. 639. *Lond.* 1893. 8°. 6095. d. 36.

MÉGNIN (P.) La faune des cadavres. Application de l'entomologie à la médecine légale. pp. 214. 1895. 8°. Encyclopédie des aide-mémoire. 8709. g.

MURRELL (W.) Aids to Forensic Medicine. pp. 114. *Lond.* 1894. 8°. 6095. a. 35.

TAYLOR (A. S.) Manual of Medical Juris-prudence. pp. 839. *Lond.* 1891. 8°.
2232. a. 21.

THIERRY (H.) De la Responsabilité atténuée. pp. 240. *Lond.* 1891. 8°. 6095. d. 34.

VERWAEST (P.) Étude sur le Secret Professional pp. 128. *Paris*, 1892. 8°. 6095. bb. 24.

See also CRIME : INSANITY : LAW, *Criminal :* TOXICOLOGY.

Medical Missions. *See* MISSIONS.

MEDICINE——continued.

Military Medicine and Sanitation.

DU CAZAL ( ) and CATRIN ( ) Médecine légale militaire. pp. 211. 1893. 8°. Encyclopédie des aide-mémoire. 8709. g.

FRANCE. *Ministère de la Guerre.* École de l'Infirmier militaire. 2 vol. *Paris*, 1894. 12°.
8823. f. 5.

GAVOY (E.) Le Service de Santé militaire en 1870. pp. 52. *Paris*, 1894. 8°. 8830. f. 38. (7.)

G. B. &. I. *Army.* Regulations for Army Medical Service. 2 pt. *Lond.* 1890. 8°.
8831. aaa. 47.

—— Manual for the Medical Staff Corps. pp. 273. *Lond.* 1893. 8°. 8824. c. 33.

—— Statement of the position of the Officers of the Army Medical Staff. pp. 53.
Lond. 1890. 8°. Pam. 2.

HART (E. A.) The State and its Servants. pp. 55. *Lond.* 1893. 8°. 7679. aaa. 6.

LEGRAND (M. A. H. A.) L'Hygiène des troupes européennes aux colonies. pp. 422. *Paris*, 1895. 8°. 8830. e. 15.

LEMOINE (M. A.) Recueil des conférences sur le Service de Santé de l'Armée. pp. 233. *Paris*, 1895. 8°. 8830. e. 14.

MAC NAMARA (W. H.) Notes on medical services in War. pp. 46. 1895. 8°. Gale and Polden's Military Series. 8838. b. 52.

MARVAUD (A.) Les Maladies du soldat. pp. 855. *Paris*, 1894. 8°. 7442. i. 5.

MORRIS (W. A.) Retrospect of the Army Medical Staff. pp. 23. *Bombay*, 1893. 8°. Pam. 2.

PRUSSIA. *Kreigsministerium.* Garnisonbeschrei-bungen, vom Standpunkt der Gesundheitspflege aus aufgestellt. *Berl.* 1893, *etc.* 8°. 8831. cc.

QUINZIO (M.) Malattie ed epidemie negli eserciti. pp. 355. *Firenze*, 1892. 8°. 7561. f. 7.

SLEMAN (R. R.) Manual for the Volunteer Medical Service. pp. 70. *Lond.* 1892. 8°.
8838. aaa. 53.

THORNTON (J. H.) Memories of Seven Campaigns. Record of service in the Indian Medical Department. pp. 359.
Westminster, 1895. 8°. 9057. c. 11.

See also AMBULANCE. For Military Surgery, *see* SURGERY.

Nautical Medicine.

FINLAY (A.) Seaman's Medical Guide. pp. 181. *Lond.* 1891. 8°. 7321. aa. 18.

HOLT (J.) Review of principles and practice of Maritime Sanitation. pp. 93.
New Orleans, 1892, 8°. 8807. c. 48.

LEET (C. H.) Shipowners and Ships' Surgeons. pp. 8. *Liverpool*, 1893. 8°. Pam. 43.

Profession of Medicine.

ANDREWS (W.) The Doctor in History, literature, folk-lore, etc. pp. 287. *Hull*, 1895. 8°.
7679. df. 43.

ALBERT (M.) Les Médecins grecs à Rome. pp. 323. *Paris*, 1894. 8°. 7679. ff. 1.

DUPOUY (E.) Médecine et Mœurs de l'ancienne Rome d'après les poètes. pp. 439.
Paris, 1892. 12°. 7679. a. 1.

LANDAU (R.) Geschichte der jüdischen Ärzte. pp. 144. *Berl.* 1895. 8°. 7680. df. 4.

Ac. London. *College of Physicians.* Charters, bye-laws and regulations of the College. pp. 104. *Lond.* 1892. 8°. Ac. 3848/6.

LONGMORE (*Sir* T.) R. Wiseman, Surgeon to Charles II. pp. 210. *Lond.* 1891. 8°.
10827. dd. 6.

MEDICINE.—Profession of—_continued._

RODGER (E. H. B.) Aberdeen Doctors at home and abroad. pp. 355. _Edinb._ 1893. 8°.
7679. df. 37.

ALLEN (C. B.) London Medical Specialists. pp. 60. _Lond._ 1890. 8°. 7679. aa. 8.

FAIDHERBE (A.) Les Médecins de Flandre avant 1789. pp. 347. _Lille_, 1892. 8°. 7680. e. 7.

CHANCEREL (R.) Les Apothicaires et l'ancienne faculté de médecine de Paris. pp. 121. _Dijon_, 1892. 8°. 7680. e. 8.

ROGER (J.) Médecins chirurgiens et barbiers. pp. 95. _Paris_, 1894. 8°. 7683. cc. 5.

PETIT (L.) Les Médecins de Molière. pp. 46. _Paris_, 1890. 8°. 11840. m. 31. (8.)

ISAMBARD (É.) La communauté des Chirurgiens de Pacy-sur-Eure aux XVII° et XVIII° siècles. pp. 119. _Pacy_, 1894. 8°. 7686. aa. 28.

CHAUVET (E.) Les Médecins-philosophes au XIX° siècle. 1890, _etc._ 8°. Ac. Caen. _Université._ Annales. An. 6. Ac. 303.

KRUL (R.) Haagsche doctoren in den ouden tijd. pp. 220. _'sGravenhage_, 1891. 8°. 7679. de. 13.

RUSSELL (G. W.) Early Medical Men in Connecticut. pp. 158. 1892. 4°. 7680. e. 10.

SUMNER (G.) Sketches of Physicians in Hartford in 1820. pp. 64. _Hartford, Conn._ 1890. 8°. 7679. cc. 6.

LEVICK (J. J.) Early Physicians of Philadelphia. pp. 16. _Phila._ 1886. 8°. Pam. 39.

BARNARD (W.) and STOCKER (G. B.) Medical Partnerships, transfers and assistantships. pp. 249. _Lond._ 1895. 8°. 6376. c. 35.

BOXALL (R.) Introductory Lecture on the public, the profession, and medical charities. pp 30. _Lond._ 1894. 8°. 7306. e. 25. (1.)

CATHELL (D. W.) Book on the Physician Himself. pp. 343. _Phila._ 1892. 8°. 7679. e. 19.

CYR (J.) Scènes de la vie médicale. pp. 292. _Paris_, 1888. 8°. 012330. f. 13.

DALBY (_Sir_ W. B.) Dr. Chesterfield's Letters to his son on Medicine as a career. pp. 60. _Lond._ 1894. 8°. 7680. a. 19.

DU STYRAP (J.) Code of medical ethics. pp. 103. _Lond._ 1895. 8°. 7679. aaa. 5.

—— The medico-chirurgical Tariffs. pp. 28. _Lond._ 1890. 8°. 7679. df. 42.

FAULKNER (A. S.) Guide to the public Medical Services. pp. 72. _Lond._ 1893. 8°. 7306. e. 22. (5.)

FIREBAUGH (E. M.) The Physician's Wife. pp. 186. _Phila._ 1894. 8°. 8415. ee. 38.

HART (E. A.) The Profession, the public and the code. pp. 16. _Lond._ 1893. 8°. 7306. df. 22. (6.)

JOACHIM (H.) Die preussische Medicinaltaxe in ihrer historischen Entwicklung. pp. 186. _Berl._ 1895. 8°. 7680. df. 5.

ORMSBY (L. H.) Social, scientific and political influence of the Medical Profession. pp. 41. _Dublin_, 1886. 8°. 7306. e. 26. (1.)

SURBLED (P. A.) Le Médecin devant la Conscience. pp. 236. _Paris_, 1890. 32°. 8410. a. 42.

TAYLOR (J. J.) The Physician as a business man. pp. 144. _Phila._ 1892. 8°. 7680. aaa. 11.

BLACKWELL (E.) Pioneer work in opening the Medical Profession to Women. pp. 265. _Lond._ 1895. 8°. 7679. aa. 11.

MUELLER (P.) Ueber die Zulassung der Frauen zum Studium der Medizin. pp. 43. 1894. 8°. Sammlung wissenschaftlicher Vorträge, N.F. Hft. 195. 12249. m.

MEDICINE.—Profession of—_continued._

RANSE (F. de) and LÉCHOPIÉ (A.) Commentaire de la nouvelle Loi sur l'exercice de la Médecine. pp. 112. _Paris_, 1891. 8°. 5406. de. 4.

THOMAS (G.) La Médecine devant la Loi. pp. 176. _Paris_, 1893. 8°. 6095. a. 33.

OPPENHEIM (L.) Das ärztliche Recht zu körperlichen Eingriffen au Kranken und Gesunden. pp. 63. _Basel_, 1892. 8°. 6095. bb. 25.

BRAND (A. T.) Pocket case-book for practitioners. _Lond._ 1892. 8°. 7321. b. 24.

KEMPE (C. M.) General Practitioner's visiting list, journal, _etc._ _Lond._ 1892. 8°. 7321. bb. 30.

SILVERLOCK (H.) Medical Practitioner's visiting list. pp. 53. _Lond._ 1892. 12°. 7321. a. 15.

SIMPSON (R.) Physicians', Surgeons' and Consultants' visiting list. pp. 260. _Bristol_, 1894. 12°. 7688. a. 58.

See also supra: Education: History: Legal: Military: Nautical: BIOGRAPHY, _Medical:_ EXAMINATIONS.

MEDINA DEL CAMPO. PÉREZ PASTOR (C.) La Imprenta en Medina del Campo. pp. 526. _Madrid_, 1895. 8°. 11906. c. 6.

MEDITATIONS. BERLIOUX ( ) Month of the souls in Purgatory. Meditations for November. pp. 156. _Dublin_, 1886. 8°. 3457. de. 76.

BOLTON (W. H.) Practice of Meditation. pp. 7. _Oxf._ 1891. 32°. 4422. c. 31. (4.)

CLARKE (R. F.) The Sacred Heart: Meditations for June. pp. 36. _Lond._ 1889. 16°. Pam. 77.

ELPHINSTONE (A. F.) _Lady._ Golden hours of Meditation. pp. 16. _Lond._ 1893. 8°. 3456. df. 60. (5.)

EVERARD (G.) All through the Day. Meditations. pp. 124. _Lond._ 1890. 8°. 3457. d. 16.

IVES (R. J.) Notes on Meditation. pp. 22. _Oxf._ 1893. 12°. 3456. df. 2.

JESUS CHRIST. The Heart of Jesus of Nazareth. Meditations. pp. 186. _Wells_, 1890. 8°. 3457. h. 33.

KIRBY ( ) _R.C. Archbp. of Ephesus._ Meditations on the truths of religion. pp. 392. _Dublin_, 1892. 8°. 3457. dd. 12.

M., M. C. Instruction on the science of Meditation. pp. 19. _Lond._ 1892. 8°. 4371. a. 40. (5.)

MATHESON (G.) Searchings in the Silence. pp. 240. _Lond._ 1894. 8°. 4399. aaa. 28.

MORRIS (J.) Notes of spiritual Retreats. pp. 353. _Lond._ 1894. 8°. 3456. ee. 31.

PERREYVE (H.) The Way of the Cross: meditations. pp. 94. _Lond._ 1892. 16°. 3457. dd. 27.

TREVELYAN (W. B.) Suggestions on the method of Meditation. pp. 23. _Lond._ 1894. 8°. 4422. d. 18. (4.)

See also PRAYERS: RETREATS.

MEDITERRANEAN SEA. Ac. Vienna. _K. Akademie._ Berichte der Commission für Erforschung des Östlichen Mittelmeeres. 1892, _etc._ fol. Denkschriften. Math.-naturwissenschaftliche Classe. Bd. 59, _etc._ Ac. 810/13.

BOULANGIER ( ) Essai sur les Origines de la Méditerranée. pp. 217. _Paris_, 1890. 8°. 10005. c. 4.

FRANCE. _Dépôt des Cartes et Plans._ Instructions nautiques sur la côte du Maroc et la côte d'Algérie. pp. 196. _Paris_, 1893. 8°. 10497. bb. 36.

GOURRET (P.) Les Pêcheries et les poissons de la Méditerranée. pp. 360. _Paris_, 1894. 12°. 7290. a. 28.

G. B. & I. _Hydrographic Office._ The Mediterranean Pilot. 4 vol. _Lond._ 1894, _etc._ 8°. 10496. g. 40.

MEDITERRANEAN SEA—*continued.*

Ac. London. *Hakluyt Society.* DALLAM (T.) Early Voyages in the Levant. Edited by J. T. Bent. pp. 305. *Lond.* 1893. 8°.　Ac. 6172/69.

BERNARD (M.) Autour de la Méditerranée. *Paris,* 1892, *etc.* 4°.　　　　　10096. i.

BLAKENEY (M. A.) Souvenirs of Travel in the Mediterranean. pp. 56. *Ramsgate,* 1895. 8°.
　　　　　　　　　　　　10026. c. 8.

DAVIS (R. H.) The Rulers of the Mediterranean. pp. 228. *Lond.* 1894. 8°　　10025. de. 4.

GIRARD (B.) Journal de bord d'une campagne en Tunisie, en Égypte et dans le Levant. pp. 664. *Paris,* 1895. 8°.　010096. ee. 46.

JOANNE (P.) Les Stations d'hiver de la Méditerranée. pp. 371. *Paris,* 1895. 8°.
　　　　　　　　　　　　10171. aa. 29.

JOUSSET (P.) Un Tour de Méditerranée. pp. 262. *Paris,* 1893. 4°.　　10026. k. 19.

LAMBART (F. E. G.) *Earl of Cavan.* With the Yacht, camera and cycle in the Mediterranean. pp. 94. *Lond.* 1895. 8°.　10107. bb. 3.

MACQUARIE (J. L.) Villes d'Hiver et plages de la Méditerranée. pp. 587. *Paris,* 1893. 8°.
　　　　　　　　　　　　10171. aaa. 27.

MERIWETHER (L.) Afloat and ashore on the Mediterranean. pp. 363. *Lond.* 1892. 8°.
　　　　　　　　　　　　10106. ccc. 30.

NYS (E.) Recherches sur l'histoire du droit. Autour de la Méditerranée. pp. 43.
Brux. 1895. 8°.　　　　　　Pam. 32.

WILCZEK (E.) *Count.* Historische Genrebilder vom Mittelmeere. pp. 253. *Wien,* 1894. 8°.
　　　　　　　　　　　　9078. ccc. 35.

See also RIVIERA : WATERING PLACES.

MEDUSAE. MAAS (O.) Die craspedoten Medusen. pp. 107. 1893. 4°. HENSEN (v.) Ergebnisse der Plankton-Expedition. Bd. 2. 1826. b.

MEDWAY. JONES (H. L.) Swin, Swale and Swatchway. Cruises down the Thames and Medway. pp. 203. *Lond.* 1892. 4°. 10358. e. 26.

MEETINGS. COOKE (J. H.) The conduct of public Meetings. pp. 64. *Lond.* 1895, 8°.
　　　　　　　　　　　　8005. bb. 14.

FRITH (H.) The Chairman's Guide. pp. 112. *Lond.* 1895. 8°.　　　　8009. b. 37.

JEPHSON (H.) The Platform : its rise and progress. 2 vol. *Lond.* 1892. 8°.　8138. g. 14.

PALGRAVE (*Sir* R. F. D.) The Chairman's Handbook. pp. 110. *Lond.* 1895. 8°. 8008. aa. 17.

PRICHARD (M. F.) Parliamentary usage for Women's Clubs, *etc.* pp. 60.
Cincinnati, 1894. 16°.　　　　8009. a. 38.

TAYLER (J.) Guide to the business of Public Meetings. pp. 132. *Lond.* 1893. 8°.
　　　　　　　　　　　　8009. aaa. 32.

WEIL (G. D.) Le Droit d'association et le droit de réunion devant les Chambres. pp. 340. *Paris,* 1893. 12°.　　　　8052. cc. 35.
See also RIOTS.

MEGALOPOLIS. *See* GREECE, *Antiquities.*

MEININGEN, City and Duchy. Ac. Meiningen. *Verein für Meiningische Geschichte.* Schriften. *Meiningen,* 1888, *etc.* 8°. Ac. 7114.

HOPPE ( ) Ueber die Stadtkirche in Meiningen. pp. 36. 1883. 8°. Ac. Meiningen. *Hennebergischer Altertumsforschender Verein.* Neue Beiträge. Lief. 4.　　　　　9325. d.

JACOB (G.) Die Ortsnamen des Herzogthums Meiningen. pp. 149. *Hildburghausen,* 1894. 8°.
　　　　　　　　　　　　10255. k. 1.

ALLERS (C. W.) Das meininger Hoftheater. 25 pl. *Liège.* 1890. fol.　　11795. k. 23.

ME-KONG. BRANDA (P.) Le Haut-Mékong, ou le Laos ouvert. pp. 64. *Paris,* 1887. 8°.
　　　　　　　　　　　　Pam. 88.

MELANCHOLIA. *See* INSANITY.

MELANESIA.
See MISSIONS : PACIFIC OCEAN.

MELBOURNE. MELBOURNE. Marvellous Melbourne. pp. 74. *Ballarat,* 1892. *obl.* 8°.
　　　　　　　　　　　　10491. de. 18.

SPRINGTHORPE (J. W.) Contamination of our Water Supply. *Melbourne,* 1893. 8°. Pam. 79.

STYLES (J.) Lecture on sanitary reform for Greater Melbourne. pp. 20.
Williamstown, 1888. 8°.　8827. bbb. 28. (3.)

VICTORIA. Cities and towns of Victoria. 2 pt. *Ballarat,* 1893. *obl.* 8°.　　10491. de. 20.

—— Victoria and its Metropolis. 2 vol. *Melbourne,* 1888, 4°.　　10491. h. 11.
See also EXHIBITIONS : VICTORIA.

MELINITE. HAMON (A.) and BACHOT (G.) Ministère et Mélinite. pp. 556.
Paris, 1891, 12°.　　　　8823. g. 22.

TURPIN (E.) Comment, pourquoi et par qui le mélinite, les obus, le détonateur de Bourges ont été livrés à l'étranger. pp. 592.
Braine-le-Comte, 1890. 8°.　8824. k. 20.

—— Comment on a vendu la mélinite. pp. 405. *Paris,* 1891. 8°.　　　　8823. bb. 31.

—— The Truth on Melinite. Mala fides of the Armstrong Company. pp. 62.
Braine-le-Comte, 1890. 8°.　8829. l. 24. (1.)

—— The Truth on Melinite. Letters, *etc.* pp. 8. *Paris,* 1891. 8°.　8829. l. 24. (2.)

MELK. LINDE (F. X.) Chronik des Marktes Melk. pp. 315. *Melk,* 1890. 8°. 10215. f. 13.

MELROSE ABBEY. ALLAN (W. G.) The Monks of Melrose. pp. 86. *Edinb.* 1892. 8°.
　　　　　　　　　　　　4735. bb. 30.

MELTON MOWBRAY. MELTON MOWBRAY. Views of Melton Mowbray.
Melton Mowbray, 1895. *obl.* 8°.　10360. aa. 32.

MEMMINGEN. BAUER (B.) Beiträge zur Geschichte der Reichstadt Memmingen.
1891. 8°. Ac. Augsburg. *Historischer Verein.* Zeitschrift. Jhrg. 18.　　　Ac. 7013/2.

MEMORY : MNEMONICS. ARRÉAT (L.) Mémoire et Imagination. pp. 171.
Paris, 1895. 12°.　　　　8462. bb. 49.

BIERVLIET (J. J. v.) La Mémoire. pp. 40. 1893. 8°. Ac. Ghent. *Université.* Recueil de travaux. Fasc. 8.　　　Ac. 2647/3.

COPNER (J.) Hints on Memory. pp. 120. *Lond.* 1891. 8°.　　　8308. aaa. 24.

—— Memoranda Mnemonica. pp. 400. *Lond.* 1893. 8°.　　　8311. b. 17.

DANDOLO (G.) La Dottrina della Memoria nella Psicologia Inglese. pp. 157.
Reggio nell' E. 1891. 8°.　　8462. f. 18.

DUTTON (G. H. J.) How to improve the Memory. pp. 24. *Skegness,* 1892. 8°.
　　　　　　　　　　　　7410. bb. 33. (7.)

FOREL (A.) Das Gedächtniss und seine Abnormitäten. pp. 45. *Zürich,* 1885. 8°.
　　　　　　　　　　　07305. e. 27. (1.)

FOWLER (O. S.) Memory and intellectual improvement. pp. 79. *Manch.* 1891. 8°.
　　　　　　　　　　　8304. e. 21. (15.)

GREEN (F. W. E.) Memory. Its logical relations and cultivation. pp. 288. *Lond.* 1891. 8°.
　　　　　　　　　　　8462. bb. 27.

LITTLE (H. C.) "My Memory." Historical date and note book. pp. 48. *Manch.* 1895. *obl.* 8°.
　　　　　　　　　　　9503. a. 7.

MEMORY—*continued.*

MIDDLETON (A. E.) Memory Systems, new and old. pp. 143. *N.Y.* 1888. 8°.   8311. aaa. 26.

ROSS (D.) Mnemonic charts of English History. *Lond.* 1890. 8°.   09504. ee. 1.

SMITH (W. K.) and WATSON (A.) Smith-Watson system of Memory Training. ff. 24. *Washington,* 1892. 4°.   Pam. 17.

MENANGKABO DIALECT.
See MALAY LANGUAGE.

MENDIP HILLS. COMPTON (T.) A Mendip Valley. pp. 288. *Lond.* 1892. 8°. 10350. de. 23.

MENINGITIS. MÉTAXAS (G.) and VER-CHÈRE (F.) De la méningite tuberculeuse. 1887. 8°. VERNEUIL (A. A.) Études sur la tuberculose. Tom. 1.   7561. k. 1.

QUINCKE (H. F.) Über Meningitis serosa. pp. 40. 1893. 8°. VOLKMANN (R. v.) Sammlung klin-ischen Vorträge. N.F. Nr. 67.   7441. g.
See also BRAIN: SPINE.

MENSURATION. BEARD (W.) Longmans' junior School Mensuration. pp. 118. *Lond.* 1893. 8°.   8535. cc. 34.

BRIGGS (W.) and EDMONDSON (T. W.) Mensura-tion of the simpler figures. pp. 112. 1893. 8°. Tutorial Series.   12205. c. 167.

BROWNE (W. J.) Mensuration for schools. pp. 104. 1895. 8°. Elementary Science Manuals.   8708. ee.

CLARKE (A. D.) Mensuration for the use of Schools. pp. 88. *Lond.* 1895. 8°. 8535. de. 19.

COTSWORTH (M. B.) Mensuration with illustra-tions. For Railway Companies. pp. 200. *Leeds,* 1893. 12°.   8548. de. 25.

EUCLID. Blackie's Euclid and Mensuration for beginners. pp. 79. *Lond.* 1892. 8°. 8532. aa. 30.

EVANS (T.) Government Examinations in Mensuration. *Lond.* 1891. 8°. 12210. cc. 3.

GOYEN (P.) Key and Companion to Arithmetic and elementary Mensuration. pp. 416. *Lond.* 1893. 8°.   8533. de. 25.

GRIFFITHS (L. F.) Mensuration. pp. 36. 1892. 8°. Army Short Course Series.   012202. eeee.

HILEY (A.) Explanatory Mensuration. pp. 211. 18. *Lond.* 1892. 8°.   8506. c. 49.

KIELY (J. V.) Civil Service Mensuration. pp. 73. *Dublin,* 1895. 8°.   8532. bbb. 46.

LODGE (A.) Mensuration for senior students. pp. 274. *Lond.* 1895. 8°.   8533. bb. 50.

MAC CARTHY (L.) Formulæ in Mensuration. pp. 16. *Agra,* 1889. 12°.   Pam. 38.

MANT (J. B.) Pocket book of Mensuration. pp. 249. *Lond.* 1891. obl. 8°.   8548. aa. 26.

MENSURATION. Mensuration. 2 pt. *Edinb.* 1892. 8°.   8532. aa. 26.

NESBIT (A.) Treatise on practical Mensuration. pp. 443. *Lond.* 1892. 8°.   3534. aa. 47.

NEWELL (A.) Problems in arithmetic and men-suration. pp. 187. *Lond.* 1892. 8°. 8506. c. 50.

PEARCE (A. J.) Longmans' School Mensuration. pp. 182. *Lond.* 1894. 8°.   8533. bb. 48.

ROBSON (J. H.) Solutions of Examination Papers in algebra and mensuration set for entrance to the R.M. College, Sandhurst, 1880–88. 2 pt. *Lond.* 1890. 8°.   8533. e. 17.

THOMSON (W. S.) Essentials of Mensuration. pp. 114. *Aberd.* 1895. 8°.   8534. df. 12.

MENTEITH. GRAHAM (R. G. B. C.) Notes on the district of Menteith. pp. 85. *Lond.* 1895. 8°.   10369. b. 44.

MENTONE. FRANCKEN (W.) Menton. Sta-tion climatique d'hiver. pp. 150. *Paris,* 1894. 12°.   10174. aaa. 47.

MENTONE—*continued.*

MENTONE. New English Guide to Mentone. pp. 179. *Mentone,* 1891. 8°.   10171. aaa. 22.
See also RIVIERA.

MERAN. MUELLER (I.) Meran. pp. 75. *Meran,* 1891. 8°.   10215. aaa. 33.

MERCHANT SHIPPING ACT, 1894.
See LAW, *Maritime.*

MERCURY. FERRARI (P. d.) Le Miniere di mercurio del Monte Amiata. pp. 173. *Firenze,* 1890. 8°.   07109. g. 23.

MERGET (A.) Mercure. Action physiologique, *etc.* pp. 402. *Bordeaux,* 1894, 8°. 7509. dd. 8.
See also METALS.

MÉRÉLESSART. BONNAULT (de) *Viscount.* Mérélessart pendant la Révolution. pp. 63. *Abbeville,* 1892. 8°.   09210. e. 1. (4.)

MERIONETH. KILMER (E. A.) Four Welsh counties. pp. 266. *Lond.* 1891. 8°.   10369. cc. 44.

MEROPIDAE. DRESSER (H. E.) Monograph of the Meropidæ, or Bee-eaters. pp. 144. *Lond.* 1884–86. fol.   7285. k. 9.
See also BIRDS.

MERV. COTARD (C.) Un Voyage à Merv. pp. 19. *Paris,* 1891. 8°.   Pam. 18.
See also ASIA, *Central.*

MERVILLE. LARRONDO ( ) Une Commune rurale avant la Révolution. pp. 552. *Toulouse,* 1891. 8°.   10174. c. 17.

MESERITZ. KADE (C.) Gründung und Namen von Stadt Meseritz. pp. 85. *Meseritz,* 1893. 8°.   10255. f. 32.

MESMERISM. *See* HYPNOTISM.

MESOPOTAMIA. TELONI (B.) Libri e docu-menti nell' antica Mesopotamia. pp. 61. *Firenze,* 1890. 8°,   7702. de. 12. (3.)
See also ASSYRIA: EDESSA: SUSA.

MESSINA. RIBERA (G.) Messina e la sua provincia. pp. 308. *Messina,* 1893. 8°.   10132. c. 7.

METALS: METALLURGY. Ac. London. *S.K. Museum.* Catalogue of the Collection of Metallurgical Specimens formed by J. Percy. pp. 435. *Lond.* 1892, 8°.   7959. g. 21.

ANDERSON (J. W.) The Prospector's handbook. *Lond.* 1891. 8°.   7106. a. 36.

ARBEL (P.) Rapport sur l'Exposition de Chicago concernant la métallurgie. pp. 100. *Saint-Étienne,* 1894. 8°.   7958. bbb. 18.

BARNES (T. W.) Hints to Prospectors. pp. 121. *Sydney,* 1892. 8°.   7105. aa. 4.

BEHRENS (H.) Das mikroskopische Gefüge der Metalle und Legierungen. pp. 170. *Hamburg,* 1894. 8°.   7108. bb. 2.

BERINGER (C.) and (J. J.) Text-book of Assay-ing. pp. 404. *Lond.* 1895. 8°.   7105. aa. 6.

CHALLOPEAU (A.) L'État de la métallurgie 1789–1889. pp. 60. *Paris,* 1890. 8°. Pam. 27.

COLLINS (J. H.) Principles of metal Mining. pp. 152. 1893. 8°. Collins' Elementary Science Series.   8708. aaa.

DAVIES (E. H.) Machinery for metalliferous Mines. pp. 564. *Lond.* 1894. 8°. 8768. cc. 23.

HASLUCK (P. N.) Milling Machines and pro-cesses. pp. 352. *Lond.* 1892. 8°. 7944. f. 38.

HIORNS (A. H.) Principles of metallurgy. pp. 388. *Lond.* 1895. 8°.   7107. a. 5.
—— Mixed Metals, or metallic alloys. pp. 384. *Lond.* 1890. 8°.   7106. aa. 33.

METALS—continued.

KEMP (J. F.) Ore Deposits of the U.S. pp. 302. *N.Y.* 1893. 8°.   07109. h. 39.

KNAB (L.) Traité de Métallurgie des métaux autres que le fer. pp. 614. *Paris*, 1891. 8°.
7104. dd. 4.

LAUNAY (L. de) Formation des gîtes métallifères. pp. 201. 1892. 8°. Encyclopédie des aide-mémoire.   8709. g.

—— Statistique de la production des gîtes métallifères. pp. 193. 1894. 8°. Encyclopédie des aide-mémoire.   8709. g.

LEDEBUR (A.) Les Alliages métalliques. pp. 222. *Paris*, 1894. 12°.   7106. a. 33.

LE VERRIER (U.) La Métallurgie en France. pp. 333. *Paris*, 1894. 12°.   7106. e. 13.

MOREAU (G.) Étude industrielle des gîtes métallifères. pp. 439. *Paris*, 1894. 8°. 7106. cc. 24.

PHILLIPS (J. A.) Elements of Metallurgy. pp. 909. *Lond.* 1891. 8°.   2248. f. 14.

POWER (F. D.) Pocket-book for miners and metallurgists. pp. 334. *Lond.* 1892. 8°
7109. aa. 23.

REMY (P. F.) Tratamiento metalúrgico por fusion. pp. 12. *Lima*, 1883. 8°.   Pam. 27.

RHEAD (E. L.) Metallurgy. pp. 282. *Lond.* 1895, 8°.   7108. a. 28.

ROWELL (H.) Manual of instruction in Hard Soldering. pp. 56. *Lond.* 1891. 4°. 07945. e. 74.

ROBERTS-AUSTEN (W. C.) New metallurgical Series. *Lond.* 1891, etc. 8°.   07108. g.

SCHNABEL (C.) Lehrbuch der allgemeinen Hüttenknnde. pp. 678. *Berl.* 1890. 8°.   7107. de. 1.

—— Handbuch der Metallhüttenkunde. *Berl.* 1894, etc. 8°.   07109. e

SEXTON (A. H.) Elementary Text-book of Metallurgy. pp. 263. *Lond.* 1895. 8°.
7105. aaa. 4.

TAYLOR (T.) "Gauges at a Glance." Containing the principal gauges of different metals. pp. 78. *Lond.* 1895. obl. 8°.   8548. aa. 41.

VILLARS (E. de) Statistique des Richesses métallurgiques de la France et des états de l'Europe. pp. 251. *Paris*, 1894. 4°.
7106. i. 20.

VILLASANTE Y GÓMEZ (F. R.) La Industria minero-metalúrgica en Mazarrón. pp. 252. *Cartagena*, 1892. 8°.   7105. dd. 1.

—— Atlas. fol.   7105. i. 7.

See also ALUMINIUM: ANTIMONY: BRASS: BRONZE: CADMIUM: COPPER: GOLD AND SILVER: IRON: LEAD: MERCURY: MINERALOGY AND MINING: NICKEL: STRONTIUM: TIN: TITANIUM: VANADIUM: ZINC.

Electro-Metallurgy. *See* ELECTRICITY.

METAL-WORK. Ac. London. *S.K. Museum.* Report on analysis of examples of Oriental metal-work. *Lond.* 1892. 8°.   Pam. 18.

—— *Burlington Fine Arts Club.* Catalogue of specimens of Japanese Metal Work. pp. 150. *Lond.* 1894. 4°.   Ac. 4644/35.

HARRISON (J.) The Decoration of Metals. pp. 132. *Lond.* 1894. 8°.   7820. bb. 24.

HIORNS (A. H.) Metal-colouring and Bronzing. pp. 336. *Lond.* 1892. 8°.   07945. e. 85.

JOHNSON (E.) Description of Irish antique art Metal Work, etc. pp. 108. *Dublin*, 1893. 8°.
7808. de. 4.

LE BRIS (G.) Les Constructions métalliques. pp. 380. *Paris*, 1894. 8°.   8768. e. 27.

LEDEBUR (A.) Metallverarbeitung. pp. 317. 1882. 8°. BOLLEY (P. A.) Handbuch der chemischen Technologie. Bd. 8. Abt. 1.
8905. eee.

METAL WORK—continued.

LELAND (C. G.) Elementary Metal Work. pp. 111. *Lond.* 1894. 8°.   7805. de. 26.

METAL TURNING. Metal Turning. pp. 168. *Lond.* 1890. 8°.   7944. cc. 37.

MILLIS (C. T.) Metal-Plate Work. pp. 377. 1893. 8°. THOMPSON (S. P.) Finsbury Technical Manuals.   7945. cc.

MOLINIER (É.) Dessins et modèles. Les Arts du métal. pp. 144. *Paris*, 1892. 8°.   7808. f. 6.

SERRAMALERA Y CAMPS (N.) Études pratiques indispensables aux Ferblantiers, Zingueurs, etc. *Paris*, 1894, etc. fol.   7943. k.

VIENNA. *Handels-Museum.* Sammlung von Abbildungen türkischer, arabischer, persischer und indischer Metallobjecte. *Wien*, 1895. fol.
K.T.C. 23. b. 8.

YOUNG (F. C.) Metal working for amateurs. pp. 110. 1893. 8°. Ward and Lock's Amateurs' Aid Series.   07944. ee.

See also ART, *Decorative:* GOLD AND SILVER WORK: IRON WORK: LEAD: PLATE.

METAPHYSICS. *See* PHILOSOPHY.

METEOROLOGY.

General.

Ac. *Comité Météorologique.* Tables météorologiques internationales. *Paris*, 1890. 4°
8750. i. 1.

—— Berlin. *Meteorologisches Institut.* Veröffentlichungen des Instituts. *Berl.* 1893, etc. fol.
8756. g.

—— Cambridge. *Harvard University. Observatory.* Meteorological Observations. pp. 6. *Camb. Mass,* 1890. 4°.   8562. h.

—— Christiania. *Observatorium.* Magnetische Beobachtungen und stündliche Temperaturbeobachtungen. pp. 36. *Christiania*, 1891. 4°.
8756. g. 29.

—— Hamburg. *Norddeutsche Seewarte.* Deutsche ueberseeische meteorologische Beobachtungen. *Hamb.* 1887, etc. fol.   8752. k.

—— Madras. *Observatory.* Results of Meteorological Observations. pp. 394. *Madras*, 1892. 4°.   8756. f. 39.

—— Vienna. *Sonnblick-Verein.* Jahres-Bericht des Sonnblick-Vereines. *Wien*, 1893, etc. 8°.
Ac. 4065.

BARNARD (C.) Talks about the Weather in its relation to plants and animals. pp. 121. *N.Y.* 1894. 8°.   7006. aaa. 22.

BEBBER (W. v.) Hygienische Meteorologie. pp. 330. *Stuttgart*, 1895. 8°.   8757. dd. 27.

BENN (T. G.) Observations in Meteorology. pp. 47. *Penrith*, 1893. 8°.   8756. cc. 43. (9.)

BERGHOLZ (P.) Ergebnisse der meteorologischen Beobachtungen in Bremen. *Bremen*, 1891, etc. fol.   8755. m. 18.

BLASIUS (W.) Drei Vorträge über Meteorologie. pp. 52. *Braunschweig*, 1892. 8°. 8708. l. 8. (7.)

BUCHAN (A.) The Meteorology of Ben Nevis. pp. 406. 1890. 4°. Ac. Edinburgh. *Royal Society.* Transactions. Vol. 34.   2099. g.

DAVIS (W. M.) Elementary Meteorology. pp. 355. *Bost.* 1894. 8°.   8756. ccc. 33.

—— Observations of the New England Meteorological Society 1889. 1890. 4°. Ac. Cambridge. *Harvard University. Observatory.* Annals. Vol. 21.   8562. h.

DICKSON (H. N.) Meteorology. pp. 192. 1893. 8°. SYMES (J. E.) University Extension Series.
012202. g.

ECKERT (F.) Resultate forstlich-meteorologischer Beobachtungen. 1890. 4°. Austria. *Staatliches Forstliches Versuchswesen.* Mittheilungen. Hft. 12.   7073. cee. 7.

METEOROLOGY.—General—_continued._

EGESON (C.) Weather System of Sun-spot causality. pp. 63. *Sydney*, 1889. 8°.
     8756. de. 48.

EPHEM. British Astronomical Weather Almanac. By B. G. Jenkins. *Lond.* 1891, *etc.* 8°.
     P.P. 2477. gac.

FERGUSSON (S. P.) Observations made at the Blue Hill Meteorological Observatory. 1892. 4°. Ac. Cambridge. *Harvard University. Observatory.* Annals. Vol. 30.   8563. k.

GLAISHER (J.) Hygrometrical Tables. pp. 28. *Lond.* 1893. 8°.   8755. dd. 31.

GOMIS (C.) Meteorología y agricultura. pp. 176. 1888. 8°. Ac. Barcelona. *Associació d'Excursions Catalana.* Biblioteca popular. Vol. 5.
     Ac. 8883.

G. B. & I. *Meteorological Office.* Meteorological Observations at foreign and colonial stations, 1852–86. pp. 261. *Lond.* 1890, 4°.
     8754. ddd. 12.

—— Ten Years Sunshine in the British Isles, 1881–90. pp. 58. *Lond.* 1891. 8°.   8755. l. 9.

—— Monthly Weather Report. *Lond.* 1884, *etc.* 4°.   8754. d.

—— Weekly Weather Report. *Lond.* 1892, *etc.* 4°.   8754. ccc.

—— Hourly means of Readings obtained from the self-recording instruments at the Four Observatories. *Lond.* 1891, *etc.* 4°.   8754. ddd.

—— Harmonic analysis of hourly observations of Air Temperature and Pressure. pp. 92. *Lond.* 1891. 4°.   8754. ddd. 10.

—— Meteorological Observations made at Sanchez, Samaná Bay, St. Domingo. pp. 64. *Lond.* 1890. 8°.   8754. ddd. 7.

—— Report of the International Meteorological Conference at Munich. 1891. pp. 93. *Lond.* 1893. 8°.   8754. cc. 12.

—— Report of the International Meteorological Committee, Upsala, 1894. pp. 48. *Lond.* 1895. 8°.   8754. cc. 13.

—— Instructions in the use of meteorological instruments. pp. 124. *Lond.* 1892. 8°.
     8754. cc. 24.

HANN (J.) Der Veränderlichkeit der Temperatur in Österreich. 1891, 8°. Ac. Vienna. *K. Akademie.* Denkschriften. Math.-naturwissenschaftliche Classe. Bd. 58. Ac. 810/13.

—— Studien über die Luftdruck- und Temperaturverhältnisse auf dem Sonnblickgipfel. 1891. 8°. Ac. Vienna. *K. Akademie.* Sitzungsberichte. Math. - naturwissenschaftliche Classe. Bd. 100. Hft. 4. Abt. 2. a. Ac. 810/6.

HAZEN (H. A.) Collection of articles on Meteorology. 1884, *etc.* 8°.   8755. dd.

—— Hand-book of meteorological Tables. pp. 127. *Wash.* 1888. 8°.   8548. dd. 34.

HELLMANN (G.) Neudrucke von Schriften und Karten über Meteorologie. *Berl.* 1893, *etc.* 4°.
     8755. dd.

HORNBERGER (R.) Grundriss der Meteorologie und Klimatologie. pp. 233. *Berl.* 1891. 8°.
     8756. c. 45.

HOUDAILLE (F.) Météorologie agricole. Le Soleil et l'Agriculteur. pp. 542. *Montpellier*, 1893. 8°.   8756. dd. 14.

INWARDS (R.) Weather Lore. pp. 190. *Lond.* 1893, 8°.   8755. cc. 58.

JAEGER (G.) Wetteransagen und Mondwechsel. pp. 127. *Stuttgart*, 1893, 8°.   8756. cc. 41.

—— Wetter und Mond. pp. 56. *Stuttgart*, 1894. 8°.   8756. cc. 42.

LEY (W. C.) Cloudland. pp. 208. *Lond.* 1894. 8°.   8756. ccc. 29.

METEOROLOGY.—General—_continued._

LIVERPOOL. *Observatory.* Meteorological Results, 1889-90-91. pp. 77 *Liverp.* 1893. 8°.
     8756. c. 46.

LOOMIS (E.) Contributions to Meteorology. 1891. 4°. Ac. Washington. *National Academy.* Memoirs. Vol. v.   Ac. 3039/4.

MARRIOTT (W.) Hints to meteorological Observers. pp. 42. *Lond.* 1892. 8°.
     8756. eee. 19.

MERLE (W.) Merle's MS. Consideraciones Temperiei pro 7 annis 1337–44. *Lat.* and *Eng.* *Lond.* 1891, fol.   8755. m. 20.

MEYER (H.) Anleitung zur Bearbeitung meteorologischer Beobachtungen für die Klimatologie pp. 187. *Lond.* 1891. 8°.   8756. de. 43.

MONT BLANC. *Observatoire.* Annales de l'Observatoire du Mont-Blanc. *Paris*, 1893, *etc.* 4°.
     8756. eee.

MOORE (J. W.) Meteorology. pp. 445. 1894. 8°. Sanitary Series. No. 1.   8756. dd.

NIPHER (F. E.) State Weather Service. pp. 6. *Jefferson City, Mo.*, 1891. 8°.   Pam. 79.

PAULSEN (A.) Lærebog i Meteorologi. pp. 123. *Kjøbenh.* 1890, 8°.   8756. de. 42.

P.P. *Detroit.* American Meteorological Journal. *Detroit*, 1884, *etc.* 8°.   P.P. 1560. h.

—— *Paris.* Les Sciences populaires. *Paris*, 1895, *etc.* 8°.   P.P. 1551. ab.

POWERS (E.) War and the Weather. pp. 202. *Delavan*, 1890. 8°.   8756. dd. 7.

RAVENSTEIN (E. G.) Report on meteorological Observations in British East Africa, 1893. pp. 12. *Lond.* 1894. 8°.   8755. dd. 33. (8.)

RAYMOND (G.) Les grands centres d'action de l'Atmosphère. pp. 84. *Paris*, 1890. 12°.
     8708. b. 23. (2.)

ROTCH (A. L.) Observations made at the Blue Hill Meteorological Observatory, Mass. 1889. pp. 75. 1890. 4°. Ac. Cambridge. *Harvard University. Observatory.* Annals. Vol. 30.
     8562. h.

RUSSELL (*Hon.* F. A. R.) Observations of Dew and Frost. pp. 47. *Lond.* 1892. 8°. Pam. 79.

RUSSELL (T.) Meteorology. pp. 277. *N.Y.* 1895. 8°.   8758. d. 1.

SAUSSURE (H. B. de) Observations météorologiques faites au Col du Géant 1788. pp. 32. 1891. 4°. Ac. Geneva. *Société de Physique.* Mémoirs. Vol. supplémentaire.   Ac. 2870.

SAUVAGE ( ) Chronique du froid en Normandie du Ier au XVIIIe siècle. pp. 110. *Rouen*, 1892. 8°.
     8755. f. 33.

SUGNY (J. de) Éléments de Météorologie nautique. pp. 472. *Paris*, 1890. 8°.
     8807. c. 37.

U.S. *Weather Bureau.* Bulletin. *Wash.* 1892, *etc.* 8°.   7053. e. 40.

—— Report of the Chief of the Weather Bureau. *Wash.* 1892, *etc.* 8°.   7053. e. 46.

—— Instructions for voluntary observers. pp. 100. *Wash.* 1892. 8°.   8755. k. 59.

—— *Geological Survey.* Instructions for observing air temperature, humidity. *etc.* pp. 7. *Wash.* 1889. 8°.   8755. h. 46. (3.)

—— *Signal Service.* Mean Temperatures and their corrections in the U.S. pp. 45. *Wash.* 1891. 4°.   8755. m. 21.

WALLO (F.) Modern Meteorology. pp. 460. 1893. 8°. ELLIS (H. H.) Contemporary Science Series.   8709. i.

See also AIR : AURORAE : CLIMATOLOGY . PHYSIOGRAPHY.

METEOROLOGY—*continued.*

Barometer.

AUSTRIA. *Reichs-Kriegs-Ministerium.* Relative Schwerebestimmungen durch Pendelbeobachtungen. pp. 630. *Wien*, 1895. 8°. 8808. aa. 5.

CHAMBERS (F.) Abnormal Variations of barometric Pressure in the Tropics. pp. 16. *Bombay*, 1880. 8°. 8706. h. 7. (3.)

G. B. & I. *Meteorological Office.* Barometer Manual. pp. 41. *Lond.* 1890. 8°. 8754. cc. 22.

—— Fishery Barometer Manual. pp. 81. *Lond.* 1887. 8°. 8754. cc. 26.

WHYMPER (E.) How to use the Aneroid Barometer. pp. 61. *Lond.* 1891. 8°. 8755. dd. 32. (5.) *See also supra: General. Infra: Weather Forecasts: Wind.*

Cyclones. *See infra: Wind.*

Hail.

PROHASKA (C.) Beobachtungen über Hagelfälle in Steiermark, Kärnten und Ober-Krain. 1893. 8°. Ac. Gratz. *Naturwissenschaftlicher Verein.* Mittheilungen. Hft. 29, Ac. 2905.

RUSSELL (*Hon.* F. A. R.) On Hail. pp. 224. *Lond.* 1893. 8°. 8756. de. 49.

RUSSELL (H. C.) Hail Storms. pp. 4, *Sydney*, 1892. 8°. 8755. dd. 7. (10.)

SARRAZIN (F.) Die Naturgesetze des Hagels und die Hagelversicherung. pp. 50. *Lichterfelde*, 1890. 8°. 8708. g. 27. (4.)

VERY (F. W.) Hail Storms. pp. 20. *Pittsburgh*, 1894. 8°. 8755. dd. 7. (14.)

—— The Hail Storm of May 20, 1893. pp. 10. 1893. 8°. 8755. dd. 7. (13.) *See also* INSURANCE. *Infra: Rainfall: Wind.*

Rainfall.

COLLINSON (J.) Rainmaking and Sunshine. pp. 280. *Lond.* 1894. 8°. 8755. aaa. 43.

POWERS (E.) Should the Rainfall Experiments be continued? pp. 15. *Delavan*, 1892. 8°. 8708. b. 23. (5.)

REDWAY (J. W.) Influence of Rainfall on commercial development. pp. 14. 1892. 8°. 8755. dd. 7. (9.)

RUSSELL (H. C.) Pictorial Rain Maps. pp. 4. *Sydney*, 1893. 8°. 8756. cc. 43. (11.)

U.S.A. *Geological Survey,* Instructions for Rainfall observers. pp. 4. *Wash.* 1889. 8°. 8755. h. 46. (4.)

SYMONS (E. J.) and WALLIS (H. S.) On the distribution of Rain over the British Isles during 1891. pp. 43. 228. *Lond.* 1892. 8°. 8755. l.

FRYER (H. F.) Rainfall in Cambridgeshire, 1884-93. *St Ives*, 1894. 8°. Pam. 79.

PRINCE (C. L.) Record of Rainfall at Uckfield, Sussex, 1843-92. pp. 22. 1893. 8°. 8756. cc. 38.

NIPHER (F. E.) Report on Missouri Rainfall for ten years. 1892. 8°. Ac. Saint Louis. *Academy of Science.* Transactions. Vol. 5. Ac. 3061.

U.S.A. *Signal Service..* Report of Rainfall in Washington Territory, Oregon, California, etc. pp. 101. *Wash.* 1889. 4°. 8756. eee. 25. *See also infra:* THUNDER: WIND.

Thunder-Storms.

KRETZER (H. F.) Lightning Record. Reports of lightning strokes in the United States. *St Louis*, 1895, *etc.* 8°. 8755. dd.

LODGE (O. J.) Lightning Conductors and Guards. pp. 544. 1892. 8°. Specialist's Series. 8708. k.

MAC ADIE (A.) Protection from Lightning. pp. 20. 1894. 8°. U.S. *Weather Bureau.* Circular. 1894. 7053. e. 44.

METEOROLOGY. — Thunderstorms — *—continued.*

SOHNCKE (L.) Gewitterstudien auf Grund von Ballonfahrten. 1895. 4°. Ac. Munich. *K. Akademie.* Abhandlungen der math.-physikalischen Classe. Bd. 18. Ac. 713/4.

U.S.A. *Weather Bureau.* Protection from Lightning. By A. McAdie. pp. 20. *Wash.* 1894. 8°. 7053. e. 44.

WARD (R. de C.) Thunderstorms in New England, 1886-87. 1893. 4°. Ac. Cambridge. *Harvard University. Observatory.* Annals. Vol. 31. 8563. k. *See also supra:* HAIL : RAINFALL. *Infra:* WIND.

Weather Forecasts.

BEBBER (W. J. v.) Die Wettervorhersage. pp. 171. :*Stuttg.* 1891. 8°. 8755. k. 56.

CLEMENTS (H.) Weather Prediction. pp. 16. *Lond.* 1892. 8°. 8708. b. 23. (4.)

DEWAR (D.) Weather Forecasts, 1891-92. *Dalkeith*, 1891. 8°. 1801. d. 1. (150.)

EPHEM. Clements' Weather Almanack. *Lond.* 1892, *etc.* 16°. P.P. 2477. tc.

FALB (R.) Neue Wetter-Prognosen, Juli—Dezember, 1894. pp. 79. *Berl.* 1894. 16°. 8758. a. 1.

G. B. & I. *Meteorological Office.* Principles of Forecasting. By Hon. R. Abercromby. pp. 123. *Lond.* 1885. 8°. 8754. cc. 20.

—— Aids to the forecast of Weather. By W. C. Ley. pp. 38. *Lond.* 1880. 8°. 8754. cc. 21.

JENKINS (B. G.) On Forecasting the Weather. pp. 6. *Brussels*, 1887. 8°. Pam. 79.

—— British Weather Chart, 1893. *Lond.* 1892. *s. sh.* fol. 1810. d. 1. (20.)

—— British Weather Chart, 1894. *Lond.* 1893. *s. sh.* fol. 1810. d. 1. (38.)

KENNEDY (E. A.) Hourly Weather Guide. *Lond.* 1892. fol. 14000. i. 30.

MAUDSLAY (A.) Nature's Weather warnings. pp. 191. *Lond.* 1891. 8°. 8756. aaa. 57.

RUSSELL (T.) Weather, and methods of forecasting. pp. 277. *N.Y.* 1895. 8°. 8758. d. 1.

T., B. My Weather-wise Companion. pp. 110. *Edinb.* 1895. 12°. 8756. a. 40.

TIMM (H.) Wie gestaltet sich das Wetter? pp. 175. *Wien*, 1892. 8°. 8755. b. 53.

TOYNBEE (H.) Weather Forecasting for the British Islands. pp. 40. 1892. 8°. LONDON. *Shipmasters' Society.* Papers. No. 22. 8806. cc.

Wind; Storms.

DAVIS (W. M.) Investigation of the Sea-breeze. 1890. 4°. Ac. Cambridge. *Harvard University. Observatory.* Annals. Vol. 21. 8562. h.

DECHEVRENS ( ) On vertical currents in Cyclones. pp. 14. 1890. 8°. 8755. dd. 7. (4.)

G. B. & I. *Meteorological Office.* Report on gales in the ocean district adjacent to the Cape of Good Hope. pp. 111. *Lond.* 1882. 4°. 8754. ddd. 2.

—— Daily Weather Charts for six weeks ending June 25, 1885, to illustrate the tracks of two cyclones in the Arabian Sea. *Lond.* 1891. 4°. 8754. ddd. 1.

JACKSON (R.) Winds and Currents of the Globe. pp. 28. *Portsmouth*, 1890. 8°. 8756. ccc. 26. (7.)

MERINO (B.) Estudio sobre las Borrascas en la costa de Galicia. pp. 65. *Tuy*, 1893. 8°. 8756. cc. 44. (10.)

NIEMEYER (J.) Die heissen Winde der Wüstengebiete. pp. 56. *Meldorf*, 1891. 8°. 8755. dd. 7. (6.)

METEOROLOGY.—Wind, etc.—cont.

SCHNEIDER (E.) Entstehung und Prognose der Wirbelstürme. pp. 112. *Regensburg*, 1895. 8°.
                          8757. d. 44.

SIEMENS (W. v.) On the General System of Winds on the Earth. *Lond.* 1890. 8°.
                       8756. ccc. 26. (10.)

RUSSELL (H. C.) Cyclonic Storm in the Gwydir district. pp. 3. *Sydney*, 1891. 8°.
                       8756. cc. 43. (7.)

ENGLAND, *West of.* The Blizzard in the West, March 9th, 1891. pp. 168. *Lond.* 1891. 8°.
                       8756. aaa. 56.

BOURGEAT (E.) La trombe-cyclone du 19 Aout 1890 dans le Jura. pp. 67. 1891. 8°. Ac. Lons-le-Saunier. *Société d'Émulation.* Mémoires. Sér. 5. Vol. 1.   Ac. 360.

FORTIER (É.) L'ouragan de 1891 à la Martinique. pp. 100. *Paris*, 1892. 8°.   8755. cc. 59.

MONET (H.) La Martinique. Hurricane of 18th Aug. 1891. pp. 411. *Asnières*, 1891. 8°.
                       10470. h. 26.

See also supra: General: Barometer: Thunder Storms.

METEORS: METEORITES. Ac. London.

British Museum. Introduction to the Study of Meteorites. pp. 94. *Lond.* 1894. 8°. 7106. c. 16.

COHEN (E.) Meteoritenkunde. *Stuttgart*, 1894, etc. 8°.   07108. h.

EASTMAN (J. R.) Progress of Meteoric Astronomy in America. 1892. 8°. Ac. Washington. *Philosophical Society.* Bulletin. Vol. 11.
                       Ac. 1876.

FLETCHER (L.) On the supposed Fall of a Meteoric Stone at Chartres. pp. 3. *Lond.* 1890. 8°.   7108. bb. 1. (3.)

—— On Meteorites found in the Desert of Atacama. pp. 42. *Lond.* 1890. 8°. 7108. bb. 1. (6.)

—— On the Mexican Meteorites. pp. 88. *Lond.* 1890. 8°.   7108. bb. 1. (8.)

—— The Meteoric Iron of Tucson. pp. 21. *Lond.* 1890. 8°.   7108. bb. 1. (7.)

LASPEYRES (H.) Die Meteoriten-Sammlung der Universität Bonn. 1894. 8°. Ac. Bonn. *Naturhistorischer Verein.* Verhandlungen. Jhrg. 51.
                       Ac. 2930.

LOCKYER (J. N.) The meteoritic Hypothesis. pp. 560. *Lond.* 1890. 8°.   2244. g. 14.

NIESSL (G. v.) Bahnbestimmung des grossen Meteores vom 2. April 1891. 1892. 8°. Ac. Vienna. *K. Akademie.* Sitzungsberichte. Math. naturwissenschaftliche Classe. Bd. 101.
                       Ac. 810/6.

PLASSMANN (J.) Zweites Verzeichniss von Meteorbahnen. pp. 28. *Köln*, 1891. 8°.   Pam. 4.

MEUNIER (S.) Les Météorites. pp. 228. 1894. 8°. Encyclopédie des aide-mémoire.   8709. g.

See also ASTRONOMY; MINERALOGY: SUN AND SOLAR SYSTEM.

METHODISM.

Lives of J. Wesley: General History and Controversy.

CURNOCK (N.) The Father of Methodism. pp. 64. *Lond.* 1891. 4°.   4906. i. 14.

LELIÈVRE (M.) J. Wesley, sa vie et son œuvre. pp. 500. *Lausanne*, 1891. 8°.   4906. de. 18.

LESTER (G.) The Wesleys in Lincolnshire. pp. 32. *Lond.* 1890. 8°.   4903. bbb. 54.

LUCKOCK (H. M.) J. Wesley's Churchmanship. pp. 55. *Lond.* 1891. 8°.   4139. dd. 2. (11.)

—— Who are Wesley's Heirs? pp. 40. *Lond.* 1891. 8°.   4139. dd. 2. (10.)

RIGG (J. H.) The Living Wesley. pp. 238. *Lond.* 1891. 8°.   4906. dd. 37.

METHODISM.—Lives, etc.—*continued.*

WESLEY (J.) Wesley his own Biographer. pp. 640. *Lond.* 1891. 8°.   4905. h. 3.

—— Homes, haunts and friends of J. Wesley. pp. 154. *Lond.* 1891. 8°.   4905. g. 7.

—— Wesley. Sermons and addresses. pp. 431. *Lond.* 1891. 8°.   4906. df. 15.

—— Living Thoughts of J. Wesley. pp. 562. *N.Y.* 1891. 8°.   3755. e. 6.

—— J. Wesley and modern "Church teaching." pp. 46. *Lond.* 1894. 8°. 4139. a. 12. (6.)

—— Wesley and his Successors. pp. 257. *Lond.* 1891. 8°.   4905. g. 3.

—— The Wesley Centenary Handbook. 2 pt. *Lond.* 1891. 8°.   4715. bb. 21.

BUOY (C. W.) Representative women of Methodism. pp. 476. *N.Y.* 1893. 8°. 4907. de. 10.

GREGORY (S. E.) Pictures of the early Methodists. pp. 96. *Lond.* 1891. 8°.   4906. aaaa. 54.

MAC GEE (J.) The March of Methodism around the globe. pp. 147. *N.Y.* 1893. 8°.
                       4715. aaa. 47.

METHODISTS. *Œcumenical Methodist Conference.* Proceedings of the Conference, 1881. pp. 610. *Lond.* 1881. 8°.   4135. f. 2.

—— Proceedings of the Second Conference, Washington, 1891. pp. 700. *Lond.* 1892. 8°.
                       4136. f. 4.

WANSBROUGH (C. E.) Handbook and index to the Minutes of the Conference, 1744–1890. pp. 311. *Lond.* 1890. 8°.   4715. bb. 22.

BALLARD (F.) Should Methodism cultivate the Liturgy? pp. 56. *Lond.* 1894. 8°.
                    4139. bbb. 23. (5.)

BURTON (A. H.) Methodism and the Bible. pp. 16. *Lond.* 1894. 8°. 4139. bbb. 23. (6.)

LAYMAN. Methodism and the Church of England. pp. 184. *Lond.* 1891. 8°.   4136. b. 29.

METHODIST PREACHER. Methodist Preacher's key-note. pp. 12. *Lond.* 1890. 8°. Pam. 16.

MOULTON (J. H.) What is Schism? pp. 16. *Lond.* 1892. 16°.   4139. a. 12. (2.)

RIGG (J. H.) The District Synod in Methodism. pp. 32. *Lond.* 1894. 8°. 4139. bbb. 23. (7.)

—— District Synods and separated chairmen of districts. pp. 26. *Lond.* 1894. 8°.
                    4139. bbb. 23. (8.)

SHAW (W. I.) Digest of doctrinal Standards. pp. 141. *Toronto*, 1895. 8°.   4136. bb. 10.

SIMON (J. S.) Manual of Instruction and advice for class leaders. pp. 199. *Lond.* 1892. 8°.
                     4136. aaa. 37.

WESLEYAN METHODISTS. The Junior Society Class Prize Essays. pp. 144. *Lond.* 1892. 16°.
                       4139. aa. 21.

WRIGHT (F. C.) Wesleyan Methodism. pp. 32. *Lond.* 1893. 8°.   4139. bbb. 23. (4.)

Methodism in England and Wales.

DYER (A. S.) Sketches of English Nonconformity. pp. 112. *Lond.* 1893. 8°. 4109. aa. 42.

SMITH (H.) Sketches of Methodist New Connexion Ministers. pp. 144. *Lond.* 1893. 8°.
                       4906. de. 27.

SWALLOW (J. A.) Methodism in the light of English literature. pp. 160. 1895. 8°. BREYMANN (H.) Münchener Beiträge. Hft. 9.
                     011824. i.

WESLEYAN METHODISTS. Third London District. Appointments and arrangements, 1890. pp. 16. *Lond.* 1890. 8°.   Pam. 16.

SENIOR (B.) A hundred years at Surrey Chapel. pp. 198. *Lond.* 1892. 8°. 4715. aaa. 45.

METHODISM.—England, etc.—*continued.*

P.P. *Penzance.* The Cornish Methodist church record. *Penzance, 1893, etc.* 4°.
                 P.P. 441. i. & 1362.

—— *Manchester.* The Circuit Magazine of the Manchester Methodist Circuit.
Manch. 1892, *etc.* 4°.   P.P. 441. o.

—— *Northampton.* The Northamptonshire Methodist Monthly. *Northampton, 1891, etc.* 4°.
            P.P. 441. m. and 1308.

Pratt (A. C.) Black Country Methodism.
pp. 174. *Lond.* 1891. 8°.   4715. aaa. 39.

Pilkington (W.) The makers of Wesleyan Methodism in Preston. pp. 275.
Lond. 1890. 8°.   4715. cc. 16.

Young (D.) Origin and history of Methodism in Wales. pp. 731. *Lond.* 1893. 8°.
              4715. cc. 19.

Kelly (C. H.) How to retain our young people.
pp. 16. *Lond.* 1894. 16°.   4139. a. 12. (5.)

Prescott (P.) The Methodist Book Room and its funds. pp. 45. *Bristol,* 1889. 8°.
              4136. a. 36.

See also supra: *General History, etc.*: England, *Nonconformists.*

South Africa.

Africa, *South.* Minutes of the Conference of the Wesleyan Methodist Church of S. Africa.
Cape Town, 1891, *etc.* 8°.   4192. aaa.

United States of America.

Alexander (G.) History of the Methodist Episcopal Church, South. pp. 142. 1894. 8°. American Church History Series. Vol. 11.
              4744. g.

Carroll (H. K.) Report of statistics of Churches in the U.S. pp. 812. 1894. 8°. Eleventh Census of the U.S.   1882. c. 1.

Curtiss (G. L.) Manual of Methodist Episcopal Church History. pp. 373. *N.Y.* 1893. 8°.
              4745. dd. 9.

Dryer (G. H.) Manual for Church Officers.
pp. 216. *N.Y.* 1893. 8°.   5155. de. 27.

Neely (T. B.) History of the governing conference in Methodism. pp. 452.
Cincinnati, 1892. 8°.   4745. de. 5.

Peck (J. O.) The Revival and the Pastor.
pp. 279. *N.Y.* 1894, 8°.   4192. b. 44.

Stuart (T. M.) Errors of Campbellism. pp. 292.
Cincinnati, 1890. 8°.   4136. e. 8.

Vincent (J. H.) Our own Church. pp. 173.
N.Y. 1890. 8°.   4715. a. 41.

See also supra: *General History, etc.*

Missions. *See* Missions.

METHWOLD. Gedge (J. D.) History of a village community in the Eastern Counties.
pp. 130. *Norwich,* 1893. 4°.   10351. g. 31.

METRIC SYSTEM. *See* Decimal System.

METROPOLITAN VALUATION ACT.
See London, *Local Government.*

METZ. Griessdorf (J.) Der Zug Kaiser Karls v. gegen Metz, 1552. pp. 55.
Halle, 1891. 8°.   9327. ccc.

Meyer (J.) Metz durch Panzerfronten verteidigt. 2 pt. *Frauenfeld,* 1894. 8°. 8824. e. 51.

Prost (A.) Les Institutions Judiciaires dans Metz. pp. 258. *Paris,* 1893. 8°. 5605. ff. 8.

Sauer (E.) Inventaire des Aveux et Dénombrements déposés aux Archives à Metz. pp. 232.
Metz, 1894. 8°.   10261. i. 7.

Thiriot (G.) Recherches sur l'ordre des Dominicains à Metz. 1893. 8°. Ac. Metz. *Gesellschaft für Lothringische Geschichte.* Jahrbuch. Jahrg. 5.
              Ac. 7112.

METZ—*continued.*

Thirion (M.) Étude sur l'histoire du Protestantisme à Metz. pp. 480. *Nancy,* 1884. 8°.
              4629. e. 28.

Wolfram (G.) Die Reiterstatuette Karls des Grossen aus der Kathedrale zu Metz. pp. 26.
Strassb. 1890. 8°.   Pam. 24.

Branchard (E. L. R.) Les trois batailles sous Metz. pp. 190. *Briey,* 1894. 8°.   9079. h. 22.

Fircks (A. R. G. H. T. v.) *Baron.* Die Vertheidigung von Metz, 1870. pp. 477.
Leipz. 1893. 8°.   9080. g.

Marchal (G.) Le Drame de Metz. pp. 384.
Paris, 1890. 8°.   9080. dd. 17.

Natzmer (G. E. v.) Bei der Landwehr, vor Metz. pp. 168. *Gotha,* 1894. 8°. 9080. cc. 32.

Metz. Nachweis der bei den Grabdenkmälern der Schlachtfelder um Metz liegenden Todten.
pp. 18. *Metz.* 1891. 8°.   9004. bbb. 14. (9.)
See also German-French War.

MEURTHE ET MOSELLE, Department. Jacquemin (M.) À la frontière de l'Est. pp. 184. *Paris,* 1894. 12°. 10105. cc. 4.

MEUSE, Department. Benoit (A.) Inscriptions de la Meuse. 1894, *etc.* 8°. Ac. Bar-le-Duc. *Société des Lettres.* Mémoires. Sér. 3. Tom. 3.   Ac. 271.

MEXICAN LANGUAGES, Aboriginal.
See Indian Languages : Mexico, *Antiquities.*

MEXICO, City and Republic.
       [*See note on page* 1.]

Antiquities : Aboriginal Races.

Bandelier (A. F.) Report of an archæological tour in Mexico in 1881. pp. 326. 1885. 8°. Ac. Boston. *Archæological Institute.* Papers. American series. Vol. 2.   Ac. 5790/8.

Batres (L.) Cuadro arqueológico de la República Mexicana. *México,* 1885. *s. sh.* fol.
              1882. c. 2. (154.)

Boban (E.) Catalogue de la collection de M. Goupil. Manuscrits figuratifs et autres, xvi° siècle. 3 pt. *Paris,* 1891. fol. 1707. c. 11.

Brinton (D. G.) The Native Calendar of Mexico.
pp. 59. *Phila.* 1893. 8°.   8563. e. 5.

Buelna (E.) Peregrinacion de los Aztecas y nombres geográficos de Sinaloa. pp. 152.
Mexico, 1892. 8°.   10481. de. 6.

Gimeno de Flaquer (C.) Civilización de los antiguos pueblos mexicanos. pp. 108.
Madrid, 1890. 8°.   7706. aa. 51.

Le Plongeon (A.) Sacred Mysteries among the Mayas and Quiches. pp. 163. *N.Y.* 1886. 8°.
              7706. c. 44.

Mexico. *Junta Colombina.* Antigüedades Mexicanas. pp. 80. *Mexico,* 1892. 4°.

—— Láminas. *Mexico,* 1892. fol.
              K.T.C. 21. b. 4.

Mexico. Histoire de la nation mexicaine. Manuscrit figuratif, suivi d'une traduction en Français. pp. 158. 63. *Paris,* 1893. 8°. 9771. c. 1.

Peñafiel (A.) Monumentos del arte mexicano antiguo. *Span., Fr. & Eng.* 3 vol.
Berl. 1890. fol.   Tab. 1282. b.

Parry (F.) Sacred Maya Stone of Mexico and its symbolism. pp. 70. *Lond.* 1893. 8°.
              7705. i. 20.

Saussure (H. F. de) Antiquités Mexicaines.
Genève, 1891, *etc. obl.* 4°.   1702. b.

Seler (E.) Altmexikanische Studien. 1890. fol.
Berlin. K. *Museen.* Veröffentlichungen. Bd. 1.
              7708. g. 24.

ME XICO.—Antiquities, etc.—*continued.*

SOTOMAYOR (D.) Los Aztecas, desde su advenimiento á la America, hasta la elevacion y caida del Imperio Mexicano. pp. 221.
Mazatlan, 1885, *etc.* 4°.   9772. g. 13.
See also AMERICA, *South and Central.*

Army.

JANVIER (T. A.) The Mexican Army. 1893. 8°. Armies of to-day.   8829. i. 9.

Dialect. *See* SPANISH LANGUAGE, *Dialects.*

History.

BUTLER (J. W.) Sketches of Mexico in prehistoric, colonial and modern times. pp. 316.
N.Y. 1894. 8°.   9771. aaa. 4.

GARCÍA Y CUBAS (A.) Diccionario de la República Mexicana. 5 tom. *México,* 1888–92. 4°.   10880. i. 11.

HALE (S.) Mexico. pp. 428. 1891. 8°. Story of the Nations.   9004. ccc. 1.

NOLL (A. H.) Short History of Mexico. pp. 294. *Chicago,* 1890. 8°.   9772. aa. 12.

SCHRYNMAKERS (A. de) Le Mexique. pp. 388. *Brux.* 1890. 8°.   9771. dd. 4.

ZAMACOIS (N. de) Historia de Méjico. 19 tom. *Barcelona,* 1888. 8°.   9770. e. 1.

TELLO (A.) Libro segundo de la Cronica, en que se trata de la conquista de la provincia de Xalisco, *etc.* pp. 886. *Guadalajara,* 1891. 8°.   9772. dd. 5.

BUTLER (W.) Mexico in transition. pp. 325. *N.Y.* 1892. 8°.   4182. cc. 26.

BIBESCŬ (G.) *Prince.* Au Mexique, 1862. pp. 280. *Paris,* 1887. 8°.   9771. f. 8.

GAULOT (P.) La Vérité sur l'expédition du Mexique, 1862. pp. 350. *Paris,* 1890. 12°.   9772. aaa. 31.

JANKOFF (T.) Die europäische Intervention in Mexiko. pp. 50. *Bern,* 1890. 8°. Pam. 65.

LOIZILLON (P. H.) Lettres sur l'expédition du Mexique. 1862-1867. pp. 446. *Paris,* 1890. 12°.   9772. aaa. 32.

MISMER (C.) Souvenirs du Mexique pendant l'intervention française. pp. 290. *Paris,* 1890. 12°.   10480. aa. 16.

TAYLOR (J. M.) Maximilian and Carlotta. pp. 209. *N.Y.* 1894. 8°.   9771. cc. 11.

SMISSEN (A. L. A. G. v. d.) *Baron.* Souvenirs du Mexique, 1864-1867. pp. 232. *Brux.* 1892. 8°.   9770. b. 5.

BURKE (U. R.) Life of B. Juarez, President of Mexico. pp. 384. *Lond.* 1894. 8°.   10883. c. 20.

ROUTIER (G.) L'Histoire du Mexique de nos jours. pp. 196. *Paris,* 1895. 12°. 9771. aaa. 14.

History, *Ecclesiastical.*

See ROMAN CATHOLIC CHURCH, *in Mexico.*

Indians. *See supra: Antiquities:* INDIAN LANGUAGES : INDIANS.

Topography.

BAEDEKER (C.) Nordamerika. pp. 488. *Leipz.* 1893. 8°.   10108. d. 4.

—— The United States with an excursion into Mexico. pp. 516. *Leipz.* 1893. 8°. 2352. a.

GARCÍA Y CUBAS (A.) Diccionario geogràfico de la República Mexicana. 5 tom. *Mexico,* 1888–92. 4°.   10880. i. 1.

JANVIER (T. A.) The Mexican Guide. pp. 531. *N.Y.* 1891. 8°.   10480. a. 37.

ORVAÑANOS (D.) Ensayo de geografía de la República Mexicana. 2 pt. *Mexico,* 1889. 4°.   7686. k. 4.

MEXICO.—Topography—*continued.*

RIEDEL (E.) Guide of the City and Valley of Mexico. pp. 427. *Mexico,* 1892. 16°.   10481. a. 26.

VELASCO (A. L.) Geografía de la República Mexicana. 14 tom. *México,* 1889–93. 8°.   10481. de. 13.

BALLOU (M. M.) Aztec Land. pp. 355. *Boston,* 1890. 8°.   10481. cc. 24.

BERTIE-MARRIOTT (C.) Un Parisien au Mexique. pp. 384. *Paris,* 1886. 8°.   10480. aa. 17.

CHABRAND (É.) De Barcelonnette au Mexique. pp. 472. *Paris,* 1892. 12°.   10026. c. 4.

CHAMBON (L.) Un Gascon au Mexique. pp. 341. *Paris,* 1892. 12°.   10480. aaa. 44.

CROONENBERGHS (C.) Le Mexique. pp. 424. *Paris,* 1893. 8°.   10481. e. 38.

DECKERT (E.) Die Neue Welt. pp. 488. *Berl.* 1892. 8°.   10413. k 20.

GRINGO. Through the land of the Aztecs. pp. 236. *Lond.* 1892. 8°.   10480. bb. 46.

HAMILTON (L. le C.) Border States of Mexico. pp. 211. *San Francisco,* 1881. 8°. 10411. bbb. 35.

HESSE-WARTEGG (E. v.) Mexico. Land und Leute. pp. 463. *Wien,* 1890. 8°. 10480. ee. 35.

LEJEUNE (L.) Au Mexique. pp. 314. *Paris,* 1892. 8°.   10480. bb. 45.

LINDAU (P.) Altes und Neues aus der Neuen Welt. *Berl.* 1893, *etc.* 8°.   10413. g.

MARTUSCELLI (E.) Appunti sul Messico. pp. 98. *Napoli,* 1892. 8°.   8180. g. 19.

PRIDA Y ARTEAGA (F. de) Le Mexique tel qu'il est aujourd'hui. pp. 376. *Paris,* 1891. 8°.   10480. ee. 39.

RABE (J. E.) Eine Erholungsfahrt nach Texas und Mexico. pp. 284. *Hamb.* 1893. 8°.   10413. h. 37.

ROGERS (T. L.) Mexico? Si, Señor. pp. 294. *Bost.* 1893. 8°.   10480. dd. 34.

ROUTIER (G.) Le Mexique. pp. 110. *Paris,* 1891. 8°.   10480. eee. 27.

RUTGERS (L.) On and off the Saddle. pp. 201. *N.Y.* 1894. 8°.   10408. aa. 31.

SCHWATKA (F.) In the Land of Cave and Cliff Dwellers. pp. 385. *N.Y.* 1893. 8°.   10480. dd. 33.

See also infra : Trade : AMERICA : TABASCO.

Trade and Finance.

BANCROFT (H. H.) Resources and development of Mexico. pp. 325. *San Fran.* 1893. 8°.   10480. dd. 38.

BUSTO (E.) La Administración Pública de Méjico. Administración de Hacienda. 2 pts. *Paris,* 1889. 4°.   8228. l. 5.

CASASUS (J. D.) La question de l'argent au Mexique. pp. 136. *Paris,* 1892. 8°. 08227. i. 6.

FERGUSSON (A. W.) Mexico. pp. 347. 1891. 8°. U.S. *Bureau of American Republics.* Bulletin. No. 9.   08225. k. 1.

GARCÍA Y CUBAS (A.) Mexico; its trade, industries and resources. pp. 436. *Mexico,* 1893. 8°.   8226. ff. 34.

HOWELL (E. J.) Mexico : its progress and possibilities. pp. 203. *Lond.* 1892. 8°. 10480. cc. 31.

LUNDY (F. G. C.) History of the Revenue Stamps of Mexico. pp. 45. *St. Louis,* 1890. 8°. Pam. 23.

MEXICO. Código de Comercio de Mexico. pp. 331. *México,* 1889. 8°.   6835. dd. 5.

—— Code de Commerce mexicain. pp. 435. *Paris,* 1894. 8°.   6784. f. 19.

—— Import Duties of Mexico. pp. 66. 1891. 8°. U.S. *Bureau of American Republics.* Bulletin. No. 21.   08225. k. 1.

MEXICO.—Trade, etc.—continued

MEXICO. Memoria de la Secretaria de Hacienda, 1886 á 1887. pp. 529. *México*, 1888. 8°.
8226. i. 10.

—— Noticias de las exportaciones de México para los Estados Unidos y de los Estados Unidos para México, 1887 á 1888. pp. 28. *Mexico*, 1889. 4°. 8223. f. 28.

—— Commercial Directory of Mexico. pp. 122. 1891. 8°. U.S. *Bureau of American Republics*. Bulletin. No. 18. 08225. k. 1.

SCHMITZ (O.) Die Finanzen Mexikos. pp. 224. 1894. 8°. Exotische Werte. Bd. 1. 08226. 1.

MEYWAR. FATH-LĀL MEHTĀ. Handbook of Meywar. pp. 50. *Bombay*, 1888. 8°.
10056. bbb. 7.

MÉZIÈRES. LAURENT (P.) Mézières illustré. *Charleville*, 1889. fol. 1786. c. 17.

MEZZOTINT. *See* ENGRAVING.

MICHIGAN. MAC LAUGHLIN (A. C.) Elements of civil government of Michigan. pp. 78. *Bost.* 1892. 8°. 8176. bbb. 20. (2.)

MICHIGAN. Michigan and its resources. pp. 287. *Lansing*, 1893. 8°. 10411. cc. 39.

MICMACS. *See* INDIANS, *American*.

MICROBES : MICRO-ORGANISMS. *See* BACTERIOLOGY.

MICROSCOPY. BEAUREGARD (H.) Le Microscope et ses applications. pp. 210. 1893. 8°. Encyclopédie des aide-mémoire. 8709. g.

BEHRENS (T. H.) Analyse qualitative microchimique. pp. 168. 1893. 8°. FREMY (E.) Encyclopédie chimique. Tom. 4. 8907. i.

BEHRENS (H.) Manual of microchemical Analysis. pp. 246. *Lond.* 1894. 8°. 8906. aa. 31.

BEHRENS (W. J.) Leitfaden der botanischen Mikroskopie. pp. 208. *Braunschweig*, 1890. 8°.
07028. h. 29.

BONNEY (T. G.) Microscope's Contributions to the Earth's physical history. pp. 16. *Camb.* 1892. 8°. Pam. 27.

BUETSCHLI (O.) Untersuchungen über mikroscopische Schäume und das Protoplasma. pp. 234. *Leipz.* 1892. 4°. 7407. g. 12.

CARPENTER (W. B.) The Microscope and its Revelations. pp. 1099. *Lond.* 1891. 8°. 2022. a.

COLE (A. C.) Methods of microscopical Research. pp. 207. *Lond.* 1895. 8°. 8716. bbb. 50.

CROSS (M. I.) Modern Microscopy. pp. 104. *Lond.* 1893. 8°. 8715. e. 35.

CROWTHER (J.) The Microscope and its lessons. pp. 286. *Lond.* 1891. 8°. 7005. b. 2.

GOSSE (P. H.) Evenings at the Microscope. pp. 434. *Lond.* 1895. 8°. 4429. bbb. 19.

HEURCK (H. v.) The Microscope : its construction and management. pp. 382. *Lond.* 1893. 8°. 8715. g. 28.

LEE (A. B.) The Microtomist's Vade-Mecum. pp. 509. *Lond.* 1893. 8°. 7421. d. 18.

MANCHESTER. *Leeuwenhoek Microscopical Club.* Review of the Work of the Leeuwenhoek Microscopical Club. pp. 28. *Manch.* 1891. 8°.
8768. l. 23. (7.)

MASON (R. G.) Practical hints on Microscopic Mounting. pp. 20. *Lond.* 1891. 8°.
8708. g. 27. (5.)

NAEGELI (C. W. v.) and SCHWENDENER (S.) The Microscope in theory and practice. pp. 374. *Lond.* 1892. 8°. 8716. d. 5.

NIAS (J. B.) On the Development of the continental form of Microscope Stand. *Lond.* 1893. 8°. Pam. 79.

MICROSCOPY—continued.

P.P. Trenton, *New Jersey*. The Microscope. *Wash.* 1892, *etc.* 8°. P.P. 1482. g.

POULSEN (V. A.) Botanisk Mikrokemi. pp. 87. *Kjøbenh.* 1891. 8°. 07028. f. 40.

SQUIRE (P. W.) Methods and formulæ used in the preparation of animal and vegetable Tissues for Microscopical Examination. pp. 93. *Lond.* 1892. 8°. 8706. aa. 32.

WETHERED (F. J.) Medical Microscopy. pp. 412. 1892. 8°. Lewis's Practical Series.
7482. a.

WHITE (T. C.) The Microscope and how to use it. pp. 133. *Lond.* 1893. 8°. 8709. aa. 2.

WRIGHT (L.) Handbook to the Microscope. pp. 256. *Lond.* 1895. 8°. 4430. de. 3.

ZIMMERMANN (A.) Die botanische Mikrotechnik. pp. 278. *Tübingen*, 1892. 8°. 7054. d. 2.

See also ANATOMY : BACTERIOLOGY : HISTOLOGY.

Photo-Micrography.

BOUSFIELD (E. C.) Guide to the science of Photo-Micrography. pp. 174. *Lond.* 1892. 8°.
8909. cc. 25.

HEURCK (H. v.) Photo-Micrography. pp. 41. *Lond.* 1894. 8°. 8909. ccc. 9.

HIS (W.) Der mikrophotographische Apparat der leipziger Anatomie. pp. 22. *Leipz.* 1892. 8°. 8906. h. 9.

MILLS (F. W.) Photography applied to the Microscope. pp. 61. *Lond.* 1891. 8°. 8909. h. 2.

NEUHAUSS (R.) Lehrbuch der Mikrophotographie. pp. 272. *Braunschweig*, 1890. 8°.
8908. l. 4.

—— Die Mikrophotographie und die Projection. pp. 58. 1894. 8°. Encyklopädie der Photographie. Hft. 3. 8909. k.

PITTION (C. P.) La Photographie appliquée à l'étude des microbes. pp. 47. *Lyon*, 1890. 8°.
8909. cc. 12.

PRINGLE (A.) Practical Photo-Micrography. pp. 159. *Lond.* 1893. 4°. 8908. b. 52.

MID-CALDER. MAC CALL (H. B.) History and antiquities of Mid-Calder. pp. 272. *Edinb.* 1894. 4°. 10369. k. 2.

MIDDLESBROUGH. MIDDLESBROUGH. Album of views of Middlesbrough. *Lond.* 1895. 8°. 10360. cc. 59.

MIDDLESEX. P.P. *London.* London and Middlesex Notebook. *Lond.* 1891, *etc.* 8°.
P.P. 1925. dg.

—— Middlesex and Hertfordshire Notes and Queries. *Lond.* 1895, *etc.* 8°. P.P. 6033. g.

RYLEY (W.) and DETHICK (H.) Visitation of Middlesex, 1663. pp. 101. *Lond.* 1887. 8°.
9902. g. 26.

MIDLAND RAILWAY. *See* RAILWAYS, *Great Britain.*

MIDNAPUR. MAHENDRALĀLA KHĀN. History of the Midnápur Ráj. pp. 99. *Calcutta*, 1889. 8°. 9057. c. 5.

MILAN. PAOLUCCI (G.) L' Origine dei comuni di Milano e di Roma. pp. 201. *Palermo*, 1892. 8°. 9167. f. 3.

BONFADINI (R.) Le Origini del comune di Milano. 1890. 8°. Gli albori della vita italiana. Vol. 1. 9166. ccc. 11.

BELTRAMI (L.) Il Castello di Milano, 1368-1535. pp. 639. *Milano*, 1894. 8°. 10136. h. 14.

ROMANO (G.) La pace tra Milano e i Carraresi del 1402. 1891. 8°. Ac. Milan. *Società Storica*. Archivio. Ser. 2. Fasc. 32. Ac. 6525.

MILAN –continued.

MOTTA (E.) Morti in Milano dal 1452 al 1552. 1891. 8°. Ac. Milan. *Società Storica.* Archivio. Sér. II. Fasc. 30.   Ac. 6525.

PÉLISSIER (L. G.) Documents pour l'histoire de la domination française dans le Milanais, 1499–1513. pp. 371. 1891. 8°. Bibliothèque méridionale. Sér. 2. Tom. 1.   12238. ee.

CASTRO (G. de) Milano e le conspirazioni lombarde, 1814–20. pp. 448. *Milano,* 1892. 8°.   9165. bbb. 4.

MILAN. Acta Ecclesiæ Mediolanensis. *Mediolani,* 1890, etc. 4°.   5035. h. 2.

BONABI (V.) I Conventi e i cappuccini di Milano. pp. 439. *Crema.* 1894, 8°. 4605. dd. 4.

BELTRAMI (L.) Guida del Castello di Milano. pp. 136. *Milano,* 1894. 8°.   10130. aa. 9.

CALVI (F.) Storia del Castello di Milano. pp. 547. *Milano,* 1892. 8°.   10132. bbb. 29.

MAYNO (L. del) Vicendo militari del Castello di Milano dal 1706 al 1848. pp. 240. *Milano,* 1894. 8°.   10135. e. 5.

FUMAGALLI (C.) Reminiscenze di storia ed arte nel suburbio e nella città di Milano. 2 pt. *Milano,* 1891. 4°.   7706. f. 25.

ROTTA (P.) Sullo Stile delle Chiese milanesi. pp. 37. *Milano,* 1892. 8°.   7808. bbb. 29. (4.)

—— Passeggiate ossia le chiese di Milano. pp. 198. *Milano,* 1891. 8°.   10136. g. 25.

SABBATINI (L.) Notizie sulle condizioni della Provincia di Milano. pp. 472. *Milano,* 1893. 8°.   08276. k. 24.

MILBORNE PORT. MAYO (C. H.) Parish Register of Milborne Port. pp. 27. *Sherborne,* 1891. 8°.   9906. e. 14. (8.)

MILDMAY PARK. COOKE (H. J.) Mildmay. The first Deaconess Institution. pp. 214. *Lond.* 1892. 8°.   4192. ee. 25.

MAYNARD (G. M.) Pictures of Mildmay. *Lond.* 1895. 8°.   4192. a. 36.

MILITARY SCIENCE.

Bibliography.

BELGIUM. *Ministère de la Guerre* Catalogue de la Bibliothèque. *Brux.* 1894, etc. 8°. 011899. i.

FORT MONROE. *Artillery School.* Catalogue of the Library. pp. 341. *Wash.* 1886. fol.   11902. l. 20.

G. B. & I. *Army.* Catalogue of English Official Military Works on sale January, 1893. *Lond.* 1894, etc. 8°.   011901. e.

MAURICE (J. F.) War. With an essay on military literature and list of books. pp. 155. *Lond.* 1891. 8°.   8830. k. 15.

General.

BRAUMUELLER (W.) Militarische Taschenbücher. *Wien,* 1895, etc. 8°.   8829. aa.

CAMBRELIN (A. L.) La Nation en armes. Service général. pp. 144. *Brux.* 1892. 8°.   8830. h. 18.

DECRISTOFORIS (C.) Che cosa sia la Guerra. pp. 312. *Modena,* 1894. 8°.   8827. aaa. 48.

DERVIEU (C.) La Conception de la victoire chez les grands généraux. pp. 108. *Paris,* 1894. 8°.   8826. ee. 40.

ESTOC (M. d') Le génie de la Guerre. pp. 101. *Paris,* 1892. 12°.   8823. aaa. 46.

GERMANY. *Army. General Staff.* Moltke's militärische Werke. *Berl.* 1892, etc. 8°. 9080. i.

GIRARD (J. S.) Livre de Poche du Soldat. pp. 256. *Paris,* 1895. 16°.   8823. aa. 18.

GOICOECHEA Y JURADO (M. de) Conferencia sobre Arte militar. pp. 364. *Coruña,* 1888. 8°.   8823. ddd. 2.

MILITARY SCIENCE.—General—cont.

HANRION (B. A.) Oeuvres militaires. pp. 416. *Paris,* 1894. 8°.   8829. k. 38.

—— Atlas. 4°.   8829. m. 11.

HART (R. C.) Reflections on the Art of War. pp. 236. *Lond.* 1894. 8°.   8829. aaa. 39.

HENNEBERT (E.) La Guerre. pp. 279. *Paris,* 1893. 8°.   8824. c. 34.

JOHN CHARLES, *Archduke of Austria.* Ausgewählte Schriften des Erzherzogs Carl von Oesterreich. *Wien,* 1893, etc. 8°.   12251. dd.

LAMIRAUX (F. G.) Études de Guerre. pp. 262. *Paris,* 1891. 8°.   8824. k. 11.

MAILLARD (L.) Éléments de la Guerre. *Paris,* 1891, etc. 8°.   8830. l. 16.

—— Atlas. fol.   8830. m. 1.

MARTÍNEZ RUIZ DE LINARES (A.) Breves consideraciones sobre Ciencia Militar. pp. 62. *Madrid,* 1892. 8°.   8824. ccc. 34.

MAURICE (J. F.) War. pp. 155. *Lond.* 1891. 8°.   8830. k. 15.

MOUSER (P.) La Guerra futura. pp. 330. *Buenos A.* 1893. 8°.   8825. cc. 34.

POWERS (E.) War and the Weather. pp. 202. *Delavan,* 1890. 8°.   8756. dd. 7.

SCHNEEGANS (L. E.) La Guerre raisonnée. pp. 345. *Paris,* 1891. 8°.   8823. ddd. 14.

THOUMAS (C. A.) Causeries militaires. pp. 328. *Paris,* 1889. 18°.   8823. g. 16.

—— Deuxième série. pp. 318. *Paris,* 1890. 18°.   8823. g. 15.

—— Les vertus guerrières. Livre du soldat. pp. 400. *Paris,* 1891. 8°.   8823. g. 18.

WAGNER (A. L.) The Service of Security and Information. pp. 265. *Wash.* 1893. 8°. 8824. c. 37.

WEIMERSKIRCHE (T.) L'Art de Guerre. pp. 149. *Brux.* 1890. 8°.   8823. dd. 40.

See also under the subheading *Army* of each country : WAR AND PEACE : WEAPONS.

Aeronautics, *Military.* See BALLOONS.

Administration. *See infra: Staff.*

Armies of various Countries.

ARMIES. The Armies of to-day. pp. 438. *Lond,* 1893. 8°.   8829. i. 9.

CENNI (Q.) Atlante militare. Organizzazione degli eserciti d'Europa. pp. 67. *Milano,* 1890. 8°.   8829. k. 30.

LAUTH (J.) L'état militaire des puissances étrangères. pp. 688. *Paris,* 1894. 8°. 8829. aaa. 41.

MOLARD (J.) Puissance militaire des États de l'Europe. pp. 501. *Paris,* 1895. 12°.   8828. aaa 28.

—— Appendice. pp. 40. *Paris,* 1893. 12°.   Pam. 2.

OFFICIERS. Les Officiers d'aujourd'hui. pp. 52. *Fribourg,* 1890. 8°.   8831. l. 11. (6.)

PARENTI (D.) Disposizioni vigenti sulle Pensioni militari in Italia ed in altre nazioni. pp. 304. *Livorno,* 1892. 8°.   8826. ff. 33.

See also under the subheading *Army* of each country.

Artillery.

FORT MONROE. *Artillery School.* Catalogue of the Library of the U.S. Artillery School. pp. 341. *Wash.* 1886. fol.   11902. l. 20.

BROWNE (C. O.) Armour and its Attack by Artillery. Supplement, 1887 to 1893. *Lond.* 1893. 8°.   8830. l. 19.

CARP ( ) Geschichte der Feld-Artillerie-Schiessschule. pp. 95. *Berl.* 1892. 8°.   8823. n. 26.

DOLLECZEK (A.) Artilleristisches Taschenbuch. pp. 191. 1895. 8°. Braumüller's militärische Taschenbücher. Bd. 3.   8829. aa.

MILITARY SCIENCE.—Artillery—cont.

Girod de l'Ain (M.) Grands Artilleurs.
pp. 465. *Paris*, 1893. 8°.   010662. k. 7.

Gauthier (J.) L'artillerie de la Place de Gray
pendant les guerres du xvii° siècle. pp. 20.
Vesoul, 1892. 8°.   Pam. 2.

Germany. *Army.* Règlement de manœuvres
pour l'artillerie de campagne allemande.
pp. 253. *Paris*, 1894. 8°.   8823. g. 28.

——— Drill Regulations of the German Field
Artillery, 1892. pp. 182. *Lond.* 1893. 8°.
          8823. h. 34.

Girardon (É.) Leçons d'Artillerie. pp. 396.
Paris, 1895. 8°.   8831. bb. 54.

Goovaerts (A. J. M. A.) Les Fondeurs d'Artillerie, par M. le général Henrard. Rapport.
pp. 11. *Anvers*, 1890. 8°.   8830. k. 31. (5.)

G. B. & I. *Army.* Manual for non-commissioned
Officers of Artillery preparing for examination.
pp. 259. *Lond.* 1891. 8°.   8831. aa. 40.

——— Garrison Artillery drill. *Lond.* 1891. *etc.* 16°.
          8831. aa. 42.

——— Siege Artillery drill. pp. 341.
Lond. 1891. 16°.   8831. aa. 38.

——— Notes on foot drill for Artillery Volunteers.
pp. 23. *Leeds*, 1891. 16°.   8831. ee. 13.

——— Mountain Artillery drill. pp. 176.
Lond. 1891. 16°.   8831. aa. 37.

——— Useful Rules and Tables. pp. 115.
Lond. 1883. 16°.   8831. aa. 1. (1.)

——— Treatise on military carriages. pp. 468.
Lond. 1895. 8°.   8831. cc. 1.

Hermida y Álvarez (G.) Nuevo material de
Artilleria. 2 pt. *Madrid*, 1894. 8°. 8827. cc. 45.

Hime (H. W. L.) Artillery Reform. pp. 31.
Lond. 1895, 8°.   Pam. 2.

Langlois (H.) L'Artillerie de Campagne en
liaison avec les autres armes. *Paris*, 1892, *etc.* 8°.
          8831. cc. 3.

Lloyd (E. W.) and Hadcock (A. G.) Artillery :
its progress and position. pp. 463.
Portsmouth, 1893. 8°.   8830. l. 22.

Longridge (J. A.) The Artillery of the future.
pp. 76. *Lond.* 1891. 8°.   8831. k. 26.

May (E. S.) Achievements of Field Artillery.
pp. 6. 171. *Woolwich*, 1893. 8°.   8829. i. 10.

Moch (G.) Vue générale sur l'Artillerie actuelle.
pp. 221. *Paris*, 1895. 8°.   8830. e. 17.

Philip, *Landgrave of Hesse.* Inventarium der
Artillerie Landgraf Philipps. 1891. 8°. Ac.
Cassel. *Verein für hessische Geschichte.* Zeit-
schrift. N.F. Bd. 16.   Ac. 7025.

Pratt (S. C.) Field Artillery. pp. 254. 1895. 8°.
Brackenbury (C. B.) Military Handbooks.
Vol. 3.   2249. a. 9.

Schubert (J.) Die Feld- und Gebirgs-Artillerien
der europäischen Staaten. pp. 47.
Wien, 1890. fol.   8825. h. 18.

Schumacher (A.) Die Vermehrung der Feld-
artillerie. pp. 78. *Bern*, 1891. 8°.
          8831. c. 24. (8.)

Timmermans (J. J. T.) Historique de l'Artillerie belge. pp. 112. *Gand*, 1886. 8°,
          8824. ccc. 28.

Veyrines (P.) L'Artillerie à l'Exposition de
1889. pp. 247. *Paris*, 1890. 8°.   8830. d. 3.

Woolwich. *Artillery College.* Handbook for
Military Artificers. pp. 531. *Lond.* 1894. 16°.
          8831. e. 26.

——— *Museum of Artillery.* Official catalogue of
the Museum of Artillery. pp. 288.
Lond. 1889. 8°.   8823. c. 53.

See also Fortification : Gunnery : Naval
Science ; and under the subheading *Army* of
each country.

MILITARY SCIENCE—continued.

Barracks.

Boynton (F.) Barrack Damages. pp. 32.
York, 1891. 8°.   8831. ee. 12.

Lange (W.) Der Baracken-Bau. pp. 96.
Leipz. 1895. 8°.   7688. k. 2.

Bicycling. *Military. See* Bicycles.

Biography, *Military. See* Biography.

Cavalry.

Biensan (R. de) Conduct of a Contact Squadron.
pp. 121. *Lond.* 1883. 8°.   8830. bbb. 4.

Bothmer (v.) *Baron.* Der Kavallerie-Unter-
führer vor dem Feinde. pp. 160. *Berl.* 1893. 8°.
          8828. bb. 32.

Cardinal von Widdern (G.) Der Grenz-
detachements-Krieg und die Kavallerie-Unter-
nehmungen in Feindesland. pp. 264.
Berl. 1892. 8°.   8830. f. 28.

Cavalier. Une révolution dans la tactique de
la Cavalerie. pp. 23. *Paris*, 1890. 8°.
          8831. l. 9. (5.)

Chézelles (H. de) *Viscount.* L'Homme de
Cheval. pp. 227. *Paris*, 1893. 8°. 07293. g. 18.

Flint (J.) Questions and Answers on Forage,
watering, feeding, and fitting saddles. pp. 32.
1892. 8°. Gale and Polden's Military Series.
          8830. a.

G. B. & I. *War Office.* Cavalry Manœuvres in
Italy and France, 1890. pp. 23. *Lond.* 1891, 8°.
          8831. c. 25. (6.)

Hohenlohe-Ingelfingen (K. K. A. E. F. zu)
Prince. Letters on Cavalry. pp. 263.
Lond. 1893. 8°.   8824. c. 32.

Kaulbars (A. v.) *Baron.* Die vorgeschobenen
Escadrons der russischen Kavallerie. pp. 76.
Hannover, 1891. 8°.   8823. n. 4.

Ouvry (H. A.) Cavalry Experiences. pp. 235.
Lymington, 1892. 8°.   8831. g. 60.

Rotenhan (H. v.) *Baron.* Die neuere Kriegsgeschichte der Cavalerie vom Jahre 1859.
2 Bde. *München*, 1891. 8°.   8823. n.

Steele (St. G. L.) Cavalry on outpost duty.
Aldershot, 1894, *s. sh.* 8°.   8830. aa. 24.

Vallet (L.) Croquis de Cavalerie. pp. 300.
Paris, 1893. 4°.   8825. h. 28.

Verdy du Vernois (J. v.) Studies in Troop
Leading. The Cavalry Division. pp. 424.
Lond. 1890. 8°.   8830. c. 31.

See also under the subheading *Army* of each
country.

Commissariat. *See infra : Transport.*

Cookery, *Military. See* Cookery.

Dictionaries and Encyclopædias.

Dictionaries. Dictionnaire militaire.
Paris, 1894, *etc.* 8°.   8828. k.

——— Military Vocabularies. *Lond.* 1892, *etc.* 8°.
          12902. ccc.

G. B. & I. *Army.* Lists of technical terms.
pp. 66. *Lond.* 1893. 8°.   Pam. 2.

Barrère (A. M. V.) Dictionary of English and
French Military Terms. *Lond.* 1895, *etc.* 8°.
          8823. h. 49.

Pardiellan (P. de) Aide-mémoire de l'Officier
français en Allemagne. pp. 141.
Paris, 1890. 16°.   8823. a. 10.

Romagné (E.) Dictionnaire militaire français-
allemand. pp. 176. *Paris*, 1894. 8°. 12962. f. 34.

Roy (P. R.) Répertoire alphabétique des termes
militaires allemands. pp. 178. *Paris*, 1891. 8°.
          8823. g. 21.

Koiransky (Z.) Russisch-deutsches militärisches Wörterbuch. *Berl.* 1892, *etc.* 8°.
          8825. bbb. 36.

MILITARY SCIENCE—*continued.*

Discipline, etc.

FONTAINE VON FELSENBRUNN (C.) Die Stellung des Subaltern-Officiers. pp. 102.
Wien, 1893. 8°.   8831. i. 37.

HANNA (H. B.) Discipline. pp. 55.
Delhi, 1889. 8°.   Pam. 2.

MUÑIZ Y TERRONES (J.) Concepto del Mando y Deber de la Obediencia. 2 tom.
Madrid, 1893. 8°.   8408. l. 19.

STELLA (S.) La Disciplina militare. pp. 45.
Torino, 1890. 8°.   8831. l. 10. (11.)

Drill. *See infra :* STRATEGY AND TACTICS.

Education.

CHWALLA (A.) Die intellectuelle Ausbildung des Infanterie-Unterofficiers. pp. 314.
Wien, 1891. 8°.   8824. e. 42.

JUNCK (A.) Les Écoles de Guerre en Allemagne. pp. 53. *Paris*, 1893. 8°.   8830. f. 38. (4.)

OXFORD MILITARY COLLEGE. Seven Years' Cadet-Life. pp. 443. *Oxf.* 1885. fol.   8365. h. 27.

PARDIELLAN (P. de) Graines d'officiers. Les Écoles militaires en France, en Russie, en Allemagne et en Autriche. pp. 288.
Paris, 1895. 8°.   8356. aa. 27.

PEREZ FERNANDEZ RUIZ (F.) Guia de Aspirantes y alumnos militares. pp. 172.
Madrid, 1892. 8°.   8824. c. 35.

PRATT (S. C.) Guide to Promotion.
Lond. 1892, *etc.* 8°.   8831. f. 39.

SCHMIDT (P. v.) Die Erziehung des Soldaten. pp. 172. *Berl.* 1894. 8°.   8831. bbb. 35.

See also EXAMINATIONS : SANDHURST : WOOLWICH.

Electric Light, *applied to Military Science.*
See ELECTRICITY, *Electric Light.*

Engineering, *Military.*

Ac. Chatham. *Royal Engineers Institute.* Professional Papers. Index. 1837–92. pp. 151.
Chatham, 1893. 8°.   Ac. 4354.

—— *School of Military Engineering.* Standing Orders. pp. 163. *Lond.* 1893. 8°. 8831. f. 42.

—— Manual of Military Engineering. pp. 187. *Lond.* 1893. 16°.   8831. e. 24.

G. B. & I. *Royal Engineers.* Instruction in Military Engineering. *Lond.* 1892, *etc.* 8°.
      2249. f. 21.

—— Text Book of Fortification and military engineering. *Lond.* 1892, *etc.* 8°. 8831. k. 30.

WRAY (H.) Instruction in Construction.
pp. 453. *Lond.* 1891. 8°.   8831. c. 21.

Exhibitions, *Military.*

LONDON. *Royal Military Exhibition.* Official Catalogue. pp. 226. *Lond.* 1890. 8°.
      7959. aaa. 53.

—— Official Report of the Honorary Director. pp. 62. *Lond.* 1891. 8°.   Pam. 18.

CHABBERT (G.) Notes sur l'Exposition Militaire de 1889. pp. 132. *Paris*, 1891. 4°. 7957. g. 12.

THOUMAS (C. A.) Exposition Militaire 1889.
Paris, 1890, *etc.* 4°.   8825. h. 10.

Fencing. *See* FENCING.

Firearms and Gunnery. *See* GUNNERY.

History.

B.-K., C. v. Zur Psychologie des grossen Krieges.
Wien, 1893, *etc.* 8°.   9080. k.

BRÉANT (H.) Lectures militaires. Narrations, batailles, *etc.* 2 pt. *Vienne*, 1891 92. 8°.
      8828. f. 16.

BURNHAM (M.) Struggles of the Nations.
2 vol. *Bost.* 1891. 8°.   9008. bbb. 1.

MILITARY SCIENCE.—History—*cont.*

GEORGE (H. B.) Battles of English History.
pp. 334. *Lond.* 1895. 8°.   2394. d. 3.

GROVES (J. P.) Some Notable Generals and their Battles. pp. 80. *Lond.* 1892. 8°.
      10804. ee. 15.

HARDŸ DE PÉRINI (M. J. F. É.) Batailles françaises. *Châteauroux*, 1894, *etc.* 8°.   9220. ccc.

JABLONSKI (L.) Histoire de l'art militaire.
pp. 458. *Paris*, 1895. 8°.   8830. bbb. 16.

LEUR (A. R. K. v. d.) Militair-historische Schetsen. pp. 122. *'s Gravenh.* 1890. 8°.
      9406. h. 13.

NOTES. Notes critiques sur l'histoire militaire.
pp. 241. *Paris*, 1891. 12°.   011824. de. 18.

QUESNOY (F.) La Guerre à toutes les époques.
pp. 309. *Paris*, 1892. 8°.   8830. bb. 43.

ROSSETTO (V.) Storia dell' Arte militare.
pp. 504. *Milano*, 1893. 8°.   012200. h. 111.

SCHNITLER (D.) Almindelig Krigshistorie.
Christiania, 1890, *etc.* 8°.   8823. n.

HORSETZKY VON HORNTHAL (A.) Tafeln zur kriegsgeschichtlichen Uebersicht der Feldzüge der letzten 100 Jahre. *Wien*, 1894. fol.
      8825. h. 31.

DELBRUECK (H.) Friedrich, Napoleon, Moltke. Aeltere und neuere Strategie. pp. 55.
Berl. 1892. 8°.   Pam. 2.

FORBES (A.) Memories and studies of War.
pp. 368. *Lond.* 1895. 8°.   12354. dd. 10.

MORRIS (W. O'C.) Great Commanders of modern times. pp. 364. *Lond.* 1891. 8°. 10604. g. 13.

ROMAGNY (C. M.) and PIALES D'AXTREZ (A. J. M. J.) Étude des Batailles d'un siècle.
2 pt. *Paris*, 1890. 4°.   8824. i. 10.

See also BIOGRAPHY, *Military,* and under the subheadings *Army* and *History* of each country.

Infantry.

CHWALLA (A.) Die intellectuelle Ausbildung des Infanterie Unterofficiers. pp. 314.
Wien, 1891. 8°.   8824. e. 42.

HEUSCH (W. de) Étude sur l'Infanterie légère.
pp. 75. *Brux.* 1891. 8°.   8830. c. 43. (10.)

HOHENLOHE-INGELFINGEN (K. C. A. E. F. zu) *Prince.* Letters on Infantry. pp. 280.
Lond. 1892. 8°.   8831. f. 36.

MOELLER ( ) Das Infanterie-Gefecht. 2 pt.
Hannover, 1890–91. 8°.   8823. ddd. 16.

JOHNSON (F.) Manual of instruction for Mounted Infantry. pp. 80. *Cape Town*, 1895. 8°.
      8831. f. 47.

PARR (H. H.) Training and Employment of Mounted Infantry. pp. 47. *Lond.* 1888. 8°.
      8831. f. 44.

For Infantry Drill and Tactics, *see infra : Tactics, etc. See also* BICYCLES : GUNNERY AND FIREARMS, and under the subheading *Army* of each country.

Law. *See* LAW, *Military.*

Medicine. *See* AMBULANCE : MEDICINE, *Military :* SURGERY, *Military.*

Mountain Warfare. *See* MOUNTAINS.

Pay. *See infra : Transport, etc.*

Photography. *See infra : Topography.*

Reconnaissance. *See infra : Topography.*

Shooting. *See* GUNNERY.

Signalling : Telegraphy : Pyrotechny.

EDYE (L.) and RHODES (E.) Catechism on the Manual of instruction in army signalling.
pp. 254. 1894. 8°. Gale and Polden's Military Series.   8830. b. 49.

MILITARY SCIENCE.—Signalling, etc. —*continued.*

G. B. & I. *Army.* Manual of instruction in signalling. pp. 146. *Lond.* 1893. 16°.
8831. aa. 45.

—— Regulations for Signallers. pp. 55. *Lond.* 1892. 16°. 8831. e. 4.

—— Manual of instruction in Army Telegraphy. pp. 214. *Lond.* 1891. 8°. 8830. c. 32.

Bovy DE LIÈGE (J.) La Pyrotechnie militaire, 1591. pp. 68. *Paris,* 1892. 8°. Pam. 2.

Staff: Organisation: Administration.

B. A General and his Duties. pp. 73. *Lond.* 1892. 16°. 8829. a. 20.

BIRKHIMER (W. E.) Military Government. pp. 521. *Wash.* 1892. 8°. 6875. eee. 12.

CARDINAL VON WIDDERN (G.) Staff Duties in the Field. pp. 251. *Lond.* 1891. 8°.
8831. aaa. 52.

CLARKE (F. C. H.) Staff Duties. pp. 298. *Lond.* 1890. 8°. 2249. c. 6.

FIX (N. T.) Le service dans les États-majors. pp. 588. *Paris,* 1891. 8°. 8823. ddd. 17.

G. B. & I. *Army.* The Duties of the General Staff. By General Bronsart von Schellendorf. pp. 534. *Lond.* 1895. 8°. 8831. bbb. 37.

—— Military Administration and Staff duties. pp. 53. *Lond.* 1891. 8°. 8831. f. 32. (4.)

LASSALLE (C.) Code de Législation et d'Administration militaires. 2 tom. *Paris,* 1894. 8°.
6875. dc. 11.

—— Manuel de l'Organisation de l'Armée. pp. 1292. *Paris,* 1892. 8°. 8831. bb. 34.

LOUVET (R.) Étude sur la Réorganisation des personnels administratifs de l'armée. pp. 108. *Paris,* 1890. 8°. 8823. dd. 38.

NETTANCOURT-VAUBÉCOURT (M. C. A. de) *Marquis.* La dépense pour une armée de 560,000 hommes sur le pied de guerre. pp. 199. *Bar-le-Duc,* 1892. 4°. 8824. k. 25.

WILKINSON (H. S.) The Brain of an Army. pp. 204. *Westminster,* 1895. 8°. 8832. bb. 6.

Strategy: Tactics: Drill.

BERNARD (H.) Tactique et stratégie. pp. 288. *Tarbes,* 1893. 8°. 8826. bbb. 43.

BIGELOW (J.) Principles of Strategy. Illustrated from American campaigns. pp. 362. *Phila.* 1894. 8°. 8822. i. 18.

CARDINAL VON WIDDERN (G.) Staff duties in the Field. pp. 251. *Lond.* 1891. 8°.
8831. aaa. 52.

CATINAT (E.) Éléments de Stratégie. pp. 160. *Paris,* 1895. 8°. 8829. aa. 23.

CHAMPOUDRY (A.) La Procédure militaire en Campagne. pp. 365. *Paris,* 1893. 8°.
6875. df. 9.

Ac. Chatham. *School of Military Engineering.* Elements of Strategy. pp. 168. *Lond.* 1887. 8°. 8831. g. 45.

DELBRÜCK (H.) Friedrich, Napoleon, Moltke. Aeltere und neuere Strategie. pp. 55. *Berl.* 1892. 8°. 8830. k. 32. (3.)

GIZYCKI (H. v.) Strategisch-taktische Aufgaben nebst Lösungen. 7 Heft. *Hannover,* 1889–91. 8°.
8830. k. 17.

HOENIG (F.) Twenty-four hours of Moltke's Strategy. pp. 184. *Woolwich,* 1895. 8°.
8828. g. 39.

HORSETZKY (A. v.) Vorträge über Strategie. pp. 314. *Wien,* 1892. 8°. 8828. ff. 23.

LEWAL (J. L.) Introduction à la partie positive de la Stratégie. pp. 99. *Paris,* 1892. 8°.
8824. e. 44.

MILITARY SCIENCE.—Strategy, etc. —*continued.*

LEWAL (J. L.) Stratégie de marche. pp. 252. *Paris,* 1893. 8°. 8831. h. 17.

—— Stratégie de combat. *Paris,* 1895, *etc.* 8°.
8830. e. 16.

MOREL (L.) La Guerre de Demain. Stratégie. pp. 56. *Paris,* 1893. 8°. 8830. f. 38. (5.)

ALLASON (U.) La polvere senza fumo e la tattica. pp. 110. *Torino,* 1893. 8°. 8828. aaa. 26.

BAKER (E. M.) Preliminary Tactics. pp. 275. *Lond.* 1892. 8°. 8831. f. 29.

BIDDECKE (A.) Taktische Entschlüsse und Befehle. pp. 114. *Berl.* 1895. 8°. 8829. i. 24.

BUSCHEK (H. W.) Taktik. *Teschen,* 1894, *etc.* 8°.
8830. k.

CARDINAL VON WIDDERN (G.) Der kleine Krieg und der Etappendienst. 2 Thl. *Leipz.* 1892. 8°. 8823. ddd. 29.

COUMÈS (H. A. G.) Aperçus sur la Tactique de demain. pp. 700. *Paris,* 1892. 8°. 8830. d. 5.

DARBISHIRE (R. N.) Pocket Tactics for officers of Militia. pp. 101. *Chatham,* 1891. 16°.
8830. a. 17.

DEMANGEL (J. C.) Questions and Answers on Tactics. pp. 212. *Yorktown,* 1894. 8°. 8831. h. 8.

DONAT (C. v.) Studies in applied Tactics. pp. 55. *Lond.* 1892. 8°. 8831. f. 38.

DYKE (F. H.) Lectures on Tactics. pp. 186. *Lond.* 1892. 8°. 8831. l. 15.

GALL (H. R.) Modern Tactics. pp. 451. *Lond.* 1894. 8°. 8830. k. 30.

—— Tactical questions and answers on the Infantry Drill Book. pp. 82. *Lond.* 1892. 8°.
8830. aaa. 46.

GÉRÔME (A. C.) Essai historique sur la Tactique de l'Infanterie. pp. 272. *Paris,* 1895. 8°.
8828. b. 63.

GRIEPENKERL ( ) Taktische Unterrichtsbriefe. pp. 384. *Berl.* 1892. 8°. 8824. k. 15.

GUNTER (E.) Outlines of modern Tactics. pp. 275. *Lond.* 1895. 8°. 8831. f. 46.

H., F. C. v. Zum Studium der Taktik. 2 Thl. *Wien,* 1891. 8°. 8823. n. 24.

HARDY DE PÉRINI (M. J. F. E.) Tactique française. La Division. pp. 131. *Paris,* 1891. 8°.
8823. dd. 13.

HOME (R.) Précis of modern Tactics. pp. 285. *Lond.* 1892. 8°. 8830. l. 17.

HUTCHINSON (H. D.) Tactics made easy. pp. 51. 1890. 16°. Gale and Polden's Military Series. Vol. 23. 8830. a. 86.

JAMES (W. H.) Handbook of Tactics. pp. 212. 1895. 8°. Gale and Polden's Military Series.
8830. b. 51.

JUPIN (L. S. M. J. J.) Tactique et chiens de guerre. pp. 153. *Paris,* 1890. 8°. 8823. dd. 39.

KVERGIĆ (G.) Beiträge zur Anlage und Durchführung taktischer Übungen. pp. 127. *Wien,* 1895. 8°. 8824. e. 49.

LUETGENDORF (C. v.) *Baron.* Aufgaben-Sammlung für das applicatorische Studium der Taktik. *Wien,* 1895, *etc.* 8°. 8831. cc.

MANCHESTER. *Manchester Tactical Society.* Order of Field Service of the German Army. 2 pt. *Lond.* 1893, 94. 8°. 8829. a. 38.

MATHES VON BILABRUCK (C.) Taktische Studie über die Schlacht von Custoza. pp. 145. *Wien,* 1891. 8°. 9080. d. 36.

VERDY DU VERNOIS (J. v.) Tactical Study, based on the battle of Custozza. pp. 112. 9. 1894. 8°. Gale and Polden's Military Series. 8830. b. 50.

MILITARY SCIENCE.—Strategy, etc.
—continued.

MUMME (Z.) La Tactique appliquée au terrain. pp. 268. *Paris*, 1894. 8°.   8824. ccc. 35.

NED-NOLL. Étude sur la Tactique de Ravitaillement dans les guerres coloniales. pp. 155. *Paris*, 1895. 8°.   8828. bbb. 32.

NIXON (J. E.) Tactical Notes and solution of problems on maps. pp. 104. *Ludhiana*, 1894. 16°.   8829. a. 40.

OMÉGA ( ) L'art de combattre. Traité de tactique. pp. 672. 4. *Paris*, 1891. 8°.   8829. m. 9.

PRUSSIA. *Army.* Moltke's Tactical Problems from 1858 to 1882. pp. 175. *Lond.* 1894. 8°.   8831. i. 35.

REGENSPURSKY (C.) Studien über den taktischen Inhalt des Exercier-Reglements für die k.k. Fusstruppen. pp. 144. *Wien*, 1892. 8°.   8830. k. 27.

ROHR (F.) Taschenbuch zum Gebrauche bei taktischen Ausarbeitungen. pp. 310. 1895. 8°. Braumüllers militärische Taschenbücher. Bd. 1.   8829. aa.

SCHERFF (W. v.) Reglementarische Studien. *Berl.* 1891, *etc.* 8°.   8828. f.

—— Praktische Taktik und taktische Theorie. pp. 107. *Berl.* 1893. 8°.   8824. ff. 45.

SHAW (W. J.) Elements of modern Tactics applied to English formations. pp. 511. 1894. 8°. BRACKENBURY (C. B.) Military Handbooks. Vol. 2.   2249. a. 8.

SIRACUSA (C.) Scettici e conservatori in Tattica. pp. 58. *Roma*, 1893. 8°.   8830. e. 11. (4.)

WATHEN (E. O.) Field Service pocket-book. pp. 25. *Lond.* 1892. 12°.   8831. e. 5.

FURSE (G. A.) Organization and administration of Lines of Communication in War. pp. 517. *Lond.* 1894. 8°..   8830. f. 31.

CHEVALME (A.) La Guerre de nuit. pp. 132. *Paris*, 1895. 8°.   8823. h. 50.

KR. (Ya.) Night Fighting. pp. 65. *Lond.* 1893. 8°.   8830. d. 10.

G. B. & I. *War Office.* Umpire Rules in Austria, France, Germany and Italy for the conduct of Peace Manœuvres. pp. 12. *Lond.* 1893, fol.   Pam. 2.

BENGOUGH (H. M.) Illustrations of Field Exercises by the Three Arms. pp. 102. *Lond.* 1891. 8°.   8823. n. 25.

GERMANY. *Army.* German Field Exercise, 1888. Part II. The Fight. pp. 80. *Lond.* 1888. 8°.   8823. aa. 25.

LA RIVE (E. de) Les Formations de Marche du Corps d'Armée suisse. pp. 46. *Genève*, 1892. 8°.   8824. i. 36.

LONDON. *Wellington Barracks.* Battle Formation. The Attack Drill. *Lond.* 1893. 16°.   1865. c. 4. (4.)

MARRIOTT ( ) Battle Formation, 1892. pp. 53. *Lond.* 1892. 8°.   8823. a. 12.

G. B. & I. *Army.* Infantry Drill, 1892. pp. 261. *Lond.* 1892. 8°.   8831. aa. 41.

MALTON (W. D.) Key to Infantry Drill, 1893. pp. 47. *Lond.* 1893. 16°.   8831. e. 14.

—— Brigade Drill and Ceremonial in accordance with Infantry Drill, 1893. pp. 57. *Lond.* 1893. 16°.   8831. e. 12.

SLACK (C.) Handbook of Brigade Drill. pp. 79. *Lond.* 1893. 32°.   8831. e. 17.

GORDON (W.) Battalion Drill made easy. pp. 288. 1893. 8°. Gale and Polden's Military Series.   8830. n. 78.

MILITARY SCIENCE.—Strategy, etc.
—continued.

SLACK (C.) Handbook of Battalion Drill. pp. 144. *Lond.* 1893. 32°.   8831. e. 18.

WRIGHT (S.) Short details of Battalion Drill, 1893. pp. 60. *Lond.* 1893. 16°.   8831. e. 13.

RICARDO (F. R.) Method of Instructing a Company in Company Drill. pp. 32. *Lond.* 1892, 16°.   8831. e. 10.

SLACK (C.) Handbook of Company Drill. pp. 64. *Lond.* 1893. 16°.   8824. a. 28.

VAN CORTLANDT (A. J. R.) Words of Command and explanation of movements. 3 pt. *Lond.* 1892. fol.   8826. i. 31. (1.)

Telegraphy. *See supra : Signalling.*

Topography : Reconnaissance: Military Sketching. etc.

GERAULT DE LANGALERIE (G. de) Guide de l'enseignement topographique dans les corps de troupe. pp. 128. *Paris*, 1889. 8°.   10001. aaa. 31.

MONTAGUE (W. E.) Military Topography. pp. 64. *Edinb.* 1893. 8°.   8830. aaa. 52.

PRIETO Y VILLARREAL (E.) Manual de Topografía. pp. 284. *Paris*, 1890. 18°.   10002. aa 35.

RHINE. Strategic Geography. Theatres of War of the Rhine and Danube. pp. 78. *Lond.* 1891. 8°.   8829. aaa. 15.

TACCHINI (A.) Trattato teorico-pratico di Topografia moderna. pp. 766. *Milano*, 1891. 8°.   8768. i. 26.

VERNER (W. W. C.) Some notes on Military Topography. pp. 127. *Lond.* 1891. 8°.   8823. ddd. 4.

WEST (J. M.) Elements of Military Topography. pp. 40. *Lond.* 1894. 12°.   8830. f. 30.

CALLWELL (C. E.) Hints on Reconnaissance. pp. 6. *Lond.* 1890. 16°.   8831. e. 3. (8.)

G. B. & I. *Army.* What to Observe and How to Report it. pp. 47. *Lond.* 1863. 16°.   8831. aa. 1. (3.)

WAGNER (A. L.) Service of Security and Information. pp. 265. *Wash.* 1893. 8°.   8824. c. 37.

HUTCHINSON (H. D.) Military Sketching made easy. pp. 208. 1891. 8°. Gale and Polden's Military Series. Vol. 31.   8830. b. 44.

VERNER (W. W. C.) Rapid sketching and reconnaissance. pp. 87. *Lond.* 1889. 8°.   8831. bbb. 33.

—— Map Reading and elements of field sketching. pp. 62. *Lond.* 1883. 8°.   8830. aaa. 55.

GODY (L.) La photographie appliquée aux arts militaires. pp. 212. *Namur*, 1890. 8°.   8909. bb. 5.

Transport : Commissariat : Pay, etc.

FERRAND (G.) Des Réquisitions militaires. pp. 396. *Paris*, 1892. 8°.   6875. ccc. 22.

GIRARDON (É.) Organisation et service du train. pp. 363. *Paris*, 1895. 8°.   8828. c. 58.

G. B. & I. *Army.* Manual for the Commissariat and transport corps. pp. 143. *Lond.* 1883. 8°.   8830. i. 11.

—— Manual for Commissariat Officers. pp. 138. *Lond.* 1885. 8°.   8831. g. 42.

—— Exercises for the Commissariat and Transport Corps. pp. 230. *Lond.* 1885. 8°. 8831. g. 38.

—— Manual of Instruction in regimental transport duties. pp. 116. *Lond.* 1892. 8°.   8830. aa. 49.

—— Manual of Military Railways, 1889. pp. 95. *Lond.* 1889. 8°.   8830. k. 24.

MILITARY SCIENCE.—Transport, etc.
—*continued.*

G. B. & I. Treatise on Military Carriages.
pp. 468. *Lond.* 1895. 8°.   8831. cc. 1.

HAUSCHKA (A.) Die Schule der Führung für
Officiere der Fusstruppen. pp. 104.
Wien, 1893. 8°.   8831. i. 36.

PERNOT (A.) Aperçu historique sur le service
des Transports. pp. 492. *Paris*, 1894. 8°.
          8829. k. 39.

RYLAND (H. G.) Army Transport. pp. 158.
Calcutta, 1891. 8°.   8830. aaa. 48.

SHARPE (H. G.) Art of subsisting Armies in
War. pp. 222. *N.Y.* 1893. 16°.   8831. e. 19.

THOUVENIN (T. E.) Précis du train des Équipages
militaires. pp. 294. *Paris*, 1895. 8°. 8828. c. 56.

TRÉMEREL (G.) and MARULLAZ (H.) Aide-mémoire de l'Officier d'administration des subsist-
ances militaires. pp. 512. *Paris*, 1895. 12°.
          8824. bbb. 35.

VERKEHRSMITTEL. Die neuen Verkehrsmittel im
Kriege. *Berl.* 1891, *etc.* 8°.   8831. cc.

DUNNE (W.) Lecture on the mode of Provision
and Inspection of soldiers' rations. pp. 22.
Lond. 1892. 8°.   8830. d. 11. (8.)

WRAIGHT (H.) Guide for keeping troop, battery or company Accounts. pp. 34.
Devonport, 1892. 16°.   8831. a. 88. (5.)
See also COOKERY, *Military ;* and under the subheading *Army* of each country.

Volunteers. *See* ENGLAND, *Army.*

MILK. *See* DAIRY MANAGEMENT.

MILLENIUM. *See* PROPHECY.

MILLS. *See* CORN : FACTORIES.

MILSTAT. MILSTAT, *Monastery.* Necrologium
des Benedictinerstiftes Milstat. 1891. 8°. Ac.
Vienna. *K. Akademie.* Archiv für österreichische Geschichte. Bd. 77.   Ac. 810/8.

MIND. Diseases of the. *See* INSANITY.

MINDANAO. *See* PHILIPPINE ISLANDS.

MINDEN. PHILIPPI (F.) Zur Verfassungsgeschichte der westfälischen Bischofsstädte.
pp. 102. *Osnabrück*, 1894. 8°.   Pam. 28.

SPANNAGEL (C.) Minden und Ravensberg, 1648–
1719. pp. 248. *Hannover*, 1894. 8°.
          10235. cc. 8.

MINERALOGY AND MINING.

Mineralogy, *General.*

Ac. London. *British Museum.* Introduction to
the study of Minerals. By L. Fletcher. pp. 123.
Lond. 1895. 8°.   7106. b. 51.

—— Guide to the Mineral Gallery. pp. 31.
Lond. 1895. 8°.   Pam. 27.

—— Student's index to the collection of Minerals.
pp. 33. *Lond.* 1895. 8°.   Pam. 27.

—— Munich. *K. Akademie.* Führer durch die
Mineralien-ammlung des Bayerischen Staates.
pp. 331. *München*, 1891. 8°.   7462. bb. 32.

—— Sydney. *Australian Museum.* Descriptive
Catalogue of the collection of Minerals. pp. 221.
Sydney, 1885. 8°.   7106. h. 25.

BAYLEY (W. S.) Summary of progress in Mineralogy, 1886–91. 9 pt. *Baltimore.* 1887–92. 8°.
          7108. b. 17.

DANA (J. D.) System of Mineralogy. pp. 1134.
Lond. 1892. 8°.   2030. d.

DICTIONARIES. Vocabulary of mineralogical terms
in English, German and Japanese. pp. 69. 35.
Tōkiō, 1890. 8°.   12901. ccc. 22.

DOELTER (C.) Allgemeine chemische Mine-
ralogie. pp. 277. *Leipz.* 1890. 8°. 07109. g. 24.

MINERALOGY.—General—*continued.*

EGLESTON (T.) Catalogue of Minerals and synonyms. pp. 7. 378. *N.Y.* 1891. 8°. 7106. i. 14.

FLETCHER (L.) Rennaissance of British Mineralogy. pp. 8. *Loud.* 1890. 8°. 7108. bb. 1. (4.)

FRANCKE (H. H. A.) Ueber die mineralogische
Nomenclatur. pp. 124. *Berl.* 1890. 8°.
          07109. g. 17.

FRIEDEL (C.) Cours de Minéralogie. pp. 416.
Paris, 1893. 8°.   07109. h. 29.

HATCH (F. H.) Mineralogy. pp. 124. 1892. 8°.
Whittaker's Library of popular Science.
          8709. aa.

HAUSHOFER (C.) Leitfaden für die Mineral-
bestimmung. pp. 235. *Braunschweig*, 1892. 8°.
          07109. h. 24.

LŒWINSON-LESSING (F.) Tables for the determination of Rock-forming Minerals. pp. 55.
Lond. 1893. 8°.   7109. f. 15.

MADRAS. *Government Central Museum.* Catalogue
of Minerals. pp. 104. *Madras*, 1890. 8°.
          07109. k. 16.

MALAISE (C.) Manuel de Minéralogie pratique.
pp. 465. *Brux.* 1893. 8°.   07109. i. 2.

MEUNIER (S.) Les méthodes de synthèse en
minéralogie. pp. 359. *Paris*, 1891. 8°.
          7109. f. 12.

OSBORN (H. S.) Practical Manual of Minerals.
pp. 369. *Phila.* 1895. 8°.   07107. h. 1.

WALLERANT (F.) Traité de Minéralogie.
pp. 7. 459. *Paris*, 1891. 8°.   07109. h. 18.

WRIGHT (B.) Native Silica. pp. 263.
Lond. 1894. 8°.   07108. g. 12.

See also ASBESTOS : CRYSTALS : GEOLOGY : JADE :
MAGNESIA : METALS : METEORS.

Mines and Mining, *General.*

Ac. Newcastle. *Federated Institution of Mining
Engineers.* Transactions.
Newcastle, 1892, *etc.* 8°.   Ac. 3232. b.

ANDERSON (J. W.) The Prospector's Handbook.
pp. 176. *Lond.* 1895. 8°.   7106. e. 14.

ARBEL (P.) Rapport sur l'Exposition de Chicago
concernant les mines. pp. 100.
Saint-Étienne, 1894. 8°.   7958. bbb. 18.

ARNDT (A.) Bergbau und Bergbaupolitik.
pp. 247. 1894. 8°. FRANKENSTEIN (K.) Handbuch der Staatswissenschaften. Bd. 11. 8009. k.

AUSTRIA. *Congress der Berg- und Hüttenarbeiter.*
Verhandlungen des Kongresses. pp. 123.
Prag, 1891. 8°.   08276. f. 30.

BECK (W.) Deutsch-russisches technisches
Wörterbuch der Bergbau- und Hüttenkunde.
pp. 496. *St. Petersburg*, 1890. 8°. 12975. n. 4.

BRIDGMAN (H. L.) New system of Ore sampling.
pp. 24. *Chicago*, 1891. 8°. 07109. e. 23. (3.)

CHARLETON (A. G.) Choice of coarse and fine-
crushing machinery. pp. 386.
Lond. 1892–94. 8°.   07107. k. 1.

CHICAGO. *Columbian Exposition.* Official Catalogue. Part V. Mines and Mining. pp. 186.
Chicago, 1893. 8°.   7958. bb. 31.

COLLINS (J. H.) Principles of Metal Mining.
pp. 152. 1893. 8°. Collins' Elementary Science
Series.   8708. aaa.

DAVIES (E. H.) Machinery for Metalliferous
Mines. pp. 564. *Lond.* 1894. 8°. 8768. cc. 23.

DORION (C. J.) Exploitation des Mines. pp. 667.
1893. 8°. LECHALAS (M. C.) Encyclopédie des
travaux publics.   012216. i.

FOSTER (C. le N.) Text-book of Ore and Stone
Mining. pp. 744. *Lond.* 1894. 8°. 07108. g. 4.

GABBOTT (E. R.) How to Invest in Mines.
pp. 91. *Lond.* 1893. 8°.   7106. aa. 40.

MINERALOGY.—Mines, etc.—continued.

GORDON (H. A.) A Miners' Guide. pp. 276.
Wellington, 1869. 8°.   07109. h. 15.

HOPTON (W.) Conversation on Mines. pp. 356.
Manch. 1891. 8°.   7106. aa. 36.

—— Examination Questions on Mines and
Mining. pp. 93. Manch. 1892. 8°. 7108. aa. 1.

KLOSTERMANN (R.) Industria mineraria.
1886, 87. 8°. Biblioteca dell' Economista. Ser. 3.
Vol. 12.   8205. 1.

KOEHLER (G.) Katechismus der Bergbaukunde.
pp. 316. Leipz. 1891. 8°.   7106. a. 39.

LAUR (F.) Les Mines et usines en 1889.
pp. 598. Paris, 1890. 8°.   07109. h. 9.

LOCK (C. G. W.) Miners' Pocket-Book.
pp. 472. Lond. 1892. 8°.   7106. aa. 38.

—— Economic Mining. pp. 668.
Lond. 1895. 8°.   07107. g. 1.

LUPTON (A.) Mining. pp. 519. Lond. 1893. 8°.
          7106. ff. 19.

MATHIESON (F. C.) Monthly Mining Handbook.
Lond. 1895, etc. 8°.   8228. aaa.

MERIVALE (J. H.) Notes and Formulæ for
Mining Students. pp. 169. Lond. 1890. 8°.
          7108. a. 23.

MILNE (J.) The Miner's Handbook. pp. 304.
Lond. 1894. 8°.   7106. de. 5.

MOORE (C. W.) Guide for Prospectors, Explorers
and Miners. pp. 286. Lond. 1893. 8°.
          07109. h. 31.

ORIOL (R.) Contabilidad minera. pp. 87.
Madrid, 1891. fol.   7109. k. 18.

OSBORN (H. S.) Manual of Minerals, Mines and
Mining. pp. 369. Phila. 1895. 8°. 07107. h. 1.

—— Prospector's Field-book and Guide.
pp. 175. Phila. 1892. 8°.   7106. ff. 13.

PALACIO (M. E.) and MORA (A. P.) Manual del
Minero y Ensayador. pp. 281.
Caracas, 1892. 8°.   7106. f. 31.

P.P. New York. Engineering and Mining
Journal. The Mineral Industry.
N.Y. 1893, etc. 8°.   P.P. 2096. ba.

POWER (F. D.) Pocket-book for Miners.
pp. 334. Lond. 1892. 8°.   7109. aa. 23.

PUYJALON (H. de) Petit Guide du chercheur de
Minéraux. pp. 194. Montreal, 1892. 8°.
          7106. aa. 41.

SÉBILLOT (P.) Les Travaux publics et les Mines
dans les traditions et les superstitions. pp. 623.
Paris, 1894. 8°.   12431. k. 22.

SNELL (S.) Miners' Nystagmus. pp. 143.
Bristol, 1892. 8°.   8715. h. 25.

THOMPSON (S. P.) Electricity in Mining, 1891.
pp. 45. Lond. 1891. 8°.   Pam. 79.

VILLARS (E. de) Statistique des richesses minérales des états de l'Europe. pp. 251.
Paris, 1894. 4°.   7106. i. 20.

AGUILLON (L.) Législation des mines. 3 tom.
1891. 8°. Encyclopédie des travaux publics.
          012216. i.

WALMESLEY (O.) Guide to Mining Laws of the
world. pp. 331. Lond. 1894. 8°. 6005. h. 14.

See also BLASTING : METALS : for Coal, Gold
and Silver Mining, see COAL : GOLD AND
SILVER.

Mineralogy and Mines of Various Countries.

Africa.

CHURCHILL (Lord R. H. S.) Men, Mines and
Minerals in South Africa. pp. 337.
Lond. 1892. 8°.   010096. f. 28.

HANBURY (H.) Handbook of the Mining Companies of South Africa. pp. 55. 1893. 8°.
          08226. h. 27.

MINERALOGY.—Africa—continued.

PAPPA (D.) Manuel des sociétés minières du
Sud-Afrique. pp. 104. Paris, 1895. 8°.
          07109. h. 42.

RUGG (R.) Gold Fields and Mineral Resources
of Mashonaland. pp. 42. Lond. 1891. 8°.
          Pam. 27.

LONDON. International Exhibition of Mining,
1890. Official Handbook. Transvaal Republic.
Lond. 1890. 8°.   Pam. 89.

SOUTH AFRICAN REPUBLIC. Witwatersrand
Chamber of Mines. Annual Report.
Cape Town, 1891, etc. 8°.   7104. dd.

—— Laws having special reference to Gold
Fields and Mining Districts. pp. 233.
Johannesburg, 1892. 16°.   6606. a. 6.

See also GOLD AND SILVER.

Argentine Republic.

HOSKOLD (H. D.) Catálogo de las Muestras de
Minerales exhibidas en la Sección Argentina á
la Exposición de París, 1889. pp. 143.
Buenos Aires, 1889. 4°.   07109. k. 15.

RAMIREZ (P. P.) La Mineria en San Juan.
pp. 161. San Juan, 1889. 8°.   7106. ff. 16.

Australasia.

P.P. Sydney. Australian Mining Standard.
Sydney, 1890, etc. fol.   P.P. 9905. a.

ALDRIDGE (E. W.) Reports on the Aldridge
collection of mineral specimens at Broken Hill.
pp. 24. Broken Hill, 1892. 8°.
          07109. m. 3. (10.)

DE LISSA (A.) Companies' Work and mining
law in New South Wales and Victoria. pp. 454.
Lond. 1894. 8°.   6605. aa. 9.

ADELAIDE. South Australian School of Mines.
Annual Report. Adelaide, 1890, etc. 8°.
          7109. aaa.

BROWN (H. Y. L.) Record of the Mines of South
Australia. pp. 139. Adelaide, 1890. 8°.
          07109. h. 7.

—— Catalogue of South Australian Minerals.
pp. 34. Adelaide, 1893. 8°. 07109. e. 21. (15.)

CALVERT (A. F.) Mineral resources of Western
Australia. pp. 179. Lond. 1893. 8°.
          7106. aa. 42.

—— West Australian mining investors' handbook. pp. 150. Lond. 1894. 8°. 08226. f. 27.

LONDON. Exhibition of Mining. Western Australia. Catalogue of Exhibits of Mining and
Metallurgy. pp. 32. Perth, 1890. 8°. Pam. 27.

WOODWARD (H. P.) Mining Handbook to Western Australia. pp. 126. Perth, 1894. 8°.
          07108. g. 17.

DUNEDIN. Mining Conference. Papers read at
the Mining Conference. pp. 117.
Wellington, 1890. 8°.   7106. cc. 22.

See also GOLD AND SILVER.

Austria.

LEDERER (L.) Das österreichische Bergschaden-
recht. pp. 137. Berl. 1893. 8°. 5549. dd. 13.

KARPELES (B.) Moravian and Silesian Miners.
Lond. 1894, etc. 4°.   8223. df. 24.

British Columbia.

See infra : Canada.

Canada.

CANADA. Geological Survey. Catalogue of Section One of the Museum of the Geological Survey. pp. 256. Ottawa, 1893. 8°. 7104. dd. 7.

INGALL (E. D.) Division of mineral statistics
and mines. Report. 1891, etc. 8°. CANADA.
Geological Survey. Report. N.S. Vol. 5. 7202. d.

CANADA. Geological Survey. Mineral wealth of
British Columbia. pp. 163. Montreal, 1889. 8°.
          7109. g. 39.

MINERALOGY.—Canada—*continued.*

GILPIN (E.) Mines and mineral lands of Nova Scotia. pp. 129. *Halifax,* 1880. 8°. 07108. g. 3.

Chili.

CHILI. [*Laws, etc.*] Código de Minería. pp. 55. *Santiago,* 1889. 8°.   Pam. 33.

LARRAIN ZAÑARTU (J. J.) Comentarios del Código de Minería. pp. 244. *Santiago,* 1889. 8°.   6784. h. 9.

VALDÉS (S.) Informe sobre el estudio minero de la region comprendida entre el paralelo 23 i la Laguna de Ascotan. 2 pt. *Santiago,* 1887. 8° & fol.   7106. i. 19.

Colombia.

COLOMBIA. Mining Laws of Colombia. pp. 107. *N.Y.* 1892. 8°.   6616. cc. 4.

England.

BALDWIN (F. S.) Die englischen Bergwerksgesetze. pp. 258. 1894. 8°. BRENTANO (L.) Münchener volkswirtschaftliche Studien. St. 6.   08276. i.

ELLIS (T. R.) Miners' wages dispute, 1893. pp. 70. *Lond.* 1894. 8°.   08277. ff. 6.

HALLAM (W.) Miners' Leaders. pp. 118. *Lond.* 1894. 8°.   10803. aaa. 33.

HUME (W. F.) Chemical and micro-mineralogical Researches on the Upper Cretaceous Zones of the South of England. pp. 103. *Lond.* 1893. 8°.   7109. e. 21.

JAMES (C. A.) Mining Royalties. pp. 277. *Lond.* 1893. 4°.   08227. i. 17.

NASSE (R.) and KRUEMMER (G.) Die Bergarbeiter-Verhältnisse in Grossbritannien. pp. 176. *Saarbrücken,* 1891. 8°.   8276. dd. 12.

SMART (W.) Miners' Wages and the sliding scale. pp. 34. *Glasg.* 1894. 8°. 8282. ff. 12. (17.)

BURROW (J. C.) 'Mongst Mines and Miners; working in Cornish mines. pp. 32. *Lond.* 1893. 4°.   7105. e. 21.

PRICE (L. L. F. R.) West Barbary : notes on the system of work and wages in Cornish mines. pp. 91. *Lond.* 1891. 8°.   08276. g. 5.

See also COAL.

France.

AGUILLON (L.) Législation des Mines françaises. 3 tom. 1891. 8°. LECHALAS (M. C.) Encyclopédie des travaux publics.   012216. i.

FRANCE. *Ministère des Travaux Publics.* Notice sur le nombre, les salaires, et la durée du travail des Ouvriers des Mines, en 1890. pp. 27. *Paris,* 1891. 4°.   8282. h. 18.

LACROIX (A.) Minéralogie de la France et de ses colonies. *Paris,* 1893, *etc.* 8°. 7104. dd. 6.

VILLARS (E. de) Statistique des richesses minérales de la France. pp. 251. *Paris,* 1894. 4°.   7106. i. 20.

India.

TOWNSEND (C. C.) Mineral wealth of India. pp. 61. *Bombay,* 1891. 8°.   7108. de. 26.

Jamaica.

SCOTLAND (H.) Lectures on the Geology of, and mining in, Jamaica. 2 pt. *Jamaica,* 1890. 8°.   07109. h. 13.

Mashonaland. See supra : Africa.

Mexico.

RAMIREZ (S.) Noticia de la riqueza minera de México. pp. 768. *México,* 1884. 8°. 7108. d. 1.

See also MEXICO, *Trade.*

Moravia. See supra : Austria.

New South Wales. See supra : Australasia.

New Zealand. See supra : Australasia.

MINERALOGY—*continued.*

Norway. See infra : Sweden.

Nova Scotia. See supra : Canada.

Peru.

LIMA. *Escuela de Construcciones civiles.* Anales de Construcciones civiles y de Minas del Perú. 6 tom. *Lima,* 1880–87.   7106. ff. 27.

Queensland. See supra : Australasia.

Roumania.

CREMÉR (H. H.) Études sur la Richesse minérale de la Roumanie. pp. 72. *Bucareste,* 1890. 8°.   07109. h. 22.

Scotland.

STEWART (D. R.) Treatise on the law relating to Mines in Scotland. pp. 442. *Edinb.* 1894. 8°.   6573. h. 8.

See also supra : England. COAL.

Spain.

BASTERRA (M. de) Vizcaya minera. pp. 362. *Bilbao,* 1894. 8°.   10161. d. 4.

VILLASANTE Y GÓMEZ (F. B.) La Industria minero-metalúrgica en Mazarrón. pp. 252. *Cartagena,* 1892. 8°.   7105. dd. 1.

—— Atlas. fol.   7105. i. 7.

Sweden and Norway.

SJÖGREN (S. A. H.) Contributions to Swedish Mineralogy. 1893, *etc.* 8°. Ac. Upsal. *R. Academia Geol. Instit.* Bulletin, *etc.* Vol. 1.   Ac. 1077/3.

HELLAND (A.) Norsk Bergret. pp. 618. *Kristiania,* 1892. 8°.   5725. c. 8.

Transvaal. See supra : Africa : GOLD.

United States of America.

DAY (D. T.) Report on mineral industries in the United States, 1890. pp. 858. 1892. 8°. U.S.A. *Census.* Eleventh census. Report.   1882. c.

KEMP (J. F.) Ore Deposits of the United States. pp. 302. *N.Y.* 1893. 8°.   07109. h. 39.

U.S.A. *Geological Survey.* Mineral Resources of the United States. *Wash.* 1883, *etc.* 8°.   1829. a. 8.

MELVILLE (W. H.) Contributions to the mineralogy of the Pacific Coast. 1890. 8°. U.S.A. *Geological Survey.* Bulletin. No. 61. 7109. cc.

CHICAGO. *Columbian Exposition.* Arizona. Mineral Exhibit. *Chicago,* 1893. fol. Pam. 18.

GENTH (F. A.) Minerals of North Carolina. pp. 119. 1891. 8°. U.S. *Geological Survey.* Bulletin. No. 74.   1829. a. 7.

COLORADO. Mines and mining men of Colorado. pp. 118. *Denver,* 1893. obl. 4°.   1824. a. 3.

KANSAS. Mineral resources of Kansas. pp. 23. *Chicago,* 1893. 8°.   Pam. 27.

OWEN (R. E.) and COX (E. T.) Report on the mines of New Mexico. pp. 59. *Wash.* 1885. 8°.   Pam. 27.

ROBIN (G. E.) Mineral resources of Sierra County, New Mexico. pp. 21. *St. Louis,* 1893. 8°.   Pam. 86.

See also GOLD AND SILVER.

Uruguay.

LONDON. *Exhibition of Mining.* Origin of the auriferous region of Tacuarembo. 2 pt. *Lond.* 1890. 8°.   07109. h. 5.

Venezuela.

VENEZUELA. Código de Minas. pp. 67. *Caracas,* 1891. 8°.   Pam. 33.

MINIATURES. *See* ILLUMINATIONS.

MINISTERS, of State. *See* GOVERNMENT.

MINNEAPOLIS

MINNEAPOLIS. HUDSON (H. B.) Directory of Minneapolis. pp. 110. *Minneapolis,* 1893. 8°.
10413. aaa. 20.

MINNEAPOLIS. Report of the trade and commerce of Minneapolis. *Minneapolis,* 1893. 8°.
8248. dd. 6.

STEVENS (J. H.) Personal recollections of Minnesota and early history of Minneapolis. pp. 432. *Minneapolis,* 1890. 8°. 10412. dd. 24.

MINNESINGERS. *See* POETRY, *Germany.*

MINNESOTA. ANDREWS (C. C.) Minnesota farmers, who are making money. pp. 18.
· *St. Paul,* 1893. 8°. 7030. g. 6. (11.)

MINNESOTA. Minnesota: brief sketch of its history, etc. pp. 123. *St. Paul,* 1893. 8°.
10412. d. 34.

—— Minnesota in the Civil and Indian Wars, 1861–65. *St Paul,* 1891, 93. 8°. 9605. ff. 11.

PYLE (J. G.) The Farmer's Opportunity.
pp. 104. *St. Paul,* 1891. 8°. Pam. 86.

STEVENS (J. H.) Personal Recollections of Minnesota. pp. 432. *Minneapolis,* 1890. 8°.
10412. dd. 24.

MINORCA. *See* BALEARIC ISLES.

MINORITES. *See* FRANCISCAN ORDER.

MIRACLE-PLAYS. ANRICH (G.) Das antike Mysterienwesen in seinem Einfluss auf das Christentum. pp. 237.
Göttingen, 1894. 8°. 4503. cc. 23.

BATES (K. L.) The English Religious drama. pp. 254. *N.Y.* 1893. 8°. 011795. h. 8.

DAVIDSON (C.) Studies in the English Mystery plays. pp. 173. 1892. 8°. 011795. f. 39.

GASTÉ (A.) Les Drames liturgiques de la Cathédrale de Rouen. pp. 81.
Évreux, 1893. 8°. 011795. i. 4.

PIOLIN (P. L.) Le Théâtre chrétien dans le Maine au moyen âge. pp. 204.
Mamers, 1891. 8°. 011795. g. 20.

POLLARD (A. W.) English Miracle plays. pp. 250. *Oxf.* 1895. 8°. 2306. b. 1.

SCHWARTZ (R.) Esther im deutschen und neulateinischen Drama des Reformationszeitalters. pp. 276. *Oldenburg,* 1894. 8°. 011850. i. 51.

WECHSSLER (E.) Die romanischen Marienklagen. pp. 104. *Halle a. S.* 1893. 8°. 11794. f. 41.

Ac. London. *Early English Text Society.* Extra Series. LXII. The Chester Plays.
Lond. 1893, etc. 8°. Ac. 9926/35.

DEIMLING (H. W. E.) Text-Gestalt und Kritik der Chester Plays. pp. 32. *Berl.* 1890. 8°.
011824. h. 28. (4.)

UNGEMACH (H.) Die Quellen der fünf ersten Chester Plays. pp. 198. 1890. 8°. BREYMANN (H.) Münchener Beiträge. Hft. 1. 011824. i.

ELCKERLIJK. Elckerlijk, fifteenth century Dutch morality and Everyman. Edited by Dr. H. Logeman. pp. 97. 1892. 8°. Ac. Ghent. *Université.* Recueil de travaux. Fasc. 5.
Ac. 2647/3.

Ac. London. *Roxburghe Club.* Le Livre et Mistère de Saint Adrien. pp. 206.
Macon, 1895. 4°. Ac. 8104/110.

LAWRENCE, *Saint.* Le Mystère de Saint Laurent. 1891. 4°. Ac. Helsingfors. *Societas Scientiarum.* Acta. Tom. 18. Ac. 1094/2.

PRA (S.) Le Mystère des Trois Doms. pp. 928. *Lyon,* 1887. 4°. 11735. l. 1.

SEPET (M.) Le Miracle de Théophile. pp. 33. *Paris,* 1894. 8°. 11826. i. 42. (10.)

REDENTIN EASTER PLAY. Die Handschrift des redentiner Osterspiels. pp. 47. ff. 12.
Schwerin, 1892. 4°. 11746. k. 23.

MISSIONS

MIRACLE-PLAYS—*continued.*
SCHMIDT-WARTENBERG (H. M.) Ein tiroler Passionsspiel des Mittelalters. pp. 127. 1890. 8°. Ac. United States. *Modern Language Association.* Publications. Vol. v. No. 3. Ac. 2683/2.

See also DRAMA : OBER-AMMERGAU.

MIRACLES. GONDAL (I. L.) Le Miracle. pp. 216. *Paris,* 1894. 12°. 3900. bb. 52.

GORDON (A. J.) The Ministry of Healing. pp. 283. *Lond.* 1882. 8°. 4018. aa. 21.

LAIDLAW (J.) The Miracles of our Lord. pp. 888. *Lond.* 1890. 8°. 4227. h. 15.

MUELLER (F. M.) Anthropological Religion.· pp. 464. *Lond.* 1892. 8°. 2208. d 2.

DICKSON (W. P.) Prof. M. Muller's Preface on "Miracles." pp. 22. *Glasg.* 1892. 8°.
4371. dd. 8. (6.)

PAUL (C. K.) Miracle. pp. 24.
Lond. 1892. 8°. Pam. 78.

RUSDEN (H. K.) Science and Miracles. pp. 16. *Melbourne,* 1882. 8°. 4371. b. 27. (3.)

TAYLOR (W. M.) The Miracles of Our Saviour expounded. pp. 449. *Lond.* 1891. 8°.
4227. h. 19.

WYLD (G.) Miracles as not contrary to nature, etc. pp. 18. *Lond.* 1892. 8° 4018. bb. 42. (7.)

IMBERT-GOUBEYRE (A.) La Stigmatisation, l'extase divine et les miracles de Lourdes. 2 tom. *Clermont-Ferrand,* 1894. 8°. 4824. de. 7.

LOTH (A.) Le Miracle en France au dix-neuvième siècle. pp. 366. *Lille,* 1894. 8°.
4630. f. 8.

See also CHRISTIANITY: LOURDES: PARAY-LE-MONIAL : TREVES.

MIRANDA. *See* VENEZUELA.

MIRI LANGUAGE. NEEDHAM (J. F.) Grammar of the Shaíyâng Miri language. pp. 157. *Shillong,* 1886. 8°. 12906. dd. 40.

MISIONES. NIEDERLEIN (G.) Mis exploraciones en el territorio de Misiones, etc. *Buenos A.* 1891, etc. 8°. 10481. i.

See also ARGENTINE REPUBLIC.

MISREPRESENTATION, Law of. *See* FRAUD.

MISSIONS, Foreign.

Bibliography.

JACKSON (S. M.) Bibliography of Foreign Missions. 1891. 8°. Encyclopædia of Missions. Vol. 1. 4766. g. 6.

SCOTLAND, *Free Church. Foreign Missions Committee.* Reference Library of the Committee. pp. 68. *Edinb.* 1891. 8°. 11903. b. 43. (4.)

General.

ADDRESSES. Addresses on intercessory prayer for Foreign Missions. pp. 73. *Lond.* 1895. 8°.
4399. cc. 8.

AFRICA. *Church Missionary Society.* Missionary motives, commands, calls, prayers and recompenses. pp. 32. *Lond.* 1890. 8°. Pam. 75.

—— Monthly missionary letter to Sunday Schools. *Lond.* 1889, etc. 8°. 4765. dd.

—— Pocket Manual of the C.M.S.
Lond. 1884, etc. 8°. 4766. aaa.

ALLEMAND-LAVIGERIE (C. M.) *Cardinal.* La nouvelle Loi militaire et les missions françaises à l'étranger. pp. 67. *Alger,* 1889. 8°. Pam. 40.

ANSON (*Hon.* A. J. R.) *Bp. of Qu' Appelle.* The Need of brotherhood for Mission-Work. pp. 20. *Lond.* 1893. 8°. Pam. 40.

ARDEN (A. H.) The Church Missionary Society. pp. 8. 1889. 8°. Pam. 40.

MISSIONS.—Foreign—continued.

B-G., B. Church Missionary Society. Motives for taking part in the evangelization of the world. pp. 8. Lond. 1892. 8°. Pam. 40.

BRAITHWAITE (A.) What can I do? Paper on "The deepening of our interest in Foreign Mission work. pp. 14 Bristol, 1887. 8°.
4766. aa. 8. (2.)

BROOMHALL (B.) Evangelisation of the world. pp. 258. Lond. 1894, 8°. 4766. g. 9.

BUCKLAND (A. R.) The heroic in Missions. pp. 112. Lond. 1894. 8°. 4767. bbb. 10.

CAIRNS (H. M. C.) Earl Cairns. Speech on the claims of the Heathen and Mohammedan world. pp. 15. Lond. 1885. 8°. 4766. aa. 8. (1.)

CANDIDATES-IN-WAITING. Candidates-in-Waiting: manual of home preparation for foreign missionary work. pp. 128. Lond. 1892. 16°.
4499. a. 31.

CANTERBURY, Province of. Reports of the Board of Missions. Lond. 1894, etc. 8°. 4429. dd.

CAREY (W.) Enquiry into the obligations of Christians, to use means for the conversion of the Heathen. pp. 87. Lond. 1891. 8°.
4765. ee. 22.

CHURTON (E. T.) Bp. of Nassau. The Missionary's foundation of Doctrine. pp. 299. Lond. 1890. 8°.
3554. ee. 1.

COWEN (B. R.) The Miracle of the Nineteenth Century. pp. 49. N.Y. 1891. 8°. Pam. 40.

CROIL (J.) The Noble Army of martyrs and roll of Protestant missionary martyrs. pp. 175. Phila. 1894. 8°. 4804. aa. 25.

CROMBIE (A.) Missionary Stories. Lond. 1892, etc. 8°. 4766. g. 7.

CUST (R. N.) Essay on the prevailing methods of the Evangelization of the non-Christian World. pp. 296. Lond. 1894. 8°. 4767. d. 15.

DENNIS (J. S.) Foreign Missions after a century. pp. 368. Edinb. 1894. 8°. 4765. bbb. 43.

EDWARDS (F.) Foreign Missions and Christian union. pp. 26. Lond. 1892. 8°. Pam. 40.

ENCYCLOPÆDIAS. Encyclopædia of Missions. 2 vol. N.Y. 1891. 8°. 4766. g. 6.

ENGLAND, Ch. of. Official report of the Missionary Conference of the Anglican Communion, 1896. pp. 720. Lond. 1894. 8°. 4429. dd. 8.

FORTS. Forts of Darkness and soldiers of light. pp. 104. Lond. 1895. 4°. 4766. e. 33.

GIBSON (A. G. S.) Missionary Work. pp. 43. Lond. 1893. 8°. Pam. 40.

GOLLOCK (G. A.) Light on our Lessons; or "What is the use?" pp. 88. Lond. 1892. 8°.
4765. e. 21.

GORDON (A. J.) The Holy Spirit in missions. pp. 241. Lond. 1893. 8°. 4767. ccc. 21.

GOULD (M. E. B.) Missionary Alphabet. pp. 36. Lond. 1894. 8°. 4766. ff. 31.

HODDER (E.) Conquests of the Cross. 3 vol. Lond. 1890. 8°. 4766. h. 2.

HORNE (C. S.) Story of the London Missionary Soc. pp. 444. Lond. 1894. 8°. 4676. de. 1.

HORSBURGH (J. H.) "Do not Say"; or, the Church's excuses for neglecting the heathen. pp. 56. Lond. 1891. 8°. Pam. 40.

JOHN (G.) Spiritual power for Missionary Work. pp. 43. Lucknow, 1888. 8°. Pam. 40.

JOHNSTON (J.) Missionary Points and pictures. pp. 127. Lond. 1892. 8°. 4765. de. 12.

KRUIJF (E. F.) Geschiedenis van het Nederlandsche Zendelingsgenootschap. pp. 695. Groningen, 1894. 8°. 4766. ff. 32.

LANDMARK (N.) Det norske Missionsselskab. pp. 320. Kristiania, 1889. 8°. 4766. ff. 25.

MISSIONS.—Foreign—continued.

LAUNAY (A.) Histoire de la Société des Missions-étrangères. 3 tom. Paris, 1894. 8°.
4766. e. 34.

LIGHTFOOT (J. B.) Bp. of Durham. Historical Essays. pp. 245. Lond. 1895. 8°. 2216. d. 1.

LEONARD (D. L.) A hundred years of missions. pp. 430. N.Y. 1895. 8°. 4765. de. 20.

LONDON. S.P.G. Digest of the Records of the Society. pp. 980. Lond. 1893. 8°. 4766. e. 31.

—— Baptist Missionary Society. Centenary celebration of the Baptist Missionary Society, 1892-3. pp. 727. Lond. 1893. 8°. 4765. ee. 27.

—— Centenary volume of the Society. pp. 344. Lond. 1892. 8°. 4765. df. 31.

TITTERINGTON (S. B.) A Century of Baptist Foreign Missions. pp. 300. Phila. 1891. 8°.
4767. c. 32.

LONDON. Wesleyan Missionary Society. The Missionary Controversy, 1890. pp. 388. Lond. 1890. 8°. 4766. e. 16.

TELFORD (J.) Pages from the lives of Methodist missionaries. pp. 191. Lond. 1895. 8°.
4767. bbb. 13.

MACLAREN (A.) The True source of Missionary zeal. pp. 52. Lond. 1894. 8°. Pam. 40.

MASON (G. E.) Round the World on a Church Mission. pp. 379. Lond. 1892. 8°. 4429. b. 18.

MILLARD (E. C.) What God hath wrought. Account of the Mission tour of the Rev. G. C. Grubb. pp. 382. Lond. 1891. 8°. 4765. ee. 21.

MISSIONARY BIRTHDAY BOOK. Missionary Birthday book. Lond. 1894. 8°. 4429. de. 43.

MISSIONS. Foreign Missions and home calls. pp. 102. Lond. 1893. 8°. 4766. b. 36.

—— Are Foreign Missions doing any good? pp. 124. Lond. 1894. 8°. 4766. b. 37.

MONOD (G.) Comment la Société des Missions évangéliques de Paris est en voie d'être dotée de la maison qu'elle souhaitait. pp. 24. Paris, 1887. 8°. Pam. 40.

NEURDENBURG (J. C.) De christelijke Zending der Nederlanders in de 17de en 18de eeuw. pp. 194. Rotterdam, 1891. 8°. 4685. g. 10.

OUTLINE MISSIONARY SERIES. Outline Missionary Series. Lond. 1881, etc. 8°. 4666. cc.

PATERSON (J. G.) Sowing beside all waters. pp. 102. Glasg. 1891. 4°. 4767. cc. 1.

P.P. London. Awake! A record of missionary work. Lond. 1891, etc. 4°. P.P. 952. ee. and 678.

—— The Missions of the world. Lond. 1894, etc. 4°. P.P. 952. fa. & 2241.

PERRY (W. S.) Bp. of Iowa. Why Not? [on the American Church Missionary Society.] pp. 8. Davenport, 1891. 12°. Pam. 40.

PIERSON (A. T.) The greatest Work in the world. pp 62. Lond. 1891. 8°. 4766. bb. 55.

—— The Miracles of Missions. pp. 193. Lond. 1891. 8°. 4767. cc. 3.

—— The Divine enterprise of Missions. pp. 333. Lond. 1892. 8°. 4767. bbb. 1.

—— The new acts of the Apostles. pp. 451. Lond. 1894. 8°. 4767. ccc. 22.

—— The Evangelisation of the world. pp. 31. Lond. 1894. 8°. Pam. 40.

PLITT (G. L.) Geschichte der lutherischen Mission. Leipz. 1894, etc. 8°. 4662. ee.

ROOKER (J.) A Missionary criticized by an outsider. pp 15. Lond. 1891. 8°. Pam. 40.

ROUVIER (F.) Loin du Pays. Les religieux français. pp. 407. Paris, 1895. 12°. 4767. bb. 26.

RUGG (H. W.) Our Word and work for Missions. Universalist Church Missions. pp. 254. Bost. 1894. 8°. 4767. f. 7.

MISSIONS.—Foreign—*continued.*

SCOTT (J. E.) Observations of an Itinerant. pp. 126. *Calcutta*, 1888. 8°.   4767. bb. 21.

SIMPSON (A. B.) Larger outlooks on Missionary Lands. pp. 595. *N.Y.* 1894. 8°.   4766. d. 40.

THOBURN (J. M.) Missionary Comity. pp. 14. *Bombay*, 1893. 8°.   Pam. 40.

THOMAS (J. W.) Statistical Tables of 1890. pp. 12. 2. *Calcutta*, 1892. 8°.   Pam. 40.

TISDALL (W. S. C.) "Diex li Vuelt!" Plea for an extension of mission work in Muhammadan lands. pp. 22. *Lond.* 1891. 8°.   Pam. 40.

TRICHT (V. v.) Les Missions belges. pp. 52. *Namur*, 1893. 8°.   Pam. 40.

TUCKER (A. B.) Witnesses of these Things. pp. 80. *Lond.* 1892. 8°.   4465. d. 22.

VAHL (J.) Missions to the heathen. *Copenh.* 1892, *etc.* 8°.   4766. ee.

WILLIAMS (T. L.) Bearers of the Lamp of Grace. pp. 181. *Lond.* 1894. 8°.   4903. ee. 42.

WISHARD (L. D.) New Programme of Missions. *N.Y.* 1895. 8°.   4767. aaa. 18.

WISSMANN (H. v.) Antwort auf den Brief des Dr. Warneck über die Thätigkeit der Missionen beider christlichen Confessionen. pp. 52. *Berl.* 1890. 8°.   Pam. 40.

DOWKONTT (G. D.) Murdered Millions. Need of medical missions. pp. 92. *Lond.* 1894. 8°.
7688. a. 55.

THOMSON (W. B.) Reminiscences of Medical Missionary work. pp. 248. *Lond.* 1895. 8°.
4192. cc. 34.

BUCKLAND (A. R.) Women in the Mission Field. pp. 122. *Lond.* 1895. 8°.   4767. bbb. 18.

ENSOR (G.) Help these Women. Church Zenana Missionary Society. pp. 15. *Lond.* 1894. 16°.
Pam. 40.

P.P. *London.* The Zenana, or, Woman's work in London. *Lond.* 1893, *etc.* 8°.
P.P. 982. bc. and 2220.

—— *Paisley.* The Helpmeet : record of woman's work in heathen lands. *Paisley*, 1891, *etc.* 12°.
P.P. 1030. bg and 298.

PITMAN (E. R.) Missionary Heroines in eastern Lands. pp. 160. *Lond.* 1895. 8°.   4767. c. 39.

TELFORD (J.) Women in the Mission field. pp. 192. *Lond.* 1895. 8°.   4767. bb. 14.

Africa.

CUST (R. N.) Africa Rediviva. pp. 118. *Lond.* 1891. 8°.   4765. e. 20.

HUGHES (W.) Dark Africa and the way out. pp. 155. *Lond.* 1892. 8°.   4767. ccc. 12.

KLEIN (F.) Le Cardinal Lavigerie et ses œuvres d'Afrique. pp. 418. *Paris*, 1890. 12°.
4856. aa. 14.

RICARD (A.) Le Cardinal Lavigerie. pp. 494. *Paris*, 1893. 8°.   4863. de. 13.

MACDONALD (J.) Light in Africa. pp. 263. *Lond.* 1890. 8°.   4766. e. 22.

MOFFAT (R.) Rivers of Water in a dry place. pp. 224. *Lond.* 1892. 8°.   4429. df. 26.

P.P. *Berlin.* Afrika. *Berl.* 1894, *etc.* 8°.
P.P. 932. gb.

—— *Vineland. New Jersey.* The African News. *Vineland*, 1891, *etc.* 8°.   P.P. 1047. bh.

PRATS (J. de) L'Église africaine, ancienne et moderne. pp. 192. *Tours*, 1892. 12°.
4534. ee. 13.

YOUNG (R.) Trophies from African heathenism. pp. 218. *Lond.* 1892. 8°.   4767. c. 31.

Central and East.

AFRICA. *Church Missionary Society.* Eastern Equatorial Africa Mission. pp. 106. *Lond.* 1891. 8°.   4766. bbb. 49.

MISSIONS.—Africa—*continued.*

BERGHEGGE (F.) Verslag eener Reis in midden Afrika. pp. 28. *'s Gravenh.* 1882. 8°. Pam. 89.

BOURNICHON (J.) L'Invasion musulmane en Afrique suivie du réveil de la Foi chrétienne dans ces contrées. pp. 351. *Tours*, 1890. fol.
9061. h. 5.

KORNRUMPF (F.) Die Anfänge der evangelischen Mission in Deutsch-Ost-Afrika. pp. 28. *Berl.* 1891. 8°.   Pam. 40.

LORIOT (C. F.) Explorations et missions dans l'Afrique équatoriale. pp. 375. *Paris*, 1890. 12°.
10097. cc. 17.

H., J. W. Story of the life of Mackay of Uganda. pp. 338. *Lond.* 1891. 8°.   4955. ee. 21.

M., J. L'Ouganda, la mission catholique, et les agents de la compagnie anglaise. pp. 326. *Paris*, 1893. 8°.   4766. ee. 23.

MACKAY (A. M.) A. Mackay : Missionary hero of Uganda. pp. 144. *Lond.* 1894. 8°.
4955. df. 1.

PRICE (W. S.) My third Campaign in East Africa. pp. 339. *Lond.* 1890. 8°. 4767. ccc. 8.

RICHTER (J.) Uganda, *etc.* pp. 268. *Gütersloh*, 1893. 8°.   4766. ee. 22.

STOCK (S. G.) The Story of Uganda. pp. 224. *Lond.* 1894. 8°.   4429. eee. 30.

TUCKER (A. R.) *Bp. of Eastern Equatorial Africa.* African Sketches : Uganda and the way thither. *Lond.* 1892. *obl.* 4°.   10096. i. 4.

MECHLIN. *Institut africain des Pères Blancs.* Près du Tanganika. pp. 103. *Anvers*, 1892. 8°.
Pam. 40.

NYASSALAND. *Livingstonia Mission.* The Lake regions of Central Africa. *Glasg.* 1891, *etc.* 8°.
4765. ee.

RICHTER (J.) Evangelische Mission im Nyassa-Lande. pp. 177. *Berl.* 1892. 8°. 4767. ccc. 11.

ROBERTSON (W.) Martyrs of Blantyre. pp. 150. *Lond.* 1892. 8°.   4955. bbb. 45.

South.

AFRICA, *South. Wesleyan Methodist Church.* Report of the S. African Missionary Society. *Cape Town*, 1893, *etc.* 8°.   4767. ccc.

CAPE TOWN. Christian Mission Home, established by the evangelical churches of Cape Town. *Cape Town*, 1893, *etc.* 8°.   4192. bbb.

COOK (T.) My mission tour in S. Africa. pp. 154. *Lond.* 1895. 8°.   4767. d. 12.

MACKENZIE (J.) London Missionary Society in S. Africa. pp. 21. *Lond.* 1888. 8°. Pam. 40.

MARRAT (J.) Missionary veterans in South Africa. pp. 176. *Lond.* 1894. 8°. 4766. b. 38.

P.P. *Cape Town.* South African Pioneer. *Cape Town*, 1890, *etc.* 4°. P.P. 952. o. & 1361.

—— South African Catholic magazine. *Cape Town*, 1891, *etc.* 8°.   P.P. 910. fg.

GIBSON (A. G. S.) Eight years in Kaffraria. pp. 178. *Lond.* 1891. 8°.   4766. cc. 33.

ASTRUP (N.) En Missionsreise til Limpopo gjennem Zululand, *etc.* pp. 206. *Kristiania*, 1891. 8°.   4766. e. 28.

LONDON. *MacKenzie Memorial Mission to Zululand.* Report. *Derby*, 1889, *etc.* 8°. 4767. ccc.

WIDDICOMBE (J.) Fourteen years in Basutoland. pp. 306. *Lond.* 1892. 8°.   4767. bbb. 6.

—— In the Lesuto : sketch of African mission life. pp. 352. *Lond.* 1895. 8°.   4430. b. 37.

BRUCE (G. W. H. K.) *Bp. of Mashonaland.* Journals of the Mashonaland mission. pp. 99. *Lond.* 1893. 8°.   4767. dd. 5.

CARNEGIE (D.) Among the Matabele. pp. 128. *Lond.* 1895. 8°.   4767. c. 37.

MISSIONS.—Africa—continued.
West.

CROWTHER (S. A.) *Bp. of the Niger Territory.* Experiences with heathens and Mohammedans in W. Africa. pp. 60. *Lond.* 1892. 8°. 4429. aa. 42.

—— Bishop Crowther : his life and work. pp. 55. *Lond.* 1892. 8°. 4906. bbb. 51. (8.)

EUCHER (F.) Le Congo. Essai sur l'histoire religieuse de ce pays. pp. 264. *Huy,* 1894. 8°. 4765. df. 34.

FERNANDO PO. Memoria de las misiones de Fernando Póo. pp. 102. *Madrid,* 1890. 8°. Pam. 40.

HILL (J. S.) |*Bp. in Western Equatorial Africa.* The West African mission field. pp. 20. *Lond.* 1893. 8°. Pam. 40.

INNES (A.) More Light. The Cameroons and the Baptist mission. pp. 73. *Liverp.* 1895. 8°. 4765. df. 33.

MILUM (J.) Freeman, Missionary pioneer to Ashanti. pp. 160. *Lond.* 1893. 8°. 4905. de. 43.

MYERS (J. B.) The Congo for Christ. pp. 163. *Lond.* 1895. 8°. 4767. bbb. 15.

P.P. *London.* The Sierre Leone messenger. *Lond.* 1893, *etc.* 8°. P.P. 1020. c.

America, South.

CARDÚS (J.) Las Misiones franciscanas entre los infieles de Bolivia, 1883–84. pp. 429. *Barcelona,* 1886. 8°. 4767. dd. 9.

MILLARD (E. C.) and GUINNESS (L. E.) South America : the neglected continent. pp. 182. *Lond.* 1894. 8°. 4767. aaa. 15.

MONNER SANS (R.) Misiones guaraníticas, 1607–1800. pp. 232. *Buenos A.* 1892. 8°. 4767. c. 34.

Annam. *See infra : Indo-China.*

Australasia.

LONDON. *London Missionary Society.* Ten Decades. Australian Centenary story. pp. 208. *Lond.* 1895. 8°. 4767. c. 14.

PAGE (J.) Among the Maoris. pp. 160. *Lond.* 1894. 8°. 4767. bbb. 12.

CHALMERS (J.) Pioneer life in New Guinea, 1877–94. pp. 255. *Lond.* 1895. 8°. 4429. k 9.

Burma. *See infra : Indo-China.*

Ceylon. *See infra : India.*

China.

BEAUCHAMP (M.) Days of blessing in inland China. pp. 198. *Lond.* 1890. 8°. 4767. bbb. 9.

BRYSON (M. I.) The Story of J. Gilmour and the Mongol mission. pp. 144. *Lond.* 1894. 8°. 4920. de. 16.

—— F. C. Roberts of Tientsin. pp. 222. *Lond.* 1895. 8°. 4906. df. 29.

CHINA. Church Work in North China. pp. 113. *Lond.* 1891. 8°. 4429. aa. 29.

CHRISTIE (D) Ten years in Manchuria. pp. 100. *Paisley,* 1895. 8°. 4767. bb. 23.

GUINNESS (M. G.) Story of the China inland mission. 2 vol. *Lond.* 1893. 8°. 4767. d. 14.

GUIOT (L.) La Mission du Su-Tchuen au XVIIIᵉ siècle. pp. 521. *Paris,* 1892. 8°. 4765. ee. 23.

GUZMAN (L. de) Historia de las misiones de la Compañía de Jesus en la India y China. pp. 674. *Bilbao,* 1891. 8°. 4766. h. 3.

HONGKONG. *Séminaire des Missions Étrangères.* Cérémonial du Séminaire. Sous-diacre. pp. 43. *Hongkong,* 1891. 8°. Pam. 75.

LAUNAY (A.) Les cinquante-deux Serviteurs de Dieu mis à mort pour la foi en Extrême-Orient, 1815–56. 2 tom. *Paris,* 1893. 8°. 4804. h. 4.

MISSIONS.—China—continued.

MICHIE (A.) Missionaries in China. pp. 107. *Lond.* 1891. 8°. 4767. ccc. 10.

MOULE (A. E.) China as a Mission field. pp. 80. *Lond.* 1891. 8°. Pam. 40.

PITCHER (P. W.) Fifty years in Amoy. pp. 207. *N.Y.* 1893. 8°. 4767. d. 16.

TAYLOR (J. H.) China's spiritual Need. pp. 95. *Lond.* 1890. 8°. 4766. i. 1.

—— Consecration and blessing in a Chinese City. pp. 19. *Lond.* 1894. 8°. Pam. 40.

TSCHHONGLOK MOUNTAINS. Das Evangelium unter den Bauern der Tschhonglok-Berge. pp. 32. *Basel,* 1890. 8°. Pam. 40.

TURNER (J. A.) Kwang Tung ; Five years in South China. pp. 192. *Lond.* 1894. 8°. 4767. bbb. 11.

WILLIAMS (F. M.) A New Thing. Incidents of missionary life in China. pp. 429. *Lond.* 1895. 8°. 4765. bb. 43.

Corea.

P.P. *London.* The Morning Calm. Magazine of Bishop Corfe's Mission to Korea. No. 1–33. *Lond.* 1890–93. 8°. P.P. 951. e.

RAMAGET (T.) Vie de M.-L. Huin décapité pour la foi, en Corée, 1866. pp. 364. *Langres,* 1893. 8°. 4864. e. 24.

Greenland.

PAGE (J.) Amid Greenland snows. pp. 160. *Lond.* 1893. 8°. 4767. bbb. 8.

India and Ceylon.

SMITH (G.) The Conversion of India. pp. 258. *Lond.* 1893. 8°. 4767. dd. 4.

—— H. Martyn, first modern missionary to the Mohammedans. pp. 580. *Lond.* 1892. 8°. 4429. f. 2.

CAREY (W.) Serampore Letters. pp. 150. *N.Y.* 1892. 8°. 4765. df. 26.

MONTEFIORE (A.) R. Heber, Bishop of Calcutta. pp. 160. *Lond.* 1894. 8°. 4905. e. 53.

SMITH (G.) Bishop Heber. pp. 370. *Lond.* 1895. 8°. 4905. df. 24.

BIRKS (H. A.) Life and correspondence of T. V. French, first Bishop of Lahore. 2 vol. *Lond.* 1895. 8°. 4906. h. 26.

————

ABHISHEKANATHAN (S.) Christianity : its relation to the Tamils. pp. 29. *Madras,* 1890. 8°. Pam. 40.

AFRICA. *Church Missionary Society.* The Bengal mission. pp. 20. *Lond.* 1892. 8°. Pam. 40.

—— The hill tribes of India. pp. 48. *Lond.* 1891. 8°. Pam. 40.

BARRY (A.) *Bp. of Sydney.* England's mission to India. pp. 214. *Lond.* 1895. 8°. 4429. a. 103.

BOOTH-TUCKER (F. de L.) Darkest India. pp. 7. 155. *Bombay,* 1891. 8°. 4766. e. 25.

CALCUTTA. *Missionary Conference.* Statistical tables of Protestant missions in India, Burma and Ceylon. pp. 66. *Calcutta,* 1892. 8°. 4766. g. 10.

CEYLON. *Wesleyan Mission.* Messages from the front. pp. 63. *Colombo,* 1893. 8°. 4767. ccc. 19.

DALHOFF (N.) Den nordiske Santhalmission 1867–92. pp. 150. *Kjøbenh.* 1892. 8°. 4767. dd. 6.

DOWNIE (D.) The Lone Star. History of the Telugu mission. pp. 232. *Phila.* 1893. 8°. 4765. de. 17.

FIELDE (A. M.) Pagoda Shadows. pp. 285. *Bost.* 1890. 8°. 10058. aa. 38.

GRUNDEMANN (R.) Missions-Studien in Verbindung mit einer Reise nach Indien. pp. 216. *Gütersloh,* 1894. 8°. 4766. e. 27.

MISSIONS.—India and Ceylon—cont.

JAFFNA. *Native Missionary Association.* Annual Report. *Jaffna*, 1892, *etc.* 8°.   4767. aaa.

KADIRVELU, C. Christianity in India. pp. 118. *Madras*, 1894. 8°.   4767. dd. 7.

MACPHAIL (J. M.) Three months in camp among the Sautals. pp. 158. *Pokhuria*, 1893. 8°.   4765. df. 30.

MURDOCH (J.) Indian Missionary manual. pp. 535. *Lond.* 1895. 8°.   4767. bbb. 17.

MURRAY (J. R.) Hindu Pastors. pp. 79. *Manch.* 1892. 8°.   4767. c. 29.

P.P. *London.* The dawn in India. Organ of the Christian Literature Society for India. *Lond.* 1892, *etc.* 8°.   2135.

—— Darkness and Light. Monthly paper of the Ceylon and Indian General Mission. *Lond.* 1894, *etc.* 8°.   P.P. 982. bb 2232.

—— Occasional paper of the Ceylon and Indian [General Mission. *Lond.* 1893. 4°.   4766. f.

—— Indian Church Quarterly Review. *Lond.* 1891, *etc.* 8°.   P.P. 910. cg.

SATYANĀTHA (S.) Missionary work in India. pp. 44. *Madras*, 1889. 8°.   4766. e. 24.

WARD (C. B.) History of Twelve years' work in the Nizam's Dominions. pp. 90. *Bombay*, 1893. 8°.   4766. e. 32.

GOLLOCK (GEORGINA A.) Winter's mails from Ceylon and India. pp. 189. *Lond.* 1895. 4°.   4767. aaa. 17.

LEITCH (Mary) and (M. W.) Seven years in Ceylon. pp 170. *Paris*, 1890. 8°. 4765. ee. 19.

MATSON (H.) A Woman's evangelistic work in India. pp. 87. *Calcutta*, 1889. 8°. 4767. cc. 2.

P.P. *London.* The Zenana, or, Woman's work in London. *Lond.* 1893, *etc.* 8°.   2220.

ENSOR (G.) "Help these Women." pp. 15. *Lond.* 1894. 16°.   Pam. 40.

See also COLOMBO, *Diocese.*

Roman Catholic Missions.

DARRAS (J. F. M.) Lourdes dans les Indes. pp. 340. *Paris*, 1890. 8°.   010055. ee. 6.

GUZMAN (L. de) Historia de las misiones de la Compañia de Jesus en la India. pp. 674. *Bilbao*, 1891. 4°.   4766. h. 3.

JEAN (A.) Le Maduré. L'ancienne et la nouvelle mission. 2 tom. *Bruges*, 1894. 8°.   4766. f. 23.

LAOUENAN (F. J. M.) *Archbp. of Pondicherry.* Lettres sur l'Inde. pp. 296. *Paris*, 1893. 8°.   010057. f. 17.

PIRES (J. O.) The Catholic Church in the East. pp. 41. *Lond.* 1890. 8°   Pam. 40.

SUAU (P.) Les bienheureux martyrs de Salsette. pp. 206. *Bruges*, 1893. 8°.   4829. f. 4.

VIZAGAPATAM. La Mission de Vizagapatam. pp. 531. *Annecy*, 1890. 8°.   4767. ff. 16.

Indies, Dutch.

DIJKSTRA (H.) Het Evangelie in onze Oost. *Leiden*, 1891, *etc.* 8°.   4767. ccc.

MOLIERE (T. B. G.) Het Protestantisme in Nederlandsch Indië. pp. 30. *Helder*, 1892. 8°.   Pam. 40.

Indo-China : Malaysia : Anam : Burma : Tung-King.

SINGAPORE. *Malaysia Mission Conference.* Minutes of the Conference of the Methodist Episcopal Church. *Singapore*, 1893, *etc.* 8°.   4766. d.

P P. *Singapore.* Sahabat [Missionary magazine in Malay]. *Singapura.* 1895, *etc.* 8°. 761. c.

MISSIONS.—Indo-China, etc—continued.

COSSERAT (J. J.) Rosæ Annamicæ, vitæ venerabilium Dei servorum qui pro fide in Cocincina sunt passi. pp. 250. *Monsterolii*, 1893. 8°.   4829. a. 52.

BROCKETT (L. P.) Story of the Karen mission in Bassein. pp. 160. *Phila.* 1892. 8°.   4765. dc. 13.

JOHNSON (T.) Mission journey among the Brecs. pp. 56. *Toungoo*, 1892. 16°.   Pam. 40.

LAUNAY (A.) Mgr. Retord et le Tonkin catholique, 1831-58. pp. 446. *Lyon*, 1893. 8°.   4766. ff. 30.

MONTEUUIS (G.) L'Ame d'un Missionnaire. Vie du P. Nempon, missionnaire du Tonkin. pp. 397. *Paris*, 1894. 8°.   4864. c. 27.

Japan.

COBBOLD (G. A.) Religion in Japan. *Lond.* 1894. 8°.   4429. c. 35.

DALTON (H.) Auf Missionspfaden in Japan. pp. 446. *Bremen*, 1895. 8°.   4765. aa. 46.

GORDON. (M. L.) An American missionary in Japan. pp 276. *Bost.* 1892. 8°. 4767. c. 33.

JAPAN. La nouvelle Église chrétienne au Japon. pp. 54. *Paris*, 1892. 8°.   Pam. 40.

—— Le Japon d'aujourd'hui. pp. 375. *Tours*, 1892. 8°.   4766. g. 8.

—— *Synodus Regionalis.* Acta et decreta primae Synodi Regionalis Japoniæ. pp. 125. *Hongkong*, 1893. 8°.   5061. aa. 10.

NARUSE (J.) A modern Paul in Japan. pp. 178. *Bost.* 1893. 8°.   4767. aaa. 14.

RITTER (H.) Dreissig Jahre protestantischer Mission in Japan, *etc.* pp. 126. *Berl.* 1890. 8°.   4766. ee. 18.

TARNIQUET (G.) Le premier Français martyrisé au Japon. pp. 214. *Lille*, 1891. 8°.   4829. df. 27.

Maoris. *See supra : Australia.*

Manitoulin Islands.

B., H. N. Manitoulin : Five years of Church work among Ojibway Indians and Lumbermen. pp. 164. *Lond.* 1895. 8°.   4767. c. 38.

New Guinea. *See supra : Australia.*

New Hebrides. *See infra : Polynesia.*

Palestine and Syria.

FRANCISCANS. Album missionis Terrae Sanctae. 2 pt. *Milan*, 1893. *obl.* 4°.   1789. a. 33.

P.P. *Florence.* Le Missioni francescane in Palestina. *Firenze*, 1891. *etc.* 8°   P.P. 929. f.

POST (G. E.) Pictures of Medical work. pp. 16. *Lond.* 1894. 8°.   Pam. 40.

WILSON (J. H.) and WELLS (J) Sea of Galilee mission of the Free Church of Scotland. pp. 94. *Edinb.* 1895. 4°.   4765. ccc. 3.

Polynesia.

ALEXANDER (J. M.) The Islands of the Pacific. pp. 503. *N.Y.* 1895. 8°.   4766. dd. 16.

COUSINS (G.) From Island to island in the South Seas. pp. 124. *Lond.* 1894. 8°. 4766. cc. 34.

GILL (W. W.) From Darkness to light in Polynesia. pp. 383. *Lond.* 1894. 8°.   4429. eee. 28.

MANGERET ( ) Mgr. Batallion et les missions de l'Océanie Centrale. 2 tom. *Lyon*, 1895. 8°.   4766. ee. 25.

MICHELSEN (O.) Cannibals won for Christ. pp. 188. *Lond.* 1893. 8°.   4766. e. 29.

MONFAT (A.) Dix années en Mélanésie. pp. 371. *Lyon*, 1891. 8°.   4766. ee. 19.

VERNON (R.) J. Calvert ; or, from dark to dawn in Fiji. pp. 160. *Lond.* 1890. 8°. 4767. aaa. 11.

MISSIONS.—Polynesia—_continued._

PAGE (J.) Bishop Patteson, the martyr of Melanesia. pp. 160. _Lond._ 1891. 8°.   4905. de. 31.

POMPALLIER (J. B. F.) _R.C. Bp. of Auckland._ Early history of the Catholic Church in Oceania. pp. 83. _Auckland,_ 1888. 8°.   4766. ff. 33.

Tibet.

MARSTON (A. W.) The great closed Land. pp. 112. _Lond._ 1894. 8°.   4766. ee. 24.

SCHNEIDER (H. G.) Working and waiting for Tibet. pp. 95. _Lond._ 1891. 8°.   4767. c. 27.

TIBET. _Pioneer Mission._ Origin of the Tibetan pioneer mission. pp. 20. _Lond._ 1894. 4°. Pam. 40.

MISSIONS, Home. DULLIN (J.) Parochial Missions. pp. 108. _Lond._ 1891. 8°. 4429. aa. 11.

HANDS. Strengthen your hands. pp. 113. _Lond._ 1895. 8°.   4192. aa. 40.

LONDON. _Conference of Diocesan Missioners,_ 1893. Report. pp. 60. _Lond._ 1893. 8°. 4192. cc. 32.

P.P. _London._ Church Army Gazette. _Lond._ 1886, _etc._ fol.   1459.

SPURR (F. C.) Special Missions. pp. 63. _Lond._ 1893. 8°.   4371. b. 14. (10.)

TREANOR (T. S.) The Log of a sky pilot. pp. 256. _Lond._ 1893. 8°.   4429. f. 25.

WINTZ (S. G.) Our Blue Jackets. Miss Weston's life and work. pp. 182. _Lond._ 1894. 8°. 4192. ee. 29.

See also LONDON, _Poor._

MISSISSIPPI, River. BAKER (J. H.) The sources of the Mississippi. pp. 28. _St. Paul,_ 1887. 8°.   10412. dd. 25. (1.)

BROWER (J. V.) The Mississippi River and its source. pp. 360. 1893. 8°. Ac. Saint Paul. _Minnesota Historical Society._ Collections. Vol. VII.   Ac. 8405.

GLAZIER (W. W.) Headwaters of the Mississippi. pp. 527. _Chicago,_ 1893. 8°.   10410. bb. 33.

PIKE (Z. M.) The Expeditions of Z. M. Pike to headwaters of the Mississippi River. 3 vol. _Lond._ 1895. 8°.   10412. i. 15.

ROZIER (F. A.) History of the early settlement of the Mississippi Valley. pp. 337. _St. Louis,_ 1890. 8°.   9551. bbb. 3.

MISSOURI, State. MISSOURI. _Geological Survey._ Bulletin. _Jefferson City,_ 1891, _etc._ 8°.   07109. l.

—— Missouri at the World's Fair. pp. 175. _St. Louis,_ 1893. 8°.   7956. g. 2.

NIPHER (F. E.) Report on Missouri rainfall. 1892. 8°. Ac. Saint Louis. _Academy of Science._ Transactions. Vol. 5. Nos. 3 & 4. Ac. 3061.

LOVE (J.) Annotations of the Missouri Supreme Court reports. 2 pt. _Columbia, Mo.,_ 1893. 8°. 6615. h. 16.

MAC QUILLIN (E.) Digest of Missouri reports. pp. 723. _St. Louis,_ 1891. 8°.   06616. g. 17.

MITES. _See_ ACARIDEA.

MNEMONICS. _See_ MEMORY.

MOA. HUTTON (F. W.) The Moas of New Zealand. 1891. 8°. Ac. Wellington. _New Zealand Institute._ Transactions. Vol. 24. Ac. 1990.

QUATREFAGES DE BRÉAU (J. L. A. de) The Moas and the moa-hunters. _Wellington,_ 1893. 8°. Pam. 42.

See also BIRDS.

MOBILE. DE LEON (J. C.) Our Creole carnivals. pp. 39. _Mobile,_ 1890. 8°. Pam. 18.

MODELLING, Scholastic. _See_ EDUCATION, _Pt. I. Manual._

MODENA. RICCARDI (P.) Note Bibliografiche modenesi. pp. 13. _Modena,_ 1895. 4°. Pam. 6.

MALAGUZZI-VALERI (I.) L'Archivio di stato in Modena, 1888–90. 1892. 4°. Ac. Modena. _R. Deputazioni di Storia Patria._ Atti. Ser. 4. Vol. I.   Ac. 6520.

—— L'Archivio di stato in Modena nell' annata 1891. 1893. 4°. Ac. Modena. _R. Deputazioni di Storia Patria._ Atti. Ser. 4. Vol. 4. Ac. 6520.

SANDONNINI (T.) Contro la soppressione della Università di Modena. pp. 13. _Modena,_ 1893. 8°.   Pam. 17.

MARANESI (E.) Vocabolario modenese-italiano. _Modena,_ 1892, _etc._ 8°.   1114.

MODUM. VETLESEN (H. J.) Fra Modums bad. pp. 14. _Kristiania,_ 1895. 8°. Pam. 39.

MOERIS, Lake. _See_ FAYOUM.

MOERS. HIRSCHBERG (C.) Geschichte der Grafschaft Moers. pp. 123. _Moers,_ 1893. 8°. 10256. c. 12.

MOHAMMEDANISM.

General : History : Religion.

AMÍR ALÍ, _Maulawí Sayyid._ Life and teachings of Mohammed. pp. 677. _Lond._ 1891. 8°. 4503. ee. 1.

GRIMME (H.) Mohammed. 1892, _etc._ 8°. Darstellungen aus dem Gebiete der nichtchristlichen Religionsgeschichte. Bd. 7.   4506. f.

MUIR (_Sir_ W.) Life of Mahomet. pp. 536. _Lond._ 1894. 8°.   10606. f. 18.

—— The Caliphate. pp. 612. _Lond._ 1892. 8°. 2386. f. 1.

POOLE (S. L.) The Mohammadan Dynasties. pp. 361. _Westminster,_ 1894. 8°. 9055. aaa. 38.

LA GARDE DE DIEU (L. de) Histoire de l'Islamisme et de l'Empire ottoman. pp. 276. _Brux._ 1892. 8°.   4503. ee. 19.

NOELDEKE (T.) Sketches from eastern History. pp. 288. _Lond._ 1892. 8°.   9055. d. 9.

POOL (J. J.) Studies in Mohammedanism. pp. 419. _Westminster,_ 1892. 8°. 4503. aaa. 4.

QUILLIAM (W. H.) Religion of the Sword. _Liverp._ 1891, _etc._ 8°.   4503. de.

BOURNICHON (J.) L'Invasion musulmane en Afrique. pp. 351. _Tours,_ 1890. 8°. 9061. h. 3.

MUHAMMAD SHĀH DĪN. Islam in Africa. pp. 27. _Lahore,_ 1893. 8°.   Pam. 41.

FERRAND (G.) Les Musulmans à Madagascar. 1891, _etc._ 8°. Ac. Algiers. _École Supérieure._ Publications. Pt. 9.   Ac. 5350/2.

AUTREMONT (F. d') Étude sur la Renaissance islamique et les puissances chrétiennes à la fin du 19° siècle. pp. 82. _Paris,_ 1893. 8°. 8028. de. 31. (9.)

'ABD AL-ḤAKK, _Dihlavi._ Articles of the Faith of Islam. pp. 44. _Bombay,_ 1894. 8°. 757. e. 42.

'ĀLIYAH, _Khānum._ Les Musulmanes contemporaines. pp. 201. _Paris,_ 1894. 8°.   758. b. 25.

AMĪR 'ALĪ, _Maulawi Saiyid._ Ethics of Islâm. pp. 51. _Calcutta,_ 1893. 8°.   14519. b. 41.

—— Woman in Islam. pp. 41. _Lahore,_ 1893. 8°.   Pam. 41.

BETTANY (G. T.) Mohammedanism. pp. 322. 1892. 8°. World's Religions Series. 4503. aaa.

BINGER (G.) Esclavage, Islamisme et Christianisme. pp. 112. _Paris,_ 1891. 8°. 8156. df. 14.

DERENBOURG (H.) La Science des religions et l'Islamisme. pp. 95. _Paris,_ 1886. 18°. 4503. aa. 45.

MOHAMMEDANISM.—General, etc.—continued.

FRISCH (R. J.) and DAVID (H. P. J. B.) Guide pratique en pays arabe. pp. 377.
Paris, 1892. 12°.   10096. aa. 9.

GHULĀM MUḤAMMAD, *Randeri.* Touchstone of philosophers. pp. 53. *Lahore*, 1893. 8°. Pam. 41.

GUYARD (S.) La Civilisation musulmane.
Paris, 1884. 18°.   4503. aa. 44.

ISLAM. Essay on the question whether Islam has been beneficial or injurious to human society.
pp. 26. *Lahore*, 1891. 8°.   Pam. 41.

LEITNER (G. W.) Mohammadanism. pp. 40.
Lahore, 1893. 8°.   Pam. 41.

MEHREN (A. F. M.) Les rapports de la philosophie d'Avicenne avec l'Islam. pp. 30.
Louvain, 1883. 8°.   14540. a. 45. (1.)

MITCHELL (J. M.) Letters to Indian youth.
pp. 276. *Madras*, 1894. 12°.   4018. bbb. 36.

MOHAMMEDAN PRAYER. True Adoration. Mohammedan prayer. *Sialkot*, 1312 [1894.] 16°.
       14519. a. 6.

MUḤAMMAD AL-MĀMŪN. Account of the rise of Islam in England. pp. 6. *Dacca*, 1891. 8°.
       Pam. 41.

MUḤAMMAD AMĪR 'ALĪ (A. AL-A.) The Moslem festivities. pp. 76. *Calcutta*, 1892. 8°. Pam. 41.

MUḤSIN AL-MULK. Propagation of Islam.
pp. 50. *Lahore*, 1893. 8°.   14119. b. 40. (1.)

MUSHTĀK ḤUSAIN KHĀN. Inter-religionary Amity. Is it possible to be friendly and affectionate to aliens in religion? pp. 8. *Lahore*, 1891. 12°.
       14104. c. 50.

P.P. *Liverpool.* The Islamic world.
Liverpool, 1893, etc. 8°.   P.P. 978. ab. & 645.

POOLE (S. L.) Studies in a Mosque. pp. 326.
Lond. 1893. 8°.   4503. e. 27.

QUILLIAM (W. H.) The Faith of Islam. pp. 78.
Liverpool, 1892. 8°.   4506. bb. 29.

RIYĀẔ AL-DĪN AḤMAD. The Moslem Guide.
pp. 18. *Bombay*, 1891. 12°.   Pam. 41.

ROUSE (G. H.) Tracts for Muhammadans.
pp. 112. *Madras*, 1893. 12°.   14104. b. 19.

ṢĀLIḤ ṢUBḤĪ. Pèlerinage à la Mecque et à Médine. pp. 129. *Le Caire*, 1894. 8°.
       10077. g. 37.

SNOW (U. B. H.) Merits of Islam. pp. 28.
Lahore, 1893. 8°.   Pam. 41.

—— Prayer book for Muslims. pp. 32.
Lahore, 1893. 8°.   Pam. 41.

THOMAS (F. W.) Mutual influence of Muhammadans and Hindus. pp. 117. *Camb.* 1892. 8°.
       8022. cc. 9.

TISDALL (W. S. C.) "Diex li Vuelt!" A plea for an extension of Mission work in Muhammadan lands. pp. 22. *Lond.* 1891. 8°. Pam. 40.

WEBB (M. A. R.) Lectures on Islam. pp. 48.
Lahore, 1893. 8°.   Pam. 41.

ZWEMER (S. M.) Jesus Christ of the Koran.
pp. 12. *Bombay*, 1893. 16°.   Pam. 41.

See also ALGERIA : ARABS : BABI : CRUSADES : MAROCCO : RELIGION : TUNIS.

Law.

ADDA (B.) and GHALIOUNGUI (E. D.) Droit Musulman. Le Wakf ou immobilisation d'après les principes du rite hanafite. 3 pt.
Alexandrie, 1893. 8°.   14528. b. 25.

AMĪR 'ALĪ, *Maulavi Saiyid.* Mahommedan Law. 1892, etc. 8°. Tagore Law Lectures. 5318. aaa.

CLAVEL (E.) Droit Musulman. Du statut personnel et des successions. 2 tom
Paris, 1895. 8°.   05319. i. 12.

FREUND (L.) Lug und Trug nach moslemischen Recht. *München*, 1893, etc. 8°.   5319. cc.

MOHAMMEDANISM.—Law.—continued.

HARANACHANDRA VANDYOPĀDHYĀYA. Synopsis of the Muhammadan Law in British India.
Allahabad, 1893. 4°.   5319. a. 12.

LUCIANI (J. D.) Traité des Successions musulmanes. pp. 573. *Paris*, 1890. 8°. 5318. dd. 7.

MACNAGHTEN (*Sir* W. H.) Principles and precedents of Moohummudan Law. pp. 586.
Madras, 1890. 8°.   5318. b. 24.

MUḤAMMAD IBN MUḤAMMAD. Traité de Droit musulman. *Alger*, 1882, etc. 8°.   05319. i.

MUḤAMMAD SAMĪ 'ALLĀH, *Khān Bahadur.* Judgment containing an exposition of the Muhammadan matrimonial Law. pp. 40. 32.
Allahabad, 1891. 8°.   14106. dd. 24.

PLEADER. Summary of Mahomedan Law.
pp. 58. 1891. 8°.   Pam. 33.

SAVVAS, *Pacha.* Étude sur la théorie du Droit musulman. *Paris*, 1892, etc. 8°.   5318. aa.

WILSON (*Sir* R. K.) Digest of Anglo-Muhammadan Law. pp. 500. *Lond.* 1895. 8°. 05319. g. 2.

—— Introduction to the study of Anglo-Muhammadan Law. pp. 151. *Lond.* 1894. 8°.
       05319. i. 6.

MOLD. TWEDDELL (H. J.) Handy guide to Mold. pp. 108. *Mold*, 1891. 8°.   10369. e. 9.

MOLDE. MOLDE. Molde og Romsdalen. pp. 319. *Kristiania*, 1892. 8°.   10280. b. 1.

MOLISE. PERRELLA (A.) L'antico Sannio e l'attuale provincia di Molise. pp. 639.
Isernia, 1889. 8°.   10129. bbb. 28.

PERRELLA (A.) Effemeride della provincia di Molise. *Isernia*, 1890, etc. 8°.   9166. de.

See also ABRUZZO.

MOLLUSCA. Ac. London. *Malacological Society.* Proceedings. *Lond.* 1893, etc. 8°.
       Ac. 3017. f.

COUPIN (H.) Les Mollusques. *Paris*, 1892, etc. 8°.
       7298. ee.

COUTAGNE (G.) Recherches sur le polymorphisme des Mollusques de France. 1895. 8°. Ac. *Lyons. Société d'Agriculture.* Annales. Sér. 7. Tom. 2.   Ac. 362/3.

COOKE (A. H.) Molluscs. 1895. 8°. HARMER (S. F.) Cambridge Natural History. Vol. 3. 7001. ee.

FROST (H.) Our common Shells. pp. 10.
Lond. 1891. 8°.   7001. de. 23. (6.)

HARROW SCHOOL. Handbook to the Mollusca in the Butler Museum, Harrow School. pp. 43.
Harrow, 1891. 8°.   7298. ee. 19.

KEW (H. W.) The dispersal of Shells. pp. 291. 1893. 8°. International Scientific Series. Vol. 75.   2324. bb. 12.

LOCARD (A.) De l'influence des milieux sur le développement des Mollusques. 1893. 8°. Ac. *Lyons. Société d'Agriculture, etc.* Annales. Tom. 5.   Ac. 362/3.

NEUMAYR (M.) Beiträge zur einer morphologischen Eintheilung der Bivalven. 1891. fol. Ac. Vienna. *K. Akademie.* Denkschriften. Math.-naturwissenschaftliche Classe. Bd. 58.
       Ac. 810/13.

P.P. *London.* Journal of Malacology. Vol. 3, etc. *Lond.* 1894. 8°.   P.P. 2028. da. & 2238.

—— *Philadelphia.* The Nautilus.
Phila. 1889, etc. 8°.   P.P. 2029. ab. & 1131.

ROEMER (A.) Catalog der Conchylien-Sammlung des Museums zu Wiesbaden. 1891. 8°. Ac. Wiesbaden. *Verein für Naturkunde.* Jahrbücher. Jahrg. 44.   Ac. 2895.

THIELE (J.) Die Stammesverwandtschaft der Mollusken. 1891. 8°. Ac. Jena. *Medizinsch-naturwissenschaftliche Gesellschaft.* Jenaische Zeitschrift. Bd. 25.   Ac. 3760.

MOLLUSCA—*continued.*

WILLIAMS (J. W.) Collecting and preserving Shells. pp. 8. *Birmingham*, 1891. 8°. Pam. 42.

BERGH (R.) System der nudibranchiaten Gasteropoden. pp. 173. *Wiesbaden*, 1892. 4°.
7299. l. 19.

NABIAS (B. de) Recherches sur les centres nerveux des Gastéropodes. 1894. 8°. Ac. Bordeaux. *Société Finnéenne.* Bulletin. Vol. 47.
Ac. 2839.

KELLOGG (J. L.) Contribution to our knowledge of the morphology of Lamellibranchiate Mollusks. pp. 47. *Wash.* 1892. 8°. 7298. g. 10.

PERRIER (R.) Recherches sur l'anatomie et l'histologie du rein des Gastéropodes Prosobranches. pp. 254. *Paris*, 1889. 8°.
7299. g. 24.

Local Mollusca Fauna.

European.

COLLINGE (W. E.) Review of the Arionidæ of the British Isles. pp. 11. *Lond.* 1892. 8°.
Pam. 42.

—— Catalogue of the Slugs of the British Isles. pp. 4. *Hartlepool*, 1892. 8°. 7298. d. 3. (9.)

WILLIAMS (J. W.) List of British land and fresh-water Shells. pp. 25. *Lond.* 1891. 8°.
7004. de. 23. (9.)

CALDERWOOD (W. L.) Mussel culture especially in Scotland. pp. 121. *Lond.* 1895. 8°.
7290. a. 24.

LOCARD (A.) Conchyliologie française. pp. 327. *Lond.* 1893. 8°. 7298. e. 3.

—— Les Coquilles marines des côtes de France. pp. 384. 1891. 8°. Ac. Lyons. *Société Linnéenne.* Annales. Nouvelle série. Tom. 37.
Ac. 2847/2.

—— Les Coquilles terrestres de France. 1895. 8°. Ac. Lyons. *Société d'Agriculture.* Annales. Sér. 7. Tom. 2. Ac. 362/3.

—— Malacologie des conduites d'eau de la ville de Paris. 1893. 8°. Ac. Lyons. *Académie des Sciences.* Mémoires. Sér. 3. Tom. 2. Ac. 364/5.

MORIN (P.) Essai sur la Faunule malacologique de la Sarthe. pp. 127. *Le Mans*, 1891. 8°.
7297. f. 18.

MERKEL (E.) Molluskenfaune von Schlesien. pp. 293. *Breslau*, 1894. 8°. 7299. f. 19.

SCHIEMENZ (P.) Mollusca. pp. 66. 1893. 8°. Ac. Naples. *Zoologische Station.* Zoologischer Jahresbericht, 1892. Ac. 3552/3.

—— Mollusca. pp. 64. 1894. 8°. Ac. Naples. *Zoologische Station.* Zoologische Jahresbericht, 1893. Ac. 3552/3.

See also PALAEONTOLOGY.

Exotic.

BOURGUIGNET (J. R.) Iconographie Malacologique du lac Tanganika. pp. 82. *Corbeil*, 1888. 8°. 7298. cc. 16.

TAPPARONE CANEFRI (C.) Viaggio di L. Fea in Birmania. Molluschi. 1889. 8°. Ac. Genoa. *Museo Civico.* Annali. Ser. 2. Vol. 7.
Ac. 2809.

HEDLEY (C.) and SUTER (H.) List of Mollusca of New Zealand. 1893. 8°. Ac. Sydney. *Linnean Society.* Proceedings. Ser. 2. Vol. 7, pt. 4. Ac. 3100.

BINNEY (W. G.) Fourth supplement to the fifth volume of the terrestrial air-breathing Mollusks of the U.S. 1892. 8°. Ac. Cambridge. *Harvard University. Museum.* Bulletin. Vol. 22.
Ac. 1736/2.

DALL (W. H.) Catalogue of shell-bearing marine Mollusks of the S.E. Coast of the U.S. pp. 221. 1889 8°. Bulletin of the U.S. National Museum. Separate Issue. No. 37. Ac. 1875/13.

MOLLUSCA—*continued.*

DALL (W. H.) Cruise of the "Wild Duck" in the Bahamas. Notes on the Shells collected. 1894. 8°. Ac. Cambridge. *Harvard University. Museum.* Bulletin. Vol. 25. No. 9. Ac. 1736/2.

MOLUCCAS. MARTIN (K.) Reisen in den Molukken. 2 pt. *Leiden*, 1894. 8°. 010055. i. 2. *See also* MALAY PENINSULA AND MALAYSIA : NETHERLANDS, *Colonies.*

MONACO : MONTE - CARLO. AMERICANUS. Monte-Carlo. Rules of Trente et Quarante. pp. 35. *Nice*, 1890. 8°.
7912. df. 2. (4.)

ANGE (d') *Countess.* À l'assaut de l'antre, Monaco. pp. 4. *Nice*, 1892. fol. Pam. 85.

—— À bas le brigandage de Monaco. pp. 4. *Nice*, 1892. 8°. Pam. 85.

BELZ DE VILLAS ( ) La Question de Monte-Carlo. pp. 21. *Paris*, 1895. 8°. Pam. 85.

BERTTY (C. J.) Roulette de Monaco. *Nice*, 1890-91. 8°. 7912. cc. 3. (2.)

BLARIMONT (N. de) Monte-Carlo. pp. 183. *Nice*, 1890. 8° 10174. bb. 16.

DISQUE. The new Chinese system as played at Monaco. pp. 14. *Lond.* 1891. 16°. 7912. a. 4.

DUMONT (P.) Monte-Carlo. *Paris*, 1892. 12°.
10169. e. 4.

GOLDBERG (W. F.) and PIESSE (G. C.) Monte Carlo. pp. 203. *Bristol*, 1891. 8°. 10135. cc. 8.

MONFALCONE (P.) Monte-Carlo intime. pp. 261. *Paris*, 1891. 12°. 8425. b. 59.

NICE. Nice, Monaco. Guide Joanne. *Paris*, 1894. 8°.. 10174. aaa. 48.

ONIMUS (E.) L'Hiver dans les Alpes Maritimes et dans Monaco. pp. 588. *Paris*, 1891. 12°.
07686. e. 3.

P.P. *Monaco.* Le Monaco. No. 1-269. *Monaco*, 1887-93. fol. P.P. 9505. g.

PHILIP. Appel aux Gouvernements. La vérité sur Monaco. pp. 16. *Paris*, 1890. 8°.
8425. bbb. 43. (9.)

SAIGE (G.) Le Protectorat espagnol à Monaco. pp. 170. *Monaco*, 1885. 8°. 9166. c. 33.

STAMEN (W. J. A.) A day at Monte Carlo. pp. 156. *Lond.* 1894. 8°. 010171. i. 3. *See also* GAMBLING.

MONARCHY. *See* GOVERNMENT.

MONDOVI. DANNA (C.) and CHIECHIO (G. C.) Storia del santuario di Mondovi. pp. 456. 75. *Torino*, 1891. 8°. 10132. h. 10.

MONEY.

General : Bimetallism.

A., F. A. How to establish a fixed ratio between Gold and Silver. pp. 24. *Lond.* 1892. 8°.
08227. g. 48. (6.)

Ac, *etc.* Brussels. *Conférence Monétaire.* Procèsverbaux. 1892. pp. 424. *Brux.* 1892. fol.
Ac. 2347.

—— Lille. *Société Industrielle du Nord.* ROGEZ (C.) Le Rouble ses fluctuations et leurs conséquences. pp. 19. *Lille*, 1890. 8°. Pam. 23.

ADAMI (J. H.) Nicht Bimetallismus, sondern Combinationswährung. pp. 31. *Berl.* 1894. 8°.
Pam. 23.

ADAMS (B.) The Gold standard. pp. 32. *Wash.* 1895. 8°. Pam. 23.

ALLARD (A.) Graphiques de la crise monétaire, 1850-92. *Brux.* 1892. 4°. 8228. l. 11.

AMERICA, *South.* A Silver currency for South America. pp. 31. *Lond.* 1892. 8°.
08227. g. 48. (7.)

ANSIAUX (M.) La Question monétaire en Belgique. pp. 130. *Liège*, 1892. 8°. 08207. cc. 16.

MONEY.—General. etc.—*continued.*

ARNAUNÉ (A.) La Monnaie, le crédit et le change. pp. 402. *Paris*, 1894. 8°. 08227. i. 43.

BAILLY (L.) La Réforme monétaire universelle. pp. 73. *Paris*, 1890. 8°. 08227. ee. 33.

BAIRD (H. C.) On Money the instrument of association. pp. 16. *Wash.* 1890. 8°. Pam. 23.

—— Money and Bank credit in the United States, France and Great Britain. pp. 24. *Phila.* 1891. 8°. Pam. 23.

BANCROFT (H.) "The Silver question." pp. 16. *Lond.* 1894. 8°. 08226. h. 15. (6.)

BARCLAY (R.) The Silver question and the Gold question. pp. 222. *Lond.* 1894. 8°. 08227. de. 45.

BARROWS (H. D.) International Bimetallism. pp. 55. *Los Angeles*, 1891. 8°. 08227. ee. 48. (4.)

BEETON (H. R.) The Case for monetary reform. pp. 48. *Lond.* 1894. 8°. 08226. h. 15. (5.)

—— Bimetallism: its advantages. pp. 24. *Lond.* 1895. 8°. 08226. h. 15. (12.)

BIMETALLISM. Bimetallism in parvo. By "Short, please!" pp. 14. *Manch.* 1893. 8°. 08227. g. 48. (1.)

BOISSEVAIN (G. M.) Le Problème monétaire. pp. 136. *Paris*, 1891. 8°.

—— The Monetary Question. pp. 151. *Lond.* 1891. 8°. 08227. ee. 26.

BOUTAN (E.) Résumé de la Question monétaire. pp. 76. *Paris*, 1895. 8°. 08226. i. 7.

BROË (C. de) Le Métal méprisé. pp. 32. *Lond.* 1892. 8°. Pam. 23.

BROOKS (F. A.) Objections to our national currency system. pp. 56. *Bost.* 1893. 8°. 08226. k. 3. (2.)

BROUGH (W.) The Natural law of Money. pp. 168. *N.Y.* 1894. 8°. 08229. de. 30.

CARON (W.) Die Beseitigung der internationalen Silberkrisis. pp. 46. *Düsseldorf*, 1895. 8°. Pam. 23.

CARNEVALI (Tito) Scienza delle Finanze. pp. 139. *Milano*, 1891. 8°. 12206. b. 55.

CARRUTHERS (G. T.) The Units in exchange. pp. 66. *Lond.* 1892. 8°. 8228. aaaa. 17 (15.)

CASASUS (J. D.) La question de l'argent au Mexique. pp. 136. *Paris*, 1892. 8°. 08227. i. 6.

—— Le problème monétaire et la Conférence monétaire de Bruxelles. pp. 189. *Paris*, 1893. 8°. 08225. h. 4.

CERNUSCHI (H.) Le grand procès de l'Union Latine. pp. 117. *Paris*, 1884. 8°. 08227. i. 20.

—— Les Assignats métalliques. pp. 37. *Paris*, 1885. 4°. 8226. g. 31. (1.)

—— La Danse des assignats métalliques. pp. 35. *Paris*, 1885. 4°. 8226. g. 31. (3.)

—— Le Monométallisme bossu. pp. 37. *Paris*, 1885. 4°. 8226. g. 31. (2.)

CHAPLIN (*Right Hon.* H.) Bimetallism. Speech. pp. 42. *Manch.* 1889. 8°. 08227. g. 36. (3.)

CHEAP-MONEY EXPERIMENTS. Cheap money experiments in past and present times. pp. 122. *N.Y.* 1892. 12°. 08227. de. 10.

CHIRAC (A.) Où est l'argent? pp. 295. *Paris*, 1892. 12°. 8228. cc. 44.

COBB (A. S.) Metallic reserves and the meeting of Parliament. pp. 28. *Lond.* 1892. 8°. Pam. 23.

COFFIN (G. M.) Silver from 1849 to 1892. pp. 45. *Wash.* 1892. 8°. 08226. g. 14. (13.)

COLLINS (J. H.) Plea for the bimetallic amalgamation of the currencies of Great Britain and Hindustan. pp. 19. *Lond.* 1895. 8°. Pam. 23.

COOPER (E. S.) Money; its mysteries and mistakes. pp. 48. *Lond.* 1895. 16°. Pam. 23.

MONEY.—General, etc.—*continued.*

COWPERTHWAIT (J. H.) Money, silver and finance. pp. 242. *N.Y.* 1892. 8°. 08227. de. 4.

CROSS (J. W.) Impressions of Dante, with a few words on Bimetallism. pp. 314. *Edinb.* 1893. 8°. 11420. c. 20.

DANIEL (J. W.) The Panic, its causes and its remedy. Speech. pp. 56. *Wash.* 1893. 8°. 08227. g. 49. (8.)

DEL MAR (A.) The Silver Question. pp. 7. *N.Y.* 1893. 8°. 08227. i. 29. (13.)

—— Story of the Gold Conspiracy. pp. 16. *Chicago*, 1895. 8°. Pam. 23.

DESERTIS (V. C.) Commerce and currency. pp. 73. *Allahabad*, 1892. 8°. Pam. 85.

DICK (G. H.) and MAVOR (J.) Call for currency reform and Mr. Goschen's response. pp. 48. *Lond.* 1892. 8°. 08227. g. 36. (14.)

—— International bullion Money. pp. 38. *Lond.* 1894. 8°. 08226. k. 3. (4.)

DOUGLAS (J. M.) Gold and silver Money. pp. 32 *Lond.* 1892. 8°. 08227. g. 48. (9.)

EHRICH (L. R.) The question of Silver. pp. 115. *N.Y.* 1892. 8°. 08227. de. 5.

ELLIS (G.) Appreciation of Gold and its effect on investments. pp. 31. *Lond.* 1895. 8°. 08226. h. 15. (13.)

ELLISSEN (A.) Errors and fallacies of bimetallism. pp. 31. *Lond.* 1895. 8°. 08226. h. 15. (14.)

ELLSTAETTER (C.) Indiens Silberwährung. pp. 127. 1894. 8°. BRENTANO (L.) Münchener Volkswirthschaftliche Studien. St. 4. 08276. i.

ETTINGER (M.) Einfluss der Goldwährung auf das Einkommen der Bevölkerungsclassen und des Staates. pp. 172. *Wien*, 1892. 08207. h. 4.

FONDA (A. I.) Honest Money. pp. 209. *N.Y.* 1895. 8°. 08226. f. 17.

FRAENKEL (J. E.) Die Zukunft des Silbers. pp. 30. 1894. 8°. Sammlung wissenschaftlicher Vorträge. N.F. Ser. 8. Hft. 191. 12249. l.

FREE CURRENCY TRACTS. Free Currency tracts. *Lond.* 1895, *etc.* 8°. 08226. h.

FRÈRE-ORBAN (H. J. W.) La Question monétaire en Belgique en 1889. pp. 146. *Brux*, 1890. 8°. 08229. g. 41.

ROCHUSSEN (J. J.) Supplement à "la Question monétaire en Belgique" de M. Frère Orban. pp. 50. *La Haye*, 1890. 8°. Pam. 23.

GAINSFORD (W. D.) What Bimetallism really is. pp. 41. *Nottingham*, 1895. 8°. 08226. f. 23. (8.)

GEORGE (E. M.) The Silver and Indian currency questions. pp. 65. *Lond.* 1894. 8°. 08226. f. 7.

GIBBS (H. C.) A Bimetallic primer. pp. 106. *Lond.* 1894. 8°. 08226. f. 10.

—— Address on Bimetallism. pp. 32. *Lond.* 1895. 8°. 08226. f. 23. (9.)

GIBBS (H. H.) *Baron Aldenham.* A Colloquy on Currency. pp. 330. *Lond.* 1894. 8°. 08226. h. 8.

GIFFEN (R.) The Case against Bimetallism. pp. 254. *Lond.* 1892. 8°. 08227. de. 8.

BAIN (F. W.) The Corner in Gold. Reply to Mr. Giffen's "Case against bimetallism." pp. 130. *Oxf.* 1893. 8°. 08227. de. 22.

GORDON (A. C.) Congressional Currency. pp. 234. *N.Y.* 1895. 8°. 8176. bbb.

GRAHAME (J.) Mr. Goschen's One Pound note. Digest of parliamentary opinion, 1797–1819. pp. 31. *Lond.* 1892. 8°. 08227. g. 36. (10.)

GRAPHEUS (D.) Darstellung der wirthschaftlichen Funktion des Geldes und Kredits. pp. 90. *Leipz.* 1892. 8°. Pam. 23.

HARVEY (W. H.) Coin's Financial School. pp. 149. *Chicago*, 1894. 8°. 08226. g. 20. (1.)

MONEY.—General. etc.—_continued._

RUSKIN (J.) Gold. A dialogue. pp. 26. _Lond._ 1891. 8°. 08227. de. 3.

SCHILLING (R.) The Silver Question. pp. 24. _Milwaukee_, 1891. 8°. 08227. ee. 48. (5.)

SCHMIDT (H.) The Indian Currency danger. pp. 37. _Lond._ 1893. 8°. 08227. g. 48. (4.)

SCHRAUT (M. v.) Currency and international Banking. pp. 42. _Lond._ 1894. 8°. Pam. 23.

SEMINARIO (M. E.) La Cuestion monetaria en la America española. pp. 264. _Paris_, 1893. 8°. 08225. h. 8.

SEWEN (M.) Studien über die Zukunft des Geldwesens. pp. 91. _Leipz._ 1892. 8°. 08225. h. 2.

SEYD (E.) The Silver question in 1893. pp. 81. _Lond._ 1893. 8°. 08227. h. 37.

SHERWOOD (S.) History and theory of Money. pp. 413. _Phila._ 1893. 8°. 08225 h. 6.

SILVER PROBLEM. The Silver Problem. pp. 23. _Lond._ 1892. 8°. 08227. g. 48. (13.)

SKARZYŃSKI (S.) Le Bimétallisme, trait d'union internationale. pp. 105. _Paris_, 1892. 8°. 08229. g. 45.

SMITH (Samuel) Bimetallism. pp. 32. _Manch._ 1889. 8°. 08227. g. 36. (5.)

SOETBEER (A.) Litteraturnachweis über Geld- und Münzwesen 1871-91. pp. 322. _Berl._ 1892. 8°. 08227. e. 35.

SOWERBY (W.) The Indian Rupee question and how to solve it. pp. 16. _Lond._ 1892. 8°. 08227. g. 48 (14.)

STALL (B.) Die Zukunft des Silbers. pp. 50. _Berl._ 1893. 8°. 08227. g. 48. (5.)

—— Internationales Gold. Nationales Silber. pp. 32. _Berl._ 1894. 8°. 08226. h. 15. (11.)

STOKES (A. P.) Joint-Metallism. pp. 216. _N.Y._ 1895. 8°. 08226. g. 11.

SUESS (E.) Die Zukunft des Silbers. pp. 227. _Wien_, 1892. 8°. 08227. i. 5.

TAUSSIG (F. W.) The Silver situation in the U.S. pp. 133. _N.Y._ 1893. 8°. 08225. ee. 9.

TEALE (J.) Notes on Indian currency and the Indian exchange. pp. 16. _Manch._ 1892. 8°. 8228. aaaa. 17. (19.)

THÉRY (E.) La Crise des changes. pp. 261. _Paris_, 1894. 8°. 08226. f. 12.

TRITTON (J. H.) The assault on the Standard. pp. 36. _Lond._ 1895. 8°. 08226. h. 15. (19.)

TWIGG (J. H.) Plain statement of the Currency question. pp. 23. _Lond._ 1893. 8°. 8227. i. 40. (11.)

VERSLUYS (J.) Munten, effecten en wissels. pp. 134. _Amsterd._ 1890. 8°. 8228. c. 50.

WALSH (W. J.) _R.C. Archbp. of Dublin._ Bi-métallisme et monométallisme. pp. 80. _Paris_, 1895. 8°. 08226. g. 15.

WALKER (F. A.) Bimetallism. pp. 24. _Bost._ 1894. 8°. 08226. k. 3. (8.)

WASHINGTON. _International American Monetary Commission._ Minutes of the Commission. pp. 123. _Wash._ 1891. 4°. 8228. h. 51.

WHEELER (E. P.) Real Bimetallism. pp. 91. _N.Y._ 1895. 8°. 8176. bbb.

WHITE (H.) The Gold Standard. pp. 50. _N.Y._ 1893. 8°. 08227. i. 29. (17.)

WILLEY (F. O.) Dawn of a new era in Finance. pp. 446. _N.Y._ 1887. 8°. 08227. i. 4.

WOLTERS (J.) L'Or et l'Argent dans leurs fonctions monétaires. pp. 138. _Brux._ 1890 8°. 08225. l. 7.

WOODFORD (A. B.) On the use of Silver as money in the U.S. pp. 60. _Phila._ 1893. 8°. 08226. h. 3.

MONEY.—General, etc.—_continued._

ZORN (J. C. L.) Theory of Bimetallism. pp. 8. _Lond._ 1895. 8°. 08226. h. 15. (20.)

See also BANKING : BILLS, _of Exchange :_ DECIMAL SYSTEM : LAW, _Commercial :_ NUMISMATICS : POLITICAL ECONOMY : PRICES : and under the subheading _Trade_ of each country.

History of Money.

DELMAR (A.) History of Monetary systems. pp. 511. _Lond._ 1895. 8°. 08226. h. 10.

CHALMERS (R.) History of currency in the British Colonies. pp. 496. _Lond._ 1893. 8°. 08229, g. 46.

DEMOLE (E.) Histoire monétaire de Genève de 1792 à 1848. pp. 139. _Genève_, 1892. 4°. 7757. h. 9.

EVANS (G. G.) Illustrated History of the U.S. Mint. pp. 179. _Phila._ 1892. 8°. 7757. c. 38.

NAGL (A.) Die Goldwährung und die handelsmässige Geldrechnung im Mittelalter. 1895. 8°. Numismatische Zeitschrift. Bd. 26. P.P. 1889. g.

RIDGEWAY (W.) Origin of Metallic currency and weight standards. pp. 417. _Camb._ 1892. 8°. 8535. d. 12.

ROSALES (J. P.) Papel moneda. Resumen de su historia. pp. 56. _Lima_, 1886. 8°. 8226. g. 40. (5.)

WITTE (A. de) Conférence monétaire internationale tenue à Bruges en 1469. pp. 16. _Brux._ 1893. 8°. Pam. 44.

_See also supra ; General : _ NUMISMATICS.

Monetary Systems of various Nations : Tables of Exchange, etc.

AMERICAN REPUBLICS. Money of the American Republics. pp. 12. 1891. 8°. U.S. _Bureau of American Republics._ Bulletin. No. 4. 08225. k. 1.

BECHER (W. S.) Sterling advance Tables for importers. _Toronto_, 1893. 8°. 8548. aaa. 34.

BROWNE (W. A.) Merchants' handbook of Money. pp. 562. _Lond._ 1892. 8°. 8548. b. 30.

CLARE (G.) A B C of the foreign Exchanges. pp. 160. _Lond._ 1893. 8°. 8227. aaa. 64.

DE MONTE (S. M.) Exchange Calculator, sterling into rupees and rupees into sterling. pp. 389. _Bombay_, 1894. 8°. 8548. de. 36.

DE VOS (H. W.) Exchange Tables, showing the conversion of £'s sterling into Rupees and Rupees into £'s sterling. pp. 136. _Colombo_, 1893. 4°. 8548. e. 33.

DOLLAR EXCHANGE TABLES. Dollars and sterling exchange Tables. _Hongkong_, 1894. 8°. 8548. df. 40.

HAUPT (O.) Arbitrages et Parités. pp. 922. _Paris_, 1894. 8°. 8227. i. 42.

LEJEUNE (A.) Monnaies des principaux pays du monde. pp. 552. _Paris_, 1894. 8°. 8548. de. 33.

MARTINI-MONTI (A. G.) Monete de' principali stati del mondo. pp. 152. _Firenze_, 1890. 8°. 7756. b. 13.

MERCES (F. A. D.) Indian and English exchange tables. _Lond._ 1894. 8°. 8548. de. 30.

MORRISON (J. R.) Currency of China. pp. 40. 1895. 8°. 08226. f. 23. (10.)

NORMAN (J. H.) Guide to the World's twenty-nine metal monetary Systems. pp. 328. _Lond._ 1892. 8°. 8228. f. 50.

—— Single Grain system for determining the par value of all money. _Lond._ 1887. 8°. 2240. bb. 12.

—— Ready reckoner of the world's Exchanges. pp. 164. _Lond._ 1893. 8°. 2240. aa. 25.

MONEY.—Systems of, etc.—_continued._

NORMAN (J. H.) Prices and Exchanges of the world. pp. 32. _Lond._ 1895. 8°.   08226. h. 15. (17.)

—— A B C of the foreign and colonial Exchanges. 1891. 8°.   8226. cc. 51.

—— Sailors' and travellers' guide to two thousand and seventy Exchanges. 2 pt. _Lond._ 1894. 12°.   1882. d. 2. (106.)

TATE (W.) Tate's modern Cambist. pp. 249. _Lond._ 1893. 8°.   2020. d.

WOOLHOUSE (W. S. B.) Measures and Moneys of all nations. pp. 252. _Lond._ 1890. 8°.   2242. a. 32.

MONEY LENDING. FARROW (T.) The Money-Lender unmasked. pp. 240. _Lond._ 1895. 8°.   08226. g. 12.

See also USURY.

MONGOLIA. Ac. St. Petersburg. _Academia Scientiarum._ Arbeiten der Orchon-Expedition. _St. Petersburg,_ 1892, _etc._ fol.   1701. b.

—— Washington. _Smithsonian Institution._ ROCK-HILL (W. W.) Diary of a journey through Mongolia. pp. 413. _Wash._ 1894. 8°.   10075. ff. 24.

BRETSCHNEIDER (E.) Itinéraires en Mongolie. 1893. 8°. Ac. Paris. _Société Asiatique._ Journal Asiatique. Sér. 9. Tom. 1.   Ac. 8808.

BRYSON (M. I.) Story of J. Gilmour and the Mongol mission. pp. 144. _Lond._ 1894. 8°.   4920. de. 16.

GILMOUR (J.) More about the Mongols. pp. 320. _Lond._ 1893. 8°.   4429. f. 6.

INDEMANS (E.) Landreis naar Ili. pp. 140. _Utrecht,_ 1891. 8°.   4765. e. 23.

MUḤAMMAD ḤAIDAR, _Dughlāt._ The Tarikh-i-Rashidi : history of the Moghuls of Central Asia. pp. 535. _Lond._ 1895. 8°.   757. ff. 1.

PRICE (J. M.) From the Arctic Ocean to the Yellow Sea. pp. 384. _Lond._ 1892. 8°.   10292. e. 5.

RADLOV (V. V.) Die alttürkischen Inschriften der Mongolei. _St. Petersburg,_ 1894, _etc._ 4°.   7705. d.

ROCKHILL (W. W.) The land of the Lamas. pp. 399. _Lond._ 1891. 8°.   010057. l. 5.

See also CHINA : ORKHON.

MONISM. _See_ PHILOSOPHY.

MONKEN HADLEY. BYFORD (S.) Reminiscences of Chipping Barnet and Monken Hadley. pp. 44. _Barnet,_ 1891. 8°.   Pam. 90.

MONKEYS. GARNER (R. L.) The Speech of Monkeys. pp. 260. _Lond._ 1892. 8°   12901. c. 48.

ROPER (F.) The "Missing Link." Consul, the chimpanzee. pp. 67. _Manch._ 1895. 8°.   7207. aaaa. 10.

SKENE (A. P.) "Ante Agamemnona" : a new departure in philology. _Oxf._ 1892, _etc._ 8°.   12902. bb. 35.

See also GORILLA.

MONMOUTHSHIRE. Ac. Caerleon. _Monmouthshire Antiquarian Association._ MITCHELL (E. H.) Crosses of Monmouthshire. pp. 45. _Newport,_ 1893. 4°   7709. h. 35.

BAGNALL-OAKELEY (M. E.) Account of the rude monuments in Monmouthshire. pp. 22. _Newport,_ 1889. 8°   7705. ee. 24. (2.)

BLACK (A.) and (C.) Black's Guide to Monmouthshire. pp. 204. _Edinb._ 1889. 8°..   10369. aaa. 45.

MONOGRAMS. RIS-PAQUOT (O. E.) Dictionnaire des Marques et monogrammes, _etc._ 2 tom. _Paris,_ 1893. 4°.   2031. f.

MONOPOLIES AND COMMERCIAL TRUSTS. BOYLE (A.) Right of the State to control monopolies of necessary articles. pp. 10. _Lond._ 1888. 8°.   08275. ee. 22. (6.)

JEANS (J. S.) Trusts, Pools and corners as affecting commerce and industry. pp. 190. 1894. 8°. GIBBINS (H. de B.) Social Questions. Vol. 11.   08276. e.

SPELLING (T. C.) Treatise on Trusts and monopolies. pp. 274. _Lond._ 1893. 8°.   06616. k. 15.

VON HALLE (E.) Trusts or industrial Combinations in the U.S. pp. 350. _N.Y._ 1895. 8°.   08226. f. 18.

MONS. DECLÈVE (J.) Le théâtre à Mons. 1891. 8°. Ac. Mons. _Société des Sciences._ Mémoires. Sér. 5. Tom. 4.   Ac. 1013.

MONSÉGUR. LÉGLISE (S.) Monségur, histoire, archéologie. pp. 71. 1894. 8°. Ac. Bordeaux. _Société Archéologique._ Société Archéologique. Tom. 19.   Ac. 5297.

MONSTERS : TERATOLOGY. BLANC (L.) Les Anomalies chez l'homme et les mammifères. pp. 324. _Paris,_ 1893. 8°.   7421. b. 17.

CORDIER (H.) Les Monstres dans la légende et dans la nature. pp. 23. _Paris,_ 1890. 8°.   12430. k. 40. (6.)

DARESTE (C.) Recherches sur la production artificielle des Monstruosités. pp. 587. _Paris,_ 1891. 8°.   07581. e. 12.

GUINARD (L.) Précis de Tératologie. pp. 552. _Paris,_ 1893. 12°.   7419. aa. 5.

P.P. _Lond._ Teratologia ; contributions to antenatal pathology. _Lond._ 1894, _etc._ 8°.   P.P. 3193. b.

See also OBSTETRICS.

MONTANA. MONTANA. Montana exhibit at the World's Fair, _etc._ pp. 64. _Butte,_ 1893. 8°.   10412. a. 50.

MONTARGIS. STEIN (H.) Inventaire des archives de Montargis. pp. 232. 1893. 8°. Ac. Fontainebleau. _Société Archéologique._ Documents. Tom. 4.   Ac. 6791.

MONTBÉLIARD. TOURNIER (C.) Le Catholicisme et le protestantisme dans Montbéliard, pp. 492. _Besançon,_ 1894. 8°.   4629. b. 41.

CHENOT (C. A.) Les églises de Montbéliard pendant la Révolution. 1889. 8°. Ac. Montbéliard. _Société Scientifique._ Mémoires. Vol. 20.   Ac. 375.

MONT BLANC. _See_ ALPS.

MONT-DIEU. Monastery. GANNERON (F.) Les Antiquités de la Chartreuse du Mont Dieu. 2 pt. _Paris,_ 1893. 8°.   4629. dd. 16.

MONT-DORE. JOANNE (P.) Le Mont-Dore. pp. 191. 19. _Paris,_ 1893. 8°.   10171. a. 20.

MONTE-AMIATA. FERRARI (P. de) Le Miniere di mercurio del Monte Amiata. pp. 173. _Firenze,_ 1890. 8°.   07109. g. 23.

MONTE-CARLO. _See_ MONACO.

MONTE-CASSINO. MONTE CASSINO, _Monastery._ Spicilegium Casinense. _Montis Casini,_ 1888, _etc._ 4°.   3622. i.

—— Tabularium Casinense. _Montis Casini,_ 1887, _etc._ 8°.   4782. l.

MONTE-CASTELLO, Pisa. KIRNER (G.) Statuti di Monte Castello. pp. 136. _Bologna,_ 1890. 8°.   12226. cc.

MONTENEGRO. TONDINI (C.) Notice sur la bibliographie du Monténégro. pp. 10. _Paris,_ 1889. 8°.   11903. aa. 22. (4.)

COQUELLE (P.) Histoire du Monténégro. pp. 490. _Paris,_ 1895. 8°.   9136. h. 9.

MONTENEGRO—*continued.*

G. B. & I. *War Office.* Handbook of the armies of the minor Balkan States. pp. 61.
Lond. 1891. 8°.   8823. g. 20.

HASSERT (C.) Reise durch Montenegro.
pp. 236. *Wien*, 1893. 8°.   10125. e. 11.

MONTENEGRO. Code des biens pour la principauté de Montenegro. pp. 285.
Paris, 1892. 8°.   5756. c. 8.
See also BALKAN MOUNTAINS AND PENINSULA.

MONTE-ROSA. *See* ALPS.

MONTESPAN. MANAUD DE BOISSE (L.) Le Château de Montespan. pp. 222.
Foix, 1891. 8°.   10168. c. 30.

MONTESSON. LEBŒUF (L.) Notice historique sur Montesson. pp. 133.
Vésinet, 1890. 8°.   10169. c. 11.

MONTEVIDEO. MARIA (I. de) Anales de la defensa de Montevideo, 1842–51. 4 tom.
Montevideo, 1883–87. 8°.   9772. ecc. 11.

MITRE (B.) Ricordi dell' assedio di Montevideo. 1843–51. pp. 24. *Firenze*, 1882. 8°.
     9004. bbb. 16. (1.)

MONTFORT-L'AMAURY. Ac. Rambouillet. *Société Archéologique.* DION (A. de) *Count.* Montfort-l'Amaury. pp. 48.
Tours, 1892. 8°.   Ac. 5340/6.

MONTGOMERYSHIRE. Ac. Welshpool. *Powysland Club.* Pedigrees of Montgomeryshire families. pp. 167. 1888. *Lond.* 1888. 8°.
     Ac. 8225/2.

WILLIAMS (R.) Montgomeryshire Worthies. pp. 340. *Newtown*, 1894. 8°.   10803. d. 1.

MONTLUÇON. DES GOZIS (M.) Les Montluçonnais de 1490–97. pp. 174.
Moulins, 1893. 8°.   9906. ee. 5.

MONTPELLIER. GUIRAUD (L.) Les fondations du pape Urbain v. à Montpellier. 3 vol.
Montpellier, 1889–91. 8°.   4629. i. 19.

COSTE (L.) Les transformations de Montpellier. 1891. 8°. Ac. Montpellier. *Société de Géographie.* Bulletin. Tom. 14.   Ac. 6033.

LA ROQUE (L. de) Les Évêques de Maguelone et de la Montpellier. pp. 312.
Montpellier, 1893. 8°.   4864. c. 18.

MANDON (L.) Histoire du Prêt-gratuit de Montpellier. pp. 272. *Montpellier*, 1891. 8°.
     8282. ff. 3.

MOUTON (E.) F. Ranchin, premier consul de la ville de Montpellier pendant la peste de 1629. pp. 103. *Marseille*, 1892. 8°.   010662. g. 12.

Ac. Montpellier. *Université.* Cartulaire de l'Université. *Montpellier*, 1890, *etc.* 4°.
     Ac. 379/4.

PÉLISSIER (L. G.) Documents sur la faculté des lettres de Montpellier. pp. 50.
Montpellier, 1892. 8°.   Pam. 17.

ROUZAUD (H.) Les Fêtes du VIᵉ centenaire de l'Université. pp. 259. *Montpellier*, 1891. 8°.
     8356. k. 18.
See also HÉRAULT, *Department.*

MONTREAL, Canada. Ac., *etc.* Ottawa. *Royal Society of Canada.* Handbook and historical sketch of Montreal. pp. 140.
Montréal, 1891. 8°.   Ac. 1884.

LEBLOND DE BRUMATH (A.) Histoire de Montréal. pp. 454. *Montréal*, 1890. 8°.   10470. f. 27.

MONTREAL. Illustrated Montreal. pp. 81.
Montréal, 1892. *obl.* 8°.   10460. df. 6.

JOHNSTON (W.) and VILLENEUVE (G.) Revue des enquêtes tenues par la Cour du Coroner du District de Montréal, 1893. pp. 11.
Montréal, 1894. 8°.   Pam. 33.

MONTREAL, Canada—*continued.*

MONTREAL. *Board of Trade.* Semi-centennial Report of the Montreal Board of Trade. pp. 224.
Montreal, 1893. 8°.   10470. g. 29.

Ac. Montreal. *University.* Graduates of McGill University. pp. 51. *Montreal*, 1890. 8°.
     8365. c. 74.

MONTRÉAL, Gers. MONTRÉAL Comptes des consuls de Montréal-du-Gers. 1411–14.
Bordeaux, 1894, *etc.* 4°.   7709. i.

MONTREUIL-SOUS-BOIS. RAVEY (A.) Le Pays des Pêches. pp. 166.
Montreuil, 1893. 8°.   10171. ccc. 5.

MONTREUIL-SUR-MER. BRAQUEHAY (A.) Essai sur l'Abbaye de Saint-Austrelerte à Montreuil-sur-Mer. pp. 84. *Abbeville*, 1895. 8°.
     4629. f. 29.

MONTROSE. LOW (J. G.) Memorials of the church of St. John the Evangelist. pp. 208.
Montrose, 1891. 8°.   010370. f. 18.

SMITH (J. M.) Montrose. *Edinb.* 1891. fol.
     1785. b. 11.

MONT SAINT MICHEL.
See SAINT MICHEL.

MONTSERRAT, Island. ALEXANDER (G. R.) The Island of Montserrat. pp. 23.
Carlisle, 1886. 8°.   10408. de. 13. (1.)

MONTSERRAT, Mountain. CORNET Y MAS (C.) Tres días en Montserrat. pp. 400.
Barcelona, 1890. 8°.   10151. aa. 5.

MONZA. FUMAGALLI (C.) and BELTRAMI (L.) La capella detta della Regina Teodolinda nella Basilica di San Giovanni in Monza. pp. 17.
Milano, 1891. fol.   7855. k. 16.

MONZA. *Società dei Mercanti.* Statuti della Società dei mercanti di Monza. pp. 243.
Monza, 1891. 4°.   8248. f. 28.

ZERBI (L.) I fortilizi di Monza prima dell' anno 1325, *etc.* pp. 54. *Milano*, 1891. 8°.
     10105. ec. 10. (7.)

—— Il Castello di Monza. 1892, *etc.* 4°. Ac Milan. *Società Storica.* Archivo Storico. Ser. 2. Fasc. 83, *etc.*   Ac. 6525.

MOON. BALL (*Sir* R. S.) Time and Tide. Romance of the moon. pp. 192. 1892. 8°. Romance of Science Series.   4421. de.

EKHOLM (N. G.) and ARRHENIUS (S.) Ueber den Einfluss des Mondes auf den elektrischen Zustand der Erde. pp. 50. 1894. 8°. Ac. Stockholm. *K. Svenska Vetenskaps-Akademien.* Bihang til handlingar. Bd. 19.   Ac. 1070/7.

ELGER (T. G.) The Moon. Description and map. pp. 173. *Lond.* 1895. 8°.   8561. i. 27.

HOLDEN (E. S.) Photographs of the Moon, made at the Lick Observatory. pp. 8. 1892. 8°.
     Pam. 4.

JAEGER (G.) Wetter und Mond. pp. 56.
Stuttgart, 1894. 8°.   8756. cc. 42.

MÉNÉTRIER (L. F. D.) Note sur l'influence de la Lune. pp. 32. *Bar-sur-Aube*, 1889. 8°.
     Pam. 4.

PEAL (S. E.) Theory of Lunar surfacing by Glaciation. pp. 25. *Calcutta*, 1889. 8°.
     8561. f. 36.

—— Possible cause for Lunar libration other than an ellipsoidal figure. pp. 8.
Lond. 1891. 8°.   Pam. 4.

VERY (F. W.) Prize Essay on the distribution of the Moon's Heat. pp. 45.
The Hague, 1891. 4°.   8560. g. 43.
See also ASTRONOMY : SUN.

MOORS. *See* ARABS.

MORALITY, General. CLEMANCE (C.) How to get on. pp. 32. *Lond.* 1895. 16°.
4422. d. 17. (7.)

BURATTI (C.) La Religione e la morale scientifica. pp. 288. *Milano*, 1894. 8°.   8409. c. 48.

DAWSON (W. J.) The Making of manhood. pp. 269. *Lond.* 1894. 8°.   8409. dd. 1.

DYMOND (J.) Essays on the principles of Morality. pp. 294. *Dublin*, 1894. 8°. 8408. g. 31.

ELLEFSEN (O.) Om Moralens oprindelse. pp. 131. *Kristiania*, 1893. 8°.   8409. l. 16.

FONTANA (G.) La Morale e l' estetica. pp. 349. *Milano*, 1889. 8°.   8409. ee. 21.

GERICHTSREFERENDAR. Ein Salongespräch über die Sittlichkeit. pp. 31. *Mülheim*, 1892. 8°.
Pam. 85.

GILES (A. E.) Moral Pathology. pp. 179. *Lond.* 1895. 8°.   08276. ee. 9.

KIDD (J.) Morality and religion. pp. 458. *Edinb.* 1895. 8°.   4372. cc. 23.

KRAMER (J. W.) The Right Road. pp. 282. *Lond.* 1892. 8°.   8409. h. 14.

LIFE. The successful Life. pp. 251. *Lond.* 1892. 8°.   8411. cc. 21.

MUNGER (T. T.) On the Threshold. pp. 248. *Lond.* 1892. 8°.   8411. cc. 20.

RONCATI (F.) La Decadenza della moralità ed il contagio morale. *Bologna*, 1895. 8°. Pam. 85.

WAGNER (C.) Courage. pp. 237. *Lond.* 1894. 8°.   8409. e. 29.

See also ETHICS.

Sexual Morality.

AMBROSE (H.) Convicted Law-breakers as law-makers. pp. 150. *Lond.* 1892. 8°. 8416. de. 25.

BEALE (L. S.) Our Morality and the moral question. pp. 244. *Lond.* 1893. 8°. 7641. aa. 35.

BEWES (W. A.) Manual of Vigilance law. pp. 71. *Lond.* 1888. 8°.   6485. aa. 26.

BLACKWELL (E.) Christian duty in regard to vice. pp. 6. *Lond.* 1891. 8°. 8411. cc. 30. (4.)

ENGLAND. *Church of England Purity Society.* Papers for men. *Lond.* 1885, *etc.* 8°. 8416. d.

HOLBROOK (M. L.) Chastity. pp. 104. *N.Y.* 1894. 8°.   8415. de. 33.

HOLLOWELL (J. H.) Brotherly Honour versus selfish passion. pp. 8. *Lond.* 1887. 8°.
8425. bbb. 43. (2.)

KELLOGG (J. H.) Social Purity. pp. 106. *North Fitzroy*, 1895. 8°.   8425. aa. 41.

LONDON. *Moral Reform Union.* Collection of pamphlets. *Lond.* 1888, *etc.* 8° & 16°. 8285. cc.

—— *National Vigilance Association.* Pernicious literature. Debate in the House of Commons, *etc.* pp. 32. *Lond.* 1889. 8°.   Pam. 85.

—— *Social Purity Alliance.* Annual Report. *Lond.* 1888, *etc.* 8°.   8285. cc. 43.

PAQUIN (P.) The Supreme Passions of man. pp. 150. *Battle Creek*, 1891. 8°.   7641. a. 34.

PATHWAY. The Pathway of Health and Happiness. pp. 128. *Lond.* 1895. 32°. 8415. a. 37.

RYDER (*Sir* A. P.) A Paper on Purity and the prevention of the degradation of women and children. pp. 112. *Lond.* 1884. 8°.
8282. de. 47.

SCUDDER (C. D.) Handbook for young men. pp. 92. *N.Y.* 1892. 8°.   8416. df. 8.

SPERRY (L. B.) Confidental Talks with young men. pp. 179. *Edinb.* 1894. 8°. 7641. aaa. 29.

WARD (E.) The Vital Question. pp. 27. *Lond.* 1892. 16°.   8416. aa. 65.

MORAT, Battle of.
See SWITZERLAND, *History.*

MORAVIA. Ao. Brunn. *K.K. Mähr.-Schl. Gesellschaft.* General-Repertorium zu den Publicationen der histor.-statist. Section du Gesellschaft. pp. 40. *Brünn*, 1889. 8°. Ac. 745/6.

BRETHOLZ (B.) Geschichte Mährens. *Brünn*, 1893, *etc.* 8°.   10255. h.

KIRCHMAYR (H.) Der altdeutsche Volkstamm der Quaden. 2 Bde. *Brünn.* 1888, 93. 8°.
9325. ff. 5.

BRETHOLZ (B.) Mähren und das Reich Herzog Boleslavs II. von Böhmen. 1895. 8°. Archiv für Kunde österreichischer Geschichts-Quellen. Bd. 82.   Ac. 810/8.

SKENE (A. v) Entstehen der slavish-nationalen Bewegung in Böhmen und Mähren im XIX. Jahrhundert. pp. 155. *Wien*, 1895. 8°.
8074. ff. 29.

DEUTSCH (E.) Die Preussen in Mähren 1866. pp. 63. *Brünn*, 1891. 8°.   9007. ff. 4. (7.)

COLE (G. A. J.) The Gypsy Road. pp. 166. *Lond.* 1894. 8°.   10108. de. 12.

KARFELES (B.) Moravian and Silesian miners. *Lond.* 1894, *etc.* 8°.   8223. df. 24.

MORAVIAN BRETHREN.
See BRETHREN.

MORAY, Province : Diocese. DUNBAR (M.) Documents relating to the Province of Moray. pp. 179. *Edinb.* 1895. 8°.   010370. f. 34.

MACDONALD (M.) The Covenanters in Moray and Ross. pp. 226. *Inverness*, 1892. 8°. 4735. aaa. 39.

See also BANFFSHIRE : INVERNESS : NAIRNSHIRE.

MORECAMBE. WADDINGTON (T. A. J.) Guide to Morecambe. pp. 35. *York*, 1894. 8°.
10348. c. 25. (13.)

MORMONISM : UTAH : SALT LAKE CITY. MORMON, *Book of.* The Book of Mormon. pp. 623. *Liverp.* 1883. 8°. 4182. aa. 35.

SMITH (J.) Doctrine and covenants of the Church of Latter-day Saints. pp. 503. *Liverp.* 1882. 8°.
4182. c. 27.

—— The Pearl of great Price ; selection from the revelations of J. Smith. pp. 90. *Liverp.* 1882. 8°.   4182. cc. 25.

GREGG (T.) The Prophet of Palmyra (Joseph Smith). pp. 552. *N.Y.* 1890. 8°. 4985. dd. 17.

CARROLL (H. K.) Report of statistics of Churches in the U.S. pp. 812. 1894. 8°. Eleventh Census of the U.S.   1882. c. 1.

CROCHERON (A. J.) Representative Women of Deseret. pp. 131. *Salt Lake City*, 1884. 8°.
10883. aaa. 33.

DONAN (P.) Utah. Peep into a mountain-walled treasury of the Gods. pp. 96. *Buffalo*, 1891. 8°.   10412. cc. 27.

H , M. Mormonismen og Saltsøstaden. pp. 76. 1893. 8°. NIELSEN (F.) Smaaskrifter til Oplysning for Kristne. Bd. 8.   3605. i.

LATTER-DAY JUDGMENTS. Latter day Judgments. pp. 4. *Southampton*, 1890. 8°. 4139. dd. 1. (7.)

LITTLEFIELD (L. O.) The Martyrs : lives of Joseph and Hyrum Smith. pp. 120. *Salt Lake City*, 1882. 8°.   4985. c. 32.

MERRIAM (F. A.) My Summer in a Mormon village. pp. 171. *Bost.* 1894. 8°. 10412. aaa. 43.

MONTGOMERY (M. W.) The Mormon Delusion. pp. 354. *Bost.* 1890. 8°.   4182. c. 23.

THOMAS (W. H.) Mormon Saints. pp. 200. *Lond.* 1890. 8°.   4182. aa. 36.

WOTHERSPOON (G.) Mormonism : its history and moral. pp. 27. 1886. 8°. London. *Sunday Lecture Society.* Selection 5.   4018. c.

SALT LAKE CITY. *Knutsford Hotel.* The Knutsford, Salt Lake City. pp. 67. 1891. 8°.
10413. bb. 36.

MOROCCO. *See* MAROCCO.

MORPHIA. Chambard (E.) Les Morphinomanes. pp. 274. *Paris*, 1893. 8°. 7660. de. 13.

Guimbail (H.) Les Morphinomanes. pp. 312. *Paris*, 1891. 8°. 8436. b. 41.

Regnier (L. R.) L'Intoxication chronique par la morphine. pp. 171. *Paris*, 1890. 8°. 7660. df. 19.

Talmeyr (M.) Les Possédés de la morphine. pp. 248. *Paris*, 1892. 12°. 8435. de. 16.

MORPHOLOGY. *See* Anatomy.

MORTGAGE, Law of. Beddoes (W. F.) Treatise on the Law of Mortgage. pp. 230. *Lond.* 1893. 8°. 6305. e. 20.

Boone (C. T.) The Law of Mortgages. pp. 552. *San Francisco*, 1886. 12°. 6615. a. 4.

Indermaur (J.) and Thwaites (C.) Student's Guide to Mortgages. pp. 102. *Lond.* 1886. 8°. 6375. de. 8.

Kelleher (J.) Mortgage in the civil Law. pp. 257. *Calcutta*, 1893. 8°. 5206. ee. 31.

Morris (R. B.) Summary of the Law of Mortgage Registration in the British Empire and foreign countries. pp. 176. *Lond.* 1895. 8°. 6306. f. 12.

Möller (E. J.) Dækningsadgang eller Fordringsret. pp. 527. *Kjøbenh.* 1892. 8°. 5725. bb. 7.

Rasavihārī Ghosha. The Law of Mortgage in India. pp. 561. *Calcutta*, 1889. 8°. 5318. d. 19. *See also* Land Tenures.

MOSAIC. Bolton (A. T.) Examples of Mosaic Pavings from rubbings of floors at Pompeii and Venice. 12 pt. *Lond.* 1891. fol. 1703. c. 12.

Demangeot (J. E.) Mosaïques gréco-romaines. pp. 34. *Paris*, 1892. 8°. 07703. f. 2. (5.)

Elis (C.) Handbuch der Mosaik- und Glasmalerei. 1891. 8°. Seemann's Kunsthandbücher. No. 8. 7805. de.

France. *Commission de la manufacture de Mosaique.* Rapport. pp. 13. *Paris*, 1890. 8°. 7806. de. 22. (7.)

Morgan (T.) Romano-British Mosaic Pavements. pp. 323. *Lond.* 1886. 8°. 7706. e. 40.

Sentex (J. F. L. O.) Les Mosaïques gallo-romaines du Gléyzia. pp. 40. *Dax*, 1891. 8°. 7706. f. 20. (9.)

MOSQUITO. Lamborn (R. H.) Dragon Flies vs. Mosquitoes. pp. 202. *N.Y.* 1890. 8°. 7297. b. 22. *See also* Diptera.

MOSQUITO INDIAN LANGUAGE. *See* Indian Languages.

MOSSES. Arnell (H. W.) Musci Asiæ Borealis. Beschreibung der von den schwedischen Expeditionen nach Sibirien gesammelten Moose. 1889, 90. 4°. Ac. Stockholm. *K. Svenska Vetenskaps Academien.* Handlingar. N.F. Bd. 23. Ac. 1070.

Bastit (E.) Recherches sur la tige et la feuille des mousses. pp. 116. *Paris*, 1891. 8°. 7028. d. 2.

Breidler (J.) Die Laubmoose Steiermarks. pp. 234. *Graz*, 1891. 8°. 07028. l. 3.

Campbell (D. H.) Structure and development of Mosses. pp. 544. *Lond.* 1895. 8°. 07028. f. 64.

Douin (J.) Flore des Mousses et des hépatiques. pp. 186. 1893. 8°. Histoire naturelle de la France. 7207. cc.

Fry (*Right Hon. Sir* E.) British Mosses. pp. 71. *Lond.* 1892. 8°. 7054. b. 22.

Jameson (H. G.) Illustrated guide to British Mosses. pp. 75. *Eastbourne*, 1893. 8°. 07028. l. 16.

MOSSES—*continued.*

Lange (J. M. C.) and Jensen (C.) Grønlands Mosser. 1887. 8°. Lange (J. M. C.) Conspectus Florae Groenlandicae. 10460. dd.

Klinggraeff (H. v.) Die Leber- und Laubmoose West- und Ostpreussens. pp. 317. *Danzig*, 1893. 8°. 07028. k. 10.

Kummer (P.) Der Führer in die Mooskunde. pp. 216. *Berl.* 1891. 8°. 07028. l. 5.

Paris (E. G.) Index Bryologicus. *Parisiis*, 1894, *etc.* 8°. 07028. i. *See also* Botany, *Cryptogamia* : Hepaticae.

MOSTAR. Peez (C.) Mostar und sein Culturkreis. pp. 245. *Leipz.* 1891. 8°. 10125. ee. 30.

MOTHS. *See* Lepidoptera.

MOTION, Physiological. Braune (W.) and Fischer (O.) Der Gang des Menschen. 1892, *etc.* 8°. Ac. Leipsic. *K. Sächsische Gesellschaft der Wissenschaften.* Abhandlungen. Bd. 35. Ac. 700/4.

Féré (C.) Sensation et Mouvement. pp. 164. *Paris*, 1887. 12°. 8462. aaa. 28.

Mac Kendrick (J. G.) Life in Motion. pp. 202. *Lond.* 1894. 8°. 7405. df. 17.

Marey (É. J.) Le Mouvement. pp. 335. *Paris*, 1894. 8°. 7405. cc. 6.

—— Movement. pp. 323. *Lond.* 1895. 8°. 7407. de. 8.

Muybridge (E.) Descriptive Zoopraxography. *Phila.* 1893. 8°. 7857. c. 30.

Blocq (P.) Les Troubles de la Marche dans les maladies nerveuses. pp. 159. *Paris*, 1893. 8°. 7630. aaa. 37.

Kirmisson (É.) Leçons sur les maladies de l'appareil locomoteur. pp. 550. *Paris*, 1890 8°. 7442. g. 19. *See also* Muscles.

MOTTOES. Dielitz (J.) Die Wahl- und Denksprüche, besonders des Mittelalters und der Neuzeit. pp. 476. *Frankfurt*, 1888. 4°. 9916. dd. 10.

Mair (J. A.) Proverbs and Mottoes. pp. 192. *Lond.* 1891. 8°. 12305. d. 38. *See also* Heraldry.

MOUFFLON. Bergerat (É.) La chasse au Mouflon. pp. 348. *Paris*, 1893. 12°. 10136. ee. 1.

MOUKDEN. *See* Manchuria.

MOULINS. Argouges (F. d') Procès-verbal de la généralité de Moulins, 1686. pp. 291. *Moulins*, 1892. 8°. 9226. h. 21.

Fodéré (J.) Le Monastère de Sainte-Claire de Moulins. pp. 35. *Moulins*, 1892. 8°. 4629. bbb. 17. (8.)

MOULTON, Lincolnshire. Foster (W. E.) All Saints' Church, Moulton. 2 pt. *Lincoln*, 1891. 8°. 010358. f. 33.

MOULTON, Northamptonshire. Madge (S.) Moulton Church and its bells. pp. 95. *Lond.* 1895. 8°. 3477. ee. 3.

MOUNTAINS : MOUNTAINEERING. Hutchinson (H. N.) The story of the Hills. pp. 357. *Lond.* 1892. 8°. 7106. ff. 12.

Pfaff (A. B. I. F.) Der Mechanismus der Gebirgsbildung. pp. 143. *Heidelberg*, 1880. 8°. 7109. g. 19.

Balch (E. S.) Mountain Exploration. 1893. 8°. Ac. Philadelphia. *Geographical Club.* Bulletin. Vol. 1. Ac. 6189.

British Islands. Climbing in the British Isles. *Lond.* 1894 *etc.* 8°. 10347. a. 25.

MOUNTAINS, etc.—_continued._

CONWAY (_Sir_ W. M.) and COOLIDGE (W. A. B.) Climbers' guides. _Lond._ 1892, _etc._ 16°. 10108. b.

DENT (C. T.) Mountaineering. pp. 481. 1892. 4°. Badminton Library. 7905. f.

MEURER (J.) and RABL (J.) Der Bergsteiger im Hochgebirge. pp. 264. _Wien_, 1893. 8°. 10196. ee. 4.

PRESTWICH (J.) On underground Temperatures, and on a special source of heat in mountain ranges. pp. 116. _Lond._ 1886. 8°. 8756. de. 41.

MUMMERY (A. F.) My Climbs in the Alps and Caucasus. pp. 360. _Lond._ 1895. 8°. K.T.C. 35. b. 2.

WILSON (C.) Mountaineering. pp. 208. 1893. 8°. All England Series. 7908. df.

TRUTAT (E.) La Photographie en montagne. pp. 137. _Paris_, 1894. 12°. 8909. bb. 63.

See also ALPS: ANDES: APENNINES: GEOLOGY: HIMALAYAS: NEW ZEALAND: PYRENEES: RIESENGEBIRGE: ROCKY MOUNTAINS: VOLCANOES: VOSGES.

Mountain Warfare.

MORIS (H.) Opérations militaires dans les Alpes pendant la guerre de la succession, 1742–48. pp. 360. _Paris_, 1886. 8°. 9079. k. 4.

KREBS (L.) and MORIS (H.) Campagnes dans les Alpes pendant la Révolution. 1792–93. pp. 399. _Paris_, 1891. 8°. 9079. k. 2.

PHILIPPE (C.) Le Général Badelaune et la défense des Alpes en 1793–94. pp. 160. _Annecy_, 1894. 8°. 9079. e. 6.

BIOT ( ) and MASSARD (É.) La Guerre de montagnes. _Paris_, 1891, _etc._ 8°.. 733.

BUTTET (M. de) Les Alpins. Étude sur les troupes cantonnées dans les Alpes. pp. 224. _Thonon-les-Bains_, 1894. 8°. 10196. f. 18.

CAMAU (É.) La Guerre dans les Alpes. pp. 282. _Paris_, 1890. 8°. 8823. g. 11.

FRANCE. _Ministère de la Guerre._ Règlement sur le service des Batteries de montagne. _Paris_, 1894, _etc._ 12°. 8832. aa.

G. B. & I. _Army._ Mountain Artillery Drill. pp. 176. _Lond._ 1891. 16°. 8831. aa. 37.

PARAZ (C.) Considérations sur la défense des Alpes franco-italiennes. pp. 48. _Albertville_, 1894. 8°. 8830. c. 43. (14.)

PERRIN (E.) Topographie et défense des Alpes françaises. pp. 758. _Périgueux_, 1894. 8°. 8830. l. 30.

MOUNT EDGCUMBE. WRIGHT (W. H. K.) Ramble round Mount Edgcumbe. pp. 42. _Plymouth_, 1892. 8°. Pam. 90.

MOUTH. BALCOMB (J. T.) Diagrams of the Mouth. _Lond._ 1891. 4°. 7616. a. 35.

BRESGEN (M.) Krankheits- und Behandlungslehre der Nasen- Mund- und Rachenhöhle. pp. 432. _Wien_, 1891. 8°. 7615. ee. 40.

JESSETT (F. B.) Cancer of the Mouth. pp. 183. _Lond._ 1892. 8°. 7616. f. 6.

MIKULICZ (J.) and MICHELSON (P. O.) Atlas der Krankheiten der Mund- und Rachenhöhle. _Berl._ 1891, _etc._ 4°. 7611. h.

ROSE (W.) On Harelip and cleft palate. pp. 172. _Lond._ 1891. 8°. 7480. ee. 11.

See also JAW: TEETH: TONGUE.

MOUTIERS. MOUTIERS. Règlement de Police pour la ville de Moutiers, 1779. pp. 144. _Chambery_, 1890. 16°. 6055. a. 5.

MOVEMENT. _See_ MOTION.

MOYLAND. SCHOLTEN (R.) Urkundliches über Moyland. 1890. 8°. Ac. Cologne. _Historischer Verein._ Annalen. Hft. 50. Ac. 7335.

MOZAMBIQUE. _See_ AFRICA, _Colonisation, Portuguese._

MULE. TEGETMEIER (W. B.) Horses, Mules, etc. _Lond._ 1895. 8°. 07293. i. 27.

MULHAUSEN. MULHAUSEN. Livre d'or—Bürgerbuch—de la ville de Mulhouse. pp. 431. _Mulhouse_, 1883. fol. 9905. k. 4.

TOURNIER (É.) Mülhausen im 16. Jahrhundert. pp. 53. _Illzach_, 1894. 8°. 4662. c. 25. (8.)

MÜLHEIM, a. d. Rhur. KLANKE ( ) and RICHTER ( ) Geschichte der Unterherrschaft Broich sowie der Stadt Mülheim an der Ruhr. pp. 390. _Mülheim_, 1891. 8°. 10255. f. 21.

MUMBLES. JARVIS (W. L.) New guide to the Mumbles and Gower. pp. 87. _Swansea_, 1895. 8°. 10368. aa. 51.

MUNICH. AHLAND (E.) München vor 40. Jahren. pp. 31. _München_, 1894. 8°. 10255. d. 5.

HAEUTLE (C.) Die fürstlichen Wohnsitze der Wittelsbacher in München. pp. 124. 1892. 8°. REINHARDSTOETTNER (C. v.) Bayerische Bibliothek. Bd. 27. 12253. g.

KHAN (J.) Münchens Grossindustrie und Grosshandel. pp. 206. _München_, 1891. 4°. 8223. f. 32.

KURZ (F.) Der Antheil der münchener Studenschaft an den Unruhen, 1847–48. pp. 112. _Münster_, 1893. 8°. 8357. bb. 35.

RUEPPRECHT (C.) Die Büchersammlungen der Universität München. pp. 50. _Regensburg_, 1892. 8°. Pam. 6.

TINSCH (H.) Das Stadtrecht von München. pp. 81. _Bamberg_, 1891. 8°. 05604. g. 6. (2.)

MUNICIPALITIES. _See_ TOWNS.

MÜNSTER, Alsace. HECKER (F.) Die Stadt und das Thal zu Münster. pp. 192. _Münster_, 1890. 8°. 10256. ee. 12.

MÜNSTEREIFEL. PLOENNIS (A.) Die Geschichte des Stiftes Münstereifel. pp. 100. _Bonn_, 1891. 8°. 4662. d. 18. (3.)

SCHEINS (M.) Urkundliche Beiträge zur Geschichte der Stadt Münstereifel. _Münstereifel_, 1894, _etc._ 8°. 10261. f.

MURCIA. MADRID. _Junta de Socorros para los pueblos de la provincia de Murcia._ Memoria de la inundación de Murcia 14 y 15 de Oct. 1879. pp. 931. _Madrid_, 1892. 8°. 8756. eee. 24.

MURDER. _See_ HOMICIDE.

MURI, Aargau. MARKWART (O.) Die Baugeschichte der Klosters Muri. pp. 97. _Aarau_, 1890. 8°. 4662. d. 14.

MURRAY ISLAND. SCHULENBURG (A. v. d.) _Count._ Grammatik der Sprache von Murray Island. pp. 133. 1892. 8°. Einzelbeiträge zur Sprachwissenschaft. Hft. 11. 12902. g. _See also_ NEW GUINEA.

MUSCLES. CHAVEAU (A.) Le Travail musculaire. pp. 373. _Paris_, 1891. 8°. 7406. f. 8.

FISCHER (O.) Die Arbeit der Muskeln. pp. 88. 1893. 4°. Ac. Leipsic. _Gesellschaft der Wissenschaften._ Abhandlungen. Bd. 33. Ac. 700/4.

HOFFA (A.) Zur Pathogenese der arthritischen Muskelatrophien. pp. 12. 1892. 8°. VOLKMANN (R. v.) Sammlung klinischer Vorträge. N.F. Nr. 50. 7441. g.

LEDOUBLE (A.) Des conformations anomales des Muscles de la face. 2 pt. _Lond._ 1884. 8°. Pam. 39.

—— Des variations morphologiques des Muscles de la main. pp. 47. _Nancy_, 1895. 8°. Pam. 39.

—— Anomalies des Muscles masticateurs de l'homme. _Paris_, 1893. 8°. Pam. 39.

MUSCLES—*continued*.

MAC KENDRICK (J. G.) Life in Motion. pp. 202. *Lond.* 1894. 8°.   7405. df. 17.

MUELLER (G. E.) Theorie der Muskelcontraktion. *Leipz.* 1891, *etc.* 8°.   7419. i. 17.

NAUWERCK (C.) Ueber Muskelregeneration nach Verletzungen. pp. 58. *Jena,* 1890. 8°.
07305. k. 11. (2.)

POTTER (S. O. L.) Traumatism of Muscle as a factor of internal disease. pp. 7. 1889. 8°.
07305. h. 4. (10.)

RIEGER (C.) Haltung, Heizung und Bewegung der Muskeln. pp. 48. 1892. 8°. Ac. Wurzburg. *Physikalisch - medicinische Gesellschaft.* Verhandlungen. N. F. Bd. 26.   Ac. 3763/3.

ROLLETT (A.) Untersuchungen über Contraction der quergestreiften Muskelfasern. 1891. 8°. Ac. Vienna. *K. Akademie der Wissenschaften.* Denkschriften. Math.-naturwissenschaftliche Classe. Bd. 58.   Ac. 810/13.

ROHDE (E.) Muskel und Nerv. 2 pt. 1892. 8°.

SCHNEIDER (A.) Zoologische Beiträge. Bd. 3.
7208. i. 8.

SAMPSON (C. A.) Strength; treatise on the development of muscle. pp. 240.
Lond. 1895. 8°.   7404. aaaa. 5.

SHUFELDT (R. W.) The Myology of the Raven. pp. 343. *Lond.* 1890. 8°.   7285. ee. 16.

UNVERRICHT (H.) Die Myoclonie. pp. 128. *Leipz.* 1891. 8°.   7620. ee. 31.

VOSSELER (J.) Untersuchungen über glatte und unvollkommen quergestreifte Muskeln der Arthropoden. pp. 149. *Tübingen,* 1891. 8°.
7297. e. 35.

WEBER (F. P.) Muscular Cramp, in relation with the phenomena of Angina Pectoris. pp. 8. *Phila.* 1894. 8°.   7305. f. 6. (16.)
See also MOTION : PHYSIOLOGY.

MUSEUMS, of Art and Antiquities.
See EXHIBITIONS, *Pt. I.*

MUSEUMS, of Natural History.
See NATURAL HISTORY.

MUSHROOMS. *See* FUNGI.

MUSIC. *See also* ART.

Bibliography.

BROWN (J. D.) Guide to the formation of a Music Library. pp. 22. 1893. 8°. Ac. Great Britain and Ireland. *Library Association.* Library Association Series. No. 4. Ac. 9115/7.

DEAKIN (A.) Musical Bibliography. Musical works published in England, 15th–18th centuries. pp. 68. *Birmingham,* 1892. 4°.
011901. ee. 15.

EITNER (R.) and KADE (O.) Katalog der Musik-Sammlung der K. Bibliothek zu Dresden. pp. 150. 1890. 8°. Ac. Berlin. *Gesellschaft für Musikforschung.* Monatshefte. Beilage.
Ac. 5144.

EITNER (R.) Quellen- und Hilfswerke beim Studium der Musikgeschichte. pp. 55. *Leipz.* 1891. 8°.   011900. f. 10. (17.)

FULLER-MAITLAND (J. A.) and MANN (A. H.) Catalogue of Music in the Fitzwilliam Museum, Cambridge. pp. 298. *Lond.* 1893. 8°.
7897. cc. 30.

KADE (O.) Die Musikalien. Sammlung des mecklenburg-schweriner Fürstenhauses. 2 Bde. *Schwerin,* 1893. 8°.   7895. dd. 11.

MUELLER (J.) Katalog der musikalischen Bibliothek J. Müller. 2 Abth. *Berl.* 1861, 82. 8°.
011903. k. 48.

P.P. *Leipsic.* Verzeichniss der im Jahre 1880–81, *etc.,* erschienenen Musikalien. *Leipz.* 1881, *etc.* 8°.   P.P. 1945. al.

MUSIC.—Bibliography—*continued*.

P.P. *Vevey.* Catalogue de toutes les publications musicales de la France, la Belgique et la Suisse. *Vevey,* 1890, *etc.* 8°.   011902. g.

PETERS (C. F.) Katalog der Musikbibliothek Peters. 2 Abth. *Leipz.* 1894. 8°. 7895. g. 18.

PFUDEL (E.) Die Musik-Handschriften der Ritter-Akademie zu Liegnitz. pp. 74. 1886. 8°. Ac. Berlin. *Gesellschaft für Musikforschung.* Monatshefte. Beilage.   Ac. 5144.

SCHEURLEER (D. F.) Catalogus der muziekbibliotheek van D. F. Scheurleer. pp. 567. *'s Gravenhage,* 1893. 8°.   011900. h. 16.

VOGEL (E.) Biblioteca della Musica vocale italiana stampata dal 1500 al 1700. 2 Bde. *Berl.* 1892. 8°.   7897. dd. 7.

General : Theory of Music.

ARLBERG (F.) Försök till en naturlig och förnuftig grundläggning af tonbildningsläran. pp. 209. *Stockholm,* 1891. 8°.   7898. l. 21.

Ac. London. *R. Academy of Music.* DAVENPORT (F.) Elements of Music. pp. 51. *Lond.* 1891. 8°.   7896. de. 38.

—— *Trinity College.* Text-Book of Musical knowledge. pp. 89. *Lond.* 1891. 8°.
7858. aa. 50. (5.)

BRIDGE (J. F.) Musical Gestures : Guide to the rudiments of music. pp. 83. 1894. 8°. Novello's Music Primers.   7895. ff.

CROTTI (P.) Musiconomia. pp. 45. *Parma,* 1890. 8°.   7896. c. 43. (5.)

DANNREUTHER (E.) Musical Ornamentation. 2 pt. 1893–95. 8°. Novello's Music Primers.
7895. ff.

DUNSTAN (R.) Manual of Music. pp. 263. *Lond.* 1894. 8°.   7898. bb. 43.

FISHER (H.) The Candidate in Music. 2 pt. *Lond.* 1894. 8°.   7898. cc. 25.

GARDINER (A.) Rudiments of the theory of Music. pp. 229. *Manch.* 1893. 8°.   7898. aaaa. 30.

GREIG (J.) The Musical Educator. *Edinb.* 1895, *etc.* 4°.   7897. dd. 9.

GUIRAUD (E.) Traité d'Instrumentation. pp. 210. *Paris,* 1892. 8°.   7897. c. 46.

HOERING (A.) Musical Students' practical guide. pp. 126. *Teddington,* 1893. 8°.   7898. f. 15.

HOLMES (G. A.) Academic Manual of the rudiments of Music. pp. 55. *Lond.* 1891. 8°.
7898. c. 42.

—— Questions and exercises on the Academic Manual. pp. 64. *Lond.* 1892. 8°. 7899. aaa. 12.

KISTLER (C.) Musikalische Elementarlehre. pp. 58. *Chemnitz,* 1880. 8°.   7897. k. 3.

KLAUSER (J.) The Septonate and centralization of the Tonal System. pp. 274. *Milwaukee,* 1890. 8°.   7896. dd. 9.

KRAUSE (C. C. F.) Zur Theorie der Musik. pp. 75. *Berl.* 1894. 8°.   7899. dd. 6.

LABATUT (L.) La Musique rendue facile par la suppression des portées et des clés. pp. 48. *Condom,* 1890. 4°.   7897. l. 9.

LONGMANS, GREEN AND Co. Longmans' Music course. *Lond.* 1894, *etc.* 8°.   7898. bbb.

LUSSY (M.) Le Rythme musical. pp. 104. *Paris,* 1884. 8°.   7895. g. 20.

—— Traité de l'Expression musicale. pp. 184. *Paris,* 1892. 8°.   7896. f. 35.

MITCHERD (J. W.) Easy system of Music. pp. 7. *Portmadoc,* 1891. obl. 4°.   1865. c. 1. (4.)

OXFORD AND CAMBRIDGE THEORY OF MUSIC. Oxford and Cambridge theory of Music. 2 vol. *Lond.* 1887. 8°.   7898. aa. 55.

MUSIC.—General, etc.—continued.

PROUT (E.) Musical Form. pp. 244.
Lond. 1893. 8°.   7898. b. 36.

—— Applied Forms. Sequel to "Musical Form."
pp. 292. Lond. 1895. 8°.   7899. d. 6.

RAMSAY (D. C.) Scientific Basis and build of
Music. pp. 121. Lond. 1893. 4°. 7895. aaa. 51.

RICHARDSON (M. I.) Elements of Music.
pp. 288. Lond. 1893. 8°.   7897. c. 48.

ROWLAND (J.) Practical aid to home advancement in Music. Lond. 1895. obl. 8°. 7898. i. 38.

SAMPSON (G.) Text-book of the elements of
Music. pp. 24. Brighton, 1892. 8°. 7896. a. 30.

SAXTON (M. J.) La Musique sans Larmes.
Paris, 1886. 8° & obl. fol.   M.M.

SIMPLIFIED MUSIC SERIES. Simplified Music
series. Lond. 1892. 8°.   1865. c. 1. (20.)

SNEDDON (J.) Musical Self-instructor. pp. 185.
Lond. 1891. 8°.   7898. c. 34.

WATSON (J. L.) A Manual of Music. pp. 271.
1893. 8°. Brown's School Series.   12210. c.

WEBSTER (C. A.) The Groundwork of Music.
Edinb. 1892, etc. 8°.   7898. cc.

—— Child's Primer of the theory of Music.
pp. 70. Lond. 1894. 8°.   7895. aa. 42.

LEWIS (J. H.) Counterpoint. pp. 70.
Lond. 1893. 8°.   7898. g. 53.

—— Double Counterpoint and Canon. pp. 91.
Lond. 1895. 8°.   7897. e. 49.

PROUT (E.) Double Counterpoint and Canon.
pp. 273. Lond. 1893. 8°.   7898. b. 35.

SAUNDERS (G.) Examples of strict Counterpoint,
old and new. pp. 240. 1893. 8°. Novello's
Music Primers.   7895. ff.

MARCHANT (A. W.) Five hundred Fugue Subjects and Answers. pp. 105. 1890. 8°. Novello's
Music Primers.   7895. ff.

PROUT (E.) Fugue. pp. 245. Lond. 1892. 8°.
                                  7898. b. 33.

—— Fugal Analysis. pp. 249. Lond. 1892. 8°.
                                  7898. b. 34.

BANISTER (H. C.) Helpful papers for Harmony
students. pp. 136. Lond. 1895. 8°. 7898. e. 35.

DUNSTAN (R.) Basses and Melodies for students
of harmony. pp. 167. 1894. 8°. Novello's
Music Primers.   7895. ff.

FLORIO (C.) Text-Book of practical Harmony.
pp. 192. Lond. 1892. 8°.   7897. l. 30.

—— Key. pp. 176. Lond. 1893. 8°. 7897. l. 41.

GEORGE (M.) Traité de Composition musicale
libre. pp. 292. Paris, 1894. 4°. 7895. f. 39.

HEYDEN (R.) Einführung in die Lehre von den
harmonischen Bewegungen. pp. 26.
Berl. 1892. 4°.   Pam. 38.

HILES (H.) Harmony. pp. 157.
Manch. 1894. 8°.   7896. aaa. 45.

MACFARREN (Sir G. A.) Lectures on Harmony.
pp. 281. Lond. 1892. 8°.   2264. e. 18.

OAKEY (G.) Figured Bass. pp. 37.
Lond. 1890. 8°.   7898. a. 63.

PROUT (E. B.) Harmonic Analysis. pp. 84.
Lond. 1894. 8°.   7896. b. 52.

RIEMANN (H.) Vereinfachte Harmonielehre.
pp. 213. Lond. 1893. 8°.   7898. i 37.

—— Handboek der Harmonieleer. pp. 95. 60.
's Gravenhage, 1894. 8°.   7899. d. 10.

DESCHAMPS (L.) New Method of Transposition.
pp. 4. Lond. 1891. 8°.   7897. l. 12. (5.)

WARRINER (J.) Transposition, keyboard and
orchestral. pp. 56. 1893. 8°. Novello's Music
Primers.   7895. ff.

MUSIC.—General, etc.—continued.

CRAIG (E. H.) The Octave Stave system of
musical Notation. Lond. 1891. fol. Pam. 24.

BOURKE (W. R.) Tonic Sol-faists and the minor
mode. pp. 23. Lond. 1894. 8°.
                                  7899. dd. 1. (11.)

VARGE (J.) Tonic Notation for players. 1893. 8°.
Simplified Music Series.   1865. c. 1. (20.)

BEAUDOIRE (T.) Manuel de Typographie musicale. pp. 60. Paris, 1891. 8°.   7896. dd. 8.

RAMBACH (L.) System einer Musik-Stenographie. pp. 90. Zürich, 1893. 8°. 7897. m. 2.

Æsthetics, etc.

BAUDIN (H.) Itinéraire d'un amateur dans le
romantisme lyrique. pp. 32. Tours, 1893. 16°.
                                  Pam. 15.

BELLAIGUE (C.) Psychologie musicale. pp. 282.
Paris, 1893. 8°.   7897. aaa. 74.

BOCK (A.) Deutsche Dichter in ihren Beziehungen zur Musik. pp. 264. Leipz. 1893. 8°.
                                  7898. g. 51.

DONOVAN (J.) From Lyre to Muse : aboriginal
union of music and poetry. pp. 208.
Lond. 1890. 8°.   7898. k. 36.

EASTMAN (E. V.) The Ethics of Music. pp. 77.
Bost. 1892. 8°.   7898. bbb. 34.

ENGEL (G.) Die Bedeutung der Zahlenverhält-
nisse für die Tonempfindung. pp. 59.
Dresd. 1892. 8°.   7898. m. 6. (9.)

HANSLICK (E.) Vom Musikalisch-Schönen.
pp. 196. Leipz. 1885. 8°.   7896. aa. 59.

—— The Beautiful in Music. pp. 174.
Lond. 1891. 8°.   7898. c. 44.

KADE (O.) Das Gelehrtenthum in der Tonkunst.
Schwerin, 1893. 4°.   7808. f. 21. (8.)

LIEBICH (L.) The Beautiful in Music. pp. 36.
Bristol, 1891. 8°.   7898. aa. 48.

LIND (P. v.) Moderner Geschmack und moderne
Musik. pp. 56. Leipz. 1891. 8°. 7897. aa. 69.

LOUIS (R.) Der Widerspruch in der Musik.
pp. 115. Leipz. 1893. 8°.   7896. c. 44.

MERTEN (F.) Harmonische Klangbildung nach
dem Grundakkord. pp. 275. Siegen, 1891. 8°.
                                  7897. l. 18.

MILLS (E.) The Modern Lyric from a musical
standpoint. pp. 4. Hobart, 1892. 8°. Pam. 24.

MUSIOL (R.) T. Körner und seine Beziehungen zur
Musik. pp. 96. Ratibor, 1893. 8°. 10708. de. 24.

PARRY (C. H. H.) The Art of Music. pp. 374.
Lond. 1893. 8°.   2264. e. 21.

POLE (W.) Philosophy of Music. pp. 328.
1895. 8°. English and Foreign Philosophical
Library. Vol. 11.   2318. d. 2.

PUDOR (H.) Krieg und Frieden in der Musik.
pp. 48. Dresd. 1891. 8°.   7808. e. 21. (5.)

—— Sittlichkeit und Gesundheit in der Musik.
pp. 32. Dresd. 1891. 8°.   7898. aa. 51. (3.)

—— Die alten und die neuen Wege in der
Musik. pp. 29. Dresd. 1892. 8°. 7898. m. 8. (11.)

—— Wiedergeburt in der Musik. pp. 94.
Dresd. 1892. 8°.   7898. cc. 18.

RAYMOND (G. L.) Rhythm and Harmony in
poetry and music. pp. 344. N.Y. 1895. 8°.
                                  7899. b. 7.

RIEMANN (H.) Catechism of musical Aesthetics.
pp. 67. Lond. 1895. 8°.   7899. b. 20.

RITTER (H.) Studien und Skizzen aus Musik-
und Kulturgeschichte. pp. 186.
Dresd. 1892. 8°.   7897. l. 35.

ROUGNON (P.) Le Mouvement et les nuances
d'expression dans la musique. pp. 218.
Paris, 1893. 8°.   7897. l. 40.

MUSIC.—Æsthetics, etc.—*continued.*

RUSKIN (J.) Ruskin on Music. pp. 158.
Orpington, 1894. 8°.   7895. ee. 30.
SCHUEZ (A.) Die Geheimnisse der Tonkunst.
pp. 348. *Stuttgart,* 1891. 8°.   7896. ff. 30.
SEYBEL (M.) Schopenhauers Metaphysik der
Musik. pp. 122. *Leipz.* 1895. 8°. 7895. c. 53.
SOULA (H.) Essai sur l'Influence de la musique
en médecine. pp. 68. *Paris,* 1883. 4°.
                                    7895. g. 17.
SPARMANN (H. M.) Attempt at an analysis of
Music. pp. 61. *Cincinnati,* 1891. 4°.
                                 7807. aaa. 11. (3.)
SPENCER (H.) Origine e funzione della Musica.
pp. 37. *Trieste,* 1894. 8°.   Pam. 24.
STAINER (*Sir* J.) Music in its Relation to the
Intellect and Emotions. pp. 64. *Lond.* 1892. 8°.
                                  7898. aaaa. 4.
STATHAM (H. H.) My thoughts on Music and
Musicians. pp. 475. *Lond.* 1892. 8°.
                                    7897. l. 10.
—— Form and design in Music. pp. 114.
Lond. 1893. 8°.   7898. k. 47.
TAPPERT (W.) Wandernde Melodien. pp. 95.
Leipz. 1890. 8°.   7897. l. 45.
THOMPSON (S. P.) Physical foundation of Music.
pp. 31. *Lond.* 1890. 8°.   7898. c. 50. (6.)
TORRE (F. la) La Musica e l'igiene. pp. 186.
Bergamo, 1886. 8°.   7896. aa. 60.
VIVIER (A. J.) Mémoire sur le désaccord qui
existe entre les mathématiciens et les musi-
ciens sur les vrais rapports des sons musicaux.
pp. 23. *Brux.* 1893. 8°.   Pam. 24.
WEBER (J.) Les Illusions musicales. pp. 223.
Paris, 1883. 8°.   7899. aaa. 33.
WOLFF (L.) Das musikalische Motiv. pp. 202.
Bonn, 1891. 8°.   7896. ff. 31.
ZAHM (J. A.) Sound and Music. pp. 452.
Chicago, 1892. 8°.   7879. cc. 51.

Biography of Musicians.

See infra : History : BIOGRAPHY.

Criticism : Concerts : Musical Societies.

BENNETT (J.) Story of ten hundred Concerts;
Monday Popular Concerts. pp. 52.
Lond. 1887. 8°.   7898. l. 15. (3.)
BOHN (E.) Fünfzig historische Concerte in
Breslau, 1881–92. pp. 188. *Breslau,* 1893. 8°.
                                    7895. dd. 9.
BOSTON. *Handel and Haydn Society.* History
of the Society. Vol. 1. *Bost.* 1893, *etc.* 8°.
                                    7897. dd. 8.
BRIDGE (J. C.) Sketch of the Chester Musical
Festivals, 1772–1829. pp. 10. *Chester,* 1891. 8°.
                                    Pam. 24.
COMETTANT (J. P. O.) La Hollande musicale à
Paris. [Concert of modern Dutch music.]
pp. 151. *Paris,* 1891. 18°.   7896. b. 50.
—— La Musique de la Garde Républicaine en
Amérique. pp. 291. *Paris,* 1894. 8°.
                                    7896. bb. 47.
CURWEN (J. S.) and GRAHAM (J.) The Tonic
Sol-fa Jubilee. pp. 76. *Lond.* 1891. 8°.
                                  7897. l. 13. (6.)
ELSON (L. C.) European Reminiscences, musical
and otherwise. pp. 301. *Chicago,* 1891. 8°.
                                    10108. f. 2.
GALLET (L.) Notes d'un librettiste. Musique
contemporaine. pp. 318. *Paris,* 1891. 12°.
                                    7897. cc. 48.
G. B. & I. *Union of Graduates in Music.* Roll
of the Union of Graduates. *Lond.* 1893, *etc.* 8°.
                                    7898. aaaa.
GRIGGS (J. C.) Studien über die Musik in
Amerika. pp. 91. *Leipz.* 1894. 8°. 7898. m. 12.

MUSIC.—Criticism, etc.—*continued.*

HAND (M.) Use of non-teaching Musical In-
stitutions. pp. 17. *Lond.* 1891. 8°.
                                 7898. l. 15. (12.)
HANSLICK (E.) Aus dem Tagebuche eines
Musikers. pp. 360. *Berl.* 1892. 8°.
                                    12249. cc. 4.
HERMANNSTADT. *Musikverein.* Die Concerte des
hermannstädter Musikvereins. pp. 75.
Hermannstadt, 1889. 8°.   7896. c. 43. (4.)
JOHNSTONE (W. H. S.) History of the first Cardiff
Festival, 1892. pp. 204. *Lond.* 1894. 8°.
                                    7895. aa. 61.
IMBERT (H.) Symphonie. Mélanges de critique.
pp. 178. *Paris,* 1891. 8°.   12357. dd. 14.
KREHBIEL (H. E.) The Philharmonic Society of
New York. pp. 183. *N.Y.* 1892. 8°.
                                    7896. de. 40.
KUFFERATH (M.) L'Art de diriger l'Orchestre.
R. Wagner et H. Richter. pp. 180.
Paris, 1891. 8°.   7897. l. 22.
LOCK (E.) History of the South London Choral
Association. pp. 35. *Lond.* 1892. 4°.
                                    7896. de. 42.
MAS (E.) Les Sociétés musicales et les droits
d'auteur. pp. 165. *Paris,* 1895. 8°.
                                    7899. aaa. 30.
MESNARD (L.) Essais de critique musicale.
pp. 671. *Paris,* 1892. 8°.   7898. aa. 56.
OUVREUSE. Lettres de l'Ouvreuse. pp. 282.
Paris, 1890. 12°.   7898. c. 32.
ROBERT (G.) La Musique à Paris, 1894–95.
pp. 248. *Paris,* 1895. 8°.   7899. aaa. 37.
PARKINSON (F.) How to understand Classical
Music. pp. 105. *Lond.* 1893. 8°. 7898. aaaa. 39.
RUBINSTEIN (A.) La Musique et ses représentants.
pp. 140. *Paris,* 1892. 8°.   7898. ee. 37.
—— Conversation on Music. pp. 108.
Lond. 1891. 8°.   7898. bbb. 33.
SANTLEY (C.) Student and singer. pp. 327.
Lond. 1892. 8°.   10827. d. 9.
SPARK (W.) Musical Reminiscences. pp. 316.
Lond. 1892. 8°.   7897. l. 32.
SPARK (F. R.) and BENNETT (J.) History of the
Leeds Musical Festivals, 1858–89. pp. 407.
Leeds, 1892. 8°.   7897. l. 19.
SPITTA (P.) Zur Musik. pp. 471.
Berl. 1892. 8°.   7897. l. 31.
WALKER (B.) My Musical Experiences.
pp. 324. *Lond.* 1892. 8°.   7897. l. 11.
WILLY. La Mouche des Croches. pp. 315.
Paris, 1894. 8°.   7899. aaa. 6.
See also infra : Periodicals. For Criticisms on
Composers, *etc.*, *see infra : History.* For Edu-
cational Institutions, *see infra : Education.*

Dictionaries and Encyclopædias.

M., K. v. Nieuw muzikaal Woordenboek.
pp. 272. *Culemborg,* 1891. 8°.   7897. aa. 66.
RIEMANN (H.) Dictionary of Music.
Lond. 1893, *etc.* 8°.   7896. c.
SOULLIER (C.) Dictionnaire de Musique.
pp. 126. *Paris,* 1892. 8°.   7898. g. 50.
SCHYTTE (H. V.) Nordisk Musik-Lexikon.
2 Bde. *Kjøbenh.* 1888, 92. 8°.   7897. l. 36.

Dramatic. *See infra : History :* OPERA.

Ecclesiastical.
General.

ANGLICAN CHANTING. Notes on Anglican Chant-
ing. pp. 16. *Lond.* 1892. 4°.   7897. l. 24.
BENTALL (E. G.) Suggestions for Training
Choir boys. pp. 8. *Lond.* 1894. 8°.
                                  7899. dd. 1. (10.)
COSSON (A.) Essai sur le chant protestant.
pp. 68. *Montauban,* 1892. 8°. 7899. dd. 2. (4.)

MUSIC.—Ecclesiastical—*continued.*

COURTOIS (D.) La Musique sacrée dans l'Église Réformée de France. pp. 101. *Paris*, 1888. 8°.
7895. e. 10.

CURWEN (J. S.) The Boy's Voice : information on training of boys for church choirs. pp. 105. *Lond.* 1891. 8°. 7898. bbb. 32.

DANIEL (R. B.) Chapters on Church Music. pp. 216. *Lond.* 1894. 8°. 7897. c. 49.

DICKSON (W. E.) Fifty Years of Church Music. pp. 80. *Ely*, 1894. 8°. 7895. aa. 63.

DOCKER (F. A. W.) Short History of Church Music. pp. 15. *Lond.* 1890. 8°.
7899. aaa. 11. (2.)

EPHEM. Organist and Choirmaster's diary. *Lond.* 1893, *etc.* 8°. P.P. 2495. dd.

GROVER (G. F.) Fifty musical hints to Clergymen. pp. 15. *Lond.* 1893. 8°. 7898. aa. 51. (9.)

HALLER (M.) Kompositionslehre für polyphonen Kirchengesang. pp. 399. *Regensburg*, 1891. 8°.
7897. l. 16.

HEYWOOD (J.) The Art of Chanting. pp. 94. *Lond.* 1893. 8°. 7898. aaaa. 29.

HOLLOWAY (H.) Singing Voice of Boys. pp. 59. *Birmingham*, 1895. 8°. 7899. aaa. 14.

INSKIP (O. D.) Church Choirs. pp. 19. *Lond.* 1892. 8°. 7898. c. 50. (11.)

KADE (O.) Die ältere Passionskomposition bis zum Jahre 1631. pp. 346. *Gütersloh*, 1891, 93. 8°. 7896. dd. 11.

KNOWLES (A.) Text-Book of Anglican Service-music. pp. 55. *Lond.* 1895. 8°. 7899. aaa. 24.

KOTHE (B.) Musikalisch-liturgisches Wörterbuch. pp. 167. *Breslau*, 1890. 8°. 7898. c. 26.

KRABBEL (C.) Prinzipien der Kirchen Musik. pp. 119. *Bonn*, 1893. 8°. 7896. aaa. 44.

LOVE (J.) Scottish Church Music. pp. 337. *Edinb.* 1891. 8°. 7898. cc. 5.

LILIENCRON (R. v.) *Baron.* Liturgisch-musikalische Geschichte der evangelischen Gottesdienste. pp. 171. *Schleswig*, 1893. 8°.
7897. m. 3.

MARTIN (G. C.) Art of training Choir-boys. pp. 92. 1892. 4°. Novello's Music Primers.
7895. ff.

MASUTTO (G.) Della Musica sacra in Italia. 3 vol. *Venezia*, 1889. 8°. 7895. f. 29.

MEE (J. H.) Principle of Choral Worship. A sermon. pp. 12. *Chichester*, 1891. 8°. Pam. 95.

P.P. *Breslau.* Cäcilia. Zeitschrift für katholische Kirchenmusik. *Breslau*, 1893, *etc.* 8°.
1014.

—— *London.* The Church Musician. *Lond.* 1891, *etc.* 4°. P.P. 1945. r. and 2078.

—— The Organist and choirmaster. *Lond.* 1894, *etc.* 4°. P.P. 1945. hde.

PERRY (W. S.) *Bp. of Iowa.* The Law of the Church respecting Music. pp. 8. *Davenport*, 1891. 8°. Pam. 95.

SHUTTLEWORTH (H. C.) The Place of Music in public worship. pp. 80. *Lond.* 1892. 8°.
3476. c. 29.

STEELE (J. N.) The Importance of Musical Knowledge to the Priesthood. pp. 21. *N.Y.* 1894. 4°. 7896. e. 34.

WULFRUM (P.) Die Entstehung des deutschen evangelischen Kirchenliedes in musikalischer Beziehung. pp. 250. *Leipz.* 1890. 8°.
7897. i. 39.

ZAHN (J.) Die Melodien der deutschen evangelischen Kirchenlieder. 6 Bde. *Gütersloh*, 1889–93. 8°. M.E. 590. a.

See also ORATORIO : VOICE.

MUSIC.—Ecclesiastical—*continued.*

Gregorian Music.

AC. London. *Plainsong Society.* The Elements of Plainsong. pp. 91. 29. *Lond.* 1895. 4°. M.H. 1.

BIBLE. *Psalms.* The Psalms, pointed to the eight Gregorian tones, by G. H. Palmer. pp. 200. *Lond.* 1894. 8°. 3408. f. 9.

BONUZZI (A.) Metodo di Canto gregoriano. pp. 361. *Solesmes*, 1894. 8°. 7895. c. 52.

BOTS (G. L.) De Gregoriaansche Organist. pp. 30. *Utrecht*, 1891. 8°. Pam. 24.

BOYER D'AGEN (A. J.) Introduction aux Mélodies grégoriennes. pp. 215. *Paris*, 1894. 8°.
7897. m. 6.

BRAMBACH (W.) Gregorianisch. Bibliographische Lösung der Streitfrage über den Ursprung des gregorianischen Gesanges. pp. 32. 1895. 8°.
DZIATZKO (C.) Sammlung bibliothekswissenschaftlicher Arbeiten. Hft. 7. 11904. b. 23.

CASTRO (J. de) Methodus Cantus ecclesiastici Graeco-Slavici. pp. 228. *Romae*, 1881. 8°.
M.F. 969.

COORNAERT (V. J.) Traité de Plain-chant sacré. pp. 454. *Bruges*, 1890. 8°. 7897. c. 46.

DENIS (P.) Études sur la question du Chant liturgique. pp. 103. *Paris*, 1891. 8°.
7897. l. 14.

DESBROUSSES (E.) and EYMIEU (H.) Études sur les origines et l'harmonisation du Plain-chant. 1892. 8°. EYMIEU (H.) Études musicales.
7899. aaa. 10.

JANSSENS (L.) Le Chant grégorien. pp. 32. *Tournay*, 1890. 8°. 7898. m. 8. (3.)

LHOUMEAU (A.) Rhythme, exécution et accompagnement du Chant grégorien. pp. 320. *Lille*, 1892. 8°. 7898. k. 49.

LOOTENS (L.) *Bp. of Castabala.* La théorie musicale du Chant grégorien. pp. 332. *Paris*, 1895. 8°. 7895. e. 33.

MORIN (G.) Les véritables origines du Chant grégorien. pp. 74. *Saint-Gerard*, 1890. 8°.
7898. m. 8. (4.)

NORMAND TORFS (T. E. X.) L'Archéologie musicale et le vrai Chant grégorien. pp. 429. *Paris*, 1890. 8°. 7895. f. 25.

PETER, *Saint, Monastery of, at Solesmes.* Der Einfluss des tonischen Accentes auf die melodische und rhythmische Struktur der gregorianischen Psalmodie. pp. 69. *Freiburg*, 1894. 4°.
7895. h. 27.

SEYMAT (A. M.) Raison du nouveau système de notation sur la vraie portée pour le Plain-chant. pp. 119. *Tournai*, 1892. 8°. 7896. bb. 46.

TRESCH (J. B.) Das Notwendigste und Wichtigste über und vom gregorianischen Choral. pp. 60. *Eichstätt*, 1891. 8°. 7807. e. 29. (5.)

WALKER (C.) Primer of Plain-Chant. pp. 35. *Lond.* 1890. 8°. 7808. aa. 42. (6.)

Education : Examination Questions.

CULWICK (J. C.) Study of Music, and its place in education. pp. 35. *Dublin*, 1882. 8°. Pam. 24.

EASTMAN (E. V.) Musical Education. pp. 171. *Bost.* 1893. 8°. 7896. b. 53.

NEUMEGEN (A.) Music as it is taught. pp. 24. *Lond.* 1892. 8°. 7898. aa. 51. (5.)

NIECKS (F.) Musical Education and culture. pp. 27. *Edinb.* 1892. 8°. 7898. c. 50. (12.)

PEDRELL (F.) Pour notre Musique. Observations sur la question d'une école lyrique espagnole. pp. 102. *Barcelone*, 1893. 8°.
7899. aaa. 32.

HAMMERICH (A.) Kjøbenhavns Musikkonservatorium. pp. 98. *Kjøbenh.* 1892. 8°. 7897. l. 34.

MARTINET (A.) Histoire du Conservatoire de Musique. pp. 302. *Paris*, 1893. 8°. 7898. cc. 22.

MUSIC.—Education, etc.—continued.

GAUDEFROY (A.) Académie de Musique de Lille. pp. 313. *Lille*, 1891. 8°. 7897. i. 40.

LEIPSIC. *K. Conservatorium der Musik.* Das Conservatorium der Musik zu Leipzig. pp. 114. *Leipz.* 1893. 4°. 7896. g. 31.

FOSCHINI (G.) Il Liceo musicale di Torino. pp. 66. *Torino*, 1892. 8°. 7898. m. 15. (2.)

A., M., *Oxon.* Memory work for examinations in elementary Theory of Music. pp. 8. *Lond.* 1891. 8°. Pam. 24.

Ac. London. *Associated Board of the R. Academy of Music and the R. College of Music.* Local Centre examinations. Syllabus. *Lond.* 1893, *etc.* 8°. 7895. aaa.

—— *Trinity College.* Questions and Exercises for practical use during the study of the Text-Book of musical Knowledge. pp. 40. *Lond.* 1891. 8°. 7858. aa. 50. (6.)

CARROLL (W.) Advice to Students preparing for examination in the theory of Music. pp. 16. *Manch.* 1894. 8°. 7899. aaa. 11. (7.)

DAVENPORT (F. W.) and BAKER (J. P.) Local examinations in Music. Questions and exercises. pp. 50. *Lond.* 1891. 8°. 7897. bb. 61.

DAVIES (J.) Whitehall Music examinations. Guide. pp. 173. *Lond.* 1892. 8°. 7898. aaaa. 14.

FISHER (H.) The Candidate in Music. 2 pt. *Lond.* 1894. 8°. 7898. cc. 25.

G., W. Leeds Music syllabus. 2 pt. *Lond.* 1892. 8°. 7898. i. 35.

HOLMES (G. A.) Questions and exercises on the Academic Manual. pp. 64. *Lond.* 1892. 8°. 7899. aaa. 12.

LONDON. *College of Musicians.* Local Examinations, 1890–91. Papers. *Lond.* 1891, *etc.* 8°. 7895. ee.

—— *National Society of Musicians.* Theoretical Examination questions and exercises. pp. 76. *Lond.* 1890. 4°. 7896. e. 32.

MACFARREN (N.) Text questions for musical Examinations. 2 pt. *Lond.* 1894. 8°. 7899. dd. 1. (13.)

VICKERS (S. E.) Local Examinations. Harmony questions. pp. 32. *Manch.* 1892. 8°. Pam. 24.

WADE (J. C.) Music Student's examiner. pp. 40. *Lond.* 1890. 16°. 7808. aa. 42. (4.)

For educational courses, works, *etc.*, *see supra: General.*

Exhibitions.

MARR (R. A.) Music and musicians at the Edinburgh Exhibition 1886. pp. 217. *Edinb.* 1887. 8°. 7898. c. 41.

—— Music for the people. Retrospect of the Glasgow International Exhibition, 1888. pp. 176. *Edinb.* 1889. 8°. 7898. aaaa. 16.

VIENNA. *Internationale Ausstellung für Musik- und Theaterwesen.* Fach-Katalog der Musik-historischen Abtheilung von Deutschland und Oesterreich-Ungarn. pp. 591. *Wien*, 1892. 8°. 7898. b. 5.

—— Fach-Katalog der Abtheilung des Königreiches Italien. pp. 294. *Wien*, 1892. 8°. 7897. cc. 50.

—— Russland. Katalog. pp. 84. *Wien*, 1892. 8°. 7958. bbb. 15.

—— Katalog der Ausstellung des Königreiches Spanien. pp. 95. *Wien*, 1892. 8°. 7958. bbb. 14.

—— Jugend-Führer. Anleitung zur Besichtigung der Ausstellung. pp. 44. *Wien*, 1892. 8°. Pam. 24.

History.
General.

BOEHME (E. E. H.) Die Geschichte der Musik in synchronistischen Tabellen. pp. 40. *Leipz.* 1890. 4°. 7896. g. 29.

MUSIC.—History—continued.

BRENET (M.) Histoire de la Symphonie à orchestre. pp. 168. *Paris*, 1882. 8°. 7896. de. 28.

CROWEST (F. J.) Catechism of musical History and Biography. pp. 168. *Lond.* 1883. 8°. 7896. a. 56.

CULVERHOUSE (E.) History of Music from the Renaissance. pp. 124. *Lond.* 1893. 8°. 7897. a. 76.

DAVEY (H.) Student's musical History. pp. 151. *Lond.* 1891. 8°. 7898. a. 66.

EITNER (R.) Quellen- und Hilfswerke beim Studium der Musikgeschichte. pp. 55. *Leipz.* 1891. 8°. 011900. f. 10. (7.)

KAPPEY (J. A.) Military Music. History of wind-instrumental Bands. pp. 100. *Lond.* 1894. 4°. 7895. e. 30.

MARSILLAC (F.) Histoire de la Musique moderne. pp. 420. *Paris*, 1881. 8°. 7899. b. 2.

MATTHEW (J. E.) Manual of musical History. pp. 462. *Lond.* 1892. 8°. 7898. k. 43.

NAUMANN (E.) The History of Music. *Lond.* 1894, *etc.* 8°. 7899. f.

NORMAND TORFS (T. E. X.) L'Archéologie musicale. pp. 429. *Paris*, 1890. 8°. 7895. f. 25.

PARRY (C. H. H.) The Art of Music. pp. 374. *Lond.* 1893. 8°. 2264. e. 21.

—— Summary of the history and development of European Music. pp. 115. Novello's Music Primer. 7895. ff.

RIEMANN (H.) Catechism of musical History. 2 pt. *Lond.* 1892. 8°. 7898 ee. 60.

RITTER (H.) Studien und Skizzen aus Musikgeschichte. pp. 186. *Dresd.* 1892. 8°. 7897. l. 35.

RITTER (F. L.) Manual of musical History. pp. 58. *Lond.* 1892. 8°. 7898. bb. 19.

ROWBOTHAM (J. F.) The History of Music. pp. 419. *Lond.* 1893. 8°. 7898. aaaa. 19.

SAMPSON (Z. S.) The Evolution of Music. 1891. 8°. Ac. Brooklyn. *Ethical Association.* Evolution Series. No. 15. 7006. bbb.

SPITTA (P.) Musikgeschichtliche Aufsätze. pp. 470. *Berl.* 1894. 8°. 7898. m. 10.

STOLZ (J.) Allgemeine Geschichte der Musik. pp. 389. *Graz*, 1894. 4°. 7899. d. 7.

TAYLOR (H. J.) Historical facts relating to Music. pp. 101. *Lond.* 1895. 8°. 7899. aaa. 15.

UNTERSTEINER (A.) Storia della Musica. pp. 298. *Milano*, 1893. 8°. 012200. h. 115.

WEBER (F.) Popular History of Music. pp. 327. *Lond.* 1891. 8°. 7897. i. 41.

WALLASCHEK (R.) Primitive Music. Inquiry into the origin and development of music of savage tribes. pp. 326. 9. *Lond.* 1893. 8°. 7895. bb. 34.

Composers and Musicians: History and Criticism.

BENNASSI-DESPLANTES (F. J.) Les Musiciens célèbres. pp. 282. *Limoges*, 1889. 8°. 10603. i. 23.

BRÉMONT (A. de) The world of Music. 3 pt. *Lond.* 1892. 8°. 7898. aaaa. 22.

DOLE (N. H.) A Score of famous Composers. pp. 540. *N.Y.* 1891. 8°. 10803. de. 1.

EYMIEU (H.) Études et Biographies musicales. pp. 180. *Paris*, 1892. 8°. 7899. aaa. 10.

GRIFFITHS (J. R.) Musicians and their compositions. pp. 160. *Lond.* 1894. 8°. 7899. aaa. 19.

HANNEDOUCHE (A.) Les Musiciens et Compositeurs français. pp. 238. *Paris*, 1890. 8°. 7895. ee. 27.

IMBERT (H.) Profils de Musiciens. pp. 150. *Paris*, 1888. 8°. 7898. l. 20.

MUSIC.—History—continued.

SCHURÉ (E.) Tannhaeuser. Lettre sur l'exécution de ce drame à Bayreuth. pp. 15. *Paris*, 1892. 8°.   Pam. 24.

EHRHARD (A.) L'Anneau du Nibelung. pp. 38. *Clermont-Ferrand*, 1894. 8°.   7898. m. 14. (10.)

KOBBÉ (G.) How to understand Wagner's Ring of the Nibelung. pp. 145. *Lond.* 1895. 8°.   7899. aaaa. 1.

PARKINSON (F.) Commentary upon Wagner's Nibelung's Ring. pp. 156. *Lond.* 1894. 8°.   7896. aa. 61.

HÉBERT (M.) Tétralogie. Tristan et Iseult. Parsifal. pp. 70. *Paris*, 1894. 8°.   7899. dd. 2. (6.)

PFOHL (F.) Führer durch R. Wagners "Die Meistersinger von Nürnberg." pp. 68. *Leipz.* 1894. 8°.   7899. b. 14.

PENA Y GOÑI (A.) Los Maestros Cantores de Nuremberg. pp. 143. *Madrid*, 1893. 8°.   11747. ee. 7.

GOULD (S. B.) Wagner's Parsifal at Baireuth. pp. 30. *Lond.* 1892. 8°.   7807. e. 30. (5.)

WADDELL (P. H.) The Parsifal of R. Wagner at Bayreuth. pp. 77. *Edinb.* 1894. 8°. 7899. b. 6.

BAIREUTH. Bayreuth, 1891. pp. 50. 1891. 8°.   7898. aaaa. 38.

BOPP (W.) Die Bühnenfestspiele in Bayreuth, 1892. pp. 56. *Mannheim*, 1892. 8°.   7898. aa. 51. (4.)

FRÉSON (J. G.) Bayreuth. Un pèlerinage d'art. pp. 46. *Brux.* 1890. 8°.   7898. m. 14. (7.)

HECKEL (C.) Die Bühnenfestspiele in Bayreuth. pp. 88. *Leipz.* 1891. 8°.   Pam. 24.

NOVER (J.) Die Buhnenfestspiele in Baireuth. pp. 102. *Leipz.* 1891. 8°   7896. de. 36.

RICCHETTI (A.) Note Wagneriane; Bayreuth 1892, Monaco 1893. pp. 112. *Milano*, 1894. 8°.   7899. h. 5.

SAINT-AUBAN (É. de) Un pèlerinage à Bayreuth. pp. 338. *Paris*, 1892. 18°.   7898. k. 44.

PFEIFFER (T.) Studien bei H. von Bülow. pp. 123. *Berl.* 1894. 8°.   7899. b. 4.

BUMPUS (J. S.) Compositions of Sir F. A. Gore Ouseley. pp. 34. *Lond.* 1892. 8°.   Pam. 24.

CLOSSON (E.) E. Grieg et la Musique scandinave. pp. 62. *Paris*, 1892. 8°.   7898. m. 8. (10.)

SCHMARSOW (A.) Masaccio. Studien. *Kassel*, 1895, etc. 8°.   7856. d.

History of Music of various Countries.

Ancient Greece.

MONRO (D. B.) Modes of ancient Greek Music. pp. 144. *Oxf.* 1894. 8°.   7895. c. 51.

PAPADOPOULOS (G. I.) Συμβολαι εἰς την ἱστοριαν της παρ' ἡμιν ἐκκλησιαστικης μουσικης. pp. 592. Ἐν Ἀθηναις, 1890. 8°. 7898. l. 14.

REINACH (T.) La Musique grecque et l'Hymne à Apollon. pp. 19. *Paris*, 1894. 8°.   Pam. 24.

ROSSBACH (A.) and WESTPHAL (R.) Theorie der musischen Künste der Hellenen. 3 Bde. *Leipz.* 1885–89. 8°.   2280. f. 2.

WILLIAMS (C. F. A.) The Music of the ancient Greeks. pp. 8. 1894. 8°. Novello's Series of the words of oratorios, etc.   7896. de.

Jews.

HELLER (S.) Die echten hebräischen Melodieen. pp. 284. *Trier*, 1893. 8°.   01979. a. 25.

SINGER (J.) Die Tonarten des traditionellen Synagogengesanges. pp. 19. 11. *Wien*, 1886. 8°.   7895. e. 29.

BIRNBAUM (E.) Jüdische Musiken am Hofe von Mantua, 1542–1628. pp. 35. *Wien*, 1893. 8°.   Pam. 24.

MUSIC.—History.—continued.

Modern European, etc.

SCHUSTER (H. M.) Das Urheberrecht der Tonkunst in Oesterreich, Deutschland und andern europäischen Staaten. pp. 356. *München*, 1891. 8°.   7897. l. 25.

BERGMANS (P.) Variétés musicologiques, documents sur l'histoire de la Musique en Belgique. *Gand*, 1891, etc. 8°.   7898. l. 10.

CHAPPELL (W.) Old English popular Music. 2 vol. *Lond.* 1893. 8°.   2031. f.

DAVEY (H.) History of English Music. pp. 518. *Lond.* 1895. 8°.   7899. ee. 3.

NAGEL (W.) Geschichte der Musik in England. *Strassburg*, 1894, etc. 8°.   7895. dd.

—— Annalen der englischen Hofmusik von der Zeit Heinrichs VIII. bis zum Tode Karls I. 1509–1649. *Leipz.* 1894. 8°. 7898. m. 14. (11.)

WILLIAMS (C. F. A.) Historical account of Degrees in Music at Oxford and Cambridge. pp. 167. *Lond.* 1894. 8°.   8367. bb. 8.

NEW SOUTH WALES. *Commissioners for the Exposition, Chicago.* The Drama and music in New South Wales. pp. 95. *Sydney*, 1892. 8°.   7958. g. 24.

AUBERTIN (C.) Quelques renseignements sur la Musique et les musiciens à Beaune. pp. 186. *Beaune*, 1891. 8°.   7898. a. 53.

COQUARD (A.) De la Musique en France depuis Rameau. pp. 288. *Paris*, 1891. 12°. 7896. de. 39.

GALINO (T.) La Musique française au moyen âge. pp. 39. *Leipz.* 1890. 8°.   11825. cc. 57. (7.)

GOUGET (E.) L'Argot musicale. pp. 431. *Paris*, 1892. 8°.   7899. aaa. 4.

LAVOIX (H.) La Musique française. pp. 320. *Paris*, 1891. 8°.   2261. c.

LEFEBVRE (L.) La Musique à Lille au XVIII° siècle. pp. 51. *Lille*, 1893. 4°.   Pam. 24.

LEROUX (A.) Rapports entre la musique bretonne et la musique orientale. pp. 14. *Vannes*, 1891. 8°.   7898. m. 14. (8.)

ROSOOR (J.) La Musique à Tourcoing. pp. 197. *Tourcoing*, 1892. 8°.   7895. g. 13.

KELLER (O.) Das Haus Habsburg als Pflegestätte der Tonkunst. pp. 22. *Wien*, 1890. 8°.   7896. c. 43. (7.)

LEMCKE (P.) Die thüringischen Musikfeste und die erfurter Napoleonsfeste. pp. 27. *Magdeburg*, 1886. 8°.   7898. k. 20. (1.)

SANDBERGER (A.) Beiträge zur Geschichte der bayerischen Hofkapelle unter O. di Lasso. *Leipz.* 1894, etc. 8°.   7895. dd.

STIEHL (C.) Musikgeschichte der Stadt Lübeck. pp. 116. *Lübeck*, 1891. 8°.   7898. l. 23.

BERTOLOTTI (A.) Musici alle Corte de Gonzaga in Mantova dal seculo XV al XVIII. pp. 130. *Milano*, 1890. 8°.   7895. f. 28.

GASPARI (G.) Ragguagli dei Musicisti bolognesi del secolo XVII. *Modena*, 1880. 8°.   Pam. 24.

GANDOLFI (R.) Illustrazioni di alcuni Cimeli concernenti l' Arte Musicale in Firenze. pp. 28. *Firenze*, 1892. fol.   K.T.C. 13. a. 1.

MASTRIGLI (L.) La Sicilia musicale. pp. 99. *Bologna*, 1891. 8°.   7898. c. 46.

MOTTA (E.) Musici alla Corte degli Sforza. pp. 150. *Milano*, 1887. 8°.   7897. l. 23.

PEDRELL (F.) Pour notre Musique. Observations sur la question d'une école lyrique espagnole. pp. 102. *Barcelona*, 1893. 8°. 7899. aaa. 32.

SOUBIES (A.) Précis de l'Histoire de la Musique russe. pp. 102. *Paris*, 1893. 12°. 7898. e. 34.

—— Musique russe et musique espagnole. pp. 16. *Paris*, 1894. 8°.   Pam. 24.

MUSIC.—History—*continued.*

TORT Y DANIEL (J.) Noticia musical del "Lied"
ó Cançо catalana. pp. 42.
Barcelona, 1892. 8°.　　　　　　　Pam. 24.

See also supra: Concerts : Composers : *infra :*
Periodicals.

　　　　　　Oriental and African.

CHINNASVAMI MUTHALIVĀR (A. M.) Oriental
Music in European notation.
Madras. 1892, *etc.* fol.　　　14053. g. 18.

DAY (C. R.) Music and musical instruments of
Southern India. pp. 173. *Lond.* 1891. 4°.
　　　　　　　　　　　　K.T.C. 4. b. 12.

MAHĪNDRALĀLA ṢĪLA. Diagram showing the posi-
tions of Srootees in relation to 7 notes used in
Hindoo Music. *Calcutta*, 1885–92. *s. sh.* fol. 8°.
　　　　　　　　　　　　　　　M. M.

SAURĪNDRAMOHANA ṬHAKURA. The seven Musical Notes of the Hindus. pp. 51.
Calcutta, 1892. 4°.　　　14053. e. 25. (2.)

PIGGOTT (F. T.) Music of the Japanese.
1891. 8°. Ac. Yokohama. *Asiatic Society.*
Transactions. Vol. 19.　　　Ac. 8828/6.

WALLS Y MERINO (M.) La Música popular de
Filipinas. pp. 46. *Madrid*, 1892. 8°.
　　　　　　　　　　　　7895. dd. 7.

DAY (C. R.) Native Music and musical instruments. pp. 18. 1892. 8°.　7898. c. 50. (9.)

　　　　　　Periodicals.

Ac. Amsterdam. *Vereeniging voor Nederlandsche Muziekgeschiedenis.* Tijdschrift der Vereeniging. *Amsterd.* 1882, *etc.* 8°. Ac. 5147/2.

P.P. Boston, *Massachusetts.* The Musical Record. *Bost.* 1888, *etc.* 4°.　　P.P. 1948. pb.

—— Musical Year-book of the U.S.
Bost. 1892, *etc.* 8°.　　　P.P. 2523. lg.

—— *Breslau.* Cäcilia. Zeitschrift für katholische Kirchenmusik. *Breslau*, 1893, *etc.* 8°.
　　　　　　　　　　　　　　1014.

—— *London.* The British Musician. Vol. 1.
Nos. 1–5. *Lond.* 1891. 4°.　　1866. c. (1.)

—— The Church Musician. *Lond.* 1891, *etc.* 4°.
　　　　　　　　　P.P. 1945. r. and 2078.

—— The Minim. *Lond.* 1893, *etc.* 8°.
　　　　　　　　　P.P. 1945. r. and 2225.

—— The Minstrel. *Lond.* 1892, *etc.* 4°.　N.R.

—— New Quarterly Musical Review.
Lond. 1893, *etc.* 8°.　　　P.P. 1946. ba.

—— The Organist and Choirmaster.
Lond. 1894, *etc.* 4°.　　　P.P. 1945. hde.

—— The Overture. Vol. 1–4. *Lond.* 1890, 94. 8°.
　　　　　　　　　　　　P.P. 1945. hdf.

—— The School Music Review.
Lond. 1892, *etc.* 8°.　　P.P. 1945. s. and 2159.

—— The Strand Musical Magazine.
Lond. 1895, *etc.* 8°.　　　P.P. 1947. cb.

—— *Sibsey.* The Brass Band Annual.
Sibsey, 1894, *etc.* 8°.　　　P.P. 2495. m.
See also supra : Bibliography.

　　Pianoforte Music. *See* PIANOFORTE.

　　Vocal Music. *See* VOICE.

MUSICAL INSTRUMENTS. AMERICA.
History of the Music trades of America. pp. 129.
N.Y. 1891. fol.　　　　　1807. c. 9.

DAY (C. R.) Music and musical instruments of
Southern India. pp. 173. *Lond.* 1891. 4°.
　　　　　　　　　　　　K.T.C. 4. b. 12.

HIPKINS (A. J.) Cantor Lectures on musical
instruments. pp. 31. *Lond.* 1891. 8°.
　　　　　　　　　　　7896. ff. 33. (1.)

KAPPEY (J. A.) Military Music. History of
wind instrumental Bands. *Lond.* 1894. 4°.
　　　　　　　　　　　　　7895. c

MUSICAL INSTRUMENTS—*cont.*

LONDON. *Royal Military Exhibition.* Descriptive
catalogue of musical instruments. pp. 253.
Lond. 1891. 4°.　　　　　7896. ff. 28.

ROSE (A. S.) Talks with Bandsmen. pp. 415.
Lond. 1895. 8°.　　　　　7899. aa. 1.

TRAVERS (É.) Les Instruments de musique au
XIV° siècle. pp. 41. *Paris*, 1882. 8°.
　　　　　　　　　　　6898. m. 6. (4.)

See also FLUTE : GUITAR : LUTE : ORGAN :
PIANOFORTE : VIOLIN.

MUSIC HALLS. STUART (C. D.) and PARK
(A. J.) The Variety Stage. pp. 255.
Lond. 1895. 8°.　　　　　011795. e. 57.

VARIETY STARS. Variety Stars. pp. 40.
Lond. 1895. 8°.　　　　　　Pam. 7.

MUSKHOGEAN LANGUAGE.
See INDIAN LANGUAGES.

MUSSELBURGH. LANGHORNE (W. H.)
Reminiscences connected with Musselburgh.
pp. 258. *Edinb.* 1893. 8°.　　12350. i. 28.

MUSSOORIE. HAWTHORNE (R.) Guide to
Mussoorie. *Mussoorie*, 1890. 8°.　　Pam. 88.

MYCENE. *See* GREECE, *Antiquities.*

MYCETOZOA. Ac. London. *British Museum.*
Monograph of the Mycetozoa. By A. Lister.
pp. 224. *Lond.* 1894. 8°.　　7054. ee. 21.

—— Guide to the British Mycetozoa. By A.
Lister. pp. 42. *Lond.* 1895. 8°.　　Pam. 1.

DE BARY (A.) Morphology and biology of the
Mycetozoa. pp. 525. *Oxf.* 1887. 8°.　2252. f.

MASSEE (G.) Monograph of the Myxogastres.
pp. 367. *Lond.* 1892. 8°.　　07028. i. 32.

MYOXIDAE. REUVENS (C. L.) Die Myoxidae oder Schlaefer. pp. 80. *Leiden*, 1890. 4°.
　　　　　　　　　　　7208. k. 1.

See also RODENTS.

MYRINA. *See* GREECE, *Antiquities.*

MYRIOPODA. ADLERZ (G.) Om digestionssekretionen hos Myriopoder. pp. 51.
1890. 8°. Ac. Stockholm. *K. Svenska Vetenskaps Academien.* Bihang till Handlingar.
Bd. 16.　　　　　　　　Ac. 1070/7.

ATTEMS (C.) *Count.* Die Myriopoden Steiermarks. 1895. 8°. Ac. Vienna. *Akademie der
Wissenschaften.* Sitzungsberichte. Math.-natur-
wissenschaftliche Classe. Bd. 104. Ac. 810/6.

GROULT (P.) Acariens, Myriapodes. pp. 248.
1887. 8°. Histoire naturelle de la France.
pt. 15.　　　　　　　　　7207. cc.

HAASE (E.) Die indisch-australischen Myriopoden. 1887. 8°. Ac. Dresden. *K. Zoologisches Museum.* Abhandlungen. 1886/87.
　　　　　　　　　　　　Ac. 3562.

HERBST (C.) Beiträge zur Kenntniss der Chilo-
poden. pp. 42. 1891. 4°. Bibliotheca Zoologica. Hft. 9.　　　　　　　25.

HUMBERT (A.) Myriopodes des environs de
Genève. pp. 92. 1894. 4°. Ac. Geneva.
Société de physique. Mémoires. Tom. 32.
　　　　　　　　　　　Ac. 2870.

PORAT (C. O. v.) Myriopoder från Vest- och
Syd.-Afrika. pp. 51. 1893. 8°. Ac. Stockholm. *K. Svenska Vetenskaps Academien.* Bihang
til Handlingar. Bd. 18.　　Ac. 1070/7.

SINCLAIR (F. G.) Myriapods. 1895. 8°. Cambridge Natural History. Vol. 5.　7001. ee.

MYSIA. *See* NUMISMATICS.

MYSORE. ELLIOT (R. H.) Gold, Sport and
coffee planting in Mysore. pp. 480.
Westminster, 1894. 8°.　　010057. ee. 27.

RICE (B. L.) Epigraphia Carnataca. Inscriptions in the Mysore District.
Bangalore, 1894, *etc.* 4°.　　14058. c. 8.

MYSORE—*continued.*

Syāma Rāvu. Ten years of native Rule in Mysore. pp. 136. *Madras*, 1891. 8°.　9057. aa. 20.

Virarāghavāchārya. Mysore representative Assembly and the Indian national Congress. pp. 28. *Madras*, 1891. 8°.　8022. de. 24. (14.)
See also Law Reports.

MYSTICISM. Auger (A.) Étude sur les Mystiques des Pays-Bas au moyen âge. pp. 355. 1892. 8°. Ac. Brussels. *Académie.* Mémoires couronnés. Tom. 46.　Ac. 985/4.

Behre (C.) Spiritisten, Mystiker und Theosophen. pp. 85. *Leipz.* 1890. 8°.　Pam. 36.

Merx (E. O. A.) Idee und Grundlinien einer Geschichte der Mystik. pp. 62.
Heidelberg, 1893. 4°.　8465. i. 3.

Nordau (M. S.) Entartung. 2 Bde.
Berl. 1892. 93 8°.　012357. i. 39.
—— Degeneration. pp. 560. *Lond.* 1895. 8°.　012357. k. 24.

Paulhan (F.) Le nouveau Mysticisme. pp. 201. *Paris*, 1891. 12°.　8470. cc. 30.

Thomas, à Vallgornera. Mystica theologia divi Thomæ, *Augustæ*, 1890, *etc.* 8°.　3676. cc. 2.

MYTHOLOGY. *See* Religion.

MYXINE. Sanders (A.) Researches in the nervous system of Myxine Glutinosa. pp. 44. *Lond.* 1894. 4°.　7290. k. 8.
See also Fish.

MYXOEDEMA. Blake (E. T.) Myxœdema, Cretinism and the goitres. pp. 89.
Bristol, 1894. 8°.　7616. dd. 1.

Wilson (A. M.) Myxœdema. pp. 36.
Lond. 1894. 8°.　7630. aa. 26.

Pel (P. K.) Myxödema. 1895, 8°. Volkmann (R. v.) Sammlung klinischer Vorträge. N.F. Nr. 123.　7441. g.

MYXOGASTRES. *See* Mycetozoa.

MYZOSTOMIDAE. Ac. Bergen. *Museum.* Nansen (F.) Bidrag til Myzostomernes Anatomi og Histologi. pp. 80. *Bergen*, 1885. fol.　7299. l. 18.

See also Vermes.

NAGAS. Prain (D.) The Angami Nagas. pp. 24. *Calcutta*, 1890. 8°.　Pam. 88.

Clark (M. M.) Ao Naga grammar. pp. 181. *Shillong*, 1893. 8°.　12910. dd. 36.

Mac Cabe (R. B.) Outline grammar of the Angāmi Nāgā language. pp. 95.
Calcutta, 1887. 8°.　12906. dd. 39.
See also Assam.

NAILS. *See* Screws.

NAIRNSHIRE. Bain (G.) History of Nairnshire. pp. 600. *Nairn*, 1893. 8°. 010370. f. 28.
See also Moray.

NAMA LANGUAGE.
See African Languages.

NAMES.
General.

Toubin (C.) Essai d'Étymologie historique et géographique. pp. 462. *Paris*, 1892. 8°.　12902. aaa. 38.

Wagner (L.) Names and their meaning. pp. 330. *Lond.* 1892. 8°.　12902. ccc. 25.
—— More about Names. pp, 287.
Lond. 1893. 8°.　12901. cc. 37.

NAMES——*continued.*
Personal Names.

Adamek (E.) Die Räthsel unserer deutschen Schülernamen. pp. 143. *Wien*, 1894. 8°.　12962. r. 6.

Barber (H.) British Family Names. pp. 235. *Lond.* 1894. 8°.　9906. ee. 7.

Batchelor (A.) Alphabetical list of curious Surnames. *Guildford*, 1892. fol.　1882. c. 2. (140.)

French (A. D. W.) Notes on the Surnames of Francus, Franceis, French, *etc.*, in Scotland. pp. 109. *Bost.* 1893. 8°.　9903. f. 16.

Gentry (T. G.) Family Names from the Irish, Ango-Saxon, Anglo-Norman and Scotch. pp. 225. *Phila.* 1892. 8°.　12902. dd. 40.

Gray (J.) Personal and Place Names in the Book of Deer. pp. 30. *Peterhead*, 1894. 4°.　12903. e. 27. (4.)

Ireland. *Registrar-General.* Varieties and synonyms of Surnames and Christian Names in Ireland. pp. 76. *Dublin*, 1890. 8°.　12978. h. 22.

Kleemann (S.) Die Familiennamen Quedlinburgs. pp. 264. *Quedlinburg*, 1891. 8°.　12962. h. 41.

M—K., M. Surnames. pp. 2. *Lond.* 1892. 8°.　9903. a. 6. (4.)

Macbain (A.) Personal and Surnames of Inverness. pp. 105. *Inverness*, 1895. 8°. 9904. bb. 9.

Moore (A. W.) Surnames of the Isle of Man. pp. 372. *Lond.* 1890. 8°.　12978. f. 27.

Nichols (T.) Christian Names explained. pp. 128. *Lond.* 1892. 8°.　12902. aaa. 37.

Nicholson (E. W. B.) The Pedigree of "Jack" and various allied names. pp. 35. *Lond.* 1892.　Pam. 47.

Schneller (C.) Tirolische Namenforschungen. pp. 373. *Innsbruck*, 1890. 8°.　12962. dd. 25.

Tobler-Meyer (W.) Deutsche Familien-namen. pp. 234. *Zürich*, 1894. 8°.　9904. f. 12.

Geographical.

Ac. London. *Royal Geographical Society.* Orthography of geographical Names. *Lond.* 1891. 4°.　12902. h. 17. (I.)

Barbier (J. V.) De l'Orthographie du nom.des pays qui s'écrivent en caractères latins. pp. 20. *Paris*, 1891. 12°.　12901. d. 33. (7.)

Ricouart (L.) Études pour servir à l'histoire des noms de lieu. *Anzin*, 1891, *etc.* 4°. 12953. k.

Schmidkontz (J.) Ortskunde und Ortsnamenforschung im Dienste der Sprachwissenschaft, *etc. Halle*, 1895, *etc.* 8°.　012901. h.

Taylor (I.) Names and their histories. pp. 392. *Lond.* 1895. 8°.　12901. ccc. 24.

Cropper (P. J.) Field-names on the Parkyns Estates, Nottinghamshire. pp. 7. 1893. 8°.　10347. d. 7. (8.)

Moore (A. W.) Surnames and Place Names of the Isle of Man. pp. 372. *Lond.* 1890. 8°.　12978. f. 27.

Gray (J.) Personal and Place Names in the Book of Deer. pp. 30. *Peterhead*, 1894. 4°.　12903. e. 27. (4.)

Johnston (J. B.) Place Names of Scotland. pp. 256. *Edinb.* 1892. 8°.　12978. c. 33.

MacDonald (J.) Place Names in Strathbogie. pp. 300. *Aberd.* 1891. 8°.　12978. c. 34.

Maxwell (Sir H. E.) Scottish Land Names. pp. 219. *Edinb.* 1894. 8°.　12978. c. 36.

Williams (C. A.) Die französischen Ortsnamen keltischer Abkunft. pp. 87. *Strassb.* 1891. 8°.　Pam. 47.

Jacob (G.) Die Ortsnamen des Herzogthums Meiningen. pp. 149. *Hildburghausen*, 1894. 8°.　10255. k. 1.

NAMES.—Geographical—*continued.*

JAKSCH (A. v.) Ueber Ortsnamen mit Rücksicht auf Kärnten. pp. 44. *Klagenfurt*, 1891. 8°.
12902. g. 33. (6.)

SCHNELLER (C.) Tirolis ·he Namenforschungen. pp. 373. *Innsbruck*, 1890. 8°.   12962. dd. 25.

—— Beiträge zur Ortsnamenkunde Tirols. *Innsbruck*, 1893, *etc.* 8°.   12962. s.

ZAHN (J. v.) Ortsnamenbuch der Steiermark. pp. 583. *Wien*, 1893. 4°.   10205. f. 5.

U.S. *Board on Geographical Names.* Bulletin. *Wash.* 1891, *etc.* 8°.   10408. ee. 22.

NAMUR. RADIGUÈS (H. de) Les seigneuries de Namur. pp. 127. 1895. 8°. Ac. Namur. *Société Archéologique.* Annales. Tom. 22.
Ac. 5531.

NANCY. BADEL (É.) Jeanne d'Arc à Nancy, 1429-1890. pp. 102. *Orléans*, 1890. 8°.
10663. i. 25.

GOUTIÈRE-VERNOLLE (E.) Les Fêtes de Nancy, Juin 1892. pp. 151. *Nancy*, 1892. 4°. 9930. h. 9.

PIERSON (N.) L'Université de Nancy et la décentralisation. pp. 176. *Paris*, 1890. 8°.
8356. aa. 14.

NANGIS. LHUILLIER (T.) L'ancien château de Nangis. pp. 28. *Paris*, 1893. 8°.
7808. bbb. 30. (7.)

NANTES. NANTES, *Cathedral.* Documents pour servir à l'histoire de la Cathédrale de Nantes. pp. 392. 1888. 8°. Ac. Nantes. *Société Archéologique.* Bulletin. Tom. 27.
Ac. 5319.

—— Inventaire des archives antérieures à 1790. 1888. 4°. Collection des inventaires-sommaires.
1814-15. b., *etc.*

PARFOURU (P.) Une saisie de navires anglais à Nantes, 1587. pp. 47. *Rennes*, 1893. 8°.
9078. g. 15. (9.)

BLOCQUEL DE CROIX (G.) *Baron de Wismes.* Une page de la Terreur à Nantes. pp. 55. *Vannes*, 1894. 8°.   4629. ee. 4.

KERVILER (R.) Le Procès des 132 Nantais, avec une relation de leur voyage à Paris, *etc.* pp. 297. *Vannes*, 1894. 8°.   09225. k. 1.

CHASSIN (C. L.) Centenaire du 29 Juin 1793. Récit de la défense de Nantes. pp. 45. *Nantes*, 1893. 8°.   9004. gg. 31. (9.)

DESTRANGES (É.) Le Théâtre à Nantes. pp. 504. *Paris*, 1893. 8°   011795. e. 45.
See also VENDÉE.

NANTGWILT. TICKELL (R. E.) The Vale of Nantgwilt. pp. 40. *Lond.* 1894. *obl.* fol.
1787. aa. 24.

NANTWICH. GARROD (A. E.) Medical Springs of Nantwich, *etc.* 1895. 8°. Ac. London. *Medical and Chirurgical Society.* Climates of Great Britain, *etc.* Vol. 1.   7462. g.

NAPHTHA : NAPHTHALENE. TAEUBER (E.) Die Sulfosäuren der beiden Naphtylamine und der beiden Naphtole. pp. 30. *Berl.* 1892. 4°.
8908. c. 15.

NAPIER. SPENCER (W. I.) Napier, N.Z., as a health resort. pp. 12. *Napier*, 1885. 8°.
7306. df. 19. (2.)

NAPLES, Kingdom and City.
History.

BELOCH (J.) Geschichte und Topographie des antiken Neapel. pp. 472. *Breslau*, 1890. 8°.
7706. ee. 32.

BONGHI (R.) Le origini della Monarchia a Napoli. 1891. 8°. Gli albori della vita italiana. Vol. 2.   9166. ccc. 11.

NAPLES. Istoria del regno di Napoli, 1040-1458. 1891. 8°. Archivio storico per le Province Napoletane. Anno 16.   Ac. 6534.

NAPLES.—History—*continued.*

PALMA (N.) Storia della regione più settentrionale del Regno di Napoli. *Teramo*, 1890, *etc.* 8°.   10132. k.

P.P. *Naples.* Archivio storico gentilizio del Napolitano. *Napoli*, 1894, *etc.* 8°. P.P. 3557. d.

HAMPE (C.) Geschichte Konradius von Hohenstaufen. pp. 394. *Innsbruck*, 1894. 8°.
10704. k. 3.

BADDELEY (W. S. C.) Queen Joanna I. of Naples. pp. 359. *Lond.* 1893. 8°.   10629. dd. 23.

PORZIO (C.) La Congiura de Baroni. pp. 177. *Torino*, 1895. 8°.   9166. c. 22.

AMABILE (L.) Il Santo Officio della Inquisizione in Napoli. 2 vol. *Città di C.* 1892. 8°.
4071. l. 12.

BADDELEY (W. S. C.) Charles III. of Naples and Urban VI. pp. 159. *Lond.* 1894. 8°.
9167. i. 25.

SWINBURNE (H.) The Courts of Europe at the close of the last century. 2 vol. *Lond.* 1895. 8°.
10600. f. 2.

ROSSI (M.) Nuova luce risultante dai veri fatti avvenuti in Napoli pochi anni prima del 1799. pp. 398. *Firenze*, 1890 8°.   9167. k. 19.

MARESCA (B.) Il Cav. A. Micheroux nella reazione napoletana del 1799. pp. 252. *Napoli*, 1895. 8°.   10629. f. 46.

ALONGI (G.) La Camorra. pp. 237. *Torino*, 1890. 8°.   6025. e. 11.

CHURCH (E. M.) Chapters in an adventurous Life. pp. 356. *Edinb.* 1895. 8°. 010817. g. 1.
See also ITALY.

Topography, etc.

CLEMENT (C. E.) Naples and its environs. pp. 340. *Lond.* 1894. 8°.   10130. c. 4.

COLONNA (F.) Notizie de Castelnuovo in Napoli. pp. 152. 3. *Napoli*, 1892. 8°.   10135. g. 16.

CONFORTI (L.) and GIACOMO (S. di) Guida di Napoli, *etc..* pp. 410. *Napoli*, 1892. 8°.
10135. bb. 38.

CONTE (C.) La civiltà di Napoli testificata con monumenti, con instituti, *etc.* *Napoli*, 1890, *etc.* 8°.   19630. g.

GIORDANO (F.) Napoli, il suo golfo e le sue colline. pp. 98. *Napoli*, 1894. 8°. 10131. cc. 11.

PELLET (M.) Naples contemporaine. pp. 321. *Paris*, 1894. 12°.   10136. bb. 2.

P.P. *Naples.* Napoli nobilissima. *Napoli*, 1892, *etc.* 4°.   193.

CROCE (B.) I teatri di Napoli. 1889, *etc.* 8°. Archivio Storico, *etc.* An. 14, *etc.* Ac. 6534.

GIACOMO (S. di) Cronaca del Teatro S. Carlino. *Napoli*, 1890, *etc.* 4°.   930.

Dialect.

ROCCO (E.) Vocabolario del Dialetto napolitano. *Napoli*, 1890, *etc.* 8°.   923.

NAR, River. *See* NORFOLK.

NARBONNE. DOUAIS (C.) L'Albigéisme et les Frères prêcheurs à Narbonne. pp. 149. *Paris*, 1894. 8°.   4629. ec. 6.

FAURE (H.) Étude de la situation hospitalière à Narbonne et dans le nord de la France. pp. 106. *Narbonne*, 1891. 8°.   7688. h. 1.

JOURDANNE (G.) Les Variations du littoral narbonnais examinées. pp. 29. *Paris*, 1892. 8°.
Pam. 27.

SABARTHÈS ( ) Étude sur l'Abbaye de Saint-Paul de Narbonne. pp. 403. *Narbonne*, 1893. 8°.   4629. e. 32.

JOURDANNE (G.) Les Littérateurs narbonnais à l'époque romaine. pp. 27. *Paris*, 1892. 8°.
11312. q. 3. (7.)

NASHVILLE, University. Ac. Nashville. *University.* Catalogue of the University of Nashville: Session 1888–89. pp. 40.
Nashville, 1889. 8°.   8366. b. 44.
—— Catalogue. Session 1889–90. pp. 52.
Nashville, 1890. 8°.   8366. de. 29.

NASSAU. SAUER (W.) Das Herzogtum Nassau in den Jahren 1813–20. pp. 186.
Wiesbaden, 1893. 8°.   9340. h. 10.
See also HESSE.

NATAL. BIRD (J.) Annals of Natal. 2 vol.
Pietermaritzburg, 1888. 8°.   9061. h. 9.
RUSSELL (R.) Natal, the Land and its story. pp. 265. *Pietermaritzburg,* 1891. 8°.
     010096. c. 36.
THOMAS (E. N.) How thankful should we be. pp. 28. *Cape Town,* 1894. 8°.   Pam. 66.
See also AFRICA, *South.*

NATIONALITY. KRETZSCHMER (F.) Die kommende Krisis des Nationalismus. pp. 108.
Auma, 1894. 8°.   8008. dd. 6.
RITTER ( ) Nationalität und Humanität. pp. 58. *Dessau,* 1891. 8°.   Pam. 64.
See also LAW, *International.*

NATURAL HISTORY.
General.

Ac. Liverpool. *Naturalists' Field Club.* Proceedings. *Liverpool,* 1893, *etc.* 8°. Ac. 3016. b.
BENISON (H. W. S. W.) Nature's Fairy-land. pp. 232. *Lond.* 1892. 8°.   7001. aaa. 19.
BEYER (O. W.) Die Naturwissenschaften in der Erziehungsschule. pp. 205. *Leipz.* 1885. 8°.
     8311. g. 15.
BUDDE (E.) Naturwissenschaftliche Plaudereien. pp. 322. *Berl.* 1891. 8°.   7002. aaa. 1.
DIXON (C.) Idle hours with Nature. pp. 278.
Lond. 1891. 8°.   7001. b. 8.
FOREST TITHES. Forest Tithes. By a Son of the Marshes. pp. 208. *Lond.* 1893. 8°.
     7001. b. 11.
FURNEAUX (W. S.) Out-door World, or young collector's handbook. pp. 411. *Lond.* 1893. 8°.
     7002. aa. 3.
GERARD (J.) Science and scientists; papers on Natural History. pp. 130. *Lond.* 1889. 8°.
     7206. b. 18.
GIBSON (W. H.) Strolls by starlight and sunshine. pp. 194. *N.Y.* 1891. 4°. 7002. gg. 13.
GRAHAM (P. A.) All the year with Nature. pp. 237. *Lond.* 1893. 8°.   7001. aa. 30.
JAPP (A. H.) Hours in my garden. pp. 340.
Lond. 1894. 8°.   7206. e. 17.
JASPERS (J.) De Natuurlijke Historie in de lagere school. pp. 168. *Amsterdam,* 1893. 8°.
     7001. b. 12.
KERR (R.) Hidden beauties of Nature. pp. 256.
Lond. 1895. 8°.   4429. k. 13.
LUBBOCK (*Right Hon. Sir* J.) The Beauties of Nature. pp. 427. *Lond.* 1892. 8°. 2250. b. 19.
MARGESSON (*Lady* I. A.) Handbook to the study of Natural History. pp. 232. *Lond.* 1894. 8°.
     7001. bb. 8.
OWEN (J. A.) and BOULGER (G. S.) The Country, month by month. (March, April, *etc.*)
Lond. 1894, *etc.* 8°.   7208. e.
P.P. *Buenos Ayres.* Revista argentina de Historia Natural. *Buenos Aires,* 1891, *etc.* 8°.
     P.P. 1989. k.
—— *Dublin.* The Irish Naturalist.
Dubl. 1892, *etc.* 8°.   44.
—— *Edinbur* . Annals of Scottish Natural History. *Edinb.* 1892, *etc.* 8°. P.P. 1980. c.
—— *London.* The British Naturalist.
Lond. 1891, *etc.* 8°.   P.P. 1976. d.

NATURAL HISTORY.—General—*cont.*
P.P. *London.* The Field Club.
Lond. 1890, *etc.* 8°.   P.P. 1989. d.
—— The Naturalists' Journal, *etc.*
Lond. 1892, *etc.* 8°. P.P. 1976. da. and 226.
—— *San Francisco.* Zoe. A biological journal.
San Francisco, 1890, *etc.* 8°.   P.P. 1985.
PIZZETTA (J.) Galerie des Naturalistes. pp. 396. *Paris,* 1891. 8°.   7002. f. 10.
POLLARD (B.) Every-day Miracles. pp. 238.
Lond. 1891. 8°.   7001. aa. 23.
POUCHET (F. A.) The Universe. pp. 564.
Lond. 1895. 8°.   7001. eee. 16.
REICHENAU (W. v.) Bilder aus dem Naturleben. pp. 286. *Leipz.* 1892. 8°.   7002. f. 11.
SHALER (N. S.) The Interpretation of Nature. pp. 305. *Bost.* 1893. 8°.   012357. h. 16.
SPRING. From Spring to Fall. By a Son of the Marshes. pp. 244. *Edinb.* 1894. 8°. 012356. f. 32.
SÖRENSEN (H. L.) Dyrerigets og Planterigets Naturhistorie. pp. 239. *Christiania,* 1891. 8°.
     7002. aaa. 2.
STEP (E.) By Sea-shore, wood and moorland. pp. 320. *Lond.* 1891. 8°.   7005. bb. 15.
TUTT (J. W.) Woodside, burnside and marsh. pp. 241. *Lond.* 1894. 8°.   7206. e. 19.
VARIGNY (H. C. de) Curiosités de l'Histoire Naturelle. pp. 413. *Paris,* 1893. 12°.
     7005. aaa. 22.
WILSON (A.) Glimpses of Nature. pp. 247.
Lond. 1891. 8°.   7001. aaa. 18.
—— Science Stories. pp. 269. *Lond.* 1892. 8°.
     7003. aa. 9.
WOOD (T.) Animal and plant Life. pp. 240. 1893. 8°. Blackie's Science Readers. No. 6.
     8703. aa.
WOODLANDERS. With the Woodlanders. By a Son of the Marshes. pp. 305. *Lond.* 1893. 8°.
     012357. h. 55.
WRIGHT (M. O.) The Friendship of Nature. pp. 238. *N.Y.* 1894. 16°.   012356. de. 4.

Museums of Natural History and Zoological Gardens.

Ac. Dresden. *Zoologisches Museum.* Abhandlungen und Berichte. *Berl.* 1887, *etc.* 4°.
     Ac. 3562.
Ac. Geneva. *Musée d'Histoire Naturelle.* Revue suisse de Zoologie et Annales du Musée.
Genève, 1893, *etc.* 8°.   Ac. 2870. b.
Ac. London. *British Museum.* Guide to the British Museum, Natural History. pp. 78.
Lond. 1893. 8°.   7003. aa. 11.
Ac. Paris. *Muséum d'Histoire Naturelle.* Bulletin. *Paris,* 1895, *etc.* 8°.   Ac. 2855/8.
—— Centenaire de la fondation du Muséum. pp. 571. *Paris,* 1893. 4°.   7003. f. 4.
GOGORZA Y GONZÁLEZ (J.) Reseña de las colecciones del Museo de Historia Natural. pp. 102.
Madrid, 1891. 8°.   Pam. 42.
Ac. Sydney. *Australian Museum.* Records.
Sydney, 1890, *etc.* 8°.   Ac. 1973.
CORNISH (C. J.) Life at the Zoo. Notes and traditions of the Regent's Park Gardens, *etc.* pp. 340. *Lond.* 1895. 8°.   7206. h. 22.
WOOD (J. G.) and (T.) The Zoo. With coloured illustrations. pp. 100. *Lond.* 1892. 8°.
     7206. h. 17.

NATURALISM, Artistic and Literary.
BAHR (H.) Die Überwindung der Naturalismus. pp. 322. *Dresden,* 1891. 8°.   8470. f. 18.
BERG (L.) Der Naturalismus. pp. 244.
München, 1892. 8°.   012357. k. 6.
BOVIO (G.) Il Naturalismo. pp. 42.
Torino, 1882. 8°.   8462. f. 40.

NATURALISM—*continued.*

DAVID-SAUVAGEOT (A.) Le Réalisme et le Naturalisme. pp. 407. *Paris*, 1890. 8°.
11840. aa. 12.

HANSSON (O.) Der Materialismus in der Litteratur. pp. 35. 1892. 8°. SCHMIDKUNZ (H.) Gegen den Materialismus. No. 3. 4016. h. 13.

KLINCKSIECK (F.) Zur Entwicklungsgeschichte des Realismus im französischen Roman. pp. 56. *Marburg*, 1891. 8°. 011824. h. 31. (9.)

KRAUS (E.) Romantik und Naturalismus. pp. 51. *Mitau*, 1891. 8°. 011850. h. 16. (9.)

LAPORTE (A.) Le Naturalisme, ou, l'immoralité littéraire. pp. 320. *Paris*, 1894. 12°.
011850. f. 66.

NORDAU (M. S.) Entartung. 2 Bde. *Berl.* 1892, 93. 8°. 012357. i. 39.

—— Degeneration. pp. 560. *Lond.* 1895. 8°.
12357. k. 24.

REISSMANN (A.) Der Naturalismus in der Kunst. pp. 74. 1891. 8°. Deutsche Zeit- und Streit-Fragen. Hft. 88, 89. 12209. f.

VALENTIN (V.) Der Naturalismus und seine Stellung in der Kunstentwickelung. pp. 45. 1891. 8°. WOLFF (E.) Deutsche Schriften. Reihe 1. Hft. 4. 12250. i.

NATURALIZATION.
See LAW, *International.*

NATURAL PHILOSOPHY. *See* PHYSICS.

NATURAL SELECTION.
See EVOLUTIONS.

NAUEN. BARDEY (E. G.) Geschichte von Nauen und Osthavelland. *Rathenow*, 1892, *etc.* 8°. 10240. i.

NAUMBURG am Saale. BRAUN (S.) Naumburger Annalen von Jahre 799 bis 1613. pp. 537. *Naumburg*, 1892. 8°. 10256. cc. 16.

SCHOEPFE (C.) Naumburgs Mundart. pp. 58. *Naumburg*, 1893. 8°. 12903. dd. 36. (15.)

NAVAL SCIENCE.
Bibliography.

GILBERT (H. M.) Catalogue of a collection of books on Naval Subjects in the possession of T. J. Bennett. pp. 63. *Southampton*, 1895. 4°.
11905. l. 4.

YOUNG (L.) Catalogue of Works by American Naval Authors. pp. 149. *Wash.* 1888. 8°.
011902. m. 10.

General : History.

CORAZZINI (F.) Storia della Marina militare antica. pp. 199. *Catania*, 1892. 8°.
8806. ddd. 7.

SERRE (P.) Les Marines de guerre de l'antiquité et du moyen âge. 2 pt. *Paris*, 1885-91. 8°.
8807. d. 27.

TORR (C.) Ancient Ships. pp. 139. *Camb.* 1894. 8°. 8806. dd. 25.

KOPECKY (J.) Die attischen Trieren. pp. 154. *Leipz.* 1890. 8°. 7705. e. 35.

LUEBECK (E.) Das Seewesen der Griechen und Römer. 2 Thle. *Hamburg*, 1890, 91. 4°.
8805. g. 33.

AC. London. *Navy Records Society.* Publications. *Lond.* 1894, *etc.* 8°. Ac. 8109.

FROUDE (J. A.) English Seamen in the sixteenth century. pp. 241. *Lond.* 1895. 8°. 2394. c. 3.

LESLIE (R. C.) Old Sea Wings, ways and words. pp. 328. *Lond.* 1890. 8°. 8807. c. 40.

MAHAN (A. T.) Influence of Sea Power upon the French Revolution, 1793-1812. 2 vol. *Lond.* 1892. 8°. 9079. g. 21.

MEULEN (M. de) La Marine moderne. pp. 249. *Paris*, 1892. 8°. 8806. g. 22.

NAVAL SCIENCE.—General, etc.—*cont.*

P.P. *Palermo.* Rassegna Navale. *Palermo*, 1893, *etc.* 8°. P.P. 4027. lb.

Q. The Story of the Sea. *Lond.* 1895, *etc.* 8°.
8807. g.

See also infra: Dictionaries and Encyclopædias: Ships of War: Steamships: BIOGRAPHY, *Military and Naval.*

Artillery.

See infra: Ships of War: FORTIFICATION: GUNNERY.

Collisions, Rule of the Road, etc.

HUETTEROTH (A.) Captains' Bridge Companion. Tables for finding the distance of an object at sea. pp. 47. *Lond.* 1893. 8°. 8806. a. 62.

MOORE (J. G.) "Keep Clear!" A nautical game. *Liverp.* 1888. 8°. 1865. c. 2. (1.)

RAIKES (F. W.) "Both to blame." Paper on the conflict of law where two vessels are held jointly in fault. pp. 26. *Lond.* 1895. 8°.
Pam. 32.

TAYLOR (H. M.) Collisions at sea. pp. 11. *Camb.* 1895. 8°. Pam. 43.

TODD (J.) Whistle Code for use in steamers. pp. 29. *Lond.* 1891. 8°. 8807. c. 43.

WILES (J. F.) Greatest peril of the Sea and its remedy. pp. 16. *Lond.* 1891. 8°. Pam. 43.

Dictionaries and Encyclopædias.

AMEZAGA (C. de) Manuale del Marino militare e mercantile. pp. 260. *Milano*, 1891. 8°.
12206. aaa. 60.

ENCYCLOPÆDIAS. Naval Encyclopædia. *Phila.* 1884. 8°. 8807. h. 23.

COWAN (F.) Contributions to a Sailor's Dictionary. pp. 18. *Greenesburgh*, 1894. 8°.
12903. dd. 37. (14.)

PATTERSON (H.) Illustrated Nautical Dictionary. pp. 392. *N.Y.* 1891. 8°. 8807. d. 22.

—— Naval Dictionary illustrated. pp. 68. *N.Y.* 1895. 8°. 8807. g. 10.

PIRRIE (W.) Technical Dictionary (English and French) of sea-terms. pp. 354. *Lond.* 1895. 8°.
8806. a. 66.

ANSTRUTHER (R. H.) and SETTEMBRINI (R.) Seafaring phrases, English and Italian. pp. 134. *Portsmouth*, 1894. 8°. 8806. bb. 31.

BERG (C. F.) Ordbog for Skibsredere, Skibsførere og Styrmænd. *Porsgrund*, 1891, *etc.* 8°.
8806. ccc.

Electrical Appliances.

CALLOU (L.) Applications de l'Électricité dans la marine. pp. 347. *Paris*, 1894. 8°.
8757. dd. 22.

MINEL (P.) Électricité appliquée à la marine. pp. 203. 1894. 8°. Encyclopédie des Aide-Mémoire. 8709. g.

URQUHART (J. W.) Electric Ship-lighting. pp. 278. *Lond.* 1892. 8°. 8757. bbb. 16.

Engineering. *See infra:* Steamships: ENGINEERING.

Examinations, Navy and Board of Trade. *See* EXAMINATIONS.

Exhibitions.

LONDON. *Naval Exhibition.* Official catalogue. pp. 542. *Lond.* 1891. 8°. 7957. aa. 9.

GREGO (J.) Naval Exhibition. Illustrated souvenir. pp. 81. *Lond.* 1891. 8°. 7959. cc. 12.

LIVERPOOL. *Naval Exhibition*, 1892. Catalogue. pp. 154. *Liverpool*, 1892. 8°. 7959. aaa. 57.

CHICAGO. *Columbian Exposition.* Catalogue. Part VII. Transportation Exhibits. pp. 60. *Chicago*, 1893. 8°. 7958. bb. 29.

NAVAL SCIENCE.—Exhibitions—cont.

DREDGE (J.) Record of the Transportation Exhibits at the Columbian Exposition. pp. 779. 1894. 4°. Engineering Series.　　　8755. m.

Gunnery. See GUNNERY.

Law, Mercantile and Naval. See LAW.

Merchant Service. See infra: Shipping.

Navigation. See NAVIGATION.

Sail-making. See SAILMAKING.

Seamanship.

ALSTON (A. H.) Seamanship. pp. 498. *Portsmouth*, 1893. 8°.　　　8806. bb. 26.

BEDFORD (F. G. D.) Sailor's Pocket book. pp. 588. *Portsmouth*, 1890. 8°.　8807. dd. 18.

CRADOCK (C. G. F. M.) "Wrinkles" in Seamanship. pp. 222. *Portsmouth*, 1894. 8°.　　　　　　　　　　8807. aa. 48.

G. B. & I. *Navy.* Manual of Seamanship for Boys' Training Ships. pp. 355. *Lond.* 1893. 8°.　　　8806. bb. 28.

IMPERATO (F.) Attrezzatura, manovra delle navi e segnalazioni marittime. pp. 360. *Milano*, 1894. 8°.　　　012200. h. 116.

WALKER (T. P.) Seamanship examination questions of the Training Squadron. pp. 49. *Portsmouth*, 1894. 8°.　　8806. ccc. 11.

See also supra: Collisions : EXAMINATIONS.

Shipbuilding. See SHIPBUILDING

Ships of War : Naval Strategy and Tactics.

ACKERMAN (A. A.) Face-hardened Armor. pp. 105. 1895. 8°. Ac. Annapolis. *Naval Institute.* Papers. Vol. 21.　　Ac. 4398.

BALINCOURT (R. de) Étude sur les Navires d'aujourd'hui. pp. 181. *Paris*, 1892. 8°.　　　　　　　　　　8807. e. 46.

BERTIN (L. E.) État actuel de la Marine de Guerre. pp. 188. 1893. 8°. Encyclopédie des aide-mémoire.　　　8709. g.

BRASSEY (T.) *Baron Brassey.* Future policy of War-Ship Building. pp. 33. *Lond.* 1891. 8°.　　　Pam. 43.

BUCHARD (H.) Marines étrangères. pp. 628. *Paris*, 1891. 8°.　　　8805. c. 79.

COLOMB (P. H.) Naval Warfare. pp. 471. *Lond.* 1895. 8°.　　　8807. f. 2.

CRONEAU (A.) Construction des Navires de Guerre. *Paris*, 1894, etc. 8°.　8808. aa. 4.
—— Atlas. *Paris*, 1894. 4°.　　8808. d. 2.

HOFF (W. B.) Elementary Naval Tactics. pp. 110. *Lond.* 1894. 8°.　　8806. dd. 26.

LANGMAID (J.) Lessons in Steam Machinery with description of the construction of a Battleship. pp. 267. *Lond.* 1893. 8°.　8768. e. 24.

LEDIEU (A.) and CADIAT (E.) Le Nouveau Matériel Naval. 2 tom. *Paris*, 1889, 90. 8°.　　　　　　　　　　8807. d. 28.
—— Atlas, etc. 4°.　　　1804. a. 5.

MONTERO Y RAPALLO (M.) Ensayo de Estrategia Naval. pp. 514. *Madrid*, 1892. 8°.　　　　　　　　　　8805. ece. 27.

PÈNE-SIEFERT (J.) Flottes Rivales. pp. 485. *Paris*, 1890. 18°.　　8807. aa. 42.

U.S. *Navy Department.* Examples, conclusions and maxims of modern Naval Tactics. pp. 149. *Wash.* 1884. 8°.　　8808. f. 2.
—— Papers on Naval Operations during the year 1885. pp. 135. *Wash.* 1885. 8°.　　　　　　　　　　8808. f. 3.

NAVAL SCIENCE,—Ships of War—cont.

U.S. *Navy Department.* Papers on Squadrons of Evolutions. pp. 265. *Wash.* 1886. 8°.　8808. f. 4.
—— Recent Naval Progress. pp. 346. *Wash.* 1887. 8°.　　　8808. f. 5.
—— Naval Mobilization and improvement in matériel. pp. 485. *Wash.* 1889. 8°. 8808. f. 7.
—— A Year's Naval Progress. *Wash.* 1890, etc. 8°.　　　8808. f.
—— Naval Reserves, training and matériel. pp. 433. *Wash.* 1895. 8°.　8808. f. 6,

WAINWRIGHT (R.) Tactical problems in Naval Warfare. 1895. 8°. Ac. Annapolis. *Naval Institute.* Papers. Vol. 21.　Ac. 4398.

WARAKER (T.) Naval Warfare of the future. Consideration of the Declaration of Paris, 1856. pp. 213. *Lond.* 1892. 8°.　8806. cc. 18.

WARFARE. Modern Naval Warfare. pp. 7. 1891. 8°.　　　　　Pam. 43.

WERNER (B. v.) Der Seekrieg. pp. 160. *Darmstadt*, 1893. 8°.　　8806. d. 53.
—— Die Kampfmittel zur See. pp. 152. *Leipz.* 1892. 8°.　　　8807. c. 45.

WEYL (É.) La Flotte de Guerre et les arsenaux. pp. 250. *Paris*, 1894. 12°.　8806. b. 48.

WHITE (W. H.) Modern War-ships. 1887. 8°. LONDON. *Company of Shipwrights.* Lectures, etc.　　　　8807. bbb. 34.

WILMOT (S. M. E.) Development of Navies during the last half-century. pp. 295. *Lond.* 1892. 8°.　　　8805. bbb. 33.
—— The next Naval War. pp. 175. *Lond.* 1894. 8°.　　　012330. h. 16.

WILKINSON (H. S.) The Command of the Sea. pp. 122. *Lond.* 1894. 8°.　　8806. a. 65.
—— The Secret of the Sea. pp. 27. *Lond.* 1895. 8°.　　　Pam. 68.

Z— and MONTÉCHANT (H.) Les Guerres navales de demain. pp. 282. *Paris*, 1891. 8°.　　　　　　　　　　8807. dd. 34.
—— Essai de Stratégie navale. pp. 527. *Paris*, 1893. 8°.　　8806. d. 51.

See also GUNNERY, *and under the subheading Navy of each country.*

Shipping : Mercantile Marine.

BLACKMORE (E.) The British Mercantile Marine. pp. 26. *Lond.* 1890. 8°.　Pam. 43.

CHAMPENOIS (C.) Les Armements maritimes. 2 tom. *Paris*, 1895. 8°.　8805. bbb. 38.

EPHEM. Brown's Almanac for the Mercantile Marine. *Glasg.* 1894, etc. 8°.　P.P. 2373. eb.

MACKIRDY (J.) Our Seamen. pp. 16. 1890. 8°. LONDON. *Shipmaster's Society.* Course of papers.　　　8806. cc.

BATES (W. W.) American Marine. The shipping question. pp. 479. *Bost.* 1893. 8°. 8806. dd. 20.

GERMANY. *Reichsamt des Innern.* Handbuch für die deutsche Handels-Marine. *Berl.* 1892, etc. 8°.　　　8806. ddd.

RAINERI (S.) La Marina Mercantile germanica. pp. 443. *Roma*, 1892. 8°.　8807. f. 40.

BENTZON (V.) Søloven og Lov om danske Skibes Registrering. pp. 188. *Kjøbenh.* 1892. 8°.　　　　　　　　　　5725. a. 10.

ENHÖRNING (E.) International Shipping guide. pp. 159. *Lond.* 1892. 8°.　8807. c. 52.

FROUD (A. G.) Heating of Ships and cargoes. pp. 30. *Lond.* 1891. 8°.　　Pam. 43.

G. B. & I. *Board of Trade.* Instructions to the measuring Surveyors employed in the measurement of shipping. pp. 109. *Lond.* 1891. 8°.　　　　　　　　　　8806. cc. 19.

NAVAL SCIENCE. — Shipping, etc.—
continued.

G. B. & I. *Board of Trade.* Instructions as to the Survey of passenger accommodation. pp. 70. *Lond.* 1892. 8°.   Pam. 43.
—— Regulations and suggestions as to the Survey of steamships carrying passengers. pp. 103. *Lond.* 1893. 8°.   8806. de. 44.
—— *Shipping Federation.* Merchant Shipping victualing scale Committee. pp. 44. *Lond.* 1893. fol.   8805. g. 36.
—— *Corporation for the Survey of Shipping.* Rules and Tables of Scantlings, and register of vessels. *Glasg.* 1893, *etc. obl.* fol.   1803. a.

HILLCOAT (C. H.) Notes on Stowage. pp. 179. *Lond.* 1894. 8°.   8807. aaa. 45.
HOLMAN (H.) Handy Book for Ship Owners and masters. pp. 208. *Lond.* 1892. 8° 8807. e. 30.
HOLT (J.) Epitomized Review of the principles and practice of maritime Sanitation. pp. 93. *New Orleans,* 1892. 8°.   8807. c. 48.
LONDON. *Shipmaster's Society.* Memorandum of Association, *etc. Lond.* 1890. 4°.   Pam. 43.
STEVENS (R. W.) On the Stowage of ships. pp. 816. *Lond.* 1894. 8°.   8805. cc. 45.
URQUHART (G. D.) Dues and Charges on shipping in foreign ports. pp. 1172. *Lond.* 1892. 8°.   8247. e. 46.
WEIGHT TABLE. Weight Table for rates of freight. *Lond.* 1890. *s. sh.* fol. 1882. d. 2. (56.)
See also infra: Steamships : LAW, Maritime.

Signals. *See* SIGNALLING.

Steamships.

History : Steamship Companies.

MACDONALD (A. F.) Our Ocean Railways. pp. 266. *Lond.* 1893. 8°.   8807. b. 61.
MAGINNIS (A. J.) Diagram illustrating development of Atlantic steamers. *Lond.* 1890. *s. sh.* fol.   1865. c. 5. (3.)
—— The Atlantic Ferry, its ships, men and working. pp. 208. *Lond.* 1893. 8°. 8806. b. 43.
OCEAN STEAMSHIPS. Ocean Steamships. pp. 298. *Lond.* 1892. 8°.   8807. d. 25.
PREBLE (G. H.) Chronological history of Steam Navigation. pp. 483. *Phila.* 1883. 8°.   8806. ddd. 16.
CASTLE LINE. South African Royal Mail service. Handbook of information. pp. 65. *Lond.* 1893. 8°.   10498. a. 25.
—— Castle Line. pp. 32. *Lond.* 1892. 4°.   10498. b. 17.
CUNARD STEAMSHIP COMPANY. Cunard Passenger's log-book. pp. 96. *Glasg.* 1893. 8°.   8807. a. 54.
LONDON. *New Zealand Shipping Company.* Handbook for passengers. pp. 35. *Lond.* 1892. 8°.   Pam. 87.
—— *Peninsular and Oriental Company.* Handbook of information. pp. 54. *Lond.* 1893. 8°.   8807. ec. 37.
LLOYD (W. W.) P. & O. pencillings. *Lond.* 1891. *obl.* fol.   1876. b. 16.
JAPAN. The Japanese Government v. the P. & O Company. Proceedings, cases, arguments, judgment pp. 484. *Lond.* 1895. 8°. 6835. dd. 9.
UNION STEAMSHIP COMPANY. Handbook of information. pp. 54. *Lond.* 1893. 8°. 10498. b. 18.
LINDEMAN (M.) Der Norddeutsche Lloyd. Geschichte und Handbuch. pp. 487. *Bremen,* 1892. 8°.   8806. dd. 22.

Engines : Machinery etc.

BOUGHTON (G. P.) Hints to young officers of Merchant Steamers. pp. 82. *Sunderland,* 1893. 8°.   8807. dd. 30.

NAVAL SCIENCE.—Steamships—*cont.*

BUSLEY (C.) The Marine Steam engine. Pt. 1. *Kiel,* 1892. 8°.   8806. ddd. 8.
CHASE (I. M.) Screw Propellers and marine propulsion. pp. 230. *N.Y.* 1895. 8°. 8805. dd. 66.
CHICAGO. *Engineering Congress.* Proceedings. Division of Marine and Naval Engineering. 2 vol. *N.Y.* 1894. 8°.   8808. a. 2.
DONALDSON (J.) Drawing for marine engineers. 2 pt. *Lond.* 1895. 8°.   8806. e. 40.
DYER (H.) Efficiency of Steamships from the owners' point of view. pp. 31. *Glasg.* 1888. 8°.   Pam. 43.
EDWARDS (E.) Examination questions and answers for engineers and firemen. pp. 240. *Phila.* 1893. *obl.* 8°.   8767. de. 2.
G. B. & I. *Board of Trade.* Regulations as to survey of steamships carrying passengers. pp. 103. *Lond.* 1893. 8°.   8806. de. 44.
HALDANE (J. W. C.) Steamships and their machinery. pp. 532. *Lond.* 1893. 8°.   8806. dd. 21.
HEAN (P.) Reminiscences of the Marine engine. pp. 8. *Hong Kong,* 1893. 8°. 8768. l. 23. (11.)
HUTCHINSON (W. E) Steering of screw steamers 1890. 8°. London. *Shipmasters' Society.* Course of papers, *etc.*   8806. cc.
JACK (R. W.) Criticism on W. Bailey's paper, "The Running of marine engines and boilers." pp. 19. *Hong Kong,* 1895. 12°.   Pam. 79.
JOHNSON (H. M. W. P.) Navigation with reference to the increased speed of Steamers. pp. 22. 1891. 8°. LONDON. *Shipmasters' Society.* Course of Papers. No. 12.   8806. cc.
"KINGDON" MACHINERY. Description of the "Kingdon" Machinery. *Lond.* 1891. 8°.   8807. cc. 34.
LANGMAID (J.) Lessons in Steam Machinery and the marine steam engine. pp. 267. *Lond.* 1893. 8°.   8768. e. 24.
LEASK (A. R.) Breakdowns at Sea. pp. 252. *Lond.* 1894. 8°.   8806. ccc. 16.
LOCKE (J.) Marine Engineers' drawing-book. *Lond.* 1892. *obl.* 8°.   8806. a. 60.
LONDON. *Institute of Marine Engineers.* Transactions. *Lond.* 1889, *etc.* 8°. 8805. bbb. 36. (2.)
MARTORELLI (G.) Le Macchine a Vapore marine. pp. 634. *Torino,* 1893. 4°.   8807. l. 24.
NEWTON (J.) Newton's Steamship examiner. pp. 115. *Lond.* 1891. 8°.   8807. aa. 44.
ROBERTS (C. W.) Advice for Marine Engineers. pp. 150. *Lond.* 1894. 8°.   8806. bb. 34.
—— Drawing for Marine Engineers. pp. 183. *Lond.* 1895. 8°.   8805. c. 82.
RASMUSSEN (A. H. M.) Læren om Skibsdampmaskinen. pp. 576. *Kjøbenh.* 1893. 8°.
—— Tegninger. *obl.* 4°.   8806. ddd. 18.
SEATON (A. E) Manual of Marine Engineering. pp. 585. *Lond.* 1895. 8°.   8768. ccc. 2.
—— and ROUNTHWAITE (H. M.) Pocket Book of Marine Engineering. pp. 426. *Lond.* 1894. 8°.   8806. aa. 61.
THORN (W. H.) Reed's Engineers' handbook to Board of Trade examinations. pp. 639. 18. 5. *Sunderland,* 1893. 8°.   8768. dd. 17.
—— Key to Reed's Engineers' handbook. pp. 336. *Sunderland,* 1894. 8°.   8768. dd. 18.
—— Hints to sea-going Engineers. pp. 203 *Sunderland,* 1891. 8°.   8766. aa. 44.
WATSON (T. H.) Naval Architects and Engineers data book. *Newcastle,* 1892. 8°.   8807. e. 47.
YEO (J.) Steam and the Marine Steam Engine. pp. 196. *Lond.* 1894. 8°.   8768. k. 18.

NAVAL SCIENCE.—Steamships—cont.

BARNABY (S. W.) Marine Propellers. pp. 115. *Lond.* 1891. 8°.   8806. dd. 15.

MARTINENQ (B.) Traité des Propulseurs employés dans la navigation à vapeur. 2 pt. *Paris*, 1893. 4°.   8807. l. 23.

WALTON (W. H.) Pitch of Propeller table. *Hexham*, 1893. 16°.   1810. d. 1. (22.)

See also supra: Ships of War: BOILERS: SHIPBUILDING : YACHTS.

Strategy and Tactics.

See supra: Ships of War.

Torpedoes. *See* TORPEDOES.

NAVARRE. BRUTAILS (J. A.) Archives de la Chambre des Comptes de Navarre, 1196–1384. pp. 194. 1890. 8°. AC. Paris. *École des Hautes Études.* Bibliothèque. Sciences philologiques. fasc. 84.   AC. 8929.

BOISSONNADE (P.) Histoire de la réunion de la Navarre à la Castille. pp. 685. *Paris*, 1893. 8°.   9180. g. 3.

NAVIGATION AND NAUTICAL AS-TRONOMY. BARHAM (W. H.) Theory and practice of Navigation. pp. 160. 1893. 8°. Collins' Science Series.   8708. aaa.

BATEMAN (J. F. R.) Short method Ex-Meridian tables. pp. 224. *Lond.* 1894. 4°. 8535. dd. 22.

BEDFORD (F. G. D.) Sailor's Pocket-book. pp. 588. *Portsmouth*, 1890. 8°.   8807. dd. 18.

BERGEN (W. C.) Practice of Navigation and nautical astronomy. pp. 393. 277. *North Shields*, 1893. 8°.   8807. e. 32.

CASPARI (É.) Les Chronomètres de marine. pp. 203. 1894. 8°. Encyclopédie des aide-mémoire.   8709. g.

DON (J.) Navigation. *Lond.* 1892, *etc.* 8°.   8807. a. 52.

FLAGG (A. J.) Primer of Navigation. pp. 104. *Lond.* 1894. 8°.   8806. a. 27.

GEELMUYDEN (C. T. H.) Lærebog i Navigationen 2 Deel. *Christiania*, 1883, 91. 8°. 8806. dd. 17.

G. B. & I. *Hydrographic Office.* Notes bearing on the Navigation of H.M. Ships. pp. 32. *Lond.* 1893. 8°.   Pam. 43.

GUILHAUMON (J. B.) Éléments de Navigation. 2 pt. *Paris*, 1891. 8° and 4°.   8807. l. 21.

INMAN (J.) Nautical Tables. pp. 567. *Lond.* 1895. 8°.   8548. g. 29.

JACKSON (R.) Ocean Passages. pp. 16. *Portsmouth*, 1890. 8°.   Pam. 43.

JOHNSON (A. C.) Combined Time and Altitude Azimuth tables. pp. 13. *Lond.* 1892. 8°.   Pam. 38.

—— Tables and rules for finding Latitude and Longitude. *Lond.* 1887. 8°.   8806. de. 42.

—— Hour-angles of the Sun, Moon and Stars. pp. 31. *Lond.* 1891. 8°.   8806. de. 40.

—— How to find the Time at Sea in less than a minute. *Lond.* 1891. 8°.   8806. de. 41.

—— On finding the Latitude and Longitude in cloudy weather. pp. 22. *Lond.* 1892. 8°.   8806. de. 39.

JOHNSON (W.) Two Stars Vertical: tables. pp. 178. *Lond.* 1891. 8°.   8561. cc. 34.

LECKY (S. T. S.) "Wrinkles" in practical Navigation. pp. 758. *Lond.* 1894. 8°.   8806. ddd. 14.

LEONARDI CATTOLICA (P.) Trattato di Navigazione. pp. 699. *Livorno*, 1893. 8°. 8805. cc. 44.

MARTIN (W. R.) Treatise on Navigation and nautical astronomy. pp. 356. *Lond.* 1891. 8°.   8807. cc. 35.

NAVIGATION, etc,—continued.

NOORDUYN (L. A. W.) Leerboek der Zeevaartkunde. pp. 352. *Gorinchem*, 1893. 8°.   8806. de. 46.

NORIE (J. W.) Epitome of practical Navigation. pp. 431. *Lond.* 1889. 8°.   8807. bb. 60.

PATTERSON (H.) Navigator's Pocket-book. pp. 177. *Lond.* 1894. 8°.   8806. aa. 21.

PETERSEN (C. T.) Navigations-Tabeller. pp. 294. *Kristiania*, 1891. 8°.   8548. df. 34.

QUIRK (H. G.) Table of Angles, and Local Marine Board Examination rules. *Dublin*, 1893. *s. sh.* 8°.   1865. c. 5. (8.)

RAPER (H.) Practice of Navigation and nautical astronomy. pp. 934. *Lond.* 1891. 8°.   8807. d. 19.

REYNOLDS (R.) Tables for finding the Latitude from ex-meridian altitudes. pp. 15. *Southampton*, 1893. 8°.   Pam. 38.

THOMSON (W.) *Baron Kelvin.* Popular Lectures. Vol. 3. *Lond.* 1891. 8°. Nature Series.   2244. b. 32.

WILSON-BARKER (D.) Development of instrumental Nautical Astronomy. pp. 19. 1890, *etc.* 8°. LONDON. *Shipmasters' Society.* Course of papers.   Pam. 43. *See also* COMPASS.

NEANDRIA. *See* GREECE, *Antiquities.*

NEBRASKA. GARNEAU (J.) Nebraska: resources and development. pp. 24. *Omaha*, 1893. 12°.   Pam. 86.

NEBULAE. *See* STARS.

NECK. *See* HEAD.

NECKAR, River. ECKART (T.) Bilder aus dem Neckarthal. pp. 88. *Heidelberg*, 1893. 8°.   10256. b. 46.

NEEDLEWORK. ARNOLD (E. J.) Examination in Needlework. Instructions to Inspectors. *Leeds*, 1894. *s. sh.* fol.   Tab. 11747. b. (52.)

CORNWELL (E.) Columbian Sewing book. pp. 22. 24. *Chicago*, 1892. 4°.   7743. ee. 16.

DILLMONT (T. de) Encyclopedia of Needlework. pp. 578. ¡*Dornach*, 1890. 8°.   7743. c. 14.

FAIT-HANDO-PE. Machine sewing compared with Hand-sewing. pp. 32. *Lond.* 1895. 8°.   7742. de. 34.

FLEMING (J. A.) A. L. Series of Pupil Teachers' Needlework patterns. *Leeds*, 1891, *etc.* fol.   7743. f.

JONES (E. G.) Manual of plain Needlework. pp. 128. *Lond.* 1890. 8°.   7743. b. 21

—— Self-teaching Needlework manuals. pp. 77. *Lond.* 1894. 8°.   7743. bbb. 71.

KNITTER. Knitter's Note-book. pp. 62. *Lond.* 1890. 16°.   7743. aa. 17.

MASTERS (E. T.) Drawn Linen work. pp. 117. *Lond.* 1890. 8°.   7742. bb. 25.

—— Gentlewoman's book of art Needlework. pp. 210. 1893. 8°. ADAMS (W. H. D.) Victoria Library.   012208. f.

—— Work-table Companion. pp. 192. *Lond.* 1893. 8°.   7743. d. 2.

MORRIS, afterwards SPARLING (M.) Decorative Needlework. pp. 121. *Lond.* 1893. 4°.   Banks. 3. e. 5.

MYRA. Myra's Knitting-books. *Lond.* 1889, *etc.* 8°.   7743. aaa. 45.

ROSEVEAR (E.) Manual of Needlework. pp. 136. *Lond.* 1894. 8°.   7743. bb. 69.

—— Needlework, Knitting and cutting out. 3 pt. *Lond.* 1894. 8°.   7743. bb. 66.

—— Text-book of Needlework. pp. 460. *Lond.* 1893. 8°.   7742. b. 19.

NETHERLANDS.—Antiquities—*cont.*

Ac. Antwerp. *Académie d'Archéologie.* Annales. Sér. in 4°. *Anvers, 1894, etc.* 4°. Ac. 5513.

ROEVER (N. de) Het leven van onze Voorouders. *Amsterdam, 1891, etc.* 8°.   7706. i.
See also infra : Topography.

Colonies.

CREMER (J. T.) Koloniale Politiek. pp. 39. *Haarlem, 1891.* 8°.   8155. ee. 18. (8.)

HAVE (J. J. ten) Land en volk onzer Koloniën. pp. 317. *'s Gravenh.* 1892. 8°.   10024. ccc. 3.

NASSAU (H. J.) Nederlandsch-Indië en andere Koloniën. pp. 147. *Groningen, 1891.* 8°.   9055. aaa. 22.

RIETSTAP (J. B.) Aardrijkskundig woordenboek van Nederland en zijne Kolonien. coll. 580. *Groningen, 1892.* 8°.   10026. ccc. 5.

WAANDERS (F. G. v. B.) Nederland's koloniale markt. pp. 60. *'s Gravenh.* 1881. 8°.   8023. g. 37. (10.)
See also ACHEEN : CELEBES : INDIES, *Dutch* : MALAY PENINSULA AND MALAYSIA : MOLUCCAS : SUMATRA.

Constitution and Politics.

BEIJNEN (L. R.) Overzicht van de Staatsregeling van ons Vaderland. pp. 230. *'s Gravenh.* 1891. 8°.   9405. aaa. 18.

BOUDEWIJNSE (J.) Regeering en Staten Generaal tijdens de Grondwet van 1848. pp. 108. *'s Gravenh.* 1890. 8°.   5686. d. 4.

HARTMAN (H. G.) Staatsrecht en staatsinrichting van Nederland. pp. 240. *'s Gravenh.* 1891. 8°.   8081. aaa. 9.

KNIPHORST (J. H. P. E.) Nogmaals de quaestie der Rijkswerven in de Nederlandsche Volksvertegenwoordiging. pp. 104. *'s Gravenh.* 1891. 8°.   Pam. 43.

LIBERAL PARTY. De Liberale Partij tegenover radicalen Volkspartij, *etc.* pp. 23. *Zierikzee,* 1891. 8°.   Pam. 73.

LOHMAN (W. H. de S.) De Verhouding tusschen het recht, den staat en de overheid. pp. 47. *Amsterdam,* 1890. 8°.   Pam. 34.

NETHERLANDS. De partijen in Nederland. pp. 31. *Amsterdam,* 1891. 8°.   Pam. 73.

SIMMER (J.) Is Revolutie noodzakelijk? pp. 41. *Amsterdam,* 1893. 8°.   Pam. 73.

TREUB (M. W. F.) De Radicalen tegenover de social-democratische partij. pp. 48. *Amsterdam,* 1891. 8°.   Pam. 73.

TROELSTRA (P. J.) Het Kiesrecht en de sociaal-demokratie. pp. 64. *Utrecht,* 1895. 8°. Pam. 82.

TROSÉE (J.) Wat wil de Radicale Partij? *'s Hertogenbosch,* 1892. 8°.   Pam. 73.

VLIET (P. v.) De Houding der Liberale Partij tegenover de candidatuur van "een man uit het volk." pp. 52. *Amsterdam,* 1891. 8°. Pam. 73.
See also SOCIALISM : SOCIAL SCIENCE.

History.

(Including the history of Belgium to 1830.)

PIRENNE (H.) Bibliographie de l'histoire de Belgique. pp. 230. *Gand,* 1893. 8°.   011902. h. 46.

Ac. Antwerp. *Académie d'Archéologie.* Annales. Sér. in 4°. *Anvers, 1894, etc.* 4°. Ac. 5513.
—— Haarlem. *Vereeniging van Archivarissen.* Nederlandsch Archievenblad. *Groningen,* 1893. *etc.* 8°.   Ac. 9012.

BEAUFORT (W. H. de) Geschiedkundige Opstellen. 2 pt. *Amsterdam,* 1893. 8°. 9414. cc. 2.

BLOK (P. J.) Geschiedenis van het Nederlandsche volk. *Groningen,* 1892, *etc.* 8°.   9406. h. 16.

GRIFFIS (W. E.) Brave little Holland. pp. 252. *Bost.* 1894. 8°.   9414. aaa. 19.

NETHERLANDS.—History—*continued.*

JORISSEN (T. T. H.) Historische Studien. pp. 480. *Haarlem,* 1893. 8°.   9009. k. 3.

JUSTE (T.) Histoire de Belgique. 3 tom. *Brux.* 1895. 8°.   9415. l. 7.

KLOPPERS (P. J.) Nederland en Oranje in beeld en schrift. *Amsterdam,* 1895, *etc.* 8°. 9407. dd.

NAVEZ (L.) La Belgique asservie. pp. 54. *Brux.* 1895. 8°.   9414. f. 13.

NIJHOFF (D. C.) Staatkundige Geschiedenis van Nederland. 2 Dl. *Zutphen,* 1893. 8°.   9407. dd. 3.

POULLET (E.) Histoire politique nationale. 2 tom. *Louvain,* 1882–92. 8°.   9414. bb. 11.

RIJSENS (F. v.) Geschiedenis des Vaderlands. pp. 246. *Te Groningen,* 1891. 8°.   9406. b. 9.

VANDERKINDERE (L.) Introduction à l'histoire des institutions de la Belgique au moyen age. pp. 301. *Brux.* 1890. 8°.   9414. h. 13.

PIRENNE (H.) Histoire du meurtre de Charles le Bon, comte de Flandre. 1891. 8°. Collection de textes. No. 10.   9210. de.

BOTS (P. M.) Van Erasmus naar Vondel, of kern der vaderlandsche vrijheidshistorie. pp. 89. *Haarlem,* 1893. 4°.   9407. g.

BRINK (R. C. B. v. d.) Cartons voor de geschiedenis van den Nederlandschen Vrijheidsoorlog. pp. 289. *'s Gravenh.* 1891. 8°.   9405. aaa. 19.

ENZINAS (F. de) Denkwürdigkeiten vom Zustand der Niederlande und von der Religion in Spanien. pp. 302. *Bonn,* 1893. 8°. 4625. dd. 2.

CAMPBELL (D.) The Puritan in Holland, England and America. 2 vol. *Lond.* 1892. 8°.   9602. dd. 1.

GRIFFIS (W. E.) Influence of the Netherlands in the making of the English Commonwealth and the American Republic. pp. 40. *Bost.* 1891. 8°.   9005. d. 26. (7.)

JURIEN DE LA GRAVIÈRE (J. P. E.) Les Gueux de Mer. pp. 339. *Paris,* 1893. 12°. 9406. b. 11.

MOTLEY (J. L.) Rise of the Dutch Republic. 3 vol. *Lond.* 1893. 8°.   9414. bb. 9.

ROGERS (J. E. T.) Lessons from the Dutch Republic. 1891. 8°. MAGNÚSSON (E.) National Life.   8486. g. 21.

KOETSVELD (C. E. v.) Bij de graven van Oranje-Nassau. pp. 61. *Amsterdam,* 1891. 8°.   10759. k. 27.

PUTNAM (R.) William the Silent, Prince of Orange. 2 vol. *N.Y.* 1895. 8°. 10759. e. 22.

X. Lodewijk van Nassau en Willem de Zwijger. pp. 104, *Roermond,* 1892. 8°.   10759. i. 44.

BRUGMANS (H.) Engeland en de Nederlanden. 1558–67. pp. 235. *Groningen,* 1892. 8°.   9079. h. 21.

Ac. Brussels. *Commission d'Histoire.* PERRENOT DE GRANVELLE (A.) *Cardinal.* Correspondance du Cardinal de Granvelle, 1565–83. pp. 764. *Brux.* 1884. 4°.   Ac. 986/24.

TEUBNER (E.) Der Feldzug Wilhelms von Oranien gegen den Herzog von Alba, 1568. pp. 71. *Halle,* 1892. 8°.   9327. ccc.

FEYS (E.) Les Députés de la Flandre à Madrid, pp. 51. 1890. 8°. Ac. Bruges. *Société d'Émulation.* Annales. Sér. 5. Tom. 2.   Ac. 5517.

FRUIN (R.) Tien Jaren uit den tachtigjarigen Oorlog, 1588–98. pp. 383. *'s Gravenh.* 1889. 8°.   9073. de. 18.

WADDINGTON (A.) La République des Provinces-Unies en 1630. pp. 62. *Paris,* 1893. 8°.   9008. l. 3. (7.)

KERNKAMP (G. W.) De Sleutels van de Sont. 1644–45. pp. 310. *'s Hage,* 1890. 8°.   9079. g. 12.

NETHERLANDS.—History—*continued.*

MITSUKURI (G.) Englisch - niederländische Unionsbestrebungen im Zeitalter Cromwells. pp. 107. *Tübingen*, 1891. 8°. 9079. i. 6.

KRÄMER (F. J. L.) De Nederlandsch-Spaansche Diplomatie vóór den Vrede van Nijmegen. pp. 287. *Utrecht*, 1892. 8°. 9079. i. 17.

DELPLACE (L.) Joseph II. et la Révolution brabançonne. pp. 247. *Bruges*, 1891. 8°. 9414. c. 4.

VERGERS (P.) De Revolutie van 1789 en Nederland. pp. 326. *Doesburg*, 1894. 8°. 9231. l.

ZEISSBERG (H. R. v.) Zwei Jahre belgischer Geschichte 1791–92. 1891, *etc.* 8°. Ac. Vienna. *K. Akademie.* Sitzungsberichte. Phil.-historische Classe. Bd. 123, *etc.* Ac. 310/6.

JOTTRAND (G.) L'Annexion de la Belgique à la France, 1792–95. pp. 47. *Brux.* 1889. 8°. Pam. 28.

ZEISSBERG (H. v.) Belgien unter Erzherzog Carls, 1793–94. pp. 168. 1893. 8°. Ac. Vienna. *K. Akademie.* Sitzungsberichte. Phil.-histoische Classe. Bd. 128. *.*Ac. 810/6.

SAHRON (F. H. A.) De Oorlog von 1794–95. *Te Breda*, 1892, *etc.* 8°. 9079. f.

FRENCH REVOLUTION. La République batave. pp. 398. *Paris*, 1894. 8°. 9414. e. 5.

LANZAC DE LABORIE (L. de) La Domination française en Belgique. 1795–1814. 2 tom. *Paris*, 1895. 8°. 9414. h. 18.

WICHERS (L.) De Regeering van Koning Lodewijk Napoleon, 1806–10. pp. 401. *Utrecht*, 1892. 8°. 9406. h. 17.

VEENENDAAL (E. J.) Levensbeschrijving van wijlen Koning Willem III. pp. 93. *Nijmegen.* 1891. 8°. 10759. f. 25.

WILLIAM III., *King.* Het leven van Koning Willem III. pp. 208. *Schiedam*, 1890. 8°. 10759. e. 16.

ISING (A. L. H.) In de Kamers der Staten-Generaal. 1850–86. pp. 211. *'s Gravenh.* 1892. 8°. 8081. b. 17.

History, *Ecclesiastical.*

BERLIÈRE (U.) Documents pour servir à l'Histoire ecclésiastique de la Belgique. *Maredsous*, 1894, *etc.* 8°. 4685. h.

DITCHFIELD (P. H.) The Church in the Netherlands. pp. 396. 1892. 8°. National Churches. 4534. de.

REITSMA (J.) Geschiedenis van de Hervorming en de Kerk der Nederlanden. *Groningen*, 1892. *etc.* 8°. 4685. g. 14.

MEER (B. v.) De Synode te Emden 1571. pp. 267. *'s Gravenh.* 1892. 8°. 5015. ee. 6.

RUTGERS (F. L.) Acta van de Nederlandsche Synoden der zestiende eeuw. 1889. 8°. Ac. Utrecht. *Marnix-Vereeniging.* Werken. Ser. II. Dl. III. Ac. 2043.

MARCELLINO, *da Civezza*, and DOMENICHELLI (T.) Epistolae missionariorum Ordinis S. Francisci ex Frisia et Hollendia. pp. 403. *Quaracchi*, 1888. 8°. 4685. h. 8.

WYLIE (J. A.) Hundert Jahre aus der Geschichte der Reformation in den Niederlanden pp. 434. *Gütersloh*, 1893. 8°. 4662. bbb. 27. *See also infra :* REFORMED CHURCH: UTRECHT, *Jansenist Church.*

Language and Literature.

See DUTCH LANGUAGE AND LITERATURE.

Law.

ALEXANDRE (P.) Histoire des Officiers fiscaux près les Conseils de Justice dans les anciens Pays-Bas. pp. 164. 1891. 8°. Ac. Brussels. *Académie.* Mémoires couronnés. Tom. 45. Ac. 985/4.

NETHERLANDS.—Law—*continued.*

BEMMELEN (P. v.) Regtsgeleerde Opstellen. *Leiden*, 1891, *etc.* 8°. 5685. f.

GROOT (H. de) Opinions of Grotius, as contained in the Hollandsche Consultatien en Advijsen. pp. 668. *Lond.* 1894. 8°. 6005. h. 21.

LINDEN (J. v. d.) Institutes of Holland. pp. 515. *Cape Town*, 1891. 8°. 5686. b. 8. *See also* LAW, *Commercial : Criminal.*

Local Government.

See LOCAL GOVERNMENT.

Politics. *See supra : Constitution.*

Reformed Church.

BOEHL (E.) Prolegomena voor eene gereformeerde Dogmatiek. pp. 108. *Amsterd.* 1892. 8°. 3925. f. 30.

CORSWAREM (A. de) Uitlegging der wetten over de Kerkfabrieken. pp. 480. *Hasselt*, 1894. 8°. 5125. aa. 5.

CORWIN (E. T.) History of the Reformed Church, Dutch, in the United States. pp. 525. 1895. 8°. American Church History Series. Vol. 8. 4744. g.

KUYPER (H. H.) De Opleiding tot den dienst des woords bij de Gereformeerden. *'s Gravenh.* 1891, *etc.* 8°. 4685. g. 11.

PANORAMA. Politiek Panorama. Een woord aan Nederlands Protestanten. pp. 40. *Arnhem*, 1891. 8°. 3925. k. 38. (5.)

ROCHUSSEN (J. J.) Christen of modern ? pp. 40. *'s Gravenh.* 1891. 8°. Pam. 77.

SEPP (C. E. A.) Het Staatstoezicht op de godsdienstige letterkunde in de noordelijke Nederlanden. pp. 258. *Leiden*, 1891. 8°. 4999. f. 5. *See also supra :* HISTORY, *Ecclesiastical.* For the Reformed Church in South Africa, *see* AFRICA, *South.*

Topography : Social Life.

BLINK (H.) Handleiding bij het onderwijs in de aardrijkskunde van Nederland. pp. 145. *Amsterd.* 1893. 8°. 10270. bb. 13.

DURAND (H.) Hollande et Hollandais d'après nature. pp. 312. *Paris*, 1893. 8°. 10270. ff. 23.

LE HIRBEC (D.) Voyages aux Pays-Bas, 1642–44. pp. 92. *Laval*, 1890. 8°. 10028. g. 12.

NIEDMEYER (J. F.) Zur Geschichte der Kartographie Hollands. pp. 32. *Rotterdam*, 1893. 4°. Pam. 91.

RIETSTAP (J. B.) Aardrijkskundig woordenboek van Nederland en zijne kolonien. coll. 580. *Groningen*, 1892. 8°. 10026. ccc. 5.

ROEVER (N. de) Van Vrijen en trouwen. pp. 243. *Haarlem*, 1891. 8°. 9406. c. 7.

BAEDEKER (C.) Belgium and Holland. pp. 423. *Leipz.* 1894. 8°. 2352. a.

BLACK (C. B.) Holland, its rail, tram and waterways. *Lond.* 1894. 8°. 10271. aa. 8.

COOK (T.) Tourists' handbook for Holland. pp. 376. *Lond.* 1895. 8°. 10271. aa. 10.

DAVIES (G. C.) Cruising in the Netherlands. pp. 208. *Lond.* 1894. 8°. 10271. aaa. 22.

JOANNE (P.) Hollande et bords du Rhin. pp. 324. *Paris*, 1895. 8°. 10271. aa. 11.

LONDON. *Association for the Promotion of Travel.* "Through Holland on skates." pp. 21. *Lond.* 1894. *obl.* 8°. Pam. 91.

MATHESON (G. E.) About Holland. pp. 188. *Lond.* 1893. 8°. 10270. aaa. 21.

WARD, LOCK AND Co. Guide to Holland. pp. 266. *Lond.* 1892. 8°. 10271. aa. 6.

Trade and Finance.

EYK (J. P. S. v.) De Rijks- en Gemeentebelastingen in Nederland. pp. 254. *s' Gravenh.* 1891. 8°. 5685. aaa. 2.

NETHERLANDS.—Trade, etc.— *cont.*

EYK (J. P. S. v.) De Wet op de Vermogensbelasting. pp. 160. *'s Gravenh.* 1893. 8°. 5685. b. 4.

LEGRAND [(L.) Les conditions du travail dans les Pays-Bas. pp. 195. 1890, *etc.* 8°. FRANCE. *M. des Affaires Étrangères.* Recueil de rapports. 08276. k.

NYPELS (L. A. D.) Het rijksfiscaal strafproces-recht. pp. 194. *Maastricht,* 1891. 8°. 5685. e. 8.

REUS (G. C. K. de) Ueberblick der Entwicklung der niederländisch-ostindischen Compagnie. pp. 323. 1894. 8°. Ac. Batavia. *Genootschap van Kunsten.* Verhandelingen. Ac. 975/6.

RÉUS (H de) and ENDT (G. S.) Die Handelspolitik der Niederlande in de letzten Jahrzehnten. 1892. 8°. Leipzic. *Verein für Socialpolitik.* Schriften. Vol. 49. Ac. 2322.

NETLEY ABBEY. JONES (E. H.) Adam's Guide to Netley Abbey. pp. 60. *Southampton,* 1883. 8°. 4705. b. 46. (7.)

NETTLE. BAROT (A.) L'Ortie; sa valeur alimentaire, *etc.* pp. 106. *Paris,* 1891. 8°. 7075. de. 21.

NEUCHÂTEL - BOURGOGNE. LOYE ( ) Histoire de la seigneurie de Neucl âtel-Bourgogne. pp. 418. *Montbéliard,* 1890. 8°, 010171. h. 34.

NEUENKAMP. FABRICIUS (F.) Urkunden des Klosters Neuenkamp. 1891. 4°. Ac. Stettin. *Gesellschaft für Pommersche Geschichte.* Quellen. Vol. 2. 10235. k.

NEUMARK. MELCHER (E. E.) Geschichte der nordwestlichen Neumark. pp. 258. *Frankfurt,* 1895. 8°. 10240. h. 22.

NEURALGIA AND NEURASTHENIA. *See* NERVES.

NEUSS. EFFMANN (W.) Die St. Quirinus-Kirche zu Neuss. pp. 46. *Düsseldorf,* 1890. 4°. 7807. m. 6. (4.)

TUECKING (C.) Geschichte der Stadt Neuss. pp. 378. *Düsseldorf,* 1891. 8°. 10261. h. 17.

NEUTRALITY. *See* LAW, *International : Military : Naval.*

NEVADA. SPEARS (J. R.) Sketches of Death Valley and other borax deserts of the Pacific. pp. 226. *Chicago,* 1892. 8°. 10412. bbb. 41.

NEVERS. BOUTILLIER ( ) Le trésor de la Cathédrale de Nevers. 1889. 8°. Ac. *Société des Sciences.* Bulletin. Sér. 3. Tom. 3. Ac. 400.

ROUVET (M.) La Commune de Nevers. pp. 201. *Nevers,* 1891. 12°. 10171. aaa. 21.

MEUNIER (P.) La Révolution en Nivernais. *Nevers,* 1891, *etc.* 12°. 9226. aa. 8.

SARRIAU (H.) Numismatique nivernaise. pp. 148. 1894. 8°. Ac. Nevers. *Société des Sciences.* Bulletin. Sér. 3. Tom. 6. Ac. 400.

NEW BRUNSWICK. CANADA. Maritime Provinces of Canada. Handbook of information. pp. 122. *Lond.* 1892. 8°. 10470. dd. 30. (10.)

LUGRIN (C. H.) New Brunswick, its resources. pp. 191. *St. John's,* 1886. 8°. 10470. c. 30.

PERLEY (M. H.) Early history of New Brunswick. pp. 29. *St. John's,* 1891. 8°. 9004. bbb. 15. (5.)

LEE (G. H.) Historical sketch of the Church of England in New Brunswick. 1783–1833. pp. 141. *St. John's,* 1880. 8°. 4744. bb. 10.

See also CANADA ; ENGLAND, *Colonies.*

NEW CALEDONIA. BERNARD (A.) L'Archipel de la Nouvelle-Calédonie. pp. 458. *Paris,* 1895. 8°. 10491. g. 25

NEW CALEDONIA— *continued.*

JEANNENEY (A.) La Nouvelle-Calédonie agricole. pp. 344. *Paris,* 1894. 16°. 7077. aaa. 16.

LEGRAND (M. A.) Au Pays des Canaques. pp. 212. *Paris,* 1893. 8°. 10491. ff. 14.

SALINIS (P. A. de) Conquête de la Nouvelle Calédonie, 1843–53. pp. 340. *Paris,* 1892. 8°. 4766. ff. 27.

VINCENT (J. B. M.) Les Canaques de la Nouvelle-Calédonie. pp. 120. *Paris,* 1895. 8°. 10491. cc. 11.

VUILLOD (J.) La Nouvelle Calédonie et ses produits en 1890. pp. 223. *Saint-Claude,* 1891. 8°. 10492. aa. 19.

C., A. La tribu de Wagap, Nouvelle Calédonie. 1890. 8°. 12910. g. 28.

DICTIONARIES. Dictionnaire français-wagap-anglais. pp. 152. *Paris,* 1891. 8°. 12910. d. 26.

WAGAP. Vocabulaire de la langue de Wagap. pp. 152. 1892. 8°. Ac. Paris. *Société Philologique.* Actes. Tom. 21. Ac. 9808.

See also PACIFIC OCEAN AND ISLANDS.

NEWCASTLE, California. NEWCASTLE. Newcastle, California. pp. 30. *San Francisco,* 1893. 12°. 1879. c. 8. (8.)

NEWCASTLE, New Hampshire. CURTIS (C. B.) Bi-Centennial Souvenir. 1693–1893. pp. 51. *Concord,* 1893. 8°. 10413. g. 20.

ALBEE (J.) New Castle, historic and picturesque. pp. 155. *Bost.* 1884. 8°. 10411. df. 29.

NEWCASTLE-ON-TYNE. NEWCASTLE-ON-TYNE. Newcastle. Illustrated. pp. 16. *Brighton,* 1893. 8°. Pam. 90.

NORTHUMBERLAND. Collectanea curiosa. pp. 64. *Newcastle,* 1892. 8°. 010358. l. 39.

WELFORD (R.) History of Newcastle. 3 vol. *Lond.* 1884, 87. 8°. 010558. l. 15.

NEW ENGLAND. WINSOR (J.) Earliest printed sources of New England history, 1602–29. pp. 14. *Camb.* 1894. 8°. 11904. l. 15. (9.)

PRINCE (T.) Chronological history of New England. 5 vol. 1887, 88. 8°. GOLDSMITH (E. M.) Bibliotheca Curiosa. 012202. de. 47.

Ac. Portland. *Gorges Society.* The Sagadahoc Colony. Voyage into New England ; Lambeth MS. pp. 276. *Portland,* 1892. 4°. Ac. 8391/4.

BORGEAUD (C.) Rise of modern Democracy in Old and New England. pp. 168. *Lond.* 1894. 8°. 08276. e. 60.

BROWN (J.) The Pilgrim Fathers of New England. pp. 368. *Lond.* 1895. 8°. 4430. f. 5.

CAMPBELL (D.) The Puritan in Holland and America. 2 vol. *Lond.* 1892. 8°. 9602. dd. 1.

GREGORY (J.) Puritanism in the Old World and in the New. pp. 406. *Lond.* 1895. 8°. 4715. df. 7.

MERRIMAN (T. M.) The Pilgrims, Puritans and R. Williams vindicated. pp. 312. *Bost.* 1892. 8°. 4745. bbb. 42.

SCOTT (B.) The Pilgrim Fathers neither Puritans nor Persecutors. pp. 52. *Lond.* 1891. 8°. Pam. 29.

STRAUS (O. S.) R. Williams, the pioneer of Liberty. pp. 257. *N.Y.* 1894, 4°. 4987. c. 2.

BLISS (W. R.) Side glimpses from the Colonial Meeting-house. pp. 256. *Bost.* 1894. 8°. 4745. de. 6.

LAUER (P. E.) Church and State in New England. pp. 106. 1892, 8°. Johns Hopkins University Studies. Series 10. Ac. 2689.

PERRY (A. L.) Scotch-Irish in New England. pp. 55. *Bost.* 1891. 8°. 9008. g. 11. (6.)

NEW ENGLAND—continued.

BOLLES (F.) Land of the lingering snow. New England from Jan. to June. pp. 234. *Bost.* 1891. 8°. 10409. aa. 32.

MABIE (H. W.) Our New England: her nature described. pp. 24. *Bost.* 1890. *obl.* fol. 10408. l. 6.

NEW ENGLAND. Summary of vital statistics of New England States, 1892. pp. 59. *Bost.* 1895. 8°. 8225. dd. 44.

See also CONNECTICUT: MAINE: MASSACHUSETTS: NEW HAMPSHIRE: RHODE ISLAND: VERMONT.

NEW FOREST. *See* HAMPSHIRE.

NEWFOUNDLAND. G. B. & I. *Hydrographic Office.* Newfoundland Pilot. pp. 532. 8. *Lond.* 1887–91. 8°. 10496. gg. 5.

GRESWELL (W. P.) Geography of Canada and Newfoundland. pp. 154. *Oxf.* 1891. 8°. 10470. dd. 25.

HARVEY (M.) Newfoundland in 1894. pp. 298. *Lond.* 1894. 8°. 10470. a. 54.

PROWSE (D. W.) History of Newfoundland. pp. 742. *Lond.* 1895. 8°. 9555. f. 9.

THOULET (J.) Un voyage à Terre-neuve. pp. 171. *Paris,* 1891. 8°. 10470. f. 31.

LANGTRY (J.) History of the Church in Newfoundland. pp. 256. 1892. 8°. Colonial Church Histories. 4421. dd.

See also ENGLAND, *Colonies.*

NEW FRANCE. *See* CANADA.

NEW GUINEA: BISMARCK ARCHIPELAGO: TORRES STRAITS. Ac. Sydney. *Royal Geographical Society.* Instructions for the guidance of the New Guinea Exploration Expedition. pp. 40. *Sydney,* 1885. 8°. Pam. 87.

—— First report on New Guinea. By J. F, Mann. pp. 36. *Sydney,* 1889, 8°. Ac. 6214/2.

CHALMERS (J.) Pioneer life in New Guinea, 1877–94. pp. 255. *Lond.* 1895. 8°. 4429. k. 9.

CLERCQ (F. S. A. de) Ethnographische Beschrijving van de West- en Noordkust van Nederlandsch Nieuw-Guinea. pp. 300. *Leiden,* 1893. fol. 10491. i. 12.

HADDON (A. C.) Decorative art of British New Guinea. pp. 279. 1894. 4°. Ac. Dublin. *Royal Irish Academy.* Cunningham Memoirs. No. x. Ac. 1540/6.

HORST (D. W.) De Rum-Serams of Nieuw-Guinea. pp. 200. *Leiden,* 1893. 8°. 4504. b. 6.

LEVEY (G. C.) Handy guide to Australasia. pp. 392. *Lond.* 1891. 8°. 10492. aaa. 49.

MAC IVER (H. R. H. D.) Rivals for supremacy in the Pacific. pp. 52. *Sydney,* 1885. 8°. Pam. 66.

MACGREGOR (*Sir* W.) Handbook for settlers in British New Guinea. pp. 34. *Brisbane,* 1892. 8°. Pam. 86.

MUELLER (F. v.) Records of observations on Sir W. Macgregor's highland plants from New Guinea. pp. 45. 1889. 4°. Ac. Melbourne. *Royal Society.* Transactions. N.S. Vol. 1. Pt. 2. Ac. 1980/8.

NEW GUINEA. New Guinea. pp. 16. *Lond.* 1890. 8°. Pam. 87.

NISBET (H.) A Colonial Tramp. 2 vol. *Lond.* 1891, 8°. 10491. ee. 24.

PITCAIRN (W. D.) Two years among the savages of New Guinea. pp. 286. *Lond.* 1891. 8°. 10492. c. 34.

QUEENSLAND. Geology and palæontology of New Guinea. 3 pt. *Brisbane,* 1892. 8°. 7109. g. 33,

RAY (S. H.) The Tugere tribe of Netherlands New-Guinea. *Leiden,* 1893. *s. sh.* 4°. 1882. c. 2. (23.)

NEW GUINEA, etc.—continued.

THOMSON (J. P.) British New Guinea. pp. 336. *Lond.* 1892. 8°. 10492. f. 30.

ZOELLER (H.) Deutsch-Neuguinea und meine Ersteigung des Finisterre-Gebirges. pp. 546. *Stuttgart,* 1891. 8°. 010057. l. 12.

HAGER (C.) Kaiser Wilhelms-Land und der Bismarck-Archipel. pp. 144. *Leipz.* 1886. 8°. 10097. cc. 26.

RAY (S. H.) Note on the People of New Ireland and Admiralty Islands. pp. 12. *Lond.* 1891. 8°. 12901. d. 36. (9.)

Languages.

LAWES (W. G.) Grammar and vocabulary of language spoken by Motu tribe, New Guinea. pp. 129. *Sydney,* 1888. 8°. 12910. b. 37.

RAY (S. H.) Languages of British New Guinea. *Lond.* 1894. 8°. 12910. bb. 47. (13.)

—— Vocabulary of the dialects of British New Guinea, etc. pp. 40. *Lond.* 1895. 8°. 4430. b. 26.

—— Note on the Languages of New Ireland and Admiralty Islands. pp. 12. *Lond.* 1891. 8°. 12901. d. 36. (9.)

—— Texts in the languages of the Bismarck Archipelago. pp. 29. *Berl.* 1895. 8°. Pam. 47.

—— and HADDON (A. C.) Study of the languages of Torres Straits. *Dublin,* 1893, *etc.* 8°. 12910. b. 36.

ZOELLER (H.) Deutsch Neuguinea. Wortverzeichniss von 46 Papua-Sprachen. pp. 546. *Stuttgart,* 1891. 8°. 010057. l. 12.

NEW HAMPSHIRE. BATCHELLOR (A. S.) List of documents in the Record Office, London, relating to the Province of New Hampshire. pp. 557. 1893. 8°. Ac. Concord. *New Hampshire Historical Society.* Collections. Vol. x. Ac. 8415.

GREEN (S. A.) Boundary line between Massachusetts and New Hampshire. pp. 30. *Lowell, Mass.,* 1894. 8°. Pam. 86.

HAZEN (H. A.) New Hampshire and Vermont. pp. 15. *Concord, N.H.,* 1894. 8°. 9551. k. 8. (12.)

STANWOOD (J. R.) Province seal of New Hampshire. 1692–94. pp. 28. *Bost.* 1889. 8°. 9916. bb. 17. (3.)

FARRAR (C. A. J.) Through the Wilds. Record of sport in the forests of New Hampshire. pp. 415. *Bost.* 1893. 8°. 10412. dd. 17.

See also NEW ENGLAND.

NEW HEBRIDES. BEAUNE (G.) Onze croisières aux Nouvelles Hébrides. pp. 330. *Lyon,* 1894. 8°. 10491. de. 19.

DAVILLÉ (E.) La Colonisation française aux Nouvelles Hébrides. pp. 176. *Paris,* 1895. 8°. 10492. f. 34.

RAY (S. H.) Languages of the New Hebrides. 1893. 8°. Ac. Sydney. *Royal Society.* Journal. Vol. 27. Ac. 1971.

—— Sketch of Aulua grammar with vocabularies. *Lond.* 1893. 8°. 12910. bb. 47. (10.)

—— Vocabulary of the Tangoa dialect. pp. 7. 1892. 8°. 12910. d. 31. (4.)

See also PACIFIC OCEAN AND ISLANDS.

NEW IRELAND. *See* NEW GUINEA.

NEW JERSEY. GANNETT (H.) Geographic dictionary of New Jersey. pp. 131. 1894. 8°. U.S. *Geographical Survey.* Bulletin. No. 118. 1829. a. 7.

NEW JERUSALEM CHURCH. *See* SWEDENBORGIANISM.

NEW MEXICO. LADD (H. O.) Story of New Mexico. pp. 473. *Bost.* 1891. 8°. 9615. ccc. 4.

NEW MEXICO—*continued.*

LUMMIS (C. F.) Land of poco tiempo. pp. 310. *Lond.* 1893. 8°.   10412. dd. 18.

NEW MEXICO. New Mexico: resources, climate, geography. pp. 216. *Santa Fe*, 1890. 8°.
                              10412. cc. 32.

EDDY, *New Mexico.* The Pecos Valley, Fruit-belt of New Mexico. pp 17. *Chicago,* 1893. 12°.
                        1879. c. 8. (6.)

OWEN (R. E.) and Cox (E. T.) Report on the mines of New Mexico. pp. 59. *Wash.* 1885. 8°.
                              Pam. 27.

ROBIN (G. E.) Resources of Sierra County, New Mexico. pp. 21. *St. Louis,* 1893. 8°. Pam. 86.

NEW ORLEANS. DIRECTORIES. Soards' New Orleans City directory. *New Orleans,* 1892, *etc.* 8°.   P.P. 2535. d.

KING (G.) New Orleans: the place and the people. pp. 404. *N.Y.* 1895. 8°. 10413. f. 8.

ZACHARIE (J. S.) New Orleans guide. pp. 159. *New Orleans,* 1893. 8°.   10410. c. 39.

NEWPORT, Fifeshire. NEISH (J. S.) History of Newport. pp. 256. *Dundee,* 1890. 8°.
                              10360. e. 21.

NEWPORT, Monmouthshire. GWYN-LLYW, *Saint, Church at Newport-on-Usk.* History of St. Gwynllyw's Church. pp. 191. *Newport,* 1893. 8°.   10368. h. 32.

NEWPORT. Pembrokeshire. JONES (E.) Historical sketch of Newport. pp. 80. *Solva,* 1890. 8°.   10369. ccc. 9.

NEW QUAY, Cardiganshire. L., J. Guide to New Quay. pp. 35. *Lampeter,* 1895. 8°.
                              Pam. 90.

NEW SIBERIA. *See* ARCTIC REGIONS.

NEW SOUTH WALES. [*See note on page* 1.] *See also* AUSTRALIA.

Aborigines. *See* AUSTRALIA, *Aborigines.*

History: Politics.

BARTON (G. B.) History of New South Wales from the Records. *Sydney,* 1889, *etc.* 8°.
                        9781. cc. 2.

NEW SOUTH WALES. Historical records of New South Wales. *Sydney,* 1892, *etc.* 8°.
                        9781. cc. 3.

—— *Commissioners for the Columbian Exposition.* N.S.W. Statistics, history and resources. pp. 160. *Sydney,* 1893. 8°.   7958. g. 28.

YOUNG (*Sir* G.) Facsimile of a Proposal for a settlement on the Coast of N.S.W. 1785. pp. 3. *Sydney,* 1888. fol.   8154. h. 2.

WHITE (C.) Convict life in New South Wales. pp. 579. *Bathurst,* 1889. 8°.   6057. b. 30.

PARKES (*Sir* H.) Fifty years in the making of Australian history. 2 vol. *Lond.* 1892. 8°.
                        2398. d. 10.

MARTIN (A. P.) Life and letters of R. Lowe, Viscount Sherbrooke. 2 vol. *Lond.* 1893. 8°.
                        10817. dd. 10.

HAGAN (J. F.) R. Lowe, Viscount Sherbrooke. pp. 350. *Lond.* 1893. 8°.   10816. b. 43.

P.P. *Sydney.* Year-book of New South Wales. *Sydney,* 1887, *etc.* 8°.   P.P. 2600. da.

ROYDHOUSE (T. R.) and TAPERELL (H. J.) The Labour Party in New South Wales. pp. 127. *Lond.* 1892. 8°.   8154. aa. 15.

HUTCHINSON (F.) The Australian Contingent. History of the movement in N.S.W. and account of the despatch of troops to the Soudan. pp. 285. *Sydney,* 1885. 8°.   9781. cc. 5. *See also* AUSTRALIA.

NEW SOUTH WALES—*continued.*

Topography.

HANSON (W.) Geographical encyclopædia of New South Wales. pp. 462. *Sydney,* 1892. 8°.
                              10491. g. 22.

JAMES (G. L.) Shall I try Australia? pp. 290. *Liverp.* 1892. 8°.   10492. b. 47.

NEW SOUTH WALES. Railway guide of New South Wales. pp. 145. *Sydney,* 1884. 4°.
                              10492. f. 31.

—— List of towns in New South Wales. pp. 67. *Lond.* 1885. 8°.   Pam. 87.

—— Stations determined in connection with trigonometrical survey, 1891. pp. 16. *Sydney,* 1892. 8°.   Pam. 4.

RUSSELL (H. C.) Physical geography and climate of New South Wales. pp. 35. *Sydney,* 1892. 8°.
                              Pam. 87.

See also AUSTRALIA.

Trade : Finance : Resources.

NEW SOUTH WALES. *Treasury.* Financial State-ments of Colonial Treasurers of New South Wales, 1855-81. pp. 506. *Sydney,* 1881. 8°.
                        08225. l. 20.

—— Statistical Register for 1889 and previous years. pp. 594. *Sydney,* 1890. 8°. 8223. dh. 12.

CHICAGO. *Columbian Exposition.* Catalogue of exhibits in the N.S.W. Courts. pp. 782. *Sydney,* 1893. 8°.   7956. k. 20.

NEW SOUTH WALES. *Commissioners for the Columbian Exposition.* Social, industrial and co-operative Associations in N.S.W., Australia : compiled by E. W. O'Sullivan, *etc.* pp. 24. *Sydney,* 1892. 8°.   7958. g. 36.

—— Rise and position of Trade in New South Wales. By E. Pulsford. pp. 51. *Sydney,* 1892. 8°.   7958. g. 33.

—— Sketch of the progress and resources of New South Wales. By G. Tregarthen. pp. 47. *Sydney,* 1893. 8°.   7958. g. 35.

—— New South Wales. Statistics and resources. [With map.] pp. 160. *Sydney,* 1893. 8°.
                              7958. g. 28.

CHICAGO. *Columbian Exhibition.* Report of the Executive Commissioner for N.S.W. pp. 671. *Sydney,* 1894. 8°.   7956. k. 21.

P.P. *Sydney.* Year Book of New South Wales. *Sydney,* 1887, *etc.* 8°.   P.P. 2600. da.

See also GOLD AND SILVER : MINERALOGY AND MINING.

NEWSPAPERS. *See* JOURNALISM.

NEWTON ABBOT. NEWTON ABBOT. Where to buy at Newton Abbot. pp. 35. *Brighton,* 1890. 4°.   10368. k. 31.

NEW YORK, City. [*See note on page* 1.]

History.

IRVING (W.) Knickerbocker's History of New York. 2 vol. *N.Y.* 1894. 8°. K.T.C. 15. a. 2.

WILSON (J. G.) Memorial history of the City of New York. *N.Y.* 1892, *etc.* 8°.   9603. f. 5.

ANDREWS (W. L.) Bradford Map. City of New York at the time of the granting of the Mont-gomerie Charter. pp. 115. *N.Y.* 1893. 4°.
                              10408. ee. 26.

JANVIER (T. A.) In old New York. pp. 285. *N.Y.* 1894. 8°.   10410. b. 33.

GUERNSEY (R. S.) New York during the war of 1812-15. 2 vol. *N.Y.* 1889-95. 8°. 9605. ff. 14.

PHISTERER (F.) New York in the war of the Rebellion, 1861-65. pp. 532. *Albany,* 1890. 8°.
                              9605. ff. 4.

FISKE (S.) Offhand portraits of prominent New Yorkers. pp. 357. *N.Y.* 1884. 8°. 10883. bb. 33.

NEW YORK—continued.

Municipal Government, etc.

COSTELLO (A. E.) History of the New York Police. pp. 572. *N.Y.* 1885. 8°.   6056. ff. 17.

FRYER (W. J.) Laws relating to buildings in the City of New York. pp. 251. *N.Y.* 1892. 8°.   06616. k. 11.

PARKHURST (C. H.) Our Fight with Tammany. pp. 296. *N.Y.* 1895. 8°.   8176. de. 4.

GARDNER (C. W.) The Doctor [C. H. Parkhurst] and the Devil : municipal corruption. pp. 80. *N.Y.* 1894. 8°.   8285. cc. 45.

NEW YORK. *Civil Service Reform League.* Proceedings. *N.Y.* 1891, *etc.* 8°.   8177. de.

PRYOR (J. W.) Statement of the Election law as in force in New York City. pp. 62. *N.Y.* 1894. 12°.   Pam. 65.

Topography.

DAVIS (R. H.) Broadway. 1892. 8°. Great Streets of the World.   10026. k. 16.

KÉRATRY (É. de) *Count.* New York. 1892. 8°. Les Capitales du Monde. No. 3.   10025. g.

KING (M.) Handbook of New York City. pp. 1008. *Bost.* 1893. 8°.   10413. g. 22.

RIIS (J. A.) How the Other Half lives : studies among the poor. pp. 304. *Lond.* 1891. 8°.   8282. df. 46.

ROSSI (A.) Nel Paese dei Dollari. Tre anni a New-York. pp. 207. *Milano,* 1893. 8°.   10412. b. 39.

SWEETSER (M. F.) and FORD (S.) How to know New York City. pp. 136. *N.Y.* 1891. 16°.   10413. a. 19.

Roman Catholic Diocese.

NEW YORK, *R.C. Diocese.* Constitutiones dioecesanae Neo-Eboracenses. pp. 88. *N.Y.* 1890. 8°.   05107. f. 4.

State.

CHAMPLAIN (S. de) Two Tracts relating to the State of New York, 1609–15. pp. 47. 1887. 8°. Collectanea Adamantæa, 23.   012202. de. 42.

Ac. New York. *Grolier Club.* Facsimile of Laws and Acts of the General Assembly of New York, 1694. pp. 84. 3. 4. 11. *N.Y.* 1894. fol.   Ac. 4714/4.

HOUGHTON (G. W. W.) Coaches of colonial New-York. pp. 31. *N.Y.* 1890. 8°.   Pam. 3.

Ac. Albany. *University.* State Library Bulletin. Summary of state legislation in 1890, *etc. Albany,* 1891, *etc.* 8°.   Ac. 2686/2.

CHEYNEY (E. P.) Anti-Rent agitation in the State of New York, 1839–46. pp. 64. 1887. 8°. Ac. Philadelphia. *University.* Publications. Political Economy Series. No. 2. Ac. 2692. p.

CHICAGO. *Columbian Exposition.* Exhibits of the State. *Chicago,* 1893. 8°.   Pam. 18.

See also ADIRONDACK AND CATSKILL MOUNTAINS : LAW, Criminal.

NEW ZEALAND. [*See note on page 1.*]
See also AUSTRALIA.

Bibliography.

BOOSÉ (J. R.) Brief reference to the literature relating to New Zealand. 1891. 8°. CROZET ( ) Voyage to Tasmania.   10492. e. 15.

C., J. Literature relating to New Zealand. pp. 235. *Wellington,* 1889. 8°.   011902. g. 26.

SYDNEY. *Public Library.* Australian Bibliography. 3 pt. *Sydney,* 1893. 4°.   2060. e.

History : Constitution : Politics.

HARVEN (É. de) La Nouvelle Zélande, histoire. pp. 245. 1883. 8°. Ac. Antwerp. *Société de Géographie.* Mémoires. Tom. 2. Ac. 6096/2.

NEW ZEALAND.—History, etc.—cont.

SUTHERLAND (A.) History of New Zealand. pp. 248. *Lond.* 1894. 8°.   9781. bb. 2.

LEYS (T. W.) Early history of New Zealand. 1890. 8°. Brett's Historical Series.   9781. g.

GUDGEON (T. W.) Defenders of New Zealand. pp. 620. *Auckland,* 1887. 8°.   10803. f. 1.

REES (W. L.) and (L.) Life and times of Sir George Grey. 2 vol. *Lond.* 1892. 8°.   10817. dd. 9.

STOUT (*Sir* R.) Notes on the progress of New Zealand, 1864–84. pp. 39. *Wellington,* 1886. 8°.   8154. cc. 14.

NEW ZEALAND. Decisions of the Speakers of the House of Representatives on points of order, *etc.,* 1867–88. pp. 135. *Wellington,* 1889. 8°.   8154. a. 11.

—— Official handbook of New Zealand. 3 pt. *Lond.* 1883, 84. 8°.   10492. cc. 8.

P.P. *Wellington.* New Zealand official Yearbook. *Wellington,* 1893, *etc.* 8°. P.P. 2666. b.

REES (W. L.) National Policy for New Zealand. pp. 11. *Auckland,* 1890. 8°.   Pam. 66.

SANDERSON (A.) A B C of New Zealand politics. 1890–94. pp. 58. *Masterton,* 1894. 8°.   Pam. 66.

See also AUSTRALIA.

Law.

NEW ZEALAND. *Statutes.* Index to the Statutes, 1840–84. pp. 61. *Wellington,* 1885. 8°.   6606. a. 5.

Maori Race and Language.

GUDGEON (T. W.) History and doings of the Maoris, 1820–40. pp. 225. *Auckland,* 1885. 8°.   9781. b. 15.

NGATA (A. T.) Past and future of the Maori. 1892. fol. P.P. *Christchurch.* Weekly Press. Vol. 33. No. 1448–50.   P.P. 9945. ab.

PAGE (J.) Among the Maoris. pp. 160. *Lond.* 1894. 8°.   4767. bbb. 12.

RUSDEN (G. W.) Tragedies in New Zealand in 1868 and 1881. pp. 284. *Lond.* 1888. 8°.   6495. e. 21.

SCOTT (J. H.) Contributions to the osteology of of the aborigines of New Zealand. 1894. 8°. Ac. Wellington. *New Zealand Institute.* Transactions. Vol. 26.   Ac. 1990.

TREGEAR (E.) Maori-Polynesian dictionary. pp. 675. *Wellington,* 1891. 8°.   12910. f. 36.

ATKINSON (A. S.) Notes on the Maori-Polynesian dictionary of E. Tregear. pp. 69. 6. *Nelson,* 1893. 8°.   12910. b 45.

WILLIAMS (W.) *Bp. of Waiapu.* Dictionary of the New Zealand language. pp. 325. *Auckland,* 1892. 8°.   12910. bb. 43.

A., S. New manual of Maori conversation. pp. 197. *Wellington,* 1885. 16.   12910. a. 23.

TREGEAR (E.) Fairy Tales and Folk Lore of New Zealand. pp. 165. *Wellington,* 1891. 8°.   12431. cc. 26.

See also MISSIONS.

Topography.

ARTHUR (J. K.) Kangaroo and Kauri. Sketches and anecdotes. pp. 132. *Lond.* 1894. 8°.   10492. e. 17.

BENTLEY (E. L.) Settler's guide to New Zealand. pp. 70 *Lond.* 1893. 8°.   10492. bb. 41.

COOK (T.) New Zealand pocket pamphlet. pp. 61. *Auckland,* 1890. 8°.   Pam. 87.

CROZET ( ) Voyage to Tasmania, New Zealand and the Philippines in 1771–72. pp. 148. *Lond.* 1891. 8°.   10492. e. 15.

FERGUSON (D.) Vicissitudes of Bush life. pp. 327. *Lond.* 1891. 8°.   012631. i. 23.

NEW ZEALAND.—Topography—*cont.*

GRAY (R.) Tongariro. pp. 49. *Lond.* 1892. 8°.
Pam. 87.

G. B. & I. *Hydrographic Office.* The New Zealand pilot. *Lond.* 1891. 8°. 10496. gg. 43.

GRENVILLE (A. A.) *Duchess of Buckingham.* Glimpses of four Continents. pp. 291. *Lond.* 1894. 8°. 10024. ccc. 6.

HOUGHTON (J.) Rural New Zealand. pp. 55. *Auckland,* 1893. 4°. Pam. 87.

LEE (R.) Longmans' geographical reader for New Zealand. pp. 272. *Lond.* 1895 8°. 10491. aaa. 46.

LEVEY (G. C.) Handy Guide to Australasia. pp. 392. *Lond.* 1891. 8°. 10492. aaa. 49.

LEYS (T. W.) New Zealand lakes, terraces, geysers and volcanoes. pp. 68. *Auckland,* 1887. 8°. 10491. ff. 17.

LYDE (L. W.) Elementary Geography of New Zealand. pp. 92. *Lond.* 1892. 8°. 10492. aa. 20.

MANNERING (G. E.) With Axe and Rope in the New Zealand Alps. pp. 139. *Lond.* 1891. 8°. 10492. f. 29.

NEW ZEALAND. New Zealand, the wonderland of the World. pp. 43. *Dunedin,* 1890. 8°. Pam. 87.

—— New Zealand Tourist's Vade Mecum. pp. 55. *Dunedin,* 1891. 8°. Pam. 87.

—— New Zealand Shipping Co. Handbook for Passengers. pp. 32. *Lond.* 1892. 8°. Pam. 43.

—— New Zealand. Description of the colony. pp. 4. 1892. 8°. Pam. 87.

PENNEFATHER (F. W.) Murray's Handbook for New Zealand. pp. 64. 172. *Lond.* 1893. 8°. 2364. b. 29.

PERCEVAL (*Sir* W. B.) New Zealand. A paper. pp. 40. *Lond.* 1892. 8°. Pam. 87.

REEVES (E.) Homeward Bound after thirty years. pp. 337. *Lond.* 1892. 8°. 10024. g. 10.

SILVER (S. W.) Handbook for New Zealand. pp. 449. *Lond.* 1888. 8°. 10492. aaa. 51.

SWANTON (W. E.) Notes on New Zealand. pp. 257. *Lond.* 1892. 8°. 10492. aaa. 50.

THOMAS (A. P. W.) Report on the eruption of Tarawera and Rotomahana. pp. 74. *Wellington,* 1888. 8°. 07109. h. 16.

WALLACE (A. R.) Australia and New Zealand. pp. 505. 1893. 8°. Stanford's Compendium of geography. 2060. a.

WILSON (E.) In the Land of the Tin. pp. 322. *Lond.* 1894. 8°. 10491. c. 38.

Trade: Finance, etc.

ATKINSON (*Sir* H. A.) Financial condition of New Zealand, 1890. pp. 63. *Wellington,* 1890. 4°. 8227. k. 15.

BROWN (M.) The Wealth and production of New Zealand. pp. 24. *Dunedin,* 1888. 12°. 8228. aaaa. 21. (2.)

BRUCE (A.) Report on stock breeding in New Zealand. pp. 16. *Sydney,* 1893. fol. Pam. 42.

GRIFFIN (G. W.) New Zealand : her commerce, etc. pp. 180. *Wellington,* 1884. 8°. 08225. l. 6.

HARVEN (É. de) Mission commerciale en Nouvelle-Zéland. pp. 427. *Brux.* 1887. 8°. 08227. f. 37.

MULVANY (T. J.) New Zealand Products and manufactures. pp. 35. *Tauranga,* 1880. 8°. Pam. 23.

NEW ZEALAND. Official Handbook. 3 pt. *Lond.* 1883–84. 8°. 10492. cc. 8.

—— Report on the Statistics of the colony. *Wellington,* 1891, *etc.* 8°. 08225. g.

NEW ZEALAND.—Trade, etc.—*cont.*

NEW ZEALAND. *Ministry of Lands.* Crown lands of New Zealand. pp. 24. *Wellington,* 1892. 8°. Pam. 87.

PERCEVAL (*Sir* W. B.) Farming and labour in New Zealand. pp. 59. *Lond.* 1892. 8°. Pam. 1.

—— Statement of the productions of New Zealand. pp. 23. *Lond.* 1893. 8°. Pam. 87.

P.P. *Wellington.* New Zealand official Year Book. *Wellington,* 1893, *etc.* 8°. P.P. 2666. b.

See also supra : Topography : GOLD AND SILVER.

NEXT-OF-KIN. DOUGAL (F. H.) AND Co. Index to advertisements for next of kin. pp. 304. *Lond.* 1891. 8°. 6355. aaa. 32.

NGONI LANGUAGE. *See* AFRICAN LANGUAGES.

NIAGARA. NIAGARA. The Niagara Book. pp. 225. *Lond.* 1893. 8°. 10413. aaa. 17.

—— New guide to Niagara Falls. pp. 159. *Chicago,* 1893. 8°. 10412. b. 41.

—— Niagara Falls from many points of view. *Chicago,* 1893. obl. 8°. 10413. e. 6.

NIBELUNGENLIED. NIBELUNGEN. Das Nibelungenlied. pp. 226. *Bielefeld,* 1892. 8°. 11517. ee. 44.

MEINCK (E.) Die sagenwissenschaftlichen Grundlagen der Nibelungendichtung R. Wagners. pp. 328. *Berl.* 1892. 8°. 011824. h. 76.

RUDOLPH (C.) Über die geeignetste Form einer Nibelungenübersetzung. pp. 24. *Berl.* 1890. 4°. 11850. m. 14. (11.)

SCHULZE (W.) Einführung in das Nibelungenlied. pp. 299. *Dortmund,* 1892. 8°. 011850. i. 14.

WEITBRECHT (C.) Die Nibelungen im modernen Drama. pp. 37. *Zürich,* 1892. 8°. 11825. q. 20. (5.)

See also GERMAN LITERATURE.

NICARAGUA. BELLY (F.) L'Isthme Américain. Notes d'un premier voyage, 1858. pp. 161. *Brux.* 1889. 8°. 10480. ee. 40.

COLQUHOUN (A. R.) The Key of the Pacific. pp. 443. *Lond.* 1895. 8°. 8235. dd. 42.

CUDMORE (P.) Buchanan's Conspiracy, the Nicaragua Canal and reciprocity. pp. 160. *N.Y.* 1892. 8°. 8176. bbb. 24.

FRYE (W. P.) Relation of the Nicaragua Canal to American commerce. pp. 16. 1893. 8°. Pam. 76.

MADRID. *Exposición Histórico-Americana.* Catálogo de los objetos que envía la República de Nicaragua. pp. 43. *Madrid,* 1892. 8°. 7959. f. 30.

NICARAGUA. Commercial Directory of Nicaragua, etc. 1891. 8°. U.S. *Bureau of American Republics.* Bulletin. No. 28. 08225. k. 1.

—— Import duties of Nicaragua. pp. 34. 1891. 8°. U.S. *Bureau of American Republics.* Bulletin. No. 20. 08225. k. 1.

ORTEGA (F.) Nicaragua en los primeros años de su emancipación. pp. 171. *Paris,* 1894. 8°. 9772. aa. 33.

See also AMERICA, *South and Central.*

NICE. ANDRÉ (G.) Nizza, 1792–1814. pp. 594. *Nizza,* 1894. 8°. 010171. k. 14.

BRUN (F. A.) Promenades d'un curieux dans Nice. 1894. 8°. Ac. Nice. *Société des Lettres.* Annales. Tom. 14. Ac. 405/4.

LETAINTURIER-FRADIN (G.) Nice de France. pp. 301. *Paris,* 1893. 8°. 9080. ee. 4.

NICE. Nice. Guide Joanne. *Paris,* 1894. 8°. 10174. aaa. 48.

PELLEGRINI (J.) Essai d'un Dictionnaire niçois, français, italien. *Nice,* 1894. *etc.* 8°. 12942. cc.

See also RIVIERA.

NICKEL. Bell (R.) Nickel and Copper deposits of Sudbury District, Canada. *Rochester*, 1891. 8°. Pam. 27.

Frossard (J. D.) Nickel ores of Sudbury. pp. 61. *Lond.* 1893. 8°. 7106. e. 9. *See also* Metals.

NICOBAR ISLANDS. Svoboda (W.) Die Bewohner des Nikobaren-Archipels. *Leiden*, 1893. 4°. 10055. i. 10.

NIDDERDALE. Speight (H.) Nidderdale and the Garden of the Nid. pp. 514. *Lond.* 1894. 8°. 010358. h. 19. *See also* Yorkshire.

NIÈVRE, Department. Nièvre, *Department*. Inventaire des archives départementales. 1891, *etc.* 4°. Collection des Inventaires-Sommaires. 1814. b., *etc.* *See also* Gâtinais.

NIGER, River and Territories. Hodges (F. E.) Consular jurisdiction on the Niger Coast. pp. 201. *Lond.* 1895. 8°. 06955. ee. 14.

Mockler-Ferryman (A. F.) Up the Niger. Narrative of Major Macdonald's mission to the Niger. pp. 326. *Lond.* 1892. 8°. 010096. ff. 15.

Péroz (M. E.) Au Niger. 1891–92. pp. 426. *Paris*, 1894. 8°. 9061. e. 27. *See also* Africa, *West*: England, *Colonies*.

NIHILISM. *See* Anarchism.

NIJMEGEN. Evers (J. W. S.) Nijmegen. pp. 113. *Arnhem*, 1891. 8°. 010271. f. 11.

Haar (B. ter) Berg-en-Dal. Gids voor de bezoekers van Nijmegen's Omstreken. pp. 72. *Nijmegen*, 1890. 8°. Pam. 91.

Nimeguen. Reglement voor der Apostolische School te Nijmegen, 1601. pp. 25. *Nijmegen*, 1894. 8°. 8385. f. 6.

NIKKO. Dautremer (J.) Nikkō passé et présent. pp. 109. *Tokio*, 1894. 8°. 010057. f. 33.

NILE, River. Budge (E. A. T. W.) The Nile. pp. 374. *Lond.* 1892. 8°. 2259. b. 14.

Chélu (A.) Le Nil, le Soudan, l'Égypte. pp. 507. *Paris*, 1891. 8°. 10096. i. 5.

Cook (T.) Tourists' handbook for the Nile. pp. 355. *Lond.* 1892. 8°. 10095. aaa. 6.

—— Programme of Cook's tickets to Egypt. pp. 62. *Lond.* 1891–92. 8°. 010096. e. 37.

Joûbert (J.) En dahabièh du Caire aux Cataractes. pp. 476. *Paris*, 1894. 8°. 010096. m. 20.

Legrand (M.) La Vallée du Nil. pp. 253. *Paris*, 1892. 8°. 10095. ee. 16.

Martino (A. de) Studio sul bacino del Nilo. pp. 248. *Napoli*, 1894. 8°. 10097. ccc. 20.

Renouf (*Sir* P. le P.) Nile Mythology. pp. 8. *Lond.* 1890. 8°. 7704. e. 17. (25.)

Rawnsley (H. D.) Notes for the Nile. pp. 324. *Lond.* 1892. 8°. 10095. de. 17.

Tirard (H. M.) and (N.) Sketches from a Nile steamer. pp. 275. *Lond.* 1891. 8°. 010096. c. 32.

Whitehouse (F. C.) The Raiyan Project. pp. 16. *N.Y.* 1890. 8°. 8768. l. 16. (9.)

Ya'kūb Ṣarrūf and Fāris Nimr. The new nationality of the Nile. pp. 20. *Cairo*, 1893. 8°. 8027. dd. 2. *See also* Egypt.

NÎMES. Bazin (H.) Nîmes gallo-romain. Guide du touriste-archéologue. pp. 300. *Nimes*, 1891. 8°. 07708. g. 12.

Bondurand (E.) Nos Textes romans. pp. 18. *Nimes*, 1891. 8°. 11826. g. 44. (1.)

NÎMES—*continued.*

Puech (A.) Les anciennes Jurisdictions de Nîmes. pp. 126. *Nimes*, 1891. 4°. 5406. de. 5.

—— La Renaissance et la réforme à Nîmes. pp. 218. *Nimes*, 1893. 8°. 4660. dd. 20.

NIORT. Berthelé (J.) Le donjon de Niort. pp. 19. *Niort*, 1890. 8°. 10601. ff. 3. (3.)

Clouzot (H.) Notes pour servir à l'histoire de l'imprimerie à Niort. 1890. 8°. Ac. Niort. *Société de Statistique*. Mémoires. Sér. 3. Tom. 7. Ac. 316.

NITHSDALE. *See* Dumfriesshire.

NITROGEN. Treatise. Treatise on Nitrogen. pp. 20. *Manch.* 1891. 8°. Pam. 13. *See also* Gas.

NOCTUIDAE. *See* Lepidoptera.

NORDERNEY. Herquet (C.) Geschichte der Insel Norderney, 1398–1711. pp. 58. 1890. 8° Ac. Emden. *Gesellschaft für bildende Kunst*. Jahrbuch. Ac. 5378.

Verhoeff (C.) Blumen und Insekten der Insel Norderney. 1894. 4°. Ac. Germany. *Academia Cæsarea*. Nova Acta. Tom. 61. Ac. 2871.

NORDHAUSEN. Eckart (T.) Gedenkblätter aus der Geschichte der Reichsstadt Nordhausen. pp. 54. *Leipz.* 1895. 4°. Pam. 91.

NÖRDLINGEN. Monninger (G.) Das Ries und seine Umgebung. pp. 280. *Nördlingen*, 1893. 8°. 10256. c. 13. For the Battle of Nördlingen, *see* Thirty Years' War.

NORFOLK. Ac. London. *Harleian Society*. Publications. Vol. 32. Visitacion of Norffolk, 1563, *etc.* pp. 375. *Lond.* 1891. 4°. 2118. d.

—— Norwich. *Archæological Society*. Norfolk Records. *Norwich*, 1886, *etc.* 8°. Ac. 5685/8.

Berlyn (A.) Sunrise-land. pp. 345. *Lond.* 1894. 8°. 10350. bb. 48.

Cozens-Hardy (H. F.) Broad Norfolk. pp. 103. *Norwich*, 1893. 8°. 10358. aa. 56.

East Anglia. Holiday notes in East Anglia. *Stratford*, 1894. 8°. 10352. bbb. 50.

Essex. Murray's Handbook for Norfolk. pp. 482. *Lond.* 1892. 8°. 2364. a. 13.

Harbour (H.) Way about Norfolk. pp. 150. 1893. 8°. Way-About Series. No. 5. 010358. e.

Jessop (A.) Studies by a Recluse. pp. 281. *Lond.* 1893. 8°. 012357. h. 2.

Knights (M.) Peeps at the past, rambles among Norfolk Antiquities. pp. 184. *Lond.* 1892. 8°. 7709. i. 21.

Norfolk. Industries of Norfolk. pp. 8. *Birmingham*, 1890. 16°. 7942. a. 64. (2.)

Ritchie (J. E.) East Anglia. pp. 344. *Lond.* 1893. 8°. 010358. f. 41.

Rye (W.) Tourist's guide to Norfolk. pp. 128. *Lond.* 1892. 8°. 10352. a. 66.

—— Monumental Inscriptions in the Hundred of Tunstead, in Norfolk. pp. 190. *Norwich*, 1891. 8°. 9914. h. 15.

White (W.) History and Directory of Norfolk. pp. 1226. *Sheffield*, 1890. 8°. N.R.

Broads of Norfolk and Suffolk.

Bickerdyke (J.) The best cruise on the Broads. pp. 142. *Lond.* 1895. 8°. 010358. e. 33.

Brittain (H.) Notes on the Broads and Rivers of Norfolk. pp. 154. *Norwich*, 1887. 8°. 10360. b. 60.

—— Rambles in East Anglia. pp. 150. *Lond.* 1891. 8°. 10358. ccc. 40.

Coulton (J. J.) Names on the Nar. pp. 20. 1891. 8°. Pam. 90.

NORFOLK.—Broads—_continued._

DAVIES (G. C.) Handbook to the Rivers and Broads of Norfolk. pp. 173. 1891. 8°. Jarrold's "Holiday" Series.   10360. d.

EMERSON (P. H.) On English Lagoons. pp. 298. _Lond._ 1893. 8°.   010358. g. 6.

—— Birds, Beasts and Fishes of the Broadland. pp. 396. _Lond._ 1895. 8°.   7205. cc. 2.

GARDYNE (A.) Log of the Lalage. Cruise on the Norfolk Broads. pp. 32. _Stratford_, 1892. 8°.   10348. e. 15. (2.)

LUNN (C.) "Norfolk Broads." pp. 13. _Lond._ 1891. _obl._ 4°.   10352. e. 6.

MOLL (R.) Illustrated guide to Fishing in Norfolk Waters. pp. 111. _Lond._ 1893. 8°.   7912. aa. 24.

NORFOLK. Summer holidays in the Land of the Broads. pp. 45. _Stratford_, 1894. 8°.   10348. d. 20. (12.)

PATTERSON (A.) Man and nature on the Broads. pp. 143. _Lond._ 1895. 4°.   10358. dd. 31.

STEBBINGS (F.) Guide to Lowestoft and the Broads. pp. 92. _Lowestoft_, 1891. 8°.   10358. cc. 54.

SUFFLING (E. R.) History and legends of the Broad District, _etc._ pp. 217. _Lond._ 1891. 8°.   10352. cc. 40.

—— How to organise a cruise on the Broads. pp. 140. _Lond._ 1891. 8°.   7907. dd. 12.

WATERS. By many Waters. pp. 8. _Stratford_, 1890. 8°.   Pam. 90.

WHERRY. En Wherry. pp. 171. _Paris_, 1892. 8°.   010358. f. 39.

NORMANDY.

History, etc.

Ac. Caen. _Université._ Annales de la Faculté des Lettres. _Paris_, 1885–90. 8°.   Ac. 303.

—— Rouen. _Société de l'Histoire de Normandie._ AMATUS. Ystoire de li Normant. pp. 384. _Rouen_, 1892. 8°.   Ac. 6890/27.

COVILLE (A.) Les États de Normandie. pp. 422. _Paris_, 1894. 8°.   5423. h. 1.

SPENCE (H. D. M.) Dreamland in History, story of the Norman Dukes. pp. 228. _Lond._ 1891. 8°.   9225. l. 15.

LAIR (J.) Étude sur la vie de Guillaume Longue-Épée. pp. 84. _Paris_, 1893. fol.   1852. d. 8.

DELISLE (L. V.) Fragments d'une Chronique relatifs aux événements militaires en Basse-Normandie de 1353 à 1389. pp. 22. _Saint-Lo_, 1895. 8°.   11903. f. 35. (12.)

Ac. Rouen. _Société de l'Histoire de Normandie._ ROBILLARD DE BEAUREPAIRE (C. de) Cahiers des États de Normandie sous le règne de Charles IX. pp. 375. _Rouen_, 1891. 8°.   Ac. 6890/24.

BERNIER (P. D.) Essai sur le Tiers état rural de Basse-Normandie au XVIIIᵉ siècle. pp. 315. _Paris_, 1892. 8°.   08276. g. 27.

DUVAL (L.) Éphémérides de la moyenne Normandie en 1789. pp. 234. _Alençon_, 1890. 12°.   9226. aaa. 38.

Ac. Paris. _Société d'Histoire Contemporaine._ MOULIN (M.) Mémoires sur la chouannerie normande. pp. 403. _Paris_, 1893. 8°.   Ac. 6885. c. 13.

MARTIN (A.) Le Clergé normand avant, pendant et après l'exil, 1791–1802. _Evreux_, 1892. 8°.   4532. g. 9. (6.)

BORDEAUX (G.) Le Président Carnot en Normandie. pp. 217. _Rouen_, 1889. 4°. 1763. d. 27.

SAUVAGE ( ) Chronique du froid en Normandie du 1ᵉʳ au XVIIIᵉ siècle. pp. 110. _Rouen_, 1892. 8°.   8755. f. 33.

NORMANDY—_continued._

Topography.

BLACKBURN (H.) Artistic travels in Normandy. pp. 320. _Lond._ 1892. 8°.   10108. f. 1.

COOK (T.) Handbook for Normandy. pp. 131. _Lond._ 1894. 8°.   10174. aaa. 49.

DODD (A. B.) In and out of three Normandy Inns. pp. 394. _Lond._ 1892. 8°. 010171. e. 10.

HARE (A. J. C.) North-Western France. pp. 409. _Lond._ 1895. 8°.   2362. b. 4.

JOANNE (P.) Normandie. pp. 301. _Paris_, 1891. 16°.   10169. de. 21.

NORMANDY. La Normandie Monumentale et pittoresque. _Havre_, 1892, _etc._ fol.   K.T.C. 9. a.

ROBIDA (A.) La vieille France. Normandie. pp. 331. _Paris_, 1890. 4°.   10172. i.

See also EURE AND ORNE, _Departments :_ ROUEN.

Dialect.

MOISY (H.) Glossaire comparatif anglo-normand. _Caen_, 1889, _etc._ 8°.   12954. e.

NORMANS. HEINEMANN (L. v.) Geschichte der Normannen in Unteritalien und Sicilien. _Leipz._ 1894, _etc._ 8°.   9167. i.

JEWETT (S. O.) The Normans, chiefly in relation to their Conquest of England. pp. 373. 1891. 8°. Story of the Nations. 9004. ccc. 3.

NORTHAMPTON, Town. BRADBURY (E.) Architectural sketches in Northampton. _Northampton_, 1894. 4°.   7816. f. 28.

NORTHAMPTON. Where to buy at Northampton. pp. 74. _Brighton_, 1891. 4°.   10368. k. 32.

NORTHAMPTONSHIRE. ADKINS (W. R. D.) Our County. Sketches of representative men of Northamptonshire. pp. 123. _Lond._ 1893. 8°.   10804. ee. 18.

ANDREWS (W.) Bygone Northamptonshire. pp. 232. _Lond._ 1891. 8°.   010358. i. 6.

MARKHAM (C. A.) Church Plate of the County of Northampton. pp. 368. _Lond._ 1894. 8°.   3478. l. 4.

NORTHAMPTONSHIRE. Northamptonshire biographical Notices. _Northampton_, 1892, _etc._ 8°.   10803. c. 9.

P.P. _Northampton._ Architectural notes relating to Churches of Northamptonshire. 2 vol. _Northampton_, 1890–92. 8°.   P.P. 1818. b.

POWYS (T. L.) _Baron Lilford._ Notes on the birds of Northamptonshire. 2 vol. _Lond._ 1895. 4°.   7284. i. 10.

NORTH BRITISH RAILWAY. _See_ RAILWAYS.

NORTH CAPE. ADELSKÖLD (C.) En resa till Nordkap. pp. 154. _Stockholm_, 1890. 8°.   10280. ee. 25.

NORTH CAROLINA. _See_ CAROLINA.

NORTH DAKOTA. _See_ DAKOTA.

NORTH EASTERN RAILWAY. _See_ RAILWAYS.

NORTHINGTON. EYRE (W. L. W.) History of the Parishes of Swarraton and Northington. pp. 79. _Lond._ 1890. 4°. 10351. k. 16.

NORTH POLE. _See_ ARCTIC REGIONS.

NORTH SEA. RUSSELL (W. C.) The British Seas. pp. 88. _Lond._ 1892. fol. K.T.C. 3. b. 10.

NORTH SEA AND BALTIC CANAL. BESEKE (C.) Der Nord-Ostsee-Kanal. pp. 148. _Kiel_, 1893. 8°.   08235. f. 35.

NORTHUMBERLAND. Ac. _Durham._ _Surtees Society._ Publ. Vol. 85. English Miscellanies illustrating the history of the northern counties. pp. 100. _Durham_, 1890. 8°.   Ac. 8045/65.

NORTHUMBERLAND.—*continued.*

Ac. Durham. *Surtees Society.* Publications. Vol. 88. Early Assize Rolls for Northumberland. Sæc. xiii. pp. 476. *Durham,* 1891. 8°.
Ac. 8045/68.

—— Newcastle. *Society of Antiquaries.* BATES (C. J.) Border Holds of Northumberland. *Newcastle,* 1891, *etc.* 8°. Ac. 5675/4.

BATES (C. J.) History of Northumberland. pp. 302. 1895. 8°. Popular County Histories.
2368. f. 20.

BRUCE (J. C.) Handbook to the Roman Wall. pp. 279. *Lond.* 1895. 8°. 2368. a. 1.

CHRISTIE (J.) Northumberland : history, features, and people. pp. 152. *Carlisle,* 1893. 8°.
10350. d°. 28.

COTTERELL (C.) Summer holidays in North East England. pp. 143. *Lond.* 1895. 8°.
010358. e. 32.

DURHAM. Murray's Handbook for Durham and Northumberland. pp. 312. *Lond.* 1890. 8°.
2364. a. 10.

ENGLAND. Survey of the Debateable and Border Lands taken A.D. 1604. pp. 136.
Alnwick, 1891. 4°. 10360. h. 25.

HALL (M. H.) Builders of the Church in Northumbria. pp. 111. *Lond.* 1890. 8°. 4828. aaa. 18.

NORTHUMBERLAND. History of Northumberland. *Newcastle,* 1893, *etc.* 4°. 10360. k. 19.

—— Collectanea Curiosa. Reprints of rare tracts, *etc.* pp. 64. *Newcastle,* 1892. 8°. 010358. l. 39.

—— Pedigrees recorded at the Heralds' Visitations of Northumberland, 1615-1666. pp. 139. *Newcastle,* 1891. 8°. 9914. cc 2.

PEASE (H.) Borderland Studies. pp. 130. *Newcastle,* 1893. 8°. 012357. h. 19.

TAIT (M.) Stories of Northumbria. pp. 239. *Hull,* 1892. 8°. 12331. i. 42.

Ac. London. *English Dialect Society.* HESLOP (O.) Northumberland Words. *Lond.* 1892, *etc.* 8°. Ac. 9934/31,

NORUMBEGA. See AMERICA, *Discovery, etc.*

NORWAY. [*See note on page 1.*]

Antiquities.

ZINCK (L.) Nordisk Archæologi. pp. 105. *Kjøbenh.* 1890. 8°. 07708. g. 8.
See also SCANDINAVIA.

Army. *See* SWEDEN.

Church of *See infra:* HISTORY, *Ecclesiastical.*

Constitution: Politics.

ASCHEHOUG (T. H.) Norges nuværende Statsforfatning. *Christiania,* 1891, *etc.* 8°. 8092. bb.

HÖJER (N.) Statsförbundet mellan Sverige och Norge. pp. 211. *Visby,* 1885. 8°. 8093. e. 2.

NORWAY. Kongeriget Norges en og ordentlige Storthings Forhandlinger i Aaret 1882-83, *etc. Kristiania,* 1882, *etc.* 4°. 8095. a, *etc.*

MARCELLUS. Den Norska Konflikten. pp. 101. *Stockholm,* 1882. 8°. 8092. de. 31.

—— Striden i Norge. Fösvar och kritik. pp. 187. *Stockholm,* 1883. 8°. 8092. de. 34.

OSCAR II., *King of Sweden.* Is King Oscar II. a constitutional king? pp. 16. *Lond.* 1895. 8°.
Pam. 74.

REUTERSKIÖLD (C. A.) Till belysning af den svensk-norska Unionsförfattningen. pp. 195. *Stockholm,* 1893. 8°. 9424. cc. 9.

Emigration.

ASTRUP (H. I. S.) Blik paa amerikanske Forhold, særlig med Hensyn paa de fra Norge Indvandrede. pp. 78. *Kristiania,* 1893. 8°.
8176. b. 35.

NORWAY.—Emigration—*continued.*

NELSON (O. N.) History of Scandinavians in the United States. *Minneapolis,* 1893, *etc.* 8°.
010882. k. 15.

History,

BRICKA (G. S.) Nordens Historia i fragmentarisk Fremstilling. pp. 175. *Kjøbenh.* 1889. 8°.
9431. cc. 9.

JENSEN (O.) Norges historie. pp. 100. *Kristiania,* 1892. 8°. 9425. bbb. 15.

STURLUSON (S.) Noregs Konunga Sögur. *Reykjavík,* 1892, *etc.* 8°. 9425. aa. 7.

Ac. Copenhagen. *Samfund til Udgivelse af nordisk Litteratur.* STURLUSON (S.) Heimskringla. Udgivne ved F. Jónsson. *Kjøbenh.* 1893, *etc.* 8°. Ac. 9057.

STURLUSON (S.) Heimskringla done into English by W. Morris and E. Magnússon. 1893, *etc.* 8°. The Saga Library, *etc.* Vol. 3. 2324. h. 3.

OLAF I., *King of Norway.* Saga of King Olaf. Translated by J. Sephton. pp. 500. 1895. 8°. Northern Library. Vol. 1. 12203. ff.

STURLUSON (S.) Das Leben Konig Olafs des Heiligen. pp. 156. *Graz,* 1895. 8°. 10761. dd. 7.

SKAVLAN (A.) Kulturbilleder fra Norges nyere Historie. pp. 175. *Kristiania,* 1892. 8°.
9431. aaa. 11.

Ac. Christiania. *Norsk Historisk Kildeskriftfond.* Historisk-topografiske Skrifter om Norge og norske Landsdele. pp. 257. *Christiania,* 1895. 8°. Ac. 5561/4.

BERING LÜSBERG (H. C.) Christian IV., Danmarks og Norges Konge. *Kjøbenh.* 1890, *etc.* 8°.
10761. g. 29.

HOLM (P. E.) Danmark-Norges Historie, 1720-30. *Kjøbenh.* 1890, *etc.* 8°. 9424. ee. 5.

BJÖRLIN (G.) Kriget i Norge 1814. pp. 348. *Stockholm,* 1893. 8°. 9435. f. 27.

—— Der Krieg in Norwegen, 1814. pp. 354. *Stuttg.* 1895. 8°. 9425. dd. 1.

GREGERSEN (N. J.) Foredrag over Norges Historie i 1814, *etc.* pp. 212. *Trondhjem,* 1889. 8°.
9431. bb. 24.

NIELSEN (Y.) Aktstykker vedkommende Norges Opgjør med Danmark, 1818-19. pp. 77. *Christiania,* 1889. 8°. Pam. 74.

See also SCANDINAVIA : SWEDEN.

History, *Ecclesiastical,* and Church of Norway.

Ac. Christiania. *Norsk Historisk Forening.* TARANGER (A.) Den angelsaksiske Kirkes Indflydelse paa den Norske. pp. 459. *Kristiania,* 1890-91. 8°. 4707. b. 30.

BANG (A. C.) Kirkehistoriske Smaastykker. pp. 348. *Kristiania,* 1890. 8°. 4530. aa. 9.

HEFFERMEHL (A. V.) Geistlige Møder i Norge. pp. 202. *Kristiania,* 1890. 8°. 4685. aaa. 26.

HANSEN (M.) Hvorfor er jeg ikke Lutheraner og Medlem af Statskirken? pp. 16. *Kristiania,* 1890. 8°. Pam. 93.

Law.

Ac. Christiania. *Stang'ske Stiftelse.* Tidsskrift for Retsvidenskab. *Christiania,* 1888, *etc.* 8°.
Ac. 2142.

P.P. *Christiania.* Norsk Lovtidende. *Kristiania,* 1887, *etc.* 8°. P.P. 1414. d.

BRANDT (F. P.) Tingsretten fremstillet efter den norske Lovgivning. pp. 558. *Kristiania,* 1892. 8°. 5725. b. 16.

AUBERT (L. M. B.) Den norske Obligationsrets specielle Del. *Christiania,* 1890, *etc.* 8°.
5725. e. 5.

Navy. *See* SWEDEN.

NORWAY.—*continued.*

Politics. *See supra: Constitution.*

Topography.

GRISWOLD (W. M.) List of Novels dealing with life in Norway. pp. 20. *Camb., Mass.,* 1892. 8°.
011902. m.

ARENTZEN (K. A. E.) En Norgesreise. pp. 136. *Kjobenh.* 1890. 8°. 10280. ee. 26.

ARGONAUTS. Narrative of the voyage of the Argonauts in 1880. pp. 134. *Edinb.* 1881. 8°.
10281. f. 10.

BAEDEKER (C.) Norway, Sweden and Denmark. 2 pt. *Leipz.* 1895. 8°. 2352. a.

BENNETT (T.) Handbook for Norway. pp. 324. *Christiania,* 1893. 8°. 10280. aaa. 41.

CHRISTIANIA. *Færder Steamship Company.* Steamship Coy. " Færder." Tours to Norway. pp. 111. *Christiania,* 1895. 8°. 10281. a. 5.

COOK (T.) Guide to Norway. pp. 206. *Lond.* 1893. 8°. 10280. aa. 24.

DYRING (J. P. M.) Kongeriget Norge. pp. 290. *Porsgrund,* 1891. 8°. 10281. f. 9.

GIERTSEN (E. B.) and HALVORSEN (A.) Norway illustrated. pp. 112. *Bergen,* 1888. 4°.
1787. c. 30.

GINISTY (P.) De Paris au Cap Nord. pp. 252. *Paris,* 1892. 8°. 10280. f. 11.

GOODMAN (E. J.) The best Tour in Norway. pp. 336. *Lond.* 1892. 8°. 10280. e. 11.

—— Handbook for Norway. pp. 85. *Hull,* 1894. obl. 16°. 10281. aa. 16.

—— Western Norway. Notes to accompany P. Lange's photogravures. pp. 14. *Lond.* 1893. obl. fol. K.T.C. 30. b. 4.

GUESSFELDT (P.) Kaiser Wilhelm's II. Reisen nach Norwegen, 1889-90. pp. 350. *Berl.* 1890. 8°. 10280. ee. 24.

HAUKENÆS (T. S.) Reiseskildringer fra Norges natur og folkeliv. *Bergen,* 1890, *etc.* 8°.
10280. aaa. 36.

KEARY (C. F.) Norway and the Norwegians. pp. 408. *Lond.* 1892. 8°. 10280. aaa. 40.

KIMBALL (D. C.) Midnight Sunbeams. pp 279. *Bost.* 1888. 8°. 10280. e. 10.

LANDAU (J.) Nordlandfahrt. pp. 151. *Berl.* 1895. 8°. 10280. aa. 27.

LE ROUX (H.) Notes sur la Norvège. pp. 320. *Paris,* 1895. 8°. 10281. b. 9.

NAYLOR (R. A.) Letters on Sweden and Norway. pp. 207. *Lond.* 1884. 8°. 10280. ccc. 16.

NIELSEN (Y.) Reischaandbog over Norge. pp. 756. *Christiania,* 1891. 8°.
10281. aa. 13.

NORWAY. Murray's Handbook for Norway. pp. 108. 187. 31. *Lond.* 1892. 8°. 2364. b. 5.

—— Land of the Midnight Sun. pp. 29. *Sheffield,* 1886. 8°. Pam. 91.

—— Most picturesque routes in Southern Norway. pp. 47. *Skien,* 1891. 8°.
10106. de. 4. (3.)

PARSON AND LAWYER. Yatching cruise to Norway. pp. 176. *Lond.* 1895. 8°.
10280. bb. 47.

P.P. *London.* Norwegian Railway and Steamer time-tables. *Lond.* 1893, *etc.* 16°. P.P. 2500. ci.

S., W. West Norway notes. pp. 86. *Lond.* 1893. 8°. 10280. bb. 46.

SPITZBERGEN. Spitzbergen and Norway in August. pp. 65. *Lond.* 1894. 8°. 10460. ff. 18.

SPRINGER (M.) De la Bastille au Cap Nord. pp. 56. *Paris,* 1889. 8°. 10107. ff. 27. (4.)

STUART (J. M.) How "No 1" became "1½" in Norway. pp. 326. *Lond.* 1891. 8°.
10280. cc. 9.

NORWAY.—Topography—*continued.*

TÖNSBERG (N. C.) Norge fremstillet i Tegninger, med kortfattet oplysende Text. pp. 102. *Christiania,* 1890. obl. 8°. 10280. aa. 17.

TWEEDIE (E. B.) Winter jaunt to Norway. pp. 316. *Lond.* 1894. 8°. 10280. ee. 28.

VERGANI (E.) Durch Skandinavien. pp. 144. *Wien,* 1894. 8°. 10281. a. 6.

WILLSON (T. B.) Handy guide to Norway. pp. 267. *Lond.* 1891. 8°. 10281. aa. 11.

See also SPORT.

Trade.

CHICAGO. *Columbian Exposition.* Catalogue of Exhibit of Norway. pp. 79. *Chicago,* 1893. 8°.
Pam. 18.

FAHLBECK (P. E.) Die Handelspolitik Schwedens und Norwegens. 1892. 8°. Ac. *Leipsic. Verein für Socialpolitik.* Schriften. Vol. 49.
Ac. 2322.

MILLET (R.) Les Conditions du travail en Norvège. pp. 178. 1890. 8°. FRANCE. *M. des Affaires Étrangères.* Recueil de rapports, *etc.*
08276. k.

NORWAY. *Handelsstands Fællesforening.* Forhandlingerne, *etc. Kristiania,* 1890, *etc.* 4°.
8245. gg.

NORWEGIAN LANGUAGE.

See DANISH LANGUAGE.

NORWEGIAN LITERATURE.

BERNARDINI (L.) La Littérature scandinave. pp. 280. *Paris,* 1894. 8°. 011850. ccc. 13.

CONSOLI (S.) Litteratura norvegiana. pp. 270. *Milano,* 1894. 8°. 012200. h. 112.

BIGEON (M.) Les Révoltés scandinaves. pp. 341. *Paris,* 1894. 12°. 011850. ccc. 14.

BOYESEN (H. H.) Essays on Scandinavian Literature. pp. 288. *Lond.* 1895. 8°.
011824. e. 61.

JÆGER (H.) Illustreret Norsk Literaturhistorie. *Kristiania,* 1892, *etc.* 8°. 011850. i.

See also DRAMA : ICELANDIC LITERATURE : SCANDINAVIAN LITERATURE.

NORWICH. Ac. Norwich. *Norfolk and Norwich Archæological Society.* KIRKPATRICK (J.) Streets and lanes of Norwich. pp. 138. *Norwich,* 1889. fol. 10352. m. 10.

HOOPER (J.) Notes on the Church of St. Peter of Mancroft, Norwich. pp. 44. *Norwich,* 1895. 8°. 7814. bb. 35.

HUDSON (W.) Leet jurisdiction in the City of Norwich during the XIIIth and XIVth centuries. pp. 39. ff. 81. 1892. 4°. Ac. London. *Selden Society.* Publications. Vol. v. Ac. 2176.

SAINT GEORGE, *Parish of, Norwich.* Parish Register of St. George of Tombland, Norwich, 1538-1707. pp. 286. *Norwich,* 1891. 4°.
9916. ee. 5.

WARD, LOCK AND CO. Historical handbook to Norwich Cathedral. *Lond.* 1890. 8°.
010358. l. 24.

NOSE. HOVORKA (O.) Die aeussere Nase. pp. 144. *Wien,* 1893. 8°. 7611. df. 27.

ÓNODI (A. D.) Anatomy of the Nasal Cavity. pp. 19. *Lond.* 1895. 8°. 7615. cc. 15.

TAYLOR (J. W.) Noses, and what they indicate. pp. 15. *Lond.* 1892. 8°. 7410. bb. 33. (11.)

Diseases.

BALL (J. B.) Handbook of diseases of the Nose. pp. 364. *Lond.* 1894. 8°. 7616. ee. 4.

BAUMGARTEN (E.) Die Neurosen des Nasenrachenraumes. pp. 18. 1892. 8°. VOLKMANN (R. v.) Sammlung klinischer Vorträge. Nr. 44.
7441. g.

NOSE.— Diseases—continued.

BRESGEN (M.) Krankheits- und Behandlungs-lehre der Nasen- und Rachenhöhle. pp. 432. *Wien*, 1891. 8°. 7615. ee. 40.

BROWNE (L.) The Throat and Nose, and their diseases. pp. 734. *Lond.* 1893. 8°. 7615. f. 43.

BURNETT (C. H.) System of diseases of the Nose. 2 vol. *Lond.* 1893. 8°. 7615. cc. 14.

HALL (F. de H.) Diseases of the Nose. pp. 524. 1894. 8°. Lewis's Practical Series. 7482. a.

HUTCHINSON (P. S.) Manual of diseases of the Nose. pp. 127. *Lond.* 1891. 8°. 7616. aaa. 4.

IVINS (H. F.) Diseases of the Nose. pp. 507. *Phila.* 1893. 8°. 7616. i. 8.

MACBRIDE (P.) Diseases of the Nose. pp. 640. 1892. 8°. Pentland's Medical Series. Vol. 3. 7641. ee.

NEWMAN (D.) Malignant disease of the Nose. pp. 213. *Edinb.* 1892. 8°. 7616. f. 7.

RETHI (L.) Die Krankheiten der Nase. pp. 352. *Wien*, 1892. 8°. 7615. d. 6.

PARKER (C. A.) Post-nasal Growths. pp. 98. *Lond.* 1894. 8°. 7615. de. 45.

ROSENTHAL (C. F. T.) Die Erkrankungen der Nase. *Berl.* 1892, *etc.* 8°. 7615. f. 42.

RUPP (A.) Perforations of the nasal Septum. pp. 24. *N.Y.* 1894. 8°. 7306. g. 18. (8.)

SAJOUS (C. E.) Diseases of the nose. 1894. 8°. BIGELOW (H. R.) International System of Electro-Therapeutics. 2024. e.

SCHROETTER (L.) Vorlesungen über die Krank-heiten der Nase. *Wien*, 1892, *etc.* 8°. 7616. i.

THUDICHUM (J. L. W.) On Polypus in the Nose. *Lond.* 1892. 8°. 7616. f. 5.

WILLIAMS (P. W.) Diseases of the upper Re-spiratory Tract. pp. 282. *Bristol.* 1894. 8°. 7616. f. 12.

ZARNIKO (C.) Die Krankheiten der Nase. pp. 313. *Berl.* 1894. 8°. 7615. c. 4.

NOSSI-BÉ. DEBLENNE (P. R.) Essai de géographie medicale de Nosi-Bé. pp. 300. *Paris*, 1883. 8°. 07686. k. 3.

NOTARIES. See LAW, *Profession of, France and Scotland.*

NOTO. See JAPAN.

NOTTINGHAM, Town. BRAMLEY (T.) Guide to Nottingham Castle. pp. 80. *Nottingham*, 1880. 8°. 10352. g. 13.

BRISCOE (J. P.) Old Guild Hall and Prison of Nottingham. pp. 16. *Nottingham*, 1895. fol. 10368. g. 47.

BRISCOE (J. P.) Allen's guide to Nottingham. pp. 63. *Nottingham*, 1891. 8°. 10351. cc. 57.

—— Caverns in Nottingham Park. pp. 8. *Nottingham*, 1893. 8°. 07703. e. 2. (8.)

CATTLE (C. H.) Guide to Nottingham. pp. 116. *Nottingham*, 1892. 8°. 10368. cc. 44.

CROPPER (P. J.) Enquiry into the origin and meaning of the name of Nottingham. pp. 10. *Derby*, 1894. 8°. Pam. 90.

EPHEM. Nottingham year-book. *Nottingham*, 1891. 8°. P.P. 2509. tab.

GODFREY (J. T.) Notes on the Parish of Brew-house Yard, Nottingham. pp. 12. *Nottingham*, 1890. 8°. 10318. c. 25. (3.)

NOTTINGHAM. Records of the Borough of Not-tingham. 4 vol. *Lond.* 1882–89. 8°. 10358. k. 2.

STAPLETON (A.) History of the Crosses of old Nottingham. pp. 66. *Nottingham*, 1893. 8°. 10348. ccc. 57. (9.)

WYLIE (W. H.) and BRISCOE (J. P.) Popular history of Nottingham. pp. 136. *Nottingham*, 1893. 8°. 10360. e. 29.

NOTTINGHAMSHIRE. GODFREY (J. T.) Notes on the Bibliography of Nottinghamshire. *Ratcliffe-on-Trent*, 1891. 8°. 11902. b. 46. (8.)

WARD (J.) Descriptive Catalogue of Books re-lating to Nottinghamshire. pp. 40. *Nottingham*, 1892. 8°. 011900. f. 12.

AC. G. B. & I. *British Association.* Contribu-tion to the geology and natural history of Not-tinghamshire. pp. 90. *Nottingham*, 1893. 8°. 7003. a. 11.

BROWN (C.) History of Nottinghamshire. pp. 306. 1891. 8°. Popular County Histories. 2368. e.

DERBY. Murray's Handbook for Derbyshire, Nottinghamshire, *etc.* pp. 38. 229. *Lond.* 1892. 8°. 2364. a. 8.

P.P. *Derby.* Nottinghamshire and Derbyshire notes and queries. *Derby*, 1892, *etc.* 8°. P.P. 6065. f. and 2210.

SHERWOOD FOREST. Guide to Sherwood Forest and "the Dukeries." pp. 175. *Lond.* 1893. 8°. 10347. aaa. 36.

STAPLETON (A.) The Crosses of Nottinghamshire, *etc.* pp. 50. *Mansfield*, 1891. 8°. 7702. de. 11. (9.)

STEVENSON (W.) Bygone Nottinghamshire. pp. 290. *Nottingham*, 1893. 8°. 010358. i. 10.

CROPPER (P. J.) Nottinghamshire printed chap-books. pp. 32. *Nottingham*, 1892. 4°. 11899. g. 43. (2.)

See also SHERWOOD FOREST.

NOUVION-EN-THIÉRACHE. MACON (G.) Un Épisode de l'histoire du Nouvion-en-Thiérache. pp. 49. *Paris*, 1891. 8°. 10106. df. 16. (5.)

NOVA SCOTIA. BLACK (H.) Memorandum respecting Nova Scotia. pp. 4. *Lond.* 1894. 8°. Pam. 86.

CANADA. Maritime Provinces of Canada. pp. 122. *Lond.* 1892. 8°. 10470. d. 30.

FRAME (E.) List of Micmac names of places in Nova Scotia. pp. 12. *Camb.* 1892. 8°. 12903. dd. 34. (11.)

GILPIN (E.) Mines and mineral lands of Nova Scotia. pp. 129. *Halifax*, 1880. 8°. 07108. g. 3.

SYMONS (B.) Gold-fields of Nova Scotia. 1892. 8°. Pam. 27.

SWANN (H. K.) Nature in Acadie. pp. 74. *Lond.* 1895. 8°. 7004. aa. 7.

EATON (A. W. H.) The Church of England in Nova Scotia. pp. 320. *Lond.* 1892. 8°. 4745. cc. 41.

O'BRIEN (C.) *R.C. Archbp. of Halifax.* Memoirs of E. Burke, Bishop of Zion. pp. 154. *Ottawa*, 1894. 8°. 4956. bbb. 14.

—— Mémoire sur les Missions de la Nouvelle Écosse. Réponse aux "Memoirs of Bishop Burke" par Mgr. O'Brien. pp. 269. *Quebec*, 1895. 8°. 8765. ee. 30.

See also CANADA: CAPE BRETON: ENGLAND, *Colonies.*

NOVA ZEMLYA. BARRY (R. v.) Zwei Fahrten in das nördliche Eismeer nach Spitz-bergen und Novaja Zemlja. pp. 169. *Pola*, 1894. 8°. 10470. h. 34.

NOVIBAZAR. NOVIBAZAR. Novibazar und Kossovo. pp. 158. *Wien*, 1892. 8°. 10125. e. 12.

NUISANCES, Law of. BROUN (J. C. C.) Law of Nuisance in Scotland. pp. 258. *Edinb.* 1891. 8°. 6583. aaa. 8.

CLARKE (C. H.) Trade Nuisances. pp. 24. *Lond.* 1893. 8°. 8777. bbb. 28. (6.)

GARRETT (E. W.) The Law of Nuisances. pp. 548. *Lond.* 1890. 8°. 6426. e. 7.

WILSON (F. R.) Guide for Inspectors of Nuis-ances. pp. 156. *Lond.* 1891. 8°. 6425. aa. 50.

See also SANITATION.

NUMBERS.

BERGER (A. F.) Recherches sur les valeurs moyennes dans la théorie des Nombres. pp. 130. 1887. 4°. Ac. Upsal. *R. Societas Scientiarum.* Nova Acta. Vol. 14.
　　　　　　　　　　　　　　　　Ac. 1076.

BULLINGER (E. W.) Number in Scripture : its design and significance. pp. 303. *Bromley,* 1894. 8°. 3127. ccc. 4.

DAVID (C. H. C.) Brochure on the number Seven. pp. 32. *Colombo,* 1890. 8°.
　　　　　　　　　　　　　　　4372. h. 28. (4.)

LUCAS (É.) Théorie des Nombres. *Paris,* 1891, *etc.* 8°. 8533. i. 28.

MATHEWS (G. B.) Theory of Numbers. *Camb.* 1892, *etc.* 8°. 8535. d. 13.

NICHOLS (H.) Our notions of Number and Space. pp. 201. *Bost.* 1894. 8°. 8532. bb. 43.

RUMPELT (H. B.) Die deutschen Zahlwörter historisch dargestellt. pp. 48. *Oxf.* 1893. 8°.
　　　　　　　　　　　　　　12962. g. 30.

SPECKMANN (G.) Beiträge zur Zahlenlehre. pp. 64. *Oldenburg,* 1893. 8°. 8534. cc. 36.

TANNERY (J.) Introduction à l'étude de la théorie des Nombres. pp. 350. *Paris,* 1895. 8°. 8534. dd. 11.

WESTCOTT (W. W.) Numbers : their occult power. pp. 52. *Lond.* 1890. 4°. 8632. h. 7.

WEISSENBORN (H.) Zur Geschichte der Einführung der jetzigen Ziffern in Europa durch Gerbert. pp. 123. *Berl.* 1892. 8°. 8507. e. 9.

NUMIDIA. *See* AFRICA, *North.*

NUMISMATICS.

General.

Ac. Berlin. *Numismatische Gesellschaft.* Festschrift zur Feier des fünfzigjährigen Bestehens der Numismatischen Gesellschaft zu Berlin. pp. 176. *Berl.* 1893. 8°. 7757. e. 38.

—— Brussels. *Société de Numismatique,* Congrès international de Numismatique. pp. 687. *Brux.* 1891. 8°. Ac. 5843/2.

—— Geneva. *Société Suisse de Numismatique.* Revue suisse de Numismatique. *Genève,* 1891, *etc.* 8°. Ac. 5817.

—— London. *South Kensington Museum.* Supplementary list of Medals, *etc.,* reproduced in metal in the Museum. pp. 17. *Lond.* 1891. 8°. Pam. 18.

—— Paris. *Bibliothèque Nationale.* Notice des monuments exposés dans le Département des Médailles. pp. 165. *Paris,* 1889. 8°.
　　　　　　　　　　　　　　7757. aaa. 8.

AMBROSOLI (S.) Numismatica. pp. 214. *Milano,* 1891. 8°. 012200. h. 1.

BLANCHET (J. A.) Études de Numismatique. *Paris,* 1892. *etc.* 8°. 7757. ee. 23.

BOLTON (H. C.) Contributions of alchemy to Numismatics. pp. 44. *N.Y.* 1890. 4°. Pam. 44.

DANNENBERG (H.) Grundzüge der Münzkunde. pp. 261. *Leipz.* 1891. 8°. 7756. b. 15.

GNECCHI (F.) and (E.) Guida numismatica universale. pp. 603. *Milano,* 1894. 8°.
　　　　　　　　　　　　　　7756. b. 31.

MORALEDA Y ESTEBAN (J.) Catálogo de la colección de Monedas reunida por Don J. Moraleda y Esteban. pp. 44. *Toledo,* 1892. 8°.
　　　　　　　　　　　　　　Pam. 14.

P.P. Colchester. Numismatology. Vols. 1–3. *Colchester,* 1892–94. 8°. P.P. 1875. ad.

—— London. Spink and Son's Numismatic circular. *Lond.* 1892, *etc.* fol. N.R.

—— Paris. Bulletin de Numismatique. *Paris,* 1891, *etc.* 8°. P.P. 1877. da.

POOLE (S. L.) Coins and Medals. pp. 286. *Lond.* 1885. 8°. 7756. de. 37.

NUMISMATICS.—*continued.*
Ancient: Greek: Roman, etc.

Ac. London. *British Museum. Department of Coins.* Guide to the gold and silver Coins of the Ancients, B.C. 700 to A.D. 1. pp. 128. *Lond.* 1895. 8°. 7755. aaa. 50.

—— Paris. *Bibliothèque Nationale.* Catalogue des Monnaies grecques. Les Rois de Syrie, d'Arménie et de Commagène. pp. 268. *Paris,* 1890. 8°. 7755. h. 26.

—— Stuttgard. *K. statistisch.-topographisches Bureau.* NESTLE (W.) Funde antiker Münzen in Württemberg. pp. 113. *Stuttg.* 1893. 8°.
　　　　　　　　　　　　　　7757. e. 33.

HEAD (B. V.) Archaic Coins of Cyrene. pp. 11. *Lond.* 1891. 8°. Pam. 44.

HILL (G. F.) Coinage of Lycia to Alexander the Great. pp. 44. *Lond.* 1895. 8°. Pam. 44.

IMHOOF-BLUMER (F.) Griechische Münzen. 1890. 4°. Ac. Munich. *K. Akademie der Wissenschaften.* Abhandlungen der phil.-philol. Classe. Bd. 18. Ac. 713/6.

MÉLIX ( ) Spicilegium de Monnaies présentant des légendes phéniciennes. pp. 62. 1894. 8°. Ac. Bona. *Académie d'Hippone.* Bulletin. No. 26. Ac. 588.

REINACH (T.) Numismatique ancienne. Trois royaumes de l'Asie Mineure. pp. 206. *Paris.* 1888. 8°. 7757. e 24.

WALCHER DE MOLTHEIN (L.) Catalogue de la collection des Médailles grecques de M. L. Walcher de Molthein. pp. 294. *Paris,* 1895. 8°. 7757. dd. 8.

WILLIAMSON (G. C.) Money of the Bible. pp. 94. 1894. 8°. By-Paths of Bible Knowledge. No. 20. 2202. a.

WROTH (W. W.) Catalogue of Greek Coins of Mysia. pp. 217. 1892. 8°. Ac. London. *British Museum.* Catalogue of Greek Coins.
　　　　　　　　　　　　　　7756. c.

FARCINET (C.) Une collection des douze Césars. Lettre sur l'authenticité de deux médaillons romains trouvés en Vendée. 2 pt. *Macon,* 1892. 8°. Pam. 44.

PRING (J. H.) Roman Coins found at Taunton. pp. 11. *Taunton,* 1882. 8°. Pam. 44.

SUCHIER (R.) Die römischen Münzen von Gross-Krotzenburg. 1882. 8°. Ac. Cassel. *Verein für Hessische Geschichte.* Zeitschrift. N.F. VIII. Ac. 7025/2.

THURSTON (E.) Discovery of Roman Coins in Southern India. pp. 4. *Madras,* 1888. 8°.
　　　　　　　　　　　　　　Pam. 44.

Ac. Paris. *Bibliothèque Nationale.* Catalogue des Monnaies gauloises de la Bibliothèque Nationale. 2 pt. *Paris,* 1889, 92. 4°. 7756. h. 8.

AMARDEL (G.) Les Monnaies de chefs gaulois attribuées à Narbonne. pp. 29. *Narbonne,* 1893. 8°. Pam. 44. *See also infra : France.*

Mediæval and Modern.
Europe.

BRAKENHAUSEN (F. v.) Vortrag über die Verschönerung der modernen Münzen in der numismatischen Gesellschaft zu Berlin. pp. 19. *Berl.* 1891. 8°. Pam. 44.

ENGEL (A.) and SERRURE (R.) Traité de Numismatique du moyen âge. *Paris,* 1891, *etc.* 8°.
　　　　　　　　　　　　　　7757. f. 33.

HAZLITT (W. C.) Coinage of the European Continent. pp. 554. *Lond.* 1893. 8°. 7757. e. 29.

HIGGINS (F. C.) Introduction to copper coins of modern Europe. pp. 95. 1892. 8°. Young Collector Series. 7001. aaa.

NUMISMATICS.—Europe—_continued._

VAISSIÈRE (P. de)　La Découverte à Augsbourg des instruments du Monnayage moderne.
pp. 29.　_Montpellier_, 1892. 8°.　　　Pam. 44.

BLANCHET (J. A.)　Manuel de Numismatique du moyen âge et moderne.　2 tom.　1890. 8°.　Encyclopédie-Roret.　　　　　　　12208. b.

ELVIN (C. N.)　Hand-book of Orders of Chivalry, War Medals, Crosses and other decorations.
Lond. 1894. 4°.　　　　　　　9906. g. 2.

HAMANN (C.)　Bildnisse einiger berühmter Persönlichkeiten des dreissigjährigen Krieges, auf Münzen u. Medaillen.　pp. 11.
Hamb. 1891. 4°.　　　　　　　Pam. 44.

MANSFELD-BÜLLNER (H. V.)　Fortegnelse over H. Mansfeld-Büllners militaire Ordens- og Medaille-Cabinet.　pp. 74.　_Kjøbenh._ 1889. 8°.
　　　　　　　　　　　　　　9905. cc. 29.

P.P.　_London._　The War Medal record.
Lond. 1895, _etc._ 4°.　　P.P. 4044. b. & 988.

Austria : Bohemia.

SCHALK (C.)　Wiens Geldwesen, 1251–1892.
pp. 95.　_Wien_, 1894. 8°.　　　7756. de. 33.

DONEBAUER (M.)　Beschreibung der Sammlung böhmischer Münzen und Medaillen des M. Donebauer.　_Prag_, 1888, _etc._ 8°.　　7757. g. 1.

FIALA (E.)　Beschreibung böhmischer Münzen und Medaillen.　_Prag_, 1891, _etc._ 8°.　7755. dd.

Belgium.

Ac.　Brussels.　_Société de Numismatique._　Médailles historiques de Belgique.
Brux. 1890, _etc._ 8°.　　　　　Ac. 5813.

SERRURE (C. A.)　Les sciences auxiliaires de l'histoire de Belgique.　Numismatique.
pp. 175.　_Brux._ 1893. 12°.　　9414. aaa. 18.

CHESTRET DE HANEFFE (J. de)　Coup d'œil sur l'Histoire monétaire de Liége.　1886. 8°.　Ac. Liége.　_Institut Archéologique._　Bulletin.　Tom. 18. Livr. 3.　　　　　　　Ac. 5527.

WITTE (A. de)　Histoire monétaire des comtes de Louvain.　1894, _etc._ 4°.　Ac.　Antwerp. _Académie d'Archéologie._　Annales.　Tom. 1.
　　　　　　　　　　　　　　Ac. 5513.

Denmark.

JØRGENSEN (C. T.)　Beskrivelse over danske Mønter.　pp. 164.　_Kjøbenh._ 1888. 8°.
　　　　　　　　　　　　　7756. de. 19.

France.

Ac.　Paris.　_Bibliothèque Nationale._　Catalogue des Monnaies françaises.　_Paris_, 1892, _etc._ 8°.
　　　　　　　　　　　　　　7757. g.

BARTHÉLEMY (A. J. B. A. de)　Numismatique de la France.　_Paris_, 1891, _etc._ 8°.　7757. e.

PARIS.　_Musée monétaire._　Médailles françaises.
pp. 572.　_Paris_, 1892. 4°.　　　7755. g. 16.

FARCINET (C.)　Étude sur les Monnaies mérovingiennes attribuées à la Vendée.　pp. 20.
Paris, 1892. 8°.　　　　　　Pam. 44.

MOREL-FATIO (A.)　Catalogue de la collection de Deniers mérovingiens des VIIᵉ & VIIIᵉ siècles de la trouvaille de Cimiez.　pp. 66.
Paris, 1890. 8°.　　　　　　7757. f. 32.

PONTON D'AMÉCOURT (G. de)　Description des Monnaies mérovingiennes.　_Paris_, 1892, _etc._ 8°.
　　　　　　　　　　　　　7757. f. 34.

VALLENTIN (R.)　La valeur de l'Écu au soleil à Avignon.　pp. 7.　_Avignon_, 1889. 8°.
　　　　　　　　　　　　　7757. e. 13. (8.)

MATER (D.)　Études sur la Numismatique du Berry.　1890. 8°.　Ac.　Bourges.　_Société des Antiquaires._　Mémoires.　Vol. 17.　Ac. 5291.

BLANCHET (J. A.)　Numismatique du Béarn.
2 tom.　_Paris_, 1893. 8°.　　　7757. e. 30.

NUMISMATICS.—France—_continued._

BLANCARD (L.)　Nouveau classement des Monnaies languedociennes.　1892. 8°.　Ac.　Marseilles.　_Académie des Belles Lettres._　Mémoires, 1888–92.　　　　　　　　Ac. 367.

LAUGIER (J.)　Notice sur le Monnayage de Marseille.　pp. 63.　_Marseille_, 1891. 8°.　Pam. 44.

VIRMAITRE (C.)　Paris-médaillé.　pp. 265.
Paris, 1890. 12°.　　　　　7858. a. 47.

AMARDEL (G.)　L'Hôtel des Monnaies de Narbonne au XVIIᵐᵉ siècle.　pp. 22.
Narbonne, 1891. 8°.　　　　　Pam. 44.

—— La fin de la Monnaie de Narbonne.　pp. 17.
Narbonne, 1892. 8°.　　　　　Pam. 44.

SARRIAU (H.)　Numismatique nivernaise.
pp. 148.　1894. 8°.　Ac.　Nevers.　_Société Nivernaise._　Bulletin.　Sér. 3.　Tom. 6.　Ac. 400.

For Gaulish coins, _see supra : Ancient._

Germany.

MENADIER (J.)　Deutsche Münzen.
Berl. 1891, _etc._ 8°.　　　　7757. e. 20.

SAURMA (H. v.)　_Baron von der Jeltsch._　Die Saurma'sche Münzsammlung deutscher Gepräge.
2 pt.　_Berl._ 1892. fol.　　　　7757. i. 13.

DOMANIG (C.)　Die deutsche Privat-Medaille der älteren Zeit.　pp. 42.　_Wien_, 1893. 8°.　7757. g. 12.

KULL (J. V.)　Repertorium zur Münzkunde Bayerns.　pp. 80.　1890. 8°.　Ac.　Munich. _Numismatische Gesellschaft._　Mittheilungen. Jahrg. 9.　　　　　　　　Ac. 5827.

—— Studien zur Geschichte der oberfälsischen Münzen des Hauses Wittelsbach.　1890. 8°. Ac.　Ratisbon.　_Historischer Verein._　Verhandlungen.　Bd 44.　　　　　　Ac. 7157.

GEBERT (C. F.)　Die Gedenk-Münzen mit dem Bilde des Prinzregenten Luitpold.　pp. 20.
Nürnberg, 1891. 4°.　　　　　Pam. 44.

BAHRFELDT (M.)　Die Münzen der Herzogthümer Bremen und Verden, 1648–1719.　pp. 156.
1892. 8°.　Ac.　Luneberg.　_Historischer Verein für Niedersachsen._　Zeitschrift.　Jhrg. 1892.
　　　　　　　　　　　　　　Ac. 7085.

HEYDEN (H. v.)　Der Concordien-Orden und die Ehren-Medaillen der Stadt Frankfurt.　Ac. Frankfort.　_Gesellschaft für Frankfurts Geschichte._　Archiv.　Folge 3.　Ac. 7049.

BAHRFELDT (E.)　Zur Münzkunde der Niederlausitz im XIII. Jahrhundert.　pp. 41.
Berl. 1892. 8°.　　　　　　Pam. 44.

GEBERT (C. F.)　Geschichte der Münzstätte der Reichstadt Nürnberg.　pp. 130.
Nürnberg, 1891. 8°.　　　　　7757. e. 22.

BAHRFELDT (E.)　Zur mittelalterlichen Münzkunde Pommerns.　pp. 21.　_Berl._ 1893. 8°.
　　　　　　　　　　　　　7757. e. 34.

GROBE (L.)　Die Münzen des Herzogtums Sachsen-Meiningen.　pp. 48.　_Meiningen_, 1891. 4°.
　　　　　　　　　　　　　7757. g. 7.

CAHN (J.)　Münz- und Geldgeschichte der Stadt Strassburg.　pp. 176.　_Strassburg_, 1895. 8°.
　　　　　　　　　　　　　7756. d. 33

Great Britain and Ireland.

THORBURN (W. S.)　Guide to the Coins of Great Britain and Ireland.　pp. 164.　_Lond._ 1892. 8°.
　　　　　　　　　　　　　7756. bb. 32.

NORMAN (J. H.)　Silver and gold Coinage of England.　pp. 14.　_Lond._ 1890, _etc._ 8°.
　　　　　　　　　　　　　8226. cc. 51.

MONTAGU (H.)　Copper, tin and bronze Coinage and Patterns for Coins of England, from Elizabeth to Her present Majesty.　pp. 150.
Lond. 1893. 8°.　　　　　　7756. de. 31.

WEBER (F. P.)　Richard, Earl of Cornwall, and his Coins as King of the Romans, 1247–1271.
pp. 9.　_Lond._ 1895. 8°.　　　　Pam. 44.

NUMISMATICS.—Great Britain—*cont.*

Montagu (H.) Catalogue of milled English Coins, from George I. to her present Majesty. ff. 175. *Lond.* 1890. 4°.   7757. c. 14.

Storer (H. R.) Les Médailles de la Princesse Charlotte d'Angleterre. 2 pt. *Brux.* 1888, 91. 8°.   Pam. 44.

Carter (T.) War Medals of the British Army. pp. 656. *Lond.* 1893. 8°.   8828. ff. 21.

Tancred (G.) Historical record of Medals conferred on the British Navy, Army and Auxiliary Forces. pp. 483. *Lond.* 1891. 4°. 7757. e. 17.

Weber (F. P.) Medals of the nineteenth century, relating to England, by foreign artists. pp. 128. *Lond.* 1894. 8°.   7756. dc. 36.

Atkins (J.) Tradesmen's Tokens of the eighteenth century. pp. 415. *Lond.* 1892. 8°. 7757. c. 33.

Davis (W. J.) Token Coinage of Warwickshire. pp. 132. *Birmingham*, 1895. 4°. 7757. g. 13.

Ac. Devizes. *Wiltshire Archæological Society.* Catalogue of collection of Wiltshire Trade Tokens. pp. 22. *Devizes*, 1893. 8°. Pam. 44.

Italy.

Ac. London. *Burlington Fine Arts Club.* Exhibition of Pictures, also of Medals of the houses of Este and Bentivoglio. pp. 57. *Lond.* 1894. 4°.   7858. c. 25.

Bossi (V.) Storia degli Ordini Equestri italiani e delle medaglie nazionali. pp. 171. *Roma*, 1894. 8°.   9914. g. 9.

Gaetano (F.) Le Monete delle Zecche di Salerno. *Salerno*, 1891, etc. 4°.   7755. f.

Ancona (A.) Medaglia satirica di Mentana ed altre medaglie garibaldine, 1870-71. pp. 20. *Milano*, 1889. 8°.   7756. dc. 20. (7.)

For Roman Coins, *see supra : Ancient.*

Netherlands. See supra : Belgium.

Russia and Poland.

Deubner (A.) Die k. russischen Orden und Medaillen. pp. 8. *Berl.* 1890. fol. Pam. 26.

Saurma (H. v.) *Baron von der Jetsch.* Die Saurma'sche Münzsammlung. 2 pt. *Berl* 1892. fol.   7757. i. 13.

Kirmis (M.) Einleitung in die polnische Münzkunde. 1888-91. Ac. Posen. *Historische Gesellschaft.* Zeitschrift. Bd. 4-6. Ac. 7365.

Savoy. See infra : Switzerland.

Spain.

Campaner y Fuertes (A.) Indicator de la Numismática española. pp. 575. *Madrid*, 1891. 8°.   7756. aaa. 9.

Moraleda y Esteban (J.) Numismática toledana. pp. 35. *Toledo*, 1893. 8°.   Pam. 44.

For Coins of the Arabs in Spain, *see infra : Oriental.*

Switzerland and Savoy.

Saurma (H. v.) *Baron von der Jetsch.* Die Saurma'sche Münzsammlung. 2 pt. *Berl.* 1892. fol.   7757. i. 13.

Mayor (J.) Les Médailles du sixième centenaire de l'Alliance Helvétique. pp. 25. *Genève*, 1891. 8°.   Pam. 44.

Demole (E.) Jetons inédits de Savoie, de Genève et de Vaud. pp. 14. *Thonon*, 1888. 8°.   7756. dc. 20. (4.)

America.

Canada.

Breton (P. N.) Le Collectionneur des Monnaies canadiennes. pp. 48. *Montréal*, 1890. 8°.   Pam. 44.

Leroux (J.) Canadian copper Coin catalogue. pp. 16. *Montreal*, 1882. 8°. 7756. dc. 20. (1.)

NUMISMATICS,—America—*continued.*

Leroux (J.) Atlas numismatique du Canada. pp. 35. *Montréal*, 1883. 8°.   7757. c. 13. (2.)

Zay (E.) Canada. Médailles d'honneur pour les Indiens. pp. 8. *Paris*, 1889. 8°. Pam. 44.

United States of America.

Betts (C. W.) American colonial history illustrated by contemporary Medals. pp. 332. *N.Y.* 1894. 8°.   7757. e. 37.

U.S.A. *Mint.* The United States Mint. History, biography, statistics. pp. 120. *Phila.* 1883. 8°.   7756. b. 19.

South America.

Rosa (A.) Monetario americano, ilustrado. pp. 560. *Buenos A.* 1892. 8°.   7757. g. 4.

—— Coleccion de Leyes, sobre condecoraciones militares, medallas conmemorativas, moneda, metálica, *etc.* pp. 411. *Buenos A.* 1891. 8°.   6784. g. 18.

Motta (J. X. da) Moeda do Brazil, 1645-1888. pp. 197. *Victoria*, 1889. 8°.   9772. b. 12.

Australasia.

New South Wales. *Commissioners for the Columbian Exposition.* Account of Coins of Australasia. pp. 159. *Sydney*, 1893. 8°.   7757. c. 40.

Oriental.

Tizengausen (V.) Notice sur une collection de Monnaies orientales. pp. 58. *St.-Pétersbourg*, 1880. 8°.   Pam. 44.

Saint-Laumer (A. de) Sur les Médailles orientales conservées au Musée de Chartres. pp. 9. *Chartres*, 1887. 8°.   7757. e. 13. (3.)

Annam. See infra : Indo-China.

Arabs, etc.

Ac. Madrid. *Museo Arqueológico.* Catálogo de Monedas arábigas españolas. pp. 264. *Madrid*, 1892. 8°.   7756. de. 30.

—— Paris. *Bibliothèque Nationale.* Catalogue des Monnaies musulmanes de la Bibliothèque Nationale. pp. 571. *Paris*, 1891. 8°. 7757. g. 3.

Palermo. *Biblioteca Comunale.* Catalogo delle Monete arabe. pp. 234. *Palermo*, 1892. 8°.   7757. e. 31.

Vives y Escudero (A.) Monedas de las Dinastías arábigo-españolas. pp. 553. *Madrid*, 1893. 8°.   7757. dd. 5.

China and Corea.

Ac. London. *British Museum.* Catalogue of Chinese Coins from the VIIth Cent. B.C., to A.D. 621. pp. 443. *Lond.* 1892. 8°.   7757. g. 6.

Courant (M.) Note sur les espèces de Monnaie qui ont été usitées en Corée. 1893. 8°. Ac. Paris. *Société Asiatique.* Journal Asiatique. Sér. 9. Tom. 2.   2098. d.

India.

Ac. Calcutta. *Indian Museum.* Catalogue of the Coins. *Calcutta*, 1893, etc. 8°. 7757. bb. 6.

Lahore. *Government Museum.* Catalogue of the coins. pp. 149. 29. *Calcutta*, 1891. 4°.   7755. e. 4.

Cunningham (Sir A.) Coins of mediæval India to the Muhammadan Conquests. pp. 108. *Lond.* 1894. 8°.   7756. de. 35.

Poole (S. L.) Coins of the Moghul Emperors of Hindustan. pp. 401. 1892. 8°. Ac. London. *British Museum.* Catalogue of Indian Coins.   7756. bb. 18.

—— History of the Moghul Emperors illustrated by their coins. pp. 177. *Westminster*, 1892. 8°.   7757. c. 36.

Tufnell (R. H. C.) Hints to Coin-collectors in Southern India. pp. 88. *Madras*, 1889. 8°.   7756. de. 24.

NYASSALAND. LUGARD (F. J. D.) Rise of our East African Empire. 2 vol. *Edinb.* 1893. 8°.   010096. h. 4.

RANKIN (D. J.) The Zambesi Basin and Nyassaland. pp. 277. *Edinb.* 1893. 8°. 010096. c. 64.

See also AFRICA, *Central and East:* MISSIONS: ZAMBEZI.

OAK TREE. *See* FORESTRY.

OAMARU. ROBERTS (W. H. S.) History of Oamaru, N.Z. pp. 483. *Oamaru,* 1890. 8°.   10191. aaa. 44.

OATHS. FORD (C.) Ford on Oaths. pp. 170. *Lond.* 1892. 8°.   6282. bb. 36.

HAPPEL (J.) Der Eid im Alten Testament. pp. 72. *Leipz.* 1893. 8°.   4372. cc. 19.

STRINGER (F. A.) Oaths and Affirmations. pp. 184. *Lond.* 1893. 8°.   6281. aaa. 42.

OBELISKS. MOLDENKE (C. E.) The New York Obelisk, Cleopatra's Needle. pp. 202. *N.Y.* 1891. 8°.   7704. aaa. 53.

See also EGYPT, *Antiquities.*

OBER-AMMERGAU. BEAUREGARD (J. de) De Paris à Vienne par Oberammergau. pp. 431. *Lyon,* 1891. 8°.   10106. ccc. 24.

BLONDEL (G.) Le Mystère de la Passion à Oberammergau. pp. 32. *Dijon,* 1891. 8°. Pam. 50.

BUTLER (W. A.) Oberammergau, 1890. pp. 46. *N.Y.* 1891. 8°.   11686. l. 9.

EICHBAUM (F. A. G.) The Country Parson at the Passion Play. pp. 57. *Lond.* 1890. 8°.   011795. e. 51.

HERBERT (M. E.) *Baroness Herbert of Lea.* The Passion Play at Ammergau. pp. 16. *Lond.* 1890. 8°.   3939. ccc. 2 (11.)

LANG (A.) Offizieller Führer zum oberammergauer Passionsspiel. 2 pt. *München,* 1890. 8°.   011795. e. 21.

NIEDENZU (A.) Eine Reise zu den oberammergauer Passionsspielen. pp. 103. *Wollstein,* 1893. 8°.   11795. dg. 42.

OBER-AMMERGAU. *Passions-Spiel.* Le Mystère de la Passion. pp. 232. *Paris,* 1890. 12°.   11746. de. 48.

—— Le Drame de la Passion à Oberammergau. pp. 251. *Paris,* 1890. 18°.   11747. cc. 39.

—— La Passion d'Oberammergau. pp. 24. *Aix,* 1890. 12°.   Pam. 50.

O'REILLY (P. J.) At Ober-Ammergau in 1890. pp. 111. *Lond,* 1890. 4°.   011795. h. 6.

TRAUTMANN (C.) Oberammergau und sein Passionsspiel. pp. 110. 1890. 8°. REINHARDSTOETTNER (C. v.) Bayerische Bibliothek. Bd. 15. 12253. g.

WYL (W.) Der Christus-Mayr. pp. 160. *Berl.* 1890. 8°.   011795. e. 33.

OBJECT LESSONS. CLARK (D.) Complete Object Lesson book. pp. 252. *Redditch,* 1894. 8°.   012200. g. 2.

FROST (H.) Six Object Lessons. ff. 71. *Lond.* 1891. 8°.   8308. aa. 38.

MIALL (L. C.) Object Lessons from nature. *Lond.* 1893, *etc.* 8°.   7006. aaa. 18.

MURCHÉ (V. T.) Object Lessons for infants. *Lond.* 1895, *etc.* 8°.   8310. bbb. 6.

POPE (W. J.) Object-Readers. 4 pt. *Lond.* 1891. 8°.   012202. de. 2.

ROSS (M. A.) How to train young Eyes and Ears. pp. 139. *Edinb.* 1891. 8°. 8310. a. 31.

SALMON (D.) Longmans' Object Lessons. pp. 280. *Lond.* 1891. 8°.   12203. dd. 21.

OBJECT LESSONS—*continued.*

STEELEY (F.) and TROTMAN (B. H.) Blackboard illustrations for Object Lessons. 1893, *etc.* 8°. The Guide Series.   12203. ff.

WILKE (E.) Anschauungsunterricht im Englischen mit Benutzung von Hölzels Bildern. pp. 108. *Leipz.* 1894. 8°.   12984. ff. 12.

OBOK. SALMA (L. de) Obock. Exploration du golfe de Tadjoura. pp. 153. *Paris,* 1893. 12°.   10076. aaa. 3.

See also AFRICA, *Colonisation, French :* FRANCE, *Colonies.*

OBSTETRICS. Ac. Germany. *Gesellschaft für Gynäkologie.* Festschrift zur Feier des Jubiläums der Gesellschaft. pp. 419. *Wien,* 1894. 8°.   Ac. 3783.

AHLFELD (F.) Lehrbuch der Geburtshilfe. pp. 488. *Leipz.* 1894. 8°.   7580. g. 23.

BALLANTYNE (J. W.) Diseases and deformities of the Fœtus. *Edinb.* 1892, *etc.* 8°. 07581. e. 18.

BARBOUR (A. H. F.) The Anatomy of labour. 2 pt. *Edinb.* 1889. fol.   07581. df. 16.

—— Atlas. 1889. fol.   1832. e. 7.

BARNES (R. S. F.) Manual of Midwifery for midwives. pp. 189. *Lond.* 1893. 8°.   07581. de. 31.

BIRCH-HIRSCHFELD (F. V.) Ueber die Pforten der placentaren Infection des Fötus. 1891. 8°. ZIEGLER (E.) Beiträge zur pathologischen Anatomie. Bd. 9.   7441. ece. 18.

BOUFFE DE SAINTE-BLAISE (G.) Lésions anatomiques que l'on trouve dans l'éclampsie puerpérale. pp. 223. *Paris,* 1891. 4°.   7383. dd. 1. (3.)

BOXALL (R.) Use of antiseptics in midwifery. *Lond.* 1894. 8°.   Pam. 39.

CHAIGNEAU (J.) Étude des divers agents anésthesiques employés dans des accouchements. pp. 174. *Paris,* 1890. 8°.   07581. df. 10.

COFFIN (R. J. M.) Obstetric hints for midwives. pp. 80. *Lond.* 1892. 16°.   7581. de. 49.

CREDÉ (C. S. F.) and LEOPOLD (G.) Guide to the Examination of lying-in-women. pp. 48. *Lond.* 1894. 8°.   7581. ccc. 5.

CULLINGWORTH (C. J.) Illustrations of the diseases of the Fallopian Tubes and of Tubal Gestation. pp. 75. *Lond.* 1895. 8°. 7581. d. 16.

DEMELIN (L. A.) Anatomie obstétricale. pp. 169. 1892. 8°. Encyclopédie des aide-mémoire.   8709. g.

DOHRN (R.) Über Leistung von Kunsthilfe in der geburtshilflichen Praxis. 1894. 8°. VOLKMANN (R. v.) Sammlung klinischer Vorträge. N.F. Nr. 94.   7441. g.

DONALD (A.) Introduction to Midwifery. pp. 188. *Lond.* 1894. 8°.   7581. b. 30.

FARABEUF (L. H.) and VARNIER (H.) Introduction à l'étude des Accouchements. pp. 475. *Paris,* 1891. 8°.   7580. g. 14.

FLYNN (M.) Normal Labour as conducted in the Frauen Universitat-Klinik, Berlin. pp. 8. *Leicester,* 1894. 8°.   7306. e. 22. (15.)

GALABIN (A. L.) Manual of Midwifery. pp. 845. *Lond.* 1893. 8°.   07581. de. 35.

GEYL (A.) Zum Oedema acutum cervicis uteri gravidi parturientis s. puerperalis intermittens. 1895. 8°. VOLKMANN (R. v.) Sammlung klinischer Vorträge. N.F. Nr. 128.   7441. g.

GRAEFE (M.) Ueber die Behandlung der Rückwärtslagerung der Gebärmutter. 1895. 8°. VOLKMANN (R. v.) Sammlung klinischer Vorträge. N.F. Nr. 125.   7441. g.

GRANDIN (E. H.) and JARMAN (G. W.) Obstetric Surgery. pp. 207. *Phila.* 1894. 8°. 7580. d. 4.

OBSTETRICS—*continued.*

GRANDIN (E. H.) and JARMAM (G. W.) Pregnancy, Labor and the puerperal state. pp. 261.
Phila. 1895. 8°.   07581. h. 1.

HARRIS (R. P.) Abdominal and uterine tolerance in pregnant Women. pp. 20. *Phila.* 1892. 8°.
       07305. h. 18. (10.)

HAULTAIN (F. W. N.) Practical handbook of Midwifery. pp. 248. *Lond.* 1894. 8°.
       7581. bbb. 40.

HEITZMANN (J.) Compendium der Geburtshilfe. pp. 371. *Wien,* 1894. 8°.   07581. c. 26.

HERFF (O. v.) Grundriss der geburtshülflichen Operationslehre. pp. 372. *Berl.* 1894. 8°.
       7580. a. 2.

HERMAN (G. E.) First lines in Midwifery. pp. 191. *Lond.* 1891. 8°.   07581. de. 21.

—— Difficult Labour. pp. 443. *Lond.* 1894. 8°.
       07581. de. 37.

HEWITT (G.) On severe vomiting during Pregnancy. pp. 147. *Lond.* 1890. 8°. 07581. df. 13.

INGERSLEV (E.) Die Geburtszange. pp. 146. *Stuttg.* 1891. 8°.   7581. e. 15.

KEHRER (F. A.) Lehrbuch der operativen Geburtshülfe. pp. 372. *Stuttg.* 1891. 8°.
       07581. i. 1.

KALTENBACH (R.) Lehrbuch der Geburtshilfe. pp. 524. *Stuttg.* 1893. 8°.   7581. d. 15.

KRUEGER (F.) Die Verdauungsfermente beim Embryo und Neugeborenen. pp. 80.
Wiesbaden, 1891. 8°.   7581. f. 17.

LAURITZEN (W.) Om Svangerskab og Fødsel ved Tvillinger. pp. 200. *Kjøbenh.* 1891. 8°.
       07581. i. 4.

LUSK (W. T.) Science and art of Midwifery. pp. 761. *Lond.* 1892. 8°.   07581. c. 13.

MANTON (W. P.) Syllabus of lectures on human Embryology. pp. 125. *Phila.* 1894. 8°.
       7580. aaa. 6.

MARTIN (A.) Beiträge zur Geburtshülfe und Gynækologie. pp. 218. *Berl.* 1895. 8°.
       7581. f. 20.

NAPIER (A. D. L.) The Thermometer in Obstetrics. pp. 30. *Lond.* 1890. 8°.
       07305. c. 21. (15.)

OLIVIER (A.) La pratique de l'Accouchement normal. pp. 200. 1892. 8°. Encyclopédie des aide-mémoire.   8709. g.

P.P. *Berlin.* Allgemeine deutsche Hebammen-Zeitung. *Berl.* 1886, *etc.* fol.
       P.P. 2982. db. & 385.

—— *London.* Teratologia : contributions to antenatal pathology. *Lond.* 1894, *etc.* 8°.
       P.P. 3193. b.

PLAYFAIR (W. S.) Treatise on Midwifery.
2 vol. *Lond.* 1893. 8°.   2256. d. 10.

STACPOOLE (F.) Advice to Women on the care of the health before and after confinement.
pp. 134. *Lond.* 1893. 8°.   7581. aa. 6.

SWAYNE (J. G.) Obstetric Aphorisms. pp. 164. *Lond.* 1893. 8°.   7581. de. 50.

WALKER (J. H.) Handbook for Mothers.
pp. 200. *Lond.* 1893. 8°.   07581. de. 32.

WEBSTER (J. C.) Tubo-Peritoneal ectopic Gestation. pp. 50. *Edinb.* 1892. 4°. 7580. g. 21.

—— Ectopic Pregnancy. pp. 240.
Edinb. 1895. 8°.   07581. e. 30.

CHAZAN (S.) Die Streitpunkte in der Puerperal-fieberfrage. pp. 48. 1890. 8°. VOLKMANN (R. v.) Sammlung klinischer Vorträge. N.F. No. 12.   7441. g.

LALLIER (A.) De la Folie puerpérale dans ses rapports avec l'éclampsie. pp. 119.
Paris, 1892. 8°.   07581. c. 17.

OBSTETRICS—*continued.*

SCHMORL (G.) Pathologisch-anatomische Untersuchungen über Puerperal-Eklampsie. pp. 106.
Leipz. 1893. 8°.   7581. g. 26.
See also ABORTION : WOMEN, *Diseases of.*

History, etc.

MORGOULIEFF (J.) Étude sur les Monuments antiques représentant des scènes d'Accouchement. pp. 76. *Paris,* 1893. 8°.   07708. g. 31.

AUDUREAU (C.) Étude sur l'Obstétrique pendant le moyen âge et la renaissance. pp. 194.
Dijon, 1892. 8°.   7580. g. 18.

WITKOWSKI (G. J. A.) Accoucheurs et sages-femmes célèbres. pp. 390. *Paris,* 1891. 8°.
       07581. e. 7.

—— Les Accouchements dans les beaux-arts. pp. 590. *Paris,* 1894. 8°.   7580. dd. 8.

—— Les Accouchements à la cour. pp. 415.
Paris, 1890. 8°.   7581. g. 23.

OGATA (M.) Beitrag zur Geschichte der Geburtshülfe in Japan. pp. 48. *Freiburg,* 1891. 8°.
       07305. h. 17. (3.)

Obstetric Nursing.

CHURCHILL (F.) A Handbook of obstetric Nursing. pp 216. *Dublin,* 1893. 8°.   07581. f. 1.

CULLINGWORTH (C. J.) Short manual for Monthly Nurses. pp. 92. *Lond.* 1891. 8°. 07581. de. 19.

DREW (M.) Monthly Nursing. pp. 82.
Lond. 1890. 8°.   7581. aa. 5.

HAULTAIN (F. W. N.) and FERGUSON (J. H.) Handbook of obstetric Nursing. pp. 243.
Edinb. 1894. 8°.   07581. f. 2.

HUMFREY (M.) Manual of obstetric Nursing. pp. 282. *Lond.* 1894. 8°.   07581. de. 39.

HUSBAND (H. A.) The Monthly Nurse. pp. 26.
Edinb. 1887. 8°.   7306. df. 20. (1.)
See also supra : General.

Veterinary Obstetrics.
See VETERINARY MEDICINE.

OCCULT SCIENCE. ABER (M. A.) Souls. pp. 176. *Chicago,* 1893. 8°.   8632. d. 26.

BADAUD (U. N.) Coup d'œil sur la Magie au XIXᵉ siècle. pp. 336. *Paris,* 1891. 8°.
       8632. bb. 56.

—— Coup d'œil sur les Thaumaturges du XIXᵉ siècle. pp. 340. *Paris,* 1891. 8°. 8632. ccc. 12.

BATHURST (J.) Atomic-consciousness. Explanation of ghosts, spiritualism, witchcraft, *etc.* pp. 284. *Exeter,* 1892. 8°.   8632. g. 19.

BEHRE (C.) Spiritisten, Occultisten und Theosophen. pp. 85. *Leipz.* 1890. 8°.
       8632. e. 36. (9.)

BOIS (J.) Le Satanisme et la Magie. pp. 427. *Paris,* 1895. 8°.   8631. g. 32.

BOLTON (H. C.) A Modern Oracle, and its prototypes. *N.Y.* 1893. 8°.   Pam. 36.

BOMBAST VON HOHENHEIM (P. A. T.) Hermetic and alchemical Writings of Paracelsus. 2 vol.
Lond. 1894. 4°.   8905. g. 2.

BOSC (E.) Addha-Nari, ou l'occultisme dans l'Inde. pp. 359. *Paris,* 1893. 8°. 8631. ee. 37.

CAHAGNET (L. A.) Magie magnétique, ou traité de fascinations, possessions, *etc.* pp. 519.
Paris, 1895. 8°.   08631. c. 1.

COLLECTANEA. Collectanea Chemica : treatises on hermetic medicine. pp. 160.
Lond. 1893. 8°.   8631. ccc. 32.

COPLEY (H. A.) Broad-thought Library.
Lond. 1891, *etc.* 8°.   8632. ccc.

DIESENBACH (J.) Besessenheit, Zauberei und Hexenfabeln. 1893. 8°. HAFFNER (P. L.) *Bishop of Mentz.* Frankfurter zeitgemässe Broschüren. N.F. Bd. 14.   12209. g.

OCCULT SCIENCE—continued.

Ducret (É.) Les Sciences occultes. pp. 180.
Paris, 1895. 8°. 8630. bbb. 33.

Du Potet de Sennevoy (J.) *Baron*. La Magie
dévoilée. pp. 334. *Paris*, 1893. 8°. 8632. f. 27.

Du Prel (C.) *Baron*. Die Entdeckung der Seele
durch die Geheimwissenschaften. pp. 258.
Leipz. 1894. 8°. 8462. g. 29.

Elworthy (F. T.) The Evil Eye. pp. 471.
Lond. 1895. 8°. 8632. f. 30.

Figuier (L.) Aujourd'hui. Les prodiges de
Cagliostro, *etc.* pp. 725. *Paris*, 1893, 4°.
8630. i. 20.

Figulus (B.) Golden and blessed Casket of
nature's marvels. pp. 361. *Lond.* 1893. 8°.
8905. bb. 29.

Gasparin (A. É. de) *Count*. Du Surnaturel.
2 vol. *Paris*, 1892, 12°. 8632. ccc. 18.

Gibier (P.) Physiologie transcendantale.
pp. 270. *Paris*, 1890. 12°. 8462. aaa. 31.

Girard (R.) and Garredi (M.) Les Messies
Esséniens et l'Eglise orthodoxe par les Esséniens
du xixe siècle. pp. 396. *Paris*, 1893. 12°.
3900. b. 58.

Gleams. Gleams of Light and glimpses thro'
the rift. pp. 724. *Lond.* 1893. 4°. 8632. h. 12.

Guaita (S. de) Essais de Sciences maudites.
Paris, 1890, *etc.* 8°. 8632. d. 14.

Harrison (C. G.) The Transcendental Universe.
pp. 168. *Lond.* 1894. 8°. 8632. c. 43.

Hartmann (F.) Cosmology; or, universal
science. 2 pt. *Bost.*, 1888. fol. 1896. b. 4.

—— Life and doctrines of Jacob Boehme.
pp. 338. *Lond.* 1891. 8°. 4888. f. 14.

—— Occult Science in medicine. pp. 100.
Lond. 1893. 8°. 8632. e. 30.

—— Magic, white and black. pp. 298.
Lond. 1893. 8°. 8632. e. 26.

—— Die weisse und schwarze Magie. pp. 255.
Leipz. 1894. 8°. 8632. e. 33.

—— Die Geheimlehre in der christlichen Religion nach den Erklärungen von Meister Eck-
hart. pp. 226. *Leipz.* 1895. 8°. 3716. bb. 36.

Henne-am-Rhyn (O.) Eine Reise durch das
Reich des Aberglaubens. pp. 175.
Leipz. 1893. 8°. 8632. d. 25.

Hermes, *Trismegistus*. Collectanea Hermetica.
Lond. 1893, *etc.* 8°. 8906. aaa.

Hermetic Museum. The Hermetic Museum,
restored and enlarged. 2 vol. *Lond.* 1893. 8°.
8905. ee. 20.

Initié. Mystères des Sciences occultes. pp. 595.
Paris, 1894. 8°. 8632. g. 20.

Jhouney (A.) Ésotérisme et socialisme: le
Christ ésotérique. pp. 193. *Paris*, 1893. 8°.
8470. f. 32.

Kiesewetter (C.) Geschichte des neueren Oc-
cultismus. pp. 799. *Leipz.* 1891. 8°.
8632. d. 17.

Kingsford (A. B.) Intima Sacra; manual of
esoteric devotion. pp. 163. *Lond.* 1891. 12°.
4503. a. 41.

Lang (A.) Cock Lane and common sense.
pp. 357. *Lond.* 1894. 8°. 8632. h. 13.

Laurent (A.) La Magie et la divination chez
les Chaldéo-Assyriens. pp. 89. *Paris*, 1894. 8°.
8632. d. 29.

Lermina (J.) Collection d'ouvrages relatifs aux
Sciences hermétiques. *Paris*, 1889, *etc.* 8°.
8905. de. 19.

—— La Science occulte. Magie pratique.
pp. 274. *Paris*, 1891. 12°. 8632. c. 40.

OCCULT SCIENCE—continued.

Lillie (A.) Modern Mystics and modern magic.
Biography of W. S. Moses. pp. 172.
Lond. 1894. 8°. 8631. aaa. 54.

Ludwig (W.) Spaziergänge eines Wahrheit-
suchers in's Reich der Mystik. pp. 257.
Leipz. 1890. 8°. 8630. cc. 32.

Maitland (E.) Story of the new Gospel of
Interpretation. pp. 175. *Lond.* 1893. 8°.
4371. df. 18.

—— The new Gospel of Interpretation. Doctrine
of the esoteric Christian Union. *Lond.* 1892. 8°.
4371. bb. 9. (1.)

Olcott (H. S.) Occultism and Truth.
1894. 8°. Pam. 36.

Palazzi (G.) Gli odierni Occultisti. pp. 85.
Roma, 1891. 8°. 8600. cc. 36. (2.)

Papus, *pseud*. Traité méthodique de Science
occulte. pp. 1092. *Paris*, 1891. 8°. 8632. i. 2.

—— Absolute key to occult science. The Tarot
of the Bohemians. pp. 355. *Lond.* 1892. 8°.
8632. g. 18.

—— La Kabbale. Tradition secrète de l'Occident. pp. 188. *Paris*, 1892. 8°. 8632. h. 8.

—— Traité élémentaire de Magie pratique.
pp. 559. *Paris*, 1893. 8°. 8632. i. 1.

—— L'Illuminisme en France, 1767–74.
pp. 283. *Paris*, 1895. 12°. 010662. g. 40.

Péladan (J.) Amphithéâtre des Sciences mortes.
Comment on devient Fée. pp. 393.
Paris, 1893. 8°. 8632. e. 27.

—— Comment on devient Mage. pp. 303.
Paris, 1892. 8°. 8632. e. 28.

P.P. Boston. *Massachusetts*. Occultism.
Bost. 1893, *etc.* 8°. P.P. 636. cp.

—— *Glasgow*. The Occult Magazine.
Glasg. 1885–86. 8°. P.P. 647.

—— *London*. Borderland. *Lond.* 1893, *etc.* 4°.
P.P. 636. cl.

—— The Mystical World. *Lond.* 1893, *etc.* 4°.
P.P. 636. ch. and 2228.

—— The Unknown World. *Lond.* 1894, *etc.* 8°.
P.P. 636. ci.

—— *Manchester*. The Unseen Universe.
Manch. 1892, *etc.* 8°. P.P. 597. cd.

—— *Paris*. Annales des Sciences psychiques.
Paris, 1891, *etc.* 8°. P.P. 597. ge.

Pazig (C.) Treatyse of magic Incantations.
pp. 54. *Edinb.* 1886. 8°. 8632. ccc. 15.

Plytoff (G.) Les Sciences occultes. pp. 320.
Paris, 1891. 8°. 8632. cc. 42.

—— La Magie, les lois occultes, *etc.* pp. 312.
Paris, 1892. 8°. 8632. ccc. 13.

R., E. J. Out of the Darkness.
Bournemouth, 1895. 8°. Pam. 36.

Rāma Prasāda. Occult Science. Science of
Breath, *etc.* pp. 28. *Lahore*, 1892. 8°. 759. b. 7.

Rouxel ( ) Spiritisme et occultisme. pp. 72.
Paris, 1892. 12°. 8630. cc. 36. (3.)

Schwab (M.) Les Coupes magiques et l'hydro-
mancie dans l'antiquité orientale. pp. 51.
Lond. 1890. 8°. 8632. f. 24.

Secret. The Great Secret and its unfoldment
in Occultism. pp. 317. *Lond.* 1895. 8°.
8631. f. 49.

Sinclair (M.) *Countess of Caithness*. Interprétation ésotérique des livres sacrés. pp. 227.
Paris, 1891. 8°. 8632. cc. 47.

Stanton (E.) Dreams of the dead. pp. 268.
Bost. 1892. 8°. 8632. cc. 48.

Styx. Hermetic Philosophy.
Phila. 1890, *etc.* 8°. 8630. d.

OCCULT SCIENCE—*continued.*

THOMPSON (A.) Magic and mystery. pp. 127. *Lond.* 1894. 8°. 8631. aaa. 55.

VITOUX (G.) Les Limites de l'inconnu. pp. 48. *Paris,* 1892. 8°. Pam. 36.

WAITE (A. E.) The Occult Sciences. pp. 292. *Lond.* 1891. 8°. 8632. ccc. 10.

—— Azoth; or, The Star in the east. pp. 239. *Lond.* 1893. 8°. 8632. m. 2.

WEATHERLY (L. A.) The Supernatural? pp. 273. *Bristol,* 1891. 8°. 8632. ccc. 8.

See also ALCHEMY : ASTROLOGY : CHARMS: FORTUNE TELLING : MAGIC SQUARES : ROSICRUCIANS : SPIRITUALISM : TELEPATHY : THEOSOPHY : WITCHCRAFT.

OHIO. THOMSON (P. G.) Catalogue of books relating to Ohio. pp. 108. *Cincinnati,* 1890. 8°. 011902. f. 34.

Ac. Washington. *Smithsonian Institution.* THOMAS (C.) Circular, square and octagonal Earthworks of Ohio. pp. 33. *Wash.* 1889. 8°. 7706. g. 6. (5.)

—— Problem of the Ohio Mounds. pp. 54. *Wash.* 1889. 8°. 7706. g. 8. (12.)

MOOREHEAD (W. K.) Primitive man in Ohio. pp. 246. *N.Y.* 1892. 8°. 7709. e. 6.

FERNOW (B.) The Ohio Valley in Colonial Days. pp. 299. *Albany,* 1890. 4°. 9605. cc. 13.

GIST (C.) Gist's Journals with notes by W. M. Darlington. pp. 296. *Pittsburgh,* 1893. 8°. 010882. m. 26.

VENABLE (W. H.) Beginnings of literary culture in Ohio. pp. 519. *Cincinnati,* 1891. 8°. 011824. i. 14.

OJIBIWAY INDIANS. *See* INDIANS.

OKLAHOMA. INDIAN TERRITORY. Statistics concerning the Indian Territory, Oklahoma. pp. 85. *St. Louis,* 1893. 8°. Pam. 86.

OKLAHOMA. Oklahoma and the Cherokee Strip. pp. 16. *Chicago,* 1893. 12°. Pam. 86.

—— Statutes of Oklahoma, 1893. pp. 1338. *Guthrie,* 1893. 8°. 6617. cc. 3.

See also LAW REPORTS.

OLD AGE : LONGEVITY. BELL (R.) Secret of Long Life. pp. 42. *Glasg.* 1894. 8°. Pam. 39.

BUECHNER (F. C. C. L.) Das Buch vom langen Leben. pp. 288. *Leipz.* 1892. 8°. 7391. df. 15.

CREAN (R.) Care of health in Old Age. 1888. 8°. MANCHESTER. *Sanitary Association.* Health Lectures. Ser. 11. No. 4. 7404. bbb.

HARDWICKE (H.) Art of Living long and happily. pp. 106. *Lond.* 1895. 8°. 7404. aaaa. 7.

HUMPHRY (G. M.) Old Age : results of information respecting persons who had attained the age of eighty. pp. 216. *Camb.* 1889. 8°. 7391. de. 4.

LEBON (L.) De l'hérédité de la Longévité. pp. 56. *Nancy,* 1894. 4°. 7383. ddd. 3. (3.)

SIMPSON (P. A.) Old Age. 1892. 8°. GLASGOW. *Insurance Society.* Transactions. Ser. 3. No. 4. 08227. c.

BOOTH (C.) Aged Poor in England and Wales. *Lond.* 1894, *etc.* 8°. 2020. c.

DRAGE (G.) Problem of the Aged Poor. pp. 375. *Lond.* 1895. 8°. 08275. f. 30.

For Old Age Pensions, *see* INSURANCE.

OLD CATHOLICS. BEYSCHLAG (W.) Der Altkatholicismus. pp. 66. *Halle,* 1883. 8°. 4662. d. 18. (1.)

OLD CATHOLICS. Der zweite internationale Altkatholiken-Kongress in Luzern. pp. 318. *Luzern,* 1892. 8°. 3908. f. 30.

OLD CATHOLICS—*continued.*

LITURGIES. Old Catholics. *Hymns.* Godsdienstig gezangboeck voor Oud-Katholicken. pp. 176. *Rotterdam,* 1890. 8°. 3434. de. 56.

See also UTRECHT, *Jansenist Church.*

OLDENBURG. KOLLMANN (P.) Das Herzogthum Oldenburg in seiner wirthschaftlichen Entwickelung. pp. 608. *Oldenburg,* 1893. 8°. 9385. g. 1.

RUETHNING (G.) Tilly in Oldenburg. pp. 24. *Oldenburg,* 1890. 4°. Pam. 28.

SCHAUENBURG (L.) Hundert Jahre oldenburgischer Kirchengeschichte, 1573–1667. *Oldenburg,* 1894, *etc.* 8°. 4662. cc.

OLIVE. CARBONE (G. A.) L' Olivo e l' olio. pp. 314. *Napoli,* 1889. 8°. 7076. i. 9.

MORELL TERRY (L.) Elaboración del aceite de olivas. pp. 55. *Granada,* 1889. 8°. 7942. g. 23. (5.)

See also FATS AND OILS.

OLIVEIRA DO HOSPITAL. ABREU (A. de) Oliveira do Hospital. Traços historico-criticos. pp. 145. *Coimbra,* 1893. fol. 10161. f. 12.

OLMÜTZ. ELVERT (C. d') Zur Geschichte des Erzbisthums Olmütz. pp. 327. 1895. 8°. Ac. Brunn. *K. K. Mährisch-Schlesische Gesellschaft.* Schriften. Bd. 29. Ac. 745/2.

MUELLER (W.) Sagen und Geschichten der Stadt Olmütz. pp. 114. *Olmütz,* 1892. 8°. 10215. c. 4.

PEYSCHA (F.) Die olmützer Kunstuhr. pp. 32. *Olmütz,* 1886. 8°. 10107. c. 11. (4.)

OLNEY. WRIGHT (T.) The Town of Cowper. pp. 224. *Lond.* 1893. 8°. 10351. c. 41.

OLYMPIA : OLYMPIC GAMES.
See GREECE, *Antiquities.*

OMBRE, Game. POLE (W.) Ombre. 1891. 8°. Cyclopædia of Card Games, *etc.* 2264. b. 20.

See also CARDS.

ONION. TAPLIN (J. A.) Cultivation of the Onion. pp. 12. *Lond.* 1891. 12°. 7074. e. 11. (7.)

See also GARDENING.

ONONDAGA LANGUAGE. *See* INDIAN LANGUAGES.

ONTARIO. KINGSFORD (W.) Bibliography of the province of Ontario. pp. 140. *Toronto,* 1892. 8°. 9555. b. 11.

MAC EVOY (J. M.) The Ontario township. pp. 43. 1889. 8°. ASHLEY (W. J.) Toronto University Studies. Ser. 1. No. 1. 8009. i. 24.

ONTARIO. *Immigration Department.* Ontario as a home for the British farmer. pp. 48. *Toronto,* 1892. 8°. 10470. dd. 30. (12.)

See also CANADA.

OOTACAMUND. OOTACAMUND. Guide to Ootacamund. pp. 82. *Madras,* 1889. 8°. 10058. a. 18. (2)

OPERA. BRICQUEVILLE (E. H. de) Le livret de l'Opéra français, 1672–1779. pp. 77. *Brux.* 1887. 8°. 7895. f. 32.

CHESNEY (F. R.) Stories of the Operas. pp. 309. *Lond.* 1891. 8°. 7897. bb. 62.

DEPPE (L.) Zwei Jahre Kapellmeister an der königlichen Oper zu Berlin. pp. 45. *Bielefeld,* 1890. 8°. 7898. cc. 14.

FITZGERALD (P.) The Savoy Opera and the Savoyards. pp. 218. *Lond.* 1894. 8°. 11795. dg. 46.

GROUCHY (E. H. de) Les abonnés de l'Opéra en 1778. pp. 13. *Paris,* 1891. 8°. Pam. 50.

OPERA—*continued.*

HEDBERG (F.) Gustaf III.s Operahus och dess minnen. pp. 138. *Stockholm*, 1891. 8°.
11795. dg. 23.

KRAUSE (E.) Abriss der Entwickelungsgeschichte der Oper. pp. 130. *Hamburg*, 1890. 8°.
7896. bb. 45.

PFOHL (F.) Die moderne Oper. pp. 401. *Leipz.* 1894. 8°. 7899. b. 8.

REGNARD (A.) La renaissance du Drame lyrique 1600–1876. pp. 152. *Paris*, 1895. 12°.
7899. aaa. 23.

ROLLAND (R.) Histoire de l'Opéra en Europe avant Lully et Scarlatti. pp. 316. 1895. 8°. Ac. Athens. *École Française.* Bibliothèque. Fasc. 71. Ac. 5206/2.

SOUBIES (A.) Soixante-sept ans à l'Opéra, 1826–93. pp. 24. *Paris*, 1893. 4°. 7896. f. 40.

SPIER (K. C.) Stories of the Operas. *Liverpool*, 1890. 8°. 11779. aa.

VALORI (H. de) *Prince.* La Musique, le bon sens et les deux Opéras. pp. 204. *Paris*, 1890. 8°.
7898. k. 40.

See also DRAMA : MUSIC. For criticisms, *etc.* of Operas by eminent Composers, *see* MUSIC, *History.*

OPHTHALMOSCOPY. *See* EYE.

OPIUM. BROWN (R.) Opium Revenue and Indian finance. pp. 24. *Glasg.* 1891. 8°.
08227. cc. 46. (5.)

CEYLON. The Use of Opium and bhang. pp. 24. *Colombo*, 1893. 8°. 8110. a. 46. (5.)

CLEIFE (H. H. T.) England's greatest national Sin. pp. 153. *Lond.* 1892. 8°. 8436. c. 4.

DYER (A. S.) Chinese Christians and the ravages of the Opium plague. pp. 4. *Lond.* 1890. 8°.
8425. bbb. 43. (4.)

—— The great Plague of Asia. pp. 4. *Lond.* 1890. 8°. 8425. bbb. 43. (5.)

HART (E. A.) On the use of Opium in India. Reports to the Parliamentary Bills Committee of the British Medical Association. pp. 31. *Lond.* 1894. 8°. 8435. bb. 63.

HEADLAND (E.) China and Opium. pp. 16. *Lond.* 1892. 8°. 8409. ccc. 27. (4.)

HEHIR (P.) Opium ; physical, moral and social effects. pp. 886. *Lond.* 1894. 8°. 8435. cc. 57.

HELD (A.) Les alcaloïdes de l'Opium. pp. 238. *Paris*, 1894. 12°. 8909. aa. 34.

INDIA. Is India to be ruined by Opium? pp. 4. *Lond.* 1890. 8°. 8425. bbb. 43. (6.)

KONING (G. A. de) De Opiumreglementen voor Nederlandsch-Indië. pp. 147. *Zalt-Bommel*, 1885. 8°. 5319. aa. 15.

LAY (H. N.) Note on the Opium question. pp. 23. *Lond.* 1893. 8°. Pam. 85.

P.P. *London.* Anti-Opium news. *Lond.* 1891, *etc.* 4°. 136.

ROO (L. W. G. de) De verkoop van opium op Java. pp. 32. *Nijmegen*, 1892. 8°. Pam. 85.

RUSTAM PESTANJĪ JAHĀNGĪR. History of the Lives of Bombay opium smokers. pp. 40. 80. *Bombay*, 1893. 8°. 8435· cc. 56.

—— Truth about the Bombay Opium defamation cases. pp. 129. *Bombay*, 1894. 8°. 5319. aa. 13.

SOETERWOUDE (W. E. v.) De Opium-vloek op Java. *'s-Gravenh.* 1890. 4°. 8435. i. 10.

WATT (G.) Papaver Somniferum-Opium. pp. 89. 1891. 8°. 07076. k. 2.

ZEGERS (J. L.) Het Opium-vraagstuk in nederlandsch Oost-Indië. pp. 523. *Nijmegen*, 1890. 8°.
8226. h. 39.

OPORTO. OPORTO. Revolta militar no Porto em 31 de janeiro de 1891. pp. 479. *Porto*, 1891. 8°. 9195. f. 3.

OPPA, River. *See* SILESIA.

OPTICS. ALLEMAN (L. A. W.) Optics as related to evolution. 1891. 8°. Brooklyn. *Ethical Association.* Evolution Series. No. 10.
7006. bbb.

BASSET (A. B.) Treatise on physical Optics. pp. 411. *Camb.* 1892. 8°. 8715. h. 26.

BIESE (A. C.) Ein neuer Typus optischer Instrumente. pp. 29. *Berl.* 1894. 8°. Pam. 79.

BURTON (W. K.) Optics for photographers. pp. 153. *Lond.* 1891. 8°. 8909. aa. 14.

GELCICH (E.) Ottica. pp. 576. *Milano*, 1895. 16°.
012200. i. 14.

GLAZEBROOK (R. T.) Physical Optics. pp. 458. 1893. 8°. GOODEVE (T. M.) Text-books of Science. 2244. a. 9.

HEATH (R. S.) Treatise on geometrical Optics. pp. 388. *Camb.* 1895. 8°. 2242. cc. 3.

ISSALY ( ) Optique géométrique. 1895. 8°. Ac. Bordeaux. *Société des Sciences.* Mémoires. Sér. 4. Tom. 5. Ac. 2840.

MYSTERIES. Collection of experiments illustrating chemical and optical Wonders. pp. 100. *Lond.* 1891. 8°. 8909. bb. 6.

POINCARÉ (H.) Électricité et Optique. Les théories de Maxwell. pp. 314. *Paris*, 1890. 8°.
8757. h. 15.

STEINHEIL (A.) and VOIT (E.) Handbuch der angewandten Optik. *Leipz.* 1891, *etc.* 8°.
8715. h. 24.

WERNDLY (L.) Klinische Optiek. pp. 182. *Leiden*, 1893. 8°. 7611. b. 48.

ZWICK (H.) Optical Experiments. A series. pp. 54. *Lond.* 1893. 8°. 8715. ce. 49.

See also EYE : LENSES : LIGHT : MICROSCOPY : PHYSICS : TELESCOPE.

OPTIMISM. *See* PESSIMISM.

ORAN. ARMENGAUD (J. L.) Le Sud oranais. Treize mois de colonnes pendant l'insurrection, 1881–82. pp. 108. *Paris*, 1893. 8°.
10096. ee. 8.

INNOCENTI (J. C. A. A.) *General.* Insurrection du Sud-Oranais en 1881. pp. 134. *Paris*, 1893. 12°. 9061. aaa. 2.

MATHIEU (A.) and TRABUT (L.) Les Hautsplateaux oranais. pp. 94. *Alger*, 1891. 8°.
010096. ff. 14.

MATHIEU (A.) Le service forestier dans le département d'Oran. pp. 44. *Alger*, 1892. 8°. Pam. 1. *See also* ALGERIA.

ORANGE. ALDERTON (G. E.) Treatise of Orange-culture in Auckland. pp. 76. *Wellington*, 1884. 8°. 07076. l. 3. *See also* GARDENING.

ORANGE FREE STATE. ORANGE FREE STATE. Orange Free State. pp. 15. *Chicago*, 1893. 8°. Pam. 89. *See also* AFRICA, *South.*

ORATORIOS. NOVELLO, EWER AND Co. Series of the words of Oratorios, cantatas, *etc. Lond.* 1890, *etc.* 8°. 7896. de. *See also* MUSIC.

ORCHARDS. *See* GARDENING.

ORCHIDS. BOHNHOF (E.) Dictionnaire des Orchidées hybrides. pp. 139. *Paris*, 1895. 8°.
07028. e. 52.

BOLUS (H.) Icones Orchidearum Austro-Africanarum extra-tropicarum. *Lond.* 1893, *etc.* 8°.
7028. d. 3.

BOYLE (F.) About Orchids. pp. 250. *Lond.* 1893. 8°. 07028. f. 52.

ORCHIDS—*continued.*

BURBERRY (H. A.) Amateur Orchid cultivators' guide book. pp. 200. *Liverp.* 1895. 8°.
07028. h. 37.

CAMUS (E. G.) Monographie des Orchidées de France. pp. 130. *Paris,* 1894. 8°. 7054. h. 25.

DENTERGHEM (O. de K. de) *Count.* Le Livre des Orchidées. pp. 601. *Gand,* 1894. 8°.
7028. ee. 4.

HANSEN (G.) The Orchid hybrids. pp. 257. *Lond.* 1895. 8°. 7028. cc. 3.

LINDEN (L.) Les Orchidées exotiques et leur culture en Europe. pp. 1019. *Brux.* 1894. 8°.
7029. h. 4.

MEASURES (R. I.) Cypripediums. pp. 63. *Lond.* 1894. obl. 12°. 7029. a. 15.

MILLICAN (A.) Travels of an Orchid Hunter in Colombia. pp. 222. *Lond.* 1891. 8°.
10481. dd. 21.

P.P. *London.* The Orchid Review. *Lond.* 1893, *etc.* 8°. P.P. 2160. c.

PUCCI (A.) Les Cypripedium et genres affines, *etc.* pp. 218. *Florence,* 1891. 8°. 07028. k. 2.

SCHULZE (M.) Die Orchidaceen Deutschlands, Deutsch-Oesterreichs und der Schweiz. *Gera-Untermhaus,* 1892, *etc.* 8°. 7028. d.

STEIN (B.) Stein's Orchideenbuch. pp. 602. *Berl.* 1892. 8°. 7028. cc. 1.

WATSON (W.) Orchids. pp. 554. *Lond.* 1895. 8°. 07028. f. 62.

WILLIAMS (B. S.) The Orchid-Grower's manual. pp. 796. *Lond.* 1894. 8°. 07028. m. 13.

WOOLWARD (F. H.) The Genus Masdevallia. Issued by the Marquess of Lothian. 9 pts. *Grantham,* 1890–96. fol. 1820. d. 4.

See also BOTANY : GARDENING.

OREGON. OREGON. *State Board of Agriculture.* Resources of Oregon. pp. 230. *Salem,* 1892. 8°. 10411. d. 31.

VICTOR (F. A.) Atlantis Arisen. Talks about Oregon. pp. 412. *Phila.* 1891. 8°. 10413. g. 19.

ORGAN. BONY (L.) Une excursion dans l'Orgue. pp. 95. *Paris,* 1892. 8°. 7895. c. 1.

BOTS (G. L.) De gregoriaansche Organist. pp. 30. *Utrecht,* 1891. 8°. Pam. 24.

BUMPUS (J. S.) Organists of S. Paul's Cathedral. pp. 272. *Lond.* 1891. 8°. 7898. l. 27.

DIENEL (O.) Die moderne Orgel. pp. 90. *Berl.* 1891. 8°. 7896. c. 43. (11.)

ELLISTON (T.) Organs and tuning. pp. 204. *Lond.* 1895. 8°. 7899. aaa. 21.

FLEURY (P. de) *Marquis.* Les Orgues de la Cathédrale d'Angoulême. 1890. 8°. Ac. Angoulême. *Société Archéologique.* Bulletin. Sér. 5. Tom. 11. Ac. 5286.

FRENZEL (R.) Die Orgel und ihre Meister. pp. 145. *Dresden,* 1894. 8°. 7899. a. 1.

HORNER (B. W.) Organ Pedal Technique. pp. 28. 1895. 8°. Novello's Music Primers.
7895. ff.

LOCHER (C.) Les Jeux d'Orgue. pp. 78. *Paris,* 1889. 8°. 7897. cc. 52.

MARCUZZI (G.) Cenni storico-artistici sull' Organo. pp. 66. *Udine,* 1890. 8°.
7896. c. 43. (8.)

MEIJER (S.) De Forte-Piano an het Orgel. pp. 40. *Groningen,* 1881. 8°. Pam. 24.

PESCHARD (A.) Les applications de l'électricité aux grandes Orgues. pp. 73. *Paris,* 1890. 8°.
7895. g. 11.

PHILBERT (C. M.) Essai sur le tuyau d'Orgue à anche battante. pp. 61. *Avranches,* 1893. 8°.
8709. c. 11. (5.)

ORGAN—*continued.*

RIETSCHEL (G.) Die Aufgabe der Orgel im Gottesdienste bis in das 18. Jahrhundert. pp. 72. *Leipz.* 1893. 8°. 7896. d. 32.

ROJAHN (F.) Kortfattet Haandbog om Orglet. *Kristiania,* 1891. 8°. 7897. g. 60.

STOCKS (W. H.) History of the Organ and organists at the Chapel of Alleyn's College at Dulwich. pp. 28. *Lond.* 1891. 8°. Pam. 24.

ZELLNER (L. A.) Vorträge über Orgelbau. pp. 148. *Wien,* 1893. 8°. 7895. ce. 28.

ORIENTAL CONGRESS. Ac. Europe. *Oriental Congress.* Actes du huitième Congrès. *Leide,* 1891, *etc.* 8°. Ac. 8806.

WEBER (A.) Quousque tandem? Der achte Orientalisten-Congress. pp. 78. *Berl.* 1891. 8°. 011824. h. 35.

Ac. Europe. *Oriental Congress.* Tranactions of the Ninth International Congress of Orientalists. 2 vol. *Lond.* 1893. 8°. Ac. 8806.

LEUMANN (E.) Persönliche Erinnerungen an den neunten Orientalisten-Congress. pp. 19. *Strassb.* 1892. 8°. Pam. 46.

ORIGNY-EN-THIÉRACHE. MICHAUX (E.) Histoire d'Origny-en-Thiérache. pp. 543. *Origny,* 1894. 8°. 10169. f. 4.

ORINOCO, River. CARVAJAL (J. de) Relación del descubrimiento del rio Apure hasta su ingreso en el Orinoco. pp. 444. *Leon,* 1892. 8°. 9771. dd. 6.

ERBACH (E. zu) *Count.* Wandertage im Strom- und Küstengebiet des Orinoko. pp. 460. *Leipz.* 1892. 8°. 10481. e. 33.

ORISSA. GAŅAPATI DĀSA. Young Orissa. pp. 26. *Cuttack,* 1890. 8°. 8409. ccc. 26. (7.)

ORKHON. Ac. Helsingfors. *Société Finno-Ougrienne.* Inscriptions de l'Orkhon. pp. 48. *Helsingfors,* 1892. fol. 7705. i. 18.

—— Saint Petersburg. *Academia Scientiarum.* Arbeiten der Orchon-Expedition. *St.-Petersburg,* 1892, *etc.* fol. 1701. b.
See also MONGOLIA.

ORKNEY AND SHETLAND ISLANDS. CURSITER (J. W.) Lists of books and pamphlets relating to Orkney and Shetland. pp. 73. *Kirkwall,* 1894. 8°. 011900. h. 22.

BADDELEY (M. J. B.) Orkney and Shetland. pp. 64. 1890. 8°. Thorough Guide Series.
10347. aaa.

EPHEMERIDES. Manson's Shetland Almanac. *Lerwick,* 1891, *etc.* 8°. P.P. 2511. yb.

GREEN (J.) Aberdeen to the Muckle Flugga. pp. 28. *Sunderland,* 1894. 8°.
10348. c. 25. (10.)

HIBBERT WARE (S.) Description of the Shetland Islands. pp. 294. *Lerwick,* 1891. 4°.
10369. i. 14.

LONDON. *Orkney and Shetland Society.* Social and literary Branch; or, Viking Club. Lawbook. 1892, *etc.* 8°. & 16°. 10348. ccc.

MILL (J.) Diary of J. Mill, Minister in Shetland, 1740–1803. pp. 227. 1889. 8°. Ac. Edinburgh. *Scottish History Society.* Publications. Vol. 5.
Ac. 8256.

PAGET (C.) *Lady.* King Bele of the Sogn District, Norway, and Jarl Angantyr of the Orkney Islands. pp. 24. *Camb.* 1894. 8°.
11840. bb. 41.

PLOYEN (C.) Reminiscences of a voyage to Shetland and Orkney in 1839. pp. 237. *Lerwick,* 1894. 8°. 10369. b. 43.

SAXBY (J. M. E.) Birds of Omen in Shetland. pp. 32. 1893. 8°. 12130. g. 37. (7.)

ORLEANS. Desnoyers ( ) Le préhistorique dans l'Orléanais. pp. 13. *Orléans*, 1892. 8°.
Pam. 3.

Guerrier (L.) Genabum. 1894. 8°. Ac. Orleans. *Société Archéologique*. Mémoires.
Tom. 25.   Ac. 5324/2.

Guillaume, *Bp. of Orleans.* Élection de Guillaume de Bussi, et actes de son épiscopat 1238–58. *Lat.* 1894. 8°. Ac. Orleans. *Société Archéologique.* Mémoires. Tom. 25. Ac. 5324/2.

Villaret (A. de) Campagnes des Anglais dans l'Orléanais, 1421–28. pp. 168.
Orléans, 1893. 8°.   9079. g. 22.

Dubois (F. N. A.) Histoire du siège d'Orléans, 1428–29. pp. 444. *Orléans*, 1894. 8°. 09210. df. 8.

Couret (A.) Les Relations d'Orléans avec l'Espagne au siège d'Orléans, 1428–29. pp. 14. *Orléans*, 1892. 8°.   09210. e. 1. (3.)

Jarry (L.) Le Compte de l'Armée anglaise au siège d'Orléans, 1428–29. pp. 240.
Orléans, 1892. 8°.   9072. f. 9.

Boucher de Molandon ( ) and Beaucorps (A. de) L'Armée anglaise vaincue par Jeanne d'Arc sous les murs d'Orléans. pp. 314.
Orléans, 1892. 8°.   9073. dd. 7.

Domet (P.) Histoire de la Forêt d'Orléans. pp. 432. *Orléans*, 1892. 12°.   10170. ccc. 3.
See also Genabum.

ORNAMENT. *See* Art, *Decorative.*

ORNE. La Sicotière (L. de) Bibliographie des Usages et des Traditions de l'Orne. pp. 35. *Vannes*, 1892. 8°.   11903. aa. 23. (10.)

Letacq (A. L.) Recherches sur la bibliographie scientifique de l'Orne. 1891, *etc.* 8°. Ac. Alençon. *Société historique.* Bulletin. Tom. 10.
              Ac. 6774.

See also Perche.

ORON, Vaud. Pasche (C.) La contrée d'Oron. pp. 630. *Lausanne*, 1895. 8°.
            10196. e. 11.

OROTAVA. *See* Canary Islands.

ORPHANAGES.
See Children, *Protection, etc.*

ORTHOPAEDIC SURGERY.
See Surgery.

ORTHOPTERA. Brunner von Wattenwyl (C.) Révision du système des Orthoptères. 1893. 8°. Ac. Genoa. *Museo di Storia Naturale.* Annali. Ser. 2. Vol. 13.   Ac. 2809.

Pantel (J.) Notes orthoptérologiques. 1890. 8°. Ac. Madrid. *Sociedad de Historia Natural.* Anales. Tom. 19.   Ac. 2826.

Finot (A.) Faune de la France. Orthoptères. pp. 322. *Fontainebleau*, 1890. 8°. 7297. g. 35.

Borde (E.) Les Sauterelles. Invasion de 1891. pp. 117. *Alger*, 1891. 8°.   7297. g. 37.

Cotes (E. C.) Locusts of Bengal, Madras, Assam and Bombay. 1891. 8°. Ac. Calcutta. *Indian Museum.* Notes. Vol. 2. No. 4.   Ac. 3693.

Pictet (A.) Locustides nouveaux. pp. 80. 1888. 8°. Ac. Geneva. *Société de Physique.* Mémoires. Tom. 30.   Ac. 2870.

—— and Saussure (H. F. de) Iconographie de quelques Sauterelles vertes. pp. 26.
Genève, 1892. 4°.   7296. g. 12.

Ac. Calcutta. *Indian Museum.* A Catalogue of the Mantodea. *Calcutta*, 1889, *etc.* 8°. 7297. bb.

Redtenbacher (J.) Monographische Uebersicht der Mecopodiden. pp. 42. 1892. 8°. Pam. 42.

Saussure (H. F. de) and Zehntner (L.) Revision de la tribu des Périsphæriens. pp. 59. 1895. 8°. Ac. Geneva. *Musée d'Histoire Naturelle.* Revue de Zoologie. Tom. 3.   Ac. 2870. b.

ORTHOPTERA—*continued.*
Tepper (J. G. O.) Blattariæ of Australia and Polynesia. pp. 20. *Adelaide*, 1894. 8°. Pam. 42.

—— Descriptions of new species of Blattariæ. pp. 5. *Adelaide*, 1895. 8°.   Pam. 42.

ORTON. Garnett (F. B.) Orton old Hall. pp. 4. *Kendal*, 1891. 8°.   10348. d. 19. (13.)

ORVAL, Abbey. Tandel (E.) Les biens de l'Abbaye d'Orval. 1888. 8°. Ac. Arlon. *Société pour la Conservation des Monuments.* Annales. Tom. 20.   Ac. 5514.

ORVIEDO. *See* Asturias.

ORVIETO. Fumi (L.) Il duomo di Orvieto e i suoi restauri. pp. 528. *Roma*, 1891. 4°.
            7815. df. 16.

OSCAN DIALECT. Bronisch (G.) Die oskischen I- und E-Vocale. pp. 193.
Leipz. 1892. 8°.   12934. g. 28.

Buck (C. D.) Der Vocalismus der oskischen Sprache. pp. 219. *Leipz.* 1892. 8°. 12934. h. 17.

Planta (R. v.) Grammatik der oskisch-umbrischen Dialekte. *Strassb.* 1892. 8°.   12933. i.

OSNABRÜCK. Ac. Osnaburg. *Historischer Verein.* Osnabrücker Geschichtsquellen.
Osnabrück, 1891, *etc.* 8°.   10250. g.

Osnaburg, *Guild of.* Die ältesten osnabrückischen Gildeurkunden bis 1500. pp. 92.
Osnabrück, 1890. 8°.   8248. e. 30.

Philippi (F.) Zur Verfassungsgeschichte der westfälischen Bischofsstädte. pp. 102.
Osnabrück, 1894. 8°.   Pam. 28.

Runge (H.) Geschichte des osnabrücker Buchdrucks. 1892, *etc.* 8°. Ac. Osnaburg. *Historischer Verein.* Mittheilungen. Bd. 17, *etc.*
            Ac. 7145.

OSSETIANS. *See* Caucasus.

OSSETT. Frankland (M.) Ossett past and present. pp. 7. *Ossett*, 1895. 8°.   Pam. 90.

OSTEND. Belleroche (E.) The Siege of Ostend. pp. 117. *Lond.* 1892. 8°.   9414. c. 5.

Henrard (P. J. J.) Histoire du Siège d'Ostende, 1601–04. pp. 148. *Brux.* 1890. 8°. 9414. h. 14.

OSTEOLOGY. *See* Bones.

OSTIA. André (P.) Restauration du théâtre d'Ostie. pp. 16. *Paris*, 1891. 8°.
           7706. f. 20. (7.)

Cumont (F.) Notes sur un Temple Mithriaque d'Ostie. pp. 23. 1891. 8°. Ac. Ghent. *Université.* Recueil de travaux. Fasc. 4.
            Ac. 2647/3.

OSTRICH. Cape of Good Hope. Ostrich farming of Cape Colony. *Lond.* 1893. 8°.
            Pam. 42.

Forest (J.) La question de l'élevage des Autruches d'Algérie. pp. 8. *Paris*, 1889. 8°.
            Pam. 42.

—— L'Autruche ; son utilité ; son élevage. pp. 71. *Paris*, 1894. 8°.   Pam. 42.

—— L'Autruche ; son présent, son avenir dans l'art décoratif. pp. 23. *Paris*, 1894. 8°. Pam. 42.

Martin (A.) Home Life on an Ostrich Farm. pp. 288. *Lond.* 1891. 8°.   010096. e. 40.

Williams (T.) Ostriches in Australia. pp. 19. *Adelaide*, 1887. 8°.   Pam. 42.

OTAGO. Roberts (W. H. S.) The History of North Otago. pp. 483. *Oamaru*, 1890. 8°.
           10491. aaa. 44.

Ross (M.) Guide to the lakes of Central Otago. pp. 67. *Wellington*, 1889. 8°. 10492. bbb. 58.

Ross (C. S.) Story of the Otago Church and Settlement. pp. 449. *Dunedin*, 1887. 8°.
           4745. b. 34.

OXFORD.—Colleges—*continued.*

SMITH (G.) Oxford and her colleges. pp. 99. *Lond.* 1894. 16°.   10351. aa. 62.

DE PARAVACINI (F.) Early History of Balliol College. pp 370. *Lond.* 1891. 8°.   8364. e. 42.

Ac. Oxford. *Historical Society.* BOASE (C.W.) Register of the Rectors, Fellows, and other members of Exeter College. pp. 399. *Oxf.* 1894. 8°.   Ac. 8126/17.

SHADWELL (C. L.) Registrum Orielense, members of Oriel College. *Lond.* 1893, *etc.* 8°.   8367. b. 12.

Ac. Oxford. *Oxford Historical Society.* FOWLER (T.) History of Corpus Christi College. pp. 482. *Oxf.* 1893. 8°.   Ac. 8126/16.

CHANCELLOR (E. B.) Christ Church, Oxford. pp. 21. *Lond.* 1891. 4°.   8365. g. 15.

JACKSON (T. G.) Wadham College, its foundation, architecture and history. pp. 228. *Oxf.* 1893. 4°.   8365. ff. 35.

Oxford. *Mansfield College.* Mansfield College, its origin and opening. pp. 250. *Lond.* 1890. 8°.   8365. f. 26.

—— *Manchester College.* Manchester College. Proceedings on the opening of the College Buildings. pp. 160. *Lond.* 1894. 8°.   8364. h. 13.

OXFORDSHIRE. OXFORD, *County.* Murray's Handbook for Oxfordshire. pp. 14. 242. *Lond.* 1894. 8°.   2364. b. 30.

OXYGEN. DISCOVERY. Discovery of Oxygen and its immediate results. pp. 59. *Lond.* 1895. 8°.   8907. aaa. 36.

MURRAY (K. S.) Handbook on the use of Compressed Oxygen. pp. 82. *Lond.* 1893. 8°.   8908. f. 45.

See also GAS.

OYSTER. STEVENSON (C. H.) Bibliography of publications relating to Oysters. 1894. 8°. UNITED STATES. *Commission of Fisheries.* Report. Pt. 18.   7290. c.

CARAZZI (D.) Ostricultura e mitilicultura. pp. 202. *Milano,* 1893. 8°.   012200. h. 110.

DRAKE (J. C.) Sounds and estuaries of Georgia, with reference to Oyster culture. 1891. 8°. U.S. *Coast Survey.* Bulletin. No. 19.   10497. g. 9.

FOWLER (G. H.) Conditions for successful Oyster culture. pp. 22. *Lond.* 1893. 8°.   Pam. 42.

KENT (W. S.) The great Barrier Reef of Australia. pp. 387. *Lond.* 1893. fol.   K.T.C. 9. b. 3.

LOCARD (A.) Les Huîtres et les mollusques comestibles. pp. 383. *Paris,* 1890. 8°.   7299. e. 4.

PHILPOTS (J. R.) Oysters, and all about them. 2 vol. *Lond.* 1890, 91. 8°.   7290. aa. 24.

STEVENSON (C. H.) Oyster industry of Maryland. 1894. 8°. U.S. *Commission of Fisheries.* Bulletin. Vol. 12.   7290. dd. *See also* MOLLUSCA.

OZONE. ANDRÉOLI (É.) Ozone: commercial production, applications. pp. 89. *Lond.* 1893. 8°.   8908. bb. 46.

—— L'Ozono: produzione, applicazioni. pp. 120. *Firenze,* 1895. 8°.   8908. bb. 37.

PACIFIC OCEAN AND ISLANDS, POLYNESIA. ALEXANDER (J. M.) The Islands of the Pacific. pp. 503. *N.Y.* 1895. 8°.   4766. dd. 16.

PACIFIC OCEAN—*continued.*

BAESSLER (A.) Südsee-Bilder. pp. 371. *Berl.* 1895. 8°.   10192. f. 35.

CLAVERIE (T.) Pages détachées. pp. 278. *Paris,* 1894. 12°.   10026. cc. 10.

CODRINGTON (R. H.) The Melanesians: studies in anthropology and folk-lore. pp. 419. *Oxf.* 1891. 8°.   10492. ee. 19.

DANA (J. D.) Corals and Coral Islands. pp. 440. *N.Y.* 1890. 8°.   7297. c. 15.

EARL AND DOCTOR. South Sea Bubbles. pp. 324. *Lond.* 1895. 8°.   10491. de. 4.

EDGE-PARTINGTON (J.) Album of weapons, tools, ornaments, *etc.* of the natives of the Pacific Islands. ff. 391. *Lond.* 1890. *obl.* 4°. 1787. aa. 6.

GUILLEMARD (F. H. H.) Stanford's Compend. of Geography. Australasia. Vol. 2. *Lond.* 1894. 8°.   2060. a.

HAURIGOT (G.) Les Établissements français en Océanie. pp. 237. *Paris,* 1891. 8°.   010057. ee. 30.

MELVILLE (H.) Omoo. pp. 365. *Lond.* 1892. 8°.   012706. h. 29.

—— Typee. pp. 389. *Lond.* 1892. 8°.   012706. h. 30.

NEW SOUTH WALES. *Commissioners for the Columbian Exposition.* South Pacific past and present. pp. 38. *Sydney,* 1892. 8°. 7958. g. 37.

POWELL (B. F. S. B.) In Savage Isles and settled lands, *etc.* pp. 438. *Lond.* 1892. 8°.   10026. g. 4.

ROMILLY (H. H.) Letters from the Western Pacific. pp. 384. *Lond.* 1893. 8°. 10028. e 29.

WAWN (W. T.) South Sea Islanders and Queensland labour trade. pp. 440. *Lond.* 1893. 8°.   10491. ff. 15.

FINDLAY (A. G.) Directory for the navigation of the South Pacific Ocean. pp. 1252. *Lond.* 1884. 8°.   10496. d. 14.

FRANCE. *M. de la Marine.* Instructions nautiques sur les îles de l'Océan Pacifique Nord. pp. 175. *Paris,* 1891. 8°.   10497. f. 20.

—— Instructions nautiques sur les îles de l'Océan Pacifique Sud. pp. 324. *Paris,* 1894. 8°.   10497. bb. 37.

G. B. & I. *Hydrographic Office.* South America Pilot. *Lond.* 1893, *etc.* 8°.   10496. h. 25.

—— Pacific Islands Pilot. *Lond.* 1893, *etc.* 8°.   10496. gg. 26.

U.S. *Coast Survey.* Pacific Coast Pilot. pp. 721. *Wash.* 1889. 4°.   10497. ff. 14. *See also* ADMIRALTY ISLAND : CAROLINE ISLANDS : EASTER ISLAND : FIJI : GILBERT ISLANDS : HAWAIIAN ISLANDS : LIFU : MARQUESAS ISLANDS : NEW CALEDONIA : NEW HEBRIDES : SAMOA : TAHITI : TONGA.

Missions. *See* MISSIONS.

Polynesian Languages.

COWAN (F.) English Words in South Sea languages. pp. 12. *Greenesburgh, Pa.,* 1894. 8°.   12903. dd. 37. (15.)

MAC DONALD (D.) South Sea languages. Series of studies. *Melbourne,* 1889, *etc.* 8°. 12910. ccc.

P.P. *Berlin.* Zeitschrift für oceanische Sprachen. *Berl.* 1895, *etc.* 8°.   P.P. 4991. ha.

RAY (S. H.) Importance and nature of the Oceanic languages. 1892. 8°.   12910. bb. 47. (7.)

TREGEAR (E.) Maori-Polynesian comparative Dictionary. pp. 675. *Wellington, N.Z.,* 1891. 8°.   12910. f. 36.

ATKINSON (A. S.) Notes on the Maori-Polynesian Dictionary of E. Tregear. pp. 69. 6. *Nelson,* 1893. 8°.   12910. b. 45.

PACY-SUR-EURE. ISAMBARD (É.) La communauté des Chirurgiens de Pacy-sur-Eure aux XVIIᵉ et XVIIIᵉ siècles. pp. 119.
Pacy, 1894. 8°.   7680. aa. 28.

PADERBORN. RICHTER (W.) Studien und Quellen zur paderborner Geschichte.
Paderborn, 1893, *etc.* 8°.   10256. f.

PHILIPPI (F.) Zur Verfassungsgeschichte der westfälischen Bischofsstädte. pp. 102.
Osnabrück, 1894. 8°.   Pam. 28.

SCHRADER (F. X.) Leben und Wirken Meinwerk's Bischofs von Paderborn, 1009–36. pp. 104. *Paderborn*, 1895. 8°.   4888. bb. 41.

ENGELSHEYM (D. v.) Liber dissencionum archiepiscopi Coloniensis et capituli Paderbornensis. 1893, *etc.* 8°. Ac. Munster. *Verein für Geschichte Westfalens.* Zeitschrift. Ergänzungshefte.   Ac. 7355.

GORGES (M.) Beiträge zur Geschichte des Hochstiftes Paderborn im 17. Jahrhundert. pp. 114. 1892. 8°. Ac. Munster. *Verein für Geschichte Westfalens.* Zeitschrift. Bd 50.   Ac. 7355.

RICHTER (W.) Geschichte der paderborner Jesuiten. *Paderborn*, 1892, *etc.* 8°.   4662. d.

PADUA. PADUA. Padova città romana. pp. 91. 1887. 4°. Ac. Venice. *Deputazione Veneta.* Monumenti. Ser. 4. Miscellanea. Vol. 10.   Ac. 6580/2.

LENEL (W.) Studien zur Geschichte Paduas im 13ᵗᵉⁿ Jahrhundert. pp. 86. *Strassb.* 1893. 8°.   9167. e. 3.

PADUA. La Obsidione di Padua del MDIX. pp. 385. *Bologna*, 1892. 8°.   12226. cc.

ZANETTI (P.) L'Assedio di Padova del 1509. 1891. 8°. P.P. *Venice.* Archivio Veneto. N.S. Anno 1. No. 3.   P.P. 3556. v.

GLORIA (A.) L'Osservatorio di Galileo Galilei in Padova. pp. 28. *Padova*, 1892. fol.   8560. i. 20.

GIOMO (G.) L'Archivio antico della Università di Padova. pp. 88. *Venezia*, 1893. 8°.   8355. e. 33.

Ac. Padua. *Università.* L'Anno accademico 1891-92. pp. 11. *Padova*, 1892. 8°.   8356. dd. 9.

—— Annuario della R. Università 1891 95, *etc.* *Padova*, 1895. *etc.* 8°.   Ac. 100. b.

PAIGNTON. PAIGNTON. Paignton illustrated. pp. 32. *Torquay*, 1891. 4°. Pam. 90.

—— Where to buy at Paignton. pp. 27. *Brighton*, 1891. 4°.   10368. k. 33.

THOMAS (W. E.) Guide to Paignton. pp. 64. *Paignton*, 1895. 8°.   Pam. 90.

PAIN. FOSTER (J. E.) Pain: its mystery and meaning. pp. 228. *Lond.* 1891. 8°. 4479. aa. 51.

MANTEGAZZA (P.) Physiologie de la Douleur. pp. 353. *Paris*, 1888. 8°.   7405. a. 3.

MARSHALL (H. R.) Pain, Pleasure and Æsthetics. pp. 364. *Lond.* 1894. 8°.   8462. e. 27.

PAINSWICK. HYETT (F. A.) Painswick during the Civil War 1642-6. pp. 8. *Gloucester*, 1894. 8°.   10348. e. 15. (10.)

PAINTING.

Pt. I. General.

ARRÉAT (L.) Psychologie du Peintre. pp. 267. *Paris*, 1892. 8°.   8462. e. 15.

BLOCKA (J.) A compendium of Painting. pp. 125. *Lond.* 1894. 8°.   7858. aa. 30.

BOUFFIER (H.) Schule der Oel-Malerei. pp. 121. 1891. 8°. Bossong's kunsttechnische Bibliothek. Bd. 4.   7858. f.

BOUVIER (J.) Handbook for Oil-Painting. pp. 72. *Lond.* 1885. 8°.   7854. ccc. 46.

PAINTING.—General—*continued.*

CUYER (É.) Le Dessein et la Peinture. pp. 304. *Paris*, 1893. 12°.   7858. a. 41.

GUAITA (L.) La Scienza dei Colori e la Pittura. pp. 248. *Milano*, 1893. 8°.   012200. h. 105.

HAREUX (E.) Manual of Painting in oil colours. 3 pt. *Lond.* 1891. 8°.   7854. bbb. 60.

JEEVES (G. C.) Guide and advice to young Painters. pp. 81. *Lond.* 1893. 8°. 7855. aa. 45.

LA FARGE (J.) Considerations on Painting. pp. 270. *N.Y.* 1895. 8°.   7858. aa. 39.

LAMPE (L.) Signatures et monogrammes des Peintres de toutes les écoles. *Brux.* 1895, *etc.* 8°.   7856. d.

MUCKLEY (W. J.) Handbook for Painters. pp. 146. *Lond.* 1893. 8°.   7858. f. 17.

NISBET (H.) Lessons in Art. pp. 119. *Lond.* 1891. 8°.   7857. aa. 58.

OUGHTON (F.) Note book on oil colour technique. pp. 46. *Lond.* 1892. 8°.   7855. b. 55.

RECOUVREUR (A.) Grammaire du Peintre. pp. 116. *Paris*, 1894. 8°.   7854. c. 56.

RAUPP (K.) Katechismus der Malerei. pp. 146. *Leipz.* 1891. 8°.   7854. b. 21.

REYNOLDS (*Sir* J.) Sir J. Reynolds's Discourses. Edited by E. G. Johnson. pp. 373. *Chicago*, 1891. 8°.   7855. c. 51.

RIS-PAQUOT (O. E.) Dictionnaire des Marques et monogrammes. 2 tom. *Paris*, 1893. 4°.   2031. f.

STEPS. My first steps in Painting. 6 pt. *Lond.* 1894. *obl.* 8°.   7858. c. 22.

TERRY (G.) Pigments, paint and painting. pp. 392. *Lond.* 1893. 8°.   7875. aa. 52.

VIBERT (J. G.) La science de la Peinture. pp. 332. *Paris*, 1891. 18°.   7855. aa. 42.

—— The Science of Painting. pp. 196. *Lond.* 1892. 8°.   7858. aa. 28.

WATTS (G. F.) What should a Picture say. pp. 4. *Lond.* 1894. 8°.   7808. bbb. 27. (8.)
See also AESTHETICS: ART: DRAWING.

Animal Painting.

LOFTIE (W. J.) Landseer and animal painting. pp. 82. 1891. 4°. V. Foster's Drawing Books.   7857. f. 22.

Biographies of Painters. *See infra:* National Schools: BIOGRAPHY.

China Painting. *See* CERAMICS.

Collections of Pictures, *Private Galleries.* *See* COLLECTIONS *and* COLLECTORS.

Collections of Pictures, *Public Galleries.* *See* EXHIBITIONS.

Decorative Painting. *See* ART, *Decorative.*

Flower Painting.

FLOWER STUDIES. Flower Studies. Facsimile reproductions.[*Lond.* 1894, *etc.* fol. K.T.C. 13. a.

HULME (F. E.) Wild Flowers drawing and painting book. 6 pt. *Lond.* 1895. 4°. 7858. f. 32.

Galleries of Pictures. *See* EXHIBITIONS.

Glass Painting. *See* GLASS.

History and Criticism, *General.*

BEAULIEU (C. de) Peintres célèbres du XIXᵉ siècle. 2 tom. *Paris*, 1894. 8°. 7858. e. 8.

BOLE (F.) Sieben Meisterwerke der Malerei. pp. 127. *Brixen*, 1893. 4°.   7858. cc. 2.

CHILD (T.) Art and criticism. pp. 313. *Lond.* 1892. 8°.   7806. dd. 8.

CHEFS-D'ŒUVRE. Les Chefs-d'Œuvre de l'art au XIXᵉ siècle. 5 tom. *Paris*, 1892. 4°.   K.T.C. 9. b. 2.

PAINTING.—National Schools—*cont.*

SCHEIBLER (L.) and ALDENHOVEN (C.) Geschichte der kölner Malerschule. 1894, *etc.* fol.
Ac. Cologne. *Gesellschaft für Rhenische Geschichtskunde.* Publicationen. No. 13. Ac. 7028.

WYZEWA (T. de) Les grands peintres contemporains de l'Allemagne, *etc.* pp. 192.
Paris, 1891. 8°.   7857. h. 49.

MURAU (C.) Wiener Malerinnen. pp. 127.
Dresd. 1895. 8°.   10707. bbb. 50.

Great Britain and Ireland.

SHEPHERD (G. H.) Short history of the British School of Painting. pp. 160. *Lond.* 1891. 8°.
         7854. e. 38.

WALPOLE (H.) *Earl of Orford.* Anecdotes of Painting in England. Revised by R. N. Wornum. 3 vol. *Lond.* 1888. 8°.   2032. c.

GRAVES (A.) Dictionary of Artists who have exhibited works in the London Exhibitions from 1760 to 1893. pp. 314. *Lond.* 1895. 4°.
         7808. g. 21.

LOFTIE (W. J.) Reynolds and Children's Portraiture in England. pp. 84. 1891. 4°. Vere Foster's Drawing Books.   7857. f. 22.

PHILLIPS (C.) Sir J. Reynolds. pp. 415.
Lond. 1894. 8°.   10825. f. 37.

GAMLIN (H.) G. Romney and his art. pp. 332.
Lond. 1894. 8°.   10825. eee. 13.

REDGRAVE (R.) and (S.) A century of Painters of the English School. pp. 479.
Lond. 1893. 8°.   7856. df. 40.

HAMERTON (P. G.) Life of J. M. W. Turner. pp. 398. *Lond.* 1895. 8°.   10825. cc. 30.

RUSKIN (J.) Lectures on Architecture and Painting. pp. 256. *Orpington*, 1891. 8°.
         7808. bbb. 20.

LOFTIE (W. J.) Landseer and Animal Painting in England. pp. 82. 1891. 4°. V. Foster's Drawing Books.   7857. f. 22.

DESTRÉE (O. G.) Les Préraphaélites. pp. 111.
Brux. 1895. 8°.   7858. f. 28.

MORRIS (W.) Address on the Paintings of the English Pre-Raphaelite School in the Birmingham Museum. pp. 16. *Birmingh.* 1891. 8°.
         7807. i. 4. (12.)

WOOD (E.) D. Rossetti and the Pre-Raphaelite movement. pp. 323. *Lond.* 1894. 8°.
         K.T.C. 26. a. 3.

RHYS (E.) Sir F. Leighton. pp. 74.
Lond. 1895. fol.   K.T.C. 9. b. 14.

BELL (M.) E. Burne-Jones. pp. 130.
Lond. 1892. 4°.   K.T.C. 1. b. 7.

CARTWRIGHT, afterwards ADY (J.) Sir E. Burne-Jones. pp. 32. 1894. 4°. P.P. *London.* Art-Union Monthly Journal.   P.P. 1931. pc.

EDINBURGH. *Scottish Artists' Club.* Album of the Club. *Edinb.* 1892. fol. K.T.C. 3. b. 16.

LETTERS. Letters to living Artists. pp. 168.
Lond. 1891. 8°.   7857. d. 7.

LITTLE (J. S.) The Wealden Painters at the summer exhibitions, 1892. pp. 20.
Arundel, 1892. 12°.   Pam. 24.

LA SIZERANNE (R. de) La Peinture anglaise contemporaine. pp. 340. *Paris*, 1895. 8°.
         7858. aa. 38.

MOORE (G.) Modern Painting. pp. 248.
Lond. 1893 8°.   7857. e. 27.

QUILTER (H.) Preferences in Art and Literature. pp. 404. *Lond.* 1892. 4°.   K.T.C. 6. b. 7.

VERDAVAINNE (G.) La Peinture anglaise. Exposition de Paris, 1889. pp. 46.
Brux. 1889. 8°.   7806. de. 22. (5.)

WYZEWA (T. de) Les grands Peintres contemporains de l'Angleterre. pp. 192.
Paris, 1891. 8°.   7857. h. 49.

PAINTING.—National Schools—*cont.*

Italy.

COLE (T.) Old Italian Masters. pp. 282.
N.Y. 1892. 8°.   K.T.C. 11. b. 7.

KÁROLY (K.) Guide to the Paintings of Florence. pp. 344. *Lond.* 1893. 8°.   7857. a. 41.

LERMOLIEFF (I.) Kunstkritische Studien über italienische Malerei. 3 Bde.
Leipz. 1890–93. 8°.   7858. e. 1.

LOGAN (M.) Guide to the Italian Pictures at Hampton Court. pp. 48. 1894. 8°. LONDON.
Kyrle Society. Kyrle Pamphlets.   7808. c.

MORELLI (G.) Italian Painters: critical studies. pp. 358. *Lond.* 1892. 8°.   7858. f. 6.

VASARI (G.) Lives of Italian Painters. Selected by H. Ellis. pp. 291. 1895. 8°. The Scott Library.   012208. ee.

BERENSON (B.) The Venetian Painters of the renaissance. pp. 141. *N.Y.* 1895. 8°.
         7858. aa. 43.

SÉAILLES (G.) Léonard de Vinci, l'artiste et le savant. pp. 547. *Paris*, 1892. 8°. 10629. dd. 22.

BUTTON (B.) Raphael and his works. pp. 24.
1890. 4°.   7808. bbb. 31. (1.)

KÁROLY (K.) Raphael's Madonnas and other great pictures. pp. 139. *Lond.* 1894. 4°.
         K.T.C. 26. b. 11.

SANZIO (R.) The Hours of Raphael in outline. pp. 19. *Lond.* 1892. fol.   1755. b. 12.

—— Lithographic reproductions of the Drawings by Raffaelle in the University Galleries, Oxford. pp. 180. *Oxf.* 1894. 8°.   K.T.C. 36. a. 1.

STEINCHEN (F.) La Madone de Sienne peinte par Raphaël. pp. 20. *Paris*, 1891. 4°.
         7808. f. 21. (5.)

—— Raphaels in St. Petersburg aufgefundene Madonna di Sienna. pp. 58.
St. Petersburg, 1894. 4°.   7857. k. 36.

BERENSON (B.) Lorenzo Lotto. pp. 362.
N.Y. 1895. 8°.   7858. gg. 28.

SYMONDS (J. A.) Life of Michelangelo Buonarroti. 2 vol. *Lond.* 1893. 8°. K.T.C. 11. a. 1.

MOLMENTI (P. G.) Carpaccio. pp. 123.
Venise, 1893. 8°.   7858. l. 18.

MOUREAU (A.) Antonio Canal, dit Le Canaletto. pp. 108. 1894. 8°. MÜNTZ (E.) Les Artistes Célèbres.   7858. i.

Japan. See ART.

Mexico.

LAMBORN (R. H.) Mexican Painting and painters. pp. 76. *Phila.* 1891. 4°.   7858. h. 27.

Netherlands and Belgium.

COLE (T.) Old Dutch and Flemish Masters. pp. 192. *N.Y.* 1895. 8°.   7851. d. 5.

MADSEN (C.) Hollandsk Malerkunst.
Kjøbenh. 1891, *etc.* 8°.   7857. d.

PIT (A.) Les origines de l'Art hollandais. pp. 112. *Paris*, 1894. 8°.   7808. aaa. 8.

DEHAISNES (C.) Les Œuvres des Maîtres de l'école flamande primitive conservée en Italie et en France. pp. 48. *Paris*, 1891. 8°. Pam. 24.

Ac. London. *Burlington Fine Arts Club.* Exhibition of Pictures by the Netherlandish schools of XV. and XVI. centuries. *Lond.* 1892. 8°.
         Ac. 4644/33.

WEALE (W. H. J.) G. David. pp. 72. 1895. fol.
P.P. *London.* Portfolio Monographs. No. 24.
         P.P. 1931. pcd.

LEQUIME (L.) Les secrets de Rubens. pp. 43.
Brux. 1892. 8°.   Pam. 24.

HYMANS (H.) L. Vorsterman. pp. 270.
Brux. 1893. 4°.   7857. h. 52.

PAINTING.—National Schools—_cont._

Ac. Saint Petersburg. _Academia Scientiarum._
ROVINSKY (D. A.) L'Œuvre gravé de Rembrandt. Coll.. 188. _St. Pétersbourg,_ 1890. 8°.
—— Atlas. 3 vol. fol. K.T.C. 16. b. 1.
LAUTNER (M.) Wer ist Rembrandt ? pp, 470.
Breslau, 1891. 8°. 7858. g. 34.
MICHEL (É.) Rembrandt, sa vie, son œuvre et son temps. pp. 630. _Paris._ 1893. 8°.
K.T.C. 11. b. 13.
WEDMORE (F.) Rembrandt. Seventeen of his masterpieces. pp. 8. _Lond._ 1894. fol.
K.T.C. 16. a. 1.
ESTAUNIÉ (É.) Impressions de Hollande. Petits maîtres. pp. 270. _Paris,_ 1893. 8°. 7857. d. 10.
ZILCKEN (P.) Peintres hollandais modernes.
Amsterdam, 1891, _etc._ 8°. 7856. g. 14.
TAEYE (E. L. de) Les Artistes Belges contemporains. _Brux._ 1894, _etc._ 4°. 7858. d.

Spain.

LEFORT (P.) La Peinture espagnole. pp. 304.
Paris, 1893. 8°. 2261. cc. 2.
WYZEWA (T. de) Les grands peintres contemporains de l'Espagne, _etc._ pp. 192.
Paris, 1891. 8°. 7857. h. 49.
STEVENSON (R. A. M.) The Art of Velasquez. pp. 124. _Lond._ 1895. 4°. K.T.C. 26. b. 17.
LEFORT (P.) Murillo et ses élèves. pp. 99.
Paris, 1892. 8°. 7858. l. 6.

Switzerland.

HAENDCKE (B.) Die schweizerische Malerei im xvi. Jahrhundert. pp. 416. _Aarau,_ 1893. 8°.
7858. e. 6.

United States of America.

SOISSONS (S. C. de) Boston Artists. Parisian Critic's notes. pp. 96. _Bost._ 1894. 8°.
7854. c. 35.

PALAEOGRAPHY. ARNDT (W.) La Paléographie latine. pp. 26. _Liège,_ 1891. 8°.
07703. g. 1. (7.)
BERGER (P.) Histoire de l'écriture dans l'antiquité. pp. 389. _Paris,_ 1891. 8°. 2268. f. 21.
BERGER (S.) and DURRIEU (P.) Les notes pour l'Enlumineur dans les manuscrits du moyen âge. pp. 30. _Paris,_ 1893. 8°. Pam. 24.
GARDTHAUSEN (V.) Éléments de Paléographie grecque. pp. 223. _Paris,_ 1891. 12°.
7706. a. 37.
GIRY (A.) Manuel de Diplomatique. pp. 944.
Paris, 1894. 8°. 2050. c.
LABITTE (A.) Les Manuscrits, et l'art de les orner. pp. 398. _Paris,_ 1893. 8°. 7709. h. 32.
MADAN (F.) Books in Manuscript. pp. 188.
1893. 8°. POLLARD (A. W.) Books about Books.
2312. d.
MAURY (A.) La Invencion de la Escritura.
pp. 146. _Madrid,_ 1891. 8°. 7706. a. 44.
MOLINIER (A.) Les Manuscrits et les Miniatures.
pp. 333. _Paris,_ 1892. 8°. 7807. e. 27.
MUÑOZ Y RIVERO (J.) Idioma y escritura de España. pp. 149. _Madrid,_ 1888. 8°. 7709. a. 12.
P.P. _Paris._ Le Manuscrit. Revue spéciale.
Paris, 1894, _etc._ 4°. 47.
PROU (M.) Recueil de fac-similés d'écritures du xii° au xvii° siècle. _Paris,_ 1892. 4°. 7709. l. 16.
QUARITCH (B.) Palæography. pp. 96.
Lond. 1894. 8°. 7709. h. 37.
REUSENS (E. H. J.) Éléments de paléographie du moyen âge. pp. 118. _Louvain,_ 1891. fol.
7708. eee. 15.
THOMPSON (Sir E. M.) Handbook of Greek and Latin Palæography. pp. 343. 1893. 8°. International Scientific Series. Vol. 73.
2324. bb. 10.

PALAEOGRAPHY—_continued._
WATTENBACH (W.) Paläographie 1895. 8°.
Pam. 6.
See also ABBREVIATIONS: ALPHABETS: ÉCOLE DES CHARTES.

Catalogues of Collections of MSS.
See MANUSCRIPTS.

Charters. _See_ CHARTERS AND DEEDS.

Facsimiles and Notes on Manuscripts.
For reproductions and descriptions of Miniatures, borders, _etc._, of illuminated MSS., _see_ ILLUMINATIONS.

Ac. London. _British Museum._ Greek Papyri in the Museum. Edited by F. G. Kenyon.
pp 296. _Lond._ 1893. 4°. 1705. a. 16.
—— Facsimiles. fol. 1705. d. 6.
—— Guide to the Manuscripts, _etc._, exhibited.
pp. 140. _Lond._ 1895. 8°. 11903. b. 42.
—— _Henry Bradshaw Society._ Vol. IV. Antiphonary of Bangor : an Irish manuscrit in the Ambrosian library at Milan. _Lond._ 1893, _etc._ 4°.
Ac. 9929/4.
—— Oxford. _Bodleian Library._ Conspectus of the cases in the Bodleian arranged to illustrate the history of Latin and West European bookhands _Oxf._ 1890. _obl._ fol. 1865. c. 1. (2.)
—— _Oxford Philological Society._ Herculanean Papyri. 7 vol. _Oxf._ 1889. 4°. Tab. 710. b.
HERCULANEAN FRAGMENTS. Engravings of texts and alphabets from the Herculanean Fragments.
Oxf. 1891. fol. 1705. c. 10.
ANZIANI (N.) Cenno storico intorno ai Codici Ashburnham. pp. 24. _Firenze,_ 1894. 8°, Pam. 6.
CERIANI (A. M.) De Codice Marchaliano.
pp. 111. _Romae,_ 1890. fol. 1705. a. 13.
CLÉDAT (L.) Collection de reproductions de Manuscrits. _Paris,_ 1890, _etc._ 8°. 12205. k.
DELISLE (L. V.) Notice sur un Psautier latin-français du xii° siècle. pp. 18. _Paris,_ 1891. 4°.
Pam. 6.
—— Un feuillet des Heures de Charles frère de Louis XI. pp. 6. _Nogent-le-Rotrou,_ 1894. 8°.
11903. aa. 24.
—— Les Heures bretonnes du xvi° siècle.
pp. 39. _Paris,_ 1895. 8°. 11904. l. 15. (10.)
DUPONT (A.) Le Propre de Saint Séverin de Château-Landon. Description d'un manuscrit.
pp. 43. _Fontainebleau,_ 1890. 8°. 4829. e. 32.
DURRIEU (P.) L'origine du manuscrit dit le Psautier d'Utrecht. pp. 21. _Paris,_ 1895. 8°.
11904. l. 17. (9.)
ELLIS (R.) Facsimiles from Latin MSS. in the Bodleian Library. _Oxf._ 1891. 4°. K.T.C. 18. b. 4.
FAVALORO (M.) Spicilegio storico paleografico di alfabeti e fac-simili. Tav. 77.
Palermo, 1893. 4°. K.T.C. 19. a. 8.
GRAUX (C.) Notices des Manuscrits grecs d'Espagne et de Portugal. pp. 321. _Paris,_ 1892. 8°.
011901. g. 13.
GUERLIN (R.) Deux Bréviares manuscrits.
pp. 59. _Paris,_ 1894. 8°. 07708. k. 3.
HAURÉAU (J. B.) Notices et extraits de quelques manuscrits latins de la Bibliothèque Nationale.
Paris, 1890, _etc._ 8°. 011899. i.
HOOLE (C. H.) Account of some Manuscripts of the New Testament contained in the library of Christ Church, Oxford. pp. 26.
Oxf. 1892. 8°. Pam. 5.
JACOB (A.) Notes sur les Manuscrits grecs palimpsestes de la Bibliothèque Nationale. pp. 14.
Paris, 1895. 8°. 11904. l. 17. (11.)
KAULEK (J.) and PLANTET (E.) Recueil de fac-simile pour servir à l'étude de la Paléographie moderne, xvii° et xviii° siècles.
Paris, 1889, _etc._ 4°. 7705. f.

PALAEOGRAPHY. — Facsimiles, etc.
—continued.

MARCEL (L.) La Calligraphie et la miniature à Langres à la fin du quinzième siècle. pp. 44. *Paris*, 1892. 4°. 　　　　　　7709. l. 17.

MARTIN (A.) Facsimilés de Manuscrits grecs d'Espagne. pp. 127. *Paris*, 1891. 8°.
—— Planches. fol. 　　　　　Tab. 1282. a.

MEYER (P.) Notices sur quelques Manuscrits français de la bibliothèque Phillips. 1891. 4°. Ac. Paris. *Académie des Inscriptions.* Notices et extraits des manuscrits. Tom. 34. 　818. l.

MONTE CASSINO. La Paleografia artistica nei Codici Cassinesi. *Montecassino*, 1888. 4°.
　　　　　　　　　　　　7743. i. 4.

MUÑOZ Y RIVERO (J.) Scripturae Hispanae veteris specimina. *Matriti*, 1891, *etc.* 8°. 7709. aa. 28.

OMONT (H.) Les Manuscrits grecs datés des xv° et xvi° siècles dans la Bibliothèque Nationale. pp. 87. *Paris*, 1892. 8°. 　　11903. aa. 23. (9.)
—— Notice sur un très ancien Manuscrit grec en onciales des Épîtres de Saint Paul. pp. 56. *Paris*, 1889. 4°. 　　　　　4999. g. 11.
—— Lettre grecque sur papyrus, émanée de la Chancellerie impériale de Constantinople. pp. 14. *Paris*, 1892. 8°. 　　　　Pam. 3.

RAINERUS, *Archduke of Austria.* Papyrus Erzherzog Rainer. Führer durch die Ausstellung. *Wien*, 1892, *etc.* 8°. 　　　　754. c. 8.

SKEAT (W. W.) Twelve facsimiles of old English Manuscripts. pp. 36. *Oxf.* 1892. 8°.
　　　　　　　　　　　　12982. f. 13.

WATTENBACH (W.) Scripturae Graecae specimina. pp. 17. *Berolini*, 1883. fol. 1704. a. 10.

WEIBULL (M. J. J.) Handskrift-prof 1500–1800. pp. 26. *Stockholm*, 1891. fol. 　1704. a. 6.

WILCKEN (U.) Tafeln zur aelteren griechischen Palæographie. *Leipz.* 1891. fol. 1704. b. 25.

AUFRECHT (S. T.) Florentine Sanskrit manuscripts. *Leipz.* 1892. 8°. 　　14096. cc. 9.

MERX (E. O. A.) Documents de Paléographie hébraïque et arabe. pp. 59. *Leyde*, 1894. fol.
　　　　　　　　　　1984. ff. 1.

NEUBAUER (A.) Introduction of the square characters in Biblical MSS. pp. 36. 1891. 8°. DRIVER (S. R.) Studia Biblica. Vol. 3. 3127. l.

Illuminated MSS. *See* ILLUMINATION.

Paper: Water-Marks, etc. *See* PAPER.

PALAEONTOLOGY.

General.

BERNARD (F.) Éléments de Paléontologie *Paris*, 1893, *etc.* 8°. 　　　7203. bb. 15.

P.P. *Bologna.* Rivista italiana di Paleontologia. *Bologna*, 1895, *etc.* 8°. 　　P.P. 2083. b.

WOODS (H.) Catalogue of the type Fossils in the Woodwardian Museum. pp. 180. *Camb.* 1891. 8°. 　　　7202. aaa. 32.

THOMAS (P.) Description de quelques Fossiles nouveaux. pp. 46. 1893. 4°. FRANCE. *Ministère de l'Instruction.* Exploration scientifique de la Tunisie, *etc.* 　　　　10105. ff.

SHALER (N. S.) On the occurrence of Fossils on the Island of Martha's Vineyard, Mass. 1889. 8°. Ac. Cambridge. *Harvard University.* Bulletin. Vol. 16. 　　　　Ac. 1736/2.

KEYES (C. R.) Paleontology of Missouri. 2 vol. 1894. 8°. MISSOURI. *Geological Survey.* Reports. Vol. iv., v. 　　　　07109. h.

MERCERAT (A.) Notas sobre la Paleontologia de la República Argentina. 1890. 8°. Ac. La Plata. *Museo.* Revista. Tom. 1. 　Ac. 3091.

PALAEONTOLOGY.—General—*cont.*

PHILIPPI (R. A.) Los Fósiles de Chile. pp. 256. *Santiago*, 1887. 4°. 　　　7202. f. 4.

ETHERIDGE (R.) Silurian and mesozoic Fossils from Central Australia. *Adelaide*, 1893. fol.
　　　　　　　　　　7105. g. 13. (5.)

QUEENSLAND. Geology and Palæontology of Queensland and New Guinea. 3 pts. *Brisbane*, 1892. 8°. 　　　7109. g. 33.

BRUNSWICK. *Cammer-Direction der Bergwerke.* Beiträge zur Geologie und Paläontologie Braunschweigs. *Braunschweig*, 1894, *etc.* 8°. 07108. g.

KISSLING (E.) Die versteinerten Thier- und Pflanzenreste der Umgebung von Bern. pp. 70. *Bern*, 1890. 8°. 　　7202. aa. 11.

WESTLAKE (E.) Tabular index to the upper cretaceous Fossils of England and Ireland. pp. 24. *Fordingbridge*, 1888. 4°. 　Pam. 42.

NAUMANN (E.) and NEUMAYR (M.) Zur Geologie und Paläontologie von Japan. pp. 42. 1890. fol. Ac. Vienna. *K. Akademie.* Denkschriften. Math.-naturwissenschaftl. Classe. Bd. 57.
　　　　　　　　　　Ac. 810/13.

See also GEOLOGY.

Botany.

Ac. London. *British Museum.* Catalogue of mesozoic Plants. *Lond.* 1894, *etc.* 8°. 7207. gg.

ETTINGSHAUSEN (C. v.) *Baron*, and KRASAN (F.) Untersuchungen über Ontogenie der Pflanzen auf paläontologischer Grundlage. 1890. fol. Ac. Vienna. *K. Akademie.* Denkschriften. Math.-naturwissenschaftl. Classe. Bd. 57.
　　　　　　　　　　Ac. 810/13.

FROMENT (A.) Les Merveilles de la flore primitive. pp. 145. *Genève*, 1895. 8°. 07028. f. 61.

SCHUMANN (C.) Lehrbuch der systematischen Botanik und Phytopaläontologie. pp. 705. *Stuttg.* 1894. 8°. 　　　7029. d. 11.

SEWARD (A. C.) Fossil Plants as tests of climate. pp. 151. *Lond.* 1892. 8°. 　07109. g. 33.

SOLMS-LAUBACH (H. zu) *Count.* Fossil Botany. pp. 401. *Oxf.* 1891. 8°. 　7202. bb. 26.

ENGELHARDT (H.) Über Tertiärpflanzen von Chile. 1891. 4°. Ac. Frankfort. *Senckenbergische Naturforschende Gesellschaft.* Abhandlungen. Bd. 16. Hft. 4. 　　Ac. 2878/2.

FEISTMANTEL (O.) Palæontological relations of the Coal and Plant-bearing Beds of palæozoic and mesozoic age in Australia. pp. 183. 1890. 8°. NEW SOUTH WALES. *Geological Survey.* Memoirs. 　　　　　　7203. h.

HEER (O.) Oversigt over Grønlands fossile Flora. 1883. 8°. DENMARK. *Commission for Ledelsen af de geologiske Undersøgelser om Grønland.* Meddelelser. Hft. 5. 　　10460. dd.

BOULAY (N.) Flore pliocène du Mont-Dore, Puy-de-Dôme. pp. 115. *Paris*, 1892. 4°.
　　　　　　　　　　　7202. g. 8.

LIGNIER (O.) Végétaux fossiles de Normandie. pp. 78. 1894. 8°. Ac. Caen. *Société Linnéenne.* Mémoires. Vol. 18. 　Ac. 2842/3.

SQUINABOL (S.) Contribuzioni alla Flora fossile dei terreni terziarii della Liguria. *Genova*, 1891, *etc.* fol. 　　　　7202. g.

KIDSTON (R.) On Fossil Plants of the coal fields, Ayrshire. 1893. 4°. Ac. Edinburgh. *Royal Society.* Transactions. Vol. 37. Pt. 2.
　　　　　　　　　　　2099. g.

ETTINGSHAUSEN (C. v.) *Baron.* Die fossile Flora von Schoenegg bei Wies. *Wien*, 1890, *etc.* 8°.
　　　　　　　　　　　7203. ee.

FRUEH (J. J.) Zur Kenntniss der Gesteinbildenden Algen der Schweizer-Alpen. pp. 102. 1890. 4°. Ac. Switzerland *Paläontologische Gesellschaft.* Abhandlungen. Vol. 17. Ac. 3122.

　　　　　　　　　　　　2 U 2

PALAEONTOLOGY.—Botany—*cont.*

KIDSTON (R.) Fossil Flora of the South Wales coal field. 1894. 4°. Ac. Edinburgh. *Royal Society.* Transactions. Vol. 37. Pt. 3. 2099. g. *See also* BOTANY.

Zoology.
General.

HUTCHINSON (H. N.) Extinct Monsters. pp. 254. *Lond.* 1892. 8°. 7202. aaa. 34.
—— Creatures of other days. pp. 270. *Lond.* 1894. 8°. 7206. f. 15.

BIGOT (A.) Contributions à l'étude de la Faune jurassique de Normandie. 1893, *etc.* 4°. Ac. Caen. *Société Linnéene.* Mémoires. Vol. 17. Ac. 2842/3.

DEPÉRET (C.) Les Animaux pliocènes du Roussillon. 1890, *etc.* 4°. Ac. Paris. *Société Géologique.* Mémoires. Paléontologie. Tom. 1. Ac. 3115/3.

COPE (E. D.) Uebersicht der eocänen Fauna von Egerkingen. 1890, 4°. Ac. Switzerland. *Paläontologische Gesellschaft.* Abhandlungen. Vol. 17. Ac. 3122.

INDIA. *Geological Society.* Index to the genera and species described in the Palæontologica Indica. pp. 186. *Calcutta,* 1892. fol. 7107. f.

PRIEM (F.) L'Évolution des formes animales avant l'apparition de l'homme. pp. 383. *Paris,* 1891. 8°. 7006. bb. 31.

Invertebrata.

BOYLE (C. B.) Catalogue and Bibliography of N. American mesozoic Invertebrata. pp. 315. 1893. 8°. U.S. *Geological Survey.* Bulletin. No. 102. 1829. a. 7.

MARCOU (J. B.) Bibliography of the collection of fossil Invertebrates in the U.S. National Museum. pp. 333. 1885. 8°. Ac. Washington. *Smithsonian Institution.* Bulletin of the U.S. National Museum. No. 30. Ac. 1875/13.

WOODS (H.) Elementary Palæontology. Invertebrate. pp. 222. 1893. 8°. SHIPLEY (A. E.) Cambridge Science Manuals. Biological Series. 8709. h.

ALLEN (E. H.) Prologomena towards the study of the chalk Foraminifera. pp. 36. *Lond.* 1894. 8°. Pam. 27.

AMICIS (G. A. de) Contribuzione alla conoscenza dei Foraminiferi pliocenici. 1893. 8°. Ac. Rome. *Società Geologica.* Bollettino. Vol. 12. Ac. 3104.

HAEUSLER (R.) Monographie der Foraminiferen-Fauna der schweizerischen Transversarius-Zone. pp. 134. 1890. 4°. Ac. Switzerland. *Paläontologische Gesellschaft.* Abhandlungen. Vol. 17. Ac. 3122.

PERNER (J.) Études sur les graptolites de Bohême. *Prague,* 1894, *etc.* 4°. 7203. f.

VOGDES (A. W.) Bibliography of the palæozoic Crustacea. pp. 412. 1893. 8°. Ac. San Francisco. *California Academy of Sciences.* Occasional Papers. No. 4. Ac. 3037/4.

SCUDDER (S. H.) Bibliography of fossil Insects. pp. 101. 1890. 8°. U.S. *Geological Survey.* Bulletin. No. 69. 1829. a. 7.
—— Index to the fossil Insects of the World. pp. 744. 1891. 8°. U.S. *Geological Survey.* Bulletin. No. 71. 1829. a. 7.
—— Two new types of carboniferous Myriapods. 1884. 4°. Ac. Boston. *Society of Natural History.* Memoirs. Vol. 3. No. 9. Ac. 3042.

AC., *etc.* London. *British Museum.* List of the Edwards Collection of British oligocene and eocene Mollusca. pp. 365. *Lond.* 1891. 8°. 7207. e. 18.

COSSMANN ( ) Essais de Paléoconchologie comparée. *Paris,* 1895, *etc.* 8°. 7204. i.

FALAEONTOLOGY.—Zoology—*cont.*

KLIKA (G.) Die tertiaeren Land- und Süsswasser-Conchylien Böhmen's. pp. 121. 1891. 8°. Ac. Prague. *Oba Komitéty pro Výskum země České.* Archiv. Bd. 7. No. 4. Ac. 2915.

DEGRANGE-TOUZIN (A.) Étude des coquilles fossiles des Faluns. 1895. 8°. Ac. Bordeaux. *Société Finnéenne.* Bulletin. Vol. 47. Ac. 2839.

ARDUINI (V.) Conchiglie plioceniche del bacino di Albenga. 1895. 8°. Ac. Genoa. *Società Ligustica di Scienze.* Atti. Vol. 6. Ac. 2809. b.

LOCARD (A.) Monographie des Mollusques tertiaires de la Suisse. 1892, *etc.* 4°. Ac. Switzerland. *Paläontologische Gesellschaft.* Abhandlungen. Vol. 18, 19. Ac. 3122.

PÉRON (A.) Description des Mollusques fossiles de la région sud de la Tunisie. 1889, *etc.* 8°. FRANCE. *Ministère de l'Instruction.* Exploration de la Tunisie. 10105. ff.

WHITFIELD (R. P.) Mollusca and Crustacea of the Miocene Formations of New Jersey. pp. 195. 1894. 4°. U.S. *Geological Survey.* Monographs. Vol. 24. 1828. b.

POMPECKJ (J. F.) Beiträge zu einer Revision der Ammoniten des schwäbischen Jura. *Stuttg.* 1893, *etc.* 8°. 7202. aaa.

HUDLESTON (W. H.) and WILSON (E.) Catalogue of British jurassic Gasteropoda. pp. 147. *Lond.* 1892. 8°. 7202. b. 1.

WHITFIELD (R. P.) Gasteropoda and Cephalopoda of New Jersey. pp. 402. 1892. 4°. U.S. *Geological Survey.* Monographs. Vol. 18. 1828. b.

HIND (W.) Monograph on Carbonicola, Anthracomya and Naiadites. 1894, *etc.* 4°. Ac. London. *Palæontographical Society.* Publications. Vol. 48. Ac. 3200.

BITTNER (A.) Brachiopoden der alpinen Trias. pp. 325. 1890. 4°. Ac. Vienna. *Geologische Reichsanstalt.* Abhandlungen. Bd. 14. 1828. a.

GAGEL (C.) Die Brachiopoden der cambrischen und silurischen Geschiebe der Provinzen Ost- und Westpreussen. pp. 79. 1890. 4°. Ac. Koenigsberg. *Physikalisch-Oekonomische Gesellschaft.* Beiträge. No. 6. Ac. 2337.

REED (F. R. C.) Brachiopods, Fossil. 1895. 8°. Cambridge Natural History. Vol. 3. 7001. ee.

Vertebrata.

DUBLIN. *Science and Art Museum.* Catalogue of fossil Mammals, Birds, Reptiles and Amphibians in the Museum. By R. Lydekker. pp. 61. *Lond.* 1891. 8°. Pam. 18.

NEWTON (E. T.) Vertebrata of the pliocene Deposits of Britain. pp. 137. 1891. 8°. G.B.&I. *Geological Survey.* Memoirs. 2248. g.

DUBLIN. *Science and Art Museum.* Catalogue of the collection of fossil Fishes, by J. W. Davis. pp. 20. *Dublin,* 1888. 8°. 7204. c. 17. (5.)

DEAN (B.) Fishes, living and fossil. pp. 300. 1895. 8°. Ac. New York. *Columbia College.* Biological Series. Vol. 3. 7002. e.

JAEKEL (O.) Die eocänen Selachier vom Monte Bolca. pp. 176. *Berl.* 1894. 8°. 7203. e. 8.

KOKEN (E.) Neue Untersuchungen an tertiären Fisch-Otolithen. 2 pt. 1888, 91. 8°. Ac. Berlin. *Geologische Gesellschaft.* Zeitschrift. Bd. 41, 43. Ac. 3137.

WOODWARD (A. S.) Fossil Fishes of the Hawkesbury series at Gosford. pp. 55. 1890. 4°. NEW SOUTH WALES. *Geological Survey.* Memoirs. 7203. h.

AC. London. *British Museum.* Catalogue of the fossil Birds. By R. Lydekker. pp. 368. *Lond.* 1891. 8°. 7207. e. 11.

PALAEONTOLOGY.—Zoology—cont.

FILHOL (H.) Études sur les Mammifères fossiles de Sansan. pp. 319. 1890. 8°. Ac. Paris. *École des Hautes Études.* Bibliothèque. Tom. 37.   Ac. 8929/5.

POHLIG (H.) Die grossen Säugetiere der Diluvialzeit. pp. 64. 1890. 8°. MARSHALL (W.) Zoologische Vorträge. Hft. 5.   7204. bb. 33.

MINGAUD (G.) Tableau des Mammifères dans le département du Gard à l'époque quaternaire. pp. 3. *Nîmes*, 1891. 8°.   Pam. 42.

SCOTT (W. B.) Mammalia of the Uinta Formation. 1890. 4°. Ac. Philadelphia. *American Philosophical Society.* Transactions. N.S. Vol. 16. Pt. 3.   Ac. 1830/3.

DAWSON (G. M.) Notes on Mammoth-remains in Canada and Alaska. pp. 9. *Lond.* 1894. 8°.   Pam. 27.

GAUDRY (A.) Quelques remarques sur les Mastodontes à propos de l'animal du Cherichira. pp. 6. 1891. 4°. Ac. Paris. *Société Géologique.* Mémoires. Paléontologie. Tom. 2. Fasc. 1.   Ac. 3115/3.

PALATE. See MOUTH.

PALERMO. GIOVANNI (V. di) La Topografia di Palermo dal secolo x al xv. 2 vol. *Palermo*, 1889, 90. 4°.   7709. k. 16.

MAGGIORE-PERNI (F.) Da popolazione di Palermo dal x. al xviii. secolo. pp. 621. *Palermo*, 1892. 8°.   8223. dh. 18.

PALERMO. Gli atti della città di Palermo dal 1311 al 1410. *Palermo*, 1892, etc. fol. 5322. g.

GENZARDI (B.) Il Comune di Palermo sotto il Dominio spagnuolo. pp. 254. *Palermo*, 1891. 8°.   10132. aaa. 11.

BOLAFFIO (L. F.) Guida di Palermo e suoi dintorni. pp. 11. 105. *Milano*, 1891. 8°.   10136. aaa. 16.

PALESTINE AND SYRIA.

Antiquities. See JEWS.

Geography: Excavations.

ROEHRICHT (R.) Bibliotheca geographica Palaestinae. Literatur von 333 bis 1878. pp. 744. *Berl.* 1890. 8°.   BB. I. d. 4.

Ac. Berlin. *Deutscher Palästina-Verein.* Mittheilungen und Nachrichten. *Leipz.* 1895, etc. 8°.   Ac. 5387/2.

BLANCKENHORN (M.) Grundzüge der Geologie von Nord Syrien. pp. 101. *Berl.* 1891. 4°.   7202. f. 3.

BUHL (F. P. W.) Palæstina i kortfattet geografisk Fremstilling. pp. 166. *Kjøbenh.* 1890. 8°.   10078. c. 30.

—— Studien zur Topographie des Ostjordanlandes. pp. 20. *Leipz.* 1894. 8°. Pam. 88.

FILLION (L. C.) and NICOLE (H.) Atlas géographique de la Bible. pp. 58. *Lyon*, 1890. 4°.   10076. i. 8.

MAC DOUGALL (J.) Geography of Palestine. pp. 103. *Lond.* 1895. 8°.   10078. aa. 24.

NICOL (T.) Recent explorations in Bible lands. pp. 76. *Edinb.* 1892. 8°.   3149. c. 5.

PALESTINE. *Exploration Fund.* The City and the land. Lectures on the work of the Society. pp 238. *Lond.* 1892. 8°.   2356. b. 4.

—— Tel el Hesy. By W. M. F. Petrie. pp. 62. *Lond.* 1891. 4°.   7703. h. 29.

—— A Mound of many cities; Tell El Hesy. By F. J. Bliss. pp. 201. *Lond.* 1894. 8°.   7704. b. 53.

SMITH (G. A.) Historical geography of the Holy Land. pp. 692. *Lond.* 1894. 8°. 10077. f. 24.

VOGELSTEIN (H.) Shechem and Bethel. pp. 22. *Lond.* 1892. 8°.   Pam. 5.

PALESTINE.—Geography, etc.—cont.

WHITTY (J. I.) Who originated the Palestine Exploration Fund? *Dublin*, 1894. 8°. Pam. 46.

Guide Books.

BAEDEKER (C.) Palestine and Syria. pp. 444. *Leipz.* 1894. 8°.   2352. a.

—— Palestine et Syrie. pp. 442. *Leipz.* 1893. 8°.   10108. d. 5.

COOK (T.) Programmes and itineraries of Cook's arrangements for Palestine tours. pp. 105. *Lond.* 1891. 8°.   10078. c. 28.

SYRIA. Murray's Handbook for Syria and Palestine. pp. 403. 20. *Lond.* 1892. 8°.   2364. b. 19.

History, *Ancient*.

See BASHAN: HITTITES: JEWS: PHOENICIA.

History, *Mediaeval*; Pilgrimages and Early Travels.

STARCK (E. v) Palaestina und Syrien von Anfang der Geschichte bis zum Siege des Islam. pp. 168. *Berl.* 1894. 8°.   9055. df. 38.

Ac. London. *Palestine Pilgrims' Text Society.* Publications. *Lond.* 1887, etc. 8°.   Ac. 6171.

CHARLES I., *Emperor*. Iter Hierosolymitanum, Voyage de Charlemagne à Jérusalem. 1892. 8°. Ac. Montpellier. *Société pour l'Étude des Langues Romanes.* Revue. Sér. 4. Tom. 6.   Ac. 9809/2.

Ac. London. *Camden Society.* N.S. 52. Expeditions to Prussia and the Holy Land by Henry Earl of Derby, aft. King Henry IV. 1390–3. pp. 360. *Lond.* 1894. 4°. Ac. 8113/137.

DIESBACH (M. de) Les Pèlerins fribourgeois à Jérusalem, 1436–1640. 1891. 8°. Ac. Fribourg. *Société d'histoire.* Archives. Tom. 5. Livr. 2.   Ac. 6938.

ROEHRICHT (R.) Die Jerusalemfahrten der Grafen Philipp Ludwig, 1484, und Reinhard von Hanau, 1550. 1891. 8°. Ac. Cassel. *Verein für hessische Geschichte.* Zeitschrift. N.F. Bd. 16.   Ac. 7025.

SCHOEN (T.) Eine Pilgerfahrt in das heilige Land, 1494. 1892. 8°. Ac. Vienna. *Universitas.* Mittheilungen des Instituts für oesterreichische Geschichtsforschung. Bd. 13. Hft. 3.   Ac. 803.

DU CLOU (L.) Itinerarium breve Terrae Sanctae. pp. 252. *Florentiae*, 1891. 8°   10077. h. 13.

See also CRUSADES: JERUSALEM.

Inscriptions. *See* INSCRIPTIONS.

Missions. *See* MISSIONS.

Modern Travels, etc.

ALBOUY (A.) Jérusalem et les sanctuaires de la Judée. pp. 276. *Paris*, 1894. 8°. 10077. l. 12.

ANDREW (A.) My visit to Palestine. pp. 206. *Paisley*, 1892. 8°.   10078. c. 31.

BALANGERO (J. B.) Trip to the Holy Land. pp. 30. *Colombo*, 1894. 8°.   Pam. 88.

BARCÍA PAVÓN (Á.) Viaje à Tierra Santa. pp. 454. *Madrid*, 1889, 8°.   10078. aa. 15.

BOUTROUE (A.) La Palestine et la Syrie à vol d'oiseau. pp. 23. *Paris*, 1894. 8°. Pam. 38.

BREWSTER (M. A.) Three months' travels in Egypt and Palestine. pp. 233. *Lond.* 1894. 8°.   10078. b. 20.

BRIDEL (P. S.) Palestine illustrated. *Lond.* 1892, etc. obl. fol.   1780. a.

BRINTON (J.) Tour in Palestine. pp. 173. *Lond.* 1893. 8°.   10076. ee. 3.

CHARMES (G.) Voyage en Syrie. pp. 327. *Paris*, 1891. 8°.   10078. aa. 16.

CHOPIN ( ) France et Syrie. pp. 368. *Tours*, 1891. 8°.   10077. i. 8.

PALESTINE.—Modern Travels, etc.—
continued.

COURET (A.) En Terre Promise. Notes de mon
voyage. pp. 259. *Paris*, 1891. 12°. 10078. aa. 19.

DALBERG (F. v.) Palästina. Ein Sommeraus-
flug. pp. 235. *Würzburg*, 1892. 8°.
10077. k. 20.

DUPUIS (J. F.) Rome et Jérusalem. pp. 540.
Québec, 1894. 8°. 10028. h. 3.

EHRNROOTH (A.) Två Finskors Lustvandringar.
Helsingfors, 1890, *etc.* 8°. 10077. h. 10.

ENEMANNUS (M.) Resa i Orienten, 1711–1712.
2 Dlr. *Upsala*, 1889. 8°. 010055. ee. 5.

FRASER (M. D.) The Pyramids, Palestine, Pompeii. pp. 111. *Glasg.* 1894. 8°. 10078. aa. 23.

H., W. H Carnatic to Canaan. pp. 131.
Madras, 1891. 12°. 10077. a. 6.

HARPER (H. A.) Walks in Palestine. pp. 128.
Lond. 1894. 4°. 4429. l. 23.

HARTUNG (B.) Sommertage im Heiligen Lande.
pp. 150. *Leipz.* 1895. 8°. 10078. bb. 1.

HOME (S.) In Christ's Country. pp. 107.
Lond. 1892. 8°. 10078. aa. 20.

JANEWAY (C.) Ten weeks in Palestine. pp. 158.
Lond. 1894. 8°. 10078. aaa. 40.

JEWRY, afterwards VALENTINE (L.) Palestine
past and present. pp. 435. *Lond.* 1893. 8°.
10077. h. 17.

JULLIEN (M.) Sinaï et Syrie. pp. 300.
Lille, 1893. 8°. 10077. i. 13.

KEAN (J.) Among the Holy Places. pp. 388.
Lond 1892. 8°. 10077. f. 23.

KING (A.) Dr. Liddon's Tour in Palestine in
1886. pp. 213. *Lond.* 1891. 8°. 010096. e. 38.

KNIGHT (A. E.) Gleanings from Bible lands.
pp. 194. *Lond.* 1891. 8°. 10077. de. 6.

LANDRIEUX (M.) Aux Pays du Christ. pp. 645.
Lond. 1895. 8°. 10077. l. 17.

LE CAMUS (É.) Notre Voyage aux pays bibliques.
2 vol. *Brux.* 1895. 8°. 10077. l. 18.

LOMBAY (G. de) Au Sinaï, Palestine et Syrie.
pp. 220. *Paris*, 1892. 12°. 10078. aaa. 34.

LOTI (P.) Le Désert. pp. 258. *Paris*, 1895. 12°.
10077. aa. 17.

—— Jérusalem. pp. 221. *Paris*, 1895. 12°.
10078. b. 22.

MARQUETTE (L.) À travers la Syrie. pp. 330.
Lille, 1892. 8°. 10078. b. 19.

MARTRIN-DONOS (J. de) Au Pays du Sauveur.
pp. 278. *Fontenay*, 1893. 8°. 10078. c. 36.

MATTHES (A.) Reisebilder aus dem Morgenland.
pp. 356. *Gütersloh*, 1891. 8°. 10024. ccc. 2.

MILLER (E. E.) Alone through Syria. pp. 330.
Lond. 1891. 8°. 10078. b. 18.

MITCHELL (E. H.) Forty days in the Holy Land.
pp. 207. *Lond.* 1890. 8°. 10078. aaa. 11.

MOTHERÉ (L. L.) Mon pèlerinage en Orient.
pp. 384. *Paris*, 1893. 8°. 10077. h. 15.

NEIL (J.) Strange Scenes. pp. 40.
Lond. 1891. 8°. 10078. c. 27.

—— Pictured Palestine. pp. 322.
Lond. 1891. 8°. 10077. f. 22.

NEWTON (R.) Rambles in Bible lands. pp. 251.
Lond. 1894. 8°. 10078. aaa. 39.

OETTLI (S.) Ideal und Leben. Gesammelte
Vorträge. pp. 338. *Gotha*, 1894. 8°. 4371. e. 31.

OPPENHEIM (M. v.) Bericht über seine Reise
durch die syrische Wüste nach Mosul.
Berl. 1894. 8°. Pam. 88.

OTTS (J. M. P.) The Fifth Gospel, the land
where Jesus lived. pp. 367. *Edinb.* 1893. 8°.
10078. aaa. 35.

PALESTINE.—Modern Travels, etc.—
continued.

PÉCHENARD (P. L.) De Reims à Jérusalem.
pp. 319. *Reims*, 1893. 8°. 10078. c. 38.

REVEL (J.) Chez nos Ancêtres. pp. 494.
Paris, 1888. 18°. 10078. b. 16.

RIDGWAY (J.) Sketches from the East, illustrating Church doctrine. *Oxf.* 1893. 8°.
4371, a. 33.

RIDPATH (J.) Jubilee Jottings, and a pilgrimage to Palestine. pp. 247. *Roehampton*, 1889. 8°.
10024. aa. 24.

ROSS (D. M.) The Cradle of Christianity:
chapters on Palestine. pp. 256.
Lond. 1891. 8°. 10078. c. 32.

SAINT CLAIR (G.) Buried cities and Bible countries. pp. 378. *Lond.* 1891, 8°. 10078. c. 29.

SCHARLING (C. H.) Reisestudier fra Palæstina.
Kjøbenh. 1891, *etc.* 8°. 10078. cc.

STAEHELIN (A.) In Algerien, Palästina und am
Roten Meere. pp. 461. *Basel*, 1891. 8°.
10024. cc. 16.

TALMAGE (T. de W.) Visit to the Holy Land.
pp. 127. *Lond.* 1891. 8°. 10078. aaa. 30.

—— Sermons on the Holy Land pp. 324.
Lond. 1891. 8°. 4487. f. 6.

TEAPE (W. M.) Through the Holy Land.
pp. 56. *Stockton*, 1895. obl. 8°. 10077. de. 18.

THOMAS (J. L.) Oxford to Palestine; notes of a
tour. pp. 113. *Lond.* 1890. 8°. 10024. cc. 11.

TRISTRAM (H. B.) Eastern customs in Bible
Lands. pp. 262. *Lond.* 1894. 8°. 10078. aaa. 38.

TROTIGNON (L.) L'Orient qui s'en va. pp. 380.
Paris, 1893. 8°. 10078 aaa. 37.

VERDAGUER (J.) Dietari d' un pelegrí á Terra
Santa. pp. 211. *Barcelona*, 1889. 8°.
10078. c. 35.

WARNER (C. D.) In the Levant. 2 vol.
Lond. 1892. 8°. 10077. bbb. 19.

WATSON (*Mrs.* P.) Palestine Pictures.
Lond. 1892. 8°. 1876. b. 19.

WILSON (E. L.) In Scripture lands. pp. 384.
Lond. 1891. 8°. 10077. i. 14.
See also JERUSALEM.

PALI LANGUAGE. Ac. London. *British
Museum.* Catalogue of Sanskrit and Pali Books
acquired during the years 1876–92. By C.
Bendall. pp. 624. *Lond.* 1893. 4°.
11899. k. 25.

FRYER (G. E.) Notes on the Páli grammarian
Kachcháyana. pp. 14. *Calcutta*, 1882. 8°.
Pam. 47.

PALLANZA. VIANI (A.) Pallanza antica
e Pallanza nuova. pp. 323. *Pallanza*, 1891. 8°.
10136. e. 13.

PALMISTRY. ALLEN (J.) Popular Palmistry,
illustrated. pp. 38. *Swansea*, 1895. 8°.
8630. aa. 4. (5.)

AROLA ( ) L'Art de lire dans la main. pp. 72.
Paris, 1890. 8°. 8632. bbb. 29.

ART. L'Art de lire dans la main. pp. 24.
Mons, 1890. 8°. 8631. a. 49. (2.)

BAUGHAN (R.) Handbook of Palmistry. pp. 32.
Lond. 1895. 8°. 8632. e. 37. (8.)

BELLO (P.) Character and fortune revealed.
pp. 127. 1894. 8°. Books for the Hour.
8632. de.

CHEIRO. Cheiro's Language of the hand.
pp. 193. *N.Y.* 1895. 4°. 8632. h. 14.

CHIROMANTIE. La Chiromancie. pp. 128.
Paris, 1895. 8° 08631. e. 3.

DALE (*Mrs.* J. B.) Indian Palmistry. pp. 66.
Lond. 1895. 8°. 8631. ee. 40.

PALMISTRY—continued.

EASTER-HENDERSON (E.) Guide to Palmistry.
pp. 132. *Lond.* 1894. 12°. 8632. de. 6.

EDMOND ( ) La Chiromancie d'Edmond.
pp. 236. *Amiens,* 1880. 8°. 8632. ccc. 9.

FRITH (H.) Practical Palmistry. pp. 138.
Lond. 1895. 8°. 08631. e. 2.

LANGRIDGE (M. C.) Key to Palmistry. pp. 40.
Lond. 1894. 16°. 8632. b. 47.

P.P. *London.* Palmist and chirological Review.
Lond. 1892, *etc. obl,* 8°. ¶ P.P. 1537 and 23.

ZOÉ. Lessons on scientific Palmistry. pp. 109.
Lond. 1895. 8°. 8631. ee. 42.

PALMYRA. DEVILLE ( ) Palmyre. Souvenirs de voyage et d'histoire. pp. 270.
7708. a. 69.

LEDRAIN (E.) Dictionnaire des Noms propres palmyréniens. pp. 59. 1886. 8°. Ac. Paris.
École du Louvre. Publications. Ac. 5329.

PALUDISM. *See* MALARIA.

PAMIRS. CUMBERLAND (C. S.) Sport on the Pamirs and Turkestan Steppes. pp. 278.
Lond. 1895. 8°. 07905. h. 25.

MURRAY (C A.) *Earl of Dunmore.* The Pamirs.
2 vol. *Lond.* 1893. 8°. 10076. e. 4.
See also ASIA, *Central.*

PAMPHYLIA and PISIDIA. LANCKOROŃSKI (C.) *Count.* Städte Pamphyliens und Pisidiens. 2 Bde. *Wien,* 1890, 92. fol. 1705. a. 10.

—— Les villes de la Pamphylie et de la Lydie.
2 tom. *Paris,* 1890, 93. 4°. 7703. d.

PANAMA: PANAMA CANAL. MINOT (G. S.) The history of Panama. pp. 84.
Kingston, 1892. 8°. 9772. b. 11.

ANDRÉ (G.) Le Canal de Panama et la nouvelle société. pp. 53. *Paris,* 1894. 8°. 8235. k. 58.

BARBOUX (H. M.) Cour d'Appel de Paris. Plaidoirie pour MM. F. et C. de Lesseps. pp. 242.
Paris, 1893. 8°. 5408. e. 20.

BRESSOLLES (P.) Liquidation de la Compagnie de Panama. Commentaire de la loi du 1er Juillet 1893. pp. 180. *Paris,* 1894. 8°.
5425. aa. 1.

CHICHÉ (A.) L'Affaire de Panama.
Bordeaux, 1894, *etc.* 12°. 8051. ccc.

COSMAO-DUMÈNEZ (S. M.) La verité sur le Panama. pp. 22. *Quimper,* 1893. 8°. Pam. 69.

DEMACHY (É.) Le scandale de Panama. pp. 13.
Paris, 1892. 8°. Pam. 69.

DÉPUTÉ. L'enquête parlementaire sur le Panama.
pp. 144. *Sceaux,* 1893. 8°. 8050. h. 7.

DU BUIT (C. H.) Affaire de Panama. Plaidoirie pour MM. Fontane. pp. 60. *Paris,* 1893. 8°.
5408. e. 16.

DUMAS (A.) Projet d'achèvement du Canal de Panama. *Paris,* 1891. 8°. 08235. h. 24.

—— Le tarif à appliquer à Panama et les revenus probables. pp. 89. *Paris,* 1891. 8°. 08235. h. 25.

DUPAS ( ) Pourquoi n'a-t-on pas pu arrêter Arton? pp. 186. *Paris,* 1893. 12°. 6057. a. 35.

ÉCONOMISTE. Panama. Canal à niveau, son achèvement possible en 5 ans. pp. 42.
Paris, 1892. 8°. Pam. 76.

EPHEM. Panama Almanach. pp. 64.
Paris, 1893. 8°. P.P. 2404. n.

FLORIDIAN (L. M.) Les coulisses du Panama.
pp. 294. *Paris,* 1891. 12°. 8235. aa. 61.

FONTBONNE (G. de) Panama, ou la vérité sur la jonction des deux Océans. pp. 31.
Paris, 1893. 12°. Pam. 76.

GIJSELAAR (N. C. de) Het Panama-Kanaal.
pp. 224. *Leiden,* 1891. 8°. 08235. f. 27.

PANAMA—continued.

LUCAS (A.) Précis de l'affaire du Panama.
pp. 252. *Paris,* 189·. 12°. 5423. de. 18.

MARCOU (J.) Souvenirs d'un géologue sur Panama et le canal. pp. 44. *Neuchâtel,* 1893. 8°.
Pam. 76.

MIMANDE (P.) Souvenirs d'un Échappé de Panama. pp. 134. *Paris,* 1893. 8°.
10481. aaa. 49.

NELSON (W.) Five years at Panama. pp. 287.
1891. 8°. 10481. cc. 25.

PANAMA. Les millions du Panama.
Paris, 1892, *etc.* 8°. 8051. ccc. 24.

—— Les scandales du Panama.
Paris, 1892, *etc.* 8°. 8051. dd. 32.

—— La comédie de Panama! pp. 4.
Paris, 1893. 8°. Pam. 69.

—— Le procès du Panama. pp. 31.
Paris, 1895. 8°. 5423. g. 2. (8.)

—— Le dernier mot de l'Affaire du Panama.
pp. 6. *Paris,* 1893. 8°. Pam. 69.

—— La chanson qu'attaque l'isthme du Panama.
Paris, 1893. *s. sh.* fol. Pam. 59.

—— Les étrangleurs du Panama. pp. 15.
Paris, 1893. 12°. Pam. 69.

PANGLOSSE ( ) Les justes lois et les responsabilités du Panama. pp. 16. *Paris,* 1893. 8°.
5405. de. 6. (4.)

PAPONOT (F.) Le Canal de Panama. Solution de la question financière. pp. 30.
Paris, 1891. 8°. Pam. 76.

—— Canal de Panama, son relèvement par le Suez. pp. 7. *Paris* 1892. 8°. Pam. 76.

—— Relèvement immédiat de l'entreprise du Canal de Panama. pp. 134. *Paris,* 1893. 8°.
8235. f. 49.

—— Canal interocéanique de Panama. 2 pt.
Paris, 1894. 8°. 8235. h. 55.

PARIS. *Société des Chemins de Fer à Navires.*
La Culebra franchie avec une dépense de 60 millions. pp. 28. *Paris,* 1892. 4°. Pam. 7.

ROUANET (G.) Les complicités du Panama: pages d'histoire sociale contemporaine. pp. 422.
Paris, 1893. 12°. 8052. cc. 29.

SÉBILLOT (A.) Résumé de la conférence de M. A. Sébillot, sur l'achèvement économique du canal de Panama. pp. 19. *Paris,* 1893. 4°.
Pam. 76.

VÉRITÉ (H.) Le Guide pratique des porteurs d'obligations de la Compagnie de Panama.
pp. 46. *Paris,* 1893. 8°. 08227. g. 49. (18.)

WYSE (L. N. B.) Canal de Panama. Mission de 1890-91 en Colombie. pp. 154.
Paris, 1891. 8°. 08235. h. 22.

—— Documents concernant le concessionnaire publiés pendant les procès de Panama.
Poissy, 1893. 8°. 8235. i. 51.

PANAY. *See* PHILIPPINE ISLANDS.

PANNAL. ROWNTREE (M.) Pannal, past and present. pp. 23. *Harrogate,* 1895. 8°.
Pam. 90.

PANTOMIME. HUGOUNET (P.) La Musique et la Pantomime. pp. 164. *Paris,* 1893. 8°.
7898. k. 46.
See also DRAMA.

PAPACY. *See* CHURCH HISTORY: ROMAN CATHOLIC CHURCH.

PAPER.

Manufacture, etc.

BENNETT (J. B.) Paper-making Processes and machinery. 2 pt. *Edinb.* 1892. 8°. 07944. g. 11.

BLONDEL (S.) Les Outils de l'écrivain. pp. 232.
Paris, 1890. 18°. 7942. cc. 30.

PAPER.—Manufacture, etc.—_continued._

CHARPENTIER (P.) Le Papier. pp. 431.
1890. 8°. FREMY (E.) Encyclopédie chimique.
Tome x. 8907. h. 1.

CHAPPERTON (G.) Practical Paper-making.
pp. 208. _Lond._ 1894. 8°. 07944. e. 30.

DÉSÉCHALIERS (E.) Répertoire des Papetiers et
Imprimeurs 1895. pp. 219. _Paris,_ 1895. 8°.
7942. f. 43.

DUNBAR (J.) Notes on the manufacture of wood
pulp papers. pp. 82. _Leith,_ 1892. 8°.
07944. g. 12.

GIRARD (A.) Le Papier. Ses ancêtres. Son
histoire. pp. 19. _Lille,_ 1892. 8°. 7942. l. 44.

GRIFFIN (R. B.) and LITTLE (A. D.) Chemistry
of Paper-making. pp. 517. _N.Y._ 1894. 8°.
07944. i. 1.

HERTZBERG (W.) Paper Testing carried out in
the German Government Laboratory at Charlottenburg. pp. 57. _Lond._ 1892. 8°. 7942. f. 30.

HOYER (E.) Die Fabrikation des Papiers.
pp. 495. 1886–87. 8°. BOLLEY (P. A.) Handbuch der chemischen Technologie. Bd. 6.
Gruppe 5. Abt. 1. 8905. eee.

KAY (J.) Paper, its history. pp. 100.
Lond. 1893. 8°. 07944. ee. 8.

LIMOGES. _Cercle d'Études Commerciales._ Le
Papier. pp. 140. _Limoges,_ 1892. 8°.
7942. dd. 8.

LEMPERTZ (H.) Beiträge zur Geschichte des
Leinen-Papiers. _Köln,_ 1891, _etc._ 8°. 7942. i. 39.

P.P. _London._ Paper-maker and Paper trade
Journal. _Lond._ 1891, _etc._ 4°. N.R.

P.P. _London._ Paper, Stationery and Printing
record. _Lond._ 1893, _etc._ 4°. N.R.

VACHON (M.) Les Arts et les industries du
Papier en France. pp. 246. _Paris,_ 1894. 4°.
7943. h. 32.

Water-Marks : Old Paper.

BRIQUET (C. M.) De la valeur des Filigranes du
Papier comme moyen de déterminer l'âge de
documents. pp. 13. _Genève,_ 1892. 8°
07703. g. 2. (6.)

—— La Légende paléographique du Papier de
Coton. pp. 18. _Genève,_ 1884. 8°. Pam. 94.

—— Lettre sur les papiers usités en Sicile, à
l'occasion de deux manuscrits en papier dit de
coton. pp. 16. _Palermo,_ 1892. 8°.
7794. i. 12. (15.)

KIRCHNER (E. D. M.) Die Papiere des 14.
Jahrhunderts im Stadtarchive zu Frankfurt
und deren Wasserzeichen. pp. 35.
Frankfurt, 1893. 8°. 7709. h. 34.

LEMON (R.) Collection of Water-Marks. 1891. 8°.
SCOTT (H. T.) and DAVEY (S.) Guide to the
Collector of Historical Documents. 11899. h. 36.

PAPYRI. _See_ EGYPT, _Antiquities :_ MANU-
SCRIPTS : PALAEOGRAPHY.

PARADISE. _See_ ESCHATOLOGY.

PARADISEIDAE. SHARPE (R. B.) Mono-
graph of the Paradiseidae ; Birds of Paradise.
Lond. 1891, _etc._ fol. 1822. d. 4.
See also BIRDS.

PARAGUAY. BRUYSSEL (E. v.) Paraguay.
Decouverte et colonisation, _etc._ pp. 219.
Brux. 1893. 8°. 10481. dd. 24.

WASHBURN (C. A.) Historia del Paraguay.
Buenos Aires, 1892, _etc._ 8°. 9772. g.

RENGGER (J. R.) and LONGCHAMP ( ) Ensayo
sobre la revolucion del Paraguay y el gobierno
del D. Francia. pp. 88. _Asuncion,_ 1882. 8°.
9772. c. 2.

JOURDAN (E. C.) Guerra do Paraguay. pp. 233.
Rio de J. 1890. 8°. 9781. e. 10.

PARAGUAY—_continued._

CERRI (D.) Campaña del Paraguay. Toma de
la ciudad de Corrientes, 25 de Mayo 1865.
pp. 91. _Buenos A._ 1892. 8°. 9772. aa. 21.

BOURGADE LA DARDYE (E. de) Paraguay. pp. 243.
Lond. 1892. 8°. 10481. c. 32.

CORDERO (F.) Artículos en "El Paraguayo"
referentes á la reclamacion Cordero. pp. 56.
Asuncion, 1888. 8°. Pam. 33.

FOERSTER (E.) Dr. B. Förster's Kolonie Neu-
Germania in Paraguay. pp. 173.
Berl. 1891. 8°. 10481. ff. 34.

P.P. _Buenos Aires._ Revista del Paraguay.
Buenos A. 1891, _etc._ 8°. P.P. 4126. fb.

RODAS (C.) El Paraguay. Bosquejo sobre su
estado. pp. 67. _Buenos A._ 1888. 8°. Pam. 65.

SCHULTZE (C. F. E.) Das Paraguayfieber.
pp. 44. _Bremen,_ 1893. 8°. Pam. 66.
See also AMERICA, _South._

PARALYSIS. BASTIAN (H. C.) Various
forms of hysterical Paralysis. pp. 199.
Lond. 1893. 8°. 7620. df. 32.

JUDSON (A. B.) Importance of early attention to
disability caused by infantile paralysis.
_N.Y._ 1893. 8°. 07305. l. 13. (3.)

KRAFFT-EBING (R. v.) Die progressive allgemeine Paralyse. pp. 108. 1894. 8°. NOTH-
NAGEL (H.) Specielle Pathologie, _etc._ Bd. 9.
7441. d.

MAGNAN (V.) and SÉRIEUX (P.) La Paralysie
générale. pp. 193. 1894. 8°. Encyclopédie
des aide-mémoire. 8709. g.

PITT (G. N.) Case of pseudo-bulbar Paralysis.
pp. 11. _Lond._ 1893, 8°. 7306. e. 26. (7.)

WEBER (F. P.) and ARKWRIGHT (J. A.) Pseudo-
bulbar Paralysis. pp. 7. 1894. 8°.
7306. e. 22. (19.)

See also NERVES : SPINE.

PARASITES. BLANCHARD (R.) Los Animales parásitos introducidos por el agua.
1890. 8°. SALAZAR (A. E.) Examen de las
aguas potables. 8777. cc. 28.

COOKE (M. C.) Vegetable Wasps. History of
entomogenous fungi. pp. 364. _Lond._ 1892. 8°.
4429. b. 25.

GÉRŽETIĆ (N.) Über Parasitismus und Krank-
heits-Erreger. pp. 130. _Karansebes,_ 1893. 8°.
7561. g. 13.

GRAHAM (J.) Hydatid Disease in its clinical
aspects. pp. 203. _Edinb._ 1891. 8°. 7560. e. 16.

JAMMES (L.) Recherches sur l'organisation des
Nématodes. pp. 205. _Paris,_ 1894. 8°. 7299. g. 28.

LABBÉ (A.) Recherches sur les Parasites endo-
globulaires du sang des vertébrés. 1894. 8°.
7299. f. 20.

KAISER (J.) Beiträge zum Kenntniss der Acan-
thocephalen. 1891, _etc._ 4°. LEUCKART (R.)
and CHUN (C.) Bibliotheca Zoologica. Hft. 7.
7205. f.

LAVERAN (A.) and BLANCHARD (R.) Les Hématozoaires de l'homme et des animaux. 2 pt.
Paris, 1894. 8°. 7405. a. 4.

LÖNNBERG (E.) Bidrag till kännedomen om i
Sverige förekommande Cestoder. pp. 69.
1889. 8°. Ac. Stockholm. _K. Svenska Vetenskaps Academien._ Bihang till Handlingar.
Bd. 14. Afd. 4. Ac. 1070/7.

—— Studien über skandinavische Cestoden.
pp. 109. 1891. 4°. Ac. Stockholm. _K. Svenska
Vetenskaps Akademi._ Handlingar. N.F. Bd. 24.
Ac. 1070.

LOOSS (A.) Ueber den Bau von Distomum hete-
rophyes und Distomum fraternum. pp. 59.
Kassel, 1894. 8°. 7296. d. 3.

PARASITES—*continued.*

LORTET (L.) and VIALLETON (L.) Étude sur le Bilharzia hæmatobia. pp. 118. 1894. fol. Ac. Lyons. *Université.* Annales. Tom. 9. Ac. 365.

MAYDL (C.) Über Echinokokkus der Pleura. pp. 97. *Wien,* 1891. 8°.   7615. f. 36.

MERCANTI (F.) Gli Animali parassiti dell' uomo. pp. 179. *Milano,* 1894. 8°.   012200. h. 107.

NEUMANN (L. G.) Traité des Maladies parisitaires des animaux domestiques. pp. 767. *Paris,* 1892. 8°.   07293. m. 10.

—— Treatise on the Parasites of domesticated animals. pp. 800. *Lond.* 1892. 8°. 07293. m. 7.

PEIPER (E.) Die Verbreitung der Echinococcen-Krankheit in Vorpommern. pp. 53. *Stuttgart,* 1894. 8°.   Pam. 39.

SCHAUMANN (O.) Zur Kenntniss der sogenannten Rothriocephalus-Anämie. pp. 214. *Helsingfors,* 1894. 8°.   7581. g. 27.

SONSINO (P.) Intestinal, hepatic and portal Entozoa. 1893. 8°. DAVIDSON (A.) Hygiene of Warm Climates.   7686. dd. 2.

SZCZYPIORSKI (S.) Des Entozoaires de l'encéphale. pp. 106. *Paris,* 1890. 8°. 7660. g. 17.

MASSART (J.) and VANDERVELDE (É.) Parasitism organic and social. pp. 124. *Lond.* 1895. 8°. 08276. ee. 10.

PARAY-LE-MONIAL. AUBERT ( ) Les merveilles de Paray-le-Monial. pp. 177. *Tours,* 1893. 12°.   4864. cc. 26.

PARIS. [*See note on page* 1.]

Bibliography and Iconography.

DESTAILLEUR (H.) Catalogue de livres relatifs à l'histoire de Paris. pp. 128. *Paris,* 1894. 8°. 011901. k. 2.

SEINE, *Department.* Inventaire des archives. Période révolutionnaire. 1789—an VIII. 1892, *etc.* 4°. Collection des Inventaires, *etc.* 1814. b, *etc.*

GRATET-DUPLESSIS (G.) Collection de dessins sur Paris. 1891. 8°. Ac. Paris. *Société de l'Histoire.* Mémoires. Tom. 17. Ac. 6883/2.

Ac. Paris. *Bibliothèque Nationale.* COURBOIN (F.) Inventaire de la collection de dessins sur Paris formée par M. H. Destailleur. *Paris,* 1891. 8°.   7858. g. 35.

Art Galleries. *See* EXHIBITIONS. Pt. I.

Bastille.

BOURNON (F.) La Bastille. pp. 364. 1893. 4°. Histoire générale de Paris.   1321. g, *etc.*

CŒURET (A.) La Bastille. pp. 93. *Paris,* 1890. 8°.   6056. c. 3.

DAVENPORT (R. A.) History of the Bastile. pp. 545. *Lond.* 1892. 8°.   012207. ee. 11.

FUNCK-BRENTANO (F.) Archives de la Bastille 1892, *etc.* 8°. France. *M. de l'Instruction.* Catalogue des manuscrits de la Bibliothèque de l'Arsenal. Tom. 9.   011901. f.

SERÉ (P.) La Bastille devant l'histoire. 1890. 8°. Ac. Havre. *Société d'Études.* Recueil. 1890. Ac. 2612.

Churches and Religious Houses.

BEALE (S. S.) The Churches of Paris. pp. 342. *Lond.* 1893. 8°.   07816. ee. 1.

GRANDPRÉ (P. de) Les légendes de Notre-Dame. pp. 328. *Paris,* 1892. 12°.   4629. aaa. 31.

PENNELL (J.) The devils of Notre Dame. Illustrations by J. Pennell. pp. 10. *Lond.* 1894. fol.   K.T.C. 21. a. 1.

VIOLET-LE-DUC (E. E.) Les Églises de Paris. Le Panthéon. pp. 294. *Paris,* 1883. 8°. 7820. cc. 11.

PARIS.—Churches, etc.—*continued.*

LODS (A.) L'Église luthérienne de Paris pendant la Révolution. pp. 21. *Paris,* 1892. 8°. Pam. 29.

PISANI (P.) La Maison des Carmes. pp. 78. *Paris,* 1891. 8°.   4629. aaa. 23.

CÉDOZ (F. M. T.) Un Couvent de Religieuses anglaises à Paris, 1634 à 1884. pp. 479. *Paris,* 1891. 8°.   4629. aaa. 25.

See also infra : TOPOGRAPHY.

Declaration of, 1856. *See* LAW, *Naval.*

Diocese.

PARIS. *Archbishops.* Les Archevêques de Paris au dix-neuvième siècle. pp. 211. *Tournai,* 1895. 8°.   4864. ee. 2.

Eiffel Tower. *See* EIFFEL TOWER.

Environs.

DESTAILLEUR (H.) Catalogue des livres relatifs à l'histoire de Paris et de ses environs. *Paris,* 1894. 8°.   011901. k. 2.

BAEDEKER (C.) Paris and its Environs. 2 pt. *Leipsic,* 1894. 8°.   2352. a.

BARONCELLI (A. de) Guide des Environs de Paris. pp. 538. *Paris,* 1894. 8°. 10174. aa. 42.

BESNARD (É.) Guide historique de Paris à Saint-Germain-en-Laye. pp. 202. *Paris,* 1894. 12°. 10174. a. 24.

DUCKETT (*Sir* G.) Paris and its environs in 1814. pp. 38. 1891. 8°.   10106. ff. 6. (6.)

GROUCHY (E. H. de) *Viscount.* Meudon, Belleville et Chaville. pp. 158. *Paris,* 1893. 8°. 010171. g. 13.

JOANNE (P.) Environs de Paris. pp. 302. *Paris,* 1895. 8°.   10171. a. 27.

MARTIN (A.) Promenades dans les Environs de Paris. *Paris,* 1891, *etc.* 8°.   010171. e.

Exposition Universelle, 1889.
See EXHIBITIONS. Pt. II.

Guide Books. *See infra :* TOPOGRAPHY.

History.

EDWARDS (H. S.) Old and new Paris. 2 vol. *Lond.* 1894. 8°.   10172. h. 3.

ROBIDA (A.) Paris de siècle en siècle. pp. 412. *Paris,* 1895. 4°.   10173. f. 5.

ROUSSEAU (P.) Les héros de Paris. pp. 312. *Paris,* 1891. 4°.   10662. i. 33.

VIRMAITRE (C.) Paris médaillé. pp. 265. *Paris,* 1890. 12°.   7858. a. 47.

Ac. Paris. *Société de l'Histoire de France.* ROYE (J. de) Journal de J. de Roye; Chronique Scandaleuse, 1460-83. *Paris,* 1894, *etc.* 8°. Ac. 6884/86.

GOMBOUST (J.) Le Paris du XVIIe siècle. Plan monumental, 1653. pp. 73. *Paris,* 1890. 8°. 10168. cc. 27.

LENÔTRE (G.) Paris révolutionnaire. pp. 420. *Paris,* 1895. 8°.   9226. c. 29.

CHALLAMEL (J. B. M. A.) Les Clubs contre-révolutionnaires, *etc.* pp. 633. 1895. 8°. Collection de documents relatifs à l'histoire de Paris.   9231. i.

PARIS. Actes de la Commune pendant la révolution. 1894, *etc.* 8°. Collection de documents relatifs à l'histoire de Paris.   9231. i.

BOURNAND (F.) La Terreur à Paris. pp. 296. *Paris,* 1891. 8°.   9230. c. 18.

REGNARD (A.) Chaumette et la Commune de 93. pp. 23. *Paris,* 1889. 8°.   Pam. 28.

HESDIN (R.) Journal of a Spy in Paris during the Reign of Terror. pp. 209. *Lond.* 1895. 8°. 9230. ccc. 5.

PARIS.—History—*continued.*

DUCKETT (*Sir* G.) Paris and its Environs in 1814. pp. 38. 1891. 8°. 10106. ff. 6. (6.)

ADLER (J. B.) Die Revolution und die pariser Commune in socialistische Geschichtsanschauung. pp. 61. *Mainz,* 1892. 16°. 9230. a. 6.

BAX (E. B.) History of the Paris Commune. pp. 135. *Lond.* 1895. 8°. 9230. b. 18.

BOURNAND (F.) Le Clergé pendant la Commune, 1871. pp. 374. *Paris,* 1892. 8°. 4629. i. 26.

GASTYNE (J. de) Une tentative de conciliation entre Versailles et Paris en mai 1871. pp. 15. *Paris,* 1893. 8°. 9004. gg. 31. (10.)

GROMIER (M. A.) La Commune. Journal d'un Vaincu. pp. 292. *Paris,* 1892. 12°. 010662. ff. 24.

KROPOTKIN (P. A.) The Commune of Paris. pp. 15. *Lond.* 1891. 8°. 8282. cc. 48. (3.)

LASSBERG (D. v.) Die pariser Commune 1871. pp. 70. *München,* 1894. 8°. Pam. 28.

MALON (B.) La terza Disfatta del proletario francese. *Milano,* 1894, *etc.* 8°. 9230. aaa. 12.

PETERSEN (N. L.) Pariserkommunen. pp. 31. *Kjøbenh.* 1891. 8°. 9004. gg. 26. (6.)

VÉSINIER (P.) Comment a péri la Commune. pp. 474. *Paris,* 1892. 12°. 9230. cc. 13.

See also infra: Topography: FRANCE, History. For the history of the Siege of Paris, 1870–71, see GERMAN-FRENCH WAR.

Louvre. *See* EXHIBITIONS. Pt. I.

Municipality : Administration.

CHAMPAGNAC (M.) Les scandales de l'Hôtel de Ville. pp. 45. *Paris,* 1890. 8°. Pam. 69.

CARRÉ (C.) La suppression des Octrois. pp. 238. *Paris,* 1890. 8°. 8225. eee. 44.

JOLTRAIN (A.) Les services sanitaires de la Ville de Paris. pp. 300. *Paris,* 1893. 12°. 8777. aaa. 33.

Palais de Justice. *See infra: Topography.*

Parlement. *See* FRANCE, *Law.*

Prisons. *See supra: Bastille : PRISONS.*

Quartiers. *See infra: Topography.*

Religious Houses. *See supra: Churches.*

Schools. *See* EDUCATION, *France.*

Sorbonne. *See infra: University.*

Topography : Social Life.

Guide Books.

BAEDEKER (C.) Paris. pp. 362. 24. *Leipz.* 1894. 8°. 2352. a.

COOK (T.) Guide to Paris. pp. 128. *Lond.* 1895. 8°. 10174. b. 39.

GALIGNANI (A.) and (W.) Paris Guide. pp. 316. *Paris,* 1894. 8°. 10169. de. 27.

JOANNE (P.) Paris-Diamant. pp. 224. *Paris,* 1895. 12°. 10171. a. 26.

NORMAND (C. P. J.) Nouvel intinéraire-guide artistique de Paris. *Paris,* 1892, *etc.* 8°. 10169. de.

PARIS. Tit-Bits guide to Paris. pp. 147. *Lond.* 1891. 8°. 10174. aaa. 40.

PINCHARD (J.) Le Compteur kilométrique parisien, dictionnaire des rues et monuments. pp. 430. *Paris,* 1890. 8°. 10174. aa. 34.

General Topography and Social Life.

ADOLPHUS (F.) Memories of Paris. pp. 308. *Edinb.* 1895. 8°. 10174. bb. 28.

BARRON (L.) Autour de Paris. pp. 497. *Paris,* 1891. 4°. K.T.C. 3. b. 14.

PARIS.—Topography, etc.—continued.

BIJVANCK (W. G. C.) Parijs, 1891. pp. 278. *Leiden,* 1892. 8°. 10169. bb. 7.

—— Un Hollandais à Paris en 1891. pp. 308. *Paris,* 1892. 8°. 011824. de. 36.

BLAVET (E.) La Vie parisienne. pp. 326. *Paris,* 1890. 18°. 12355. cc. 28.

BOIS (J.) Les petites religions de Paris. pp. 215. *Paris,* 1894. 12°. 4506. de. 8.

BONNEFONT (G.) Les Parisiennes chez elles. *Paris,* 1895, *etc.* 4°. 10659. g.

BOUCARD (M.) La Vie de Paris. pp. 375. *Paris,* 1892. 8°. 10171. de. 4.

BUGUET (H.) and BENJAMIN (E.) L'Univers dans Paris. pp. 394. *Paris,* 1889. 12°. 10171. de. 3.

CHILD (T.) The praise of Paris. pp. 299. *N.Y.* 1893. 8°. 010171. k. 7.

CHING KE-TUNG. Les Parisiens peints par un Chinois. pp. 282. *Paris,* 1891. 12°. 10169. de. 16.

CROQUEVILLE. Paris en Voiture, à Cheval, *etc.* pp. 393. *Paris,* 1892. 12°. 7907. de. 46.

CUERVO (Á.) Curiosidades de la vida americana en París. pp. 353. *París,* 1893. 8°. 012330. g. 27.

DAUDET (E.) Les Coulisses de la société parisienne. pp. 288. *Paris,* 1895. 8°. 10174. bbb. 2.

DRUMONT (É. A.) Mon vieux Paris. pp. 384. *Paris,* 1893. 12°. 10174. aaa. 45.

EDWARDS (H. S.) Old and new Paris. 2 vol. *Lond.* 1894. 8°. 10172. h. 3.

ENGLISHMAN. An Englishman in Paris. 2 vol. *Lond.* 1892. 8°. 9231. f. 4.

FALGAIROLLE (E.) Notes et souvenirs de Paris. pp. 117. *Nîmes,* 1892. 8°. 10174. aa. 43.

GOUDEAU (É.) Paysages parisiens. pp. 175. *Paris,* 1892. 8°. 10172. f. 22.

—— Tableaux de Paris. Paris qui consomme. pp. 325. *Paris,* 1893. 4°. 10171. dd. 2.

HASE (C. B.) Briefe von der Wanderung und aus Paris. pp. 115. *Leipz.* 1894. 8°. 010171. f. 46.

LAFOND DE SAINT-MÜR (O.) Impressions de voyage dans Paris. pp. 447. *Paris,* 1893. 12°. 010171. e. 21.

LESAGE (H.) Souvenirs d'un Maire-Adjoint de Paris. pp. 307. *Paris,* 1895. 12°. 10174. c. 19.

MARTIN (A.) Les Étapes d'un touriste en France. Paris. *Paris,* 1892, *etc.* 8°. 10174. a.

PARIS NOTE-BOOK. My Paris note-book. pp. 384. *Lond.* 1894. 8°. 010171. k. 12.

PAULIAN (L.) Paris qui mendie. pp. 302. *Paris,* 1893. 12°. 08275. e. 16.

PAVLOVSKY (I.) Aus der Welthauptstadt Paris. pp. 548. *Paris,* 1895. 4°. 10174. b. 40.

STRAUSS (P.) Paris Ignoré. pp. 486. *Paris,* 1893. 4°. 1787. c. 32.

TOMEL (G.) Le Bas du pavé parisien. pp. 272. *Paris,* 1894. 8°. 12350. aaa. 51.

ZED. La Société parisienne. pp. 230. *Paris,* 1891. 12°. 012330. f. 17.

Quartiers, Streets, Buildings, etc.

HARRISON (W.) Memorable Prais houses. pp. 276. *Lond.* 1893. 8°. 10170. bb. 7.

CHERRIER (P.) La Cité à travers les âges. pp. 240. *Paris,* 1894. 8°. 10174. g. 28.

VIBERT (P.) Mon berceau. Histoire du premier arrondissement. pp. 429. *Paris,* 1893. 12°. 10170. ccc. 6.

HUYSMANS (J. K.) Les vieux Quartiers de Paris. La Bièvre. pp. 43. *Paris,* 1890. 8°. 10105. ee. 12. (5.)

PARIS.—Topography, etc.—continued.

CLUSERET (G. P.) Les Halles. pp. 126. Paris, 1890. 8°. 08227. ee. 27.

PITON (C.) Le quartier des Halles. pp. 639. Paris, 1891. 8°. 10169. c. 16.

JONQUET (E.) Montmartre autrefois et aujourd'hui. pp. 348. Paris, 1890. 4°. 10172. g. 5.

SARCEY (F.) Boulevards of Paris. 1892. 8°. Great Streets of the World. 10026. k. 16.

UZANNE (O.) Bouquinistes et Bouquineurs. Physiologie des quais de Paris. pp. 318. Paris, 1893. 8°. 10174. f. 23.

—— The Book-hunter in Paris. pp. 232. Lond. 1893. 4°. 11903. m. 4.

Ac. Paris. Société de l'Histoire de Paris. COYECQUE (E.) L'Hôtel-Dieu de Paris au moyen âge. 2 tom. Paris, 1891. 8°. Ac. 6883/10.

PARIS. Le Palais de Justice; son monde et ses mœurs. pp. 400. Paris, 1892. 8°. 6005. k. 2.

—— The Paris Law Courts. pp. 293. Lond. 1894. 8°. 6006. cc. 14.

LAURENT (A.) Les Prisons du vieux Paris. pp. 271. Paris, 1893. 8°. 6056. g. 7.

JULLIEN (A.) Un vieil hôtel du Marais. pp. 37. Paris, 1891. 4°. 10172. f. 19.

PARIS. Société des Amis des Monuments. Protestations contre la mutilation de l'Esplanade des Invalides par l'établissement d'une gare. pp. 32. Paris, 1894. 8°. 10105. ee. 10. (13.)

MARTIN (A. T.) Mutilation de l'Esplanade des Invalides. pp. 13. Paris, 1894. 8°.
    10105. ee. 10. (12.)

University.

FOURNIER (M.) La Faculté de décret de l'Université au xv° siècle. 1895, etc. 4°. Histoire générale de Paris. 1321. i.

GRÉARD (O.) Nos adieux à la vieille Sorbonne. pp. 406. pp. 406. Paris, 1893. 8°. 8356. e. 41.

PÉRIES (G.) La Faculté de Droit dans l'ancienne Université 1160–1793. pp. 391. Paris, 1890. 8°.
    8356. f. 34.

FERET (P.) La Faculté de Théologie de Paris. Paris, 1894, etc. 8°. 8356. h.

LEFRANC (A.) Histoire du Collège de France. pp. 432. Paris, 1893. 8°. 8355. df. 18.

MARION (H.) L'Éducation dans l'Université. pp. 400. Paris, 1893. 12°. 8356. aa. 24.

Ac. Paris. Université. Conseil général des facultés. Rapports, 1890–91. pp. 137. Paris, 1892. 8°. 8356. e. 42.

—— Le livret de l'étudiant de Paris. 2 pt. Paris, 1891. 12°. 8355. aa. 20.

See also EDUCATION, France, University.

PARISH COUNCILS. See LOCAL GOVERNMENT.

PARISHES. ARCHBOLD (J. F.) Shaw's Parish Law. pp. 699. Lond. 1895. 8°.
    2232. a. 1.

BLACK (W. G.) Handbook of the parochial ecclesiastical Law of Scotland. pp. 236. Edinb. 1891. 8°. 5157. b. 11.

—— Handbook of Scottish parochial Law other than ecclesiastical. pp. 213. Edinb. 1893. 8°.
    6583. aa. 12.

DOLBY (J.) The Parochial Valuer's assistant. Lond. 1890. fol. 8548. f. 22.

HOLDSWORTH (W. A.) Handy book of Parish Law. pp. 296. Lond. 1891. 8°. 5155. cc. 25.

MACKENZIE (W. W.) The Overseer's handbook. pp. 310. Lond. 1895. 8°. 6425. aaa. 35.

MARIE (J.) Traité du régime légal des Paroisses catholique. pp. 588. Rennes, 1892. 8°.
    05107. ee. 23.

PARISHES—continued.

MIGNAULT (P. B.) Le Droit paroissial. pp. 690. Montréal, 1893. 8°. 5155. f. 11.

TRENCH (W. R.) Parochial church finance. pp. 16. Lond. 1894. 8°. 4429. c. 21. (19.)

See also LAW, Ecclesiastical: LOCAL GOVERNMENT: PAUPERISM: THEOLOGY, Pastoral.

PARISH REGISTERS. BOYCE (E. J.) History of Parochial Registers. pp. 57. Winchester, 1895. 8°. 9904. i. 42.

For the Registers of various Parishes, see ADEL: ASHBY: BIDSTON: BRAMFIELD: BRUTON: BURNSALL: CAMBRIDGE: CANTERBURY: CARLTON: CHILLESFORD: COLMER: CULPHO: DORSETSHIRE: DURHAM: ELMSTONE: FELKIRK: GAINSBOROUGH: GREAT HAMPDEN: GREENSTED: GRIMSBY: GULVAL: HAYNES: HORBLING: HOUGHTON: ICKWORTH: IRBY: KINGSTON: LAMBOURNE: LEWISHAM: LEYLAND: LIVERPOOL: LONDON, Parish Registers: MARSHAM: MARSHFIELD: MAXEY: MILBORNE PORT: NORWICH: PENRITH: PERLETHORPE: PRIORS DEAN: RAVENSTONEDALE: READING: ROCHESTER: RYLSTONE: SADDLEWORTH: SAINT GEORGE: SKIPTON: SOUTHAM: SOUTHAMPTON: STAPLEFORD: STOCKPORT: WALSALL.

PARKS. See FORESTRY: GARDENING.

PARLIAMENTS. BENITO Y VARELA (P. de) La Inviolabilidad parlamentaria. pp. 39. Madrid, 1894. 8°. Pam. 71.

BUCHER (L.) Der Parlamentarismus wie er ist. pp. 286. Stuttgart, 1894. 8°. 8006. cc. 10.

DICKINSON (R.) Summary of the constitution and procedure of foreign Parliaments. pp. 580. Lond. 1890. 8°. 8006. cc. 3.

FIGDOR (S.) Parlamentswissenschaft. 2 pt. Berl. 1885, 91. 8°. 8074. bb. 17.

MEAD (E. D.) Representative government. 1892. 8°. Ac. Brooklyn. Ethical Association. Evolution Series. No. 20. 7006. bbb.

MICELI (V.) Il Concetto moderno della Rappresentanza politica. pp. 270. Perugia, 1892. 8°. 8009. i. 30.

POUDRA (J.) and PIERRE (E.) Trattato di Diritto parlamentare. pp. 715. 1888. 8°. BRUNIALTI (A.) Biblioteca di scienze politiche. Vol. 4.
    8010. f. 4.

REED (T. B.) Reed's Rules. Manual of general Parliamentary Law. pp. 223. Chicago, 1894. 8°. 8175. de. 2.

SÁNCHEZ DE TOCA (J.) Necesidad del poder real en el régimen parlamentario. 1894. 8°. Ac. Madrid. R. Academie. Discursos. Tom. 5.
    Ac. 142/2.

TODD (A.) Parliamentary government in the British Colonies. pp. 929. Lond. 1894. 8°.
    8155. ee. 20.

WALPOLE (S.) The Electorate and the Legislature. pp. 163. 1892. 8°. The English Citizen.
    2238. bb.

See also ELECTIONS: GOVERNMENT; and for the Parliament of each country, under the country required.

PARODIES. ADAMS (W. D.) A Book of Burlesque. pp. 220. 1891. 8°. ADAMS (W. H. D.) Whitefriars Library. 012202. g.

UMLAUFT (F.) Das Buch der Parodien und Travestien. pp. 274. Wien, 1894. 8°.
    011528. g. 27.

LAYS. Lays of the Links: parodies. pp. 68. Edinb. 1895. 8°. 011652. e. 45.

PARROT. GREENE (W. T.) The Grey Parrot. pp. 94. Lond. 1893. 8°. 7291. aa. 23.

PATENTS.—Austria—_continued._

BRUNSTEIN (J. L.) Die Patentreform in Österreich. _Wien,_ 1894, _etc._   05549. k.

Canada. _See infra : United States._

France.

BEAUME (A.) and DUMONT (E.) Code pratique de l'Inventeur breveté. pp. 340. _Paris,_ 1895. 8°.
     6005. bb. 1.

BRUSSAUX (P.) and GUITTIER (P.) Dictionnaire des Patentes. pp. 842. _Paris._ 1891. 8°.
     5406. e. 1.

COUHIN (C.) La Propriété industrielle, _etc._ _Paris,_ 1894, _etc._ 8°.   5423. f.

PELLETIER (M.) Droit industriel. Brevets d'invention. pp. 428. 1893. 8°. LECHALAS (M. C.) Encyclopédie des travaux publics.   012216. i.

Germany.

BERLIN. _Conferenz für den Schutz des gewerblichen Eigenthums._ Sind die Industrie-Schutzgesetze verbessert? pp. 132. _Berl._ 1891. fol.
     5605. h. 18.

MITTLER (H.) Beiträge zur Theorie des Patentrechtes. pp. 165. _Berl._ 1894. 8°. 05604. i. 32.

PIEPER (C.) Gewerbe- und Industrieschutz. pp. 98. _Berl._ 1890. 8°.   08276. h. 3.

WITT (O. N.) Die deutsche chemische Industrie in ihren Beziehungen zum Patentwesen. pp. 143. _Berl._ 1893. 8°.   8908. d. 13.

New Zealand.

NEW ZEALAND. The Patents Act, 1889. pp. 428. _Wellington,_ 1889. 8°.   6605. ff. 7.

Switzerland.

MEILI (F.) Prinzipien des schweizerischen Patentgesetzes. pp. 131. _Zürich,_ 1890. 8°.
     5551. cc. 5.

SIMON (A.) Der Patentschutz mit Berücksichtigung der schweizerischen Gesetzgebung. pp. 113. _Bern,_ 1891. 8°.   05551. g. 1.

United States, Canada, and South and Central America.

AMERICA. Patent Laws of America. pp. 48. 1891. 8°. U.S. _Bureau of American Republics._ Bulletin. No. 3.   08225. k. 1.

KNIGHT (G. H.) Patent Franchise in the United States. pp. 24. 1891. 4°.   Pam. 33.

RIDOUT (J. G.) Treatise on the Patent law of Canada. pp. 590. _Toronto,_ 1894. 8°.
     6605. bb. 21.

ROBINSON (W. C.) The law of Patents. 3 vol. _Boston,_ 1890. 8°.   6615. h. 13.

U.S. _Patent Office._ Women Inventors to whom Patents have been granted. pp. 44. _Washington,_ 1888. 4°.   8228. k. 30.

PATHOLOGY. Ac. Manchester. _Pathological Society._ Transactions. _Manch._ 1892, _etc._ 8°.   Ac. 3825. f.

—— Toronto. _Pathological Society._ Proceedings and Transactions. _Toronto,_ 1890, _etc._ 8°.
     Ac. 3868. h.

ARNOLD (J.) Arbeiten aus dem pathologischen Institute zu Heidelberg. pp. 244. 1890. 8°. ZIEGLER (E.) Beiträge zur pathologischen Anatomie. Bd. 8.   7441. eee. 18.

BANNATYNE (G. A.) Aids to general Pathology. pp. 64. _Lond._ 1892. 8°.   7321. aaa. 22. (6.)

—— Aids to special Pathology. pp. 102. _Lond._ 1892. 8°.   7441. a. 21.

BOUCHARD (C.) Traité de Pathologie générale. _Paris,_ 1895, _etc._ 8°.   7441. h.

CARRINGTON (R. E.) Notes on Pathology. pp. 150. _Lond._ 1892. 8°.   7441. aa. 1.

COATS (J.) Manual of Pathology. pp. 1130. _Lond._ 1895. 8°.   2256. h. 2.

PATHOLOGY—_continued._

COATS (J.) Fundamental conceptions as to the characteristics of life, with reference to Pathology. pp. 30. _Glasg._ 1894. 8°. 7306. g. 18. (4.)

DAVIDSON (A.) Geographical Pathology. 2 vol. _Edinb._ 1892. 8°.   7686. f. 6.

GIBBES (H.) Practical Pathology. pp. 320. _Edinb._ 1891. 8°.   7441. ee. 22.

HALL (H. N.) Compend of general Pathology. pp. 204. _Edinb._ 1894. 8°.   7442. aa. 17.

HALLIBURTON (W. D.) Text-book of chemical Physiology and Pathology. pp. 874. _Lond._ 1891. 8°.   7419. i. 7.

HERRINGHAM (W. P.) Handbook of medical Pathology. pp. 313. _Lond._ 1894. 8°.
     7440. de. 10.

HOWDEN (J. C.) Index Pathologicus, for registration of lesions recorded in pathological records. pp. 86. _Lond._ 1894. fol. 7440. k. 2.

KREHL (L.) Grundriss der klinischen Pathologie. pp. 238. _Leipz._ 1893. 8°.   7441. e. 9.

MOYNAC (L.) Manuel de Pathologie. pp. 663. _Paris,_ 1888. 8°.   7441. aaa. 1.

NOORDEN (C. v.) Lehrbuch der Pathologie des Stoffwechsels. pp. 492. _Berl._ 1893. 8°.
     7441. f. 11.

NOTHNAGEL (H.) Specielle Pathologie. _Wien,_ 1894, _etc._ 8°.   7441. d.

ORTH (J.) Arbeiten aus dem pathologischen Institut in Göttingen. pp. 267. _Berl._ 1893. 8°.
     7680. df. 2.

P.P. _Edinburgh._ Journal of comparative Pathology. Edited by J. M'Fadyean. _Edinb._ 1888, _etc._ 8°.   P.P. 2856. aa.

—— The Journal of Pathology. Edited by G. S. Woodhead. _Edinb._ 1892, _etc._ 8°. P.P. 3295. b.

—— _Jena._ Centralblatt für allgemeine Pathologie. _Jena,_ 1890, _etc._ 8°. P.P. 3201. c. and 1079.

SCHWALBE (J.) Grundriss der speciellen Pathologie. pp. 763. _Stuttg._ 1892. 8°.   7442. i. 3.

STRICKER (S.) Fragmente aus dem Gebiete der experimentellen Pathologie. _Leipz._ 1894, _etc._ 8°.
     7442. ee.

SUTTON (H. G.) Lectures on Pathology. pp. 503. _Lond._ 1891. 8°.   7441. e. 7.

WHITAKER (J. R.) Notes on Pathology. pp. 245. _Edinb._ 1890. 8°.   7440. aaa. 2.

WOODHEAD (G. S.) Practical Pathology. pp. 652. _Edinb._ 1892. 8°.   2255. d. 12.

See also BACTERIOLOGY : CHEMISTRY, _Medical :_ DISEASE : MEDICINE : PHYSIOLOGY.

Pathological Anatomy. _See_ ANATOMY.

Pathological Specimens.

GUY'S HOSPITAL. Catalogue of pathological Specimens in the Museum. _Lond._ 1894, _etc._ 8°.
     7419. g.

NETLEY HOSPITAL. Catalogue of pathological Specimens in the Museum. _Lond._ 1892, _etc._ 8°.
     7419. i. 29.

Ac. London. _University College._ Catalogue of the Specimens in the Museum. pp. 153. _Lond._ 1890. 8°.   7321. ee. 18.

Surgical Pathology.

BOWLBY (A. A.) Surgical Pathology. pp. 640. _Lond._ 1895. 8°.   7481. b. 18.

PEPPER (A. J.) Elements of surgical Pathology. pp 607. _Lond._ 1894. 8°.   7481. aa. 29.

MOYNAC (L.) Éléments de Pathologie chirurgicale. 2 tom. _Paris,_ 1890. 8°.   7440. de. 9. _See also_ SURGERY.

PATIENCE. Game. HOFFMANN (L.) Book of Patience games. pp. 4. 123. _Lond._ 1892. 8°.
     7913. e. 12.

PATIENCE—continued.

POLE (W.) Patience games. 1891. 8°. Cyclopædia of Card Games. 2264. b. 20.
See also CARDS.

PATNA. WADDELL (L. A.) Discovery of the site of Asoka's capital of Pātaliputra. pp. 29. *Calcutta*, 1892. 4°. 7706. f. 29.

PAU. DUBARAT (V.) Mélanges de bibliographie et d'histoire locale. *Pau*, 1894, *etc.* 8°. 011900. f.

BARTHETY (H.) Le Berceau d'Henri IV. pp. 136. *Pau*, 1893. 8°. 010662. i. 26.

DUBONÉ (H.) Pau and its neighbourhood. pp. 103. *Pau*, 1882. 8°. 7686. aa. 5.

DELFOUR (J.) Histoire du Lycée de Pau. pp. 479. *Pau*, 1890. 8°. 8355. df. 14.
See also BEARN : WATERING-PLACES.

PAULHAN. DELOUVRIER (A.) Histoire de Paulhan. pp. 325. 55. *Montpellier*, 1892. 8°. 4629. dd. 15.

PAUPERISM : MENDICITY : POOR LAWS, Ac. Manchester. *Statistical Society.*

RHODES (J. M.) Pauperism. *Lond.* 1891. 8°. Ac. 2455/2.

BOEHMERT (C. V.) Das Armenwesen in 77. deutschen Städten und einigen Landarmenverbänden. 3 Thle. *Dresden*, 1886-88. 4°. 8282. h. 19.

BOOTH (C.) Pauperism and Endowment of Old Age. pp. 188. *Lond.* 1892. 8°. 08276. g. 28.

—— The aged Poor in England and Wales. *Lond.* 1894, *etc.* 8°. 2020. e.

BOOTH (W.) In Brightest England, or "General" Booth's scheme eclipsed. pp. 63. *Lond.* 1892. 8°. 8276. aa. 53.

BOSANQUET (B.) "In Darkest England" on the wrong track. pp. 72. *Lond.* 1891. 8°. 8282. aa. 52.

DWYER (P.) General Booth's "Submerged Tenth." pp. 99. *Lond.* 1891. 8°. 8276. aa. 49.

ELIHU. Is General Booth's Darkest England scheme a failure? pp. 31. *Manch.* 1893. 8°. 8377. ee. 30. (20.)

KASPARY (J.) Salvation General Humbug [W. Booth]. pp. 32. *Lond.* 1892. 8°. 8277. de. 30. (9.)

—— Wise social projects and the Darkest England Enquiry. pp. 48. *Lond.* 1893. 8°. 8277. de. 29. (16.)

NIEUWENHUIS (F. D.) "General" Booth en zijn "Plan." pp. 78. *Amsterd.* 1891. 8°. 8277. h. 20. (7.)

ROBERTS (W. H.) General Booth's Scheme and the Municipal alternative. pp. 49. *Lond.* 1891. 8°. 08276. f. 21. (16.)

ROXBY (R. B.) General Booth, limited. pp. 150. *Lond.* 1892. 8°. 8277. de. 18.

SALVATION ARMY. The Salvation Army and its social scheme. By W. T. Stead. pp. 32. *Lond.* 1891. 4°. Pam. 82.

SCRUTATOR. On the Watch tower. Queries respecting General Booth's Book. pp. 20. *Lond.* 1891. 8°. 4139. bb. 14. (3.)

CARLILE (W.) What is the Church Army social scheme for "Darkest England"? pp. 52. *Lond.* 1891. 16°. Pam. 92.

BURNS (J.) The Unemployed. pp. 18. 1893. 8°. LONDON. *Fabian Society.* Fabian Tracts. No. 47. 8275. dd. 7.

DALLAS (D. C.) How to solve the unemployed problem. pp. 16. *Lond.* 1895. 8°. Pam. 82.

DODD (J. T.) To Boards of Guardians. How to provide for the unemployed. pp. 7. *Lond.* 1894. 8°. 8282. ff. 12. (9.)

PAUPERISM—continued.

DRAGE (G.) The Unemployed. pp. 277. *Lond.* 1894. 8°. 08275. ee. 5.

—— The Problem of the aged Poor. pp. 375. *Lond.* 1895. 8°. 08275. f. 30.

ENGLAND AND WALES. *Local Government Board.* Pauperism and Distress. Circular respecting provision of work for the unemployed. pp. 3. *Lond.* 1892. fol. Pam. 82.

FLOWER (B. O.) Civilization's Inferno. pp. 237. *Bost.* 1893. 8°. 8277. de. 57.

GODARD (J. G.) Poverty, its genesis and exodus. pp. 160. *Lond.* 1892. 8°. 08276. e. 26.

GOLDIE (J.) The Poor and their happiness. pp. 212. *Lond.* 1895. 8°. 8277. b. 71.

GRAHAM (A. D.) Our Town Poor. pp. 19. *Lond.* 1883. 12°. 8277. de. 29. (4.)

GREENE (W. T.) Population and pauperism. pp. 23. *Lond.* 1891. 8°. 8277. de. 29. (1.)

HOWARD ASSOCIATION. Suggestions for the diminution of Pauperism. *Lond.* 1892. 8°. 8277. ee. 28. (11.)

LONDON. *Toynbee Hall.* Draft Report of the Toynbee Hall "Unemployed" committee. ff. 4. *Lond.* 1892. fol. 1890. b. 3. (65.)

PAULIAN (L.) Paris qui mendie. pp. 302. *Paris*, 1893. 12°. 08275. e. 16.

PEEK (F.) The Workless, the Thriftless and the worthless. pp. 56. *Lond.* 1892. 8°. 8277. de. 30. (12.)

RAUSCH (C.) Das Problem der Armuth. pp. 123. *Berl.* 1891. 8°. 08276. g. 19.

RUBBRECHT (L. A.) Remèdes contre le paupérisme. pp. 140. *Brux.* 1892. 8°. 8276. aa. 54.

THÉRON (E.) Individualisme, socialisme et paupérisme. pp. 456. *Paris*, 1894. 12°. 08275. e. 31.

TRAP (C.) Om Statens Stilling til ubemidledes Alderdomsforsørgelse i flere europæiske Lande. pp. 311. *Kjøbenh.* 1892. 8°. 8276. d. 64.

WHITE (A.) The destitute Alien in Great Britain. pp. 191. *Lond.* 1892. 8°. 08276. e. 31.
See also CAPITAL AND LABOUR : LONDON, *Poor :* SOCIAL SCIENCE.

Poor Laws.

Great Britain and Ireland.

BARRISTER. A B C Guide to the Poor Law. pp. 32. *Lond.* 1895. 16°. 6345. a. 9.

CHANCE (W.) Better Administration of the Poor Law. pp. 260. 1895. 8°. Charity Organisation Series. 08276. f.

CHEVALLIER (É.) La Loi des pauvres et la société anglaise. pp. 412. *Paris*, 1895. 8°. 08277. g. 16.

DODD (J. T.) "Casual Paupers" and how we treat them. pp. 8. *Lond.* 1890. 8°. Pam. 82.

FOWLE (T. W.) The Poor Law. pp. 175. 1890. 8°. The English Citizen. 2238. bb.

—— The Poor Law, Friendly Societies and Old Age Destitution. pp. 23. *Oxf.* 1892. 8°. 8277. de. 30. (8.)

FRY (D. P.) Handbook for the election of Guardians of the Poor. pp. 205. *Lond.* 1892. 8°. 6426. aaaa. 7.

HOARE (H. N. H.) On the development of the English Poor Law. pp. 27. *Lond.* 1893. 8°. 8282. cc. 47. (8.)

LUBBOCK (G.) Some poor relief Questions. With the arguments on both sides. pp. 329. *Lond.* 1895. 8°. 08275. ee. 37.

MACKENZIE (W. W.) The Poor Law Guardian. pp. 360. *Lond.* 1895. 8°. 6426. aaaa. 34.

—— The Overseers' Handbook. pp. 310. *Lond.* 1895. 8°. 6426. aaaa. 35.

PAUPERISM.—Poor Laws—*continued.*

MACMORRAN (A.) and (M. S. J.) The Poor Law statutes. *Lond.* 1890. 8°.   6425. ee. 2.

PELL (A.) Out-Relief. A paper. pp. 16. *Lond.* 1890. 8°.   8277. de. 29. (8.)

P.P. London. *British Medical Journal.* The sick poor in Workhouses. *Lond.* 1894, *etc.* 8°.   7688. eee.

DODD (T.) Better treatment of aged Poor in the Workhouses. pp. 7. *Lond.* 1892. 8°.   Pam. 82.

SYMONDS (J. F.) The Law of Settlement. pp. 256. *Lond.* 1891. 8°.   6426. aaaa. 2.

VULLIAMY (A. F.) The Law of Settlement. pp. 274. *Lond.* 1895. 8°.   6425. aaaa. 18.

WORDS. Plain Words on out-relief. pp. 65. *Lond.* 1894. 8°.   8276. aa. 66.

LAMOND (R. P.) The Scottish Poor Laws. pp. 398. *Glasg.* 1892. 8°.   6583. b. 23.

SCOTLAND. *Board of Supervision for Relief of the Poor.* Rules and regulations for the management of Poorhouses. pp. 65. *Edinb.* 1892. 8°.   6583. b. 24.

See also LOCAL GOVERNMENT.

Continent of Europe.

KOBATSCH (R.) Die Armenpflege in Wien. pp. 92. *Wien*, 1893. 8°.   8276. ee. 65.

PUSSEMIER (L.) La Répression de la mendicité et du vagabondage. pp. 23. *Paris*, 1894. 8°.   Pam. 82.

RÆDER (J. G. F.) Forsørgelse af Trængende. pp. 272. *Kjøbenh.* 1892. 8°.   08276. f. 61.

RUBIN (M.) Om Alderdomsforsørgelsen. pp. 32. *Kjøbenh.* 1891. 8°.   Pam. 82.

SEEGER (V.) Bidrag til Asminderød og Grønholt Sognes Fattigvæsens Historie i Tidsrumuret. pp. 63. *Helsingør*, 1893. 8°.   Pam. 82.

BALCH (E. G.) Public assistance of the Poor in France. pp. 179. 1893. 8°. Ac. Saratoga. *Economic Association.* Publications. Vol. 8. No. 4 & 5.   Ac. 2388.

BERTSCH (M.) Ueber Landstreicherei und Bettel. pp. 101. *Tübingen*, 1894. 8°.   05604. i. 27.

SMISSAERT (H.) Het aandeel van den staat in de Verzorging der Armen. pp. 200. *Utrecht*, 1893. 8°.   8276. f. 35.

DAHLBERG (B. H.) Bidrag till Svenska fattiglagstiftningens historia. pp. 103, 36. *Upsala*, 1893. 8°.   08276. i. 18.

See also LOCAL GOVERNMENT.

PAVIA. BELTRAMI (L.) La certosa di Pavia. pp. 6. *Milano*, 1891. fol.   1730. c. 9.

PAWNBROKING. HARDAKER (A.) Brief history of Pawnbroking. pp. 367. *Lond.* 1892. 8°.   8226. aaa. 49.

LENZ (A.) Der Strafrechtliche Schutz des Pfandrechts. pp. 271. *Stuttg.* 1893. 8°.   6006. c. 39.

P.P. *London.* Pawnbrokers' Magazine. *Lond.* 1891, *etc.* fol.   2105.

PEACE. *See* WAR.

PEAK, Derbyshire. *See* DERBY.

PEARLS. CALVERT (A. F.) Pearls: their origin and formation. pp. 32. *Lond.* 1892. 8°.   Pam. 42.

KENT (W. S.) The Great Barrier Reef of Australia. pp. 387. *Lond.* 1893. fol. K.T.C. 9. b. 3.

KUNZ (G. F.) On Pearls, and the utilization and application of the shells. 1894. 8°. U.S. *Commission of Fisheries.* Bulletin. Vol. 13.   7290. dd.

MADRAS. *Government Central Museum.* Notes on Pearl fisheries. *Madras*, 1890. 8°. 7299. e. 5.

PEARLS—*continued.*

THOMAS (H. S.) Report on Pearl fisheries. pp. 79. *Madras*, 1884. fol.   7290. k. 5.

THURSTON (E.) Pearl fisheries of the Gulf of Manaar. pp. 62. 1894. 8°. MADRAS. *Government Museum.* Bulletin. No. 1.   7958. f.

See also GEMS.

PEAT. BURKE (J.) Moss Peat and its products. pp. 32. *Lond.* 1895. 8°.   07031. de. 1. (14.)

PECOS VALLEY. *See* NEW MEXICO.

PEEBLES. RENWICK (R.) Gleanings from the records of Peebles, 1604–52. pp. 267. *Peebles*, 1892. 12°.   10369. ccc. 21.

WILLIAMSON (A.) Glimpses of Peebles. pp. 322. *Selkirk*, 1895. 8°.   10369. ccc. 38.

PEGU. DHAMMACHETI. The Kalyānī Inscriptions erected at Pegu in 1476 A.D. *Rangoon*, 1892. 8°.   14098. dd. 9.

PEKIN. PALÉOLOGUE (M.) Pékin. 1892. 4°. Les Capitales du Monde. No. 10.   10025. g.

P.P. *Tientsin.* Peking and Tientsin Times. *Tientsin*, 1894, *etc.* fol.   P.P. 9990. ff.

PELASGIANS. *See* GREECE, *History.*

PELLAGRA. BERGER (L.) Pellagra. 1893. 8°. Ac. London. *New Sydenham Society.* Monographs. Vol. 143.   Ac. 3838/57.

TUCZEK (F.) Studien über die Pellagra. pp. 113. *Berl.* 1893. 8°.   7620. df. 37.

PELOPONNESUS. *See* GREECE: SPARTA.

PEMBROKESHIRE. KILNER (E. A.) Four Welsh counties. pp. 266. *Lond.* 1891. 8°.   10369. cc. 44.

OWEN (G.) Description of Pembrokeshire. 1892, *etc.* 8°. Cymmrodorion Record Series. No. 1, *etc.*   Ac. 8227/10.

TIMMINS (H. T.) Nooks and corners of Pembrokeshire. pp. 203. *Lond.* 1895. 4°.   10369. l. 12.

PENANCE. CHILDREN. Children's Confession book. pp. 56. *Manch.* 1892. 12°.   Pam. 11.

DAVIS (C. H.) Scriptural and Ecclesiastical Absolution. pp. 4. *Lond.* 1887. 8°.   4371. dd. 8. (3.)

ENGLAND, *Church of.* Hints to those who go to Confession. pp. 32. *Lond.* 1894. 8°.   4422. bbb. 64. (5.)

HITCHENS (J. H.) "The Priest in Absolution." pp. 20. *Lond.* 1891. 8°.   4108. de. 32. (10.)

MOEREN (A. B. v. d.) Practatus de sacramento Pœnitentiæ. pp. 152. *Gandavi.* 1888. 8°.   4061. f. 14.

NOEL (M. H.) Confession. A sermon. pp. 30. *Oxf.* 1894. 12°.   4476. de. 13. (5.)

PIJPER (F.) Geschiedenis der Boete en biecht in de Christelijke Kerk. 's *Gravenh.* 1891, *etc.* 8°.   4061. dd.

PUSEY (E. B.) Hints for a first Confession. pp. 40. *Lond.* 1892. 24°.   3455. aaaa. 2.

SCHIELER (K. E.) Die Verwaltung des Busssakramentes. pp. 644. 1894. 8°. Wissenschaftliche Handbibliothek. Theol. Lehrbücher. 7.   3558. e.

WAINWRIGHT (C. H.) Debate on auricular Confession in the Church of England. pp. 32. *Lond.* 1891. 8°.   4108. de. 32. (12.)

WILMOT (E. A. E.) The Prayer-Book and Absolution. 1895. 8°. Four Foundation Truths.   4109. aa. 44.

PENANG. P.P. *Penang.* The Penang Herald. *Penang*, 1888, *etc.* fol. P.P. 9979. c. *See also* MALAY PENINSULA: STRAITS SETTLEMENTS.

PENCHANT, Game. SMARTE (J.) Penchant: a game of cards. pp. 111.
Lond. 1893. 8°.　　　　　7913. ccc. 39.

PEN DRAWING. *See* DRAWING.

PENINSULAR AND ORIENTAL STEAMSHIP COMPANY.
See NAVAL SCIENCE.

PENINSULAR WAR. CLERC (J. C. A.) Campagne du Maréchal Soult dans les Pyrénées en 1813–14. pp. 464. *Paris,* 1894. 8°. 9180. ee. 5.

CRAUFURD (A. H. G.) General Craufurd and his Light Division. pp. 298. *Lond.* 1891. 8°.
　　　　　　　　　　10817. i. 27.

G., L. F. Les prisoniers de Cabrera. pp. 298.
Paris, 1892. 12°.　　　　　9078. b. 18.

LAGERHJELM (G. R.) Napoleon och Wellington på Pyreneiska Halfön 1808–10. pp. 213.
Stockholm, 1889. 8°.　　　　　9080. c. 26.

NAPIER (*Sir* W. F. P.) History of the War in the Peninsula. 3 pt. *Lond.* 1893. 8°. 9080. e. 2.

TOMKINSON (W.) Diary of a Cavalry Officer in the Peninsula, *etc.,* 1809–1815. pp. 358.
Lond. 1894. 8°.　　　　　9080. dd. 19.
See also ENGLAND, EUROPE, FRANCE, SPAIN, *Histories.*

PENMANSHIP. *See* HANDWRITING.

PENNSYLVANIA. BUCK (W. J.) W. Penn in America. pp. 424. *Phila.* 1888. 8°.
　　　　　　　　　　10825. c. 52.

HOTCHKIN (S. F.) Early clergy of Pennsylvania. pp. 280. *Phila.* 1890. 8°.　　4744. e. 34.

GRESHAM (J. M.) Cyclopedia of Fayette County, Pennsylvania. pp. 602. *Chicago,* 1889. 4°.
　　　　　　　　　　10880. g. 37.

PENNSYLVANIA. *Board of World's Fair Managers.* Pennsylvania and the World's Columbian Exposition. pp. 191. *Harrisburg,* 1893. 8°.
　　　　　　　　　　7956. f. 6.

CHICAGO. *Columbian Exhibition.* Catalogue of Exhibits of Pennsylvania. pp. 218.
Phila. 1893. 8°.　　　　　7956. f. 5.

VICKERS (G.) The Fall of Bossism : history of the reform movement in Pennsylvania. Vol. I.
Phila. 1883. 8°.　　　　　8176. a. 55.

BRINTON (D. G.) Reminiscences of Pennsylvania folk-lore. 1892. 8°.　　　　Pam. 22.

HOFFMAN (W. J.) Notes and vocabulary of the Pennsylvania German dialect. 1889. 8°. Ac. Philadelphia. *American Philosophical Society.* Proceedings. Vol. 26. No. 129.　　Ac. 1830.

LEARNED (M. D.) Pennsylvania German dialect. pp. 114. *Baltimore,* 1889. 8°.　12972. o. 2.

University.

Ac. Philadelphia. *University of Pennsylvania.* Biographical catalogue of matriculates of the College. pp. 567. *Phila.* 1894. 8°. 8366. g. 26.

PENRITH. FURNESS (W.) History of Penrith. pp. 376. *Penrith,* 1894. 8°.　010358. h. 23.

PENRITH. Bygone Penrith. Arrangement of the Parish Registers. *Penrith,* 1893, *etc.* 8°.
　　　　　　　　　　9914. g. 5.

PENS. BLONDEL (S.) Les outils de l'Écrivain. pp. 232. *Paris,* 1890. 18°.　7942. cc. 30.

BORE (H.) Story of the invention of steel Pens. pp. 67. *Lond.* 1892. 8°.　07944. ee. 3. (4.)

GLASS (J.) Pens and Pen-making. pp. 21.
Edinb. 1889. 16°.　　　　　Pam. 94.

GOLD PEN. The everlasting gold Pen.
Lond. 1894. 8°.　　　　　Pam. 94.

MORDAN (F.) History of the invention of Mordan's gold Pens. ff. 16. *Lond.* 1892. 8°.
　　　　　　　　　07944. ee. 3. (5.)

PENSIONS, Old Age. *See* INSURANCE.

PEPPER. HOUTEN (P. J. v.) Handleiding voor de Pepercultuur. pp. 185.
Amsterdam, 1890. 8°.　　　　07076. g. 21.

PERAK. PERAK. Perak Museum notes.
Taiping, 1893, *etc.* 4°.　　　　7297. bb.

SWETTENHAM (F. A.) About Perak. pp. 78.
Singapore, 1893. 8°.　　　　10055. ee. 15.
See also MALAY PENINSULA.

PERCHE. Province, LE PERCHE. Documents sur la Province de Perche.
Mortagne, 1890, *etc.* 8°.　　　　10169. dd.
See also EURE, ORNE, *Departments.*

PERFUMERY. ASKINSON (G. W.) Perfumes and their preparation. pp. 312.
Lond. 1892. 8°.　　　　07945. m. 14.

DURVELLE (J. P.) Fabrication des Parfums.
pp. 448. *Paris,* 1893. 12°.　　7945. g. 27.

PIESSE (C. H.) Art of Perfumery. pp. 498.
Lond. 1891. 8°.　　　　07945. h. 28.

SAWER (J. C.) Odorographia natural history of raw materials used in the perfume industry.
pp. 383. *Lond.* 1892. 8°.　　7054. e. 17.

PERGAMUS. *See* GREECE. *Antiquities.*

PERICARDIUM. *See* HEART.

PÉRIERS. LEROSEY (A.) Histoire de Périers.
pp. 331. *Paris,* 1892. 8°.　　010171. g. 1.

PÉRIGORD AND PÉRIGUEUX.
CUMONT (M. P. T. de) *Marchioness.* Recherches sur la Noblesse du Périgord. pp. 376.
Paris, 1890. 8°.　　　　9916. b. 22.

BRUGIÈRE (H.) Le Livre d'Or des diocèses de Périgueux et de Sarlat pendant la période révolutionnaire. pp. 326. *Montreuil,* 1893. 8°.
　　　　　　　　　　4629. e. 34.

PECOUT (T.) Périgueux. Souvenirs historiques.
pp. 397. *Lille,* 1890. 8°.　　10172. f. 15.
See also DORDOGNE.

PERIMETRY. *See* EYE.

PERIPATUS. SEDGWICK (A.) Peripatus.
1895, *etc.* 8°. HARMER (S. F.) Cambridge Natural History. Vol. 5, *etc.*　　7001. ee.

PERITONEUM, PERITONITIS. BALLANTYNE (J. W.) and WILLIAMS (J. D.) Structures in the Mesosalpinx. pp. 81.
Edinb. 1893. 8°.　　　　Pam. 39.

KRAFT (L.) Studier over akut Peritonitis.
pp. 148. *Kjøbenh.* 1891. 8°.　　7620. df. 35.

WALLACE (J.) On localised Peritonitis. pp. 36.
Lond. 1890. 8°.　　　　7306. df. 14. (8.)

PERLEBERG. LIESEGANG (E.) Zur Verfassungsgeschichte von Perleberg. 1891. 8°. Ac. Berlin. *Verein für Geschichte der Mark Brandenburg.* Forschungen. Bd. 4. Hälfte 2.
　　　　　　　　　　Ac. 7325.

PERLETHORPE. PERLETHORPE. Register of Perlethorpe. pp. 66. *Worksop,* 1887. fol.
　　　　　　　　　　9916. f. 40.

PERNAMBUCO. OLIVEIRA LIMA (M. de) Pernambuco. pp. 327. *Leipz.* 1895. 8°.
　　　　　　　　　　9772. cc. 3.

PERSEPOLIS. EASTON (M. W.) Observations on the Platform at Persepolis. pp. 18. 1892. 8°. Ac. Philadelphia. *University.* Publications. Philology. Vol. 2.　　Ac. 2692. p./2.

PERSIA.

Antiquities and History, Ancient.

MASPERO (G.) Histoire ancienne, *etc.* pp. 811.
Paris, 1893. 8°.　　　　9055. bb. 34.

VAUX (W. S. W.) Ancient history from the Monuments. Persia. *Lond.* 1893. 8°. 2378. a

PERSIA.—Antiquities, etc.—*continued*.

KĀVASJĪ DĪNSHĀH KIASH. Ancient Persian sculptures. pp. 234. *Bombay*, 1889. 8°.
14146. h. 17.

WEISSBACH (F. H.) and BANG (W.) Die altpersischen Keilinschriften. 1893, *etc.* 4°. DELITZSCH (F.) Assyriologische Bibliothek. Bd. 10, *etc.* 12903. h. 19.

WEISSBACH (F. H.) Die Achämenideninschriften zweiter Art. pp. 126. *Leipz.* 1890. 4°.
7702. i. 28.

PERROT (G.) and CHIPIEZ (C.) History of art in Persia. pp. 508. *Lond.* 1892. 8°. 2259. f. 14.

RAWLINSON (G.) Parthia. pp. 432. 1893. 8°. Story of the Nations. 9004. ccc. 9.

BILLERBECK (A.) Susa. pp. 184. *Leipz.* 1893. 8°. 7702. c. 37.

DIEULAFOY (J.) At Susa. Narrative of travel and excavations. pp. 266. *Phila.* 1890. 8°.
10076. i. 9.

EVERS (E.) Der historische Wert der griechischen Berichte über Cyrus und Cambyses. pp. 26. *Berl.* 1888. 4°. 11312. ee. 1. (3.)

HOONACKER (A. v.) Néhémie en l'an 20 d'Artaxerxès I.; Esdras en l'an 7 d'Artaxerxès II. pp. 90. *Gand*, 1892. 8°. 3166. ee. 46.

FEIS (L. de) La Battaglia di Cunassa in un mosaico pompeiano. pp. 15. *Firenze*, 1893. 8°.
Pam. 24.

TERRIEN DE LACOUPERIE (A. É. J. B.) L'Ère des Arsacides en 248 avant J.-C. pp. 42. *Louvain*, 1891. 8°. 07703. i. 2. (4.)

See also ASSYRIA : HISTORY, *Ancient :* MEDIA.

History, Medieval and Modern: Politics.

POOLE (S. L.) The Mohammadan Dynasties. pp. 361. *Westminster*, 1894. 8°. 9055. aaa. 38.

ODORICUS. Voyages en Asie au XIV° siècle. pp. 602. 1891. 8°. Recueil de voyages. No. 10.
10024. i.

TAHMĀSP I., *Shah of Persia.* Die Denkwürdigkeiten Schâh Tahmâsp's, 1515-76. pp. 156. *Strassb.* 1891. 8°. 757. b. 40.

VECCHIETTI (G. B.) Vecchiettis till Philip II. afgifna relation om Persiens tillstånd 1586-87, *etc.* 1894. 4°. Ac. Helsingfors. *Societas Scientiarum.* Öfversigt, *etc.* Ac. 1094.

Ac. Paris. *École des Langues Orientales.* DU MANS (R.) Estat de la Perse en 1660. pp. 464. *Paris*, 1890. 8°. 10075. k. 4.

CASTONNET DES FOSSES (H.) Les relations de la France avec la Perse. pp. 52. *Angers*, 1889. 8°.
9007. ff. 6. (5.)

LE BRUN-RENAUD (C. G. N.) La Perse politique et militaire au XIX° siècle. pp. 34. *Paris*, 1894. 12°. 9004. bbb. 16. (8.)

BĀB, *Sect of the.* Traveller's narrative to illustrate the Épisode of the Báb. 2 vol. *Camb.* 1891. 8°. 757. c. 38.

HUSAIN, *Mirzā.* History of the Bab, from the Persian. pp. 459. *Camb.* 1893. 8°. 757. c. 42.

CURZON (*Hon.* G. N.) Persia and the Persian question. 2 vol. *Lond.* 1892. 8°. 2356. h.

Religion. *See* MOHAMMEDANISM : ZEND-AVESTA.

Topography: Social Life.

BIDDULPH (C. E.) Four months in Persia. pp. 137. *Lond.* 1892. 8°. 10076. ff. 15.

BIRD, *afterwards* BISHOP (I. L.) Journeys in Persia. 2 vol. *Lond.* 1891. 8°. 10075. f. 5.

DE WINDT (H.) A Ride to India across Persia. pp. 340. *Lond.* 1891. 8°. 10075. ff. 19.

LACOIN DE VILMORIN (A.) De Paris à Bombay par la Perse. pp. 368. *Paris*, 1895. 8°.
10076. ff. 19.

PERSIA.—Topography, etc.—*continued*.

LAYARD (*Right Hon. Sir* A. H.) Early adventures in Persia. pp. 34. 436. *Lond.* 1894. 8°.
10075. bb. 20.

MORGAN (J. de) Mission scientifique en Perse. *Paris*, 1894, *etc.* 4°. 10075. k. and 14000. h. 14.

MUELLER-SIMONIS (P.) Relation des missions scientifiques, *etc.* pp. 628. *Wash.* 1892. 8°.
10075. k. 7.

PONTEVÈS-SABRAN (J. B. E. M. C. de) *Count.* Notes de voyage d'un Hussard. pp. 445. *Paris*, 1890. 12°. 10075. aa. 9.

SAFAR-NĀMAH. Persian pictures. pp. 294. *Lond.* 1894. 8°. 010057. e. 32.

REISENDER. Persien. Das Land der Sonne und des Löwen. pp. 211. *Freiburg*, 1894. 8°.
10075. ff. 25.

STANLEY (H. M.) My early Travels. 2 vol. *Lond.* 1895. 8°. 10027. ee. 4.

WILLS (C. J.) In the land of the Lion and Sun. pp. 446. 1891. 8°. BETTANY (G. T.) Minerva Library. 012207. h.

WILSON (*Sir* C. W.) Murray's Handbook for Persia, *etc. Lond.* 1895. 8°. 2364. b. 32.

PERSIAN GULF. G.B. & I. *Hydrographic Office.* The Persian Gulf pilot. pp. 332. *Lond.* 1890. 8°. 10496. gg. 29.

PERSIAN LANGUAGE. 'ABD AL-KARĪM. Dictionary of Anglo-Persian homogeneous words. pp. 68. *Bombay*, 1889. 8°. 757. d. 38. (4.)

ADĀLAT KHAN. Vocabulary of one thousand words in Hindustani, Persian and Bengalī. pp. 67. *Calcutta*, 1890. 8°. 12907. b. 39.

RICHARDSON (J.) Comprehensive Persian-English dictionary. pp. 1539. *Lond.* 1892. 8°.
12906. i. 17.

SOHRĀBSHĀH BEHRĀMJĪ. The Student's English-Persian dictionary. pp. 733. *Surat*, 1892. 8°.
12907. eee. 41.

Ac. Allahabad. *University.* English translation of the Persian entrance course, 1891-92. 2 pt. *Allahabad*, 1890, 91. 8°. 757. cc. 23.

AMJAD 'ALĪ. Key to the Persian entrance course, 1891. pp. 111. *Allahabad*, 1889. 8°.
757. d. 38. (3.)

—— English translation of the Persian entrance course, 1895. pp. 106. 131. *Allahabad*, 1894. 8°.
757. cc. 26.

ADALAT KHAN. A Book of exercises. pp. 325. *Calcutta*, 1890. 8°. 12907. bbb. 42.

AMĪR 'ALĪ, *Mashhadi.* Anglo-Persian grammar. Vol. 1. *Bombay*, 1890. 8°. 12907. aa. 67.

—— First book of Persian. pp. 92. *Bombay*, 1890. 12°. 12907. aa. 72.

—— Second book of Persian. pp. 135. *Bombay*, 1890. 12°. 12907. aa. 68.

'AZMAT ALLĀH (M.) Anglo-Persian translation guide. Pt. 1. pp. 64. *Meerutt*, 1890. 12°.
14117. aa. 27.

DOSABHAI BAHRAMJI HAKIM. First reading-book in Persian. pp. 32. *Surat*, 1890. 8°. 757. a. 27.

GEIGER (W.) Grundriss der iranischen Philologie. *Strassb.* 1895, *etc.* 8°. 12906. i.

HIKĀYĀT I LAṬĪF. First step in Persian on a new plan. pp. 76. 96. *Bombay*, 1890. 8°.
757. d. 42.

HORMASJĪ TEMULJĪ DĀDĀCHANDJĪ. Guide to Persian composition. 2 pt. *Bombay*, 1890. 8°.
12907. c. 33.

HUEBSCHMANN (H.) Persische Studien. pp. 287. *Strassb.* 1895. 8°. 12906. df. 42.

JAMSHEDJĪ BEJANJĪ KĀNGĀ and PESTANJĪ KĀVASJĪ KĀNGĀ. Hints on the study of Persian. pp. 249. *Bombay*, 1892. 8°. 12907. aa. 73.

2 x

PERSIAN LANGUAGE—continued.

JAMSHEDJĪ BEJANJĪ KĀNGĀ. Persian Standard Series. New Persian readers.
Bombay, 1895, etc. 8°.   757. cc. 25.

NANNU-MIYĀN AḤMAD-MIYĀN. Tarjuma-āmoz; exercises for translation into Persian. pp. 41.
Surat, 1891. 12°.   12907. aa. 71.

NŪR-BAKHSH. Manual of Anglo-Persian grammar. Delhi, 1894, etc. 8°.   12907. bbb. 44.

PLATTS (J. T.) Grammar of the Persian language.
Lond. 1894, etc. 8°.   12907. b. 43.

RĀMAKRISHNA. Anglo-Persian translation exercises, etc. 3 pt. Lucknow, 1889. 16°.
                                             12907. a. 52.

SAQIB KHURASANI (M. S.) Modern Persian idioms and proverbs. Bombay, 1892, etc. 8°.
                                             757. e. 40.

TALBOT (A. C.) Translations into Persian.
2 vol. Calcutta, 1890. 8°.   757. c. 9.

WILMOT (H. E.) Manual of Persian phrases.
pp. 95, 17. Madras, 1887. 8°.   757. g. 54.

ZHUKOVSKY (V.) Persische Grammatik. 1889. 8°.
PETERMANN (J. H.) Porta Linguarum Orientalum, etc. Pt. 12.   12904. de.

PERSIAN LITERATURE. JAMSHEDJĪ

BEJANJĪ KĀNGĀ. Gems of Persian prose and poetry. pp. 169. Bombay, 1892. 8°. 757. e. 39.

MEHRJIBHĀĪ NAUSHĪRVĀNJĪ KŪKĀ. Wit and humour of the Persians. pp. 255.
Bombay, 1894. 8°.   757 e. 43.

MONTAGNE (É.) Les légendes de la Perse.
pp. 367. Paris, 1890. 18°.   12410. ee. 19.

PIZZI (I.) Storia della poesia persiana. 2 vol.
Torino, 1894. 8°.   011850. h. 58.

REED (E. A.) Persian Literature. pp. 419.
Chicago, 1893. 8°.   011850. h. 23.

RASMUSSEN (H.) Studier over Hâfiz, etc.
pp. 235. Kjøbenh. 1892. 8°.   011850. i. 18.

PERSONALITY. BLACKWELL (A. L.) The

Philosophy of Individuality. pp. 519.
N.Y. 1893. 8°.   8468. k. 21.

DRESCHER (H.) Die Bedeutung und das Recht der Individualitaet. pp. 289. Haarlem, 1893. 8°.
                                             8408. g. 29.

GERBER (G.) Das Ich als Grundlage unserer Weltanschauung. pp. 429. Berl. 1893. 8°.
                                             8462. g. 7.

ILLINGWORTH (J. R.) Personality, human and divine. pp. 274. Lond. 1894. 8°. 4453. f. 25.

JUNCKER (A.) Das Ich und die Motivation des Willens im Christentum. pp. 75. Halle, 1891. 8°.
                                             8465. ee. 24. (8.)

KUECHENMEISTER (C.) Der Kampf um die Persönlichkeit. pp. 136. Leipz. 1894. 8°.
                                             8463. h. 16.

LANDMANN (S.) Die Mehrheit geistiger Persönlichkeiten in einem Individuum. pp. 186.
Stuttgart, 1894. 8°.   8462. e. 34.

SETH (A.) Hegelianism and Personality.
pp. 242. Edinb. 1893. 8°.   8470. df. 5.

STARKENBURG (H.) Die Wertung der Persönlichkeit als Faktor in dem Entwicklungsgang der moralischen Anschauungen. pp. 143.
Leipz. 1894. 8°.   8462. h. 4.

THOMPSON (H. M.) Bp. of Mississippi. The World and the wrestlers. Personality and responsibility. pp. 142. Lond. 1895. 8°.
                                             4487. aa. 25.

PERSPECTIVE. BAKER (E. G.) Theory and

practice of Perspective Projection. pp. 61.
Lond. 1892. 4°.   7855. i. 22.

BERGHUIS (F.) Perspectief. pp. 142.
Tiel, 1891. 8°.   7855. f. 46.

PERSPECTIVE—continued.

BOUFFIER (H.) Lehre des malerischen Perspektive. pp. 52. 1891. 8°. Bossong's kunsttechnische Bibliothek. Bd. 5.   7858. f.

CARROLL (J.) Principles and practice of linear Perspective. pp. 76. Lond. 1892. 8°.
                                             7854. e. 39.

CARTLIDGE (S. J.) Elementary Perspective drawing. 4 pt. 1884. 4°. Poynter's S.K. Drawing Book.   7855. i.

DENNIS (H. J.) Elementary Perspective. pp. 60.
Lond. 1895. obl. fol.   7856. df. 44.

EMERSON (P. H.) and GOODALL (T. F.) Notes on Perspective drawing and vision. pp. 7.
Lond. 1891. 8°.   [Pam. 39.

FERGUSON (F. O.) Architectural Perspective.
pp. 41. Lond. 1895. 8°.   7817. f. 31.

KNIGHT (J. P.) New Perspective guide. pp. 49.
Lond. 1890. obl. fol.   7856. df. 35.

PERSPECTIVE. Practical Perspective. 3 pt.
Hammersmith, 1890. fol.   1801. d. 1. (144.)

PETTY (J.) Government second grade examination test papers in Perspective. Leeds, 1893. fol.
                                             7854. k. 14.

SPENCER (J.) Practical Perspective. pp. 128.
Lond. 1891. 4°.   7855. g. 49.

TROBRIDGE (G.) Principles of Perspective.
pp. 48. Lond. 1891. obl 8°.   7856. de. 16.

VAUGHAN (J.) Moffatt's Perspective for second grade art students. pp. 104. Lond. 1892. obl. fol.
                                             1752. a. 4.

VERSLUYS (J.) Perspectief. 3 dl.
Amsterd. 1890. 8°.   7854. ff. 42.

—— Aanvulling van het Leerboek der Perspectief. pp 47. Amsterd. 1887. 8°.
                                             7854. h. 30.

—— Inleiding tot de Perspectiefs. pp. 59.
Amsterd. 1891. 8°.   7807. k. 17. (14.)

WALKER (J. A.) Theory and practice of Perspective. Glasg. 1893, etc. 8°.   7858. d.

WARE (W. R.) Modern Perspective. pp. 321.
Bost. 1894. 8°.   7817. ee. 6.

See also DRAWING.

PERTH. DOMINICANS. The Blackfriars of

Perth: Chartulary, etc. pp. 290.
Edinb. 1893. 4°.   4735. f. 15.

PERTHSHIRE. FORD (R.) The Harp of

Perthshire: Songs and ballads. pp. 519.
Paisley, 1893. 8°.   11621. f. 39.

See also MENTEITH.

PERU. [See note on page 1.]

See also AMERICA, South.

Antiquities: Aborigines.

CASAS (B. de las) Bp. of Chiapa. De las antiguas gentes del Perú. pp. 290. 1892. 8°. RAMIREZ DE ARELLANO (F.) Marquis de la Fuensanta del Valle. Colección de libros españoles. Tom. 21.
                                             12230. aa.

TSCHUDI (J. J. v.) Culturhistorische Beiträge zur Kenntniss des alten Perú. pp. 220.
1891. fol. Ac. Vienna. K. Akademie. Denkschriften. Phil.-Hist. Classe. Bd. 39. Ac. 810/12.

Ac. Washington. Smithsonian Institution.
HOLMES (W. H.) Textile Fabrics of ancient Peru. pp. 17. Wash. 1889. 8°. 7706. g. 8. (11.)

STUEBEL (A.) and UHLE (F. M.) Die Ruinenstaette von Tiahuanaco im Hochlande des Perú.
pp. 67. Breslau, 1892. fol.   1706. c. 15.

See also INDIANS.

Constitution: Politics.

LAMA (M. A. de la) La Constitucion explicada.
pp. 95. Lima, 1888. 8°.   Pam. 65.

PERU.—Constitution, etc.—_continued._

MIRÓ QUESADA (J. A.) Estudio sobre el sufragio en el Peru. pp. 22. _Lima,_ 1893. 8°. Pam. 65.

ARRÓSPIDE (A.) Manual para el servicio de los registros del estado civil. pp. 57.
Lima, 1889. 8°.   Pam. 33.

PERU. Reglamento consular del Perú. pp. 209.
Lima, 1888. 8°.   8179. aaa. 4.

—— Colección de los tratados y otros actos diplomaticos y politicos. _Lima,_ 1890, _etc._ 8°. 8180. k.

PROAÑO (V.) Refutacion à las aseveraciones hechas por "El Diario Judicial" sobre la cuestion límites entre el Perú y el Ecuador. pp. 24.
Lima, 1892. 8°.   Pam. 65.

VAZQUEZ (H.) Límites entre el Ecuador y el Perú. Alegato del Gobierno del Ecuador ante el árbitro. pp. 384. _Quito,_ 1892. fol. 8180. i. 19.

History.

PRESCOTT (W. H.) Conquest of Peru. Edited by J. F. Kirk. pp. 459. 302. _Lond._ 1893. 8°.
            9772. df. 1.

XERES (F. de) Relacion de la conquista del Perú. pp. 174. 1891. 8°. AMERICA. Colección de libros. Tom. 1.   9551. bbb.

MARKHAM (C. R.) History of Peru. pp. 556.
Chicago, 1892. 8°.   2398. d. 11.

PARODI Y VIVANCO (A.) Apuntes de historia del Perú. pp. 165. 45. _Lima,_ 1889. 8°. 9772. aa. 14.

SALAZAR (M. M.) Historia del Peru. pp. 238.
Lima, 1893. 8°.   9772. a. 31.

WIESSE (C.) Resumen de la historia del Péru. pp. 211. _Lima,_ 1892. 8°.   9772. aaa. 34.

LAVALLE (J. A. de) Galería de retratos de los Gobernadores del Perú, 1532–1824. pp. 88.
Lima, 1891. fol.   10880. k. 15.

—— Galería de retratos de los Arzobispos de Lima, 1541–1891. pp. 48. _Lima,_ 1892. fol.
            4985. h. 1.

PRADO Y UGARTECHE (J.) Estado social del Peru durante la Dominación española. pp. 190.
Lima, 1894. 8°.   9772. c. 14.

SALILLAS (R.) El pacificador del Perú, P. Gasca. pp. 28. _Madrid,_ 1892. 8°.   9009. m. 8. (6.)

PAZ SOLDAN (M. F.) Historia del Perú independiente, 1835–39. pp. 408.
Buenos A. 1888. 8°.   9772. f. 15.

AHUMADA MORENO (P.) Guerra del Pacifico. Documentos oficiales. 6 tom.
Valparaiso, 1884–89. fol.   9781. i. 1.

CHILI. Partes oficiales de las batallas de Chorrillos i Miraflores, Enero, 1881. pp. 420.
Santiago de C. 1881. 8°.   9772. g. 10.

FIGUEROA (P. P.) Atacama en la guerra del Pacífico. pp. 142. _Santiago de C._ 1888. 8°.
            12354. dd. 2. (5.)

PAZ SOLDAN (M. F.) Narracion de la guerra de Chile contra el Perú. pp. 917.
Buenos A. 1884. 8°.   9772. g. 9.

RIQUELME (D.) Recuerdos de la campaña al Perú i Bolivia, 1879–84. pp. 276.
Santiago de C. 1890. 8°.   9772. b. 17.

RIVAS (E. A.) Episodios de la guerra del Pacífico, 1879–83. pp. 153. _Lima,_ 1891. 8°. 9772. aaa. 35.

Immigration. _See infra : Trade._

Topography.

CLARK (E. B.) Twelve months in Peru. pp. 158. _Lond._ 1891. 8°.   10481. de. 3.

FRY (C.) La gran region de los bosques o rios peruanos navegables. 2 pt. _Lima,_ 1889. fol.
            10480. h. 16.

MIDDENDORF (E. W.) Peru: Beobachtungen und Studien. _Berl._ 1893, _etc._ 8°. 10481. de.

PERU.—Topography—_continued._

ROMÁN DE IDIÁQUEZ (J.) Prospecto sobre demarcacion del Perú. pp. 79. _Lima,_ 1893. 8°.
            10481. f. 29.

VILLAREAL (F.) Determinacion de la longitud, latitud y altura de los lugeres del Peru. pp. 75.
Lima, 1889. 8°.   8562. aaa. 39.

Trade : Finance, etc.

ARONA (J. de) La Immigracion en el Perú. pp. 160. _Lima,_ 1891. 8°.   9772. b. 13.

CHACALTANA (C.) Immigracion. Informe del Sr. Ministro del Peru en las Republicas del Plata. pp. 23. _Lima,_ 1888. 8°.   Pam. 65.

LIMA. _Escuela de Construcciones, etc._ Anales. 6 tom. _Lima,_ 1880–87. 8°.   7106. ff. 27.

MADRID. _Exposición Histórico._ Catálogo de los objetos que presenta la República del Perú, _etc._ pp. 9. _Madrid,_ 1892. 8°.   7959. f. 32.

PERU. El Contrato Donoughmore. pp. 12. 1888. fol.   Pam. 65.

—— Ferrocarriles del Sur. pp. 190.
Lima, 1888. 8°.   08235. f. 17.

—— _Cámara de Diputados._ La deuda externa y la Camara de Diputados. pp. 32.
Lima, 1888. fol.   Pam. 65.

PESARO. BONAMINI (D.) Pesaro nella Repubblica Cisalpina, 1796–99. pp. 97.
Pesaro, 1892. 8°.   10136. c. 25.

PESMES. PERCHET (E.) Le Culte à Pesmes. pp. 403. _Groy,_ 1892. 8°.   4629. k. 22.

PESSARY. _See_ WOMEN, _Diseases, etc._

PESSIMISM AND OPTIMISM. BOURCHENIN (D.) La Trace du Pessimisme dans la société et les lettres françaises.
Paris, 1893, _etc._ 8°.   8470. df. 7.

FRIEDLAENDER (J.) and BERENDT (M.) Der Pessimismus im Lichte einer höheren Weltauffassung. pp. 111. _Berl._ 1893. 8°.
            8462. f. 23.

GOITEIN (H.) Der Optimismus und Pessimismus in der jüdischen Religionsphilosophie. pp. 111. _Berl._ 1890. 8°.   Pam. 31.

HARTMANN (C. R. E. v.) Zur Geschichte des Pessimismus. pp. 373. _Leipz._ 1892. 8°.
            8486. e. 5.

HOPPS (J. P.) Pessimism, Science and God. pp. 71. _Lond._ 1894. 8°.   4016. df. 24.

JOUVIN (L.) Le Pessimisme. pp. 512.
Paris, 1892. 8°.   8408. h. 32.

KNAUER (V.) R. Hamerling gegen den Pessimismus Schopenhauer's und Hartmann's. pp. 22. _Wien,_ 1892. 8°.   8460. i. 15. (4.)

LORM (H.) Der grundlose Optimismus. pp. 329. _Wien,_ 1894. 8°.   08464. f. 1.

METMAN (E.) Le Pessimisme moderne. pp. 192. 8°. Ac. Dijon. _Académie des Sciences._ Mémoires. Sér. 4. Tom. 3.   Ac. 318.

MORANDO (G.) Ottimismo e Pessimismo. pp. 484. _Milano,_ 1890. 8°.   8467. h. 16.

MORSELLI (E.) Il Pessimismo di T. Lucrezio Caro. _Torino,_ 1892. 8°.   8468. k. 28. (5.)

PASTORE (L.) Il Pessimismo di Leopardi e de Musset. _Torino,_ 1892. 8°.   8362. c. 31. (6.)

SCHOPENHAUER (A.) Studies in Pessimism. pp. 142. _Lond._ 1891. 8°.   8463. c. 38.

SULLY (J.) Pessimism. pp. 477. _Lond._ 1891. 8°.
            2236. cc. 15.

WENLEY (R. M.) Aspects of Pessimism. pp. 337. _Edinb._ 1894. 8°.   8462. h. 8.

XERE (A.) Unselfish Pessimism. pp. 31.
Lond. 1892. 8°.   8425. b. 62. (10.)

PEST. _See_ BUDA-PEST.

PHARMACY: PHARMACOLOGY.

Bibliography.

Ac. London. *Pharmaceutical Society.* Catalogue of the Library. pp. 657. *Lond.* 1894. 8°.
    011903. e. 28.

See also MEDICINE, *Bibliography.*

General.

Ac. Erlangen. *Academia Fridericiana.* Mittheilungen aus dem pharmaceutischen Institute. *München,* 1889, *etc.* 8°.   Ac. 2629/2.

—— London. *Pharmaceutical Society.* Chemical papers from the Research Laboratory. *Lond.* 1892, *etc.* 8°.   Ac. 3924/9.

AULDE (J.) The Pocket Pharmacy. pp. 204. *Lond.* 1892. 8°.   07509. de. 18.

BEASLEY (H.) The book of Prescriptions. pp. 599. *Lond.* 1892. 8°.   07509. de. 16.

BERENDES (J.) Die Pharmacie bei den alten Culturvölkern. 2 Bde. *Halle,* 1891. 8°.
    07509. f. 2.

BINZ (C.) Vorlesungen über Pharmakologie. pp. 732. *Berl.* 1891. 8°.   07509. i. 5.

BRADBURY (J. B.) Inaugural lecture on Pharmacology. pp. 35. *Camb.* 1894. 8°.
    7306. e. 25. (2.)

BRESTOWSKI (A.) Handwörterbuch der Pharmacie. *Wien,* 1892, *etc.* 8°.   07509. l.

BROOKES (A. F.) Definition of processes used in Pharmacy. pp. 12. *Liverpool,* 1890. 24°.
    7509. a. 8.

CERNA (D.) Notes on the newer Remedies. pp. 177. *Phila.* 1893. 8°.   7509. b. 12.

CHRISTY (T.) and Co. New and rare Drugs. pp. 24. *Lond.* 1888. 8°.   Pam. 39.

DODDS (W.) Guide to the preliminary Examination of the Pharmaceutical Society. pp. 86. *Lond.* 1893. 8°.   8909. aa. 24.

DUJARDIN-BEAUMETZ (G.) L'Art de formuler. pp. 291. *Paris,* 1894. 12°.   07509. de. 37.

DUPUY (E.) Cours de Pharmacie. 2 tom. *Paris,* 1894, 95. 8°.   07509. g. 2.

DYMOCK (W.) Pharmacographia Indica. History of drugs of vegetable origin, met with in British India. Part III., *etc. Lond.* 1890, *etc.* 8°.
    07509. e. 16.

GILBERT (É.) La Pharmacie à travers les Siècles. pp. 455. *Toulouse,* 1886. 8°.
    7509. i. 21.

GILLE (N.) Falsifications des principaux médicaments simples. pp. 409. *Brux.* 1891. 12°.
    07509. de. 32.

HÉRAIL (J.) and BONNET (V.) Manipulations de Botanique médicale et pharmaceutique. pp. 320. *Paris,* 1891. 8°.   07509. l. 6.

HOLFERT (J.) Schule der Pharmacie. *Berl.* 1893, *etc.* 8°.   07509. f.

INCE (J.) Latin grammar of Pharmacy. pp. 306. *Lond.* 1894. 8°.   12935. cc. 38.

JOLIN (S.) Nyare läkemedel ur farmaceutiskkemisk synpunkt. pp. 354. *Stockholm,* 1892. 8°.
    8909. k. 1.

LERCH (J. Z.) Pharmaceutisches Handlexicon. Synonyma in lateinischer, deutscher, böhmischer und polnischer Sprache. pp. 448. *Prag,* 1890. 8°.   07509. l. 4.

MARTINDALE (W.) Analyses of twelve thousand Prescriptions. *Lond.* 1894. 8°.   07509. f. 9.

MEADOWS (A.) Prescriber's Companion. pp. 287. 10. *Lond.* 1891. 16°.   7509. de. 57.

MOELLER (J.) Pharmakognostischer Atlas. pp. 443. *Berl.* 1892. 8°.   07509. l. 7.

NORDIN (I.) and SCHIMMELPFENNIG (C.) Svensk farmaceutisk Matrikel för 1893. *Stockholm,* 1893. 16°.   7509. df. 50.

PHARMACY.—General—*continued.*

PEARMAIN (T. H.) and MOOR (C. G.) Aids to the analysis of drugs. pp. 160. *Lond.* 1895. 8°.
    8909. eee. 1.

P.P. *London.* British, Foreign and colonial Drug review. *Lond.* 1892, *etc.* fol.   N.R.

PHILLIPS (C. D. F.) Materia Medica and Pharmacology. *Lond.* 1894, *etc.* 8°.   07509. f. 10.

POTTER (S. O. L.) Handbook of Pharmacy. pp. 767. *Phila.* 1891. 8°.   07509. e. 14.

PROCTOR (B. S.) Lectures on Pharmacy. pp. 539. *Lond.* 1892. 8°.   07509. e. 17.

SOULIER (H.) Traité de Pharmacologie. 2 tom. *Paris,* 1891. 8°.   7442. d.

STARK (A. C.) Practical Pharmacy. pp. 205. *Lond.* 1893. 8°.   07509. de. 29.

STEPHENSON (J. B.) Notes on medicinal Remedies. pp. 72. *Lond.* 1893. 8°.   07509. de. 30.

STIRLING (G.) Notes on dispensing. pp. 64. *Ealing,* 1894. 8°.   7509. de. 83.

STOKVIS (B. J.) Voordrachten over geneesmiddelleer. *Haarlem,* 1891, *etc.* 8°.   7460. ff. 23.

TSCHIRCH (A.) and OESTERLE (O.) Anatomischer Atlas der Pharmakognosie. *Leipz.* 1893, *etc.* fol.
    7029. i.

WARNCKE (T. S.) Forelæsninger over Pharmacologi. 2 Dle. *Kjøbenh.* 1890. 4°. 7510. g. 8.

WEDDERBURN (A. J.) Report on the extent and character of drug adulteration. pp. 64. 1894. 8°. U.S. *Department of Agriculture, Chemical Division.* Bulletin. No. 41.   7053. e. 9.

WHITE (W. H.) Materia Medica and Pharmacy. pp. 614. *Lond.* 1892. 8°.   07509. de. 21.

WHITLA (W.) Elements of Pharmacy. pp. 646. *Lond.* 1892. 8°.   2256. a. 25.

See also BOTANY, *Medical :* CHEMISTRY, *Medical :* CHEMISTS AND DRUGGISTS : MATERIA MEDICA : MEDICINE : PHARMACOPOEIAS : THERAPEUTICS.

Law relating to Pharmacy.

G. B. & I. Pharmacy and Poison laws of the United Kingdom. pp. 220. *Lond.* 1892. 8°.
    6095. a. 34.

BELL (*Sir* W. J.) Sale of Food and Drugs Acts, 1875 and 1879. pp. 146. *Lond.* 1894. 8°.
    6426. aaaa. 25.

HEDDERWICK (T. C. H.) Sale of Food and Drugs Acts. pp. 101. *Lond.* 1894. 8°.   6425. c. 33.

ROBINSON (H. M.) and CRIBB (C. H.) Law of Food and Drugs. pp. 499. *Lond.* 1895. 8°.
    6425. de. 33.

WEDDERBURN (A. J.) Compilation of Pharmacy laws of the States and Territories. pp. 152. 1894. 8°. U.S. *Department of Agriculture, Chemical Division.* Bulletin. No. 42.
    7053. e. 9.

Patent Medicines.

MEDICINES. Patent alias quack medicines. pp. 128. *Lond.* 1892. 8°.   7509. b. 11.

P.P. London. *Patent Medicines' Journal.* Patent Medicines' journal. *Lond.* 1893, *etc.* 8°.
    P.P. 2505. gmb.

See also supra : General.

PHARYNX. SAJOUS (C. E.) Diseases of the Pharynx. 1894. 8°. BIGELOW (H. R.) System of Electro-Therapeutics.   2024. e.

THORNER (M.) Acute Pharyngitis. pp. 23. *Phila.* 1893. 8°.   Pam. 39.

WILLIAMS (P. W.) Diseases of the upper Respiratory Tract. pp. 282. *Bristol,* 1894. 8°.
    7616. f. 12.

See also DIGESTION : DIPHTHERIA : THROAT.

PHEASANT. COOK (W.) Pheasants, Turkeys and Geese. pp. 69. *Lond.* 1894. 8°.
    7294. bbb. 16.

PHEASANT—*continued.*

GRANT (W. R. O.) Handbook to Game Birds. 1895, *etc.* 8°. Allen's Naturalist's Library.
7001. eee.

MACPHERSON (H. A.) The Pheasant. pp. 265. 1895. 8°. WATSON (A. E. T.) Fur and Feather Series.
7906. dd.

WITTMANN (P.) Der Edelfasan-Phasianus colchicus. pp. 245. *Wien*, 1891. 8°. 7285. g. 13.
See also BIRDS : SPORT.

PHILADELPHIA. ALLINSON (E. P.) and PENROSE (B.) Ground Rents in Philadelphia. pp. 19. 1888. 8°. Ac. Philadelphia. *University.* Publications. Pol. Econ. Series. No. 3.
Ac. 2692. p.

BRINLEY (C. A.) Handbook for Philadelphia voters. pp. 210. *Phila.* 1894. 8°. 8176. aa. 30.

BROTHERHEAD (W.) Forty years among the Booksellers of Philadelphia. pp. 122.
Phila. 1891. 8°.   11899. b. 50.

CHRIST CHURCH. Handbook of Christ Church, Philadelphia. pp. 58. *Phila.* 1892. 8°.
4745. aaa. 40.

HOTCHKIN (S. F.) Ancient and modern Germantown. pp. 538. *Phila.* 1889. 8°. 10411. i. 21.

PHILADELPHIA. *Commission for the Erection of the Public Buildings on Penn Square.* Proceedings, Feb. and March, 1891. pp. 109.
Phila. 1891. 8°.   06616. df. 18.

—— Supreme Court of Pennsylvania. Proceedings, Jan. 1891. pp. 35. *Phila.* 1891. 8°.
Pam. 33.

SMYTH (A. H.) Philadelphia Magazines and their contributors, 1741-1850. pp. 264.
Phila. 1892. 8°.   11852. df. 18.

VICKERS (G. E.) Philadelphia : the story of an American city, pp. 232. *Phila.* 1893. 8°.
10411. c. 32.

—— The Fall of Bossism. History of the Committee of one hundred, *etc.* Vol. 1.
Phila. 1883. 8°.   8176. a. 55.
See also PENNSYLVANIA.

PHILIPPINE ISLANDS. ABELLA Y CASARIEGO (E.) Descripción de la isla de Panay. pp. 203. *Manila*, 1890. 8°. 07109. l. 4.

—— Terremotos experimentados en la Isla de Luzón, 1892. pp. 110. *Manila*, 1893. 8°.
7109. dd. 13.

BLUMENTRITT (F.) Consideraciones acera de la situación política de Filipinas. pp. 51.
Barcelona, 1889. 8°.   8028. de. 30. (5.)

CABEZAS DE HERRERA (J.) Apuntes sobre la organizacion de Filipinas. pp. 29.
Manila, 1883. fol.   Pam. 66.

CHÁPULI NAVARRO (A.) Siluetas. Galería filipina. pp. 321. *Madrid*, 1894. 8°. 12354. de. 21.

CROZET (   ) Crozet's Voyage to the Philippines, 1771–72. pp. 148. *Lond.* 1891. 8°. 10492. e. 15.

ESPINA (M. A.) Apuntes para hacer un libro sobre Joló. pp. 899. *Manila*, 1888. 8°.
9055. d. 31.

FECED (P.) Filipinas. Esbozos. pp. 361.
Manila, 1888. 8°.   10055. df. 3.

FERNANDEZ ÁRIAS (E.) Paralelo entre la conquista de América y el descubrimiento de Filipinas. pp. 62. *Madrid*, 1893. 8°. 9551. bb. 28.

FOREMAN (J.) The Philippine Islands. pp. 495.
Lond. 1890. 8°.   10055. df. 21.

GOVANTES (F. M. de) Episodios historicos de Filipinas. pp. 260. *Manila*, 1881. 8°.
9056. a. 46.

JORDANA Y MORERA (R.) La Inmigracion china en Felipinas. pp. 48. *Madrid*, 1888. 8°.
Pam. 67.

PHILIPPINE ISLANDS—*continued.*

LACALLE Y SANCHEZ (J. de) Tierras y razas del Archipiélago filipino. pp. 290.
Manila, 1886. 8°.   010055. gg. 1.

MADRID. *Exposición de Filipinas.* Collección de artículos publicados en El Globo. pp. 220.
Madrid, 1887. fol.   7959. k. 19.

MARTÍNEZ DE ZUÑIGA (J.) Estadismo de las Islas Filipinas. 2 tom. *Madrid*, 1893. 8°.
010055. g. 1.

MEYER (A. B.) and SCHADENBERG (A.) Die Philippinen. 1890, *etc.* fol. Ac. Dresden. *K. Ethnographisches Museum.* Publicationen. No. 8.
1700. c. 1.

MOLO AGUSTÍN PATERNO (P. A.) El Regimen municipal en las Islas Filipinas. pp. 280.
Madrid, 1893. 8°.   5384. de. 3.

NIETO AGUILAR (J.) Colonización de Filipinas. pp. 414. *Madrid*, 1893. 8°. 10055. d. 2.

—— Mindanao. pp. 152. *Madrid*, 1894. 8°.
010055. gg. 2.

PARDO DE TAVERO (T. H.) El Mapa de Filipinas del P. Murillo Velarde. pp. 19.
Manila, 1894. 8°.   Pam. 88.

—— Noticias sobre la imprenta en Filipinas. pp. 48. *Madrid*, 1893. 8°. 11904. l. 14. (6.)

PERINAT Y LASSO DE LA VEGA (A.) Operaciones militares en Rio Grande de Mindanao. 2 pt.
Madrid, 1891. 4°.   9056. cc. 4.

P.P. *Manila.* El Eco de Filipinas.
Manila, 1890, *etc.* fol.   P.P. 9900. c.

—— La España oriental. *Manila*, 1889, *etc.* fol.
29.

PHILIPPINE ISLANDS. Filipinas. Problema fundamental. pp. 60. *Madrid*, 1891. 8°. Pam. 66.

BLUMENTRITT (F.) Filipinas. Problema fundamental. [A criticism.] pp. 31.
Madrid, 1891. 8°.   Pam. 66.

PUYA RUIZ (A.) Description de la provincia de Cagayan. pp. 78. *Manila*, 1895. 8°.
10055. aaa. 11.

RETANA (W. E.) Frailes y clérigos. pp. 142.
Madrid, 1891. 8°.   4766. aaa. 10.

—— Cuestiones filipinas. pp. 367.
Madrid, 1892. 8°.   8023. a. 4.

REYES Y FLORENTINO (I. de los) Historia de Ilocos. 2 tom. *Manila*, 1890. 8°. 9055. aa. 8.

SANCIANCO Y GOSON (G.) El progreso di Filipinas. pp. 260. *Madrid*, 1881. 8°. 8023. cc. 31.

SCHNEIDNAGAL (M.) El Archipielado de Legaspi. pp. 320. *Madrid*, 1890. 8°. 10055. aaaa. 30.

SPAIN. Viva Espana, viva el Rey, viva el Ejército, fuera los frailes. pp. 38.
Manila, 1888. 8°.   Pam. 67.

VAZQUEZ DE ALDANA (A.) and GONZALEZ SERRANO (V.) Espana en la Oceanía. 2 pt.
Manila, 1880. 8°.   9772. h. 3.

VERA Y LOPEZ (R.) Solucion filipina. pp. 142.
Manila, 1888. 8°.   08227. i. 30. (2.)

WALLS Y MERINO (M.) El general Despujol en Filipinas. pp. 31. *Madrid*, 1892. 8°. Pam. 67.

Ethnology, Native Languages, etc.

BLUMENTRITT (F.) Alphabetisches Verzeichniss der eingeborenen Stämme der Philippinen und der Sprachen. pp. 20. 1890. 8°.
12901. d. 20. (7.)

MARCILLA Y MARTIN (C.) Estudio de los antiguos alfabetos filipinos. pp. 107.
Malabón, 1895. fol.   12910. k. 20.

CAMPA (B.) Los Mayóyaos y la Raza Ifugao. pp. 165. *Madrid*, 1894. 8°. 10007. aa. 8.

MINGUELLA (T.) Estudios comparativos entre el Tagalog, Filipinas y el Sanscrito. pp. 8.
1885. fol.   Pam. 47.

PHILIPPINE ISLANDS.—Ethnology,
etc.—*continued.*

MOLO AGUSTÍN PATERNO (P. A.) La Familia
tagálog en la historia universal. pp. 152.
Madrid, 1892. 8°.   9055. a. 20.

RETANA (W. E.) Supersticiones de los Indios
filipinos. pp. 104. *Madrid,* 1894. 12°.
                                       12489. e. 20.

BARRANTES (V.) El Teatro tagalo. pp. 199.
Madrid, 1889. 8°.   011795. g. 12.

TENORIO O SIGAYÁN (J.) Costumbres de los
Indios tirurayes. pp. 91. *Manila,* 1892. 8°.
                                       010055. e. 18.

BENNÁSAR (G.) Diccionario tiruray-español.
pp. 201. *Manila,* 1892. 8°.   12910. cc. 18.

See also CAROLINE ISLANDS : MALAY PENINSULA
AND MALAYSIA : MANILA : SPAIN, *Colonies.*

PHILOLOGY. *See* LANGUAGE.

PHILOSOPHY.

Metaphysical and General.

BALFOUR (*Right Hon.* A. J.) The Foundations
of Belief. pp. 356. *Lond.* 1895. 8°. 8463. e. 31.

BARLET (F. C.) Essai sur l'évolution de l'Idée.
pp. 174. *Paris,* 1891. 12°.   8465. aaa. 41.

BARTHÉLEMY SAINT-HILAIRE (J.) La Philosophie
dans ses rapports avec les sciences et la religion.
pp. 280. *Paris,* 1889. 8°.   8468. cc. 36.

BAX (E. B.) The problem of Reality. pp. 177.
Lond. 1892. 8°.   8470. e. 7.

BILHARZ (A.) Metaphysik als Lehre vom Vorbe-
wussten. *Wiesbaden,* 1890, *etc.* 8°. 8463. i. 18.

BOIRAC (É.) L'Idée du phénomène. pp. 350.
Paris, 1894. 8°.   8463. dd. 36.

BONGHI (R.) Le prime armi. Filosofia e filologia. pp. 472. *Bologna,* 1894. 8°. 8462. h. 11.

BRADLEY (F. H.) Appearance and reality.
pp. 558. 1893. 8°. MUIRHEAD (J. H.) Library
of Philosophy.   8486. h.

BRAIG (C.) Die Freiheit der philosophischen
Forschung. pp. 64. *Freiburg,* 1894. 8°.
                                       8462. b. 42.

BRENTANO (F.) Ueber die Zukunft der Philosophie. pp. 74. *Wien,* 1893. 8°. 8462. g. 15.

BUECHNER (F. C. C. L.) Fremdes und Eignes
aus dem geistigen Leben der Gegenwart.
pp. 397. *Leipz.* 1890. 8°.   4018. i. 25.

CAIRD (E.) Essays on Philosophy. 2 vol.
Glasg. 1892. 8°.   012357. f. 53.

CALDERWOOD (H.) Vocabulary of Philosophy.
pp. 359. *Lond.* 1894. 8°.   8462. bb. 29.

CARUS (P.) Fundamental Problems. Method of
Philosophy as a systematic arrangement of
knowledge. pp. 373. *Lond.* 1891. 8°. 8468. d. 22.

—— Primer of Philosophy. pp. 232.
Chicago, 1893. 8°.   8462. bb. 37.

CERETTI (P.) Saggio circa la ragione logica di
tutte le cose, Pasaelogices Specimen.
Torino, 1888, *etc.* 8°.   8467. i.

CHARAUX (C. C.) De l'Esprit philosophique.
pp. 303. *Paris,* 1892. 8°.   8463. bb. 30.

DAURELLA Y RULL (J.) Instituciones de Meta-
física. pp. 814. *Valladolid,* 1891. 8°. 8462. e. 17.

DEUSSEN (P.) Elements of Metaphysics.
pp. 337. *Lond.* 1894. 8°.   8462. b. 36.

DORMAN (M. R. P.) From Matter to mind.
pp. 319. *Lond.* 1895. 8°.   8462. c. 27.

DRAKELOWE. "From the Known to the unknown." pp. 49. *Derby,* 1891. 8°.   Pam. 85.

DUNAN (C.) Cours de Philosophie. pp. 336.
Paris, 1893. 8°.   8462. e. 25.

EITLE (J.) Grundriss der Philosophie.
pp. 304. *Freiburg,* 1891. 8°.   8468. dd. 37.

PHILOSOPHY. — Metaphysical, etc. —
continued.

ENGEL (G.) Entwurf einer ontologischen Begründung des Seinsollenden. pp. 212.
Berl. 1894. 8°.   8462. cc. 24.

ERHARDT (F.) Metaphysik. *Leipz.* 1894, *etc.* 8°.
                                      8462. e. 36.

FAWCETT (E. D.) The Power behind the
universe. pp. 30. *Madras,* 1891. 8°. 8463. g. 33.

—— The Riddle of the universe. pp. 440.
Lond. 1893. 8°.   8462. f. 36.

FELDEGG (F. v.) Das Gefühl als Fundament der
Weltordnung. pp. 234. *Wien,* 1890. 8°.
                                      8466. ee. 29.

—— Das Verhältnis der Philosophie zur empirischen Wissenschaft von der Natur. pp. 48.
Wien, 1894. 8°.   8462. d. 20. (9.)

FISCHER (E. L.) Das Grundproblem der Metaphysik. pp. 203. *Mainz,* 1894. 8°. 8462. e. 31.

FONSEGRIVE (G. L.) La Causalité efficiente.
pp. 170. *Paris,* 1893. 12°.   8463. bb. 33.

FRANCHI (A.) Ultima Critica. 3 pt.
Milano, 1889–93. 8°.   8463. b. 34.

FROHSCHAMMER (J.) Ueber das Mysterium
magnum des Daseins. pp. 183. *Leipz.* 1891. 8°.
                                      8469. g. 30.

—— System der Philosophie im Umriss.
München, 1892, *etc.* 8°.   8462. f. 35.

GALLONE (G.) L'Olos svolto dal lato filosofico
religioso politico. *Napoli,* 1893, *etc.* 8°.
                                      8462. dd. 7.

GREPPO (C.) L'existence "dont la semence est
en soi-même," ou qui porte en soi son principe.
2 tom. *Paris,* 1894. 8°.   8462. h. 3.

GRIMMISCH (V.) Lehrbuch der theoretischen
Philosophie. pp. 565. *Freiburg,* 1893. 8°.
                                      8462. g. 23.

HAGEMANN (G.) Elemente der Philosophie.
3 pt. *Freiburg,* 1894. 8°.   8463. e. 36.

HALVORSON (G.) Grundtræk af Metafysik, Na-
turfilosofi og Aandsfilosofi.
Kristiania, 1891, *etc.* 8°.   8462. f. 7.

HILL (D. J.) Genetic Philosophy. pp. 382.
N.Y. 1893. 8°.   8470. df. 8.

HUGONIN (F. A. A.) Bp. of Bayeux. Études
philosophiques. pp. 152. *Paris,* 1894. 8°.
                                      8462. aa. 23.

KLEFFLER (H.) Philosophie du Sens commun.
Paris, 1894, *etc.* 8°.   8462. e.

KNIEPF (A.) Theorie der Geisteswerthe.
pp. 158. *Leipz.* 1892. 8°.   8462. e. 14.

KRALIK (R.) Weltweisheit. *Wien,* 1894. 8°.
                                      8409. ccc.

KRAUSE (C. C. F.) Das Eigenthümliche der
Wesenlehre. pp. 292. *Leipz.* 1890. 8°.
                                      8463. i. 19.

—— Der Begriff der Philosophie. pp. 115.
Leipz. 1893. 8°.   8462. g. 34.

LADD (G. T.) Introduction to Philosophy.
pp. 426. *Lond.* 1891. 8°.   8462. e. 13.

MAACK (F.) Geeinte Gegensätze.
Leipz. 1894, *etc.* 8°.   8462. e.

MATURI (S.) La Filosofia e la Metafisica.
pp. 266. 1895. 8°. Ac. Naples. *Reale
Accademia.* Atti. Vol. 27.   Ac. 96/2.

MENDEL (T. H.) Geist und Stoff. pp. 100.
Leipz. 1894. 8°.   8465. cc. 27.

MENÉNDEZ Y PELAYO (M.) Ensayo de Crítica
filosófica. pp. 397. *Madrid,* 1892. 8°.
                                      8463. bb. 34.

MEYER (J. G.) Telaëtia oder der Weltknoten.
pp. 146. *Leipz.* 1894. 8°.   8462. f. 41.

MIVART (St. G.) The helpful Science. pp. 178.
Lond. 1895. 8°.   8462. c. 24.

PHILOSOPHY. — Metaphysical, etc. — *continued*.

NARDI (P. de) Della parte che ebbero la Filosofia ed i Filosofi nel Risorgimento dei popoli. *Città di C.*, 1892, *etc.* 8°. 8462. g. 10.

NAVILLE (E.) La définition de la Philosophie. pp. 289. *Genève*, 1894. 8°. 8462. g. 41.

OLLÉ-LAPRUNE (L.) La Philosophie et le temps présent. pp. 379. *Paris*, 1890. 12°. 8462. aaa. 25.

PAGNANI (C.) *Bp. of Kandy*. First notions of Logic and Metaphysics. pp. 272. *Colombo*, 1891. 8°. 8470. ccc. 17.

P.P. *Boston*. The Philosophical Review. *Bost.* 1892, *etc.* 8°. P.P. 1253. i.

—— *Edinburgh*. The Critical Review of philosophical literature. *Edinb.* 1890, *etc.* 8°. P.P. 409. c.

—— *New York*. The Metaphysical Magazine. *N.Y.* 1895, *etc.* 8°. P.P. 1247. f.

—— *Paris*. Revue de Métaphysique. *Paris*, 1893, *etc.* 8°. P.P. 1236. ba.

PLUMPTRE (C. E.) Natural Causation. pp. 198. *Lond.* 1888. 8°. 8463. g. 28.

POZZO DI MOMBELLO (E. dal) Il Monismo. pp. 410. *Città di C.*, 1890. 8°. 8463. ccc. 35.

PREVITI (L.) La Tradizione del Pensiero italiano. pp. 591. *Roma*, 1891, 8°. 8486. c. 1.

PROBLEM. The great problem of Substance and its attributes. pp. 197. *Lond.* 1895. 8°. 8462. h. 15.

REVEL (P. C.) Esquisse d'un système de la Nature fondé sur la loi du hasard. pp. 291. *Lyon*, 1890. 8°. 8463. aaa. 22.

RIEHL (A.) Principles of the critical Philosophy. pp. 346. 1894. 8°. English and Foreign Philosophical Library. 2318. d. 1.

ROBERTY (E. de) La Recherche de l'unité. pp. 230. *Paris*, 1893. 8°. 8463. bb. 32.

ROMUNDT (H.) Ein Band der Geister. pp. 129. *Leipz.* 1895. 8°. 8466. aaa. 44.

SALA Y VILLARET (P.) Materia, forma y fuerza. pp. 348. *Madrid*, 1891. 8°. 8470. f. 25.

SCHELLWIEN (R.) Der Geist der neueren Philosophie. *Leipz.* 1895, *etc.* 8°. 8470. i.

SEGALL-SOCOLIU (I.) Zur Verjüngung der Philosophie. *Berl.* 1893, *etc.* 8°. 8462. g.

—— Die Grundprobleme der Philosophie. pp. 261. *Bern*, 1895. 8°. 8465. c. 55.

SEWALL (F.) The new Metaphysics. pp. 208. *Lond.* 1888. 8°. 8462. b. 34.

SIEGFRIED (A.) Radicaler Realismus. pp. 145. *Leipz.* 1892. 8°. 8462. e. 16.

SINCLAIR (D.) Lux Naturae : Nerve system of the universe. pp. 188. *Lond.* 1894. 8°. 8704. bbb. 31.

SONNEN (C.) Vom Dichter zum Philosophen. *Leipz.* 1894, *etc.* 8°. 8462. bb. 38.

SPICKER (G.) Die Ursachen des Verfalls der Philosophie. pp. 280. *Leipz.* 1892. 8°. 8485. f. 16.

STEUDEL (A.) Das goldene A B C der Philosophie. pp. 215. *Berl.* 1891. 8°. 8462. c. 17.

T., T. E. S. Two Spheres, or, mind versus instinct. pp. 518. *Lond.* 1894. 8°. 8462. e. 20.

TROGLODYTE. Riddles of the Sphinx. pp. 468. *Lond.* 1891. 8°. 8469. g. 29.

URRÁBURU (J. J.) Institutiones philosophicæ. *Vallisoleti*, 1890, *etc.* 8°. 8467. h. 18.

VARNBUELER (T. L. F. v.) Der Organismus der Allvernunft und das Leben der Menschheit in ihm. pp. 679. *Prag*, 1891. 8°. 8467. i. 5.

PHILOSOPHY. — Metaphysical, etc. — *continued*.

WAHLE (R.) Das Ganze der Philosophie und ihr Ende. pp. 539. *Wien*, 1894. 8°. 8465. h. 17.

WALLER (B.) The Microcosm and the Macrocosm. pp. 95. *Lond.* 1894. 8°. 8470. bbb. 13.

WEISS (B.) Aphoristische Grundlegung einer Philosophie des Geschehens. pp. 73. *Berl.* 1895. 8°. Pam. 49.

WETTERHAN (D.) Das Verhältnis der Philosophie zu der empirischen Wissenschaft von der Natur. pp. 110. *Leipz.* 1894. 8°. 8462. g. 43.

WHITTAKER (T.) Essays and notices. pp. 370. *Lond.* 1895. 8°. 8462. e. 42.

WINTER (N.) Pan-Gnosticism. pp. 184. *N.Y.* 1895. 8°. 8470. df. 9.

WOLFF (H.) Κοσμος. Die Weltentwickelung nach monistisch-psychologischen Prinzipien. 2 Bde. *Leipz.* 1890. 8°. 8466. gg. 30. *See also* LOGIC : PSYCHOLOGY.

History.

BASCOM (J.) Historical interpretation of Philosophy. pp. 518. *N.Y.* 1893. 8°. 8486. bb. 15.

BAUMANN (J.) Geschichte der Philosophie. pp. 383. *Gotha*, 1890. 8°. 8486. g. 18.

BERGMANN (F. W. E. J.) Geschichte der Philosophie. *Berl.* 1892, *etc.* 8°. 8486. g. 26.

BRASCH (M.) Lehrbuch der Geschichte der Philosophie. pp. 441. *Leipz.* 1893. 8°. 8486. b. 10.

DEUSSEN (P.) Allgemeine Geschichte der Philosophie. *Leipz.* 1894, *etc.* 8°. 8486. d.

ERDMANN (B.) Abhandlungen zur Philosophie und ihrer Geschichte. *Halle*, 1893, *etc.* 8°. 8462. g.

ERDMANN (J. E.) History of Philosophy. 3 vol. 1893. 8°. MUIRHEAD (J. H.) Library of Philosophy. 8486. h.

GONZÁLEZ (Z.) *Cardinal*. Histoire de la Philosophie. 2 tom. *Paris*, 1890. 8°. 8486. de. 16.

HEGEL (G. W. F.) Lectures on the history of Philosophy. 1892, *etc.* 8°. English and Foreign Philosophical Library. 2318. e.

HODGSON (S. H.) Philosophy in relation to its History. pp. 28. *Lond.* 1880. 8°. Pam. 49.

KNAUER (V.) Die Hauptprobleme der Philosophie in ihrer Entwicklung von Thales bis R. Hamerling. pp. 408. *Wien*, 1892. 8°. 8462. g. 2.

LEWES (G. H.) Biographical history of Philosophy. pp. 656. 1891. 8°. Sir J. Lubbock's Hundred Books. Vol. 16. 012207. l. 16.

SCHWEGLER (F. C. A.) Geschichte der Philosophie im Umriss. pp. 397. *Stuttg.* 1891. 8°. 8486. g. 25.

WINDELBAND (W.) History of Philosophy. pp. 659. *N.Y.* 1893. 8°. 8486. dd. 3.

SCOTT (W. R.) Simple history of ancient Philosophy. pp. 91. *Lond.* 1894. 8°. 8486. bb. 14.

WINDELBAND (W.) Geschichte der alten Philosophie. pp. 313. 1894. 8°. MUELLER (I. E. P. v.) Handbuch der klassischen Altertums-Wissenschaft. Bd. 5. 2259. g.

APELT (O.) Beiträge zur Geschichte der griechischen Philosophie. pp. 401. *Leipz.* 1891. 8°. 8486. e. 3.

BURNET (J.) Early Greek Philosophy. pp. 378. *Lond.* 1892. 8°. 8486. e. 4.

GOMPERZ (T.) Griechische Denker *Leipz.* 1893, *etc.* 8°. 8486. ee.

KRAUSE (C. C. F.) Abriss der Geschichte der griechischen Philosophie. pp. 107. *Leipz.* 1893. 8°. 8486. e. 8.

PHILOSOPHY—History.—*continued.*

MARSHALL (J.)   Short history of Greek Philosophy. pp. 253. *Lond.* 1891. 8°.   8486. de. 15.

MITCHELL (E. M.)   Study of Greek Philosophy. pp. 282. *Chicago*, 1891. 8°.   8486. b. 9.

ZELLER (E.)   Outlines of the history of Greek Philosophy. pp. 363. *Lond.* 1892. 8°. 2234. a. 19.

—— The Stoics, Epicureans and Sceptics. pp. 585. *Lond.* 1892. 8°.   2234. b. 22.

WOLFF (M.)   Credo ut Intelligam : studies on early Greek Philosophy and its relation to Christianity. pp. 84. *Oxf.* 1891. 8°.
                     8460. bb. 31.

BÉNARD (C.)   Platon, sa Philosophie. pp. 546. *Paris*, 1892. 8°.   8461. d. 39.

OORDT (J. W. G. v.)   Plato and the times he lived in. pp. 266. *The Hague*, 1895. 8°.
                     8460. dd. 14.

PATER (W. H.)   Plato and Platonism. pp. 259. *Lond.* 1893. 8°.   2234. cc. 15.

BULLINGER (A.)   Aristoteles' Metaphysik. pp. 254. *München*, 1892. 8°.   8461. ee. 35.

KAPPES (M.)   Aristoteles-Lexikon. pp. 70. *Paderborn*, 1894. 8°.   Pam. 49.

BONHOEFFER (A.)   Epictet und die Stoa. pp. 316. *Stuttg.* 1890. 8°.   8460. g. 11.

ZENO.   Fragments of Zeno and Cleanthes. pp. 344. *Lond.* 1891. 8°.   2280. aa. 3.

SCHMEKEL (A.)   Die Philosophie der mittleren Stoa. pp. 483. *Berl.* 1892. 8°.   8485. df. 19.

NASMITH (D.)   Makers of modern thought—1200–1699. 2 vol. *Lond.* 1892. 8°.   8485. de. 3.

BAEUMKER (C.)   Beiträge zur Geschichte der Philosophie des Mittelalters. *Münster*, 1891, *etc.* 8°.   8485. f.

BURT (B. C.)   History of modern Philosophy from the Renaissance. 2 vol. *Chicago*, 1892. 8°   8485. b. 23.

FALCKENBERG (R.)   History of modern Philosophy. pp. 655. *Lond.* 1895. 8°. 8485. ee. 11.

BRASCH (M.)   Leipziger Philosophen vom 15.–19. Jahrhundert. pp. 371. *Leipz.* 1894. 8°.
                     010707. ee. 23.

THOMAS (P. F.)   La Philosophie de Gassendi. pp. 320. *Paris*, 1889. 8°.   8467. cc. 42.

SPINOZA (B. de)   Philosophy of Spinoza. Translated by G. S. Fullerton. pp. 204. *N.Y.* 1892. 8°.   8462. b. 27.

BERENDT (M.) and FRIEDLAENDER (J.)   Spinoza's Erkenntnisslehre in ihrer Beziehung zur modernen Naturwissenschaft. pp. 315. *Berl.* 1891. 8°.   8470. e. 6.

BUSSE (L.)   Beiträge zur Entwicklungsgeschichte Spinoza's. pp. 88. *Berl.* 1885. 8°.   Pam. 49.

VOLD (J. M.)   Spinozas Erkjendelsestheori. pp. 384. *Kristiania*, 1888. 8°.   8468. dd. 36.

KANT (I.)   Premiers principes métaphysiques de la science de la nature. Traduits, par C. Andler et E. Chavannes. pp. 96. *Paris*, 1891. 8°.
                     8467. h. 20.

—— Fundamental Principles of the Metaphysic of Ethics. Translated by T. K. Abbott. pp. 102. *Lond.* 1895. 8°.   8411. cc. 32.

APEL (M.)   Kants Erkenntnistheorie, und seine Stellung zur Metaphysik. pp. 147. *Berl.* 1895. 8°.   8464. cc. 45.

ARNOLDT (E.)   Kritische Excurse im Gebiete der Kant-Forschung. pp. 651. *Königsberg*, 1894. 8°.   8462. g. 38.

CICCHITTI-SURIANI (F.)   I Primordii del Kantismo in Italia. *Roma*, 1892, *etc.* 8°. 8462. g. 13.

DREWS (A.)   Kants Naturphilosophie als Grundlage seines Systems. pp. 497. *Berl.* 1894. 8°.
                     8462. dd. 11.

PHILOSOPHY.—History—*continued.*

EISLER (R.)   Die Weiterbildung des Kant'schen Aprioritätslehre bis zur Gegenwart. pp. 88. *Leipz.* 1894. 8°.   8462. e. 43.

GARTELMANN (H.)   Sturz der Metaphysik als Wissenschaft. Kritik des Idealismus I. Kants. pp. 246. *Berl.* 1893. 8°.   8470. f. 31.

HARTMANN (C. R. E. v.)   Kants Erkenntnistheorie und Metaphysik. pp. 256. *Leipz.* 1894. 8°.   8462. g. 26.

KANT (I.)   Kant's Philosophy adapted to a natural system. pp. 214. *Edinb.* 1893. 8°.
                     8462. aaa. 29.

LIND (P. v.)   "Kant's mystische Weltanschauung," ein Wahn der modernen Mystik. pp. 144. *München*, 1892. 8°.   8462. g. 3.

MAUXION (M.)   La Métaphysique de Herbart et la Critique de Kant. pp. 339. *Paris*, 1894. 8°.
                     8465. gg. 12.

WEGNER (G.)   Kantlexikon. pp. 347. *Berl.* 1893. 8°.   8462. f. 32.

DREWS (A.)   Die deutsche Spekulation seit Kant. 2 Bde. *Berl.* 1893. 8°.   8462. g. 14.

LÉVY-BRUHL (L.)   La Philosophie de Jacobi. pp. 263. *Paris*, 1894. 8°.   8462. f. 42.

RITCHIE (D. G.)   Darwin and Hegel. pp. 285. *Lond.* 1893. 8°.   8470. e. 11.

LEHMANN (R.)   Schopenhauer. pp. 200. *Berl.* 1894. 8°.   8462. g. 39.

JONES (H.)   Critical account of the Philosophy of Lotze. pp. 375. *Glasg.* 1895. 8°. 8462. h. 13.

KÁATZ (H.)   Die Weltanschauung F. Nietzsches. *Dresd.* 1892, *etc.* 8°.   8462. f. 8.

STEINER (R.)   F. Nietzsche, ein Kämpfer gegen seine Zeit. pp. 125. *Weimar*, 1895. 8°.
                     010707. i. 12.

ADAM (C.)   La Philosophie en France. Première moitié du XIX° siècle. pp. 444. *Paris*, 1894. 8°.   8485. f. 18.

PICAVET (F.)   Les Idéologues. Essai sur l'histoire des idées en France depuis 1789. pp. 628. *Paris*, 1891. 8°.   8486. g. 22.

PUGLIA (F.)   Il Risorgimento filosofico in Italia. pp. 198. *Napoli*, 1891. 8°.   8467. aaa. 45.

ROYCE (J.)   The Spirit of modern Philosophy. pp. 519. *Boston*, 1892. 8°.   8470. e. 1.

ROBERTY (E. de)   La Philosophie du siècle. pp. 234. *Paris*, 1891. 8°.   8486. g. 24.

BENZONI (R.)   Il Monismo nella filosofia contemporanea. pp. 118. *Palermo*, 1892. 8°.
                     8462. e. 21.

MAUMUS (É. V.)   Les Philosophes contemporains. *Paris*, 1891, *etc.* 12°.   8469. d. 30.

SCHULTZE (F.)   Der Zeitgeist in Deutschland. pp. 194. *Leipz.* 1894. 8°.   8485. f. 17.

SETH (A.)   Present position of the Philosophical Sciences. pp. 32. *Edinb.* 1891. 8°.
                     8461. bbb. 48. (4.)

VOLKELT (J.)   Vorträge zur Einführung in die Philosophie der Gegenwart. pp. 230. *München*, 1892. 8°.   8462. e. 9.

    Moral Philosophy.   *See* ETHICS.

    Scholastic Philosophy.   *See* THEOLOGY.

PHOENICIA.   BEZOLD (C.)   Oriental Diplomacy. Text of the Tell el-Amarna Tablets. pp. 124. *Lond.* 1893. 8°.   7704. aaa. 54.

PALESTINE.   *Palestine Exploration Fund.*   Tell Amarna Tablets. Translated by C. R. Conder. pp. 212. *Lond.* 1893. 8°.   2356. b. 5.

SCHEIL (F. V.)   Tablettes d'El-Amarna. 1892. 8°. Mémoires de la Mission Archéologique au Caire. Tom. 6.   7703. k.

PHOENICIA—*continued.*

HAMDI (O.) Une Nécropole royale à Sidon. Fouilles de Hamdy Bey. *Paris*, 1892, *etc.* 4°.
—— Planches. fol. 1711. d.

PARIS. *Louvre.* Notice des Monuments phéniciens. Par E. Ledrain. pp. 191.
Paris, 1888. 12°. 7706. a. 26.

PELLEGRINI (A.) Studii d'Epigrafia fenicia. 1891, *etc.* 4°. Ac. Palermo. *Accademia di Scienze.* Atti. Ser. 3. Vol. 1. Ac. 99.

JOHNSTON (T. C.) "Did the Phœnicians discover America?" 1892. 8°. Ac. San Francisco. *Geographical Society.* Special Bulletin.
9551. k. 8. (1.)

WALKER (R.) Phœnicia in Freshwater. pp. 20. *Freshwater*, 1892. 8°. Pam. 3.

BLOCH (A.) Phœnicisches Glossar. pp. 64. *Berl.* 1890. 8°. 12901. d. 20. (11.)
See also HISTORY, *Ancient.*

PHONETICS. *See* LANGUAGE; and for the Phonetics of each language, under the language required.

PHONOGRAPH. GILLETT (W.) The Phonograph and how to construct it. pp. 87. *Lond.* 1892. 8°. 8757. bb. 15.

VILLON (A. M.) Le Phonographe et ses applications. pp. 92. *Paris*, 1894. 8°. 8757. aaaa. 52.

PHONOGRAPHY. *See* SHORTHAND.

PHONOPHORE.
See TELEGRAPHY : TELEPHONE.

PHOSPHATES. BLAKE (W. P.) Early history of the industry of Phosphate of lime in the United States. *New Haven, Conn.* 1892. *s. sh.* 8°.
Pam. 27.

DECKERS (A.) Étude sur les Phosphates. 2 vol. *Liège*, 1894. 8°. 8908. h. 44.

D'INVILLIERS (E. V.) Phosphate deposits of Navassa. 1891. 8°. Ac. United States. *Geological Society.* Bulletin. Vol. 2. Ac. 3187.

MILLAR (C. C. H.) Florida, South Carolina and Canadian Phosphates. pp. 223. *Lond.* 1892. 8°.
7106. i. 13.

STOKLASA (J.) Die wasserlöslichen Verbindungen der Phosphorsäure in den Superphosphaten. *Prag*, 1894, *etc.* 8°. 8908. c.

WRIGHT (C. D.) Phosphate industry of the United States. pp. 145. 1895. 8°. U.S. *Bureau of Labour.* Report 6. 8275. k.

WYATT (F.) Phosphates of America. pp. 191. *N.Y.* 1894. 8°. 07109. h. 38.
See also MANURES.

PHOTOGRAPHY.
Bibliography.

Ac., *etc.* London. *Photographic Society.* Catalogue of the Library. pp. 32. *Lond.* 1893. 8°.
11903. aa. 23. (12.)

LONDON. *Camera Club.* Catalogue of the Library. pp. 27. *Lond.* 1894. 8°. 11901. h. 25.

General.

ABNEY (W. de W.) Treatise on Photography. pp. 374. 1893. 8°. GOODEVE (T. M.) Text-books of Science, *etc.* 8707. bb.
—— Instruction in Photography. pp. 388. *Lond.* 1892. 8°. 8908. e. 59.
—— Instantaneous Photography. pp. 96. *Lond.* 1895. 8°. 8909. aaa. 20.
—— and CLARK (L.) Platinotype. pp. 174. *Lond.* 1895. 8°. 8909. b. 26.

ALFIERI (B.) Half-holidays with the Camera. pp. 160. *Lond.* 1893. 8°. 8908. e. 63.

ANDREWS (J.) Studies in Photography. pp. 202. *Lond.* 1892. 8°. 8909. f. 19.

PHOTOGRAPHY.—General—*continued.*

ARNOLD (H.) Die Negativ-Retouche nach Kunst- und Naturgesetzen. pp. 480. *Wien*, 1892. 8°. 8909. bb. 23.

BALAGNY (G.) Les Contre-types. pp. 48. *Paris*, 1893. 12°. 8909. bb. 32.

BECK (R.) and (J.) Principles of a Photographic Lens explained. pp. 20. *Lond.* 1892. 8°. Pam. 13.
—— The Frena Handbook. 2 pt. *Lond.* 1893-4. 8°. 8909. aa. 29.

BEGINNER. Beginner's guide to Photography. pp. 119. *Lond.* 1894. 8°. 8909. g. 11.

BENNETT (R. A. R.) Experiences with a Hand-camera. pp. 10. *Blackburn*, 1891. 8°. Pam. 13.

BERGERET (A.) and DROUIN (F.) Les Récréations photographiques. pp. 224. *Paris*, 1893. 8°. 8909. ccc. 5.

BLACK (A.) Photography indoors and out. pp. 240. *Bost.* 1894. 8°. 8909. f. 6.

BOLAS (T.) The Photographic studio. pp. 94. *Lond.* 1895. 8°. 8909. f. 25.

BOTHAMLEY (C. H.) Ilford manual of Photography. pp. 207. *Ilford*, 1891. 8°.
8909. bb. 12.

BROTHERS (A.) Photography; its history and processes. pp. 364. *Lond.* 1892. 8°. 8909. cc. 23.

BURTON (W. K.) Modern Photography. pp. 208. *Lond.* 1892. 8°. 8909. aaa. 40.
—— Manual of Photography. pp. 184. *Bradford*, 1895. 16°. 8909. f. 37.
—— Practical guide to Photographic Printing. pp. 355. *Lond.* 1887. 8°. 8909. cc. 8.
—— Optics for Photographers. pp. 153. *Lond.* 1891. 8°. 8909. aa. 14.

BURNABY, afterwards MAIN (E. A. F.) Hints on snow Photography. pp. 14. *Lond.* 1895. 8°.
8909. cc. 11.

CHAPEL D'ESPINASSOUX (G. de) Traité de la détermination du temps de pose. pp. 121. *Paris*, 1890. 12°. 8908. i. 24.

CHÉRI ROUSSEAU (G.) Méthode pour le Tirage des épreuves de petit format. pp. 20. *Paris*, 1894. 12°. 8909. bb. 62.

CLARK (L.) Development; including instructions for the use of eikonogen as a developer. pp. 46. *Lond.* 1891. 8°. 8909. aaa.
—— Platinum Toning. pp. 96. *Lond.* 1892. 8°.
8909. aaa.

COLSON (R.) La Perspective en photographie. pp. 72. *Paris*, 1894. 12°. 8209. bb.

DAVID (L.) and SCOLIK (C.) Photographisches Notiz- und Nachschlage-Buch für die Praxis. pp. 204. *Halle*, 1893. 8°. 8909. aa. 26.

DILLAYE (F.) Les Nouveautés photographiques. *Paris*, 1893, *etc.* 8°. 8909. ccc.

DONNADIEU (A. L.) Traité de Photographie stéréoscopique. 2 pt. *Paris*, 1892. 8°.
8909. ccc. 1.

DRESSER (A. R.) Bromide Enlarging and Contact printing. pp. 60. *Lond.* 1892. 8°.
8908. aa. 55.

DUCHOCHOIS (P. C.) Photographic reproduction processes. pp. 122. *Lond.* 1892. 8°. 8909. g. 3.
—— Lighting in photographic studios. pp. 66. *Lond.* 1895. 8°. 8908. e. 26.

DUNMORE (E.) Photographer's Companion. pp. 136. *Lond.* 1892. 8°. 8909. aa. 17.

EMERSON (P. H.) Death of naturalistic Photography. pp. 7. *Lond.* 1890. 8°. Pam. 13.

ENCYCLOPÆDIAS. Encyklopädie der Photographie. *Halle*, 1893, *etc.* 8°. 8909. k.

FISCH (A.) Les Phototirages aux encres d'imprimerie. pp. 86. *Paris*, 1894. 12°.
8908. aa. 33.

PHOTOGRAPHY.—General—*continued.*

FOREST (M.) Ce qu'on peut faire avec des Plaques voilées. pp. 52. *Paris*, 1893. 8°.
8909. bb. 29.

FOURTIER (H.) Les Positifs sur verre. pp. 205. *Paris*, 1892. 8°.   8909. d. 5.

—— La Pratique des projections. *Paris*, 1892, *etc.* 12°.   8909. bb.

—— Les Tableaux de projections mouvementés. pp. 95. *Paris*, 1893. 12°.   8909. bb. 36.

FRY (S. H.) Photographic Manuals. *Lond.* 1895, *etc.* 8°.   8909. h.

GANICHOT (P.) La Photographie et ses applications. 2 pt. *Paris*, 1893. 12°.   8909. g. 5.

GAUTHIER-VILLARS (H.) Manuel de ferrotypie. pp. 36. *Paris*, 1891. 12°.   8909. bb. 30.

GEYMET (T.) Traité pratique de photographie. pp. 267. *Paris*, 1894. 12°.   8909. bb.

GIOPPI (L.) La Fotografia secondo i processi moderni. pp. 726. *Milano*, 1891. 8°. 8908. k. 14.

GOERZ (P.) Ausführliche Anleitung zur Herstellung von Photographien für Liebhaber. pp. 209. *Berl.* 1893. 8°.   8909. f. 4.

GUERRONNAN (A.) Dictionnaire français, allemand, anglais, italien et latin des mots employés en Photographie. pp. 175. *Paris*, 1895. 8°.
12902. i. 10.

HALL (F.) Amateur photography. How to become an unsuccessful amateur. pp. 31. *Lond.* 1895, 8°.   12316. i. 63.

HASCHEK (A. M.) Photographische Optik. pp. 94. *Halle*, 1891. 8°.   8909. d. 3.

HASTINGS (C. W.) Holidays with the Camera. pp. 59. *Lond.* 1891. 4°.   10106. h. 2.

HEIGHWAY (W.) Hand-book of photographic terms. pp. 226. *Lond.* 1891. 8°. 8909. bb. 11.

—— Photographic printers' assistant. pp. 86. *Lond.* 1892. 8°.   8909. bb. 16.

HEPWORTH (T. C.) Evening work for amateur photographers. pp. 196. *Lond.* 1890. 8°.
8909. c. 29.

HODGES (J. A.) Elementary photography. pp. 159. *Lond.* 1893. 8°.   8909. aaa.

HUME (W.) Cantilever enlarging apparatus for the use of photographers. pp. 12. *Edinb.* 1890. 8°.   Pam. 13.

JARDIN (G.) Recettes et conseils à l'amateur photographe. pp. 74. *Paris*, 1893. 8°.
8909. g. 7.

KAPTEIJN (J. C.) De beteekenis der Photographie. pp. 24. *Groningen*, 1891. 8°. Pam. 4.

KLARY (C.) L'Éclairage des portraits photographiques. pp. 67. *Paris*, 1893. 12°. 8909. bb.

—— La Photographie nocturne. pp. 174. *Paris*, 1893. 8°.   8909. cc. 30.

KODAK MANUAL. The Kodak Manual. 5 pt. *Lond.* 1892. 16°.   8909. de.

KRUEGER (J.) Die Photographie, oder die Anfertigung von bildlichen Darstellungen auf künstlichem Wege. pp. 495. *Wien*, 1893. 8°.
8909. f. 2.

LA BAUME PLUVINEL (A. de) La Photographie au gélatino-bromure d'argent. pp. 213. *Paris*, 1891. 12°.   8909. bb. 51.

—— La théorie des procédés photographiques. pp. 226. 1894. 8°. Encyclopédie des aide-mémoire.   8709. g.

LEAPER (C. J.) Experimental photography. pp. 102. *Lond.* 1893. 8°.   8909. aaa.

—— First principles of photography. pp. 269. *Lond.* 1892. 8°.   8908. e. 64.

LEGROS (V.) L'Aristotypie. pp. 95. *Paris*, 1891. 8°.   8909. bb. 2.

LIÉBERT (A.) La photographie en Amerique. pp. 679. 24. *Paris*, 1884. 8°.   8909. cc. 29.

PHOTOGRAPHY.—General—*continued.*

LONDE (A.) Aide-mémoire de photographie. pp. 337. *Paris*, 1893. 12°.   8909. aa. 27.

—— Traité pratique du Développement. pp. 104. *Paris*, 1892. 12°.   8909. bb. 26.

LONDON. *Camera Club.* Journal of the Camera Club. *Lond.* 1894, *etc.* 8°.   2234.

—— *Eastman Photographic Materials Co.* Directions for developing and printing with Eastman's Outfit. pp. 16. *Lond.* 1892. *obl.* 16°. 8909. de. 3.

—— *Photographic Club.* Transactions, *etc. Lond.* 1880, *etc.* 8°.   8909. cc.

LUMIÈRE (A.) and (L.) Les Développateurs organiques en photographie. pp. 82. *Paris*, 1893. 12°.   8908. aa. 56.

MAIMBRESSY (C. de) La Photographie. pp. 176. *Paris*, 1892. 8°.   8909. aaa. 43.

MANN (W. J.) Photographic Tourist's equipment. pp. 20. *Lond.* 1890. 8°.   Pam. 13.

MARTIN (A.) Méthode pour la détermination des courbures des objectifs de photographie. pp. 67. *Paris*, 1894. 8°.   8909. ccc. 8.

MATHET (L.) La Photographie durant l'hiver. pp. 314. *Paris*, 1895. 12°.   8909. g. 22.

MERCIER (P.) Virages et Fixages. 2 pt. *Paris*, 1892-93. 8°.   8909. aa. 25.

MILLS (F. W.) Exterior and interior Photography. pp. 68. *Lond.* 1895. 8°. 8909. c. 31.

—— Art and practice of Interior Photography. pp. 123. *Huddersfield*, 1890. 8°. 8909. c. 27.

—— and PONTON (A. C.) Stenopaic or pin-hole Photography. pp. 27. *Lond.* 1895. 8°.
8909. c. 32.

MUFFONE (G.) Come il sole dipinge. Fotografia per i dilettanti. pp. 315. *Milano*, 1895. 16°.
012200. i. 11.

NIEWĘGLOWSKI (G. H.) Notions de Photographie à l'usage des amateurs. pp. 95. *Paris*, 1892. 12°.   8909. bb. 59.

—— L'Objectif photographique. pp. 59. *Paris*, 1892. 8°.   8909. l. 2.

—— Le Matériel de l'amateur photographe. pp. 74. *Paris*, 1894. 12°.   8909. g. 12.

PAAR (J.) Die Retouche der Photographie. pp. 70. *Halle*, 1890. 8°.   8908. l. 3.

PANAJOU (F.) Manuel du Photographe amateur. pp. 191. *Paris*, 1892. 8°.   8909. aaa. 44.

PAPERS. Competitive papers on Photography. *Lond.* 1890, *etc.* 8°.   8909. aaa.

PELIGOT (M.) Traitement des Résidus photographiques. pp. 44. *Paris*, 1891. 12°.
8909. bb. 34.

P.P. *Ashtead.* Dry Plates. A magazine. *Ashtead*, 1892, *etc.* 8°. P.P. 1912. cd. and 2103.

—— *Bradford.* The practical Photographer. *Bradford*, 1890, *etc.* 8°.   P.P. 1912. ec.

—— The junior Photographer. *Bradford*, 1894, *etc.* 4°.   P.P. 1912. eca.

—— *Geneva.* Revue de Photographie. *Genève*, 1891, *etc.* 8°.   P.P. 1913. n.

—— *Lavender Hill.* The Photographic Gazette. *Lavender Hill*, 1893, *etc.* 8°.   1866. a. 14.

—— *London.* Adams and Co.'s photographic Annual. *Lond.* 1893, *etc.* 8°. P.P. 2495. cae.

—— The Photogram. *Lond.* 1894, *etc.* 8°.
P.P. 1912. eb. and 843.

—— The amateur Photographer's Annual. *Lond.* 1891, *etc.* 8°.   P.P. 2495. cac.

—— Photographic Review of reviews. *Lond.* 1892, *etc.* 8°.   P.P. 1912. faa.

—— *Photography.* Photography Annual. *Lond.* 1891, *etc.* 8°.   P.P. 2495. cab.

PHOTOGRAPHY.—General—continued.

—— *New York.* American amateur Photographer. *N.Y.* 1893, *etc.* 8°.　　　P.P. 1912. qa.

—— International annual of Anthony's photographic Bulletin. *N.Y.* 1890, *etc* 8°. P.P. 2523. ld.

—— Photo American Review.
N.Y. 1891, *etc.* 8°.　　　　　　P.P. 1912. q.

—— *Paris.* Annuaire général de la Photographie. *Paris*, 1892, *etc.* 8°.　P.P. 1913. bac.

—— Paris-Photographe. Revue mensuelle
Paris, 1891. 8°.　　　　　　P.P. 1913. bad.

PHOTOGRAPHY. Practical Photography for amateurs. pp. 127. *Lond.* 1893. 8°.　8909. g. 4.

PICKERING (W. H.) A Method of measuring the sensitiveness of photographic dry plates.
pp. 11. *Camb. Mass.* 1884. 8°.　　　Pam. 13.

—— Methods of determining the speed of photographic exposers. *Camb. Mass.* 1885. 8°.
　　　　　　　　　　　　　　　　　Pam. 13.

REYNER (A.) La Photographie dans les appartements. pp. 124. *Paris*, 1894. 8°. 8909. aa. 32.

ROBERT (K.) La Photographie, aide du paysagiste. pp. 169. *Paris*, 1890. 8°.　8908. l. 11.

—— Traité de la Photominiature. pp. 87.
Paris, 1893. 8°.　　　　　　　8909. f. 7.

ROBINSON (H. P.) Art Photography in short chapters. pp. 60. *Lond.* 1890. 8°.　8909. aaa.

—— The Studio: and what to do in it. pp. 143.
Lond. 1891. 8°.　　　　　　8909. aaa. 36.

ROGERS (W. I.) One Hundred photographic Formulæ. pp. 32. *Lond.* 1892. 8°.　Pam. 13.

ROOSVAL (A.) Handbok i Fotografi.
Stockholm, 1890, *etc.* 8°.　　　8909. cc. 22.

ROUILLÉ-LADEVÈZE (A.) Sépia-photo et Sanguino-photo. pp. 24. *Paris*, 1894. 8°. 8909. bb.

SACHSE (J. F.) Philadelphia's share in the development of Photography. pp. 17.
Phila. 1893. 8°.　　　　　　　Pam. 13.

SASSI (L.) Ricettario fotografico. pp. 150.
Milano, 1893. 8°.　　　　　012200. i. 6.

SCHMIDT (F.) Compendium der practischen Photographie. pp. 339. *Karlsruhe*, 1891. 8°.
　　　　　　　　　　　　　　　　8909. cc. 21.

SCHNAUSS (H.) Die Blitzlicht-Photographie.
pp. 136. *Düsseldorf*, 1893. 8°.　8909. cc. 31.

SERIES. Popular photographic series.
Bradford, 1895, *etc.* 8°.　　　　　8909. h.

STOLZE (F.) Photographische Bibliothek.
Berl. 1893. 8°.　　　　　　　8909. dd.

SUN ARTISTS. Sun Artists. 8 pt.
Lond. 1889–91. 8°.　　　　　1757. b. 14.

TAYLOR (J. T.) Optics of Photography and photographic lenses. pp. 244. *Lond.* 1892. 8°.
　　　　　　　　　　　　　　　8909. aaa. 39.

TOUCHE (P. de) Notions de Photographie.
pp. 87. *Paris*, 1894. 8°.　　　　8908. k. 8.

TRUTAT (E.) La Photographie en montagne.
pp. 137. *Paris*, 1894. 12°.　　　8909. bb. 63.

VOGEL (E.) Practical pocket-book of Photography. pp. 202. *Lond.* 1893. 8°. 8909. aa. 23.

VIDAL (L.) Manuel d'Orthochromatisme.
pp. 127. *Paris*, 1891. 8°.　　　8909. bb. 22.

WALL (E. J.) Dictionary of Photography.
pp. 237. *N.Y.* 1889. 8°.　　　8908. i. 25.

—— Carbon Printing. pp. 69. *Lond.* 1894. 8°.
　　　　　　　　　　　　　　　　8909. aaa.

WALLON (E.) Traité élémentaire de l'Objectif photographique. pp. 299. *Paris*, 1891. 8°.
　　　　　　　　　　　　　　　8908. l. 6.

—— Choix et usage des Objectifs photographiques. pp. 196. 1893. 8°. Encyclopédie des Aide-Mémoire.　　　　　　　　　8709. g.

PHOTOGRAPHY.—General—continued.

WATKINS (A.) Exposure Notes. Instructions for the use of the Watkins' Exposure Meter.
pp. 99. *Hereford*, 1890. obl. 8°.　8909. a. 19.

WELFORD (W. D.) The Hand camera Manual.
pp. 116. *Lond.* 1893. 8°.　　　8909. g. 6.

WHEELER (G.) Photographic Enlargements.
pp. 48. *Manch.* 1892. 8°.　　　Pam. 13.

WOODBURY (W. E.) Encyclopædia of Photography. *Lond.* 1892. 8°.　　　8909. cc. 28.

—— Gelatino-chloride of silver printing-out Process. pp. 121. *Lond.* 1891. 8°. 8909. bb. 10.

Applications to Engraving and Illustration.

See ENGRAVING.

Applications, *Scientific, Professional, etc.*

GANICHOT (P.) La Photographie et ses applications. 2 pt. *Paris*, 1893. 12°.　8909. g. 5.

GODY (L.) La Photographie appliquée aux arts militaires et civils. pp. 212. *Namur*, 1890. 8°.
　　　　　　　　　　　　　　　　8909. bb. 5.

KŒHLER (R.) Applications de la Photographie aux sciences naturelles. pp. 199. 1893. 8°.
Encyclopédie des aide-mémoire.　　　8709. g.

STEINER (F.) Die Photographie im Dienste des Ingenieurs. *Wien*, 1891, *etc.* 8°.　8908. m.

LEGROS (V.) Sommaire de Photogrammétrie.
pp. 272. *Paris*, 1891. 8°.　　　8909. bb. 20.

BERTILLON (A.) La Photographie judiciaire.
pp. 115. *Paris*, 1890. 8°.　　　8909. cc. 11.

—— Die gerichtliche Photographie. pp. 111.
1895. 8°. Encyklopädie der Photographie.
Hft. 14.　　　　　　　　　　　　8909. k.

BIGEON (A.) La Photographie et le droit.
pp. 305. *Paris*, 1894. 12°.　　　8909. f. 21.

LONDE (A.) La Photographie médicale. pp. 220.
Paris, 1893. 8°.　　　　　　　8909. ccc. 3.

Astronomical Photography.

Ac. Sydney. *Government Observatory.* Description of the Star Camera. pp. 15.
Sydney, 1892. 4°.　　　　　　8563. i. 22.

—— Photographs of the Milky Way and Nubeculæ. *Sydney*, 1891. 4°.　　　8560. h. 40.

BALTIN (P.) Ueber die neuesten Fortschritte, Astrophotographie. pp. 12. 1891. 8°. HUTH (E.) Sammlung naturwissenschtlicher Vorträge.
Bd. 3.　　　　　　　　　　　　8705. ff.

BATUT (A.) La Photographie aérienne. pp. 74.
Paris, 1890. 8°.　　　　　　　8909. cc. 7.

JACOBY (H.) The Rutherfurd photographic measures of the group of the Pleiades. 1892. 8°.
Ac. New York. *Academy of Sciences.* Annals.
Vol. 6. Nos. 5, 6.　　　　　　　Ac. 3048.

MOUCHEZ (E.) La Photographie astronomique à l'Observatoire de Paris. pp. 107.
Paris, 1887. 8°.　　　　　　　8563. aa. 24.

ROBERTS (I.) Selection of Photographs of Stars, Star Clusters and Nebulæ. pp. 134.
Lond. 1893. 4°.　　　　　　　8563. i. 24.

Chemistry of Photography

FOURTIER (H.) Dictionnaire de Chimie photographique. pp. 348. *Paris*, 1892. 8°.
　　　　　　　　　　　　　　　　8909. d. 4.

MAUMENÉ (E. J.) Manuel de Chimie photographique. pp. 496. *Paris*, 1893. 8°. 8909. bb. 40.

NAMIAS (R.) Fotochimica dei Sali di Mercurio.
pp. 51. *Modena*, 1894. 8°.　　　Pam. 13.

SEYEWETZ (A.) Contribution de la Chimie aux récents progrès réalisés par la photographie.
1895. 8°. Ac. Lyons. *Société d'Agriculture, etc.* Annales des sciences. Sér. 7. Tom. 2.
　　　　　　　　　　　　　　　Ac. 362/3.

PHOTOGRAPHY—continued.
Exhibitions of Photography.
GLASGOW. *Photographic Exhibition.* Catalogue. pp. 65. *Glasg.* 1886. 8°.   7959. b. 32. (4.)

LEEDS. *Municipal Art Gallery.* International Photographic Exhibition. 2 pt. *Leeds,* 1891. 8°.   8909. bb. 18.

LINCOLN. *Camera Club.* Official catalogue. Photographic Exhibition. pp. 15. *Lincoln,* 1892. 8°.   Pam. 13.

Ac. London. *Photographic Society.* Photographs of the Year. pp. 8. *Lond.* 1891. fol.   1757. b. 12.

—— Photographs of the Pall Mall Exhibition, 1892. pp. 8. *Lond.* 1892. fol.   1758. b. 7.

History of Photography.
SCHIENDL (C.) Geschichte der Photographie. pp. 380. *Wien,* 1891. 8°.   8908. k. 16.

ARATA (P. N.) Documentos históricos relativos al descubrimiento de la Fotografía. pp. 11. 1892. fol. Ac. La Plata. *Museo.* Anales.   Tab. 1227. a.

MENTIENNE ( ) La découverte de la Photographie en 1839. pp. 162. *Paris,* 1892. 8°.   8909. ccc. 2.

HARRISON (W. J.) Proposal for a national photographic record. pp. 14. *Lond.* 1892. 8°.   Pam. 13.

Photomicrography. *See* MICROSCOPY.

Photography in Colours.
BERTHIER (A.) Manuel de Photochromie interférentielle. pp. 169. *Paris,* 1895. 12°.   8909. bb. 64.

BRANDT (C.) La Photographie des couleurs. pp. 66. *Paris,* 1892. 8°.   8909. f. 33.

DUMOULIN (E.) Les Couleurs reproduites en photographie. pp. 55. *Paris,* 1894. 8°.   8909. bb. 60.

IVES (F. E.) Handbook to the Photochromoscope. pp. 50. *Lond.* 1894. 8°.   8909. aa. 30.

VALENTA (E.) Die Photographie in natürlichen Farben. pp. 82. 1894. 8°. Encyklopädie der Photographie. Hft. 2.   8909. k.

PHOTOGRAVURE: PHOTOLITHOGRAPHY AND PHOTOTYPE.
See ENGRAVING.

PHOTOMETRY. *See* LIGHT.

PHRENOLOGY: PHYSIOGNOMY,
etc. ACKROYD ( ) Astro-Phrenology, the planet reader, *etc.* pp. 56. *Rochdale,* 1885. 8°.   Pam. 36.

CHARACTER. Character in the Face. pp. 256. *Lond.* 1893. 8°.   7410. c. 35.

CHEETHAM (A.) Character Reading explained. pp. 8. *Rhyl.* 1893. 8°.   7410. de. 57. (1.)

—— Phrenology in a nutshell. pp. 18. *Rhyl.* 1893. 8°.   7410. de. 57. (5.)

—— Noses, and how to read them. pp. 10. *Rhyl.* 1893. 8°.   7410. de. 57. (4.)

COATES (J.) How to read Faces. pp. 128.' *Lond.* 1891. 8°.   7410. de. 48.

—— Self Help: a phrenological and physiological register. pp. 76. *Lond.* 1892. 8°.   7410. bb. 33. (6.)

COMBE (G.) Select works of G. Combe. *Lond.* 1893, *etc.* 8°.   12273. cc. 5.

DONOVAN (C.) Some observations of C. Donovan on the Mastoid Process, as an indication of walking energy. pp. 15. *Lond.* 1894. 8°.   Pam. 39.

DUTTON (G. H. J.) Delineation of the character of C. S. Parnell and W. H. Smith. pp. 7. *Skegness,* 1891. 8°.   7410. bb. 33. (2.)

PHRENOLOGY—continued.
DUTTON (G. H. J.) Music and phrenology. pp. 7. *Skegness,* 1892. 8°.   7410. bb. 33. (8.)

FARMERY (J. R.) and LARDER (F. T.) The Character-Reader *Rotherham,* 1893, *etc.* 8°.   7410. de. 53.

FRITH (H.) How to read Character in features, forms and faces. pp. 114. *Lond.* 1891. 8°.   7410. df. 38.

HOLLANDER (B.) Contribution to a scientific phrenology. *Lond.* 1891. 8°. 07305. h. 6. (6.)

HORNER (J. H.) The new phrenological Chart. pp. 16. *Manch.* 1893. 8°.   Pam. 36.

KESWICK (J. B.) The new phrenological and physiological Register. pp. 97. *Scarborough,* 1895. 8°.   7410. ccc. 7.

LEDOS (E.) Traité de la Physionomie humaine pp. 440. *Paris,* 1894. 8°.   7410. f. 4.

MERTON (H. W.) Descriptive mentality. 2 pt. *Bost.* 1893. 8°.   7410. c. 45.

O'DELL (S. E.) Phrenology. pp. 248. *Lond.* 1894. 8°.   7410. df. 52.

OPPENHEIM (A. I.) Phreno-Physiognomy. pp. 75. *Lond.* 1892. 8°.   7410. dg. 45.

P.P. *Batley.* Know Thyself. *Batley,* 1891, *etc.* 4°.   P.P. 1257. c. and 2106.

—— *London.* Phrenological Record. No. 1–7. *Lond.* 1892, 93. 4°. & 8°.   1866. c. 6.

ROBINSON (W.) Phrenological Chart. pp. 13. *Blackpool,* 1895. 8°.   07305. f. 20. (11.)

ROGERSON (R.) What the eye can see in human and animal character. pp. 228. *Edinb.* 1892. 8°.   012330. f. 32.

SAPIRA (M. I.) Studii physiognomice. pp. 128. *Roman,* 1885. 8°.   7410. d. 39.

SPARK (J. J.) Confessions of a Phrenologist. pp. 22. *Lond.* 1891. 8°.   7306. df. 16. (8.)

—— The human Face divine. pp. 64. *Lond.* 1891. 8°.   07305. e. 23. (15.)

TAYLOR (J. W.) New Register and self-instructor in Phrenology. pp. 85. *Morecambe,* 1893. 8°.   7410. bb. 33. (14.)

—— Noses, and what they indicate. pp. 15. *Lond.* 1892. 8°.   7410. bb. 33. (11.)

THORNTON (W. P.) Phrenology, or, heads and what they tell us. pp. 120. *Lond.* 1894. 8°.   7410. df. 53.

WEBB (J.) Phrenological aspect of modern research. pp. 27. *Lond.* 1890. 8°.   07305. h. 16. (6.)

—— Phrenology and religion. pp. 13. *Lond.* 1894. 8°.   7306. e. 25. (14.)

WHEELER (M.) Moles or birth-marks. pp. 145. *Lond.* 1894. 8°.   8610. b. 92.

WILLIAMS (W. M.) Vindication of Phrenology. pp. 428. *Lond.* 1894. 8°.   7410. ee. 43.

WILSON (W.) Chart of new Phrenology. pp. 59. *Lond.* 1895. 8°.   Pam. 39.

PHRYGIA. LEGRAND (P. E.) and CHAMONARD (J.) Inscriptions de Phrygie. 1893. 8°. Ac. Athens. *École Française.* Bulletin de correspondance hellénique. Année 17. Ac. 5206/3.

RAMSAY (W. M.) Cities and bishoprics of Phrygia. *Oxf.* 1895, *etc.* 8°.   9055. g.

PERROT (G.) and CHIPIEZ (C.) History of Art in Phrygia, *etc.* pp. 405. *Lond.* 1892. 8°.   2259. f. 20.

See also ASIA MINOR.

PHTHISIS. *See* CONSUMPTION.

PHYCOMYCETES. *See* FUNGI.

PHYLLOXERA. *See* VINE.

PHYSICAL EDUCATION, DRILL, etc.
See GYMNASTICS.

PHYSICIANS. *See* MEDICINE, *Profession of.*
PHYSICS: PHYSICAL SCIENCE.

Bibliography.

Ac. London. *S.K. Museum.* Catalogue of the science Library. pp. 501. *Lond.* 1891. 8°.
　　　　　　　　　　　　　　　　Centre Desk.
CATALOGUES. Catalogue of works on Science and technology. pp. 8. 128. *Lond.* 1893. 8°.
　　　　　　　　　　　　　　　　011901. i. 1.
LEHFELDT (R. A.) List of Memoirs on the Physics of matter. pp. 41. *Lond.* 1894. 8°.
　　　　　　　　　　　　　　　　8707. f. 21.

General.

Ac. Ithaca. *Cornell University.* The Physical Review. *N.Y.* 1893, *etc.* 8°. Ac. 2692. g. 4.
—— Madison. *University.* Bulletin. Science Series. *Madison,* 1894. 8°. Ac. 1792.
—— Manchester. *Owens College.* Studies from the physical Laboratory. *Manch.* 1893, *etc.* 8°.
　　　　　　　　　　　　　　　　Ac. 2672/7.
BARKER (G. F.) Physics. Advanced course. pp. 902. *Lond.* 1892. 8°. 8705. cc. 31.
BARKER (L. H.) Elementary Physics. pp. 254. *Lond.* 1893. 8°. 8705. aaa. 47.
BARRETT (W. F.) and BROWN (W.) Practical Physics. *Lond.* 1892, *etc.* 8°. 8703. b. 54.
BEAUMONT (L. de) Les curiosités de la Science. 1re série. pp. 186. *Paris,* 1895. 16°.
　　　　　　　　　　　　　　　　8704. a. 37.
BICKERTON (A. W,) Materials for lessons in Science. *Wellington,* 1893, *etc.* 8°. 8706. df. 20.
BONNEFONT (G.) Les miettes de la Science. pp. 309. *Paris,* 1893. 8°. 8706. f. 22.
BOWER (J. A.) Simple Experiments for Science teaching. pp. 164. *Lond.* 1894. 8°. 8708. g. 33.
BRITANNIA PHYSICS NOTE BOOK. Britannia Physics note book. pp. 150. *Lond.* 1894. 4°.
　　　　　　　　　　　　　　　　8705. df. 38.
BROWN (R.) Science for all. 5 vol. *Lond.* 1894. 8°. 8703. i. 5.
BUCKLEY, *afterwards* FISHER (A. B.) Moral teachings of Science. pp. 122. *Lond.* 1891. 8°.
　　　　　　　　　　　　　　　　8411. cc. 14.
CAVERNI (R.) Storia del metodo sperimentale in Italia. 2 tom. *Firenze,* 1891, 92. 8°.
　　　　　　　　　　　　　　　　8705. dd. 14.
CERRITELLI (P.) L' obbietto della Scienza moderna. pp. 163. *Chieti,* 1891. 8°. 8469. c. 32.
CHAPPUIS (J.) and BERGET (A.) Leçons de Physique générale. 2 tom. *Paris,* 1891. 8°.
　　　　　　　　　　　　　　　　8709. c. 14.
CHRISTENSEN (K.) and SCHMIDT (C. H. P.) Natur-lære for Realskoler. pp. 200. *Odense,* 1891. 8°.
　　　　　　　　　　　　　　　　8705. c. 32.
CONTA (B.) Premiers principes composant le monde. pp. 112. *Jassy,* 1888. 8°. 8470. ccc. 9.
CUTLER (C. W.) Essentials of Physics. pp. 296. *N.Y.* 1889. 8°. 8908. bb. 32.
DANIELL (A.) Text Book of the principles of physics. pp. 782. *Lond.* 1895. 8°. 2244. g. 2.
DELAURIER (É.) Critique et perfectionnement de la Science. pp. 98. *Paris,* 1891. 8°.
　　　　　　　　　　　　　　　　8704. aaa. 34.
DINGLE (E.) A final effort on Physics in a supplement. pp. 36. *Edinb.* 1895. 4°.
　　　　　　　　　　　　　　　　8707. d 47.
DOLBEAR (A. E.) Matter, Ether and Motion. pp. 407. *Bost.* 1894. 8°. 8708. i. 30.
DU BOIS-REYMOND (P.) Über die Grundlagen der Erkenntnis in den exacten Wissenschaften. pp. 130. *Tübingen,* 1890. 8°. 8708. dd. 11.
EGAN (C. J.) Scraps of modern Science. pp. 352. *Cape Town,* 1895. 8°. 7002. aaa. 5.
ELLINGER (H. O. G.) Lærobog i Fysik. pp. 283. *Kjøbenh.* 1891. 8°. 8704. bb. 42.

ERHARDT (F.) Mechanismus und Teleologie. pp. 160. *Leipz.* 1890. 8°. 8768. c. 25.
EVERETT (J. D.) Illustrations of the C.G.S. system of units. pp. 220. *Lond.* 1891. 8°.
　　　　　　　　　　　　　　　　8534. aa. 37.
FARGES (A.) Matière et forme en présence des sciences modernes. pp. 274. *Paris,* 1892. 8°.
　　　　　　　　　　　　　　　　8462. g. 5.
FESSENDEN (C. E.) Elements of Physics. pp. 229. *Lond.* 1892. 8°. 8705. aa. 29.
FOY (P. B.) Elements of Natural Philosophy. pp. 181. 1895. 8°. FINLAY (T. A.) School and college series. 012202. h.
FRICK (J.) Physikalische Technik. *Braunschweig,* 1890, *etc.* 8°. 8708. dd.
GAGE (A. P.) Principles of Physics. pp. 634. *Bost.* 1895. 8°. 8707. cc. 20.
GANOT (A.) Elementary treatise on physics. pp. 1115. *Lond.* 1893. 8°. 2022. a,
GAUTIER (É.) Les étapes de la Science. pp. 393. *Paris,* 1892. 8°. 8704. a. 33.
GAY (J.) Lectures scientifiques. pp. 790. *Paris,* 1891. 8°. 8708. g. 26.
GLAZEBROOK (R. T.) and SHAW (W. N.) Practical Physics. pp. 633. 1893. 8°. GOODEVE (T. M.) Text-Books of Science. 2244. a. 10.
GORDON (H.) Elementary course of practical Science. *Lond.* 1893, *etc.* 8°. 8704. aa. 32.
GOSS (W. H.) Review of modern Science and modern Thought [by S. Laing]. pp. 587. *Stoke-upon-Trent,* 1895. 8°. 8707. d. 45.
GRASSMANN (H.) Gesammelte physikalische Werke. *Leipz.* 1894, *etc.* 8°. 8535. h
GREGORY (R. A.) Exercise book of elementary Physics, *etc.* pp. 172. *Lond.* 1895. 4°.
　　　　　　　　　　　　　　　　8707. ee. 17.
HASSELL (J.) Familiar Objects of everyday life. pp. 328. *Lond.* 1891. 8°. 8708. i. 20.
HELMHOLTZ (H. L. F. v.) Popular Lectures on scientific subjects. 2 series. *Lond.* 1893. 8°.
　　　　　　　　　　　　　　　　8708. b. 21.
HOPKINS (W. J.) Preparatory Physics. pp. 147. *Lond.* 1894. 8°. 8704. ee. 31.
HUME (W.) Solutions to exercises in experimental Physics. 2 pt. *Edinb.* 1889. 8°.
　　　　　　　　　　　　　　　　8768. l. 23. (3.)
HUXLEY (T. H.) Collected Essays. *Lond.* 1894, *etc.* 8°. 2344. d.
JAMIN (J. C.) Cours de Physique de l'École Polytechnique. 4 tom. *Paris,* 1888–91. 8°.
　　　　　　　　　　　　　　　　8709. cc. 1.
JONES (D. E.) Examples in Physics. pp. 323. *Lond.* 1893. 8°. 8708. f. 7.
JUUL (C.) Naturlære. pp. 315. *Kjøbenh.* 1893. 8°. 8704. de. 26.
KENNEDY (D.) Natural Philosophy for junior students. pp. 163. *Dublin,* 1894. 8°.
　　　　　　　　　　　　　　　　8704. a. 36.
LAGRANGE (C.) Étude sur le Système des forces du monde physique. pp. 728. 1892. 4°. Ac. Brussels. *Académie.* Nouveaux Mémoires. Tom. 48. Ac. 985/7.
LEHMANN (O.) Physikalische Technik. pp. 419. *Leipz.* 1885. 8°. 8707. h. 27.
LA GRASSERIE (R. de) De la Classification des arts et des sciences. pp. 304. *Paris,* 1893. 8°.
　　　　　　　　　　　　　　　　8464. eee. 30.
LOMMEL (E. v.) Lehrbuch der Experimental-physik. pp. 643. *Leipz.* 1893. 8°. 8705. de. 30.
LONDON. *Royal College of Science.* Syllabus of the course of instruction. *Lond.* 1892, *etc.* 8°.
　　　　　　　　　　　　　　　　7958. cc.

PHYSICS.—General—*continued.*

LONDON (W. J.) and MAC LENNAN (J. C.) Laboratory Course in experimental Physics. pp. 302. *N.Y.* 1895. 8°. 8705. dd. 16.

LUBBOCK (*Sir* J.) Modern Science. *Lond.* 1891, *etc.* 8°. 8709. f.

MAC PHERSON (J. G.) Fairyland tales of Science. pp. 281. *Lond.* 1891. 8°. 8703. c. 35.

MAJOR (H.) Teacher's Manual of lessons in elementary Science. pp. 415. *Lond.* 1894. 8°. 8706. aaaa. 33.

MAXWELL (J. C.) Scientific Papers. 2 vol. *Camb.* 1890. 4°. 8706. g. 11.

MERCHANT (F. W.) and FESSENDEN (C. E.) High School physical Science. *Toronto*, 1895, *etc.* 8°. 8708. h. 14.

MIVART (St. G.) Introduction to the elements of Science. pp. 392. *Lond.* 1894. 8°. 8704. bb. 41.

MOELLER (M.) Die Naturkraft. pp. 176. *Hamb.* 1891. 8°. 8705. e. 20.

MURCHÉ (V. T.) Object lessons in elementary Science. *Lond.* 1894, *etc.* 8°. 8707. cc. 17.

—— Science Readers. *Lond.* 1895, *etc.* 8°. 8708. ee.

MYSTERIES. Scientific Mysteries. Collection of simple experiments. pp. 100. *Lond.* 1891. 8°. 8909. bb. 6.

NABER (H. A.) Standard methods in Physics criticised. pp. 114. *Lond.* 1894. 8°. 8757. f. 33.

NEUMANN (C.) Beiträge zur einzelnen Theilen der mathematischen Physik. pp. 314. *Leipz.* 1893. 8°. 8705. ee. 16.

NICHOLS (E. L.) Laboratory manual of Physics. *N.Y.* 1894, *etc.* 8°. 8704. ff 15.

OLMSTED (D.) Introduction to Natural Philosophy. pp. 465. *N.Y.* 1891. 8°. 8707. f. 20.

ORGANISATION. On the organisation of Science. pp. 32. *Lond.* 1892. 8°. 8708. g. 27. (13.)

PARVÉ (D. J. S.) Leerboek der Natuurkunde. 4 Stuk. *Tiel*, 1888, 1887–92. 8° 8708. b. 20.

PAULSEN (A. F. W.) Naturkræfterne deres Lov og vigtigste Anvendelser. *Kjøbenh.* 1893, *etc.* 8°. 8705. ff.

PEARSON (K.) The grammar of Science. pp. 493. 1892. 8°. ELLIS (H. H.) Contemporary Science Series. 8709. i.

PEDDIE (W.) Manual of Physics. pp. 501. 1892. 8°. University Series. 012202. de.

P.P. *Freiburg.* Jahrbuch der Naturwissenschaften. *Freiburg*, 1886, *etc.* 8°. P.P. 1452. c.

—— *London.* Natural Science. *Lond.* 1892, *etc.* 8°. P.P. 1976. c.

—— Science Progress. *Lond.* 1894, *etc.* 8°. P.P. 1463. d.

—— Year-book of Science. *Lond.* 1892, *etc.* 8°. P.P. 2495. ce.

—— *Philadelphia.* New Science Review. *Phila.* 1894, *etc.* 8°. P.P. 1437. b.

POCHE (G.) Origine des forces de la nature. pp. 342. *Paris*, 1891. 12°. 8708. g. 25.

POPULAR SCIENCE LECTURES. Popular Science Lectures. Nos. 1–4. *Lond.* 1881. 8°. 8709. de.

PRIVAT-DESCHANEL (A.) Elementary treatise on Natural Philosophy. 4 pt. *Lond.* 1894. 8°. 2022. d.

RÒITI (A.) Elementi di Fisica. 2 vol. *Firenze*, 1891, 94. 8°. 8707. e. 25.

SCHEFFLER (H.) Die Äquivalenz der Naturkräfte. pp. 585. *Leipz.* 1893. 8°. 8768. cc. 30.

SCHIÖTZ (O. E.) Lærebog i Fysik. pp. 461. *Kristiania*, 1889. 8°. 8709. bbb. 7.

SHORTER (A.) Notes of lessons for a course in elementary Science. pp. 46. *Bradford*, 1892, *etc.* 8°. 8705. aaa. 45.

PHYSICS.—General—*continued.*

SIEMENS (W. v.) Scientific and technical papers. *Lond.* 1892, *etc.* 8°. 8757. g. 34.

STEELE (J.) Thoughts on Natural Philosophy. pp. 15. *Norwich*, 1891. 8°. Pam. 69.

STEEL (R. E.) The world of Science. pp. 239. *Lond.* 1891. 8°. 8703. de. 39.

STEWART (B.) Lessons in elementary Physics. pp. 475. *Lond.* 1895. 8°. 8703. aaa. 39.

STOURDZA (G.) *Prince.* Les Lois fundamentales de l'Univers. pp. 564. *Paris*, 1891. 8°. 8705. de. 28.

TODD (S. R.) Elementary Science. *Lond.* 1894. 8°. 8705. bb. 40.

UTNE (A. J.) Naturkundskab for folkeskolen. *Drammen*, 1890, *etc.* 8°. 8707. cc.

WATERDALE. Waterdale Researches: fresh light on dynamic action of matter. pp. 293. *Lond.* 1892. 8°. 8767. f. 17.

WEBER (J. L.) Über das galilei'sche Princip. pp. 40. *Kiel*, 1891. 8°. Pam. 38.

WETTSTEIN (H.) Elements of natural science. *Lond.* 1894, *etc.* 8°. 8707. d. 44.

WOODHULL (J. F.) First Course in science. *N.Y.* 1893, *etc.* 8°. 8707. k. 11.

WOOLLCOMBE (W. G.) Practical work in general physics. pp. 83. *Oxf.* 1894. 8°. 8704. de. 27.

WRIGHT (C. R. A.) The threshold of science. pp. 389. *Lond.* 1891. 8°. 8906. df. 21.

ZIMMER (G. C.) Über das Wesen der Naturgesetze. pp. 101. *Giessen*, 1893. 8°. 8705. d. 32.

See also ACOUSTICS : ASTRONOMY : ELECTRICITY : FORCE : HEAT : LIGHT.

Biography of Scientific Discoverers, etc.
See BIOGRAPHY.

History of Physical Science, etc.

BUCKLEY, *afterwards* FISHER (A. B.) Short history of natural science. pp. 509. *Lond.* 1894. 8°. 2244. d. 2.

GERLAND (E.) Geschichte der Physik. pp. 356. *Leipz.* 1892. 8°. 8707. cc. 16.

MARMERY (J. V.) Progress of science : origin, course and results, *etc.* pp. 358. *Lond.* 1895. 8°. 8705. d. 33.

MUELLER (F.) Zeittafeln zur Geschichte der Physik. pp. 103. *Leipz.* 1892. 8°. 8704. e. 29.

CORNOLDI (G. M.) The physical system of S. Thomas Aquinas. pp. 228. *Lond.* 1893. 8°. 3805. b. 4.

RENAN (J. E.) L'Avenir de la science. pp. 541. *Paris*, 1890. 8°. 8469. h. 20.

See also BIOGRAPHY, *Scientific.*

Methods of Teaching Science, etc.

ACLAND (*Sir* H. W.) Science in secondary schools. pp. 35. *Lond.* 1891. 8°. 8310. cc. 42.

DYER (H.) Science teaching in schools. pp. 128. *Lond.* 1893. 8°. 8311. b. 18.

LISHMAN (R.) and BESZANT (S. L.) Experimental Science as a class subject. pp. 158. *Lond.* 1892. 8°. 8704. a. 34.

PAGET (*Sir* J.) Scientific Study. 1894. 8°. LONDON. *Society for the Extension of University Teaching.* Aspects of modern study. 8367. aa. 19.

Physical Measurement.

AC. Cambridge. *Harvard University.* List of experiments in physical Measurements, *etc.* pp. 55. *Camb.* 1890. 12°. 8703. aaa. 40.

EARL (A. G.) Lessons in physical Measurement. pp. 350. *Lond.* 1894. 8°. 8351. aa. 49.

PHYSICS. — Physical Measurement.— continued.

KOHLRAUSCH (F.) Introduction to physical Measurements. pp. 476. *Lond.* 1894. 8°.
8704. ff. 16.

OSTWALD (W.) Manual of physico-chemical Measurements. pp. 255. *Lond.* 1894. 8°.
8704. ff. 17.

SABINE (W. C.) Student's Manual of a laboratory course in physical Measurements. pp. 126. *Bost.* 1893. 8°.   8705. de. 31.

WHITING (H.) Course of experiments in Physical Measurement. 4 pt. *Bost.* 1892, 91. 8°.
8707. dd. 15.

PHYSIOGNOMY. *See* PHRENOLOGY.

PHYSIOGRAPHY : PHYSICAL GEO-GRAPHY. COFFINIÈRES DE NORDECK ( ) Essais sur les Phénomènes cosmogoniques. pp. 372. *Paris,* 1893. 8°.   8705. de. 29.

DICKIE (H.) Elements of Physiography. pp. 168. 1893. 8°. Collins' Science Series.   8708. aaa.

FINDLATER (A.) Physiography. Elementary Course. pp. 194. *Lond.* 1891. 8°. 8704. a. 30.

—— Advanced course. pp. 227. *Lond.* 1892. 8°.
8704. a. 32.

GEE (W.) Short Studies in nature knowledge. pp. 313. *Lond.* 1895. 8°.   8708. b. 24.

GREGORY (R. A.) Elementary Physiography. pp. 463. *Lond.* 1895. 8°.   8707. bbb. 35.

—— Advanced Physiography. pp. 277. *Lond.* 1893. 8°.   8563. aa. 29.

—— and WELLS (H. G.) Honours Physiography. pp. 181. *Lond.* 1893. 8°. 8705. aaa. 46.

GUENTHER (S.) Lehrbuch der Geophysik, *etc.* 2 Bde. *Stuttgart,* 1884, 85. 8°.   8705. dd. 15.

HOFFMEYER (J.) Mathematisk og fysisk Geografi. pp. 21. *Aarhus,* 1889. 8°.   Pam. 91.

KROPOTKIN (P. A.) On the teaching of physiography. pp. 10. *Lond.* 1893. 8°.   Pam. 91.

LAWSON (W.) Text-book of physical Geography. pp. 380. *Edinb.* 1891. 8°.   2352. b.

—— Elements of physical Geography. pp. 96. *Edinb.* 1894. 12°.   10005. aa. 23.

MARTIN (H. C.) Notes on elementary Physiography. pp. 194. *Manch.* 1891. 8°.
8703. aaa. 36.

MILL (H. R.) The Realm of Nature. pp. 369. 1892. 8°. University Extension Manuals.
12204. f.

SPENCER (J.) Physiography. pp. 229. *Lond.* 1891. 8°.   8704. a. 31.

THORNTON (J.) Elementary Physiography. pp. 328 *Lond.* 1894. 8°.   8708. i. 28.

—— Advanced Physiography. pp. 350. *Lond.* 1892. 8°.   8708. i. 21.

See also ASTRONOMY : EARTH : GEOGRAPHY.

PHYSIOLOGY. ARTHUS (M.) Éléments de Chimie physiologique. pp. 347. *Paris,* 1895. 8°.
8909. aa. 37.

ASHBY (H.) Notes on Physiology. pp. 380. *Lond.* 1893. 8°.   2254. aa. 1.

BELFAST. *Society for the Extension of University Teaching.* The Body and its health. pp. 205. *Belfast,* 1892. 8°.   7391. cc. 10.

BERNSTEIN (J.) Lehrbuch der Physiologie des thierischen Organismus. pp. 755. *Stuttgart,* 1894. 8°.   07293. m. 16.

BOLLAND (G. J. P. J.) Die Lebenserscheinungen in der Physiologie der Gegenwart. 1891. 8°. Ac. Batavia. *Natuurkundige Vereeniging.* Natuurkundig Tijdschrift. Deel. 50. Ac. 3096.

CALLEJA (C.) Introducción à la Fisiología. pp. 937. *Madrid,* 1892. 8°.   7405. d. 2.

PHYSIOLOGY.—continued.

CHATIN (J.) Organes de nutrition et de reproduction chez les vertébrés. pp. 176. 1894. 8°. Encyclopédie des aide-mémoire.   8709. g.

—— Les organes de relation chez les vertébrés. pp. 172. 1894. 8°. Encyclopédie des aide-mémoire.   8709. g.

DURHAM (W.) Food, physiology, *etc.* pp. 123. 1891. 8°. Science in Plain Language. 8709. aaa.

FICK (A.) Compendium der Physiologie des Menschen. pp. 499. *Wien,* 1891. 8°.
7407. f. 24.

FOSTER (M.) A Text Book of Physiology. *Lond.* 1893, *etc.* 8°.   2024. bb.

—— and SHORE (L. E.) Physiology for beginners. pp. 241. *Lond.* 1894. 8°. 7406. de. 8.

FREDERICQ (L.) Manipulations de Physiologie. pp. 283. *Paris,* 1892. 8°.   7407. e. 4.

FURNEAUX (W. S.) Animal Physiology. pp. 247. *Lond.* 1892. 8°.   7407. aaa. 10.

GAD (J.) and HEYMANS (J. F.) Lehrbuch der Physiologie des Menschen. pp. 515. 1892. 8°. Wredens Sammlung Lehrbücher. Bd. 16.
7321. h.

GÉRARDIN (L.) L'Homme. Éléments de Physiologie. pp. 360. *Paris,* 1890. 12°. 7419. aa. 2.

GRIFFITHS (A. B.) Physiology of the Invertebrata. pp. 477. *Lond.* 1892. 8°.   7299. h. 8.

H. My Body. Its use and abuse. pp. 79. *Lond.* 1890. 8°.   Pam. 37.

HALLIBURTON (W. D.) Text-book of chemical Physiology. pp. 874. *Lond.* 1891. 8°.
7419. i. 7.

—— Essentials of chemical Physiology. pp. 166. *Lond.* 1893. 8°.   8908. b. 47.

HAMMARSTEN (O.) Lehrbuch der physiologischen Chemie. pp. 425. *Wiesbaden,* 1891. 8°.
7407. f. 23.

—— Text-book of physiological Chemistry. pp. 511. *N.Y.* 1893. 8°.   7407. e. 5.

HANSGIRG (A.) Physiologische und phycophytologische Untersuchungen. pp. 286. *Prag,* 1893. 4°.   7029. i. 15.

HARRIS (V. D.) and POWER (D.) Manual for the physiological Laboratory. pp. 345. *Lond.* 1892. 8°.   2254. b. 7.

HILL (A.) The Physiologist's note-book. pp. 200. *Lond.* 1893. 8°.   7405. ee. 28.

HIRTH (G.) Aufgaben der Kunstphysiologie. 2 Thle. pp. 611. *München,* 1891. 8°.
7807. k. 16.

KELLOGG (J. H.) Second Book in Physiology. pp. 291. *N.Y.* 1894. 8°.   7404. df. 9.

KIMBER (D. C.) Text-book of Physiology for nurses. pp. 268. *N.Y.* 1895. 8°.   7419. c. 1.

KIMMINS (C. W.) Chemistry of life and health. pp. 167. 1892. 8°. University Extension Series.
012202. g.

KIRKES (W. S.) Hand-book of Physiology. pp. 884. *Lond.* 1892. 8°.   2024. a.

KRABBE (H.) Huspattedyrenes, særlig Hestens, Bygning og Liv. pp. 194. *Kjøbenh.* 1892. 8°.
07293. m. 11.

LANDOIS (L.) Lehrbuch der Physiologie des Menschen. *Wien,* 1893, *etc.* 8°.   7406. dd.

—— Text-Book of human Physiology. 2 vol. *Lond.* 1891. 8°.   2254. f. 12.

LANGENDORFF (O.) Physiologische Graphik. pp. 316. *Leipz.* 1891. 8°.   7405. f. 15.

LANKESTER (O.) The human Body. pp. 16. *Lond.* 1892. 16°.   7419. i. 23.

LARKIN (F. C.) and LEIGH (R.) Outlines of practical physiological Chemistry. pp. 86. *Lond.* 1891. 8°.   8909. aaa. 37.

PHYSIOLOGY—continued.

LEA (A. S.) Chemical Basis of the Body. pp. 290. *Lond.* 1892. 8°.   2024. bb.

LEFFINGWELL (A.) Physiology in our Public Schools. pp. 4. *Bost.* 1895. 8°.   Pam. 85.

LINDÉN (A.) Människokroppens byggnad, förrättninger och vård. pp. 48. *Stockholm*, 1891. 8°.   7419. a. 3.

LUDWIG (C.) Beiträge zur Physiologie. pp. 121. *Marburg*, 1891. 4°.   7407. g. 11.

MACKENDRICK (J. G.) and SNODGRASS (W.) Physiology of the Senses. pp. 318. 1893. 8°. University Extension Manuals.   12204. f.

MARXOW (E. F. v.) Gesammelte Abhandlungen. pp. 548. *Leipz.* 1893. 8°.   7305. ee. 20.

MURCHÉ (V. T.) Elementary text-book of Physiology. pp. 202. 1891. 8°. Blackie's Science Text Books.   8703. bb.

NEUMEISTER (R.) Lehrbuch der physiologischen Chemie. *Jena*, 1893, *etc.* 8°.   7406. dd.

NOORDEN (C. v.) Beiträge zur Lehre vom Stoffwechsel des gesunden und kranken Menschen. *Berl.* 1892, *etc.* 8°.   7442. g. 23.

OVEREND (W.) Elements of human Physiology. pp. 192. *Lond.* 1891. 8°.   7407. aa. 7.

P.P. *Hamburg.* Zeitschrift für Physiologie der Sinnesorgane. *Hamb.* 1890, *etc.* 8°.
                    P.P. 1253. bb.

RICHET (C.) Dictionnaire de Physiologie. *Paris*, 1895, *etc.* 8°.   7407. g.

—— Physiologie. Travaux du laboratoire. *Paris*, 1893, *etc.* 8°.   7407. cc.

ROBERTSON (J. M.) Elementary text-book of Physiology. pp. 384. 1893. 8°. Blackie's Science Text-Books.   8703. bb.

SCHIFF (J. M.) Beiträge zur Physiologie. *Lausanne*, 1894, *etc.* 8°.   7406. h.

SCHOFIELD (A. T.) Physiology for schools. 3 pt. *Lond.* 1891. 8°.   7405. aaa. 25.

—— Elementary Physiology. pp. 372. *Lond.* 1892. 8°.   7405. aaa. 26.

SCIENCES. Les Sciences biologiques, *etc.* pp. 800. *Paris*, 1893. 8°.   7001. g. 7.

STEWART (G. N.) A Manual of Physiology. pp. 796. 1895. 8°. University Series.
                    012202. e.

STARLING (E. H.) Elements of human Physiology. pp. 454. *Lond.* 1895. 4°.   2254. a. 27.

STIRLING (W.) Outlines of practical Physiology. pp. 402. *Lond.* 1895. 8°.   7405. dd. 1.

SWANSON (J.) Guide to the Examinations in animal Physiology. pp. 57. 1893. 8°. Blackie's Guides to the Science Examinations.   8703. aa.

THORNTON (J.) Human Physiology. pp. 440. *Lond.* 1894. 8°.   7405. aa. 6.

UNDERWOOD (J. C.) Revision notes on elementary Physiology. pp. 64. *Lond.* 1893. 8°.
                    7406. de. 7.

WALLER (A. D.) Introduction to human Physiology. pp. 632. *Lond.* 1893. 8°.   7405. de. 6.

YEO (G. F.) Manual of Physiology. pp. 679. *Lond.* 1893. 8°.   2254. b. 25.

ZIEHEN (T.) Leitfaden der physiologischen Psychologie. pp. 176. *Jena*, 1891. 8°.
                    7660. g. 21.

ZOFF (W.) Beiträge zur Physiologie und Morphologie niederer Organismen. *Leipz*, 1892, *etc.* 8°.   7299. f. 16.

See also BLOOD : CHEMISTRY, *Medical* : MEDICINE : MUSCLES : PATHOLOGY.

PIACENZA. GIARELLI (F.) Storia di Piacenza. 2 vol. *Piacenza*, 1889. 8°.
                    10129. cc.

PIACENZA—continued.

BIANCHI (G.) Il Clero piacentino dal Concilio di Trento. pp. 79. *Piacenza*, 1891. 8°.
                    4535. bb. 17. (8.)

PIANOFORTE. BECKER (A. G.) On a new method of fingering extended arpeggios. pp. 7. *Godalming*, 1894. 8°.   Pam. 24.

BIGGS (H.) All the major and minor Scales for the Pianoforte played at sight. pp. 8. *Lond*, 1891. obl. 4°.   Pam. 24.

BLANCHETT AND SONS. Blanchett's Scale fingering Chart. *Slough*, 1893. 4°.   1865. c. 1. (24.)

—— Scale examiner for the Pianoforte. 2 pt. *Slough*, 1893. 8°.   7898. aaaa. 21.

BOURMAN-HART (M. H.) Practical hints on Pianoforte playing. pp. 14. *Lond.* 1893. 8°.
                    7899. dd. 1. (9.)

BRESLAUR (E.) Methodik des Klavier-Unterrichts in Einzelaufsätzen. 2 pt. *Berl.* 1886. 8°.
                    7898. l. 2.

BROADWOOD (J.) Information concerning Pianofortes. pp. 173. *Lond.* 1895. 8°. 7898. e. 36.

COMETTANT (J. P. O.) Histoire de cent mille Pianos. pp. 364. *Paris*, 1890. 8°. 7899. aaa. 5.

DAVENPORT (F. W.) and BAKER (J. P.) Guide for Pianoforte students. pp. 74. *Lond.* 1891. 8°.
                    7898. aaa. 64.

EHRLICH (A.) Celebrated pianists of the past and present time. pp. 367. *Lond.* 1894. 8°.
                    10601. e. 19.

EHRENFECHTER (C. A.) Technical study in the art of pianoforte-playing. pp. 112. *Lond.* 1892. 8°.
                    7898. aaaa. 2.

—— Delivery in the art of pianoforte playing. pp. 64. *Lond.* 1895. 8°.   7899. b. 13.

FILLMORE (J. C.) Pianoforte Music ; history, *etc.* pp. 253. *Phila.* 1892. 8°.   7899. b. 15.

FISHER (C. R.) Synopsis of musical facts for Pianoforte students. pp. 8. *Lond.* 1894. 8°.
                    7808. df. 15. (7.)

GLEN (A.) How to Accompany. pp. 173. *Lond.* 1894. 4°.   7895. g. 21.

GOODWIN (A.) Practical hints on the technique and touch of pianoforte playing. pp. 72. *Lond.* 1892. 8°.   7898. ee. 61.

GUILFORD (C. C.) and CHASE (H. E.) The Chromatic Stave. 1895. *s. sh.* fol.
                    1865. c. 1. (22.)

HANSMANN (R.) Die Janko-Klaviatur. pp. 7. *Leipz.* 1891. 8°.   7898. m. 8. (5.)

MEIJER (S.) De Forte-Piano en het orgel. pp. 40. *Groningen*, 1881. 8°.   Pam. 24.

PASCAL (J.) A few hints on Technique. pp. 6. *Lond.* 1894. 8°.   Pam. 24.

P.P. *London.* The Keyboard. Monthly journal. Vol. 1. *Lond.* 1892, 94. 4°.   P.P. 1947. cc.

RIEMANN (H.) Catechism of pianoforte playing. pp. 92. *Lond.* 1892. 8°.   7898. bbb. 35.

—— Analysis of J. S. Bach's wohltemperirtes Clavier. 2 pt. *Lond.* 1893. 8°. 7895. aa. 62.

ROMEU (J.) L'Art du pianiste. pp. 320. *Paris*, 1893. 8°.   7898. cc. 21.

SHEDLOCK (J. S.) The Pianoforte sonata. pp. 245. *Lond.* 1895. 8°.   7899. b. 12.

WEBBE (W. H.) Pianoforte playing. Jottings. *Lond.* 1893, *etc.* 8°.   7898. bbb.

HIPKINS (A. J.) History of the pianoforte. pp. 14. 2. *Lond.* 1883. 8°.   7896. ff. 33. (2.)

MARMONTEL (A.) Histoire du Piano. pp. 464. *Paris*, 1885. 18°.   7898. cc. 16.

C., C. E. Hints on how to take care of the Pianoforte. pp. 13. *St. Leonard's*, 1891. 16°.
                    Pam. 24.

                    2 Y

PIANOFORTE—*continued.*

NORTON (E. Q.) Construction, tuning, and care of the pianoforte. pp. 96. *Lond.* 1893. 8°.
7898. aaaa. 24.

SPILLANE (D.) The Piano. Instructions relating to tuning, *etc.* pp. 101. *N.Y.* 1893. 8°.
7898. bbb. 40.

WORDS. A few words about the Pianoforte, hints for preserving the instrument. pp. 16.
Camb. 1891. 16°.   Pam. 24.

See also MUSIC: MUSICAL INSTRUMENTS.

PICKERING. Ac. Yorkshire. *North Riding Record Society.* Vol. 1. N.S. Honor and Forest of Pickering. pp. 280. *Lond.* 1894. 8°.
Ac. 8190/2.

GOLDSBOROUGH (A.) History of the Independent Church, Pickering. pp. 20. *Pickering*, 1889. 8°.
4715. bb. 24.

PICTS. *See* SCOTLAND, *Antiquities.*

PICTURE GALLERIES: PICTURES.
See EXHIBITIONS : PAINTING.

PIEDMONT. GABOTTO (F.) Storia del Piemonte, 1292–1349. pp. 271. *Torino*, 1894. 8°.
9166. g. 18.

CORDOVA (F.) Inghilterra e Piemonte. pp. 42. *Roma*, 1893. 8°.   9078. ff. 34.

BONFADINI (R.) Le origini della Monarchia in Piemonte. 1891. 8°. Gli albori della vita italiana. Vol. 2.   9166. ccc. 11.

NEUMANN (L.) Die deutschen Gemeinden in Piemont. pp. 40. *Freiburg*, 1891. 8°.
10105. e. 4. (3.)

AGUITON (d') Guerre de la France contre le Piémont, et du Piémont contre la France.
pp. 34. 3. *Grenoble*, 1891. 8°.   8823. dd. 41.

FORTI-CASTELLI (G.) Saggio sui provincialismi del Piemonte, *etc.* pp. 84. *Mondovi*, 1892. 8°.
Pam. 47.

See also ALPS, *Italian :* ITALY, *History.*

PIG. DOUGLAS (L. M.) Manual of the Pork trade. pp. 107. *Lond.* 1893. 8°. 7942. f. 35.

GARRATT (R. D.) Practical Pig-keeping.
pp. 80. *Lond.* 1892. 8°.   7293. b. 37.

GINEBREDA (A.) Ensayo sobre la cria del Cerdo. pp. 240. *Barcelona*, 1891. 8°.   07293 g. 3.

MONOSTORI (K.) Die Schweine Ungarns.
pp. 99. *Berl.* 1891. 8°.   07293. k. 2.

OHLSEN (C. T. A.) Concorso internazionale di animali riproduttori tenuto a Parigi, 1889.
1890. 4°. Ac. Naples. *R. Istituto d'Incoraggiamento.* Atti, *etc.* Ser. 4. Vol. 3.
Ac. 2815.

PIGS. Pigs for profit. pp. 149. 1890. 8°. P.P. Dublin. *Weekly Freeman.* Freeman Handbook. No. 5.   07944. ee. 10.

PORK BUTCHER. Pork Butcher's guide and receipt book. *Manch.* 1890. 8°. 7942. g. 23. (7.)

SCHLIEBEN (A.) Das Schwein in der Kulturgeschichte. pp. 60. *Wiesbaden*, 1891. 8°.
7704. c. 18. (7.)

See also ANIMALS, *Domestic.*

For diseases of Swine. *See* VETERINARY MEDICINE.

PIGEON. ANDRÉ (F.) Notice historique sur le Pigeon voyageur. pp. 18.
La Roche-sur-Yon, 1894. 8°.   Pam. 42.

BOEVE (R. de) Traité de l'élevage de tous les Pigeons. pp. 153. *Roubaix*, 1894. 8°.
07293. m. 13.

FULTON (R.) Book of pigeons.
Lond. 1893, *etc.* 8°.   07293. m.

HEPWORTH (A. F.) The Tippler Pigeon. pp. 99.
Lond. 1893. 8°.   7293. b. 38.

PIGEON—*continued.*

HEWITT (W. E.) National Peristeronic Society. Presidential address. pp. 19. *Lond.* 1894. 8°.
07293. k. 16,

KENDRICK (H.) Chats about Pigeon fanciers.
pp. 74. *Lond.* 1893. 8°.   7291. aa. 21.

KEUCKER (A.) L'Aérostation et les Pigeonniers militaires. pp. 105. *Paris*, 1884. 8°.
Pam. 79.

LUMLEY (W. F.) The Turbit Pigeon. pp. 81.
Lond. 1894. 8°.   7293. f. 12. (5.)

LYELL (J. C.) Pigeon-keeping for amateurs.
pp. 135. *Lond.* 1892. 8°.   7293. bbb. 36.

ROSOOR (J.) La Colombophilie. pp. 208.
Tourcoing, 1891. 8°.   7295. dd. 6.

SALVADORI (T.) Catalogue of the Pigeons in the British Museum. pp. 676. 1893. 8°. Ac. London. *British Museum.* Catalogue of Birds. Vol. 21.   7207. f.

WITTOUCK (S.) La Colombophilie moderne.
pp. 280. *Bruges*, 1894. 8°.   7291. b. 17.

WOODS (R.) The Dragon Pigeon. pp. 148.
Lond. 1892. 8°.   07293. g. 2.

—— Guide to successful Pigeon-culture. pp. 190.
Lond. 1891. 8°.   7293. c. 33.

See also ANIMALS, *Domestic :* BIRDS.

PIGEON SHOOTING. HURLINGHAM CLUB. Pigeon Shooting. Rules. pp. 34.
Lond. 1893. 16°.   7908. a. 103.

PILGRIMAGES. *See* LORETTO : LOURDES: PALESTINE : ROMAN CATHOLIC CHURCH, *in France.*

PILLNITZ. MINCKWITZ (A. v.) Geschichte von Pillnitz. pp. 128. *Dresd.* 1893. 8°.
10255. f. 30.

PILOTAGE. JACKSON (R.) Questions and notes on the Sub-lieutenants' Pilotage course.
pp. 23. *Portsmouth*, 1891. 8°.   Pam. 43.

PILTON. Ac. Somerset. *Record Society.* Church-Wardens' Accounts of Pilton, *etc.*
pp. 277. *Lond.* 1890. 4°.   Ac. 8133/4.

PINEROLO. CAFFARO (P.) Notizie della Chiesa pinerolese. *Pinerolo*, 1893, *etc.* 8°.
4606. ee.

PITTAVINO (A.) L'Assedio di Pinerolo nel 1693. pp. 31. *Pinerolo*, 1893. 8°. 9165. dd. 18. (9.)

PIQUET. CAVENDISH. Pocket guide to Piquet.
pp. 23. *Lond.* 1894. 16°.   7915. de. 14. (7.)

—— Laws of Piquet. pp. 208. *Lond.* 1892. 8°.
7913. ccc. 35.

See also CARDS.

PIRACY. BURNEY (J.) History of the Buccaneers of America. pp. 382. *Lond.* 1891. 8°.
9551. i. 14.

EXQUEMELIN (A. O.) Buccaneers and Marooners of America. 1891. 8°. Adventure Series.
012207. k.

ROCHE (J. J.) Story of the Filibusters. pp. 373. 1891. 8°. Adventure Series.   012207. k.

PIRNA. HOFMANN (R.) Zur Geschichte der Stadt Pirna. pp. 68. *Pirna*, 1891. 8°.
10105. ee. 10. (5.)

—— Reformationsgeschichte der Stadt Pirna.
pp. 329. 1893. 8°. DIBELIUS (F.) Beiträge zur sächsischen Kirchengeschichte. Hft. 8.
4662. e.

PISA. TRENTA (G.) La Tomba di Arrigo VII. in Pisa. pp. 100. *Pisa*, 1893. 8°.
10703. dd. 5.

VIGO (P.) Una festa popolare a Pisa nel medio evo. pp. 103. *Pisa*, 1888. 8°.   10129. cc. 1.

PISIDIA. *See* PAMPHYLIA.

PISTOJA. Pistoja. Breve et ordinamenta Populi Pistorii, A.D. 1283. pp. 271. *Mediolani*, 1891. 4°.   5327. e. 11.

Pistoja and Prato. *Diocese.* Synodus dioecesana Pistoriensis et Pratensis habita Pistorii an. 1892. pp. 303. *Pistorii*, 1893. 8°.   5051. bb. 10.

PITCAIRN ISLAND. Young (R. A.) Mutiny of the Bounty and Story of Pitcairn Island. pp. 254. *Oakland*, 1894. 8°.   10491. b. 40.

PLAGUE. Ammann (H.) Die Pest des Jahres 1636 in Neustift bei Brixen. pp. 57. *Brixen*, 1891. 8°.   07305. h. 18. (2.)

Barnes (H.) Visitations of the Plague in Cumberland and Westmoreland. pp. 28. *Kendal*, 1890. 8°.   Pam. 39.

—— On Quarter Sessions orders relating to the Plague in Durham, 1665. 1890. 8°.   Pam. 39.

Charvériat (È) La Peste en Allemagne pendant le 17° siècle. pp. 29. *Lyon*, 1892. 8°.   07305. k. 14. (7.)

Creighton (C.) History of Epidemics in Britain. 2 vol. *Camb.* 1891–94. 8°.   2255. f. 8.

Gasquet (F. A.) The great Pestilence, A.D. 1348-9, now known as the Black Death. pp. 244. *Lond.* 1893. 8°.   7561. k. 20.

Malaga. Relación de la Peste en Málaga en 1637. pp. 4. *Sevilla*, 1892. 4°.   07305. h. 17. (9.)

Mouton (E.) F. Ranchin, premier consul de Montpellier pendant la Peste de 1629. pp. 103. *Marseille*, 1892. 8°.   010662. g. 12.

Murray (D.) Sir John de Mandeville, and the Pestilence. pp. 33. *Paisley*, 1891. 8°.   7561. i. 38.

Tuerler (H.) Die Pest im Oberland im Jahre 1669. pp. 28. *Bern*, 1893. 8°. 7306. c. 23. (13.)

Zerbi (L.) La Peste di San Carlo in Monza. 1891. 8°. Ac. Milan. *Società Storica Lombarda.* Archivio Storico Lombardo. Ser. 2. Vol. 8.   Ac. 6525.

See also Diseases, *Infectious.*

PLAISTOW. Curwen (J. S.) Old Plaistow. pp. 68. *Plaistow*, 1893. 8°.   10347. d. 7. (9.)

PLANETS. *See* Sun and Solar System.

PLASTERING. Kemp (W.) The practical Plasterer. pp. 184. *Lond.* 1893. 12°.   8703. c. 57.

See also Art, *Decorative :* Building.

PLATE. Ac. Cambridge. *Antiquarian Society.* Catalogue of loan collection of Plate exhibited at the FitzWilliam Museum. pp. 107. *Camb.* 1895. 8°.   7805. b. 36.

Cripps (W. J.) Old English Plate. pp. 462. *Lond.* 1894. 8°.   2031. b.

—— Old French Plate. pp. 113. *Lond.* 1893. 8°.   2266. d. 3.

Ellis (H. D.) Description of the Silver Plate belonging to the Company of Armourers. pp. 24. *Lond.* 1892. 4°.   7709. k. 25.

Jewitt (L.) Corporation Plate of the cities and towns of England and Wales. 2 vol. *Lond.* 1895. 4°.   7709. l. 21.

Ris-Paquot (O. E.) Dictionnaire des marques et monogrammes. 2 tom. *Paris*, 1893. 2031. f.

Redman (W.) Hall Marks, illustrated. pp. 48. *Bradford*, 1894. 8°.   7709. bb. 65.

Watney (J.) The Hospital of St. Thomas of Acon, and the Plate of the Mercers' Company. pp. 308. *Lond.* 1892. 4°.   4705. g. 25.

See also Gold and Silver.

PLATE—*continued.*
Church Plate.
Peet (H.) Inventory of the Plate in the two Parish Churches of Liverpool. pp. 128. *Liverp.* 1893. 8°.   4707. cc. 13.

Wordsworth (C.) Inventories of Plate belonging to the Cathedral of Lincoln. pp. 82. 1892. 4°. Archaeologia. Vol. 53.   Cat. Desk I.

Freshfield (E.) Communion Plate of the churches in the city of London. pp. 152. *Lond.* 1894. 4°.   3475. i. 2.

—— Communion Plate of the parish Churches in the county of London. pp. 111. *Lond.* 1895. 4°.   3475. i. 4.

Paul, *Saint. Cathedral Church, London.* St. Paul's Cathedral in the time of Edward VI. Inventarie of the Plate, 1552. pp. 30. *Lond.* 1893. 8°.   9902. ccc. 10.

Crichton (L.) and (P.) Church Plate of the Chapel Royal, Kensington Palace. pp. 11. *Lond.* 1894. 8°.   Pam. 3.

Markham (C. A.) Church Plate of the County of Northampton. pp. 368. *Lond.* 1894. 8°.   3478. l. 4.

Nightingale (J. E.) Church Plate of the County of Wilts. pp. 256. *Salisbury*, 1891. 8°.   3478. g. 15.

Burns (T.) Old Scottish Communion Plate. pp. 651. *Edinb.* 1892. 8°.   3478. l. 2.

Knoepfler (A.) Die Kelchbewegung in Bayern unter Herzog Albrecht v. pp. 223. 129. *München*, 1891. 8°.   4662. f. 3.

Neumann (W. A.) Der Reliquienschatz des Hauses Braunschweig-Lüneburg. pp. 368. *Wien*, 1891. fol.   1706. a. 19.

Rogadeo di Torrequadra (E.) Di un calice della cattedrale di Bitonto. pp. 38. *Bitonto*, 1893. 8°.   7805. de. 23

PLATE, River. *See* La Plata.

PLEURA. *See* Lungs.

PLEVNA.
See Russian-Turkish War, 1877-78.

PLÖN. Kinder (J. C.) Urkundenbuch zur Chronik der Stadt Plön. pp. 620. *Plön*, 1890. 8°.   10255. h. 2.

Zacharias (O.) Forschungsberichte aus der biologischen Station zu Plön. *Berl.* 1893, *etc.* 8°.   7004. df.

PLUMBING. Allison (J.) How to elevate the status of Plumbers. pp. 8. *Manch.* 1892. 8°.   08275. ee. 21. (3.)

Clarke (J. W.) Pocket-book for Plumbers. pp. 217. *Lond.* 1891. *obl.* 32°.   8548. a. 30.

—— Lectures to Plumbers. pp. 223. *Lond.* 1893. 4°.   8777. k. 22.

Hellyer (S. S.) Principles and practice of Plumbing. pp. 294. 1893. 8°. Wood (*Sir* H. T.) Technological Handbooks.   2266. a. 37.

Smeaton (J.) Plumbing, drainage, *etc.* pp. 236. *Lond.* 1893. 8°.   8777. b. 46.

Vacher (F.) Defects in Plumbing and drainage work. pp. 83. *Manch.* 1894. 8°.   8777. d. 37.

See also Drainage : Sanitation.

PLYMOUTH, Devonshire. Dent (R. K.) Pictorial Plymouth. pp. 36. *Birmingham*, 1891. fol.   1785. b. 12.

G. B. & I. Victoria, *Queen.* Order in Council amending the regulations with reference to Plymouth. pp. 12. *Lond.* 1891. 8°. Pam. 42.

Peek (*Sir* H. W.) Prospectus-Makers and the Public. The Plymouth Tramways case. pp. 147. *Lond.* 1890. 8°.   6375. de. 4.

PLYMOUTH, Massachusetts.

DAVIS (W. T.) History of the town of Plymouth. pp. 188. *Phila.* 1885. 8°.   10411. h. 26.

KINGMAN (B.) Epitaphs from Burial Hill, Plymouth. pp. 330. *Brookline*, 1892. 8°. 9902. e. 28.

PLYMOUTH BRETHREN.

ADAM (G.) "The Ground of one Body." pp. 16. *Glasg.* 1885. 16°.   4422. aaa. 65. (6.)

DYER (A. S.) Sketches of English Nonconformity. pp. 112. *Lond.* 1893. 8°. 4109. aa. 42.

GREGORY (J. R.) The Gospel of Separation. pp. 39. *Lond.* 1894. 16°.   4139. a. 12. (4.)

LATIMER (W. T.) Lecture on the doctrines of Plymouth Brethren. pp. 16. *Belfast*, 1893. 8°.   4139. bbb. 23. (2.)

PLYMOUTH BRETHREN. Life among the close Brethren. pp. 116. *Lond.* 1890. 8°. 4136. aa. 33.

TREGELLES (S. P.) Three letters to the author of "A Retrospect of Events that have taken place amongst the Brethren." pp. 76. *Lond.* 1894. 8°.   4136. aa. 41.

PNEUMATICS. *See* HYDRODYNAMICS.

PNEUMONIA.

FINKLER (D.) Die acuten Lungentzündungen als Infectionskrankheiten. pp. 574. *Wiesbaden*, 1891. 8°.   7615. f. 39.

AULD (A. G.) Pathological histology of Pneumonia and fibroid Pneumonia. pp. 207. *Lond.* 1891. 8°.   7616. h. 17.
See also LUNGS.

PODOPHTHALMA. *See* CRUSTACEA.

POETRY.

General.

ARISTOTLE. Aristotle's Theory of Poetry. pp. 384. *Lond.* 1895. 8°.   2234. cc. 17.

BIERFREUND (T.) Kulturbærere. pp. 222. *Kjøbenh.* 1892. 8°.   011850. i. 23.

COOK (A. S.) The poetical treatises of Horace, Vida and Boileau. Edited by A. S. Cook. pp. 303. *Bost.* 1892. 8°.   11386. f. 20.

CROMBIE (J. W.) Some Poets of the people in foreign lands. pp. 169. *Lond.* 1891. 8°.   011824. de. 1.

DONOVAN (J.) From Lyre to muse. History of the union of music and poetry. pp. 208. *Lond.* 1890. 8°.   7898. k. 36.

HUNT (J. H. L.) An Answer to the question, "What is Poetry?" pp. 98. *Bost.* 1893. 8°.   011850. g. 12.

NEWMAN (J. H.) *Cardinal.* Poetry, with reference to Aristotle's Poetics. pp. 36. *Bost.* 1891. 8°.   11312. f. 52.

PEREIRA DA SILVA (J. M.) Considerações sobre poesia epica e poesia dramatica. pp. 300. *Rio de J.* 1889. 18°.   11824. df. 44.

PESCI (D.) Bellezza e Amore. Studio sui principali poeti. pp. 348. *Roma*, 1890. 8°. 011824. de. 20.

PUGLISI PICO (M.) La poesia dell' avvenire. pp. 26. *Acireale*, 1892. 8°.   11825. q. 20. (4.)

RAGUSA-MOLETI (G.) Poesie dei popoli selvaggi. pp. 300. *Torino*, 1891. 8°.   011850. h. 10.

RAYMOND (G. L.) Rhythm and harmony in poetry and music. pp. 344. *N.Y.* 1895. 8°. 7899. b. 7.

SCHMIDT (A.) Das Madrigal. pp. 19. *Wien*, 1890. 8°.   Pam. 24.

STANLEY (W. H.) Poetry. A popular analysis. pp. 78. *Eastbourne*, 1895. 8°.   Pam. 15.

STEDMAN (E. C.) Nature and elements of Poetry. pp. 338. *Bost.* 1892. 8°. 011824. g. 34.

SWANWICK (A.) Poets the interpreters of their age. pp. 392. *Lond.* 1892. 8°. 011824. g. 22.

WESTPHAL (R.) Allgemeine Metrik der indogermanischen und semitischen Völker. pp. 514. *Berl.* 1892. 8°.   011824. e. 56.

Poetry.—General—*continued.*

PIZZI (I.) Antologia Epica. pp. 352. *Torino*, 1891. 8°.   11422. c. 26.

STRETTELL, afterwards HARRISON (A.) Lullabies of Many Lands collected, *etc.* pp. 127. *Lond.* 1894. 4°.   11601. g. 25.

Biographies of Poets. *See* BIOGRAPHY.

Poetry of Various Countries.

For the history of the poetry of each country, *see* under the *Literature* of the country required.

America, *Spanish. See infra : Spain.*

Arabs.

ARABIC POETS. Studien in arabischen Dichtern. *Berl.* 1893, *etc.* 8°.   011850. k.

FAIZ ALLĀH BHĀĪ. Essay on pre-Islamite Arabic Poetry. *Bombay*, 1893. 8°. 11825. cc. 57. (8.)

GIESE (F.) Untersuchungen über die 'Addâd auf Grund von Stellen in altarabischen Dichtern. pp. 57. *Berl.* 1894. 8°. 11825. q. 22. (13.)
See also ARABIC LITERATURE : BALLADS, *Oriental.*

Australia.

SLADEN (D. B. W.) Australian ballads and rhymes. Selected. pp. 301. 1888. 8°. Canterbury Poets.   11604. aa.
See also infra : England.

Belgium.

DEFRECHEUX (C.) Anthologie des Poètes wallons. *Liège*, 1889, *etc.* 8°.   11498. i.

PARNASSUS. Parnasse de la jeune Belgique. pp. 306. *Paris*, 1887. 8°.   11483. h. 32.

WATTEZ (O.) La Poésie néerlandaise contemporaine en Belgique. pp. 141. *Tournai*, 1893. 8°. 011850. f. 33.
See also infra : Netherlands.

Bohemia.

ALBERT (E.) Neueste Poesie aus Böhmen. *Wien*, 1895, *etc.* 8°.   011528. f.

P.P. *Eichwald.* Böhmens deutsche Poesie. Monatsschrift. *Wien*, 1891, *etc.* 8°.   775.

Bolivia. *See infra : Spain.*

Canada.

LIGHTHALL (W. D.) Canadian poems : selections. pp. 276. pp. 1893. 8°. Canterbury Poets.   11604. aaaa. 1.

ROBERTS (G. B.) Younger Canadian Poets. 1891. 8°. SLADEN (D. R. W.) Younger American poets.   11687. e. 42.
See also infra : England.

Denmark. *See infra : Scandinavia.*

England.

History and Criticism.

See BIOGRAPHY, *Literary :* ENGLISH LITERATURE.

Versification.

BREWER (R. F.) Orthometry. Treatise on the art of versification. pp. 376. *Lond.* 1893. 8°. 11805. de. 42.

CORSON (H.) Primer of English Verse. pp. 232. *Bost.* 1892. 8°.   011824. g. 19.

LAWRENCE (J.) Chapters on alliterative Verse. pp. 113. *Lond.* 1893. 8°.   011840. k. 75.

PARSONS (J. C.) English Versification. pp. 162. *Bost.* 1891. 8°.   011824. e. 25.

P.P. *London.* Versification : monthly magazine. *Lond.* 1891, *etc.* 8°. P.P. 5126. g. and 2056.

SYMONDS (J. A.) Blank Verse. pp. 113. *Lond.* 1895. 8°.   011805. g. 3.

VERRIER (P.) Notions de Versification anglaise. pp. 38. *Paris*, 1891. 8°. 011824. f. 32. (10.)

POETRY.—England—*continued.*

MOELLER (H.) Das altenglische Volksepos in der ursprünglichen strophischen Form. 2 pt. *Kiel*, 1883. 8°.   11595. d. 17

CROW (C. L.) Zur Geschichte des kurzen Reimpaars in Mittelenglischen. pp. 63. *Göttingen*, 1892. 8°.   011850. i. 13.

KOENIG (G.) Der Vers in Shaksperes Dramen. pp. 138. 1888. 8°. BRINK (B. ten) and SCHERER (W.) Quellen und Forschungen. Hft. 61.   2338. h.

BEECHING (H. C.) Prosody of Paradise Regained and Samson Agonistes. pp. 12. *Oxf.* 1889. 8°.   011840. h. 53. (5.)

BRIDGES (R.) Milton's Prosody. pp. 80. *Oxf.* 1893. 4°.   11826. e. 32.

MAACK (R.) Über Popes Einfluss auf die Idylle in Deutschland. pp. 16. *Hamburg*, 1895. 4°   Pam. 15.

Selections, General.

BEECHING (H. C.) Paradise of English Poetry. 2 vol. *Lond.* 1893. 8°.   11602. g. 29.

BRADSHAW (J.) An English Anthology. pp. 509. *Lond.* 1894. 8°.   11601. ff. 25.

CALENDAR. A Calendar of Verse. *Lond.* 1895. 8°.   11601. aa. 56.

CARVENALI (L.) Canti inglesi. pp. 102. *Mantova*, 1890. 8°.   011653. i. 60.

CHAMBERS (E. K.) English Pastorals. pp. 280. 1895. 8°. Warwick Library.   11601. ddd.

COLE (E. W.) Thousand best Poems in the world. 2 Series. *Lond.* 1891, 94. 8°.   11601. g. 21.

COUCH (A. T. Q.) The Golden Pomp. Procession of English lyrics. pp. 382. *Lond.* 1895. 8°.   11601. ee. 40.

CRAWFORD (O. J. F.) Lyrical Verse from Elizabeth to Victoria. pp. 452. *Lond.* 1895. 8°.   11601. ccc. 41.

DAVENPORT (E.) Girl's own Poetry book. pp. 544. *Lond.* 1890. 8°.   11602. ee. 41.

DE VERE (A. T.) Household Poetry book. pp. 308. *Lond.* 1893. 8°.   11601. ccc. 37.

FORSHAW (C. F.) Yorkshire Poets past and present. 2 vol. *Bradford*, 1888, 89. 8°. 11602. ee. 39.

HEATLEY (H. R.) Ballad and other Poetry. pp. 156. *Lond.* 1892. 8°.   11601. aaa. 40.

HENLEY (W. E.) Lyra Heroica: book of verse for boys. pp. 362. *Lond.* 1892. 8°. 11603. g. 27.

LANG (A.) The Blue Poetry book. pp. 243. *Lond.* 1892. 8°.   11601. c. 39.

MILES (A. H.) The Aldine Speaker. 2 pt. *Lond.* 1891. 8°.   12269. c. 7.

NICHOLS (J. B. B.) Words and days. Table book of prose and verse. pp. 382. *Lond.* 1895. 8°.   12274. c. 25.

PALGRAVE (F. T.) Golden Treasury of songs and lyrical poems. pp. 448. *Lond.* 1890. 4°.   11603. g. 25.

PEARLS. Pearls of Poetry. *Lond.* 1893. 4°.   11601. ff. 23.

POETRY. Poetry for recitation. 12 pt. 1891. 8°. Cassell's Modern School Series.   12205. aa.

POETRY BOOK. A new Poetry book. pp. 148. *Lond.* 1892. 8°.   11601. aaa. 39.

POETS. The Lyrical Poets. *Lond.* 1895, *etc.* 12°.   11607. ccc.

REPPLIER (A.) Book of famous Verse. pp. 244. *Bost.* 1892. 8°.   11601. dd. 8.

SHARP (W.) Great Odes. pp. 257. 1890. 8°. Canterbury Poets.   11604. aaa.

WHITE (J. G.) Ballads and Rondeaus, chants royal, sestinas, villanelles, *etc.* pp. 296. 1887. 8°. Canterbury Poets.   11604. aa.

POETRY.—England—*continued.*

FITZGIBBON (H. M.) Early English Poetry. pp. 334. 1887. 8°. Canterbury Poets.   11604. aa.

LAING (D.) Early Popular Poetry of Scotland and the northern Border. 2 vol. *Lond.* 1895. 8°.   2292. h. 2.

PERCY (T.) Bp. of Dromore. Reliques of ancient English Poetry. 3 vol. *Lond.* 1891. 8°.   11621. f. 37.

BULLEN (A. H.) Lyrics from the dramatists of the Elizabethan Age. pp. 301. *Lond.* 1891. 8°.   11602. ccc. 23.

—— Lyrics from the song-books of the Elizabethan Age. pp. 233. *Lond.* 1891. 8°.   11601. d. 17.

GARRETT (E. H.) Elizabethan Songs in honour of love and beautie. pp. 178. *Lond.* 1893. 8°.   11626. e. 18.

SCHELLING (F. E.) Book of Elizabethan Lyrics. pp. 327. *Bost.* 1895. 8°.   11601. dd. 23.

DIRCKS (W. H.) Cavalier and Courtier Lyrists: anthology of 17th century minor verse. pp. 234. 1891. 8°. Canterbury Poets.   11604. aaa.

SAINTSBURY (G. E. B.) Seventeenth Century Lyrics. pp. 326. 1893. 8°. Pocket Library of English Literature. Vol. v.   012207. g.

ENGLISH POETS. Living English Poets. pp. 285. *Lond.* 1893. 8°.   11601. i. 19.

EYLES (F. A. H.) Popular Poets of the period. pp. 376. *Lond.* 1888, 89. 8°.   11602. f. 28.

MILES (A. H.) Poets and poetry of the century. 8 vol. *Lond.* 1891–93. 8°.   11603. cc.

SHARP (E. A.) Women poets of the Victorian era. pp. 295. 1890. 8°. Canterbury Poets.   11604. aaa.

WRIGHT (K. A.) Dainty poems of the nineteenth century. pp. 304. *Birmingham*, 1895. 8°.   11601. aa. 58.

See also BALLADS: RECITATIONS: SONNETS.

Humourous: Vers de Société.

JACKSON (W. S.) Merry Minstrelsy. pp. 320. *Lond.* 1892. 16°.   11601. aaa. 41.

MORLEY (H.) Playful Poems. pp. 192. 1891. 8°. Companion Poets.   11622. e.

POWELL (G. H.) Musa Jocosa: choice pieces of comic Poetry. pp. 192. *Lond.* 1894. 8°.   11601. ff. 26.

See also RECITATIONS.

Poems on Special Subjects.

ADAMS (E. D.) The Poets' Praise, from Homer to Swinburne. pp. 407. *Lond.* 1894. 8°.   11602. ff. 22.

STRACHEY (J. M.) Poets on Poets. pp. 324. *Lond.* 1894. 8°.   11602. cc. 34.

WHITE (J. G.) Book-Song: anthology of poems of books. pp. 185. 1893. 8°. WHEATLEY (H. B.) Book-Lover's Library.   11900. aa.

PATON (F. N.) Bards and the Birds. pp. 514. *Lond.* 1894. 8°.   11601. ee. 39.

BEECHING (H. C.) Book of Christmas Verse. pp. 174. *Lond.* 1895. 8°.   11602. cc. 35.

LEONARD (R. M.) The Dog in British Poetry. pp. 350. *Lond.* 1893. 8°.   11603. g. 26.

ROBINSON (P.) The Poets and Nature. Reptiles, fishes and insects. pp. 300. *Lond.* 1893. 8°.   011824. g. 32.

FORD (R.) Ballads of Bairnhood. pp. 348. *Paisley*, 1894. 8°.   11601. dd. 15.

ROBERTSON (E. S.) Children of the Poets. pp. 273. 1886. 8°. Canterbury Poets.   11604. aaa.

HENLEY (W. E.) A London Garland. pp. 203. *Lond.* 1895. 4°.   K.T.C. 11. b. 16.

POETRY.—England—*continued.*

CAINE (R. H.) Love Songs of English Poets, 1500-1800. pp. 277. *Lond.* 1892. 8°.
11601. d. 18.

CHANDLER (H. P.) Lover's year-book of Poetry. 2 vol. *Bost.* 1892, 93. 8°. 11601. dd. 19.

GARRETT (E. H.) Elizabethan Songs in honour of love, *etc. Lond.* 1893. 8°. 11626. c. 18.

HULBURD (P.) English Love Lyrics. pp. 221. 1891. 8°. Canterbury Poets. 11604. aaa.

WATSON (W.) Lyric Love. An anthology. pp. 238. *Lond.* 1892. 8°. 11601. e. 41.

BRUCE (R.) Oxford Verses. pp. 80. *Oxf.* 1894. 8°. 011652. e. 32.

SAINTSBURY (G. E. B.) Political Verse. pp. 276. 1891. 8°. Pocket Library of English Literature. Vol. 2. 012207. g.

SEA BREEZES. [Selected Poems.] *Lond.* 1891. obl. 8° 011653. i. 39.

KNIGHT (J.) Pipe and Pouch. Smoker's book of poetry. pp. 182. *Bost.* 1895. 8°.
11602. bb. 36.

Religious.

HERNAMAN (C. F.) Lyra Consolationis. pp. 228. *Lond.* 1890. 8°. 11602. ce. 38.

HORDER (W. G.) The Poets' Bible. 2 vol. *Lond.* 1895. 8°. 11601. ff. 27.

SHIPLEY (O.) Carmina Mariana ; English anthology in honour of the B. V. Mary. pp. 461. *Lond.* 1894. 8°. 11602. ccc. 25.

See also HYMNS.

France.

History and Criticism. See FRENCH LITERATURE.

Versification.

BANVILLE (T. de) Petit traité de Poésie française. pp. 336. *Paris,* 1891. 12°. 11851. aaa. 9.

BIBESCO (A.) *Prince.* La Question du Vers français et la tentative des poètes décadents. pp. 47. *Paris,* 1893. 4°. 11805. m. 27.

EICHTHAL (E. d') Du rythme dans la Versification française. pp. 55. *Paris,* 1892. 12°.
011824. e. 50.

GALINO (T.) Musique et Versification françaises au moyen-âge. pp. 39. *Leipz.* 1890. 8°.
Pam. 15.

NAETEBUS (G.) Die nicht-lyrischen Strophenformen des Altfranzösischen. pp. 227. *Leipz.* 1891. 8°. 011824. i. 13.

P.P. *Paris.* Revue de Métrique et de Versification. *Paris,* 1894, *etc.* 8°. P.P. 4316. b.

SOURIAU (M.) L'évolution du Vers français au 17e siècle. *Paris,* 1893. 8°. 011824. k. 26.

SOUZA (R. de) Le Rythme poétique. pp. 304. *Paris,* 1892. 8°. 011824. g. 18.

SULLY PRUDHOMME (R. F. A.) Réflexions sur l'art des Vers. pp. 85. *Paris,* 1892. 8°.
011824. e. 49.

TISSEUR (C.) Modestes observations sur l'art de Versifier. pp. 355. *Lyon,* 1893. 8°. 11824. h. 30.

TOBLER (A.) Le Vers français ancien et moderne. pp. 207. *Paris,* 1885. 8°. 011850. i. 33.

Selections.

BATAILLE (F.) Anthologie de l'enfance. pp. 342. *Paris,* 1893. 12°. 11483. de. 19.

FLORESCU (B.) Morceaux choisis, XVII° siècle. Poésie. pp. 145. *Giurgevo,* 1889. 8°.
11483. ccc. 2.

FUSTER (C.) L'Année des Poètes. *Paris,* 1891, *etc.* 8°. 11483. ff. 28.

LENIENT (C.) La Poésie patriotique en France. 2 tom. *Paris,* 1894. 8°. 011850. ccc. 18.

ROBERTSON (W. J.) A century of French Verse. pp. 317. *Lond.* 1895. 4°. 11483. dd. 12.

POETRY.—France—*continued.*

SAINT-JEAN, *Comte de.* Les Femmes Poètes bretonnes. pp. 169. *Nantes,* 1892. 12°.
11850. cc. 42.

See also BALLADS: SONNETS.

Germany.

History and Criticism. See GERMAN LITERATURE.

Versification.

FUHR (C.) Die Metrik des westgermanischen Allitterationsverses. pp. 147. *Marburg,* 1892. 8°. 11805. i. 34.

HEINZE (P.) and GOETTE (R.) Deutsche Poetik. pp. 363. *Dresden,* 1891. 8°. 011824. f. 5.

HEUSLER (A.) Über germanischen Versbau. pp. 139. 1894. 8°. ROEDIGER (M.) Schriften zur germanischen Philologie. Hft. 7.
12963. k. 28.

—— Zur Geschichte der altdeutscher Verskunst. pp. 161. 1891. 8°. WEINHOLD (C.) Germanistische Abhandlungen. Hft. 8. 12208. gg.

KALUZA (M.) Studien zum germanischen Alliterationsvers. *Berl.* 1894, *etc.* 8°. 11825. q.

KASSEWITZ (J.) Darlegung der dichterischen Technik von Goethes Elegie "Alexis und Dora." pp. 27. *Leipz.* 1893. 8°. Pam. 15.

MINOR (J.) Neuhochdeutsche Metrik. pp. 490. *Strassburg,* 1893. 8°. 11825. q. 15.

SANDERS (D. H.) Abriss der deutschen Silbenmessung und Verskunst. pp. 133. *Berl.* 1891. 8°. 011824. i. 22.

SCHREIBER (J.) Die Vaganten-Strophe der mittellateinischen Dichtung, und das Verhältnis derselben zu mittelhochdeutschen Strophenformen. pp. 204. *Strassburg,* 1894. 8°. 11312. p. 8.

SIEVERS (E.) Altgermanische Metrik. pp. 252. 1893. 8°. BRAUNE (W.) Sammlung kurzer Grammatiken. Ergänzungsreihe. Bd. 2.
12901. e. 33.

Selections.

BONTÉ (H.) Deutsche Lyrik. pp. 145. *Wien,* 1895. 12°. 011528. e. 71.

BUCHHEIM (C. A.) Balladen und Romanzen. Selected, *etc.* pp. 318. *Lond.* 1891. 8°. .
11527. ccc. 51.

CIBRARIO (L.) Saggio di versioni poetiche dal Tedesco. pp. 180. *Torino,* 1892. 8°.
11527. dd. 30.

DITTMAR (F.) Vaterländische Gedichte zur Geschichte Bayerns. pp. 267. *Bamberg,* 1891. 8°. 11527. f. 23.

HUB (I.) Deutschland's Balladen- und Romanzen-Dichter. pp. 728. *Karlsruhe,* 1884, 85. 8°. 11522. g. 18.

PARRY (C. H.) and ROBINSON (G. G.) German Poetry for Schools. pp. 208. *Lond.* 1886. 8°.
11528. aa. 4.

—— German Poetry for repetition. pp. 64. *Godalming,* 1882. 8°. 11517. bbb. 42.

MUELLENHOFF (C. V.) and SCHERER (W.) Denkmäler deutscher Poesie aus dem VIII.-XII. Jahrhundert. 2 Bde. *Berl.* 1892. 8°.
11517. h. 2.

KRAUS (C.) Deutsche Gedichte des zwölften Jahrhunderts. pp. 283. *Halle,* 1894. 8°.
11517. f. 34.

ELLINGER (G.) Deutsche Lyriker des 16ten Jahrhunderts. pp. 122. 1891. 8°. HERMANN (M.) Lateinische Litteraturdenkmäler. Hft. 7.
11305. d.

FREILIGRATH-KROEKER (K.) Century of German Lyrics. pp. 225. *Lond.* 1894. 8°.
11528. bbb. 62.

JOYNES (J. L.) Songs of a Revolutionary Epoch. pp. 176. *Lond.* 1888. 8°. 11526. d. 49.

POETRY.—Germany—_continued._

DAHMS (G.) Germania. Deutsche Dichter der Gegenwart. pp. 150. _Berl._ 1891. fol.
                  11522. k. 2.

BRUNO (C. G.) Deutsche Lyrik von 1891, _etc._ _Stuttgart_, 1892, _etc._ 8°.   011528. g.
See also BALLADS : NIBELUNGENLIED.

Greece.

History and Criticism. _See_ GREEK LITERATURE.

Prosody.

ALLEN (F. D.) On Greek Versification in Inscriptions. 1888. 8°. Ac. Boston. _School of Classical Studies at Athens._ Papers. Vol. 4.
                  Ac. 5790/9.

DINGELDEIN (O.) Der Reim bei den Griechen. pp. 131. _Leipz._ 1892. 8°.   11312. c. 66.

GLEDITSCH (H.) Allgemeine Theorie der griechischen Metrik. 1887. 8°. ROSSBACH (A.) and WESTPHAL (R.) Theorie der musischen Künste. Bd. 2. Abt. 1.   2280. f. 2.

MUELLER (L.) Greek and Roman Versification. pp. 121. _Bost._ 1892. 8°.   11312. c. 68.

RIEMANN (O.) and DUFOUR (M.) Traité de Rythmique et de métrique grecques. pp. 152. _Paris_, 1893. 8°.   11312. f. 59.

USSING (J. L.) Græsk og romersk Metrik. pp. 207. _Kjøbenh._ 1893. 8°.   11312. e. 31.

VERNIER (L.) Traité de Métrique grecque et latine. pp. 230. _Paris_, 1894. 8°.
               11312. bbb. 26.

WESTPHAL (R.) and GLEDITSCH (H.) Allgemeine Theorie der griechischen Metrik. pp. 368. 1887. 8°. ROSSBACH (A.) Theorie der musischen Künste der Hellenen. Bd. 2. Abt. 1. 2280. f. 2.

WILLIAMS (J. H.) Damon, manual of Greek Iambic composition. pp. 107. _Lond._ 1894. 8°.
               11312. aaa. 39.

Selections.

APPLETON (W. H.) Greek Poets in English Verse. pp. 360. _Bost._ 1893. 8°. 11340. de. 1.

BAKER (W.) Latin and Greek Verse translations. pp. 133. _Lond._ 1895. 8°.   11409. c. 46.

BERGK (T.) Poetae lyrici Graeci. 2 vol. _Lipsiae_, 1882. 8°.   11340. g. 8.

COBET (C. G.) Fragmenta inedita Poetarum graecorum. pp. 16. _Lugduni-Bat._ 1880. 8°.
               Pam. 63.

EVANS (T. S.) Latin and Greek verse. pp. 276. _Camb._ 1893. 8°.   11409. c. 44.

FARNELL (G. S.) Greek Lyric Poetry. pp. 490. _Lond._ 1891. 8°.   2282. c. 1.

GARNETT (R.) A Chaplet from the Greek Anthology. 1892. 8°. The Cameo Series.
               12205. ee.

GREEK ANTHOLOGY. From the Garden of Hellas. Translations by L. C. Perry. pp. 142. _N.Y._ 1891. 8°.   11340. b. 11.

—— Selections. Edited by G. R. Tomson. pp. 277. 1889. 8°. The Canterbury Poets.
               11604. aaa.

GREECE. Poètes moralistes de la Grèce. Notices et traductions. pp. 320. _Paris_, 1892. 12°.
               11312. bbb. 21.

HOFFMANN (E.) Sylloge epigrammatum Graecorum, _etc._ pp. 245. _Halis S._ 1893. 8°.
               7706. c. 48.

HOUBRON (G.) and DANIAUX (J.) Études antiques. pp. 119. _Paris_, 1890. 8°. 11340. bbb. 4.

MURR (J.) Altgriechische Weisheit. _Innsbruck_, 1891, _etc._ 8°.   11340. aa.

PALEY (F. A.) Fragments of the Greek comic Poets. pp. 145. _Lond._ 1892. 8°. 11340. aa. 15.

POLLARD (A. W.) Odes from the Greek Dramatists. pp. 208. _Lond._ 1890. 4°. 11705. c. 15.

POETRY.—Greece—_continued._

SCHULTZ (J.) and GEFFCKEN (J.) Altgriechische Lyrik in deutschen Reim. pp. 104. _Berl._ 1895. 8°.   11340. aa. 32.

Hebrew.

HARTMANN (M.) Die hebräische Verskunst. pp. 100. _Berl._ 1894. 8°.   012904. h. 18.

HERDER (J. G. v.) Vom Geist der ebräischen Poesie. 2 Tle. 1890. 8°. Bibliothek theologischer Klassiker. Bde. 30, 31.   3605. l.
See also HEBREW LITERATURE.

Hungary.

LACHMANN (H.) Ungarische Gedichte : uebertragen von H. L. pp. 132. _Berl._ 1891. 8°.
               011586. e. 34.

India.

RAMESACHANDRA DATTA. Lays of ancient India. Selections. pp. 224. 1894. 8°. Trübner's Oriental Series.   2318. h. 9.

Ireland.

IRELAND. Poems of young Ireland. pp. 80. _Dubl._ 1890. 8°.   11601. ccc. 28. (6.)

MAC CALL (P. J.) Irish Nóiníns : collection of historical poems. pp. 128. _Dubl._ 1894. 8°.
               11621. aaa. 61.

MONTGOMERY (H. R.) Specimens of early native poetry of Ireland in English translations. pp. 311. _Dubl._ 1892. 8°.   11595. c. 35.

SPARLING (H. H.) Irish Minstrelsy. pp. 368. 1887. 8°. Canterbury Poets.   11604. aa.

YEATS (W. B.) Book of Irish Verse. pp. 256. _Lond._ 1895. 8°.   11622. e. 20.

See also supra: England: ENGLISH LITERATURE : IRISH LITERATURE.

Italy.

History and Criticism. _See_ ITALIAN LITERATURE.

Versification and Selections.

PLATANIA D'ANTONI (R.) Rimario universale della lingua italiana. pp. 592. 3. _Acireale_, 1892. 8°.   12941. g. 22.

BARBIERA (C. R.) Poesie veneziane. pp. 308. _Firenze_, 1886. 8°.   11429. c. 16.

BARSOTTINI (G.) Poesie italiane. pp. 528. _Prato_, 1891. 8°.   11429. e. 28.

ESTELRICH (J. L.) Antología de poetas liricos italianos traducidos en catellano. pp. 884. _Palma de Mallorca_, 1889. 8°.   11427. ee. 12.

FERRARI (S.) Antologia della Lirica moderna italiana. pp. 334. _Bologna_, 1891. 8°.
               11436. e. 45.

GREENE (G. A.) Italian Lyrists of to-day. pp. 232. _Lond._ 1893. 8°.   11436. cc. 8.

LEVI (E.) Dai nostri Poeti viventi. pp. 272. _Firenze_, 1891. 8°.   11429. b. 14.

See also BALLADS.

Japan.

FLORENZ (K.) Dichtergrüsse aus dem Osten. Japanische Dichtungen. pp. 97. _Leipz._ 1894. 4°.   011528. g. 46.

Latin.

History and Criticism. _See_ LATIN LITERATURE.

Prosody.

AINGER (A. C.) and WINTLE (H. G.) English-Latin Gradus. pp. 442. _Lond._ 1890. 8°.
               12934. c. 33.

BENECKE (E. F. M.) Poetarum Latinorum Index, in usum versificatorum nostratum conflatus. pp. 166. _Lond._ 1894. 8°.   11312. e. 36.

DINGELDEIN (O.) Der Reim bei den Griechen und Römern. pp. 131. _Leipz._ 1892. 8°.
               11312. c. 66.

HIME (M. C.) Introduction to Latin Verse composition. pp. 43. _Dublin_, 1893. 8°. 11312. c. 67.

POETRY.—Latin—continued.

MORICE (F. D.) Latin Verse composition.
pp. 123. *Lond.* 1893. 8°. 11312. bb. 16.
—— Key. pp. 67. *Lond.* 1893. 8°.
11312. aaa. 36.

MUELLER (L.) Greek and Roman Versification.
pp. 121. *Bost.* 1892. 8°. 11312. c. 68

NIXON (J. E.) and SMITH (E. H. C.) Parallel
Verse extracts for translation into English and
Latin. pp. 151. *Lond.* 1893. 8°. 11375. ee. 30.

OPITZ (C. R.) De argumentorum metricorum
Latinorum arte. 1883. 8°. CURTIUS (G.)
Leipziger Studien. Bd. 6. P.P. 5044. c.

RASI (P.) De Carmine Romanorum elegiaco.
pp. 165. *Patavii*, 1890. 8°. 11312. l. 47.

RITCHIE (F.) First Latin Verse book. pp. 64.
Lond. 1894. 8°. 11312. aaa. 38.

SKUTSCH (F.) Forschungen zur lateinischen
Metrik. *Leipz.* 1892, *etc.* 8°. 12934. g.

USSING (J. L.) Græsk og romersk Metrik.
pp. 207. *Kjøbenh.* 1893. 8°. 11312. e. 31.

VERNIER (L.) Petit traité de Métrique latine.
pp. 230. *Paris*, 1894. 8°. 11312. bbb. 26.

BENECKE (E. F. M.) Apospasmata critica, suggestion as to the origin of the Horatian Sapphic
stanza. pp. 15. *Oxf.* 1892. 8°. 11312. p. 4. (13.)

EICKHOFF (P.) Der horazische Doppelbau der
sapphischen Strophe. pp. 54.
Wandsbeck, 1895. 8°. Pam. 14.

GABRIEL (J. E.) Étude sur la Métrique d'Horace.
pp. 32. *Bergerac*, 1891. 8°. 11312. p. 2. (8.)

HILBERG (I.) Die Gesetze der Wortstellung in
Pentameter des Ovid. pp. 892.
Leipz. 1894. 8°. 11312. p. 7.

DECHEVEENS (A.) Du Rythme dans l'hymnographie latine. pp. 159. *Paris*, 1895. 8°.
7899. bb. 2.

SCHREIBER (J.) Die Vaganten-Strophe der mittellateinischen Dichtung. pp. 204.
Strassb. 1894. 8°. 11312. p. 8.

Selections.

BUECHELER (F.) and RIESE (A.) Anthologia
Latina. *Lipsiae*, 1893, *etc.* 8°. 2278. c. 29.

LATIN ANTHOLOGY. Anthologiae Latinae sup-
plementa. *Lipsiae*, 1895, *etc.* 8° 2278. i. 8.

BAKER (W.) Latin and Greek verse translations.
pp. 133. *Lond.* 1895. 8°. 11409. c. 46.

CAREY (S. W. S.) Selection of Latin Verse for
lower forms. pp 102. *Lond.* 1893. 8°. 11352. c. 2.

EVANS (T. S.) Latin and Greek verse. pp. 276.
Camb. 1893. 8°. 11409. c. 44.

MERRY (W. W.) Selected fragments of Roman
Poetry. pp. 260. *Oxf.* 1891. 8°. 11355. e. 12.

NIXON (J. E.) and SMITH (E. H. C.) Parallel
verse extracts, *etc.* pp. 151. *Lond.* 1893. 8°.
11375. ee. 30.

POSTGATE (J. P.) Corpus Poetarum Latinorum.
Londini, 1893, *etc.* 4°. 2282. f. 1.

Ac. Aberdeen. *New Spalding Club.* GEDDES
(*Sir* W. D.) Musa Latina Aberdonensis.
Aberd. 1892, *etc.* 4°. Ac. 8245/8.

Mexico. *See infra:* Spain.

Netherlands.

HASEBROEK (J. P.) Een Dichter-Album. pp. 333.
Amsterd. 1890. 8°. 10760. c. 25.
See also supra: BELGIUM : DUTCH LITERATURE.

Norway. *See infra:* Scandinavia.

Persia

KRISHNALĀL MOHANLĀL JHĀVERĪ. Outlines of
Persian Prosody. pp. 108. *Bombay*, 1892. 8°.
757. bb. 18.

See also PERSIAN LITERATURE.

POETRY—continued.

Russia.

ASCHARIN (A.) Nordische Klänge. Russische
Dichtungen. pp. 237. *Riga*, 1894. 8°.
011586. e. 60.

POLLEN (J.) Rhymes from the Russian. pp. 118.
Lond. 1891. 8°. 011586. de. 67.

SAINT-ALBIN (E. de) Les Poètes russes. Anthologie. pp. 451. *Paris*, 1893. 12°. 11586. cc. 32.
See also RUSSIAN LITERATURE.

Scandinavia.

HJELMQVIST (T.) Naturskildringarna i den
norröna Diktningen. pp. 215.
Stockholm, 1891. 8°. 011824. h. 33.

DANISH LYRICS. Nyere dansk Lyrik. pp. 370.
Kjøbenh. 1883. 8°. 11557. bbb. 23.

KROHN (J.) Dansk Versebog. pp. 160.
Kjøbenh. 1890. 8°. 11565. d. 1.

ROLFSEN (N.) Norske Digtere.
Christiania, 1894, *etc.* 8°. 11565. g.

VEDEL (V.) Studien over Gudalderen i dansk
Digtning. pp. 262. *Kjøbenh.* 1890. 8°.
011824. f. 22.

See also DANISH, ICELANDIC, NORWEGIAN AND
SWEDISH LITERATURE.

Scotland.

Ac. Edinburgh. *Scottish Text Society.* AMOURS
(F. J.) Scottish alliterative Poems.
Edinb. 1892, *etc.* 8°. Ac. 9943/13.

LAING (D.) Early popular Poetry of Scotland,
etc. 2 vol. *Lond.* 1895. 8°. 2292. h. 2.

TODD (G. E.) Abbotsford series of the Scottish
Poets. *Glasg.* 1891, *etc.* 8°. 11622. ee.

VEITCH (J.) History and Poetry of the Scottish
Border. 2 vol. *Edinb.* 1893. 8°. 2308. c. 20.

DOUGLAS (*Sir* G. H. S.) *Bart.* Poems of the
Scottish minor Poets. pp. 327. *Lond.* 1891. 8°.
11604. aaa.

Ac. Edinburgh. *Scottish Text Society.* CRANS-
TOUN (J.) Satirical Poems of the time of the
Reformation. *Edinb.* 1890, *etc.* 8°. Ac. 9943/11.

MAC ALLISTER (D.) Poets and Poetry of the
Covenant. pp. 300. *Edinb.* 1894. 8°.
11622. df. 32.

MACFARLANE (J.) The harp of the Scottish
Covenant. pp. 341. *Lond.* 1895. 8°. 11622. ee. 12.

CROCKETT (W. S.) Minstrelsy of the Merse
Poets of Berwickshire. pp. 343.
Paisley, 1893. 8°. 11622. e. 19.

DOUGLAS (*Sir* G. B. S.) Contemporary Scottish
Verse. pp. 348. 1893. 8°. Canterbury Poets.
11604. aaaa.

See also supra: England : BALLADS : ENGLISH
LITERATURE : SCOTCH LITERATURE. For Gaelic
poetry, *see* GAELIC LANGUAGE.

Spain and Spanish America.

LÓPEZ PINCIANO (A.) Filosofía antiqua poética.
pp. 511. *Valladolid*, 1894. 8°. 8465. ee. 26.

MENÉNDEZ Y PELAYO (M.) Antología de Poetas
líricos castellanos. *Madrid*, 1890, *etc.* 8°.
11450. d.

SPANISH POETS. Poetas castellanos modernos.
pp. 189. *Barcelona*, 1892. 16° 11450. bb. 32.

Ac. Madrid. *Real Academia Española.* Antología de poetas hispano-americanos.
Madrid, 1893, *etc.* 8°. Ac. 144/9.

TESORO. Poetas del Nuevo Mundo. 2 pt.
Barcelona, 1890. 8°. 11450. a. 32.

MARTINEZ (B. T.) Antologia argentina. pp. 467.
Buenos A. 1890. 8°. 12296. d. 4.

RIVAS (B.) Lira boliviana.
Cochabamba, 1885, *etc.* 8°. 11452. f.

AÑEZ (J.) Parnaso colombiano. 2 tom.
Bogotá, 1886, 87. 8°. 11450. f. 32.

POLAND—*continued.*

PR. Das polnisch-russische Staatskirchen-
" Recht." *Leipz. 1890, etc.* 8°.   3926. h.

SEMBRZYCKI (J.) Die polnischen Reformirten
und Unitarier in Preussen. pp. 100.
Königsberg, 1893. 8°.   4695. e. 36.

POLICE.

General.

HALE (G. W.) Police Cyclopædia. pp. 273.
Camb., Mass. 1892. 8°.   6057. de. 4.

See also CRIME : LAW, *Criminal.*

Austria.

ZUCKER (A.) Die Polizeiaufsicht nach österreichischen Rechte. pp. 125. *Prag, 1894.* 8°.
5549. df. 11.

Belgium.

BELVAL (T.) Police des Mœurs. pp. 16.
Bruges, 1889. 8°.   08276. i. 2. (6.)

France.

PAISANT (A.) La Police au dix-huitième siècle.
pp. 42. *Paris, 1894.* 8°.   5423. g. 1. (11.)

MOUTIERS. Règ'ement de Police pour la ville de
Moutiers, 1779. pp. 144. *Moutiers, 1890.* 16°.
6055. a. 5.

Germany.

GERLAND (O.) Ueber den Begriff der Polizei
und insbesondere der Sicherheits-Polizei.
pp. 72. 1890. 8°. LABAND (P.) Archiv für
öffentliches Recht. Bd. v. Hft. 1.
P.P. 1403. k.

KIESLING ( ) Organisation und Bekleidung
der k. p. Leib-Gendarmerie. pp. 28.
Berl. 1890. 8°.   8831. l. 9. (6.)

WICKEDE (F. v.) Handbuch der Polizeiverwal-
tung für Wiesbaden. pp. 566.
Wiesbaden, 1893. 8°.   05605. g. 1.

Great Britain and Ireland.

DALGARNIE (F.) Plea for the appointment of
Police Matrons, *etc.* pp. 58. *Lond. 1894.* 8°.
6057. bb. 39. (7.)

BICKNELL (P. B.) Police manual. pp. 296.
Lond. 1894. 8°.   6485. a. 24.

CHILDS (H.) Policeman's guide to promotion.
pp. 24. *Lond. 1893.* 12°.   6057. a. 34.

DAWSON (J.) Facts for the people. Truth about
the Police. pp. 8. *Lond. 1887.* 4°.
1882. c. 2. (204.)

KIRCHNER (F. J.) Index to the Police Forces of
the British Empire. pp. 126. *Manch. 1893.* 8°.
6057. b. 29.

LEES (T. O. H.) Police Acts, 1839–93. pp. 66.
Lond. 1893. 8°.   6145. aa. 36. (2.)

—— The Constable's Pocket book. pp. 154.
Lond. 1894. 8°.   6057. a. 39.

MARRIOTT (T.) A Constable's duty and how to
do it. pp. 164. *Lond. 1894.* 8°.   6057. bb. 38.

SNOWDEN ( ) Police Officer's guide. pp. 567.
Lond. 1892. 8°.   6191. aa. 17.

G. B. & I. Victoria, *Queen.* Abstract of the
Burgh Police, Scotland, Act, 1892. pp. 15.
Aberdeen, 1893. 8°.   6146. bbb. 26. (4.)

GLASGOW. Acts relating to the Glasgow Police.
pp 556. *Glasg. 1893.* 8°.   6583. g. 15.

IRONS (J. C.) The Burgh Police, Scotland, Act,
1892. pp. 913. *Edinb. 1893.* 8°.   6583. cc. 1.

MUIRHEAD (J.) The Law relating to Police
government in Burghs in Scotland. pp. 691.
Glasg. 1893. 8°.   6583. g. 12.

—— List of offences and penalties under the
Burgh Police, Scotland, Act, 1892. pp. 50.
Glasg. 1893. 8°.   6583. a. 5.

POLICE.—Great Britain, etc.—*continued.*

SCOTLAND. *Constabulary.* Rules made by H.M.
Secretary for Scotland for the government of
the Police. pp. 8. *Lond. 1892.* fol.
6126. l. 1. (3.)

DOWNS (A. J.) Relations of the public in the
Dublin metropolitan district with the Police
Force, *etc.* pp. 30. *Dubl. 1889.* 8°.   Pam. 32.

BENT (J.) Criminal Life : reminiscences.
pp. 322. *Manch. 1891.* 8°.   6057. aa. 26.

CAMINADA (J.) Twenty-five years of detective
Life. pp. 464. *Manch. 1895.* 8°.   6057. cc. 2.

CAVANAGH ( ) Scotland Yard past and present.
pp. 229. *Lond. 1893.* 8°.   12331. ee. 30.

LANSDOWNE (A.) A Life's reminiscences. Scotland Yard. pp. 202. *Lond. 1893.* 8°.   6057. aa. 40.

LITTLECHILD (J. G.) Reminiscences. pp. 238.
Lond. 1894. 8°.   6057. a. 40.

India.

ARTHUR (T. C.) Reminiscences of an Indian
police official. pp. 285. *Lond. 1894.* 8°.
6057. de. 7.

United States of America.

KIRCHNER (F. J.) Index to Police Forces of the
British Empire and the United States. pp. 126.
Manch. 1893. 8°.   6057. b. 29.

COSTELLO (A. E.) History of the New York
Police. pp. 572. *N.Y. 1885.* 8°.   6056. ff. 17.

**POLISH LANGUAGE AND LITERA-
TURE.** BOOCH-ÁRKOSSY (F.) Polnisch-deutsches und deutsch-polnisches Taschenwörterbuch. 2 pt. *Leipz. 1890.* 8°.   12975. b. 1.

KURTZMANN (L.) Die polnische Literatur in
Deutschland. pp. 89. *Posen, 1881.* 8°.
011902. g. 23.

POLITICAL ECONOMY.

Bibliography.

BOWKER (R. R.) and ILES (G.) Reader's Guide
in Economic and Political Science. pp. 169.
N.Y. 1891. 8°.   11900. bb. 54.

MARTELLO (T.) Dizionario bibliografico dell'
Economia politica. *Bologna, 1893.* 8°. 011900. f.

MUEHLBRECHT (O.) Wegweiser durch die neue
Litteratur der Rechts- und Staatswissenschaften.
pp. 748. *Berl. 1893.* 8°.   011900. h. 15.

General.

Ac. Cambridge. *Harvard University.* Quarterly
Journal of Economics. *Bost. 1887, etc.* 8°.
P.P. 1423. ce.

—— London. *British Economic Association.* The
Economic Journal. Edited by F. Y. Edgeworth.
Lond. 1891, etc. 8°.   2020. c.

—— Philadelphia. *University of Pennsylvania.*
Publications. Political Economy Series.
Phila. 1890, etc. 8°.   Ac. 2692. p.

ASHLEY (W.) Introduction to English Economic
Theory. *Lond. 1892, etc.* 8°.   2240. aa. 1.

AVELING (E. B.) The Students' Marx. Introduction to K. Marx's " Capital." pp. 180.
Lond. 1892. 8°.   08276. e. 25.

BAGEHOT (W.) Economic Studies. pp. 280.
Lond. 1895. 8°.   2240. e. 2.

BAILLAIRGÉ (F. A.) Traité d'Économie politique
selon la doctrine de Léon XIII. pp. 324.
Quebec, 1892. 8°.   8207. a. 18.

BAIN (F. W.) On the Principle of Wealth-crea-
tion. pp. 237. *Lond. 1892.* 8°.   08227. cc. 52.

—— Body and Soul. pp. 466. *Lond. 1894.* 8°.
8465. k. 24.

BARBIERI (V.) La proprietà fondiaria nell'Economia sociale. pp. 100. *Lodi, 1891.* 8°.
8225. eee. 45.

POLITICAL ECONOMY. — General —
continued.

BARDI (F. de') *Count.* Del Benessere nella società moderna. pp. 269. *Roma*, 1892. 8°.
    08276. h. 50.

BERG (R.) Der wirthschaftliche Nothstand und ein Weg zum Bessern. pp. 99. *Berl.* 1891. 8°.
    08227. f. 29.

BRENTANO (L.) and LESER (E.) Sammlung staatswissenschaftlicher Schriften des In- und Auslandes. *Leipz.* 1893, *etc.* 8°.   08276. i. 4.

BRUDER (A.) Staatslexikon. *Freiburg*, 1889, *etc.* 8°.   012216. i.

BUECHER (C.) Die Entstehung der Volkswirtschaft. pp. 304. *Tübingen*, 1893. 8°. 08276. i. 11.

CAIRE (F.) L'Economia politica applicata. pp. 361. *Casale*, 1891. 8°.   08207. g. 21.

CAMPBELL (G. D.) *Duke of Argyll.* The Unseen Foundations of Society. pp. 591. *Lond.* 1893. 8°.   2238. d. 15.

CHASE (H. S.) Letters to Farmers' Sons on the questions of the day. pp. 166. *N.Y.* 1891. 8°.
    08207. ee. 2.

CLAMAGERAN (J. J.) La Réaction Économique et la démocratie. pp. 103. *Paris*, 1891. 12°.
    8277. aa. 67.

COHN (G.) System der Nationalökonomie. 2 Bde. *Stuttgart*, 1885-89. 8°.   08207. h. 1.

COMMONS (J. R.) The Distribution of Wealth. pp. 258. *N.Y.* 1893. 8°.   08207. ee. 19.

COPE (R.) The Distribution of Wealth. pp. 364. *Phila.* 1890. 8°.   08207. g. 10.

COSSA (L.) Introduzione allo studio dell' Economia politica. pp. 594. *Milano*, 1892. 8°.
    08207. g. 23.

—— Introduction to the study of Political Economy. pp. 587. *Lond.* 1893. 8°.   2020. c.

CUNNINGHAM (W.) Use and abuse of money. pp. 219. 1891. 8°. University Extension Lectures.   12204. f.

DEVAS (C. S.) Political Economy. pp. 578. 1892. 8°. Manuals of Catholic Philosophy.
    8470. ccc.

EFFERTZ (O.) Arbeit und Boden. *Berl.* 1890, *etc.* 8°.   08276. h. 2.

ELY (R. T.) Introduction to Political Economy. pp. 358. *Lond.* 1891. 8°.   08207. ee. 3.

—— Outlines of Economics. pp. 432. *N.Y.* 1893. 8°.   08207. ee. 18.

FLUERSCHEIM (M.) Rent, Interest and Wages. pp. 238. *Lond.* 1895. 8°.   08275. f. 25.

FRANKENSTEIN (K.) Hand- und Lehrbuch der Staatswissenschaften. *Leipz.* 1893, *etc.* 8°.
    8009. k.

GANS-LUDASSY (J. v.) Die wirtschaftliche Energie. *Jena*, 1893, *etc.* 8°.   08207. k.

GIBSON (*Hon.* W.) Future of Political Economy. pp. 14. *Oxf.* 1891. 8°.   8228. aaaa. 17. (4.)

GIDE (C.) Principes d'Économie Politique. pp. 638. *Paris*, 1894. 12°.   08207. ee. 22.

—— Principles of Political Economy. pp. 581. *Bost.* 1891. 8°.   08207. ee. 8.

GRAHAM (R. G. B. C.) Economic Evolution. pp. 18. *Aberd.* 1891. 16°.   Pam. 82.

GROSSMANN (L.) Compendium der praktischen Volkswirthschaft. pp. 80. *Wien*, 1892. 8°.
    8227. k.

GUNTON (G.) Principles of social Economics. pp. 451. *N.Y.* 1892. 8°.   08277. ff. 4.

HERRMANN (E.) Technische Fragen und Probleme der modernen Volkswirthschaft. pp. 475. *Leipz.* 1891. 8°.   08276. g. 14.

—— Wirthschaftliche Fragen der Gegenwart. pp. 480. *Leipz.* 1893. 8°.   08207. h. 15.

POLITICAL ECONOMY. — General —
continued.

KENWORTHY (J. C.) The Anatomy of misery. pp. 98. *Lond.* 1893. 8°.   8277. de. 42.

KEYNES (J. N.) Scope and method of Political Economy. pp. 359. *Lond.* 1891. 8°.
    8207. e. 25.

KOENIG (F.) Die Volkswirtschaftslehre. *Leipz.* 1893, *etc.* 8°.   08276. i.

LABRA (R. M. de) Estudios de Economía social. pp. 312. *Madrid*, 1892. 8°.   08276. f. 78.

LALOR (J. J.) Cyclopædia of Political Science, *etc.* 3 vol. *Chicago*, 1881-88. 8°. 8176. ce. 1.

LANGE (J. E.) Socialøkonomiens grundsætninger. pp. 77. *Odense*, 1890. 8°.   Pam. 82.

LAVELEYE (É. de) Luxury. pp. 179. 9. *Lond.* 1891. 8°.   08276. e. 17.

LEHR (J.) Grundbegriffe und Grundlagen der Volkswirtschaft. pp. 375. 1893. 8°. FRANKENSTEIN (K.) Lehrbuch der Staatswissenschaften. Abth. i. 1.   8009. k.

—— Produktion und Konsumtion in der Volkswirtschaft. pp. 261. 1895. 8°. FRANKENSTEIN (K.) Lehrbuch der Staatswissenschaften. Abth. 1. Bd. 4.   8009. k.

LE PLAY (P. G. F.) Économie sociale. pp. 252. *Paris*, 1892. 8°.   08276. dc. 2.

LEROY-BEAULIEU (P. P.) Précis d'Économie politique. pp. 409. *Paris*, 1894. 8°.
    08207. ee. 25.

LEVI (G. G.) Lavoro e libertà. *Torino*, 1893, *etc.* 8°.   08207. g.

LIBERATORE (M.) Principles of Political Economy. pp. 295. *Lond.* 1891. 8°.   08207. g. 13.

LIMA (A. H. de) Primeiros Estudios economicos. pp. 87. *Rio de J.* 1892. 8°.   Pam. 82.

LONDON. *School of Economics.* Prospectus. pp. 11. *Lond.* 1895. 8°.   Pam. 23.

—— *National Liberal Club.* Political Economy Circle. Transactions. *Lond.* 1891, *etc.* 8°.
    08207. g.

LUPORINI (C.) Il Principio etico e giuridico in relazione all' Economia civile. pp. 359. *Lucca*, 1892. 8°.   08207. h. 9.

MACKAY (T.) A Policy of Free Exchange. pp. 292. *Lond.* 1894. 8°.   08225. k. 5.

MACLEOD (H. D.) Theory of Credit. *Lond.* 1894, *etc.* 8°.   08207. g. 25.

MALLET (*Sir* L.) Free Exchange. pp. 356. *Lond.* 1891. 8°.   08207. g. 2.

MACLEOD (H. D.) Address to the Civil Service Commissioners on the teaching of Economics in the public service. pp. 12. *Lond.* 1892. fol.
    8228. l. 17. (7.)

MARSHALL (A.) Principles of Economics. *Lond.* 1895, *etc.* 8°.   2020. f.

—— Elements of Economics of industry. pp. 416. *Lond.* 1892. 8°.   08207. ee. 4.

MILL (J. S.) Principles of Political Economy. pp. 640. *Lond.* 1892. 8°.   8207. aa. 31.

MOLINARI (G. de) Notions d'Économie politique. pp. 466. *Paris*, 1891. 8°.   08207. g. 17.

—— Précis d'Économie politique. pp. 278. *Paris*, 1893. 12°.   08207. ee. 17.

NICHOLSON (J. S.) Principles of Political Economy. *Lond.* 1893, *etc.* 8°.   08207. h. 11.

NOVICOW (J.) Les Gaspillages des sociétés modernes. pp. 344. *Paris*, 1894. 8°. 08276. h. 62.

OSBORNE (G. P.) Principles of Economics. pp. 454. *Cincinnati*, 1893. 8°.   8207. c. 33.

OTT (A.) Traité d'Économie sociale. 2 tom. *Paris*, 1892. 8°.   08207. ee. 12.

POLITICAL ECONOMY. — General — *continued*.

PALGRAVE (R. H. I.) Dictionary of Political Economy. *Lond.* 1894, *etc.* 8°.   2020. c.

PATTEN (S. N.) Premises of Political Economy. pp. 244. *Phila.* 1885. 12°.   08207. ee. 11.

—— Theory of dynamic Economics. pp. 153. 1892. 8°. Ac. Philadelphia. *University.* Political Economy Series. Vol. III. No. 2.
   Ac. 2692. p.

—— Educational value of Political Economy. pp. 36. 1890. 8°. Ac. Saratoga. *American Economic Association.* Publications. Vol. 5. No. 6.   Ac. 2388.

PÉRIN (C.) Premiérs principes d'Economie politique. pp. 375. *Paris*, 1895. 12°.
   8207. b. 23.

P.P. *Chicago.* Journal of Political Economy. *Chicago*, 1892, *etc.* 8°.   P.P. 1423. eg.

—— *London.* The Economic Review. *Lond.* 1891, *etc.* 8°   P.P. 1423. ad.

—— *New York.* The Social Economist. *N.Y.* 1891, *etc.* 8°.   P.P. 1423. ef.

PERRY (A. L.) Principles of Political Economy. pp. 599. *Lond.* 1891. 8°.   08207. g. 12.

PICK (G. V.) Digest of Political Economy. pp. 156. *Lond.* 1892. 8°.   08207. ee. 7.

PLATTER (J.) Kritische Beiträge zur Erkenntnis unserer socialen Zustände und Theorien. pp. 558. *Basel.* 1894. 8°.   08276. h. 58.

PROTHERO (M.) Political Economy. pp. 266.¦ *Lond.* 1895. 8°.   8206. aa. 30.

RAMBAUD (J.) Éléments d'Économie politique. pp. 796. *Paris*, 1895. 8°.   08207. g. 28.

RICARDO (D.) Principles of Political Economy. Edited by E. C. K. Gonner. pp. 455. 1891. 8°. Bohn's Economic Library. 2500. i.

ROBERTSON (J. M.) The Fallacy of Saving. pp. 148. *Lond.* 1892. 8°.   08276. e. 37.

ROSCHER (W.) System der Volkswirthschaft. *Stuttgart*, 1892, *etc.* 8°.   2240. f.

ROSE (H.) The new Political Economy. pp. 152. *Lond.* 1891. 8°.   8207. e. 29.

ROSSI (G.) La Matematica applicata alla teoria della ricchezza sociale. *Reggio-Emilia*, 1889, *etc.* 8°.   8276. i.

SAINT-MARC (H.) Étude sur l'enseignement de l'Économie politique dans les Universités d'Allemagne et d'Autriche. pp. 140. *Paris*, 1892. 8°.   8206. h. 21.

SANZ Y ESCARTÍN (E.) La Cuestión Económica, *etc.* pp. 319. *Madrid*, 1890. 8°.   08207. g. 9.

SCHOENBERG (G. v.) Manuale di Economia politica. 1886, *etc.* 8°. Biblioteca dell' economista. Ser. 3. Vol. 11, *etc.*   8205. l.

SCHULZE-DELITZSCH (H.) Catechismo di Economia politica. 1889, *etc.* 8°. Biblioteca dell' economista. Ser. 3. Vol. 9.   8205. l.

SHIRRES (L. P.) Analysis of the ideas of Economics. pp. 260. *Lond.* 1893. 8°. 08207. ee. 13.

SMART (W.) Studies in Economics. pp. 341. *Lond.* 1895. 8°.   8297. bb. 45.

SMITH (A. M.) System of Political Economy. pp. 492. *Lond.* 1891. 8°.   08207. ee. 1.

SMITH (J. C.) Distribution of the produce. pp. 77. *Lond.* 1892. 8°.   8282. de. 48.

STOCKHOLM. *Nationalekonomiska Föreningen.* Förhandlingar. *Stockholm*, 1891, *etc.* 8°. 8206. h.

SULZER (G.) Die wirtschaftlichen Grundgesetze in der Gegenwartsphase ihrer Entwicklung. pp. 620. *Zürich*, 1895. 8°.   05551. e. 3.

SWARTWOUT (W. H. v.) Olombia; the new Political Economy. *N.Y.* 1893, *etc.* 4°. 08276. k.

POLITICAL ECONOMY. — General — *continued*.

VIDAURRE Y ORUETA (C.) Economía política. 3 tom. *Tolosa*, 1891–93. 8°.   08207. g. 26.

WAGNER (A.) Lehr- und Handbuch der politischen Oekonomie. *Leipz.* 1892, *etc.* 8°.
   08207. h.

WALRAS (L.) Éléments d'Économie politique pure. pp. 523. *Lausanne*, 1889. 8°.
   08207. h. 18.

WESTERGAARD (H. L.) Indledning til studiet af Nationaløkonomien. pp. 88. *Kjøbenh.* 1891. 8°.   8207. e. 30.

WICKSELL (K.) Über Wert, Kapital und Rente. pp. 143. *Jena*, 1893. 8°.   08276. k. 21.

WOOD (H.) Political Economy of natural law. pp. 305. *Bost.* 1894. 8°.   08275. ee. 15.

See also CAPITAL AND LABOUR : GOVERNMENT : MONEY : PRICES : SOCIALISM : SOCIAL SCIENCE : TRADE.

History.

ASHLEY (W. J.) Introduction to English Economic History. *Lond.* 1892, *etc.* 8°. 2240. aa. 1.

—— On the study of Economic History. *Bost.* 1893. 8°.   08227. i. 29. (12.)

BONAR (J.) Philosophy and Political Economy, in their historical relations. pp. 410. 1893. 8°.

MUIRHEAD (J. H.) Library of Philosophy.
   8486. h.

BRANTS (V. L. J. L.) L'Économie politique au moyen âge. pp. 279. *Louvain*, 1895. 8°.
   8207. bbb. 38.

CAMPBELL (G. D.) *Duke of Argyll.* Application of the historical method to Economic Science. 1894. 8°. LONDON. *Society for the Extension of University Teaching.* Aspects of Modern Study.   8367. aa. 19.

CANNAN (E.) History of the theories of production and distribution in English Political Economy, 1776–1848. pp. 410. *Lond.* 1893. 8°.
   08207. h. 8.

ESPINAS (A.) Histoire des Doctrines économiques. pp. 359. *Paris*, 1892. 12°. 08207. ee. 10.

FEILBOGEN (S.) Smith und Turgot. pp. 170. *Wien*, 1892. 8°.   08207. h. 6.

OERTMANN (P.) Die Volkswirtschaftslehre des Corpus Juris Civilis. pp. 154. *Berl.* 1891. 8°.
   5206. ee. 19.

P.P. *Freiburg.* Zeitschrift für Social- und Wirthschaftsgeschichte. *Freiburg*, 1893, *etc.* 8°.
   P.P. 1423. hac.

PRICE (L. L. F. R.) Short history of Political Economy in England. pp. 201. 1891. 8°.

SYMES (J. E.) University Extension Series.
   012202. g.

PRUSSIA. Dokumente zur Geschichte der Wirthschaftspolitik im deutschen Reich. *Berl.* 1889, *etc.* 8°.   8074. ff.

SCHEEL (H. v.) Storia della Economia politica. 1886, 87. 8°. Biblioteca dell' economista. Ser. 3. Vol. 11 and 12. Pt. 2.   8205. l.

SCHUELLER (R.) Die klassische Nationalökonomie. Zur Geschichte der Nationalökonomie seit Adam Smith. pp. 71. *Berl.* 1895. 8°.   Pam. 23.

STUART (C. A. V.) Ricardo en Marx. pp. 99. *'s Gravenh.* 1890. 8°.   08276. h. 14.

WALCKER (C.) A. Smith, der Begründer der modernen Nationalökonomie. pp. 50. *Berl.* 1890. 8°.   Pam. 7.

POLITICS. *See* GOVERNMENT.

POLO. BROWN (J. M.) Polo. 1891. 8°. Badminton Library.   7905. f.

See also GAMES.

POLYGAMY. *See* MARRIAGE.

POLYNESIA.
See PACIFIC OCEAN AND ISLANDS.

POLYTHEISM. *See* RELIGION.

POLYZOA. BRAEM (F.) Die Bryozoen des
süssen Wassers. 2 pt. 1890. 4°. LEUCKART
(R.) and CHUN (C.) Bibliotheca Zoologica.
Hft. 6.   7205. f.
LEVINSEN (G. M. R.) Polyzoa. 1891. 4°.
PETERSEN (G. C. J.) Det videnskabelige Ud-
bytte af Kanonbaaden "Hauchs" Togter. No. 4.
                     7299. l. 15.
See also VERMES.

POMMERANIA. BAIER (R.) Zwei stralsundische Croniken des 15ten Jahrhunderts.
pp. 47. *Stralsund,* 1893. 8°.   Pam. 28.
BLUEMCKE (O.) Pommern während des nordischen
siebenjährigen Krieges. pp. 445.
Stettin, 1890. 8°.   9076. cc. 1.
GAEHTGENS (P.) Die Beziehungen zwischen
Brandenburg und Pommern, 1440-70. pp. 152.
Giessen, 1890. 8°.   9386. f. 13.
KNOOP (O.) Allerhand Scherz, Reime und Erzäh-
lungen über pommersche Orte und ihre Be-
wohner. 1891. 8°. Ac. Stettin. *Gesellschaft
für Pommersche Geschichte.* Baltische Studien.
Jhrg. 41.   Ac. 7380/2.
RUDEL (R.) Die Lage Pommerns vom Beginn
des 30-jährigen Krieges, 1620-30. Ac. Stettin.
Gesellschaft für Pommersche Geschichte. Bal-
tische Studien. Jhrg. 40.   Ac. 7380/2.
WEHRMANN (M.) Aus Pommerns Vergangenheit.
pp. 135. *Stettin,* 1891. 8°.   9386. g. 3.

POMPEI. FURCHHEIM (F.) Bibliografia di
Pompei. pp. 118. *Napoli,* 1891. 8°.
                  011902. i. 13.
CERILLO (E.) Pompei. Dipinti murali scelti, *etc.*
pp. 20. *Napoli,* 1892. fol.   K.T.C. 17. a. 1.
KALINDERU (J.) Viaţa municipala la Pompei.
pp. 123. *Bucuresci,* 1890. 8°.   7706. e. 32.
MARRIOTT (H. P. F.) Facts about Pompei.
pp. 89. *Lond.* 1895. 4°.   7705. ee. 35.
MAU (A.) Führer durch Pompeji. pp. 103.
Neapel, 1893. 8°.   7706. a. 45.
—— Scavi di Pompei. 1890. 8°. Ac. Rome.
Istituto di Corrispondenza. Bullettino. Sezione
Romana. Vol. 5.   557. c.

PONDICHERRY.
See INDIA, *History, French in India.*

PONT-À-MOUSSON. MARTIN (E.) L'Université de Pont-à-Mousson. pp. 455.
Paris, 1891. 8°.   8356. cc. 25.

PONTARLIER. PONTARLIER. Inventaire
des archives communales antérieures à 1790.
pp. 145. 1889. 4°. Collection des inventaires-
sommaires.   1814-15. b., *etc.*

PONT D'AIN. CUAZ (E.) Histoire du château
de Pont-d'Ain. pp. 246. *Lyon,* 1892. 8°.
                  010171. k. 6.

PONTHIEU. LEDIEU (A.) Étude sur cinq
dénombrements de Seigneuries. 1889. 8°. Ac.
Abbeville. *Société d'Émulation.* Mémoires.
Sér. 4. Tom. 1.   Ac. 230.

PONTUS. REINACH (T.) Mithradates Eupator
König von Pontos. pp. 488. *Leipz.* 1895. 8°.
                  10606. h. 22.

PONY. *See* HORSE.

POPULATION. ANTEN (W. M. H.) Het
Nieuw-Malthusianisme. pp. 64.
Amersfoort, 1890. 8°.   Pam. 23.
BERTHEAU (C.) Essai sur les lois de la Popula-
tion. pp. 480. *Paris,* 1892. 8°. 8223. dh. 14.

POPULATION—*continued.*
DUMONT (A.) Essai sur la natalité dans le
Canton de Beaumont-Hague. pp. 49. 1893. 8°.
Ac. Paris. *Société d'Anthropologie.* Mémoires.
Sér. 3. Tom. 1.   Ac. 6227/2.
FETTER (F.) Versuch einer Bevölkerungslehre.
pp. 97. 1894. 8°. Ac. Halle. *Academia
Fridericiana.* CONRAD (J.) Sammlung na-
tionalökonomischer Abhandlungen. Bd. 7,
                  Ac. 2320.
FLORENCE. La Popolazione e la mortalità del
centennio 1791-1890. pp. 158.
Firenze, 1893. 8°.   8223. de. 9.
GEFFCKEN (F. H.) Politica della Popolazione.
1889. 8°. Biblioteca dell' economista. Sér. 3.
Vol. 13.   8205. l.
HOFFMANN (L.) Die Bevölkerungszunahme ist
keine Gefahr. pp. 155. *Stuttgart,* 1892. 8°.
                  08276. f. 67.
JANKE (H.) Die Uebervölkerung. pp. 160.
Leipz. 1893. 8°.   8277. ee. 46.
KÖRÖSI (J.) Demologische Beiträge zur Erwei-
terung der Natalitäts- und Fruchtbarkeits- Sta-
tistik. pp. 98. *Berl.* 1892. 8°. 8223. de. 41.
LAINÉ (A.) De la Dépopulation en France.
pp. 60. *Tours,* 1891. 12°. 08276. f. 24. (3.)
LAW. The law of Population. pp. 55.
Lond. 1893. 8°.   7641. e. 5. (3.)
LEROUX (A.) La question de la Dépopulation
devant l'Académie de Médecine. 1891. 8°. Ac.
Nantes. *Société Académique.* Annales. Sér. 7.
Vol. 2.   Ac. 387.
LEVASSEUR (É.) La Population et la richesse.
1891. 8°. Ac. Paris. *Conservatoire des Arts.*
Annales. Sér. 2. Tom. 3. Fasc. 2. Ac. 4415.
NEWSHOLME (A.) Elements of vital Statistics.
pp. 326. *Lond.* 1892. 8°.   08225. ee. 7.
NITTI (F. S.) La Popolazione e il sistema
sociale. pp. 212. *Torino,* 1894. 8°. 08277. g. 2.
—— Population and the social system.
pp. 192. *Lond.* 1894. 8°.   08276. e. 64.
ROBERTSON (J. M.) Over-population. pp. 24.
Lond. 1890. 8°.   07305. f. 5. (3.)
RUEMELIN (G.) Teoria della Popolazione.
1889. 8°. Biblioteca dell' economista. Sér. 3.
Vol. 13.   8205. l.
SMISSEN (É. v. d.) La Population. pp. 561.
Bruz. 1893. 8°.   8223. dh. 17.
WOODHULL MARTIN (V. C. W.) Rapid Multi-
plication of the unfit. pp. 39. *Lond.* 1891. 8°.
                  Pam. 37.
See also POLITICAL ECONOMY : STATISTICS.

PORCHESTER CASTLE. PORCHESTER
CASTLE. History of Portchester Castle.
Landport, 1880. 8°.   10348. bbbb. 14. (3.)

PORLOCK. HOOK (W.) History of the Church
of Porlock. pp. 95. *Lond.* 1893. 8°. 4707. aaaa. 28.

PORT ELIZABETH. Guide to Port Elizabeth. pp. 98. *Cape Town.* 1894. 8°. 010096. e. 69.

PORTLAND. PORTLAND. *Urban Sanitary
Authority.* Advantages of Portland Harbour as
a steam-packet station. pp. 23.
Portland, 1892. obl. 4°.   8806. b. 41.
MUDGE (R. C.) Coast Gems. pp. 23.
Weymouth, 1895, 4°.   Pam. 90.

PORTOGRUARO. DEGANI (E.) Il Comune
di Portogruaro, 1140-1420. pp. 177.
Udine, 1891. 8°.   10130. c. 2.

PORTO MAURIZIO. *Consiglio Provinciale.*
Atti. Sessioni, 1891. pp. 419. *Oneglia,* 1892. 8°.
                  5359. ee. 33.

PORTO RICO. *See* PUERTO RICO.
PORT PHILLIP BAY. PORT PHILLIP
BAY. Illustrated Handbook. pp. 52.
Melbourne, 1880. 8°.   Pam. 87.

PORTRAITS. Ac. New York. *Grolier Club.* Catalogue of an exhibition of engraved Portraits of Women Writers. pp. 24. *N.Y.* 1895. 12°.   Pam. 24.

—— London. *Royal College of Surgeons.* Catalogue of Portraits and Busts. pp. 68. *Lond.* 1892. 8°.   7808. cc. 2.

—— Paris. *École Spéciale des Beaux-Arts.* Salles des Portraits. pp. 49. *Paris*, 1894. 8°.   7858. a. 42.

BRUCKMANN (F.) Griechische und römische Porträts. *München*, 1891, *etc.* fol.   1703. c.

CASSELL (J.) Universal Portrait Gallery. *Lond.* 1894, *etc.* 8°.   10600. f.

DAYOT (A.) Napoléon raconté par l'image. pp. 497. *Paris*, 1895. 4°.   K.T.C. 26. b. 18.

EBERS (G.) Eine Gallerie antiker Porträts. pp. 41. *Berl.* 1889. 8°.   7807. k. 17. (4.)

—— Antike Porträts. Die hellenistischen Bildnisse aus den Fajjûm. pp. 73. *Leipz.* 1893, 8°.   07703. h. 1. (13.)

ENGLISH POETS. Portraits of English poets. *Bristol*, 1891. 8°.   K.T.C. 6. b. 7.

EHRLICH (A.) Berühmte Geiger. pp. 316. *Leipz.* 1893. 8°.   10601. df. 2.

HAMERTON (P. G.) Man in Art. Studies in art, portrait and genre. pp. 344. *Lond.* 1892. 4°.   K.T.C. 3. b. 17.

MANUEL. Manuel de bibliographie et d'Iconographie des femmes célèbres. pp. 895. *Turin*, 1892. 8°.   10601. ee. 17.

MARIANI (A.) Figures contemporaines tirées de l'album Mariani. *Paris*, 1894, *etc.* fol. 10601. g.

MUSICIANS. Celebrated Musicians. Collection of portraits. pp. 40. *Dresd.* 1883. 4°. 10602. m. 7.

O'DONOGHUE (F. M.) Catalogue of Portraits of Queen Elizabeth. pp. 121. *Lond.* 1894. 8°.   7858. l. 17.

PARIS. *Association des Journalistes parisiens.* Catalogue de l'Exposition des portraits des écrivains du siècle. pp. 267. *Paris*, 1893. 12°.   7854. aaa. 40.

ROSE (J. A.) Collection of engraved Portraits. 2 vol. *Lond.* 1894. 4°.   K.T.C. 37. b. 2.

SCHLICHTEGROLL (C. F. v.) Portrait Gallerie der regierenden Fürsten und Fürstinnen. *Stuttgart*, 1890, *etc.* fol.   1764. c.

SEIDLITZ (W. v.) Allgemeines historisches Porträtwerk. 12 Bde. *München*, 1884-90. 4°.   1765. a. 19.

TIFFIN (W. F.) Catalogue of a collection of English portraits in mezzo-tint. pp. 136. *Salisbury*, 1883. 8°.   7858. gg. 19.

See also PRINTS.

PORT ROYAL, Jamaica. *See* JAMAICA.

PORTS, HARBOURS AND DOCKS.
BAILEY (C. H.) Tables of Distances from port to port. pp. 380. *Newport*, 1895. *obl.* 16°.   10004. a. 6.

BELLET (D.) Les grands Ports maritimes. pp. 186. *Paris*, 1893. 16°.   8807. a. 55.

BENNASSI-DESPLANTES (F. J.) Les cinq Ports militaires de la France. pp. 157. *Limoges*, 1894. 8°.   10174. g. 29.

BOOTH (C.) Dock and Wharf labour. *Lond.* 1892. *obl.* fol.   14001. c. 23.

CARVER (T. G.) Expenses at a Port of refuge. pp. 16. *Lond.* 1892. 8°.   6190. cc. 4. (5.)

COLSON (C.) Notes on Docks and dock construction. pp. 426. *Lond.* 1894. 8°. Longmans' Civil Engineering Series.   8768. f.

CORNAGLIA (P.) Sul regime delle spiagge e sulla regolazione dei Porti. pp. 569. *Torino*. 1891, 8°.   8777. g. 4.

PORTS, HARBOURS, etc.—*continued*
CROWTHER (F. J.) Orders of the Board of Trade in reference to Piers and Harbours. pp. 48. *Lond.* 1893. 8°.   6426. aaaa. 18.

G. B. & I. *Hydrographic Office.* Additions and corrections to Dock book 1890. pp. 25. *Lond.* 1893. fol.   10497. ff. 16.

LAROCHE (F.) Ports maritimes. 4 tom. *Paris*, 1893. 8°. and 4°. LECHALAS (M. C.) Encyclopédie des Travaux Publics.   012216. i. and n. 2.

SHIELD (W.) Principles of Harbour construction. pp. 299. 1895. 8°. Longmans' Civil Engineering Series.   8768. f.

VOLPRIGNANO (P. T.) The future of the Port of London. pp. 8. *Lond.* 1890. fol.   Pam. 79.

PORTSMOUTH AND SOUTHSEA, Hants. CHARPENTIER (W. H.) Guide to Southsea, *etc.* pp. 118. *Portsmouth*, 1893. 12°.   010358. e. 24.

HARPER (C. G.) The Portsmouth Road and its tributaries. pp. 372. *Lond.* 1895. 8°.   010358. h. 24.

PORTSMOUTH. Up to Date Guide for Portsmouth and Southsea. *Southsea*, 1893, *etc.* 8°.   10351. ccc. 4.

PORTSMOUTH, New Hampshire.
ALDRICH (T. B.) An old Town by the Sea. pp. 128. *Bost.* 1893. 8°.   10410. bb. 30.

PORTUGAL.

Antiquities.

BOUTROUE (A.) Rapport sur une mission archéologique en Portugal. pp. 57. *Paris*, 1893. 8°.   07703. i. 1. (16.)

VILHENA BARBOSA (I. de) Monumentos de Portugal. pp. 500. *Lisboa*, 1886. 8°.   10162. f. 1.

Colonies.

ANDRADE CORVO (J. de) Estudos sobre as Provincias ultramarinas. 4 vol. *Lisboa*, 1883-87. 8°.   8155. ee. 14.

D'ORSEY (A. J. D.) Portuguese Discoveries, dependencies and missions. pp. 434. *Lond.* 1893. 8°.   4767. d. 13.

P.P. *Lisbon.* As Colonias portuguezas. *Lisboa*, 1883-92. fol.   P.P. 9017. b.

PINHEIRO CHAGAS (M.) As Colonias portuguezas no seculo XIX. pp. 228. *Lisboa*, 1890. 8°.   8155. ee. 10.

See also infra: Politics, Foreign: AFRICA, Colonisation, Portuguese: GOA: MACAO: MADEIRA. For the early voyages and discoveries of the Portuguese, *see* VOYAGES.

Constitution and Government.

PORTUGAL. *Cortes.* Documentos para a historia das Cortes. *Lisboa*, 1889, *etc.* 8°.   9195. i.

TAVARES DE MEDEIROS (J. J.) Das Staatsrecht Portugal's. pp. 145. 1892. 8°. MARQUARDSEN (H.) Handbuch des oeffentlichen Rechts. Bd. 4. Hlbbnd 1. Abt. 9.   6006. k.

History.

ALVES NOGUEIRA (M. T.) Evoluções da civilisação em Portugal. pp. 129. *Paris*. 1893. 8°.   9195. h. 3.

LE GRAND (M.) Le Portugal. Notice historique au point de vue du développement de ses relations avec la France. pp. 64. *Fécamp*, 1895. 8°.   9195. g. 11.

LEITE MACHADO BASTOS (A.) Glorias nacionaes. pp. 328. *Lisboa*, 1891. 8°.   9195. aa. 2.

P.P. *Paris.* Revue hispanique. *Paris*, 1894, *etc.* 8°.   P.P. 4331. aea.

PORTUGAL.—History—*continued.*

RODRIGUES CORDEIRO (A. X.) Factos de historia portugueza. 2 tom. *Lisboa*, 1889, 90. 8°.
     9195. de. 1.

OLIVEIRA MARTINS (J. P.) Historia de Portugal. 2 tom. *Lisboa*, 1894. 8°.   9195. de. 4.

SALISBURY (W. A.) Portugal and its people. pp. 334. *Lond.* 1893. 8°.   9195. de. 2.

SILVERCRUYS (É.) Le Portugal. pp. 169. *Lille*, 1892. 8°.   9195. bb. 20.

OLIVEIRA MARTINS (J. P.) Os Filhos de D. João I. pp. 471. *Lisboa*, 1891. 8°. 9195. e. 4.

MENEZES (C. J. de) A Inquisição em Portugal. 2 tom. *Porto*, 1893. 8°.   4625. a. 35.

—— Os Jesuitas e o Marquez de Pombal. 2 vol. *Porto*, 1893. 8°.   4625. a. 36.

CORNIDE DE SAAVEDRA (J.) Estado de Portugal en el año de 1800. 2 tom. 1894. 8°. Ac. Madrid. *R. Academia de la Historia.* Memorial. Tom. 26, 27.   Ac. 6630.

See also PENINSULAR WAR.

Law.

PORTUGAL. Code Civil portugais. pp. 483. *Paris*, 1894. 8°.   5384. ff. 11.

LABRA (R. M. de) La Legislación portuguesa contemporánea. pp. 212. *Madrid*, 1890, *etc.* 8°.   6025. de. 2.

Politics, *Domestic.*

FERNANDES (J.) O Portugal jacobino. pp. 202. *Braga*, 1893. 8°.   8042. aaa. 36.

GUERREIRO (D. A.) Portugal agonisante. pp. 88. *Vianna*, 1893. 8°.   8042. aa. 26.

PORTUGUESE REPUBLICANS. Aos republicanos portuguezes. 1890. *s. sh.* fol.   1240. k. (18.)

VÉZELAY (R. de) Le Portugal politique. pp. 154. *Paris*, 1890. 8°.   8042. g. 20.

Politics, *Foreign.*

PORTUGAL. *Ministerio dos Negocios Estrangeiros.* Documentos. Negocios de África. Correspondencia com a Inglaterra. pp. 269. *Lisboa*, 1890. fol.   8028. g. 16.

—— Documentos. Negociações do tratado com a Inglaterra [of 20 Aug. 1890]. pp. 227. *Lisboa*, 1890. fol.   8028. g. 17.

—— Documentos. Negociações do tratado com a Inglaterra. IV. pp. 262. *Lisboa*, 1891. 4°.   8028. g. 20.

Ac. Lisbon. *Sociedade de Geographia.* O Ultimatum britannico. Correspondencia. pp. 250. *Lisboa*, 1890. 8°.   Ac. 6020/6.

BARJONA DE FREITAS (A. C.) A Questão ingleza. Discurso. pp. 24. *Lisboa*, 1891. 8°. Pam. 71.

BARROS GOMES (H. de) As Negociações com a Inglaterra no periodo de 1886 a 1889. Discurso. pp. 59. *Lisboa*, 1891. 8°.   Pam. 71.

GROMIER (M. A.) Portugal, Angleterre & France. pp. 48. *Paris*, 1890. 16°   Pam. 67.

HINTZE RIBEIRO (E. R.) Portugal e a Inglaterra. Discurso. pp. 48. *Lisboa*, 1891. 8°. Pam. 71.

LISBOA (C.) Apreciações ao Tratado anglo-portuguez, 1890. *Lisboa*, 1890. 8°. 8028. de. 31. (7.)

MELLO (C. de) A Questão ingleza. O tratado. *Lisboa*, 1890, *etc.* 8°.   8027. bb. 11.

OLIVEIRA MARTINS (J. P.) Carteira de um jornalista. Portugal em Africa; o conflicto anglo-portuguez. pp. 240. *Porto*, 1891. 8°.   8022. aaa. 3.

TESTA (C.) Incidentes da politica externa de Portugal. pp. 144. *Lisboa*, 1890. 8°. 8042. g. 19.

BRAZIL. *Ministerio dos Negocios Estrangeiros.* Correspondence in regard to the surrender of insurgent refuges on board Portuguese corvettes. pp. 38. *Rio de J.* 1894. 8°.   Pam. 65.

PORTUGAL.—Politics—*continued.*

CARQUEJA (B.) Conflict diplomatique entre le Portugal et le Brésil. pp. 38. *Porto*, 1894. 8°.   Pam. 65.

MARTENS FERRÃO (J. B. de) La question entre le Portugal et le Brésil. pp. 16. *Rome*, 1894. 8°.   Pam. 32.

PORTUGAL. Portugal e Brazil. Conflicto diplomatico. 5 vol. *Lisboa*, 1894, 95. 8°. 8180. h. 35.

Topography : Social Life.

BOUTROUE (A.) Une heure en Sicile. Un coup d'œil sur le Portugal. pp. 57. *Paris*, 1895. 8°.   10107. ff. 29.

DESCAMPS (M.) Souvenirs de Portugal. pp. 336. *Lille*, 1892. 8°.   10160. c. 2.

GERMOND DE LAVIGNE (L. A. G.) Espagne et Portugal. Guide Joanne. pp. 750. *Paris*, 1893. 12°.   10160. bbb. 14.

LABRA (R. M. de) Portugal contemporaneo. pp. 292. *Madrid*, 1889. 8°.   10162. aaa. 5.

LORING (G. B.) A year in Portugal. pp. 313. *N.Y.* 1891. 8°.   10162. g. 12.

MORRIS (M. O'C.) Peeps at Portugal. pp. 129. *Lond.* 1891. 8°.   10162. aaa. 1.

NOLHAC (S. de) En Portugal. pp. 290. *Paris*, 1891. 12°.   10162. aaa. 3.

O'SHEA (H.) Guide to Spain and Portugal. pp. 563. *Lond.* 1895. 8°.   2362. b. 6.

P.P. *Oporto.* Revista lusitana. *Porto*, 1887, *etc.* 8°.   P.P. 4979.

QUILLINAN (D.) Journal of a few months' residence in Portugal. pp. 288. *Lond.* 1895. 8°.   10161. bb. 22.

ROSNY (L. L. de) Taureaux et mantilles. pp. 372. *Paris*, 1894. 12°.   10160. aaa. 22.

SAINT-VICTOR (G. de) Portugal. Souvenirs et impressions. pp. 264. *Paris*, 1891. 12°.   10162. aaa. 2.

TODA (E.) Guía de España y Portugal. pp. 482. *Madrid*, 1892. 8°.   10161. aa. 14.

Trade and Finance.

CORUCHE (de) *Viscount.* Problema financeiro. pp. 87. *Lisboa*, 1895. 8°.   Pam. 23.

GIACARDY (E.) Le Portugal au point de vue commercial. pp. 30. *Paris*, 1890. 8°. Pam. 23.

LE GRAND (M.) Le Portugal. Notice commerciale au point de vue du développement de ses relations avec la France. pp. 64. *Fécamp*, 1895. 8°.   9195. g. 11.

BIHOURD (G.) Les conditions du travail en Portugal. 1890. 8°. FRANCE. *Ministère des Affaires étrangères.* Recueil de rapports, *etc.* 08276. k.

PORTUGUESE LANGUAGE. CASTRO DE LA FAYETTE (L.) Novo Vocabulario da lingua portugueza. pp. 1172. *Paris*, 1889. 8°.   12941. aa. 48.

—— Novo Diccionario inglez-portuguez e portuguez-inglez. 2 pt. *Pariz*, 1892. 16°.   12941. b. 43.

MICHAELIS (H.) New Dictionary of the Portuguese and English languages. 2 vol. *Lond.* 1893. 8°.   12943. dd. 3.

ENENKEL (A.) and SOUZA PINTO ( ) Novo Diccionario portuguez-allemão e allemão-portuguez. 2 pt. *Paris*, 1894. 8°.   12943. a. 50.

FOULCHÉ-DELBOSC (R.) Abrégé de Grammaire portugaise. pp. 270. *Paris*, 1894. 8°.   12942. aaa. 44.

GRAUERT (E. F.) New Method for learning Portuguese. pp. 346. *Lond.* 1892. 8°.   12943. c. 28.

MONTEIRO LEITE (F. J.) Subsidios para o estudo da lingua portugueza. pp. 280. *Porto*, 1882. 8°.   12941. d. 6.

PORTUGUESE LANGUAGE—continued.

WALL (C. H.) Grammar of the Portuguese language. pp. 256. *Lond.* 1892. 8°.
12942. cc. 13.

HOSSFELD (C.) Portuguese Dialogues. pp. 150. *Lond.* 1894. 16°. 12942. a. 49.

PORTUGUESE LITERATURE. GARCIA

PERES (D.) Catalogo de los Autores portugueses que escribieron en castellano. pp. 660.
Madrid, 1890. 8°. 11899. h. 41.

BRAGA (T.) Curso de historia da Litteratura portugueza. pp. 411. *Lisboa,* 1885. 8°. 011850. k. 6.

—— Questões de Litteratura portugueza.
pp. 408. *Lisboa,* 1881. 8°. 011850. k. 7.

—— Camões e o Sentimento nacional. pp. 324. *Porto,* 1891. 8°. 011850. f. 56.

—— As modernas ideas na Litteratura portugueza. 2 vol. *Porto,* 1892. 8°. 011850. f. 38.

P.P. *Oporto.* Revista lusitana.
Porto, 1887, *etc.* 8°. P.P. 4979.

—— *Paris.* Revue hispanique.
Paris, 1894, *etc.* 8°. P.P. 4331. aea.

POSEN. Ac. Posen. *Historische Gesellschaft.*

Zeitschrift. *Posen,* 1885, *etc.* 8°. Ac. 7365.

—— Sonder-Veröffentlichungen.
Posen, 1892, *etc.* 8°. Ac. 7365/2.

POSITIVISM. AUDIFFRENT (G.) Centenaire

de la Fondation de l'École Polytechnique. A. Comte sa plus puissante émanation. pp. 258.
Paris, 1894. 8°. 010662. i. 31.

BEESLY (E. S.) Some public aspects of Positivism. pp. 32. *Lond.* 1881. 8°. Pam. 49.

BLAKE (W. F.) Some neglected passages on the Culte historique from Comte's Appeal. pp. 32.
Lond. 1890. 8°. 8463. d. 38. (10.)

BROGLIE (E. de) La réaction contre le Positivisme. pp. 297. *Paris,* 1894. 8°. 3900. c. 29.

COMTE (I. A. M. F. X.) Système de Politique positive. *Paris,* 1890, *etc.* 8°. 8009. k.

—— Religion of Humanity. Vol. 1.
Lond. 1891. 8°. 8466. ff. 38.

—— Der Positivismus in seinem Wesen und seiner Bedeutung. pp. 384. *Leipz.* 1894. 8°.
8463. e. 33.

—— The Catechism of Positive Religion.
pp. 304. *Lond.* 1891. 8°. 3554. f. 15.

—— The Positivist Calendar of 558 Worthies.
pp. 16. *Lond.* 1894. 8°. 8463. a. 5.

GRUBER (H.) A. Comte, sa vie, sa doctrine.
pp. 343. *Paris,* 1892. 8°. 010662. ff. 36.

—— Le Positivisme depuis Comte jusqu'à nos jours. pp. 528. *Paris,* 1893. 8°. 8462. bb. 30.

HARRISON (F.) New Year's address to the Positivists of New York. pp. 8. *Lond.* 1886. 8°.
8470. f. 9. (3.)

—— Marriage : discourse to the Positivist Society. pp. 29. *Lond.* 1887. 8°. Pam. 37.

—— A New Era. Address. pp. 15.
Lond. 1889. 8°. 8470. f. 9. (7.)

—— The presentation of Infants. Discourse.
pp. 20. *Lond.* 1891. 8°. Pam. 49.

—— The New Calendar of great men. Biographies of the 558 worthies. pp. 644.
Lond. 1892. 8°. 10601. ee. 7.

HIGGINSON (C. G.) The more excellent Way. Address. pp. 11. *Lond.* 1889. 8°. Pam. 49.

HOLLANDER (B.) The Positive Philosophy of the mind. pp. 11. *Lond.* 1891. 8°. Pam. 49.

HUTTON (H. D.) Comte, the man and the founder. pp. 47. *Lond.* 1891. 8°. 10601. e. 5. (5.)

—— Comte's Life and work. Address. pp. 29.
Lond. 1892. 8°. 8461. b. 28. (7.)

KAINES (J.) The Beauty of holiness. Discourse.
pp. 18. *Lond.* 1884. 8°. Pam. 49.

POSITIVISM—continued.

KAINES (J.) Our daily Faults and Failings.
pp. 13. *Lond.* 1891. 8°. 8461. b. 28. (1.)

LAGARRIGUE (J.) Apostolat positiviste. Le faux et le vrai Positivisme. pp. 47.
Paris, 1892. 8°. 8461. b. 28. (8.)

—— L'Apostolat positiviste à Paris. pp. 44.
Paris, 1893. 8°. Pam. 93.

LEMOS (M.) Religion de l'Humanité. L'Apostolat positiviste au Brésil.
Rio de J. 1884, *etc.* 8°. 8467. aa.

—— Le Calendrier positiviste et le Ministre des Finances de Brésil. pp. 7. *Rio de J.* 1890. 8°.
8461. b. 28. (4.)

LONDON. *London Positivist Committee.* Report, 1881-89. *Lond.* 1882-90. 8°. 8470. f. 9. (10.)

P.P. *London.* The Positivist Review.
Lond. 1893, *etc.* 8°. P.P. 5939. n.

PERCIVAL (P.) The position of Positivism.
pp. 8. *Manch.* 1891. 8°. 4371. g. 1. (5.)

POMPERY (É. de) La Morale naturelle et la Religion de l'Humanité. pp. 298. *Paris,* 1891. 8°.
8409. cc. 20.

THAMIN (R.) Éducation et Positivisme. pp. 186.
Paris, 1892. 12°. 8311. aa. 19.

POSTS : POSTAGE AND OTHER STAMPS.

Posts : General.

GALLOIS (E.) La Poste et les moyens de communication à travers les siècles. pp. 382.
Paris, 1894. 8°. 08247. eee. 5.

MAURY (L.) Les Postes romaines. Notice sur la service des postes chez différentes peuples anciens et modernes. pp. 112. *Paris,* 1890. 18°.
7708. a. 64.

RUEBSAM (J.) Zur Geschichte des internationalen Postwesens im 16. und 17. Jahrhunderte.
1892. 8°. Ac. Bonn. *Görres-Gesellschaft.* Historisches Jahrbuch. Bd. 13. Hft. 1.
Ac. 2026/3.

SCHRANKA (E. M.) Datenzieger der Weltpost-Geschichte. pp. 212. *Leipz.* 1893. 8°.
08247. df. 1.

TRAVERS (A.) Vocabulaire postal et télégraphique anglais-français et français-anglais.
pp. 346. *Paris,* 1894. 8°. 8247. aaa. 41.

VEREDARIUS. Das Buch von der Weltpost.
pp. 367. *Berl.* 1894. 4°. 8248. k. 3.

WEITHASE (H.) Geschichte des Weltpostvereins.
pp. 87. *Strassburg,* 1893. 8°. 08247. g. 3.

Great Britain and Ireland and Colonies.

HYDE (J. W.) The Post in grant and farm.
pp. 355. *Lond.* 1894. 8°. 08235. e. 11.

JOYCE (H.) History of the Post Office to 1836.
pp. 460. *Lond.* 1893. 8°. 08247. g. 2.

NORWAY (A. H.) History of the Post-Office packet service, 1793-1815. pp. 312.
Lond. 1895. 8°. 08247. ff. 30.

G. B. & I. *Post Office.* Account of the celebration of the Jubilee of inland Penny Postage.
pp. 331. *Lond.* 1891. 8°. 8247. dd. 23.

HYDE (J. W.) A Hundred Years by Post.
pp. 144. *Lond.* 1891. 8°. 8247. bbb. 40.

CHALMERS (P.) Adhesive Postage Stamp. Petition to the Lords of H.M. Treasury. pp. 35.
Lond. 1891. 8°. 08247. ff. 22. (3.)

—— Adhesive Postage Stamp. Removal of official documents from H.M Treasury by Sir R. Hill. pp. 20. *Lond.* 1891. 8°. 08247. ff. 22. (4.)

FELLOWS (E. C.) Truth v. Fiction, re the Chalmers' Claim. pp. 15. *Lond.* 1892. 8°.
08247. ff. 22. (5.)

BAINES (F. E.) Forty years at the Post Office.
2 vol, *Lond.* 1895. 8°. 08247. ee. 4.

POSTS.—Great Britain, etc.—*continued.*

BAINES (F. E.) On the Track of the Mail-coach·
pp. 351. *Lond.* 1895. 8°. 08247. ee. 6.

BEADON (R. J.) Uniform imperial Postage.
pp. 56. *Lond.* 1891. 8°. 08227. i. 30. (3.)

G. B. & I. *Post Office.* Foreign and Colonial
Post: principal regulations. pp. 78.
Lond. 1892. 8°. 8247. aaa. 39.

MILLAR (F.) Evils of state trading as illustrated
by the Post Office. 1891. 8°. MACKAY (T.)
Plea for Liberty. 8276. g. 44.

P.P. *London.* G.P.O. Mail Drivers' despatch.
Lee Green, 1892, etc. 4°. 2175.

TOMBS (R. C.) London Postal service of to-day.
pp. 136. *Lond.* 1891. 8°. 8247. aaa. 36.

BAUER (W.) AND Co. List of Australian and New
Zealand mails. *Lond.* 1891. *s. sh.* fol.
1865. c. 5. (1.)

ROYLE (A.) and WILLAN ( ) Table of Australian and New Zealand mails. 1892. *s. sh.* fol.
1882. d. 1. (93.)

P.P. *Cape Town.* The Post Office guide.
Cape Town, 1892, etc. 8°. P.P. 2579. o.

Europe.

KOSEL (M.) Österreichische Postvorschriften.
Wien, 1893, etc. 8°. 08247. ff.

WANKA (J.) Das Postwesen in Oesterreich.
Prag, 1891, etc. 8°. 08247. g.

ARNOUX (J.) Administrations des Postes. Conditions d'admission à tous les emplois. pp. 81.
Lille, 1895. 8°. 08247. ff. 29.

FRAULT (A.) Manuel postal. pp. 544.
Paris, 1893. 8°. 08247. ff. 25.

JACCOTTEY (P.) Traité de Législation et d'exploitation postales. pp. 1017. *Paris,* 1891. 8°.
8247. g. 38.

HULL (C. H.) Die deutsche Reichspacket-post.
pp. 161. 1892. 8°. Ac. Halle. *Academia
Fridericiana.* CONRAD (J.) Sammlung statistischer Abhandlungen. Bd. 8. Hft. 3.
Ac. 2320.

MITTELSTEIN (M.) Beiträge zum Postrecht.
pp. 144. *Berl.* 1891. 8°. 8247. e. 44.

MOLLI (G.) La Marina postale. pp. 205.
Milano, 1893. 8°. 8807. dd. 40.

SWITZERLAND. *Postdepartment* Post- und Telegraphenwesen. pp. 125. 1895. 8°. Ac. Berne.
*Centralkommission für schweizerische Landes-
kunde.* Bibliographie, *etc.* Fasc. v. Ac. 3147.

United States of America.

CUSHING (M.) Story of our Post Office. pp. 1034.
Bost. 1893. 8°. 08247. g. 1.

Postage and other Stamps, *Collections of,*
etc.

SUPPANTSCHITSCH (V.) Bibliographie zugleich
Nachschlagebuch der deutschen philatelisti-
schen Literatur. pp. 748. *München,* 1892. 8°.
011900. h. 18.

BARBARIN (J.) Nouveau catalogue de Timbres-
poste. pp. 351. *Paris,* 1895, 8°. 08247. eee. 8.

BELIN (M.) Catalogue descriptif illustré; Prix-
courant de tous les Timbres. pp. 360.
Brux. 1893. 8°. 08247. ff. 28.

BOSSAKIEWICZ (S.) Manuel du Collectionneur de
Timbres-poste. pp. 254. *Paris,* 1894. 12°.
08247. eee. 6.

BUTLER, *Brothers.* "Excelsior" Postage Stamp
album. *Lond.* 1893. 4°. 8247. cc. 48.

—— Oblong series. pp. 448. *Oxf.* 1894. *obl.* 4°.
1879. a. 6.

EARÉE (R. B.) Album Weeds; how to detect
forged stamps. pp. 726. *Lond.* 1892. 8°.
08247. ff. 23.

POSTS.—Postage Stamps. etc.—*continued.*

EPHEM. The Philatelist's Almanack.
Lond. 1892, etc. 16°. P.P. 2491. zb.

EVANS (E. B.) Stamps and stamp collecting.
pp. 66. *Lond.* 1894. 8°. 08247. ff. 26.

GIBBONS (E. S.) Descriptive catalogue and price
list of Postage Stamps. *Lond.* 1891. 8°.
08247. h. 7.

—— Imperial Postage Stamp album.
Lond. 1892, etc. 4°. 8247. g. 41.

—— Stanley Gibbons Philatelic handbooks.
Lond. 1893, etc. 8°. 08247. g.

HEALEY (E.) Postage Stamp album. pp. 100.
Lond. 1891. 4°. 8247. bbb. 39.

KALCKHOFF (F.) Illustrated catalogue of all
known reprints of Postage Stamps. pp. 74.
Lond. 1892. 8°. 8247. aaa. 37.

LINCOLN (W.) Catalogue of foreign, colonial
and British Postage Stamps. pp. 148.
Lond. 1892. 8°. 08247. ff. 3.

MAURY (A.) Catalogue de Timbres poste. 3 pt.
Paris, 1889–91. 8°. Pam. 23.

MOENS (J. B.) Catalogue prix courant de Timbres-poste. *Brux.* 1891, etc. 8°. 08247. h. 3.

P.P. *Birmingham.* Philatelic Chronicle.
Birmingham, 1891, etc. 8°.
P.P. 1424. apb. and 2140.

P.P. *Forest Gate.* The Stamp collector.
Forest Gate, 1891–93. 8°. P.P. 1424. age.

—— *Geneva.* Revue philatélique suisse. Année I. II. *Genève,* 1891–92. 8°. P.P. 1424. hi.

—— *London.* The Fiscal Philatelist and revenue stamp guide. *Lond.* 1892, etc. 8°
PP. 1424. aqc.

—— The London Philatelist. *Lond.* 1892, etc. 8°.
P.P. 1424. aqb.

—— The Stamp News. A monthly journal.
Lond. 1882, etc. 4°. P.P. 1424. aqa. and 2067.

—— *Munich.* Die Postwertzeichenkunde.
München, 1891, etc. 8°. P.P. 1424. hfc. and 750.

—— *Salisbury.* Philatelic Journal of Great
Britain. *Salisbury,* 1891, etc. 8°.
P.P. 1424. aot.

—— *Walthamstow.* Stamp Collectors' Herald.
Walthamstow, 1893, etc. 8°. 1866. a. 14.

PIET-LATAUDRIE (F.) Les réimpressions de
Timbres-poste, timbres-taxe, télégraphe, fiscaux
etc. pp. 78. *Niort,* 1894. 8°. 08247. ee. 2.

ROBERT (V.) Catalogue de tous les Timbres-
poste émis depuis 1840 jusqu'à 1894. pp. 349.
Paris, 1895. 8°. 08247. ff. 27.

MORLEY (W.) Catalogue and price list of Stamps
of Great Britain. pp. 140. *Lond.* 1895. 8°.
8247. c. 28.

SKIPTON (S. C.) British Empire Postage Stamp
album. *Salisbury,* 1895, etc. *obl.* 4°.
1879. b. 4.

WESTOBY (W. A. S.) Catalogue of all the Postage
Stamps of the United Kingdom. pp. 94.
Lond. 1891. 8°. 8247. de. 28.

EVANS (E. B.) Description of the Mulready
envelope. pp. 240. *Lond.* 1891. 8°. 8247. de. 30.

LUNDY (F. G. C.) Embossed deed Stamps of
Great Britain. pp. 14. *Lond.* 1893. 4°.
Pam. 23.

LONDON. *Philatelic Society.* The Postage stamps,
envelopes, wrappers, *etc.* of British India and
Ceylon. pp. 100. *Lond.* 1892. fol.
08247. h. 8.

WALKER (L. H. J.) and MOENS (J. B.) Les
Timbres de Natal. pp. 60 *Brux.* 1883. 8°.
08247. ff. 5.

HULL (A. F. B.) The Stamps of Tasmania.
pp. 136. *Lond.* 1890. 8°. 8247. g. 39.

POSTS.—Postage Stamps, etc.—_continued._

LONDON. _Philatelic Society._ The Postage Stamps, envelopes, wrappers, _etc.,_ of the British West Indies, _etc._ pp. 180. _Lond._ 1891. 8°.
8247. g. 40.

MOENS (J. B.) Les Timbres de Belgique. 2 tom. _Brux._ 1880. 8°. 08247. ff. 4.

SALEFRANQUE (L.) Le Timbre à travers l'histoire. pp. 126. _Rouen,_ 1890. 4°. 7709. i. 18.

LEROY (L.) Histoire du Timbre-poste français. pp. 204. _Paris,_ 1891. 8°. 08247. e. 1.

MOENS (J. B.) Catalogue de Timbres-poste locaux de l'Empire d'Allemagne. pp. 76. _Brux._ 1891. 8°. 08247. eee. 3.

—— Les Timbres de Prusse. pp. 142. _Brux._ 1887. 8°. 08247. ff. 20.

—— Timbres des duchés de Schleswig, Holstein & Lauenbourg. pp. 94. _Brux._ 1884. 8°.
08247. ff. 6.

—— Timbres de l'office Tour et Taxis. pp. 107. _Brux._ 1880. 8°. 08247. ff. 13.

—— Les Timbres du Wurtemberg. 2 tom. _Brux._ 1881. 8°. 08247. ff. 11.

FRIEDERICH (R.) Die Postwertzeichen Spaniens & seiner Kolonien. 2 pt. _Berl._ 1894. 8°.
8247. ee. 37.

MOENS (J. B.) Histoire des Timbres-poste en Espagne. pp. 564. _Brux._ 1891. 8°. 08247. h. 2.

—— Timbres d'Égypte. pp. 116. _Brux._ 1880. 8°.
08247. ff. 12.

COSTER (C. H.) Les postes privées des États-Unis. 2 vol. _Brux._ 1882, 85. 8°. 08247. ff. 18.

TIFFANY (J. K.) Les Timbres des États-Unis. 3 tom. _Brux._ 1883. 8°. 08247. ff. 7.

—— History of the Postage Stamps of the U.S. pp. 272. _St. Louis,_ 1887. 8°. 8247. cc. 45.

U.S. _National Philatelical Society._ The Stamped Envelopes, wrappers and sheets of the U.S. pp. 126. _N.Y._ 1892. 8°. 8247. g. 42.

MOENS (J. B.) Timbres de la République Argentine. 2 tom. _Brux._ 1882. 8°. 08247. ff. 19.

AC. Lima. _Sociedad Filatélica Sud-Americana._ Catalogue des Timbres-poste, enveloppes et cartes postales dans la République du Pérou. pp. 52. _Lima,_ 1887. 8°. 08247. ff. 21

POTATOE. DOBBIE (J.) Instructions for the propagation and culture of the Potato. pp. 16. _Rothesay,_ 1893. 8°. 7074. e. 10. (10.)

POTATO. The best Potato: how to grow it. pp. 52. 1891. 8°. P.P. Dublin. _Weekly Free-man._ Freeman Handbook. No. 6.
07944. ee. 10.

VEITCH (R.) AND SON. Report upon experiments made for the prevention of Potato disease. pp. 15. _Plymouth,_ 1892. 8°. 7073. de. 13. (13.)

WARD (H. W.) Potato Culture for the million. pp. 24. _Lond._ 1891. 8°. 7074. i. 8. (11.)

WARNER (W. H.) Potato Culture. pp. 22. _Lond._ 1892. 8°. 7074. i. 8. (14.)

WILTSHIRE. _Technical Education Committee._ Potato Culture and disease prevention. pp. 33. _Lond._ 1893. 4°. 7054. g. 17.
See also GARDENING.

POTTERY. _See_ CERAMICS.

POULTRY. ATKINSON (H.) The old English Game-fowl. pp. 66. _Lond._ 1891. 8°.
7004. df. 22. (7.)

BEALE (S.) Profitable Poultry keeping. pp. 276. _Lond._ 1891. 8°. 7295. b. 6.

BRÉCHEMIN (L.) Élevage moderne des Animaux de basse-cour. pp. 374. _Paris,_ 1894. 4°.
7295. i. 18.

POULTRY—_continued._

BROWN (E.) Poultry keeping as an industry. pp. 138. _Lond._ 1891. 8°. 07293. m. 3.

—— Pleasurable Poultry keeping. pp. 236. _Lond._ 1894. 8°. 07293. g. 15.

—— Poultry Fattening. pp. 156. _Lond._ 1895. 8°. 7293. bbb. 40.

BUTLIN (W. H.) £300 a Year from my Poultry. pp. 32. 1895. 8°. Pam. 42.

COLLINGWOOD (H. W.) The business Hen. pp. 150. _N.Y._ 1892. 8°. 07293. g. 9.

CORNEVIN (A. M. C. I.) Les Oiseaux de basse-cour. pp. 322. _Paris,_ 1895. 8°. 07293. m. 18.

DE SALIS (H. A.) New-laid Eggs. Hints for poultry-rearers. pp. 101. _Lond._ 1892. 8°.
7291. aa. 14.

ENGLEFIELD (H.) New Laid Eggs all the year round for ½d. each. pp. 31. _Croydon,_ 1893. 8°.
Pam. 42.

ENTWISLE (W. F.) Bantams. pp. 116. _Wakefield,_ 1894. 8°. 7294. g. 4.

HARRISON (T. H.) The Minorca Fowl. pp 80. _Lond._ 1893. 8°. 07293. k. 7.

HEARSON (C. E.) The Problem solved. pp. 142. _Lond._ 1894. 8°. 7291. ua. 26.

HAY (W.) Incubation and rearing of Chickens. pp. 125. _Paisley,_ 1893. 16°. 7293. b. 39.

KEAYS (A. M.) Keays' patent Incubator. pp 18. _Lond._ 1892. 8°. Pam. 42.

LARBALÉTRIER (A.) Les Animaux de basse-cour. pp. 417. _Paris,_ 1895. 12°. 07293. g. 23.

LA PERRE DE ROO (V.) Monographie des Races de Poules. pp. 379. _Paris,_ 1894. 8°.
07293. m. 14.

MAC KENZIE (F. A.) Popular Poultry-keeping for Amateurs. pp. 118. _Lond._ 1892. 8°.
7293. c. 35.

MORANT (G. F.) How to keep laying Hens and rear Chickens. pp. 32. _Lond._ 1891. 8°.
7293. f. 12. (2.)

PERCHERON (G.) Les Oiseaux de basse-cour. pp. 372. _Paris,_ 1894. 12°. 7294. df. 7.

POPOV (D.) Die Dottersack-Gefässe des Huhnes. pp. 43. _Wiesbaden,_ 1894. 4°. 7285. k. 14.

POULTRY. Popular Poultry. pp. 115. 1889. 8°. P.P. Dublin. _Weekly Freeman._ Freeman Handbook. No. 3. 07944. ee. 10.

ROBERTSHAW (H. A.) Pedigree Register for Poultry. _Halifax,_ 1892. 8°. 7291. aa. 16.

ROSS (G. G.) £50 a year in your spare time, from Incubators. pp. 44. _Lond._ 1893. 8°.
7293. f. 12. (4.)

ROUILLÉ (L.) Ornithotechnie. Monographies de races de poules. _Paris,_ 1893, _etc._ 8°.
7291. aaa.

SAINT-LOUP (R.) Les Oiseaux de basse-cour. pp. 368. _Paris,_ 1895. 12°. 7293. b. 45.

SMITH (T.) Investigations concerning infectious diseases among Poultry. pp. 90. 1895. 8°. U.S. _Animal Industry, Bureau of._ Bulletin. No. 8.
7053. e. 41.

TEGETMEIER (W. B.) Cottager's manual of Poultry keeping. pp. 46. _Lond._ 1895. 8°.
Pam. 42.

—— Poultry for the table and market versus fancy fowls. pp. 129. _Lond._ 1893. 8°.
07293. i. 21.

VERREY (L. C.) French breeds of Poultry. pp. 71. _Lond._ 1891. 8°. 07293. m.

WATTS (E.) The Poultry-yard. pp. 155. _Lond._ 1893. 8°. 7291. aaa. 30.

WIESE (V.) De nordiske Stuefugle. pp. 88. _Kjøbenh._ 1891. 8°. 7285. de. 23.

POULTRY—*continued.*

WRIGHT (L.) The Book of Poultry. pp. 591.
Lond. 1893. 4°.

See also ANIMALS, *Domestic:* DUCK: GOOSE:
TURKEY.

POURRAIN. MEMAIN (T.) Histoire de la
commune de Pourrain, 1789-1800. pp. 94.
Auxerre, 1892. 12°. 9225. a. 20.

PRAEMONSTRATENTIAN ORDER.
MARTIN (E.) De Canonicis Praemonstraten-
sibus in Lotharingia. pp. 86.
Nanceii, 1891. 8°. 4629. aaa. 26.

See also RELIGIOUS ORDERS.

PRAGUE. HELFERT (J. A. v.) *Baron.* Drei
Stadtpläne vom alten Prag. pp. 34.
Prag, 1893. 8°. 10105. ff. 4. (8.)

Ac. Vienna. *K.K. Centralcommission zur Erforschung der Baudenkmale.* TOMEK (V. V.)
and MOCKER (J.) Das Agnes-Kloster in Prag.
pp. 18. *Wien,* 1891. 4°. Ac. 4792/3.

ECKHARDT (C.) Geschichte der deutschen
evangelischen Gemeinde in Prag. pp. 141.
Prag, 1891. 8°. 4662. e. 10.

PRAKRIT. *See* SANSKRIT.

PRAYER: PRAYERS.

Works on Prayer.

ADDRESSES. Addresses on intercessory Prayer
for foreign missions. pp. 73. *Lond.* 1895. 8°.
4399. cc. 8.

BUXTON (H. J. W.) Prayer and practice. Sermons. pp. 431. *Lond.* 1894. 8°. 4466. cc. 7.

CELESTINE-EDWARDS (S. J.) Does God answer
Prayer? pp. 14. *Portsmouth,* 1895. 8°.
4422. ddd. 56. (6.)

EYTON (R.) The Lord's Prayer: sermons.
pp. 234. *Lond.* 1892. 8°. 4478. dd. 13.

GOODHART (C. A.) Advent thoughts on the
Lord's Prayer. pp. 71. *Lond.* 1894. 8°.
4430. aaa. 6.

GRIFFITHS (C.) Nature of true Prayer. pp. 16.
Lond. 1891. 8°. Pam. 84.

GRIMLEY (H. N.) Prayer of Humanity. Sermons. pp. 199. *Lond.* 1890. 8°. 4478. h. 31.

HOLLINGS (G. S.) Porta Regalis : considerations
on prayer. pp. 76. *Lond.* 1894. 8°.
4371. aaaa. 4.

HOULT (P.) Dialogues on the efficacy of Prayer.
pp. 151. *Lond.* 1892. 8°. 3476. f. 11.

LEROY (R.) La Prière chrétienne. pp. 47.
Lausanne, 1894. 8°. 3477. dd. 7. (12.)

LORD'S PRAYER. Our Father; talks about the
Lord's Prayer. pp. 144. *Lond.* 1893. 16°.
4421. de. 23.

MASON (F. A.) Lessons on the Creed and Lord's
Prayer. pp. 127. *Lond.* 1891. 8°. 4429. b. 33.

MILLIGAN (G.) The Lord's Prayer. Sermons.
pp. 158. *Edinb.* 1895. 8°. 4462. a. 12.

PIERSON (A. T.) Lessons in the school of Prayer
as taught by the Lord. pp. 151.
Lond. 1895. 8°. 4399. d. 1.

PRAYER. On Prayer for special occasions.
pp. 20. *Lond.* 1890. 8°. 4371. de. 4. (8.)

RAINSFORD (M.) Thoughts on St. John xvii.,
the Lord's Prayer. pp. 479. *Lond.* 1895. 8°.
4406. i. 27.

RIDGEWAY (C. J.) Plain teachings on Prayer
for children. pp. 71. *Lond.* 1891. 8°.
3455. cc. 51.

SIMPSON (W. J. S.) Pater Noster. Addresses
on the Lord's Prayer. pp. 150. *Lond.* 1893. 8°.
4404. d. 43.

SMITH (R. T.) Lessons on Thought and Prayer,
etc. pp. 21. *Lond.* 1895. 8°. 4399. a. 55.

PRAYER—*continued.*

TAFEL (R. L.) The Lord's kingdom. Sermons.
pp. 112. *Lond.* 1893. 8°. 3716. ccc. 26.

VAUGHAN (B.) Prayer : the food of the soul.
pp. 20. *Lond.* 1892. 8°. Pam. 95.

VAUGHAN (C. J.) The Prayers of Jesus Christ.
pp. 123. *Lond.* 1891. 8°. 4473. bb. 35.

WALROND (F. F.) Thou, when thou prayest.
pp. 64. *Lond.* 1892. 8°. 3478. aa. 12.

Prayers.

BOUTRAIS (C. M.) Ancient devotions to the
Sacred Heart by Carthusian Monks. pp, 317.
Lond. 1895. 8°. 3456. df. 50.

LITURGIES. Rome, *Church of.* Primers. The
Prymer or Prayer-Book of the lay people in
the Middle Ages. *Lond.* 1891, *etc.* 8°.
3405. f. 13.

ANDREWES (L.) *Bp. of Winchester.* Devotions of
Bishop Andrewes, Graece et Latine. pp. 431.
Lond. 1895. 8°. 3457. h. 44.

—— Greek Devotions of L. Andrewes. pp. 196.
Lond. 1892. 8°. 4429. aa. 51.

ALPHONSO MARIA, *Saint, Bp. of Sant' Agata dei
Goti.* The Mission Book. pp. 536. 150.
Dubl. 1891. 8°. 3457. d. 28.

BAXTER (C. P.) Hospital Service Book and
supplement. pp. 185. 73. *Lond.* 1895. 8°.
3408. b. 51.

BEECHER (H. W.) Book of Prayer. Prayers in
the congregation. pp. 211. *Lond.* 1892. 8°.
3405. bbb. 12.

HUNTER (J.) Devotional Services for public
worship. pp. 271. *Glasg.* 1895. 8°. 3408. de. 25.

LITURGIES. Liturgies for Divine Worship.
pp. 174. *Lond.* 1892. 8°. 3457. h. 40.

MURRAY (W. R.) Church Prayer. Services of
public devotion. pp. 56. *Lond.* 1892. 8°.
3456. ddd. 3.

PRAYERS. Public Prayers. pp. 50.
Lond. 1894. 8°. 3457. ddd. 12.

RIDDETTE (J. H.) Responsive Services. pp. 64.
Lond. 1892. 8°. 3408. df. 17.

SPURGEON (C. H.) The Pastor in Prayer. Selection of C. H. Spurgeon's Sunday Morning
prayers. pp. 163. *Lond.* 1893. 8°. 3456. ccc. 47.

VOYSEY (C.) Revised Prayer Book. pp. 462.
Lond. 1892. 8°. 3406. a. 54.

BARRETT (G. S.) Family Worship : morning
and evening. pp. 248. *Lond.* 1894. 8°.
3456. ee. 32.

C., S. Book of family Prayers. pp. 58.
Cardiff, 1893. 4°. 3455. i. 12.

CARPENTER (W. B.) *Bp. of Ripon.* Churchman's
household Prayers. pp. 142. *Lond.* 1893. 8°.
3455. f. 34.

CRAIB (A. R.) Prayers for family Worship.
pp. 164. *Aberdeen,* 1894. 8°. 3457. h. 42.

DU TOIT (S. J.) De Huiskerk : bevattende 57
Preeken voor alle Zon- en Feestdagen. pp. 484.
De Paarl, 1893. 8°. 4427. cc. 13.

FORM. Liturgical form of family Prayers.
pp. 115. *Lond.* 1892. 8°. 3456. dd. 20.

FORMS. Forms of short family Prayer for each
day. pp. 64. *Lond.* 1892. 8°. 3457. dd. 39.

GARBETT (E.) and MARTIN (S.) The family
Prayer Book. *Lond.* 1894, *etc.* 8°. 3455. k. 2.

GURNEY (J. H.) Family Prayers. pp. 167.
Lond. 1891. 8°. 3457. h. 38.

HARKNESS (H. L.) and NORTON (P.) Steps to
the Throne ; four weeks' family Prayers.
pp. 120. *Lond.* 1892. 8°. 3457. i. 15.

HOUSEHOLD PRAYERS. Household Prayers.
pp. 95. *Lond.* 1891. 8°. 3455. d. 44.

PRAYER—*continued.*

LITURGIES. England, *Church of. Common Prayer.*
Little Prayer Book for use in families.
Lond. 1894. 8°.   4429. a. 74.

MORN. Morn and Eventide. Prayers. pp. 87.
Lond. 1894. 8°.   3456. df. 32.

MOULE (H. C. G.) Prayers for the home.
pp. 254. *Lond.* 1892. 8°.   3457. ddd. 10.

MURRAY (J.) Het Huisaltaar en de Binnen-
kamer. pp. 449. *Kaapstad,* 1890. 8°.
                                     3157. g. 33.

PRAYERS. Prayers for Households. pp. 11.
Lond. 1891. 8°.   Pam. 75.

SCOTLAND, *Church of. General Assembly.* Church
of Scotland. Aids to devotion; prayers for
family worship. pp. 108. *Edinb.* 1894. 16°.
                                     3456. df. 56.

SENEX, *Scotus.* Off-hand notes on "Prayers for
social and family Worship prepared by a Committee of the General Assembly. pp. 56.
Edinb. 1892. 8°.   3457. bb. 63. (4.)

STOBART (H.) Short Prayers for family worship.
pp. 64. *Lond.* 1891. 8°.   4429. a. 5.

VITA. Week's morning and evening Prayers for
families. *Lond.* 1892. 4°.   3455. dd. 37.

ABT ( ) To Calvary. New method of making
the Stations. pp. 24. *Lond.* 1890. 8°.
                                     3939. ccc. 2. (13.)

BARTRAM (R.) Home Devotions. pp. 144.
Lond. 1893. 8°.   3408. df. 15.

BELL (J.) The Home-Altar. Daily prayers.
pp. 160. *Lond.* 1894. 8°.   3457. cc. 40.

BELLARS (W.) In the King's Presence. Daily
prayers for Holy Communion. pp. 119.
Lond. 1893, 16°.   4324. aa. 19.

BLACK (W.) Brief heads for mental Prayer for
Advent. pp. 35. *Lond.* 1892. 8°.
                                     3456. df. 60. (3.)

—— Brief heads for Lent. pp. 55.
Lond. 1893. 8°.   3456. df. 60. (4.)

—— Brief heads from Easter to Whitsuntide.
pp. 54. *Lond.* 1894. 8°.   3456. df. 37.

—— Brief heads for Trinity. *Lond.* 1894, *etc.* 8°.
                                     3456. df. 36.

BURROUGHS (H. C.) Short private morning
Prayers. pp. 90. *Dublin,* 1894. 16°.
                                     3456. dd. 45.

CHRISTIAN. Christian's handy book of Prayer.
pp. 143. *Lond.* 1893. 8°.   3457. bbb. 86.

COBBE (F. P.) Alone to the Alone. pp. 110.
Lond. 1894. 8°.   3457. h. 41.

COLLINS (*Mrs.* H.) Short daily Prayers. pp. 175.
Glasg. 1891. 8°.   3456. dd. 17.

COMPTON (B.) The Armoury of Prayer. pp. 231.
Lond. 1891. 12°.   3457. d. 19.

GARDEN. The Garden of the Soul. pp. 464. 134.
Dublin, 1892. 8°.   3456. df. 10.

H., E. L. Prayers—at bed-time. pp. 83.
Oxf. 1890. 8°.   3457. ddd. 6.

HAYWARD (*Sir* J.) Brief course of Prayers and
Meditations. pp. 28. *Folkestone,* 1890. 8°.
                                     Pam. 75.

IGNATIUS, *de Loyola, Saint.* Spiritual exercises
of St. Ignatius. pp. 64. *Lond.* 1893. 32°.
                                     Pam. 77.

LEE (W.) Threefold cords of the Holy Scriptures. pp. 154. *Lond.* 1890. 8°.   3128. de. 18.

LEONARD, *of Porto Maurizio, Saint.* Prayers for
Mass. pp. 39, 45. *Lond.* 1889. 32°. 3457. dd. 9.

LITURGIES. Rome, *Church of. Offices.* The Gate
of Heaven. pp. 298. *Lond.* 1891. 24°.
                                     3356. a. 40.

—— The Spirit of the Sacred Heart. pp. 732.
Lond. 1892. 8°.   3366. aaaa. 4.

PRAYER—*continued.*

MALTUS (J. A.) Charity is the greatest created
gift of God. pp. 40. *Lond.* 1895. 8°.
                                     3456. df. 51.

MANNER. Manner of mental Prayer according to
the Sulpician method. *Lond.* 1893. 16°.
                                     Pam. 75.

MEYER (F. B.) Prayers for heart and home.
pp. 123. *Lond.* 1895. 8°.   3457. h. 43.

MILLER (J. R.) For a Busy Day. A morning
prayer. pp. 32. *Lond.* 1895. 8°.   4402. d. 27.

NUTTALL (E.) *Bp. of Jamaica.* The Churchman's manual. pp. 318. *Lond.* 1894. 8°.
                                     4430. a. 1.

OFFICES Seven little Offices. pp. 55.
Lond. 1894. 16°.   3456. df. 49.

OLDKNOW (J.) and CRAKE (A. D.) Priest's book
of private Devotion. pp. 532. *Oxf.* 1891. 8°.
                                     3457. bbb. 85.

PAGANI (G. B.) Book of Novenas. pp. 216.
Lond. 1892. 8°.   3456. df. 29.

PERREYVE (H.) Spiritual Communion for the
sick. pp. 30. *Oxf.* 1891. 8°.   4324. aa. 14.

PRAYER BOOK. A simple Prayer Book. pp. 68.
Lond. 1895. 16°.   3457. aaa. 72.

RUSSELL (M.) Moments before the Tabernacle.
pp. 62. *Lond.* 1892. 16°.   4324. aa. 17.

SAINT VERONICA MANUAL. St. Veronica manual
of Divine Love. pp. 217. *Lond.* 1894. 8°.
                                     3456. df. 45.

TWINING (L.) Morning and evening Prayers.
pp. 157. *Lond.* 1892. 8°.   3457. dd. 17.

VIZARD (P. E.) Prayers new and old. pp. 66
Lond. 1894. 8°.   3457. cc. 39.

VOYSEY (C.) Prayers and Meditations. pp. 53.
Lond. 1892. 8°.   3457. dd. 28.

W., E. Book of simple Prayers. pp. 109.
Reading, 1893. 4°.   3457. i. 18.

WARDEN. Heads of Intercession. For the use
of Religious. pp. 63. *Lond.* 1893. 16°.
                                     3456. df. 6.

WILBERFORCE (F. B.) Easy method of mental
Prayer. pp. 24. *Lond.* 1890. 8°.
                                     3939. ccc. 2. (21.)

YATES (H. S. B.) Quiet Thoughts for morning
devotion. pp. 365. *Lond.* 1895. 8°.
                                     3456. ee. 33.

See also EUCHARIST : LENT : MEDITATIONS : RE-
TREATS : ROSARY.

Prayers for Children and Schools.

B., C. W. A., and W., F. Manual of children's
Worship. 6 pt. *Lond.* 1895. 32°. 3455. aaaa. 5.

BARRETT (G. S.) Service Book for church and
school. pp. 64. *Lond.* 1891. 8°.
                                     3406. de. 36. (4.)

CATHOLIC CHILDREN. Collection of Prayers for
Catholic children. pp. 18. *Colombo.* 1893. 16°.
                                     Pam. 75.

CHAMBERS (A.) Children's Service. pp. 8.
Lond. 1892. 16°.   Pam. 75.

CHILDREN. Children's Prayers. pp. 22.
Lond. 1894. 16°.   Pam. 75.

DALTON (H. A.) Helps to self-examination for
boys. pp. 16. *Oxf.* 1892. 8°.   Pam. 77.

GOING (J.) With Angels and Archangels.
Manual for the use of children. pp. 49.
Oxf. 1892. 8°.   4324. aa. 18.

HOWATT (J. R.) Children's Prayer Book.
pp. 80. *Lond.* 1895. 18°.   3455. b. 84.

HUNT (C. W.) Daily Prayers for schools. pp. 68.
Lond. 1892. 8°.   3408. bbb. 31.

MANUAL. Manual of Prayers for youth. pp. 256.
Lond. 1893. 8°.   3456. df. 28.

PRAYER—*continued.*

PRAYERS. Daily Prayers for little children. pp. 70. *Oxf.* 1891. 32°.   3457. dd. 34.

RAYMOND (V.) The faithful Guide. Prayers and devotions. pp. 264. *Lond.* 1892. 8°.   3456. aa. 86.

S., A. Manual of Prayers for Catholic youth. pp. 263. *Lond.* 1892. 8°.   3456. dd. 19.

SAINT PAUL'S SCHOOL. Latin Prayers used in St. Paul's School in 1644. pp. 14. *Lond.* 1890. 8°.   Pam. 75.

THICKNESSE (F. H.) *Bp. of Leicester.* Prayers for schools. pp. 27. *Lond.* 1894. 12°.   3457. bb. 63. (6.)

WILLIAMS (C. E. E.) Morning and evening Devotions for preparatory schools. pp. 51. *Lond.* 1892. 16°.   3408. aa. 51.

Prayers for the Sick. *See* SICKNESS.

PRECIOUS STONES. *See* GEMS.

PRÉCIS WRITING. SKERRY (G. E) Indexing and Précis writing. pp. 184. *Lond.* 1893. 8°.   011824. e. 53.

THOMSON (W. S.) Guide to Indexing and Précis writing. pp. 324. *Aberd.* 1895. 8°.   12982. bb. 48.

PREDESTINATION. *See* CALVINISM.

PRENZLAU. ARNOLDT ( ) Geschichte des Gymnasiums zu Prenzlau. pp. 308. *Prenzlau,* 1893. 8°.   8357. f. 25.

PRESBYTERIANISM.

General.

BANNERMAN (D. D.) Worship, order and polity of the Presbyterian Church. 4 pt. *Edinb.* 1894. 8°.   4175. de. 46.

BELL (J.) J. Calvin : his errors, and the errors of Presbyterianism. pp. 82. *N.Y.* 1891. 8°.   4182. f. 36.

BOYD (J.) Plea for the responsive element in Presbyterian worship. pp. 20. *Glasg.* 1894. 8°.   4175. bb. 27. (9.)

CHRISTIANITY. Outline of practical Christianity. Text-book for those preparing for the Lord's Supper. pp. 48. *Edinb.* 1893. 8°.   Pam. 77.

ELDER. The Ru'ing Elder : his place and work. pp. 336. *Lond.* 1892. 8°.   4136. aaa. 39.

MIDDLEMISS (J. T.) Lecture on Presbyterian polity. pp. 11. *Sunderland,* 1894. 8°.   4139. dd. 2. (15.)

RAINY (R.) Presbyterianism as a form of church life. pp. 23. *Camb.* 1894. 8°. 4175. bb. 27. (11.)

VAN DYKE (H. J.) The Church : her ministry and sacraments. pp. 265. *Lond.* 1890. 8°.   4182. f. 35.

WRIGHT (A.) The Presbyterian Church ; its worship, functions and ministerial orders. pp. 282. *Edinb.* 1895. 8°.   4735. b. 42.

See also CALVINISM.

Presbyterian Church in England.

Ac. Manchester. *Chetham Society.* Remains. N.S. Vol. 20, *etc.* Minutes of the Manchester Presbyterian classes. *Manch.* 1890, *etc.* 4°.   Ac. 8120.

DYER (A. S.) Sketches of English Nonconformity. pp. 112. *Lond.* 1893. 8°. 4109. aa. 42.

ENGLAND, *Presbyterian Church.* Official Handbook. *Lond.* 1892, *etc.* 8°.   P.P. 2485. kea.

FRASER (D.) Sound Doctrine. Commentary on the articles of Faith of the Presbyterian Church of England. pp. 237. *Lond.* 1892. 8°.   3506. aaaa. 2.

GIBSON (J. M.) Presbyterian Church of England. Address. pp. 40. *Lond.* 1891. 8°.   Pam. 9.

PRESBYTERIANISM.—*continued.*

MIDDLEMISS (J. T.) How far is a Directory of worship necessary ? pp. 8. *Sunderland,* 1893. 8°.   Pam. 75.

P.P. *London.* Year Book of the Presbyterian Church of England. *Lond.* 1887, *etc.* 8°.   P.P. 2485. ke.

See also ENGLAND, *History, Ecclesiastical : Nonconformists.*

Ireland.

EDGAR (R. M.) Progressive Presbyterianism. pp. 186. *Belfast,* 1894. 8°.   4165. a. 3.

LATIMER (W. T.) History of the Irish Presbyterians. pp. 238. *Belfast,* 1893. 8°.   4735. aaa. 40.

Netherlands.

See NETHERLANDS, *Reformed Church.*

Scotland.

See SCOTLAND, *Church of, and History, Ecclesiastical.*

Switzerland.

See SWITZERLAND, *Evangelical and Free Churches.*

United States of America.

CARROLL (H. K.) Report of statistics of Churches in the U.S. pp. 812. 1894. 8°. Eleventh Census of the U.S.   1882. c. 1.

P.P. *New York.* The Presbyterian Review. Vols. 1–10. *N.Y.* 1880–89. 8°.   P.P. 899. c.

—— The Presbyterian and Reformed Review. *N.Y.* 1890, *etc.* 8°.   P.P. 899. d.

SCOULLER (J. B.) History of the United Presbyterian Church of N. America. 1894. 8°. American Church History Series. Vol. XI.   4744. g.

THOMPSON (R. E.) History of Presbyterian Churches in the U.S. pp. 424. 1895. 8°. American Church History Series. Vol. VI.   4744. g.

MAC COOK (J. J.) Appeal in the Briggs Heresy case before the General Assembly of the Presbyterian Church in the U.S. pp. 378. *N.Y.* 1893. 8°.   5155. h. 11.

HALSEY (Le R. J.) History of the McCormick Theological Seminary. pp. 537. *Chicago,* 1893. 8°.   8366. f. 29.

JOHNSON (T. C.) History of the southern Presbyterian Church. 1894. 8°. American Church History Series, *etc.* Vol. XI.   4744. g.

MAC ILVAIN (J. W.) Early Presbyterianism in Maryland. pp. 33. 1890. 8°. Johns Hopkins University Studies. Notes, 1890, No. 3.   Ac. 2689.

ALEXANDER (J. E.) History of the Synod of Tennessee. pp. 155. *Phila.* 1890. 8°.   4744. ee. 27.

PRESCRIPTION, Law of. HERBERT (T. A.) History of the Law of Prescription. pp. 210. *Lond.* 1891. 8°.   6306. bb. 12.

PRESS. Laws, etc., relating to the.

CARQUEJA (B.) A Liberdade de imprensa. pp. 140. *Porto,* 1893. 8°.   6005. h. 16.

COULON (H.) De la Liberté de la Presse. Commentaire de la loi du 28 juillet 1894. pp. 414. *Paris,* 1894. 8°.   8050. g. 8.

FISHER (J. R.) and STRAHAN (J. A.) The Law of the Press. pp. 297. *Lond.* 1891. 8°.   6375. h. 25.

HUBER (H.) Zum Begriff der Pressfreiheit nach schweizerischem Rechte. pp. 70. *Bern,* 1891. 8°.   5510. cc. 1. (3.)

NAGRADOW (W. J.) Moderne russische Censur und Presse. pp. 482. *Berl.* 1894. 8°.   8093. b. 31.

PRESS.—Laws, etc.—*continued.*

OETKER (F.)　Die strafrechtliche Haftung des verantwortlichen Redakteurs.　pp. 120.
Stuttgart, 1893. 8°.　　　　　6055. df. 23.
See also JOURNALISM : LIBEL.

PRESSBURG.　KIRALY (J.)　Geschichte des Donau-Mauth- und Urfahr-Rechtes der Freistadt Pressburg.　pp. 252.　*Pressburg*, 1890. 8°.
5549. c. 23.

ORTVAY (T.)　Geschichte der Stadt Pressburg.
Pressburg, 1892, etc. 8°.　　　　10215. i.

PRESTON, Yorkshire.　SMITH (T. C.)　Records of the Parish church of Preston.　pp. 299.
Preston, 1892. 4°.　　　　10360. g. 41.

PREUILLY-SUR-CLAISE.　PICARDAT (G.)　Un Joyau d'architecture chrétienne en 1009, l'Eglise de Preuilly-sur-Claise.　pp. 416.
Preuilly, 1895. 8°.　　　　07816. l. 1.

PRIBYLOV ISLANDS.　*See* BEHRING SEA.

PRICES AND VALUE.　ALLARD (A.)　Graphiques de la crise monétaire 1850–92.
Bruxelles, 1892. 4°.　　　　8228. l. 11.

ARMSDEN (J.)　Value : criticism of political economy and socialism.　pp. 144.
Lond. 1892. 8°.　　　　8275. aa. 60.

AVENEL (G. d') *Viscount.*　Histoire économique de la propriété, des salaires et des prix en géneral, 1200–1800. 2 tom.　*Paris*, 1894. 4°.
8207. m. 1.

BARCLAY (R.)　Disturbance in the Standard of Value.　pp. 107.　*Lond.* 1893. 8°. 8228. ccc. 50.

BOEHM-BAWERK (E. v.)　The ultimate Standard of Value.　1895. 8°. Ac. Philadelphia, *American Academy of Political Science.* Annals. Vol. v. No. 2.　　　　Ac. 2383.

DENIS (H.)　La Dépression économique et l'histoire des prix.　pp. 412.　*Brux.* 1895. 8°.
8226. h. 42.

FISHER (I.)　Mathematical investigations in the theory of Value and Prices. 1892. 8°. Ac. New Haven. *Connecticut Academy.* Transactions. Vol. IX.　　　　Ac. 1805.

FREWEN (M.)　Mr. Frewen on Prices.　pp. 26.
Lond. 1889. 8°.　　　　Pam. 23.

HAMMER (E.)　Die Hauptprincipien des Geld- und Währungswesens, *etc.*　pp. 32.
Wien, 1891. 8°.　　　　Pam. 23.

HERTZKA (T.)　Das internationale Währungs-problem.　pp. 136.　*Leipz.* 1892. 8°. 8225. cc. 44.

JOWETT (E.)　The Ruinous fall in Prices.
pp. 24.　*Melbourne*, 1894. 8°.　　Pam. 23.

LEVY (J. H.)　A symposium on Value.　pp. 58.
Lond. 1895. 8°.　　　　Pam. 82.

MARX (C.)　The theory of Value complete.
pp. 189.　1893. 8°.　Bellamy Series.　12205. e.

MELLAND (E.)　The financial Depression and the standard of Value.　pp. 12.　*Dunedin*, 1894. 8°.
Pam. 23.

MENGER (C.)　Der Übergang zur Goldwährung.
pp. 36.　*Wien*, 1892. 8°.　　08227. i. 30. (9.)

MEINONG (A.)　Philologisch-ethische Unter-suchungen zur Werth-Theorie.　pp. 232.
Graz, 1894. 8°.　　　　08207. i. 2.

NEUMANN (F. J.)　La formazione del Prezzo.
1886, 87. 8°.　Biblioteca dell' Economista. Ser. 3.　Vol. 11, & 12, pt. 2.　　　8205. l.

NORMAN (J. H.)　Prices and monetary Exchanges of the world.　pp. 32.　*Lond.* 1895. 8°. Pam. 23.

OSTERSETZER (A.)　Währungswechsel und Auf-nahme der Baarzahlungen. 2 Thle.
Wien, 1892. 8°.　　　　08225. k. 3.

SAUERBECK (A.)　Prices of commodities during the last seven years.　pp. 40.　*Lond.* 1893. 8°.
08227. g. 49. (15.)

PRICES AND VALUE—*continued.*

SAUERBECK (A.)　Course of average Prices in England, 1820–93.　*Lond.* 1894. *s. sh.* fol.
1882. d. 2. (66.)

SCHROEDER (H.)　Wertverteilung und Renten-theorie.　pp. 146.　*Berl.* 1894. 8°.　08207. i. 1.

SMART (W.)　Introduction to the theory of Value.
pp. 88.　*Lond.* 1891. 8°.　　　8206. bb. 29.

SOETBEER (A.)　Materialien zur Erläuterung der wirtschaftlichen Edelmetallverhältnisse und der Währungsfrage.　*Berl.* 1886. 4°.　8228. i. 72.

VOLKMAR (G.)　Die Währungs- und die Arbeiter-frage.　pp. 86.　*Wien*, 1893. 8°.　　Pam. 82.

WHARTON (J.)　The unit of Value.　pp. 14.
Phila. 1892. 8°.　　　　08226. k. 3. (1.)
See also MONEY : POLITICAL ECONOMY : TRADE.

PRIMOGENITURE.　*See* SUCCESSION.

PRIMULACEAE.　WIDMER (E.)　Die europä-ischen Arten der Gattung Primula.　pp. 154.
München, 1891. 8°.　　　　07028. h. 34.
See also FLOWERS.

PRINCE EDWARD ISLAND. CANADA.
The Maritime Provinces of Canada.　pp. 122.
Lond. 1892. 8°.　　　10470. dd. 30. (10.)

CASGRAIN (H. R.)　Île du Prince-Édouard sous le régime français.　pp. 419.　*Québec*, 1894. 8°.
9555. eee. 17.

See also CANADA.

PRINCETON COLLEGE.　SLOANE (W. M.)　Princeton University. 1895. 4°.　Four American Universities.　　　　8364. i. 9.

WALLACE (G. R.)　Princeton Sketches.　Story of Nassau Hall.　pp. 200.　*N.Y.* 1893. 8°.
8366. de. 35.

PRINKNASH PARK.　BAZELEY (W.)　History of Prinknash Park.　pp. 39.
Gloucester, 1890. 8°.　　10348. d. 19. (3.)

PRINTS. Ac. London. *British Museum.*
Guide to an exhibition of Engravings from the Malcolm Collection.　pp. 118.　*Lond.* 1895. 8°.
7858. b. 50.

—— *Burlington Fine Arts Club.*　Exhibition illustrative of the French revival of Etching.
pp. 21.　*Lond.* 1891. 4°.　　　7854. g. 36.

—— Nuremberg. *Germanisches Nationalmuseum.*
Katalog der deutschen Kupferstiche des XV. Jahrhunderts.　pp. 64. 1888. 4°. P.P. *Munich.* Anzeiger für Kunde des deutschen Mittelalters.
P.P. 3542. aa.

—— Paris. *École des Beaux-Arts.*　Exposition de la lithographie.　pp. 59.　*Paris*, 1891. 8°.
K.T.C. 27. b. 2.

BARRITT (L.)　Engravings. How to estimate their cost.　*N.Y.* 1890. 4°.　　　7875. ee. 16.

BERALDI (H.)　Mes Estampes.　pp. 95.
Lille, 1884. 8°.　　　　7875. aa. 54.

BLOCK (J. C.)　Das Kupferstich-Werk des W. Hondius.　pp. 80.　*Danzig*, 1891. 8°. 7856. eee. 47.

BOSTON, *Mass. Museum of Fine Arts.*　Exhibition of the Society of American wood-engravers.
pp. 28.　*Bost.* 1890. 8°.　　　Pam. 24.

BOUCHOT (H.)　Les Livres à vignettes du XVᵉ au XIXᵉ siècle, *etc.*　2 pt.　*Paris*, 1891. 8°.
11899. ee. 30.

—— Le Cabinet des Estampes de la Biblio-thèque Nationale ; guide du lecteur.　pp. 392.
Paris, 1895. 8°.　　　　7857. bbb. 47.

BOURCARD (G.)　Dessins, gouaches et estampes du dix-huitième siècle.　pp. 675.
Paris, 1893. 8°.　　　　7858. gg. 20.

CHAMPFLEURY.　Catalogue des lithographies, caricatures et aquarelles formant la collection Champfleury.　pp. 127.　*Paris*, 1891. 4°.
7858. c 17.

PRISONS.—Europe—continued.

MERRICK (G. P.) Work among the Fallen in the prison cell. pp. 62. Lond. 1891. 8°.
8285. aa. 59.

RENDER (W. H.) Through Prison Bars. Lives of J. Howard and E. Fry, etc. pp. 160.
Lond. 1894. 8°.   4907. b. 39.

PARIS. Société Générale des Prisons. Les Institutions pénitentiaires de la France en 1895. pp. 487. Paris, 1895. 8°.   6057. e. 29.

LAURENT (A.) Les Prisons du vieux Paris. pp. 271. Paris, 1895. 8°.   6056. g. 7.

BRU (P.) Histoire de Bicêtre. pp. 480.
Paris, 1890. 4°.   10172. f. 21.

GRANDPRÈ (P. de) La Prison Saint-Lazare depuis vingt ans. pp. 434. Paris, 1889. 12°.
6057. aaa. 33.

COURET (É.) Le Pavillon des Princes. Histoire complète de la prison de Sainte-Pélagie.
pp. 360. Paris, 1895. 18°.   6057. d. 1.

VALLÈS (J. L. J.) Mazas. Paris, 1895. fol.
6055. h. 2.

ARBOUX (J.) Manuel des visiteurs de prisons.
pp. 123. Paris, 1894. 12°.   6057. a. 42.

BAILLY (C.) Les Pénitenciers agricoles de la Corse. pp. 93. Saint-Valery, 1884. 8°
6095. f. 26.

COR (H.) Questions coloniales de la Transportation considérée. pp. 180. Paris, 1895. 8°.
6057. c. 15.

PIERRET (G.) Transportation et colonisation pénale. pp. 107. Paris, 1892. 8°. 6056. f. 25.

TEISSEIRE (É.) La Transportation pénale et la relégation. pp. 508. Paris, 1893. 8°.
5424. dd. 11.

WOLLENZIEN (J.) Die Gefängniss-Verwaltung bei den preussischen Justizbehörden. pp. 305.
Breslau, 1890. 8°.   6056. ee. 30.

WULFF (C.) Die Gefängnisse der Justizverwaltung in Preussen. pp. 712. Hamb. 1890. 8°.
6056. ee. 31.

LECCI (A.) Il sistema delle pene nel Codice italiano. pp. 408. Turin, 1891. 8°.
5359. bb. 13.

KENNAN (G.) Siberia and the Exile system.
2 vol. Lond. 1891. 8°.   010055. f. 1.

CORBOUD (T.) Les Maisons pénitentiaires du Canton de Fribourg. pp. 251.
Fribourg, 1890. 8°.   6057. b. 23.
See also PARIS, Bastille.

United States of America.

FALKNER (R P.) Prison statistics of the U.S. for 1888. pp. 34. 1889. 8°. Ac. Philadelphia. University. Publications. Political Economy Series. No. 5.   Ac. 2692. p.

POWELL (J. C.) The American Siberia; a Southern convict camp. pp. 355. Lond. 1892. 8°.
6057. b. 25.

U.S. Bureau of Labour. Convict Labour.
pp. 612. 1887. 8°. Annual Report, etc. Report II.   8275. k.

ELMIRA. New York State Reformatory. Seventeenth Year book. Elmira, 1892. 8°.
6057. b. 40.

WINTER (A.) New York State Reformatory in Elmira. pp. 172. Lond. 1891. 8° 6057. aaa. 26.
See also CHILDREN : CRIME : LAW, Criminal : POLICE : PUNISHMENT.

PROBABILITIES. BOBEK (C. J.) Lehrbuch der Wahrscheinlichkeitsrechnung. pp. 296.
1891. 8°. Kleyer's Encyclopädie.   8705. g.

SELANDER (E.) Sannolikhets-Kalkylen i korthet framställd. pp. 117. Helsingfors, 1891. 8°.
8535. ccc. 44.

PROBATE AND PROBATE AND SUCCESSION DUTIES. See SUCCESSION.

PROCIDA. PARAS-CANDOLA (M.) Cenni storici intorno alla città di Procida. pp. 306.
Napoli, 1892. 8°.   10135. ee. 17.

PROCLAMATIONS. LINDSAY (J. L.) Earl of Crawford. Bibliotheca Lindesiana.
Aberdeen, 1893, etc. fol.   11901. i.

PROPERTY.

General.

FOUILLÉE (A.) La Propriété sociale et la démocratie pp. 282 Paris, 1895. 8°. 08275. f. 35.

KIELE (M. de T.) Propriété individuelle et collectivisme. pp. 17. Brussels, 1894. 8°.
Pam. 82.

KOVALEVSKY (M. M.) Tableau des origines et de l'évolution de la propriété. pp. 202. 1890. 8°.
Ac. Stockholm. Lorénska Stiftelse. Skrifter. No. 2.   Ac. 3475.

LABOULAYE (R. de) T. Rogers, ses théories sur la propriété. pp. 24. Paris, 1891. 8°.
08276. k. 4. (3.)

LAVELEYE (É. de) Baron. De la Propriété et de ses formes primitives. pp. 562. Paris, 1891. 8°.
08276. h. 31.

LETOURNEAU (C. J. M.) Property ; its origin and development. pp. 401. 1892. 8°. ELLIS (H. H.) Contemporary Science Series. 8709. i.

SIMCOX (E. J.) Primitive Civilizations. Outlines of the history of ownership. 2 vol.
Lond. 1894. 8°.   2238. d. 17.

Law of.

Austria.

RANDA (A.) Der Besitz nach österreichischem Rechte. pp. 814. Leipz. 1895. 8°. 05551. k. 1.

Germany.

BLUMENSTOK (A. H.) Entstehung des deutschen Immobiliareigenthums. Innsbruck, 1894, etc. 8°.
6005. de.

Great Britain and Ireland.

INDERMAUR (J.) and THWAITES (C.) Student's Guide to the Law of real and personal property.
pp. 192. Lond. 1893. 8°.   6306. aa. 43.

POLLOCK (Sir F.) Essay on possession in the Common Law. pp. 244. Oxf. 1888. 8°.
6145. e. 24.

STRAHAN (J. A.) and BAXTER (J. S.) View of the Law of Property. pp. 352. Lond. 1895. 8°.
6306. g. 2.

GOODEVE (L. A.) Modern Law of personal Property. pp. 482. Lond. 1892. 8°. 2230. f. 3.

WILLIAMS (J.) Principles of the Law of personal Property. pp. 620. Lond. 1894. 8°.
6325. h. 1.

CHALLIS (H. W.) Law of real Property. pp. 466.
Lond. 1892. 8°.   6306. h. 8.

DIGBY (K. E.) Introduction to the History of the Law of real Property. pp. 446. 1892. 8°.
Clarendon Press Series.   2320. h. 7.

GOODEVE (L. A.) Modern Law of real Property.
pp. 566. Lond. 1891. 8°.   6306. b. 7.

KELKE (W. H. H.) Epitome of real Property Law. pp. 160. Lond. 1892. 8°. 6306. aa. 39.

SHELFORD (L.) Shelford's real property Statutes.
pp. 847. Lond. 1893. 8°.   6306. h. 14.

WILLIAMS (J.) Principles of the Law of real Property. pp. 703. Lond. 1892. 8°. 6305. dd. 12.
See also CONVEYANCING : LAND.

India.

AVINĀSACHANDRA MITRA. Transfer of Property Act, 1882. pp. 85. Calcutta, 1891. 8°. 6306. e. 7.

GRIFFITH (W.) Indian Transfer Acts. pp. 293.
Madras, 1892. 8°.   5319. b. 21.

PROPERTY.—Law of—*continued.*

KIṢORAMOHANA CHAṬṬOPĀDHYĀYA. Law relating to the Transfer of immoveable Property. pp. 503. 1890. 8°. Tagore Law Lectures. 1886.   5318. a.a.

Italy.

PICCIONE (E.) Concetto positivo del Diritto di Proprietà. pp. 337. *Bologna,* 1890. 8°.   8276. ee. 58.

Roman Law.

BEKKER (E. I.) Das Recht des Besitzes bei den Römern. pp. 417. *Leipz.* 1880. 8°. 5207. df. 23.

PROPHECY. BEN-OLIEL (M. M.) Prophecy an evidence of Inspiration. pp. 120. *Lond.* 1891. 8°.   3186. df. 43.

BIBLE. Old Testament. *Prophets.* How to read the Prophets. *Edinb.* 1892, *etc.* 8°. 3186. df. 44.

DARMESTETER (J.) Les Prophètes d'Israël. pp. 386. *Paris,* 1892. 8°.   3166. ee. 43.

GREEN (W. H.) Moses and the Prophets. The Old Testament in the Jewish Church, by W. R. Smith, reviewed by W. H. Green. pp. 369. *N.Y.* 1891. 8°.   3155. de. 27.

HAVET (E.) La modernité des prophètes. pp. 264. *Paris,* 1891. 8°.   3166. ee. 34.

KIRKPATRICK (A. F.) The Doctrine of the Prophets. pp. 540. *Lond.* 1892. 8°. 4456. de. 11.

REICH (W.) Das prophetische Schrifttum. *Wien,* 1892, *etc.* 8°.   3186. dd.

SIMCOX (W. H.) Cessation of Prophecy. pp. 319. *Lond.* 1891. 8°.   4479. dd. 25.

BRIGGS (C. A.) Messiah of the Apostles. pp. 562. *Edinb.* 1895. 8°.   4227. cc. 6.

DELITZCH (F.) Messianic Prophecies. pp. 232. *Edinb.* 1891. 8°.   3186. df. 37.

HOARE (J. G.) Christ Revealed in title and prophecy. pp. 142. *Lond.* 1894. 8°. 4224. c. 78.

MEIGNAN (G.) *Archbp. of Tours.* Les Prophètes et le Messie depuis Salomon jusqu'a Daniel. pp. 607. *Paris,* 1893. 12°.   3165. dd. 47.

—— Les Prophètes depuis Daniel jusqu'à Jean Baptiste. pp. 579. *Paris,* 1894. 12°.   3165. dd. 48.

MEYER (F. B.) Christ in Isaiah. pp. 211. *Lond.* 1895. 8°.   3187. aaaa. 15.

RIEHM (E. C. A.) Messianic Prophecy. pp. 348. *Edinb.* 1891. 8°.   3186. i. 23.

BIBLE. *Isaiah.* The Prophecies of Isaiah. New translation by T. K. Cheyne. Vol. I. pp. 310. *Lond.* 1889. 8°.   2202. e. 1.

KENNEDY (J.) Argument for the unity of Isaiah. pp. 196. *Lond.* 1891. 8°.   3185. df. 37.

DOUGLAS (G. C. M.) Isaiah one and his book one. pp. 417. *Lond.* 1895. 8°.   3187. c. 5.

GAUTIER (L.) La Mission du prophète Ézéchiel. pp. 376. *Lausanne,* 1891. 8°.   3185. df. 36.

ANDERSON (R.) Defence of the Book of Daniel against the Higher Criticism. pp. 45. *Lond.* 1895. 8°.   3187. d. 4. (7.)

HINKLEY (W. H.) The Book of Daniel: its prophetic character. pp. 191. *Bost.* 1894. 8°.   3187. aaaa. 12.

KAMPHAUSEN (A.) Das Buch Daniel und die neuere Geschichtsforschung. pp. 46. *Leipz.* 1893. 8°.   3187. d. 4. (5.)

MENSI (G.) Studi sulle Profezie di Daniele. pp. 78. *Milano,* 1890. 8°.   3105. de. 5. (3.)

PATERSON (D. D.) Lectures on Daniel. pp. 77. *Glasg.* 1891. 8°.   3186. de. 27.

BELLETT (J. G.) Musings on the Apocalypse. pp. 48. *Lond.* 1895. 16°.   Pam. 5.

PROPHECY—*continued.*

BOUSSET (W.) Der Antichrist in der Überlieferung des Judentums des neuen Testaments und der alten Kirche. pp. 186. *Göttingen,* 1895. 8°.   3186. f. 35

BROWN (D.) The Apocalypse. pp. 224. *Lond.* 1891. 8°.   3186. i. 26.

CLARK (J.) Seven ages of the Church: exposition of the Apocalypse. pp. 48. *Lond.* 1891. 8°.   3187. aaa. 6. (4.)

DICE (A.) The Revelation a book for to-day. pp. 277. *Lond.* 1894. 8°. 3187. aaaa. 14.

H., W. R. The Apocalypse. pp. 44. *Lond.* 1892. 8°.   3187. d. 4. (3.)

HIRSCHT (A.) Die Apokalypse und ihre neueste Kritik. pp. 175. *Leipz.* 1895. 8°. 3186. f. 34.

MILLIGAN (W.) Discussions on the Apocalypse. pp. 290. *Lond.* 1893. 8°.   3187. c. 4.

SLIGHT (H. S.) An attempt to interpret portions of the Book of Revelation. pp. 54. *Bath,* 1893. 8°.   3186. d. 3.

SMITH (C. E.) The World lighted: study of the Apocalypse. pp. 218. *N.Y.* 1890. 8°.   3186. df. 42.

BLIGH (*Hon.* E. V.) Prophetical signs of the Second Coming. pp. 111. *Lond.* 1891. 8°.   3186. de. 20.

BROWN (A.) The great Day of the Lord. pp. 403. *Lond.* 1894. 8°. 3187. aaaa. 10.

DIMBLEBY (J. B.) "The appointed Time." pp. 231. *Lond.* 1895. 8°.   3187. aaa. 11.

GILBERT (M.) The Signs, manner and time of our Lord's Second Coming. pp. 18. *Toronto,* 1895. 8°.   3187. aaaa. 23.

KELLY (W.) The Second Advent premillennial. pp. 95. *Lond.* 1888. 8°.   3187. aaa. 15.

OVERTON (J.) His Appearing and his Kingdom. pp. 20. *Lond.* 1893. 8°.   4422. ddd. 55. (11.)

RUSSELL (C. T.) Millennial Dawn. *Lond.* 1891. 8°.   3186. de.

STEED (A. J.) The second Coming of Christ. pp. 50. *Lond.* 1893. 8°.   3187. d. 4. (6.)

TRENCH (G. F.) After the thousand Years. The glorious reign of Christ. pp. 120. *Lond.* 1894. 8°.   3186. a. 70.

TROTTER (W.) Lectures on the second Coming of Christ. pp. 293. *Lond.* 1892. 8°.   3186. de. 33.

WILSON (J.) The Millennium. pp. 174. *Lond.* 1895. 8°.   3187. aaaa. 19.

ANTICHRIST. The Computation of 666 and its relation to Antichristian systems. pp. 398. *Lond.* 1891. 8°.   3186. dd. 3

BAXTER (M. P.) 15 predicted Events from 1892 until 1901. pp. 40. *Lond.* 1892. 16°. Pam. 5

—— The great Crisis from 1890 to 1901. pp. 32. *Lond.* 1887. 8°.   Pam. 5.

CLARK (M. S.) Thoughts of Peace, or the purpose of God regarding Israel. pp. 219. *Lond.* 1895. 8°.   4034. i. 50.

DINGLE (E.) On Prophecies fulfilled during the 19th century. pp. 52. *Tavistock,* 1895. 8°.   3186. cc. 27.

FRY (H. W.) God's plan in the Bible. pp. 141. *Lond.* 1891. 8°.   3186. df. 40.

GRIFFITHS (W.) Divine footprints in the Bible. pp. 272. *Lond.* 1891. 8°.   3109. df. 23.

HIGGINS (C.) The Future unveiled. pp. 362. *Oxf.* 1894. 8°.   3187. aaa. 3.

HOWARD (E.) The Sword's coming. pp. 32. *Taunton,* 1894. 8°.   3187. aaa. 6. (7.)

PROTOZOA—*continued.*

TORTORI (E.) Genesi, organizzazione e meta-
morfosi degli Infusori. pp. 196.
Firenze, 1895. 8°.   7296. f. 15.

WALLENGREN (H. D. J.) Studier öfver Ciliata
Infusorier. 1894, *etc.* 4°. Ac. Lund. *R. Academia.* Acta. Tom. 30.   Ac. 1067.

KLEBS (G.) Über die Organisation einiger
Flagellaten-Gruppen. 1883. 8°. Ac. Leipzig.
Botanisches Institut. Untersuchungen. Bd. 1.
      Ac. 3260.

EGGER (J. G.) Foraminiferen aus Meeresgrund-
proben. 1893. 4°. Ac. Munich. *K. Akademie.*
Abhandlungen der math.-physikalischen Classe.
Bd. 18.   Ac. 713/4.

GOES (A.) Synopsis of the Arctic and Scandi-
navian marine Foraminifera. pp. 127. 1893. 4°.
Ac. *etc.* Stockholm. *K. Svenska Vetenskaps-
Akademien.* Handlingar. N.F. Bd. 25. Ac. 1070.

HAEUSLER (R.) Monographie der Foraminiferen-
Fauna der schweizerischen Transversarius-Zone.
pp. 134. 1890 4°. Ac. Switzerland. *Paläontologische Gesellschaft.* Abhandlungen.
Vol. 17.   Ac. 3122.

DREYER (F.) Die Principien der Gerüstbildung
bei Rhizopoden, *etc.* 1891. 8°. Ac. Jena.
Medizinisch-Naturwissenschaftliche Gesellschaft
Zeitschrift für Naturwissenschaft. Bd. 26.
Hft. 2.   Ac. 3760.

MOEBIUS (C.) Bruchstücke einer Rhizopoden
fauna der Kieler Bucht. pp. 31. 1889. 4°. Ac.
Berlin. *Societas Scientiarum.* Abhandlungen.
1888.   Ac. 855/6.

PENARD (E.) Études sur les Rhizopodes d'eau
douce. pp. 230. 1890. 4°. Ac. Geneva. *Société
de Physique.* Mémoires. Tom. 31. Pt. 1.
      Ac. 2870.

See also MYCETOZOA: PALAEONTOLOGY:
SPOROZOA.

**PROVENCAL LANGUAGE AND
LITERATURE.** PIAT (L.) Dictionnaire
français-occitanien. *Montpellier*, 1893, *etc.* 8°.
      12953. h. 18.

CRESCINI (V.) Manualetto provenzale. pp. 256.
Verona, 1892. 8°.   12950. cc. 31.

KOSCHWITZ (E.) Grammaire de la langue des
Félibres. pp. 181. *Greifswald*, 1894. 8°.
      12950. c. 40.

KALEPKY (T.) Von der Negation in Provenzalischen. pp. 28. *Berl.* 1891. 4°. 12902. h. 19. (1.)

STICHEL (C.) Beiträge zur Lexicographie des
altprovenzalischen Verbums. pp. 86. 1890. 8°.
STENGEL (E. M.) Ausgaben und Abhandlungen.
No. 86.   11498. i.

WIECHMANN (E.) Provenzalisches geschlossenes
E nach den Grammatiken, *etc.* pp. 38.
Leipz. 1890. 8°.   12902. dd. 27. (10.)

KOSCHWITZ (E.) Ueber die provenzalischen
Feliber. pp. 38. *Berl.* 1894. 8°.
      011850. g. 62. (6.)

LINTILHAC (E.) Les Félibres à travers leur
monde. pp. 136. *Paris*, 1895. 8°.
      011850. g. 67.

MICHEL (S.) Notes et documents pour servir à
l'histoire du mouvement félibréen à Paris.
pp. 283. *Paris*, 1894. 12°. 011850. eee. 15.

P.P. *Montpellier.* Le Félibrige latin.
Montpellier, 1890, *etc.* 8°.   PP. 4382. bca.

RESTORI (A.) Letteratura provenzale. pp. 220.
Milano, 1891. 8°.   012200. h. 22.

—— Histoire de la Littérature provençale.
Montpellier, 1894, *etc..* 8°.   011850. g.

ROQUE-FERRIER (A.) Le Midi de la France; ses
poètes et ses lettrés. pp. 534. *Paris*, 1892. 8°.
      011824. h. 58.

PROVENÇAL LANGUAGE, etc.—*cont.*

TERRIS (J. de) Roumanille et la Littérature provençale. pp. 78. *Paris*, 1894. 8°.
      011850. i. 61. (10.)

See also FRENCH LANGUAGE, *Dialects and History :* ROMANCE LANGUAGES.

PROVENCE. CASTANIER (P.) Histoire de
la Provence dans l'antiquité.
Paris, 1893, *etc.* 8°.   010171. m.

BABEAU (A.) Le Maréchal de Villars, gou-
verneur de Provence. pp. 306. *Paris*, 1892. 8°.
      010662. h. 17.

GOULD (S. B.) In Troubadour-land. pp. 339.
Lond. 1891. 8°.   010171. h. 36.

JANVIER (T. A.) An embassy to Provence.
pp. 132. *N.Y.* 1893. 8°.   010171. e. 22.

MARIÉTON (P.) La Terre provençale. pp. 566.
Paris, 1890. 8°.   10174. bb. 17.

NICATI (W.) À propos de la Constitution d'une
Université à créer en Province. pp. 47.
Paris, 1891. 8°.   Pam. 17.

PARROCEL (É.) Les beaux-arts en Provence.
pp. 102. *Paris*, 1889. 8°.   7807. m. 1.

PENNELL (J.) and (E. R.) Play in Provence.
pp. 202. *Lond.* 1892. 8°.   010171. e. 11.

PRADELLE (J.) En Provence. pp. 322.
Paris, 1890. 8°.   10174. bb. 21.

See also AIX: BASSES-ALPES : BOUCHES DU
RHONE, *Departments.*

PROVERBS. COWAN (F.) Dictionary of
proverbs of the English language relating to
the Sea. pp. 144. *Greenesburgh*, 1894. 8°.
      12304. g. 34.

MAIR (J. A.) Proverbs and family mottoes.
pp. 192. *Lond.* 1891. 8°.   12305. d. 38.

MACKAY (Æ. J. G.) Century of Scottish Proverbs and sayings. pp. 55.
Cupar-Fife, 1891. 16°.   12304. cc. 26.

STANDING (B.) Anecdotes and proverbs. pp. 183.
Lond. 1891. 8°.   12305. c. 47.

KRISTENSEN (E. T.) Danske Ordsprog og mund-
held. pp. 656. *Kjøbenh.* 1890. 8°. 12305. k. 1.

NEES (F.) Bevingede engelske Ordsprog.
pp. 40. *Christiania*, 1890. 8°.   12305. d. 47.

GUICHARD (G.) Uno pugna de Prouverbes dou-
finens. 1889. 8°. Ac. Grenoble. *Académie
Delphinale.* Bulletin. Ser. 4. Tom. 2.
      Ac. 3401.

LESPY (V.) Dictons et Proverbes du Béarn.
pp. 285. *Pau*, 1892. 8°.   12305. k. 11.

LORENZO, *da Volturino.* La Scienza pratica.
Dizionario di proverbi. pp. 701.
Quaracchi, 1894. 4°.   12304. l. 19.

LOUBENS (D.) Les Proverbes de la langue française. pp. 304. *Paris*, 1888. 8°. 12305. d. 36.

M., M. L. Proverbs. With glossary. pp. 211.
Arbroath, 1895. 16°.   012305. i. 1.

PAYNE (J. B. de V. P.) French Idioms and
Proverbs. pp. 162. *Lond.* 1893. 8°.
      12950. cc. 24.

SCHOLLEN (M.) Aachener Sprichwörter und
Redensarten. 1886. 8°. Ac. Aix-la-Chapelle.
Aachener Geschichtsverein. Zeitschrift. Bd. 8.
      Ac. 7008.

OTTO (A.) Die Sprichwörter der Römer.
pp. 436. *Leipz.* 1890. 8°.   12933. f. 34.

MUSATTI (C.) Proverbi veneziani. pp. 34.
Venezia, 1891. 8°.   012305. ee. 5. (2.)

ECKART (R.) Niederdeutsche Sprichwörter.
pp. 586. *Braunschweig*, 1893. 8°. 12972. h. 20.

B. y M., D. L. Paremiología, ó tratado exposi-
tivo de los apotegmas proverbiales. pp. 304.
Valladolid, 1889. 8°.   12305. k. 5.

PROVERBS—*continued.*

SBARBI (J. M.) Monografía sobre los refranes y proverbios castellanos. pp. 412.
Madrid, 1891. 8°.   11899. h. 44.

DOYENHART (A.) A. D. et son Supplément des proverbes basques. pp. 24. *Bayonne*, 1892. 8°.
                                                012305. ee. 5 (3.)

HOERMANN (L. v.) Haussprüche aus den Alpen. pp. 201. *Leipz.* 1890. 32°.   12304. a. 57.

BAYAN (G.) Armenian Proverbs and sayings. pp. 58. *Venice*, 1889. 12°.   889. g. 15.

Ac., *etc.* The Hague. *K. Istituut voor de Taal-, en Volkenkunde van Nederlandsch Indië.* HUR-GRONJE (C. S.) Mekkanische Sprichwörter. pp. 144. *Haag*, 1886. 8°.   14579. d. 22.

JEWETT (J. R.) Arabic Proverbs. 1891. 8°. Ac. *Boston. American Oriental Society.* Journal. Vol. 15. No. 1.   Ac. 8824.

BOUCHE (P.) Les Noirs peints par eux-mêmes. pp. 144. 1883. 8°. JEROME, *Saint.* Œuvre de Saint Jérome, *etc.* Fasc. 1.   12902. cc.

TAYLOR (W. E.) African Aphorisms. pp. 182. *Lond.* 1891. 8°.   4429. aa. 7.

SMITH (A. H.) Proverbs of the Chinese. pp. 2. 384. *Shanghai*, 1888. 8°.   12304. f. 34.

AIMAN (S.) and NARASIMHA RAU, *Ubhayada.* Popular Canarese Proverbs. pp. 22.
Mangalore, 1894. 12°.   14176. d. 43.

HANAMANTA GOVINDA JŌSI. Samati-Sangraha. Collection of Canarese Proverbs. pp. 52.
Belgaum, 1894. 8°.   14176. d. 44.

MAHĀSUKHA CHUNĪLĀLA SHĀH. Proverbs, Gujarati and English. pp. 40.
Ahmedabad, 1892. 16°.   14146. e. 29.

CHHANŪ LĀLA GUPTA. Bunch of Proverbs. English with equivalents in Urdu, Hindi and Persian. pp. 60. *Delhi*, 1892. 12°.
                                            14119. a. 26. (2.)

CHRISTIAN (J.) Behar Proverbs. pp. 256. 1891. 8°. *Trübner's Oriental Series.* 2318. f.

MENDIS (N.) Sinhalese and European Proverbs, *etc.* pp. 74. *Colombo*, 1890. 8°. 14165. f. 34.

LAZARUS (J.) Dictionary of Tamil Proverbs. pp. 662. *Madras*, 1894. 8°.   14170. k. 76.

TAMIL PROVERBS. Tamil Proverbs with English equivalents. pp. 12. *Madras*, 1893. 8°.
                                              14170. k. 58.

WAZĪR AḤMAD. English Proverbs, with Urdu equivalents. pp. 52. *Bareilly*, 1892. 16°.
                                            14119. a. 26. (1.)

PROVIDENCE, Rhode Island. PROVIDENCE. Early records of the town of Providence. pp. 139. *Providence*, 1892. 4°.   10409. d. 27.

PRUSSIA. [*See note on page 1.*]

Army. *See* GERMANY.

Constitution and Government.

BAUMANN (J.) Preussisch? oder zugleich Deutsch und allgemeinmenschlich? pp. 181.
Frankf. 1894. 8°.   8074. bb. 45.

GNEIST (H. R. v.) Die nationale Rechtsidee von den Ständen und das preussische Dreiklassen-wahlsystem. pp. 272. *Berl.* 1894. 8°.
                                              8008. dd. 7.

LEIDIG (E.) Preussisches Stadtrecht. pp. 552. *Berl.* 1891. 8°.   5606. e. 10.

Ac. Berlin. *Societas Scientiarum.* Acta Borussica. Denkmäler der preussischen Staatsverwaltung im 18. Jahrhundert. *Berl.* 1892, *etc.* 8°.
                                              Ac. 855/10.

PRUSSIA. Constitution of the Kingdom of Prussia. 31 Jan. 1850. pp. 54. 1894. 8°. Ac. *Philadelphia. American Academy.* Annals (Supplement). Vol. v. No 2.   Ac. 2383.

PRUSSIA.—Constitution, etc.—*continued.*

KUERSCHNER (J.) Das preussische Abgeordnetenhaus. pp. 455. *Stuttgart*, 1894. 32°.
                                              8073. aa. 9.

See also infra: History: GERMANY: LOCAL GOVERNMENT.

Evangelical Church.

See EVANGELICAL CHURCH.

History.

BERNER (E.) Geschichte des preussischen Staates. *München*, 1890, *etc.* 8°. 9386. g.

BUSSLER (W.) Preussische Feldherren und Helden. *Gotha*, 1890, *etc.* 8°.   010707. h.

COLLMANN (K. F.) Preussische Geschichte. *Greiz*, 1892, *etc.* 8°.   9385. h. 9.

DONDORFF (H.) Aus drei Epochen preussischer Geschichte. pp. 118. *Berl.* 1892. 8°.
                                              9385. f. 11.

EVERS (E.) Brandenburgisch-preussische Geschichte. pp. 623. *Berl.* 1892. 8°. 9385. e. 1.

P.P. *Berlin.* Hohenzollerische Forschungen. *Berl.* 1891, *etc.* 8°.   P.P. 3545. h.

PRINZ (P.) Quellenbuch zur brandenburgisch-preussischen Geschichte. *Freiburg*, 1892, *etc.* 8°.
                                              9385. f. 12.

ROGGE (B.) Das Buch von den preussischen Königen. pp. 544. *Hannover*, 1891. 8°.
                                              9386. g. 1.

SCHMID (L.) Die Könige von Preussen sind Hohenzollern nicht Abenberger. pp. 113.
Berl. 1892. 8°.   9914. f. 21.

ROGGE (B.) Vom Kurhut zur Kaiserkrone. *Hannover*, 1892, *etc.* 8°.   9906. ee.

BISCHOFF (E.) Die Camarilla am preussischen Hofe. pp. 50. *Leipz.* 1895. 8°.   9386. e. 6.

RICHTER (J. W. O.) Brandenburg-Preussens Vorzeit. pp. 255. *Hannover*, 1892. 8°.
                                              9385. eee. 6.

JOACHIM (E.) Die Politik des letzten Hochmeisters in Preussen. 1892, *etc.* 8°. Prussia. Staatsarchive. Publicationen. Bd. 50. 9386. eee.

Ac. Konigsberg. *Verein für die Geschichte der Provinz Preussen.* Rechnungen über Heinrich von Derby's Preussenfahrten 1390-92. pp. 228. *Leipz.* 1893. 8°.   Ac. 7351/5.

LEWINSKI (L.) Die brandenburgische Kanzlei, 1411-70. pp. 188. *Strassb.* 1893. 8°.
                                              09325. h. 9.

BRANDENBURG (E.) König Sigmund und Kurfürst Friedrich I. von Brandenburg. pp. 220. *Berl.* 1891. 8°.   9326. dd. 4.

GAEHTGENS (P.) Die Beziehungen zwischen Brandenburg und Pommern, 1440-70. pp. 152. *Giessen*, 1890. 8°.   9386. f. 13.

Ac. Konigsberg. *Verein für die Geschichte der Provinz Preussen.* NOSTITZ (C. v.) Kaspars von Nostitz Haushaltungsbuch des Fürstenthums Preussen. 1578. pp. 420.
Leipz. 1893. 8°.   Ac. 7351/4.

BONNELL (W.) Bilder aus drei Jahrhunderten preussischer Geschichte. *Berl.* 1891, *etc.* 8°.
                                              9385. f. 10.

MUELVERSTEDT (G. A. v.) Die brandenburgische Kriegsmacht unter dem Grossen Kurfürsten. pp. 813. *Magdeburg*, 1888. 8°.   8830. l. 24.

SCHROETTER (F. v.) Die preussische Heeresverfassung unter dem Grossen Kurfürsten. pp. 157. 1892. 8°. SCHMOLLER (G.) Staatswissenschaftliche Forschungen. Bd. 11.   8205. dd.

FEY (C.) Der Anteil der Jesuiten an der preussischen Königskrone von 1701. pp. 46.
Leipz. 1892. 8°.   9008. g. 10. (7.)

THOEMES (N.) Der Anteil der Jesuiten an der preussischen Königskrone von 1701. pp. 112.
Berl. 1892. 8°.   9008. g. 12. (8.)

PRUSSIA.—History—*continued.*

REIMANN (G.) Abhandlungen zur Geschichte Friedrichs des Grossen. pp. 163.
Gotha, 1892. 8°. 10704. i. 16.

LAVISSE (E.) La Jeunesse du grand Frédéric. pp. 451. *Paris*, 1891. 8°. 10704. f. 32.

—— The Youth of Frederick the Great. pp. 471. *Lond.* 1891. 8°. 10704. ccc. 22.

—— Le grand Frédéric avant l'avènement. pp. 373. *Paris*, 1893. 8°. 10704. k. 1.

HUELSEN (C. W.) Unter Friedrich dem Grossen. pp. 207. *Berl.* 1890. 8°. 10704. ccc. 21.

CARLYLE (T.) Battles of Frederick the Great. Abstracted from Carlyle's Frederick the Great. pp. 245. *Lond.* 1892. 8°. 9077. ccc. 12.

GERMANY. *Army. Staff.* Die Kriege Friedrichs des Grossen. *Berl.* 1890, *etc.* 8°. 9072. g.

LEHMANN (M. L. E.) Friedrich der Grosse. pp. 140. *Leipz.* 1894. 8°. 9078. ee. 38.

NAUDÉ (A.) Friedrichs des Grossen Angriffspläne gegen Oesterreich im 7-jährigen Kriege. *Marburg*, 1893, *etc.* 4°. 9073. h.

IMMICH (M.) Die Schlacht bei Zorndorf, 1758. pp. 156. *Berl.* 1893. 8°. 9073. e. 19.

DOPSCH (A.) Das Treffen bei Lobositz, 1756. *Graz*, 1892. 8°. 9079. i. 16.

WITTE (L.) Friedrich der Grosse und die Jesuiten. pp. 114. *Bremen*, 1892. 8°. 9008. g. 11. (8.)

UNZER (A.) Hertzbergs Anteil an den preussisch-österreichischen Verhandlungen, 1778/79. pp. 182. *Frankf.* 1890. 8°. 9079. h. 10.

RIQUETTI (H. G.) *Count de Mirabeau.* Secret History of the Court of Berlin. 2 vol. *Lond.* 1895. 8°. 10703. ee. 35.

HUEFFER (H.) Die Kabinetsregierung in Preussen und J. W. Lombard, 1797–1810. pp. 579. *Leipz.* 1891. 8°. 9386. f. 15.

BELLARDI (P.) Königin Luise. pp. 112. *Berl.* 1893. 8°. 10703. de. 34.

BONNAL (E.) La reine Louise de Prusse. pp. 322. *Paris*, 1891. 12°. 10703. de. 27.

MENZEL (P.) Königin Luise von Preussen. pp. 49. *Brieg*, 1892. 8°. 10601. aa. 32. (9.)

LETTOW-VORBECK (O. v.) Der Krieg von 1806 und 1807. 2 Bde. *Berl.* 1891, *etc.* 8°. 9079. k. 1.

TREUENFELD (B. v.) Auerstedt und Jena. 2 vol. *Hannover*, 1893. 8°. 9079. l. 11.

CAVAIGNAC (G.) La formation de la Prusse contemporaine. Le ministère de Stein. pp. 510. *Paris*, 1891. 8°. 9386. g. 2.

ECKART (T.) Erinnerungen an Friedrich Wilhelm IV. von Preussen. pp. 108. *Hannover*, 1891. 8°. 10703. de. 28.

KESSEL-ZEUTSCH (v.) *Baron.* Erinnerungen aus der Regierungszeit des Königs Friedrich Wilhelm IV. pp. 96. *Wiesbaden*, 1891. 8°. 010707. g. 32.

WALDOW, afterwards ERNSTHAUSEN (E. v.) Erinnerungen eines preussischen Beamten. pp. 432. *Bielefeld*, 1894. 8°. 9386. e. 5.

ONCKEN (W.) Das Zeitalter des Kaisers Wilhelm. 2 Bde. 1888, 90. 8°. Allgemeine Geschichte, *etc.* Hauptabth. IV. Th. 6. 2068. (31.)

KANNGIESSER (O.) Geschichte des Krieges von 1866. *Basel*, 1892, *etc.* 8°. 9080. f.

LUNEBURG. Von Lüneburg bis Langensalza. pp. 152. *Bremen*, 1894. 8°. 9080. d. 40.

DEUTSCH (E.) Die Preussen in Mähren, 1866. pp. 63. *Brünn*, 1891. 8°. 9007. ff. 4. (7.)

SCHMITT (R.) Die Gefechte bei Trautenau, Juni, 1866. pp. 271. *Gotha*, 1892. 8°. 9314. cc. 10.

GUTBIER (H.) Der Kampf bei Langensalza. pp. 275. *Langensalza*, 1891. 8°. 9366. bbb.

PRUSSIA.—History—*continued.*

WAGNER (A. L.) The campaign of Königgrätz. pp. 121. *Fort Leavenworth*, 1889. 8°. 9080. bbb. 21.

KOENIGGRAETZ. Führer über die Schlachtfeld. pp. 82. *Königgrätz*, 1892. 8°. 10215. aa. 20.

RATHLEF (G.) Bismarck and Oesterreich bis 1866. pp. 92. *Reval*, 1893. 8°. 8072. f. 4.

See also GERMAN-FRENCH WAR: GERMANY: HOHENZOLLERN, *House of.*

Law.

PRUSSIA. Beiträge zur brandenburg-preussischen Rechtsgeschichte. *Berl.* 1890, *etc.* 8°. 05604. i.

HASSENPFLUG (R.) Die erste Kammergerichts-ordnung Kurbrandenburgs. pp. 76. *Breslau*, 1895. 8°. 05604. h. 31.

DICKEL (C.) Beiträge zum preussischen Rechte. *Marburg*, 1891, *etc.* 8°. 5604. d.

GROTEFEND (G. A.) Das gesammte preussisch-deutsche Gesetzgebungs-Material. *Düsseldorf*, 1890, *etc.* 8°. 5605. ff.

WOLLENZIEN (J.) Die Bureau-Verwaltung bei den preussischen Justizbehörden. pp. 409. *Breslau*, 1890. 8°. 05604. h. 5.

See also GERMANY: LAND TENURES: LAW, *Profession of.*

Politics. *See* GERMANY.

Topography.

AC. Konigsberg. *Geographische Gesellschaft.* Die landeskundliche Litteratur der Provinzen Ost- und Westpreussen. *Königsberg*, 1892, *etc.* 8°. 011840. h.

GRITZNER (A. M. F.) Landes- und Wappenkunde der brandenburgisch-preussischen Monarchie. pp. 310. *Berl.* 1894. 8°. 9906. g. 15.

Trade and Finance.

FUISTING (B.) Das preussische Einkommen-steuergesetz, 24 Juni, 1891. pp. 605. *Berl.* 1892. 8°. 5606. cc. 3.

JASTROW (I.) Die Selbsteinschätzung und die geistige Arbeit. pp. 39. 1891. 8°. Volkswirthschaftliche Zeitfragen. Hft. 103. 8207. i.

NEUKAMP (E.) Das Gewerbesteuer-Gesetz für die preussische Monarchie. pp. 168. *Essen*, 1891. 8°. 5000. aaa. 14.

KEERL (A.) Das preussische Stempelrecht in den neuen Landestei'en der Monarchie. pp. 262. *Wiesbaden*, 1891. 8°. 5606. aaa. 13.

SATTLER (C.) Das Schuldenwesen des preussischen Staates. pp. 414. *Stuttgart*, 1893. 8°. 8228. ccc. 49.

BRAUN (C.) Von Friedrich dem Grossen bis zum Fürsten Bismarck. Geschichte der preussisch deutschen Wirthschaftspolitik. pp. 334. *Berl.* 1882. 8°. 8074. f. 36.

PRUSSIA. Dokumente zur Geschichte der Wirthschaftspolitik in Preussen. *Berl.* 1889, *etc.* 8°. 8074. ff.

RING (V.) Asiatische Handlungscompagnien Friedrichs des Grossen. pp. 336. *Berl.* 1890. 8°. 08227. f. 14.

ZIMMERMANN (A.) Geschichte der preussisch-deutschen Handelspolitik. pp. 850. *Oldenburg*, 1892. 8°. 08227. h. 21.

See also GERMANY.

PRUSSIA, East and West. *See* EAST PRUSSIA: WEST PRUSSIA.

PSORIASIS. *See* SKIN.

PSYCHIATRY. *See* INSANITY.

PSYCHOLOGY. AC. *International Congress of Psychology.* Proceedings. *Lond.* 1892, *etc.* 8°. AC. 3833. b.

PSYCHOLOGY—*continued.*

Ac. Germany. *Gesellschaft für psychologische Forschung.* Schriften. *Leipz.* 1891, *etc.* 8°.
Ac. 3782.

—— New Haven. *Yale College.* Studies from the Yale psychological Laboratory.
New Haven, 1893, *etc.* 8°. Ac. 2692. m.

APEL (M.) Kants Erkenntnistheorie, und seine Stellung zur Metaphysik. pp. 147.
Berl. 1895. 8°. 8464. cc. 45.

ARRÉAT (L.) Mémoire et Imagination. pp. 171.
Paris, 1895. 12°. 8462. bb. 49.

BAIN (A.) The Senses and the Intellect.
pp. 703. *Lond.* 1894. 8°. 2023. b.

BAKER (A.) Outlines of Logic and Psychology.
pp. 161. *Lond.* 1891. 8°. 8462. b. 21.

BALDWIN (J. M.) Handbook of Psychology.
pp. 394. *Lond.* 1891. 8°. 8467. dd. 31.

—— Elements of Psychology. pp. 372.
Lond. 1893. 8°. 8470. cc. 29.

—— Mental Development in the child and the race. pp. 496. *N.Y.* 1895. 8°. 8462. b. 41.

BIERVLIET (J. J. v.) Éléments de Psychologie humaine. pp. 317. *Gand,* 1895. 8°. 8466. d. 24.

BINET (A.) Introduction à la Psychologie expérimentale. pp. 146. *Paris,* 1894. 12°. 8462. h. 7.

—— Psychologie des grands calculateurs.
pp. 364. *Paris,* 1894. 8°. 8462. bb. 44.

BLEIBTREU (C.) Zur Psychologie der Zukunft.
pp. 292. *Leipz.* 1890. 8°. 8467. ff. 40.

BONFIGLIO (G.) Esame delle piu comuni opinioni sull' origine delle Idee. pp. 76.
Napoli, 1893. 8°. 8468. k. 27. (8.)

BOSURGI (D.) Studii di Psicologia applicata alla letteratura. pp. 76. *Catania,* 1892. 8°.
8461. b. 29. (8.)

BURNEY (S. G.) Studies in Psychology.
pp. 535. *Nashville,* 1890. 8°. 8462. b. 19.

CALDERWOOD (H.) Relations of Mind and Brain.
pp. 551. *Lond.* 1892. 8°. 2236. c. 6.

CARSTANJEN (F.) R. Avenarius' biomechanische Grundlegung der neuen allgemeinen Erkenntnistheorie. pp. 129. *München,* 1894. 8°.
8462. f. 46.

CARTWRIGHT (T.) Mental Science for teachers.
pp. 194. *Lond.* 1892. 8°. 8462. b. 23.

CHAMORRO (E. R.) Psicologia y logica. pp. 317.
Madrid, 1890. 8°. 8469. bbb. 50.

COMPAYRÉ (G.) Psychology applied to education.
pp. 216. 1895. 8°. Heath's Pedagogical Library.
8311. aaa.

DESSOIR (M.) Geschichte der neueren deutschen Psychologie. *Berl.* 1894, *etc.* 8°. 8485. ff.

ERNY (A.) Le Psychisme expérimental.
pp. 232. *Paris,* 1895. 12°. 8469. a. 1.

EXNER (S.) Entwurf zu einer physiologischen Erklärung der psychischen Erscheinungen.
Leipz. 1894, *etc.* 8°. 08461. i.

FÉRÉ (C.) La Pathologie des émotions. pp. 605.
Paris, 1892. 8°. 7660. g. 1.

FONSEGRIVE (G. L.) La causalité efficiente.
pp. 170. *Paris,* 1893. 12°. 8463. bb. 33.

FORD (C. L.) The synthesis of Mind. pp. 58.
Ann Arbor, 1893. 8°. 8462. g. 20.

FOUILLÉE (A.) La Psychologie des idées-forces.
2 tom. *Paris,* 1893. 8°. 8468. d. 26.

FULLERTON (G. S.) On Sameness and identity.
pp. 156. 1890. 8°. Ac. Philadelphia. *University of Pennsylvania.* Publications. Philosophical Series. No. 1. Ac. 2692. p./3.

GODFERNAUX (A.) Le Sentiment et la pensée.
pp. 224. *Paris,* 1894. 8°. 8462. e. 38.

GRANGER (F. S.) Psychology. pp. 235. 1891. 8°.
University Extension Series. 012202. g.

PSYCHOLOGY—*continued.*

GRIMM (E.) Zur Geschichte des Erkenntnisproblems. pp. 596. *Leipz.* 1890. 8°.
8486. e. 1.

HALLECK (R. P.) Psychology and psychic culture. pp. 368. *N.Y.* 1895. 8°. 08464. ee. 3.

HARTMANN (C. R. E. v.) Kants Erkenntnistheorie. pp. 256. *Leipz.* 1894. 8°.
8462. g. 26.

HAUFFE (G.) E. Beneckes Psychologie als Naturwissenschaft. pp. 116. *Leipz.* 1891. 8°.
8470. ccc. 12.

HEGEL (G. W. F.) Hegel's Philosophy of Mind.
pp. 202. *Oxf.* 1894. 8°. 2319. b. 12.

HEGLER (A.) Die Psychologie in Kants Ethik.
pp. 331. *Freiburg,* 1891. 8°. 8462. e. 8.

HIRSCH (W.) Genie und Entartung. Ein psychologische Studie. pp. 340. *Berl.* 1894. 8°.
8462. g. 40.

HÖFFDING (H.) Outlines of Psychology.
pp. 365. *Lond.* 1891. 8°. 8470. ccc. 10.

JACOBS (J.) The Need of a Society for experimental Psychology. pp. 5. *Lond.* 1886. 8°.
8463. d. 38. (6.)

JAESCHE (E.) Seele und Geist in streng wissenschaftlicher Auffassung. pp. 119.
Leipz. 1893. 8°. 8462. g. 21.

JAMES (W.) Text-book of Psychology. pp. 478.
Lond. 1892. 8°. 8467. bb. 34.

JANET (P.) Cours de Psychologie et de morale.
pp. 486. *Paris,* 1891. 12°. 8470. df. 2.

JASTROW (J.) Time-relations of mental phenomena. pp. 60. *N.Y.* 1890. 8°. 8470. ccc. 14.

JERUSALEM (W.) Die Urtheilsfunction. pp. 269.
Wien, 1895. 8°. 8465. ff. 30.

KAUFFMANN (M.) Fundamente der Erkenntnisstheorie. pp. 52. *Leipz.* 1890. 8°.
8463. d. 38. (11.)

KELLOGG (A. M.) Elementary Psychology.
pp. 50. *N.Y.* 1894. 8°. 8463. aaa. 36.

KERRY (B.) System einer Theorie der Grenzbegriffe. *Leipz.* 1890, *etc.* 8°. 8535. h. 22.

KODIS (J.) Zur Analyse des Apperceptionsbegriffes. pp. 202. *Berl.* 1893. 8°. 8462. c. 22.

KOEBER (R. v.) Jean Paul's Seelenlehre.
pp. 37. 1893. 8°. Ac. Germany. *Gesellschaft für psychologische Forschung.* Schriften.
Hft. 5. Ac. 3782.

KRAEPELIN (E.) Psychologische Arbeiten.
Leipz. 1895, *etc.* 8°. 8463. g.

KRAUSE (C. C. F.) Anfangsgründe der Erkenntnisslehre. pp. 224. *Leipz.* 1892. 8°.
8462. f. 14.

KROMAN (K.) Kurzgefasste Logik und Psychologie. pp. 389. *Kopenhagen,* 1890. 8°.
8469. d. 29.

KUELPE (O.) Grundriss des Psychologie.
pp. 478. *Leipz.* 1893. 8°. 8462. g. 33.

—— Outlines of Psychology. pp. 462.
Lond. 1895. 8°. 8465. gg. 13.

—— Ueber die Gleichzeitigkeit und Ungleichzeitigkeit von Bewegungen. 1891, *etc* 8°.
WUNDT (W.) Philosophische Studien.
Bd. 6, *etc.* 8463. e. 12.

LADD (G. T.) Outlines of Physiological Psychology. pp. 505. *Lond.* 1891. 8°. 8463. i. 23.

—— Psychology, descriptive and explanatory.
pp. 676. *Lond.* 1894. 8°. 8463. e. 1.

—— Primer of Psychology. pp. 244.
Lond. 1894. 8°. 8463. cc. 37.

—— Philosophy of Mind. pp. 414.
Lond. 1895. 8°. 8463. e. 32.

LEHMANN (A.) Die Hauptgesetze des menschlichen Gefühlslebens. pp. 356. *Leipz.* 1892. 8°.
8462. f. 20.

PSYCHOLOGY—*continued*.

LOMBROSO (P.) Saggi di Psicologia del bambino. pp. 284. *Torino*, 1894. 8°.   8462. h. 16.

LOMBROSO (C.) The Man of Genius. pp. 370. 1891. 8°. ELLIS (H. H.) Contemporary Science Series.   8709. i.

LONDON. *Psychological Association.* Journal of the Psychological Association. *Lond.* 1892, *etc.* 8°.   8632. ccc.

MEDLICOTT (H. B.) Evolution of Mind in man. pp. 48. *Lond.* 1892. 8°.   8461. b. 29. (9.)

MONRAD (M. J.) Psychologie. Grundrids til Brug ved Forelæsninger. pp. 59. *Christiania*, 1892. 8°.   8462. bb. 31.

MORGAN (C. L.) Introduction to comparative Psychology. pp. 382. 1894. 8°. ELLIS (H. H.) Contemporary Science Series.   8709. i.

—— Psychology for Teachers. pp. 251. *Lond.* 1894. 8°.   8462. bb. 41.

MUENSTERBERG (H.) Beiträge zur experimentellen Psychologie. *Freiburg*, 1889, *etc.* 8°.   8463. i. 21.

—— Ueber Aufgaben der Psychologie. pp. 182. 1891. 8°. Ac. Germany. *Gesellschaft für psychologische Forschung.* Schriften. Hft. 2.   Ac. 3782.

NIETO Y SERRANO (M.) Biología del Pensamiento. pp. 426. *Madrid*, 1891. 8°.   8462. f. 17.

NISBET (J. F.) The Insanity of Genius and inequality of human faculty. pp. 340. *Lond.* 1891. 8°.   8463. i. 25.

PAULHAN (F.) Les Caractères. pp. 237. *Paris*, 1894. 8°.   8409. l. 21.

PEILLAUBE (P.) Théorie des Concepts. Existence, origine, valeur. pp. 466. *Paris*, 1895. 8°.   8468. l. 4.

P.P. *Hamburg.* Zeitschrift für Psychologie der Sinnesorgane. *Hamb.* 1890, *etc.* 8°.   P.P. 1253. bb.

—— *London.* The Psychological Magazine. *Lond.* 1891, *etc.* 8°.   P.P. 597. be.

—— *New York.* The Psychological Review. *N.Y.* 1894, *etc.* 8°.   P.P. 1247. e.

—— *Paris.* L'Année psychologique. *Paris*, 1895, *etc.* 8°.   P.P. 1236. eb.

PIAT (C.) L'Intellect actif. pp. 199. *Paris*, 1890. 8°.   8466. gg. 28.

PRZYBYSZEWSKI (S.) Zur Psychologie des Individuums. *Paris*, 1892, *etc.* 8°.   8362. b. 26.

QUEYRAT (F.) L'Imagination et ses Variétés chez l'enfant. pp. 162. *Paris*, 1893. 12°.   8463. b. 44.

—— L'Abstraction et son rôle dans l'éducation intellectuelle. pp. 143. *Paris*, 1895. 8°.   8462. aa. 24.

REHMKE (J.) Lehrbuch der allgemeinen Psychologie. pp. 582. *Hamb.* 1894. 8°.   8462. dd. 9.

RICKERT (H.) Der Gegenstand der Erkenntniss. pp. 91. *Freiburg*, 1892. 8°.   8462. g. 17.

ROYSE (N. K.) A Study of Genius. pp. 312. *Chicago*, 1891. 8°.   8469. d. 28.

SANCTIS (S. de) I Fenomeni di contrasto in psicologia. 1895. 8°. Ac. Rome. *Società di Antropologia.* Atti. Vol. 2.   Ac. 6222.

SARLO (F. de) Le basi della Psicologia secondo il Rosmini. pp. 175. *Roma*, 1893. 8°.   8462. h. 6.

SAROLI (P.) Il Pensiero come movimento è una forza che può trasmettersi. pp. 42. *Napoli*, 1893. 8°.   Pam. 49.

SCHMID (A.) Erkenntnisslehre. 2 Bde. *Freiburg*, 1890. 8°.   8467. cc. 40.

SCHNEIDER (O.) Transcendentalpsychologie. pp. 467. *Leipz.* 1891. 8°   8467. h. 19.

PSYCHOLOGY—*continued*.

SCHOLTEN (H.) De Ziu en zijne deelen. pp. 112. *Deventer*, 1891. 8°.   8462. bb. 22.

SCHULTZE (F.) Vergleichende Seelenkunde. *Leipz.* 1892, *etc.* 8°.   8462. f. 13.

SCHUPPE (W.) Grundriss der Erkenntnistheorie. pp. 186. *Berl.* 1894. 8°.   8463. f. 34.

SCHWARZ (H. C.) Das Wahrnehmungsproblem. pp. 408. *Leipz.* 1892. 8°.   8462. e. 12.

—— Die Umwälzung der Wahrnehmungshypothesen durch die mechanische Methode, *etc.* 2 pt. *Leipz.* 1895. 8°.   8470. k. 1.

SCRIPTURE (E. W.) Ueber den associativen Verlauf der Vorstellungen. 1891. 8°. WUNDT (W.) Philosophische Studien. Bd. 7.   8463. e. 12.

SOMMER (R.) Grundzüge einer Geschichte der deutschen Psychologie. *Würzburg*, 1892, *etc.* 8°.   8486. ee.

SOURY (J.) Histoire des doctrines de Psychologie physiologique. pp. 464. *Paris*, 1891. 8°.   7660. e. 6.

STANLEY (H. M.) Studies in the evolutionary Psychology of feeling. pp. 392. *Lond.* 1895. 8°.   8463. e. 35.

STIBARIUS ( ) Die Kategorien der sinnlichen Perception. pp. 144. *Leipz.* 1890. 8°.   8466. gg. 31.

STRASOSKY (H.) J. F. Fries als Kritiker der kantischen Erkenntnistheorie. pp. 75. *Hamburg*, 1891. 8°.   8465. ee. 24. (11.)

STUMPF (C.) Psychologie und Erkenntnistheorie. 1891. 4°. Ac. Munich. *K. Akademie.* Abhandlungen. Bd. 19. Abt. 2.   Ac. 713/6.

SULLY (J.) Outlines of Psychology. pp. 490. *Lond.* 1892. 8°.   8469. c. 33.

—— The human Mind. 2 vol. *Lond.* 1892. 8°.   2023. c.

TWARDOWSKI (K.) Idee und Perception. pp. 46. *Wien*, 1892. 8°.   8468. k. 27. (7.)

UPHUES (G. K.) Psychologie des Erkennens. *Leipz.* 1893, *etc.* 8°.   8462. dd.

VIGNOLI (T.) Peregrinazioni psicologiche. pp. 404 *Milano*, 1895. 8°.   8470. cc. 32.

VOLKMANN VON VOLKMAR (W. F.) Lehrbuch der Psychologie vom Standpunkte des Realismus. *Cöthen*, 1894, *etc.* 8°.   8462. dd.

VORBRODT (G.) Psychologie des Glaubens. pp. 257. *Göttingen*, 1895. 8°.   4017. h. 10.

WHITTAKER (T.) Essays philosophical and psychological. pp. 370. *Lond.* 1895. 8°.   8462. e. 42.

WINN (J. M.) Exposition of the fallacies of the materialistic theory of physiological Psychology. pp. 29. *Lond.* 1894. 8°.   8461. b. 29. (12.)

WUNDT (W.) Vorlesungen ueber die Menschen- und Thierseele. pp. 495. *Hamburg*, 1892. 8°.   8462. g. 11.

—— Lectures on human and animal Psychology. pp. 454. *Lond*, 1894. 8°.   8463. h. 4.

—— Grundzüge der physiologischen Psychologie. 2 Bde. *Leipz.* 1893. 8°.   7407. cc. 15.

ZIEHEN (T.) Leitfaden der physiologischen Psychologie. pp. 176. *Jena*, 1891. 8°.   7660. g. 21.

—— Introduction to physiological Psychology. pp. 305. *Lond.* 1895. 8°.   8470 c. 37.

See also INSANITY AND PSYCHIATRY : PHILOSOPHY : SOUL. For the Psychology of the lower animals, *see* INSTINCT.

PTOMAINES. SARLES (É.) Contribution à l'étude des Ptomaines. pp. 47. *Montpellier*, 1891. 8°.   07305. k. 11. (5.)

See also BACTERIOLOGY : PUTREFACTION.

PUBLIC HEALTH. *See* SANITATION.

PUBLISHING. *See* BOOKSELLING.

PUERTO RICO. CEPIDO (F.) Conferencias de Abuli, celebradas con R. M. de Labra sobre política antillana. pp. 304. *Ponce*, 1890. 8°.
8042. aaa. 28.

DOMÍNGUEZ (J. de J.) La autonomia administrativa en Puerto-Rico. pp. 98.
Puerto-Rico, 1887. 8°. 8180. aaa. 16.

GÓMEZ (J. G.) La Isla de Puerto Rico.
Madrid, 1891, *etc.* 8°. 9771. cc. 7.

GOVIN Y TORRES (A.) El Enjuiciamiento civil en Puerto Rico. pp. 632. *Habana*, 1886. 8°.
6784. f. 12.

PORTO-RICO. Import Duties of Puerto Rico. 1891. 8°. U.S. *Bureau of American Republics.* Bulletin. No. 10. 08225. k. 1.

SARDÀ (A.) La Isla de Puerto Rico.
Madrid, 1889, 8°. Pam. 86.

See also SPAIN, *Colonies :* WEST INDIES.

PUGLIA. *See* APULIA.

PUJOLS, *Lot et Garonne.* GERBEAU (J. B.) Essai sur la Baronnie de Pujols. pp. 575 *Agen*, 1891. 8°. 010171. k. 2.

PULSE. EWART (W.) How to feel the Pulse. pp. 112. *Lond.* 1892. 8°. 7442. a. 29.

FREY (M. v.) Die Untersuchung des Pulses. pp. 260. *Berl.* 1892. 8°. 7461. gg. 18.

KRIES (J. v.) Studien zur Pulslehre. pp. 146. *Freiburg*, 1892. 8°. 7460. ff. 24.

See also BLOOD : HEART.

PUMPS. BALE (M. P.) Pumps and pumping. pp. 121. *Lond.* 1892. 8°. 8767. g. 7.

BARR (W. M.) Pumping Machinery. pp. 447. *Phila.* 1893. 8°. 8768. e. 29.

BJÖRLING (P. R.) Construction of Pump details. pp. 208. *Lond.* 1892. 8°. 8777. aaa. 30.

—— Pumps and pump motors.
Lond. 1895, *etc.* 4°. 8765. g.

COLYER (F.) Pumps and pumping machinery. *Lond.* 1892, *etc.* 8°. 8777. b. 40.

INNES (C. H.) The centrifugal Pump. Turbines and water-motors. pp. 178.
Manch. 1893. 8°. 8777. aaa. 31.

See also HYDRAULICS.

PUNISHMENT. STEINMETZ (S. R.) Ethnologische Studien zur ersten Entwicklung der Strafe. 2 Bde. *Leiden*, 1894. 8°. 6055. f. 8.

WINES (F. H.) Punishment and Reformation. Rise of the penitentiary system. pp. 339.
Lond. 1895. 8°. 6057. b. 39.

See also CRIME : LAW, *Criminal.*

Capital Punishment.

MAC MASTER (J.) Divine purpose of Capital Punishment. pp. 379. *Lond.* 1892. 8°.
8425. b. 61.

MANTEL (A.) Étude ethnographique sur la Peine de mort. pp. 47. *Paris*, 1894. 8°.
8425. c. 70. (12.)

OLIVECRONA (S. R. D. K.) De la Peine de mort. pp. 325. *Paris*, 1893. 8°. 8425. f. 23.

BERRY (J.) My Experiences as an Executioner. pp. 144. *Lond.* 1892. 8°. 6057. aa. 33.

HARTSHORNE (A.) Hanging in Chains. pp. 120. *Lond.* 1891. 12°. 6057. aa. 28.

CARDEVACQUE (A. de) Le bourreau à Arras. 1893. 8°. Ac. Arras. *Société pour l'Encouragement des Sciences.* Mémoires. Sér. 2. Tom. 24.
Ac. 255.

LENÔTRE (G.) La Guillotine et les exécuteurs des arrêts pendant la Révolution. pp. 378. *Paris*, 1893. 8°. 6056. ec. 33.

PUNISHMENT, Capital—*continued.*

LUCAS (J. M. C.) De l'état anormal en France de la répression en matière de crimes capitaux. 1888. 4°. Ac. Paris. *Académie des Sciences Morales.* Mémoires. Tom. 16. 2098. ff.

MAC DONALD (C. F.) Infliction of the death-penalty by means of Electricity. pp. 37.
N.Y. 1892. 8°. 07305. h. 19. (11.)

PUNJAB. MUHAMMAD LATÎF. History of the Panjáb. pp. 652. *Calcutta*, 1891. 4°.
9056. ff. 23.

GRIFFIN (*Sir* L. H.) Ranjit Singh. pp. 223. 1892. 8°. HUNTER (*Sir* W. W.) Rulers of India. 10603. dd.

—— The Panjab Chiefs. Historical and biographical notices. 2 vols. *Lahore*, 1890. 8°.
9056. ff. 24.

MASSY (C. F.) Chiefs and families of note in the Panjab. pp. 670. *Allahabad*, 1890. 8°.
9056. ff. 25.

RADFORD (O. C.) Notes for Panjab Probationers. pp. 65. *Lahore*, 1894. 8°. 8829. bbb. 50.

SIMPSON (W.) Sikh Initiation. pp. 10. 1893. 8°. Pam. 22.

GORE (F. St. J.) Light and shades of hill life in the Highlands of the Punjab. pp. 269.
Lond. 1895. 8°. 010057. i. 4.

MUHAMMAD LATIF. Lahore. pp. 426.
Lahore, 1892. 8°. 010057. k. 7.

PUNJAUB. A Note on administration of Justice in the Punjab. pp. 70. *Lahore*, 1890. 8°.
Pam. 33.

JAISÎ RĀMA. The Punjab Civil Law Manual. pp. 4. 97. 13. *Lahore*, 1892. 8°. 05319. i. 11.

FENTON (M. W.) Municipal manual for the Punjab. *Lahore*, 1890. 8°. 05319. k. 1.

Ac. London. *British Museum.* Catalogues of the Hindi and Panjabi printed books. By J. F. Blumhardt. 4 pt. *Lond.* 1893. 4°. 11901. i. 24.
See also AMBALA : AMRITSAR : FIROZPUR : LAW REPORTS.

PURGATORY. *See* ESCHATOLOGY.

PUS. *See* SUPPURATION.

PUSHTU LANGUAGE. Ac. London. *British Museum.* Catalogues of the Hindi and Pushtu printed books. By J. F. Blumhardt. 4 pt. *Lond.* 1893. 4°. 11901. i. 24.

DAMES (M. L.) Text book of the Balochi Language. 4 pt. *Lahore*, 1891. fol. 12907. g. 24.

GEIGER (W.) Etymologie und Lautlehre des Afghänischen. 1894. 4°. Ac. Munich. K. *Akademie.* Abhandlungen der phil.-philologischen Classe. Bd. 20. Ac. 713/6.

MUHAMMAD ISMA'IL KHĀN. Guide to Pukhto. pp. 215. *Abbottabad*, 1894. 12°. 14163. f. 1.

PUTREFACTION. BORDAS (F.) Étude sur la Putréfaction. pp. 220. *Paris*, 1892. 8°.
7407. f. 25.

See also BACTERIOLOGY : FERMENTATION : PTOMAINES.

PUY DE DÔME, Department. PUY DE DÔME, *Department.* Collection des inventaires des archives hospitalières. *Paris*, 1887, *etc.* 4°.
1814-15. b., *etc.*

BONNEFOY (G.) Histoire de l'administration civile dans le département du Puy-de-Dôme. *Paris*, 1895, *etc.* 8°. 10174. f.
See also AUVERGNE.

PWLLHELI. PWLLHELI. Guide to Pwllheli. pp. 45. *Pwllheli*, 1891. 8°. 10347. aa. 37. (4)

PYAEMIA. *See* SEPTIC DISEASES.

PYCNOGONIDAE. Morgan (T. H.) Contribution to the embryology and phylogeny of the Pycnogonids. pp. 76. *Baltimore*, 1891. 8°.
         7297. f. 17.

PYGMIES. *See* Dwarfs.

PYRAMIDS.
See Egypt, *Antiquities and Religion.*

PYRENEES. Blackburn (H.) Artistic travels in Normandy, the Pyrenees, *etc.* pp. 320. *Lond.* 1892. 8°.   10101. f. 1.

Camena d'Almeida (P.) Les Pyrénées. pp. 328. *Paris*, 1893. 8°.   010171. f. 43.

Dujardin (V.) Voyages aux Pyrénées. pp. 571. *Céret*, 1890. 8°.   10169. cc. 14.

Hugo (V. M.) *Viscount.* En Voyage. Alpes et Pyrénées. pp. 316. *Paris*, 1891. 12°.
         10106. ccc. 27.

Joanne (P.) Pyrénées. Guide Joanne. pp. 432. *Paris*, 1895. 8°.   10171. aaa. 29.

Leclercq (J.) Promenades dans les Pyrénées. pp. 240. *Tours*, 1890. 8°.   010171. k. 10.

Penck (A.) Die Eiszeit in den Pyrenäen. pp. 69. *Paris*, 1884. 8°.   Pam. 27.

Sacaze (J.) Inscriptions antiques des Pyrénées. pp. 576. 1892. 8°. Bibliothèque Méridionale. Sér. 2. Tom. 2.   12238. ee.

Trutat (E.) Les Pyrénées. pp. 371. *Paris*, 1894. 8°.   10174. b. 36.
See also Andorra : Mountains.

PYRENOMYCETES. *See* Fungi.

PYROTECHNY. *See* Fireworks.

QUADI. *See* Moravia.

QUAKERS. *See* Friends, *Society of.*

QUARANTINE. Lutsch (W.) Die Handhabung der Schiffs-Quarantäne. pp. 25. 1892. 8°. Deutsche Zeit- und Streit-Fragen. Hft. 96.   12209. f.

Wyman (W,) Quarantine. 1894. 8°. Rohé (G. H.) Text-Book of Hygiene.   7390. g. 26.

QUATERNIONS. Hardy (A. S.) Elements of Quaternions. pp. 230. *Bost.* 1881. 8°.
         8530. h. 21.

Hime (H. W. L.) Outlines of Quaternions. pp. 190. *Lond.* 1894. 8°.   8535. aa. 42.

Mac Aulay (A.) Utility of Quaternions in physics. pp. 107. *Lond.* 1893. 8°. 3533. d. 22.

Molenbroek (P.) Theorie der Quaternionen. pp. 284. *Leiden*, 1891. 8°.   8548. dd. 39.

—— Anwendung der Quaternionen auf die Geometrie. pp. 257. 8. *Leiden*, 1893. 8°.
         8535. c. 13.

Wettum (T. B. v.) Researches on Quaternions. pp. 26. *Leyden*, 1894. 4°.   Pam. 38.
See also Mathematics.

QUEBEC, City. Buies (A.) Québec en 1900. pp. 65. *Québec*, 1893. 8°.   Pam. 45.

Chambers (E. T. D.) Guide to Quebec. pp. 129. *Quebec*, 1895. 8°.   10470. aaa. 54.

Chouinard (M.) Acte d'incorporation de la cité de Québec. pp. 237. *Québec*, 1890. 8°.
         06606. f. 18.

Fairchild (G. M.) Short account of ye Quebec Winter Carnival, 1894. pp. 140. *Quebec*, 1894. 8°.   10470. e. 30.

Gagnon (E.) Le Fort et le Château Saint-Louis, Québec. pp. 376. *Québec*, 1895, 8°.
         10470. dd. 37.

Holiwell (C. E.) Guide to Quebec and environs. pp. 90. *Quebec*, 1892. 8°.   Pam. 86.

QUEBEC, City—*continued.*
Le Moine (J. M.) Historical notes on Quebec. pp. 152. *Quebec*, 1890. 8°.   10470. aa. 47.

Würtele (F. C.) English Cathedral of Quebec. 1891. 8°. Ac. Quebec. *Literary Society.* Transactions. No. 20.   Ac. 8560.

QUEBEC, Province.
Adam (G. M.) Illustrated Quebec. pp. 90. *Montreal*, 1892. obl. 4°.   10460. df. 5.

Quebec. Guide to historic Quebec and Lower St. Lawrence. pp. 138. *Quebec*, 1892. 16°.
         10470. aa. 44.

—— *Legislative Assembly.* Nouvelle-France. Correspondance entre les autorités françaises et les gouverneurs. *Quebec*, 1893, *etc.* 4°. 9555. g.

Myrand (J. E.) 1690. Sir W. Phips devant Québec. pp. 428. *Québec*, 1893. 8°. 9555. e. 11.

Casgrain (H. R.) Instructions, ordres, plans de campagne et de défense, 1756–60. pp. 367. *Québec*, 1891. 4°.   8824. k. 33.

Quebec, *Legislative Assembly.* Assemblée législative. Séance du 28 mars 1883. Les Canadiens-Français aux États-Unis. pp. 34. *Quebec*, 1883. 8°.   Pam. 66.

Mercier (H.) Élections provinciales. 1890. Le Gouvernement Mercier. pp. 354. *Québec*, 1890. 8°.   8154. a. 9.

Tarte (J. I.) 1892. Procès Mercier. Les causes qui l'ont provoqué. pp. 195. *Montréal*, 1892. 8°.
         8154. dd. 11.
See also Canada.

Law.
Quebec. Les Codes de Québec. *Montréal*, 1889, *etc.* 12°.   6606. a.

—— Code Civil de Québec. pp. 687. *Montréal*, 1893. 8°.   6614. a. 8.

—— Code de Procédure civile de Québec. pp. 616. *Montréal*, 1893. 8°.   6614. a. 7.

Bedard (J. E.) Code-manuel des huissiers et des sherifs. pp. 346. *Québec*, 1892. 12°.
         6606. a. 8.

Quebec. Code municipal de Québec. pp. 639. *Montréal*, 1894. 8°.   6605. a. 6.

QUEDLINBURG. Duening (H. H. A.) Stift und Stadt Quedlinburg im 30-jährigen Kriege. pp. 65. *Quedlinburg*, 1894. 8°.   10240. c. 14.

—— Das Ende des Stifts Quedlinburg. pp. 43. *Quedlinburg*, 1891. 8°.   10106. de. 8. (4.)

Kleemann (S.) Die Familiennamen Quedlinburgs. pp. 264. *Quedlinburg*, 1891. 8°.
         12962. h. 41.

Quedlinburg. *K. Gymasium.* Festschrift zur Feier des dreihundertundfünfzigjährigen Bestehens des Gymnasiums. 5 pt. *Quedlinburg*, 1890. fol.   8357. l. 17.

QUEENSLAND. Coote (W.) History of Queensland, 1770–1881. Vol. 1. pp. 256. *Brisbane*, 1882. 8°.   9781. aaa. 5.

Russell (H. S.) Genesis of Queensland. pp. 633. *Sydney*, 1888. 8°.   9781. g. 2.

Bicknell (A. C.) Travel in northern Queensland. pp. 219. *Lond.* 1895. 8°. 10491. d. 33.

Coote (W.) Capital Value and indebtedness of the Colony. pp. 14. *Brisbane*, 1883. 8°.
         8228. g. 59. (5.)

Hardie (D.) Notes on some common diseases in Queensland. pp. 132. *Brisbane*, 1893. 8°.
         07686. k. 7.

London. *Colonial Exhibition.* Queensland : its resources and institutions. *Lond.* 1886. 8°.
         7959. d. 8.

—— Catalogue of Exhibits in the Queensland Court. pp. 173. *Brisbane*, 1886. 8°. 7959. d. 11.

QUEENSLAND—*continued.*

PITCAIRN (W. D.) Two years among the savages of New Guinea. With notes on north Queensland. pp. 286. *Lond.* 1891. 8°.   10492. c. 34.

RANDALL (G.) Letters from Queensland farmers. pp. 20. *Lond.* 1885. 8°.   Pam. 1.

QUEENSLAND. Handbook for Queensland. pp. 71. *Lond.* 1893. 8°.   Pam. 87.

—— Letters from Queensland. By "The Times" special correspondent. pp. 110. *Lond.* 1893. 8°.   10492. aaa. 52.

—— Queensland. Fresh fields and pastures new. pp. 15. *Lond.* 1892. 4°.   Pam. 87.

—— Souvenir of Floods. Southern Queensland, Feb. 1893. *Brisbane,* 1893. 4°.   1787. aa. 22.

TYRWHITT (W. S. S.) The new chum in Queensland. pp. 214. *Oxf.* 1887. 8°.   10491. bb. 35.

WAWN (W. T.) South Sea Islanders and the Queensland labour trade. pp. 440. *Lond.* 1893. 8°.   10491. ff. 15.

See also AGRICULTURE: AUSTRALIA: GOLD AND SILVER: MINERALOGY.

QUEVILLY, Petit. DUCHEMIN (P.) Petit-Quevilly et le Prieuré de Saint-Julien. pp. 301. *Pont-Audemer,* 1890. 8°. 010171. f. 23.

QUIBERON. CADOUDAL (L. G. de) Auray et Quiberon. 1892. fol. BRITTANY. Paysages et Monuments. Livr. 1-13.   K.T.C. 15. b.

QUICHUA LANGUAGE.
See INDIAN LANGUAGES.

QUICKSILVER. *See* MERCURY.

QUOITS. WALKER (J. M.) Rounders, Quoits, *etc.* pp. 71. 1892. All England Series.
                                        7908. df.

See also GAMES.

QUOTATIONS. BARTLETT (J.) Familiar Quotations. pp. 1158. *Lond.* 1891. 8°.
                                        2288. a. 5.

BELTON (J. D.) Literary manual of foreign Quotations. pp. 249. *N.Y.* 1891. 8°. 12305. k. 9.

BLACK (A.) Treasure trove. pp. 100. *Lond.* 1894. 8°.   012357. h. 60.

BOMBAUGH (C. C.) Gleanings for the curious. pp. 864. *Lond.* 1890. 8°.   12331. i. 25.

BREWER (E. C.) Dictionary of phrase and fable. pp. 1440. *Lond.* 1895. 8°.   2035. b.

BUECHMANN (G.) Geflügelte Worte. pp. 699. *Berl.* 1895. 8°.   012305. k. 1.

CLOUSTON (W. A.) Book of wise sayings, from Eastern sources. pp. 134. *Lond.* 1893. 8°.
                                        12305. cc. 48.

COXETER (G. M.) Vera Verba. pp. 79. *Lond.* 1891. 16°.   3457. dd. 7.

HUNT (V.) Great Poets birthday album. *Lond.* 1894. 8°.   11601. dd. 16.

LUMSDEN (H. S.) Thoughts for Book-lovers. pp. 95. *Aberd.* 1895. 8°.   011850. g. 60.

MOODIE (W.) Tools for Teachers. pp. 488. *Lond.* 1893. 8°.   4192. ee. 28.

SOUTHGATE (H.) Wealth and wisdom of Literature. [Collection of extracts, cuttings, *etc.*] 21 vol. 1880. 8°.   Banks. 4 d-ee.

SOUTHWICK (A. P.) Wisps of Wit and wisdom. pp. 265. *Lond.* 1892. 16°.   12314. d. 27.

W., C. M. Being and Doing: selection of helpful thoughts. pp. 370. *Liverp.* 1892. 8°.
                                        4401. p. 30.

WALSH (W. S.) Handy-book of Literary Curiosities. pp. 1104. *Lond.* 1893. 8°. 011824. f. 58.

WEBSTER (W. G.) Quotations from Greek, Latin, and modern foreign languages. 1890. 4°.
Webster's International Dictionary.   2112. g.

QUOTATIONS—*continued*

WOOD (J.) Dictionary of Quotations from English and foreign sources. pp. 659. *Lond.* 1893. 8°.
                                        12305. dd. 21.

MURR (J.) Altgriechische Weisheit. *Innsbruck,* 1891, *etc.* 8°.   11340. aa.

EICHHOLZ (C.) Lateinische Citate mit deutscher Uebersetzung. pp. 176. *Hamb.* 1893. 8°.
                                        12935. bb. 56.

ALEXANDRE (R.) Répertoires de Citations françaises. pp. 446. *Paris,* 1892. 8°. 12305. d. 49.

FINOD (J. de) Thousand flashes of French wit. pp. 251. *Lond.* 1890. 8°.   012314. e. 58.

EICHNER (W.) Aus Werkstätten des Geistes. pp. 800. *Frankf.* 1893. 8°.   012305. ee. 2.

KOFAHL (A.) Deutscher Zitaten-Schatz. pp. 281. *Leipz.* 1890. 8°.   12253. ccc. 1.

See also ANECDOTES.

RABBIT. CHRISTY (R. M.) Extermination of the Rabbit in Australasia. 1892. 8°.
                                7204. c. 17. (12.)

KEITH (G. W.) The Rabbit question. Across the rabbit warrens of New South Wales. pp. 32. *Brisbane,* 1892. 8°.   Pam. 42.

P.P. *Norwood.* The Fur Fanciers' Journal. *South Norwood,* 1891-93. 8°.   PP. 1859. cb.

SIMPSON (J.) The wild Rabbit in a new aspect. pp. 176. *Edinb.* 1895. 8°.   7206. b. 23.

WIGG (H. C.) The Rabbit question. pp. 6. *Melbourne,* 1888. 8°.   10827. bbb. 26. (2.)

See also RODENTS.

RABY, Durham. HODGSON (J. F.) Raby. 1887-93. 8°. Ac. Durham. *Architectural Society.* Transactions.   Ac. 5635.

RACING. CONTADES (G. de) *Count.* Bibliographie sportive. Les Courses en France, 1651-1890. pp. 154. *Paris,* 1892. 8°.
                                        011900. h. 2.

ASTLEY (*Sir* J. D.) Fifty years of my Life. 2 vol. *Lond.* 1894. 8°.   10816. cc. 26.

BAUME (L.) Autour des Courses. pp. 300. *Paris,* 1895. 8°.   07905. f. 33.

BLACK (R.) The Jockey Club and its founders. pp. 420. *Lond.* 1891. 8°.   7905. cc. 27.

—— Horse-Racing in England. pp. 356. *Lond.* 1893. 8°.   07905. h. 8.

CHETWYND (*Sir* G.) Racing Reminiscences. 2 vol. *Lond.* 1891. 8°.   7907. dd. 11.

COLOMBO. *Ceylon Turf Club.* Rules and orders. pp. 77. *Colombo,* 1891. 12°. 7907. df. 17. (1.)

CONSTABLE (H. S.) Something about Horses, *etc.* pp. 293. *Lond.* 1891. 8°.   012357. f. 10.

CURZON (L. H.) Mirror of the Turf. pp. 372. pp. 372. *Lond.* 1892. 8°.   7908. eee 13.

CUSTANCE (H.) Riding Recollections. pp. 304. *Lond.* 1894. 4°.   7905. g. 32.

DAY (W.) Reminiscences of the Turf. pp. 345. *Lond.* 1891. 8°.   7908. df. 11.

—— Turf celebrities I have known. pp. 290. *Lond.* 1891. 8°.   10804. e. 8.

DIXON (H. H.) "The Druid" Sporting Library. 5 vol. *Lond.* 1895. 8°.   {07905. f. 29.

G., A. Les Courses à Maurice de 1812-67. pp. 82. *Port-Louis,* 1894. 8°.   07905. i. 8.

GOODMAN (R.) The golden key to Turf Mysteries. 1895. 24°.   7912. a. 37.

GOULD (N.) On and off the Turf in Australia. pp. 244. *Lond.* 1895. 8°.   07905. ee. 1.

RACING—*continued.*

HOWARD (H. C.) *Earl of Suffolk and Berkshire.* Racing and Steeplechasing. pp. 439. 1893. 4°. Badminton Library.   2264. aa.

KENT (J.) Racing life of Lord G. C. Bentinck. pp. 482. *Edinb.* 1892. 8°.   10825. g. 4.

LONG ODDS. Horse Racing and the winners. pp. 58. *Lond.* 1892. 8°.   7907. ee. 34.

LOWE (C. B.) Breeding Racehorses by the figure system. pp. 262. *Lond.* 1895. 8°.   07905. l. 6.

MABBESSAN (de) *Baron.* Dictionnaire des Courses. pp. 88. *Paris,* 1895. 8°. 7912. aa. 39.

MUIR (J. B.) Ye Olde New-Markitt calendar. 1619 to 1719, *etc.* pp. 76. *Lond.* 1892. 8°.   7908. dd. 29.

PEDDIE (J.) Racing for Gold. pp. 308. *Lond.* 1891. 8°.   7912. aa. 5.

P.P. *Colombo.* Guide to the Ceylon turf. *Colombo,* 1890, *etc.* 8°.   P.P. 2575. t.

—— *Dublin.* Racing Calendar. By George Quin. *Dublin,* 1885, *etc* 12°.   P.P. 2512. l.

—— *London.* Sportsman's Monthly guide to the Turf. *Lond.* 1884, *etc.* 12°. & 8°. P.P. 2489. th.

RUSSELL (F.) In Scarlet and silk. pp. 295. *Lond.* 1895. 8°.   07905. g. 9.

SILBERER (V.) Turf-Lexicon. pp. 634. *Wien,* 1890. 8°.   7907. d. 37.

SIMPSON (J.) Ancient Stamford race articles, 1619-20. *Stamford,* 1890. 8°. 7912. ee. 1. (8.)

WARBURTON (F. T.) The Race Horse. pp. 270. *Lond.* 1892. 8°.   7906. d. 34.

COLOURS. Colours at a glance of the leading owners. *Manch.* 1889. 8°.   7906. ccc. 26.

MUIR (J. B.) Raciana; or Riders' colours of the British Turf, 1762—1883. pp. 188. *Lond.* 1890. 8°.   7907. i. 23.

B., L. L. Money-Making on the Stock Exchange and Racecourse. pp. 14. *Blackburn,* 1894. 8°.   08226. f. 23. (6.)

BRANDON. Practicable system of "Backing horses." *Manch.* 1893. 24°. 7915. de. 14. (6.)

CHILTON (C.) New Turf system. *Manch.* 1893. 12°.   Pam. 83.

—— Horses worth following. *Liverp.* 1890, *etc.* 8°.   7912. de.

—— New Book of Form. *Manch.* 1894, *etc.* 8°.   07905. e.

JONATHAN. Jonathan's Calculator. *Liverp.* 1893. 32°.   8548. aa. 33.

KING ( ) King's Electric S.P. ready reckoner. *Lond.* 1892. 8°.   8548. b. 32.

SUTCLIFFE (R.) Instantaneous Starting-price ready reckoner. *Lond.* 1893. 8°.   1882. d. 2. (78.)

TURF COUPLING SYSTEM READY RECKONER. The Turf Coupling System. *Lond.* 1891. 8°.   7906. aaa. 47.

WAY. Way to win money on Races. pp. 16. *Lond.* 1892. 16°.   7915. de. 19. (3.)

See also BETTING : HORSE : HORSEMANSHIP : TROTTING RACES.

RACKETS. BOUVERIE (E. O. P.) Rackets. 1894. 8°. Badminton Library.   2264. aa. 11.

MARSHALL (J.) Tennis, Rackets, *etc.* pp. 104. 1890. 8°. All England Series.   7908. df.

See also GAMES.

RADLEY COLLEGE. RADLEY. *College of St. Peter.* Calendar. *Oxf.* 1841, *etc.* 12°.   8364. a.

RAGLAN, Monmouthshire. RAGLAN. Views in Raglan. *Lond.* 1895. 8°. 10360. bbb. 68.

RAGUSA. GELCICH (G.) Di Ragusa e de' monumenti che sono in essa. pp. 123. *Ragusa,* 1883. 8°.   10105. ee. 12. (1.)

PISANI (P.) Num Ragusini ab omni jure Veneto usque ad sæc. XIV. immunes fuerint disputavit P. P. pp. 79. *Lutetiæ P.* 1893. 8°. 9314. g. 35.

RAILWAYS.

General : History : Finance.

ACWORTH (W. M.) The State in relation to railways. 1894. 8°. MACKAY (T.) Policy of Free Exchange.   08225. k. 5.

BEHR (F. B.) Lightning Express Railway service. pp. 32. *Lond.* 1893. 4°. 8766. ee. 41.

BARRY (J. W.) Railway appliances. pp. 331. 1890. 8°. GOODEVE (T. M.) Text-Books of science.   2244. a. 7.

BRICKA (C.) Cours de Chemins de fer. 1894, *etc.* 8°. LECHALAS (M. C.) Encyclopédie des Travaux Publics.   012216. i.

BOWES (I.) Rails and waterways. G. Stephenson and M. F. de Lesseps. pp. 62. *Manch.* 1893. 8°.   08235. f. 31.

CARPENTIER (A.) and MAURY (G.) Traité des Chemins de fer. 3 tom. *Paris,* 1894. 8°.   08235. i. 6.

CHICAGO. *Columbian Exposition.* Official Catalogue. Pt. VII. Transportation exhibits. pp. 60. *Chicago,* 1893. 8°.   7958. bb. 29.

COTSWORTH (M. B.) Railway measurer and calculator. pp. 225. *Leeds,* 1893. 12°.   8548. de. 26.

DREDGE (J.) Record of the Transportation exhibits at the Columbian Exposition. pp. 779. 1894. 4°. Engineering Series.   8755. m.

FRITH (H.) The Flying Horse. Story of the locomotive. pp. 290. *Lond.* 1893. 8°.   08235. g. 15.

HAARMANN (A.) Das Eisenbahn-Geleise. *Leipz.* 1891, *etc.* 8°.   8767. l. 27.

HACKWORTH (T.) Jubilee of the World's first public Railway. pp. 51. *Leamington,* 1892. 8°.   10827. aa. 39.

HOLE (J.) National Railways. pp. 408. *Lond.* 1895. 8°.   08235. g. 21.

HUMBERT (G.) Traité des Chemins de fer. 2 tom. *Paris,* 1891. 8°.   08235. m. 2.

KIRKMAN (M. M.) Science of Railways. 12 vol. *Chicago,* 1894. 8°.   08235. g. 19.

LEYGUE (L.) Chemins de fer. pp. 605. 1892. 8°. LECHALAS (M. C.) Encyclopédie des Travaux Publics.   012216. i.

MAC CAIN (C. C.) Compendium of Transportation theories. pp. 295. *Wash.* 1893. 8°.   08235. f. 43.

P.P. *London.* Railway Herald Magazine. *Lond.* 1895, *etc.* 8°.   P.P. 1804. g. and 741.

RAILWAYS. Railways and railway men. pp. 128. *Lond.* 1892. 8°.   08235. e. 5.

STRETTON (C. E.) Safe railway working. pp. 230. *Lond.* 1893. 8°.   8767. f. 26.

SÉBILLOT (A.) Les Chemins de fer à navires et leurs applications. pp. 24. *Paris,* 1890. 8°.   Pam. 76.

WILCZEK (E.) *Count.* Gedanken über die Sicherheit und Oekonomie des Eisenbahnbetriebes. pp. 62. *Wien,* 1893. 8°.   8235. f. 48.

BERNE. *Bernsche Spoorweg-Conventie.* De Bernsche Spoorweg-Conventie van 14 Oct. 1890. pp. 103. *'s Gravenh.* 1893. 8°.   08235. k. 1.

BOLAS (T.) Address to the International Railway Congress, London, 1895. *Lond.* 1895. 4°.   Pam. 76.

FISHER (J. A.) Railway Accounts and finance. pp 546. *Lond.* 1893. 8°.   08235. k. 3.

RAILWAYS.—General, etc.—*continued.*

GILPIN (W.) The Cosmopolitan Railway.
pp. 369.   *San Francisco,* 1890.   8°.
08235. f. 21.

H. A Zone System of passenger fares. pp. 55.
Lond. 1891. 8°.   Pam. 76.

HOLE (J.) National Railways. pp. 385.
Lond. 1893. 8°.   08235. g. 12.

KAUFMANN (W.) Die mitteleuropäischen Eisenbahnen, *etc.* pp. 289. *Leipz.* 1893. 8°.
6916. b. 25.

MAC EWEN (R.) How should Railway fares be
charged ? pp. 8. *Lond.* 1893. 8°.   Pam. 76.

ROSENTHAL (E.) Internationales Eisenbahn-
Frachtrecht. pp. 398. *Jena,* 1894. 8°.
05604. k. 8.

TROILIUS (C. R. W.) Staten og jernvägarne.
pp. 237. 77. *Stockholm,* 1890. 8°. 08235. f. 20.

TODD (M.) Railways of Europe and America.
pp. 293. *Bost.* 1893. 8°.   08235. g. 14.
See also infra : Railways of various Countries :
MACHINERY : TRANSPORTATION.

Accidents. *See* ACCIDENTS.

Engines. *See* MACHINERY.

Electric Railways.

CROSBY (O. T.) and BELL (L.) The Electric
Railway. pp. 409. *N.Y.* 1892. 8°. 8757. g. 41.

HASSLER (A.) Die elektrischen Eisenbahnsig-
nale. pp. 117. *Stuttgart,* 1895. 8°. 8757. d. 42.

HEDGES (K.) American Electric Street Railways. pp. 205. *Lond.* 1894. 4°.   8757. l. 16.

HERING (C.) Recent progress in Electric Railways. pp. 389. *N.Y.* 1892. 8°.   8757. bb. 35.

KOHLFUERST (L.) Die Fortentwicklung der elektrischen Eisenbahn-Einrichtung. pp. 296.
Wien, 1891. 8°.   8757. b. 18.

LUIGGI (L.) La nuova Ferrovia elettrica sotte-
ranea di Londra. pp. 20. *Roma,* 1891. 8°.
Pam. 76.

MARTINEZ (G.) La Trazione elettrica. pp. 347.
Milano, 1894. 8°.   8757. g. 35.

MUELLENDER (A.) Projet de Chemin de fer
électrique souterrain à Bruxelles. pp. 190.
Verviers, 1895. 4°.   8767. m. 10.

RECKENZAUN (A.) Electric Traction on railways
and tramways. pp. 422. *Lond.* 1892. 8°.
8757. cc. 32.

TREVERT (E.) Electric Railway engineering.
pp. 186. *Lynn,* 1892. 8°.   8757. g. 39.

WEISSENBRUCH (L.) Les Avantages de l'Électricité pour le freinage des trains de mar-
chandises. pp. 34. *Brux.* 1890. 8°. Pam. 79.

Law of Railways. *See infra : America :*
Germany : Great Britain and Ireland : India.

Light and Mountain Railways.

THOMPSON (C. L.) Catalogue of books and
articles, relating to Light Railways. pp. 39.
Lond. 1895. 8°.   11903. f. 33. (12.)

BALLARD (S.) Cheap Railways for rural districts.
pp. 11. *Malvern,* 1884. 8°.   Pam. 76.

SALWEY (E. R.) Light Railways as a means of
exploration. pp. 109. *Lond.* 1890. 8°.
08235. f. 14.

UNRUH (C. M. v.) Die Kleinbahnen. pp. 141.
Bromberg, 1893. 8°.   08235. i. 3.

WHITE (J. W.) Light Railways. Papers.
pp. 128. *Lond.* 1895. 4°.   8768. l. 25.

LÉVY-LAMBERT (A.) Chemins de fer funicu-
laires. pp. 334. 1894. 8°. LECHALAS (M. C.)
Encyclopédie des travaux publics.   012216. i.

Machinery. *See* MACHINERY.

RAILWAYS—*continued.*

Military Railways, etc.

AUSTRIA. Normen für die Feldausrüstung der K.
K. Eisenbahn Compagnien. *Wien,* 1894, *etc.* 8°.
8825. bbb.

FERRARIUS (M.) Die Eisenbahnen und die
Kriegführung. pp. 30. 1890. 8°. Deutsche
Zeit- und Streitfragen. No. 66.   12209. f.

FROELICH (L.) Du Transport des blessés sur voies
ferrées. pp. 27. 4. *Frauenfeld,* 1892. 8°. Pam. 29.

G. B. & I. *Royal Engineers.* Manual of military
Railways. 1889. pp. 95. *Lond.* 1889. 8°.
8830. k. 24.

Street Railways.

HEDGES (K.) American electric Street Railways.
pp. 205. *Lond.* 1894. 4°.   8757. l. 16.

HIGGINS (E. E.) Street Railway investments.
pp. 102. *N.Y.* 1895. 8°.   08235. f. 57.

HAUPT (H.) Street Railway motors. pp. 213.
Phila. 1893. 8°.   8767. f. 30.

MACDERMOTT (F.) Railway system of London.
pp. 20. *Lond.* 1891. 8°.   Pam. 76.

SMITH (J. B.) Treatise upon cable or rope
traction as applied to street railways. pp. 195.
Lond. 1887. 8°.   8767. l. 21.

DEMAREST (T. F. C.) Rise and growth of Elevated Railroad Law. pp. 278.
N.Y. 1894. 8°.   6615. dd. 1.

BOOTH (H. J.) Treatise on the law of Street
Railways. pp. 749. *Phila.* 1892. 8°.
06616. g. 22.

Railways of various Countries.
Algeria, the Sahara, etc.

COURAN (J.) Les Chemins de fer de l'Algérie-
Tunisie. pp. 190. *Paris,* 1891. 8°. 08235. h. 34.

FRANCE. *Ministère des Travaux Publics.* Chemin
de fer transsaharien. *Paris,* 1890, *etc.* 4°.
08235. m.

ROLLAND (G.) Le Transsaharien. pp. 131.
Paris, 1891. 8°.   8028. e. 27.

SÉBILLOT (A.) Le Transafricain. pp. 67.
Paris, 1893. 8°.   Pam. 76.

America, North, United States and
Canada.

BERG (W. G.) Building and Structures of
American Railroads. pp. 500. *N.Y.* 1893. 4°.
7820. h. 15.

BUSBEY (T. A.) Biographical directory of the
railway officials of America. pp. 418.
Chicago, 1893. 8°.   08235. i. 8.

CLARK (F. C.) State Railroad commissions, and
how they may be made effective. pp. 110.
1891. 8°. Ac. *Saratoga. American Economic
Association.* Publications. Vol. 6. No. 6.
Ac. 2388.

DORSEY (E. B.) English and American Railroads. pp. 142. *N.Y.* 1887. 8°.   08235. f. 36.

GOMEL (C.) Les droits de l'État sur les tarifs de
Chemins de fer en Angleterre et aux États-unis.
pp. 28. *Paris,* 1891. fol.   Pam. 76.

GREGORY (G.) Principal American Railroads.
History and Prospects. pp. 64. *Lond.* 1892. 8°.
Pam. 76.

LARRABEE (W.) The Railroad question. pp. 488.
Chicago, 1893. 8°.   08235. g. 17.

LEWIS (G. H.) National Consolidation of the
Railways of the U.S. pp. 326. *N.Y.* 1893. 8°.
08235. g. 18.

MANN (E. D.) Shall the Government own our
Railways. pp. 16. *N.Y.* 1894. 8°.   Pam. 76.

RAPALJE (S.) and MACK (W.) Digest of Railway decisions. *Northport,* 1895, *etc.* 8°. 6617. e.

STERNE (S.) The Railway problem.
N.Y. 1880. 8°.   08235. f. 54.

RAILWAYS.— America, North, etc. — *continued.*

STERNE (S.) The Railway question. Statement made to the U.S. Select Committee on interstate commerce. pp. 39. *Wash.* 1885. 4°. 08235. f. 48.

—— Railway reorganization. pp. 53. *N.Y.* 1890. 8°.   08235. f. 47.

—— Recent Railroad failures and their lessons. pp. 20. *N.Y.* 1894. 8°.   08235. f. 55.

STICKNEY (A. B.) The Railway problem. pp. 249. *St. Paul, Minn.,* 1891. 8°. 08235. g. 8.

U.S. *Bureau of Labour.* Railway labour. pp. 888. 1890. 8°. Annual Report of the Bureau.   8275. k.

VAN OSS (S. F.) American Railways as investments. pp. 815. *Lond.* 1893. 8°. 08235. f. 28.

—— American Railroads and British investors. pp. 188. *Lond.* 1893. 8°.   08235. g. 13.

BOOTH (H. J.) Treatise on the law of Street Railways. pp. 749. *Phila.* 1892. 8°. 06616. g. 22.

DEMAREST (T. F. C.) Rise and growth of elevated Railway Law. pp. 278. *N.Y.* 1894. 8°.   6615. dd. 1.

CANADA. *Grand Trunk Railway Company.* Official Time Tables. pp. 64. *Toronto,* 1892. 8°.   08235. f. 37.

INVESTOR. Handbook of Railway Statistics. pp. 36. *Lond.* 1893. 12°.   8235. aa. 67.

PÉRISSÉ (L.) and ROY (A. V.) Le Canadian Pacific Railway. 1894. 8°. Ac. Paris. *Société des Ingénieurs.* Mémoires. Sér. 5. Ann. 47.   Ac. 4305.

CANADA. *Grand Trunk Railway.* Useful information for Tenant Farmers. *Toronto,* 1892. 16°.   Pam. 86.

BUGLER, GRAHAM AND PHILLIPS. Grand Trunk Railway. Traffic book. *Lond.* 1890. obl. 16°.   8235. a. 98.

ANGERS (A. R.) Chemin de fer de la Baie des Chaleurs. Dossier officiel. pp. 67. *Québec,* 1891. 8°.   Pam. 76.

PENNSYLVANIA RAILROAD. Pennsylvania Railroad to the Columbian Exposition. pp. 123. *Phila.* 1893. 8°.   10411. cc. 40.

DAVIS (J. P.) The Union Pacific Railway. pp. 247. *Chicago,* 1894. 8°.   08235. f. 39.

SAN FRANCISCO. Ocean to Ocean. San Francisco, Chicago, New York. pp. 24. *San Francisco,* 1893. obl. 12°.   10413. a. 16.

See also supra : General : Electric : Street Railways.

America, South.

CARTER (J. R.) S. American Railways. Argentina and Uruguay. pp. 204. *Lond.* 1891. 12°.   8235. aa. 59.

URUGUAY. *M. de Fomento.* Treatise on the South American Railways. pp. 601. *Montevideo,* 1893. 4°.   8245. g. 20.

—— Maps. fol.   Tab. 11747. b. (6.)

ROSS (A.) Memoria sobre los Ferrocarriles de Chile. pp. 61. *Paris,* 1892. 8°. 08235. h. 28.

PERU. Ferrocarriles del Sur. Documentos. pp. 190. *Lima,* 1888. 8°.   08235. f. 17.

BLUME (F.) Ferrocarril de Tarma á Chanchamayo. pp. 43. *Lima,* 1887. 8°. Pam. 76.

Australia.

KANDT (M.) Ueber die Entwickelung der australischen Eisenbahnpolitik. pp. 263. *Berl.* 1894. 8°.   08235. k. 4.

VICTORIA. Victorian Railways. Regulations. *Melbourne,* 1885. 8°.   8235. aa. 63.

Austria.

EDER (A.) Die Eisenbahnpolitik Oesterreichs. pp. 124. *Wien,* 1894. 8°.   08235. k. 8.

RAILWAYS.—Austria—*continued.*

DIMCHOV (R. M.) Das Eisenbahnwesen auf der Balkan-Halbinsel. pp. 266. *Bamberg,* 1894. 8°.   08235. k. 9.

ZIFFER (E. A.) Die Localbahnen in Galizien und der Bukowina. pp. 190. *Wien,* 1891. 4°.   08235. m. 4.

See also supra : Military Railways.

Bulgaria.

DIMCHOV (R. M.) Das Eisenbahnwesen auf der Balkan-Halbinsel. pp. 266. *Bamberg,* 1894. 8°.   08235. k. q.

Canada. *See supra : America, North.*

Ceylon. *See infra : India.*

Chili. *See supra : America, South.*

France.

CARRO (T.) La lutte entre la Navigation et les Chemins de fer. pp. 32. *Meaux,* 1895. 8°.   Pam. 76.

COLLARD (W.) Proposed London and Paris Railway. pp. 26. *Lond.* 1895. 8°. Pam. 76.

DUFOUR (É.) Les Employés de Chemins de fer. pp. 160. *Paris,* 1891. 8°.   8282. bb. 75.

—— and ARMAND (E.) Les Agents des Chemins de fer et les Employés de l'industrie privée. pp. 146. *Paris,* 1893. 12°.   8277. de. 55.

FRANCQ (L.) Chemin de fer métropolitain. pp. 95. *Paris,* 1892. 4°.   8235. k. 54.

GUÉRARD (E.) Sul movimento dei Ferrovieri francesi. pp. 36. *Firenze,* 1893. 8°. Pam. 76.

PICARD (A.) Les Chemins de fer français. 6 tom. *Paris,* 1884. 8°.   08229. f. 51.

ROCHE (A.) Tendresse des compagnies de Chemin de fer envers le public. pp. 28. *Nantes,* 1893. 8°.   Pam. 76.

THÉRY (E.) Histoire des grandes compagnies françaises de Chemins de fer. pp. 234. *Paris,* 1894. 8°.   8235. aaa. 60.

See also supra : General : Electric.

Germany : Switzerland.

BAZAINE (P. D.) Chemin de fer de Strasbourg à Bâle. pp. 156. *Paris,* 1892. 8°. 08235. h. 26.

ENGELHARD (F. R.) Sammlung von Gesetzen, Verordnungen, u.s.w. in Bezug auf den Eisenbahn-Dienst. *Berl.* 1895, *etc.* 8°.   8235. i.

GERMANY. Unsere Staats-Eisenbahnen. pp. 34. *Berl.* 1892. 8°.   Pam. 76.

GLEIM (W.) Das Recht der Eisenbahnen in Preussen. *Berl.* 1891, *etc.* 8°.   05604. i.

KROENIG (F.) Die Verwaltung der preussischen Staats-Eisenbahnen. *Breslau,* 1891, *etc.* 8°.   08235. k.

MAYER (A. v.) Geschichte und Geographie der deutschen Eisenbahnen. 2 Bde. *Berl.* 1891. 8°.   08235. h. 9.

ODRICH (O.) Zur Reformfrage des Personen-Tarifs der Eisenbahnen. pp. 36. 1891. 8°. Deutsche Zeit- und Streit-Fragen. Hft. 86.   12209. f.

SCHWABE (H.) Geschichtlicher Rückblick auf die ersten 50. Jahre des preussischen Eisenbahnwesens. pp. 111. *Berl.* 1895. 8°. 08235. e. 16.

ULRICH (F.) Staffeltarife und Wasserstrassen. pp. 234. *Berl.* 1894. 8°.   08225. k. 6.

VOGT (G.) Was nun ? Ein Beitrag zu Lösung der Eisenbahnfrage. pp. 39. 1891. 8°. Schweizer-Zeitfragen. Hft. 22.   8074. f.

See also supra : General : Electric : Military.

Great Britain and Ireland.
General.

COOK (W. W.) Corporation Problem. pp. 262. *Lond.* 1891. 8°.   08227. de. 1.

RAILWAYS.—Great Britain, etc.—cont.

DORSEY (E. B.) English and American Railroads compared. pp. 142. *N.Y.* 1887. 8°.
08235. f. 36.

FINDLAY (*Sir* G.) Working and management of an English Railway. pp. 412. *Lond.* 1894. 8°.
08235. g. 20.

GORDON (W. J.) Every-day life on the Railroad. pp. 192. *Lond.* 1892. 8°.   4429. df. 29.

G. B. & I. *Railways.* Transfer arrangements of the railways of the United Kingdom. pp. 29. *Lond.* 1893. 8°.   08235. h. 30.

INVESTORS. Handbook of Railway statistics. pp. 36. *Lond.* 1893. 12°.   8235. aa. 67.

KEANE (E.) Heroes of the line. pp. 128. *Lond.* 1893. 8°.   4414. df. 46.

KEMMANN (G.) Der Verkehr Londons mit besonderer Berücksichtigung der Eisenbahnen. pp. 197. *Berl.* 1892. fol.   1802. b. 11.

MACDERMOTT (F.) The Railway system of London. pp. 20. *Lond.* 1891. 8°.   Pam. 76.

MATHIESON (F. C.) AND SON. Dividends paid, and highest and lowest prices, 1875–90, of British Railways. *Lond.* 1891. *s. sh.* fol.
1882. d. 2. (78.)

MAVOR (J.) Scottish Railway strike, 1891. pp. 66. *Edinb.* 1891. 8°.   8282. aa. 51.

OLIVER (H.) and AIREY (J.) Handbook of Stations, Junctions, Works, &c., on the Railways in the United Kingdom. pp. 412. *Lond.* 1895. 4°.   8235. bb. 83.

PATTINSON (J. P.) British Railways: their passenger services, locomotives, gradients, and speeds. pp. 252. *Lond.* 1893. 8°.   08235. i. 2.

PENDLETON (J.) Our Railways: their origin and romance. 2 vol. *Lond.* 1894. 8°.
08235. i. 5.

SCOTT (W. J.) The Best Way there. Handbook of competitive railway routes. pp. 116. *Lond.* 1892. 8°.   10347. cc. 23.

—— Kinnaber; or the great Railway race of 1895. pp. 46. *Lond.* 1895. 8°.   Pam. 76.

WOLFE (A. G.) Nationalisation of the Railway system. pp. 31. *Lond.* 1895. 8°.   Pam. 82.

WORKS. Round the works of our great Railways. pp. 232. *Lond.* 1893. 8°.   8767. g. 12.

See also supra: General: Electric: Light Railways: Military: Street Railways.

Law.

BROWNE (J. H. B.) Railway and Canal Traffic Act 1888. pp. 191. *Manch.* 1890. 8°.
08235. f. 15.

FERGUSON (J.) Five Years' Railway cases, 1889–93. pp. 124. *Edinb.* 1894. 8°.   6375. bb. 30.

GOMEL (C.) Les droits de l'État sur les tarifs de chemins de fer en Angleterre. pp. 28. *Paris*, 1891. fol.   Pam. 76.

PARSONS (A.) Liability of Railway Companies for negligence towards passengers. pp. 196. *Lond.* 1893. 8°.   6875. k. 11.

PRESTON (F. M.) Manual of Railway law. pp. 318. *Lond.* 1892. 8°.   6376. d. 25.

RAPALJE (S.) and MACK (W.) Digest of Railway decisions. *Northport*, 1895, *etc.* 8°.   6617. l.

TAYNTON (H. J.) Outline of the law relating to the private ownership of Railway Rolling Stock. pp. 79. *Lond.* 1893. 8°.   6376. a. 57.

See also infra : Rates.

Railway Companies.

MASON (T.) Caledonian Railway Budget. pp. 108. *Glasg* 1893. 32°.   10369. aa. 23.

GREAT EASTERN RAILWAY. Official Guide. pp. 100. *Lond.* 1895. 8°.   10351. cc. 64.

RAILWAYS.—Great Britain, etc.—cont.

GREAT NORTHERN RAILWAY. Tourist Programme. pp. 48. *Lond.* 1895. 8°.   10347. cc. 27.

SEKON (G. A.) History of the Great Western Railway. pp. 373. *Lond.* 1895. 8°. 08235. f. 44.

GREAT WESTERN RAILWAY. Official guide. pp. 384. *Lond.* 1893. 8°.   10351. d. 41.

VINTER (P. J.) Great Western Expresses. pp. 37. *Plymouth*, 1894. 8°.   Pam. 76.

LIVERPOOL AND MANCHESTER RAILWAY. Travelling on the Liverpool and Manchester Railway, 1831. *Lond.* 1894. 8°. Tab. 11747. a. (62.)

LONDON AND NORTH-WESTERN RAILWAY. Official Guide. pp. 90. *Lond.* 1895. 8°. 10347. a. 24.

LONDON AND SOUTH-WESTERN RAILWAY. Official Guide. pp. 96. *Lond.* 1895. 8°. 10348. bbbb. 15.

MIDLAND COUNTIES RAILWAY. Official Guide. pp. 432. *Lond.* 1893. 8°.   10358. aa. 58.

NORTH BRITISH RAILWAY. Tourist Guide. pp. 253. *Edinb.* 1891. 8°.   10369. e. 8.

BRECKON (J. R.) North Eastern Railway Company: analysis of the capital expended from 1868 to 1889. pp. 38. *Newcastle*, 1890. 8°.
8235. ee. 46. (10.)

SEKON (G. A.) History of the South Eastern Railway. pp. 40. *Lond.* 1895. 8°.   Pam. 76.

SOUTH EASTERN RAILWAY COMPANY. The South Eastern Railway: passenger services, rolling stock and express speeds. pp. 32. *Lond.* 1895. 8°.
Pam. 76.

COLLARD (W.) Proposed London and Paris Railway. pp. 26. *Lond.* 1895. 8°.   Pam. 76.

Rates and Charges.

ACWORTH (W. M.) The Railways and the traders. pp. 378. *Lond.* 1891. 8°. 08235. g. 7.

COTSWORTH (M. B.) Railway Maximum rates and charges. pp. 130. *Lond.* 1892. 8°.
8235. aa. 65.

DARLINGTON (H. R.) The Railway rates. pp. 581. *Lond.* 1893. 8°.   6376. d. 26.

DAVIES (J.) Railway Rates, charges, and regulations. pp. 234. *Lond.* 1892. 8°. 08235. i. 4.

LONDON. *Mansion House Association on Railway Traffic.* Report on the Railway Rates and Charges Order Confirmation Acts, 1891. pp. 39. *Lond.* 1892. 4°.   08235. m. 7.

TABLES. Tables for ascertaining the charges on merchandise by Railway. pp. 121. *Lond.* 1893. 4°.   8548. df. 28.

Greece.

NIKOLAIDES (N. S.) AND Co. Guide des Chemins de fer en Grèce. *Athènes*, 1891, *etc.* 16°. 8235. aa.

India and Ceylon.

ALPHA. Some Railway Servants. pp. 66. *Lahore*, 1890. 8°.   012330. f. 46.

ANDREW (*Sir* W. P.) Indian Railways as connected with British Empire in the East. pp. 279. *Lond.* 1884. 8°.   08235. f. 32.

BELL (H.) Railway Policy in India. pp. 359. *Lond.* 1894. 8°.   08235. k. 2.

GEORGE (E. M.) Railways in India. pp. 94. *Lond.* 1894. 8°.   8767. bbb. 40.

PRIESTLEY (N.) Route table for Indian Railways. 2 pt. *Bombay*, 1891. fol. & 8°. 08235. h. 27.

RUSSELL (L. P.) and BAYLEY (V. B. F.) Indian Railways Act IX. of 1890. pp. 332. *Bombay*, 1891. 8°.   5318. b. 28.

STRACHEY (R.) East Indian Railway Company. Address of the Chairman. pp. 18. *Lond.* 1893. 8°.   Pam. 76.

TREVOR (H. E.) Law relating to Railways in British India. pp. 447. *Lond.* 1891. 8°.
5318. b. 23.

RAILWAYS.—India and Ceylon—cont.

CEYLON. *Railways.* Ceylon Government Railways. Notes on the views. pp. 14.
Colombo, 1893. 8°.   08235. i. 11.

GALLE. Railway extension to Galle and Matara. pp. 43. *Galle*, 1894. 8°.   Pam. 76.

JAFFNA RAILWAY. Proposed Jaffna Railway. pp. 105. *Colombo*, 1890. 8°.   8235. l. 46

Italy.

COMPAGNA (A.) La questione delle Ferrovie. pp. 88. *Napoli*, 1890. 8°.   Pam. 17.

YOUNG (L.) Relazione sul progetto di una Ferrovia metropolitana per la città di Napoli. Vol. 5. *Napoli*, 1888. 4°.   08235. m. 6.

Japan.

TREVITHICK (F. H.) History of the railway system in Japan. 1894. 8°. Ac. *Yokohama. Asiatic Society.* Transactions. Vol. 22.
     Ac. 8828/6.

Peru. *See supra: America, South.*

Prussia. *See supra: Germany.*

Roumania and Servia.

DIMCHOV (R. M.) Das Eisenbahnwesen auf der Balkan-Halbinsel. pp. 266. *Bamberg*, 1894. 8°.
     08235. k. 9.

Sahara. *See supra: Algeria.*

Scotland.

See supra: Great Britain and Ireland.

Switzerland. *See supra: Germany.*

United States of America.

See supra: America, North.

RAINFALL. *See* METEOROLOGY.

RAISINS. LISBONNE (G.) Législation sur les Raisins secs. pp. 170.
Montpellier, 1891. 8°.   5423. cc. 4.

SORGUES (P. de) and BERTHAULT (R.) Les Raisins secs. pp. 290. *Paris*, 1890. 8°.
     07076. h. 47.

See also VINE.

RAJPUTANA. AMRITALĀLA DE. Students' history of Rajpootana. pp. 78.
Calcutta, 1889. 12°.   9057. a. 37.

LÆSSÖE (A.) Haremsbesøg og Djungleliv i Radjputana. pp. 197. *Kjøbenh.* 1893. 8°.
     010057. k. 10.

RAJPUT. A Rajput's Observations on social reform. pp. 50. *Delhi*, 1893. 8°.   Pam. 67.

WEBB (W. W.) Currencies of Hindu states of Rájputána. pp. 135. *Lond.* 1893. 8°. 7757. e. 26.

RAMBOUILLET. MAILLARD (J.) Les Yvelines. Histoire de Rambouillet. pp. 260. *Paris*, 1891. 8°.   10170. i. 9.

RAMSBOTTOM. ELLIOT (W. H.) Country and Church of the Cheeryble Brothers. pp. 406. *Selkirk*, 1893 8°.   10360. d. 37.

RAMSGATE. RICHARDSON (C. T.) Fragments of history pertaining to Ramsgate. pp. 212. *Ramsgate*, 1885. 8°.   10358. e. 24.

RAPPOLTSTEIN. ALBRECHT (C.) Rappoltsteinisches Urkundenbuch, 759–1500. *Colmar*, 1891, *etc.* 8°.   10250. i. 3.

RAT. BARKLEY (H. C.) Studies in the Art of Rat-catching. pp. 185. *Lond.* 1891. 8°.
     7908. ee. 23.

See also RODENTS.

RATES, *Local. See* ENGLAND, *Trade and Finance:* LOCAL GOVERNMENT: TAXATION.

RATIONALISM. BRUN (C.) Rationalismen i dens historiske. pp. 276.
Kristiania, 1891. 8°.   3925. i. 46.

RATIONALISM—*continued.*

GALLETTI (B.) Saggio di Razionalismo. pp. 328. *Palermo*, 1891. 4°.   8462. g. 4.

UTOPY (F.) Le Rationalisme philosophique et religieux. pp. 233. *Paris*, 1891. 12°.
     4018. g. 31.

RATISBON. NEUMANN (C. W. v.) Die Fürstenherberge zum "goldenen Kreuz" in Regensburg. pp. 64. *Regensburg*, 1892. 16°.
     Pam. 28.

GEYER (W.) Die Einführung der Reformation in Regensburg. pp. 48.
Regensburg, 1892. 8°.   4535. b. 16. (4.)

WILL (C. J. C.) Beiträge zur Geschichte der Erstürmung von Regensburg, 23. April 1809. 1895. 8°. Ac. *Ratisbon. Historischer Verein.* Verhandlungen. Bd. 47.   Ac. 7157.

RAUCOURT. GOFFART (N.) and (E.) Notice sur le Canton de Raucourt. pp. 222. *Sedan*, 1889. 8°.   010171. h. 33.

RAVEN. SHUFELDT (R. W.) The Myology of the Raven. pp. 343. *Lond.* 1890. 8°.
     7285. ee. 16.

RAVENSBERG. SPANNAGEL (C.) Minden und Ravensberg, 1648–1719. pp. 248. *Hannover*, 1894. 8°.   10235. cc. 8.

RAVENSTONEDALE. RAVENSTONEDALE. Parish Registers, 1571–1812. 3 vol. *Kendal*, 1893–94. 8°.   9906. bb 1.

RÉ., Ile de. *See* LA ROCHELLE.

READING. READING. Reading Records. *Lond.* 1892, *etc.* 8°.   010350. k. 2.

SAINT MARY, *Reading.* Registers of the parish, 1538–1812. *Reading*, 1891, *etc.* 8°.   9916. f. 5.

READY RECKONERS. ACCOUNTANT. Handy aid to interest and commission Calculations. pp. 16. *Edinb.* 1892. 8°.   Pam. 23.

BARFF (L. C.) Merchants and shipmasters' calculator of freight. pp. 134.
Hongkong, 1892. *obl.* 8°.   8548. de. 23.

BARLOW (A. C.) Railway invoice and shipping clerks' Ready Reckoner. pp. 100. *Wellington, N.Z.* 1895. *obl.* 8°.   8548. aa. 40.

BUNTING (H. A.) Standard English and foreign Calculator of prices. pp. 99. *Manch.* 1895. 8°.
     8548. c. 54.

CARNAFFAN (W.) Reid's 48 hours' Wages book. *Lond.* 1892. 8°.   Pam. 38.

CHADWICK (W.) Number, weight and fractional Calculator. pp. 842. *Lond.* 1890. 4°.
     8548. df. 22.

CHERRY (H.) Forget-me-not Calculator. pp. 6. *Putney*, 1895. 8°.   8531. c. 47. (6.)

COTSWORTH (M. B.) Railway and traders' Calculator. *Leeds*, 1893. fol.   8505. k. 10.

ELBOROUGH (J.) Ready discount Reckoner. pp. 24. *Lond.* 1893. 8°.   8548. c. 52.

ELLIOTT (N.) Ready wages Calculator. *Leeds*, 1893. 8°.   8504. f. 35.

FISHER ( ) Fisher's Ready Reckoner. pp. 247. *Lond.* 1892. 8°.   8548. aaa. 35.

NORMAN (J. H.) Ready Reckoner of foreign and colonial Exchanges. pp. 164.
Lond. 1893. 8°.   8548. c. 51.

POCKET READY RECKONER. Pocket Ready Reckoner. pp. 320. *Lond.* 1895. 12°.
     8548. a. 33.

READY RECKONER. Rapid Ready Reckoner. *Lond.* 1895. 8°.   8548. aa. 39.

SHEPPARD (W. A.) Ready Reckoner showing superficial measurement. pp. 34. *Bath*, 1892. 16°.   8548. aa. 29.

READY RECKONERS—*continued.*

SOULARY (J.) Ready Reckoner for ascertaining English nett prices to the yard of goods sold to the metre or the aune. 2 pt. *Lyon,* 1892. 8°.
             8548. b. 33.

STEVENSON (J.) The Tradesman's ready calculator of measurements. pp. 80.
Lond. 1894. 8°.   8506. b. 64.

STOCK EXCHANGE READY RECKONER. Stock Exchange Ready Reckoner. *Lond.* 1893.
            1882. d. 2. (1.)

WAGES CALCULATOR. Wages Calculator. *Sheffield,* 1891. 16°.   8548. aaa. 32.

WAISTCOAT POCKET READY RECKONER. Waistcoat pocket Ready Reckoner for stationers. pp. 244. *Halifax,* 1891. 16°.   8548. aa. 24.

WATERMAN (W. H.) New Method of instantaneous calculation of simple Interest, *etc.* pp. 8. *Worthing,* 1893. 16°.   Pam. 39.

WILLIAMS (J.) British and French Calculator. pp. 24. *Walsall,* 1892. 8°.   8535. gg. 7. (4.)
See also MONEY : TABLES.

REALISM, Artistic and Literary.
See NATURALISM.

RECEIPTS. *See* INDUSTRIES.

RECEIVERS. KERR (W. W.) Treatise on the law as to Receivers. pp. 252. *Lond.* 1891. 8°.   2230. c. 9.

RECITATIONS. BAKER (G. M.) Baker's Dialect Reciter. 5 pt. *Lond.* 1892. 8°.
            12296. e. 23.

BELL (D. C.) and (A. M.) Bell's standard Elocutionist. pp. 600. *Lond.* 1892. 8°.
            12272. bbb. 17.

BOYS. The Boys' Reciter. 2 pt
Lond. 1893. 8°.   12273. bbb. 11.

BURRELL (A.) Recitation. Handbook for teachers. pp. 239. *Lond.* 1891. 8°.   11824. de. 43.

—— Exercises in speech and Recitations for standards. 3 pt. *Lond.* 1891. 8°. 11824. bb. 54.

CARPENTER (J. E.) Popular Elocutionist and reciter. pp. 564. *Lond.* 1894. 8°.
            12273. bb. 18.

CLARKE (H. S.) and WAGNER (L.) The Century Reciter. pp. 364. *Lond.* 1895. 8°. 12272. i. 10.

ELLIS (G. A.) The handy pocket Reciter. pp. 174. *Lond.* 1893. 8°.   12274. aaa. 35.

FLETCHER (E.) Monologues à la mode and Ballads. pp. 63. *Lond.* 1895. 8°. 012330. g. 85.

FORD (R.) Popular English readings. pp. 130. *Paisley,* 1891. 8°.   12273. f. 21.

—— Popular Scotch Readings. pp. 128. *Paisley,* 1891. 8°.   12273. f. 19.

—— Popular American readings. pp. 128. *Paisley,* 1892. 8°.   12296. e. 24.

GIRLS. The Girls' Reciter. pp. 128. *Lond.* 1893. 8°.   12274. aaa. 36.

HALLSWORTH (T. E.) Onward Reciter. pp. 186. *Lond.* 1892. 8°.   12274. aaa. 31.

HENRY (R.) Recitations and readings. pp. 64. *Lond.* 1891. 8°.   12331. i. 22.

HEYWOOD (A.) Modern Reciter. pp. 100. *Manch.* 1893. 8°.   12274. f. 11.

—— New series of Recitations.
Manch. 1893, *etc.* 8°.   11779. cc.

JULIAN (F.) Original Readings for entertainments. pp. 54. *Ross,* 1893. 8°. 012330. e. 11.

KIRTON (J. W.) Standard little folks' Reciter. pp. 244. *Lond.* 1891. 8°.   11601. ee. 31.

KNIGHT (A. F.) The "Original Reciter." pp. 38. *Reading,* 1894. 8°.   12354. de. 15.

LLOYD (H.) Smoking Concert Reciter. pp. 160. *Lond.* 1890. 8°.   12273. c.

RECITATIONS—*continued.*

MAC HARDY (M.) M. McHardy's Elocutionist. pp. 135. *Lond.* 1892. 8°.   11601. ee. 37.

MACMILLAN AND Co. Recitation Cards & Books. 36 pt. *Lond.* 1892. 8°.   11603. ee. 22.

MILES (A. H.) The Aldine Speaker. 2 pt. *Lond.* 1891. 8°.   12269. e. 7.

—— The Browning Reciter. pp. 248.
Lond. 1889. 8°.   12273. e.

—— The Ladies' Reciter. pp. 192.
Lond. 1891. 8°.   12273. e.

—— The Library of Elocution. 6 pt.
Lond. 1891. fol.   12272. m. 6.

—— Modern Humour for recitation. pp. 192. *Lond.* 1892. 8°.   12273. e.

—— New standard Elocutionist. pp. 640. *Lond.* 1895. 8°.   12273. f. 27.

—— The Platform Reciter. 3 pt.
Lond. 1891. 8°.   12273. cc. 3.

MOORE (J. S.) Six-penny Pieces. pp. 48. *Liverpool,* 1890. 4°.   Pam. 22.

OVERTON (R.) The Overton Reciter. pp. 150. *Lond.* 1889. 8°.   12273. e.

RECITING WORLD. The Reciting World. *Lond.* 1892, *etc.* 8°.   2021.

RICHARDSON (M. A.) Original little Recitations. pp. 24. *Manch.* 1894. 12°. 11601. ccc. 39. (16.)

ROUTLEDGE (E.) Modern Speaker and Reciter. pp. 571. *Lond.* 1892. 8°.   12273. f. 23.

STEWART (A.) Young Folks' Reciter. pp. 75. *Edinb.* 1891. 8°.   11601. dd. 14. (7.)

SUCKLING (F. H.) Humane Educator and Reciter. pp. 528. *Lond.* 1891. 8°. 11601. i. 3.

WAGNER (L.) Modern Readings and Recitations. pp. 44. *Lond.* 1886. 8°.   12272. aaa. 13.

WESTON (J.) Recitations for Bands of Hope and Sunday Schools. pp. 112. *Lond.* 1892. 8°.
            11601. dd. 7.

YOXALL (J. H.) Choice of standard recitations. *Lond.* 1891, *etc.* 8°.   11601. ccc.
See also ELOCUTION.

RECTUM AND ANUS. BALL (C. B.) The Rectum and Anus. Diseases and treatment. pp. 439. *Lond.* 1894. 8°.   7630. aa. 23.

COOPER (A.) Diseases of the Rectum and the Anus. pp. 324. *Lond.* 1892. 8°.
            7630. e. 13.

EDGELOW (G.) Immediate and painless cure of Hæmorrhoids and Prolapsus. pp. 32. *Lond.* 1890. 12°.   7630. a. 10.

FAYARD (J.) Des Indications opératoires dans le Cancer du Rectum. pp. 62. *Lyon,* 1891. 8°.
            Pam. 39.

MACAULEY (W. R.) Hæmorrhoids, fistula, and other diseases of the Rectum. pp. 58. *Lond.* 1891. 8°.   7630. aa. 17.

See also CANCER : COLEOTOMY.

RED CROSS SOCIETY. *See* AMBULANCE.

REDHILL. REDHILL. Visitor's guide to Redhill. pp. 68. *Redhill,* 1891. 8°.
            10360. e. 24.

RED RIVER, Tung-King. FRANCE. *Navy.* Notice sur le Fleuve Rouge. pp. 84. *Paris,* 1895. 8°.   10497. b. 47.

RED SEA. MAGNIN (P. de) Le passage de la Mer Rouge. pp. 8. *Nîmes,* 1891. 8°. Pam. 5.

CASTONNET DES FOSSES (H.) La France, l'Angleterre et l'Italie dans la Mer Rouge. pp. 24. *Lille,* 1889. 8°.   Pam. 67.

G. B. & I. *Hydrographic Office.* Red Sea Pilot. pp. 564. *Lond.* 1892. 8°.   10496. gg. 35.

REFERENDUM. DEPLOIGE (S.) Le Referendum en Suisse. pp. 190. *Brux.* 1892. 8°. 8072. f. 2.

LA SIZERANNE (R. de) Le Referendum communal. pp. 86. *Paris*, 1895. 8°. 8050. aaa. 10.

OBERHOLTZER (E. P.) Referendum in America. pp. 225. 1892. 8°. Ac. Philadelphia. *University.* Publications. Ac. 2692. p.

See also GOVERNMENT : SWITZERLAND.

REFORMATORIES. *See* PRISONS.

REFRIGERATION. LEASK (A. R.) Refrigerating Machinery. pp. 266. *Lond.* 1895. 8°. 8767. g. 26.

MARCHENA (R. E. de) Machines frigorifiques à air. pp. 196. 1894. 8°. Encyclopédie des aide-mémoire. 8709. g.

REDWOOD (I. I.) Ammonia Refrigeration. pp. 146. *N.Y.* 1895. 16°. 8909. a. 29.

REGGIO NELL' EMILIA. CHIESI (L.) Reggio nell' Emilia sotto i pontefici Giulio II., Leone X., Adriano VI. pp. 132. *Reggio-Emilia*, 1892. 8°. 10136. c. 27.

REGICIDE. *See* HOMICIDE.

REICHENAU, Abbey. Ac. Carlsruhe. *Badische Historische Commission.* Quellen zur Geschichte der Abtei Reichenau. *Heidelberg*, 1890, *etc.* 4°. 4662. g.

REICHENHALL. CHLINGENSPERG-BERG (M. v.) Das Gräberfeld von Reichenhall. pp. 164. *Reichenhall*, 1890. 4°. 7709. l. 12.

REIGATE. REDHILL. Visitor's guide to Reigate, *etc.* pp. 68. *Redhill*, 1891. 8°. 10360. e. 24.

REIMS. DEMAISON (L.) Les Architectes de la cathédrale de Reims. 1894. 8°. Ac. Paris. *Comité des Travaux historiques.* Bulletin. Archéologie. 1894. Liv. I. Ac. 437.

GIVELET (C.) Répertoire archéologique de l'arrondissement de Reims. 1891. 8°. Ac. Rheims. *Académie.* Travaux. Vol. 85. Ac. 510.

JADART (H.) Les anciennes bibliothèques de Reims, leur sort en 1790-91. pp. 39. *Reims*, 1891. 8°. Pam. 6.

Les Portraits rémois du Musée de Reims. pp. 33. *Paris*, 1894. 8°. Pam. 24.

RELICS. NEUMANN (W. A.) Der Reliquien-Schatz des Hauses Brunschweig-Lüneburg. pp. 368. *Wien*, 1891. fol. 1706. a. 19.

See also ABBEVILLE : ARGENTEUIL : BOURBON L'ARCHAMBAULT : TREVES.

RELIGION AND MYTHOLOGY.

General : Natural Theology, etc.

BALFOUR (*Right Hon.* A. J.) The Foundations of Belief. pp. 350. *Lond.* 1895. 8°. 8463. e. 31.

BLAKE (J. V.) Natural Religion, in sermons. pp. 228. *Chicago*, 1892. 8°. 4487. aaa. 19.

BOEDDER (B.) Natural Theology. pp. 480. 1891. 8°. Manuals of Catholic Philosophy. 8470. ccc.

BURATTI (C.) La Religione e la morale scientifica. pp. 288. *Milano*, 1894. 8°. 8409. c. 48.

CARPENTER (W. B.) *Bp. of Ripon.* Permanent elements of Religion. pp. 423. *Lond.* 1891. 8°. 4456. g. 17.

CESCA (G.) La Religione della morale. pp. 100. *Padova*, 1893. 8°. 8409. g. 45.

CONWAY (J.) Rational Religion. pp. 175. *Milwaukee*, 1890. 8°. 3940. bbb. 20.

DAVIDSON (W. L.) Theism as grounded in Human Nature. pp. 469. *Lond.* 1893. 8°. 4371. cc. 18.

RELIGION.—General, etc.—*continued.*

DENYS (J.) L'Évangile de l'humanité ou le Christianisme universel. pp. 203. *Paris*, 1891. 8°. 4374. e. 4.

EMERY (L.) Religion et Théologie. pp. 26. *Lausanne*, 1890. 8°. 4371. ee. 2. (5.)

FAGGI (A.) La Religione e il suo avvenire secondo E. Hartmann. pp. 91. *Firenze*, 1892. 8°. 3910. f. 20.

FERRARS (M. H.) Religion. From an agnostic point of view. pp. 140. *Lond.* 1892. 8°. 4017. df. 2.

FOGAZZARO (A.) L'Origine dell' uomo e il sentimento religioso. pp. 109. *Milano*, 1893. 8°. 3900. c. 25.

GAṆAPATARĀVA RAGHUNĀTHA NAVALAKARA. Elementary truths of Religion. pp. 41. *Bombay*, 1891. 16°. Pam. 77.

GHEYN (G. v. d.) La Religion ; son origine et sa définition. pp. 131. *Gand*, 1891. 8°. 4503. ee. 8.

GOPĪNĀTHA SADĀSIVAJĪ HĀTĒ. Natural Religion. pp. 622. *Bombay*, 1890. 8°. 4372. ee. 28.

GOULD (G. M.) Meaning and method of life. pp. 297. *N.Y.* 1893. 8°. 7003. aa. 10.

H., A. Vernunftreligion. pp. 46. *Leipz.* 1890. 8°. 3911. ee. 51. (5.)

HARTE (B.) The new Theology. pp. 233. *Lond.* 1894. 8°. 4015. df. 19.

HAVEN (T. W.) Natural Religion. pp. 622. *N.Y.* 1892. 8°. 4371. de. 5.

HEGEL (G. W. F.) Lectures on the philosophy of Religion. 3 vol. 1895. 8°. English and Foreign Philosophical Library. 2318. d. 3.

HUMMEL (F.) Die Bedeutung der Schrift von Carl Schwarz über das Wesen der Religion. pp. 175. *Braunschweig*, 1890. 8°. 3908. f. 24.

JOHNSON (F. H.) What is Reality? Inquiry as to the reasonableness of natural religion, *etc.* pp. 510. *Bost.* 1891. 8°. 8470. f. 22.

KENNEDY (J. H.) Natural Theology and modern thought. pp. 276. *Lond.* 1891. 8°. 4018. f. 17.

KIDD (J.) Morality and religion. pp. 458. *Edinb.* 1895. 8°. 4372. cc. 23.

KRAUSE (C. C. F.) Zur Religions-philosophie und speculativen Theologie. pp. 180. *Leipz.* 1893. 8°. 4371. ee. 12.

LOTZE (R. H.) Outlines of a philosophy of Religion. pp. 176. *Lond.* 1892. 8°. 4017. c. 13.

VORBRODT (G.) Principien den Ethik und Religionsphilosophie Lotzes. pp. 186. *Dessau*, 1891. 8°. 8409. cc. 4.

LOVELL (A.) The Ideal of man. pp. 250. *Lond.* 1891. 8°. 4018. f. 21.

LUETGENAU (F.) Natürliche und soziale Religion. pp. 260. *Stuttgart*, 1894. 8°. 8409. cc. 30.

LYALL (*Sir* A. C.) Natural Religion in India. pp. 64. *Camb.* 1891. 8°. 4503. aa. 40.

MOLINARI (G. de) Religion. pp. 195. *Lond.* 1894. 8°. 4017. c. 18.

MOMERIE (A. W.) The Religion of the future. pp. 141. *Edinb.* 1893. 8°. 4107. de. 13.

PFLEIDERER (O.) Philosophy and Development of Religion. 2 vol. *Edinb.* 1894. 8°. 4371. b. 17.

PORUCK (J.) Die Religion der Zukunft. pp. 24. *Berl.* 1894. 8°. 4371. dd. 8. (11.)

RAṄGĀCHĀRYA. Function of Religion in social evolution. pp. 58. *Madras*, 1894. 8°. Pam. 82.

ROLFES (E.) Die aristotelische Auffassung von Verhältnisse Gottes zur Welt. pp. 202. *Berl.* 1892. 8°. 8460. dd. 26.

SANTI (V.) La questione fondamentale della Teologia Naturale. pp. 33. *Perugia*, 1890. 8°. Pam. 77.

RELIGION.—General, etc.—*continued.*

SCHLEIERMACHER (F. E. D.) On Religion.
pp. 287. *Lond.* 1893. 8°. 4374. l. 26.

SCHOPENHAUER (A.) Religion : a dialogue.
pp. 140. *Lond.* 1891. 8°. 8470. f. 23.

SEELEY (*Sir* J. R.) Natural Religion. pp. 305.
Lond. 1895. 8°. 4018. bbb. 33.

SEYDEL (R.) Religionsphilosophie im Umriss.
pp. 396. *Freiburg i. B.,* 1893. 8°. 4371. f. 4.

SIEBECK (H.) Lehrbuch der Religionsphilosophie. pp. 456. 1893. 8°. Sammlung theologischer Lehrbücher. 3554. i.

STEINTHAL (H.) Zu Bibel und Religionsphilosophie. pp. 237. *Berl.* 1890. 8°. 4016. f. 34.

STERRETT (J. M.) Reason and authority in
Religion. pp. 184. *Lond.* 1891. 8°. 3940. c. 5.

—— Studies in Hegel's Philosophy of Religion.
pp. 348. *Lond.* 1891. 8°. 8467. e. 35.

STOKES (*Sir* G. G.) Natural Theology. pp. 272.
Lond. 1893. 8°. 2208. a. 4.

STRAUSS (J.) Religion and morals. pp. 25.
Lond. 1890. 12°. 4372. aa. 34.

STRUEMPELL (L. H.) Gedanken über Religion
und religiöse Probleme. pp. 242.
Leipz. 1888. 8°. 4380. aa. 3.

TROGLODYTE. Riddles of the Sphinx. pp. 468.
Lond. 1891. 8°. 8469. g. 29.

TUTTLE (H.) Religion of Man and ethics of
science. pp. 313. *N.Y.* 1890. 8°. 4018. f. 23.

UPTON (C. B.) Lectures on the bases of Religious
Belief. pp. 364. *Lond.* 1894. 8°. 2212. e. 2.

VODSKOV (H. S.) Sjæledyrkelse og Naturdyr-
kelse. *Kjøbenh.* 1890, *etc.* 8°. 4506. bb. 27.

WEIL (S.) The Religion of the future. pp. 267.
Boston, 1894. 8°. 8631. cc. 37.

See also CHRISTIANITY : DEITY : THEOLOGY.

History, etc., of Religions.

ACHELIS (T.) Max Müller und die vergleichende
Religionswissenschaft. pp. 33. 1893. 8°.
Sammlung wissenschaftlicher Vorträge. N.F.
Hft. 182. 12249. m.

ANDRIAN (F. v.) *Baron.* Der Höhencultus
asiatischer und europäischer Völker. pp. 385.
Wien, 1891. 8°. 4503. cc. 16.

ARYAN SUN-MYTHS. Aryan Sun-myths the
origin of Religions. pp. 192. *Lond.* 1889. 8°.
4506. aa. 15.

BETTANY (G. T.) Primitive Religions. pp. 267.
1891. 8°. World's Religious Series. No. 1.
4503. aaa.

BOETTGER (H.) Sonnencult der Indogermanen.
pp. 167. *Breslau,* 1890. 8°. 4506. bb. 26.

CAIRD (E.) The Evolution of Religion. Gifford
lectures. 2 vol. *Glasg.* 1893. 8°. 2212. c. 2.

CANNING (*Hon.* A. S. G.) Words on existing
Religions. pp. 220. *Lond.* 1893. 8°. 4503. de. 3.

CARPENTER (J. E.) Place of the history of
Religion in theological study. pp. 87.
Lond. 1890. 8°. Pam. 41.

CHAPMAN (J.) Ancient Worship. pp. 191.
Liverp. 1892. 8°. 4503 de. 8.

CHICAGO. *Columbian Exposition. World's Congress Auxiliary.* The World's Congress of
religions. pp. 363. *Chicago,* 1894. 8°.
4182. de. 3.

BARROWS (J. H.) The World's Parliament of
Religions. Story of the first Parliament of
Religions. 2 vol. *Chicago,* 1893. 8°. 4182. ff. 1.

BONET-MAURY (G.) Le Congrès des Religions à
Chicago en 1893. pp. 345. *Paris,* 1895. 8°.
4182. aaa. 41.

RELIGION.—History, etc.—*continued.*

HUGENHOLTZ (F. W. N.) Het Parlement der
Godsdiensten, Chicago, 1893. pp. 123.
Rotterdam, 1893. 8°. 4182. ff. 4.

JONES (J. L.) Chorus of Faith as heard in the
Parliament of Religions, Chicago, 1893.
pp. 333. *Chicago,* 1893. 8°. 4182. de. 2.

MERCER (L. P.) Review of the World's Religious
Congresses, Chicago, 1893. pp. 334.
Chicago, 1893. 8°. 4182. de. 1.

CLODD (E.) The childhood of Religions.
pp. 288. *Lond.* 1889. 8°. 4503. a. 39.

—— Myths and Dreams. pp. 251.
Lond. 1891. 8°. 4503. aaa. 2.

CUST (R. N.) Essay on the ancient Religions of
the world. pp. 34. *Hertford,* 1894. 8°.
Pam. 41.

—— Essay on the common features which
appear in all forms of Religious Belief. pp. 194.
Lond. 1895. 8°. 4503. b. 16.

DARSTELLUNGEN. Darstellungen aus dem Gebiete der nichtchristlichen Religionsgeschichte.
Münster, 1890, *etc.* 8°. 4506. f.

DERENBOURG (H.) La Science des Religions.
pp. 95. *Paris,* 1886. 18°. 4503. aa. 45.

DEUSSEN (P.) Allgemeine Geschichte der Philosophie, mit Berücksichtigung der Religionen.
Leipz. 1894, *etc.* 8°. 8486. d.

DREXLER (W.) Mythologische Beiträge.
Leipz. 1890, *etc.* 8°. 4505. ccc. 4.

EDKINS (J.) Early spread of religious Ideas in
the Far East. pp. 144. 1893. 8°. By paths of
Bible Knowledge. No. 19. 2202. a.

ELLINWOOD (F. F.) Oriental religions and
Christianity. pp. 384. *Lond.* 1892. 8°.
4503. aaa. 6.

EVANS (E. E.) History of Religions. pp. 128.
N.Y. 1892. 8°. 4016. df. 22.

FORCHHAMMER (P. W.) Prolegomena zur Mythologie als Wissenschaft. pp. 127.
Kiel, 1891. 4°. 4504. h. 10.

FRADENBURGH (J. W.) Fire from strange Altars.
pp. 324. *Cincinnati,* 1891. 8°. 4503. bb. 27.

GOBLET (E.) *Count d'Alviella.* La Migration des
symboles. pp. 343. *Paris,* 1891. 8°.
4503. cc. 19.

—— Migration of Symbols. pp. 277.
Westminster, 1894. 8°. 4503. ee. 34.

—— L' "Idée" de Dieu. pp. 328.
Bruxelles, 1892. 8°. 4371. ee. 8.

—— Lectures on the conception of God as illustrated by anthropology and history. pp. 296.
Lond. 1892. 8°. 2212. e.

GRANT (G. M.) Religions of the world. pp. 206.
1895. 8°. The Guild Library. 3622. g

JASTROW (M.) Handbooks on the history of
Religions. *Bost.* 1895, *etc.* 8°. 4503. c.

JENKINS (R. W.) Religions old and new. pp. 19.
Colombo, 1890. 8°. 4372. h. 28. (5.)

JUNKER VON LANGEGG (F. A.) Krypto-Monotheismus in den Religionen der alten Chinesen
und anderer Völker. pp. 79. *Leipz.* 1892. 8°.
Pam. 41.

KELLOGG (S. H.) Genesis and growth of Religion.
pp. 275. *Lond.* 1892. 8°. 4503. aaa. 7.

KING (J. H.) The Supernatural : its origin and
evolution. 2 vol. *Lond.* 1892. 8°. 4503. ee. 9.

KLEINPAUL (R.) Menschenopfer und Ritualmorde. pp. 80. *Leipz.* 1892. 8°. Pam. 41.

KUENEN (A.) Volksreligion und Weltreligion.
pp. 339. *Berl.* 1883. 8°. 4503. b. 10.

LANG (A.) Custom and Myth. pp. 312.
Lond. 1893. 8° 2348. aa.

RELIGION.—History, etc.—continued.

LEFÈVRE (A.) La Religion. pp. 586. 1892. 8°. Bibliothèque des Sciences contemporaines. No. 17.   8709. b.

LELORRAIN (C.) Le Polythéisme juif et chrétien. pp. 164. *Épinal,* 1892. 8°.   4017. e. 16.

LETHABY (W. R.) Architecture, mysticism and myth. pp. 272. *Lond.* 1892. 8°.   7820. cc. 13.

LETOURNEAU (C. J. M.) L'Évolution religieuse dans les diverses races. pp. 607.
Paris, 1892. 8°.   4503. ee. 14.

LEWIS (A. H.) Paganism surviving in Christianity. pp. 309. *N.Y.* 1892. 8°. 3940. cc. 12.

LINDSAY (A. W. C.) *Earl of Crawford.* The Creed of Japhet, the race popularly surnamed Indo-Germanic. pp. 829. *Lond.* 1891. 8°.   4503. ee. 6.

LONDON. *South Place Institute.* Religious Systems of the world. pp. 824. *Lond.* 1892. 8°.   4503. ee. 18.

LUKAS (F.) Die Grundbegriffe in den Kosmogonien der alten Völker. pp. 277. *Leipz.* 1893. 8°.   4503. b. 5.

MACDONALD (J.) Religion and myth. pp. 240. *Lond.* 1893. 8°.   4503. ee. 17.

MATHESON (G.) The distinctive Messages of the old Religions. pp. 342. *Edinb.* 1892. 8°.   4503. bb. 33.

MENZIES (A.) History of Religion. pp. 438. 1895. 8°. University Extension Manuals.   12204. f.

MOLLOY (J. F.) Faiths of the peoples. 2 vol. *Lond.* 1892. 8°.   4136. g. 6.

MUELLER (F. M.) Lectures on the origin and growth of Religion. pp. 408. *Lond.* 1891. 8°.   4503. b. 13.

—— Physical Religion. Gifford Lectures. pp. 410. *Lond.* 1891. 8°.   2208. b. 1.

—— Anthropological Religion. Gifford Lectures. pp. 464. *Lond.* 1892. 8°.   2208. d. 2.

—— Natural Religion. pp. 608. *Lond.* 1892. 8°.   4503. bb. 34.

—— Theosophy. Gifford Lectures. pp. 585. *Lond.* 1893. 8°.   2212. c. 3.

—— Chips from a German Workshop. 4 vol. *Lond.* 1894-95. 8°.   2342. bb.

O'NEILL (J.) The Night of the Gods. Vol. 1. *Lond.* 1893. 8°.   4506. d. 16.

PAPILLAUD (J.) Le Faux Dieu des Juifs, des Chrétiens et des Mahométans. pp. 240. *S. Martin-de-Ré,* 1889. 12°.   4018. df. 10.

QUILLIAM (W. H.) The Religion of the Sword. Judaism, Christianity and Islam. *Liverp.* 1891, *etc.* 8°.   4503. de.

RECLUS (J. J. É.) La formation des Réligions. pp. 11. *Brux.* 1894. 8°.   Pam. 77.

REGNAUD (P.) Le Rig-Véda et les origines de la mythologie indo-européenne. 1892, *etc.* 8°. Annales du Musée Guimet. Bibliothèque d'Études. Tom. 1.   7704. i.

RENAN (J. E.) Studies of religious History. pp. 303. *Lond.* 1893. 8°.   2212. f. 1.

SAINT-PATRICE. Plagiats bibliques : Brahmanisme de Moïse : Bouddhisme de Jésus. pp. 115. *Paris,* 1891. 12°.   4018. df. 16.

SANDER (N. F.) Rigveda und Edda. Eine vergleichende Untersuchung. pp. 71. *Stockholm,* 1893. 8°.   4503. ee. 27.

SAUSSAYE (P. D. C. de la) Manual of the science of Religion. pp. 672. *Lond.* 1891. 8°. 4506. df. 7.

SCHNEIDER (W.) Die Religion der afrikanischen Natur-völker. pp. 283. 1891. 8°. Darstellungen aus dem Gebiete der nichtchristlichen Religionsgeschichte. Bd. 5, 6.   4506. f.

RELIGION.—History, etc.—continued.

SCOTT (A.) Sacrifice, its prophecy and fulfilment. Baird lecture. pp. 372. *Edinb.* 1894. 8°.   4466. cc. 5.

SCOTT (C. N.) Foregleams of Christianity. pp. 223. *Lond.* 1893. 8°.   4503. aaa. 10.

SMITH (W. R.) Lectures on the religion of the Semites. pp. 507. *Lond.* 1894. 8°. 2212. e. 3.

TIELE (C. P.) Geschiedenis van den godsdienst in de oudheid. *Amsterd.* 1891, *etc.* 8°. 4530. d.

—— Geschichte der Religion im Altertum. *Gotha,* 1895, *etc.* 8°.   4504. cc.

—— Histoire comparée des anciennes Religions de l'Égypte et des peuples sémitiques. pp. 510. *Paris,* 1882. 8°.   4504. h. 8.

—— Manuel de l'histoire des Religions. pp. 360. *Paris,* 1885. 12°.   4503. a. 34.

TORMA (S. v.) Ethnographische Analogieen. pp. 76. *Jena,* 1894. 8°.   4503. cc. 22.

TYLER (C. M.) The Study of the history and philosophy of Religion. pp. 23. *Ithaca, N.Y.,* 1891. 8°.   8304. e. 24. (6.)

VAN ENDE (U.) Histoire naturelle de la Croyance. pp. 320. *Paris,* 1887. 8°.   8462. g. 44.

VANNUTELLI (V.) L'Oriente e l'Occidente. Usi e tradizioni religiose. pp. 151. *Roma,* 1892. 8°.   3926. aaa. 36.

WHEELER (J. M.) Bible Studies. Essays on phallic worship and other rites. pp. 136. *Lond.* 1892. 8°.   4505. aa. 5.

WORLD'S RELIGIOUS SERIES. The World's Religious series. *Lond.* 1891, *etc.* 8°. 4503. aaa.

See also ASSYRIA : DEITY : EGYPT : GREECE : HINDUISM : MOHAMMEDANISM : ROME : TEUTONIC MYTHOLOGY.

RELIGIOUS ORDERS.

General : History : Controversy.

SMITH (I. G.) Christian Monasticism from the fourth to the ninth centuries. pp. 351. *Lond.* 1892. 8°.   4782. g. 21.

AMÉLINEAU (E.) Histoire des Monastères de la Basse-Égypte. pp. 429. 1894. 4°. Annales du Musée Guimet. Tom. 25.   7704. h. 21.

GIACHI (V.) Il Monachismo romano nel quarto secolo. pp. 30. *Città di C.* 1892. 8°.   4534. c. 30. (9.)

SPREITZENHOFER (E.) Die Entwicklung des alten Mönchthums in Italien bis zum Auftreten des heil. Benedict. pp. 136. *Wien,* 1894. 8°.   4571. f. 27.

MONTALEMBERT (C. F. de) *Count.* Monks of the West from St. Benedict to St. Bernard. 6 vol. *Lond.* 1895. 8°.   2214. c. 2.

WEISS (C. F.) Die kirchlichen Exemtionen der Klöster bis zur gregorianisch-cluniacensischen Zeit. pp. 88. *Basel,* 1893. 8°.   4534. c. 30. (11.)

FAURE ( ) Récits et Légendes du moyen âge. pp. 514. *Saint-Amand,* 1893. 8°.   4532. df. 3.

AQUILLO LÓPEZ DE TURISO (J.) Los Institutos religiosos. pp. 861. *Barcelona,* 1891. 8°.   4784. de. 11.

BERTHIER (J.) L'État religieux. pp. 448. *La Salette,* 1893. 8°.   4061. de. 9.

BIOGRAPHIES. Biographies monastiques. *Ligugé,* 1892, *etc.* 8°.   4855. aaa.

DEMANTE (H.) La Femme forte et l'état religieux. pp. 266. *Paris,* 1890. 12°. 3900. bb. 34.

DUCKETT (*Sir* G. F.) Notices on monastic Costume. pp. 24. 1891. 8°.   Pam. 25.

FORAN (W.) All about Monks and Nuns. pp. 24. *Lond.* 1894. 8°.   3939. ccc. 18. (16.)

RELIGIOUS ORDERS.—*continued.*

GARCÍA MACEIRA (A.) Los Monjes y el suelo pátrio. pp. 85. *Salamanca*, 1893. 8°.
4535. b. 15. (9.)

GASQUET (F. A.) Some notes on mediæval Monastic Libraries. pp. 20. *Yeovil*, 1891. 8°.
011900. ee. 5. (11.)

—— Sketches of mediæval Monastic Life. The Scriptorium. pp. 12. *Yeovil*, 1894. 8°. Pam. 25.

HARNACK (A.) Das Mönchthum, seine Ideale und seine Geschichte. pp. 62.
Giessen, 1895. 8°.   4061. f. 16.

HUMPHREY (W.) Elements of Religious Life. pp. 342. *Lond.* 1895. 8°.   4092. bb. 2.

KITCHIN (G. W.) Organisation of a Convent, *etc.* 1892. 8°. Ac. Hampshire. *Record Society.* Compotus Rolls of St. Swithun's Priory, Winchester.   Ac. 8123. (7.)

LONDON. *Conventual Enquiry Society.* Abstract of Parliamentary evidence on monastic Institutions. pp. 32. *Lond.* 1890. 8°.   Pam. 78.

MULLER (S.) Over claustraliteit. pp. 228. 1890. 4°. Ac. Amsterdam. *K. Akademie van Wetenschappen.* Verhandelingen. Afdeeling Letterkunde. Deel. 19.   Ac. 944/3.

RÈGLES. Quelques règles canoniques sur la conduite des Religieuses. pp. 103.
Montréal, 1885. 8°.   4401. c. 44.

THURSTON (H.) The immuring of Nuns. pp. 28. 1892. 8°. MORRIS (J.) Historical Papers. No. 5.   3939. ccc.

—— Mr. R. Haggard and the myth of the walled-up Nun. pp. 24. *Lond.* 1894. 8°.
Pam. 78.

HOLLAND (W. L.) Walled-up Nuns and nuns walled in. pp. 237. *Edinb.* 1895. 8°.
3939. bb. 22.

TOCCO (F.) Gli ordini religiosi e l' eresia. 1891. 8°. Gli albori della vita italiana. Vol. 2.
9166. ccc. 11.

History, etc., in various Countries.

GRITZNER (A. M. F.) Handbuch der im deutschen Reiche, in Oesterreich-Ungarn, Dänemark, Schweden und der russischen Ostseeprovinzen bestehenden Damen-Stifter. pp. 245.
Frankfurt, 1893. 8°.   04789. h. 3.

BERLIÈRE (U.) Monasticon belge.
Bruges, 1890, *etc.* 4°.   4695. h. 2.

SPENCE (H. D. M.) Cloister Life in the days of Cœur de Lion. pp. 203. *Lond.* 1892, 4°.
4707. g. 12.

ARCHBOLD (W. A. J.) Somerset Religious Houses. pp. 407. 1892. 8°. Cambridge Historical Essays. No. VI.   9009. c.

LEFROY (W. C.) Ruined Abbeys of Yorkshire. pp. 296. *Lond.* 1891. 8°.   10358. ccc. 39.

GASQUET (F. A.) Henry VIII. and the English monasteries. 2 vol. *Lond.* 1892–95 8°.
4707. cc. 12.

SOUSA AMADO (J. de) Progresso das ordens religiosas dos dois sexos na Inglaterra, 1867–87. pp. 58. *Lisboa*, 1887. 8°.   4784. bb. 51. (14.)

MOLINIER (A.) Les Obituaires français au moyen âge. pp. 354. *Paris*, 1890. 8°.
7709. g. 28.

ZIMMERMANN (A.) Die Klöster in Frankreich, 1766–89. pp. 32. 1893. 8°. Frankfurter zeitgemässe Broschüren. N.F. Bd. 14. 12209. d.

PARIS. *Comité Congréganiste Le Franc de Taviers.* Frère Malapion, ou les Frères Congréganistes sous la 3° Republique. pp. 199. 8.
Paris, 1895. 8°.   8308. aaa. 32.

RELIGIOUS ORDERS.—*continued.*

ROBERT (A.) Comparison des impôts des congrégations religieuses avec ceux des contribuables ordinaires. pp. 94. *Rouen*, 1892. 8°. 8225. cc. 49.

ROUVIER (F.) Les Religieux français le l'influence de la France dans les missions. pp. 407. *Paris*, 1895. 12°.   4767. bb. 26.

SIMONNET (R.) Les Congrégations religieuses non autorisées. pp. 223. *Paris*, 1891. 8°.
4061. dd. 12.

THOMAS (J.) Les Coulisses d'un cloître. pp. 238. *Paris*, 1890. 12°.   4071. de. 22.

See also ATHOS, *Mount :* BEGUINES : CAPUCHINS : CARMELITES : CARTHUSIANS : CHURCH HISTORY : CISTERCIANS : CLUNIAC ORDER : DOMINICANS : FRANCISCANS : PRAEMONSTRATENSIAN ORDER : SACRED HEART : SERVITES : SISTERHOODS : TEMPLARS : TEUTONIC ORDER : URSULINES.

REMAUVILLE. GUILLOT (H.) Notice sur Remauville. pp. 240. *Troyes*, 1892. 8°.
10170. bb. 5.

REMIREMONT. BECK (F. W.) Remiremont, its Chapter. pp. 15. *Yeovil*, 1892. 8°.
4629. bbb. 17. (6.)

BUISSON (E.) Les Élections de 1789 à Remiremont. pp. 29. *Remiremont*, 1890. 8°. 9072. e. 9. (8.)

RENAISSANCE. BRISTOL (F. M.) Providential Epochs. pp. 269.
Cincinnati, 1894. 8°.   9004. g. 25.

CREIGHTON (M.) *Bp. of London.* The early Renaissance in England. pp. 44.
Camb. 1895. 8°.   011850. eee. 66.

LEE (V.) Renaissance fancies and studies. pp. 260. *Lond.* 1895. 8°.   012356. ff. 9.

VOIGT (G.) Die Wiederbelebung des classischen Alterthums. 2 Bde. *Berl.* 1893. 8°.
11312. p. 10.

See also ARCHITECTURE : ART, *History*, *Italy*, *Netherlands :* ITALIAN LITERATURE : ITALY, *History.*

RENNES. ORAIN (A.) Au Pays de Rennes. pp. 252. *Rennes*, 1892. 4°.   10174. h. 20.

BELLEVUE (   ) *Count.* L'Hôpital Saint-Yves de Rennes. pp. 469. *Rennes*, 1895. 8°.
4629. ee. 8.

REPRESENTATION, Parliamentary.
See ELECTIONS.

REPTILES. Ac. Frankfort. *Senckenbergische Naturforschende Gesellschaft.* Katalog der Reptilien-Sammlung. *Frankfurt*, 1893, *etc.* 8°.
Ac. 2878/5.

—— London. *British Museum.* Guide to the galleries of Reptiles. *Lond.* 1893. 8°.
7206. f. 10.

BEDRIAGA (J. v.) Amphibiens et reptiles recueillis en Portugal. pp. 87. *Coimbra*, 1889. 8°.
7290. e. 23.

BOWDICH, afterwards LEE (S.) Anecdotes of the habits and instincts of Reptiles, *etc.* pp. 323. *Lond.* 1891. 8°.   7204. a. 21.

COPE (E. D.) Catalogue of Reptiles of Central America. pp. 98. 1887. 8°. Bulletin of the U.S. National Museum. No. 32. Ac. 1875/13.

COOKE (M. C.) Our Reptiles and batrachians. pp. 200. *Lond.* 1893. 8°.   7290. a. 22.

COLOMBO. *Museum.* Report on the collection of Reptilia. pp. 39. *Colombo*, 1891. 8°.
7290. aaa. 12.

DUERIGEN (B.) Deutschlands Reptilien. *Magdeburg*, 1890, *etc.* 8°.   7290. f. 19.

GRANGER (A.) Reptiles. pp. 186. 1888. 8°. FRANCE. Histoire naturelle. Pt. 4.   7207. cc.

REPTILES—*continued.*
LACHMANN (H.) Die Reptilien Deutschlands.
pp. 229. *Berl.* 1890. 8°. 7290. e. 22.
See also LIZARDS: PALAEONTOLOGY: SNAKES:
TORTOISE.

REPTON. HIPKINS (F. C.) Repton. pp. 64.
Derby, 1894. 8°. 010358. f. 51.
REPTON SCHOOL. Repton School register, 1620–
1894. pp. 416. *Lond.* 1895. 8°. 8364. de. 42.

REPUBLICAN GOVERNMENT.
See DEMOCRACY: GOVERNMENT.

RESPIRATORY ORGANS. *See* LUNGS.

RETHEL. JADART (H.) Essai d'une Bibliographie rethéloise. pp. 84. *Réthel,* 1894. 8°.
11903. f. 34. (11.)
CARUEL (J. B.) Essai sur Réthel. pp. 432.
Réthel, 1891. 8°. 10174. f. 22.

RETREATS. NEWBOLT (W. C. E.) Quiet
days and Retreats. pp. 40. *Oxf.* 1894. 8°.
3457. dd. 44.

REUDNITZ. *See* LEIPSIC.

REUSS-SCHLEIZ. *See* GERA.

REUTLINGEN. Ac. Stuttgard. *K. statis-
tisch-topographisches Bureau.* Beschreibung
des Oberamts Reutlingen. 2 pt.
Stuttgart, 1893. 8°. Ac. 2432/6.
REVAL. STIEDA (W.) Revaler Zollbücher
und Quittungen des 14. Jahrhunderts. pp. 107.
1887. 8°. Hansische Geschichtsquellen. Bd. 5.
Ac. 7079. (2.)
RHAETO-ROMANSCH LANGUAGE.
See ROMANSCH.

RHEA. Ac. Paris. *Société d'Agriculture.*
Ramie or Rhea : cultivation and preparation.
pp. 28. *Lond.* 1891. 8°. 07076. e. 17.

RHETORIC. CLARK (J. S.) Practical Rhe-
toric. pp. 307. *N.Y.* 1891. 8°. 011824. e. 26.
CORNUTUS (L. A.) Cornuti Artis Rhetoricae epi-
tome. pp. 55. *Berolini,* 1891. 8°. 11805. k. 43.
DOYLE (F. C.) Introduction to the study of
Rhetoric. 3 pt. *Lond.* 1893. 8°. 011824. g. 11.
HONGKONG. *Collegium Missionum ad Exteros.*
Elementa Rhetoricæ. pp. 92.
Hongkong, 1890. 8°. 11824. aaa. 39.
RAYMOND (G. L.) and WHEELER (G. P.) The
Writer. Correlation of the principles of elocution
and rhetoric. pp. 203. *N.Y.* 1893. 8°.
011850. eee. 47.
See also ELOCUTION.

RHEUMATISM. ALLINSON (T. R.) Articles
on Rheumatism. pp. 24. *Lond.* 1892. 8°.
7306. df. 20. (4.)
GUYOT (T.) L'Arthritis. pp. 160.
Paris, 1890. 8°. 7620. df. 22.
LANE (H.) Differentiation in rheumatic Diseases.
pp. 121. *Lond.* 1892. 8°. 7470. b. 13.
THORNER (M.) Rheumatic throat affections.
pp. 8. 1893. 8°. 7305. f. 6. (12.)
WILDE (P. R.) Rheumatism : investigations
respecting its cause and cure. pp. 72.
Lond. 1893. 4°. 7616. f. 13.
See also GOUT.

RHINE, River and Provinces. RITTER (F.)
Katalog der Stadtbibliothek in Koeln.
1894, *etc.* 8°. Ac. Cologne. *Stadtbibliothek.*
Veröffentlichungen. Hft. 5 & 6. Ac. 9614.
QUETSCH (F. H.) Geschichte des Verkehrswesens
am Mittelrhein. pp. 416. *Freiburg,* 1891. 8°.
08225. k. 2.
CLEMEN (P.) Die Kunstdenkmäler der Rhein-
provinz. *Düsseldorf,* 1891, *etc.* 8°. 7806. de.

RHINE, RIVER, etc.—*continued.*
COHAUSEN (A. v.) Die Altertümer im Rheinland.
pp. 80. *Wiesbaden,* 1891. 4°. 7708. aa. 57.
KRAUS (F. X.) Die christlichen Inschriften der
Rheinlande. *Freiburg,* 1890, *etc.* 4°. 7707. g.
LAMPRECHT (C.) Fränkische Wanderungen
vornehmlich in Rheinland. 1882. 8°. Ac. Aix-
la-Chapelle. *Aachener Geschichtsverein.* Zeit-
schrift. Bd. 4. Ac. 7008.
P.P. *Bonn.* Rheinische Geschichtsblätter.
Bonn, 1894, *etc.* 8°. P.P. 3533. c. & 1126.
RIESE (A.) Das rheinische Germanien in der
antiken Litteratur. *Leipz.* 1892. 8°. 9340. f. 3.
SOMMERLAD (T.) Die Rheinzölle im Mittelalter.
pp. 175. *Halle,* 1894. 8°. 08227. i. 37.
BECK (C.) Zur Verfassungsgeschichte des Rhein-
bunds. pp. 48. *Mainz,* 1890. 4°.
9004. n. 10. (4.)

BADEN. *Centralbureau für Meteorologie.* Ergeb-
nisse der Untersuchung der Hochwasser Ver-
hältnisse im deutschen Rheingebiet. 2 Hft.
Berl. 1891. fol. 8755. m. 19.
CHAMBALU (A.) Die Stromveränderungen des
Niederrheins. *Köln,* 1892, *etc.* 4°. 10261. h.
BAEDEKER (C.) The Rhine. pp. 396.
Leipz. 1892. 8°. 2352. a.
COOK (T.) Tourists' handbook for Holland and
the Rhine. pp. 376. *Lond.* 1895. 8°. 10271. aa. 10.
JOANNE (P.) Hollande et bords du Rhin.
pp. 324. *Paris,* 1895. 8°. 10271. aa. 11.
VIGNERON (L.) Au-delà du Rhin. pp. 320.
Lyon, 1892. 12°. 10256. b. 43.
LEITHAEUSER (J.) Gallicismen in niederrhein-
ischen Mundarten. *Barmen,* 1891, *etc.* 4°.
12962. s. 2.

See also BERG : GERMANY.

RHIZOPODA. *See* PROTOZOA.

RHODE ISLAND. GANNETT (H.) Geo-
graphic dictionary of Rhode Island. pp. 31.
1894. 8°. U.S. *Geological Survey.* Bulletin.
No. 15. 1829. a. 7.
RHODE-ISLAND. Charter, Acts and Laws of the
Colony of Rhode Island, 1719. pp. 102.
Providence, 1895. fol. 6625. h. 6.
TOLMAN (W. H.) History of higher Education
in Rhode Island. pp. 210. 1894. 8°.
8366. bb. 43.

See also NEW ENGLAND.

RHODES. 'ABD AL-RAḤMĀN (J. al-D. A.
al-F.) Unternehmungen der Mamluken gegen
Cypern 1423–44. pp. 43. 16. *Wien,* 1884. 8°.
14555. b.

RHONE, Department. JOANNE (A. L.)
Géographie du département du Rhône. pp. 62.
Paris, 1895. 8°. 10105. aa. 2.

RHONE, River. BARRON (L.) Le Rhône.
pp. 454. *Paris,* 1892. 8°. 010171. g. 7.
LENTHÉRIC (C.) Le Rhône. 2 tom.
Paris, 1892. 8°. 10108. g. 1.
GENEVA. Utilisation des forces motrices du
Rhône. Travaux exécutés par la Ville de
Genève. pp. 279. *Genève,* 1890. 8°.
8775. h. 20.

RHOPALOCERA. *See* LEPIDOPTERA.

RHUBARB. GAUTIER (H.) Nouvelle étude
sur la Rhubarbe du Thibet. pp. 19.
La Rochelle, 1890. 8°. 7030. g. 6. (5.)
RICHELIEU, Indre-et-Loire. BOSSEBŒUF
(L. A.) Histoire de Richelieu. pp. 504.
1890. 8°. Ac. Tours. *Société Archéologique.*
Mémoires. Tom. 35. Ac. 5345.

RICHMOND, Surrey. CHANCELLOR (E. B.) History of Richmond. pp. 410.
Richmond, 1894. 4°.   10349. k. 3.

BURT (C.) The Richmond Vestry. Notes of its history, 1614–1890. pp. 82. 21.
Richmond, 1890. 8°.   010358. f. 22.

RICHMOND, Virginia. RICHMOND. Snapshots at Richmond. pp. 128. *Richmond*, 1895. 8°.
      10413. d. 4.

RICKETS. JENNER (*Sir* W.) Clinical lectures and essays on Rickets, *etc.* pp. 329.
Lond. 1895. 8°.   7616. h. 23.

RIDDLES. COLLECTION. Penny Collection of Conundrums. pp. 32. *Manch.* 1893, 8°.
      12316. ee. 14. (3.)

DONALD (M) Birthday book of Riddles.
Edinb. 1893. 32°.   7913. de. 9.

ECKART (K.) Allgemeine Sammlung niederdeutscher Rätsel. pp. 136. *Leipz.* 1894. 8°.
      012305. e. 7.

HUMPHREYS (J.) Christmas Conundrums.
1885–93. fol.   1882. c. 2. (196.)

JEAN (F.) Le nouveau Sphinx. pp. 356.
Olivet, 1890. 18°.   012314. i. 28.

LAKSHMĪNĀTHA UPĀSANI. Collection of Riddles. pp. 32. *Patna*, 1888. 32°.   12316. a. 55.

LEMON, *Don.* Everybody's book of Puzzles. pp. 125. *Lond.* 1890. 8°.   7913. f. 38.

RIDING. *See* HORSE.

RIES. *See* NORDLINGEN.

RIESENGEBIRGE. PETRÁK (E. R.) Illustrirter Führer durch das Riesengebirge. pp. 348. *Wien*, 1891. 8°.   10215. aa. 16.

RIFLE. *See* GUNNERY.

RIGA. METTIG (C.) Geschichte der Stadt Riga. *Riga*, 1895, *etc.* 8°.   10292. h.

Ac. Riga. *Gesellschaft für Geschichte der Ostseeprovinzen.* NEUMANN (W.) Das mittelalterliche Riga. pp. 56. *Berl.* 1892. fol.
      1788. b. 24.

SCHMIEDT (J.) Die Aufzeichnungen des rigaschen Rathssecretärs J. Schmiedt zu den Jahren 1558–62. pp. 164. *Leipz.* 1892. 8°.   9454. e. 2.

Ac. Riga. *Gesellschaft für Geschichte der Ostseeprovinzen.* BODECKER ( ) Chronik livländischer Ereignisse, 1593–1638. pp. 158. *Riga*, 1890. 8°.
      9456. g. 6.

BUCHHOLTZ (A.) Zur Geschichte des rigaschen Rathhauses. 1892. 8°. Ac. Riga. *Gesellschaft für Geschichte der Ostsee-Provinzen.* Mittheilungen. Bd. 15. Hft. 1.   Ac. 7900.

BULMERINCQ (A. v.) Der Ursprung der Stadtverfassung Rigas. pp. 83. *Leipz.* 1894. 8°.
      10105. ee. 10. (11.)

TOBIEN (A.) Ergebnisse der rigaer Handelsstatistik 1866–91. pp. 161. *Riga*, 1893. 4°.
      8228. l. 12.

See also LIVONIA.

RINGSTED. LÖFFLER (J. B.) Gravmonumenterne i Ringsted Kirke. pp. 45.
Kjøbenh. 1891. fol.   1706. c. 13.

RINGWORM. BURNETT (J. C.) Ringworm. pp. 132. *Lond.* 1892. 8°.   7630. aa. 18.

WHITEHOUSE (H. H.) Case of Ringworm of the scalp simulating Alopecia Areata. pp. 4.
N.Y. 1893. 8°.   7305. f. 5. (10.)
See also SKIN.

RIO DE JANEIRO. P.P. *Rio de Janeiro.* Archivo do Districto Federal. Revista de documentos. *Rio de J.* 1894, *etc.* 8°.   P.P. 4127. d.

RIO DE LA PLATA. *See* LA PLATA.

RIO GRANDE DO SUL, State. GRIMM (J. T.) Heimatkunde des Staates Rio Grande do Sul. pp. 247. *Santa Cruz*, 1891. 8°.
      10481. aa. 36.

RIOLO, LORENZINI (E.) Riolo. Stabilimento idrotorapico. pp. 30. *Bologna*, 1884. 8°.
      7462. ee. 4. (20.)

RIOM. RIOM. Inventaire sommaire des archives. pp. 194. 1892. 8°. Collection des inventaires-sommaires.   1814. b. *etc.*

RIOTS. ORDWAY (A.) Drill regulations for Street Riot Duty. *Wash.* 1891. 8°.
      8830. e. 11. (3.)
See also MEETINGS.

RIPON. RIPON. Ripon Millenary; a record of the festival. 2 pt. *Ripon*, 1892. 4°.
      Banks. 3. g. 1.

WARD, LOCK AND CO. Handbook to Ripon Cathedral. *Lond.* 1890. 8°.   010358. l. 25.

RIVERS. BOULÉ (A.) and LESCUYER (P.) Code des cours d'eau non navigables. pp. 453.
Paris, 1893. 12°.   5403. cc. 7.

BROWN (S. H.) Diagrams and tables of tidal Streams. pp. 54. *Lond.* 1895. 8°. 10498. c. 23.

DAVIS (G. E.) and (A. R.) The River Irwell: monograph on river pollution. pp. 96.
Manch. 1890. 8°.   8777. aaa. 21.

GREAT BRITAIN. The Rivers of Great Britain. 2 vol. *Lond.* 1892, *etc.* 4°.   10348. k. 18.

G. B. & I. Victoria, *Queen.* Public Health Act and Rivers Pollution Prevention Act, 1876.
Lond. 1892. 8°.   6426. cc. 4.

LAUER (J.) Zerstörung von Felsen in Flüssen. pp. 137. *Wien*, 1892. 8°.   8768. k. 12.

PARTIOT (H. L.) Étude sur les Rivières à marée et sur les estuaires. pp. 127. *Paris*, 1892. 8°.
      10172. f. 25.

PATERSON (M. McC.) Pollution of the Aire and Calder. pp. 32. *Lond.* 1893. 8°.   Pam. 79.

PICARD (A.) Traité des eaux. Droit, *etc.* 4 tom. *Paris*, 1890. 8°.   5403. g. 7.

U.S. *Corps of Engineers.* Index to the Reports of the Chief of Engineers upon river and harbour improvement. 2 vol.
Wash. 1881–89. 8°.   8768. l. 21.

THIÉRY (E.) Restauration des montagnes, correction des torrents. pp. 413. 1891. 8°.

LECHALAS (M. C.) Encyclopédie des travaux publics.   012216. i.

WHEELER (W. H.) Tidal Rivers. pp. 467. 1893. 8°. Longmans' Civil Engineering Series.
      8768. f.

—— Transporting Power of Water, as applied to the deepening of Rivers. pp. 20.
Bost. 1893. 8°.   8767. cc. 30. (13.)
See also CANALS: ENGINEERING: HYDRAULICS; and under the name of each river.

RIVIERA. ADENIS (J.) De Marseille à Menton. pp. 396. *Paris*, 1892. 8°.
      010171. e. 13.

AMBAYRAC (H.) Ligne de Nice à Grasse et à Puget-Théniers. pp. 67. *Nice*, 1892. 8°.
      10171. ee. 18.

ANSTED (A.) The Riviera. Etchings and vignettes. pp. 80. *Lond.* 1894. fol. K.T.C. 39. b. 1.

BALL (E. A. R) Mediterranean Winter resorts. pp. 336. 1892. 8°. Winter Resorts Guides.
      10025. aa.

BERNARD (M.) Autour de la Méditerranée.
Paris, 1892, *etc.* 4°.   10096. i.

BLACK (C. B.) The Riviera. pp. 260. 8.
Edinb. 1890. 8°.   10105. bb. 4.

BUCKLAND (A W.) The World beyond the Esterelles. 2 vol. *Lond.* 1884. 8°. 10136. f. 6.

COOK (T.) Handbook to the Riviera, *etc.*
pp. 174. *Lond.* 1893. 8°   10174. aa. 38.

D., R. B. Illustrated guide to the Riviera.
pp. 246. *Lond.* 1891. 8°.   10135. cc. 9.

RIVIERA—*continued.*

Dodge (W. P.) As the Crow Flies. From Corsica to Charing Cross. pp. 132.
N.Y. 1893. 12°.   10106. dd. 5.

Fitz Frederick. Letters from southern Shores.
pp. 50. *Sunderland*, 1894. 12°.   Pam. 91.

Joanne (P.) Les Stations d'hiver de la Méditerranée. pp. 371. *Paris*, 1895. 8°.
                                        10171. aa. 29.

Lenthério (C.) The Riviera ancient and modern. pp. 464. *Lond.* 1895. 8°.
                                        10170. bb. 8.

Liégeard (S.) La Côte d'azur. pp. 430.
Paris, 1887. fol.   10173. g. 8.

Macmillan (H.) The Riviera. pp. 304.
Lond. 1892. 8°.   10107. ee. 23.

Macquarie (J. L.) Villes d'hiver et plages de la Méditerranée. pp. 587. *Paris*, 1893. 8°.
                                        10171. aaa. 27.

Onimus (E.) L'Hiver dans les Alpes Maritimes.
pp. 588. *Paris*, 1891. 12°.   07686. e. 3.

Riviera. Murray's Handbook for the Riviera.
pp. 138. *Lond.* 1892. 8°.   2364. b. 25.

Sauvaigo (É.) Les Cultures sur le littoral de la Méditerranée. pp. 318. *Paris*, 1894. 12°.
                                        7078. e. 5.

Scott (C. W.) The Land of Flowers. pp. 186.
Bristol, 1892. 8°.   10135. aaa. 9.

See also Alassio : Grasse : Mediterranean Sea : Mentone : Monaco : Nice : Watering Places.

ROADS. *See* Highways.

ROANNE. Dumoulin (M.) En Pays roannais. pp. 274. *Roanne*, 1892. 8°.
                                        010171. m. 37.

ROCHESTER. O'Gorman (R. A.) Haymo of Hythe, Bishop of Rochester. pp. 131.
Lond. 1895. 8°.   4707. bb. 15.

Rochester. *Cathedral Church.* Registers of the Cathedral, 1657–1837. pp. 103.
Canterbury, 1892. 8°.   9906. i. 5.

Ward, Lock and Co. Handbook to Rochester Cathedral. *Lond.* 1890. 8°.   010358. l. 26.

ROCKALL. Christy (R. M.) About Rockall.
pp. 8. *Lond.* 1895. 8°.   Pam. 90.

ROCKINGHAM CASTLE. Wise (C.) Rockingham Castle and the Watsons. pp. 256.
Lond. 1891. 4°.   9914. d. 12.

ROCKY MOUNTAINS. Beaugrand (H.) Six Mois dans les Montagnes-Rocheuses.
pp. 323. *Montréal*, 1890. 8°.   10409. cc. 31.

Edwords (C. E.) Camp-fires of a Naturalist.
pp. 304. *N.Y.* 1893. 8°.   07905. f. 14.

Heclawa. In the Heart of the Bitter-Root Mountains. pp. 259. *N.Y.* 1895. 8°.
                                        10412. b. 42.

Ingersoll (E.) The Crest of the Continent.
pp. 344. *Chicago*, 1890. 8°.   10412. bbb. 42.

Rocky Mountains. What may be seen Crossing the Rockies. pp. 35. *Chicago*, 1893. 16°.
                                        Pam. 86.

—— One thousand miles through the Rocky Mountains. pp. 56. *Chicago*, 1893. 8°.
                                        Pam. 86.

Rutgers (L.) On and off the Saddle. pp. 201.
N.Y. 1894. 8°.   10408. aa. 31.

Wallihan (A. G.) Hoofs, claws and antlers of the Rocky Mountains. *Denver*, 1894. 4°.
                                        7208. k. 3.

See also Canada, *North West* and *Topography :* Sport : United States of America, *Western States.*

RODENTS. Herrick (C. L.) and Tight (W. G.) Central nervous system of Rodents.
1890, *etc.* 8°. Ac. Granville. *Denison University.* Bulletin of Scientific Laboratories.
Vol. 5.   Ac. 2692. c.
See also Myoxidae : Rabbit : Rat.

ROLLER, Bird. *See* Coraciidae.

ROMAGNA. Pasolini Dall' Onda (P. D.) I Tiranni di Romagna e i Papi. pp. 340.
Imola, 1888. 8°.   9166. ccc. 5.

ROMAN CATHOLIC CHURCH.

General.

Addis (W. E.) and Arnold (T.) A Catholic Dictionary. pp. 961. *Lond.* 1893. 8°. 2015. b.

Neher (S. J.) Conspectus Hierarchiæ Catholicæ in toto orbe terrarum. *Ger.* pp. 92.
Regensburg, 1895. 8°.   4050. c. 7.

Werner (O.) Orbis Terrarum Catholicus.
pp. 266. *Friburgi*, 1890. 4°.   4570. f. 11.
See also Church History.

Doctrines: Controversy.

A., C. F. B. Which is the true Church?
pp. 94. *Lond.* 1890. 8°.   3939. g 6. (5.)

A., J. M., *Missionnaire.* Conversions au xix° siècle. pp. 191. *Lille*, 1891. 8°.   4866. h. 16.

Allnatt (C. F. B.) The Church and the Sects.
2 Ser. *Lond.* 1887–90. 8°.   3940. g. 9.

Armstrong (R. C.) Romanism versus Protestantism. pp. 125. *Nashville*, 1894. 8°.
                                        3939. bb. 26.

Armytage (N. G.) Anglo-Catholicism the safer way. pp. 4. *Lond.* 1890. 8°. 3939. de. 20. (2.)

Aylmer (H.) Transformers and spiritual Chameleons. pp. 200. *Lond.* 1891. 8°.
                                        3940. cc. 7.

Bachmann (P.) Die wichtigsten Symbole der reformierten und katholischen Kirche. pp. 244.
Erlangen, 1891. 8°.   3506. ee. 5.

Bagshawe (J. B.) What do Anglicans mean by "the Church"? pp. 299. *Lond.* 1890. 8°.
                                        3940. b. 11.

Beer (E. de) Three Testimonies against Romanism. 2 pt. *Capetown*, 1890. 8°. 3939. g. 6. (7.)

Best (K. D.) The Victories of Rome and the Temporal Power. pp. 80. *Lond.* 1893. 8°.
                                        3940. aaa. 23.

Bridgett (T. E.) A Flag of Truce : or, must we fight for ever? pp. 69. *Lond.* 1893. 8°.
                                        3939. ccc. 16.

—— England for Our Lady. pp. 32.
Lond. 1893. 8°.   3940. g. 12. (4.)

Brinckman (A.) Disloyalty to Our Lord, or, the sin of Rome. pp. 37. *Lond.* 1891. 8°. Pam. 78.

Britten (J.) Why I left the Church of England.
pp. 24. *Lond.* 1894. 8°.   3939. ccc. 18. (8.)

Brown (N. F.) A Momentous Question ! Is killing heretics murder? pp. 15.
Lond. 1889. 8°.   3939. de. 22. (2.)

Brown (R.) Popery : a swindle of the Devil, *etc.*
pp. 122. *Lond.* 1894. 8°.   3940. b. 9.

Brownlow (W. R. B.) *R.C. Bishop of Clifton.* The Reunion of England with Rome. pp. 44.
Lond. 1895. 8°.   3939. ccc. 18. (13.)

Carrasquilla (R.) Sofismas anticatólicos.
pp. 63. *Bogotá*, 1881. 16°.   Pam. 93.

Catholic Church. The Catholic Church and the Bible. pp. 16. *Lond.* 1890. 8°.
                                        3939. ccc. 1. (9.)

Catholic Doctrine. Readings in Catholic doctrine. *Lond.* 1893, *etc.* 8°.   3939. ccc.

Clarke (R. F.) The Pope and the Bible. Attitude of the Church to Bible-reading. pp. 80.
Lond. 1889. 8°.   Pam. 78.

ROMAN CATHOLIC CHURCH.—Doctrines, etc.—continued.

COLLETTE (C. H.) Illegal ecclesiastical territorial Titles. pp. 56. Lond. 1894: 8°.
3940. g. 12. (7.)
—— Roman Priests as described by themselves.
pp. 31. Lond. 1894. 8°.　3939. de. 21. (11.)

SMITH (S. F.) Mr. Collette as a Historian.
pp. 24. Lond. 1893. 8°.　3939. ccc. 18. (7.)

CONNELLAN (T.) Landmarks. pp. 100.
Dublin, 1893. 8°.　3939. de. 20. (7.)

COSTELLOE (B. F. C.) The Church Catholic.
pp. 28. Lond. 1890. 8°.　3939. ccc. 1. (10.)

CROFT (W.) The continuity of the English
Church. pp. 28. Lond. 1890. 8°.
3939. ccc. 1. (12.)

CULLEN (P. J.) A Guide to the true Faith.
pp. 192. Lond. 1893. 8°.　3940. bbb. 27.

CUSACK (M. F.) A Remarkable Book and two
remarkable relics. pp. 116. Lond. 1892. 8°.
3940. aa. 10.
—— What Rome teaches. pp. 166.
Lond. 1892. 8°.　3940. aa. 11.

DELITZSCH (F.) Selbsterlebte römische Pro-
paganda. pp. 24. Leipz. 1894. 8°.　Pam. 93.

ENGLAND. Catechism for Catholics in England.
pp. 40. Lond. 1893. 16°.　Pam. 11.

ENGLISHMAN. England under St. Peter. pp. 15.
Lond. 1893. 8°.　3940. g. 12. (5.)

EVEREST (W. F.) The Gift of the Keys and
other essays. pp. 185. Lond. 1895. 8°.
3939. bb. 24.

FALLACIES. Some popular historical Fallacies
examined. Lond. 1893, etc. 8°.　3939. c. 13.

FERNANDEZ Y VALBUENA (R.) La Herejia
liberal. pp. 179. Toledo, 1893. 8°. 3901. ee. 7.

FRY (J. H.) The Church of England, never a
part of the Church of Rome. pp. 89.
Lond. 1893. 8°.　3939. b. 9.

GATTY (C. T.) Letter to the people of England
on the revival of the Catholic Faith. pp. 92.
Lond. 1891. 16°.　3940. a. 4.

GIBBONS (J.) Cardinal. The Faith of our Fathers.
pp. 480. Baltimore, 1890. 8°.　3940. aa. 9.

GILDEA (W.) The Catholic Church. pp. 24.
Lond. 1893. 8°.　3939. ccc. 15.

GORE (C.) Roman Catholic claims. pp. 184.
Lond. 1892. 8°.　3939. cc. 21.

G. B., Roman Catholic Bishops in. Declaration of
the Roman Catholic Bishops in Great Britain.
1826. pp. 16. Lond. 1891. 8°.　Pam. 78.

GRETTON (G.) Stranger's guide to the Church.
pp. 31. Lond. 1881. 8°.　3939. aa. 42. (3.)

GROOT (J. V. de) Summa apologetica de Ecclesia
Catholica. 2 vol. Ratisbonae, 1890. 8°.
4050. c. 6.

HAMMOND (W.) The Roman Catholic System
destructive of our welfare. pp. 125.
Capetown, 1890. 8°.　Pam. 78.

HARDWICKE (W. W.) Missing links of the
English religious Establishments. pp. 36.
Lond. 1894. 8°.　Pam. 78.

HECKER (I. T.) The Church and the age.
pp. 322. N.Y. 1887. 8°.　4183. de. 26.

HOCHSTETTER (C.) Einfluss des Protestantismus
und Katholizismus. pp. 158. Gütersloh, 1892. 8°.
3908. f. 27.

HOENIG (W.) Der katholische und der protestan-
tische Kirchenbegriff. pp. 133. Berl. 1894. 8°.
4662. f. 11.

JENKINS (R. C.) Letter to Cardinal Vaughan
on the unity of the church. pp. 24.
Folkestone, 1895. 8°.　Pam. 78.

ROMAN CATHOLIC CHURCH.—Doctrines, etc.—continued.

JOSEPH, de Saint-François. Syllogismes religieuses. pp. 192. Paris, 1892. 8°. 4371. ee. 10.

LA RIVE (T. de) De Genève à Rome. Impressions et souvenirs. pp. 243.
Paris, 1895. 12°.　3900. c. 33.

LETA (B. M. la) La Chiesa Cattolica difesa.
pp. 439. Milano, 1891. 8°.　4050. aa. 33.

LONDON. Catholic Truth Society. Controversial
tracts. Lond. 1890, etc. 8°.　3939. ccc.
—— Leaflets and religious tracts.
Lond. 1888, etc. 16°.　3939. a.
—— Papers read at the annual conference, 1890.
Lond. 1890. 8°.　3940. aaa. 16.

LYNCH (P.) The old religion in England. pp. 34.
Lond. 1890. 8°.　3939. ccc. 1. (14.)

M., J. H. Before and after the Reformation.
pp. 16. Lond. 1890. 8°.　3939. ccc. 1. (15.)

MACKLEM (S.) A few words from a convert from
Anglicanism. pp. 12. Lond. 1893. 8°.　Pam. 78.

MICHEL (P.) L'Orient et Rome: étude sur
l'union. pp. 344. Saint-Amand, 1894. 8°.
3926. aa. 26.

MOORE (T.) and BRINCKMAN (A.) Anglican
Brief against Roman claims. pp. 682.
Lond. 1895. 8°.　3939. bb. 23.

MOORHOUSE (J.) Bp. of Manchester. The Roman
claim to Supremacy. pp. 45. Manch. 1895. 8°.
Pam. 78.

VAUGHAN (B.) B. Vaughan's Lectures in reply to
the Bishop of Manchester. pp. 158.
Lond. 1895. 8°.　3939. c. 18.

MOYES (J.) Canon Moyes and his facts as to the
ancient connection of the Church of England
with that of Rome. pp. 11. Lond. 1892. 8°.
Pam. 78.

NEWMAN (J. H.) Cardinal. Eight lectures on
the position of Catholics in England. 9 pt.
Lond. 1890. 8°.　3940. cc. 6.
—— Analysis of Cardinal Newman's "Apologia
pro vitâ sua." By J. N. Darby. pp. 282.
Lond. 1891. 8°.　3940. c. 6.

NUS (E.) Vivisection du Catholicisme. pp. 278.
Paris, 1894. 8°.　3900. c. 28.

O'REILLY (E. J.) Relations of the Church to
society. pp. 384. Lond. 1892. 8°.　3940. i. 9.

PATON (J.) British History and papal claims.
2 vol. Lond. 1893. 8°.　9503. dd. 5.

PAUL (C. K.) Confessio Viatoris. pp. 66.
Lond. 1891. 8°.　3940. aaa. 22.

P.P. London. Faith of our Fathers. A magazine. Lond. 1887, etc. 8° & 4°. P.P. 199. & 2187.

PEREZ-CORTÉS Y GARCIA (A.) Catolicismo y
racionalismo. pp. 275. Alicante, 1891. 8°.
3900. aa. 7.

PITTAR (F. M.) Protestant converted to Catholicity by her Bible and Prayer-Book. pp. 200.
Lond. 1895. 8°.　3939. cc. 28.

PROCTER (M. J.) Points of difference between
the English, Roman and Protestant Churches.
pp. 204. Camb. 1894. 8°.　3940. b. 10.

PROTESTANT FICTIONS. Some Protestant Fictions
exposed. 8 pt. Lond. 1894. 8°.　3939. b. 12.

RIVINGTON (L.) Anglican Fallacies. Lord
Halifax on reunion. pp. 114. Lond. 1895. 8°.
3939. aaa. 50.

ROMAN CAMP. The War in the Roman camp.
pp. 35. Lond. 1894. 8°.　Pam. 78.

ROMAN IMPRESSIONS. Recent Roman Impressions.
Paganism and Roman Catholicism. pp. 23.
Lond. 1893. 8°.　Pam. 78.

ROME, Church of. Roma Antiqua et Recens.
pp. 174. Lond. 1889. 8°.　3940. bbb. 19.

**ROMAN CATHOLIC CHURCH.—Doc-
trines, etc.—** *continued.*

Rome. Why I came out from Rome. pp. 101.
Lond. 1892. 12°.   3939. aaa. 46.

Rome, *Church of.* Apostolic Letter of Pope
Leo XIII. to the English people. April 14, 1895.
pp. 16. *Lond.* 1895. 8°.   Pam. 96.

Armytage (G. N.) The Pope and the People;
comments on the letter of Leo XIII. pp. 26.
Lond. 1895. 8°.   3939. de. 20. (12.)

Ruffoni (A. G.) La Chiesa cattolica. pp. 418.
Novara, 1893. 8°.   3553. aa. 2.

S., L. On the Infallibility of the Catholic
Church. pp. 8. *Lond.* 1895. 8°.   Pam. 78.

Salmon (G.) The Infallibility of the Church.
pp. 500. *Lond.* 1890. 8°.   3940. g. 10.

Smith (S. F.) Reasons for rejecting Anglican
Orders. pp. 150. *Lond.* 1895. 8°. 3939. aaa. 49.

Soames (W. H. K.) Sacrifice, altar, priest and
absolution. pp. 92. *Blackheath,* 1894. 8°.
     4371. b. 16.

Spinoza (B. de) The Reply of B. Spinoza, to the
letter of A. de Burgh, a convert to Romanism.
pp. 8. *Folkestone,* 1890. 8°.   3940. bb. 31. (7.)

Taute (R.) Die katholische Geistlichkeit und
die Freimaurerei. pp. 94. *Leipz.* 1895. 8°.
     4785. cc. 45.

Titherington (J.) Roman Catholicism, the
Friend of superstition. pp. 16.
Lower Darwen, 1893. 8°.   Pam. 78.

Toupet (A.) Essai sur le Catholicisme. 2 tom.
Lille, 1890. 8°.   4376. ee. 16.

Vaughan (B.) Faith and reason. pp. 20.
Lond. 1890. 8°.   3939. ccc. 2. (20.)

Vaughan (H.) *Cardinal.* England's Conversion
by the power of prayer. pp. 28.
Lond. 1890. 8°.   3939. ccc. 1. (21.)

Waterworth (W.) The Popes and the English
Church. pp. 20. *Lond.* 1890. 8°.
     3939. ccc. 1. (22.)

Wilberforce (W. I.) What is the Object?
Correspondence on the Anglican theory of Continuity. *Bognor,* 1895. 8°.   3939. aaa. 48.

Wright (C. H. M.) Primer of Roman Catholicism. pp. 160. 1895. 8°.   Present Day
Primers.   4429. eee.

Wyss (L. v.) Der neuere Katholizismus, in
seiner dogmatischen und praktischen Entfaltung.
pp. 78. *Zürich,* 1892. 8°.   4427. cc. 19. (15.)

Zahm (J. A.) Catholic Science and Scientists.
pp. 217. *Phila.* 1893. 8°.   4182. b. 41.

See also Christianity: Clergy: England,
Church of: Indulgences: Liturgiology:
Theology: Vatican Council.

History.

See Church History, and under the subheading
History, Ecclesiastical, of each country.

Law. *See* Law, *Ecclesiastical.*

Papacy: Cardinals: Conclave.

Allnatt (C. F. B.) Was St. Peter Bishop of
Rome? pp. 28. *Lond.* 1887. 8°.
     3939. ccc. 1. (2.)

—— Notes on passages of Holy Scripture, alleged
by Dr. Littledale against the Supremacy of St.
Peter. pp. 32. *Lond.* 1887. 8°.
     3939. ccc. 1. (1.)

Bell (C. D.) The Supremacy of St. Peter.
pp. 16. *Lond.* 1894. 8°.   3939. de. 20. (10.)

Berthelet (G.) Muss der Papst ein Italiener
sein? pp. 171. *Leipz.* 1894. 8°.   4050. g. 39.

Brandi (S. M.) Die Politik des Papstes Leo XIII.
vertheidigt gegenüber der "Contemporary Review." pp. 63. *Trier,* 1893. 8°.   Pam. 64.

**ROMAN CATHOLIC CHURCH—Doc-
trines, etc.—** *continued*

Briganti (A.) *Archbp. of Apamœa.* L' impero
dell' uomo e l' impero di Dio. pp. 445.
Torino, 1893. 8°.   4050. aaa. 19.

C., C. F. P. The Theandric Kingdom. pp. 60.
Lond. 1894. 8°.   4050. aaa. 21.

Calatayud y Bonmati (V.) Necesidad del
principado civil del Romano Pontifice. pp. 42.
Alicante, 1890. 8°.   Pam. 70.

Collinridge (C. F. P.) "Then the Pontiffs are
free." pp. 173. *Lond.* 1890–93. 8°.
     3940. cc. 17.

Courtial (L.) La Papauté est-elle d'institution
divine? pp. 58. *Montauban,* 1891. 8°.
     4050. h. 17. (2.)

Doellinger (J. J. I. v.) Das Papstthum.
pp. 579. *München,* 1892. 8°.   5015. cc. 3.

Fava (A. J.) *Bp. of Grenoble.* Letter treating of
the Divine Institution of the Papacy. pp. 90.
Lond. 1891. 8°.   4050. aaa. 15.

Forti-Mancinelli (G.) Da Papa a Papa.
pp. 92. *Milano,* 1892. 8°.   4050. a. 31.

Froehlich (R.) The Vatican and the Italian
Kingdom. Bishop of Salford's address to the
R.C. Congress at Liège. pp. 84.
Manch. 1891. 8°.   4050. g. 33.

Maglione (L.) The Vatican and the Kingdom
of Italy. [Reply to R. Froehlich.] pp. 148.
Lond. 1892. 8°.   4571. cc. 13.

Gallagher (M.) Was the Apostle Peter ever
at Rome? pp. 249. *N.Y.* 1894. 8°.
     3939. bb. 25.

Genet de Châtenay (L. M. C. G. A.) *Countess.*
Rome chrétienne. Les noces d'or de sa Sainteté
Léon XIII. pp. 237. *Tours,* 1891. 8°.
     4571. ee. 8.

Goyau (G.) Le Vatican, les Papes, *etc.*
Brux. 1895. 4°.   K.T.C. 30. b. 7.

Guérin (P.) Le Pouvoir temporel. pp. 384.
Lyon, 1892. 8°.   4050. g. 35.

Hall (H. E.) Leadership not lordship: instructions on the Roman question. pp. 75.
Lond. 1892. 8°.   3940. bbb. 25.

Hitchens (J. H.) Papal Supremacy. pp. 20.
Lond. 1891. 8°.   Pam. 78.

Hollweck (J.) Der apostolische Stuhl und
Rom. pp. 190. *Mainz,* 1895. 8°. 4050. bbb. 18.

Imbart Latour (J.) La Papauté en droit international. pp. 251. *Paris,* 1893. 8°.
     4050. h. 19.

Italy. Il Papa e l'Impero italiano. pp. 15.
Roma, 1890. 8°.   Pam. 70.

Kannengieser (A.) Les Adversaires du Pouvoir
Temporel et la Triple Alliance. pp. 336.
Paris, 1893. 8°.   8026. aa. 28.

Kiryeev (A. A.) Zur Unfehlbarkeit des Papstes.
pp. 71. *Leipz.* 1891. 8°.   4050. h. 17. (3.)

L'Étoile (G. A.) Lösung der römischen Frage
durch Kaiser Wilhelm II. pp. 46.
Paderborn, 1890. 8°.   Pam. 70.

López Pelaez (A.) El Pontificado y el actual
pontifice. pp. 703. *La Coruña,* 1893. 8°.
     4571. e. 3.

Lyons (D.) Christianity and infallibility.
pp. 284. *Lond.* 1891. 8°.   3939. cc. 18.

Malvezzi (N.) Il caso della partenza del Papa
da Roma. pp. 67. *Bologna,* 1891. 8°.
     4050. h. 17. (4.)

Morvan (J. N.) Un Pape chrétien frappant
d'anathème le Pape infaillible. pp. 52.
Brest, 1890. 24°.   Pam. 93.

Nitti (F.) Leone X. e la sua politica. pp. 463.
Firenze, 1892. 8°.   4855. bb. 17.

ROMAN CATHOLIC CHURCH.—Doctrines, etc.—continued.

OCHINO (B.) Des Papstthums Entstehung und Fall. pp. 68. Halle, 1893. 8°. Pam. 93.

OLIVART (de) Marquis. Del Aspecto internacional de la Cuestión romana. Madrid, 1893, etc. 4°. 8032. ccc.

PALMIERI (D.) Tractatus de Romano Pontifice. pp. 791. Prati, 1892. 8°. 4050. g. 37.

PAPACY. Present Position and future prospects of the Papacy. pp. 8. Lond. 1890. 8°. 4136. a. 42. (4.)

PESARO (A. A. di) La Diplomazia Vaticana e la questione del potere temporale. pp. 128. Firenze, 1890. 8°. 4050. h. 22.

PETAVEL OLLIFF (E.) Les droits et les torts de la Papauté. pp. 74. Lausanne, 1890. 8°. 4050. h. 17. (1.)

PONTREMOLI (P.) L'Opusculo d'un monomane sulla Questione romana. pp. 25. Genova, 1890. 8°. Pam. 71.

POPE. The Temporal Power of the Pope, definable or indefinable. pp. 21. Lond. 1891. 8°. Pam. 78.

PULLER (F. W.) Primitive Saints and the See of Rome. pp. 428. Lond. 1893. 8°. 3940. bb. 28.

RIVINGTON (L.) The Primitive Church and the See of Peter. pp. 488. Lond. 1894. 8°. 4534. ee. 15.

—— Primitive and Roman. A reply to the Church Quarterly Review. pp. 36. Lond. 1894. 8°. Pam. 78.

ROLF (A.) Das Papsttum und seine Unfehlbaren. pp. 176. Wiesbaden, 1895. 8°. 4050. a. 34.

ROME, Church of. Rights and pretensions of the Roman See. pp. 272. 1894. 8°. NEW YORK. Church Club. Lectures. 3940. dd.

S., C. Sul Dominio temporale dei Papi. pp. 110. Roma, 1891. 8°. 8033. h. 18.

SANDOVAL (A. de) Estado actual de la Cuestion romana. pp. 74. Madrid, 1890. 8°. Pam. 70.

SCHMID (J.) Petrus in Rom. pp. 229. Luzern, 1892. 8°. 4050. g. 38.

TRIPEPI (L.) Erudizione alcuni avversari dei Papi. pp. 207. Roma, 1892. 8°. 4050. h. 20.

VAL D'EREMAO (J. P.) The Keys of Peter. pp. 30. Dublin, 1891. 8°. Pam. 78.

VEGA DE ARMIJO (de la) Marquis. Les Relations entre le Saint-Siège et le Royaume d'Italie. pp. 84. Paris, 1889. 8°. 8033. g. 40.

———

GRIMALDI (F.) Les Congrégations romaines. pp. 556. Sienne, 1890. 8°. 4050. bbb. 15.

PASCAL (G. de) Notice sur les Congrégations romaines. pp. 82. Marseille, 1894. 8°. 5051. bb. 11.

PIEPER (A.) Zur Entstehungsgeschichte der ständigen Nuntiaturen. pp. 222. Freiburg, 1894. 8°. 4571. f. 26.

LECTOR (L.) Le Conclave: origines, histoire, etc. pp. 784. Paris, 1894. 8°. 5015. aa. 7.

GRABINSKI (G.) Count. Il Conclave. [Criticism on Le Conclave par L. Lector.] pp. 123. Firenze, 1894. 8°. 5015. aaa. 9.

SAEGMUELLER (J. B.) Die Papstwahlbullen und das staatliche Recht der Exklusive. pp. 308. Tübingen, 1892. 8°. 5015. aaa. 8.

See also supra : Doctrines. Infra : Italy : VATICAN COUNCIL.

For the History of the Papacy, see CHURCH HISTORY.

ROMAN CATHOLIC CHURCH.—cont.

Roman Catholic Church in various Countries.

Africa. See MISSIONS.

Argentine Republic.

CHACALTANA (C.) Patronato Nacional argentino. pp. 658. Buenos A. 1885. 8°. 4183. cc. 42.

Australia.

KENNY ( ) History of Catholicity in Australia to 1840. pp. 243. Sydney, 1886. 8°. 4745. cc. 43.

Austria.

ENSIAN (H. v.) Clericale Umstürzler. Studie zur Geschichte der Ultramontanen "Volkspartei" in Ungarn. pp. 66. Berl. 1895. 8°. 3914. bbb. 18.

MAYERHOFER (H.) Oesterreich - ungarisches Pfarrorte-Lexikon. Wien, 1895, etc. 8°. 10235. ee.

VIENNA. Zweiter Katholikentag, 1889. Verhandlungen. 2 Bde. Wien, 1889. 8°. 3908. f. 23.

WAHRMUND (L.) Das Kirchenpatronatrecht in Oesterreich. Wien, 1894, etc. 8°. 05107. i.

See also AUSTRIA, History, Ecclesiastical : EDUCATION, Ecclesiastical : LAW, Ecclesiastical.

Bavaria. See infra : Germany.

Belgium.

BELGIUM. Assemblée des Catholiques. Assemblée générale des catholiques. Session de 1891. Malines, 1892, etc. 8°. 3900. k.

EBUR. Propos chrétiens d'un Catholique belge. pp. 107. Liège, 1895. 12°. 3900. c. 32.

GHENT, Diocese of. L'Œuvre du Denier de Saint Pierre. Histoire du Denier de Saint Pierre depuis sa restauration 1860–85. pp. 589. Gand, 1886. 8°. 4685. e. 33.

VERSPEYEN (G.) Le Parti catholique belge. pp. 153. Gand, 1893. 8°. 3925. b. 50.

WASSENHOVE (A. v.) Le Parti catholique en face de la représentation proportionnelle. pp. 43. Brux. 1895. 8°. 8081. f. 9.

See also BELGIUM, Politics : NETHERLANDS, History, Ecclesiastical.

Canada.

EPHEM. Le Canada ecclésiastique. Almanach-annuaire du Clergé. pp. 216. Montréal, 1889. 12°. P.P. 2539. f.

HUARD (V. A.) L'Apôtre du Saguenay, D. Racine. pp. 154. Québec, 1895. 8°. 4986. f. 61.

LACASSE (Z.) Le Prêtre et ses détracteurs. pp. 276. Montréal, 1892. 8°. 4182. a. 38.

—— Dans le Camp ennemi. pp. 220. Montréal, 1893. 12°. 4182. aaa. 35.

O'BRIEN (C.) Archbp. of Halifax, N.S. Memoirs of E. Burke, Bishop of Zion. pp. 154. Ottawa, 1894. 8°. 4956. bbb. 14.

—— Mémoire sur les missions de la Nouvelle Écosse de 1760 à 1820. pp. 269. Québec, 1895. 8°. 8765. cc. 30.

TANGUAY (C.) Répertoire du Clergé canadien. pp. 526. Montréal, 1893. 8°. 4985. f. 13.

Chili.

BELMAR (F. S.) Carta demostrativa del patronato canónico de Chile. pp. 180. Santiago, 1883. 8°. 4183. f. 28.

China. See MISSIONS.

England.

ENGLAND. Short history of the Catholic Church in England. pp. 502. Lond. 1895. 8°. 4707. bb. 14.

ROMAN CATHOLIC CHURCH. —
England—*continued*.

INGRAM (T. D.) England and Rome : history of
the relations between the Papacy and the Eng-
lish State. pp. 430. *Lond.* 1892. 8°. 3910. h. 14.
MORRIS (J.) Historical Papers.
Lond. 1892, *etc.* 8°.   3939. ccc.
—— The English Martyrs. pp. 32.
Lond. 1887. 8°.   3939. ccc. 1. (3.)
POLLEN (J. H.) Acts of English Martyrs.
pp. 400. 1891. 8°. The Quarterly Series.
Vol. 75.   3605. dd.
GASQUET (F. A.) Hampshire Recusants; their
troubles in the reign of Queen Elizabeth.
pp. 58. *Lond.* 1895. 8°.   4705. bbb. 32.
COURSON (R. de) *Countess*. Quatre portraits de
femmes. Épisodes des persécutions d'Angleterre.
pp. 455. *Paris,* 1895. 12°.   4906. de. 31.
THOMPSON (E. H.) Before and after Gunpowder
Plot. pp. 24. *Lond.* 1890. 8°. 3939. ccc. 1. (20.)
POLLEN (J. H.) Father H. Garnet and the Gun-
powder Plot. pp. 52. *Lond.* 1888. 8°.
                                 4804. dd. 6. (3.)
STONYHURST COLLEGE. Souvenir of the Centenary
Celebration, July 1894. *Belfast,* 1894, *obl.* 8°.
                                 8364. h. 14.
WARD (B.) History of St. Edmund's College,
Old Hall. pp. 344. *Lond.* 1893. 8°. 8364. f. 20.
SHEPHERD (J.) Reminiscences of Prior Park.
pp. 148. *Lond.* 1894. 8°.   8364. bb. 72.
UFTON COURT. Catholic register of Ufton Court.
pp. 22. 1889. 8°.   9916. f. 32.
MURPHY (T.) Position of the Catholic Church
during the last two centuries. pp. 112.
Lond. 1892. 8°.   4705. d. 20.
CASARTELLI (L. C.) Forgotten chapter of the
Second Spring, 1835–1846. pp. 44.
Lond. 1895. 8°.   Pam. 29.
ULLATHORNE (W. B.) *Bp. of Birmingham.*
Autobiography. *Lond.* 1893, *etc.* 8°. 4905. g. 9.
WARD (W.) W. G. Ward and the Catholic
revival. pp. 468. *Lond.* 1893. 8°. 2217. d. 2.
GRABINSKI (G.) *Count.* La Renaissance catho-
lique en Angleterre et le Cardinal Newman.
pp. 395. *Lyon,* 1893. 8°.   4705. e. 33.
LEMIRE (J.) Le Cardinal Manning et son action
sociale. pp. 285. *Paris,* 1893. 12°. 4856. aa. 19.

ASHBURNHAM (B.) *Earl of Ashburnham.* English
Catholics and home rule. pp. 8.
Lond. 1886. 8°.   Pam. 68.
WYNDHAM (F. M.) English Catholics and home
rule. pp. 7. *Lond.* 1886. 8°.   Pam. 68.
BOWDEN (H. S.) Guide to the Oratory, S. Ken-
sington. pp. 112. *Lond.* 1893. 8°. 4707. aaa. 39.
DYER (A. S.) Sketches of English nonconformity.
pp. 112. *Lond.* 1893. 8°.   4109. aa. 42.
GLADSTONE (*Right Hon.* W. E.) The Religious
Disabilities Bill. Speech in moving the Second
Reading. pp. 16. *Westminster,* 1891. 8°. Pam. 68.
GREAT BRITAIN. Handbook of Catholic charities
in Great Britain. pp. 103. *Lond.* 1894. 8°.
                                 4192. b. 42.
LILLY (W. S.) and WALLIS (J. E. P.) Manual of
the law affecting Catholics. pp. 266.
Lond. 1893. 8°.   6325. df. 20.
P.P. *London.* The Newman House chronicle :
Lond. 1891, *etc.* 8°.   2095.
See also EDUCATION, *Ecclesiastical :* STONYHURST :
WARE. For Anglican and Roman Controversy,
see supra : Doctrines, *etc.* For Pre-Reformation
History, *see* CHURCH HISTORY and ENGLAND,
History, Ecclesiastical.

ROMAN CATHOLIC CHURCH.—*cont.*

France.

APER DE M. (J.) La Lutte. pp. 66.
Bar-le-Duc, 1893. 12°.   Pam. 69.
AT (J. A.) Questions de morale contemporaine.
pp. 168. *Tarbes,* 1892. 8°.   3900. b. 52.
AUDIFFRENT (J. B. G.) Aux vrais Catholiques.
pp. 26. *Marseille,* 1892. 8°.   3900. i. 18. (6.)
BASCOUL (L.) Étude sur la Décomposition de la
France après 89. pp. 368. *Paris,* 1893. 8°.
                                 3900. bb. 50.
BAUNARD (L.) Espérance, un réveil de l'idée
religieuse en France. pp. 241. *Paris,* 1892. 12°.
                                 3900. bb. 44.
BAZIN (G.) Politique et religion. pp. 416.
Paris, 1892. 12°.   3900. bb. 39.
BELLER (J.) Le Pèlerinage des vingt mille à
Rome. pp. 546. *Reims,* 1892. 8°. 4571. aa. 7.
BESSIÈRES (X.) Le Recrutement du Clergé
en Corse. pp. 50. *Bar-le-Duc,* 1892. 8°.
                                 3900. g. 12. (8.)
BONNEFON (J. de) Soutanes politiques.
pp. 329. *Paris,* 1893. 12°.   3900. bb. 51.
BOYER D'AGEN (A. J.) Le Clergé devant la
République. pp. 220. *Paris,* 1892. 12°.
                                 3900. a. 56.
BROGLIE (P. de) Le Présent et l'avenir du
Catholicisme en France. pp. 273.
Paris, 1892. 12°.   3900. c. 20.
C., J. C. Pro Patria et pro Petri Sede. pp. 80.
Paris, 1891. 8°.   3900. h. 49. (9.)
CATHOLIC. Les Catholiques et la République.
pp. 70. *Paris,* 1891. 12°.   Pam. 69.
—— La situation en France. pp. 16.
Toulouse, 1891. 8°.   Pam. 69.
CATHOLIC INTERESTS. Les Intérêts catholiques
en 1891. pp. 259. *Paris,* 1891. 12°.
                                 3900. bb. 37.
CHAMARD (F.) La Révolution, le Concordat et
la liberté religieuse. pp. 296. *Paris,* 1891. 12°.
                                 4629. b. 28.
CHARLES * * * La révolution dans la société
chrétienne. pp. 445. *Paris,* 1893. 8°.
                                 3900. bb. 48.
CHAVARD (F.) Le Célibat, le prêtre et la femme.
pp. 521. *Paris,* 1894. 8°.   8416. f. 49.
CHESNELONG (P. C.) Discours prononcé dans la
séance de la XXI° Assemblée annuelle des
catholiques. pp. 34. *Paris,* 1892. 8°. Pam. 93.
COCHIN (A.) L'Hôpital Cochin. La Laicisation,
1780–1885. pp. 202. *Paris,* 1890. 8°.
                                 7688. g. 6.
DELACROIX (J.) La Déclaration du Cardinal
Lavigerie. pp. 60. *St. Amand,* 1891. 8°.
                                 Pam. 69.
DESPREZ (F.) *Cardinal.* Exposé de la situation
faite à l'Église en France. pp. 16.
Paris, 1892. 8°.   3900. g. 12. (10.)
FÈVRE (J. L. P.) La défense de l'Église en
France sous Léon XIII. pp. 136. *Paris,* 1894. 8°.
                                 3900. i. 26.
FRANCE. Traité sur la séparation de l'Église
et de l'Etat. pp. 149. *Beauvais,* 1890. 8°.
                                 4050. g. 31.
—— Le Clergé français en 1890. pp. 101.
Paris, 1890. 8°.   4629. k. 9.
GOUTHE-SOULARD (F. X.) *Archbp. of Aix.* Mon
procès, mes avocats. pp. 288. *Paris,* 1891. 8°.
                                 3900. b. 45.
GRÉZEL ( ) Par ici la sortie. pp. 343.
Paris, 1893. 8°.   8051. de. 19.
GROSJEAN (G.) La question religieuse. pp. 59.
Paris, 1892. 8°.   Pam. 93.

ROMAN CATHOLIC CHURCH. —
Ireland—*continued.*

MORAN (P. F.) *Cardinal.* Occasional Papers.
pp. 292. *Dublin,* 1890. 8°.   4531. aaa. 28.

P.P. *Dublin.* The Irish Catholic directory.
Dublin, 1892, etc. 8°.   P.P. 2513. bc.

WEBB (A.) Opinions of some Protestants regarding their Irish Catholic fellow-countrymen.
pp. 32. *Dublin,* 1886. 8°.   Pam. 68.

See also IRELAND, *History, Ecclesiastical* and *Politics.*

India. *See* MISSIONS.

Italy.

CHIARI (A.) È Opportuno che i cattolici scendano alle urne politiche? pp. 53. *Roma,* 1891. 8°.
    3900. i. 25. (1.)

GALANTE (A.) Il Diritto di Placitazione e l'economato dei benefici vacanti in Lombardia.
pp. 128. *Milano,* 1894. 8°.   05107. h. 2.

ITALY. *Congresso Cattolico.* Atti e documenti dell' octavo Congresso. 2 pt.
Bologna, 1890, 91. 8°.   3900. i. 15.

LAICO. Il Prete cattolico e il nuovo codice penale.
pp. 69. *Piacenza,* 1888. 8°.   8033. g. 34 (3.)

LAMPERTICO (F.) L'Italia e la chiesa. pp. 108.
Firenze, 1890. 8°.   8033. g. 36.

MAGANI (F.) D' un bisogno urgente della chiesa in Italia. pp. 186. *Milano,* 1890. 8°. 3900. h. 43.

MARIANO (R.) L' Italia cattolica è cristiana o pagana? pp. 107. *Napoli,* 1892. 8°.
    3900. i. 19.

MUENZ (S.) Aus Quirinal und Vatikan.
pp. 210. *Berl.* 1891. 8°.   10629. cc. 29.

ROBERTSON (A.) Count Campello and Catholic reform in Italy. pp. 203. *Lond.* 1891. 8°.
    3900. bb. 33.

See also ITALY, *History, Ecclesiastical* : LAW, *Ecclesiastical.* For works on the position of the Pope, *see supra* : *Papacy.*

Mexico.

VERA (F. H.) Coleccion de documentos ecclesiásticos de Mexico. 3 tom.
Amecameca, 1887. 8°.   05107. k. 1.

Netherlands.

KERKHOFF (F. A. v.) Een terugblik op het herstel der Hiërarchie in Nederland. pp. 144.
Vlaardingen, 1893. 8°.   4685. g. 17.

See also NETHERLANDS, *History, Ecclesiastical.*

Polynesia. *See* MISSIONS.

Portugal.

PAPERS. Papers on the Padroado.
Lond. 1891, *etc.* 8°.   3940. cc.

INDIA. Portuguese royal patronage in British India. pp. 93. *Bombay,* 1893. 8°. 3940. bb. 29.

Spain.

FERNANDEZ VÍTORA Y ENSULVE (A.) El Papa y España. pp. 275. *Madrid,* 1890. 8°. 3900. f. 7.

ORTI Y LARA (J. M.) El Reconocimiento de D. Alfonso XIII. por los católicos españoles.
pp. 46. *Madrid,* 1893. 8°.   Pam. 71.

—— La Encíclica de 16 de Febrero 1892 y la union de los católicos. pp. 77.
Madrid, 1893. 8°.   Pam. 71.

SPAIN. *Congreso Católico.* Crónica del Congreso, *etc. Madrid,* 1889, *etc.* 8°. 3900. i. 12.

SPANISH CATHOLICS. Pequeñeces de los católicos españoles. pp. 277. *Tortosa,* 1893. 8°.
    3900. b. 59.

TOUS Y FERRÁ (R.) El Papa y los católicos españoles. pp. 211. *Barcelona,* 1894. 8°.
    3900. c. 36.

ROMAN CATHOLIC CHURCH. —
Spain—*continued.*

ZOZAYA (A.) La crísis contemporánea. pp. 223.
Madrid, 1891. 8°.   3900. b. 47.

See also SPAIN, *History, Ecclesiastical.*

Switzerland.

LAUCHERT (F.) Bibliographie der christkatholischen Kirche der Schweiz. pp. 30. 1893. 8°.
Ac. Berne. *Central Kommission fur Landeskunde.* Bibliographie. Fasc. v. 10. *etc.*
    Ac. 3417.

AGRIGENTE (J. B. d') Le Cardinal Mermillod.
pp. 312. *Lyon,* 1893. 8°.   4863. de. 15.

BELLOC (J. T. de) Le Cardinal Mermillod.
pp. 617. *Fribourg,* 1892. 8°.   4863. ee. 22.

Turkey.

BELIN (F. A.) Histoire de la Latinité de Constantinople. pp. 547, *Paris,* 1894. 8°.
    4534. d. 2.

United States of America.

BOLTON (H. W.) America's next War. pp. 285.
Chicago, 1892. 8°.   8177. de. 41.

BUGG (L. H.) The correct thing for Catholics.
pp. 213. *N.Y.* 1892. 8°.   4182. a. 37.

CARROLL (H. K.) Report of statistics of Churches in the U.S. 1890. pp. 812. 1894. 4°. U.S. *Census.* Eleventh Census. Reports. 1882. c. 1.

HECKER (I. T.) The Church and the age.
pp. 322. *N.Y.* 1887. 8°.   4183. de. 26.

HUNTINGDON (B. A.) The Coming American civil war. pp. 301. *Minneapolis,* 1893. 8°.
    4182. bbb. 44.

KNORTZ (C.) Rom in Amerika. pp. 59.
Zürich, 1891. 8°.   Pam. 78.

MEAUX (C. de) *Viscount.* L'Église catholique et la liberté aux Etats-Unis. pp. 426.
Paris, 1893. 12°.   4182. aaa. 42.

NEW YORK, *R.C. Diocese.* Constitutiones dioecesanae Neo-Eboracenses. pp. 88.
N.Y. 1890. 8°.   05107. f. 4.

PERRY (W. S.) *Bp of Iowa.* Catholicism and Columbus. pp. 16. 1893. 8°.   Pam. 78.

SHEPHERD (M. L.) Pope Leo's demand. pp. 24.
Phila. 1892. 8°.   Pam. 78.

WALBURG (A. H.) Question of nationality in its relations to the Catholic Church in the U.S.
pp. 62. *Cincinnati,* 1889. 8°.   Pam. 93.

ROMANCE LANGUAGES. BREYMANN (H.) Münchener Beiträge zur romanischen Philologie. *Erlangen,* 1890, *etc.* 8°. 011824. i.

PARIS (G.) Études romanes dédiées à G. Paris.
pp. 552. *Paris,* 1891. 8°.   011824. i. 8.

GREGORIO (G. de) Per la storia comparata delle Letterature neo-latine. pp. 65.
Palermo, 1893. 8°.   011824. k. 25.

GORRA (E.) Lingue neolatine. pp. 147.
Milano, 1894. 8°.   012200. h. 108.

EBERING (E.) Berliner Beiträge zur romanischen Philologie. *Berl.* 1893, *etc.* 8°.   12901. d.

PARIS (G.) L'Altération romaine du c latin.
1893. Ac. Paris. *École des Hautes Études.* Section des sciences historiques. Annuaire. 1893.   Ac. 8929/8.

See also FRENCH, ITALIAN, SPANISH, PORTUGUESE, PROVENÇAL, ROMANSCH and ROUMANIAN LANGUAGES.

ROMANCES.

Classical.

ALEXANDER, *the Great.* Beiträge zur Geschichte des Alexanderromans von T. Nöldeke. 1890. 4°.
Ac. Vienna. *K. Akademie.* Denkschriften. Phil. historische Classe. Bd. 38. Ac. 810/12.

ROMANCES.—Classical—continued.

HERMANN (A.) Untersuchungen über das schottische Alexanderbuch. pp. 87. *Berl.* 1893. 8°.
11850. dd. 31.

Ac. Paris. *Société des Anciens Textes.* Le Roman de Thèbes, publié par L. Constans. 2 tom. *Paris,* 1890. 8°. Ac. 9811/32.

British.

ARTHUR, *King of Britain.* Birth, life and acts of King Arthur. The text by Sir T. Malory imprinted by W. Caxton. 3 vol.
Lond. 1893–94. 4°. K.T.C. 19. a. 11.

PERCEVAL, *le Gallois.* Een paar fragmenten van den Roman van Perchevael. pp. 54.
Brux. 1890. 8°. 11498. d. 26.

Ac. Edinburgh. *Scottish Text Society.* THOMAS, *of Ercildoune.* Sir Tristrem. Edited by G. P. MacNeill. pp. 148. *Edinb.* 1886. 8°.
Ac. 9943/6.

GURTEEN (S. H.) Arthurian Epic. Study of the Cambrian, Breton and Anglo-Norman versions. pp. 437. *N.Y.* 1895. 8°. 11850. cc. 44.

HARPER (G. McL.) Legend of the Holy Grail. pp. 66. *Baltimore,* 1893. 8°. 11824. dd. 45.

HEINZEL (R.) Über die französischen Gralromane. pp. 196. 1892. fol. Ac. Vienna. *K. Akademie.* Denkschriften. Phil. historische Classe. Bd. 40.
Ac. 810/12.

LÖSETH (E.) Le roman de Tristan, de Palamède, et de Rusticien de Pise. pp. 542. 1890. 8°. Ac. Paris. *École des Hautes Études.* Bibliothèque. Sciences philologiques. Fasc. 82.
Ac. 8929.

LOTH (J.) Des nouvelles Théories sur l'origine des Romans Arthuriens. pp. 31.
Paris, 1892. 8°. 011850. i. 5. (10.)

French.

Charlemagne Cycle.

REICHEL (C.) Die mittelenglische Romanze Sir Fyrumbras und ihr Verhältnis zum altfranzösischen Fierabras. pp. 86. *Treibnitz,* 1892. 8°.
Pam. 15.

HUON, *of Bordeaux.* Huon of Bordeaux: done into English by Sir J. Bourchier. pp. 304.
Lond. 1895. 8°. 12403. f. 26.

VORETZSCH (C.) Über die Sage von Ogier dem Dänen. pp. 127. *Halle,* 1891. 8°. 011840. k. 68.

ROLAND. Della "Chanson de Roland," esperimento di traduzione di M. Vanni. pp. 29.
Milano, 1891. 8°. Pam. 59.

—— Extraits de la Chanson de Roland publiés, par G. Paris. pp. 160. *Paris,* 1891. 8°.
11498. aaa. 18.

—— The Song of Roland. Summary by A. Way and F. Spencer. pp. 62. *Lond.* 1895. 8°.
11498. d. 39.

—— La Chanson de Roland. Histoire, par L. Petit de Julleville. pp. 121. *Paris,* 1894. 12°.
11498. bbb. 28.

EICKE (T.) Zur neueren Literaturgeschichte der Rolandsage. pp. 56. *Leipz.* 1891. 8°.
011850. c. 2. (3.)

HOEFFT (C. T.) France, Franceis und Franc im Rolandsliede. pp. 74. *Strassb.* 1891. 8°.
11825. i. 42

Other Romances.

EUSTACHE, *le Moine.* Wistasse le Moine. Altfranzösischer Abenteuer-roman. pp. 88.
1891. 8°. FOERSTER (W.) Romanische Bibliothek. Vol. 4. 12238. e.

A°. London. *Chaucer Society.* 1st series. LXXXIII., *etc.* Romaunt of the Rose. Edited by M. Kaluza. *Lond.* 1891, *etc.* 8°. Ac. 9924/33.

—— Paris. *Société des Anciens Textes.* Le Roman de la Rose. Publié par G. Servois. pp. 204. *Paris,* 1893. 8°. Ac. 9811/34

ROMANCES.—French—continued.

LANGLOIS (E.) Origines du Roman de la Rose. pp. 203. 1891. 8°. Ac. Athens. *École Française.* Bibliothèque. Fasc. 58. Ac. 5206/2.

GUILLAUME, *de Dole.* Guillaume de Dole. "Roman de la Rose." Edited by H. A. Todd. 1887. 8°. Ac. Baltimore. *Modern Language Association.* Transactions. Vol. II.
Ac. 2683/2.

Spanish.

RENNERT (H. A.) Spanish pastoral Romances. pp. 119. 1892. 8°. Ac. Baltimore. *Modern Language Association.* Publications. Vol. VII.
Ac. 2683/2.

Reynard the Fox.

REYNARD THE FOX. Le Roman de Renart, publié par E. Martin. 4 pt.
Strasb. 1882–87. 8°. 11515. dd.

—— Le Roman du Renard. Introduction par C. Potvin. pp. 252. *Paris,* 1891. 8°.
12411. e. 31.

—— History of Reynard the Fox. Edited by J. Jacobs. pp. 260. *Lond.* 1895. 8°.
12411. b. 7.

BUETTNER (H.) Studien zu dem Roman de Renart. 2 Hefte. *Strassb.* 1891. 8°.
011824. h. 32.

SUDRE (L.) Les Sources du Roman de Renart. pp. 356. *Paris,* 1893. 8°. 011824. k. 18.

PARIS (G.) Le Roman de Renard. [Review of L. Sudre "Les Sources de Renart."] pp. 72.
Paris, 1895. 4°. 11840. m. 41.

Moralized Tales.

ROMANS. Select tales from the Gesta Romanorum. Translated by C. Swan. pp. 253.
N.Y. 1887. 16°. 012202. eeee 1.

ROMANS, Drôme. CHEVALIER (C. U. J.) Le Comité de Surveillance révolutionnaire de Romans, 1793–94. pp. 48. *Valence,* 1890. 8°.
Pam. 28.

ROMANSCH LANGUAGE AND LITERATURE. Ac. Ithaca. *Cornell University.* Catalogue of the Rhaeto-Romanic Collection presented to the Library. pp. 32.
Ithaca, 1894. 8°. Pam. 6.

PALLIOPPI (Z.) and (E.) Dizionari dels idioms romauntschs d'Engiadin, *etc.*
Samedan, 1893, *etc.* 8°. 12942. d.

VIENNA GLOSSES. Les Gloses de Vienne: vocabulaire réto-romain du XIᵐᵉ siècle. pp. 48.
Fribourg, 1895. 8°. Pam. 47.

BUEHLER (J. A.) Carta instrucziun per emprender il Lungatg Tudestg en scolas romonschas. pp. 112. *Cuera,* 1889. 8°. 12943. c. 24.

Ac. St. Gall. *Hist. Verein.* GOETZINGER (W.) Die romanischen Ortsnamen des Kantons St. Gallen. *St. Gallen,* 1891. 8°. 10196. ee. 8.

MUOTH (G. C.) Grammatica romontscha-tudestga. pp. 184. *Cuera,* 1890. 8°. 12942. c. 28.

DECURTINS (C.) Rätoromanische Chrestomathie. *Erlangen,* 1888, *etc.* 8°. 885. l. 8.

TUOR (A.) Poësias romonschas. pp. 48.
Cuera, 1891. 8°. Pam. 12.

ROME. [*See note on page 1.*]

Bibliography.

FOCK (G.) Catalogus Dissertationum philologicarum classicarum. 3 pt. *Leipz.* 1893. 8°.
011900. ee. 31.

P.P. *Rome.* Romanae Res. Rassegna di bibliografia romana. *Roma,* 1894, *etc.* 8°. 776.

VALMAGGI (L.) Manuale storico-bibliografico di filologia. pp. 336. *Torino,* 1894. 8°.
12933. i. 12.

ROME.—Bibliography—*continued.*

CERROTI (F.) Bibliografia di Roma medievale e moderna. *Roma,* 1893, *etc.* 4°.   11906. k.

Antiquities.

Ac. London. *British Museum.* Photographic reproductions of Greek and Roman Antiquities. *Lond.* 1891, *etc.* fol.   Tab. 1226. c.

BALLERINI (F.) La vitalità delle Belle Arti annichilita in Roma, *etc.* pp. 202. *Roma,* 1893. 8°.   7807. k. 26.

BERLIN DISSERTATIONS. Abhandlungen zur klassischen Altertumswissenschaft. *Berl.* 1894, *etc.* 8°.   11312. dd.

BERTOGLIO-PISANI (N.) Un nuovo ed un vecchio Museo. pp. 86. *Milano,* 1891. 8°. 7708. aa. 56.

BOLTON (H. C.) The Porta Magica, Rome. pp. 5. *N.Y.* 1895. 8°.   8632. g. 25. (11.)

BONNET (M.) La Philologie classique. Six conférences. pp. 224. *Paris,* 1892. 8°. 8311. b. 5.

BOULFROY (A.) Rome, ses monuments. pp. 302. *Lille,* 1890. 8°.   10132. m. 1.

BURN (R.) Ancient Rome and its neighbourhood. pp. 292. 1895. 8°. Bohn's Illustrated Library.   2502. c.

CENTERWALL (J.) Romas ruiner. pp. 252. *Stockholm,* 1889. 8°.   7706. c. 43.

GOYAU (G.) Lexique des antiquités romaines. pp. 332. *Paris,* 1895. 8°.   7706. b. 37.

HELBIG (W.) Guide to the collections of classical Antiquities in Rome. *Leipz.* 1895, *etc.* 8°.   07707. e. 1.

HUELSEN (C.) Jahresbericht uber neue Funde zur Topographie der Stadt Rom. 1891. 8°. Ac. Rome. *Instituto di Corrispondenza Archeologica.* Bulletino. Sezione Romana. Vol. 6.   557. c.

LANCIANI (R. A.) Topografia di Roma antica. pp. 404. *Roma,* 1880. fol.   7706. h. 28.

—— Pagan and Christian Rome. pp 374. *Lond.* 1892. 8°.   7705. b. 51.

LELAND (C. G.) Etruscan Roman Remains in popular tradition. pp. 385. *Lond.* 1892. 4°.   4504. i. 7.

LEVY (L.) and LUCKENBACH (H.) Das Forum Romanum. pp. 17. *München,* 1895. 4°.   7706. ee. 43.

MIDDLETON (J. H.) Remains of Ancient Rome. 2 Vol. *Lond.* 1892. 8°.   2258. b. 10.

MUELLER (I. E. P. v.) Handbuch der klassischen Altertums-Wissenschaft. *München,* 1891, *etc.* 8°.   2259. g.

OEHLER (R.) Klassisches Bilderbuch. pp. 105. *Leipz.* 1892. 8°.   7706. ee. 36.

PASDERA (A.) Dizionario di Antichità classica. *Torino,* 1891, *etc.* 8°.   7706. d.

PAULI (C.) Altitalische Forschungen. *Leipz.* 1885, *etc.* 8°.   7706. de.

—— Altitalische Studien. *Hannover,* 1883, *etc.* 8°.   7706. e. 16.

PAULY (A. F. v.) Real-Encyclopädie der classischen Altertumswissenschaft. *Stuttgart,* 1893, *etc.* 8°.   2282. f. 2.

PÉLADE ( ) Rome. Histoire de ses monuments. pp. 239. *Lyon,* 1894. 8°.   7706. d. 1.

PERSICHETTI (N.) Viaggio archeologico sulla Via Salaria nel circondario di Cittaducale. pp. 212. *Roma,* 1893. 8°.   07708. f. 42.

PULLEN (H. W.) Handbook of ancient Roman Marbles. pp. 205. *Lond.* 1894. 8°. 7706. a. 51.

RAMSAY (W.) Manual of Roman Antiquities. pp. 573. *Lond.* 1894. 8°.   2259. b. 17.

REINACH (S.) L'Arc de Titus. pp. 31. *Paris,* 1890. 8°.   7705. ee. 25. (6.)

ROME. Murray's Handbook of Rome. pp. 91. 492. *Lond.* 1894. 8°.   2364. b. 9.

ROME.—Antiquities—*continued.*

ROMF, *City of.* Lo scoppio della polveriera della Vigna Pia. pp. 64. *Roma,* 1891. 8°. Pam. 91.

SCHLIMMER (J. G.) and COHEN DE BOER (Z.) Woordenboek der grieksche en romeinsche Oudheid. pp. 588. *Haarlem,* 1890. 8°. 7706. f. 15.

SCHOEN (G.) Das capitolinische Verzeichnis der römischen Triumphe. pp. 90. 1893. 8°. Ac. Vienna. *Universitas.* Abhandlungen des epigraphischen Seminares. Hft. 9. 1880, *etc.* 8°.   Ac. 803/2.

SCHREIBER (T.) Atlas of classical Antiquities. pp. 202. *Lond.* 1895. obl. 8°.   1702. b. 4.

SEYFFERT (A. O.) Dictionary of classical Antiquities. pp. 716. *Lond.* 1895. 8°.   2051. e.

VALMAGGI (L.) Manuale di filologia classica. pp. 336. *Torino,* 1894. 8°.   12933. i. 12.

WINNEFELD (H.) Die Villa des Hadrian bei Tivoli. pp. 168. 1895. 4°. Ac. Berlin. *Deutsches Archäologisches Institut.* Jahrbuch. Erganzungsheft 3.   Ac. 5388.

WYNDHAM (C.) The Capitol. Descriptive catalogue. pp. 170. *Rome,* 1891. 8°. 7706. a. 39.

See also infra: Social Life, Religion and Topography; ART, *Ancient:* INSCRIPTIONS: ITALY, *Antiquities:* NUMISMATICS: POMPEI: SCULPTURE: VASES.

Christian Antiquities.

Ac. Fribourg, *in Switzerland. Université de Fribourg.* BERTHIER (J. J.) La porte de Sainte-Sabine à Rome. pp. 90. *Fribourg,* 1892. 4°.   Ac. 607.

ARMELLINI (M.) Gli antichi cimiteri cristiani di Roma. pp. 779. *Roma,* 1893. 8°. 7706. d. 3.

DAVIN (V.) Les Antiquités chrétiennes rapportées à la Cappella Greca du cimetière de Priscille. pp. 867. *Paris,* 1892. 8°.   7706. cc. 13.

LANCIANI (R. A.) Pagan and Christian Rome. pp. 374. *Lond.* 1892. 8°.   7705. b. 51.

MARUCCHI (O.) Il Cimitero e la Basilica di S. Valentino. pp. 140. *Roma,* 1890. 8°.   7708. aaa. 51.

WILPERT (J.) Ein Cyclus christologischer Gemälde aus der Katakombe. pp. 58. *Freiburg,* 1891. 4°.   7705. h. 27.

WIEGAND (F.) Eine Wanderung durch den römischen Katakomben. pp. 39. *Erlangen,* 1893. 8°.   07703. e. 3. (5.) *See also* ART, *Christian :* CHURCH HISTORY.

Antiquities in Africa.

See AFRICA, *North.*

Antiquities in Bosnia and the Herzgovina.

Ac. Sarajevo. *Zemaljski Muzej u Bosni.* BALLIF (P.) Römische Strassen in Bosnien und der Hercegovina. *Wien,* 1893, *etc.* fol.   7707. h.

Antiquities in Dalmatia.

MODRICH (G.) La Dalmazia romana. pp. 506. *Torino,* 1892. 8°.   10125. dc. 3.

Antiquities in England.

BRUCE (J. C.) Hand-book to the Roman Wall. pp. 279. *Lond.* 1895. 8°.   2368. a. 1.

NEILSON (G.) Per lineam valli. New argument touching the rampart between Tyne and Solway. pp. 62. *Glasg.* 1891. 8°   7706. a. 38.

Antiquities in France.

Ac. Paris. *Comité des Travaux historiques.* L'épigraphie chrétienne en Gaule. pp. 140. *Paris,* 1890. 8°.   07708. f. 24.

BAZIN (H.) Vienne et Lyon gallo-romains. pp. 407. *Paris,* 1891. 8°.   7708. cc. 53.

BLANCHET (J. A.) Mélanges d'Archéologie gallo-romaine. *Paris,* 1893, *etc.* 8°.   7706. d.

ROME.—Antiquities in France—*cont.*

GABUT (F.) Archéologie préhistorique et gallo-romaine. pp. 52. *Lyon*, 1894. 8°. 7706. f. 31.

LE BLANT (E.) Nouveau recueil des Inscriptions chrétiennes de la Gaule. pp. 483. *Paris*, 1892. 4°. 7709. c. 22.

LIÈVRE (A. F.) Les Chemins romains entre la Loire et la Gironde. 1892. 8°. Ac. Poitiers. *Société des Antiquaires*. Mémoires. Sér. 2. Tom. 14. Ac. 5326.

LOMBARD-DUMAS (A.) Sépultures gallo-romaines, à Saint-Clément. pp. 17. *Nimes*, 1893. 8°. 07703. h. 2. (9.)

MALÈGUE (H.) Antiquités gallo-romaines de la Haute-Loire. pp. 99. *Le Puy*, 1894. 8°. 07708. k. 2.

MENTIENNE ( ) L'ancien pays du Parisis. Cimetière gallo-romain à Bry-s.-Marne. pp. 48. *Paris*, 1892. 8°. Pam. 3.

PILLOY (J.) Les cimetières de Vermand du quatrième siècle. 1891. 8°. Ac. Saint-Quentin. *Société des Sciences*. Mémoires. Sér. 4. Tom. 9. Ac. 530.

THEURIET (C.) Une Station gallo-romaine en Bourgogne. pp. 310. *Dijon*, 1890. 8°. 10174. bb. 22.

ZANGEMEISTER (C.) Zur Geographie des römischen Galliens. pp. 36. *Heidelberg*, 1892. 8°. 07703. h. 2. (8.)

Antiquities in Germany and Hungary.

KUZSINSZKY (B.) Die Ausgrabungen zu Aquincum 1879–1891. pp. 125. *Budapest*, 1892. 8°. 7708. de. 40.

Ac. Frankfort. *Gesellschaft für Frankfurts Geschichte*. Mittheilungen über römische Funde in Heddernheim. *Frankf.* 1894. 4°. 7706. h. 29.

—— Stuttgard. *Anthropologischer Verein*. Fundberichte aus Schwaben. *Stuttgart*, 1893, *etc.* 8°. Ac. 6229. c.

HETTNER (F.) Die römischen Steindenkmäler zu Trier. pp. 294. *Trier*, 1893. 8°. 7705. c. 38.

MILLER (C.) Die römischen Kastelle in Württemburg. pp. 48. *Stuttgart*, 1892. 8°. 07703. h. 1. (10.)

SARWEY (O. v.) and HETTNER (F.) Der obergermanisch-raetische Limes des Roemerreiches. *Heidelberg*, 1894. *etc.* 8°. Ac. 7706. h.

WOLFF (G.) Das Römercastell zu Gross-Krotzenburg am Main. 1882. 8°. Ac. Cassel. *Verein für Hessische Geschichte*. Zeitschrift. N. F. VIII. Supplement. Ac. 7025/2.

ZANGEMEISTER (C.) Zur Geographie des römischen Galliens und Germaniens. pp. 36. *Heidelberg*, 1892. 8°. 07703. h. 2. (8.)

Antiquities in Switzerland.

DUBI (H.) Studien zur Geschichte der römischen Altertümer in der Schweiz. pp. 42. *Bern*, 1891. 4°. 7705. ee. 26. (10.)

Army, Ancient.

FERRERO (H.) Iscrizioni e ricerche intorno all' ordinamento delle armate dell' Impero Romano. pp. 88. *Torino*, 1884. 4°. 7705. h. 25.

MARQUARDT (J.) De l'organisation militaire chez les Romains. pp. 411. 1891. 8°. MOMMSEN (T.) and MARQUARDT (J.) Manuel des antiquités romaines. Vol. 11. 9041. i. 2.

SCHILLING (O.) De legionibus Romanorum. pp. 128. 1893. 8°. CURTIUS (G.) Leipziger Studien. Bd. 15. P.P. 5044. c.

Campagna.

GSELL-FELS (T.) Rom und die Campagna. Col. 1255. 1889. 8°. Meyer's Reisebücher. 10195. aaa.

ROME.—Campagna—*continued.*

SOMBART (W.) La Campagna romana. pp. 212. *Torino*, 1891. 8°. 08227. g. 25.

THOMPSON (G. E.) Around the Roman Campagna. pp. 156. *Liverp.* 1893. 8°. 10132. c. 3.

Capitol. *See supra: Antiquities.*

Climate.

TOMMASI-CRUDELI (C.) Climate of Rome and Roman malaria. pp. 163. *Lond.* 1892. 8°. 7686. a. 6.

Constitution and Government, Ancient.

FOWLER (W. W.) City-state of the Greeks and Romans. pp. 332. *Lond.* 1893. 8°. 8009. aaa. 31.

GARAGNANI (R.) I tributi e le tasse dei Romani. pp. 184. *Bologna*, 1892. 8°.. 9041. g. 15.

MARABELLI (G.) Di un Processo politico avvenuto negli ultimi tempi della Republica romana. pp. 75. *Savona*, 1890. 8°. Pam. 14.

MOMMSEN (T.) Abriss des römischen Staatsrechts. pp. 363. 1893. 8°. BINDING (C.) Systematisches Handbuch, *etc.* Abt. 1. Th. 3. 5605. ff.

REICH (E.) Graeco-Roman institutions. pp. 100. *Oxf.* 1890. 8°. 5205. aa. 22.

SCHULTEN (A.) De conventibus civium Romanorum. pp. 132. *Berolini*, 1892. 8°. 5254 aaa. 14.

STEPHENSON (A.) Public Lands and agrarian laws of Rome. pp. 101. 1891. 8°. Johns Hopkins University Studies. Ser. 9. No. 7–8. Ac. 2689.

See also infra: Social Life: LAW, *Roman:* SLAVERY.

History.

ALLCROFT (A. H.) and MASOM (W. F.) Tutorial history of Rome to 14 A.D. pp. 416. 1893. 8°. Tutorial Series. 12205. c. 161.

BICKERSTETH (A.) Outlines of Roman history, B.C. 753 to A.D. 180. *Lond.* 1891. 4°. 9041. d. 24.

BURGER (C. P.) Neue Forschungen zur ältern Geschichte Roms. *Amsterd.* 1894, *etc.* 8°. 9040. f.

CORTESI (G.) The silent company of the Pincio. Biographical sketches of great men of Italy. pp. 241. *Rome*, 1893. 8°. 10631. b. 46.

COULTON (J. J.) Roma. [Enquiry into the meaning of the name.] pp. 14. *Lond.* 1893. 8°. 12903. c. 51. (11.)

DOESBURG (J. J.) Geschiedenis der Romeinen. *Amsterd.* 1890, *etc.* 8°. 9041. h. 2.

HARDIE (W. R.) Character and genius of the Roman People. pp. 29. *Lond.* 1895. 8°. Pam. 28.

JOY (B.) Synopsis of Roman history, from the Expulsion of the Kings to the Accession of Octavian. pp. 129. *Lond.* 1894. 8°. 9039. bb. 36.

MACDERMOT (T. B.) Outlines of Roman history. pp. 83. *Dublin*, 1892. 12°. 9040. aa. 19.

MOMMSEN (T.) History of Rome. 5 vol. *Lond.* 1894. 8°. 2069. b.

PAGANELLI (A.) La Cronologia romana. pp. 171. *Milano.* 1892. 4°. 9039. l. 6.

PAIS (E.) Storia d'Italia sino alle guerre puniche. *Torino*, 1894, *etc.* 8°. 9166. dd.

PELHAM (H. F.) Outlines of Roman history. pp. 542. *Lond.* 1895. 8°. 9041. f. 12.

POLLARD (A.) Stories from Roman history. pp. 312. *Lond.* 1892. 8°. 9041. f. 6.

ROBINSON (W. S.) First history of Rome. pp. 358. *Lond.* 1890. 8° 9040. aa. 11.

SHUCKBURGH (E. S.) History of Rome to the battle of Actium. pp. 809. *Lond.* 1894. 8°. 9041. f. 10.

ROME.— History—*continued.*

CHURCH (R. W.) Beginning of the middle ages. pp. 269. *Lond.* 1895. 8°. 9073. a. 22.

GREGOROVIUS (F.) History of the City of Rome in the middle ages. *Lond.* 1894, *etc.* 8°. 9167. f. 5.

BRUNENGO (G.) Il Patriziato romano di Carlomagno. pp. 416. *Prato,* 1893. 8°. 9166. dd. 17.

OLIPHANT (M. O.) The makers of Modern Rome. pp. 507. *Lond.* 1895. 8°. 2388. f. 1.

PAOLUCCI (G.) L'Origine dei comuni di Milano e di Roma. pp. 201. *Palermo,* 1892. 8°. 9167. f. 3.

GNOLI (D.) Descriptio urbis o censimento della popolazione di Roma avanti il sacco Borbonico. 1894. 8°. Ac. Rome. *Società di Storia.* Archivio. Vol 17. Ac. 6540.

SCHULZ (H.) Der sacco di Roma, 1527–28. pp. 188. *Halle,* 1894. 8°. 9327. ccc.

VICCHI (L.) Les Français à Rome pendant la Convention, 1792–95. pp. 182. *Rome,* 1892. 4°. 9167. m. 3.

VICINI (G.) La Rivoluzione dell' anno 1831 nello Stato Romano. pp. 454. *Imola,* 1889. 8°. 9166. dd. 11.

See also HISTORY, *Ancient :* BYZANTINE EMPIRE : CHURCH HISTORY, *Papacy :* ITALY.

Jews in Rome. *See* JEWS.

Language and Literature. *See* LATIN.

Law. *See* LAW, *Roman.*

Navy.

LUEBECK (E.) Das Seewesen der Griechen und Römer. pp. 55. *Hamb.* 1890. 4°. Pam. 3.

GUGLIELMOTTI (A.) Storia della Marina pontificia. 10 vol. *Roma,* 1886–93. 8°. 8808. cc. 1.

For other works on Naval Antiquities, *see* NAVAL SCIENCE, *History.*

Religion and Mythology, *Ancient.*

BEER (R.) Heilige Höhen der alten Griechen und Römer. pp. 86. *Wien,* 1891. 8°. 4503. cc. 17.

BEURLIER (É.) Le Culte impérial. Son histoire et son organisation. pp. 357. *Paris,* 1891. 8°. 4504. f. 22.

BONGHI (R.) Le Feste romane. pp. 218. *Milano,* 1891. 8°. 4504. h. 9.

—— Die römischen Feste. pp. 216. *Wien,* 1891. 8°. 4503. g. 3.

BROWN (J. B.) Stoics and Saints: Lectures on the later Heathen moralists. pp. 296. *Glasg.* 1893. 8°. 4534. ee. 14.

CUMONT (F.) Textes et monuments figurés relatifs aux mystères de Mithra. *Brux.* 1894, *etc.* 4°. 7705. f.

DICTIONARIES. Dictionary of Roman Mythology, *etc.* pp. 163. *Lond.* 1892. 16°. 7706. a. 42.

DRESSLER (F. R.) Triton und die Tritonen. *Wurzen,* 1892, *etc.* 4°. 4503. g.

FARRER (J. A.) Paganism and Christianity. pp. 256. *Lond.* 1891. 8°. 4503. bb. 31.

GRANGER (F.) The Worship of the Romans in relation to the Roman temperament. pp. 313. *Lond.* 1895. 8°. 4503. aaa. 28.

KUNTZE (J. E.) Prolegomena zur Geschichte Rom's. Oraculum. Auspicium. Templum. pp. 222. *Leipz.* 1882. 8°. 9041. g. 5.

LINDE (S.) De Iano summo Romanorum deo. pp. 54. *Lundae,* 1891, 4°. Pam. 41.

PLOIX (C.) La Nature des Dieux. pp. 474. *Paris,* 1888. 8°. 4503. cc. 33.

ROME.— Religion, etc.—*continued.*

PRELLER (L.) Römische Mythologie. 2 Bde. *Berl.* 1881–83. 8°. 4503. bb. 44.

SCHULTESS (C.) Die sibyllinischen Bücher in Rom. pp. 56. 1895. 8°. Sammlung wissenschaftlicher Vorträge. Hft. 216. 12249. m.

SIEMERING (F.) Die Behandlung der Mythen und des Götterglaubens bei Lukrez. pp. 18. *Tilsit,* 1891. 4°. Pam. 41.

SMITH (*Sir* W.) Classical Dictionary of Greek and Roman Mythology, *etc.* pp. 1018. *Lond.* 1894. 8°. 2259. b. 16.

See also RELIGION.

Social Life.

Ancient.

ALBERT (M.) Les Médecins grecs à Rome. pp. 323. *Paris,* 1894. 8°. 7679. ff. 1.

DELOUME (J. A.) Les manieurs d'argent à Rome, jusqu'à l'Empire. pp. 351. *Paris,* 1892. 8°. 8229. e. 32.

DUPOUY (E.) Médecine et mœurs de l'ancienne Rome. pp. 439. *Paris,* 1892. 12°. 7679. a. 1.

FRIEDLAENDER (L.) Darstellungen aus der Sittengeschichte Roms. 3 Thle. *Leipz.* 1888–90. 8°. 9041. i. 11.

FOUGÈRES (G.) La Vie des Grecs et ·des Romains. pp. 116. *Paris,* 1894. 4°. 7701. k. 4.

GUHL (E.) and KONER (W.) Leben der Griechen und Römer. *Berl.* 1893, *etc.* 8°. 7704. cc.

MAURY (L.) Les Postes romaines. pp. 112. *Paris,* 1890. 18°. 7708. a. 64.

MARQUARDT (J.) La Vie privée des Romains. 1892, *etc.* 8°. MOMMSEN (T.) and MARQUARDT (J.) Manuel des Antiquités romaines. Tom. 14. 9041. i. 2.

OPITZ (C. R.) Das häusliche Leben der Griechen und Römer. pp. 302. 1894. 8°. Kulturbilder 6. 7709. aaa.

PRESTON (H. W.) and DODGE (L.) Private life of the Romans. pp. 167. *Bost.* 1893. 8°. 7705. a. 33.

Mediaeval and Modern.

RODOCANACHI (E.) Les corporations ouvrières à Rome depuis la chute de l'Empire. 2 tom. *Paris,* 1894. 4°. 8248. k. 2.

—— Le Carnaval à Rome au XV° et au XVI° siècle. pp. 17. *Amiens,* 1890. 4°. Pam. 91.

ELLIOT (F. M.) Roman Gossip. pp. 362. *Lond.* 1894, 8°. 012357. i. 48.

HUGO (C.) *Countess.* Rome en 1886. pp. 505. *Rome,* 1886. 8°. 10136. h. 11.

See also infra : Topography.

Topography.

BAEDEKER (C.) Italy and Rome. pp. 410. 14. *Leipz.* 1893. 8°. 2352. a

COOK (T.) Tourist's Handbook for Rome, *etc.* pp. 398. 8. *Lond.* 1892. 8°. 10136. bbb. 28.

GSELL-FELS (T.) Rom. Col. 1255. 1889. 8°. Meyer's Reisebücher. 10195. aaa.

JOANNE (P.) Rome. *Paris,* 1893. 8°. 10136. aaa. 18.

ROME. Murray's Handbook of Rome. pp. 492. *Lond.* 1894. 8°. 2364. b. 9.

—— Guia de Roma para los romeros españoles. pp. 132. *Roma,* 1894. 8°. 10136. b. 3.

ALEXIS (F.) Rome et l'Italie. pp. 208. *Tournai,* 1895. 8°. 10135. ee. 19.

BOISSIER (G.) Rome. 1892. 4°. Les Capitales du Monde. No. 5. 10025. g.

BUATHIER (J. M.) À Rome et en Italie. pp. 166. *Paris,* 1892. 8°. 10129. a. 5.

ROME.—Topography—*continued.*

BUCKLAND (A. W.) The World beyond the Esterelles. 2 vol. *Lond.* 1884. 8°. 10136. f. 6.

DUPUIS (J. F.) Rome et Jérusalem. pp. 540. *Québec,* 1894. 8°. 10028. h. 3.

HARE (A. J. C.) Walks in Rome. 2 vol. *Lond.* 1893. 8°. 2360. b.

JOLY (H.) La Rome d'aujourd-hui. pp. 265. *Paris,* 1895. 12°. 10132. bb. 29.

M., F. C. How we went to Rome in 1857. pp. 103. *Lond.* 1892. 8°. 10136. bb. 4.

MAC SWINEY ( ) Souvenirs du pèlerinage espagnol à Rome. pp. 110. *La Chapelle-M.* 1895. 12°. 10136. bb. 5.

MAGNAN ( ) Trois ans à Rome. pp. 339. *Paris,* 1891. 12°. 10131. cc. 5.

MICHELET (J.) Rome. pp. 392. *Paris,* 1891. 12°. 10129. bbb. 29.

MONTET (C. É.) Choses de Rome. pp. 344. *Paris,* 1892. 12°. 10130. aa. 7.

PÉLADE ( ) Rome. Histoire de ses monuments. pp. 239. *Lyon,* 1894. 8°. 7706. d. 1.

POISSON ( ) Italie—Rome. *Orléans,* 1893, *etc.* 8°. 10131. cc.

RICARD (A.) Mes pèlerinages. Rome sous Léon XIII. pp. 239. *Paris,* 1892. 12°. 10105. e. 3.

STORY (W. W.) The Corso of Rome. 1892. 8°. Great Streets of the World. 10026. k. 16.

WITTE (J. de) *Baron.* Rome sous Léon XIII. pp. 516. *Paris,* 1892. 8°. 10131. bbb. 39.

———

GOYAU (G.) Le Vatican. pp. 796. *Brux.* 1895. 4°. K.T.C. 30. b. 7.

TESORONE (G.) L' antico pavimento delle logge di Raffaello in Vaticano. pp. 48. *Napoli,* 1891. 4°. 7807. m. 3.

BORGATTI (M.) Castel Sant' Angelo in Roma. pp. 215. *Roma,* 1890. 8°. 10135. e. 2.

ARMAILHACQ (d') L'Église nationale de Saint Louis à Rome. pp. 224. *Rome,* 1894. 4°. 7814. i. 2.

See also supra : Antiquities.

ROMNEY, New. MARTIN, *Saint, Church of, New Romney.* [St. Martin's Church, New Romney. pp. 8. *Lond.* 1893. 8°. 4705. cc. 14. (10.)

ROMORANTIN, Abbey. ROMORANTIN. *Abbaye.* Cartulaire de l'abbaye. pp. 200. *Romorantin,* 1892. 8°. 4630. e. 4.

RONCE-LES-BAINS. LÉTELIÉ (J. A.) Une plage sur l'océan. Ronce-les-Bains. pp. 284. *Paris,* 1890. 12°. 10174. bb. 20.

ROPE-MAKING. ALHEILIG (A.) Corderie. pp. 163. 1892. 8°. Encyclopédie des aide-mémoire. 8709. g.

RORSCHACH, Ac. St. Gall. *Historischer Verein.* HARDEGGER (A.) Mariaberg bei Rorschach. pp. 63. *St. Gallen,* 1891. 4°. 4662. g. 3.

HAENE (J.) Der Klosterbruch in Rorschach und der St. Galler Krieg 1489-90. pp. 272. 1895. 8°. Ac. Saint Gall. *Historischer Verein.* Mittheilungen. Bd. 26. Ac. 6970.

ROSARY. GASQUET (F. A.) English Rosary book of the 15th century. pp. 16. *Yeovil,* 1894. 8°. 3477. ee. 5. (8.)

RYAN (A.) The Holy Rosary. pp. 24. *Lond.* 1890. 8°. 3939. ccc. 2. (18.)

ROSE, VERGARA (M.) Bibliografia de la Rosa. pp. 318. *Madrid,* 1892. 8°. 011901. e. 14.

BIENENGRAEBER (M.) Die Rose in Geschichte und Dichtung. pp. 31. *Berl.* 1891. 8°. 011824. f. 23. (8.)

ROSE—*continued.*

BURNSIDE (F. R.) Tea Roses. pp. 23. *Hereford,* 1893. 16°. 7054. de. 4.

CHASTAINGT (G.) Prodrome d'une monographie des Roses d'Indre-et-Loire. 1891. 8°. Ac. Angers. *Académie des Sciences.* Mémoires. Ac. 247/4.

ELLWANGER (H. R.) The Rose. pp. 310. *Lond.* 1893. 8°. 7029. a. 13.

FOSTER-MELLAIR (A.) Book of the Rose. pp. 336. *Lond.* 1894. 8°. 07028. e. 45.

GANDOGER (M.) Monographia Rosarum Europæ et Orientis. *Parisiis,* 1892, *etc.* 8°. 07076. m. 14.

HOLE (S. R.) Book about Roses. pp. 213. *Lond.* 1891. 8°. 07076. e. 21.

JORET (C.) La Rose dans l'antiquité et au moyen âge. pp. 480. *Paris,* 1892. 8°. 12431. ee. 24.

PAUL (W.) Observations on the cultivation of Roses in pots. pp. 86. *Lond.* 1892. 8°. 7054. aaa. 39.

ROEMER (H.) Der tausendjährige Rosenstock am Dome zu Hildesheim. pp. 40. *Hildesheim,* 1892. 8°. 7054. d. 7.

RYDER (S.) How to grow Roses. pp. 58. *Manch.* 1888. 8°. 7074. e. 10. (1.)

SAWER (J. C.) Rhodologia. pp. 93. *Brighton,* 1894. 8°. 07028. l. 27.

SCHULZE (M.) Jenas Wilde Rosen. pp. 57. 1886. 8°. Ac. Jena. *Geographische Gesellschaft.* Mitteilungen. Bd. 5. Hft. 1 and 2. Ac. 6086.

SULZBERGER (R.) La Rose. pp. 148. *Namur,* 1891. 8°. 07028. m. 9.

TYRNO. Propagation of the Rose, by cuttings or eyes. pp. 8. *Worthing,* 1892. 8°. 7074. e. 9. (5.)

See also FLOWERS : GARDENING.

ROSENBORG. BROCK (P. M. J.) Musée chronologique des Rois de Danemark au Rosenborg. pp. 113. *Copenhague,* 1892. 8°. 7808. c. 25.

ROSEOLA. DUKES (C.) On the features which distinguish epidemic Roseola from Measles and Scarlet Fever. pp. 39. *Lond.* 1894. 8°. 7306. e. 22. (14.)

ROSICRUCIANS. HARTMANN (F.) In the Pronaos of the Temple of Wisdom. pp. 134. *Lond.* 1890. 8°. 8632. e. 24.

LONDON. *Rosicrucian Society.* Transactions of the Metropolitan College. *Lond.* 1885, *etc.* 8°. 4785. ccc.

—— Zelator. The ceremonies of the Society. pp. 21. *Lond.* 1881. 8°. 4785. bb. 15

—— Ordinances. pp. 16. *Lond.* 1892. 8°. 4785. cc. 39.

PELADAN (J.) L'Art idéaliste. Doctrine de l'ordre et du salon annuel des Rose Croix. pp. 280. *Paris,* 1894. 12°. 8632. bb. 60.

ROSICRUCIANS. Mysteries of the Rosie Cross. pp. 134. *Lond.* 1891. 8°. 8632. cc. 35.

See also OCCULT SCIENCE

ROSNEATH. MAUGHAN (W. C.) Rosneath past and present. pp. 269. *Paisley,* 1893. 8°. 10370. e. 29.

ROSSALL SCHOOL. BEECHEY (St. V.) Rise and progress of Rossall School. pp. 55. *Lond.* 1894. 8°. 8364. e. 3.

ROSSALL SCHOOL. Rossall Register, 1844-89. pp. 390. *Lond.* 1890. 8°. 8364. ee. 39.

—— Memorial of the Jubilee of Rossall School. pp. 66. *Manch.* 1894. 8°. 8364. de. 38.

ROWBOTHAM (J. F.) History of Rossall School. pp. 447. *Manch.* 1894. 8°. 8364. f. 25.

ROSSANO, Abbey. Batiffol (P.) L'Abbaye de Rossano. pp. 182. *Paris*, 1891. 8°.
4571. f. 21.

ROSSBACH, Battle of. See Prussia, *History.*

ROSSENDALE. Newbigging (T.) History of the Forest of Rossendale. pp. 369. *Rawtenstall*, 1893. 8°.   10352. dd. 6.

ROSS-SHIRE. Kennedy (J.) Days of the Fathers in Ross-shire. pp. 260. *Inverness*, 1895. 8°.   4735. b. 43.

ROSTOCK. Rostock. Sammlung der rostocker Verordnungen, 1861–92. pp. 341. *Rostock*, 1893. 4°.   5604. g. 19.

ROTHENBURG, ob der Tauber. B., E. A Run round Rothenburg o. Tauber. pp. 47. *Lond.* 1893. 8°.   10106. df. 18. (7.)
Rothenburg. A Franconian City. pp. 31. *Lond.* 1894. 8°.   10106. de. 4. (5.)

ROTHERHAM. Rotherham. Reminiscences of Rotherham. pp. 120. *Rotherham*, 1891. 8°.
010358. f. 21.
R., F. Proposed ship canal between Rotherham and Goole. pp. 34. *Rotherham*, 1883. 8°.
Pam. 76.

ROTTERDAM. Rotterdam. Bronnen voor de Geschiedenis van Rotterdam. *Rotterdam*, 1892, *etc.* 4°.   10270. ff.
—— *Scotch Church.* Scotch Church, Rotterdam. 250th anniversary. pp. 58. *Amsterd.* 1894. 8°.
Pam. 29.

ROTTHALMÜNSTER. Traeger (J. A.) Zur Chronik des Marktes Rotthalmünster. 1895. 8°. Ac. Landshut. *Historischer Verein.* Verhandlungen. Bd. 31.   Ac. 7118.

ROUBAIX. Leuridan (T.) Histoire de Notre-Dame des Victoires de Roubaix. pp. 216. 1891. 8°. Ac. Roubaix. *Société d'Émulation.* Mémoires. Sér. 2. Tom. 6.   Ac. 520.

ROUEN. Robillard de Beaurepaire (C. M. de) Dernier recueil de notes historiques. pp. 360. *Rouen*, 1892. 8°.   010171. g. 20.
Le Lieur (J.) Rouen au xvime siècle. 4 pt. *Rouen*, 1891. fol.   1788. a. 26.
Laffleur de Kermaingant (P.) Le siège de Rouen par Henri iv. 1591–92. pp. 36. *Rouen*, 1891. 8°.   9007. g. 23. (1.)
P., G. Documents sur le ban et l'arrière-ban, et les fiefs de Rouen. 1594. 1895. 8°. Ac. Rouen. *Société de l'Histoire.* Mélanges. Sér. 3. 1895.
Ac. 6890/23.
Rouen. Inventaire-sommaire des archives antérieures à 1790. 1887, *etc.* 4°. Collection des inventaires-sommaires.   1814. b., *etc.*
Louvet (L.) Rouen, et la révolution. pp. 33. *Rouen*, 1892. 8°.   9226. h. 20.
Loth (J.) Histoire du Cardinal De La Rochefoucauld et du diocèse de Rouen pendant la révolution. pp. 756. *Écreux*, 1893. 8°.
4863. ee. 24.
Glanville (L. de) Histoire du Prieuré de Saint-Lô. 2 tom. *Rouen*, 1890–91. 8°.   4629. k. 17
Aubé (R.) Le Lycée de Rouen. pp. 244. *Rouen*, 1892. 8°.   8356. e. 39.
Collette (A.) Histoire de la Maîtrise de Rouen. pp. 277. 16. *Rouen*, 1892. 8°.   7897. dd. 6.
Noel (E.) Rouen, rouennais, rouenneries. pp. 228. *Rouen*, 1894. 8°.   10171. c. 5.
Spalikowski (E.) Étude sur les logements des ouvriers de Rouen. 1894. 8°. Ac. Rouen. *Société d'Émulation.* Bulletins. 1892–4.   Ac. 527.
Noury (J.) Les comédiens à Rouen, au xvii. siècle. pp. 41. *Rouen*, 1893. 8°.   Pam. 50.
—— Le Théâtre Français de Rouen en 1793. pp. 67. *Rouen*, 1893. 8°.   Pam. 50.

ROUEN—*continued.*
Arras (P. d') Assainissement de la ville de Rouen. 1890. 8°. Ac. Rouen. *Société Industrielle.* Bulletin. An. 18.   Ac. 4412.
Gogeard ( ) Assainissement de la ville de Rouen. 1891. 8°. Ac. Rouen. *Société Industrielle.* Bulletin. An. 19.   Ac. 4412.

ROUERGUE. Vissac (M. de) Les révolutionnaires du Rouergue. pp. 284. *Riom*, 1893. 8°.
09200. e. 6.
Macquarie (J. L.) Les bains du Centre. pp. 363. *Paris*, 1891. 8°.   10169. de. 18.

ROUMANIA.
See also Balkan Mountains and Peninsula.

Army.

A., H. Die türkische Wehrmacht und die Armeen der Balkanstaaten. pp. 207. *Wien*, 1892. 8°.
8823. ddd. 23.
G. B. & I. *War Office.* Handbook of the armies of the Balkan States. pp. 61. *Lond.* 1891. 8°.
8823. g. 20.
P.P. *Bucharest.* Anuarul al Armatei române. *Bucuresci*, 1889. 8°.   P.P. 2459. ad.
Socecu (A. I. V.) Die rumänische Armee. pp. 54. *Leipz.* 1895. 8°.   Pam. 2.

Evangelical Church.

See Evangelical Church.

History.

Tamm (T.) Über den Ursprung der Rumänen. pp. 150. *Bonn*, 1891. 8°.   10007. g. 45.
Bibescŭ (G.) *Prince.* Roumanie. D'Andrinople à Balta-Liman, 1829–49. Correspondance et documents, 1843–56. *Paris*, 1893, *etc.* 8°.
9136. h. 7.
Roumania. Analele parlamentare ale Romaniei. 1831–33. 3 tom. *Bucuresci*, 1890–92. 8°.
8028. g. 21.
Bamberg (F.) Geschichte der orientalischen Angelegenheit. pp. 622. 1888. 8°. Oncken (W.) Allgemeine Geschichte. Hauptabth. iv. Th. 5.   2068. (30.)
Augenzeuge. Aus dem Leben König Karls von Rumänien. *Stuttgart*, 1894, *etc.* 8°.   010795. g.
Boteanu (G.) La Guerre russo - roumaine. 1877–1878. pp. 36. *Paris*, 1893. 8°.
9135. d. 19. (6.)
Rochefort (L. de) Les Roumaines pendant la guerre russo-turque 1877–1878. pp. 19. *Amiens*, 1894. 8°.   9004. h. 30. (9.)
Roumania. Istoriculu rĕsboiului din 1877–78. Participarea României la acestŭ rĕsboiŭ. *Bucuresci*, 1887, *etc.* 8°.   9135. ee.
Bibescŭ (G.) *Prince.* La Roumanie sur la rive droite du Danube. pp. 258. *Paris*, 1883. 8°.
9136. f. 10.
Blancard (T.) Les Mavroyéni. Essai d'étude additionnelle à l'histoire moderne. pp. 916. *Paris*, 1893. 8°.   9916. aaa. 26.
Puscariu (I. de) Date istorice privitorie la familiele nobile române. pp. 184. *Sibiiu*, 1892. 4°.
9906. g. 22.
P.P. *Bucharest.* Anuarul national al României. *Bucuresci*, 1891, *etc.* 8°.   P.P. 2459. ac.

Law.

Roumania. Codicele Române anotate. *Bucuresci*, 1890, *etc.* 8°.   5756. a. 2.
Flaischlen (G. G.) De l'initiative consulaire en fait de tutelle et de curatelle. pp. 89. *Paris*, 1891. 8°.   Pam. 34.
See also infra: Trade.

Politics.

Danubian. La Fin d'une monarchie. pp. 24. *Bucarest*, 1890. 8°.   8028. de. 30. (6.)

ROUMANIA.—Politics—*continued.*

La Schey (de) Hitrowo şi Kotzebue. pp. 163. *Bucurescĭ,* 1890. 8°.   8027. b. 2.

Pascal (A. C. J.) Un Cri d'alarme. pp. 22. *Bucharest,* 1888. 8°.   8026. i. 5. (1.)

—— Un Cri d'espérance. pp. 15. *Bucharest,* 1888. 8°.   8026. i. 5. (2.)

Gonzalez y Mendoza (E.) Les Juifs et les étrangers en Roumanie. pp. 98. *Nancy,* 1894. 12°.   4034. c. 51. (6)

For the Roumanians in Hungary and Transylvania, *see* Hungary.

Topography.

Fava (R.) Ricordi rumeni. pp. 311. *Parma,* 1894. 8°.   10215. aa. 25.

Trade and Finance.

Arion (C. C.) La Situation économique et sociale du paysan. pp. 127. *Paris,* 1895. 8°.   08277. h. 2.

Bibescŭ (G.) *Prince.* 1889. Exposition universelle. La Roumanie. pp. 442. *Paris,* 1890. 8°.   7959. f. 21.

Roumania. Code de commerce roumain. pp. 470. *Paris,* 1895. 8°.   5756. d. 7.

—— Traités de Commerce. 5 pt. *Bucurescĭ,* 1886–87. 4°.   08227. h. 13. (1–4.)

—— Buletinul legiuirilor financiare, *etc.* *Bucurescĭ,* 1886, *etc.* 8°.   08227. f.

Stroell (M.) Die Handelspolitik der Balkan-staaten. pp. 65. 1892. 8°. Ac. Leipsic. *Verein für Socialpolitik.* Schriften. No. 51. Bd. 3.   Ac. 2322.

ROUMANIAN LANGUAGE AND LITERATURE. Damé (F.) Dictionnaire roumain-français. *Bucarest,* 1893, *etc.* 8°.   12950. l.

Alexi (T.) Dicţionar româno-german. pp. 337. *Kronstadt,* 1894. 8°.   12943. cc. 9.

Grossmann (S. J.) Dicţionar german-romîn. *Iaşi,* 1890, *etc.* 4°.   273.

Ac. Leipsic. *Institut für Rumänische Sprache.* Jahresbericht. *Leipz.* 1894, *etc.* 8°. Ac. 9831.

Lovera (R.) Grammatica della Lingua rumena. pp. 200. *Milano,* 1892. 8°.   012200. h. 88.

Mangiuca (S.) Daco-romanische Sprachforschung. *Oravicza,* 1890, *etc.* 8°. 12941. h. 30.

Nădejde (I.) Gramatica limbeĭ române. pp. 240. *Iaşi,* 1884. 8°.   12941. e. 19.

Oprescu (G.) Conversaţiunĭ româneştĭ. pp. 146. *Leipz.* 1892. 8°.   12941. de. 12.

Rudow (M.) Geschichte des rumänischen Schrifttums. pp. 237. 1892. 8°.   11825. dd. 51.

Stoenescu (S. I.) Gramatica limbeĭ române. pp. 84. *Bucurescĭ,* 1891. 8°. 12903. c. 51. (9.)

Gaster (M.) Chrestomathie roumaine. *Roum.* 2 vol. *Leipz.* 1891. 8°.   12941. f. 38.

Nădejde (I.) Istoriea limbeĭ şi literatureĭ române. pp. 516. *Iaşi,* 1886. 8°. 011824. e. 1.

Philippide (A.) Introducere in Istoria Limbei şi literaturei romîne. pp. 212. *Iaşi,* 1888. 8°.   011810. h. 46.

ROUMANIANS, in Hungary and Transylvania. *See* Hungary.

ROUNDERS. Walker (J. M.) Rounders. pp. 71. 1892. 8°. All England Series. 7908. df. *See also* Games.

ROUSSILLON. Brutails (J. A.) Étude sur la condition des populations du Roussillon au moyen âge. pp. 314. *Paris,* 1891. 8°.   08276. k. 5.

ROWING. Ac. Cambridge. *University.* Records of the Jesus College Boat Club. Vol. 2, *etc.* *Lond.* 1886, *etc.* 8°.   7912. aaa.

—— Oxford. *University.* Spiers and Son's chart of the Oxford University eight-oared boat-races. *Oxf.* 1890, *etc.* fol.   1865. c. 2. (10.)

Forster (R. H.) and Harris (W.) History of the Lady Margaret Boat club, St. John's College, Cambridge. pp. 187. *Camb.* 1890. 8°.   7908. dd. 10.

Hayward (J. D.) Canoeing. pp. 152. 1893. 8°. Bell (E.) Handbook of Sports.   2502. e.

Hints. A few hints on Rowing. pp. 11. *Camb.* 1892. 12°.   7907. df. 17. (4.)

Winn (W.) Boating Man's vade-mecum. pp. 336. *Lond.* 1891. 8°.   8807. dd. 25.

Woodgate (W. B.) Boating. pp. 352. 1891. 8°. Badminton Library.   2264. aa.

ROXBURGHSHIRE. Robson (J.) Illustrated Scottish borders. *Hawick,* 1891, *etc.* 8°.   10369. ccc. 19.

ROYAL ACADEMY OF ARTS. *See* Exhibitions.

RUBY. *See* Gems.

RUDOLF AND STEFANIE, Lakes. *See* Africa, *Central and East.*

RUGBY, School and Town. Jex-Blake (T. W.) Farewell Sermon in Rugby School Chapel, April 3, 1887. Events relating to Rugby School, from 1567 to 1887. pp. 19. *Rugby,* 1887. 12°.   8305. ff. 7. (2.)

P.P. *Rugby.* The Sibyl. *Rugby,* 1890, *etc.* 8°.   P.P. 6145. bac.

Satchell (R. J.) Old familiar Rugby faces. pp. 16. *Rugby,* 1892. 8°.   Pam. 46.

Benson (R. S.) Rugby School Hare and hounds. pp. 50. *Rugby,* 1894. 8°.   7906. de. 39.

Rimmer (A.) Rambles round Rugby. pp. 270. *Lond.* 1892. 8°.   10360. h. 26.

Treen (A. E.) Walks in and around Rugby. pp. 132. *Rugby,* 1895. 8°.   10360. bbb. 69.

RÜGEN. Credner (R.) Rügen. Eine Inselstudie. pp. 122. 1893. 8°. Lehmann (R.) Forschungen zur deutschen Landeskunde, *etc.* Bd. 7.   10235. i. 10.

Haas (A.) Rügensche Sagen und Märchen. pp. 263. *Greifswald,* 1891. 8°. 12430. bbb. 20.

Jacob (G.) Das wendische Rügen in seinen Ortsnamen. pp. 151. *Stettin,* 1894. 8°.   10240. ee. 1.

RUM. Davis (N. D.) Etymology of the word Rum. pp. 6. *Demerara,* 1895. 8°.   Pam. 47.

RUNCORN. Nickson (C.) History of Runcorn. pp. 232. *Lond.* 1887. 4°. 10368. h. 28.

RUNIC INSCRIPTIONS, etc. Kermode (P. M. C.) Catalogue of Manks Crosses. pp. 60. *Ramsay,* 1892. 8°.   7708. cc. 50.

Köbke (P.) Om Runerne i Norden. pp. 94. *Kjøbenh.* 1890. 8°.   7706. f. 19. (3.)

Bugge (E. S.) Norges Indskrifter med de aeldre Runer. *Christiania,* 1895, *etc.* 4°.   7709. l.

—— Om Runeindskrifterne paa Rök-stenen i Östergötland. pp. 111. 1888. 8°. Ac. Stockholm. *K. Vitterhets-Historie Academi.* Handlingar. N.F. Del. 11.   Ac. 7800.

Phillips (H.) Supposed Runic Inscription at Yarmouth, Nova Scotia. pp. 2. 1884. 8°.   Pam. 3.

Rasmussen (R. C.) De aeldste Nordiske Runealfabeter. pp. 8. *Kjøbenh.* 1892. 8°.   12902. i. 5. (5)

RUSSIA.—History—*continued.*

SAINT PETERSBURG, *Court of.* Secret Memoirs. Translated from the French [of Count L. P. : de Ségur]. pp. 390. *Lond.* 1895. 8°. 10290. cc. 1.

RUSSIA. Secret Memoirs. Translated from the French [of C. F. P. Masson]. pp. 390. *Lond.* 1895. 8°. 10290. cc. 1.

HARTMANN (O.) Der Antheil der Russen am Feldzug von 1799 in der Schweiz. pp. 198. *Zürich,* 1892. 8°. 9079. g. 17.

VANDAL (A.) Napoléon et Alexandre 1er. *Paris,* 1891, *etc.* 8°. 9079. i. 5.

BLEIBTREU (C.) Der russische Feldzug 1812. pp. 143. *Leipz.* 1893. 8°. 9079. g. 14.

JENSEN (N. P. v.) Napoleons Felttog i Rusland, 1812. pp. 395. *Kjøbenh.* 1893. 8°. 9079. k. 8.

KAUSLER (F. v.) Campagne de Russie, 1812. pp. 319. *Paris,* 1895. 8°. 9079. l. 15.

MARENZI (F.) *Count.* Beiträge zum Studium des Feldzuges des Jahres 1812 in Russland. pp. 23. *Wien,* 1895. 8°. Pam. 2.

BAMBERG (F.) Geschichte der orientalischen Angelegenheit, *etc.* pp. 622. 1888. 8°. ONCKEN (W.) Allg. Geschichte. Hauptabth. IV. Th. 5. 2068. (30.)

LATIMER (E. W.) Russia and Turkey in the 19th Century. pp. 413. *Chicago,* 1893. 8°. 9136. de. 3.

PUIPIN (A. N.) Die geistigen Bewegungen in Russland in der ersten Hälfte des XIX. Jahrhunderts. pp. 690. *Berl.* 1894. 8°. 9456. d. 2.

PUZUIREVSKY (A. K.) Der polnisch-russische Krieg 1831. *Wien,* 1892, *etc.* 8°. 9456. ee. 9.

DALLAS (G. M.) Diary of G. M. Dallas, while United States Minister to Russia 1837–39. pp. 443. *Phila.* 1892. 8°. 010882. e. 16.

THOUVENEL (L.) Les préliminaires de la guerre de Crimée 1852–54. pp. 389. *Paris,* 1891. 8°. 9080. cc. 10.

PETROV (A. N.) Der russische Donaufeldzug im Jahre 1853/54. pp. 350. *Berl.* 1891. 8°. 9080. i. 14.

MORNY (C. A. L. J. de) *Count.* Une Ambassade en Russie, 1856. pp. 244. *Paris,* 1892. 8°. 9080. bbb. 36.

DE ARNAUD (C. A.) The new Era in Russia. pp. 166. *N.Y.* 1891. 8°. 8094. e. 28.

FLOURENS (L. É.) Alexandre III. pp. 364. *Paris,* 1894. 8°. 010795. i. 4.

GRANDIN (L.) Alexandre III. pp. 376. *Paris,* 1895. 8°. 10795. i. 16.

LACOMBE (H. de) L'Empereur Alexandre III. pp. 19. *Paris,* 1894. 8°. Pam. 8.

LOWE (C.) Alexander III. pp. 370. *Lond.* 1895. 8°. 010795. de. 14.

MILLINGEN (F.) [OSMAN-BEY.] Tod Alexanders III. und Alexanders II. pp. 223. *Bern,* 1895. 8°. 10790. bb. 50.

NEUBUERGER (F.) Russland unter Kaiser Alexander III. pp. 97. *Berl.* 1895. 8°. 9456. e. 6.

NOTOVICH (N.) Livre d'or à la mémoire d'Alexandre III. pp. 202. *Paris,* 1894. 4°. 10790. i. 17.

—— L'Empereur Alexandre III. et son entourage. pp. 284. *Paris,* 1893. 8°. 010795. e. 36.

—— Alexander III. und seine Umgebung. pp. 244. *Leipz.* 1895. 8°. 010795. ee. 17.

PEDDIE (J. A.) The dead Czar (Alexander III.). pp. 16. *Lond.* 1894. 8°. Pam. 8.

BAUER (E.) Die Gefahr im Osten. Beiträge zur neuesten Geschichte Russlands. pp. 236. *Berl.* 1895. 8°. 8028. aa. 13.

See also infra: Topography: CRIMEAN WAR: EUROPE: HISTORY, *Mediaeval* and *Modern.* RUSSIAN TURKISH WAR, 1877–78.

RUSSIA.—*continued.*

Law.

FRANCE. *Ministère de la Justice.* Code d'organisation judiciaire de l'empire de Russie. pp. 528. *Paris,* 1893. 8°. 5756. c. 10.

KOVALEVSKY (M. M.) Modern Customs and ancient Laws of Russia. pp. 260. *Lond.* 1891. 8°. 5756. c. C.

Navy.

ALEXANDER MIKHAILOVICH, *Grand-Duke of Russia.* La Marine russe. *St. Pétersbourg,* 1892. obl. 4°. 1803. a. 18.

NOTOVICH (N.) Le Tsar, son armée et sa flotte. pp. 164. *Paris,* 1893. 8°. 8827. cc. 44.

Politics, *General: Domestic.*

ALEXANDER III., *Emperor of Russia.* Der Czar irrsinnig. pp. 27. *Lond.* 1891. 8°. 10601. e. 12. (5.)

DE ARNAUD (C. A.) The new Era in Russia. pp. 166. *Lond.* 1891. 8°. 8094. aa. 13.

EEDEN (F. v.) Lettre à Sa Majesté l'Empereur. pp. 16. *Genève,* 1891. 8°. 8277. h. 20. (5.)

LEGER (L.) Russes et Slaves. Études politiques. pp. 346. *Paris,* 1890. 8°. 8094. aa. 12.

LONDON. *Society of Friends of Russian Freedom.* Annual Report of the Executive Committee. *Lond.* 1890, *etc.* 8°. 8093. b.

MIROWO (I.) Mene tekel upharsin! Russische Visionen. pp. 48. *Hermannstadt,* 1891. 8°. Pam. 74.

NOTOVICH (N.) L'Empereur Nicolas II. et la politique russe. pp. 200. *Paris,* 1895. 8°. 8092. aaa. 4.

P.P. *Zürich.* Frei Russland. *Zürich,* 1892, *etc.* 4°. 699.

REHBINDER (N.) *Count.* "Heiliges Russland erwache!" pp. 97. *Leipz.* 1892. 8°. Pam. 74.

RUSSIAN ALP. Der russische Alp. pp. 68. *Dresd.* 1891. 8°. Pam. 74.

RUSSIAN ASCENDANCY. Die Emancipation des vierten Standes. pp. 48. *Leipz.* 1891. 8°. 8026. i. 5. (8.)

TIKHOMIROV (L. A.) Russia political and social. 2 vol. *Lond.* 1892. 8°. 10292. f. 8.

WESTLAENDER (A.) Russland vor einem Regime-Wechsel. pp. 115. *Stuttgart,* 1894. 8°. 8093. e. 3.

YAKSAKOV (V.) Aus den sibirischen Bleibergwerken. pp. 183. *Berl.* 1892. 8°. 6057. aaa. 28.

See also infra: Topography: ANARCHISM: POLAND.

Foreign.

ASIA. Antagonismus der englischen und russischen Interessen in Asien. pp. 187. *Wien,* 1890. 8°. 8028. e. 21.

BISMARCK-SCHOENHAUSEN (O. E. L. v.) *Prince.* Fürst Bismarck und Russlands Orientpolitik. pp. 55. *Berl.* 1892. 8°. Pam. 67.

F. Darf Russland einen Angriff auf den Bosporus wagen? pp. 326. *Wien,* 1892. 8°. 8028. f. 31.

LEE (F.) The Suppressed Truth. Revelations regarding Russian conquests in Asia. pp. 70. *Lahore,* 1893. 8°. 9055. a. 25.

LEHAUTCOURT (P.) La Russie et l'invasion de l'Inde. pp. 21. *Paris,* 1892. 8°. 8028. de. 30. (15.)

LEONOV (R.) Documents secrets de la politique russe en Orient 1881–90. pp. 237. *Berl.* 1893. 8°. 8028. ec. 29.

—— Geheime Documente der russischen Orient-Politik, 1881–90. pp. 247. *Berl.* 1893. 8°. 8028. de. 32.

RUSSIA.—Politics—*continued.*

MARIN (P.) Autour des dépouilles de l'Empire ottoman. pp. 347. *Paris, 1891.* 12°.
8028. aaaa. 17.

MARVIN (C.) Letters to the "Morning Post." 1888-90. pp. 427. *Allahabad, 1891.* 8°.
8023. ee. 23.

NEVINS (W. P.) Apologia for Russia and plea for an Anglo-Russian alliance. pp. 118. *Lond. 1895.* 8°.
8027. aa. 11.

POPOWSKI (J.) ·The rival powers in Central Asia. pp. 235. *Westminster, 1893.* 8°.
8028. de. 29.

RUSSIA. Russia's march towards India. 2 vol. *Lond. 1894.* 8°.
8023. ee. 42.

COLLEVILLE (de) *Viscount,* and ZEPELIN (F. de) L'Empereur de Russie et la Cour de Danemark. pp. 34. *Paris, 1894.* 8°.
Pam. 67.

BERTOL-GRAIVIL (E.) and BOYER (P.) Le Livre d'Or des fêtes franco-russes. pp. 215. *Paris, 1894.* 4°.
9930. gg. 35.

BOURNAND (F.) Le Livre d'Or franco-russe. pp. 382. *Tours, 1894.* 8°.
8026. e. 9.

DAUDET (E.) Histoire diplomatique de l'Alliance franco-russe. 1873-93. pp. 339. *Paris, 1894.* 8°.
9079. f. 12.

GEFFCKEN (F. H.) Frankreich, Russland und der Dreibund. pp. 179. *Berl. 1893.* 8°.
8026. e. 7.

HÉNAUT (F. de) Douze ans d'alliance franco-russe. pp. 186. *Paris, 1892.* 8°. 8026. d. 4.

POPOWSKI (J.) Die französisch-russische Allianz pp. 30. *Wien, 1891.* 8°. Pam. 67.

VACHON (M.) Les Marins russes en France. pp. 204. *Paris, 1893.* 4°. 9930. k. 1.

BIGELOW (P.) The German Emperor and his eastern neighbours. pp. 179. *Lond. 1892.* 8°.
10703. c. 36.

HELM (W. v.) Das russische Schreckgespenst und sein innerer Werth. pp. 54. *Hannover, 1892.* 8°. 8026. i. 6. (14.)

STEIN (A.) Wer wird siegen? Betrachtungen über dem Kampf Russlands gegen das Deutschthum. pp. 48. *Berl. 1893.* 8°. Pam. 93.

WILLIAM II., *Emperor of Germany.* Wilhelm II. und Alexander III. pp. 32. *Dresd. 1892.* 8°.
Pam. 67.

Topography : Social Life : Travels and General Works on Russia.

GRISWOLD (W. MacC.) Descriptive list of novels dealing with life in Russia. *Camb., Mass., 1892.* 8°. 011902. m.

BALCAM (E.) Promenades en Russie. pp. 215. *Paris, 1895.* 4°. 10292. g. 14.

BARBOU (A.) Nos amis les Russes. pp. 159. *Paris, 1893.* 4°. 10292. l. 3.

BÉNAR (N.) À la découverte de la Russie. pp. 71. *Paris, 1892. obl.* 4°. 1876. b. 17.

BIGELOW (P.) The Borderland of Czar and Kaiser. pp. 343. *Lond. 1895.* 8°. 10024. aa. 29.

BODDY (A. A.) With Russian Pilgrims. pp. 317. *Lond. 1893.* 8°. 10291. aaa. 37.

BROWNE (G. F.) *Bp. of Stepney.* Memorials of a short life. Sketch of W. F. A. Gaussen, with essays on Russian life. pp. 263. *Lond. 1895.* 8°. 10292. b. 2.

BUEHLER (A.) Von den Vogesen zum Balkan. 2 vol. *Magd. 1890.* 8°. 10105. ee. 5.

CARLETTI (T.) La Russia contemporanea. pp. 506. *Milano, 1894.* 8°. 10292. aaa. 15.

CONSUL (S.) De France en Russie. Journal d'un écolier. pp. 190. *Paris, 1895.* 8°. 10106. h. 3.

CYON (E. v.) La Russie contemporaine. pp. 380. *Paris, 1892.* 8°. 8094. c. 30.

RUSSIA.—Topography, etc.—*continued.*

DUPRAT (É.) La Russie. pp. 336. *Limoges, 1893.* 4°. 10291. i. 15.

GUÉNIN (E.) La Russie. pp. 351. *Paris, 1891.* 12°. 10292. aaa. 8.

HAPGOOD (I. F.) Russian Rambles. pp. 369. *Lond. 1895.* 8°. 10291. aaa. 39.

HEHN (V.) De moribus Ruthenorum. Zur Characteristik der russischen Volksseele. pp. 251. *Stuttgart, 1892.* 8°. 10291. d. 4.

JEFFERSON (R. L.) Awheel to Moscow and back. pp. 172. *Lond. 1895.* 8°. 10107. b. 2.

KELLER (F. C.) Wild-, Wald- und Sumpfbilder aus Westrussland. pp. 117. *Klagenfurt, 1890.* 8°.
10291. aaa. 30.

LAJOYE (R.) Mes vingt-huit Jours en Russie. pp. 235. *Paris, 1892.* 8°. 10291. aaa. 22.

LALLIÉ (N.) Choses de Russie. pp. 388. *Lyon, 1895.* 8°. 10292. e. 8.

LEROY-BEAULIEU (A.) The Empire of the Tsars and the Russians. *N.Y. 1893, etc.* 8°.
10291. d. 3.

MEYER VON WALDECK (F.) Russland. 2 Abt. *Leipz. 1884, 86.* 8°. 10292. aaa. 10.

—— Unter dem russischen Scepter. pp. 313. *Heidelberg, 1894.* 8°. 10292. b. 1.

MICHELL (T.) Murray's Handbook for Russia. 2 pt. *Lond. 1893.* 8°. 2364. b. 28.

MODRICH (G.) Russia. pp. 550. *Torino, 1892.* 8°. 10291. bb. 31.

MOORE (J.) Journey from London to Odessa. pp. 320. *Paris, 1883.* 8°. 10292. e. 3.

NITROF. Au Pays des roubles. pp. 688. *Paris, 1891.* 12°. 10291. aaa. 29.

PRET (C. A.) La Lutte des civilisations et l'Accord des peuples. pp. 96. *Paris, 1892.* 8°.
10007. cc. 14.

QUESADA (E.) Un invierno en Rusia. *Buenos A. 1888, etc.* 8°. 10292. aaa.

RABOT (C.) À travers la Russie boréale. pp. 320. *Paris, 1894.* 8°. 10292. aaa. 14.

REVEL (J.) Six semaines en Russie. pp. 376. *Paris, 1893.* 8°. 10292. aaa. 12.

RUSSIA. The Tsar and his People. pp. 435. *N.Y. 1891.* 8°. 10291. f. 6.

—— La Russie. pp. 496. *Paris, 1892.* 8°.
10292. e. 7.

RUSSIA. La Russie en images. pp. 90. *Paris, 1893.* 4°. 10291. bb. 32.

SAMSON-HIMMELSTJERNA (H. v.) Russland unter Alexander III. pp. 448. *Leipz. 1891.* 8°.
10292. h. 11.

—— Russia under Alexander III. pp. 306. *Lond. 1893.* 8°. 10292. c. 1.

SCHWEITZER (G.) Streifzüge durch Russland. pp. 227. *Berl. 1895.* 8°. 8027. bb. 15.

SELVOV (S.) Lettres russes. pp. 243. *Paris, 1891.* 8°. 10290. aaa. 13.

SILVESTRE (A.) La Russie. pp. 362. *Paris, 1892.* 4°. 10291. i. 13.

SINGELS (N. J.) Van de Noordkaap naar het Kremlin en Alhambra. pp. 280. *Leiden, 1892.* 8°. 10106. df. 13.

STERN (B.) Aus dem modernen Russland. pp. 168. *Berl. 1893.* 8°. 10291. aaa. 38.

STEVENS (T.) Through Russia on a mustang. pp. 334. *Lond. 1891.* 8°. 10292. f. 6.

STODDARD (C. A.) Across Russia from Baltic to Danube. pp. 258. *Lond. 1892.* 8°. 10292. f. 7.

WHISHAW (F. J.) Out of doors in Tsarland. pp. 380. *Lond. 1893.* 8°. 10291. bb. 30.

PIERLING (P.) L'Italie et la Russie au XVIe siècle. pp. 134. *Paris, 1892.* 8°. 9078. bb. 28.

RUSSIA.—Topography, etc.—*continued.*

ADAMS (C.) Chancellor's Voyage to Muscovy, 1630. pp. 78. 7. 1886. 8°. GOLDSMID (E. M.) Bibliotheca Curiosa.   012202. de. 27.

JUEL (J.) En Rejse til Rusland under Tsar Peter. pp. 473. *Københ.* 1893. 8°.
                   10292. k. 8.

FITZ-JAMES (J.) *Duke of Liria and Berwick.* Diario del viaje á Moscovia del Duque de Liria y Xerica. pp. 503. 1889. 8°. FERNANDEZ DE NAVARRETE (M.) Colección de documentos. Tom. 93.   9197. h.

See also SLAVONIC RACES.

Trade and Finance.

HOSKIER ET CIE. Les Finances de la Russie. pp. 409. *Paris*, 1891. 4°.   8226. i. 11.

RAVALOVICH (A.) Note sur les Stocks d'or et de la Banque de Russie. pp. 22. *Paris*, 1892. 8°.   08227. i. 29. (11.)

RUSSIA. Règlement du budget de l'Empire pour l'exercice 1888. pp. 80. *St.-Pétersbourg*, 1889. 8°.   Pam. 23.

—— Les Finances de la Russie. Le Budget de 1893. pp. 115. *Paris*, 1893. 4°.   8227. k. 14.

—— Règlement du Budget de l'Empire pour l'exercice 1893. *St.-Pétersbourg*, 1894, *etc.* 8°.   08226. k.

SKAL'KOVSKY (K. A.) Les Ministres des finances de la Russie, 1802–90. pp. 325. *Paris*, 1891. 8°.   08227. ee. 41.

AC. Lille. *Société Industrielle du Nord.* ROGEZ (C.) Le Rouble, ses fluctuations et leurs conséquences. pp. 19. *Lille*, 1890. 8°.   Pam. 23.

BIANCONI (F.) La Russie au point de vue commercial. pp. 68. *Paris*, 1893. 8°.   8229. k. 5.

CHICAGO. *Columbian Exposition.* The Industries of Russia. 5 vol. *St. Petersburg*, 1893. 8°.
                  7956. l. 7.

—— Catalogue of the Russian section. pp. 572. *S.-Petersburg*, 1893. 8°.   7956. l. 8.

CYON (E. v.) M. Witte et les finances russes. pp. 224. *Paris*, 1895. 8°.   08226. h. 29.

—— Les Finances russes et l'épargne française. pp. 66. *Paris*, 1895. 8°.   08226. i. 5.

FRIEDE. Der Friede auf dem Papier und der Friede eines thatsächlichen status quo. pp. 30. *Berl.* 1894. 8°.   Pam. 67.

GERMANY. *Zollkonferenz.* Zur deutsch-russischen Zollkonferenz. pp. 22. *Berl.* 1893. 8°. Pam. 23.

HENCKEL (W.) Russlands wirthschaftliche Lage im Jahre 1891. pp. 68. 1892. 8°. Deutsche Zeit- und Streit-Fragen. Hft. 98.   12209. f.

HOURWICH (I. A.) Economics of the Russian village. 1892. 8°. Ac. New York. *Columbia College.* Studies in History. Vol. 2.
                Ac. 2088/2.

MAYER (H.) Münzwesen und Edelmetallproduktion Russlands. pp. 130. *Leipz.* 1893. 8°.
                8226. i. 13.

ROUMANIA. Traité de Commerce entre la Roumanie et la Russie. pp. 16. *Bucarest*, 1886. 8°.   08227. h. 13. (2.)

WINIARSKI (L.) Les Finances russes 1867–94. pp. 80. *Genève*, 1894. 8°.   08226. h. 12.

RUSSIAN LANGUAGE AND LITE-RATURE. DICTIONARIES. Pocket-dictionary of English and Russian. 2 pt. *Leipz.* 1893. 16°.
                12976. ccc. 7.

BECK (W.) Deutsch-russisches Wörterbuch der Bergbau- und Hüttenkunde. pp. 496. *St. Petersburg*, 1890. 8°.   12975. n. 4.

KOIRANSKY (Z.) Russisch-deutsches militärisches Wörterbuch. *Berl.* 1892, *etc.* 8°. 8825. bbb. 36.

RUSSIAN LANGUAGE AND LITE-RATURE—*continued.*

MANASEVICH (B.) Russisch-deutsches und deutsch-russisches militärisches Wörterbuch. pp. 396. *Berl.* 1892. 8°.   8823. aa. 29.

ALEKSANDROV (F.) Russian and English idiomatic phrases, *etc.* pp. 136. *Lond.* 1891. 8°.
                12976. a. 22.

BOLTZ (A.) Lehrgang der russischen Sprache. 2 Thle. *Berl.* 1880–84. 8°.   12975. i. 24.

BOUGE (X. de) Le Maître Populaire, ou le Russe sans maître. pp. 500. 124. *Paris*, 1894. 8°.
                12976. h. 28.

COMBES (E.) Cours de Langue russe. pp. 124. *Paris*, 1893. 12°.   12976. bb. 31.

CREMAT ( ) Wortschatz und Phraseologie der russischen Sprache. 2 Thle. *Leipz.* 1894. 8°.
                12975. f. 18.

DEML (J.) Lese- und Uebungsbuch der französischen und russischen Sprache. pp. 138. *Leipz.* 1890. *obl.* 8°.   12902. a 28.

DIMITRIEVICH (N.) Russisches Lesebuch. pp. 265. 36. *Lemberg*, 1891. 8°. 12976. cc. 44.

G. B. & I. *War Office.* Table of the Russian characters, with English equivalents. *Lond.* 1892. *s. sh. obl.* 4°.   1865. c. 1. (12)

KOERNER (W.) Ausführliches Lehrbuch der russischen Sprache. *Sondershausen*, 1891, *etc.* 8°.
                12975. i.

LEGER (L.) and BARDONNAUT (G.) Les Racines de la Langue russe. pp. 264. *Paris*, 1894. 8°.
                12976. c. 45.

LUNDELL (J. A.) Études sur la Prononciation russe. 1891, *etc.* 8°. Ac. Upsal. *R. Academia Upsaliensis.* Årsskrift, 1891.   Ac. 1075/6.

MINZES (B.) Ueber die Transscription russischer Namen. pp. 5. *Freiburg*, 1893. 8°.   Pam. 47.

PETRI ( ) Anleitung zu systematischen Selbstunterricht im Russischen. pp. 187. *Berl.* 1893. 8°.   12975. k. 43.

SIDORATSKY (V.) Petit Manuel de la Langue russe. pp. 15. *Paris*, 1895. 16°.   Pam. 47.

GUÉNIN (E.) La Russie. Littérature. pp. 351. *Paris*, 1891. 12°.   10292. aaa. 8.

LEGER (L.) La Littérature russe. pp. 556. *Paris*, 1892. 8°.   011850. h. 5.

—— Chrestomathie russe. Morceaux choisis. pp. 278. *Paris*, 1895. 8°.   12976. b. 41.

LONDON. *Anglo-Russian Literary Society.* Office bearers, Rules, opening address, *etc.* pp. 28. *Westminster*, 1893. 8°.   11825. dd. 50.

NAGRADOW (W. J.) Moderne russische Censur und Presse. pp. 482. *Berl.* 1894. 8°. 8093. b. 31.

VOYNICH (E. L.) The Humour of Russia. pp. 349. *Lond.* 1895. 8°.   012314. g.

See also SLAVONIC RACES AND LANGUAGES.

RUSSIAN TURKISH WAR, 1877–78.

BAMBERG (F.) Geschichte der orientalischen Angelegenheit. pp. 622. 1888. 8°. ONCKEN (W.) Allgemeine Geschichte. Hauptabth. IV. Th. 5.   2068. (30.)

BOTEANU (G.) La Guerre russo-roumaine. 1877–78. pp. 36. *Paris*, 1893. 8°. 9135. d. 19. (6.)

HEÏMANN (R. de) À cheval de Varsovie à Constantinople. pp. 271. *Paris*, 1893. 12°.
                10106. dd. 3.

HERBERT (W. V.) The Defence of Plevna, 1877. pp. 488. *Lond.* 1895. 8°.   9135. d. 22.

LATIMER (E. W.) Russia and Turkey in the Nineteenth Century. pp. 413. *Chicago*, 1893. 8°.   9136. de. 3.

LEVAUX (P. F.) Ghazi Osman Pacha. Souvenirs de la guerre des Balkans. pp. 180. *Liège*, 1891. 8°.   9135. ee. 19.

RUSSIAN TURKISH WAR—continued.

OLLIER (E.) Cassell's History of the Russo-Turkish War. *Lond.* 1895, *etc.* 8°.   9136. i. 2.

PFEIL (R. v.) *Count.* Erlebnisse eines preussischen Offiziers während des türckischen Krieges 1877–78. pp. 234. *Berl.* 1892. 8°.   9135. cc. 20.

—— Experiences of a Prussian Officer during the Turkish War of 1877–78. pp. 362.
Lond. 1893. 8°.   9135. dd. 4.

PUZIREVSKY (A. K.) Die russische Armee bei Ausbruch des Feldzuges 1877–78. pp. 56.
Graudenz, 1891. 8°.   8831. l. 11. (7.)

SPRINGER (A. H.) Der russisch-türkische Krieg 1877–1878. *Wien,* 1891, *etc.* 8°.   9135. ee.

VERESHCHAGIN (V.) Kriegsfahrten in Asien und Europa. Erinnerungen. pp. 296.
Leipz. 1895. 8°.   9009. c. 18.

—— Vom Kriegsschauplatze in Asien und Europa. pp. 359. *Berl.* 1895. 8°.
    010026. ee. 1.

See also RUSSIA : TURKEY.

RUTHENIAN RACE AND LANGUAGE.

DASZKIEWICZ (S.) Die Lage der gr.-or. Ruthenen in der bukowinær Erzdiöcese.
pp. 171. *Czernowitz,* 1891. 8°.   3926. h. 23.

KAINDL (R. F.) Die Rutenen in der Bukowina. 2 Thl. 1889, 90. 8°. Der Buchenwald.
    10215. bb. 21.

—— Die Huzulen. pp. 129. *Wien,* 1894. 8°.
    10215. i. 1.

PRET (C. A.) La Lutte des civilisations, *etc.*
pp. 96. *Paris,* 1892. 8°.   10007. cc. 14.

LEVITSKY (I. E.) Bibliographie des Publications ruthéniennes du XIX-ème siècle.
Léopol, 1888, *etc.* fol.   11901. l.

MITROFANOWICZ (M.) Grammatik der klein-russischen, ruthenischen, Sprache. pp. 184.
1891. 8°. Die Kunst der Polyglottie. Th. 36.
    12902. c.

OGONOVSKY (O.) Studien auf dem Gebiete der ruthenischen Sprache. pp. 244.
Lemberg, 1880. 8°.   12975. k. 2.

See also SLAVONIC RACES AND LANGUAGES.

RUTHERGLEN.

GRAY (G.) Burgh School of Rutherglen. pp. 107. *Rutherglen,* 1891. 8°.
    8364. cc. 65.

RUTLAND.

P.P. *Leicester.* Leicestershire and Rutland notes and queries.
Leicester, 1891, *etc.* 8°.   P.P. 6056. bc.

Ac. London. *English Dialect Society.* WORDSWORTH (C.) Rutland Words. pp. 43.
Lond. 1891. 8°.   Ac. 9934/29.

RYE, Sussex.

MASTERS (J. N.) Catalogue of antiquities and historical manuscripts of Rye. pp. 14. *Rye,* 1894. 8°. 07703. e. 2. (9.)

RYLSTONE.

SAINT PETER, *Rylstone, Parish of.* Register of St. Peter's, Rylstone. pp. 204.
Leeds, 1895. 8°.   9906. b. 6.

RYSWICK, Peace of.

LEGRELLE (A.) Notes et documents sur la paix de Ryswick. pp. 136.
Lille, 1894. 8°.   9078. g. 16.

SAARBRÜCKEN.

KNIEBE (H.) Bilder aus Saarbrückens Vergangenheit.
Saarbrücken, 1894, *etc.* 8°.   10240. bb.

AUGENZEUGE. Die Franzosen in Saarbrücken, 1792–94. 2 Bdchn. *Saarbrücken,* 1890. 8°.
    9079. i. 2.

SABAEANS.

DERENBOURG (H.) Les Monuments sabéens de la Bibliothèque Nationale.
pp. 45. *Paris,* 1891. 8°.   7705. aa. 35.

SABAEANS—continued.

MORDTMANN (J. H.) and MUELLER (D. H.) Sabäische Denkmäler. pp. 114. *Wien,* 1883. 4°,
    7705. f. 51.

See also MANDAEANS : YEMEN.

SACCHARIN.

ADVANTAGES. Advantages of Saccharin in the manufacture of aërated waters.
pp. 52. *Lond.* 1891. 8°.   07945. m. 1.

STUTZER (R.) Das Fahlberg'sche Saccharin.
pp. 67. *Braunschweig,* 1890. 8°.   Pam. 13.

SACKINGEN.

SCHULTE (A.) Gilg und Säckingen. 1893. 8°. Archiv für schweizerische Geschichte. Bd. 18.   Ac. 6995/2.

SACRAMENTS.

BILLOT (L.) De Ecclesiae Sacramentis commentarius.
Romae, 1893, *etc.* 8°.   4323. cc.

DIX (M.) The Sacramental system as the extension of the Incarnation. pp. 239. 1893. 8°.
Bishop Paddock Lectures.   4487. f.

HASLEHURST (   ) Notes for addresses at mother's meetings. The Sacraments. pp. 108.
Lond. 1895. 8°.   4429. a. 112.

SCHANZ (P.) Die Lehre von den heiligen Sacramenten. pp. 757. *Freiburg,* 1893. 8°.
    4323. f. 5.

STALEY (V.) Plain words on the Sacraments.
pp. 92. *Lond.* 1892. 8°.   4324. bb. 10.

WARREN (*Right Hon.* R. R.) Ex opere operato : or, a Condition precedent ? Essay on the Sacraments. pp. 30. *Lond.* 1891. 8°.
    4371. de. 3. (3.)

See also BAPTISM : EUCHARIST, *etc.*

SACRED HEART, Order of the.

LE DORÉ (A.) Les Sacrés-Cœurs. 2 pt.
Paris, 1891. 8°.   4534. ee. 6.

SADDLERY. *See* HORSE.

SADDLEWORTH.

BRIERLEY (M.) Chapter from a MS. history of Saddleworth. pp. 92.
Oldham, 1891. 8°.   8304. a. 8. (6.)

CHAD, *Saint, Church of.* The Parish Registers.
pp. 675. *Uppermill,* 1891. 8°.   9902. e. 23.

SADOWA. *See* KÖNIGGRÄTZ.

SAGALLA LANGUAGE. *See* AFRICAN LANGUAGES.

SAGAS. *See* ICELANDIC LITERATURE.

SAGUENAY, River.

SAGUENAY. Historical sketch of the Saguenay. pp. 22.
Quebec, 1883. 12°.   Pam. 86.

SAHARA.

BAURON (P.) De Carthage au Sahara. pp. 301. *Tours,* 1893. 8°. 10096. i. 17.

CAT (É.) À travers le désert. pp. 253.
Paris, 1892. 8°.   10096. i. 12.

DEPORTER (V.) À propos du Transsaharien. Extrême-sud de l'Algérie. 2 pt. *Alger,* 1890. 8°.
    10105. g. 1.

FOCK (A.) Algérie, Sahara, Tchad. pp. 75.
Paris, 1891. 8°.   8155. ee. 11.

FOLLIE (L. G.) Voyage dans les déserts du Sahara. pp. 158. *Tours,* 1892. 8°.
    010096. f. 29.

FOUREAU (F.) Une mission au Tademayt.
pp. 133. *Paris,* 1890. 8°.   010096. m. 8.

—— Rapport sur ma mission au Sahara.
pp. 277. *Paris,* 1894. 8°.   010096. m. 28.

FRANCE. *Ministère des Travaux Publics.* Chemin de Fer Transsaharien. Documents relatifs à la mission dirigée au Sud de l'Algérie par M. A. Choisy. *Paris,* 1890, *etc.* 4°.   08235. m.

DU PATY DE CLAM (   ) *Count.* Étude sur le Djérid. 1893. 8°. Ac. Paris. *Comité des Travaux historiques.* Bulletin de Géographie.
Année 1893.   Ac. 437/6.

SAHARA—*continued.*

LE ROUX (H.) Au Sahara. pp. 308.
Paris, 1891. 12°.   10097. cc. 23.

PHILEBERT (C.) La France en Afrique et la Transsaharien. pp. 96. *Paris*, 1890. 8°.
         8028. ff. 16. (7.)

SCHIRMER (H.) Le Sahara. pp. 443.
Paris, 1893. 8°.   010096. m. 17.
See also SOUDAN : TIMBUKTU.

SAIDA. *See* SIDON.

SAILMAKING. SADLER (S. B.) Art and science of Sailmaking. pp. 137.
Lond. 1892. 8°.   8805. c. 80.

SAINT ALBANS. ASHDOWN (C. H.) Gossiping guide to St. Albans. pp. 40.
St. Albans, 1891. 8°.   10348. ccc. 60. (1.)

—— St. Albans, historical and picturesque.
pp. 307. *Lond.* 1893. 4°. K.T.C. 18. b. 2.

GASQUET (F. A.) The Making of St. Alban's Shrine. pp. 8. 1894. 8°. 4705. cc. 14. (13.)

JESSOPP (A.) Studies by a Recluse. pp. 281.
Lond. 1893. 8°.   012357. h. 2.

SAINT AMAND. MALLARD (C. N. V.) Histoire de Saint-Amand et du Château de Montrond. pp. 508. *Saint-Amand*, 1895. 8°.
         10171. dd. 6.

SAINT ANDREWS, City and University. ANDERSON (J. M.) Heraldry of St. Andrews University. pp. 24. *Edinb.* 1895. 8°.
         9905. b. 31.

FLEMING (D. H.) Register of the Christian Congregation of St. Andrews, 1559–1600.
1889, 90. 8°. Ac. Edinburgh. *Scottish History Society.* Publications. Vol. 4, 7. Ac. 8256.

KERR (D. R.) St. Andrews in 1645–46. pp. 128.
Lond. 1895. 8°.   10369. ccc. 37.

BOYD (A. K. H.) Twenty-five years of St. Andrews. 2 vol. *Lond.* 1892. 8°. 4955. f. 14.

—— St. Andrews and elsewhere. pp. 384.
Lond. 1894. 8°.   4955. f. 17.

KNIGHT (W.) Rectorial Addresses delivered at the University of St. Andrews. 1863–93.
pp. 401. *Lond.* 1894. 8°. 012301. f. 20.

LANG (A.) St. Andrews. pp. 347.
Lond. 1893. 8°.   K.T.C. 11. b. 15.

SAINT BRIEUC. LE SAGE (G.) Notices sur le diocèse de Saint-Brieuc. pp. 144.
Saint-Brieuc, 1890. 8°.   4629. k. 7.

DU BOIS DE LA VILLERABEL (A.) *Viscount.* L'École Saint-Charles à Saint-Brieuc. pp. 393.
Saint-Brieuc, 1891. 8°.   8355. df. 12.

TRÉBUCHET (L.) Les baies de Saint-Malo et de Saint-Brieuc. pp. 293. *Paris*, 1893. 8°.
         010168. e. 2.

SAINT CHAFFRE. ARSAC (G. O.) Notes sur les abbés de Saint-Chaffre. pp. 72.
Le-Puy-en-V. 1881. 8°.   Pam. 9.

SAINT CHAMOND. SAINT-CHAMOND. Registre des procès-verbaux de la Société Républicaine de Saint-Chamond. *Lyon*, 1890, *etc.* 4°.
         8051. f. 26.

SAINT CLAUDE. BENOIT (D. P.) Histoire de l'Abbaye et de la terre de Saint-Claude.
pp. 672. *Montreuil*, 1890. 8°. 4629. k. 10.

BRUNE (M. P.) Diplômes de l'Abbaye de Saint Claude. pp. 33. *Montreuil*, 1890. 8°.
         4629. k. 15.

DIJON (H.) La Cathédrale de Saint-Claude.
pp. 75. *Lons-le-Saunier*, 1894. 8°. 7817. c. 6.

THURIET (C.) Saint-Claude et ses environs.
pp. 387. *Bourg*, 1890. 8°. 10169. c. 17.

SAINT CLÉMENT. LOMBARD-DUMAS (A.) Nouvelle hypothèse sur le rôle de l'Hipposandale. Sépultures à Saint-Clément. pp. 17.
Nîmes, 1893. 8°.   Pam. 3.

SAINT CYR, Seine et Oise. SAINT-CYR. *École Militaire.* L'Argot de Saint-Cyr.
pp. 71. *Paris*, 1893. 12°. 12954. a. 55.

SAINT CYR DE FAVIÈRES. PRAJOUX (J.) Notes et documents sur Saint-Cyr-de-Favières. pp. 188. *Roanne*, 1892. 8°.
         10170. ccc. 4.

SAINT DENIS. BOURNON (F.) Histoire de Saint-Denis. pp. 167. *Paris*, 1892. 12°.
         10174. b. 34.

SAINTE ANNE, River. SAINTE ANNE, *River.* Le cataclysme de la rivière Ste.-Anne.
pp. 48. *Québec*, 1894. 8°.   Pam. 86.

SAINTE ANNE DE LA PÉRADE. SAINTE-ANNE DE LA PÉRADE. Autre fois et aujourd'hui à Sainte-Anne de la Pérade. 2 pt.
Trois-Rivières, 1895. 8°. 4745. cc. 44.

SAINTE BAZEILLE. ALIS (R. L.) Histoire de Ste.-Bazeille. pp. 607. *Agen*, 1892. 8°.
         10172. g. 7.

SAINT EDMUND'S COLLEGE, Ware.
See WARE.

SAINTE ÉTIENNE DU ROUVRAY. DUCHEMIN (P. P.) Histoire de Saint-Étienne-du-Rouvray. pp. 391. *Rouen*, 1892. 8°. 10171. e. 5.

SAINT FLOUR. BOUDET (M.) Assauts et blocus de Saint-Flour par les Anglais, 1356–91.
pp. 34. *Clermont-Ferrand*, 1893. 8°.
        9078. gg. 9. (6.)

SAINT FRANÇOIS DE LA BEAUCE, Quebec. DEMERS (B.) Notes sur la paroisse de St.-François de la Beauce. pp. 151.
Québec, 1891. 12°.   4745. aa. 47.

SAINT GALL, Canton. Ac. Saint Gall. *Historischer Verein.* GOETZINGER (W.) Die romanischen Ortsnamen des Kantons St. Gallen.
St. Gallen, 1891. 8°.   10196. ee. 8.

SAINT GEORGE, Denbighshire. SAINT GEORGE, *Denbighshire.* Parish Registers.
pp. 52. *Lond.* 1890. fol.   9916. f. 38.

SAINT GEORGE'S CHANNEL AND IRISH SEA. SAINT GEORGE'S CHANNEL. Sailing Directions for the St. George's Channel.
2 pt. *Lond.* 1893, 91. 8°. 10496. b. 36.

COWPER (F.) Sailing Tours. Pt. IV. Irish Sea.
Lond. 1892, *etc.* 8°.   10360. e.

SAINT GERMAIN DES PRÉS. BROGLIE (E. de) *Prince.* La société de l'Abbaye de Saint Germain des Prés au 18ᵉ siècle. 2 tom.
Paris, 1891. 8°.   4866. h. 17.

SAINT GERMAIN EN LAYE. BESNARD (É.) Guide de Paris à Saint-Germain-en-Laye.
pp. 202. *Paris*, 1894. 12°. 10174. a. 24.

SAINT GERVAIS, Puy de Dôme. TARDIEU (A.) and MADEBÈNE (A.) Histoire de Saint-Gervais d'Auvergne. pp. 232.
Herment, 1892. 8°.   10171. aaa. 24.

SAINT HELENA. FIRMIN-DIDOT (G.) La captivité de Sainte-Hélène d'après les rapports du marquis de Montchenu. pp. 330.
Paris, 1894. 8°.   010663. g. 10.

HALIBURTON (R. G.) Letters on the withdrawal of the garrison from St. Helena. pp. 24.
Jamestown, 1890. 8°.   Pam. 66.
See also ENGLAND, *Colonies.*

SAINT HILAIRE DE BRIOUZE. GOURDEL ( ) Saint-Hilaire-de-Briouze. 1893, *etc.* 8°.
Ac. Alençon. *Société Historique.* Bulletin.
Tom. 12, *etc.*   Ac. 6774.

SAINT HYACINTHE, Quebec. BERNARD (A. X.) Mandements des Évêques de Sᵗ Hyacinthe. 4 vol. *Montréal*, 1888–90. 8°. 4446. f. 5.

SAINT IVES. MATTHEWS (J. H.) History of Saint Ives. pp. 560. *Lond.* 1892. 4°. 10368. h. 30.

SAINT JACUT-DE-LA-MER. JUHEL (T.) Notice sur Sᵗ Jacut-de-la-Mer. pp. 95. *Dinan*, 1890. 8°. 4629. bbb. 17. (2.)

SAINT JOHN, Lake. BUIES (A.) La Région du lac Saint-Jean. pp. 51. *Québec*, 1890. 8°. 10460. e. 36. (3.)

MAC CARTHY (E.) The leaping Ouananiche: where and how to catch it. pp. 66. *N.Y.* 1894. 8°. 7290. de. 9.

SAINT JOHN, *Lake.* Guide. *Montreal*, 1892. *obl.* 8°. 10460. de. 3.

SAINT JOHN, Order of.
See MALTA, *Knights of.*

SAINT JOSEPH, Maison de, at Saint Pol de Léon. KERNÉ ( ) Saint-Joseph autrefois Bel-Air. Maison de repos pour les prêtres âgés. pp. 374. *Morlaix*, 1891. 8°. 4629. b. 31.

SAINT-JUST-EN-CHEVALET. PRAJOUX (J.) Le canton de Saint-Just-en-Chevalet. pp. 310. *Roanne*, 1893. 8°. 10170. ccc. 5.

SAINT LÉON, Haute Garonne. ARAGON (H.) La seigneurie de Saint-Léon, 1030–1793. pp. 116. *Toulouse*, 1895. 8°. 10171. d. 13.

SAINT LEONARDS. *See* HASTINGS.

SAINT LÔ. CLAUDIN (A.) Les origines de l'imprimerie à Saint-Lô. pp. 37. *Paris*, 1894. 8°. 11903. f. 34. (8.)

SAINT MAIXENT. LÉVESQUE (L.) Inscriptions de la ville de Saint-Maixent. 1891. 8°. Ac. Niort. *Société de Statistique.* Mémoires. Sér. 3. Tom. 8. Ac. 316.

SAINT MALO. HERPIN (E.) Saint Malo. Ses souvenirs. pp. 502. *Rennes*, 1894. 8°. 10173. de. 10.

TRÉBUCHET (L.) Les baies de Saint-Malo et de Saint-Brieuc. pp. 293. *Paris*, 1893. 8°. 010168. e. 2.

SAINT MARTIN DE RÉ.
See LA ROCHELLE.

SAINT MARYCHURCH. BROWNLOW (W. R. B.) Visitation of St. Marychurch, A.D. 1301. pp. 20. *Lond.* 1893. 8°. 4705. cc. 14. (9.)

SAINT MAURICE, River. CARON (N.) Deux voyages sur le Saint-Maurice. pp. 322. *Trois-Rivières*, 1890. 8°. 10470. h. 31.

SAINT MAURICE AND SAINT LAZARUS, Order of. CLARETTA (G.) Dell' Ordine Mauriziano nel primo secolo dalla sua ricostituzione. pp. 332. *Firenze*, 1890. 8°. 9905. cc. 28.

SAINT MAXAIRE. DESAIVRE (L.) Sᵗ Maxaire. pp. 130. *Niort*, 1894. 8°. 10173. ee. 6.

SAINT MICHEL, Mont. DUBOUCHET (G.) L'Abbaye de Mont St.-Michel. pp. 297. *Paris*, 1895. 8°. 7815. aa. 36.

TRÉBUCHET (L.) La baie de Cancale, le Mont-Saint-Michel. pp. 160. *Paris*, 1888. 8°. 010171. e. 12.

POLI (O. de) Les défenseurs du Mont Saint-Michel 1417–50. pp. 245. *Paris*, 1895. 12°. 9225. a. 30.

POTICHE (de) La baie du Mont Saint-Michel. pp. 308. *Paris*, 1891. 8°. 10173. f. 4.

VEUCLIN (E. V.) Ma première excursion au Mont S. Michel. pp. 4. *Bernay*, 1891. 8°. 10106. i. 1. (13.)

SAINT MOMELIN. DU TEIL (J.) Le village de Saint-Momelin. pp. 134. *Paris*, 1891. 8°. 10171. ee. 17.

SAINT MORITZ. COOK (T. A.) Notes on Tobogganing at St. Moritz. pp. 103. *Lond.* 1894. 8°. 7912. bb. 1.

VERAGUTH (C.) The baths of St. Moritz. pp. 155. *Zurich*, 1890. 8°. 7462. e. 27.
See also ENGADINE.

SAINT NEOTS. COOPER (R. D.) History of the "Old Meeting House," St. Neots. pp. 62. *St. Neots*, 1890. 8°. 4715. aaa. 38.

SAINT NICHOLAS, Quebec. PAQUET (É. T.) Fragments de l'histoire de la Paroisse de Saint Nicolas. *Lévis*, 1894, *etc.* 8°. 10470. cc. 40.

SAINT OMER. LAUWEREYNS DE ROOSENDAELE (L. de) Comment la ville de Saint-Omer fit retour à la France en 1677. pp. 199. *Saint-Omer*, 1893. 8°. 10174. aa. 39.

SAINTONGE. Ac. Saintes. *Société des Archives.* AUSSY (D. d') La Saintonge pendant la guerre de cent ans, 1372–1453. pp. 49. *La Rochelle*, 1894. 8°. Ac. 6892/3.

DELAVAUD (L.) Troubles en Poitou et Saintonge, 1643–44. 1891. 8°. Ac. Saintes. *Société des Archives.* Archives, *etc.* Vol. 19. Ac. 6892.

ÉVEILLÉ (A.) Glossaire saintongeais. pp. 408. *Paris*, 1887. 8°. 12954. ff. 30.

JOANNE (P.) Itinéraire. Poitou et Saintonge. pp. 290. *Paris*, 1891. 8°. 10174. aa. 36.

MONGIS (T.) Récits saintongeois. pp. 350. *Lyon*, 1894. 8°. 12430. c. 37.

SAINT PAUL, Minnesota. SAINT PAUL, *Minnesota.* Salient facts about St. Paul. *St. Paul*, 1893. *obl.* 12°. Pam. 86.

SAINT PAUL'S CATHEDRAL, London. *See* LONDON, *Churches.*

SAINT PAUL'S SCHOOL, London. LONDON. *Saint Paul's School.* Honours and distinctions obtained, 1889–90. pp. 24. *Lond.* 1890. 8°. 8304. e. 20. (9.)

SAINT PETERSBURG. HAPGOOD (I. F.) The Névsky Prospékt. 1892. 8°. Great Streets of the World. 10026. k. 16.

VULLIET ( ) Quinze jours à St. Pétersbourg. pp. 23. *Paris*, 1891. 8°. 07305. k. 9. (16.)

SAINT PIAT. LA GRANGE (A. de) Obituaire de la paroisse de Saint-Piat. 1890. 8°. Ac. Tournay. *Société historique.* Bulletins. Tom. 23. Ac. 7600.

SAINT PIERRE-ÉGLISE. DROUET (L.) Recherches sur les communes du canton de Saint-Pierre-Église. pp. 488. *Cherbourg*, 1893. 8°. 010171. m. 38.

SAINT POL DE LÉON.
See SAINT JOSEPH, *Maison de.*

SAINT-PRIX. REY (A.) Les cahiers de Saint-Prix, 1789. pp. 354. *Paris*, 1892. 8°. 9226. k. 18.

SAINT QUENTIN. ECK (T.) Saint Quentin dans l'antiquité et au moyen-âge. pp. 51. *Paris*, 1894. 8°. 7704. i. 12. (10.)

POETTE (C.) Origine des noms des rues de Saint-Quentin. pp. 460. *Saint-Quentin*, 1891. 8°. 10170. aa. 1.

SAINT RIQUIER, Abbey. BONNAULT (L. de) Étude sur Saint-Riquier. pp. 69. 1887. 8°. Ac. Abbeville. *Société d'Émulation.* Mémoires. Ser. 3. Tom. 4. Ac. 230.

HARIULPHUS, *Abbas.* Chronique de l'Abbaye de Saint-Riquier. pp. 362. 1894. 8°. Collection de textes. 09210. de.

SAINTS. Ac. Paris. *Bibliothèque Nationale.* Catalogus Codicum hagiographicorum latinorum saeculo XVI. 4 tom. *Bruxellis*, 1889–93. 8°.
4999. ff. 2.

Ac. Edinburgh. *Scottish Text Society.* Legends of the Saints in the Scottish dialect. Edited by W. M. Metcalfe. *Edinb.* 1888, *etc.* 8°. Ac. 9943/9.

BOWDEN (H. S.) The witness of the Saints. pp. 94. *Lond.* 1893. 8°.   3939. b. 7.

BUTLER (A.) Lives of Women Saints. pp. 256. *Lond.* 1887. 8°.   4829. cc. 4.

COUANIER DE LAUNAY (E. L.) Légendaire, ou, vies des Saints de Laval. pp. 304.
Laval, 1891. 8°.   4829. c. 6.

D., E. C. The Saints of God. pp. 158.
Lond. 1894. 8°.   4465. f. 24.

FLORES. Flores historiæ, seu Sanctorum historicæ lectiones. pp. 479. *Hongkong*, 1891. 8°.
4827. aaa. 3.

GUÉRIN (P.) Vie des Saints d'après les Bollandistes. 4 tom. *Paris*, 1890. 18°.
4829. de. 8.

NARBEY (C.) Supplément aux Bollandistes pour l'époque mérovingienne.
Paris, 1894, *etc.* fol.   45.

NOELDEKE (T.) Sketches from Eastern History. pp. 288. *Lond.* 1892. 8°.   9055. d. 9.

P., L. The inheritance of the Saints. pp. 374. *Lond.* 1891. 8°.   4257. f. 23.

PAGANI (G. B.) The science of the Saints in practice. *Lond.* 1891. 8°.   4400. cc. 1.

PROFILLET ( ) Les Saints militaires. 6 tom. *Paris*, 1890. 12°.   4829. de. 13.

ROHAULT DE FLEURY (C.) Les Saints de la Messe et leurs monuments. *Paris*, 1893,*etc.* 4°.
K.T.C. 20. b. 3.

SAMSON (H.) Die Heiligen als Kirchenpatrone. pp. 431. *Paderborn*, 1892. 8°.   4824. ccc. 8.

SHEA (J. G.) Little pictorial lives of the Saints. pp. 625. *N.Y.* 1894. 8°.   4827. df. 23.

SMALLPEICE (F. A.) The English Saints of the English Calendar. *Oxf.* 1894. 8°. 4829. bb. 19.

SMEDT (C. de) Acta Sanctorum Hiberniae nunc primum edita opera C. de Smedt et J. de Backer. col. 975. *Edinburgi*, 1888. 4°.
4828. f. 6.

STOKES (M. M.) Six months in the Apennines, in search of vestiges of the Irish Saints. pp. 313. *Lond.* 1892. 8°.   10136. f. 12.

For the symbolism of the Saints, *see* ART, *Christian.*

SAINT VALERY-EN-CAUX. LELOUTRE (N. P. C.) Saint-Valery-en-Caux. pp. 351.
Paris, 1895. 18°.   10174. bbb. 3

SAINT VALLIER, Drome. FAYARD (E.) Notice sur Saint-Vallier. pp. 335.
Lyon, 1894. 8°.   10174. f. 26.

CAISE (A.) Le Registre baptistaire de Saint Vallier. 1568–75. pp. 18. *Valence*, 1892. 8°.
9906. bb. 12. (6.)

SAINT VINCENT, Island. MUSGRAVE (T. B. C.) Historical sketch of the Colony of St. Vincent. pp. 26. *Kingston*, 1891. 8°.
Pam. 86.

See also ENGLAND, *Colonies* : WEST INDIES.

SAIS. *See* EGYPT, *Religion.*

SAKHALIN. HOWARD (B. D.) Life with Trans-Siberian Savages. pp. 209.
Lond. 1893. 8°.   10075. bbb. 7.

SALAMANDER. *See* AMPHIBIA.

SALASSI. DUC (J. A.) *Bp. of Aosta.* La Religion des Salasses. pp. 45. *Aoste*, 1894. 16°.
Pam. 41.

SALCOMBE REGIS. MORSHEAD (J. Y. A.) History of Salcombe Regis. pp. 19.
Sidmouth, 1894. 8°.   10347. g. 5. (8.)

SALE, Bills of. *See* BILLS, *of Sale.*

SALE, Law of. BROWN (R.) Notes and commentaries on the Sale of goods act, 1893. pp. 399. *Edinb.* 1895. 8°.   6376. ee. 13.

CAMPBELL (R.) The Law relating to the Sale of goods. pp. 870. *Lond.* 1891. 8°.
6375. k. 2.

CHALMERS (M. D. E. S.) The Sale of goods act, 1893. pp. 212. *Lond.* 1894. 8°.
6376. ee. 11.

KER (W. C. A.) and PEARSON GEE (A. B.) Commentary on the Sale of goods act, 1893. pp. 380. *Lond.* 1894. 8°.   6376. g. 2.

MOYLE (J. B.) Contract of Sale in the civil law. pp. 271. 1892. 8°. Clarendon Press Series.   2320. g. 22.

NEWBOLT (F.) Sale of goods act, 1893. pp. 181. *Lond.* 1894. 8°.   6376. ee. 9.

ROME, *Empire of.* Roman Law of Sale with modern illustrations. By J. Mackintosh. pp. 272. *Edinb.* 1892. 8°.   5206. ee. 20.

RUSSELL (W. H.) Hire-purchase System. Epitome of the Law. pp. 71. *Lond.* 1895. 8°.
6376. de. 16.

STEWART (C. E.) Treatise on the Law relating to the Sale of goods. pp. 129. 1891. 8°. Wilson's Legal Handy Books.   6426. aaa. 39.

TRAVIS (J.) Commentaries on the Law of Sales. 2 vol. *Lond.* 1892. 8°.   6825. eee. 8.

TURNER (E. F.) Duties of solicitor to client as to Sales. pp. 264. *Lond.* 1893. 8°. 6306. e. 5.

See also AUCTIONS : LAW, *Commercial.*

SALEM. Massachusetts. GREEN (S. A.) S. Skelton, the first Minister of Salem. pp. 8. 1895. 8°.   Pam. 9.

NEVINS (W. S.) Witchcraft in Salem Village, 1692. pp. 273. *Salem*, 1892. 8°. 8632. d. 22.

SALEM DISTRICT, Madras. RĀMASVĀMI MUDALIYAR. Dissertation on the hill tribes of Eastern Kongu. pp. 35. *Salem*, 1892. 8°.
Pam. 88.

SALERNO. GAETANO (F.) Le Monete delle zecche di Salerno. *Salerno*, 1891, *etc.* 4°.
7755. f.

SALFORD. *See* MANCHESTER.

SALINS-MOUTIERS. DELASTRE (P.) Eaux minérales de Salins-Moutiers. pp. 86.
Moutiers, 1892. 8°.   7462. e. 24.

SALISBURY. JONES (W. H. R.) Documents illustrating the history of the Cathedral, City and Diocese of Salisbury in the 12th and 13th centuries. pp. 446. 1891. 8°. Chronicles and Memorials.   2073. (97.)

SALISHAN LANGUAGES.
See INDIAN LANGUAGES.

SALLINGLAND. SALLINGLAND. Sallinglands Kirker. *Kjøbenh.* 1884, *etc.* fol. 1736. c.

SALMONIDAE. *See* FISH, *Culture and Angling.*

SALOMO, Game. ROBERTS (H. O.) Instructions and rules for the game of Salomo. *Gloucester*, 1894. 24°.   Pam. 83.

SALSOLACEAE. MUELLER (F. v.) *Baron.* Iconography of Australian salsolaceous plants. *Melbourne*, 1890, *etc.* 4°.   7029. l.

SALT : SALTS. MUIR (M. M. P.) Tables and directions for the qualitative analysis of complex mixtures of Salt. pp. 44.
Lond. 1895. 8°.   8909. b. 19.

SALT, etc.—*continued.*

ĀNNASVAMI AIYAR. The Madras Salt act. pp. 197. *Madras*, 1891. 8°. 5318. b. 29.

SALT. Salt in relation to agricultural depression. pp. 7. *Lond.* 1894. 8°. Pam. 1.

WUTKE (C.) Die Versorgung Schlesiens mit Salz, 1772–90. pp. 135. *Berl.* 1894. 8°. 07108. g. 8.

SALT LAKE CITY. *See* MORMONISM.

SALTPETRE. FRANCE. *Service des Poudres.* Mémorial des poudres et salpêtres. *Paris*, 1882, *etc.* 8°. 8909. ccc.

KRULL (W.) Studie der Saltpeterwüste und ihrer Industrie. 1892. 8°. Ac. Greifswald. *Naturwissenschaftlicher Verein.* Mittheilungen. Jahrg. 24. Ac. 2940.

POLAKOWSKY (H.) Der Chilisalpeter und die Zukunft der Salpeterindustrie. pp. 76. *Berl.* 1893. 8°. 08227. i. 29. (15.)

SAINT-ANDRÉ (J. A. de) La Question des monopoles. Les Poudres et Salpêtres. pp. 337. *Paris*, 1890. 8°. 08227. ee. 15.

SALVADOR. DAWSON (G. J.) Geografía del Salvador. pp. 72. *Paris*, 1890. 4°. 10481. i. 15.

TULIO ( ) El 22 de Junio de 1890. Homenaji à la redentora idea de la revolucion de El Salvador. pp. 78. *San Salvador*, 1892. 8°. 8180. m. 3.

SAN SALVADOR. Commercial directory of Salvador. 1891. 8°. U.S. *Bureau of American Republics.* Bulletin. No. 28. 08225. k. 1.

—— Import duties of Salvador. pp. 39. 1891. 8°. U.S. *Bureau of American Republics.* Bulletin. No. 23. 08225. k. 1.

See also AMERICA, *South and Central.*

SALVAGE. *See* LAW, *Maritime.*

SALVATION ARMY. BOOTH (W.) "General" Booth and others. pp. 24. *Lond.* 1892. 8°. 8277. de. 30. (2.)

BOOTH–TUCKER (F. de L.) The life of Catherine Booth. 2 vol. *Lond.* 1893. 8°. 4906. i. 17.

BOOTH (C.) C. Booth, mère de l'Armée du Salut. pp. 61. *Lausanne*, 1891. 8°. 4906. de. 25. (4.)

BOOTH (B.) From Ocean to ocean, the Salvation Army's march. pp. 186. *N.Y.* 1891. 4°. 4136. e. 9.

CHARLESWORTH (S. B.) Sensational Religion; as resorted to in the system called the Salvation Army. pp. 120. *Ipswich*, 1885. 8°. 4136. aa. 42.

CLIBBORN (A. S.) and BOOTH-CLIBBORN (C.) Chants de l'Armée du Salut. pp. 159. *Paris*, 1892. 16°. 3435. aaa. 57.

FEHR (J.) Die Heilsarmee. pp. 80. 1891. 8°. Frankfurter zeitgemässe Broschüren. N.F. Bd. 12. Hft. 9 & 10. 12209. aa.

HEATHCOTE (W. S.) My Salvation Army experience. pp. 86. *Lond.* 1891. 8°. 4136. b. 32.

JOHANSSON (G.) Bp. of Kuopio. Frälsningsarmén. pp. 162. *Kuopio*, 1890. 8°. 8275. aaa. 53.

P.P. *Torre-Pellice.* Grido di guerra. Gazzetta dell' Esercito della Salvezza. *Torre Pellice*, 1891, *etc.* fol. P.P. 9005. d.

PRICE (J.) Salvation Army tested by their works. pp. 25. *Chester*, 1882. 8°. 4139. cc. 3. (9.)

RED–HOT LIBRARY. Red-Hot Library. *Lond.* 1894, *etc.* 8°. 4136. de.

ROBERTS (W.) Review of "The Doctrine and discipline of the Salvation Army" by W. Booth. pp. 19. 11. *Madras*, 1889. 8°. 4371. ee. 2. (4.)

ROOPER (W. H.) General Booth and the Salvation Army. pp. 16. *Lond.* 1892. 8°. Pam. 16.

SALVATION ARMY—*continued.*

WHITE (A.) Truth about the Salvation Army. pp. 59. *Lond.* 1892. 8°. 4136. g. 9.

BOOTH–TUCKER (F. de L.) The life of Colonel Weeresooriye. pp. 16. *Lond.* 1888. 4°. Pam. 9.

—— Darkest India. pp. 155. *Bombay*, 1891. 8°. 4766. e. 25.

SALVATION ARMY. A handful of Corn; annual report of the Indian Salvation Army. pp. 33. *Bombay*, 1893. 8°. 4766. ff. 34.

For W. Booth's plan of social reform, *see* PAUPERISM.

SALZBRUNN. MAYER ( ) Effects of the Kronenquelle water in the treatment of Gout. pp. 11. *Breslau*, 1891. 8°. 07305. e. 23. (13.)

SALZBURG. MARETICH VON RIV-ALPON (G.) Baron. Die Gefechte in der Umgebung von Salzburg, 1800, 1805 und 1809. pp. 104. *Wien*, 1893. 8°. 9080. dd. 18.

SALZUNGEN. HERTEL (D.) Die salzunger Mundart. pp. 150. 1888. 8°. Ac. Meiningen. *Hennebergischer Altertumsforschender Verein.* Neue Beiträge. Lief. 5. 9325. d.

SAMARKAND. *See* TURKESTAN.

SAMOA. BASTIAN (A.) Die samoanische Schöpfungs-Sage. pp. 50. *Berl.* 1894. 8°. Pam. 41.

FRASER (M.) In Stevenson's Samoa. pp. 190. *Lond.* 1895. 8°. 10491. b. 39.

MOORE (F. F.) Coral and cocoa-nut. Cruise of the yacht "Fire-Fly." pp. 379. *Lond.* 1890. 8°. 4419. f. 28.

STEVENSON (R. L.) Footnote to history. Eight years of trouble in Samoa. pp. 322. *Lond.* 1892. 8°. 9781. aaa. 2.

—— Vailima Letters. pp. 366. *Lond.* 1895. 8°. 010920. k. 4.

FUNK (B.) Anleitung zum Verständniss der samoanischen Sprache. pp. 82. *Berl.* 1893. 8°. 12910. cc. 15.

NEWELL (J. E.) Chief's language in Samoa. pp. 17. *Lond.* 1893. 8°. 12910. d. 31. (8.)

See also PACIFIC OCEAN AND ISLANDS.

SAMOËNS. TAVERNIER (H.) Histoire de Samoëns. pp. 291. 1892. 8°. Ac. Chambéry. *Société Savoisienne.* Mémoires. Tom. 31. Ac. 5240.

SAMSÖE. SCHLEISNER (G. E. V.) Samsø og dens Befolkning, 1815–89. pp. 116. *Kjøbenh.* 1891. 8°. 8223. dh. 9.

SAN ANTONIO, Texas. CORNER (W.) San Antonio de Bexar. pp. 164. *San Antonio*, 1890. 8°. 10412. h. 24.

SANCHI. MAISEY (F. C.) Sánchi and its remains. pp. 142. *Lond.* 1892. 4°. 7705. h. 30.

SANDBACH. HARPER (W. J.) "Old Sandbach" and neighbourhood. pp. 53. *Sandbach*, 1894. 8°. 10360. d. 39.

SANDEFJORD. POULSSON (C.) Sandefjords bad. pp. 23. *Kristiania*, 1895. 8°. Pam. 39.

VIBE (J.) Sandefjord bad. pp. 163. *Kristiania*, 1893. 8°. 10280. a. 4.

SANDGATE. BIRCH (W. P.) AND Co. Guide to Folkestone and Sandgate. *Folkestone*, 1891. 32°. Pam. 90.

RULTON (W. L.) Sandgate Castle, A.D. 1539–40. pp. 32. *Lond.* 1892. 8°. 10348. e. 15. (3.)

SANDHURST, Royal Military College. SANDHURST. *Royal Military College.* Regulations respecting admission to the R.M.C. pp. 10. *Lond.* 1893. 8°. 8830. aaa. 57.

SANDHURST.—Royal Military College
—continued.

SANDHURST, *Royal Military College.* Synopsis
of the Course of instruction.
pp. 17. *Lond.* 1888. fol.   8825. h. 19. (4.)

SAN FRANCISCO. JENNESS (C. K.) The
charities of San Francisco. pp. 93.
San Francisco, 1894. 8°.   8285. ee. 45.

SANITATION: PUBLIC HEALTH.
Ac. *Congrès International des Sciences Médicales.*
Anstalten und Einrichtungen des öffentlichen
Gesundheitswesens in Preussen. pp. 413.
Berl. 1890. 8°.   Ac. 3699/2.
—— Deutsches Gesundheitswesen. pp. 309.
Berl. 1890. 8°.   Ac. 3699/3.
—— Great Britain. *Sanitary Institute.* List of
exhibits to which medals and certificates have
been awarded at Exhibitions, Worcester, 1889,
Brighton, 1890. pp. 124. *Lond.* 1892. 8°.
                                     8777. bbb. 27.
—— London. *British Institute of Public Health.*
Journal of State Medicine. *Lond.* 1892, *etc.* 8°.
                                     Ac. 3820. c.
—— Officers and members. *Lond.* 1895, *etc.* 8°.
                                     Ac. 3820. c/2.
ADLER (M. N.) Health Laws of the Bible.
pp. 11. *Lond.* 1892. 8°.   4034. h. 51. (5.)
—— Sanitation as taught by the Mosaic Law.
pp. 12. *Lond.* 1893. 8°.   4034. h. 51. (7.)
ALLAN (F. J.) Aids to Sanitary Science, for
candidates for Public Health qualifications.
Dublin, 1890, *etc.* 8°.   8777. aa. 1.
ARLIDGE (J. T.) Hygiene, diseases and mortality
of Occupations. pp. 568. *Lond.* 1892. 8°.
                                     7404. de. 7.
ARRAS (P. D') Assainissement de la ville de
Rouen. 1890–91. 8°. Ac. Rouen. *Société In-
dustrielle.* Bulletin. An. 18, 19.   Ac. 4412.
BLASIUS (R.) Die Städtereinigung. Einleitung,
Abfuhrsysteme, Kanalisation. pp. 304.
1894. 8°. WEYL (T.) Handbuch der Hygiene.
Bd. 2.   7391. dd.
—— Die Stadt Braunschweig in hygienischer
Beziehung. pp. 260. *Braunschweig,* 1890. 8°.
                                     7686. ee. 21.
BOYLE (R.) Sanitary crusade round the World.
pp. 34. *Lond.* 1890. 8°.   8708. g. 27. (3.)
—— Sanitary crusade through the East and
Australasia. pp. 44. *Lond.* 1892. 8°.
                                     8777. aaa. 28.
CAMERON (J. S.) Is my House healthy?
pp. 204. *Leeds,* 1892. 8°.   8777. aaa. 26.
CHEYNE (W. W.) and CASSAL (C. E.) Public
Health laboratory work. 1884. 8°. London.
International Health Exhibition. Handbooks.
                                     7958. d.
CLARKE (C. H.) Calculation of cubic space for
sanitary officers. pp. 25. *Leyton,* 1894. 8°.
                                     8531. dd. 28. (11.)
COLYER (F.) Treatise on modern sanitary ap-
pliances. pp. 118. *Lond.* 1892. 8°. 8777. aaa. 29.
CORFIELD (W. H.) Dwelling houses. pp. 125.
Lond. 1894. 8°.   8777. aaa. 37.
DENMARK. Denmark; its hygiene, *etc.* pp. 474.
Copenh. 1891. 8°.   7680. e. 9.
DIBBLE (F. L.) Vagaries of Sanitary Science.
pp. 462. *Phila.* 1893. 8°.   8777. b. 53.
DOMESTIC HOUSE PLANNER. Domestic House
planner and sanitary architect. pp. 263.
Lond. 1891. 8°.   7817. e. 12.
ELLIS (H. H.) Nationalisation of Health.
pp. 244. *Lond.* 1892. 8°.   7404. df. 3.
ENGLAND AND WALES. *Local Government Board.*
Model Byelaws for the use of Sanitary autho-
rities. 2 pt. *Lond.* 1893. 8°.   6426. cc. 1.

SANITATION, etc.—*continued.*

FAWCETT (E. A. S.) Sanitary Engineer's pocket
report-book. *Lond.* 1894. *obl.* 8°. 8777. dc. 2.
GERMANY. *Kaiserliches Gesundheitsamt.* Medi-
zinal-statistische Mittheilungen.
Berl. 1892, *etc.* 8°.   7689. g. 2.
GILLESPIE (C. G. K.) Claims of Sanitary Science
upon the Clergy. pp. 23. *Lond.* 1891. 8°.
                                     8708. g. 27. (10.)
GOSLETT (C.) The Science of home life. pp. 63.
Lond. 1895. 8°.   8777. a. 6.
HART (E. A.) The State and its servants.
pp. 55. *Lond.* 1893. 8°.   7679. aaa. 6.
HART (R. C.) Sanitation and Health. pp. 57.
Lond. 1894. 8°.   7404. cc. 22.
INNES (C.) and BURTON (W. K.) Sanitary In-
spection of dwelling houses. pp. 6.
Lond. 1880. 8°.   Pam. 79.
JOLTRAIN (A.) Les Services sanitaires de Paris.
pp. 300. *Paris,* 1893. 12°.   8777. aaa. 33.
JONES (H.) Guide to the examinations in Sani-
tary Science, *etc.* pp. 99. *Lond.* 1892. 8°.
                                     8777. aa. 2.
KENWOOD (H. R.) Public Health laboratory
work. pp. 491. 1893. 8°. Lewis's Practical
Series.   7482. a.
LONDON. *Ladies' Sanitary Association.* Report
to the seventh International Congress of Hy-
giene. pp. 14. *Lond.* 1891. 8°.   7404. a. 42.
LOW (S.) Sanitary Suggestions. pp. 100.
Lond. 1885. 8°.   8776. aaa. 6.
MANFREDI (L.) Sulla contaminazione della
superficie stradale nelle grandi città dal punto
di vista dell'igiene. pp. 79. 1891. 4°. Ac.
Naples. *Accademia delle Scienze.* Atti. Ser. 2.
Vol. 4.   Ac. 96.
MARSDEN (J. A.) Health on one Hand, death on
the other. pp. 31. *Manch.* 1893. 8°.
                                     8777. bbb. 28. (9.)
NEWSHOLME (A.) Hygiene. Personal and public
health. pp. 448. *Lond.* 1892. 8°. 7404. df. 2.
NIGHTINGALE (F.) Health teaching in Towns
and Villages. pp. 27. *Lond.* 1894. 8°.
                                     7306. c. 22. (17.)
NOTTER (J. L.) and FIRTH (R. H.) Hygiene.
pp. 374. *Lond.* 1894. 8°.   7404. df. 10.
PALMBERG (A.) Treatise on Public Health.
pp. 539. *Lond.* 1895. 8°.   8777. cc. 35.
PARKES (L. C.) Elements of Health. pp. 246.
Lond. 1895. 8°.   7404. aaaa. 4.
—— Hygiene and Public Health. pp. 531.
1895. 8°. Lewis's Practical Series. 7482. a.
PERETMÈRE (H.) Les grandes villes devant la
Loi Sanitaire française. pp. 49.
Paris, 1893. 4°.   8709. c. 13. (8.)
P.P. *London.* Lancet reports on the Con-
gresses of Hygiene, 1876–89. pp. 81.
Lond. 1891. 8°.   7404. de. 13.
—— *Newton Abbot.* Sanitation in the West.
Newton Abbot, 1892, *etc.* 4°.
                                     P.P. 2706. al. and 1182.
PIGNANT (P.) Génie sanitaire. pp. 527.
Dijon, 1889, 90. 8°.   8777. d. 34.
—— Atlas. fol.   7053. b. 1.
PIOGER (J.) La Question Sanitaire dans ses
rapports avec les intérêts de l'individu et de la
société. pp. 239. *Paris,* 1895. 12°. 5424. b. 21.
POORE (G. V.) Essays on rural Hygiene.
pp. 372. *Lond.* 1894. 8°.   8776. a. 69.
—— Dry methods of Sanitation. pp. 15.
Lond. 1894. 8°.   8777. bbb. 28. (12.)
POPE (J. J.) Number One and how to take care
of him. pp. 188. *Lond.* 1883. 8°. 7404. a. 34.

SANITATION, etc.—continued.

REID (G.) Practical Sanitation. pp. 331.
Lond. 1895. 8°.   8777. df. 2.

REYNOLDS (E. S.) Primer of Hygiene. pp. 164.
Lond. 1894. 8°.   7404. a. 44.

RICHARD (E.) Précis d'Hygiène appliquée.
pp. 779. *Paris*, 1891. 8°.   7404. cc. 12.

ROHÉ (G. H.) Text book of Hygiene. pp. 553.
Phila. 1894. 8°.   7390. g. 26.

ROTHERY (G. C.) Healthy Households. pp. 114.
Lond. 1892. 8°.   7942. de. 13.

RUFF (J.) Illustriertes Gesundheits-Lexikon.
Strassb. 1894. 8°.   7390. g. 27.

SANITARY SERIES. Sanitary Series.
Lond. 1894, etc. 8°.   8756. dd.

SKELTON (J.) Supplement to Skelton's handbook
of Public Health. pp. 33. *Edinb.* 1891. 8°.
                 6583. aa. 10.

SLAGG (C.) Sanitary Work in the smaller towns
and in villages. pp. 270. *Lond.* 1893. 8°.
                8776. aaaa. 24.

STEVENSON (T.) and MURPHY (S. T.) Treatise
on Hygiene and Public Health.
Lond. 1892, etc. 8°.   7391. g. 18.

STYAN (T. G.) Address to the Sanitary Inspectors' Association at Ramsgate. pp. 8.
Ramsgate, 1894. 8°.   8827. bbb. 28. (13.)

STYLES (J.) Lecture on Sanitary Reform for
greater Melbourne. pp. 20.
Williamstown, 1888. 8°.   8827. bbb. 28. (3.)

SYKES (J. F. J.) Public Health problems.
pp. 370. 1892. 8°. ELLIS (H. H.) Contemporary Science series, etc.   8709. i.

TAYLOR (A.) The Sanitary Inspector's handbook. pp. 243. *Lond.* 1893. 8°. 8777. aaa. 32.

TAYLER (A. J. W.) Sanitary Arrangement of
dwelling-houses. pp. 196. *Lond.* 1894. 8°.
                 8777. b. 50.

WERNICH (A.) and WEHMER (R.) Lehrbuch
oeffentlichen Gesundheitswesens. pp. 788.
Stuttgart, 1894. 8°.   7442. i. 9.

WEYL (T.) Studien zur Strassenhygiene.
pp. 142. *Jena*, 1893. 8°.   8776. ee. 51.

WHARAM (R. M.) Hints on Sanitary Fittings and
their application. pp. 31. *Lond.* 1891. 8°.
                 8777. b. 36.

WHITELEGGE (B. A.) Hygiene and Public
Health. pp. 586. 1894. 8°. Manuals for
Students.   2255. a. 34.

WILLIS (W. A.) Public Health. Guide for the
inhabitants of the County of London. pp. 61.
Lond. 1892. 8°.   6426. cc. 16.

WILLOUGHBY (E. F.) Handbook of Public Health.
pp. 509. *Lond.* 1893. 8°.   8777. aa. 4.

—— Health Officer's pocket-book. pp. 376.
Lond. 1893. 8°.   8777. aa. 3.

—— Notes of the essentials of House Sanitation.
pp. 39. *Lond.* 1895. 8°.   Pam. 79.

WILSON (G.) Handbook of Hygiene and Sanitary
Science. pp. 751. *Lond.* 1892. 8°. 2254. c. 26.

See also DRAINAGE : HYGIENE : PLUMBING.

Laws relating to Public Health.

ANGELL (J. A.) and MORLEY (J. G.) Practical
guide to Sanitary Legislation. pp. 638.
Lond. 1895. 8°.   6425. aaaa. 14.

BLYTH (A. W.) Lectures on Sanitary Law.
pp. 287. *Lond.* 1893. 8°.   6426. e. 13.

CHAMBERS (G. F.) Handy digest of cases relating
to Public Health. pp. 222. *Lond.* 1893. 8°.
                 6426. e. 12.

CLARKE (C. H.) Notes on Sanitary Law. pp. 32.
Lond. 1893. 8°.   6190. cc. 3. (7.)

**SANITATION.—Laws relating to Public
  Health—continued.**

GLEN (W. C.) and (A.) Law relating to Public
Health. 2 vol. *Lond.* 1895. 8°. 6426. de. 24.

G. B. & I. Victoria, *Queen*. Public Health Act,
1875, and other statutes. *Lond.* 1894. 8°.
               6425. aaaa. 4.

LUMLEY (W. G.) and (E.) Public Health Acts,
annotated. pp. 1272. *Lond.* 1893. 8°.
               2232. d. 12.

MONOD (H.) Les mesures sanitaires en Angleterre depuis 1875. pp. 74. *Paris*, 1891. 8°.
               8777. g. 3.

MACMORRAN (A.) Public Health Acts, 1888–
1890. pp. 434. *Lond.* 1891. 8°. 6426. df. 21.

SMITH (B.) Public Health Acts Amendment
Act, 1890. pp. 202. *Lond.* 1891. 8°.
               6425. cc. 13.

HOLDSWORTH (W. A.) Public Health (London)
Act, 1891. pp. 192. *Lond.* 1891. 8°.
               6426. aaaa. 3.

MACMORRAN (A.) Public Health (London) Act,
1891. pp. 306. *Lond.* 1891. 8°. 6426. aaaa. 9.

ROBERTS (J.) and GOLLAN (H. C.) Law relating
to the Public Health of London. pp. 382.
Lond. 1891. 8°.   6426. cc. 14.

THOMAS (E. L.) Public Health (London) Act,
1891. pp. 393. *Lond.* 1891. 8°. 6426. e. 8.

G. B. & I. Victoria, *Queen*. Public Health
(London) Act, 1891. Model Byelaws. pp. 8.
Lond. 1893. fol.   7560. k. 7. (6.)

MAGUIRE (T. M.) The London Householder's
chart. pp. 20. *Lond* 1891. 8°.   Pam. 32.

ENGLAND AND WALES. *Local Government Board.*
Legislation of 1892 affecting urban Sanitary
Authorities. pp. 10. *Lond.* 1893. fol.
               7560. k. 7. (5.)

GLASGOW. *Social Union.* Glasgow Sanitary
Summary. pp. 15. *Glasg.* 1891. 8°.
            6190. aa. 31. (9.)

CHILI. Disposiciones vigentes en Chile sobre
Policía sanitaria. pp. 172. *Santiago*, 1889. 8°.
               6784. f. 14.

—— La Administracion sanitaria en Chile. Recopilacion de las disposiciones. pp. 365.
Santiago, 1895. 8°.   6784. g. 21.

See also LOCAL GOVERNMENT : NUISANCES.

    Military and Naval Sanitation.
See MEDICINE, *Military and Nautical.*

SAN MARINO. HAUTTECOEUR (H.) La République de San Marino. pp. 256.
Brux. 1894. 8°.   10135. e. 6.

FATTORI (M.) Ricordi storici della repubblica
di S. Marino, etc. pp. 101. *Firenze*, 1893. 8°.
               9167. e. 4.

FRANCIOSI (P.) Garibaldi e la repubblica di S.
Marino. pp. 71. *Bologna*, 1891. 8°.
           9004. gg. 24. (7.)

MONTALBO (de) La République de Saint-
Marin. Gouvernement, administration. pp. 40.
Paris, 1895. 8°.   8033. h. 21.

SAN MINIATO. PIOMBANTÍ (G.) Guida
della città di San Miniato. pp. 148.
S. Miniato, 1894. 8°.   10136. b. 4.

SANQUHAR. BROWN (J.) History of Sanquhar. pp. 450. 47. *Dumfries*, 1891. 8°.
             010370. f. 20.

SANSKRIT LANGUAGE. CAPPELLER
(C.) Sanskrit-English dictionary. pp. 672.
Lond. 1891. 8°.   2115. e.

LAKSHMAṆA RĀMACHANDRA VAIDYA. Standard
Sanskrit-English dictionary. pp. 889.
Bombay, 1889. 8°.   12906. dd. 28.

MACDONNELL (A. A.) Sanskrit-English dictionary. pp. 384. *Lond.* 1893. 4°. 12906. i. 19.

SANSKRIT LANGUAGE—*continued.*

VAMANA SIVARĀMA ĀPTE. Sanskrit-English dictionary. pp. 13. 1196. *Poona,* 1890. 4°.
　　　　　　　　　　　　　12906. i. 18.

—— Student's English-Sanskrit dictionary. pp. 462. *Bombay,* 1893. 8°.　12907. ee. 48.

DAVIS (B.) Nine Hundred Sanscrit words, compared with corresponding terms in English, *etc.* pp. 36. *Banaras,* 1888. 8°. 12903. dd. 34. (5.)

AMBIKĀDATTA VYĀSA. Practical Sanskrit. Grammar and composition, *etc.* 2 pt.
Benares, 1888. 12°.　　　　　14092. a. 8.

—— Children's Sanskrit grammar. pp. 88.
Bhagalpur, 1890. 12°.　　12901. ccc. 18. (3.)

ANDERSEN (D.) Om Brugen og Betydningen af Verbets Genera i Sanskrit. pp. 123.
Kjøbenh. 1892. 8°.　　　　12907. d. 27.

ANUBHŪTISVARŪPA ĀCHĀRYA. Sarosati, a Sanskrit grammar translated into English.
Bankipore, 1890, *etc.* 8°.　　14093. b. 27.

ARYĀ. Grammar of the Sanskrit language.
Benares, 1889, *etc.* 8°.　　14093. d. 13.

BERGAIGNE (A.) and HENRY (V.) Manuel pour étudier le Sanscrit védique. pp. 336.
Paris, 1890. 8°.　　　　　12907. eee. 38.

CHHOTĀLĀLA CHUNILĀLA SUTARIYA. Notes on Sanscrit grammar. *Bombay,* 1890. 8°.
　　　　　　　　　　　　　14150. a. 43.

EDGREN (H.) Jämförande grammatik, omfattande Sanskrit, Grekiska, Latin och Gotiska.
Göteborg, 1893, *etc.* 8°.　　　12901. cc.

FICK (R.) Praktische Grammatik der Sanskrit-Sprache. pp. 184. 1891. 8°. Die Kunst der Polyglottie. Th. 33.　　　12902. c.

GOPĀLACHANDRA VIDYĀRATNA. Companion to Sanskrit grammar. pp. 76. *Calcutta,* 1891. 12°.
　　　　　　　　　　14092. a. 11. (2.)

JOHNSTON (C.) Useful Sanskrit nouns and verbs. pp. 30. *Lond.* 1892. 8°.　12906. df. 38.

KEDĀRANĀTHA. Manual of Sanskrit grammar.
Lucknow, 1890, *etc.* 8°.　　12907. aa. 75.

LUDWIG (A.) Die Genesis der grammatischen Formen des Samskṛt. pp. 164. 1891. 4°. Ac. Prague. *Gesellschaft der Wissenschaften.* Abhandlungen. Folge VII. Bd. 4.　　Ac. 801.

NĪLAMANI MUKHOPĀDHYĀYA NYĀYĀLAMKĀRA. Laghumanjari, or the Elements of Sanskrit grammar. pp. 232. *Calcutta,* 1888. 12°. 12906. aaa. 54.

MORESVARA RĀMACHANDRA KALE. Higher Sanskrit grammar. pp. 632. *Bombay,* 1894. 8°.
　　　　　　　　　　　　12906. de. 10.

RĀJAKUMĀRA TARKARATNA. Student's Sanskrit grammar. pp. 237. *Calcutta,* 1888. 12°.
　　　　　　　　　　　　12906. aa. 46.

SCERBO (F.) Radici sanscritte. pp. 85.
Firenze, 1892. 8°.　　　　12907. ee. 46.

VASCONCELLOS-ABREU (G. de) Manual para o estudo do sãoskrito classico. pp. 186.
Lisboa, 1881. 8°.　　12906. g. 33. (2.)

VASUDEVA SAHĀYA. Principles of Sanskrit grammar. pp. 176. *Allahabad,* 1892. 8°. 12906. aaa. 57.

VĀLMĪKI. Matriculation Examination for Madras University, 1889. Sanskrit text, prose and poetry. 2 pt. *Bombay,* 1889. 8°. 14072. cc. 44. (1.)

VĀMANA SIVARĀMA ĀPTE. Student's Handbook of progressive exercises. *Poona,* 1894, *etc.* 12°.
　　　　　　　　　　　　14092. a. 14.

VASCONCELLOS-ABREU (G. de) Exercicios e primeiras leituras de Sanscritto.
Lisboa, 1889. 4°.　　　　12906. g. 34.

JACKSON (A. V. W.) Avesta grammar in comparison with Sanskrit. *Stuttgart,* 1892, *etc.* 8°.
　　　　　　　　　　　　12907. dd. 32.

SANSKRIT LANGUAGE—*continued.*

KIRSTE (J.) Die Bedeutung der orientalischen Philologie. pp. 16. *Wien,* 1892. 8°.
　　　　　　　　　　12903. dd. 34. (12.)

MINGUELLA (T.) Estudios comparativos entre el Tagalog y el Sanscrito. pp. 8. 1885. fol.
　　　　　　　　　　　　　　Pam. 47.

UHLENBECK (C. C.) De plaats van het Sanskrit in de vergelijkende Taalwetenschap. pp. 31.
Leiden, 1892. 8°.　　　12901. f. 43. (4.)

SANSKRIT LITERATURE. Ac. *British Museum.* Catalogue of Sanskrit Books acquired during the years 1876–92. By C. Bendall.
col. 624. *Lond.* 1893. 4°.　　11899. k. 25.

—— Germany. *Deutsche morgenländische Gesellschaft.* Catalogus Catalogorum. Alphabetical register of Sanskrit works and authors, by T. Aufrecht. pp. 795. *Leipz.* 1891. 4°. Cat. Desk. B.

MANMATHANĀTHA DATTA. The Wealth of India. Magazine devoted to English translation of Sanskrit works. *Calcutta,* 1892, *etc.* 8°.
　　　　　　　　　　　　14085. d. 32.

MONIER WILLIAMS (*Sir* M.) Indian Wisdom. pp. 576. *Lond.* 1893. 8°.　　4506. dd. 3.

OMAN (J. C.) The great Indian Epics. pp. 231. *Lond.* 1894. 8°.　　011850. g. 39.

RAMAKRISHNA GOPĀLA BHĀNDARAKARA. Lists of Sanskrit Manuscripts in private libraries in the Bombay Presidency. *Bombay,* 1893, *etc.* 8°.
　　　　　　　　　　　　14096. c. 12.

REED (E. A.) Hindu Literature. pp. 410.
Chicago, 1891. 8°.　　　011824. f. 2.
See also HINDUISM.

SANTALS. AFRICA. *Church Missionary Society.* The Hill Tribes of India. pp. 48.
Lond. 1891. 8°.　　　　　Pam. 40.

DALHOFF (N.) Den Nordiske Santhalmission pp. 150. *Kjøbenh.* 1892. 8°.　4767. dd. 6.

MACPHAIL (J. M.) Three Months in Camp among the Santals. pp. 158.
Pokhuria, 1893. 8°.　　　4765. df. 30.

THOMSEN (V.) Bemaerkninger om Santhalsproget. pp. 7. *Kjøbenh.* 1893. 8°.
　　　　　　　　　　12910. bb. 47. (12.)

CAMPBELL (A.) Santal Folk Tales. pp. 127.
Pokhuria, 1891. 8°.　　　14178. g. 24.

SANTO DOMINGO. *See* HAYTI.

SAÔNE-ET-LOIRE, Department. BELOT (A.) Le Département de Saône-et-Loire.
pp. 63. *Paris,* 1892. 8°.　　10174. aa. 37.

AUTUN. Cahiers des paroisses du Bailliage d'Autun, 1789. Suivis d'une iconographie des députés de Saône-et-Loire. pp. 95*, 407.
Autun, 1895, 8°.　　　　　9231. k. 9.
See also BURGUNDY.

SÃO PAULO, Province. SÃO PAULO. *Commissao Geographica.* Boletim.
S. Paulo, 1889, *etc.* 8°.　　　Ac. 6199.

SARAJEVO. Ac. *etc.* Sarajevo. *Zemaljski Muzej.* Die neolithische Station von Butmir bei Sarajevo. pp. 54. *Wien,* 1895. fol.
　　　　　　　　　　　　1700. b. 8.

SARATOGA, New York. *See* UNITED STATES OF AMERICA, *History.*

SARCOMA. *See* CANCER.

SARDINIA, Kingdom and Island. TODA Y GÜELL (E.) Bibliografia española de Cerdeña. pp. 326. *Madrid,* 1890. 4°.　011902. f. 24.

CAMBONI (A.) Storia della Sardegna. pp. 209. *Sassari,* 1890. 8°.　　　9150. f. 2.

DU BOIS-MELLY (C.) Relations de la cour de Sardaigne et de Genève, 1754–92.
pp. 319. *Genève,* 1891. 8°.　　9080. c. 30.

SARDINIA—*continued.*

NAPOLI (T.) La Flotta francese e la Sardegna nel 1793. pp. 9. *Cagliari*, 1893. fol. Pam. 28.

MELONI-SATTA (P.) L'Arma di Sardegna. pp. 16. *Cagliari*, 1892. 8°.   9905. aaa. 31. (3.)

CHIESI (G.) In Sardegna. Note di un Delegato della Cooperativa Agricola. pp. 55. *Bergamo*, 1892. 8°.   10107. e. 12. (5.)

CUGIA (P.) Nuovo itinerario di Sardegna. 2 vol. *Ravenna*, 1892. 8°.   10130. bb. 22.

MAFFI (A.) Dieci giorni in Sardegna. pp. 59. *Roma*, 1892. 8°.   10106. de. 8. (5.)

SERGI (G.) Di alcune varietà umane della Sardegna. pp. 17. *Roma*, 1892. 8°. 7365. f. 6. (3.)

VUILLIER (G.) Les Îles oubliées. pp. 503. *Paris*, 1893. 4°.   K.T.C. 1. b. 11.

CHIMIRRI (B.) Disegno di Legge. Colonizzazione della Sardegna. pp. 6. 1892. 8°. Pam. 70.

VIVANET (F.) Colonizzazione della Sardegna. pp. 61. *Cagliari*, 1893. 8°.   8282. g. 25. (9.)

See also ITALY, *History :* PIEDMONT : SAVOY.

SARK. *See* CHANNEL ISLANDS.

SASKATCHEWAN. MANITOBA. Experience of farmers cultivating lands of Saskatchewan, *etc.* pp. 16. *Lond.* 1892. 8°.   Pam. 86.

—— Report Delegates. Proceedings of a Delegation to examine Saskatchewan. pp. 24. *Lond.* 1892. 8°.   Pam. 86.

See also CANADA, *North-West Provinces.*

SATAN. *See* DEMONOLOGY.

SATIRE. SCHNEEGANS (H.) Geschichte der grotesken Satire. pp. 523. *Strassb.* 1894. 8°.   011850. i. 54.

SOLDINI (E.) Breve storia della Satira. pp. 140. *Cremona*, 1891. 8°.   11312. d. 55.

SATURN. EICHELBERGER (W. S.) Orbit of Hyperion. pp. 13. *Lynn, Mass.* 1892. 8°.   Pam. 4.

KEELER (J. E.) Spectroscopic proof of the meteoric constitution of Saturn's Rings. *Chicago*, 1895. 8°.   Pam. 4.

—— Conditions affecting form of lines in the Spectrum of Saturn. *Chicago*, 1895. 8°. Pam. 4.

See also SUN AND SOLAR SYSTEM.

SAUZÉ-VAUSSAIS. PICANON (A. E.) Notice sur l'église réformée de Sauzé-Vaussais. pp. 12. *Paris*, 1892. 8°.   4535. c. 9. (6.)

SAVANNAH. JONES (C. C.) Siege and evacuation of Savannah, Dec. 1864. pp. 30. *Augusta*, 1890. 8°.   9004. m. 5. (6.)

SAVERDUN. BARRIÈRE-FLAVY (C.) Histoire de la ville de Saverdun. pp. 334. *Toulouse*, 1891. 8°.   10174. g. 23.

SAVINGS BANKS. *See* BANKING.

SAVONA. BRUNO (A.) Gli antichi archivi di Savona. pp. 87. *Savona*, 1890. 8°.   11899. ee. 23.

SAVOY.

History, etc.

MUGNIER (F.) Les Savoyards en Angleterre au XIII° siècle. *Chambéry*, 1890. 8°. pp. 324.   010661. i. 25.

GABOTTO (F.) Le Stato Sabaudo da Amedeo VIII. ad Emanuele Filiberto. 2 vol. *Torino*, 1892, 93. 8°.   9167. h. 12.

—— Curiosità giudiziarie del tempo di Amedeo VIII. pp. 17. *Torino*, 1891. 8°.   Pam. 34.

CLAPARÈDE (T.) Histoire de la réformation en Savoie. pp. 380. *Genève*, 1893. 12°.   4660. aaa. 34.

SAVOY.—History, etc.—*continued.*

CLARETTA (G.) Emanuele Filiberto e la corte di Londra, 1554-55. pp. 76. 47. *Pinerolo*, 1892. 8°.   9166. dd. 13.

CHARLES EMANUEL I., *Duke of Savoy.* Carlo Emanuele I. pp. 263. *Torino*, 1891. 8°.   10631. e. 50.

RUA (G.) L'Epopea savoina alla corte di Carlo Emanuele I. pp. 52. *Torino*, 1893. 8°.   11826. i. 42. (6.)

FAZI (H.) Les Suisses et la neutralité de la Savoie. 1703-04. pp. 349. *Genève*, 1895. 8°.   9304. de. 5.

LARACINE (H.) 1745. Occupation espagnole de Savoie. pp. 30. *Chambéry*, 1891. 8°.   9007. ff. 5. (6.)

CARUTTI (D.) Storia di Savoia durante la rivoluzione e l'impero francese. *Torino*, 1892, *etc.* 8°.   9166. dd. 12.

MASSE (J.) Histoire de l'annexion de la Savoie à la France, 1792. *Grenoble*, 1891, *etc.* 8°.   9080. f.

BURDIN (C.) L'Annexion de 1792 et son centenaire. pp. 132. *Chambéry*, 1890. 8°.   9226. aa. 7.

DUVAL (C.) L'invasion de la Savoie par l'armée sarde en 1793. pp. 202. *Saint-Julien*, 1892. 8°.   9072. e. 11.

ROUX (X.) L'Invasion de la Savoie par les Autrichiens, 1813-14. *Grenoble*, 1892, *etc.* 8°.   7094. k. 5.

SAVOY. La Neutralité militaire de la Savoie. pp. 30. *Annecy*, 1893. 8°.   9165. d. 39. (9.)

P.P. *Grenoble.* Revue du Dauphiné et de la Savoie. *Grenoble*, 1894, *etc.* fol.   277.

Topography.

JOANNE (P.) Dauphiné et Savoie. pp. 492. *Paris*, 1894. 8°.   10171. a. 24.

JUGE (S.) Guide bleu des Alpes françaises. *Paris*, 1894, *etc.* 8°.   10174. aa.

See also ALPS.

Dialect.

DURET (V.) Grammaire savoyarde. pp. 91. *Berl.* 1893. 8°.   12950. f. 36.

SAXE-COBURG-GOTHA. LERP (C.) Die alten Völker im Lande Gotha. pp. 157. *Gotha*, 1892. 4°.   10250. g. 3.

LOTZ (A.) Coburgische Landesgeschichte. pp. 112. *Coburg*, 1892, 8°.   9384. c. 4.

BERBIG (M.) Die Gemahlinnen der Regenten des gothaischen Landes. pp. 164. *Gotha*, 1890. 8°.   10704. e. 39.

KREYENBERG (G.) Ernst der Fromme. pp. 110. *Frankfurt*, 1890. 8°.   010707. e. 9.

OSTEN (J. v. d.) Luise Dorothee Herzogin von Sachsen-Gotha 1732-67. pp. 428. *Leipz.* 1893. 8°.   10703. ff. 7.

OHORN (A.) Herzog Ernst II. pp. 239. *Leipz.* 1894. 8°.   10703. ee. 34.

RUETE (H.) Herzog Ernst II. und sein Anteil an den Einheitsbestrebungen Deutschlands. pp. 29. *Gotha*, 1892. 8°.   8074. ee. 47. (8.)

WELTIG (H.) 1867-91. Gothaer Chronik. *Gotha*, 1892. 8°.   10106. df. 18. (6.)

SAXE-MEININGEN. *See* MEININGEN.

SAXE-WEIMAR. *See* WEIMAR.

SAXONY, Kingdom. KLEIST (U.) Die sächsischen Städtebünde zwischen Weser und Elbe im XIII. und XIV. Jahrhundert. pp. 101. 1892. 8°. Ac. *Wernigerode. Harz-Verein.* Zeitschrift. Jahrg. 25.   Ac. 7172.

TREFFTZ (J.) Kursachsen und Frankreich 1552-57. pp. 164. *Leipz.* 1891. 8°.   9077. ccc. 11.

SAXONY—*continued.*

Troska (F.) Die Publizistik zur sächsischen Frage auf dem Wiener Kongress. pp. 47. *Halle*, 1891. 8°.   9327. ccc.

Bangert (F.) Die Sachsengrenze im Gebiete der Trave. pp. 35. *Oldesloe*, 1893. 4°.   Pam. 91.

Bebel (A.) Zu den Landtagswahlen iu Sachsen. pp. 31. *Berl.* 1891. 8°.   08276. f. 40. (1.)

Lommatzsch (G.) Die Bewegung der Bevolkerungsstandes in Sachsen, 1871–1890. pp. 157. *Dresden*, 1894. 8°.   8223. aa. 78.

Dibelius (F.) Beiträge zur sächsischen Kirchengeschichte. *Leipz.* 1882, *etc.* 8°.   4662. e.

Fricker (C. V.) Die Verfassungsgesetze des Königreichs Sachsen. pp. 370. *Leipz.* 1895. 8°.   5604. de. 19.

—— Grundriss des Staatsrechts des Königreichs. pp. 261. *Leipz.* 1891. 8°.   8072. eee. 8.

Saxony. Codex des geltenden Kirchen- und Schulrechts. pp. 1173. *Leipz.* 1890. 8°.   5605. h. 17.

Mueller (O.) Das sächsische Privatrecht. *Leipz.* 1892, *etc.* 8°.   95604. i.

See also Germany : Lusatia.

SAXONY, Province. Ac. Halle. *Provinzial-Museum.* Mittheilungen. *Halle*, 1894, *etc.* 8°.   Ac. 5470.

—— *Saxony.* Die Geschichtsquellen der Provinz Sachsen im Mittelalter und in der Reformationszeit. pp. 202. *Halle*, 1893. 8°. Ac. 7161/4.

—— Halle. *Verein für Erdkunde.* Archiv für Landes- und Volkskunde der Provinz Sachsen. *Halle*, 1891, *etc.* 8°.   Ac. 6083/2.

SCANDERBORG. Lund (T.) Christian den Fjerdes Skib paa Skanderborg Sø. 2 vol. *Kjøbenh.* 1893. 8°.   9431. c. 19.

SCANDINAVIA.

Antiquities and History.

Ac. Stockholm. *Nordiska Museet.* Bidrag till vår odlings häfder. *Stockholm*, 1881, *etc.* 8°.   10281. k. 2.

—— Afbildningar af föremål i Nordiska Museet. *Stockholm*, 1888, *etc.* fol.   7709. k.

—— Führer durch die Sammlungen des nordischen Museums, Stockholm. pp. 50. *Stockholm*, 1888. 8°.   7706. g. 6. (2.)

Hazelius (A. I.) Guide to the collections of the Northern Museum, Stockholm. pp. 52. *Stockholm*, 1889. 8°.   Pam. 3.

Ac. Stockholm. *Nordiska Museet.* Meddelanden. Utgifna af A. Hazelius. *Stockholm*, 1890, *etc.* 8°.   7709. c. 9.

Undset (I. M.) University-Museum of Northern Antiquities in Christiania. pp. 23. *Christiania*, 1889. 8°.   7706. f. 21. (9.)

Bååth (A. U.) Nordiskt forntidslif. pp. 241. *Stockholm*, 1890. 8°.   07708. g. 7.

Montelius (O.) Les temps préhistoriques en Suède et dans les autres pays scandinaves. pp. 352. *Paris*, 1895. 8°.   7708. d. 38.

Rygh (O.) Discovery of a Viking Ship at Sandefjord, Norway. pp. 7. *Christiania*, 1881. 8°.   Pam. 3.

Undset (I. M.) Guide for the use of visitors to the Viking-ship from Gokstand. pp. 16. *Christiania*, 1887. 8°.   Pam. 3.

Ac. Copenhagen. *Íslenzka Bókmentafèlag.* Melsted (P.) Norðurlandasaga, eða Dana, Norðmanna og Svía soga. pp. 324. *Reykjavík*, 1891. 8°.   Ac. 9052/27.

Jorgensen (A. D.) Fortœllinger af Nordens Historie. *Kjøbenh.* 1891, *etc.* 8°. 9425. bbb. 17.

SCANDINAVIA. — Antiquities, etc. — *continued.*

Ottosen (J.) Lærebog i Nordens Historie. pp. 318. *Kjøbenh.* 1893. 8°.   9424. cc. 10.

Paget (C.) *Lady.* The Northmen in Wales. pp. 16. *Camb.* 1891. 8°.   Pam. 3.

See also Denmark : Iceland : Normans : Norway : Runic Inscriptions : Sweden. For Scandinavian Voyages to America, *see* America.

Literature. *See* Danish : Icelandic.

Mythology.

Bugge (E. S.) Prof. Bugge's Studies on Northern Mythology. 1884. 8°. Ac. Copenhagen. *K. Nordisk Oldskrift-Selskab.* Mémoires.   Ac. 5538/7.

Rydberg (A. V.) Fädernas Gudasaga. pp. 248. *Stockholm*, 1887. 8°.   4503. c. 17.

Sander (N. F.) La Mythologie du Nord, éclairée par des inscriptions latines. pp. 188. *Stockholm*, 1892. 8°.   4503. g. 6.

Schierenberg (G. A. B.) Die Götter der Germanen. pp. 224. *Detmold*, 1894. 8°.   4503. ee. 35.

SCARABS. Myer (I.) Scarabs. pp. 177. *Leipz.* 1894. 8°.   7704. a. 48.

See also Egypt, *Religion.*

SCARBOROUGH. Adey ( ) Annual guide to Scarborough. *Lond.* 1888, *etc.* 8°.   010358. f.

Waddington (T. A. J.) Guide to Scarborough. pp. 44. *York*, 1894. 8°.   10348. c. 26. (8.)

SCARLET FEVER. *See* Fevers.

SCEPTICISM. *See* Agnosticism.

SCEY–EN–VARAIS. Favrot (J.) Histoire de Scey-en-Varais. pp. 227. *Besançon*, 1890. 8°.   10174. aa. 32.

SCHAFFHAUSEN. Schaffhausen, *Kadettenkorps.* Das Kadettenkorps der Stadt Schaffhausen. pp. 81. *Schaffhausen*, 1891. 8°.   8830. k. 31. (7.)

Stickelberger (H.) Lautlehre der Mundart der Stadt Schaffhausen. pp. 59. *Aarau*, 1881. 8°.   12903. dd. 36. (5.)

SCHELDT. Cardevacque (A. de) Promenades sur les bords de l'Escaut. 1893. 8°. Ac. Cambray. *Société d'Émulation.* Mémoires. Tom. 48.   Ac. 307.

Lütken (O.) Les Danois sur l'Escaut, 1809–13. pp. 172. *Copenhague*, 1891. 8°. 9080. bbb. 35.

Rochet (E.) Description hydrographique de l'Escaut. pp. 120. *Brux.* 1894. 8°. 10270. g. 7.

SCHIERMONNIKOOG. Sluijs (P. J. A.) Schiermonnikoog als Noordzeebad geschetst. pp. 45. *Groningen*, 1891. 8°. 10106. de. 6. (4.)

SCHIZOPODA. *See* Crustacea.

SCHLESWIG-HOLSTEIN. Frahm (L.) Lebensbilder der Heldengeister Schleswig-Holsteins. *Lübeck*, 1892, *etc.* 8°.   010707. ee.

Mejborg (R.) Slesvigske Bøndergaarde i det 16de, 17de og 18de Aarhundrede. *Kjøbenh.* 1891, *etc.* 4°.   7820. h.

Schleiden (R.) Erinnerungen eines Schleswig-Holsteiners. N.F. 1841–48. *Wiesbaden*, 1890, *etc.* 8°.   010707. h. 18.

Boeger ( ) Die Wohnplätze der Provinz Schleswig-Holstein. pp. 188. *Kiel*, 1891. 8°.   10235. k. 21.

Clausen (H. V.) Sønderjylland. pp. 107. *Kjøbenh.* 1890. 8°.   10280. aa. 16.

Detlefsen (D.) Geschichte der holsteinischen Elbmarschen. *Glückstadt*, 1891, *etc.* 8°. 10255. f.

SCHLESWIG-HOLSTEIN—*continued.*

FISCHER-BENZON (R. v.) Die Moore der Provinz Schleswig-Holstein. pp. 78. 1891. 4°. Ac. Hamburg. *Naturwissenschaftlicher Verein.* Abhandlungen. Bd. 11. Hft. 3.   Ac. 2885.

OTTOSEN (J.) Sønderjylland. *Kjøbenh.* 1892. 4°.   10280. f. 12.

THOMSEN (K.) Fra danske Hjem i Sønderjylland. pp. 70. *Kolding,* 1892. 8°.   Pam. 62. *See also* ALTONA. For the War of 1864, *see* DENMARK.

SCHMALKALD, League of. WINCKELMANN (O.) Der schmalkaldische Bund, 1530–32, pp. 313. *Strassb.* 1892. 8°.   4662. e. 18.

SCHWARZBURG-RUDOLSTADT. OSSBAHR (C. A.) Das fürstliche Zeughaus in Schwarzburg. pp. 216. *Rudolstadt,* 1895. 8°.   8828. bbb. 33.

SCHWEINFURT. OPPEL (C.) Die alten Schweinfurter. pp. 137. *Schweinfurt,* 1892. 8°.   10255. bbb. 11.

SCHWYZ, Canton. SOWERBY (J.) Forest Cantons of Switzerland. pp. 288. *Lond.* 1892. 8°.   10196. cc. 11.

SCIATICA. ECCLES (A. S.) Sciatica. Record of clinical observations. pp. 88. *Lond.* 1893. 8°.   7620. de. 23.

SIMPSON (R.) Sciatic Neuritis. pp. 46. *Bristol,* 1893. 8°.   7630. aa. 24.

SCIENCE. *See* PHYSICS.

SCILLY ISLANDS. COWPER (F.) Sailing Tours. Pt. II. Scilly Isles. *Lond.* 1892, *etc.* 8°.   10360. e.

TREGELLAS (W. H.) Guide to Cornwall and the Scilly Isles. pp. 156. *Lond.* 1895. 8°.   10352. a. 55.

SCLAYN. BARBIER (V.) Histoire du Chapitre de Sclayn. pp. 384. *Namur,* 1889. 8°.   4685. e. 32.

SCORPION. *See* ARACHNIDAE.

SCOTCH DIALECT AND LITERATURE. CLEISHBOTHAM, *the Younger.* Dictionary of the Scottish language. pp. 66. *Glasg.* 1895. 8°.   12983. aa. 59.

CURTIS (F. J.) Investigation of the rimes and phonology of the Middle-Scotch romance Clariodus. pp. 168. *Halle,* 1894. 8°.   011850. i. 57.

Ac. Edinburgh. *Scottish Text Society.* Legends of the Saints in the Scottish dialect of the 14th century. Edited by W. M. Metcalfe. *Edinb.* 1888, *etc.* 8°.   Ac. 9943/9.

REEVES (W. P.) Study in the language of Scottish prose before 1600. pp. 100. *Baltimore,* 1893. 8°.   12982. ccc. 16.

HALLIBURTON (H.) Furth in Field. Essays on the language and literature of old Scotland. pp. 280. *Lond.* 1895. 8°.   10369. ccc. 33.

MACKINTOSH (J.) History of civilisation in Scotland. 4 vol. *Paisley,* 1892–96. 8°. 2396. d. 9.

WALKER (H.) Three Centuries of Scottish Literature. 2 vol. *Glasg.* 1893. 8°. 011824. g. 25.

BLACKIE (J. S.) Life of R. Burns. pp. 183. 1888. 8°.   ROBERTSON (E. S.) Great Writers.   10601. de. 5.

GAIRDNER (M. S.) R. Burns. pp. 79. *Lond.* 1887. 8°.   10856. aa. 4.

HIGGINS (J. C.) Life of R. Burns. pp. 231. *Edinb.* 1893. 8°.   10856. bb. 17.

MACRAE (D.) R. Burns. pp. 32. *Dundee,* 1886. 8°.   10803. c. 6. (4.)

SINTON (J.) Burns. A vindication. pp. 19. *Carlisle,* 1895. 8°.   10803. e. 23. (12.) *See also* BALLADS: ENGLISH LITERATURE: GAELIC LANGUAGE AND LITERATURE: POETRY.

SCOTLAND. [*See note on page* 1.] For all works relating to the United Kingdom, *see* ENGLAND.

Antiquities.

Ac. Edinburgh. *Society of Antiquaries.* Catalogue of the National Museum of Antiquities. pp. 380. *Edinb.* 1892. 8°.   7958. bbb. 13.

ANNANDALE (C.) Scotland in prehistoric Times. pp. 38. *Lond.* 1892. 8°.   7704. i. 12. (4.)

PATON (J.) Scottish National Memorials. Historical and archæological collection in the Bishop's Castle, 1888. pp. 359. *Glasg.* 1890. fol.   K.T.C. 3. b. 6.

P.P. *Edinburgh.* The Scottish Antiquary. *Edinb.* 1890, *etc.* 8°.   P.P. 6214. b. & 662.

MACLAGAN (C.) "What mean these Stones?" *Edinb.* 1894. 8°.   07708. g. 35.

MAC RITCHIE (D.) The Underground Life. pp. 47. *Edinb.* 1892. 4°.   7708. aa. 58.

CARNEGIE (J.) *Earl of Southesk.* Origins of Pictish symbolism. pp. 95. *Edinb.* 1893. 8°.   07708. g. 18.

MACKINNON (J.) Culture in Early Scotland. pp. 239. *Lond.* 1892. 8°.   9509. h. 9.

MACRITCHIE (D.) Fians, fairies and picts. pp 77. *Lond.* 1893. 8°.   07708. g. 21.

MUIR (T. S.) Ecclesiological notes on the Islands of Scotland. *Edinb.* 1885. 8°.   7708. b. 48.

RHYS (J.) Inscriptions and languages of the Northern Picts. 1892. 4°. Ac. Edinburgh. *Society of Antiquaries.* Proceedings. Vol. 26.   Ac. 5770/2.

SKENE (W. F.) Celtic Scotland. 3 vol. *Edinb.* 1886–90. 8°.   2071. d.

Church of (after 1688).

BANNERMAN (D. D.) Worship, order and polity of the Presbyterian Church. 4 pt. *Edinb.* 1894. 8°.   4175. de. 46.

BOYD (A. K. H.) Church life in Scotland. pp. 34. *Edinb.* 1890. 8°.   4175. cc. 24. (2.)

CROMARTY (D.) Scottish Ministerial miniatures. pp. 285. *Lond.* 1892. 8°.   4956. e. 13.

DICKSON (N.) The Auld Scotch Minister. pp. 175. *Glasg.* 1892. 8°.   4175. de. 40.

HEAD (J.) My Attitude, as a Catholic candidate, towards disestablishment of the Church of Scotland. pp. 32. *Lond.* 1892. 8°.   Pam. 92.

HILL (H. E.) The Catholic movement in the Church of Scotland. pp. 14. *Edinb.* 1894. 8°.   Pam. 92.

HOWIE (R.) Churches and churchless in Scotland. pp. 12. *Glasg.* 1893. 4°.   4175. i. 3.

INNES (A. T.) Studies in Scottish History, chiefly ecclesiastical. pp. 341. *Lond.* 1892. 8°.   4735. cc. 25.

MAC CLYMONT (J. A.) The Church of Scotland. Course of lectures. pp. 214. *Aberd.* 1892. 8°.   4175. cc. 25.

MAC CRIE (C. G.) Public Worship of presbyterian Scotland. pp. 465. *Edinb.* 1892. 8°. 3476. h. 23.

MACGREGOR (J.) Reunion of the Scottish Church on the lines of the Reformation. pp. 47. *Edinb.* 1891. 8°.   4175. cc. 24. (10.)

MAIR (W.) The truth about the Church of Scotland. pp. 56. *Edinb.* 1891. 8°.   4175. de. 34. (4.)

MUIR (P. M.) The Church of Scotland. pp. 229. *Lond.* 1891. 8°.   4735. b. 38.

SCOTLAND, *Church of.* The Church of Scotland, its position and work. pp. 6. 1885. 8°. Pam. 92.

—— Regulations for election and appointment of ministers. pp. 14. *Edinb.* 1889. 8°.   4175. cc. 24. (1.)

SCOTLAND.—Church of—*continued.*

SCOTLAND, *Church of.* Mr. Gladstone's position on the Church question. *Edinb.* 1890. 8°. Pam. 92.

—— *Churches in.* Statistics of Scottish churches. 1890. *s. sh.* 8°.   1897. c. 8. (98.)

SIMPSON (W.) Facts and fictions concerning the Church of Scotland. pp. 78. *Glasg.* 1895. 8°.
4175. bb. 27. (14.)

STORY (R. H.) The Church of Scotland, its present and its future. pp. 51. *Edinb.* 1894. 8°.
4175. bb. 27. (12.)

THOMSON (A.) T. Boston of Ettrick: his life and times. pp. 263. *Lond.* 1895. 8°. 4955. df. 4.

WILLIAMSON (A.) Is the Church of Scotland to stand or fall? pp. 37. *Edinb.* 1890. 8°. Pam. 92.

SCOTLAND, *Church of.* A Miners' crack about the Kirk. No. 1, 2. *Edinb.* 1892. 8°.
1897. c. 8. (79.)

—— Principal Acts of the General Assembly, May 19, 1892. pp. 138. *Edinb.* 1892. fol.
4175. i. 2.

—— Report of the Committee on Church Interests to the General Assembly, May, 1892. pp. 21. *Edinb.* 1892. 8°.   Pam. 92.

—— To the Electors of Scotland. A reply, issued by the Committee on Church Interests to a pamphlet entitled: "Disestablishment and disendowment in Scotland." pp. 8. *Edinb.* 1892. 8°.   Pam. 92.

—— What would the taxpayer gain by Disestablishment? pp. 4. *Edinb.* 1892. 8°.
4175. bb. 27. (5.)

—— Recommendations for the proper conduct of public worship by a Committee of the General Assembly. pp. 30. *Edinb.* 1894. 8°. Pam. 75.

FORSYTH (J. S.) Forms of service for Baptism, Marriage, Burial of the Dead and Ordination of Elders. pp. 48. *Lond.* 1894. 8°.
3425. cc. 37.

See also infra: History, Ecclesiastical: PRESBYTERIANISM: TITHES.

County Councils. *See* LOCAL GOVERNMENT.

Crofters. *See* LAND TENURES.

Dialects. *See* SCOTCH DIALECTS.

Episcopal Church (after 1688.)

SCOTLAND. *Episcopal Church of.* Code of Canons of the Episcopal Church. pp. 82. *Edinb.* 1890. 8°.   5157. aaa. 7.

BRUCE (J.) The national element in the Scottish Episcopal Church. pp. 31. *Edinb.* 1894. 8°.
4175. bb. 27. (10.)

P.P. *Edinburgh.* Year Book for the Episcopal Church. *Edinb.* 1891, *etc.* 8°. P.P. 2510. mac.

RORISON (V. L.) Why am I a Scottish Episcopalian? pp. 2. *Edinb.* 1892. *s. sh.* 8°.
1897. c. 8. (70.)

—— Claims of the Episcopal Church of Scotland. pp. 2. *Edinb.* 1892. *s. sh.* 8°. 1897. c. 8. (70.)

CURRIE (H. P.) Notes on the Scottish Liturgy. pp. 28. *Oxf.* 1892. 8°.   3477. dd. 7. (8.)

LITURGIES. Scotland, *Episcopal Church.* Proposed revision of the Scottish Communion Office. pp. 11. *Glasg.* 1890. 8°.   4175. cc. 24. (5.)

WORDSWORTH (C.) *Bp. of Saint Andrew's.* A plain tract on the Scotch Communion Office. pp. 24. *Edinb.* 1894. 8°.   Pam. 92.

See also infra: HISTORY, Ecclesiastical.

Free Church.

BAYNE (P.) The Free Church of Scotland. pp. 346. *Edinb.* 1894. 8°.   4735. c. 32.

BLAIKIE (W. G.) After Fifty Years; letters of a grandfather on the jubilee of the Free Church. pp. 144. *Lond.* 1893. 8°.   4735. bb. 28.

SCOTLAND.—Free Church—*continued.*

BROWN (T.) Annals of the Disruption. pp. 841. *Edinb.* 1893. 8°.   4735. cc. 14.

FLØYSTRUP (C. E.) Folkekirken og den Frie Kirke i Skotland, 1843-93. pp. 52. 1894. 8°.

NIELSEN (F.) Smaaskrifter til Oplysning for Kristne. Bd. 8.   3605. i.

HAMILTON (D. S.) Strictures on the Free Church "Declaratory Act anent the Confession of Faith." pp. 19. *Glasg.* 1892. 8°.   Pam. 92.

MAC CANDLISH (J. M.) Why are we Free Churchmen? pp. 96. *Edinb.* 1893. 8°. 4175. cc. 26.

ALISON (J.) Why we are not Free Churchmen. A reply to Mr. McCandlish. pp. 32. *Edinb.* 1893. 8°.   4175. ff. 7. (4.)

—— Remarks on Mr. M'Candlish's "Rejoinder" to "Why we are not Free Churchmen." pp. 24. *Edinb.* 1893. 8°.   4175. ff. 7. (5.)

MACKINNON (D. A.) Souvenir of the jubilee of the Free Church of Scotland. pp. 254. *Edinb.* 1893. 8°.   4735. b. 40.

MONCREIFF (*Sir* H. W.) The Free Church principle. pp. 344. *Edinb.* 1883. 8°.
4735. ee. 11.

SCOTLAND, *Free Church.* Statement by ministers and office-bearers in regard to the decisions of last General Assembly in the cases of Drs. Dods and Bruce. pp. 16. *Glasg.* 1890. 8°.
4175. cc. 24. (7.)

RYLEY (G. B.) Scotland's Free Church. A historical retrospect. pp. 392. *Westminster*, 1893. 4°.   4735. f. 14.

WALKER (N. L.) Chapters from the history of the Free Church. pp. 364. *Edinb.* 1895. 8°.
4735. ee. 13.

See also supra: Church of. MISSIONS.

Highlands.

SKENE (W. F.) Celtic Scotland. 3 vol. *Edinb.* 1886-90. 8°.   2071. d.

CAMPBELL (*Lord* A.) The Children of the mist. pp. 55. *Edinb.* 1890. 8°.   10369. h. 25.

SCOTCH CLANS. The Scottish Clans and their tartans. *Edinb.* 1892. 16°.   7743. aa. 19.

STEWART (D. W.) Old and rare Scottish Tartans. *Edinb.* 1893. 4°.   K.T.C. 1. b. 9.

STUART (J. S. S.) and (C. E.) The costume of the Clans. pp. 171. *Edinb.* 1892. fol.
Tab. 612. a.

CAMERON (J.) The Clan Cameron. pp. 95. *Kirkintilloch*, 1894. 8°.   9903. c. 20.

MACKENZIE (A.) History of the Camerons. pp. 478. *Inverness*, 1884. 8°.   9914. h. 24.

EDINBURGH. *Clan Donnachaidh Society.* Brief Account of the Clan Donnachaidh. By D. Robertson. pp. 60. *Glasg.* 1894. 8°.
9904. g. 24.

MACKINTOSH (C. F.) The last Macdonalds of Isla. pp. 99. *Glasg.* 1895. 4°.   9906. d. 4.

MENZIES (D. P.) The "Red and White" Book of Menzies. py. 529. *Glasg.* 1894. 8°.
9906. h. 4.

SMITH (R. A.) Loch Etive and the Sons of Uisnach. pp. 376. *Lond.* 1885. 8°.
10370. e. 27.

———————————

Ac. *Montreal. Celtic Society.* Transactions of the Celtic Society of Montreal. pp. 231. *Montreal*, 1887. 8°.   Ac. 9978.

CAMPBELL (*Lord* A.) Waifs and strays of Celtic Tradition. Argyllshire series. *Lond.* 1889, *etc.* 8°.   12341. k.

MACGREGOR (A.) Highland Superstitions. pp. 64. *Inverness*, 1891. 8°.   8631. aaa. 60.

SCOTLAND.—Highlands—*continued.*

MACKENZIE (A.) The Prophecies of the Brahan Seer. pp. 93. *Inverness,* 1894. 8°. 8631. b. 43.

MACKENZIE (W.) Gaelic Incantations, charms and blessings of the Hebrides. pp. 86. *Inverness,* 1895. 8°. 8631. f. 48.

MACPHERSON (A.) Glimpses of church and social Life in the Highlands. pp. 528. *Edinb.* 1893. 4°. 10370. f. 22.

P.P. *Glasgow.* The Celtic Monthly. *Glasg.* 1892, *etc.* 8°. P.P. 6223. c. & 523.

BADDELEY (M. J. B.) The Northern Highlands. pp. 145. 1894. 8°. Thorough Guide Series. 10347. aaa.

BROWN (C. R.) A Cockney in kilts. pp. 181. *Glasg.* 1892. 8°. 012314. ee. 29.

GLASGOW. Glasgow and its environs. pp. 358. *Lond.* 1891. 4°. 12369. i. 11.

HILLS. Our western Hills: how to reach them. pp. 154. *Glasg.* 1892. 8°. 10369. ccc. 17.

IMRAY (J. F.) Sailing directions for the West Coast and Islands of Scotland. pp. 224. *Lond.* 1893. 8°. 10496. b. 41.

KELLY (*Mrs.* T.) Highland Lochs and glens. pp. 63. *Lond.* 1894. *obl.* 8°. 10369. e. 13.

LESLIE (D.) Tourist's guide to the Scottish Highlands. 3 pt. *Perth,* 1892. 16°. 10369 aa. 22.

MAC BRAYNE (D.) Summer Tours. Guide from Glasgow to the Highlands viâ Crinan and Caledonian Canals. *Glasg.* 1880, *etc.* 8°. 10369. ccc.

MOUNTAIN. "Mountain, Moor and Loch" illustrated by pen and pencil. pp. 180. *Lond.* 1894. 8°. 010370. f. 13.

NAIRNE (D.) Memorable floods in the Highlands during the nineteenth century. pp. 177. *Inverness,* 1895. 8°. 8757. bbb. 35.

—— Notes on Highland woods. 1892. 8°. Ac. *Inverness. Gaelic Society.* Transactions. Vol. 17. Ac. 8260.

P.P. *Edinburgh.* Scottish Mountaineering Club Journal. *Edinb.* 1892, *etc.* 8°. P.P. 3909. ab.

WALKER (R.) The Clyde and the western Highlands. pp. 96. *Lond.* 1892. *obl.* 8°. 10369. e. 10.

See also infra: History *and* Topography : ENGLAND, *Army:* FOLK LORE : GAELIC LANGUAGE AND LITERATURE : HEBRIDES : INVERNESS : LAND TENURES, *Scotland :* SPORT.

History.

SCOTLAND. Calendar of documents relating to Scotland. Edited by J. Bain. *Edinb.* 1881, *etc.* 8°. 2075. d.

ENGLAND AND WALES. *Public Record Office.* Catalogue of English and Scotch Record Publications, *etc. Lond.* 1888, *etc.* 8°. 011901. f.

Ac. Edinburgh. *Scottish History Society.* Publications. *Edinb.* 1887, *etc.* 8°. Ac. 8256.

CAMPBELL (D.) The Scots Reader: history of Scotland for Junior pupils. pp. 192. 1890. 8°. Century Historical Readers. 9503. d.

CORNER (J.) History of Scotland. pp. 185. *Lond.* 1889. 8°. 9509. c. 1

FITTIS (R. S.) Curious episodes in Scottish History. pp. 326. *Paisley,* 1895. 8°. 9509. f. 26.

LYDE (L. W.) History of Scotland for junior classes. pp. 192. *Lond.* 1892. 8°. 9509. c. 22.

MACKINTOSH (J.) History of civilisation in Scotland. 4 vol. *Paisley,* 1892, 96. 8°. 2396. d. 9.

MAJOR (J.) History of Greater Britain. pp. 476. 1892. 8°. Ac. *Edinburgh.* Scottish History Society. Publications. Vol. 10. Ac. 8256.

MAXWELL (D.) Bygone Scotland. pp. 313. *Edinb.* 1894. 8°. 010358. i. 12.

SCOTLAND.—History—*continued.*

OLIPHANT (M. O.) Child's history of Scotland. pp. 233. 1895. 8°. Children's Study. 9004. bb.

PATON (J.) Scottish National Memorials. Historical collection in the Bishop's Castle. pp. 359. *Glasg.* 1890. fol. K.T.C. 3. b. 6.

PATRICK (R. W. C.) Mediaeval Scotland. pp. 200. *Glasg.* 1892. 8°. 7709. bb. 61.

SMITH (G. B.) History of the English Parliament, with an account of the Parliament of Scotland. 2 vol. *Lond.* 1892. 8°. 09504. f. 10.

TAYLOR (J.) Great historic families of Scotland. 2 vol. *Lond.* 1891–94. 4°. 9906. i. 20.

THOMSON (T.) History of the Scottish people. *Lond.* 1893, *etc.* 8°. 9509. l.

VEITCH (J.) History and poetry of the Scottish border. 2 vol. *Edinb.* 1893. 8°. 2308. c. 20.

HAMILTON PAPERS. The Hamilton Papers. Edited by J. Bain. A.D. 1532–1543, *etc. Edinb.* 1890, *etc.* 8°. 2075. d.

BALLESTREM (E.) *Countess.* Maria Stuart, Königin von Schottland. pp. 409. *Hamburg,* 1889. 4°. 10805. k. 6.

KERVYN DE LETTENHOVE (J. M. B. C.) *Baron.* Marie Stuart. 2 tom. *Paris,* 1889. 8°. 10806. f. 15.

PHILIPPSON (M.) Histoire du règne de Marie Stuart. *Paris,* 1891, *etc.* 8°. 9509. c.

SCARSE (C. E.) Letters relating to Mary, Queen of Scots. *Birimingham,* 1895. 4°. Pam. 35.

SKELTON (J.) Mary Stuart. pp 207. *Lond.* 1893. 4°. K.T.C. 9. b. 5.

STORM (G.) Maria Stuart. pp. 263. *München,* 1894. 8°. 10806. f. 22.

RUBLE (A. de) *Baron.* La première jeunesse de Marie Stuart. pp. 320. *Paris,* 1891. 8°. 10806. ee. 2.

FORST (H.) Maria Stuart und der Tod Darnleys. pp. 42. *Bonn,* 1894. 8°. 9004. k. 15. (6.)

DE PEYSTER (J. W.) Mary Stuart, Bothwell and the Casket letters. pp. 40. *N.Y.* 1890. 8°. 9004. m. 7. (12.)

MARY, *Queen of Scotland.* The genuine Letters of Mary, Queen of Scots, to James Earl of Bothwell. Edited by W. de Peyster. pp. 24. *N.Y.* 1891. 12°. Pam. 35.

SCOTT (*Hon* M. M. M.) The tragedy of Fotheringay. pp. 271. *Lond.* 1895. 8°. 10806. ee. 4.

W., A. Mary, Queen of Scots. Narrative and defence. pp. 161. *Aberdeen,* 1889. 8°. K.T.C. 33. a. 5.

SCOTLAND. *General Register House.* The Border Papers. Letters and papers relating to the affairs of the Borders of England and Scotland. *Edinb.* 1894, *etc.* 8°. 2075. e.

LINDSAY (J. L.) *Earl of Crawford.* Hand list of Proclamations. *Aberd.* 1883, *etc.* fol. 11901. i.

Ac. Edinburgh. *Scottish History Society.* LAW (T. G.) Documents illustrating Catholic policy in the Reign of James VI. 1596, 1598. pp. 70. *Edinb.* 1893. 8°. Ac. 8256/2.

SALOMON (F.) Frankreichs Beziehungen zu dem schottischen Aufstand, 1637–40. pp. 58. *Berl.* 1890. 8°. Pam. 28.

MORRIS (M.) Montrose. pp. 229. 1892. 8°. English Men of Action. 10803. bbb.

WISHART (G.) *Bp. of Edinburgh.* Memoirs of James Marquis of Montrose. pp. 551. *Lond.* 1893. 4°. 10816. g. 14.

SIMPSON (H. F. M.) Civil War papers, 1643–50. 1893. 8°. Ac. Edinburgh. *Scottish History Society.* Publications. Vol. 15. Ac. 8256.

SCOTLAND.—History—*continued.*

GARDINER (S. R.) Letters and papers illustrating relations between Charles II. and Scotland, 1650. 1894. 8°. Ac. Edinburgh. *Scottish History Society.* Publications. Vol. 17. Ac. 8256.

FIRTH (C. H.) Scotland and the Commonwealth. Letters and papers, 1651–53. pp. 383. 1895. 8°. Ac. Edinburgh. *Scottish History Society.* Publications. Vol. 18. Ac. 8256.

PATON (V. A. N.) Masterton Papers. 1660–1719. 1893. 8°. Ac. Edinburgh. *Scottish History Society.* Publications. Vol. 15. Ac. 8256.

MAITLAND (J.) *Duke of Lauderdale.* Thirty-four Letters written to J. Sharp, Archbishop of St. Andrews, by the Duke and Duchess of Lauderdale, 1660–77. Edited by J. Dowden. 1893. 8°. Ac. Edinburgh. *Scottish History Society.* Publications. Vol. 15. Ac. 8256.

ERSKINE (Hon. J.) Journal of J. Erskine, 1683–87. Edited by W. Macleod. pp. 259. 1893. 8°. Ac. Edinburgh. *Scottish History Society.* Publications. Vol. 14. Ac. 8256.

MELVILLE (A. P.) The Last Scots Parliament. pp. 66. *Perth,* 1894. 8°. 9008. bbb. 20. (5.)

Ac. Edinburgh. *Scottish History Society.* Papers about the Rebellions of 1715 and 1745. Edited by H. Paton. pp. 52. *Edinb.* 1893. 8°. Ac. 8256/4.

BUTLER (J.) *Duke of Ormonde.* Jacobite attempt of 1719. Letters of the Duke of Ormonde. Edited by W. K. Dickson. pp. 306. 1895. 8°. Ac. Edinburgh. *Scottish History Society.* Publications. Vol. 19. Ac. 2856.

SCOTLAND. List of persons concerned in the Rebellion of 1745. pp. 425. 1890. 8°. Ac. Edinburgh. *Scottish History Society.* Publications. Vol. 8. Ac. 8256.

FORBES (R.) *Bp. of Ross.* The Lyon in mourning. Speeches, *etc.,* relative to Prince Charles Edward Stuart. Edited by H. Paton. 1895, *etc.* 8°. Ac. Edinburgh. *Scottish History Society.* Publications. Vol. 20, *etc.* Ac. 8256.

MACQUOID (G. S.) Jacobite Songs and Ballads. pp. 360. 1887. 8°. Canterbury Poets. 11604. aa.

WILKIE (T.) Representation of Scotland. Parliamentary elections since 1832. pp. 388. *Paisley,* 1895. 8°. 8142. d. 5.

See also infra : Social Life : ENGLAND, *History.*

History, Ecclesiastical (*until* A.D. 1688).

BEALE (J.) The Story of the Scottish Church. pp. 33. *Edinb.* 1892. 8°. 4705. b. 46. (3.)

MUIR (P. M.) The Church of Scotland. History. pp. 96. 1890. 8°. CHARTERIS (A. H.) Guild Text-Books. 3605. aaa.

STEPHEN (W.) History of the Scottish Church. *Edinb.* 1894, *etc.* 8°. 4735. ee. 12.

SKENE (W. F.) Celtic Scotland. 3 vol. *Edinb.* 1886–90. 8°. 2071. d.

ADAMNAN, *Saint.* Adamnani Vita S. Columbæ. A new translation. pp. 140. *Lond.* 1895. 8°. 4829. cc. 5.

ARCHIBALD (J.) Historic episcopate in the Columban Church and in the Diocese of Moray. pp. 406. *Edinb.* 1893. 8°. 4735. cc. 15.

CHARLES (E.) Early Christian missions of Scotland. pp. 425. *Lond.* 1893. 8°. 4429. c. 1.

COOKE (E. A.) Saint Columba; his life and work. pp. 153. *Edinb.* 1893. 8°. 4829. b. 15.

DOWDEN (J.) *Bp. of Edinburgh.* The Celtic Church in Scotland. pp. 338. *Lond.* 1894. 8°. 4429. c. 37.

SCOTLAND.—History, etc.—*continued.*

JAMIESON (J.) Historical account of the ancient Culdees of Iona. pp. 257. *Glasg.* 1890. 8°. 4735. c. 30.

MACKINNON (J.) Culture in early Scotland. pp. 239. *Lond.* 1892. 8°. 9509. h. 9.

MUIR (T. S.) Ecclesiological notes on some of the Islands. pp. 315. *Edinb.* 1885. 8°. 7708. b. 48.

STEWART (R. M.) The Church of Scotland from the time of Queen Margaret to the Reformation. pp. 402. *Paisley,* 1892. 8°. 4735. bbb. 12.

Ac. Aberdeen. *New Spalding Club.* BOETHIUS (H.) Hectoris Boetii Murthlacensium et Aberdonensium episcoporum vitae. Translated by J. Moir. pp. 210. *Aberd.* 1894. 4°. Ac. 8245/12.

BROWN (P. H.) J. Knox. A biography. 2 vol. *Lond.* 1895. 8°. 4955. dd. 15.

SMITH (G. B.) J. Knox and the Scottish Reformation. pp. 160. *Lond.* 1895. 8°. 4955. b. 37.

ZIMMERMANN (A.) Die vermeintlichen Segnungen der schottischen Reformation. 1895. 8°. Frankfurter zeitgemässe Broschüren. N.F. Bd. 16. 12209. g.

RANKEN (A.) Sketches of the history of the Church of Scotland from the Reformation. pp. 38. *Edinb.* 1894. 8°. Pam. 29.

MAC CRIE (C. G.) Public worship of Presbyterian Scotland historically treated. pp. 465. *Edinb.* 1892. 8°. 3476. h. 23.

MILROY (A.) Scottish theologians and preachers during the first Episcopal Period, 1610–38. pp. 41. *Edinb.* 1891. 8°. 4705. b. 46. (2.)

Ac. Aberdeen. *New Spalding Club.* WODROW (R.) Selections from Wodrow's Biographical Collections. pp. 360. *Aberd.* 1890. 4°. Ac. 8245/5.

BROWN (J. W.) The Covenanters of the Merse. pp. 259. *Edinb.* 1893. 8°. 4735. bb. 31.

MACDONALD (M.) The Covenanters in Moray and Ross. pp. 226. *Inverness,* 1892. 8°. 4735. aaa. 39.

SPROTT (G. W.) Worship of the Church of Scotland during the Covenanting Period, 1638–61. pp. 50. *Edinb.* 1893. 8°. 4735. aaa. 41.

See also ARCHITECTURE.

For Ecclesiastical History after 1688, *see supra :* Church of : Episcopal Church : Free Church.

Law.

BARCLAY (H.) Justice's Digest of the Law of Scotland. pp. 707. *Edinb.* 1894. 8°. 6583. cc. 9.

ERSKINE (J.) Principles of the Law of Scotland. pp. 682. *Edinb.* 1895. 8°. 2018. c.

GOUDY (H.) Inaugural lecture on the fate of the Roman Law north and south of the Tweed. pp. 33. *Lond.* 1894. 8°. Pam. 32.

LITTLEJOHN (D. S.) Sketch of the Law of Scotland. pp. 89. *Edinb.* 1890. 8°. 6573. aaa. 1.

—— Popular sketch of the Law of Scotland. pp. 139. *Edinb.* 1893. 8°. 6583. cc. 3.

LORIMER (J.) Handbook of the Law of Scotland. pp. 633. *Edinb.* 1894. 8°. 2228. b. 18.

BALFOUR (D.) Handbook of Court of Session practice. pp. 268. *Edinb.* 1891. 8°. 6583. c. 4.

SMITH (R. E. M.) Law of expenses in the Supreme and Sheriff Courts. pp. 442. *Edinb.* 1892. 8°. 6583. g. 11.

LEES (J. M.) Sheriff Court styles. pp. 632. *Edinb.* 1892. 8°. 6583. c. 6.

SCOTLAND.—Law—continued.

WILSON (J. D.) Practice of the Sheriff Courts of Scotland in civil causes. pp. 975. Edinb. 1891. 8°.   6583. g. 8.

IRONS (J. C.) Manual of the law and practice of the Dean of Guild Court. pp. 667. Edinb. 1895. 8°.   6583. b. 27.

MILLAR (J. H.) Handbook of Prescription according to the Law of Scotland. pp. 232. Edinb. 1895. 8°.   6573. e. 1.

STEVENSON (J. H.) The Law of Scotland in relation to the presumption of life of absent Persons. pp. 159. Edinb. 1893. 8°. 6583. aa. 13.

WATT (J. C.) J. Inglis, Lord Justice-General of Scotland. pp. 507. Edinb. 1893. 8°.   10816. d. 21.

See also LAW, Criminal, Profession of : LAW REPORTS.

Literature. See ENGLISH LITERATURE : POETRY : SCOTCH LITERATURE.

Local Government. See LOCAL GOVERNMENT.

Politics.

EDINBURGH. Scottish Home Rule Association. Scottish Home Rule debate, 19th, 20th Feb. 1890. pp. 22. Edinb. 1890. 8°. 8139. bb. 51. (6.)

WADDIE (C.) The Government of Scotland bill. pp. 15. Edinb. 1892. 8°.   8138. aa. 20. (6.)

DAVIDSON (J. M.) Scotia Rediviva, Home rule for Scotland. pp. 113. 1893. 8°. Bellamy Series. No. 6.   12205. e.

SCOTLAND. National Union of Conservative Associations. The Campaign guide. pp. 636. Edinb. 1895. 8°.   8139. d. 3.

Reformed Presbyterian Church.

HUTCHINSON (M.) The Reformed Presbyterian Church, 1680–1876. pp. 450. Paisley, 1893. 8°.   4735. bbb. 13.

Social Life.

PATRICK (R. W. C.) Mediaeval Scotland. pp. 200. Glasg. 1892. 8°.   7709. bb. 61.

ADAMS (W. H. D.) Romantic stories of our Scottish towns. pp. 160. Glasg. 1894. 8°.   10369. bb. 52.

BARR (A. E.) Scottish Sketches. pp. 320. Edinb. 1890. 8°.   4408. k. 5.

BROWN (P. H.) Scotland before 1700, from contemporary documents. pp. 368. Edinb. 1893. 8°.   010370. f. 27.

HALIBURTON (H.) Furth in Field. Essays on the life of old Scotland. pp. 280. Lond. 1895. 8°.   10369. ccc. 33.

—— In Scottish Fields. pp. 249. Lond. 1890. 8°.   12357. l. 37.

HENDERSON (T. F.) Old-world Scotland. pp. 263. Lond. 1893. 8°.   012357. i. 37.

INGRAM (J.) Graphic Scotch anecdotes. pp. 168. Glasg. 1892. 8°.   012314. ee. 37.

MACINTOSH (J.) History of civilisation in Scotland. Paisley, 1892, etc. 8°.   2396. d. 9.

MAXWELL (D.) Bygone Scotland. pp. 313. Edinb. 1894. 8°.   010358. i. 12.

SALMOND (J. B.) Silvaceas, or the manners, customs, and superstitions of the fisher folks of Scotland. pp. 9. Lowestoft, 1892. 8°. Pam. 90.

VEITCH (J.) History and poetry of the Scottish border. 2 vol. Edinb. 1893. 8°.   2308. c. 20.

WALLACE (W.) Scotland Yesterday. Some old Friends. pp. 240. Lond. 1893. 8°.   012330. g. 50.

See also supra : Highlands. Infra : Topography.

Sport. See SPORT.

SCOTLAND—continued.

Taxation.

ARMOUR (S. B.) Valuation of property for Rating in Scotland. pp. 380. Edinb. 1892. 8°. 6583. c. 7.

Topography.

BADDELEY (M. J. B.) Scotland. Part III. The Lowlands. pp. 184. 1894. 8°. Thorough Guide series.   10347. aaa.

BAEDEKER (C.) Great Britain. Handbook. pp. 547. Leipsic, 1894. 8°.   2352. a.

BURNABY (E. H. V.) Ride from Land's End to John o' Groat's. pp. 146. Lond. 1893. 8°.   10351. e. 42.

CALEDONIAN RAILWAY. Tours in Scotland. pp. 144. Glasg. 1893. 8°.   10370. bbb. 37.

G. B. & I. Round the coast. Photographs. Lond. 1895, etc. obl. fol.   1558.

GROOME (F. H.) Ordnance Gazetteer of Scotland. Lond. 1894, etc. 8°.   2059. c.

HALL (M.) Notes on the geography of the British Isles. pp. 110. Dublin, 1895. 8°.   10348. b. 27.

KNIGHT (F. A.) By Moorland and sea. pp. 215. Lond. 1893. 8°.   012356. f. 3.

LAWSON (R.) Famous places of Scotland. pp. 123. Paisley, 1893. 8°.   10369. e. 11.

—— Sacred places of Scotland. pp. 124. Paisley, 1891. 8°.   10369. ccc. 13.

MACLEOD (D.) Border Abbeys and Abbotsford. pp. 124. Edinb. 1891. 8°.   10369. ccc. 12.

P.P. Glasgow. Elliots' Scottish Hotel and Steamship Directory. Glasg. 1891, etc. 4°.   P.P. 2511. s.

—— Frazer's Time Tables and Conveyance guide. Glasg. 1884, etc. 8°.   P.P. 2511. caa.

ROBERTSON (J.) Scottish Abbeys and Cathedrals. pp. 110. Aberdeen, 1891. 8°. 010370. f. 14.

ROBSON (J.) The illustrated Scottish Borders. Hawick, 1891, etc. 8°.   10369. ccc. 19.

SCOTLAND. Murray's Handbook for Scotland. pp. 475. Lond. 1894. 8°.   2364. b. 10.

SHENNAN (H.) Boundaries of Counties and Parishes in Scotland. pp. 397. Edinb. 1892. 8°.   010370. f. 23.

SPURRIER (W. J.) Cyclists Route Book. pp. 188. Lond. 1893. 8°.   10348. cc. 24.

SUMMER RESORTS. Summer Resorts. pp. 64. Lond. 1895. 8°.   10348. d. 22.

TODD (G. E.) Scotland picturesque and traditional. pp. 320. Lond. 1895. 8°.   10370. dd. 24.

ULLRICH (T.) Reise-Studien aus England und Schottland. pp. 417. Berl. 1893. 8°.   12249. ccc. 2.

BROWN (P. H.) Early travellers in Scotland. pp. 300. Edinb. 1891. 8°.   10370. dd. 17.

LOWTHER (C.) Our journall into Scotland anno domini 1629. pp. 56. Edinb. 1894. 8°.   010370. f. 32.

KIRK (T.) Tours in Scotland 1677 and 1681. pp. 60. Edinb. 1892. 8°.   010370. f. 26.

POCOCKE (R.) Bishop of Meath. Tours in Scotland 1747, 1750, 1760. pp. 375. 1887. 8°. Ac. Edinburgh. Scottish History Society. Publications. Vol. 1.   Ac. 8256.

WORDSWORTH (D.) Recollections of a tour in Scotland, A.D. 1803. pp. 316. Edinb. 1894. 8°.   10369. ccc. 27.

See also supra : Highlands : Social Life : ENGLAND, Topography : NAMES, Geographical : SPORT.

SCREWS. HASLUCK (P. N.) Screw Threads and methods of producing them. pp. 108. Lond. 1890. obl. 16°.   8767. a. 31.

SCREWS—*continued.*

SCREWS. Screws and Screw-making. pp. 208. *Colchester*, 1891. 8°.   07945. e. 25.

WHARTON (W. E.) Turner's handbook on Screw cutting. pp. 60. *Lond.* 1892. 8°. 7820. aa. 24.

SCULPTURE.

General.

DAVIDSON (T.) The evolution of Sculpture. 1891. 8°. Ac. Brooklyn. *New York Ethical Association.* Evolution Series. No. 13. 7006. bbb.

FARRAR (C. S.) Art topics in the history of Sculpture. pp. 196. *Chicago*, 1890. 4°.   7808. bbb. 21.

HENKE (W.) Vorträge über Plastik. pp. 248. *Rostock*, 1892. 8°.   7805. de. 19.

MEYER (A. G.) Studien zur Geschichte der plastischen Darstellungsformen. *Leipz.* 1894, *etc.* 4°.   7875. ee.

PARTRIDGE (W. O.) Technique of Sculpture. pp. 118. *Bost.* 1895. 8°.   7875. aa. 60.

SIMMONDS (T. C.) Art of Modelling in clay and wax. pp. 62. *Lond.* 1892. 8°.   7942. aa. 70.

Ancient (Oriental, Greek and Roman).

BOSTON. *Museum of Fine Arts.* Catalogue of Casts. pp. 369. *Bost.* 1891. 8°.   7807. aa. 3.

PARIS. *Louvre.* Catalogue de Sculpture égyptienne, par E. Revillout. pp. 68. *Paris*, 1890. 8°.   7702. de. 8.

CHAVANNES (É.) La Sculpture sur pierre en Chine au temps des deux dynasties Han. pp. 88. *Paris*, 1893. 4°.   7709. i. 23.

KĀVASJĪ DĪNSHĀH KIASH. Ancient Persian Sculptures. pp. 234. *Bombay*, 1889. 8°.   14146. h. 17.

Ac. Constantinople. *Musée Impérial.* Catalogue des Sculptures grecques, romaines et byzantines. pp. 83. *Constantinople*, 1893. 8°.   Pam. 24.

—— London. *British Museum.* Catalogue of Sculpture in the Department of Greek and Roman Antiquities. By A. H. Smith. *Lond.* 1892, *etc.* 8°.   7875. aaa.

AMELUNG (W.) Florentiner Antiken. pp. 41. *München*, 1893. 8°.   7875. dd. 12.

BARRACCO (G.) La Collection Barracco. [Illustrations of antique sculpture.] *Munich*, 1892, *etc.* fol.   1704. c.

BIE (O.) Kampfgruppe und Kämpfertypen in der Antike. pp. 160. *Berl.* 1891. 8°.   7706. e. 37.

BRUCKMANN (F.) Griechische und römische Porträts. *München*, 1891, *etc.* fol.   1703. c.

GEORGE (G.) De la Sculpture de figures dans la décoration des Monuments antiques. pp. 72. *Lyon*, 1890. 8°.   7875. de. 24.

LABAN (F.) Der Gemüthsausdruck des Antinous. pp. 92. *Berl.* 1891. 8°.   7875. b. 46.

MASSI (H. J.) Description of the Museums of ancient Sculpture in the Vatican. pp. 232. *Rome*, 1892. 8°.   7875. aa. 51.

PARIS (P.) Manual of ancient Sculpture. Edited by J. E. Harrison. pp. 369. *Lond.* 1890. 8°.   7875. aaa. 33.

ROME. *Museo Boncompagni.* Catalogue des Sculptures antiques du Musée Ludovisi. pp. 32. *Foligno*, 1891. 8°.   7808. bbb. 28. (5.)

Ac. London. *British Museum.* Catalogue of archaic Greek Sculpture. pp. 89. *Lond.* 1892. 8°.   7706. a. 46.

COLLIGNON (M.) Histoire de la Sculpture grecque. *Paris*, 1892, *etc.* 8°.   7875. e. 24.

CONZE (A. C. L.) Die attischen Grabreliefs. *Leipz.* 1890, *etc.* fol.   7701. k.

SCULPTURE.—Ancient, *etc.—continued.*

FURTWAENGLER (A.) Meisterwerke der griechischen Plastik. pp. 767. *Leipz.* 1893. 8°. & fol.   K.T.C. 18. a.

—— Masterpieces of Greek Sculpture. Edited by E. Sellers. 2 vol. *Lond.* 1895. 4°.   K.T.C. 26. b. 15.

JONES (H. S.) Passages from ancient writers, illustrative of the history of Greek Sculpture. pp. 231. *Lond.* 1895. 8°.   7875. a. 45.

OVERBECK (J. A.) Geschichte der griechischen Plastik. 2 Bde. *Leipz.* 1893, 94. 4°.   7875. de. 33.

SITTL (C.) Würzburger Antiken. pp. 20. *Würzburg*, 1890. fol.   1706. a. 21.

Ac. London. *British Museum.* Catalogue of the Sculptures of the Parthenon. pp. 125. *Lond.* 1892. 8°.   7875. a. 38.

KEKULÉ (R.) Ueber eine weibliche Gewandstatue aus der Werkstatt der Parthenongiebelfiguren. pp. 26. *Berl.* 1894. 4°.   7875. g. 7.

BALLHORN (D.) Der Antheil der Plastik an der Entstehung der griechischen Götterwelt und die Athene des Phidias. 1893. 8°. Sammlung wissenschaftlicher Vorträge. N.F. Serie 8. Hft. 174.   12249. 1.

STORY (W. W.) Excursions in Arts and letters. pp. 295. *Bost.* 1891. 8°.   012357. e. 38.

Ac. London. *British Museum.* Catalogue of Sculptures by the successors of Pheidias. pp. 159. *Lond.* 1892. 8°.   7875. a. 39.

RHOMAÏDES (C.) Olympia. The Hermes of Praxiteles. pp. 33. *Athens*, 1890. fol.   K.T.C. 4. a. 1.

HAYAUX DE TILLY (L.) Notice sur la Vénus de Milo. pp. 16. *Paris*, 1894. 8°.   Pam. 24.

RAVAISSON (F.) La Vénus de Milo. 1892. 4°. Ac. Paris. *Académie des Inscriptions.* Mémoires. Tom. 34.   2099. f.

SALOMAN (G.) Die Restauration der Venus von Milo. pp. 74. *Stockholm*, 1895. 4°. 7875. ee. 21.

LOEWY (E.) Lysipp und seine Stellung in der griechischen Plastik. pp. 35. 1891. 8°. Sammlung wissenschaftlicher Vorträge. Hft. 127. 1866, *etc.* 8°.   12249. m.

FREERICKS (H.) Der Apoll von Belvedere. pp. 78. *Paderborn*, 1894. 8°.   7875. bb. 33.

SAUER (B.) Der Torso von Belvedere. pp. 116. *Giessen*, 1894. 8°.   7875. cc. 4.

BERLIN. *K. Museen.* Beschreibung der antiken Skulpturen mit Ausschluss der pergamenischen Fundstücke. pp. 554. *Berl.* 1891. 8°.   7875. cc. 2.

MUELLER (G. A.) Die Reitergruppe auf den römisch-germanischen Giganten-Säulen. pp. 30. *Strassb.* 1894. 8°.   7875. bb. 32.

HETTNER (F.) Die römischen Steindenkmäler des Provinzialmuseums zu Trier. pp. 294. *Trier*, 1893. 8°.   7705. c. 38.

See also ART, *Ancient,* and under the subheading Antiquities of ASSYRIA, GREECE, EGYPT, ROME : TERRA-COTTA.

Mediaeval and Modern.

Ac. Nuremberg. *Germanisches Nationalmuseum.* Katalog der Originalskulpturen. pp. 92. 1890. 8°. P.P. *Munich.* Anzeiger für Kunde des deutschen Mittelalters. Jahrg. 1890.   P.P. 3542. aa.

PARIS. *Palais du Trocadéro.* Musée de Sculpture comparée. *Paris*, 1892, *etc.* 8°. 7875. de.

CLEMEN (P.) Merowingische und karolingische Plastik. pp. 146. 1892. 8°. Ac. Bonn. *Verein von Alterthumsfreunden.* Jahrbücher. Hft. 92.   Ac. 5153.

SCULPTURE.—Mediaeval and Modern
—*continued.*

GONSE (L.) L'Art gothique. pp. 476.
Paris, 1891. fol. 7805. g. 7.

JAMES (M. R.) The Sculptures in the Lady Chapel at Ely. pp. 68. *Lond.* 1895. 4°. 7875. e. 29.

VOEGE (W.) Die Anfänge des monumentalen Stiles im Mittelalter. pp. 376.
Strassb. 1894. 8°. 7875. aaa. 39.

BODE (W.) Die italienische Plastik. pp. 188. 1893. 8°. BERLIN. *K. Museen.* Handbücher. 7808. a. 41.

PAOLETTI (P.) L'Architettura e la Scultura del Rinascimento in Venezia. 2 pt.
Venezia, 1893. fol. 1733. d. 21.

SEMRAU (M.) Donatellos Kanzeln in S. Lorenzo. pp. 232. 1891. 8°. SCHMARSOW (A.) Italienische Forschungen, *etc.* Bd. 2. 7806. de. 19.

COURAJOD (L.) Histoire du département de la Sculpture moderne au Louvre. pp. 266.
Paris, 1894. 12°. 7875. a. 40.

HELBIG (J.) La Sculpture au pays de Liège. pp. 212. *Bruges*, 1890. 4°. 7806. c. 16.

DUCOURTIEUX (P.) La sculpture à Limoges au XVIᵉ siècle. 1895. 8°. Ac. Limoges. *Société archéologique.* Bulletin. Tom. 44. Ac. 5312.

TAEYE (L. de) and (E. L. de) Études sur les arts plastiques en Belgique. pp. 490.
Brux. 1891. 8°. 7875. bb. 31.

GONSE (L.) La Sculpture française depuis le XIVᵉ siècle. pp. 360. *Paris*, 1895. 4°.
K.T.C. 24. b. 9.

BERTAUX (E.) Les Artistes picards.
Paris, 1894, etc. 8°. 7858. aa.

CHILD (T.) Art and criticism. pp. 343.
Lond. 1892. 8°. 7806. dd. 8.

MARIONNEAU (C.) Travaux du statuaire Francin à Bordeaux, 1748–65. pp. 19.
Bordeaux, 1890. 8°. Pam. 24.

SMITH (J. T.) Nollekens and his times.
pp. 425. *Lond.* 1894. 8°. 10825. h. 5.

MÜLLER (S.) Thorvaldsen, hans Liv og hans Vaerker. *Kjøbenh.* 1889, etc. 4°. 7875. ee. 19.

RHYS (E.) Sir F. Leighton. pp. 74.
Lond. 1895. fol. K.T.C. 9. b. 14.

BAUZON (L.) La Sculpture décorative, statues, groupes, bas-reliefs. pp. 144. *Paris*, 1892. 8°.
7875. de. 32.

CARRIER-BELLEUSE (A.) Decorative Statuetten allegorische und mythologische Figuren.
Berl. 1891, etc. fol. 1759. c. 15.
See also ART.

SCYLLA AND CHARYBDIS. WASER (O.) Skylla und Charybdis in der Literatur der Griechen und Römer. pp. 147.
Zürich, 1894. 8°. 11312. r. 2.

SEA.

General.

CHILI. Anuario hidrográfico de la Marina de Chile. *Santiago*, 1892, etc. 8°. 10498. i.

FILOZ (N.) Les mers de France. pp. 293.
Paris, 1894. 12°. 7005. aaa. 23.

FRANCE. *Dépôt des Cartes et Plans de la Marine.* Service hydrographique. Catalogue des cartes, plans, vues de côtes, mémoires, *etc.* pp. 423.
Paris, 1892. 8°. 011901. g. 5.

GROSSMANN (J.) Die Bekämpfung der Sturzwellen durch Öl. pp. 140. *Wien*, 1892. 8°.
8805. bbb. 37.

KARSTENS (K.) Eine neue Berechnung der mittleren Tiefen der Oceane. pp. 32.
Kiel, 1894. 8°. 10498. c. 24.

LESAGE (P.) Influence du bord de la Mer sur la structure des feuilles. pp. 112.
Rennes, 1890. 8°. 07028. i. 28.

SEA.—General—*continued.*

MURRAY (J.) Report on Deep-sea deposits: specimens collected during the voyage of H.M.S. Challenger. pp. 525. 1891. 4°. Report on Scientific Results of the voyage of H.M.S. Challenger. 1825. aa.

NATTERER (C.) Zur Chemie des Meeres. pp. 31.
Wien, 1892. 8°. Pam. 13.

RÉVEILLÈRE (P. É. M.) La conquête de l'Océan. pp. 320. *Paris*, 1894. 8°. 8806. b. 49.

RICHTER (M. M.) Die Lehre von der Wellenberuhigung. pp. 99. *Berl.* 1894. 8°. Pam. 13.

ROBINSON (J. L.) Elements of marine Surveying. pp. 263. *Lond.* 1894. 8°. 10498. aa. 22.

SHALER (N. S.) Sea and Land : features of coasts and oceans with reference to the life of man.
pp. 252. *Lond.* 1895. 8°. 7001. ee. 8.

THOULET (J.) Guide d'Océanographie. pp. 224. 1894. 8°. Encyclopédie des aide-mémoire.
8709. g.

WEA (G. v.) Periodische Meeresanschwellungen an den Polen und am Aequator. pp. 59.
Wien, 1891. 8°. 8755. k. 58.

WHYMPER (F.) The Sea. 4 vol.
Lond. 1887–90. 8°. 10498. cc. 26.

COWAN (F.) Dictionary of proverbs relating to the Sea. pp. 144. *Greensburgh*, 1894. 8°.
12304. g. 34.

PAVOLINI (P. E.) I Nomi e gli epiteti Omerici del mare. pp. 37. *Pisa*, 1890. 8°. Pam. 14.

- *See also* ANTARTIC OCEAN : ATLANTIC OCEAN : ARCTIC REGIONS : MEDITERRANEAN SEA.

Fauna. *See* FISH : ZOOLOGY.

Flora. *See* ALGAE : BOTANY.

Tides.

BALL (*Sir* R. S.) Time and Tide. pp. 192. 1895. 8°. The Romance of Science Series.
4421. de.

HATT (P.) Des Marées. pp. 222. 1894. 8°. Encyclopédie des aide-mémoire. 8709. g.

WIJKANDER (A.) Observations de Marées faites à Polhem au Spitzberg. pp. 11. 1889. 8°. Ac. Stockholm. *K. Svenska Vetenskaps Academi.* Bihang till handlingar. Bd. 15. Ac. 1070/7.

SEAL. *See* BEHRING SEA.

SEALS. Ac. Bruges. *Société d'Émulation.* Les Sceaux de la prévôté et des prévôts de Saint-Martin à Ypres. pp. 8. *Bruges*, 1884. 4°.
Ac. 5517/8.

—— London. *British Museum.* Guide to the Manuscripts and Seals exhibited. pp. 140.
Lond. 1895. 8°. 11903. b. 42.

—— Paris. *Bibliothèque Nationale.* Inventaire des Sceaux de la Collection Clairambault. 2 tom. 1885, 86. 8°. FRANCE. Collection des documents inédits. Sér. 3. 9210. g.

—— Troyes. *Société Académique.* LE CLERT (L.) Catalogue de Sigillographie du Musée de Troyes. pp. 114. *Troyes*, 1887. 8°. Ac. 261/2.

—— Zurich. *Stiftung von Schnyder von Wartensee.* Sigelabbildungen zum Urkundenbuch der Stadt Zürich. *Zürich*, 1891, etc. 8°. 523.

BERTRAND DE BROUSSILLON (A.) Sigillographie des seigneurs de Craon. 1890, etc. 8°. MAYENNE. *Commission historique.* Procès-verbaux. Sér. 2. Tom. 2. 010171. m. 18.

—— Sigillographie des seigneurs de Laval.
pp. 152. 1888. 8°. MAYENNE. *Commission historique.* Procès-verbaux. Tom. v.
010171. m. 18.

BOSREDON (P. de) Notes pour servir à la Sigillographie de la Haute-Vienne. pp. 268.
Limoges, 1892. 8°. 7757. e. 28.

SEALS—*continued.*

BOSREDON (P. de) Répertoire des Sceaux des rois et reines de France. pp. 240. *Périgueux, 1893.* 4°.   7757. e. 35.

DAUCHEZ (H.) Essai de Sigillographie. Saint Luc, patron des facultés de médecine. pp. 35. *Paris, 1891.* 8°.   Pam. 44.

DONY (P.) Monographie des Sceaux de Verdun. 2 pt. *Verdun, 1880-90.* 4°.   7757. c. 15.

DOUËT D'ARCQ (L. C.) Répertoire des Sceaux des villes françaises. pp. 49. *Paris, 1891.* 8°.   7756. de. 25.

STANWOOD (J. R.) Province Seal of New Hampshire, 1692-94. pp. 28. *Bost. 1889.* 8°.   9916. bb. 17. (3.)

VALLIER (G.) Sigillographie de l'Ordre des Chartreux. pp. 508. *Montreuil, 1891.* 8°.   7757. e. 21.

WURMANN (F.) Sammlung aller Amts Siegel und Wappen der Magistrate der deutschen Städte. *Kaufbeuren, 1894, etc.* 4°.   9906. i.

SEAMANSHIP. *See* NAVAL SCIENCE.

SEASCALE. MOSSOP (M.) Seascale as a health and pleasure Rest. pp. 30. *Cockermouth, 1895.* 8°.   Pam. 90.

SEA SERPENT. OUDEMANS (A. C.) The great Sea-Serpent. pp. 592. *Leiden, 1892.* 8°.   7290. f. 25.

SEA-SICKNESS. AILHAUD-CASTELET (E. d') Étude du Mal de mer. pp. 132. *Paris, 1895.* 8°.   7620. df. 38.

DUTTON (T.) Sea-sickness. pp. 125. *Lond. 1892.* 8°.   7620. de. 20.

ROSENBACH (O.) Studien über die Seekrankheit. pp. 56. *Berl. 1891.* 8°.   07305. h. 8. (9.)

SEASONS, Ecclesiastical. BULKELEY-OWEN (*Hon.* F. M. C.) Readings for mothers' unions, upon the Seasons. pp. 120. *Lond. 1893.* 8°.   4429. b. 41.

D., A. Thoughts for holy Seasons. pp. 47. *Lond. 1892.* 16°.   3437. a. 56.

HELPS. Helps for Holy Days. pp. 87. *Lond. 1895.* 8°.   3225. df. 32.

MACPHERSON (A. C.) Teachings from the Church's year. pp. 178. *Lond. 1894.* 8°.   3476. h. 8.

STORY. The Story of the year. pp. 55. *Lond. 1895.* 8°.   4371. aaaa. 50.

TUCKER (A. B.) Simple thoughts for the Seasons. pp. 380. *Lond. 1891.* 8°. 3457. d. 31.

TOWNSEND (J. H.) Spiral Stairs, or the heavenward course of the Seasons. pp. 262. *Lond. 1895.* 8°.   4463. gg. 15.

WATSON (J.) Church teaching for the Church's year. pp. 197. *Hull, 1895.* 8°.   3554. bb. 2. *See also* ADVENT : CHRISTMAS : EASTER : LENT.

SEAWEED. *See* ALGAE.

SEBASTOPOL, Siege of. *See* CRIMEAN WAR.

SEBENICO. FOSCO (A. G.) *Bishop of Sebenico.* La cattedrale di Sebenico. pp. 96. *Sebenico, 1893.* 8°.   7814. g. 2.

SECLIN. SECLIN. Inventaire des archives antérieures à 1790. pp. 74. *1888.* 4°. Collection des inventaires-sommaires. *1814-15.* b., *etc.*

—— *Hôpital.* Inventaire des archives antérieures à 1790. pp. 62. *1892.* 4°. Collection des inventaires-sommaires. *1814.* b., *etc.*

SEDAN. LEROY (S.) Essai sur les institutions de la Principauté de Sedan. pp. 120. *Sedan, 1890.* 8°.   5424. dd. 8. For the Battle of Sedan, *see* GERMAN FRENCH WAR.

SEDBERGH. THOMPSON (W.) Sedbergh, Garsdale and Dent. pp. 280. *Leeds, 1892.* 8°.   10360. k. 12.

SEDBERGH SCHOOL. School Register, 1546-1895. pp. 446. *Leeds, 1895.* 8°.   8364. ee. 40.

SÉES. DUMAINE (L. V.) La Cathédrale de Sées. pp. 75. *Sées, 1892.* 8°.   4629. c. 13.

SEFTON. CAROË (W. D.) and GORDON (E. J. A.) Sefton. Descriptive and historical account. pp. 520. *Lond. 1893.* 8°. 10352. dd. 5.

SEILLON. BULLIAT (A. M.) Chartreuse de Seillon. pp. 350. *Montreuil, 1890.* 8°.   4629. c. 7.

SEINE ET OISE, Department. MINZES (B.) Die Nationalgüterveräusserung während der Revolution, mit Berücksichtigung des Departement Seine und Oise. pp. 167. *1892.* 4°. ELSTER (L.) Staatswissenschaftliche Studien. Bd. 4.   8207. h. *See also* VEXIN.

SEINE INFÉRIEURE, Department. ROBILLARD DE BEAUREPAIRE (C. M. de) Recueil de notes concernant le département de la Seine-Inférieure. pp. 360. *Rouen, 1892.* 8°.   010171. g. 20.

SELANGOR. SELANGOR. List of names of places in Selangor. pp. 9. *Kuala Lumpur, 1891.* 8°.   Pam. 88.

SELBORNE. Ac. Hampshire. *Record Society.* Calendar of Documents relating to Selborne. pp. 177. *Lond. 1891.* 8°.   Ac. 8123/4.

SELBY. FOWLER (J. T.) Coucher Book of Selby. 2 vol. 1891-93. 8°. Ac. Huddersfield. *Yorkshire Archæological Association.* Record Series. Vol. 10, 13.   Ac. 5652/8.

SEMINARIES, Ecclesiastical. *See* EDUCATION, *Ecclesiastical.*

SEMITIC LANGUAGES. BARTH (J.) Etymologische Studien zum Semitischen. pp. 76. *Leipz. 1893.* 8°.   012904. h. 13.

—— Die Nominalbildung in den semitischen Sprachen. pp. 495. *Leipz. 1894.* 8°.   12904. cc. 27.

CUST (R. N.) Essays on the languages of the Bible. pp. 89. *Lond. 1890.* 8°.   3128. h. 12.

HOMMEL (F.) Aufsätze arabistisch-semitologischen Inhalts. *München, 1892, etc.* 8°.   012904. h.

HUIZINGA (A. H.) Analogy in the Semitic Languages. pp. 63. *Baltimore, 1891.* 8°.   12901. d. 34. (7.)

LEWY (H.) Die semitischen Fremdwörter im Griechischen. pp. 266. *Berl. 1895.* 8°.   12924. f. 41.

MUSS-ARNOLT (W.) On Semitic words in Greek and Latin. 1892. 8°. Ac. U.S. *American Philological Association.* Transactions. Vol. 23.   Ac. 9965.

WRIGHT (W.) Lectures on the comparative grammar of the Semitic languages. pp. 288. *Camb. 1890.* 8°.   2268. d. 18. *See also* ARABIC, ARAMAIC, ASSYRIAN, HEBREW and SYRIAC LANGUAGES : LANGUAGE.

SEMITIC RACES. CLERMONT-GANNEAU (C.) Les Antiquités sémitiques. pp. 62. *Paris, 1890.* 12°.   7702. de. 11. (8.)

P.P. *Paris.* Revue Sémitique d'épigraphie et d'histoire. *Paris, 1893, etc.* 8°.   P.P. 37. cf.

SAYCE (A. H.) Races of the Old Testament. pp. 180. 1891. 8°. By-Paths of Bible Knowledge.   2002. a.

SMITH (W. R.) Lectures on the religion of the Semites. pp. 507. *Lond. 1894.* 8°. 2212. e. 3.

SEMITIC RACES—*continued.*

VIBERT (C. T.) La Race sémitique. pp. 294. *Paris*, 1883. 12°.   10007. b. 28.
See also ARABS : ASSYRIA : HISTORY, *Ancient* : JEWS : PHOENICIA.

SEMRIACH. GASPARITZ (A.) Semriach mit Schöckel und Lurloch dargestellt. pp. 139. *Graz*, 1894. 8°.   10215. bbb. 13.

SENEGAL. CLAVERIE (P.) Notes de voyages. pp. 278. *Paris*, 1894. 12°.   10026. cc. 10.
DECRESSAC-VILLAGRAND (M.) Souvenirs du Sénégal. pp. 292. *Guéret*, 1890. 8°.   010096. e. 34.
DOMERGUE (A.) Sénégal et Soudan. pp. 91. *Paris*, 1895. 8°.   010095. g. 2.
GAFFAREL (P.) Le Sénégal et le Soudan français. pp. 237. *Paris*, 1892. 8°. 010096. m. 16.
VIGNÉ (P.) Au pays des fétiches. pp. 287. *Paris*, 1890. 12°.   10095. de. 15.
See also AFRICA, *Colonisation, and West*: FRANCE, *Colonies.*

SENLIS. MÜLLER (E.) Guide dans les rues de Senlis. pp. 139. *Senlis*, 1887. 8°. 10171. d. 9.
—— Monographie des rues de Senlis. pp. 743. *Senlis*, 1880–84. 8°.   10169. dd. 15.

SENS. JULLIOT (G.) Épitaphes des Archevêques de Sens. pp. 114. *Sens*, 1894. 8°.   4864. e. 28.
QUESVERS (P. L. M.) and STEIN (H.) Pouillé de l'ancien Diocèse de Sens. pp. 407. *Paris*, 1894. 4°.   4630. f. 9.

SEPTIC DISEASES. BLAKE (E. T.) Septic Intoxication. pp. 66. *Lond.* 1892. 8°. 7630. b. 21.
DENNIG (A.) Über septische Erkrankungen. pp. 213. *Leipz.* 1891. 8°.   7560. i. 8.
EPPINGER (H.) Die Hadernkrankheit. pp. 119. *Jena*, 1894. 8°.   7560. d. 8.
ÉTIENNE (G.) Les Pyosepticémies médicales. pp. 389. *Paris*, 1893. 8°.   07482. k. 2.

SERFDOM. *See* SLAVERY.

SERIGNY. CARRÉ DE BUSSEROLLE (J. X.) Une Coutume bizarre à Sérigny. pp. 12. *Montsoreau*, 1890. 18°.   Pam. 3.

SERVANTS, Domestic.
See HOUSEHOLD MANAGEMENT.

SERVIA. A., H. Die türkische Wehrmacht und die Armeen der Balkanstaaten. pp. 207. *Wien*, 1892. 8°.   8823. ddd. 23.
G. B. & I. *War Office.* Handbook of the Armies of the Minor Balkan States. pp. 61. *Lond.* 1891. 8°.   8823. g. 20.
APPLETON (L.) Servia, Austria, Turkey and Russia, 1356–1889. pp. 28. *Lond.* 1891. 8°.   Pam. 67.
BAMBERG (F.) Geschichte der orientalischen Angelegenheit. pp. 622. 1888. 8°. ONCKEN (W.) Allgemeine Geschichte. Hauptabth. IV. Th. 5.   2068. (30.)
COQUELLE (P.) Le Royaume de Serbie. pp. 294. *Paris*, 1894. 8°.   9136. bb. 18.
CUNIBERTI (F.) La Serbia e la dinastia degli Obrènovitch, 1804–93. pp. 113. *Torino*, 1893. 8°.   9136. ee. 3.
OUTIS. Le roi Stanko [King Milan] et la reine Xenia [Queen Natalie]. pp. 334. *Paris*, 1891. 12°.   8028. aaa. 10.
BUETTNER (H.) Aus dem Tagebuch der Königin Natalie. pp. 96. *Berl.* 1891. 8°. 10790. c. 35.
CHOLET (A. P. de) *Count.* Étude sur la Guerre bulgaro-serbe. pp. 198. *Paris*, 1891. 8°.   9077. f. 2.
REGENSPURSKY (C.) Die Kämpfe bei Slivnica, Nov. 1885. pp. 179. *Wien*, 1895. 8°. 9136. g. 8.

SERVIA—*continued.*

TUMA (A.) Serbien. pp. 307. *Hannover*, 1894. 8°.   10125. de. 26.
MIRKOVIĆ (T.) Étude sur les Eaux minérales en Serbie. pp. 155. *Paris*, 1892. 8°. 7462. g. 6.
STROELL (M.) Die Handelspolitik der Balkanstaaten. pp. 65. 1892. 8°. Ac. Leipsic. *Verein für Socialpolitik.* Schriften. Bd. 3.   Ac. 2322.
See also BALKAN MOUNTAINS AND PENINSULA.

SERVITES. SERVITES, *Order of.* The Servite Manual. pp. 488. *Lond.* 1892. 8°.   4071. aa. 7.
SPOERR (B. M.) Lebens-Bilder aus dem Serviten-Orden. *Innsbruck*, 1892, *etc.* 8°.   4828. dd. 6.
See also RELIGIOUS ORDERS.

SESENHEIM. MUELLER (G. A.) Sesenheim, wie es ist. pp. 123. *Bühl*, 1894. 8°.   010707. ff. 3.
—— Führer durch Sesenheim und Umgebung. pp. 31. *Bühl*, 1894. 12°.   Pam. 91.

SETTLED LAND ACTS.
See LAND TENURES.

SEVEN WEEKS' WAR.
See AUSTRIA : HANOVER : PRUSSIA.

SEVEN YEARS' WAR.
See EUROPE : PRUSSIA.

SEVERN TUNNEL. WALKER (T. A.) The Severn Tunnel. pp. 195. *Lond.* 1891. 8°.   8767. dd. 14.

SEVILLE. CANDAU Y PIZARRO (F.) Prehistoria de la provincia de Sevilla. pp. 224. *Sevilla*, 1894. 8°.   7707. cc. 37.
CONTRERAS (R.) Estudio de los monumentos árabes de Sevilla y Córdova. pp. 378. *Madrid*, 1885. 8°.   7706. f. 35.
GESTOSO Y PEREZ (J.) Sevilla monumental y artística. *Sevilla*, 1889, *etc.* 8°.   10160. dd.
MAS Y PRAT (B.) La Tierra de María Santísima. pp. 499. *Barcelona*, 1891. 4°. 10160. i. 3.

SEWAGE. *See* DRAINAGE.

SEX. BLACKWELL (E.) The human element in Sex. pp. 76. *Lond.* 1894. 8°. 8415. df. 27.
CHEVALIER (J.) L'inversion sexuelle. pp. 520. *Lyon*, 1893. 8°.   7641. a. 37.
DAILLIEZ (G.) Les Sujets de Sexe douteux. pp. 112. *Lille*, 1892. 8°.   7641. i. 20.
ELLIS (H. H.) Man and Woman. pp. 409. 1894. 8°. Contemporary Science Series.   8709. i.
GEDDES (P.) and THOMSON (J. A.) Evolution of Sex. 1890. 8°. Contemporary Science Series.   8709. i.
HARTMANN (C. R. E. v.) The Sexes compared and other essays. pp. 164. *Lond.* 1895. 8°.   8415. df. 31.
KRAFFT-EBING (R. v.) Neue Forschungen auf dem Gebiet der Psychopathia sexualis. pp. 131. *Stuttgart*, 1891. 8°.   7660. cc. 25.
LAURENT (É.) L'Amour morbide. pp. 286. *Paris*, 1891. 12°.   8416. e. 27.
MOLL (A.) Die conträre Sexualempfindung. pp. 296. *Berl.* 1891. 8°.   7405. e. 1.
PASCAL ( ) Das sexuelle Problem in der modernen Litteratur. pp. 48. *Berl.* 1890. 8°.   011824. h. 30. (12.)
PENTA (P.) I Pervertimenti sessuali nell' uomo. pp. 307. *Napoli*, 1893. 8°.   7660. c. 7.
RYDER (J. A.) Origin of Sex through cumulative integration. 1890. 8°. Ac. Philadelphia. *American Philosophical Society.* Proceedings. Vol. 28. No. 132.   Ac. 1830.

SEX—*continued.*

SCHROEDER (P.) Theorien über die willkürliche Hervorbringung des Geschlechts beim Menschen. pp. 47. *Berl.* 1890. 8°.   Pam. 39.

TRALL (R. T.) Sexual Physiology and hygiene. pp. 266. *Glasg.* 1891. 8°.   7641. ee. 8.

VENTURI (S.) Le Degenerazioni psico-sessuali. pp. 519. *Torino*, 1892. 8°.   7660. dd. 6.
See also LOVE.

SHAFTESBURY. MAYO (C. H.) Municipal records of Shaftesbury. pp. 87. *Sherborne*, 1889. 8°.   010358. f. 37.

SHAKERS. AVERY (G. B.) Sketches of Shakers and Shakerism. pp. 50. *Albany*, 1884. 8°.   4182. aaa. 39.

SHANGHAI. MACFARLANE (W.) Sketches in the foreign settlements and native city. *Shanghai*, 1881. 4°.   10058. l. 11.

SHANGHAI. 1843—Shanghai—1893. pp. 96. *Shanghai*, 1893. 4°.   10057. e. 6.

—— Manual of Customs' practice at Shanghai. pp. 228. *Shanghai*, 1894. 8°.   8245. e. 71.

SHANS AND SHAN LANGUAGE.
See LAOS.

SHAVINGTON. HARROD (H. D.) History of Shavington. pp. 3. 139. *Shrewsbury*, 1891. fol.   10368. k. 14.

—— Muniments of Shavington. pp. 216. *Shrewsbury*, 1891. fol.   10368. k. 13.

SHAWNEES. *See* INDIANS.

SHEEP. ALGERIA. Des conditions d'existence des troupeaux sur les hauts-plateaux d'Algérie. pp. 533. *Alger*, 1893. fol.   7294. h. 6.

ARMATAGE (G.) The Sheep: its varieties and management. pp. 220. *Lond.* 1893. 8°.   7291. aa. 18.

CARMAN (E. A.) Report on the history and condition of the Sheep Industry of the U.S. 1892. 8°. U.S. *Animal Industry, Bureau of.* Publications.   7053. e. 6.

COOPER (W.) AND NEPHEWS. The world's Sheep farming for fifty years, 1843–93. pp. 104. *Berkhamsted*, 1893. 8°.   7291. aaa. 33.

COTSWOLD SHEEP SOCIETY. The Cotswold Flock book. *Cirencester*, 1892, *etc.* 8°.   07293. i.

FISON (E. H.) Flocks and Fleeces. pp. 94. *Lond.* 1894. 8°.   07293. i. 28.

GIBSON (H.) History and present state of the sheep-breeding industry in the Argentine Republic. pp. 297. *Buenos A.* 1893. 8°. 07293. l. 2.

GRINNELL (J. S.) History of Sheep husbandry in Massachusetts. pp. 49. *Bost.* 1892. 8°.   7204. c. 16. (8.)

HAMPSHIRE. *Sheep Breeders' Association.* Hampshire Downs Flock Book. *Salisbury*, 1890, *etc.* 8°.   07293. k.

HEYNE (J.) Die Entwickelung der Schafzucht in Sachsen. pp. 72. *Dresd.* 1890. 8°. Pam. 42.

LEWIS (W. D.) Our Sheep and the tariff. pp. 158. 1890. 8°. Ac. Philadelphia. *University.* Publications. Political Economy Series.   Ac. 2692. p.

NEW SOUTH WALES. *Commissioners for the Exposition, Chicago.* Sheep and wool in New South Wales. pp. 23. *Sydney*, 1893. 8°.   7958. g. 31.

NEW ZEALAND. On the best method of dipping Sheep. pp. 12. *Melbourne*, 1884. 8°.   7293. i. 12. (3.)

OHLSEN (C. T. A.) Concorso internazionale di animali riproduttori della specie bovina. Relazione, 1889. 4°. Ac. Naples. *R Istituto d'Incorragiamento.* Atti. Ser. 4. Vol. 3. Ac. 2815.

SHEEP—*continued.*

SHEPHERDS. The Shepherds' guide. pp. 70. *Cockermouth*, 1892. 8°.   07293. i. 9.

SUFFOLK. *Sheep Society.* Flock-book of Suffolk Sheep. *Bury St Edmunds*, 1887, *etc.* 8°.   07293. k.

WENSLEYDALE. *Long Wool Sheep Breeders' Association.* Flock-book of Wensleydale Long Wool Sheep. *Bedale*, 1890, *etc.* 8°. 07293. g.

WOOD (D.) Sheep-dipping. pp. 68. *Lond.* 1892. 8°.   7294. bbb. 14.

WRIGHTSON (J.) Sheep. Breeds and management. pp. 235. 1893. 8°. SINCLAIR (J.) Live Stock handbooks. No. 1.   7291. c.
See also ANIMALS, *Domestic:* DOG. For diseases of Sheep, *see* VETERINARY MEDICINE: WOOL.

SHEERNESS. COPLAND (J.) The Taking of Sheerness by the Dutch. pp. 40. *Sheerness*, 1895. 16°.   9512. de. 1.

SHEFFIELD. ADDY (S. O.) The Hall of Waltheof; or, the early Condition of Hallamshire. pp. 295. *Lond.* 1893. 4°.   7709. g. 33.

LEADER (J. D.) Old Sheffield jottings. pp. 24. *Sheffield*, 1891. 12°.   10352. e. 8. (5.)

SMITH (W.) Characteristics of some inhabitants of Sheffield, at the close of the 18th century. pp. 22. *Sheffield*, 1889. 8°.   10803. bbb. 6.

SNELL (S.) History of the medical societies of Sheffield, *etc.* pp. 74. *Sheffield*, 1890. 8°.   7679. df. 38.

HESTER (G.) N. Simmons, bookseller and publisher, of Sheffield. pp. 50. *Lond.* 1893. 8°.   Pam. 7.

SHERIFFS. MATHER (P. E.) Compendium of Sheriff Law. pp. 578. *Lond.* 1894. 8°.   6405. f. 11.

DIXON (G. Y.) and GILLILAND (W. L.) Law relating to Sheriffs in Ireland. pp. 558. *Dubl.* 1888. 8°.   6503. bb. 5.

SHERWOOD FOREST. SHERWOOD FOREST. Guide to Sherwood Forest. pp. 175. *Lond.* 1893. 8°.   10347. aaa. 36.
See also NOTTINGHAMSHIRE.

SHETLAND. *See* ORKNEY.

SHEVAROY. WILSON (F. H.) The Shevaroys. pp. 96. *Madras*, 1888. 8°. 10056. aaa. 24.

SHINTOISM. *See* JAPAN, *Religions.*

SHIPBUILDING. BRASSEY (T.) *Baron Brassey.* Future policy of War-ship Building. pp. 33. *Lond.* 1891. 8°.   Pam. 43.

CRONEAU (A.) Construction pratique des navires de guerre. *Paris*, 1894, *etc.* 8°. 8808. aa. 4.

—— Atlas. *Paris*, 1894. 4°.   8808. d. 2.

—— Construction du navire. pp. 206. 1894. 8°. Encyclopédie des aide-mémoire.   8709. g.

DREDGE (J.) Records of the Transportation Exhibits at the Columbian Exposition. pp. 779. 1894. 4°. Engineering Series.   8755. m.

FITGER (E.) Schiffsbau und Seeschifffahrt in den letzten Jahren. pp. 34. 1892. 8°. Volkswirthschaftliche Zeitfragen. Hft. 105. 8207. i.

GUYOU (E.) Théorie du Navire. pp. 426. *Paris*, 1894. 8°.   8807. bbb. 42.

LEDIEU (A.) and CADIAT (E) Le nouveau Matériel naval. 2 tom. *Paris*, 1889, 90. 8°.   8807. d. 28.

LLOYDS. Report to the Committee of Lloyd's concerning the dismasting of large iron Sailing Ships. pp. 185. *Lond.* 1886. 8°. 8807. e. 33.

LONDON. *Thames Ironworks.* Exhibit of models of Ships. pp. 32. 1891. 8°.   Pam. 43.

SHIPBUILDING—continued.

MACKROW (C.) Naval Architect's and Ship-Builder's pocket-book. pp. 700.
Lond. 1892. 8°.   8806. b. 42.

P.P. *London.* Shipbuilding of the whole world.
Lond. 1895, *etc.* 8°.   P.P. 2491. ci.

POLLARD (J.) and DUDEBOUT (A.) Architecture Navale. *Paris,* 1890, *etc.* 8°.   8807. d.

RAMAGE (A. G.) On the resistance of Ships and a method of estimating it. pp. 16.
Leith, 1895. 8°.   8806. ccc. 18.

SCHMIDT (A.) Die Stabilität von Schiffen.
pp. 313. *Berl.* 1892. 8°.   8806. dd. 5.

TAYLOR (D. W.) On a method for calculating the stability of Ships. 1891. 8°. Ac. Annapolis. *U.S. Naval Institute.* Papers. Vol. 17.
                                          Ac. 4398.

WATSON (T. H.) Naval Architect's data-book.
Newcastle, 1892. 8°.   8807. c. 47.

—— S. Kensington Questions in Honours, Naval Architecture. pp. 32. *Newcastle,* 1893. 8°.
                                          Pam. 43.

WHITE (W. H.) Manual of Naval Architecture.
pp. 729. *Lond.* 1894. 8°.   2249. g. 13.

For the construction of Steam Engines and Machinery *see* BOILERS: NAVAL SCIENCE, *Steamships, etc.*

SHIPLAKE. CLIMENSON (E. J.) History of Shiplake. pp. 494. *Lond.* 1894. 8°.
                                       10358. k. 13.

SHIPPEN. LYMAN (B. S.) Shippen and Wetherill Tract. pp. 36. *Phila.* 1893. 8°.
                                          Pam. 27.

SHIPPING. *See* NAVAL SCIENCE.

SHIPWRECKS. DIBDIN (J. C.) and AYLING (J.) Book of the Lifeboat. pp. 270.
Edinb. 1894. 4°.   8806. ccc. 17.

FISHER (W. P.) Lifeboat Saturday. pp. 26.
Manch. 1893. fol.   8808. i. 2.

G. B. & I. *Board of Trade.* Instructions relating to the Rocket Apparatus for saving life from shipwreck. pp. 73. *Lond.* 1893. 8°.
                                       8807. ee. 36.

—— Tables relating to Life salvage on the coasts of the United Kingdom, 1889-90.
Lond. 1890. 8°.   Pam. 43.

HOARE (E. N.) Perils of the Deep. Account of remarkable shipwrecks. pp. 379.
Lond. 1885. 8°.   4421. aaa. 12.

KENNEDY (W. R.) Treatise on the law of civil Salvage. pp. 255. *Lond.* 1891. 8°. 6835. h. 4.

LOCKHART (W. C.) Records of Steamers lost. 1886-89. pp. 61. *Lond.* 1890. fol. 8808. aa. 2.

—— Record of Steamers and Ships lost, &c., 1890. pp. 56. *Lond.* 1891. obl. 8°. 8808. aa. 3.

LUSSICH (A. D.) Naufragios célebres en el Cabo Polonio, *etc.* pp. 262. *Montevideo,* 1893. 8°.
                                       8806. dd. 27.

—— Celebrated Shipwrecks at Cape Polonio, *etc.* pp. 462. *Monte Video,* 1894. 8°.
                                       8806. ddd. 10.

MUNDELL (F.) Stories of the Lifeboat. pp. 160.
Lond. 1895. 8°.   4400. dd. 12.

TREANOR (T. S.) Heroes of the Goodwin Sands.
pp. 255. *Lond.* 1892. 8°.   4429. ee. 35.

BOKHARA, *Steamship.* The "Bokhara" disaster.
pp. 25. *Hongkong,* 1892. 8°.   Pam. 43.

M., C. Narrative of the Rescue of the passengers of the S.S. Danmark by the S.S. Missouri. pp. 69. *Lond.* 1891. 8°. 10498. a. 22.

SHIRONGA LANGUAGE.
See AFRICAN LANGUAGES.

SHOOTING. *See* GUNNERY: SPORT.

SHORTHAND.
Bibliography.

FAULMANN (C.) Geschichte und Litteratur der Stenographie. pp. 173. *Wien,* 1895. 8°.
                                       12991. h. 34.

MANCHESTER. *Public Libraries.* The Shorthand Collection. pp. 44. *Manch.* 1891. 8°.
                                       011901. g. 16.

WALFORD (C.) Statistical review of the literature of Shorthand. pp. 24. *Lond.* 1885. 8°.
                                       12991. b. 50. (7.)

ROCKWELL (J. E.) The teaching and literature of Shorthand. 1885. 8° U.S. *Bureau of Education.* Circular. No. 2.   8308. i.

Works on Shorthand.

AXON (W. E. A.) C. Dickens and Shorthand.
pp. 10. *Manch.* 1892. 8°.   Pam. 48.

FAULMANN (C.) Geschichte und Litteratur der Stenographie. pp. 173. *Wien,* 1895. 8°.
                                       12991. h. 34.

HARTLEY (L.) Employment for Girls. Typewriting and Shorthand. pp. 8.
Woolwich, 1894. 8°.   Pam. 94.

JUNGE (A.) Die Vorgeschichte der Stenographie in Deutschland während des 17. und 18. Jahrhunderts. pp. 127. 1890. 8°. MITZSCHKE (P.) Handbibliothek der stenographischen Wissenschaft. Bd. 1.   12991. d.

LANTERN LECTURE. Lantern lecture on Shorthand. pp. 16. *Lond.* 1893. 8°.   Pam. 48.

LONDON. *International Shorthand Congress.* Transactions. *Lond., Paris, etc.* 1888. 8°.
                                       12991. g. 25.

—— Report of the Committee on contractions in writing for the press. pp. 7. *Lond.* 1888. 8°.
                                       12991. bb. 65. (8.)

MARTIN (J. P. A.) Quelle est la meilleure Sténographie? pp. 62. *Paris,* 1894. 8°.
                                       12991. cc. 20.

P.P. *Elgin.* Scottish Phonographer.
Elgin, 1894, *etc.* 8°.   P.P. 1892.

PITMAN (*Sir* I.) History of Shorthand. pp. 192.
Lond. 1891. 8°.   12991. b. 49.

—— Life and work of Sir I. Pitman. pp. 108.
Lond. 1894. 8°.   10856. aa. 8.

REED (T. A.) Biography of I. Pitman. pp. 191.
Lond. 1890. 8°.   10827. cc. 5.

POCKNELL (E.) Paper on principles hitherto used in Shorthand. pp. 16. *Lond.* 1885. 8°.
                                          Pam. 48.

ROCKWELL (J. E.) Teaching of Shorthand. 1885. 8°. U.S. *Bureau of Education.* Circular. No. 2.   8308. i.

STOLZE (F.) Von der Bilderschrift zur Stenographie. *Berl.* 1891, *etc.* 8°.   12991. d.

THOMPSON (H.) The humourous side of Shorthand. pp. 53. *Lond.* 1891. 8°. 12991. b. 46.

WATT (J. C.) Monograph on Shorthand. pp. 87.
Lond. 1890. 8°.   Pam. 48.

Systems of Shorthand, etc.

ABBOTT (F.) Swiftograph. pp. 20.
Lond. 1893. 8°.   12991. cc. 16.

ANDERTON (H.) Speed-o-Graf. pp. 16.
Sheffield, 1895. 16°.   Pam. 48.

ARTEAGA PEREIRA (E. de) Nueva taquigrafía.
pp. 45. *Madrid,* 1888. 8°.   Pam. 48.

AVERY (R. S.) Phonetic Alphabet. pp. 48.
Wash. 1893. 8°.   12902. de. 1. (8.)

BAKER (A.) Reporting Hints and practice.
pp. 56. *Lond.* 1889. 8°.   11852. b. 19.

BARLOW (W. H.) The Celestial Writing; or, the Normal Script phonetic writing. pp. 15.
Lond. 1894. fol.   12991. k. 5.

SHORTHAND—*continued.*

BARTER (J.) Manual of ABC Shorthand.
pp. 31. *Lond.* 1885. 8°.   Pam. 48.

—— The A B C Shorthand Reporter. pp. 32.
Lond. 1886. 8°.   12991. b. 50. (5.)

BELL (A. M.) Popular Shorthand or Steno-
phonography. pp. 16. *N.Y.* 1892. 8°.
12991. h. 32.

BROOKES (H. C.) Figure Shorthand. pp. 4.
1895. 16°.   Pam. 48.

BROWNE (A. M.) Phonetic Shorthand. pp. 20.
Lond. 1887. 8°.   12991. b. 50. (9.)

BROWNE (W. T.) Simplex Shorthand. pp. 32.
Manch. 1891. 8°.   12991. aaa. 9.

CALLENDAR (H. L.) Manual of Orthographic
Cursive Shorthand. pp. 32. *Lond.* 1891. 4°.
Pam. 48.

COOMBE (J. E.) Graduated Exercises for students
of Coombe's Comprehensive Shorthand.
Lond. 1891, *etc.* 8°.   12991. c. 26.

COPE (E. A.) Acquisition of Speed in Phonography. pp. 19. *Lond.* 1886. 8°.
12991. b. 50. (8.)

EVERETT (J. D.) Card of Everett's Shorthand.
Lond. 1883. 8°.   Pam. 48.

—— Shorthand Lessons. 2 pt.
Manch. 1892. 8°.   12991. b. 47.

REES (D.) Comparison of Phonography and
Everett's Shorthand. pp. 14. *Bath,* 1884. 8°.
Pam. 48.

FAULMANN (C.) Historische Grammatik der
Stenographie. pp. 376. *Wien,* 1887. 8°.
12991. h. 24.

FRANCINI (G.) Manuale di Fonografia italiana.
pp. 33. *Roma,* 1893. 8°.   Pam. 48.

GREGG (J. R.) Light-line Phonography. pp. 40.
Liverp. 1892. 8°.   Pam. 48.

—— The Shorthand for the Million! pp. 24.
Liverp. 1892. 8°.   12991. b. 50. (15.)

—— Gregg's Shorthand. pp. 24.
Lond. 1894. 12°.   Pam. 48.

—— Synopsis of Gregg's Shorthand.
Liverp. 1893. 8°.   Pam. 48.

ÆSOP. Aesop's Fables translated into Light-line
Phonography. pp. 25. *Edinb.* 1893. 8°.
Pam. 48.

P.P. *Exeter.* The Light-line Magazine. Vol. I.
No. 1–9. *Exeter,* 1892, 93. 8°. P.P. 1892. ah.

—— *Liverpool.* The Light liner. Monthly
magazine. *Liverp.* 1893, *etc.* 8°. P.P. 1892. m.

REFORM. Educational Reform. Specimens of
Light-line Phonography, *etc.* pp. 20.
Liverp. 1889. 8°.   Pam. 48.

HARRIS (G. A.) Manual of Harrisonian.
pp. 10. *Gloucester,* 1890. 8°.   Pam. 48.

HAY (W.) Shorthand, simplified and improved.
pp. 46. *Lond.* 1892. 8°.   12991. ff. 7.

HOPSON (J.) The Invention of Space-links; being
a help to speed. pp. 12. *Cranbrook,* 1893. 24°.
Pam. 48.

JANES (A.) Shorthand without complications.
pp. 24. *Lond.* 1892. 8°.   Pam. 48.

—— Shorthand without complications. Reading
book, No. 1. pp. 48. *Lond.* 1894. 8°.
12991. c. 29.

—— Reading book, No. 2. pp. 48. 23.
Lond. 1894. 8°.   12991. c. 30.

—— Circulars on Janes's system of Shorthand.
Lond. 1894. 8°.   Pam. 48.

KAMLOOPS PHONOGRAPHER. The Kamloops Phonographer. No. 1–7.
Kamloops, B.C., 1892–93. 8°.   12991. cc. 18.

LESSON. Practical Lesson in G. R. Phonography.
pp. 7. *Lond.* 1890. 8°.   Pam. 48.

SHORTHAND—*continued.*

LOCKETT (A. B.) Lockett's Shorthand Alphabet.
Lond. 1888. 8°.   Pam. 48.

MENGELKAMP (A.) Roller's Light-lined Phonography. pp. 11. *Breda, Iowa,* 1894. 8°.
Pam. 48.

MALONE (T. S.) Script Phonography. pp. 96.
Glasg. 1893. 8°.   12991. g. 39.

—— Script Phonography. School edition. 6 pt.
Lond. 1893. 8°.   12991. cc. 15.

MAC EWAN (O.) Script Phonography versus
Pitman's. pp. 8. *Lond.* 1888. 8°.   Pam. 48.

P.P. *Glasgow.* Script Phonographic Journal.
No. 2, *etc.* *Glasg.* 1887, *etc.* 4°.
P.P. 1892. hb. & 951.

PITMAN (*Sir* I.) Great Shorthand controversy.
Script versus Pitman. Reply to Pitman's mis-
representations. pp. 31. *Glasg.* 1889. 8°.
Pam. 48.

SCIENCE. Science victorious! Script or Long-
hand Movement. pp. 27. *Glasg.* 1891. 4°.
Pam. 48.

WARDEN (J. M.) The Claims and fallacies of
Script Phonography. pp. 16. *Bath,* 1888. 8°.
12991. b. 50. (11.)

MILLER (R. E.) Exercises in Shorthand on
Gurney's System. pp. 47. *Lond.* 1890. 8°.
Pam. 48.

MORRELL (C.) System of Phonoscript and Phono-
typy. pp. 56. *Chicago,* 1894. 8°. Pam. 48.

MOUIS (J. J.) Méthode de sténographie à portée.
pp. 24. *Lisieux,* 1893. 8°.   Pam. 48.

NANKIVELL (E. J.) Fac-Simile Reporting notes.
Lond. 1891, *etc.* 8°.   12991. g. 37.

OXFORD SHORTHAND. The Oxford Shorthand.
pp. 8. *Dover,* 1894. 8°.   Pam. 48.

EPHEM. Oxford Shorthand Almanac.
Dover, 1892, *etc.* 8°.   P.P. 2495. ia.

P.P. *Dover.* Oxford Shorthand Chronicle.
Dover, 1890, *etc.* 4°.   2113.

GUÉNIN (L. P.) La Sténographie Aimé Paris et
ses imitations. pp. 204. *Paris,* 1893. 8°.
12991. cc. 19.

PATERSON (H. G.) Paterson's Phonography and
Typewriting manual. pp. 100.
Lond. 1895. obl. 8°.   1879. a. 8.

P.P. *London.* The Monthly illustrated re-
porters' Journal [in shorthand].
Lond. 1887, *etc.* 8°.   P.P. 1891. q.

—— The London Phonographer.
Lond. 1891, *etc.* 8°.   P.P. 1891. pc.

—— Phonographic Quarterly Review.
Lond. 1894, *etc.* 8°.   P.P. 1891. nb.

—— Shorthand and Typewriting.
Lond. 1895, *etc.* 8°.   P.P. 1891. pd. & 732.

PITMAN (*Sir* I.) Phonographic and Pronouncing
Dictionary. pp. 299. *Lond.* 1890. 8°.
12991. f. 12.

—— Abridged Shorthand Dictionary. pp. 224.
Lond. 1895. 8°.   12991. a. 9.

—— Phonographic Phrase Book. pp. 88.
Lond. 1893. 8°.   12991. aaa. 11.

—— Manual of Phonography. 2 pt.
Lond. 1890, 91. 8°.   12991. c. 27.

—— The Phonographic Teacher. pp. 45.
Lond. 1894. 8°.   Pam. 48.

—— Shorthand Instructor. pp. 231.
Lond. 1893. 8°.   12991. aaa. 12.

—— Shorthand Instructor. (Key.) 3 pt.
Lond. 1894. 8°.   12991. b. 52.

—— Shorthand Primers. 3 pt. *Lond.* 1892. 8°.
12991. b. 48.

—— The Reporter's Assistant. pp. 80.
Lond. 1890. 8°.   12991. b. 51.

SHORTHAND—*continued.*

PITMAN (*Sir* I.) Fonografik Improovments.
Bath, 1894. 8°.   Pam. 48.

—— An eksplanashon respekting the Fonografik Improovments. pp. 8. *Bath*, 1895. 8°.
       Pam. 48.

—— Grammalogues of Phonography. pp. 4.
Bath, 1894. 8°.   Pam. 48.

—— How to form Classes in Pitman's Shorthand. pp. 8. *Lond.* 1892. 8°.   Pam. 48.

COPE (E. A.) Handbook for Shorthand teachers: guide to the art of teaching Pitman's Phonography. pp. 139. *Lond.* 1893. 8°.
       12991. aaa. 10.

ÆSOP. Æsop's Fables. Printed in the learners' style of phonography by I. Pitman. pp. 48.
Lond. 1891. 8°.   Pam. 48.

EPHEM. Pitman's Shorthand Year book.
Lond. 1892, *etc.* 8°.   P.P. 2496. n.

LEARNER. Learner's Shorthand Reader. Pitman's Shorthand. pp. 48. *Lond.* 1893. 8°.
       12991. b. 53.

NIXON (A.) New Code for Evening Continuation schools, with reference to classes in Pitman's Shorthand. pp. 12. *Lond.* 1893. 8°.
       Pam. 17.

P.P. *London.* Phonographic Miscellany. Illustrated magazine in an easy style of Pitman's Shorthand. *Lond.* 1895, *etc.* 8°.   385.

—— Pitman's Shorthand Weekly.
Lond. 1892, *etc.* 4°.   P.P. 1895. b.

REED (T. A.) The Shorthand Writer. pp. 222.
Lond. 1892. 8°.   12991. ff. 8.

RELTON (W.) Points of difference between the Benn Pitman and I. Pitman's present style of Phonography. pp. 8. 1890. 8°.   Pam. 48.

SHORTHAND. Practical Shorthand. Applicable to Pitman's Phonography. pp. 11.
Lond. 1892. 8°.   Pam. 48.

STONE (F. C.) Pitman's Shorthand as a specific subject. pp. 16. *Lond.* 1892. 8°.
       12991. b. 50. (16.)

TURNER (T. A.) Progressive Studies in Phonography. pp. 107. *Lond.* 1893. 8°.
       12991. aaa. 13.

BARRUÉ (P.) La Sténographie apprise sans professeur. Phonographie Isaac Pitman.
Paris, 1881. 8°.   Pam. 48.

BRUCE (J. R.) Sténographie phonétique. Phonographie Pitman. pp. 78. *Londres*, 1895. 12°.
       12991. b. 56.

HODGES (J. G.) Irish Notes, 1843–48; and other work with the Purton System of Shorthand. pp. 31. *Lond.* 1888. 8°.   Pam. 48.

RAMBACH (L.) System einer Musik-Stenographie. pp. 90. *Zürich*, 1893. 8°. 7897. m. 2.

SCHWAB (J.) Nederlandsch snelschrift naar het Stenographiesysteem van F. X. Gabelsberger bewerkt door J. Schwab. pp. 26.
Rotterdam, 1892. 4°.   12991. k. 5.

SHORTHAND PILOT. The Shorthand Pilot.
pp. 8. *Bradford*, 1893. 16°.   Pam. 48.

SIMSON (J.) Manual of Syllabic Shorthand.
pp. 16. *Lond.* 1892. 8°.   12991. g. 38.

SKINNER (F.) Skinner's Rapid Long-Hand.
pp. 15. *Teddington*, 1892. 8°.   Pam. 48.

SLOAN-DUPLOYAN SHORTHAND. Sloan-Duployan Shorthand. pp. 20. *Bath*, 1885. 8°.
       12991. b. 50. (6.)

P.P. *London.* Sloan-Duployan Phonographic Journal. Vol. 1–3. *Lond.* 1884–88. 8°.
       P.P. 1891. pb.

REED (T. A.) Review of Duployé's Shorthand.
pp. 13. *Bath*, 1885. 8°.   12991. b. 50. (3.)

SHORTHAND—*continued.*

SÖGAARD (N. P.) Stenografiske Skriveøvelser etter L. A. F. Arends' syst. Lærebog i Stenografi. pp. 60. 14. *Kjøbenh.* 1893. *obl.* 4°.
       12991. e. 28.

SPEED SECRET. The Speed Secret. Short-cut to rapid work. pp. 58. *N.Y.* 1894. 12°.
       12981. aa. 66.

SPENCER (W. G.) System of Lucid Shorthand.
pp. 28. *Lond.* 1894. 8°.   12991. cc. 17.

SUTCLIFFE (J. A.) How to pass the Society of Arts' examination in shorthand. pp. 32.
Lond. 1895. 8°.   Pam. 48.

SWEET (H.) Manual of current Shorthand, orthographic and phonetic. pp. 137.
Oxf. 1892. 8°.   12991. cc. 14.

TAYLOR (E. W.) Taylor's Exercises on the Grammalogues and Contractions of Phonography. pp. 7. *Lond.* 1886. 8°.   Pam. 48.

VALPY (F. H.) Audeography: the new Shorthand. pp. 8. *Lond.* 1886. 8°.   Pam. 48.

VENTRE (C. C.) Nouvelle méthode de sténographie horizontale. *Marseille*, 1893. *s. sh.* 4°.
       1882. d. 2. (106.)

WÉRY (J. L.) De Stenographie en het Stolze'sche Systeem. pp. 40. *Amsterd.* 1894. 12°.
       Pam. 48.

WORMS (A.) Letfattelig dansk Stenografi. pp. 6.
Kjøbenh. 1893. 8°.   Pam. 48.

SHREWSBURY. FLETCHER (W. G. D.) Poll-Tax for Shrewsbury, 1380. pp. 12.
1891. 8°.   10348. d. 19. (12.)

SHREWSBURY. Inquisition of the Liberties of Shrewsbury, 1515. pp. 4. 1892. 8°.
       10348. d. 20. (3.)

HIBBERT (F. A.) Influence of English Gilds, illustrated by the history of the Gilds of Shrewsbury. pp. 168. 1891. 8°.   Cambridge Historical Essays. No. 5.   9009. c.

KENT (A. E.) Album of photographs of Shrewsbury. *Shrewsbury*, 1895. *obl.* 4°. 10360. aa. 38.

BRADLEY (R.) Guide to Shrewsbury. pp. 88.
Shrewsbury, 1893. 8°.   10351. e. 43.

BLAKEWAY (J. B.) History of Shrewsbury School. pp. 241. *Shrewsbury*, 1889. 4°.
       8365. ff. 23.

SHREWSBURY. *Royal School.* Regestum Scholarium, 1562–1635. pp. 333.
Shrewsbury, 1892. 8°.   8365. c. 76.

P.P. *Shrewsbury.* The Salopian. Magazine of Shrewsbury School. *Shrewsbury*, 1885, *etc.* 4°.
       P.P. 6152. bc.

SHROPSHIRE. CRANAGE (D. H. S.) Architectural account of the churches of Shropshire.
Wellington, 1894, *etc.* 4°.   7814. h.

FLETCHER (W. G. D.) Religious census of Shropshire in 1676. pp. 18. 1891. 8°.
       4705. cc. 14. (5.)

P.P. *Shrewsbury.* Shropshire Notes and Queries.
Shrewsbury, 1885, *etc.* 4°.   P.P. 6019. fga.

SALOP. Shropshire topographical Manuscripts in the British Museum. pp. 29. 1892. 8°.
       011902. m. 22. (9.)

SIAM. Ac. London. *R. Geographical Society.* Notes of a journey on the Upper Mekong. By H. W. Smyth. pp. 109. *Lond.* 1895. 8°.
       010055. c. 20.

FOURNEREAU (L.) Le Siam ancien. 1895, *etc.* 4°.
Annales du Musée Guimet. Tom. 27.
       7704. h. 21.

—— Les Ruines khmères. *Paris*, 1890. fol.
       7704. l. 26.

GERINI (G. E.) Chūlākantamaṅgala, or the Tonsure ceremony. pp. 187.
Bangkok, 1893. 8°.   4503. g. 11.

SILK—*continued.*

MARINI (A.) La Campagna serica italiana nel 1894. pp. 381. *Torino*, 1894. 8°. 7297. c. 21.

—— Il Crivello bombicino per la cernita del seme serico. pp. 16. *Torino*, 1894. 8°.
Pam. 42.

PINCHETTI (P.) L'Industria della Seta sul finire del secolo XIX. pp. 187. *Como*, 1894. 8°.
7743. e. 26.

SCHMOLLER (G.) and HINTZE (O.) Die preussische Seidenindustrie im 18. Jahrhundert. 3 Bde. 1892. 8°. Ac. *Berlin. Societas Regia Scientiarum. Acta Borussica.* Ac. 855/10.

STORCK (A.) and MARTIN (H.) Lyon à l'Exposition Universelle. L'industrie de la soie. pp. 120. *Lyon*, 1891. 4°. 7743. g. 18.

U.S. *Dept. of Agriculture. Silk Section.* Bulletin. *Wash.* 1890, *etc.* 8°. 7053. e. 26.

VILLON (A. M.) Éducation des vers à soie, *etc.* pp. 320. *Paris*, 1890. 8°. 7742. b. 14.

VIGNON (L.) La Soie au point de vue scientifique et industriel. pp. 359. *Paris*, 1890. 12°.
7742. b. 13.

—— Recherches sur la soie. pp. 124. *Lyon*, 1891. 8°. 7298. f. 9.

VISZKOCSILL (J. L.) Anleitung zur praktischen Ausübung der Seidenraupenzucht, *etc.* pp. 115. *Gran*, 1881. 8°. 7297. a. 51.

WARDLE (T.) On the development of Power-Loom weaving of silk fabrics at Lyons. pp. 36. *Manch.* 1893. 8°. 7743. b. 55.

WHITER (J. S.) The Silk industry of Great Britain. pp. 53. *Lond.* 1882. 8°. 08227. e. 50.

WRAY (L.) Experimental culture of Silkworms in Perak. pp. 29. 1893. 4°. Perak Museum Notes. No. 1. 7297. bb.

YOSHIDA (T.) Entwickelung des Seidenhandels und der Seidenindustrie. pp. 111. *Heidelberg*, 1895. 8°. 7297. b. 27.

SILVER. *See* GOLD AND SILVER : MONEY.

SIMANCAS. DÍAZ SÁNCHEZ (F.) Guía de la villa y archivo de Simancas. pp. 299. *Madrid*, 1885. 8°. 011901. ee. 24.

SIN. *See* EVIL.

SINAI PENINSULA. BÉNÉDITE (G.) La Péninsule sinaïtique. pp. 23. *Paris*, 1891. 8°.
10078. aaa. 31.

GIBSON (M. D.) How the Codex was found. Narrative of two visits to Sinai. pp. 141. *Camb.* 1893. 8°. 10076. b. 3.

HART (H. C.) Some Account of the fauna and flora of Sinai, *etc. Lond.* 1891. 4°. 2057. c.

HAYNES (A. E.) Man-hunting in the Desert, narrative of the Palmer Search-Expedition, 1882–83. pp. 305. *Lond.* 1894. 8°. 9055. ece. 30.

JULLIEN (M.) Sinaï et Syrie. pp. 300. *Lille*, 1893. 8°. 10077. i. 13.

LOMBAY (G. de) Au Sinaï. pp. 220. *Paris*, 1892. 12°. 10078. ana. 34.

LOTI (P.) Le Désert. pp. 258. *Paris*, 1895. 8°.
10077. aa. 17.

PALMER (H. S.) Ancient history from the Monuments. Sinai. pp. 224. *Lond.* 1892. 8°. 2378. a.

SIND. JAMES (H. E. M.) Sind as a field for the naturalist and antiquarian. pp. 27. *Karachi*, 1893. 8°. Pam. 42.

SINDHI LANGUAGE AND LITERATURE. UMMED 'ALĪ KARĪM MUḤAMMAD. Manual of Anglo-Vernacular grammar for Sindhi students. pp. 87. *Karachi*, 1883. 8°. 14164. c. 5.

Ac. *London. British Museum.* Catalogues of the Hindi and Sindhi printed books. By J. F. Blumhardt. 4 pt. *Lond.* 1893. 4°. 11901. i. 24.

SINGAPORE. D'ARANJO (B. E.) Stranger's Guide to Singapore. pp. 76. *Singapore*, 1890. 8°. 10055. c. 4.

P.P. *Singapore.* The Daily Advertiser. *Singapore*, 1890, *etc.* fol. P.P. 9974. i.

REITH (G. M.) Handbook to Singapore. pp. 135. *Singapore*, 1892. 8°. 10055. aaaa. 34.

SINGAPORE. Photographic views of Singapore. *Singapore*, 1893. 8°. 10058. bb. 40.

WORSFOLD (W. B.) Visit to Java, with account of the founding of Singapore. pp. 283. *Lond.* 1893. 8°. 010055. e. 13.

See also ENGLAND, *Colonies :* MALAY PENINSULA : STRAITS SETTLEMENTS.

SINGING. *See* VOICE.

SINHALESE LANGUAGE. CLOUGH (B.) Sinhalese-English dictionary. pp. 824. *Colombo*, 1892. 4°. 12906. dd. 44.

DE SILVA (D. S.) English-Sinhalese pronouncing dictionary. *Colombo*, 1885, *etc.* 8°. 12906. df. 21.

GUNASĒKARA (A. M.) Comprehensive grammar of the Sinhalese language. pp. 516. *Colombo*, 1891. 8°. 12907. cc. 29.

CEYLON. Glossary of native and foreign Words occurring in official correspondence. pp. 33. *Colombo*, 1893. fol. 12910. l. 7.

MENDIS (N.) Sinhalese and European Proverbs. pp. 74. *Colombo*, 1890. 8°. 14165. f. 34.

SION-VANDÉMONT. DIDRIT (T.) Étude sur Sion-Vandémont en Lorraine. pp. 122. *Nancy*, 1894. 8°. 10171. e. 9.

SIOUX INDIANS. *See* INDIAN LANGUAGES : INDIANS.

SIPHONOPHORAE. CHUN (C.) Die canarischen Siphonophoren. 1891. 4°. Ac. *Frankfort. Senckenbergische Naturforschende Gesellschaft.* Abhandlungen. Bd. 16. Hft. 3.
Ac. 2878/2.

SISTERHOODS : DEACONESSES.

BOURNAND (F.) Les Sœurs des hôpitaux, *etc.* pp. 346. *Paris*, 1891. 12°. 4061. bbb. 32.

COOKE (H. J.) Mildmay, story of the first Deaconess institution. pp. 214. *Lond.* 1892. 8°.
4192. ee. 25.

D., A. The Anglican Sister of Mercy. pp. 162. *Lond.* 1895. 8°. 4071. cc. 6.

FRANCISCANS, *Third Order of.* Deacons, Deaconesses, *etc.* pp. 89. *Lond.* 1891. 8°. 4071. aaa. 4.

N., H. Thirty-two years in a House of Mercy. pp. 96. *Lond.* 1895. 8°. 4429. a. 98.

STEPHENSON (T. B.) Concerning Sisterhoods. pp. 96. *Lond.* 1890. 8°. 4108. dc. 36.

See also BEGUINES : RELIGIOUS ORDERS.

SISTERON. CLAUDIN (A.) Les origines de l'Imprimerie à Sisteron. pp. 23. *Paris*, 1894. 8°. 11903. f. 34. (9.)

SITTINGBOURNE. PAYNE (G.) Collectanea Cantiana ; archæological researches in the neighbourhood of Sittingbourne. pp. 218. *Lond.* 1893. 8°. 7709. aa. 30.

SKÅRA. HILDEBRAND (H. O. H.) Skara Domkyrka. pp. 112. 1895. 8°. Ac. *Stockholm. K. Vitterhets Akademien.* Antiqvarisk Tidskrift. Del 15. Ac. 7800/4.

OLSON (J.) and HÖRLÉN (M.) Illustrerad beskrifning öfver Skåre. pp. 40. *Stockholm*, 1889. 8°. 10106. de. 5. (3.)

SKAT. DIEHL (L. V.) Skat. pp. 72. 1891. 8°. The Club Series. *Lond.* 1891. 8°. 7908. cc.

—— Skat scoring book. *Lond.* 1891. 8°.
7913. ccc. 25.

HERTEFELD (A.) The game of Skat. pp. 8. 152. *Lond.* 1893. 8°. 7913. c. 17.

SKAT—*continued.*

Mon. Rules of the game of Skât. pp. 24.
Lond. 1890. 16°.   7915. de. 14. (3.)
See also Games.

**SKATING: CURLING: SKI: TOBOG-
GANING.** Deney (G.) Traité du Patinage.
pp. 166. *Paris,* 1891. 8°.   7908. ece. 15.

Digby (J. D.) Skating and Curling. The
Glaciarium. pp. 34. *Lond.* 1893. 8°. 7912. f. 1. (9.)

Heathcote (J. M.) and Tebbutt (C. G.) Skating,
Curling, Tobogganing. pp. 464. 1894. 8°.
Badminton Library.   2264. aa. 12.

Martinez (F. N.) The Roller Skating pocket
guide. pp. 48. *Lond.* 1893. 16°. 7913. de. 17. (5.)

Meagher (G. A.) Figure and fancy Skating.
pp. 160. *Lond.* 1895. 8°.   07905. f. 42.

Williams (M. S. F. M.) and (S. F. M.) Figure-
Skating. pp. 322. *Lond.* 1892. 8°. 7907. de. 44.

Urdahl (L.) Haandbog i Skiløbning. pp. 113.
Kristiania, 1893. 8°.   07905. i. 13.

—— Vom Skilaufen und Schlittenrutschen.
pp. 16. *Kristiania,* 1893. 4°.   7905. i. 20.

Wangenheim (W. v.) Die norwegischen Schnee-
schuhe. Ski. pp. 23. *Hamb.* 1892. 8°.
     7912. g. 1. (6.)

Witham (T. M.) System of Figure-Skating.
pp. 319. *Lond.* 1893. 8°.   07905. f. 13.

Cook (T. A.) Notes on Tobogganing at St.
Moritz. pp. 103. *Lond.* 1894. 8°. 7912. bb. 1.

Gibson (*Hon.* H.) Tobogganing on Crooked
Runs. pp. 255. *Lond.* 1894. 8°.   7912. c. 4.

SKEGNESS. Avery (J.) Popular penny
Guide to Skegness. pp. 26. *Skegness,* 1894. 8°.
     10348. c. 25. (8.)

SKIASCOPY. *See* Eye.

SKIN. Ac. *Congrès International de Der-
matologie. Comptes rendus.*
Paris, 1890, *etc.* 8°.   Ac. 3699. c.
—— Germany. *Dermatologische Gesellschaft.
Verhandlungen der Gesellschaft.* pp. 419.
Wien, 1892. 8°.   Ac. 3774. b.
—— London. *Dermatological Society.* Trans-
actions. *Lond.* 1895, *etc.* 8°.   Ac. 3826. b.
—— *New Sydenham Society.* Selected Mono-
graphs on Dermatology. Vol. 143. pp. 613.
Lond. 1893. 8°.   Ac. 3838/57.

Anderson (T. M.) Treatise of diseases of the
Skin. pp. 761. *Lond.* 1894. 8°. 7641. h. 26.

Brocq (L.) and Jacquet (L.) Précis de Dermatologie. Pathologie générale. pp. 172. 1893. 8°.
Encyclopédie des aide-mémoire.   8709. g.

—— Précis. Maladies en particulier. pp. 232.
1894. 8°. Encyclopédie des aide-mémoire. 8709. g.

Bulkley (L. D.) Clinical study and analysis of
1,000 cases of Psoriasis. pp. 16.
Baltimore, 1891. 8°.   07305. l. 13. (1.)
—— Clinical notes on Psoriasis. pp. 14.
N.Y. 1895. 8°.   Pam. 39.
—— On the relation of Eczema to disturbances
of the nervous system. pp. 35. *N.Y.* 1891. 8°.
     07305. f. 14. (6.)

Burnett (J. C.) Diseases of the Skin. pp. 240.
Lond. 1893. 8°.   7641. a. 38.

Crocker (H. R.) Diseases of the Skin. pp. 939.
Lond. 1893. 8°.   2024. bb.

Dockrell (M.) The Skin: how to keep it
healthy. pp. 40. *Lond.* 1893. 16°. 7630. a. 13.

Du Mesnil ( ) Beiträge zur Anatomie und
Aetiologie einiger Hautkrankl.eiten. pp. 56.
1890. 8°. Ac. Wurzburg. *Physikalisch-Medicinische Gesellschaft.* Verhandlungen. N. F.
Bd. 24.   Ac. 3763/3.

Dühring (L. A.) Cutaneous Medicine.
Phila. 1895, *etc.* 8°.   7640. g. 6.

SKIN—*continued.*

Gemmell (W.) Dermic Memoranda.
pp. 116. *Glasg.* 1892. 8°.   7640. aaa. 17.

Hammer (F.) Über den Einfluss des Lichtes auf
die Haut. pp. 56. *Stuttgart,* 1891. 8°.
     8708. l. 8. (5.)

Hayes (P. S.) Electricity in diseases of the
Skin. 1894. 8°. Bigelow (H. R.) International system of Electro-Therapeutics. 2024. e.

Joseph (M.) Lehrbuch der Hautkrankheiten für
Aerzte und Studirende. pp. 299.
Leipz. 1892. 8°.   7640. h. 25.

Jessner (S.) Haut-Anomalieen bei inneren
Krankheiten. *Berl.* 1893. 8°.   7620. ee. 34.

Jamieson (W. A.) Diseases of the Skin.
pp. 660. 1894. 8°. Pentland's Medical Series.
Vol. 1.   7641. ee.

Kaposi (M.) Ueber die Behandlung von Lupus,
und anderen Hautkrankheiten mittels Koch-
'scher Lymphe, "Tuberculin." pp. 122.
Wien, 1891. 8°.   7640. g. 4.

Lewin (G.) and Heller (J.) Die Sclerodermie.
pp. 236. *Berl.* 1895. 8°.   7641. i. 21.

Manson (P.) Diseases of the Skin in tropical
countries. 1893. 8°. Davidson (A.) Hygiene
of Warm Climates.   7686. dd. 2.

Marie (P.) Leçons sur les maladies de la Moelle.
pp. 504. *Paris,* 1892. 8°.   7630. g. 21.

Morris (M.) Diseases of the Skin. pp. 556.
Lond. 1894. 8°.   7640. aaa. 18.

—— Internationaler Atlas seltener Hautkrankheiten. *Ger., Eng.* and *Fr.*
Hamburg, 1889, *etc.* fol.   1832. d.

Neumann (I.) Atlas der Hautkrankheiten.
Wien, 1890. fol.   1831. d. 1.

Nouran (D. v. H.) Casuistique et diagnostic
photographique des maladies de la peau.
Haarlem, 1889, *etc.* fol.   531.

Patteson (R. G.) Synopsis of diseases of the
Skin. pp. 15. *Lond.* 1891. 16°.   7640. a. 5.

P.P. *Berlin. Dermatologische Zeitschrift.*
Berl. 1894, *etc.* 8°.   P.P. 3015. f.

Phillips (L.) Medicated baths in the treatment
of Skin diseases. pp. 103. *Lond.* 1893. 8°.
     7461. de. 9.

Piffard (H. G.) Treatise on diseases of the
Skin. pp. 157. *Lond.* 1891. 4°.   7620. i. 5.

Robinson (T.) Illustrations of diseases of the
Skin. *Lond.* 1890, *etc.* fol.   1749.

Rohé (G. H.) Manual of diseases of the Skin.
pp. 303. *Phila.* 1892. 8°.   7640. ee. 7.

Rossi (A.) Lo stato attuale della Dermatologia.
pp. 250. *Napoli,* 1891. 8°.   7640. i. 6.

Savill (T. D.) On an epidemic Skin disease in
the Western District of London, 1891. pp. 64.
Lond. 1892. 8°.   7630. f. 20.

Smith (P. H. P.) Introduction to the study of
diseases of the Skin. pp. 367. *Lond.* 1893. 8°.
     7641. b. 31.

Startin (J.) The Skin and complexion. pp. 84.
Lond. 1893. *obl.* 8°.   7641. a. 35.

Steiger (A.) Beiträge zur Physiologie und
Pathologie der Hornhautrefraction.
Wiesbaden, 1895, *etc.* 8°.   7611. h.

Thibierge (G.) Thérapeutique des maladies de
la Peau. 2 tom. *Paris,* 1895. 12°.
     7640. aa. 28.

Unna (P. G.) Die Histopathologie der Hautkrankheiten. pp. 1225. 1894. 8°. Orth (J.)
Lehrbuch der pathologischen Anatomie. Lief. 8.
     7442. g. 9.

Van Harlingen (A.) Diseases of the Skin.
1893. 8°. Allen (H.) Handbook of local
Therapeutics.   7442. g. 26.

SKIN—*continued.*

WINIWARTER (A. v.) Die chirurgischen Krankheiten der Haut. pp. 754. 1892. 8°.

BILLROTH (T.) Deutsche Chirurgie. Lief. 23.   7482. cc.

LONDON. *Saint John's Hospital.* Formulæ used at the Hospital. pp. 48. *Lond.* 1891. 16°.   07509. de. 12.

STARTIN (J.) Pharmacopœia for diseases of the Skin. pp. 39. *Lond.* 1892. 8°.   7509. de. 80.

See also COUNTER IRRITATION : LEPROSY : LUPUS : RINGWORM.

SKIPTON IN CRAVEN. SKIPTON. Parish Register of Skipton-in-Craven. pp. 355. *Skipton,* 1894. 8°.   9902. ccc. 13.

DAWSON (W. H.) A Day at Skipton. pp. 32. *Bingley,* 1895. 8°.   Pam. 90.

SKIVE. LOHMANN (J. J.) Kalkmalerierne i Skive Kirke. pp. 91. *Kjøbenh.* 1890. 8°.   7808. aa. 43. (3.)

SKULL. BUSCH ( ) *Dr.* Ueber die Schädelbildung bei niederen Menschenrassen. 1894. 8°. Ac. Berlin. *Odontologische Gesellschaft.* Verhandlungen. Bd. 6.   Ac. 3774.

HÄLLSTÉN (K. G.) Matériaux pour servir à la connaissance des crânes des peuples finnois. 1893. 8°. Ac. Helsingfors. *Societas Scientiarum.* Bidrag till Kännedom af Finlands Natur. Hft. 52.   Ac. 1094/4.

MATIEGKA (H.) Crania Bohemica. *Prag,* 1891, *etc.* 8°.   10007. l.

RUEDINGER (N.) Die Rassen-Schädel in der K. anatomischen Anstalt in München. pp. 207. 1892. 4°. Ac. Vienna. *Anthropologische Gesellschaft.* Die anthropologischen Sammlungen. No. 10.   Ac. 6230/2.

STUDER (T.) Crania Helvetica antiqua. pp. 55. *Leipz.* 1894. fol.   7420. h. 3.

MACEWEN (W.) Atlas of Head Sections. *Glasg.* 1893. 4°.   7440. i. 3.

TÖRÖK (A.) Grundzüge einer systematischen Kraniometrie. pp. 631. *Stuttgart,* 1890. 8°.   7419. l. 4.

BARKER (A. E. J.) Hunterian lectures on intracranial Inflammations. pp. 72. *Lond.* 1890. 8°.   Pam. 39.

FAWCETT (E.) On the localisation of the Foramina at the base of the skull. pp. 16. *Bristol,* 1895. 8°.   Pam. 39.

GUBLER (R.) Beiträge zur Kasuistik der komplizierten Frakturen des Schädeldachs. 1895. 8°. BRUNS (P.) Mittheilungen aus des chirurgischen Klinik zu Tübingen. Bd. 13.   7481. ccc. 16.

LEDIARD (H. A.) Compound comminuted fracture of the skull. pp. 7. 1893. 8°.   7306. df. 20. (11.)

MOISSON (J. L.) Des différentes méthodes d'oblitération des pertes de substance du crâne. pp. 84. *Paris,* 1891. 8°.   7383. ddd. 1. (4.)

POIRIER (P.) Topographie cranio-encéphalique. Trépanation. pp. 92. *Paris,* 1891. 8°. Pam. 39.

See also ANTHROPOLOGY : BRAIN : HEAD.

SKYE. *See* HEBRIDES.

SLANDER. *See* LIBEL.

SLAVERY.

General : History.

ABIGNENTE (G.) La Schiavitù nei suoi rapporti colla Chiesa e col laicato. pp. 333. *Torino,* 1890. 8°.   8156. ec. 10.

BIANCHETTI (C.) L'Antischiavismo alla fine del secolo XIX. pp. 407. *Torino,* 1893. 8°.   8156. df. 18.

BINGER (G.) Esclavage, Islamisme et Christianisme. pp. 112. *Paris,* 1891. 8°. 8156. df. 14.

BROWNLOW (W. R. B.) Lectures on Slavery and Serfdom in Europe. pp. 248. *Lond.* 1892. 8°.   8156. aa. 5.

HENSON (H. H.) Christianity and Slavery. pp. 27. 1887. 8°. Oxford House Papers. No. 18.   4017. bbb.

INGRAM (J. K.) A History of Slavery and Serfdom. pp. 285. *Lond.* 1895. 8°.   8155. aaaa. 9.

O'BRIEN (J. B.) Rise, progress and phases of Slavery. pp. 148. *Lond.* 1885. 8°.   08276. i. 22.

SALADIN. Christianity and the Slave trade. pp. 91. *Lond.* 1894. 8°.   8155. aaa. 4.

ANDRÉ (T.) L'Esclavage chez les anciens Hébreux. pp. 197. *Paris,* 1892. 8°. 4516. cc. 5.

PINCHES (T. G.) Documents relating to Slave-dealing in Babylonia. *Lond.* 1884. 8°.   7704. d. 10. (9.)

SCHNEIDER (A.) Zur Geschichte der Sclaverei im alten Rom. pp. 52. *Zürich,* 1892. 8°. Pam. 81.

CRESCENZIO (N. de) La personalità dello Schiavo nel diritto romano. 1891, *etc.* 4°. Ac. Naples. *R. Accademia di Scienze Morali.* Atti. Vol. 24.   Ac. 96/2.

SALKOWSKI (C.) Zur Lehre vom Sklavenerwerb. pp. 256. *Leipz.* 1891. 8°.   5207. df. 16.

Africa.

AFRICA. L'Esclavage en Afrique. pp. 518. *Paris,* 1890. 12°.   8156. de. 6.

ALLEMAND LAVIGERIE (C. M.) *Cardinal.* L'Esclavage africain. pp. 17. *Gand,* 1891. obl. 4°.   1790. b. 4.

—— Documents sur la fondation de l'œuvre anti-esclavagiste. pp. 724. *Saint-Cloud,* 1889. 8°.   8156. e. 15.

BOURNAND (F.) Le Cardinal Lavigerie. pp. 329. *Paris,* 1893. 8°.   4863. e. 19.

SALLÈS (A.) Le Cardinal Lavigerie et l'influence française en Afrique. pp. 58. *Lyon,* 1893. 12°.   Pam. 40.

BELGIUM. *Société Antiesclavagiste.* Les conférences antiesclavagistes. pp. 114. *Brux.* 1892. 8°.   8156. f. 6.

BONARDI DU MÉNIL (de) *Marquis.* La Croisade noire. pp. 69. *Paris,* 1889. 8°.   Pam. 81.

IMBART LATOUR (J.) L'Esclavage en Afrique et la Croisade noire. pp. 184. *Paris,* 1894. 8°.   8155. aaaa. 10

LENTNER (F.) Der schwarze Kodex. Der afrikanische Sklavenhandel und die brüsseler General-Akte vom 2. Juli 1890. pp. 140. *Innsbruck,* 1891. 8°.   8156. e. 18.

NOYANT ( ) Les Horreurs de l'Esclavage en Afrique. pp. 95. *Paris,* 1891. 8°.   8156. df. 15.

PEASE (J. A.) How we countenance Slavery. pp. 14. *Lond.* 1895. 8°.   Pam. 81.

P.P. *Brussels.* Le Mouvement antiesclavagiste. *Brux.* 1888, *etc.* 8°.   P.P. 1046. n.

VIGNERON (L.) Sang noir. Scènes de la vie esclavagiste dans l'Afrique. pp. 293. *Paris,* 1893. 12°.   10096. bb. 11.

WALLER (H.) Slaving and slavery in our Protectorates. pp. 8. *Lond.* 1894. 8°. Pam. 81.

See also AFRICA, *Central and East* : NEGROES.

Brazil.

BRAZIL. L'Abolition de l'esclavage au Brésil. pp. 146. *Paris,* 1889. 8°.   8156. e. 14.

SLAVERY.—Brazil—continued.

Rome, Church of. Leo XIII., Pope. Sendschreiben an die Bischöfe Brasiliens. Ueber die Aufhebung der Sklaverei. pp. 41. Freiburg, 1889. 8°. Pam. 96.

Spont (A.) L'abolition de l'esclavage au Brésil. pp. 47. Paris, 1888. 8°. Pam. 81.

United States of America.

Botume (E. H.) First days among the Contrabands. pp. 286. Bost. 1893. 8°. 8155. aaa. 1.

Grimke (A. H.) W. L. Garrison. pp. 405. 1891. 8°. Martyn (C.) American Reformers. 10883. bbb. 4.

Harrison (W. P.) The Gospel among the Slaves. pp. 394. Nashville, 1893. 8°. 8155. aaa. 2.

Hope (A. R.) Heroes in Homespun. Scenes from the Emancipation movement. pp. 380. Lond. 1894. 8°. 8155. aaaa. 8.

Maillard (R. Q.) Plantation life before Emancipation. pp. 237. Richmond, 1892. 8°. 8157. b. 15.

Michael (C. D.) The Slave and his champions. pp. 160. Lond. 1891. 8°. 8155. aaaa. 6.

Tuckerman (B.) W. Jay and the constitutional movement for the Abolition of Slavery. pp. 185. N.Y. 1893. 8°. 8156. e. 22.

Thoreau (H. D.) Anti-Slavery and reform papers. pp. 141. Lond. 1890. 8°. 8157. c. 5.

See also Negroes: United States of America, History, and Southern States.

SLAVONIA. See Croatia.

SLAVONIC LANGUAGES & LITERATURE. Leskien (A.) Untersuchungen über Quantität und Betonung in den slavischen Sprachen. pp. 84. 1893. 8°. Ac. Leipsic. K. Gesellschaft der Wissenschaften. Abhandlungen. Bd. 30. Ac. 700/4.

Masing (L.) Zur Laut- und Akzentlehre der macedoslavischen Dialekte. pp. 146. St. Petersburg, 1891. 8°. 12975. l. 24.

Weiske (G.) Slavische Sprachreste aus dem Havellande. Rathenow, 1890, etc. 8°. 12975. m.

Ciàmpoli (D.) Letterature Slave. pp. 141. Milano, 1891. 8°. 012200. h. 57.

Krek (G.) Einleitung in die slavische Literaturgeschichte. pp. 887. Graz, 1887. 8°. 011824. i.

See also Bohemian, Croatian, Polish, Russian, Slovakian, Slovenisch Languages and Literature.

SLAVONIC RACES. Eim (G.) Die Slaven und der Dreibund. Rede, etc. pp. 41. Wien, 1892. 8°. 8026. i. 6. (13.)

Krauss (F. S.) Volksglaube der Südslaven. pp. 176. 1890. 8°. Darstellungen aus dem Gebiete der nichtchristlichen Religionsgeschichte. Bd. 2. 4506. f.

Leger (L.) Russes et Slaves. pp. 346. Paris, 1890. 8°. 8094. aa. 12.

Moravičanský (F. S. P.) Das slavische Altgermanien. pp. 125. Brünn, 1882. 8°. 9325. aaa. 12.

Popowski (J.) Nationalität—Race. Slavismus—Panslavismus. pp. 112. Wien, 1893. 8°. 8092. ee. 14.

See also Balkan Mountains: Bohemia: Bulgaria: Croatia: Poland: Russia: Servia, etc.

SLEEP AND DREAM. Browne (Sir J. C.) On Dreamy Mental States. pp. 32. Lond. 1895. 8°. Pam. 39.

Giessler (M.) Aus den Tiefen des Traumlebens. pp. 210. Halle, 1890. 8°. 8464. dd. 36.

SLEEP AND DREAM—continued.

Graffunder (P.) Traum und Traumdeutung. pp. 38. 1894. 8°. Virchow (R. v.) Sammlung wissenschaftlicher Vorträge. Hft. 197. 12249. m.

Greenwood (F.) Imagination in Dreams. pp. 198. Lond. 1894. 8°. 8462. b. 37.

Macfarlane (A. W.) Dreaming. pp. 52. Edinb. 1891. 8°. 07305. h. 6. (8.)

Maillard (E.) Étude sur le Sommeil. pp. 72. Savenay, 1893. 8°. 7410. c. 46.

Mumford (A. A.) Waking, sleeping and dreaming. pp. 32. Manch. 1893. 8°. 8462. d. 20. (5.)

Rosenbaum (E.) Warum müssen wir schlafen? pp. 62. Berl. 1892. 8°. 07305. h. 18. (11.)

Schmick (J. H.) Die nachirdische Fortdauer der Persönlichkeit. pp. 149. Leipz. 1891. 8°. 7410. ee. 33.

Scholz (F.) Sleep and Dreams. pp. 147. N.Y. 1893. 8°. 7410. bb. 44.

Schultze (F.) of Bonn. Über Neurosen und Neuropsychosen nach Traum. pp. 28. 1891. 8°. Volkmann (R. v.) Sammlung klinischer Vorträge. N.F. No. 14. 7441. g.

Edgelow (G.) Modern Sleeplessness. pp. 16. Lond. 1891. 8°. 7620. a. 13.

Reichenbach (C. v.) Baron. Ein schwerer sensitiv somnambuler Krankheitsfall geheilt, etc. pp. 160. Leipz. 1891. 8°. 7410. e. 35.

See also Hypnotism.

SLIDE RULE. Chadwick (J.) Slide-Rule Instructor. pp. 88. Manch. 1894. 8°. 8767. b. 36.

Nasmith (J. W.) The Slide Rule. pp. 272. Manch. 1895. 8°. 8532. bbb. 45.

Pickworth (C. N.) The Slide Rule. pp. 56. Manch. 1894. 8°. 8533. de. 30.

See also Engineering: Logarithms.

SLIGO, County and Town. O'Rorke (T.) History of Sligo. 2 vol. Dubl. 1890. 8°. 10390. f. 7.

SLIVNICA, Battles of. See Bulgaria: Servia.

SLOUGH. Slough. Stray notes upon Slough. pp. 79. 1892. 8°. 10368. g. 43.

SLOVAKIAN LANGUAGE. Maršall (G.) Die Kunst die slovakische Sprache zu erlernen. pp. 180. 1890. 8°. Die Kunst der Polyglottie. Th. 24. 12902. c.

SLOVENISCH LANGUAGE. Janežič (A.) Deutsch-slovenisches Hand-Wörterbuch. pp. 841. Klagenfurt, 1889. 8°. 12975. i. 15.

Pečnik (C. J.) Lehrbuch der slovenischen Sprache. pp. 191. 1890. 8°. Die Kunst der Polyglottie. Th. 31. 12902. c.

SLOYD. See Education, Manual.

SLUGS. See Mollusca.

SLYMBRIDGE. Bazeley (W.) Slymbridge Church. pp. 9. Gloucester, 1890. 8°. 10348. d. 19. (6.)

SMALL HOLDINGS ACT, 1892. See Land, England.

SMALL-POX AND VACCINATION. Ac. Paris. Académie de Médecine. Rapport sur les vaccinations en France, 1890. pp. 175. Melun, 1892. 8°. 7561. k. 12.

Crookshank (E. M.) Prevention of Small-Pox. pp. 40. Lond. 1894. 8°. 7561. k. 26. (7.)

Edwardes (E. J.) Vaccination and small-pox, showing that compulsory re-vaccination is necessary. pp. 78. Lond. 1892. 8°. 7306. df. 20. (6.)

SMALL-POX, etc.—*continued.*

ENGLAND AND WALES. *Local Government Board.* Memorandum on the steps to be taken in places where Small-pox is prevalent. pp. 6.
Lond. 1893. fol.   7560. k. 7. (1.)

—— Memoranda as to Certificates of "Insusceptibility" to Vaccination. pp. 3.
Lond. 1891. 8°.   07305. h. 16. (7.)

FUERST (L.) Der Stand der animalen Vaccination. pp. 44. 1891. 8°. VOLKMANN (R. v.) Sammlung klinischer Vorträge. Nr. 30. 7441. g.

HART (E. A.) Essays on State Medicine. Compulsory vaccination. 2 pt. *Lond.* 1894. 8°.
         6095. b. 33.

—— The Truth about Vaccination. pp. 59.
Lond. 1895. 8°.   7561. d. 8.

HAY (M.) Die Kuhpockenimpfung in Deutschland, Holland, Belgien und Österreich. pp. 97.
Wien, 1890. 8°.   7561. i. 32.

HUTTON (A. W.) The Vaccination Question.
pp. 195. *Lond.* 1895. 8°.   7561. aaa. 29.

IRELAND. *Local Government Board.* Rules for the performance of vaccination. pp. 89.
Dubl. 1892. 8°.   7561. aaa. 27.

LEVY (J. H.) The Bird that laid the Vaccination egg. pp. 11. *Lond.* 1892. 8°.
       7306. df. 19. (14.)

LIGUE. Ligue universelle des antivaccinateurs. Congrès de Paris, 1889. pp. 106.
Brux. 1890. 8°.   7561. g. 12.

LONDON. *Society for the Abolition of Compulsory Vaccination.* Catalogue of anti-vaccination Literature. pp. 44. *Lond.* 1895. 8°. Pam. 6.

—— The legend of the Smallpox Hospital Nurses saved from small-pox by re-vaccination. pp. 20. *Lond.* 1895. 8°.   Pam. 39.

MILNES (A.) Theory and practice of Vaccinosyphilis. pp. 24. *Lond.* 1891. 8°.
       07305. f. 5. (7.)

—— What about Vaccination? pp. 80.
Lond. 1893. 8°.   7561. aaa. 24.

NEUMAN (F. W.) The Vaccination Question.
pp. 15. *Lond.* 1895. 8°.   Pam. 39.

PICKERING (J.) Which? Sanitation or vaccination. pp. 362. *Lond.* 1892. 8°.   7561. k. 11.

POOLE (T. D.) Vaccination eruptions. pp. 120.
Edinb. 1893. 8°.   7561. e. 7.

POWER (W. H.) Distribution of Small-Pox in the Metropolis, 1876–85. *Lond.* 1888. 8°.
       7687. eee. 34.

TEBB (W.) Story of fourteen years' Struggle for parental emancipation from the vaccination tyranny. pp. 20. *Lond.* 1894. 8°.
       7306. e. 22. (8.)

—— Public Health. The Increase of Cancer.
Lond. 1892. 8°.   07305. f. 17. (4.)

—— Public Health. Leprosy and Vaccination. pp. 20. *Lond.* 1891. 8°.   07305. e. 23. (16.)

—— Personal statement of the results of Vaccination. pp. 4. 1891. 8°.   7306. e. 22. (3.)

THÉRY (L.) Statistique de la mortalité par variole en Angleterre, 1871–92. pp. 83.
Paris, 1894. 8°.   7560. e. 20.

VINCENTI (C.) La Vaccinazione nel secolo XIX.
pp. 110. *Milano*, 1894. 8°.   7561. cc. 4.

WALLACE (A. R.) Forty-five years of registration statistics, proving vaccination to be useless and dangerous. pp. 45. *Lond.* 1889. 8°.
       7306. df. 22. (4.)

WINTERBURN (G. W.) The Value of Vaccination. pp. 182. *Phila.* 1886. 8°. 7560. de. 20.
See also DISEASE, *Infectious.*

SMOKE ABATEMENT, etc. GOODACRE (W. G.) Scheme for drawing off Smoke, *etc.* pp. 6. *Lond.* 1891. 8°.   8708. h. 16. (7.)

SMOKE ABATEMENT, etc.—*continued.*

HORSFALL (T. C.) Nuisance of Smoke from domestic fires. pp. 20. 1892. 8°. MANCHESTER. *Noxious Vapours Abatement Association.* Air Pollution.   8755. bbb. 31.

MAC LEOD (M. C. V.) Life or Death. pp. 303.
Lond. 1892. 8°.   8703. aa. 27.

SMUGGLING. SHORE (*Hon.* H. N.) Smuggling Days and smuggling ways. pp. 287.
Lond. 1892. 8°.   6057. bb. 31.

SMYRNA. ROUGON (F.) Smyrne. Situation commerciale. pp. 706. *Paris*, 1892. 8°.
       08227. e. 43.

SNAKES. &c. London. *British Museum.* Catalogue of the Snakes in the Museum.
Lond. 1893, *etc.* 8°.   7207. gg.

—— Calcutta. *Indian Museum.* List of Snakes in the Museum. pp. 79. *Calcutta*, 1891. 8°.
       7290. b. 8.

BLEYER-HEYDEN (G.) Schlangenfauna Deutschlands. pp. 87. *Kolmar*, 1891. 8°. 7290. f. 20.

CEYLON. Concerning Snakes in Ceylon. pp. 29.
Colombo, 1891. 12°.   Pam. 42.

CLARKE (J. H.) Therapeutics of the serpent poisons. pp. 31. *Lond.* 1893. 8°. 7321. e. 14.

HINDU. Snake-bites and their treatment.
pp. 62. *Calcutta*, 1889. 8°. 07305. h. 8. (2.)

SUNDOWNER. Snakes. pp. 116. *Lond.* 1895. 8°.
       7290. a. 26.

See also REPTILES.

SNEINTON. CROPPER (P. T.) Enquiry into the origin of the names of Nottingham and Sneinton. pp. 10. *Derby*, 1894. 8°. Pam. 90.

SNOWDON. HUSON (T.) Round about Snowdon. *Lond.* 1894. fol.   K.T.C. 25. b. 3.

SNOW SHOES. *See* SKATING.

SOAP. CARPENTER (W. L.) Treatise on the manufacture of Soap. pp. 446.
Lond. 1895. 8°.   07944. e. 53.

GADD (W. L.) Soap Manufacture. pp. 224.
1893. 8°. WOOD (*Sir* H. T.) Technological Handbooks.   2266. a. 39.

LEFEVRE (J.) Savons et Bougies. pp. 424.
Paris, 1894. 12°.   07944. c. 45.

WILLIAMS (T.) Soap Bubbles. pp. 14.
Liverpool, 1890. 8°.   8708. i. 25. (8.)

See also FATS AND OILS.

SOAVE. CAMUZZONI (G.) Soave e il suo castello. pp. 291. *Verona*, 1893. 8°. 10136. h. 13.

SOCIALISM.

Bibliography.

STAMMHAMMER (J.) Bibliographie des Socialismus und Communismus. pp. 303.
Jena, 1893. 8°.   BBC. c. 17.

General.

ADDERLEY (C. B.) *Baron Norton.* Socialism. pp. 35. *Lond.* 1895. 8°.   08277. h. 4.

AMMON (O.) Der Darwinismus gegen die Sozialdemokratie. pp. 112. *Hamburg*, 1891. 8°.
       8277. ee. 28. (1.)

ANDELFINGER (A.) Der Sozialismus und die Arbeitgeber. *N.Y.* 1892. 8°.   08276. f. 50.

ARNOLD, *Meister.* Socialismus, der Erzfeind steht von der Thüre. pp. 61.
Strassb. 1891. 16°.   8277. a. 60. (8.)

ASHBURN (W.) Socialism re-considered. pp. 32.
Manch. 1895. 8°.   Pam. 82.

BARBECK (H.) Die soziale Frage und das Programm Bebel's. pp. 31. *Nürnberg*, 1890. 8°.
       Pam. 82.

BAX (E. B.) Outlooks from the new standpoint. pp. 203. *Lond.* 1891. 8°.   08276. e. 13.

SOCIALISM.—General—*continued.*

PISACANE (C.) Saggio sulla rivoluzione.
pp. 269. *Bologna*, 1894. 8°. 08275. f. 17.

POLOZOW (A. L.) *Countess.* Sul Socialismo.
pp. 29. *Napoli*, 1893. 8°. 8282. cc. 48. (11.)

POMPERY (É. de) Le dernier Mot du Socialisme
rationnel. pp. 131. *Paris*, 1894. 12°.
08275. e. 24.

PROGRAM. Det socialistiske Program. pp. 253.
1888. 8°. WÜNBLAD (E.) Socialistiske Skrifter.
No. 7, 8. 8277. a.

RAE (J.) Contemporary Socialism. pp. 508.
Lond. 1891. 8°. 2240. bb. 15.

REICHESBERG (N.) Sozialismus und Anarchismus.
pp. 40. *Bern*, 1895. 8°. Pam. 82.

REID (A.) Vox Clamantium. The Gospel of
the People. pp. 365. *Lond.* 1894. 8°.
8409. h. 19.

RHENANUS. Der Himmel der Sozialdemokratie
in Traum und Wirklichkeit. pp. 78.
Stuttgart, 1893. 8°. 08276. df. 13.

RICHARDSON (J.) How it can be done; constructive socialism. pp. 184. *Lond.* 1895. 8°.
08276. ee. 2.

RICHESSE. Richesse et misère. pp. 72.
Paris, 1888. 8°. Pam. 82.

RICHTER (E.) Richter gegen Bebel. pp. 40.
Berl. 1893. 8°. 8282. ff. 10. (7.)

—— Pictures of the socialistic future. pp. 134.
Lond. 1893. 8°. 012554. g. 54.

RIENZI. Socialisme en Vrijheid. pp. 212.
Amsterd. 1893. 8°. 08275. f. 1.

ROBERTSON (E. S.) The impracticability of
Socialism. 1891. 8°. MACKAY (T.) Plea for
Liberty. 8276. g. 44.

ROCQUIGNY DU FAYEL (H. M. R. de) *Count.* Les
Syndicats agricoles et le socialisme agraire.
pp. 344. *Paris*, 1893. 8°. 08275. e. 6.

ROMANO-CATANIA (G.) Sul Comunismo. Notizie
storiche. pp. 80. *Palermo*, 1892. 8°.
8277. h. 20. (11.)

SCHAEFFLE (A. E. F.) Impossibility of Social
Democracy. pp. 419. *Lond.* 1892. 8°.
08276. e. 32.

SCHALL (E.) Die Socialdemokratie in ihren
Wahrheiten und Irrthümern. pp. 372.
Berl. 1893. 8°. 8277. cc. 44.

SCHEEL (H. v.) Socialismus und Kommunismus.
1890. 8°. SCHOENBERG (G. v.) Handbuch der
politischen Oekonomie. Bd. 1. 8207. k. 8.

SCHMIDT-WARNECK (F.) Zur Sache: "Innerliche
Überwindung der Socialdemokratie." pp. 79.
Braunschweig, 1894. 8°. 8277. h. 31.

SCHNEIDT (C.) Die eiserne Maske. pp. 48.
Berl. 1892. 8°. 8277. de. 38.

SHAW (G. B.) Anarchism versus State Socialism.
pp. 8. *Lond.* 1889. 8°. Pam. 82.

SMART (H. R.) Socialism and Drink. pp. 16.
Manch. 1890. 8°. Pam. 85.

SOZIALDEMOKRAT. Der Sozialdemokrat kommt!
pp. 24. *Freiburg*, 1890. 8°. 08276. i. 2. (11.)

SOZIALDEMOKRATIE. Die Sozialdemocratie und
der moderne Statt. pp. 52. *Berl.* 1890. 8°.
08276. i. 1. (5.)

—— Die Sozialdemokratie eine Zuchtruthe
Gottes. pp. 16. *Leipz.* 1892. 8°.
8277. h. 20. (12.)

SOCIALISM. Socialism and Individualism. pp. 19.
1890. 8°. 8277. ee. 29. (14.)

SPARLING (H. H.) [Collection of cuttings, *etc.*,
relating to socialism.] 2 vol. 1868–94. fol.
1850. d. 18.

STACKELBERG (F.) La République sociale.
pp. 34. *Paris*, 1890. 8°. 8277. aa. 69. (4.)

SOCIALISM.—General—*continued.*

STEGMANN (C.) and HUGO (C.) Handbuch des
Socialismus. *Zürich*, 1894, *etc.* 8°. 08276. g.

STIRLING (J.) The New State; or, unorthodox
socialism. pp. 79. *Lond.* 1891. 8°.
8276. a. 77.

TERRE. Une Terre promise, ou le Paradis des
socialistes. pp. 32. *Bruges*, 1891. 16°.
8282. a. 85. (1.)

THÉRON (E.) Individualisme, socialisme et
paupérisme. pp. 456. *Paris*, 1894. 12°.
08275. e. 31.

THOMSON (W.) Prospectus of Socialism. pp. 270.
Lond. 1894. 8°. 08275. ee. 4.

TOENNIES (F.) Gemeinschaft und Gesellschaft.
pp. 294. *Leipz.* 1887. 8°. 08276. h. 45.

TOUPET (A.) Examen du Socialisme. pp. 368.
Lille, 1893. 8°. 08276. f. 80.

TRAUB (T.) Warum gehen wir nicht mit der
Sozialdemokratie. pp. 43. *Stuttgart*, 1891. 8°.
8277. de. 28. (8.)

TRICOT (H.) Demain je serai des vôtres. pp. 20.
Cette, 1890. 8°. Pam. 69.

TUCKER (B. R.) State Socialism and Anarchism.
pp. 16. *Lond.* 1895. 8°. Pam. 82.

TUERK (J.) Hervorbringung und Vertheilung
der Werthe in der sozialistischen Gesellschaft.
pp. 106. *Hamb.* 1892. 8°. 8277. de. 43.

ULFERS (S.) Middelen door Socialisten in het
werk gesteld tot het bereiken van hun doel.
pp. 44. *Utrecht*, 1891. 8°. 08276. i. 1. (10.)

VALLI (E.) L'Imperatore socialista. pp. 65.
Roma, 1890. 8°. 8277. ee. 3. (13.)

VARGAS MACCIUCCA (M. de) *Prince di Migliano.*
Il socialismo e la questione sociale. pp. 119.
Napoli, 1894. 8°. 8277. h. 29.

VILLARD (A.) Le Socialisme moderne. pp. 298.
Paris, 1889. 12°. 08276. f. 39.

VILLEY (E.) Le Socialisme contemporain.
pp. 245. *Paris*, 1895. 8°. 08277. h. 11.

VINTON (A. D.) Looking further backward.
pp. 236. *Albany*, 1890. 8°. 012705. eee. 53.

WEBB (S.) Progress of Socialism. pp. 18.
Lond. 1888. 8°. 8282. ff. 11. (2.)

—— The Fabian Society. pp. 9.
Netherfield, 1891. 8°. 08275. ee. 22. (12.)

WIINBLAD (E.) Socialistiske Skrifter.
Kjøbenh. 1888, *etc.* 8°. 8277. a.

WINTERER (L.) Le Socialisme contemporain.
pp. 406. *Paris*, 1894. 12°. 08275. f. 10.

ZANETTI (F.) Il Socialismo, sue cause e suoi
effetti. pp. 666. *Torino*, 1893. 8°. 08275. f. 6.

BELLOT (É.) Poètes et chansonniers socialistes.
pp. 94. *Paris*, 1892. 8°. 011824. e. 39.

SOCIALISTS. Poems for Socialists. pp. 20.
Aberd. 1891. 16°. 08276. de. 8. (9.)

—— Songs for Socialists. pp. 40.
Aberd. 1890. 16°. 08276. de. 8. (5.)

SONG BOOK. Songbook for Socialists. pp. 34.
Lond. 1893. 16°. Pam. 82.

See also ANARCHISM: CAPITAL AND LABOUR:
POLITICAL ECONOMY: SOCIAL QUESTIONS.

Christianity and Socialism.

ABRAHAM (W. H.) Studies of a Socialist Parson.
pp. 220. *Hull*, 1892. 8°. 8277. de. 13.

AUERSWALD (O. T.) Die Religion der Socialdemokratie. pp. 32. *Leipz.* 1892. 8°.
8282. ff. 10. (3.)

BERGSTRÖM (L.) Kristendom och Socialism.
pp. 19. 1893. 8°. Svenska Spörsmål. No. 9.
8093. bb.

BIERBOWER (A.) Socialism of Christ. pp. 202.
Chicago, 1890. 8°. 4017. f. 16.

SOCIALISM.—Christianity, etc.—*cont.*

BLISSARD (W.) Socialism of Christianity.
pp. 121. *Lond.* 1891. 8°. 08276. f. 10.

CONWAY, afterwards GLASIER (K. St. J.) The Religion of Socialism. pp. 16.
Manch. 1890. 8°. 8282. cc. 47. (2.)

CAMAUËR (J.) Évangile contre Socialisme.
pp. 55. *Louvain*, 1895. 8°. Pam. 82.

DIETZGEN (J.) Die Religion der Sozialdemo-kratie. pp. 48. *Berl.* 1891. 8°.
08276. f. 40. (4.)

HARRISON (F.) Moral and religious Socialism.
pp. 26. *Lond.* 1891. 8°. 8277. ee. 3. (15.)

HIRD (J. D.) Jesus the Socialist. pp. 27.
Lond. 1896. 12°. Pam. 82.

JOLY (H.) Le Socialisme chrétien. pp. 336.
Paris, 1892. 8°. 8277. de. 16.

KALTHOFF (A.) Christliche Theologie und socialistische Weltanschauung. pp. 22.
Berl. 1894. 8°. 8282. ff. 10. (10.)

KIRCHE. Kirche und Sozialismus.
Erfurt, 1892, *etc.* 8°. 08276. h.

LAAN (C. L.) Het Socialisme en het christelijk huisgezin. pp. 29. *Utrecht*, 1893. 8°.
8282. g. 26. (9.)

LAPEYRE (P.) Le Socialisme catholique.
Paris, 1894, *etc.* 8°. 3900. c. 26.

NICHOLAS (W.) Christianity and Socialism.
pp. 220. *Lond.* 1893. 8°. 08275. m. 1.

NITTI (F. S.) Il Socialismo cattolico. pp. 417.
Torino, 1891. 8°. 08276. g. 26.

—— Catholic Socialism. pp. 432.
Lond. 1895. 8°. 08276. i. 43.

—— Le Socialisme catholique. pp. 410.
Paris, 1894. 8°. 08276. i. 37.

P., A. Der Sozialismus als Feind der Religion und die Volksschule. pp. 32. *Berl.* 1892. 8°.
Pam. 82.

PALLEN (C. B.) The Catholic Church and Socialism. pp. 48. *St. Louis*, 1890. 8°.
08276. f. 23. (9.)

SCHALL (E.) Das Wesen der Sozialdemokratie und die christliche Religion. pp. 47. 1894. 8°.
Kirche und Sozialismus. No. 2. 08276. h.

SPRAGUE (P. W.) Christian Socialism. pp. 204.
N.Y. 1891. 8°. 8276. aa. 57.

TUCKWELL (W.) Christian Socialism. pp. 101.
Lond. 1891. 8°. 8275. aa. 53.

VALEZ (A.) Le socialisme catholique en France.
pp. 144. *Montauban*, 1892. 8°. 08276. h. 30.

WESTCOTT (B. F.) *Bp. of Durham.* Socialism.
pp. 14. *Lond.* 1890. 8°. 08276. f. 20. (14.)
See also SOCIAL SCIENCE, *Christianity and Social Questions.*
For the Papal Encyclical of 15 May, 1891, *see* CAPITAL AND LABOUR.

History, and Socialism in various Countries.

BERNSTEIN (E.) and KAUTSKY (C.) Die Geschichte des Sozialismus in Einzeln-Darstellungen. *Stuttgart*, 1894, *etc.* 8°. 08276. k.

JANET (P.) Les Origines du Socialisme contemporain. pp. 169. *Paris*, 1893. 12°.
08275. f. 5.

KIRKUP (T.) History of Socialism. pp. 301.
Lond. 1892. 8°. 8277. ee. 11.

MALON (B.) Histoire du Socialisme. 5 tom.
Paris, 1882–85. 8°. 8285. ff. 5.

ONCLAIR (A.) Le Communisme dans l'histoire.
pp. 219. *Namur*, 1895. 8°. 08277. h. 7.

SOCIALISM.—History, etc.—*continued.*

WARSCHAUER (O.) Geschichte des Socialismus.
Leipz. 1892, *etc.* 8°. 08276. g.

POEHLMANN (R.) Geschichte des antiken Kommunismus und Sozialismus.
München, 1893, *etc.* 8°. 08276. i.

JAURÈS (J.) De primis socialismi Germanici lineamentis apud Lutherum, Kant, Fichte et Hegel. pp. 83. *Tolosae*, 1891. 8°. 08276. g. 33.

MUEHLHAUSEN (A.) Goethe ein Sozialist?
pp. 30. *Leipz.* 1892. 8°. Pam. 82.

SCULL (W. D.) Goethe and Socialism. pp. 16.
Lond. 1888. 8°. Pam. 82.

WEILL (G.) Un Précurseur du Socialisme; Saint-Simon. pp. 247. *Paris*, 1894. 8°. 08275. f. 15.

WEISENGRUEN (P.) Die socialwissenschaftlichen Ideen Saint-Simon's. pp. 17. *Basel*, 1895. 8°.
8277. g. 51.

ALHAIZA (A.) Historique de l'École sociétaire fondée par C. Fourier. pp. 152.
Paris, 1894. 8°. 08276. f. 85.

LUX (H.) E. Cabet und der ikarische Communismus. pp. 294. *Stuttgart*, 1894. 8°.
08275. ec. 16.

BERNSTEIN (E.) F. Lassalle as a social reformer.
pp. 192. *Lond.* 1893. 8°. 08276. e. 52.

DAWSON (W. H.) German Socialism and F. Lassalle. pp. 300. *Lond.* 1891. 8°. 08276. e. 3.

MAYER (G.) Lassalle als Sozialökonom.
pp. 138. *Berl.* 1894. 8°. 08276. g. 72.

LASSALLE (F. J. G.) Arbejderprogram. pp. 49.
1891. 8°. WÜNBLAD (E.) Socialistiske Skrifter.
No. 12. 8277. a.

JONES (L.) The Life of R. Owen. pp. 443.
Lond. 1895. 8°. 10827. bbb. 33.

BACCI (G.) Mazzini e il Socialismo. pp. 42.
Mantova, 1893. 8°. 8282. ff. 11. (6.)

SPERBER (O. v.) Die socialpolitischen Ideen A. Herzens. pp. 147. *Leipz.* 1894. 8°. 08276. i. 23.

Australia.

ADELAIDE. *South Australian Fabian Society.*
Tracts. *Adelaide*, 1893, *etc.* 8°. 08276. i.

FAIRFIELD (C.) State Socialism in the Antipodes.
1891. 8°. MACKAY (T.) Plea for Liberty.
8276. g. 44.

FORTESCUE (*Hon.* J. W.) State Socialism and the collapse in Australia. 1894. 8°. MACKAY (T.) Policy of Free Exchange. 08225. k. 5.

Europe.

MAGALHÃES LIMA (S. de) O Socialismo na Europa.
pp. 369. *Lisboa*, 1892. 8°. 08277. f. 10.

WYZEWA (T. de) Le Mouvement socialiste en Europe. pp. 283. *Paris*, 1892. 8°. 08276. f. 41.

DEMARTEAU (J.) Le Socialisme belge. pp. 96.
Liège, 1895. 8°. 8277. ee. 21.

MARTINET (C.) Le Socialisme en Danemark.
pp. 116. *Paris*, 1893. 12°. 8277. de. 54.

INTERNATIONAL WORKING MEN'S ASSOCIATION.
Der Bürgerkrieg in Frankreich. pp. 71.
Berl. 1891. 8°. 8282. ff. 11. (4.)

BOURDEAU (J.) Le Socialisme allemand et le Nihilisme russe. pp. 318. *Paris*, 1892. 12°.
8277. de. 35.

BISMARCK-SCHOENHAUSEN (O. E. L. v.) *Prince.*
Bismarck und die Sozialdemocratie. pp. 38.
Dresden, 1895. 8°. Pam. 72.

GERMANY. *Sozialdemokratische Partei.* Protokoll über die Verhandlungen des Parteitages zu Halle, 1890. pp. 320. *Berl.* 1890. 8°.
8073. d. 15.

—— Protokoll über die Verhandlungen des Parteitages zu Erfurt, 1891. pp. 368.
Berl. 1891. 8°. 8073. d. 14.

SOCIALISM.—History, etc.—_continued._

GERMANY. Programm der sozialdemokratischen Partei Deutschlands beschlossen, auf dem Parteitag zu Erfurt, 1891. pp. 8. _Berl._ 1891. 8°.
Pam. 82.

SAVIGNY (M.) Le Mouvement socialiste en Allemagne. pp. 143. _Niort_, 1890. 8°.
8277. aa. 66.

BUHR (V.) Der Sozialismus in der deutschen Armee. pp. 46. _Berl._ 1893. 8°.
08275. ee. 21. (6.)

CLAUSS (O.) Der Kampf gegen die Sozialdemokratie in der Armee, _etc._ pp. 55. 1891. 8°.
GERMANY. _Army._ Schriften zur deutschen Heeresreform. No. 3.
8831. l.

CEBALLOS Y CRUZADA (C. G. de) El 1° de Mayo en España. pp. 128. _Madrid_, 1892. 8°.
8277. ee. 40.

LLUNAS (J.) Los Partidos socialistas españoles. pp. 15. _Barcelona_, 1892. 8°. 8282. ff. 11. (5.)

BERGHOFF-ISING (F.) Die socialistische Arbeiterbewegung in der Schweiz. pp. 415.
Leipz. 1895. 8°. 08277. g. 10.

United States of America.

COGNETTI DE MARTIIS (S.) Il Socialismo negli Stati Uniti. 1886, _etc._ 8°. Biblioteca dell' economista. Ser. 3. Vol. 9. 8205. l.

GILMAN (N. P.) Socialism and the American Spirit. pp. 376. _Lond._ 1893. 8°. 8277. ee. 38.

SARTORIUS VON WALTERSHAUSEN (F. H. W. A. v.) _Baron._ Der moderne Socialismus in den Vereinigten Staaten. pp. 422. _Berl._ 1890. 8°.
8276. h. 24.

SAVIGNY (M.) Le Mouvement socialiste en Amérique. pp. 143. _Niort_, 1890. 8°.
8277. aa. 66.

SOTHERAN (C.) H. Greeley and other pioneers of American socialism. pp. 343. _N.Y._ 1892. 8°.
08276. f. 53.

For other works on Socialism in each country, _see_ CAPITAL AND LABOUR : SOCIAL SCIENCE.

SOCIAL SCIENCE: SOCIAL QUESTIONS. Ac. Oxford. _Society for the Study of Social Ethics._ Journal. _Oxf._ 1892, _etc._ 8°.
2131.

—— Philadelphia. _Academy of Political Science._ Annals. _Phila._ 1890, _etc._ 8°. Ac. 2383.

ADDAMS (J.) Philanthropy and Social Progress. pp. 268. _N.Y._ 1893. 8°. 08276. g. 55.

ALBERTI JÀCONA (A.) Iniziativa privata e Legislazione sociale. pp. 256. _Palermo_, 1890. 8°.
8277. a. 53.

AMSTERDAM. _Sociaal Congres._ Proces-verbaal van het Sociaal Congres. pp. 580.
Amsterd. 1892. 8°. 08276. k. 16.

ANDRADE (D. A.) Our Social System, how it affects those who work for their living.
Melbourne, 1890. 8°. 8277. ee. 3. (7.)

B., A. Wie das Volk denkt. Ein Beitrag zur Beantwortung socialer Fragen auf Grundlage ethnischer Elementargedanken. pp. 223.
Berl. 1892. 8°. 8277. h. 25.

BACKHAUS (W. E.) Allen die Erde ! pp. 211.
Leipz. 1893. 8°. 8277. cc. 49.

BAECKER (C.) Die Volksunterhaltung von sozialpolitischen Standpunkte. pp. 83. _Berl._ 1893. 8°.
Pam. 82.

BARNETT (S. A.) Practicable Socialism. pp. 328. _Lond._ 1894. 8°. 08275. ee. 8.

BAYLY (M.) and (E. B.) Home Weal and home woe. pp. 367. _Lond._ 1892. 8°.
8409. cc. 26.

BERGERET ( ) Plan d'Organisation sociale, selon les lois naturelles. pp. 98.
Orléans, 1893. 8°. 08276. i. 8.

SOCIAL SCIENCE, etc.—_continued._

BORIN-FOURNET (J.) La Société moderne et la question sociale. pp. 456. _Paris_, 1893. 12°.
08276. g. 56.

BOSANQUET (B.) Aspects of the Social Problem. pp. 334. _Lond._ 1895. 8°. 08275. ee. 27.

BRABAZON (R.) _Earl of Meath._ Social Aims. pp. 262. _Lond._ 1893. 8°. 08276. g. 53.

BRAITHWAITE (J.) Social Enigmas. pp. 100.
Lond. 1895. 8°. 08276. df. 16.

BRETTES (F.) Conférences sur la Vie sociale. pp. 292. _Paris_, 1890. 12°. 8282. aa. 55.

BRINKMANN (W.) Kirche und Humanität im Kampfe gegen die sittliche Noth der Gegenwart. pp. 128. _Berl._ 1891. 8°. 08276. h. 10.

BROICH (F. A. C. M. v.) _Baron._ Sozialreform und Genossenschaftswesen. pp. 356. _Berl._ 1890. 8°.
8277. a. 52.

C., J. La Question sociale résolue. pp. 250.
Brux. 1893. 8°. 08277. g. 6.

CALABER ( ) Essai sur la Question sociale. pp. 217. _Paris_, 1893. 8°. 08275. f. 3.

CALDWELL (G. P.) Causa Causæ; primary Laws of Liberty and Freedom. pp. 54.
Lond. 1892. 8°. Pam. 64.

CARNERI (B.) Der moderne Mensch. pp. 235.
Bonn, 1893. 8°. 8462. h. 19.

CERVERD (V.) La Justicia social. pp. 88.
Madrid, 1892. 16°. 8282. a. 85. (2.)

CHAPOT (L.) La Révolution et la question sociale. pp. 79. _Paris_, 1882. 8°. Pam. 82.

CIMBALI (G.) Il diritto del più forte. pp. 215.
Roma, 1892. 8°. 8275. i. 1.

COIT (S.) Neighbourhood Guilds. pp. 150.
Lond. 1891. 8°. 08276. e. 15.

COPENHAGEN. _Sociale Oplysnings Forening._ Den sociale Oplysnings Forenings Smaaskrifter. _København._ 1894, _etc._ 16°. 08276. de.

COSSA (C.) La Riforma sociale. pp. 38.
Genova, 1891. 8°. 8277. h. 20. (4.)

CROISDALE (L.) Social Progress. pp. 4.
Loughborough, 1895. 8°. Pam. 82.

CUNNINGHAM (W.) The Path towards knowledge. pp. 241. _Lond._ 1891. 8°. 4173. cc. 19.

DARNAUD (É.) La Société future. pp. 38.
Foix, 1890. 8°. 8277. ee. 2. (11.)

DAUVISTER-MARY (J.) La Question sociale. pp. 55. 1895. 16°. Pam. 82.

DECKER (P. J. F. de) La Providence dans les faits sociaux. pp. 332. _Brux._ 1893. 8°.
08276. i. 7.

DELBERT (P.) Social Evolution. pp. 319.
Lond. 1891. 8°. 08276. f. 9.

DEMOFILO (A.) La Democrazia e la questione sociale. 2 pt. _Firenze_, 1892. 8°. 8277. de. 37.

DENSLOW (V. B.) The "Why I Ams." An economic symposium. pp. 82. _N.Y._ 1892. 8°.
08276. f. 52.

DIDIER (E.) Des Misères humaines et sociales. pp. 248. _Paris_, 1892. 12°. 8277. de. 19.

DURKHEIM (É.) De la division du Travail social. pp. 471. _Paris_, 1893. 8°. 8277. d. 36.

EMSLEY (B.) Social Questions and national problems. pp. 59. _Bradford_, 1892. 8°.
8277. de. 30. (7.)

ESPAÑA MARTÍN (T.) La Sociedad. Estudio de cuestiones palpitantes. _Toro_, 1894, _etc._ 16°.
8285. a.

FARRAR (F. W.) Social and present-day questions. pp. 377. _Lond._ 1891. 8°. 012357. k. 2.

FAVA (N.) Sulle Cose di stato e Questione sociale. pp. 423. _Milano_, 1890. 8°.
8282. ee. 27.

SOCIAL SCIENCE, etc.—*continued.*

FEATHERMAN (A.) Thoughts and reflections on Modern Society. pp. 352. *Lond.* 1894. 8°.
8409. l. 18.

FRAGAPANE (S.) Contrattualismo e Sociologia contemporanea. pp. 252. *Bologna*, 1892. 8°.
08276. h. 49.

FRANCE. *Ministère de l'Instruction. Comité des travaux historiques, etc.* Bulletin. Section des sciences sociales. *Paris*, 1892, *etc.* 8°. 08225. l.

GIBBINS (H. de B.) English social Reformers. pp. 229. 1892. 8°. SYMES (J. E.) University Extension Series. 012202. g.

GILON (E.) Der Kampf um die Wohlfahrt. 2 Th. *Leipz.* 1892. 8°. 08276. f. 68.

GIRÁLDEZ Y ERRASTI (J.) Observaciones sobre la cuestión social. pp. 16. *Madrid*, 1890. 8°.
Pam. 82.

GREEF (G. de) Les Lois sociologiques. pp. 181. *Paris*, 1893. 8°. 08275. e. 7.

—— Le Transformisme social. pp. 520. *Paris*, 1895. 8°. 08277. g. 24.

GREY (W.) Social work in Australia and London. pp. 12. 1889. 8°. Johns Hopkins University Studies. Notes, 1889. No. 2. Ac. 2689.

GRODTCZINSKY (N.) Moderner Kastengeist in unseren Kultureinrichtungen. pp. 72. *Berl.* 1894. 8°. 8464. bb. 51.

GUÉRIN (U.) L'Évolution sociale. pp. 361. *Paris*, 1891. 12°. 08276. f. 4.

GUMPLOWICZ (L.) Die sociologische Staatsidee. pp. 134. *Graz*, 1892. 8°. 08276. h. 51.

GUNTON (G.) Principles of Social Economics. pp. 451. *Lond.* 1892. 8°. 08277. ff. 4.

HARTMANN (C. R. E. v.) Die sozialen Kernfragen. pp. 571. *Leipz.* 1894. 8°. 08276. h. 60.

HEINRICH (W.) Das Testament des neunzehnten Jahrhunderts. pp. 176. *Berl.* 1893. 8°.
08276. i. 5.

HELLENBACH (L. B.) Das neunzehnte und zwanzigste Jahrhundert. pp. 136. *Leipz.* 1893. 8°.
8276. c. 87.

HORN (E. F. B.) I Dagens Strid. pp. 148. *Kristiania*, 1892. 8°. 012357. e. 85.

JACQUES (L.) Critique sociale, ou comédie humaine. pp. 210. *Brux.* 1893. 8°. 08275. f. 21.

JAMES (W.) Wife-lending. How to preserve the poor, *etc.* pp. 110. *Lond.* 1894. 8°. 08275, e. 18.

JAY (A. O. M.) The Social Problem. pp. 142. *Lond.* 1893. 8°. 08276. df. 12.

JONKER (A. J. T.) Het sociale Vraagstuk. pp. 215. *Rotterdam*, 1893. 8°. 08275. ee. 3.

KAMPF. Kampf oder Kompromiss? Versuch einer Lösung der socialen Frage. pp. 133. *Dresden*, 1895. 8°. 8282. d. 53.

KATÔ (H.) Der Kampf ums Recht des Stärkeren. pp. 154. *Berl.* 1894. 8°. 08276. k. 25.

KAUFFMANN (G.) Die Lösung der socialen Frage. pp. 139. *Leipz.* 1894. 8°. 8282. d. 52.

KIDD (B.) Social Evolution. pp. 388. *Lond.* 1895. 8°. 08275. i. 1.

KOEHLER (O.) Die wahre Natur des Menschen und der sociale Fortschritt. *Leipz.* 1894, *etc.* 8°. 08275. m.

LANGE (J. E.) Socialøkonomiens grundsætninger. pp. 77. *Odense*, 1890. 8°. 8277. ee. 2. (14.)

LEADAM (I. S.) Social Problems and working men. pp. 8. *Altrincham*, 1890. 4°. Pam. 82.

LEGAY (C.) La Question sociale. pp. 238. *Paris*, 1891. 8°. 08276. f. 15.

LINARES NIVAS (A.) Problema social en la España. 1894. 8°. Ac. Madrid. *R. Academia de Ciencias morales.* Discursos de recepcion. Tom. 5. Ac. 142/2.

LINDEN (P. W. A. C. v. d.) De Staat huishoudkunde als sociale wetenschap. pp. 45. *'s Gravenh.* 1891. *etc.* 8°. 08276. k. 4. (4.).

LLUNÄS (J.) Estudios filosófico-sociales. pp. 219. *Barcelona*, 1883. 8°. 08275. de. 4.

—— Questions sociales. pp. 128. *Barcelona*, 1891. 8°. 08275. de. 3.

LOESER (J.) Führer durch die sociale Frage, *etc.* pp. 172. *Karlsruhe*, 1895. 8°. 08276. h. 63.

LILLY (W. S.) On Shibboleths. pp. 261. *Lond.* 1892. 8°. 8009. i. 26.

MACCLELLAND (J.) Social Science and social schemes. pp. 213. *Lond.* 1894. 8°.
08275. ee. 12.

MACKAY (T.) A Plea for Liberty. pp. 326. *Lond.* 1892. 8°. 08276. f. 26.

—— A Policy of Free Exchange. pp. 292. *Lond.* 1894. 8°. 08225. k. 5.

MACKENZIE (J. S.) Intoduction to social philosophy. pp. 454. *Glasg.* 1895. 8°. 08275. ee. 25.

MALLOCK (W. H.) Studies of contemporary Superstition. pp. 302. *Lond.* 1895. 8°.
012356. ff. 1.

MASQUARD (E. de) Études d'économie sociale. pp. 442. *Saint-Césare-les-Nimes*, 1891. *etc.* 8°.
08276. f. 19.

MASSART (J.) and VANDERVELDE (E.) Parasitism organic and social. pp. 124. *Lond.* 1895. 8°.
08276. ee. 10.

NATORP (P.) Pestalozzis Ideen über Arbeiterbildung und soziale Frage. pp. 34. *Heilbronn*, 1894. 8°. 08275. ee. 19.

NORDAU (M. S.) Conventional Lies of our civilization. pp. 346. *Lond.* 1895. 8°.
8409. l. 25.

—— Entartung. 2 Bde. *Berl.* 1892, 93. 8°. 012357. i. 39.

—— Degeneration. pp. 500. *Lond.* 1895. 8°.
012357. k. 24.

—— Regeneration: reply to M. Nordau. pp. 315. *Lond.* 1895. 8°. 8409. l. 30.

OFFERMANN (A.) Ueber die Zukunft der Gesellschaft. pp. 167. *Leipz.* 1893. 8°. 08207. h. 17.

OSENSKY (J.) Beitrag zur Lösung der socialen Frage. pp. 55. *Prag*, 1892. 8°. Pam. 82.

OSTRANDER (D.) Social Growth and stability. pp. 191. *Chicago*, 1895. 8°. 08275. ee. 34.

OUGUELLA (de) *Viscount.* A Lucta social. pp. 446. *Lisboa*, 1893. 8°. 08276. i. 25.

PARIS. *Société d'Économie Sociale.* La Réforme sociale et le centenaire de la Révolution. pp. 645. *Paris*, 1890. 8°. 8275. k. 3.

PEARSON (C. H.) National Life and character. pp. 381. *Lond.* 1894. 8°. 08275. ee. 6.

P.P. *Freiburg.* Zeitschrift für Social- und Wirthschaftsgeschichte. *Freiburg*, 1893, *etc.* 8°. P.P. 1423. hac.

—— *Paris.* La Réforme sociale. *Paris*, 1881, *etc.* 8°. P.P. 1122. b.

—— *Turin.* La Riforma sociale. *Torino*, 1894, *etc.* 8°. P.P. 1423. bk.

PHILIPPOVICH (E. v.) Wirtschaftlicher Fortschritt und Kulturentwicklung. pp. 56. *Freiburg*, 1892. 8°. 8277. ee. 18.

PIERSON (N.) Les délicieuses après-midi du Palais-Bourbon. pp. 339. *Paris*, 1891. 8°.
08276. aa. 56.

PINETON DE CHAMBRUN (J. D. A. de) *Count.* Aux Montagnes d'Auvergne. pp. 148. *Paris*, 1893. 8°. 8277. g. 49.

PLATTER (J.) Kritische Beiträge zur Erkenntnis unserer socialen Zustände. pp. 558. *Basel*, 1894. 8°. 08276. h. 58.

SOCIAL SCIENCE, etc.—*continued.*

POCHHAMMER (M.) and ERMAN (G.) Die moderne Gesellschaft. pp. 42. 1892. 8°. WOLFF (F.) Deutsche Schriften. Reihe 2. Hft. 2. 2250. l.

QUAGLINO (R.) Studi e fenomeni sociali. *Milano*, 1894, *etc.* 8°.   08275. ee.

REID (A.) Vox Clamantium. The Gospel of the people. pp. 365. *Lond.* 1894. 8°. 8409. h. 19.

—— The New Party, described by some of its members. pp. 310. *Lond.* 1895. 8°.
08276. f. 84.

REPUBLIC. The New Republic. pp. 62. *N.Y.* 1894. 16°.   8282. aa. 61. (5.)

ROBERTSON (J. M.) Modern Humanists. Sociological studies. pp. 275. *Lond.* 1891. 8°.
08276. e. 16.

ROSTAND (E.) L'Action sociale par l'initiative privée. pp. 860. *Paris*, 1892. 8°. 8277. h. 26.

SALAMERO Y MARTÍNEZ (J.) La Crisis religiosa, causa de la crisis social. 1894. 8°. Ac. Madrid. *R. Academia de Ciencias morales.* Discursos. Tom. 5.   Ac. 142/2.

SANZ Y ESCARTÍN (E.) El Estado y la reforma social. pp. 292. *Madrid*, 1893. 8°. 8277. 9. 35.

—— De la Autoridad política en la sociedad contemporánea. 1894. 8°. Ac. Madrid. *R. Academia de Ciencias morales.* Discursos. Tom. 6.   Ac. 142/2.

SAROLEA (C.) La question sociale en Angleterre. pp. 40. *Brux.* 1892. 8°.   8282. g. 27. (6.)

SBARBARO (P.) La Sapienza della vita. 2 vol. *Roma*, 1891. 8°.   8411. e. 1.

SCHOT (J. G.) Ons overzeesch bezit en de Sociale Quaestie. pp. 39. *Amsterdam*, 1891. 8°.
08276. i. 1. (9.)

SCRIVENER (S. C.) Our Fields and Cities; misdirected industry. pp. 173. *Lond.* 1891. 8°.   8277. d. 28.

SECRÉTAN (C.) Mon Utopie. pp. 302. *Lausanne*, 1892. 8°.   8405. cc. 37.

SIMON (J. F.) De l'Initiative privée et de l'État en matière de Réformes sociales. pp. 20. *Bordeaux.* 1892. 8°.   Pam. 82.

SIMONIN (A. H.) Synthèse sociale. Fin de l'enfer politique. pp. 502. *Paris*, 1894. 8°.
08276. i. 42.

SINCLAIR (D.) Vera Vita. Philosophy of sympathy. pp. 186. *Lond.* 1892. 8°. 8411. cc. 23.

SIOTTO - PINTÓR (M.) Lo Riforma sociale in Italia, *etc.* pp. 450. *Firenze*, 1894. 8°.
08277. ff. 9.

SMALL (A. W.) Introduction to the study of Society. pp. 384. *N.Y.* 1894. 8°. 08276. g. 70.

SMITH (Goldwin) Essays on Questions of the day. pp 360. *N.Y.* 1893. 8°.   8139. c. 12.

SOCIALARISTOKRAT. Volksdienst. pp. 397. *Berl.* 1893. 8°.   08276. i. 9.

SOCIAL RESTORATION. Social Restoration. pp. 30. *Lond.* 1891. 8°.   8277. ee. 1. (13.)

SPENCER (H.) Social Statics, abridged and revised. pp. 424. *Lond.* 1892. 8°. 2236. e. 11.

STARCKE (C. N.) Samvittighedslivet. *Kphenh.* 1894, *etc.* 8°.   08276. k.

STATHAM (F. R.) The New Kingdom. pp. 157. *Lond.* 1895. 8°.   08275. i. 5.

STEAD (W. T.) If Christ came to Chicago! pp. 472. *Chicago*, 1894. 8°.   08275. f. 20.

STOECKER (A.) Die sociale Lage und Frage. pp. 24. *Gernsbach*, 1890. 8°. 08276. f. 23. (10.)

STRONG (J.) The new Era. pp. 374. *Lond.* 1893. 8°.   4371. aaa. 25.

THÖNNISSEN (T.) La Lutte pour la Vie. pp. 31. *Brux.* 1894. 8°.   Pam. 82.

SOCIAL SCIENCE, etc.—*continued.*

UTOPIA. Towards Utopia. pp. 252. *Lond.* 1894. 8°.   08276. f. 82.

VALDARNINI (A.) Saggi di Filosofia sociale. pp. 264. *Torino*, 1890. 8°.   08276. f. 14.

VAULABELLE (G. de) Théorie de la Société. Les lois caduques. pp. 279. *Paris*, 1891. 8°.
8282. de. 45.

VEGA-REY FALCÓ (L.) La Cuestión social en España. pp. 106. *Madrid*, 1893. 8°.
8282. g. 26. (13.)

VÉRITÉ (É.) Esquisse d'un Plan de réorganisation sociale. pp. 30. *Bordeaux*, 1891. 8°.
8277. ee. 1. (14.)

WENGLER (H.) The Rights of Man. pp. 31. *Lond.* 1894. 8°.   8282. cc. 47. (16.)

WERNER (J.) Sozialrevolution oder Sozialreforme. pp. 64. *Halle*, 1891. 8°. 8276. k. 4. (7.)

WHITE (A.) Tries at Truth. pp. 150. *Lond.* 1891. 8°.   08276. f. 1.

WILLE (B.) Philosophie der Befreiung durch das reine Mittel. pp. 399. *Berl.* 1894. 8°. 8462. d. 18.

WILLIAMSON (A. W.) Social Unrest. pp. 32. *Edinb.* 1895. 8°.   08275. e. 37.

WOLDEMAR. Briefe von der Grenze. pp. 209. *Magdeburg*, 1890. 8°.   8282. df. 43.

WOLF (J) System der Sozialpolitik. *Stuttgart*, 1892, *etc.* 8°.   08276. h. 44.

WOODS (R. A.) English social Movements. pp. 277. *Lond.* 1895. 8°.   08276. ee. 8.

WORTE. Worte an die Zeit. *Döbeln*, 1891, *etc.* 8°.
08276. h. 13.

WYNN (W.) Social Inequalities. pp. 146. *Lond.* 1894. 8°.   8411. b. 52.

ZIEGLER (T.) La Question Sociale est une question morale. pp. 172. *Paris*, 1893. 12°.
08275. f. 2.

ZIMMERMANN (C.) Die Störungen im Mechanismus der Gesellschaft. pp. 100. *Karlsruhe.* 1892. 8°.   8228. aa. 56.

See also CAPITAL AND LABOUR : COOPERATION : FAMILY : LONDON, *Poor:* MARRIAGE : PAUPERISM : POLITICAL ECONOMY : SOCIALISM : SOCIOLOGY : WOMEN.

Christianity and Social Questions.

ADDERLEY (*Hon.* J. G.) The new Floreat. pp. 96. *Lond.* 1894. 8°.   08275. g. 1.

—— Christ and Social Reform. pp. 31. *Lond.* 1893. 8°.   Pam. 77.

ALDA Y SANCHO (V.) *Bp. of Huesca.* Catecismo católico sobre la llamada cuestión social. pp. 152. 1894. 8°.   08275. de. 6.

BOSANQUET (B.) Civilization of Christendom and other studies. pp. 383. 1893. 8°. MUIRHEAD (J. H.) Ethical Library.   8409. i.

COMMONS (J. R.) Social Reform and the Church. pp. 176. *N.Y.* 1894. 8°.   08276. df. 15.

CRAFTS (W. F.) Practical Christian Sociology. pp. 524. *N.Y.* 1895. 8°.   08275. i. 6.

DAVIES (J. L.) Order and growth as involved in the spiritual constitution of society. pp. 141. *Lond.* 1891. 8°.   4456. de. 1.

FRY (T. C.) A social Policy for the Church. pp. 128. *Lond.* 1893. 8°.   08275. e. 3.

GENEVA. *Société chrétienne d'économie sociale.* Le Christianisme et la question sociale. pp. 127. *Genève*, 1892. 8°.   08276. g. 42.

HALSTEAD (W. R.) Civil and religious Forces. pp. 198. *Cincinnati*, 1890. 8°.   4182. c. 28.

HARKER (B. J.) Christianity and the new social demands. pp. 15. *Manch.* 1892. 8°.
8277. ee. 28. (10.)

HODGES (G.) The heresy of Cain. pp. 290. *N.Y.* 1894. 8°.   08275. f. 31.

SOCIAL SCIENCE.—Christianity and Social Questions—*continued.*

LONDON. *Christian Social Union.* Lombard Street in Lent. Sermons on social subjects. pp. 206. *Lond.* 1894. 8°.   4463. dd. 6.

—— Lent in London. Sermons on social subjects. pp. 239. *Lond.* 1895. 8°.   4473. bb. 38.

HYDE (W. de W.) Outlines of social theology. pp. 260. *N.Y.* 1895. 8°.   4371. c. 6.

LEMIRE (J.) Le Cardinal Manning et son action sociale. pp. 285. *Paris,* 1893. 12°.   4856. aa. 19.

MACLEOD (D.) Christ and society. pp. 312. *Lond.* 1892. 8°.   4371. df. 12.

MATHESON (A. S.) The Church and social problems. pp. 375. *Edinb.* 1893. 8°. 8277. de. 53.

MAUMUS (E. V.) L'Église et la Démocratie. pp. 384. *Paris,* 1893. 8°.   8275. aa. 66.

—— La Iglesia y la Democracia. pp. 340. *Madrid,* 1893. 8°.   08275. e. 20.

MUECKE (A.) Die staatlich-reformatorische oder die ultramontane Lösung der socialen Krisis. *Berl.* 1891, *etc.* 8°.   8282. dd.

NATHUSIUS (M. v.) Die Mitarbeit der Kirche an der Lösung der sozialen Frage. *Leipz.* 1893, *etc.* 8°.   8277. dd.

PALIEZ (F.) Le Monde humain. 2 tom. *Paris,* 1894. 8°.   08275. f. 33.

PEARSE (M. G.) Jesus Christ and the People. pp. 253. *Lond.* 1891. 8°.   4223. a. 25.

PRINCE (H. J.) The World's Malady. pp. 310. *Lond.* 1894. 8°.   4371. b. 26.

ROME, *Church of.* Leo XIII., Pope. Letters and addresses on Social Questions. pp. 266. *Lond.* 1895. 8°.   5018. aaa. 4.

SNOW (A.) Christian aspects of the Labour Question. pp. 32. *Lond.* 1894. 8°. Pam. 82.

STUBBS (C. W.) Christ and Economics. pp. 292. *Lond.* 1893. 8°.   8277. ee. 35.

THOMPSON (R. E.) De Civitate Dei. The Divine order of human society. pp. 274. *Phila.* 1891. 8°.   4487. f. 7.

ULFERS (S.) Christendom en sociale quaestie voor achtien eeuwen. pp. 37. *Rotterdam,* 1893. 8°.   8282. g. 26. (12.)

VAUGHAN (D. J.) Questions of the day. pp. 260. *Lond.* 1894. 8°.   4465. f. 22.

VILLECROSE (J.) Le Christ et sa réforme sociale. pp. 318. *Paris,* 1892. 12°.   4224. b. 83.

WEBSTER (W.) Jesus and Democracy. pp. 113. *Manch.* 1895. 8°.   08275. e. 38.

WERNER (J.) Soziales Christentum. pp. 223. *Dessau,* 1895. 8°.   8276. g. 36.

For the Papal Encyclical of 15th May, 1891, *see* CAPITAL AND LABOUR.

SOCIETY ISLANDS. *See* TAHITI.

SOCIOLOGY. TOLMAN (W. H.) and HULL (W. J.) Bibliography of selected sociological references. pp. 73. *N.Y.* 1893. 8°.   Pam. 6.

Ac. Brooklyn. *Ethical Association.* Sociology. pp. 403. *Bost.* 1890. 8°.   7006. bbb. 29.

ANZILOTTI (D.) La Filosofia del diritto e la Sociologia. pp. 220. *Firenze,* 1892. 8°.   8277. g. 50.

AZCÁRATE (G. de) Concepto de la Sociología, 1894. Ac. Madrid. *Real Academia de Ciencias morales, etc.* Discursos, *etc.* Tom. 6.   Ac. 142/2.

BOCCARDO (G.) La Sociologia nella storia, *etc.* pp. 119. 1881. 8°. Biblioteca dell' economista. Ser. 3. Vol. 8.   8205. l.

BRAGA (T.) Systema de Sociologia. pp. 528. *Lisboa,* 1884. 8°.   08276. i. 20.

SOCIOLOGY—*continued.*

DURKHEIM (É.) Les Règles de la méthode sociologique. pp. 186. *Paris,* 1895. 12°.   08275. ee. 35.

ECCLES (R. G.) The Study of applied Sociology. 1892. 8°. Ac. Brooklyn. *Ethical Association.* Evolution Series. No. 19.   7006. bbb.

GUMPLOWICZ (L.) Sociologie und Politik. pp. 162. *Leipz.* 1892. 8°.   08276. g. 32.

LETOURNEAU (C. J. M.) La Sociologie d'après l'ethnographie. pp. 608. 1892. 8°. Bibliothèque des Sciences contemporaines. Tom. 6. 8709. b.

P.P. *Paris.* Revue internationale de Sociologie. *Paris,* 1893, *etc.* 8°.   P.P. 1122. c.

SMALL (A. W.) and VINCENT (G. E.) Introduction to the study of Society. pp. 384. *N.Y.* 1894. 8°.   08276. g. 70.

SPENCER (H.) Social Statics. pp. 424. *Lond.* 1892. 8°.   2236. c. 11.

WINIARSKI (L.) La méthode mathématique dans la Sociologie. pp. 15. *Paris,* 1894. 8°. Pam. 82.

YOUNG (A.) The Three Plates, or Synopsis of Sociology. pp. 47. *Lond.* 1892. 4°. 8282. h. 17.

See also ANTHROPOLOGY : SOCIAL SCIENCE, *etc.*

SODA. LUNGE (G.) Handbuch der Soda-Industrie. 1893, *etc.* 8°. BOLLEY (P. A.) Handbuch der chemischen Technologie. N. F. Lief. 7.   8905. eee.

SODOR AND MAN, Diocese of. *See* MAN, *Isle of.*

SOGN. SOGN. Sognefjordens Turistruter. *Dan., Engl. and Germ.* pp. 64. *Kristiania,* 1893. 8°.   Pam. 91.

SOILS. *See* AGRICULTURE : MANURES.

SOISSONS. BERLETTE (N.) Les antiquitez de Soissons. 1891. 8°. Ac. Soissons. *Société historique.* Bulletin. Sér. II. Tom. 19.   Ac. 6893.

SOLDERING. PROBERT (W.) The art of Soldering. pp. 30. *Birmingham,* 1894. 8°.   Pam. 94.

SOLENT. CUTHELL (T. G.) Sailing guide to the Solent and Poole harbour. pp. 100. *Lond.* 1893. 8°.   10498. au. 18.

HANNEN (R.) Dinghy Cruises in and about the Solent. pp. 59. *Lond.* 1893. 8°.   10350. bbb. 47.

See also ENGLISH CHANNEL.

SOLESMES. COUTEL DE LA TREMBLAYE (F. M.) Solesmes. Les Sculptures de l'Église Abbatiale, 1496–1553. pp. 186. *Solesmes,* 1892. fol.   1733. c. 12.

SOLICITORS, at Law. *See* LAW, *Profession of.*

SOLMS. HIMMELREICH (F. H.) Greifensteiner Chronik. pp. 108. *Wetzlar,* 1894. 8°.   10256. b. 47.

SOLOGNE. SAINT-VENANT (J. de) La vieille Sologne militaire et ses fortifications. pp. 86. *Vendôme,* 1892. 8°. 07703. i. 1. (13.)

SOLOTHURN, Canton and Town. AMIET (J. J.) Die Gründungs-Sage der Schwesterstädte Solothurn, Zürich und Trier. pp. 104. *Solothurn,* 1890. 8°.   10660. g. 16.

—— Solothurn im Bunde der Eidgenossen. pp. 91. *Solothurn,* 1881. 8°.   9304. de. 6.

MEISTERHANS (K.) Aelteste Geschichte des Kantons Solothurn. pp. 171. *Solothurn,* 1890. 8°.   9304. de. 1.

SOMALILAND. GLYN (F.) *Baron Wolverton.* Five months' sport in Somali Land. pp. 108. *Lond.* 1894. 8°.   07905. i. 2.

SOMALILAND—*continued.*

Hoyos (E.) *Count.* Zu den Aulihan. Reise- und Jagderlebnisse im Somâlilande. pp. 190. *Wien*, 1895. 8°.   010096. i. 28.

Melliss (C. J.) Lion-hunting in Somaliland. pp. 186. *Lond.* 1895. 8°.   07905. i. 11.

Ruspoli (E.) Nel Paese della mirra. pp. 70. *Roma*, 1892. 8°.   010096. g. 19.

Swayne (H. G. C.) Seventeen trips through Somáliland. pp. 386. *Lond.* 1895. 8°. 10096. g. 13.
See also Africa, *Central and East:* African Languages.

SOMERSET. Ac. Somerset. *Record Society.* Pedes Finium, Feet of Fines for Somerset. Richard I. to Edward I. pp. 426. *Lond.* 1892. 4°.   Ac. 8133/6.

—— Kirby's Quest for Somerset. Nomina Villarum 16 Edward III. Exchequer Lay Subsidies, County Rate of 1742, *etc.* pp. 360. *Lond.* 1889. 4°.   Ac. 8133/3.

—— Survey and rental of the chantries, colleges, guilds, *etc.*, in Somerset, 1548. pp. 371. *Lond.* 1888. 4°.   Ac. 8133/2.

Archbold (W. A. J.) Somerset Religious Houses. pp. 407. 1892. 8°. Cambridge Historical Essays. No. VI.   9009. c.

Green (E.) Preparations in Somerset against the Spanish Armada, A.D. 1558–88. pp. 137. *Lond.* 1888. 8°.   9510. f. 23.

—— The March of William of Orange through Somerset. pp. 78. *Lond.* 1892. 8°. 9510. f. 24.

Barrett (C. R. B.) Somerset highways, byways, and waterways. pp. 366. *Lond.* 1894. 4°.   K.T.C. 18. a. 1.

—— Plates. fol.   K.T.C. 18. a. 1.

Batten (J.) Historical and topographical Collections relating to South Somerset. pp. 200. *Yeovil*, 1894. 8°.   010358. h. 17.

Bruce (J. M.) Climate of Somerset. 1895. 8°. Ac. London. *Medical and Chirurgical Society.* Climates of Great Britain. Vol. 1.   7462. g.

Kinglake (R. A.) Somerset Worthies. pp. 30. *Lond.* 1891. 8°.   10348. d. 19. (15.)

Nichols (W. L.) The Quantocks and their Associations. pp. 109. *Lond.* 1891. 8°.   010358. g. 18.

Rogers (W. H. H.) West-Country stories and sketches. pp. 203. *Exeter*, 1895. 4°.   010358. h. 21.

Worth (R. N.) Tourist's guide to Somersetshire. pp. 168. *Lond.* 1894. 8°.   10352. a. 74.

SOMERSHAM. Dawes (C. E.) Somersham. pp. 172. 1890. 12°. Huntingdon. Occasional Hunts Sketches. IX.   10368. aa.

SOMNAMBULISM. *See* Sleep.

SOMPTING. Dallaway (J.) Sompting. pp. 12. *Birmingham*, 1886. 4°.   010358. l. 12. (4.)

SONGKOI, River. *See* Red-River.

SONNETS. Birks (H. A.) Sonnets for saints' days. pp. 47. *Lond.* 1890. 8°.   4429. a. 1.

De Vere (A. T.) Mediaeval records and Sonnets. pp. 270. *Lond.* 1893. 8°.   011652. g. 14.

Forshaw (C. F.) Yorkshire Sonneteers. *Bradford*, 1889, *etc.* 4°.   11652. ff. 53.

Livre. Le Livre des Sonnets. pp. 228. *Paris*, 1893. 8°.   11482. aa. 51.

Lusted (C. T.) Studies in life and literature, with introductory Sonnets. pp. 301. *Lond.* 1893. 8°.   012357. h. 6.

Martonne (L. G. A. de) Le Sonnet dans le midi de la France. pp. 59. *Aix*, 1894. 8°.   11840. i. 47. (4.)

SONNETS—*continued.*

Murphy (J. J.) Sonnets and other poems. pp. 148. *Lond.* 1890. 8°.   011653. k. 5.

Noble (J. A.) The Sonnet in England : essays. pp. 211. *Lond.* 1893. 8°.   011824. g. 33.

Waddington (S.) The Sonnets of Europe : translations. pp. 280. 1886. 8°. Canterbury Poets.   11604. aaa.

Webster (A.) Mother and Daughter. Uncompleted sonnet-sequence. pp. 51. *Lond.* 1895. 8°.   11644. eee. 31.

Wordsworth (W.) Selection from the Sonnets of Wordsworth. pp. 86. *Lond.* 1891. 8°.   11645. h. 19.

See also Poetry.

SORIA. Palacios (P.) Descripción de la provincia de Soria. pp. 558. 1890. 8°. Spain. *Comision del Mapa Geológico.* Memorias. 1890.   7108. gg.

SOUDAN. Baumgarten (J.) Ostafrika, der Sudan und das Seeengebiet. pp. 563. *Gotha*, 1890. 8°.   010096. e. 15.

Chélu (A.) De l'Équateur à la Méditerranée. pp. 507. *Paris*, 1891. 8°.   10096. i. 5.

Frobenius (H.) Die Heiden-Neger des ägyptischen Sudan. pp. 483. *Berl.* 1893. 8°.   010096. i. 2.

Gessi (R.) Sette anni del Sudan egiziano. pp. 489. *Milano*, 1891. 8°.   010096. ff. 7.

—— Seven years in the Soudan. pp. 467. *Lond.* 1892. 8°.   010096. f. 25.

Jaeger (H.) Kamerun und Sudan. *Berl.* 1892, *etc.* 8°.   8027. c.

Junker (W.) Travels in Africa. 1875–78. pp. 582. *Lond.* 1890. 8°.   010096. i. 9.

Ohrwalder (J.) Ten Years' Captivity in the Mahdi's Camp, 1882–92. pp. 471. *Lond.* 1893. 8°.   9061. ccc. 15.

Pensa (H.) L'Égypte et le Soudan égyptien. pp. 403. *Paris*, 1895. 8°.   10097. cc. 29.

Staudinger (P.) Im Herzen der Haussaländer. pp. 758. *Berl.* 1889. 8°.   010096. ff. 5.

Vugliano (C.) Gli ultimi avvenimenti del Sudan egiziano. pp. 28. *Frosinone*, 1891. 4°. Pam. 67.

Wingate (F. R.) Mahdiism and the Egyptian Soudan. pp. 617. *Lond.* 1891. 8°. 2386. f. 2
See also Africa, *Central and East :* Egypt.

French Soudan.

Archinard (L.) Le Soudan français en 1889–90. pp. 96. *Paris*, 1891. 8°.   010096. g. 17.

Bonnetain (Mme. P.) Une Française au Soudan. pp. 377. *Paris*, 1894. 8°.   10097. cc. 15.

Broussais (É.) De Paris au Soudan, Marseille-Alger-Transsaharien. pp. 296. *Alger*, 1891. 8°.   010096. i. 15.

Burgès (J.) Notice sur le Soudan français. pp. 162. *Paris*, 1893. 8°.   7686. bb. 12.

Descostes (F.) Au Soudan, 1890–91. pp. 69. *Paris*, 1893. 8°.   010096. i. 21.

Dupouy (É.) Les Chasses du Soudan. pp. 357. *Paris*, 1894. 12°.   07905. f. 24.

Gaffarel (P.) Le Sénégal et le Soudan français. pp. 237. *Paris*, 1892. 8°. 010096. m. 16.

Gallieni (J. S.) Deux Campagnes au Soudan français, 1886–88. pp. 638. *Paris*, 1891. 4°.   9061. g. 6.

Habert (C.) Au Soudan. Excursion dans l'ouest africain, *etc.* pp. 240. *Paris*, 1894. 8°.   010096. m. 24.

Monnier (M.) Mission Binger. Côte d'Ivoire et Soudan. pp. 298. *Paris*, 1894. 8°.   010096. e. 68.

SOUDAN.—French—*continued.*

OLIVIER (A.) *Viscount de Sanderval.* Soudan français. pp. 442. *Paris*, 1893. 8°.
010096. m. 18.

VIGNÉ D'OCTON (P.) Terre de Mort—Soudan. pp. 285. *Paris*, 1892. 12°.   10097. ccc. 14.

VIVAREZ (M.) Le Soudan algérien. pp. 174. *Paris*, 1890. 18°.   010096. e. 22.

See also AFRICA, *West*: FRANCE, *Colonies*: SAHARA.

SOUL. ABER (M. A.) Souls. pp. 176. *Chicago*, 1893. 8°.   8632. d. 26.

ARISTOTLE. Aristotelis de anima Liber. *Berol.* 1891. 8°.   8465. e. 24. (9.)

—— Das zweite Buch der aristotelischen Schrift über die Seele. pp. 94. *Jena*, 1894. 8°.
8460. h. 19.

ARUNDALE (F.) The Idea of Re-birth. pp. 155. *Lond.* 1890. 8°.   4503. a. 37.

CARUS (P.) The Soul of Man pp. 458. *Chicago*, 1891. 8°.   8470. ccc. 13.

CROS (A.) Nouvelles hypothèses sur la destinée des êtres. pp. 295. *Paris*, 1890. 8°.
8467. dd. 27.

ESSER (G.) Die Seelenlehre Tertullians. pp. 234. *Paderborn*, 1893. 8°.   3623. b. 19.

GUENTZEL (F. E.) Was lehrt die Natur über das Schicksal unserer Seele? pp. 184. *Leipz.* 1891. 8°.   8468. d. 24.

HEMSTREET (W.) Mind is Matter. pp. 252. *N.Y.* 1891. 8°.   8468. c. 35.

LUTOSŁAWSKI (W.) On the difference between knowledge and belief as to the Immortality of the Soul. *N.Y.* 1894. 8°.   8468. k. 27. (9.)

MAN Why I do not believe Man has a Soul. pp. 12. *Edinb.* 1891. 8°.   4018. df. 13. (8.)

RIEMANN (O.) Was wissen wir über die Existenz und Unsterblichkeit der Seele? pp. 47. *Magdeburg*, 1891. 8°.   8468. k. 27. (2.)

RODRÍGUEZ-NAVAS Y CARRASCO (M.) El alma según las escuelas filosóficas de la India. pp. 156. *Madrid*, 1890. 8°.   8465. aa. 25.

See also ESCHATOLOGY : PSYCHOLOGY.

SOULIGNÉ-SOUS-VALLON. POMMIER (A.) Chroniques de Souligné-sous-Vallon. pp. 669. *Angers*, 1880. 4°.   10172. i. 7.

SOUND. *See* ACOUSTICS.

SOUTH AFRICAN REPUBLIC. *See* TRANSVAAL.

SOUTHAM. SMITH (W. L.) Historical notices relating to the Parish of Southam. *Lond.* 1894, *etc.* 8°.   10352. dd.

SOUTHAMPTON. Ac. Hampshire. *Record Society.* Collection of records relating to the Hundred of Crondal, in the county of Southampton. *Lond.* 1891, *etc.* 8°.   Ac. 8123/3.

DE GRAVE (J. W.) Notes on the Register of the Walloon Church of Southampton. 1890. 8°. Ac. London. *Huguenot Society.* Proceedings. Vol. 5.   Ac. 2073.

MAC FADDEN (F.) Vestiges of Old Southampton. pp. 24. *Southampton*, 1891. fol.   10351. l. 7.

SOUTHAMPTON. Photographic views of Southampton. *Southampton*, 1895. obl. 8°.
10360. aa. 40.

SOUTH CAROLINA. *See* CAROLINA.

SOUTH CAVE. HALL (J. G.) History of South Cave. pp. 295. *Hull*, 1892. 8°.
10360. f. 37.

SOUTH DAKOTA. *See* DAKOTA.

SOUTH EASTERN RAILWAY. *See* RAILWAYS.

SOUTHEND. SOUTHEND. Where to buy at Southend. pp. 42. *Brighton*, 1891. 4°.
10368. k. 36.

SOUTHLAND. *See* OTAGO.

SOUTH POLE. *See* ANTARCTIC REGIONS.

SOUTHPORT, Lancashire. PLATT (J.) Handy guide to Southport. pp. 28. *Southport*, 1894. 16°.   10352. e. 16. (5.)

SOUTHPORT. Southport Centenary celebrations. pp. 80. *Liverp.* 1892. obl. 4°.   10368. cc. 45.

SOUTHSEA. *See* PORTSMOUTH.

SOUTHWARK. *See* LONDON, *Parishes, etc.*

SOUTH WEALD. FRASER (D.) South Weald. Its history, its churches, *etc.* *South Weald*, 1895. 4°.   10358. k. 9.

SOUTHWELL. Ac. London. *Camden Society.* N.S. XLVIII. Visitations and memorials of Southwell Minster. pp. 234. *Lond.* 1891. 4°.   Ac. 8113/134.

SOUTH WRAXALL. The Old Manor House, South Wraxall. pp. 23. *Bath*, 1893. 8°.   10347. d. 7. (10.)

SPA. BODY (A.) Les Actes notariaux passés à Spa, 1565-1828. 1887. 8°. Ac. Liège. *Institut archéologique.* Bulletin. Tom. 20. Livr. 1.   Ac. 5527.

—— Le Club anglais de Spa, 1766. 1886. 8°. Ac. Liège. *Institut Archéologique.* Bulletin. Tom. 19. Livr. 1.   Ac. 5527.

SPACE, Dimensions of. *See* TIME AND SPACE.

SPAIN. [*See note on p.* 1.]

Antiquities.

BOUTROUE (A.) Rapport sur une mission archéologique dans le sud de l'Espagne. pp. 57. *Paris.* 1893. 8°.   07703. i. 1. (16.)

CANDAU Y PIZARRO (F.) Prehistoria de la provincia de Sevilla. pp. 224. *Sevilla*, 1894. 8°.
7707. cc. 37.

CUVEIRO PIÑOL (J.) Iberia protohistorica. *Valladolid.* 1891. 8°.   7708. aaa. 54.

HUEBNER (E) Monumenta Linguae Ibericae. pp. 264. *Berolini*, 1893. 4°.   7705. h. 33.

MARIANO VIDAL (L.) Mas monumentos megalíticos en Cataluña. pp. 24. *Barcelona*, 1894. 8°.
Pam. 3.

For Moorish antiquities, *see infra*: History.

Army.

BARADO (F.) Mis estudios historicos. pp. 148. *Madrid*, 1893. 8°.   9181. bb. 7.

C. (S. R.) Division territorial militar. pp. 30. *Madrid*, 1893. 8°.   Pam. 71.

DÍAZ Y BENZO (A.) Las grandes maniobras en España. pp. 559. *Madrid*, 1890. 8°. 8830. l. 21.

GIL ÁLVARO (A.) Glorias de la Infanteria española. pp. 383. *Madrid*, 1893. 8°. 8828. ff. 30.

RUIZ FORNELLS (E.) and MELGAR MATA (A.) Organizacion militar de España. pp. 226. 15. *Toledo*, 1893. 8°.   8828. b. 61.

SAROU Y FERNANDEZ (J. M. de) Organizacion defensiva de las costas, *etc.* pp. 276. *Madrid*, 1890. 8°.   8831. k. 34.

Colonies.

LABRA (R. M. de) La autonomía colonial en España. pp. 314. *Madrid*, 1892. 8°.
8154. aa. 19.

REPARÁZ (G.) España en África y estudios de política colonial. pp. 218. *Madrid*, 1891. 8°.
8027. aa. 8.

SCHEIDNAGEL (M.) Colonización española. pp. 117. *Madrid*, 1893. 8°.   8154. aaa. 44.

See also AFRICA, *Colonisation*: CANARY ISLANDS : CAROLINE ISLANDS : CUBA : LADRONE ISLANDS : PHILIPPINE ISLANDS : PUERTO RICO.

SPAIN—*continued.*

Constitution and Government.

CASAS Y ABAD (S.) Catecismo político. pp. 47. *Barcelona*, 1891. 8°. Pam. 71.

EPHEM. Agenda de administración municipal y general. pp. 140. *Barcelona*, 1891. 8°. P.P. 2387. o.

HUNEEUS GANA (J.) Estudios sobre España. 2 tom. *Santiago*, 1889. 8°. 11840. aa. 8.

MELLADO (F.) Tratado de derecho administrativo. pp. 976. *Madrid*, 1894. 8°. 5383. ff. 7.

POSADA (A.) Estudios sobre el régimen parlamentario en España. pp. 198. *Madrid*, 1891. 8°. 8042. a. 28.

See also infra : Politics : ELECTIONS.

Finance. *See infra : Trade.*

History.

BURKE (U. R.) History of Spain to the death of Ferdinand the Catholic. 2 vol. *Lond.* 1895. 8°. 9180. eee. 2.

CÁNOVAS DEL CASTILLO (A.) Historia general de España. *Madrid*, 1893, *etc.* 8°. 9181. ee.

DIERCKS (G.) Geschichte Spaniens. *Berl.* 1895, *etc.* 8°. 9181. dd. 9.

FERNÁNDEZ DURO (C.) Viajes regios. pp. 390. *Madrid*, 1893. 8°. 9181. dd. 8.

GRAHAM (G. C.) Spain. 1891. 8°. MAGNÚSSON (E.) National Life and Thought. 8486. g. 21.

MOLÈNES (É. de) L'Espagne du quatrième Centenaire de la découverte du Nouveau-Monde. pp. 344. *Paris*, 1894. 8°. 7956. f. 3.

P.P. *Paris.* Revue hispanique. *Paris*, 1894, *etc.* 8°. P.P. 4331. aea.

ZABÁLBURU (F. de) and RAYON (J. S.) Neuva colección de documentos para la historia de España. *Madrid*, 1892, *etc.* 8°. 9180. ff.

FERNANDEZ VALBUENA (R.) Estudio sobre la influencia de la conversión de Recaredo en la unidad de España. pp. 139. *Badajoz*, 1890. 8°. 10632. aaa. 41.

SAAVEDRA (E.) Estudio sobre la invasión de los Árabes en España. pp. 157. *Madrid*, 1892. 8°. 9180. ff. 14.

SCHWENKOW (L.) Die lateinisch Quellen zur Geschichte der Eroberung Spaniens durch die Araber. pp. 99. *Göttingen*, 1894. 8°. 9195. ccc. 4.

POOLE (S. L.) The Mohammedan Dynasties. pp. 361. *Westminster*, 1894. 8°. 9055. aaa. 38.

WATTS (H. E.) Spain from the Moorish conquest to the fall of Granada. pp. 315. 1893. 8°. Story of the Nations. 9004. ccc. 11.

'ABD AL-WĀHID IBN 'ALI (M. al-D. A. M.) Histoire des Almohades. pp. 331. *Alger*, 1893. 8°. 14555. e. 17.

MUHAMMAD IBN MUHAMMAD, *al-Idrīsī.* La Geografía de España del Edrisí. *Madrid*, 1881–89. 8°. 14566. b.

AMADOR DE LOS RIOS (R.) Estudio acerca de las enseñas musulmanas del Monasterio de las Huelgas, Burgos. pp. 207. *Madrid*, 1893. 8°. 7807. m. 10.

ALMAGRO CÁRDENAS (A.) Museo Granadino de antigüedades árabes. pp. 190. *Granada*, 1886–93. 8°. 7709. l. 22.

CONTRERAS (R.) Estudio de los monumentos árabes de Granada, Sevilla y Córdova. pp. 378. *Madrid*, 1885. 8°. 7706. b. 35.

GUILLEN ROBLES (F.) Malaga musulmana. pp. 712. *Malaga*, 1880. 4°. 10161. f. 10.

DANVILA Y COLLADO (M.) La expulsión de los Moriscos españoles. pp. 351. *Madrid*, 1889. 8°. 9181. dd. 4.

SPAIN.—**History**—*continued.*

SWIFT (F. D.) Life and Times of James I. King of Aragon. pp. 311. *Oxf.* 1894. 8°. 10632. e. 33.

RODRÍGUEZ VILLA (A.) La reina doña Juana la Loca. pp. 578. *Madrid*, 1892. 8°. 10631. g. 39.

BOISSONNADE (P.) Historie de la réunion de la Navarre à la Castille. pp. 685. *Paris*, 1893. 8°. 9180. g. 3.

SCHWARTZ (F.) 1492; historia de un año. pp. 348. *Barcelona*, 1892. 8°. 9073. de. 22.

MARIÉJOL (J. H.) L'Espagne sous Ferdinand et Isabelle. pp. 356. *Paris*, 1892. 8°. 9180. ee. 3.

PRESCOTT (W. H.) History of Ferdinand and Isabella. pp. 684. *Lond.* 1892. 8°. 9181. dd. 7.

HAEBLER (K.) Der Streit Ferdinand's des Katholischen und Philipp's I. um die Regierung von Castilien. pp. 134. *Dresden*, 1882. 8°. Pam. 28.

ARENBERGH (E. v.) Charles-Quint. 2 tom. *Lille*, 1890, 8°. 10658. f. 21.

NAMÈCHE (A. J.) L'Empereur Charles-Quint. 5 tom. *Louvain*, 1889. 8°. 9073. de. 20.

FERNÁNDEZ MONTAÑA (J.) Nueva luz sobre Felipe II. pp. 591. *Madrid*, 1891. 8°. 10631. f. 48.

—— Más Luz de Verdad histórica sobre Felipe II. pp. 664. *Madrid*, 1892. 8°. 9180. ee. 4.

HINOJOSA (R. de) Felipe II. y el Cónclave de 1559. pp. 109. *Madrid*, 1889. 8°. 4571. f. 16.

PHILIPPSON (M.) Ein Ministerium unter Philipp II., Kardinal Granvella, 1578–86. pp. 642. *Berl.* 1895. 8°. 9072. f. 17.

SAN CLEMENTE (G. de) Correspondencia de Don G. de San Clemente, embajador en Alemania de los Reyes Don Felipe II. y III., 1581–1608. pp. 406. *Zaragoza*, 1892. 8°. 9079. i. 18.

FROUDE (J. A.) The Spanish Story of the Armada. pp. 328. *Lond.* 1892. 8°. 2342. f. 2.

LAUGHTON (J. K.) State Papers relating to the Spanish Armada. 1894, *etc.* 8°. Ac. London. *Navy Records Society.* Publications. Vol. 1, *etc.* Ac. 8109.

TILTON (W. F.) Die Katastrophe der spanischen Armada. pp. 150. *Freiburg*, 1894. 8°. 9077. eee. 39.

MOREL-FATIO (A.) Espagne. 1894, *etc.* 8°. FRANCE. *Ministère des Affaires Étrangères.* Recueil des instructions données aux ambassadeurs, 1649, *etc.* Tom. 11. 9080. l. 6.

KRÄMER (F. J. L.) De nederlandsch-spaansche Diplomatie vóór den Vrede van Nijmegen. pp. 287. *Utrecht*, 1892. 8°. 9079. i. 17.

VILLARS (P. de) *Marquis.* Mémoires de la Cour d'Espagne, 1679–81. pp. 348. *Paris*, 1893. 8°. 12234. bbb. 8.

LEGRELLE (A.) La Diplomatie française et la Succession d'Espagne. 3 tom. *Paris*, 1888–90. 8°. 9072. g. 9.

MORPURGO (A.) Notizie intorno alla guerra della successione spagnuola. 1891. 8°. Ac. Trieste. *Società del Gabinetto di Minerva.* L'Archeografo Triestino. N.S. Vol. 17. Fasc. 1. Ac. 6548.

BAUDRILLART (A.) Philippe V. et la cour de France, 1700–15. pp. 711. 1889. 8°. Revue d'histoire diplomatique. Supp. tom. 3. Ac. 6885.

SPAIN.—History—continued.

COURCY (de) *Marquis.* L'Espagne après la paix d'Utrecht, 1713-15. pp. 439.
Paris, 1891. 8°.   9180. ff. 11.

BERMEJO (I. A) Historia de la Corte de Carlos IV.
2 tom. *Madrid,* 1894. 8°.   9180. cc. 21.

GEOFFROY DE GRANDMAISON (C. A.) L'ambassade française en Espagne, 1789-1804.
pp. 356. *Paris,* 1892. 8°.   9079. f. 5.

U.S. *Department of State.* The U.S. and Spain in 1790. pp. 109. 1890. 8°. Winnowings in American History. Diplomatic Series. No. 1.
9551. d.

CASTAÑOS Y MONTIJANO (M.) Narración de algunos hechos de armas de la guerra separatista de América. pp. 144. *Toledo,* 1892. 8°.
9772. b. 15.

RODRÍGUEZ-SOLÍS (E.) Historia del partido republicano. *Madrid,* 1893, *etc.* 8°.   9180. i.

ANTIOCHE (F. M. A. d') *Count.* Deux Diplomates: le Comte Raczynski et Donoso Cortès. Dépêches et correspondance. pp. 334.
Paris, 1880. 8°.   8042. f. 6.

SPAIN. *Army.* Narración militar de la Guerra Carlista, 1869-76. 14 tom.
Madrid, 1883-89.   9195. h. 1.
—— Maps. fol.   14001. k. 21.

GRABINSKI (G.) *Count.* Amédée de Savoie, Roi d'Espagne. pp. 55. *Paris,* 1891. 8°.
10601. f. 9. (11.)

HOUGHTON (A.) Les origines de la restauration des Bourbons en Espagne. pp. 403.
Paris, 1890. 8°.   9181. df. 20.

See also ARAGON : EUROPE: GRENADA : LEPANTO : PENINSULAR WAR.

History, Ecclesiastical.

MEYRICK (F.) The Church in Spain. pp. 450.
1892. 8°. DITCHFIELD (P H.) National Churches.
4534. de.

FOERSTER (P.) Der Einfluss der Inquisition auf das geistige Leben der Spanier. pp. 24.
Berl. 1890. 4°.   11850. m. 14. (6.)

LEA (H. C.) Chapters from the religious history of Spain connected with the Inquisition.
pp. 522. *Phila.* 1890. 8°.   4625. aaa. 3.

GRAHAM (G. C.) Santa Teresa. 2 vol.
Lond. 1894. 8°.   4829. f. 6.

PLUNKET (W. C.) *Baron Plunket, Archbp. of Dublin.* An Era in the history of religious liberty in Spain. pp. 11. *Lond.* 1891. 8°.
3900. c. 31. (3.)

Law.

BARRIO Y MIER (M.) Historia del derecho español.
2 tom. *Madrid,* 1894. 8°.   5384. aa. 11.

HINOJOSA (E. de) Historia del derecho español.
Tom. 1. *Madrid,* 1887. 8°.   5383. f. 4.

MORET Y REMISA (L.) Lecciones de historia del derecho español. pp. 364. *Madrid,* 1892. 8°.
5385. cc. 4.

MANRESA Y NAVARRO (J. M.) Repertorio de la jurisprudencia civil española. pp. 580.
Madrid, 1890. 8°.   5385. dd. 4.

MHARTIN Y GUIX (E.) Manual del empleado.
pp. 319. *Madrid,* 1890. 8°.   5384. aaa. 24.

SPAIN. Los códigos españoles. 6 pt.
Madrid, 1890. 8°.   5384. aa. 7.
—— Código civil español. pp. 644.
Madrid, 1889. 8°.   5384. f. 9.

PASO Y DELGADO (N. de) Derecho civil español.
pp. 687. *Madrid,* 1890. 8°.   5385. dd. 2.

ARENAL DE GARCIA CARRASCO (C.) El derecho de gracia ante la justicia y el reo. pp. 280.
Madrid, 1893. 8°.   6005. a. 7.

SPAIN.—Law—continued.

CODERCH MANAU (S.) El consejo de familia en España. pp. 526. *Barcelona,* 1893. 8°.
5383. e. 11.

MARTINEZ IBAÑEZ (E.) El jurado.
Madrid, 1891. 8°.   6005. a. 5.

TODA Y GÜELL (E.) Derecho consular de España.
pp 407. *Madrid,* 1889. 8°.   5385. cc. 2.

See also LAW, *Commercial : Ecclesiastical.*

Politics.

BARCELONA (J. P.) Doctrina republicana federal.
pp. 62. *Madrid,* 1891. 8°.   Pam. 71.

BARK (E.) El programa comun del Republicanismo iberico. pp. 32. *Madrid,* 1892. 8°.
Pam. 71.

BERMÚDEZ DE CASTRO (S.) *Duke de Ripalda* El problema social y las escuelas politicas. pp. 98.
Madrid. 1891. 8°.   8276. ee. 64.

BORREGO (A.) La Torre de Babel en estado de construccion. pp. 197. *Madrid,* 1890. 8°.
8042. aaa. 27.

CEBALLOS Y CRUZADA (C. G. de) El 1° de Mayo en España. pp. 128. *Madrid,* 1892. 8°.
8277. ee. 40.

CERVERA (V.) Los Procedimientos del sufragio.
pp. 111. *Madrid,* 1890. 8°.   8009. a. 25.

CRUZ (V. de la) La República y sus hombres.
Madrid, 1894, *etc.* 8°.   10631. bb. 59.

GIRALDEZ Y ERRASTI (J.) Observaciones sobre la cuestión social. pp. 16. *Madrid,* 1890. 8°.
Pam. 82.

LINARES NIVAS (A.) Problema social en la España. 1894. 8°. Ac. Madrid. *R. Acad. de Ciencias morales.* Discursos. Tom. 5. Ac. 142/2.

LLUNAS (J.) Estudios filosófico-sociales. pp. 219.
Barcelona, 1883. 8°.   08275. de. 4.
—— Questions socials. pp. 128.
Barcelona, 1891. 8°.   08275. de. 2.
—— Los partidos socialistas. pp. 15.
Barcelona, 1892. 8°.   8282. ff. 11. (5.)

MARTÍ-MIGUÉL (J.) La Evolución y la revolución. pp. 255. *Madrid,* 1893. 8°. 8009. bb. 35.

MORENO NIETO (E.) Apuntes políticos. pp 143.
Madrid, 1891. 8°.   8042. aaa. 32.

OLIVIÉ (M.) Aspiraciones nacionales de España.
Vigo, 1890, *etc.* 8°.   8042. cc.

SANZ Y ESCARTIN (E.) El Estado y la reforma social. pp. 292. *Madrid,* 1893. 8°. 8277. d. 35.
—— De la autoridad politica. 1894. 8°. Ac. Madrid. *R. Acad. de Ciencias morales.* Discursos. Tom. 5.   Ac. 142/2.

VEGA-REY FALCÓ (L.) La Cuestión social en España. pp. 106. *Madrid,* 1893. 8°.
8282. g. 26. (13.)

ZOZAYA (A.) La Crisis contemporanea. pp. 144.
Madrid, 1894. 8°.   8008. a. 3.
See also supra : Constitution : History.

Foreign.

SPAIN. *Ministerio de Estado.* Boletín del Ministerio de Estado. *Madrid,* 1891, *etc.* 8°.
8042. l.

Roman Catholic Church. *See supra :* HISTORY, *Ecclesiastical :* ROMAN CATHOLIC CHURCH, *in Spain.*

Topography : Social Life.

SPAIN. *Direción del Instituto Geográfico.* Nomenclátor de las ciudades, *etc.,* de España.
Madrid, 1894. 4°.   8225. b. 2.

ENCYCLOPÆDIAS. Diccionario Enciclopedico hispano-americano. *Barcelona,* 1887, *etc.* 4°.
1878. c.

HOYOS SAINZ (L. de) and ARANZADI Y UNAMUNO (T. de) Un avance á la antropología de España. pp. 71. *Madrid,* 1892. 8°. 8225. d. 67.

SPAIN.—Topography, etc.—_continued._

JIMENO AGIUS (J.) Territorio y población de España. pp. 114. _Madrid,_ 1890. 8°.
                           8223. dh. 4.

FORD (R.) Murray's Handbook for Travellers in Spain. 2 pt. _Lond._ 1892. 8°.   2364. b. 13.

GERMOND DE LAVIGNE (L. A. G.) Espagne. Guide Joanne. pp. 750. _Paris,_ 1893. 12°.
                        10160. bbb. 14.

O'SHEA (H.) Guide to Spain and Portugal. pp. 563. _Lond._ 1895. 8°.   2362. b. 6.

BALSA DE VEGA (R.) Los bucólicos. pp. 145. _Barcelona,_ 1892. 8°.   10161. a. 3.

BAZIN (R.) Terre d'Espagne. 336. _Paris,_ 1895. 18°.   10160. bbb. 16.

BLACKBURN (H.) Artistic travels. pp. 320. _Lond._ 1892. 8°.   10108. f. 1.

CHAPMAN (A.) and BUCK (W. J.) Wild Spain. pp. 472. _Lond._ 1893. 8°.   7908. f. 25.

DESCAMPS (M.) Souvenirs d'Espagne. pp. 336. _Lille,_ 1892. 8°.   10160. c. 2.

DIGNAM (J.) London to Madrid. pp. 60. _Dublin,_ 1891. 8°.   10106. df. 18. (4.)

FANCY (J.) Quelques jours en Espagne. pp. 150. _Paris,_ 1891. 8°.   10024. c. 26.

FINCK (H. T.) Spain and Morocco. pp. 182. _Lond._ 1891. 8°.   10160. bbb. 12.

FITZ FREDERICK. Letters from Southern Shores. pp. 50. _Sunderland,_ 1894. 12°. 10106. de. 6. (5.)

FOREMAN (T. B.) Notes of a Spring Trip to Spain. pp. 121. _Lond._ 1893. 8°. 10161. de. 24.

GIRONDE (L. de) _Count._ Retour d'Espagne, 1891. pp. 88. _Montauban,_ 1892. 8°.
                        10161. cc. 14.

JAMES (W. H.) A Tandem-trip to Spain. pp. 36. _Lond._ 1892. 8°.   10107. e. 11. (10.)

LUFFMANN (C. B.) A vagabond in Spain. pp. 345. _Lond._ 1895. 8°.   10160. b. 3.

MANTEGAZZA (P.) Ricordi di Spagna. pp. 216. _Milano,_ 1894. 8°.   10160. b. 4.

MONNER SANS (R.) La España de Hoy. pp. 56. _Buenos-A._ 1893. 8°.   Pam. 71.

NYROP (K.) La España moderna. pp. 232. _Copenhague,_ 1892. 8°.   10160. c. 3.

OLIVEIRA MARTINS (J. P.) Cartas peninsulares. pp. 226. _Lisboa,_ 1895. 8°.   10160. c. 4.

O'SHEA (H.) Guide to Spain. pp. 562. _Lond._ 1892. 8°.   2362. b.

PERRODIL (É. de) De Paris à Madrid à bicyclette. pp. 326. _Paris,_ 1893. 12°. 10106. df. 14.

QUILLINAN (D.) Journal of a residence in Portugal and glimpses of the south of Spain. pp. 288. _Lond._ 1895. 8°.   10161. bb. 22.

REEVES (E.) Homeward bound after thirty years. pp. 337. _Lond._ 1892. 8°. 10024. g. 10.

ROSNY (L. L. de) Taureaux et Mantilles. Souvenirs d'un voyage en Espagne et en Portugal. pp. 372. _Paris,_ 1894, 12°.   10160. aaa. 22.

ROTHSCHILD (H. de) Souvenirs d'Espagne. pp. 119. _Macon,_ 1890. 8°.   10151. aa. 4.

SESSIONS (F. C.) In Western Levant. pp. 252. _N.Y._ 1890. 8°.   10024. cc. 15.

SINGELS (N. J.) Van de Noordkaap naar het Kremlin en Alhambra. pp. 280. _Leiden,_ 1892. 8°.   10106. df. 13.

STODDARD (C. A.) Spanish cities. pp. 228. _Lond._ 1892. 8°.   10161. de. 26.

THOMAS (M.) A Scamper through Spain. pp. 302. _Lond._ 1892. 8°.   10161. de. 22.

TODA (E.) Guía de España. pp. 482. _Madrid,_ 1892. 8°.   10161. aa. 14.

SPAIN.—Topography. etc.—_continued._

WHITWELL (_Mrs._ E. R.) Spain: as we found it. pp. 160. _Lond._ 1892. 8°.   10160. aaa. 17.

WOERL (L.) Spanien in Wort und Bild. col. 606. _Würzburg,_ 1894. 8°.   10160. f. 8.

Trade and Finance.

ALCOVER (J.) La Industria Nacional. _Madrid,_ 1888, _etc._ 8°.   07945. f.

BLAS Y MARTIN (J. de D.) El debe y haber de la Nacion. pp. 159. _Madrid,_ 1892. 8°.
                        08227. h. 32.

BRAÑAS (A.) Curso de Hacienda pública española. pp. 462. _Santiago,_ 1891. 8°. 08225. l. 18.

CAMBON (P. P.) Les conditions du travail en Espagne, _etc._ 1890. 8°. FRANCE. _Ministère des Affaires étrangères._ Recueil de rapports.
                        08276. k.

CASCÓN Y MARTÍNEZ (J.) Estudio sobre la organización del crédito agrícola. pp. 28. _Madrid,_ 1891. 8°.   Pam. 23.

CHICAGO. _Columbian Exposition._ Catálogo de la sección española. pp. 1053. _Madrid,_ 1893. 8°.   7959. f. 39.

GWINNER (A.) Die Handelspolitik Spaniens in den letzten Jahrzehnten. 1892. 8°. Ac. Leipsic. _Verein für Socialpolitik._ Schriften. No. 51. Bd. 3.   Ac. 2322.

PEROJO (J. del) Comercio de España con las repúblicas hispano-americanas. pp. 38. _Madrid,_ 1892. 8°.   08227. i. 30. (10.)

TORRENTS Y MONNER (A.) Concepto de la Contabilidad administrativa. pp. 62. _Barcelona,_ 1890. 8°.   Pam. 67.

See also LAW, _Commercial._

SPALATO. ZARBARINI (G.) Il palazzo di Diocleziano. pp. 98. _Spalato,_ 1890. 8°.
                        Pam. 3.

SPANDAU. RITTBERG (C. G. H. B. v.) _Count._ Ein Beitrag zu 1813. Die Belagerung der Festung Spandau. pp. 343. _Graudenz,_ 1891. 8°.   9079. g. 16.

SCHALL (M.) Urkundliche Nachrichten zur Geschichte der Garnison u. Garnisongemeinde in Spandau. 2 Bde. _Spandau,_ 1888. 8°.
                        10235. g. 9.

SPANISH LANGUAGE.

Bibliography.

VIÑAZA (de la) _Count._ Biblioteca de la filología castellana. pp. 1112. _Madrid,_ 1893. 8°.
                        011900. k. 10.

General.

BLANCO (B.) La Lengua castellana. pp. 4. _Cochabamba,_ 1892. 8°.   Pam. 47.

P.P. _Paris._ Revue hispanique. _Paris,_ 1894, _etc._ 8°.   P.P. 4331. aea.

ZEROLO (E.) La Lengua, la Academia y los académicos. pp. 71. _Paris,_ 1889. 12°.
                        12901. ccc. 9. (4.)

Accentuation. _See infra :_ PRONUNCIATION.

Dialects (_Spanish and Spanish American._)

MUGICA (P. de) Dialectos castellanos. _Berl._ 1892, _etc._ 8°.   12941. g.

RATO Y HÉVIA (A. de) Vocabulario de las palabras y frases que se hablan en Asturias. pp. 149. _Madrid,_ 1891. 8°.   12942. d. 8.

LENTZNER (C.) Tesoro de voces hispano-americanos. _Halle,_ 1892, _etc._ 4°.   12943. h. 11.

SEIJAS (J.) Diccionario de barbarismos cotidianos. pp. 112. _Buenos A._ 1890. 8°.
                        12942. aaa. 40.

SPANISH LANGUAGE. — Dialects —
—continued.

FERNÁNDEZ FERRAZ (J.) Nahuatlismos de Costa Rica. pp. 148. *San José,* 1892. 8°.
12910. bb. 42.

GAGINI (C.) Diccionario de barbarismos de Costa Rica. pp. 604. *San José,* 1893. 4°.
12941. g. 24.

SÁNCHEZ SOMOANO (J.) Modismos, locuciones y términos mexicanos. pp. 95.
Madrid, 1892. 12°.   11451. de. 42. (7.)

GRANADA (D.) Vocabulario rioplatense razonado. pp. 409. *Montevideo,* 1890. 8°.
12941. h. 29.

See also CATALAN LANGUAGE.

Dictionaries.

BENLLOCH (F. J. J.) Vocabulario científico-etimológico. *Madrid,* 1891, *etc.* 8°.
12942. bbb. 31.

CAMPANO (L.) Diccionario Castellano enciclopédico. pp. 1082. *Paris,* 1891. 8°. 12942. cc. 9.

DOCE (J. M.) Diccionario ortográfico etimológico español. pp. 348. *Madrid,* 1893. 8°.
12941. aa. 49.

MONLAU Y ROCA (P. F.) Diccionario etimológico de la lengua castellana. pp. 1168.
Madrid, 1881. 8°.   12942. d. 9.

OCHOA (C. de) Novísimo Diccionario de la lengua castellana. 3 pt. *Paris,* 1893. 4°.
12942. k. 10.

OLIVE (P. M. de) Diccionario de Sinónimos. pp. 208. *Paris,* 1895. 4°.   12943. h. 13.

ZEROLO (E.) Diccionario enciclopédico de la lengua castellana. 2 tom. *Paris,* 1895. 4°.
12943. i. 7.

VALBUENA (A. de) Fe de erratas del Nuevo Diccionario de la Academia. 3 tom.
Madrid, 1891. 8°.   12941. cc. 3.

SIMONET (F. J.) Glosario de voces ibéricas y latinas usadas entre los Mozárabes. pp. 628.
Madrid, 1888. 8°.   12902. h. 13.

LERCHUNDI (J.) Vocabulario español-arábigo del dialecto de Marruecos. pp. 863.
Tánger, 1892. 8°.   012904. h. 11.

BEALE (A. M. A.) Excelsior English-Spanish and Spanish-English Dictionary. pp. 314. 342.
Lond. 1895. 8°.   12943. aa. 50.

LOPES (J. M.) and BENSLEY (E. R.) Nuevo Diccionario inglés-español y español-inglés. 2 pt.
Paris, 1891. 8°.   12942. k. 8.

REDFERN (C.) Pocket Dictionary of Spanish technical terms. pp. 99. *Birmingham,* 1892. 8°.
12942. bbb. 30.

SOLER Y ARQUÉS (C.) Novísimo diccionario franco-español é hispano-francés. pp. 802.
Madrid, 1893. 8°.   12950. e. 38.

Grammars, etc.

BELLO (A.) Gramática de la lengua castellana. 2 pt. *Paris,* 1891. 8°.   12943. e. 22.

CLARKE (H. B.) A Spanish grammar. pp. 195. 1892. 8°. SONNENSCHEIN (E. A.) Parallel Grammar Series.   12902. aa.

—— First Spanish reader and writer. pp. 85. 1891. 8°. SONNENSCHEIN (E. A.) Parallel Grammar Series.   12902. aa.

DELBOS (L.) Introduction to commercial Spanish. pp. 205. 1894. 8°. Macmillan's Commercial Class Books.   012202. h.

EDGREN (A. H.) Brief Spanish Grammar. pp. 123. *Bost.* 1891. 8°.   12941. e. 21.

FOULCHÉ-DELBOSC (R.) Abrégé de Grammaire espagnole. pp. 160. *Paris,* 1892. 8°. 12942. cc. 10.

—— Exercices espagnols. pp. 229.
Paris, 1892. 8°.   12942. cc. 11.

SPANISH LANGUAGE. — Grammars,
etc.*—continued.*

HARVEY (W. F.) Practical Spanish Manual, &c. pp. 168. *Lond.* 1891. 8°.   12943. c. 23.

HOSSFELD (C.) Hossfeld's deutsch-spanischer Handels Correspondent. pp. 400.
Lond. 1891. 16°.   10920. aa. 25.

HUGO (C.) Simplified system. Spanish.
Lond. 1890. 8°.   12902. ccc. 22.

IBARRA (A.) Método para aprender lenguas modernas. Ingles-Español. pp. 319.
Bost. 1884. 8°.   12902. bb. 39.

JORDAN (F. W.) Pocket guide to Spanish verbs. pp. 16. *Lond.* 1894. 8°.   12901. de. 17. (10.)

KELLER (A.) Historische Formenlehre der spanischen Sprache. pp. 84. *Murrhardt,* 1894. 8°.
12941. g. 25.

KORTH (O.) Commercial and conversational Spanish grammar. pp. 131. *Lond.* 1891. 8°.
12943. aaa. 31.

MUGICA (P. de) Gramática del Castellano antiguo. *Berl.* 1891, *etc.* 8°.   12941. f. 37.

ORTUZAR (C.) Diccionario manual de locuciones viciosas. pp. 320. *S. Benigno,* 1893. 8°.
12942. cc. 23.

RALFS (J. W.) Rapid road to Spanish. 2 pt. *Lond.* 1891. 8°.   12942. bb. 38.

RAMSEY (M. M.) Text-book of modern Spanish. pp. 653. *N.Y.* 1894. 8°.   12943. c. 30.

ROSENTHAL (R. S.) Meisterschaft System. Spanish Language. pp. 473. *Lond.* 1892. 8°.
12942. cc. 22.

TOLRÁ Y FORNÉS (E.) New Spanish-English dialogues. pp. 377. *Lond.* 1893. 16°.
12941. a. 43.

—— First steps in Spanish Idioms. pp. 117. *Lond.* 1894. 16°.   12942. a. 48.

Pronunciation : Orthography.

AMUNÁTEGUI REYES (M. L.) Acentuaciones viciosas. pp. 479. *Santiago de C.* 1887. 8°.
12942. g. 14.

ARAUJO (F.) Estudios de Fonétika kastelana. pp. 154. *Toledo,* 1894. 8°.   12943. a. 51.

CABEZON (C.) Notas sobre la reforma ortográfiga. pp. 67. *Santiago de C.* 1892. 8°.
12901. bbb. 45. (2.)

JIMENO AGIUS (J.) La reforma de la Ortografía qastellana. pp. 84. *Paris,* 1892. 8°.
12941. aaa. 47.

MALGORRY (C. A.) Ortografía castellana. pp. 13. *Madrid,* 1890. 8°.   12903. e. 52. (4.)

URDANETA (A.) ¡ Eureka ! La verdadera acentuacion castellana. pp. 41. *Lérida,* 1894. 8°.
Pam. 47.

SPANISH LITERATURE.

History and Criticism.

CLARKE (H. B.) Spanish Literature. Handbook. pp. 288. *Lond.* 1893. 8°.   011824. f. 59.

ENCYCLOPÆDIAS. Diccionario Enciclopedico hispano-americano. *Barcelona,* 1887, *etc.* 4°.
1878. c.

FARINELLI (A.) Spanien und die spanische Litteratur im Lichte der deutschen Kritik.
Berl. 1892, *etc.* 8°.   011850. i.

FREXAS (E.) El Españolismo literario. pp. 63. *Buenos A.* 1890. 8°.   Pam. 15.

GONZALEZ SERRANO (U.) Estudios críticos. pp. 155. *Madrid,* 1892. 8°.   11824. de. 44.

HUNEEUS-GANA (J.) Estudios sobre España. 2 tom. *Santiago,* 1889. 8°.   11840. aa. 8.

JARINELLI (A.) Die Beziehungen zwischen Spanien und Deutschland in der Litteratur.
Berl. 1892, *etc.* 8°.   011840. h.

SPANISH LITERATURE. — History, etc.—*continued.*

Morel-Fatio (A.) Études sur l'Espagne.
Paris, 1895, *etc.* 8°.   011824. f. 68.

P.P. *Paris.* Revue hispanique.
Paris, 1894, *etc.* 8°.   P.P. 4331. aea.

Garcia Peres (D.) Catalogo de los Autores portugueses que escribieron en castellano.
pp. 660. *Madrid*, 1890. 8°.   11899. h. 41.

Martínez Añíbarro y Rives (M.) Intento de un diccionario de autores de la provincia de Burgos. pp. 570. *Madrid*, 1889. 8°. 10632. f. 34.

Boudet de Puymaigre (T. J. de) *Count.* Les vieux Auteurs castillans. *Paris*, 1888, *etc.* 8°.
                                             011824. e. 16.

Picatoste y Rodríguez (F.) Apuntes para una biblioteca española del siglo XVI. pp. 416.
Madrid, 1891. 8°.   11899. h. 46.

Cat (É.) M. Cervantes. pp. 220.
Paris, 1892. 8°.   10631. ee. 47.

Kelly (J. F.) Life of M. de Cervantes Saavedra. pp. 396. *Lond.* 1892. 8°.   10631. f. 46.

Watts (H. E.) M. de Cervantes : his life and works. pp. 292. *Lond.* 1895. 8°. 10632. c. 55.

Ac. Madrid. *Real Academia.* Vega Carpio (L. F. de) Obras. *Madrid*, 1890, *etc.* 4°.
                                             11726. m.

Rennert (H. A.) The Spanish pastoral Romances. pp. 119. *Baltimore*, 1892. 8°.
                                             011824. i. 34.

Garriga (F. J.) Estudio de la Novela picaresca española. pp. 39. *Madrid*, 1891. 8°.
                                             011850. i. 2. (4.)

Blanco García (F.) La Literatura española en el siglo XIX. 2 pt. *Madrid*, 1891. 8°.
                                             011824. h. 83.

Selections.

Gómez Carrillo (E.) Cuentos escogidos de los mejores autores castellanos contemporáneos.
pp. 434. *Paris*, 1894. 8°.   12489. g. 1.

Taylor (S. M.) Humour of Spain. pp. 362.
1894. 8°. Dircks (W. H.) International Humour.   012314. g.
See also Poetry, *Spanish.*
For the literature of Spanish America, *see* American Literature, *Spanish :* Poetry, *Spanish.*

SPARTA. Hallström (A.) Agis och Kleomenes. pp. 63. *Karlstad*, 1891. 4°.
                                             9007. h. 4. (4.)

Stern (E. v.) Geschichte der spartanischen und thebanischen Hegemonie. pp. 248.
Dorpat, 1884. 8°.   9026. ff. 33.

Gilbert (G.) Constitutional antiquities of Sparta. pp. 463. *Lond.* 1895. 8°. 9026. c. 17.

Stern (E. v.) Zur Entstehung und ursprünglichen Bedeutung des Ephorats in Sparta.
pp. 62. 1894. 8°. Ascherson (C. E. F.) Berliner Studien. Bd. 15.   P.P. 4991. e.

Fustel de Coulanges (N. D.) Études sur la propriété à Sparte. 1888. 4°. Ac. *Paris. Académie des Sciences Morales.* Mémoires.
Tom. 16.   2098. f.
See also Greece : Peloponnesus.

SPECIFIC PERFORMANCE, Law of.

Indermaur (J.) and Thwaites (C.) Student's Guide to specific Performance. pp. 102.
Lond. 1886. 8°.   6375. de. 8.

SPECTACLES. *See* Eye.

SPECTRUM ANALYSIS. Ames (J. S.)
On relations between the lines of various Spectra. pp. 15. 1890. 8°.   8708. i. 25. (6.)

—— On some gaseous Spectra. 1890. 8°. Pam. 13.

SPECTRUM ANALYSIS—*continued.*

Cowan (F.) D. Alter, the discoverer of Spectrum Analysis. pp. 16.
Greenesburgh, 1894. 8°.   Pam. 7.

Demarçay (E.) Spectres électriques. pp. 91.
Paris, 1895. 4°.   8755. k. 59.
—— Atlas. fol.   8755. m. 22.

Draper (H.) The Draper catalogue of Stellar Spectra. 1890. 4°. Ac. *Cambridge. Harvard University. Astronomical Observatory.* Annals.
Vol. 27.   8562. h.

Gaenge (C.) Anleitung zur Spectralanalyse.
pp. 96. *Leipz.* 1893. 8°.   8716. aa. 11.

Gothard (J.) On the spectrum of the new star in Auriga. *Lond.* 1892. 8°.   Pam. 4.

Hénocque (A. W. L.) Spectroscopie du sang.
pp. 199. 1895. 8°. Encyclopédie des aide-mémoire.   8709. g.

Kayser (H.) and Runge (C.) Über die Spectren der Elemente. pp. 93. 1889. 4°. Ac. *Berlin. Societas Regia Scientiarum.* Abhandlungen.
1888.   Ac. 855/6.

Keeler (J. E.) Spectroscope of the Alleghany Observatory. pp. 11. *Northfield*, 1892. 8°. Pam. 4.

—— Elementary principles governing the Efficiency of Spectroscopes for astronomical purposes. pp. 21. 1892. 8°.   Pam. 4.

—— On the Spectra of the Orion Nebula and the Orion Stars. pp. 18. *Northfield*, 1894. 8°.
                                             Pam. 4.

Kruess (G.) and (H.) Kolorimetrie und quantitative Spektralanalyse in ihrer Anwendung in der Chemie. pp. 291. *Hamb.* 1891. 8°.
                                             8715. h. 22.

Mac Clean (F.) Comparative photographic Spectra of the Sun and the Metals. 3 pt.
Lond. 1892. fol. & 8°.   8753. b. 4.

P.P. *Northfield.* The Astrophysical Journal.
Chicago, 1895, *etc.* 8°.   P.P. 1565. e.

Salet (G.) Traité élémentaire de Spectroscopie.
Paris, 1888, *etc.* 4°.   8715. i.

Scheiner (J.) Die Spectralanalyse der Gestirne.
pp. 474. *Leipz.* 1890. 8°.   8561. k. 4.

Watts (W. M.) Index of Spectra. pp. 232.
Manch. 1889. 8°.   8716. cc. 34.
See also Astronomy : Light.

SPEECH, Defects and Diseases of.
See Voice.

SPEECHES. *See* Elocution.

SPEEN. Money (W.) Collections for the history of Speen. pp. 103. *Newbury*, 1892. 8°.
                                             10358. dd. 21.

SPESSART. Buecking (H.) Der nordwestliche Spessart. pp. 274. 1892. 8°. Prussia. Abhandlungen zur geologischen Specialkarte.
N.F. Hft. 12.   7109. i.

Craemer (P.) Die Jagd im Spessart in Sage und Geschichte. pp. 166. *München*, 1892. 8°.
                                             07905. h. 5.

SPHINGIDAE. *See* Lepidoptera.

SPIDERS. Ac. *London. British Museum.* Descriptive catalogue of the Spiders of Burma.
pp. 406. *Lond.* 1895. 8°.   7207. gg. 1.

Mac Cook (H. C.) American Spiders. 3 vol.
Phila. 1889. 4°.   7297. h. 15.

Peckham (G. W.) and (E. G.) Ant-like Spiders of the family Attidæ. pp. 83. 1892. 8°. Ac. *Milwaukee. Naturhistorischer Verein.* Occasional Papers. Vol. 2.   Ac. 3069/2.

—— Spiders of the Homalattus group of the Family Attidæ. 1895. 8°. Ac. *Milwaukee. Naturhistorischer Verein.* Occasional Papers.
Vol. 2.   Ac. 3069/2.

SPIDERS—continued.

PECKHAM (G. W.) and (E. G.) Spiders of the Marptusa group of the Family Attidæ. 1894. 8°. Ac. Milwaukee. *Naturhistorischer Verein.* Occasional Papers. Vol. 2. Ac. 3069/2.

—— Sense of Sight in Spiders. pp. 30. *Milwaukee*, 1894. 8°. Pam. 42.

SKUSE (F. A. A.) British stalk-eyed Crustacea and Spiders. pp. 128. 1887. 8°. Young Collector Series. 7001. aaa.

THORELL (T.) Studi sui ragni malesi e papuani. 1889, *etc.* 8°. Ac. Genoa. *Museo Civico.* Annali. Ser. 2. Vol. 8. Ac. 2809.

See also ARACHNIDAE.

SPINE. Ac. London. *New Sydenham Society.*
MARIE (P.) Lectures on diseases of the Spinal Cord. pp. 511. *Lond.* 1895. 8°. Ac. 3838/62.

BARWELL (R.) Causes and treatment of lateral curvature of the Spine. pp. 216. *Lond.* 1895. 8°. 7640. aaa. 19.

BRAMWELL (J. B.) Diseases of the Spinal Cord. pp. 659. *Edinb.* 1895. 8°. 7630. h. 35.

CUTTER (E.) Treatment of sclerosis of the Spine. pp. 8. *N.Y.* 1893. 8°. 07305. i. 9. (5.)

HORSLEY (V. A. H.) Structure and functions of the Brain and Spinal Cord. pp. 223. *Lond.* 1892. 8°. 7630. ff. 31.

LEDOUBLE ( ) De l'interprétation des variations morphologiques du grand Dorsal dans l'espèce humaine. *Paris*, 1893. 8°. Pam. 39.

LEWIS (P. G.) Early Scoliosis. pp. 49. *Lond.* 1895. 8°. 7482. e. 20.

MARSH (H.) Diseases of the Joints and Spine. pp. 532. *Lond.* 1895. 8°. 7620. de. 34.

MORTON (W. J.) Diseases of the Spinal Cord. 1894. 8°. BIGELOW (H. R.) International System of Electro-Therapeutics. 2024. e.

NEUGEBAUER (F. L.) Spondyl-olisthésis et spondyl-izème. pp. 176. *Paris*, 1892. 8°. 7482. k. 17.

SMITH (E. N.) More severe forms of lateral Curvature of the Spine. pp. 24. *Lond.* 1892. 8°. 07305. h. 16. (12.)

—— Spinal Caries. Spondylitis. pp. 146. *Lond.* 1894. 8°. 7620. de. 31.

SMITS (J.) Die Chirurgie des Rückenmarkes. 1894. 8°. VOLKMANN (R. v.) Sammlung klinischer Vorträge. N.F. Nr. 104. 7441. g.

SWAN (R. L.) Manual of diseases and deformities of the Spine. pp. 194. *Dublin*, 1894. 8°. 7481. aaa. 37.

WALDEYER (W.) Das Gorilla-Rückenmark. pp. 147. 1889. 4°. Ac. Berlin. *Societas Regia Scientarum.* Abhandlungen. 1888. Ac. 855/6.

WILLIAMSON (R. T.) On the relation of diseases of the Spinal Cord to the distribution of the spinal Blood Vessels. pp. 43. *Lond.* 1895. 8°. 7630. g. 24.

See also LOCOMOTOR ATAXIA : PARALYSIS.

SPIRES. MEYER-SCHWARTAU (W.) Der Dom zu Speier. pp. 170. *Berl.* 1893. fol. 7815. e. 18.

SPIRITUALISM. AKSAKOV (A. N.) Animismus und Spiritismus. *Leipz.* 1894, *etc.* 8°. 8632. g.

ASHCROFT (T.) Spiritualism, and why I object to it. pp. 24. *Manch.* 1891. 8°. 8632. e. 36. (11.)

BEHRE (C.) Spiritisten, Occultisten, Mystiker und Theosophen. pp. 85. *Leipz.* 1890. 8°. 8632. e. 36. (9.)

BESANT (A.) Dangers of Spiritualism. (On occasion of Mrs. Besant's visit to Bellary.) pp. 15. *Bellary*, 1894. 16°. Pam. 36.

SPIRITUALISM—continued.

CHRISTIANITY. Primitive Christianity and modern Spiritualism. *Melbourne*, 1890. 8°. 8632. e. 36. (10.)

CLARKE (R. F.) Spiritualism : its character and results. pp. 48. *Lond.* 1892. 8°. 8630. cc. 39. (2.)

CLERK (A. M.) Spiritism the keystone of Christianity. pp. 60. *Lond.* 1894. 8°. 8630. cc. 39. (7.)

CURTIS (J.) Rustlings in the Golden City. *Ballarat*, 1894. 8°. 8631. aaa. 62.

CYRIAX (B.) Wie ich ein Spiritualist geworden bin. pp. 153. *Leipz.* 1893. 8°. 8630. ee. 26.

DAVIS (P.) Le spiritisme devant la raison et la science. pp. 294. *Paris*, 1892. 12°. 8632. ccc. 20.

DEAD. Do the Dead Return ? Experiences in Spiritualism. pp. 127. *Lond.* 1893. 8°. 8632. ccc. 22.

DELANNE (G.) Le Phénomène spirite. pp. 296. *Paris*, 1893. 12°. 8632. ccc. 28.

DOWIE (J. A.) Spiritualism unmasked. pp. 50. *Melbourne*, 1882. 8°. 8632. e. 36. (8.)

DRAMA. The Drama of Life, or the Evolution of Man. pp. 264. *Lond.* 1895. 8°. 8631. ee. 47.

EDELWEISS. Spiritism. pp. 135. *N.Y.* 1891. 8°. 8632. ccc. 17.

ERIKSEN (R.) Det Oversanselige. pp. 165. *Kristiania*, 1891. 8°. 8631. aaa. 52.

ESOTERIC CHRISTIAN UNION. A Message to Earth. pp. 86. *Lond.* 1892. 8°. 4136. aa. 36.

FIGUIER (L.) Les Mystères de la Science. pp. 725. *Paris*, 1893. 4°. 8630. i. 20.

FRONTAURA (J. M.) Historias de espiritismo e hipnotismo. *Santiago de C.* 1887. 8°. 8631. ee. 38.

GAILHARD (G.) Darwinisme et Spiritualisme pp. 371. *Paris*, 1891. 8°. 7006. bbb. 31.

GARDY (L.) Cherchons! Réponse aux conférences de M. E. Yung. pp. 273. *Paris*, 1890. 8°. 8632. cc. 40.

GASPARIN (A. É. de) Count. Du Surnaturel. 2 vol. *Paris*, 1892. 12°. 8632. ccc. 18.

GEIJERSTAM (C. af) Modern Vidskepelse. pp. 197. *Stockholm*, 1892. 8°. 8631. aaa. 53.

GIBIER (P.) Le Spiritisme. pp. 398. *Paris*, 1891. 12°. 8632. cc. 41.

GLEAMS. Gleams of Light, *etc.* pp. 724. *Lond.* 1893. 4°. 8632. h. 12.

GLENDINNING (A.) The Veil Lifted. pp. 164. *Lond.* 1894. 8°. 8632. ccc. 30.

GOLDEN LIGHT. Angels' visits to my farm in Florida. pp. 283. *Lond.* 1892. 8°. 10409. aa. 33.

GONDAL (I. L.) Du Spiritualisme au Christianisme. pp. 409. *Paris*, 1894. 8°. 4371. bb. 6.

HAFNER (J.) Spiritismus oder Philosophie? pp. 83. *Leipz.* 1894. 8°. 8632. f. 29.

HARDING, afterwards BRITTEN (E.) The Lyceum Manual. *Newcastle*, 1894. 8°. 8632. de. 9.

HARTMANN (C. R. E. v.) Die Geisterhypothese des Spiritismus. pp. 126. *Leipz.* 1891. 8°. 8632. g. 17.

HATCH, afterwards RICHMOND (C. L. V.) Spiritual Spheres. pp. 68. *Lond.* 1894. 8°. Pam. 36.

HOPPS (J. P.) Death a Delusion. pp. 46. *Lond.* 1893. 8°. 8632. ccc. 27.

HUDSON (T. J.) The Law of psychic Phenomena. pp. 409. *Lond.* 1893. 8°. 7410. dg. 46.

I. "I awoke," *etc.* pp. 151. *Lond.* 1893. 8°. 8632. de. 1.

LADY. From over the Tomb. pp. 102. *Lond.* 1889. 12°. 4257. e. 13.

SPIRITUALISM—*continued.*

LASHBROKE (H.) The spiritualistic Experiences of W. J. Champernowne. pp. 25.
Lond. 1893. 8°. Pam. 36.

LAZARE (B.) La Télépathie et le Neo-Spiritualisme. pp. 36. *Paris,* 1893. 8°. Pam. 36.

MARRYAT, afterwards LEAN (F.) There is no Death. pp. 295. *Lond.* 1892. 8°. 8632. cc. 45.

—— The Spirit world. pp. 299. *Lond.* 1894. 8°. 8631. ec. 34.

MAYNARD (N.) Was A. Lincoln a Spiritualist? pp. 264. *Phila.* 1891. 8°. 010882. e. 9.

MEDIUM. Confessions of a Medium. pp. 232. *Lond.* 1892. 8°. 8632. cc. 44.

MORTON (D.) Animal Electricity and Spiritualism unmasked. *Brighouse,* 1893, *etc.* 8°. 8632. ccc. 23.

MOSES (W. S.) Spirit Teachings through the mediumship of W. S. Moses. pp. 291. *Lond.* 1894. 8°. 8632. e. 31.

MUELLER (E.) Diesterweg und der Spiritismus. pp. 19. *Berl.* 1891. 8°. Pam. 36.

OTERO ACEVEDO (M.) Los Espíritus. *Madrid,* 1893, *etc.* 8°. 8631. ee.

PARIS. *Congrès international spirite.* Les Étudiants swédenborgiens libres au Congrès. pp. 27. *Argenteuil,* 1889. 8°. Pam. 84.

P.P. *Edinburgh.* The New Age. *Edinb.* 1894, *etc.* 8°. 830.

—— *London.* Astarte. Organ of the London Spiritualist Federation. *Lond.* 1893, *etc.* 4°. 1865. a. 13.

—— Borderland. *Lond.* 1893, *etc.* 8°. P.P. 636. ch.

—— The mystical World. *Lond.* 1893, *etc.* 4°. P.P 636. ch. and 2228.

—— The Spiritual Review. *Lond.* 1895, *etc.* 4°. P.P. 597. bf.

—— *Manchester.* The Unseen Universe. Vol. 1. *Manch.* 1892–93. 8°. P.P. 597. cd.

—— *Oldham.* The Spiritualists' Lyceum Magazine. Vol. 1. No. 1-9. *Oldham,* 1890. 8°. P.P. 597. cb.

RAMBAUD (Y.) Force psychique. pp. 52. *Paris,* 1889. 4°. 8630. l. 5.

RENUCCI (J. É.) Conciliation scientifique du matérialisme et du spiritualisme. pp. 46. *Paris,* 1894. 8°. Pam. 36.

ROBERTSON (J.) Rise and progress of modern Spiritualism in England, *etc.* pp. 92. *Manch.* 1893. 8°. Pam. 36.

ROUXELL ( ) Rapports du Spiritisme. pp. 384. *Paris,* 1892. 8°. 8632. h. 9.

—— Spiritisme et occultisme. pp. 72. *Paris,* 1892. 12°. Pam. 36.

SAVAGE (M. J.) Psychics; facts and theories. pp. 153. *Boston,* 1893. 8°. 8632. d. 24.

SENILLOSA (F.) Concordancia del espiritismo con la ciencia. 2 vol. *Buenos A.* 1891. 8°. 8632. d. 21.

SINCLAIR (M.) *Countess of Caithness.* Le Spiritualisme dans la Bible. pp. 64. *Paris,* 1894. 8°. 8632. bb. 59.

SINNETT (A. P.) Phenomena of Spiritualism in the light of theosophic Teaching. pp. 18. 1895. 8°. THEOSOPHICAL SOCIETY. Transactions. No. 23. 8631. cc.

TIBERGHIEN (G.) La nouveau Spiritualisme. 1892. 8°. Ac. Brussels. *Académie.* Mémoires couronnés. Tom. 46. Ac. 985/4.

TUTTLE (H.) Philosophy of Spirit, and the Spirit world. pp. 207. *Lond.* 1895. 8°. 8632. e. 35.

WEATHERLY (L. A.) The Supernatural? pp. 273. *Bristol,* 1891. 8°. 8632. ccc. 8.

SPIRITUALISM—*continued.*

WHITE (E.) Modern Spiritualism in the light of Revelation. pp. 80. *Lond.* 1893. 8°. Pam. 36.

WILMOT (T. S.) Twenty photographs of the Risen Dead. pp. 56. *Birmingham,* 1894. 8°. 8632. cc. 49.

See also GHOSTS: OCCULT SCIENCE: THEOSOPHY.

SPITZBERGEN.

BARRY (R. v.) Zwei Fahrten in das nördliche Eismeer nach Spitzbergen. pp. 169. *Pola,* 1894. 8°. 10470. h. 34.

BIENAIMÉ (A. P. L.) Voyage de "La Manche" au Spitzberg. pp. 268. *Paris,* 1894. 8°. 10460. ff. 22.

KLINCKOWSTRÖM (A.) Tre Månaders Dag Minnew från Svenska Spetsbergs-Expeditionen. pp. 176. *Stockholm,* 1891. 8°. 10460. b. 37.

NORDENSKIOLD (N. A. E.) *Baron.* Projet d'une Exploration norvégienne au Spitzberg. 1892. 8°. Ac. Paris. *Société de Géographie.* Bulletin. 1891. Ac. 6035.

RABOT (C.) Explorations dans l'océan glacial. pp. 69. 1894. 8°. Ac. Paris. *Société de Géographie.* Bulletin. 1894. Ac. 6035.

SPITZBERGEN. Spitzbergen and Norway in August 1894. pp. 65. *Lond.* 1894. 8°. 10460. ff. 18.
See also ARCTIC REGIONS.

SPONGES.

DENDY (A.) Monograph of the Victorian Sponges. 1891, *etc.* 8°. Ac. Melbourne. *Royal Society.* Transactions. N. S. Vol. 3. Ac. 1980/8.

DREYER (F.) Die Principien der Gerüstbildung bei Spongien. 1891. 8°. Jenaische Zeitschrift für Naturwissenschaft. Bd. 26. Hft. 2. Ac. 3760.

HEAD (W. R.) Palæozoic Sponges of North America. 1895. 4°. Pam. 27.

LENDENFELD (R. v.) Das System der Spongien. 1890. 4°. Ac. Frankfort. *Senckenbergische Naturforschende Gesellschaft.* Abhandlungen. Bd. 16. Ac. 2878/2.

SOLLAS (W. J.) Sponges. 1891. 4°. LANKESTER (E. R.) Zoological Articles. 7206. m. 2.

TOPSENT (E.) Contribution à l'étude des Spongiaires de l'Atlantique Nord. pp. 165. 1892. 4°. ALBERT HONORÉ CHARLES, *Prince of Monaco.* Résultats des campagnes scientifiques. Fasc. 2. 7299. l. 14.

SPOROZOA.

KOROTNEV (A.) Sporozoen als Krankheitserreger. *Berl.* 1893, *etc.* fol. 7620. i.
See also PROTOZOA.

SPORT.

Bibliography.

UHAGON Y GUARDAMINO (F. de) Estudios bibliográficos. La caza. pp. 114. *Madrid,* 1888. 8°. 011902. l. 27.

General.

ASTLEY (*Sir* J. D.) Fifty Years of my Life. 2 vol. *Lond.* 1894. 8°. 10816. cc. 26.

BARRON (L.) Les Jeux. Sports modernes, *etc.* pp. 237. *Paris,* 1892. 8°. 7908. eee. 14.

BUXTON (E. N.) Short Stalks. pp. 405. *Lond.* 1893. 8°. 7906. dd. 10.

CASSELL (J.) Book of Sports and Pastimes. *Lond.* 1891-2. 8°. 07905. h. 10.

CONSTABLE (H. S.) Something about horses, sport, and war. pp. 293. *Lond.* 1891. 8°. 7908. ee. 21.

GÉRUZEZ (P.) A pied, à cheval, en voiture. pp. 223. *Paris,* 1895. 8°. 07905. g. 10.

ELMHIRST (E. P.) Fox-hound, forest and prairie. pp. 584. *Lond.* 1892. 8°. 7908. dd. 17.

GILLMORE (P.) Gun, Rod, and saddle. pp. 341. *Lond.* 1893. 8°. 07905. f. 3.

SPORT.—General—*continued.*

GILMORE (P.) Leaves from a Sportsman's diary. pp. 341. *Lond.* 1893. 8°.   07905. f. 4.

JENSEN (G. G.) Jagtstemninger. pp. 173. *Kjøbenh.* 1893. 8°.   07905. g. 5.

KELLOGG (W. F.) Hunting in the Jungle with gun and guide. pp. 340. *Lond.* 1888. 8°.
   7908. d. 33.

KOLB (G.) Physiology of Sport. pp. 184. *Lond.* 1893. 8°.   07905. f. 8.

LYDEKKER (R.) Horns and Hoofs, chapters on hoofed animals. pp. 411. *Lond.* 1893. 8°.
   7206. h. 21.

MONTAGUE (C.) Tales of a Nomad. pp. 208. *Lond.* 1894. 8°.   010096. e. 65.

P. P. *London.* Badminton Magazine of Sports. *Lond.* 1895. *etc.* 8°.   P.P. 1832. fb.

POLLOK (F. T.) Incidents of foreign Sport. pp. 427. *Lond.* 1894. 8°.   07905. i. 4.

SARGENT (H. R.) Thoughts upon Sport. pp. 446. *Lond.* 1895. 8°.   07905. h. 26.

SKIZZEN. Gesammelte ornithologische und jagdliche Skizzen. pp. 167. *Wien,* 1884. 8°.
   7284. ee. 17.

SNAFFLE. Gun, rifle and hound in east and west. pp. 376. *Lond.* 1894. 8°.   07905. i. 7.

STEPHEN (O. L.) Sir V. Brook, Sportsman and Naturalist. pp. 266. *Lond.* 1894. 8°.
   10825. eee. 12.

WARD (R.) The Sportsman's handbook. pp. 192. *Lond.* 1894. 8°.   7206. e. 18.

—— Horn Measurements and Weights of the great game of the world. pp. 264. *Lond.* 1892. 8°.   7208. g. 25.

WOLLEY (C. P.) Big Game shooting. 2 vol. 1894. 4°. Badminton Library.   7905. f.

See also BOXING : COURSING : DEER : FALCONRY : GROUSE : HUNTING : PHEASANT : RACING : ROWING : TAXIDERMY : WRESTLING.

Shooting.

ADAMS (W. A.) Bores and loads for sporting Guns. pp. 24. *Lond.* 1894. 8°.   7905. a. 51.

EXPERT. Notes on Shooting. pp. 67. *Lond.* 1894. 8°.   7912. ee. 3. (7.)

GALLWEY (*Sir* R. P.) Letters to young shooters. 3 Series. *Lond.* 1890–96. 8°.   7908. df.

GREENER (W. W.) The Gun and its development. pp. 742. *Lond.* 1892. 8°.   2264. d. 10.

—— Modern shot Guns. pp. 202. *Lond.* 1891. 8°.   7908. ee. 13.

—— The Breech-Loader, and how to use it. pp. 351. *Lond.* 1894. 8°.   07905. f. 18.

LANCASTER (C.) Illustrated treatise on the art of Shooting. pp. 221. *Lond.* 1891. 8°. 7908. ee. 19.

LEHMANN (R. C.) Conversational hints for young Shooters. pp. 114. *Lond.* 1894. 8°.
   012314. ee. 56.

LOADS. Loads for modern Game-Guns. pp. 36. *Lond.* 1893. 8°.   7905. c. 50.

SHARP (H.) Practical Wildfowling. pp. 300. *Lond.* 1895. 8°.   07905. h. 29.

For works on Military Shooting, *see* GUNNERY.

Sports of various Countries.

Africa.

BAILEY (H.) Travel and adventures in the Congo State. pp. 335. *Lond.* 1894. 8°. 07905. i. 3.

BALDWIN (W. C.) African Hunting and adventure. pp. 428. *Lond.* 1894. 8°. 010096. h. 5.

BRYDEN (H. A.) Gun and camera in S. Africa. pp. 544. *Lond.* 1893. 8°.   010096. ff. 26.

CUMMING (R. G.) Five years' hunting Adventures in S. Africa. pp. 349. *Lond.* 1892. 8°.
   7908. c. 40.

SPORT.—Africa—*continued.*

DUPOUY (É.) Les Chasses du Soudan. pp. 357. *Paris,* 1894. 12°.   07905. f. 24.

FOÀ (É.) Mes grandes Chasses dans l'Afrique centrale. pp. 340. *Paris,* 1895. 8°. 07905. l. 5.

GLYN (F.) *Baron Wolverton.* Five months' Sport in Somali Land. pp. 108. *Lond.* 1894. 8°.
   07905. i. 2.

HOYOS (E.) *Count.* Zu den Aulihan. Jagderlebnisse im Somâlilande. pp. 190. *Wien,* 1895. 8°.   010096. i. 28.

KNOX (T. W.) Hunters Three. Sport in S. Africa, *etc.* pp. 256. *Lond.* 1895. 8°.
   012808. h. 20.

MELLISS (C. J.) Lion-hunting in Somali-Land. pp. 186. *Lond.* 1895. 8°.   07905. i. 11.

SWAYNE (H. G. C.) Seventeen trips through Somáliland. Record of big game shooting. pp. 386. *Lond.* 1895. 8°.   10096. g. 13.

America, North.

EDWORDS (C. E.) Camp-fires of a Naturalist. pp. 304. *Lond.* 1893. 8°.   7001. aa. 27.

KARR (H. W. S.) Bear-hunting in the White Mountains. pp. 156. *Lond.* 1891. 8°.
   7908. eee. 3.

RALPH (J.) On Canada's Frontier. Sketches of Sport. pp. 325. *Lond.* 1892. 8°. 10470. f. 34.

ROOSEVELT (T.) and GRINNELL (G. B.) American Big-Game hunting. pp. 345. *Edinb.* 1893. 8°.
   7907. d. 41.

WALLIHAN (A. G.) and (*Mrs.* A. G.) Hoofs, Claws and Antlers of the Rocky Mountains. *Denver,* 1894. 4°.   7208. k. 3.

See also supra: General.

America, South.

KENNEDY (W. R.) Sporting sketches in S. America. pp. 269. *Lond.* 1892. 8°. 7908. df. 14.

Asia, Central.

CUMBERLAND (C. S.) Sport on the Pamirs and Turkestan Steppes. pp. 278. *Lond.* 1895. 8°.
   07905. h. 25.

France.

FAURE (E.) La Sauvagine, sa chasse en bateau. pp. 89. *Bordeaux,* 1889. 8°.   7912. aaa. 3.

LACROIX-DANLIARD ( ) Nos animaux des bois et de la plaine. pp. 171. *Paris,* 1890. 4°.
   7208. h. 30.

LIGNIVILLE (J. de) *Count de Bey.* Les Meuttes et veneries de J. de Ligniville. 2 pt. *Paris,* 1892. 4°.   7908. dd. 23.

ONSENBRAY (H. d') *Viscount.* École du Piqueur. pp. 117. *Paris,* 1894. 12°.   07905. f. 25.

OSMOND (R. E. d') *Count.* Les Hommes des bois. pp. 372. *Paris,* 1892. 8°.   07905. h. 3.

VAGABOND. An original Wager. pp. 318. *Lond.* 1895. 8°.   07905. f. 40.

Germany.

ANDREAE (E. C. A.) Die Geschichte der Jagd im Taunus. pp. 423. *Frankf.* 1894. 8°.
   07905. h. 23.

CRAEMER (P.) Die Jagd im Spessart. pp. 166. *München,* 1892. 8°.   07905. h. 5.

Great Britain and Ireland.

SAHLENDER (P. M.) Englische Jagd im 14. 15. und 16. Jahrhundert. pp. 31. *Leipz.* 1895. 8°.
   7912. f. 2. (8.)

—— Der Jagdtraktat Twici's, des Hofjägers bei Edward II. von England. pp. 60. *Leipz.* 1894. 8°.   7912. f. 2. (9.)

DITCHFIELD (P. H.) Old English Sport. pp. 132. *Lond.* 1891. 8°   7912. aa. 6.

HARTOPP (E. C. C.) Sport in England. pp. 190. *Lond.* 1894. 8°.   07905. g. 3.

SPORT.—Great Britain, etc.—continued

BROWN (J. M.) Stray Sport. 2 vol.
Edinb. 1893. 8°.   07905. g. 1.

CANK (T.) Forty Years mingled in Game, fur
and feathers. pp. 133. Preston, 1891. 8°.
      7908. eee. 1.

CORBALLIS (J. H.) Forty-five Years of Sport.
pp. 502. Lond. 1891. 8°.   7908. dd. 18.

CRAWFURD (O. J. F.) A Year of Sport and
natural history. pp. 331. Lond. 1895. 4°.
      7906. b. 23.

DIXON (C.) The Game Birds and wild fowls of
the British islands. pp. 468. Lond. 1893. 8°.
      7285. f. 16.

GREVILLE (B. V.) Baroness Greville. Ladies
in the Field. pp. 287. Lond. 1894. 8°.
      07905. f. 15.

—— Gentlewoman's book of Sports. 1892. 8°.
ADAMS (W. H. D.) Victoria Library. 012208. f.

GRIMBLE (A.) Shooting and Salmon fishing.
pp. 259. Lond. 1892. 4°.   7908. f. 17.

LEFFINGWELL (W. B.) Wild Fowl Shooting.
pp. 373. Lond. 1890. 8°.   7908. ee. 10.

MORRIS (B. R.) British Game Birds and wild-
fowl. 2 vol. Lond. 1895. 8°.   7285. g. 21.

SHOOTING. Making a shooting. pp. 92.
Lond. 1894. 8°.   07905. f. 22.

WATSON (A. E. T.) Fur and feather series.
Lond. 1893, etc. 8°.   7906. dd.

WHITNEY (C. W.) A sporting Pilgrimage.
pp. 397. Lond. 1895. 8°.   07905. i. 6.

FITTIS (R. S.) Sports and pastimes of Scotland.
pp. 212. Paisley, 1891. 8°.   7908. dd. 12.

BICKERDYKE (J.) Days in Thule. pp. 180.
Westminster, 1894. 8°.   7907. ff. 5.

GRIMBLE (A.) Highland Sport. pp. 268.
Lond. 1894. 4°.   K.T.C. 22. c. 12.

CREALOCK (H. H.) Deer-stalking in the Highlands. pp. 194. Lond. 1892. 8°. K.T.C. 13. b. 1.

MACKENZIE (E. G.) In Grouseland. pp. 248.
Lond. 1895. 8°.   07905. f. 30.

MASON (J.) Twelve years' residence on the
West Coast of Scotland. pp. 90. Lond. 1894. 8°.
      7908. ee. 26.

SAINT JOHN (C. W. G.) Short sketches of the
Wild Sports of the Highlands. pp. 319.
Lond. 1893. 8°.   7906. dd. 9.

—— Sportsman's Tour in Sutherlandshire.
pp. 320. Lond. 1891. 8°.   7908. ee. 16.

MAXWELL (W. H.) Wild sports in the West of
Ireland. pp. 337. Lond. 1892. 8°. 012634. k. 39.

See also supra: General.

India.

A., F. E. S. Sport in Ladakh. pp. 32.
Lond. 1895. 4°.   7905. i. 30.

BRADDON (Sir E. N. C.) Thirty Years of Shikar.
pp. 373. Edinb. 1895. 8°.   07905. i. 12.

BROWN (J. M.) Stray Sport. 2 vol.
Edinb. 1893. 8°.   07905. g. 1.

GARDNER (N.) Rifle and spear with the Raj-
poots. pp. 336. Lond. 1895. 4°. 10056. h. 10.

HAMILTON (D.) Records of Sport in Southern
India. pp. 284. Lond. 1892. 4°.   7908. f. 24.

J., K. C. A. Sportsman's Vade-Mecum for
the Himalayas. pp. 120. Lond. 1891. 8°.
      7908. dd. 13.

MURRAY (J. A.) Mammalian Game of British
India. pp. 85. Bombay, 1891. 8°. 7208. dd. 5.

POLLOCK (A. J. O.) Sporting days in Southern
India. pp. 252. Lond. 1894. 8°.   7907. h. 39.

SCLATER (W. L.) Notes on Indian horned Game.
pp. 24. Calcutta, 1893. 8°.   Pam. 42.

SPORT.—India—continued.

TYACKE (R. H.) Sportsman's Manual in quest
of game in Kullu, Lahoul, and Ladak. pp. 128.
Calcutta, 1893. 8°.   7912. aa. 33.

WILLIAMSON (T.) Illustrations of Indian Sports.
pp. 20. Lond. 1892. obl. 8°.   7908. df. 17.

See also supra: General.

Ireland. See supra: Great Britain and Ireland.

Norway. See infra: Sweden.

Scotland. See supra: Great Britain and Ireland.

Spain.

CHAPMAN (A.) and BUCK (W. J.) Wild Spain.
Records of sport. pp. 472. Lond. 1893. 8°.
      7908. f. 25.

Sweden and Norway.

BAXTER (G. W.) Elk Hunting in Sweden.
pp. 43. Dundee, 1893. 16°.   Pam. 83.

GULDBERG (F. O.) Jagtminder fra det Sønden-
fjeldske Norge. pp. 288. Kristiania, 1891. 8°.
      7905. bbb. 44.

HANSEN (J. E. V.) Illustreret Idrætsbog. 2 Dlr.
Kjøbenh. 1890, 93. 8°.   7908. dd. 7.

SCHRÖDER (G.) Jagtminnen från skog och slätt.
pp. 272. Stockholm, 1891. 8°.   7908. dd. 21.

URDAHL (L.) Norsk Idræt. pp. 192.
Christiania, 1891, 92. 4°.   7908. f. 27.

SPRAINS. MOULLIN (C. W. M.) Sprains.
pp. 153. Lond. 1894. 8°.   7482. e. 18.
See also JOINTS.

SPUTUM. COUPLAND (S.) Notes on the
examination of the sputum. pp. 57.
Lond. 1891. 8°.   7461. aaa. 20.

STAFFORD. CHERRY (J. L.) Stafford in
Olden Times. pp. 152. Stafford, 1890. 8°.
      010358. l. 40.

STAFFORDSHIRE. SIMMS (R.) Bibliotheca Staffordiensis. pp. 546.
Lichfield, 1894. 4°.   11905. d. 9.

DERBYSHIRE. Murray's Handbook for Derbyshire
and Staffordshire. pp. 229. Lond. 1892. 8°.
      2364. a. 8.

SHELDON (J. P.) Through Staffordshire Stiles.
pp. 21. Derby, 1894. 4°.   10368. h. 33.

WROTTESLEY (Hon. G.) Pedes Finium. Fines
which include manors in Staffordshire. 1891. 8°.
Ac. Stafford. William Salt Society. Collections. Vol. 12.   Ac. 5704.

STAGLIENO. RESASCO (F.) La Necropoli
di Staglieno. pp. 352. Genova, 1892. 8°.
      10132. f. 15.

STAGLIENO. Staglieno. Genova, 1894, etc. fol.
      465.

STAINDROP. HODGSON (J. F.) Staindrop
Church. 1887. 8°. Ac. Durham. Architectural
Society. Transactions.   Ac. 5635.

STAINES. ENGLAND AND WALES. Local
Government Board. Report upon the sanitary
condition of the district of Staines. pp. 10.
Lond. 1891. fol.   Pam. 79.

STAIR-BUILDING. WOOD (W. H.) Prac-
tical Stair-building and Hand-railing. pp. 83.
Lond. 1894. 4°.   7817. i. 7.
See also CARPENTRY.

STALACTITES. See CAVES.

STAMBOURNE. BEDDOW (B.) Memories
of Stambourne. pp. 144. Lond. 1892. 8°.
      4715. aaa. 42.

STAMMERING. See VOICE.

STAMP DUTIES. See ENGLAND, Trade and
Finance.

STAMPS, Postage, etc. See POSTS.

STAPLEFORD TAWNEY. STAPLEFORD TAWNEY. Parish Registers. pp. 91.
Lond. 1892. fol.   9916. f. 8.

STARCH. LARBALÉTRIER (A.) Nouveau manuel de l'Amidonnier. 1890. 18°. Encyclopédie-Roret.   12208. b.

STARGARD. REDLIN ( ) Beiträge zur Geschichte der Marienkirche in Stargard.
Stargard, 1895, *etc.* 8°.   4662. cc.

STARS. Ac. Cambridge, *Mass. Astronomical Observatory.* Variable Stars of long period.
pp. 8. *Cambridge,* 1891. 4°.   8562. h.

Ac. Cape Town. *Observatory.* Catalogue of 12,441 Stars. pp. 565. *Lond.* 1881. 4°.
                                            8563. i. 7.

—— Greenwich. *Observatory.* Ten-Year Catalogue of 4059 stars. pp. 57. *Lond.* 1889. 4°.
                                            8566. i.

—— Madras. *Observatory.* Results of Observations of fixed Stars. pp. 168.
Madras, 1892. 4°.   8563. g. 3.

—— Oxford. *Radcliffe Observatory.* Catalogue of 6424 Stars. pp. 287. *Oxf,* 1894. 4°.
                                            8534. f. 26.

—— Sydney. *Observatory.* Results of Double Star Measures. pp. 22. *Sydney,* 1891. 8°.
                                            8561. f. 35.

BAUSCHINGER (J.) Zweites münchener Sternverzeichniss enthaltend die mittleren Oerter von 13200 Sternen. pp. 172. 1891. 4°. Ac. Bogenhausen. *Sternwarte.* Neue Annalen. Bd. 2.
                                            8564. dd.

BIRMINGHAM (J.) The Red Stars : observations and catalogue. pp. 201. 1890. 4°. Ac. Dublin. *R. Irish Academy.* Cunningham Memoirs. No. 5.   Ac. 1540/6.

Boss (L.) Catalogue of 8241 stars made at the Dudley Observatory of Albany. pp. 40. 238. 1890. 4°. Ac. Leipsic. *Astronomische Gesellschaft.* Catalog. Abtheil. 1, *etc.* St. 14.
                                            Ac. 4140/3.

FEARNLEY (C.) and GEELMUYDEN (H.) Zonenbeobachtungen der Sterne auf der Sternwarte in Christiania. pp. 318. *Christiania,* 1888. 4°.
                                            8563. i. 21.

GEF (W.) Die Wärmequelle der Gestirne in mechanischem Maass. pp. 11.
Heidelberg, 1892. 8°.   Pam. 79.

HAHN (R.) Mikrometrische Vermessung des Sternhaufens Σ 762. 1891. 8°. Ac. Leipsic. *Gesellschaft der Wissenschaften.* Abhandlungen. Bd. 29.   Ac. 700/4.

KEELER (J. E.) On the motions of the Planetary Nebulæ in the line of sight.
San Francisco, 1890. 8°.   Pam. 4.

KERZ (F.) Die Scholablagerungstheorie.
pp. 64. *Leipz.* 1891. 8°.   Pam. 4.

KNOBEL (E. B.) On a Catalogue of Stars in the Calendarium of Mohammad al Achsasi al Mouakket. *Lond.* 1895. 8°.   Pam. 4.

KRUEGER (A.) Catalog von 14680 Sternen nach Beobachtungen auf der Sternwarte der Universität Helsingfors. pp. 17. 295. 1890. 4°. Ac. Leipsic. *Astronomische Gesellschaft.* Catalog. Abtheil. 1. St. 4.   Ac. 4140/3.

LOEWY (M.) Determination des ascensions droites des étoiles de culmination lunaire et de longitude. pp. 117. 1890. 4°. Ac. *Paris. Bureau des Longitudes.* Annales. Tom. 4.
                                            8752. i.

OERTEL (C.) Neue Beobachtung des Sternhaufens 38h Persei am münchener grossen Refractor. pp. 94. 1891. 4°. Ac. Bogenhausen. *Sternwarte.* Neue Annalen. Bd. 2.
                                            8564. dd.

STARS—*continued.*

PARKHURST (H. M.) Observations of variable Stars. 1893. 4°. Ac. Cambridge, *Mass. Astronomical Observatory.* Annals. Vol. 29. No. 4.   8563. k.

PRIGENT (G.) De l'habitabilité des Astres.
pp. 456. *Landerneau,* 1892. 8°. 8563. aaa. 37.

ROGERS (W. A.) Catalogue of 8267 stars. pp. 39. 176. 1892. 4°. Ac. Cambridge, *Mass. Astronomical Observatory.* Annals. Vol. 15. Part 2.   8563. k.

—— Comparison of positions of Stars between 49° 50′ and 55° 10′ N. Declination in 1855 and 1870-84. 1893. 4°. Ac. Cambridge, *Mass. Astronomical Observatory.* Annals. Vol. 25.
                                            8563. k.

SEELIGER (H.) and BAUSCHINGER (J.) Erstes münchener Sternverzeichniss. pp. 717. 1890. 4°. Ac. Bogenhausen. *Sternwarte.* Neue Annalen. Bd. 1.   8564. c. and dd.

STARS. The Stars and the Earth. pp. 60.
Lond. 1895. 16°.   8562. aa. 33.

STRUVE (O. W.) Sammlung der Beobachtungen von Sternbedeckungen. pp. 58.
St. Petersburg, 1889. 8°.   8560. h. 38.

VOGEL (H. C.) Untersuchung über die Eigenbewegung der Sterne im Visionsradius. pp. 166. 1892. 4°. Ac. Potsdam. *Astrophysikalisches Observatorium.* Publicationen. Bd. 7. Tl. 1.
                                            8752. i. 6.

ZONA (T.) Osservazioni di stelle. 1890. 4°. Ac. Palermo. *Consiglio di Perfezionamento.* Giornale. Vol. 20.   Ac. 2814.
See also ASTRONOMY : PHOTOGRAPHY, *Astronomical :* SUN AND SOLAR SYSTEM : SPECTRUM ANALYSIS.

STATICS. BRIGGS (W.) and BRYAN (G. H.) Text-book of Statics. pp. 220. 1894. 8°. Tutorial Series.   12205. c. 233.

GELDARD (C.) Statics and dynamics. pp. 308.
Lond. 1893. 8°.   8767. f. 28.

HOSKINS (L. M.) Elements of Graphic Statics. pp. 191. *Lond.* 1892. 8°.   8768. l. 19.

KLIMPERT (R.) Lehrbuch der Statik flüssiger Körper. pp. 350. 1891. 8°. Kleyer's Encyclopädie.   8705. g.

LOCK (G. H.) Key to J. B. Lock's Elementary Statics. pp. 187. *Lond.* 1893. 8°. 8767. aaa. 50.

LONEY (S. L.) Elements of Statics and dynamics. 2 pt. 1893. 8°. Pitt Press Mathematical Series.
                                            2322. cc. 37.

—— Solutions of Examples. pp. 332.
Camb. 1893. 8°.   8531. de. 8.

PRINCE (J. J.) Graphic Statics. pp. 48.
Lond. 1895. 8°.   8533. aa. 20.

ROUTH (E. J.) Treatise on analytical Statics.
Camb. 1891, *etc.* 8°.   8535. d. 2.

PETERSEN (J.) Lehrbuch der Statik fester Körper. pp. 165. *Kopenhagen,* 1882. 8°. 8535. c. 30.
See also MATHEMATICS : MECHANICS.

STATISTICS, General. KETTLER (J. I.) Beiträge zur Statistik. *Weimar,* 1894, *etc.* 8°.
                                            10003. de.

KŐRÖSI (J.) Die internationale Classificierung der Berufsarten. pp. 26. *Wien,* 1893. 8°.
                                            Pam. 47.

MEITZEN (P. A.) History, theory and technique of Statistics. 1891, *etc.* 8°. Ac. Philadelphia. *American Academy.* Annals. Vol. 1. Supplement.   Ac. 2383.

MISCHLER (E.) Handbuch der Verwaltungs-Statistik. *Stuttgart,* 1892, *etc.* 8°. 8223. dh.

MULHALL (M. G.) Dictionary of Statistics. pp. 632. *Lond.* 1892. 8°.   2020. h.

                                            3 F 2

STATISTICS.—General—*continued.*

P.P. *San Francisco.* The Statistician. *San Francisco,* 1893, *etc.* 8°.   P.P. 3896. ad.

—— *Tübingen.* Allgemeines statistiches Archiv. *Tübingen,* 1890, *etc.* 8°.   P.P. 3874. cb.

RUEMELIN (G.) Statistica. 1889. 8°. Biblioteca dell' economista. Ser. 3. Vol. 15. 8205. l.

SMITH (R. M.) Science of Statistics. 1895, *etc.* 8°. Columbia University Biological Series.   7002. e.

WESTERGAARD (H.) Die Grundzüge der Theorie der Statistik. pp. 286. *Jena,* 1890. 8°.   8535. f. 34.

—— Statistikens Theori i Grundrids. pp. 308. *Kjøbenh.* 1890. 8°.   8223. dh. 8.

For Vital Statistics, *see* POPULATION; and for the Statistics of each country or subject, *see* under the country or subject required.

STAVANGER. LÖWOLD (O. A.) Biographiske Eft. rretninger om Præster i Stavanger. pp. 33. *Stavanger,* 1890. 8°.   Pam. 9.

STAVELOT-MALMEDY. NOUÉ (P. de) La législation de l'ancienne principauté de Stavelot-Malmedy. 1890, *etc.* 8°. Ac. Antwerp. *Académie d'Archéologie.* Bulletin. Sér. 4. Tom. 6.   Ac. 5513.

STEAM. *See* BOILERS: MACHINERY, *Steam.*

STEARIN. *See* FATS AND OILS.

STEEL. *See* IRON.

STEEPLECHASING. *See* RACING.

STEFANIE, Lake. *See* AFRICA, *Central and East.*

STEINBACH - HALLENBERG. KOEBRICH (A.) Geschichte von Steinbach. pp. 240. *Steinbach,* 1894. 8°.   10255. ee. 10.

STENAY. GILBERT (A.) Le Siège de Stenay en 1654. pp. 154. 1893. 8°. Ac. Bar-le-Duc. *Société des Lettres.* Mémoires. Sér. 3. Tom. 3.   Ac. 271.

STEREOTOMY. DELITALA (G.) Ricerche di Stereometria. pp. 76. *Sassari,* 1890. 8°.   8535. g. 38.

STERILITY. CASPER (L.) Impotentia et Sterilitas virilis. pp. 168. *München,* 1890. 8°.   7640. h. 23.

EDIS (A. W.) Sterility in women. pp. 112. *Lond.* 1890. 8°.   07581. de. 11.

RYLEY (J. B.) Sterility in women. pp. 88. *Lond.* 1895. 8°.   07581. f. 11.

See also GENITO-URINARY ORGANS: WOMEN, *Diseases of, etc.*

STERNBERG. SCHMIDT (K.) Geschichte der sterberger Hospitalien. 1890. 8°. Ac. Schwerin. *Verein für mecklenburgische Geschichte.* Jahrbücher. Jahrg. 55.   Ac. 7165.

STETTIN. *See* POMMERANIA.

STEYR. ROLLEDER (A.) Heimatkunde von Steyr. *Steyr.* 1893, *etc.* 8°.   10215. i.

STIGMATISATION. *See* MIRACLES.

STIRLINGSHIRE. SIBBALD (*Sir* R.) History and Description of Stirlingshire, 1707. pp. 81. *Stirling,* 1892. 4°.   10370. d. 34.

STOCKHOLM. ANTILITHANDER (E. N.) Stockholm om hundra år härefter. pp. 15. *Stockholm,* 1890. 4°.   Pam. 22.

BARRÈS (M.) Stockholm. 1892. 4°. Les Capitales du Monde. No. 14.   10025. g.

WACHTMEISTER (H.) Vägvisare för Turister. pp. 160. *Stockholm,* 1891. 8°.   10108. bb. 19.

STOCKPORT. CONNELL AND BAILEY. Express Guide to Stockport. pp. 64. *Stockport,* 1894. 8°.   10348. e. 15. (9.)

STOCKPORT. Parish Registers. ff. 118. *Stockport,* 1889. 8°.   9914. f. 9.

STOCKS AND SHARES. APPEALS. Public appeals for Capital in 1890. pp. 71. *Lond.* 1891. 8°.   08227. ee. 17.

B., L. L. Money making on the Stock Exchange and Race-course. *Blackburn,* 1894. 8°.   08226. f. 23. (6.)

BUCHÈRE (A.) Traité des opérations de la Bourse. pp. 850. *Paris,* 1892. 8°. 08227. e. 44.

CLARE (G.) Money-market primer. pp. 149. *Lond.* 1893. 8°.   08227. ee. 49.

CORDINGLEY (W. G.) Guide to the Stock Exchange. pp. 130. *Lond.* 1893. 8°. 8228. aa. 59.

DÉCOURDEMANCHE (J. A.) Manuel des valeurs cotées hors parquet à la Bourse de Paris. pp. 357. *Paris,* 1893. 12°.   08226. f. 1.

DUNCAN (W. W.) Investment and speculation in Stocks and Shares, *etc.* pp. 227. *Lond.* 1894. 8°.   08227. de. 49.

DUNSFORD (F.) Handbook of Railway and other securities. pp. 160. *Lond.* 1892. 12°.   8235. aa. 69.

DYCK-FOURY (A. v.) Les Secrets de la Finance. pp. 148. *Brux.* 1893. 12°.   8228. aa. 62.

ENNIS (G.) and (G. F. M.) Registration of transfers of transferable Stocks and Securities. pp. 128. *Lond.* 1893. 8°.   6375. ec. 17.

FENN (C.) Compendium of the English and foreign Funds. pp. 687. *Lond.* 1893. 8°.   2020. e.

GABBOTT (E. R.) How to invest Money. pp. 84. 1894. 12°. Wilson's Legal Handy books.   6426. aaa. 39.

GIBSON (G. R.) The Stock Exchanges of London, Paris and New York. pp. 125. *N.Y.* 1889. 8°.   08227. de. 23.

GREGORY (G.) Hints to Speculators and investors. pp. 420. *Lond.* 1895. 8°. 08226. h. 20.

INVESTMENTS. Investments. List of British, Colonial and Foreign Securities. pp. 79. *Lond.* 1891. 4°.   8228. l. 7.

KENNEDY (E. E.) Stockbroker's Handbook. pp. 58. 1892. 12°. Wilson's Legal Handy books.   6426. aaa. 39.

KENNEDY (S. S.) System of Share Transfer work. *Lond.* 1895. fol.   8228. l. 17. (9.)

KILLIK (S. H. M.) Stock Exchange Accounts. pp. 67. *Lond.* 1895. 8°.   8246. aaa. 7.

KOLK (F.) Das Geheimnis der Börsen-Kurse. pp. 63. *Leipz.* 1893. 8°. 8227. i. 40. (9.)

MANSON (E.) Debentures and debenture Stock of trading and other companies. pp. 248. *Lond.* 1894. 8°.   6376. ce. 3.

MARTIN (J.) The Broker's correspondent. pp. 67. 1892. 12°. Wilson's Legal Handy books.   6426. aaa. 39.

MATHIESON (F. C.) Fluctuation Chart showing business in the principal securities on the Stock Exchange, 1890–91. *Lond.* 1891–92. fol.   1882. d. 2. (118.)

—— Stock Exchange Values. 1885 to 1895. pp 194. *Lond.* 1895. 8°.   08226. k. 1.

MELSHEIMER (R. E.) and LAURENCE (W.) Law and customs of the Stock Exchange. pp. 199. *Lond.* 1891. 8°.   6376. d. 10.

MENZIES (W. J.) America as a field for investment. pp. 24. *Edinb.* 1892. 8°.   08227. ee. 46. (18.)

PALMER (F. B.) Shareholders', directors' and voluntary liquidators' legal Companion. pp. 231. *Lond.* 1895. 8°.   6376. de. 11.

STOCKS AND SHARES—*continued.*

P.P. *Leeds.* Dunsford's Stock Exchange Hand
book. *Leeds,* 1893, *etc.* 8°. P.P. 2490. nd.

—— *London.* The Investors' Review.
Lond. 1892, *etc.* 8°. PP. 1423. fb.

—— Investment Index. Supplement to the " Investors' Review." *Lond.* 1895, *etc.* 8°.
P.P. 1423. fb.

—— *The Times.* Issues. Prospectuses of public
companies. *Lond.* 1891, *etc.* 4°. N.R.

—— *London.* Joint Stock registration manual.
Lond. 1890, *etc.* 8°. P.P. 2501. ek.

—— *New York.* Poor's Handbook of Investment
securities. *N.Y.* 1891, *etc.* 8°. P.P. 2524. gm.

POUNDS. Pounds Sterling : how to make money.
pp. 12. *Lond.* 1894. 16°. Pam. 23.

QUINET (H.) and BOURNAND (F.) Les pièges de
la Bourse. pp. 274. *Paris,* 1892. 12°. 08235. e. 9.

RAVALOVICH (A.) Le Marché financier en
1892. pp. 174. *Paris,* 1893. 8°. 8225. eee. 48.

—— Le Marché financier en 1893–94. pp. 475.
Paris, 1894. 8°. 08225. l. 25.

RENNEX (A. de) L'Existence du rentier.
pp. 326. *Lausanne,* 1894. 8°. 08235. l. 1.

SENEX. Counsel to ladies and men on their
Business Investments. pp. 135.
Lond. 1892. 8°. 08227. de. 9.

SOLANO (A.) Der Geheimbund der Börse.
pp. 48. *Leipz.* 1893. 8°. 8227. i. 40. (10.)

STUTFIELD (G. H.) Rules and usages of the
Stock Exchange. pp. 181. *Lond.* 1893. 8°.
08227. e. 52.

URSA MINOR. On the science and practice of
Stock Exchange speculation. pp. 32.
Lond. 1893. 8°. 8228. aa. 58.

WALKER (J. D.) Investor's and shareholder's
guide. pp. 272. *Edinb.* 1894. 8°. 8227. ee. 50.

WAHL (A.) Traité des Titres au porteur français
et étrangers. 2 tom. *Paris,* 1891. 8°. 6825. b. 7.

WALL (R. E.) Hints to intending Investors.
pp. 125. *Lond.* 1893. 8°. 8227. bb. 68.

WHITE ( ) White's Reference book of Railroad
securities. pp. 526. *N.Y.* 1894. *obl.* 8°.
8235. a. 100.

WILLDEY (C. J.) Parities of American stocks in
London, New York, and Amsterdam. pp. 11.
Lond. 1894. 8°. 1882. d. 2. (106.)

WILSON (A. J.) Handbooks for Investors.
Lond. 1893, *etc.* 8°. 8229. a.

—— Glossary of colloquial, slang and technical
terms, in use on the Stock Exchange. pp. 210.
Lond, 1895. 8°. 8228. aaaa. 23.

WONTNER (A. J.) Colonial Government securities. pp. 4. *Lond.* 1887. 4°. Pam. 23.

Investment of Trust Funds.

ELLIS (A. L.) Trustees' guide to Investments.
pp. 122. *Lond.* 1892. 8°. 6355. aaa. 33.

MATHIESON (F. C.) Statutory Trust Investment
guide. pp. 216. *Lond.* 1891. 8°. 8226. aa. 29.

URLIN (R. D.) Handy book on the investment
of Trust Funds. pp. 76. *Lond.* 1894. 12°.
6426. aaaa. 22.

See also COMPANIES : LAW, *Commercial* : TABLES :
TRADE.

STOKE-ON-TRENT. HUTCHINSON (S. W.)
The Archdeaconry of Stoke-on-Trent. pp. 211.
Lond. 1893. 8°. 9902. c. 27.

STOMACH. FLEINER (W.) Erfahrungen über
die Therapie der Magenkrankeiten. 1894. 8°.

VOLKMANN (R. v.) Sammlung klinischer Vorträge. N.F. Nr. 103. 7441. g.

HAUSER (G.) Das Cylinderepithel-Carcinom des
Magens. pp. 268. *Jena,* 1890. 8°. 7620. f. 6.

STOMACH—*continued.*

JESSETT (F. B.) Surgical diseases and injuries
of the Stomach. pp. 327. *Lond.* 1892. 8°.
7480. de. 10.

LEDDERHOSE (G.) Die chirurgischen Erkrankungen der Bauchdecken. pp. 194. 1890. 8°.
BILLROTH (T.) Deutsche Chirurgie. Lief. 45 b.
7482. cc.

MARTIN (S.) Functional and organic diseases
of the Stomach. pp. 505. 1895. 8°. Pentland's Medical series. 7641. ce.

MARTIUS (F.) and LUETTKE (J.) Die Magensäure
des Menschen. pp. 193. *Stuttgart,* 1892. 8°.
7407. f. 26.

PICK (A.) Vorlesungen über Magen- und Darmkrankheiten. *Leipz.* 1895. 8°. 7630. ddd.

WILHELM (E.) De la Gastro-entérostomie.
pp. 360. *Nancy.* 1893. 4°. 7481. i. 11.

See also ABDOMEN : DIGESTION.

STONE. FOSTER (C. Le N.) Quarrying.
pp. 18. *Lond.* 1894. 8°. 07109. m. 1. (13.)

PULLEN (H. W.) Handbook of ancient Roman
Marbles. pp. 205. *Lond.* 1894. 8°. 7706. a. 51.

SAILLON. The antique Cipollino marbles of
Saillon. pp. 12. *Lond.* 1893. 4°. Pam. 27.

STONEHENGE. BARCLAY (E.) Stonehenge
and its earth-works. pp. 152. *Lond.* 1895. 4°.
7705. ee. 36.

JUDD (W. A.) Stonehenge : probable origin, age,
and uses. pp. 59. *Maddington,* 1893. 8°. Pam. 3.

STONYHURST. FITZGERALD (P. H.) Stony-
hurst memories. pp. 411. *Lond.* 1895. 8°.
08365. f. 1.

GERARD (J.) Stonyhurst College, 1592–1894.
pp. 316. *Belfast,* 1894. 4°. 8364. i. 7.

P.P. *Stonyhurst.* Stonyhurst Magazine.
Stonyhurst, 1881, *etc.* 8°. P.P. 6145. bda. & 75.

STONYHURST COLLEGE. Illustrations of Stonyhurst College. *Lond.* 1891. *obl.* 4°. 1787. aa. 3.

—— Our Tercentenary, June, 1892. pp. 31.
Clitheroe, 1892. 8°. 8365. f 32.

—— Souvenir of the centenary celebration,
July 1894. *Belfast,* 1894. *obl.* 8°. 8364. h. 14.

STORK. ZIEGLER (J.) Storchnester in Frank-
furt. 1893. 8°. Ac. Frankfurt on the Main.
Senckenbergische Naturforschende Gesellschaft.
Bericht, etc. Ac. 2878/3.

See also BIRDS.

STORMS. *See* METEOROLOGY.

STRAINS AND STRESSES. COVENTRY
(W. B.) On the Stresses in masonry dams.
pp. 11. *Lond.* 1894. 8°. 8767. cc. 30. (16.)

GEORGE (E M.) Pocket-book of calculations in
Stresses. pp. 140. *Lond.* 1895. *obl.* 8°. 8767. de. 4.

JOHNSON (F. R.) Stresses in girder and roof
Trusses. pp. 215. *Lond.* 1894. 8°. 8767. g. 23.

MIDDLETON (G. A. T.) Stresses and Thrusts.
pp. 148. *Lond.* 1895. 8°. 7817. b. 4.

TIMMINS (T.) Instructions for using Timmins'
Mechanical Girder calculator.. pp. 30.
Lond. 1895. 8°. Pam. 79.

WILLIAMSON (B.) Introduction to the Mathematical theory of the Stress and Strain of elastic
solids. pp. 135. *Lond.* 1894. 8°. 8768. bb. 8.

See also BUILDING : ELASTICITY : ENGINEERING.

STRAITS SETTLEMENTS. MAC LARTY
(F. M.) Affairs of the Colony. pp. 138.
Penang, 1893. 8°. 9056. bb. 35.

HUTTENBACH (A.) Critique on what ought to
have been the main point of Mr. McLarty's
Book, " Affairs of the Colony." pp. 29.
Penang, 1893. 8°. 8228. l. 17. (8.)

P.P. *Penang.* The Straits Independent.
Penang, 1889, *etc.* fol. P.P. 9979. b.

STRAITS SETTLEMENTS—*continued.*

P.P. *Singapore.* The Straits-Chinese Herald. *Singapore*, 1894, *etc.* fol. P.P. 9974. l.

STRAITS SETTLEMENT. Précis of information concerning the Straits Settlements. pp. 178. *Lond.* 1892. 8°. 010055. e. 12.

KYSHE (J. W. N.) Index to the Laws of the Straits Settlements. 2 pt. *Singapore*, 1882, 83. 8°. 06606. f. 17.

See also LAW REPORTS: MALAY PENINSULA: PENANG: SINGAPORE.

STRALSUND. BAIER (R.) Zwei stralsundische Chroniken des xv. Jahrhunderts. pp. 47. *Stralsund*, 1893. 8°. 9008. l. 2. (8.)

STRASBURG. SCHMIDT (C.) Répertoire bibliographique strasbourgeois jusque vers 1530. *Strasbourg*, 1893, *etc.* 4°. 011900. k.

CAHN (J.) Münzgeschichte der Stadt Strassburg im Mittelalter. pp. 176. *Strassb.* 1895. 8°. 7756. d. 33.

DACHEUX (L.) La petite Chronique de la Cathédrale. 1887. 8°. Ac. Strasburg. *Société pour la Conservation des Monuments.* Fragments des anciennes chroniques. Vol. 1. Ac. 5284/2.

MEYER-ALTONA (E.) Die Sculpturen des strassburger Münsters. 1894, *etc.* 8°. Studien zur deutschen Kunstgeschichte. Hft. 2. 7808. e.

ERICHSON (A.) Das theologische Studienstift Collegium Wilhelmitanum. pp. 210. *Strassb.* 1894. 8°. 8357. g. 50.

S. A. Ansichten des alten Strassburg. *Strassb.* 1892. fol. 1788. a. 25.

SCHMIDT (C.) Strassburger Gassen- und Häuser-Namen im Mittelalter. pp. 206. *Strassb.* 1888. 8°. 10256. b. 31.

—— Zur Geschichte der ältesten Bibliotheken zu Strassburg. pp. 200. *Strassb.* 1882. 8°. 11899. g. 11.

SCHWENDT (F. É.) Correspondance et pièces relatives à l'histoire de Strasbourg. 1880. 8°. REUSS (R.) L'Alsace pendant la Révolution. Vol. II. 9231. l. 7.

SEYBOTH (A.) Strassbourg historique. pp. 704. *Strasbourg*, 1894. fol. 1790. b. 12.

STRASBURG. *Architekten-Verein.* Strassburg und seine Bauten. pp. 686. *Strassb.* 1894. 8°. 10250. i. 8.

STRICKER (E.) Calvin als erster Pfarrer der reformirten Gemeinde zu Strassburg. pp. 65. *Strassb.* 1890. 8°. Pam. 9.

TOUCHEMOLIN (A.) Strasbourg militaire. pp. 150. *Paris*, 1894. 4°. 1855. c. 7.

ZAISS (J.) Schilderung der Belagerungen von Strassburg, 1870, 71. pp. 157. *Karlsruhe*, 1894. 8°. 9080. c. 39.

See also ALSACE: GERMAN-FRENCH WAR.

STRATFORD-ON-AVON. H., W. H. Historic Stratford. pp. 6. *Birmingham*, 1893. 16°. 10349. a. 33. (3.)

MOTT (J.) Old landmarks of Stratford-on-Avon. pp. 39. *Lond.* 1893. 12°. 10352. e. 8. (6.)

WILLIAMS (J. L.) Home and haunts of Shakespeare. 5 pt. *Lond.* 1892. fol. K.T.C. 2. a. 7.

STRATHBOGIE. MACDONALD (J.) Place names in Strathbogie. pp. 300. *Aberd.* 1891. 8°. 12978. c. 34.

STRATHFIELD SAYE. GRIFFITH (C. H.) History of Strathfield Saye. pp. 48. *Lond.* 1892. 4°. 10352. l. 10.

STRAWBERRIES. HARRISON (W. H.) Strawberries. pp. 69. *Lond.* 1891. 8°. 07076. c. 19.

See also GARDENING, *Fruit, etc.*

STREATLEY. TAUNT (H. W.) Goring, Streatley and the neighbourhood. pp. 122. *Oxf.* 1894. 8°. 10350. aaa. 52.

STREETS. *See* HIGHWAYS: LONDON: TOWNS.

STRONTIUM. MALBEC (A.) Les Sels de Strontium. pp. 98. *Paris*, 1892. 8°. 07509. g. 1.

See also METALS.

STUNDISTS. *See* RUSSIA, *Church of and Sects.*

STURGEON. RYDER (J. A.) Sturgeons and sturgeon industries of the Eastern Coast of the U.S. 1890. 8°. U.S. *Commission of Fish.* Bulletin. Vol. 8. 7290. dd.

See also FISH.

STYRIA. Ac. Gratz. *Historische Landes-Commission.* Bericht. *Graz*, 1893, *etc.* 8°. Ac. 7197.

GRATZ. *Landes-Archiv.* Das steiermärkische Landesarchiv zu Graz. pp. 35. *Graz*, 1893. 4°. 11906. c. 3.

STYRIA. Culturbilder aus Steiermark. pp. 290. *Graz*, 1890. 8°. 08225. l. 4.

ZAHN (J. v.) Styriaca. Gedrucktes und Ungedrucktes zur steierm. Geschichte. pp. 277. *Graz*, 1894. 8°. 10215. bbb. 12.

—— Ortsnamenbuch der Steiermark im Mittelalter. pp. 583. *Wien*, 1893. 4°. 10205. f. 5.

MELL (A.) Die mittelalterlichen Urbare in Steiermark. 1893. 8°. Ac. Gratz. *Historischer Verein.* Beiträge. Jhrg. 25. Ac. 7196.

BIDDERMANN (H. I.) Steiermarks Beziehungen zum kroatisch-slavon. Königreich im xvi. und xvii. Jahrhunderte. pp. 125. 1891. 8°. Ac. Gratz. *Historischer Verein.* Mittheilungen. Hft. 39. Ac. 7196/2.

ZWIEDINECK-SUEDENHORST (H. v.) Zur Geschichte des Kriegs von 1809 in Steiermark. 1891. 8°. Ac. Gratz. *Historischer Verein.* Beiträge. Jhrg. 23. Ac. 7196.

Ac. Gratz. *Steirischer Gebirgsverein.* Jahresbericht, 1883, *etc. Graz*, 1884, *etc.* 8°. 10210. bb. 22.

See also AUSTRIA-HUNGARY.

SUAHILI LANGUAGE. *See* AFRICAN LANGUAGES.

SUCCESSION, Law of.

General : Roman Law.

CECIL (E.) Primogeniture. Short history of its development. pp. 16. 231. *Lond.* 1895. 8°. 6005. e. 10.

LAPOUGE (G. de) Études sur la nature du droit de Succession. pp. 42. *Paris*, 1885. 8°. 5423. g. 2. (2.)

GREIFF (F.) De l'origine du Testament romain. pp. 150. *Paris*, 1888. 8°. 5206. cc. 13.

PALUMBO (L.) Testamento romano e testamento longobardo. pp. 406. *Lanciano*, 1892. 8°. 5323. df. 2.

Austria–Hungary.

STEINLECHNER (P.) Das schwebende Erbrecht und die Unmittelbarkeit der Erbfolge. *Innsbruck*, 1893, *etc.* 8°. 05549. i.

SPERL (H.) Succession in den Process. *Graz*, 1895, *etc.* 8°. 05549. h.

TELESZKY (I.) Entwurf des ungarischen Erbrechts. pp. 142. *Budapest*, 1887. 8°. 5549. g. 28.

Denmark.

DEUNTZER (J. H.) Den danske Skifteret. pp. 150. *Kjøbenh.* 1889. 8°. 5725. aaa. 8.

—— Den danske Arveret. pp. 237. *Kjøbenh.* 1892. 8°. 5725. bb. 13.

SUCCESSION—continued.
France.

CHARDENET (P.) Des droits de Succession accordés par la loi au conjoint survivant. pp. 280. *Lyon*, 1892. 8°. 5408. e. 12.

LAMBERT (É.) De l'exhérédation et des legs faits au profit d'héritiers présomptifs. pp. 818. *Paris*, 1895. 8°. 5423. eee. 17.

LE SELLYER (A. F.) Commentaire sur le titre des Successions. 2 tom. *Paris*, 1892. 8°. 5406. de. 11.

Germany.

GOLDFELD (J.) Streitfragen aus dem deutschen Erbrecht. pp. 110. *Hamburg*, 1893. 8°. 05604. i. 23.

JAEGER (E. L.) Die Voraussetzungen eines Nachlasskonkurses. pp. 63. *München*, 1893. 8°. 6005. e. 9.

KADEN (E.) Hand-Lexikon des im Sachsen Familien- und Erbrechts. pp. 553. *Meissen*, 1894. 8°. 05604. ee. 3.

ZELTER ( ) Die statutarischen Güter- und Erbrechte in Pommern. *Stettin*, 1892, etc. 8°. 05604. i. 4.

Great Britain and Ireland.
General.

BROWNE (G.) Law and practice relating to Probate and Administration. pp. 903. *Lond.* 1892. 8°. 2018. a.

CALDICOTT (O. H.) Executorship Accounts. pp. 80. *Lond.* 1889. 8°. 6355. aaa. 36.

DENDY (F. W.) Duties of Executors. pp. 59. *Lond.* 1892. 8°. 6355. df 14.

ENGLAND. *Probate Court.* Additional rules for the Registrars of the Principal Probate Registry in respect of non-contentious business. pp. 7. *Lond.* 1892. 8°. Pam. 32.

FARWELL (G.) Concise treatise on Powers. pp. 708. *Lond.* 1893. 8°. 6306. h. 13.

GIBSON (A.) and WELDON (A.) Student's Probate. pp. 359. *Lond.* 1895. 8°. 6355. ee. 12.

HARRISON (J. C.) Epitome of the Law of Probate. pp. 240. *Lond.* 1891. 8°. 6355. aaa. 31.

HAYES (W.) and JARMIN (T.) Concise forms of Wills. pp. 582. *Lond.* 1893. 8°. 2232. d. 9.

HOLDSWORTH (W. A.) Law of Wills, Executors and Administrators. pp. 255. *Lond.* 1894. 8°. 6355. a. 41.

JARMEN (T.) Treatise on Wills. 2 vol. *Lond.* 1893. 8°. 2017. f.

MARSHALL (G. W.) Handbook to the ancient Courts of Probate. pp. 75. *Lond.* 1895. 8°. 6355. aa. 22.

RANKING (D. F.) Executorship Law and accounts. pp. 123. *Lond.* 1895. 8°. 6190. cc. 6.

RUMSEY (A.) Legal handbook for Executors and Administrators. pp. 238. 1891. 8°. *Legal Handbooks.* 6191. de.

SERRELL (G.) Equitable doctrine of Election. pp. 258. *Lond.* 1891. 8°. 6355. aaa. 30.

THEOBALD (H. S.) Concise treatise on the law of Wills. pp. 787. *Lond.* 1895. 8°. 2232. ccc. 11.

TYSSEN (A. D.) The new law of Charitable Bequests. pp 26. *Lond.* 1891. 8°. Pam. 32.

WEST (B. B.) Wills, and how not to make them. pp. 186. *Lond.* 1893. 8°. 6355. aa. 19.

WILL. How to Prove a Will. pp. 37. *Wolverhampton*, 1895. 16°. 6355. a. 42.

WILLIAMS (Sir E. V.) Treatise on the Law of Executors and Administrators. 2 vol. *Lond.* 1893. 8°. 2017. f.

WILLIAMS (J.) Wills and intestate Succession. pp. 284. *Lond.* 1891. 8°. 6355. aa. 18.

SUCCESSION.—Great Britain, etc.—cont.

WOOD (F.) Digest of the Law of Administrations, Executorships and Trusteeships. pp. 470. *Lond.* 1894. 8°. 6355. df. 17.

MAC LAREN (J.) Law of Wills and Succession in Scotland. 2 vol. *Edinb.* 1894. 8°. 6583. g. 16.

Death Duties: Finance Act, 1894.
See ENGLAND, *Trade, etc., Taxation.*

Collections of Wills, etc.

BLAYDES (F. A.) Calendar of some Bedfordshire Wills. pp. 43. *Bedford*, 1893. 8°. 9906. b. 2.

Ac. Cumberland. *Antiquarian Society.* Carlisle, *Diocese of.* Testamenta Karleolensia. Wills from the registers of the Bishops of Carlisle. 1353–1386. pp. 182. *Kendal*, 1893. 8°. Ac. 5630/10.

CHESTER. An Index to the Wills preserved in the Court of Probate at Chester, 1621–1650. 1881. 8°. Ac. Manchester. *Record Society.* Publications. Vol. 2, *etc.* Ac. 8121.

—— Index to the Wills, 1660–80. 1887. 8°. Ac. Manchester. *Record Society.* Publications. Vol. 15. Ac. 8121.

—— Index to the Wills, 1701–40. 2 pt. 1889. 90. 8°. Ac. Manchester. *Record Society* Publications. Vols. 20, 22. Ac. 8121.

—— Index to the Wills, 1741–60. pp. 264. 1892. 8°. Ac. Manchester. *Record Society.* Publications. Vol. 25. Ac. 8121

HARVEY (W. J.) Calendar of Harvey Wills and Administrations in the Prerogative Court of Chancery, 1418–1789. pp. 60. 1890. 8°. 9902. f. 29.

CRISP (F. A.) Calendar of Wills at Ipswich, 1444–1600. pp. 524. 1895. 4°. 9906. i. 15.

WEAVER (F. W.) Wells Wills. pp. 234. *Lond.* 1890. 8°. 9916. a. 21.

COLLINS (F.) Index of Wills in the York Registry, 1514–53. pp. 246. 1891. 8°. Ac. Huddersfield. *Yorkshire Archaeological Association.* Record Series. Vol. 11. Ac. 5652 8.

GIBBONS (A.) Index of Wills in the York Registry, 1554–68. pp. 212. 1893. 8°. Ac. Huddersfield. *Yorkshire Archaeological Association.* Record Series. Vol. 14. Ac. 5652/8.

India.

HENDERSON (G. S.) Law of testamentary Devise in India. pp. 551. 1889. 8°. Tagore Law Lectures. 5318. aaa.

RĀMACHANDRA AIYAR. Collection of decisions of the High Courts and Privy Council on the Law of Succession. pp. 55. 2. *Madras*, 1892. 8°. 5319. bb. 8.

—— Collection of decisions of the Hindu Law of Adoption, *etc.* pp. 73. 2. *Nellore*, 1893. 8°. 05319. i. 8.

YOGENDRANĀTHA BHATTĀCHĀRYA, called SMĀRTA-ŚIROMANI. Commentaries on the Hindu Laws of inheritance. pp. 768. *Calcutta*, 1893. 8°. 05319. g. 1.

AVINĀŚACHANDRA MITRA. Hindu Law of Adoption. pp. 77. *Calcutta*, 1890. 8°. Pam. 34.
See also HINDUISM.

Mohammedan Law.

LUCIANI (J. D.) Traité des Successions Musulmanes. pp. 573. *Paris*, 1890. 8°. 5318. dd. 7.

TCHACOS (G.) De la Succession en droit ottoman. pp. 103. *Paris*, 1893. 8°. 5319. b. 20.
See also MOHAMMEDANISM.

Roman Law. *See supra: General.*
Scotland.

See supra: Great Britain and Ireland.

SUMATRA—continued.

BRENNER (J. v.) *Baron*. Besuch bei den Kannibalen Sumatras. *Würzburg*, 1893, *etc.* 8°.
　　　　　　　　　　10058. i.

CARTHAUS (E.) Sumatra und der malaiische Archipel. pp. 267. *Leipz.* 1891. 8°. 10470. g. 28.

COUPERUS (F. E.) Het Rechtswezen op Sumatra's westkust. pp. 244. *Leiden*, 1882. 8°.
　　　　　　　　　　8023. ee. 37.

FENNEMA (R) Topographische beschrijving van het noordelijk gedeelte van het Gouvernement Sumatra's Westkust. pp. 124.
Amsterd. 1887. 8°.　　　010055. ee. 7.

G. B. & I. *Hydrographic Office.* Eastern Archipelago. 2 pt. *Lond.* 1890–93. 8°. 10496. ff. 20.

JEEKEL (L. J. P. J.) Het Sumatra-tractaat. pp. 85. *Leiden*, 1881. 8°.　8023. f. 23. (8.)

KIELSTRA (E. B.) Sumatra's Westkust van 1841–49. 1891, *etc.* 8°. Ac. The Hague. *K. Instituut voor de Volkenkunde van Nederlandsch-Indië.* Bijdragen. Volgreeks v.　Ac. 7519.

MODIGLIANI (E.) L'Isola delle Donne-Viaggio ad Engano. pp 312. *Milano*, 1894. 8°.
　　　　　　　　　　010055. h. 3.

SUMATRA. Tabaks-Ondernemingen op de oostkust van Sumatra. pp. 21.
Amsterd. 1891. obl. 4°.　　　Pam. 23.

VORDERMAN (A. G.) Les oiseaux de Sumatra. 1890. 8°. Ac. Batavia. *Natuurkundige Vereeniging.* Natuurkundig Tijdschrift. Ser. 8. Deel. 10.　　　　　　Ac. 3096.

WESSELS (L.) De voorstellen van de Indische Regeering omtrent de gouvernements-koffiecultur op Sumatra's westkust. pp. 55.
's Gravenh. 1892. 8°.　　　Pam. 23.

WILKEN (G. A.) Over het huwelijks en erfrecht bij de volken van Zuid-Sumatra. 1891. 8°. Ac. The Hague. *K. Instituut voor de Volkenkunde van Nederlandsch-Indië.* Bijdragen. Volgreeks v. Deel 6.　　　　　　　Ac. 7519.

See also ACHEEN : INDIES, *Dutch* : MALAY PENINSULA AND MALAYSIA : NETHERLANDS, *Colonies.*

SUN AND SOLAR SYSTEM.

Sun.

Ac. Greenwich. *Royal Observatory.* Recomputation of the position of the Ecliptic from observations of the sun. pp. 67. *Lond.* 1889. 4°.
　　　　　　　　　　8566. i.

—— Vienna. *Sonnblick Verein.* Jahres-Bericht des Sonnblick-Vereines. *Wien*, 1893, *etc.* 8°.
　　　　　　　　　　Ac. 4065.

ÅNGSTRÖM (K.) Beobachtungen über die Strahlung der Sonne. pp. 19. 1889. 8°. Ac. Stockholm. *Vetenskaps Academi.* Bihang till handlingar. Bd. 15.　　　　　Ac. 1070/7.

BALL (*Sir* R. S.) The Story of the Sun. pp. 376. *Lond.* 1893. 8°.　　　8562. eee. 41.

BARTOLI (A.) and STRACCIATI (E.) Formula empirica pel calore solare. 1892. 4°. Ac. Catania. *Accademia Gioenia.* Atti. Ser. 4. Vol. 4.
　　　　　　　　　　Ac. 2805.

BECQUEREL (A. E.) and (H.) Mémoire sur la température de l'air à la surface du sol et de la terre. 1888. 4°. Ac. Paris. *Académie des Sciences.* Mémoires. Sér. 2. Tom. 44. 2099. b.

BERGMANN (H.) Die electrische Kraft des Sonnenlichtes in ihrer Wirkung auf das Protoplasma der Zelle hierdurch. pp. 179. *Danzig*, 1892. 8°.
　　　　　　　　　　8757. k. 5.

BOULTON (M. P. W.) On Solar or stellar heat. pp. 48. *Lond.* 1891. 8°.　　8563. b. 43.

BRESTER (A.) Théorie du Soleil. pp. 168. 1892. 8°. Ac. Amsterdam. *K. Akademie van Wetenschappen.* Verhandelingen. Sectie 1. Deel 1.　　　　　　　Ac. 944/2.

SUN—continued.

DUBOIS (E.) Die Klimate der geologischen Vergangenheit und ihre Beziehung zur Entwickelungsgeschichte der Sonne. pp. 85.
Nijmegen, 1893. 8°.　　　07109. e. 18.

DUNER (N. C.) Recherches sur la rotation du Soleil. pp. 78. 1891. 4°. Ac. Upsal. *R. Societas Scientiarum.* Nova Acta. Vol. 14.
　　　　　　　　　　Ac. 1076.

HARKNESS (W.) The Solar Parallax and its related constants. pp. 169. 1891. 4°. Ac. Washington. *Naval Observatory.* Astronomical and meteorological Observations for 1885. Appendix III.　　　　　　8567. e.

HEYSINGER (I. W.) Source and mode of Solar Energy. pp. 363. *Lond.* 1895. 8°. 8563. aa. 37.

HONORÉ (C.) Loi du rayonnement solaire. pp. 12. *Montévideo*, 1894. 8°.　　Pam. 4.
—— Polaires thermiques du soleil. pp. 30.
Montévideo, 1895. 8°.　　　Pam. 4.

JOHNSON (A.) Sunshine. pp. 502. 1892. 8°. *Nature's Story-books.*　　　8716. aa.

RICCÒ (A.) Sulla variazione in latitudine della sede dei principali fenomeni solari. pp. 5. 1892. 4°. Ac. Catania. *Accademia di Scienze.* Atti. Ser. 4. Vol. 4.　　Ac. 2805.

BERTHOLD (G.) Der Magister J. Fabricius und die Sonnenflecken. pp. 60. *Leipz.* 1894. 8°.
　　　　　　　　　　Pam. 4.

G. B. *Committee on Education.* Solar Physics Committee. Measures of positions and areas of sun spots. pp. 78. *Lond.* 1891. 4°. 8563. i. 19.

SPOERER (G.) Beobachtungen von Sonnenflecken, 1885–93. pp. 147. 1894. 8°. Ac. Potsdam. *Astrophysikalisches Observatorium.* Publicationen. Bd. 10.　　　　　8752. i. 6.

JAFFRÉ (P. V.) Éclipse de soleil. pp. 137. *Paris*, 1891. 8°.　　　8560. f. 38.

TODD (M. L.) Total Eclipses of the Sun. pp. 244. 1894. 8°. TODD (D. P.) Columbian Knowledge Series. No. 1.　　　　　8709. e.

Ac. Saint Louis. *Academy of Science.* Total Eclipse of the Sun, Jan. 1, 1889. pp. 39. *Camb.* 1891. 4°.　　　8563. i. 18.

—— Berkeley. *Lick Observatory.* Reports on the observations of the Total Eclipse of the Sun, Dec. 21, 1889. 2 pt. *Sacramento*, 1891. 8°.
　　　　　　　　　　8561. f. 37.

AUBERTIN (J. J.) By order of the Sun : to Chile to see his eclipse, April 16, 1893. pp. 152. *Lond.* 1894. 8°.　　　8563. aa. 36.

Solar System.

BACKLUND (J. O.) Über die Bewegung einer gewissen Gruppe der kleinen Planeten. pp. 54. 1892. 4°. Ac. Saint Petersburg. *Academia Scientiarum.* Mémoires. Sér. 7. Tom. 38.
　　　　　　　　　　Ac. 1125/3.

BONNET (O.) Note sur le mouvement elliptique d'une planète. pp. 27. 1890. 4°. Ac. Paris. *Bureau des Longitudes.* Annales. Tom. 4.
　　　　　　　　　　8752. i.

CHAMBERS (G. F.) Story of the Solar System. pp. 202. *Lond.* 1895. 8°.　　8563. a. 27.

GYLDEN (J. A. H.) Traité analytique des orbites absolues des huit planètes principales.
Stockholm, 1893, *etc.* 4°　　　8563. i.

H., E. The revolution of the Solar System. pp. 72. *Lond.* 1892. 8°.　　8563. b. 39.

LAIDLAW (S.) The Powers which propel and guide the planets. pp. 105. *Lond.* 1891. 8°.
　　　　　　　　　　8561. aaaa. 43.

LOHSE (O.) Planetographie. pp. 192. *Leipz.* 1894. 8°.　　　8563. aa. 39.

SUN AND SOLAR SYSTEM.—*continued.*

MASAL (H.) Formeln und Tafeln zur Berechnung der absoluten Störungen der Planeten. pp. 31. 1889. 4°. Ac. Stockholm. *Vetenskaps Academien.* Handlingar. N.F. Bd. 23.
　　　　　　　　　　　　　　Ac. 1070.

MUELLER (G.) Helligkeitsbestimmungen der grossen Planeten und einiger Asteroiden. pp. 197. 1893. 4°. Ac. Potsdam. *Astrophysikalisches Observatorium.* Publicationen. Nr. 30.　　　　　　　　8752. i. 6.

OAKDEN (A. B.) Child's Solar System. pp. 38. *Lond.* 1890. 16°.　　　　　　8563. a. 10.

REICHENBACH (O.) *Count.* Misapprehensions of Le Verrier and Adams as evidence for the existence of two Trans-Neptunian planets. pp. 12. *Lond.* 1892. 8°.　　　Pam. 4.

—— Birth and evolution of the Solar System. pp. 23. *Lond.* 1891. 8°.　　　Pam. 4.

TISCHNER (A.) Le Phénomène fondamental du système solaire. pp. 48. *Leipz.* 1895. 8°. Pam. 4.

VALENTINER (C. W. F. J.) Atlas des Sonnensystems. 1884. fol. Grimm's Atlas der Astrophysik. Lief. 2.　　　　　　8564. k. 3.

See also ASTRONOMY : EARTH : JUPITER : MARS : METEORS : NEPTUNE : PHYSIOGRAPHY : SATURN : VENUS. For sun-worship, *see* RELIGION.

SUNDAY. BITTINGER (J. Q.) Plea for the Sabbath and for man. pp. 236. *Bost.* 1892. 8°.
　　　　　　　　　　　　4355. df. 19.

BROWN (A.) A Christian Minister's duty with reference to the Sabbath. pp. 187. *Edinb.* 1890. 8°.　　　4355. de. 22.

BYLES (A. H.) The Pleasant Sunday Afternoon Society. pp. 42. *Lond.* 1891. 8°.
　　　　　　　　　　08276. f. 21. (11.)

CONWAY (M. D.) Civilizing the Sabbath. 1892. 8°. LONDON. *South Place Society,* Publications.　　　　　　　4109. f.

DELTA. Sunday versus the Puritan Sabbath. pp. 73. *Edinb.* 1894. 8°.　　4355. b. 3.

DU TOIT (S. J.) De Leerstukken der Sabbattariers. pp. 70. *Paarl,* 1893. 8°.　Pam. 77.

EARLE (A. M.) The Sabbath in Puritan New England. pp. 335. *Lond.* 1892. 8°. 4744. dd. 7.

FAIRLY (J. S.) Sunday Observance and Sunday Desecration. pp. 48. *Charleston,* 1893. 8°.
　　　　　　　　　　4371. ee. 27. (3.)

FERGUSON (F.) Speech at the anniversary of the Sabbath Protection Association. pp. 15. *Glasg.* 1894. 8°.　　4371. dd. 8. (9.)

GALTON (C.) The Christian Sabbath. pp. 12. 1893. 8°. Readings in Catholic Doctrine. No. 4.
　　　　　　　　　　　　3939. ccc.

GIBON (F.) La Nécessité sociale du Dimanche. pp. 119. *Paris,* 1891. 8°.　4355. aaa. 8.

—— Le Dimanche en action. pp. 166. *Tours,* 1894. 8°.　　　　4355. e. 15.

HARRIS (G. E.) Treatise on Sunday Laws. pp. 338. *Rochester, N.Y.* 1892. 8°. 6616. de. 7.

HELPS. Helps for the Day of Rest. *Lond.* 1891, *etc.* 4°.　　　4380. i.

HILL (C.) Tales about Sunday. pp. 164. *Lond.* 1891. 8°.　　　4406. i. 7.

LEFROY (W.) The Pastor's duty in regard to the non-observance of Sunday. pp. 28. *Norwich.* 1893. 8°.　4371. b. 25. (7.)

LINKLATER (R.) The Lord's Day. Series of essays. pp. 226. *Lond.* 1892. 8°. 4355. aaa. 9.

LORD'S DAY. The Lord's Day or Man's? pp. 15. *Lond.* 1890. 8°.　　　Pam. 77.

MILLER (J.) Physiology in accordance with the Bible respecting the Sabbath. pp. 64. *Edinb,* 1891. 4°.　　4371. a. 3. (8.)

SUNDAY—*continued.*

MORGAN (R. A.) Bible teaching on the sanctification of one day in seven. pp. 164. *Lond.* 1892. 8°.　　　4355. aaa. 11.

PENANRUN (D. de.) La Société centrale des Architects français et le Repos du Dimanche. pp. 27. *Paris,* 1893. 8°.　4371. ee. 27. (6.)

PERRAUD (A. L. A.) *Bp. of Autun.* La sanctification du Dimanche. pp. 73. *Autun,* 1891. 8°.
　　　　　　　　　　　　Pam. 96.

RAUTLIN DE LA ROY (R. de) Le travail et le repos du Dimanche. pp. 72. *Paris,* 1891. 12°.
　　　　　　　　　　4371. de. 4. (16.)

RINGGOLD (J. T.) The Legal Sunday. pp. 252. *Battle Creek,* 1895. 8°.　4355. bb. 31.

ROWLAND (A.) Sunday Observance. 1891. 8°. P.P. *London.* The People's Pulpit. No. 39.
　　　　　　　　　　　　P.P. 790. gc.

RYLE (J. C.) *Bp of Liverpool.* Thoughts about Sunday. pp. 64. *Lond.* 1893. 8°. 4355. a. 2.

SABBATH DAY. Is the seventh day of the Week or the first day of the Week the real Sabbath Day? pp. 31. *Belfast,* 1891. 8°.
　　　　　　　　　　4371. de 3. (1.)

WAGGONER (E. J.) Sunday : origin of its Observance. pp. 102. *Lond.* 1891. 8°.
　　　　　　　　　　4371. de. 3. (2.)

WEICH (A. A.) De Sabbatariërs. pp. 35. *Kaapstad,* 1890. 8°.　4372. h. 28. (12.)

WERNER (M.) Die Sonntagsruhe in Industrie und Handwerk. pp. 228. *Berl.* 1895. 8°.
　　　　　　　　　　　　4355. df. 21.

WOODHOUSE (F. C.) Manual for Sundays. pp. 376. *Lond.* 1891. 8°.　　3456. dd. 9.

SUNDAY SCHOOLS. CLARKE (H. F.) The Sunday School in relation to the Band of Hope. pp. 8. *Lond.* 1892. 8°.　8436. f. 1. (21.)

COOPER (J. A.) Counsels addressed to Sunday School teachers. pp. 166. *Lond.* 1895. 8°.
　　　　　　　　　　　4192. aaa. 50.

DAVIS (C. A.) Relation of Sunday School teachers to the Band of Hope movement. pp. 4. *Lond.* 1894. 8°.　　8436. f. 3. (16.)

GRAY (J. C.) The Class and the Desk. *Lond.* 1891, *etc.* 8°.　　3126. e. 2.

GREEN (B. L.) What more can the Sunday School do for the culture of Spiritual Life. pp. 20. *Lond.* 1894. 8°.　4371. bb. 9. (2.)

GREENWOOD (T.) Sunday-school and village Libraries. pp. 95. *Lond.* 1892. 8°. 011902. i. 16.

HANSTEEN (C.) Sondagsskolen. *Kristiania,* 1893, *etc.* 8°.　　　4192. g.

HARMER (E. G.) By-paths of Sunday School work. pp 110. *Lond.* 1892. 16°. 4192. a. 30.

HELLIER (A. M.) In the Sunday School. Thoughts and suggestions. pp. 96. *Lond.* 1894. 8°.　　　4192. a. 32.

HOCKING (W. J.) The Teacher in Class. pp. 11. *Lond.* 1893. 16°.　　　Pam. 17.

LEES (A. D. D.) Sunday School teaching. pp. 36. *Lond.* 1893. 12°.　4192 aa. 37.

MILES (A. H.) The new Sunday School reciter. pp. 200. *Lond.* 1891. 8°.　12273. e.

NORTHCOTE (S. C.) Lesson notes for Sunday School teachers. pp. 123. *Lond.* 1884. 8°.
　　　　　　　　　　　4192. ee. 14.

PALMER (J.) The Sunday School manual. pp. 426. *Lond.* 1894. 16°.　4193. a. 66.

P.P. *London.* Sunday School helps. *Lond.* 1893, *etc.* 4°.　P.P. 1175. cca. and 2230.

SILL (E. R.) How to teach a class. pp. 29. *Lond.* 1892. 8°.　8304. aa. 22. (4.)

SMITH (W. J. S.) Teacher's Practical companion. pp. 139. *Lond.* 1890. 16°.　4192. aa. 33.

SUNDAY SCHOOLS—*continued.*

SUNDAY SCHOOL TEACHERS. Papers for Sunday School teachers. *Lond.* 1890, *etc.* 8°. 4192. ee.

WATSON (J.) Church teaching for Sunday Schools. pp. 216. *Lond.* 1895. 8°. 3224. aa. 40.

WICKS (W. A.) What Sunday School teachers ought to be. pp. 13. *Ross,* 1889. 8°.
4193. bb. 68. (10.)

YATES (H. S. B) The Teacher and the class. pp. 77. *Lond.* 1895. 8°. 4192. aaa. 48.
See also EDUCATION, *Religious.*

SUNDERLAND. POTTS (T.) Sunderland. pp. 326. *Sunderland,* 1892. 8°. 010358. g. 25.

SUN DIALS. DAWBARN (A. Y.) Sun-Dial. Explanation of the principle, construction and use of the Sundial. [With a diagram.] *Lond.* 1891. 4°. & 8°. 1801. d. 1. (146.)

SACHSE (J. F.) Horologium Achaz. pp. 14. *Phila.* 1895. 8°. 8561. g. 36.

TUCKWELL (W.) Tongues in Trees, *etc.* pp. 151. *Lond.* 1891. 8°. 12355. f. 36.

SUNSTROKE. FAYRER (*Sir* J.) Sunstroke. 1893. 8°. DAVIDSON (A.) Hygiene of warm Climates. 7686. dd. 2.

SUPERPHOSPHATES. *See* PHOSPHATES.

SUPPURATION. LETULLE (M.) Pus et suppuration. pp. 196. 1894. 8°. Encyclopédie des aide-mémoire. 8709. g.
See also INFLAMMATION.

SURBITON. KINGSTON, *upon Thames.* Kingston-upon-Thames and Surbiton in 1891. pp. 70. *Brighton,* 1891. 4°. 10368. k. 30.

SURGERY, General. Ac. Cincinnati. *College of Medicine and Surgery.* Archives. *Cincinnati,* 1893, *etc.* 8°. 8366. g.

BELL (J.) Manual of the operations of Surgery. pp. 360. *Edinb.* 1892. 8°. 7482. e. 16.

—— Notes on Surgery for nurses. pp. 180. *Edinb.* 1895. 8°. 07482. e. 19.

BISHOP (E. S.) Lectures to Nurses on antiseptics in surgery. pp. 66. 1890. 8°. RIDEAL (C. F.) Nursing Record Series. No. 1. 7688. a.

CAIRD (F. M.) and CATHCART (C. W.) Surgical Handbook. pp. 278. *Lond.* 1893. 8°.
07481. de. 1.

EPITOMES. Epitomes of modern Surgical Progress. *Bristol,* 1894, *etc.* 8°. 07481. f.

ERICHSEN (*Sir* J. E.) Science and art of Surgery. 2 vol. *Lond.* 1895. 8°. 2024. bb.

ESMARCH (F. v.) and KOWALZIG (E.) Chirurgische Technik. pp. 372. *Kiel,* 1892. 8°. 07482. e. 11.

FESSLER (J.) Klinisch-experimentelle Studien über chirugische Infectionskrankheiten. pp. 176. *München,* 1891. 8°. 07482. g. 10.

FISCHER (H.) Specielle Chirurgie. pp. 890. 1892. 8°. Wreden's Sammlung. Bd. 9. 7321. h.

GOULD (A. P.) Address on the recent evolution of Surgery. pp. 63. *Lond.* 1895. 8°.
07481. de. 3.

GRAY (W.) Progress of Surgery in Bombay during the last twenty years. pp. 28. *Bombay,* 1890. 8°. 07305. h. 16. (5.)

GUILLEMAIN (A.) La Pratique des opérations nouvelles. pp. 334. *Paris,* 1895. 8°.
7481. de. 3.

HARRIS (J. D.) Scab healing and its application in surgery. pp. 28. *Lond.* 1893. 8°.
07305. h. 16. (14.)

HARTE (R. H.) General Surgery. 1893. 8°. ALLEN (H.) Handbook of local Therapeutics. 7442. g. 26.

HEATH (C.) Manual of minor Surgery. pp. 389. *Lond.* 1894. 8°. 2255. a. 4.

SURGERY.—General—*continued.*

HEATH (C.) Clinical lectures on surgical subjects. pp. 401. *Lond.* 1895. 8°. 07481. g. 1.

JACOBSON (W. H. A.) Operations of Surgery. pp. 1224. *Lond.* 1891. 8°. 07482. g. 9.

KOCHER (T.) Text-book of operative Surgery. pp. 303. *Lond.* 1895. 8°. 7482. l. 19.

LENNANDER (K. G.) Aus der chirurgischen Klinik zu Upsala. pp. 45. *Upsala,* 1893. 8°.
7306. e. 23. (12.)

LONDON. *North London Hospital.* Reports. Surgical Cases. 1886–89. *Lond.* 1887–89. 8°.
7688. c. 23.

MAC CORMAC (*Sir* W.) Surgical Operations. *Lond.* 1891, *etc.* 8°. 07482. f. 1.

MARTIN (E.) Minor Surgery. pp. 166. *Lond.* 1891. 8°. 7482. bb. 25.

MIDDLETON (G. S.) Clinical records from the Glasgow Royal Infirmary. pp. 82. *Glasg.* 1894. 8°. 7687. eee. 40.

MOULLIN (C. W. M.) Surgery. pp. 1413. *Lond.* 1891. 8°. 07482. g. 7.

NORTON (A. T.) Clinical lectures on recent Surgery. pp. 70. *Lond.* 1894. 8°. 07482. e. 14.

OLLIER (L.) Résections des grandes articulations des Membres. pp. 200. 1894. 8°. Encyclopédie des aide-mémoire. 8709. g.

PAGET (*Sir* J.) Studies of old Case-books. pp. 168. *Lond.* 1891. 8°. 07305. e. 18.

P.P. *Bombay.* Indian Medico-Chirurgical Review. *Bombay,* 1893, *etc.* 8°. P.P. 2889. da.

—— *London.* Annals of Surgery. *Lond.* 1892, *etc.* 8°. P.P. 3302.

—— The Clinical Journal. *Lond.* 1892, *etc.* 8°.
PP. 2707. g. and 2152.

PLICQUE (A. F.) Précis de Diagnostic chirurgical. pp. 693. *Paris,* 1893. 8°. 07482. e. 12.

PORTER (J. H.) Surgeon's Pocket-book. pp. 274. *Lond.* 1891. 8°. 7481. a. 10.

POWER (D'A.) Surgical Diseases of children. pp. 548. 1895. 8°. Lewis's Practical Series.
7482. a.

PYE (W.) Surgical Handicraft. pp. 570. *Bristol,* 1891. 8°. 2255. c. 8.

ROBB (H.) Aseptical Surgical Technique. pp. 264. *Phila.* 1894. 8°. 07482. e. 16.

RULES. Golden rules of surgical Practice. pp. 54. *Bristol,* 1891. 16°. 7482. e. 14.

SILVERLOCK (H.) Medical and surgical Emergency reference book. pp. 120. *Lond.* 1890. 12°. 7321. aaa. 18.

STOKES (*Sir* W.) Jubilee meeting of the British Medical Assoc. Address in Surgery. pp. 44. *Lond.* 1882. 8°. 7305. de. 17. (13)

THOMSON (S.) Dictionary of household Surgery. pp. 736. *Lond.* 1894. 8°. 2255. g. 14.

TILLAUX (P. J.) Leçons de Clinique chirurgicale. pp. 530. *Paris,* 1895. 8°. 07482. ee. 18.

TILLMANNS (H.) Die moderne Chirurgie. 1891. 8°. VOLKMANN (R. v.) Sammlung klinischer Vorträge. N.F. Nr. 27. 7441. g.

TRÉLAT (U.) Clinique chirurgicale. 2 tom. *Paris,* 1891. 8°. 07482. g. 11.

TREVES (F.) Manual of operative Surgery. 2 vol. *Lond.* 1891. 8°. 7480. ee. 12.

—— Student's handbook of Surgical Operations. pp. 495. *Lond.* 1892. 8°. 07482. e. 9.

—— System of Surgery. *Lond.* 1895, *etc.* 8°.
07482. f. 6.

WAGNER (P.) Abriss der Nieren-Chirurgie. pp. 244. *Leipz.* 1893. 8°. 7630. aa. 28.

WALSHAM (W. J.) Surgery: its theory and practice. pp. 786. *Lond.* 1895. 8°. 2256. c. 15.

SURGERY—continued.

WHARTON (H. R.) Minor Surgery. pp. 497.
Edinb. 1891. 8°.　　　　　　07482. e. 10.

WHERRY (G. E.) Preventive Surgery. pp. 29.
Camb. 1895. 8°.　　　　　　7481. aaa. 38.

WYETH (J. A.) Text-Book on Surgery. pp. 777.
Lond. 1888. 8°.　　　　　　7482. m. 18.

See also ACCIDENTS : ANAESTHETICS : ANTISEPTIC
MEDICINE : BONES : FRACTURES : WOUNDS.

Abdominal. See ABDOMEN.

Anatomy. See ANATOMY.

History.

DENEFFE (V.) Étude sur la trousse d'un chi-
rurgien gallo-romain du IIIme siècle. pp. 66.
Anvers, 1893. 8°.　　　　　07482. f. 4.

GUIDO, de Cauliaco. La Grande Chirurgie de
Guy de Chauliac, 1363. pp. 747.
Paris, 1890. 8°.　　　　　　7481. i. 9.

HENRI, de Mondeville. Leben, Lehre und Leistungen des Heinrich von Mondeville.
Berl. 1892, etc. 8°.　　　　07482. g. 18.

KJÆRGAARD (N.) Om Drainagen i den ældre
Chirurgi. pp. 179. Københ. 1892. 8°.
　　　　　　　　　　　　　　7679. ee. 4.

STOKES (Sir W.) Cavendish Lecture. Altered
relations of Surgery to medicine. pp. 40.
Lond. 1888. 8°.　　　　07305. g. 6. (11.)

See also MEDICINE, History.

Military Surgery.

CHAUVEL (J.) and NIMIER (H.) Traité de Chirurgie d'Armée. pp. 664. Paris, 1890. 8°.
　　　　　　　　　　　　　　07482. g. 4.

HAASE (W.) Die Unterbringung der Verwun-
deten und Kranken auf dem Kriegsschauplatze.
pp. 150. Berl. 1891. 8°.　　　8831. k. 22.

HABART (J.) Das Kleincaliber und die Behandlung der Schusswunden im Felde. pp. 55.
Wien, 1894. 8°.　　　　　7306. h. 15. (8.)

LONGMORE (Sir T.) Gunshot Injuries. pp. 821.
Lond. 1895. 8°.　　　　　2254. e. 13.

WAGNER (V.) Die Aseptik in der Kriegs-
Chirurgie. pp. 68. 1893. 8°. VOLKMANN (R.)
Sammlung klinischer Vorträge. N.F. Nr. 65.
　　　　　　　　　　　　　　7441. g.

See also AMBULANCE.

Orthopaedic Surgery.

ADAMS (W.) On the Surgical Treatment of
deformities. pp. 55. Lond. 1893. 8°.
　　　　　　　　　　　　7481. aaa. 35.

BIGG (H. H.) Short manual of Orthopædy.
Lond. 1892, etc. 8°.　　　07581. df. 20.

JUDSON (A. B.) Orthopædic Surgery as a
specialty. pp. 4. N.Y. 1891. 8°. 07305. f. 5. (6.)

LANDERER (A.) Mechanotherapie. Ein Handbuch der Orthopädie. pp. 406.
Leipz. 1894. 8°.　　　　　7460. bb. 1.

P.P. Stuttgard. Zeitschrift für orthopädische
Chirurgie. Stuttgart, 1892, etc. 8°. 07481. i.

REYNIER (J. B.) Leçons d'orthopédie. pp. 300.
Paris, 1889. 8°.　　　　　07482. e. 2.

YOUNG (J. K.) Practical treatise on Orthopedic
Surgery. pp. 446. Lond. 1895. 8°. 07482. g. 23.

See also supra : General.

Pathology. See PATHOLOGY.

Profession of. See MEDICINE, Profession of.

SURINAM. See GUIANA, Dutch.

SURREY. BARRETT (C. R. B.) Surrey :
highways, byways and waterways. pp. 251.
Lond. 1895. 4°.　　　　10352. dd. 13.

BEVAN (G. P.) Tourist's guide to Surrey.
pp. 138. Lond. 1891. 8°.　10352. a. 55.

SURREY—continued.

CARTWRIGHT, afterwards ADY (J.) The Pilgrims' Way from Winchester to Canterbury.
pp. 157. Lond. 1893. 8°.　10349. h. 32.

CLINCH (G.) and KERSHAW (S. W.) Bygone
Surrey. pp. 252. Lond. 1895. 8°. 010358. i. 13.

DUNN (S. T.) Flora of South-west Surrey, etc.
pp. 106. Lond. 1893. 8°.　7054. df. 13.

EWART (W.) The climate of the South Eastern
Counties. 1895. 8°. Ac. London. Medical and
Chirurgical Society. Climates of Great Britain.
Vol. 1.　　　　　　　　　7462. g.

HARPER (C. G.) The Portsmouth Road and its
tributaries. pp. 372. Lond. 1895. 8°.
　　　　　　　　　　　　010358. h. 24.

NAPPER (H. F.) Roman Roads in Surrey.
pp. 17. Lond. 1888. 8°.　7706. g. 4. (7.)

—— Caesar in Surrey. pp. 5. 1894. 8°.
　　　　　　　　　　　07703. f. 1. (6.)

SURREY. Picturesque Surrey. pp. 56.
Guildford, 1895. fol.　　10351. i. 14.

SURREY HILLS. On Surrey Hills. pp. 301.
Edinb. 1891. 8°.　　　　010358. f. 28.

V., H. S. The Way about Surrey. pp. 168.
1891. 8°. Way-About Series. No. 1. 010358. e.

Ac. London. English Dialect Society. GOWER
(G. W. G. L.) Glossary of Surrey Words.
pp. 46. Lond. 1893. 8°.　Ac. 9934/34.

SURVEYING. BAKER (T.) Rudimentary
Treatise on Surveying. pp. 231.
Lond. 1891. 8°.　　　　　8767. f. 1.

GRIBBLE (T. G.) Preliminary Survey and estimates. pp. 420. 1890. 8°. GOODEVE (T. M.)
Text-books of Science.　　2244. a. 28.

HENDERSON (R.) Data for Surveyors. pp. 28.
Lond. 1891. 8°.　　　　　Pam. 79.

HOLLOWAY (T.) The Practical Surveyor.
pp. 114. Lond. 1895. 8°.　8768. c. 37.

LEANING (J.) Specifications for the use of Surveyors. pp. 140. Lond. 1894. 8°. 7817. b. 5.

MIDDLETON (G. A. T.) Surveying and surveying
instruments. pp. 116. 1894. 8°. Specialist's
Series.　　　　　　　　　8708. k.

MOUNTFORT (C. A.) Surveyors' Pocket-book for
reducing in the field distances measured on the
slope, etc. pp. 64. Napier, 1890. 8°. 8765. aa. 44.

ORLANDI (G.) Tacheometria. pp. 361.
Sassari, 1894. 8°.　　　　8534. d. 39.

ROBINSON (J. L.) Elements of marine Surveying.
pp. 203. Lond. 1894. 8°.　10498. aa. 22.

SCOTT (J.) Agricultural Surveying. pp. 128.
Lond. 1884. 8°.　　　　　8703. ccc. 50.

STANLEY (W. F.) Surveying and Levelling
Instruments. pp. 555. Lond. 1895. 8°.
　　　　　　　　　　　　8768. bb. 16.

STRAHAN (G.) Hand-book of professional instruc-
tions for the Trigonometrical Branch, Survey of
India Department. pp. 332.
Dehra Dun, 1891. 8°.　　10058. dd. 11.

TACCHINI (A.) Trattato di Topografia moderna.
pp. 766. Milano, 1891. 8°.　8768. i. 26.

USILL (G. W.) Practical Surveying. pp. 330.
Lond. 1893. 8°.　　　　　8767. f. 33.

See also GEODESY : MENSURATION.

SUSA : SUSIANA : ELAM. BILLERBECK
(A.) Susa. Eine Studie zur alten Geschichte
Westasiens. pp. 184. Leipz. 1893. 8°.
　　　　　　　　　　　　7702. c. 37.

DIEULAFOY (J.) At Susa. Narrative of Travel.
pp 266. Phila. 1890. 8°.　10076. i. 9.

LAYARD (Right Hon. Sir A. H.) Early adventures in Susiana, etc. pp. 436. Lond. 1894. 8°.
　　　　　　　　　　　　10075. bb. 20.

SUSA—*continued.*

TERRIEN DE LACOUPERIE (A. É. J. B.) Onomastic similarity of Nai Kwang-ti of China and Nak-hunte of Susiana. pp. 10. *Lond.* 1890. 8°.
Pam. 3.

—— Western origin of the early Chinese civilisation. pp. 418. *Lond.* 1894. 8°. 9055. g. 5.

WEISBACH (F. H.) Die Achämenideninschriften. pp. 126. *Leipz.* 1890. 8°. 7702. i. 28.
See also ASSYRIA : PERSIA.

SUSSEX. CHAMBERS (G. F.) Tourists' guide to Sussex. pp. 158. *Lond.* 1891. 8°.
10352. a. 60.

COWPER (F.) Sailing Tours. Pt. II. Coasts of Sussex. *Lond.* 1892, *etc.* 8°. 10360. e.

EGERTON (J. C.) Sussex folk and Sussex ways. pp. 172. *Lond.* 1892. 8°. 012357. f. 69.

ELLIS (W. S.) Parks and forests of Sussex. pp. 255. *Lewis,* 1885. 8°. 010358. g. 27.

EWART (W.) Climate of the South Eastern Counties. 1895. 8°. Ac. London. *Medical and Chirurgical Society.* Climates of Great Britain. Vol. 1. 7462. g.

HARE (A. J. C.) Sussex. pp. 239. *Lond.* 1894. 8°. 2366. b. 2.

HARPER (C. G.) The Brighton Road. pp. 272. *Lond.* 1892. 8°. 010358. h. 10.

SKINNER (E. F.) Handbook of Sussex. pp. 156. *Lond.* 1893. 12°. 10360. aa. 27.

SUSSEX. Murray's Handbook for Sussex. pp. 22. 173. *Lond.* 1893. 8°. 2364. b. 15.

SUTHERLAND. BROWN (J. A. H.) and BUCKLEY (T. E.) Vertebrate Fauna of Sutherland. pp. 344. *Edinb.* 1887. 8°. 7206. k. 8.

SAINT JOHN (C. W. G.) Sportsman's Tour in Sutherlandshire. pp. 320. *Lond.* 1891. 8°.
7908. ee. 16.

SUTTON COLDFIELD. SIDWELL (G.) and DURANT (W. J.) The Popular Guide to Sutton. pp. 61. *Birmingham,* 1893. 8°. 10360. e. 31.

SUTTON PLACE, Guildford. HARRISON (F.) Annals of an old Manor-House, Sutton Place. pp. 231. *Lond.* 1893. 4°. K.T.C. 11. b. 9.

SWABIA AND SWABIAN DIALECT.
See GERMAN LANGUAGE : GERMANY, *Antiquities.*

SWAINSWICK. PEACH (R. E. M.) Annals of the Parish of Swainswick. pp. 183. *Lond.* 1890. 4°. 010358. f. 29.

SWANAGE. SWAINE (H.) Artist's rambles round Swanage. *Lond.* 1893, *obl.* 8°.
10360. e. 28.

SWARRATON. EYRE (W. L W.) History of the Parishes of Swarraton and Northington. pp. 79. *Lond.* 1890. 4°. 10351. k. 16.

SWATOW DIALECT. *See* CHINESE LANGUAGE.

SWAZILAND. GRIFFITHES (T. P.) From Bedford Row to Swazieland. pp. 80. *Lond.* 1890. 8°. 010096. ff. 4.

BARTLETT (*Sir* E. A.) British, Natives and Boers in the Transvaal. Appeal of the Swazis. pp. 24. *Lond.* 1894. 8°. Pam. 66.
See also AFRICA, *South :* TRANSVAAL.

SWEDEN. [*See note on page 1.*]
See also SCANDINAVIA.

Antiquities.

HOLLANDER (A. G.) Ur Svearnes förskandinaviska historia. pp. 74. *Stockholm,* 1892. 8°.
9008. l. 1. (8.)

MONTELIUS (O.) Les temps préhistoriques en Suède. pp. 352. *Paris,* 1895. 8°. 7708. d. 38.

SWEDEN.—**Antiquities**—*continued.*

N——N. En svensk bondgård för 1500 år sedan. pp. 51. *Visby,* 1891. 8°. 7704. e. 19. (7.)

SCHÜRER VON WALDHEIM (J. W.) Uppländska stenåldersfynd kända år 1884. pp. 64. 1891. 8°. Ac. Stockholm. *K. Vitterhets Historie Akademien.* Antiqvarisk Tidskrift. Del. 8.
Ac. 7800/4.
See also RUNIC INSCRIPTIONS : SCANDINAVIA.

Army.

P.P. *Stockholm.* Svenska Arméens Rulla, *etc. Stockholm,* 1894, *etc.* 4°. P.P. 2457. f.

NORWAY. *Army.* Plan for den norske Armees Organisation. pp. 48. *Kristiania,* 1891. 8°.
8830. h. 28. (4.)

TIDANDER (L. G. T.) Öfversigt af svenska befästningsväsendets utveckling. *Motala,* 1890. *etc.* 8° 8823. n. 5.

WEIDENHIELM (C. H.) Samling af gällande föreskrifter angående indelta armén. pp. 583. *Stockholm,* 1891. 8°. 8823. n. 19.

For Swedish Military History, *see infra :* History : THIRTY YEARS' WAR.

Church of.

NORBORG (L.) I den kyrkliga bekännelsefrågan. pp. 361. *Lund,* 1893. 8°. 3925. d. 42.

QUENSEL (J. O.) Bidrag till svenska liturgiens historia. *Upsala,* 1890, *etc.* 8°. 3478. g.

WIDÉN (J.) Studier i Kyrkotuktsfrågan. pp. 70. *Hernösand,* 1892. 8°. 3926. bb. 46. (8.)

Constitution, Government and Politics.

BLOMBERG (H.) Om svenskt statsborgarskap. pp. 145. *Upsala,* 1891. 8°. 5725. e. 3.

HILDEBRAND (E.) Lärobok i svensk statskunskap. pp. 153. *Stockholm,* 1892. 8°. 8092. de. 39.

HÖJER (N.) Statsförbundet mellan Sverige och Norge. pp. 211. *Visby,* 1885. 8°. 8093. e. 2.

KARLSSON (C. H.) Den svenske konungens domsratt under medeltiden. *Stockholm,* 1890. *etc.* 8°. 5725. bb. 6.

KJELLÉN (R.) Studier rörande ministeransvarigheten. pp. 226. *Upsala,* 1890. 8°. 8006. cc. 6.

JOHANSSON (J.) Sakregister till Rikets ständers protokoll. 2 Bde. *Stockholm,* 1891-93. 4°.
8093. ee. 1.

NARCELLUS. Från 1881 års Andra Kammare. 2 vol. *Stockholm,* 1881. 8°. 8092. de. 33.

SCIPIO. Andra Kammarens män, 1888-90. pp. 164. *Stockholm,* 1890. 8°. 10761. a. 34.

OSCAR II., *King.* Is Oscar II. a constitutional king? pp. 16. *Lond.* 1895. 8°. Pam. 74.

SWEDEN. Zur auswärtigen Ministerfrage in Schweden-Norwegen. pp. 31. *Leipz.* 1895. 8°. Pam. 74.

SWEDISH QUESTIONS. Svenska Spörsmål. *Upsala,* 189-, *etc.* 8°. 8093. bb.
See also NORWAY.

History.

MANKELL (J.) Öfversigt af svenska krigens historia. *Stockholm,* 1890, *etc.* 8°. 9431. g.

MEIJER (B.) Svensk-historisk handbok. pp. 397. *Stockholm.* 1882. 8°. 9431. aaa. 9.

SETTERWALL (K.) Förteckning öfver Acta Svecica i Calendars of State Papers. *Stockholm,* 1889, *etc.* 8°. 9435. f.

STRINDBERG (A.) Les Relations de la France avec la Suède. pp. 249. *Paris,* 1891, 8°.
9080. cc. 17.

ANDERSSON (T.) Svenska underhandlingar med Ryssland 1537. pp. 54. *Stockholm,* 1892, 93. 8°.
Pam. 28.

WRANGEL (F. U.) *Count.* Liste des diplomates français en Suède, 1541-1891. pp. 95. *Stockholm,* 1891, 8°. 10664. l. 16.

SWEDEN.—History—*continued.*

HILDEBRAND (E.) Karl IX.'s testamente 1611. 1895. 8°. Ac. Stockholm. *Historiska Föreningen.* Historisk Tidskrift. 15 årg. Ac. 7798.

BAUMGARTEN (H.) Gustav-Adolf und die deutschen Protestanten. pp. 19. *Coburg,* 1893. 8°. 10601. d. 33. (7.)

BIENEMANN (F.) Gustav Adolf und Livland. pp. 26. *Riga,* 1894, 8°. Pam. 28.

BJÖRLIN (G.) Gustaf Adolf. pp. 401. *Stockholm,* 1890. 8°. 10761. ee. 29.

BLUEMEL (E.) Gustav Adolf, König von Schweden. pp. 226. *Eisleben,* 1894. 8°. 10761. aa. 63.

BURG (J.) Gustav Adolph im Lichte der neueren Geschichtsforschung. pp. 47. *Essen,* 1894. 8°. Pam. 8.

FLETCHER (C. R. L.) Gustavus Adolphus. pp. 316. 1892. 8°. ABBOTT (E.) Heroes of the Nations. 10601. f.

GUTJAHR (E.) Gustaf Adolfs Beweggründe zur Teilnahme am deutschen Kriege. pp. 72. *Leipz.* 1894. 8°. Pam. 28.

LAMPARTER (E.) Gustav Adolf. pp. 652. *Barmen,* 1892. 8°. 10761. cc. 21.

TREITSCHKE (H. v.) Gustav Adolf und Deutschlands Freiheit. pp. 29. *Leipz.* 1895. 8°. Pam. 28.

WIBLING (C.) Sveriges förhållande till Siebenbürgen, 1623-48. pp. 211. *Lund,* 1890, 8°. 9431. bb. 23.

WITZ (C. A.) Gustav Adolf und Jesus-Christus. pp. 39. *Wien,* 1895. 8°. 3910. cc. 88. (6.)

RYDFORS (A.) De diplomatiska förbindelserna mellan Sverige och England 1624-30. pp. 154. *Upsala,* 1890. 8°. 9080. ee. 15.

HEIMER (A.) De diplomatiska förbindelserna mellan Sverige och England 1633-54. pp. 159. *Lund,* 1892. 8°. 9077. eee. 37.

KJÆR (S.) Gjøngehøvdingen Svend Povlsen og Snaphanerne (1643-79). pp. 293. *Kjøbenh.* 1892. 8°. 10761. e. 11.

CLARETTA (G.) La Regina Cristina in Italia, 1655-89. pp. 456. *Torino,* 1892. 8°. 10761. dd. 2.

BÖRJESSON (N. M.) Riksdagen i Stockholm, 1655. pp. 80. *Norrköping,* 1891. 8°. 9007. ff. 4. (6.)

HAUMANT (É.) La Guerre du Nord et la paix d'Oliva, 1655-60. pp. 319. *Paris,* 1893. 8°. 9078. ff. 31.

FÅHRÆUS (G. R.) Om förandringen af Sveriges allianssystem åren 1680-82. pp. 162. *Upsala,* 1891. 8°. 9431. c. 4.

BAIN (R. N.) Charles XII. and the collapse of the Swedish Empire, 1682-1719. pp. 320. 1895. 8°. ABBOTT (E.) Heroes of the Nations. Vol. 16. 10601. f.

CHARLES XII., *King.* Die eigenhändigen Briefe König Karls XII. pp. 435. *Berl.* 1894. 8°. 010920. f. 42.

PUAUX (N. A. F.) Historie de l'établissement des Protestants français en Suède. pp. 212. *Paris,* 1891. 8°. 4629. i. 20.

KRMANN (D.) Historia ablegationis D. Krmann ad regem Sveciae Carolum XII. 1708-9. 1894. 8°. Ac. Pest. *Magyar Tudományos Akadémia.* Monumenta Hungariae. Osztály II. Köt. 23. Ac. 825.

SCHENSTRÖM (C. F.) Armfeltska Karolinernas sista tåg. pp. 111. *Stockholm,* 1890. 8°. 9125. aaa. 9.

OSCAR II., *King.* Några bidrag till Sveriges Krigshistoria åren 1711, 1712 och 1713. *Stockholm,* 1892. 8°. 9435. f. 28.

SCHYBERGSON (M. G.) Riksdagsmannavalen i Åbo under frihetstiden. 1891. 8°. Ac. Helsingfors. *Svenska Literatursällskapet i Finland.* Skrifter. No. 18. Ac. 9082.

SWEDEN.—History—*continued.*

STAVENOW (L.) Om riksrådsvalen under frihetstiden. pp. 156. *Upsala,* 1890. 8°. 9435. f. 14.

BAIN (R. N.) Gustavus III. and his contemporaries. 2 vol. *Lond.* 1894. 8°. 10761. g. 29.

BROWN (J.) Memoirs of the Sovereigns of Sweden, 1766-1818. 2 vol. *Lond.* 1895. 8°. 10600. f. 1.

GUSTAVUS III., *King.* König Gustav III. in Aachen 1780 und 1791. 1880. 8°. Ac. Aix-la-Chapelle. *Geschichtsverein.* Zeitschrift. Bd. 2. Ac. 7008.

KOERSNER (P. V.) Gustaf III.'s yttre politik under tiden närmast före ryska krigens utbrott. pp. 80. *Falun,* 1882. 8°. Pam. 28

ÅKESON (N.) Förmyndarestyrelsens planer rörande Gustaf IV. Adolfs förmälning. pp. 71. *Lund,* 1891, 8°. Pam. 28.

KEY-ÅBERG (K. V.) De diplomatiska förbindelserna mellan Sverige och Storbritannien under Gustaf IV. Adolfs krig emot Napoléon. pp. 125. *Upsala,* 1890. 8°. 9080. bbb. 29.

—— De diplomatiska Förbindelserna mellan Sverige och Storbritannien under Gustaf IV. Adolfs senaste regeringsår. pp. 100. *Upsala,* 1891. 8°. 9435. dd. 7.

ALMÉN (J.) Älten Bernadotte. pp. 338. *Stockholm,* 1893. 8°. 10761. h. 11.

SWEDEN. Sveriges krig åren 1808 och 1809. *Stockholm,* 1890, *etc.* 8°. 9080. dd. 15.

SANDEGREN (T.) Till historien om statshvälfningen i Sverige, 1809. pp. 86. *Göteberg,* 1890. 4°. 8276. f. 26.

LAGERHJELM (G. R.) Napoleon och Carl Johan under kriget i Tyskland 1813. pp. 421. *Stockholm,* 1891. 8°. 9080. cc. 18.

WOYNAR (C.) Österreiches Beziehungen zu Schweden und Dänemark, 1813-14. 1891. 8°. Ac. Vienna. *K. Akademie.* Archiv für österreichische Geschichte. Bd. 77. Hlfte 2. Ac. 810/8.

BJÖRLIN (G.) Kriget i Norge 1814. pp. 348. *Stockholm,* 1893. 8°. 9435. f. 27.

REUTERSKIÖLD (C. A.) Till belysning af den Svenska-Norska Unionsförfattningen. pp. 195. *Stockholm,* 1893. 8°. 9424. cc. 9.

HOLMBERG (C.) Carl XV. pp. 700. *Stockholm,* 1890, 91. 8°. 10761. ee. 37.

ADLERSPARRE (A.) Tre Episoder i Konung Karl XV.'s lif. pp. 82. *Stockholm,* 1893. 8°. 10761. aa. 59.

CHARLES XV., *King.* Caroliana. Hågkomster ur Carl XV.'s lefnad. pp. 62. *Stockholm,* 1889. 8°. 10761. a. 29. (7.)

See also THIRTY YEARS' WAR.

Law.

SWEDEN. Les codes suédois de 1734. pp. 527. *Paris,* 1895. 8°. 5705. g. 4.

—— Sveriges Rikes Lag. pp. 962. *Stockholm,* 1890. 8°. 5725. aaa. 9.

—— *Nya Lagberedningen.* Nya Lagberedningens betänkande angående rättegångsväsendets ombildning. 3 Del. *Stockholm,* 1884. 8°. 5725. e. 4.

SWEDEN. Östgötalagen. pp. 280. 1895. 8°. Ac. Helsingfors. *Svenska Literatur sällskapet.* Skrifter 29. Ac. 9082.

Ac. Upsal. *Juridiska Föreningen.* NORLING (E. V.) Anteckningar efter Nordlings föreläsningar i svensk civilrätt. pp. 301. *Upsala,* 1891. 8°. 5725. bb. 14.

Navy.

BORCHGREVINK (A.) Haandbog i norsk fløningsvæsen. *Kristiania,* 1889, *etc.* 8°. 8807. dd. 28.

SWEDEN.—Navy—*continued.*

P.P. *Stockholm.* Svenska Arméens Rulla och Flottans Rulla. *Stockholm,* 1894, *etc.* 4°.
P.P. 2457. f.

ZETTERSTEN (A.) Svenska flottans historia, 1522–1634. pp. 511. *Stockholm,* 1890. 8°.
8807. cc. 33.

Politics.

See supra : CONSTITUTION.

Sport. *See* SPORT.

Topography: Social Life.

BAEDEKER (C.) Norway, Sweden and Denmark. pp. 392. 42. *Leipz.* 1892. 8°.   2352. a.

COOK (T.) Guide to Norway, Sweden and Denmark. pp. 206. *Lond.* 1893. 8°. 10280. aa. 24.

BAKER (*Mrs.* W.) Pictures of Swedish Life. pp. 408. *Lond.* 1894. 8°.   10280. ee. 29.

COOPER (S. W.) Rambles in Sweden. pp. 204. *Gothenburg,* 1884. 8°.   10281. aaa. 19.

GINISTY (P.) De Paris au Cap Nord. pp. 252. *Paris,* 1892. 8°.   10280. f. 11.

LIND (C.) Handbok i fäderneslandets geografi. pp. 327. *Stockholm,* 1890. 8°. 10280 aa. 19.

NAYLOR (R. A.) Letters on Sweden and Norway. pp 207. *Lond.* 1884. 8°.   10280. eee. 16.

SWEDISH FOLKLIFE. Vårt Folk, verklighetsbilder ur svenskt folklif. *Stockholm,* 1894, *etc.* fol.
10281. l.

THOMAS (W. W.) Från slott till koja. *Stockholm,* 1891, *etc.* 8°.   10280. f. 10.

VERGANI (E.) Durch Skandinavien. pp. 144. *Wien,* 1894. 8°.   10281. a. 6.

See also SPORT.

Trade and Finance.

CORDIER (H.) Les débuts de la Compagnie royal de Suède en extrême Orient au XVIII° siècle. pp. 45. *Paris,* 1889. 8°.   9055. e. 6.

CHICAGO. *Columbian Exposition.* Swedish Catalogue. 2 pt. *Stockholm,* 1893. 8°.   7959. e. 3.

FAHLBECK (P. E.) Sveriges national-förmögenhet. pp. 131. *Stockholm,* 1890. 8°.   08227. e. 23.

—— Die Handelspolitik Schwedens und Norwegens. 1892. 8°. Ac. Leipsic. *Verein für Socialpolitik.* Schriften. Vol. 49. Ac. 2522.

HÖRNELL (R.) and KÔERSNER (V.) Export of Sweden. pp. 210. *Stockholm,* 1889. 8°.
08227. e. 27.

MILLET (R.) Les Conditions du travail en Suède. pp. 178. 1890. 8°. France. *M. des Affaires Étrangères.* Recueil de rapports.   08276. k.

THULIN (G.) Om Konungens ekonomiska lagstiftning. pp. 260. *Lund,* 1890. 8°. 5725. d. 3.

SWEDENBORGIANISM. SWEDENBORG (E.) Delights of Wisdom relating to conjugal love. pp. 544. *Lond.* 1891. 8°.   3716. i. 2.

ODHNER (C. T.) Account of the life and work of E. Swedenborg. pp. 41. *Phila.* 1893. 8°.
Pam. 84.

DĀDĀBHĀI PĀṆḌURĀṄGA. Opinion d'un lettré Hindou sur les doctrines de Swedenborg. pp. 120. *Paris,* 1892. 12°.   3716. cce. 25.

SEWALL (F.) Swedenborg and Aristotle. pp. 21. *Bost.* 1895. 8°.   Pam. 84.

ADVANTAGE. On the relative advantage of Tubs with bottoms and Tubs without. Letter to a Swedenborgian clergyman. pp. 4. 345. *N.Y.* 1890. 8°.   3716. df. 24.

COLLINGWOOD (C.) The new Church doctrine of correspondence, *etc.* pp. 9. *Lond.* 1887. 8°.
Pam. 84.

GILES (C.) Hvarför jag tillhör Nya Kirkan. pp. 97. *Stockholm,* 1891. 8°.   3925. de. 2.

SWEDENBORGIANISM—*continued.*

MAC GOWAN (J.) Indian New Church leaflets. 11 pt. *Allahabad,* 1891. 8°.   4371. b. 28. (9.)

NEW JERUSALEM CHURCH. *Home Reading Union.* Solutions of questions and difficulties, 1892. pp. 79. *Lond.* 1893. 8°.   3716. df. 22.

—— Solutions of questions and difficulties during 1893. pp. 175. *Edinb.* 1894. 8°. 3716. aa. 39.

P.P. *Boston.* New-Church Review. Quarterly journal. *Bost.* 1894, *etc.* 8°.   P.P. 867. b.

SMITH (F.) History of the Peter Street Society of the New Church, Manchester. pp. 79. *Lond.* 1892. 8°.   4715. aaa. 44.

WILKINSON (J. J. G.) The African and the true Christian religion. Study in the writings of Swedenborg. pp. 245. *Lond.* 1892. 8°.
3716. df. 20.

See also ENGLAND, *Nonconformists.*

SWEDISH LANGUAGE.

Dictionaries.

SUNDÉN (D. A.) Ordbok öfver svenska språket. 2 Delen. *Stockholm,* 1885–92. 8°. 12972. ee. 34.

TAMM (F. A.) Etymologisk svensk ordbok. *Stockholm,* 1890, *etc.* 8°.   12972. o.

WENSTRÖM (O. E.) and JEURLING (O.) Svenska språkets ordförråd. coll. 1096. *Visby,* 1891. 8°.
12976. a.

BJÖRKMAN (C. G.) Svensk-engelsk Ordbok. pp. 1360. *Stockholm,* 1889. 8°. 12972. e. 13.

DICTIONARIES. New pocket-dictionary of the English and Swedish Languages. 2 pt. *Leipz.* 1894. 16°.   12972. a. 20.

KLINT (A.) Fransk-svensk Ordbok. pp. 678. *Stockholm,* 1893. 8°.   12972. c. 47.

HOPPE (O.) Schwedisch-deutsches Wörterbuch. pp. 400. *Stockholm,* 1892. 8°.   12972. f. 22.

VIDMARK (P. F.) Tysk-svensk Ordbok. *Stockholm,* 1883, *etc.* 8°.   12972. c. 41.

DICTIONARIES. [*Latin-Swedish.*] Variarum Rerum Vocabula cum Sueca interpretatione, Stockholm, 1538. *Uppsala,* 1890. *etc.* 8°.   12972. o.

Old Swedish.

NOREEN (A. G.) Altschwedisches Lesebuch. pp. 180. *Halle,* 1892–94. 8°.   12260. k. 1.

Orthography.

LUNDGREN (O.) Svensk staflista angifvande skolstafning jämte gammalstafning och nystafning. pp. 123. *Lund,* 1891. 8°. 12972. bbb. 30.

LUNDELL (J. A.) Svensk Ordlista med reformstavning och uttalsbeteckning. pp. 384. *Stockholm,* 1893. 8°.   12972. cc. 55.

NORDLANDER (J.) Ordbok för rättskrifning. pp. 128. *Stockholm,* 1890. 8°.   12976. aaa. 32.

SWEDISH LITERATURE. BERNARDINI (L.) La Littérature scandinave. pp. 280. *Paris,* 1894. 8°.   011850. eee. 13.

NOREEN (A. G.) and MEYER (E. P. L.) Valda stycken af svenska författare 1526–1732. pp. 301. *Uppsala,* 1893. 8°.   12260. c. 9.

P.P. *Lund.* Skandinavisches Archiv. *Lund,* 1891, *etc.* 8°.   P.P. 5044. h.

BAIN (R. N.) Gustavus III. Introduction to the history of Swedish belles-lettres. 2 vol. *Lond.* 1894. 8°.   10761. g. 29.

SKARSTEDT (E.) Svensk-amerikanska-poeter. pp. 335. *Minneapolis,* 1890. 8°.   11557. c. 7.

SWIMMING. AUCKLAND. *Amateur Swimming Association.* Amateur Swimming Association Annual. 1892–93, *etc.* *Auckland,* 1893, *etc.* 8°.   7912. b.

SWIMMING—*continued.*

HIMMEL (J.) Schule der Schwimmkunst.
pp. 152. 1895. 8°. Braumüller's militärische
Taschenbücher. Bd. 4.   8829. aa.

LONDON. *Swimmers' Life-saving Society.* Illustrated Handbook, containing Drill for teaching
rescue and resuscitation. pp. 56.
Lond. 1891. 16°.   7907. a. 75.

SINCLAIR (A.) and HENRY (W.) Swimming.
pp. 456. 1894. 8°. Badminton Library.
                                 2264. aa. 13.

SWINDON. MORRIS (W.) Swindon fifty
years ago. pp. 527. *Swindon,* 1885. 8°.
                                 010358. e. 16.

SWISS DIALECTS AND LITERATURE.

French.

ZIMMERLI (J.) Die deutsch-französische Sprachgrenze in der Schweiz. *Basel,* 1891, *etc.* 8°.
                                 12962. q. 3.

PLUDHUN (W.) Parlons français. pp. 34.
Genève, 1890. 8°.   12953. b. 56.

RITTER (E.) Glossaires et lexicographes génevois. pp. 19. *Genève,* 1893. 8°.
                             12903. c. 52. (8.)

Ac., *etc.* Neuchâtel. *Société d'Histoire.* Le
Patois neuchâtelois. pp. 417.
Neuchâtel, 1894. 8°.   12236. h. 2.

DUPERTUIS (F.) Recueil des locutions vicieuses
dans le Canton de Vaud. pp. 69.
Lausanne, 1892. 8°.   12954. bb. 31.

P.P. *Chaux-de-Fonds.* La Muse romande.
Chaux-de-F. 1891, *etc.* 8°.   P.P. 4299. h.

German.

ZIMMERLI (J.) Die deutsch-französische Sprachgrenze in der Schweiz. *Basel,* 1891. *etc.* 8°.
                                 12962. q. 3.

BLATTNER (H.) Ueber die Mundarten des
Kantons Aargau. pp. 80. *Brugg,* 1890. 8°.
                             12901. d. 20. (6.)

HOFFMANN (E.) Der mundartliche Vokalismus
von Basel-Stadt. pp. 94. *Basel,* 1890. 8°.
                             12902. dd. 27. (7.)

SCHILD (P.) Brienzer Mundart.
Basel, 1891, *etc.* 8°.   12962. o. 1.

BRANDSTETTER (R.) Prolegomena zu einer Geschichte der luzerner Mundart. pp. 88.
Einsiedeln, 1890. 8°.   011824. h. 11. (3.)

—— Die Reception der neuhochdeutschen
Schriftsprachen in Luzern. pp. 90.
Einsiedeln, 1891. 8°.   Pam. 47.

STICKELBERGER (H.) Lautlehre der lebenden
Mundart der Stadt Schaffhausen. pp. 59.
Aarau. 1881. 8°.   Pam. 47.

BAECHTOLD (J.) Geschichte der deutschen Literatur in der Schweiz. pp. 687. 244.
Frauenfeld, 1892. 8°.   11851. e. 33.

SAITSCHIK (R.) Meister der schweizerischen
Dichtung des XIX. Jahrhunderts. pp. 428.
Frauenfeld, 1894. 8°.   011850. eee. 27.

SWITZERLAND. [*See note on page 1.*]

Bibliography.

Ac. Basle. *Historische Gesellschaft.* Acta Pontificum Helvetica. Quellen schweizerischer Geschichte aus dem päpstlichen Archiv.
Basel, 1891, *etc.* fol.   Ac. 6924/6.

—— Berne. *Centralkommission für Schweizerische Landeskunde.* Bibliographie.
Bern, 1893, *etc.* 8°.   Ac. 3417.

—— Zurich. *Allgemeine geschichtsforschende
Gesellschaft.* BRANDSTETTER (J. L.) Repertorium über die in Zeit- und Sammelschriften der
Jahre 1812–1890 enthaltenen Aufsätze schweizergeschichtlichen Inhaltes. pp. 467.
Basel, 1892. 8°.   Ac. 6995/4.

SWITZERLAND.—**Bibliography**—*cont.*

WYSS (G. v.) Geschichte der Historiographie
in der Schweiz. *Zürich,* 1894, *etc.* 8°. 9007. g.

OECHSLI (W.) Quellenbuch zur Schweizergeschichte. 2 pt. *Zürich,* 1886, 93. 8°.
                                 9304. ee. 22.

SWITZERLAND. *Commission pour la Bibliographie
Suisse.* Bibliographie nationale Suisse.
Bern, 1892, *etc.* 8°.   11899. ee.

Antiquities.

Ac. Lausanne. *Musée Archéologique.* Antiquités
lacustres. *Lausanne,* 1894, *etc.* fol.   289.

STUDER (T.) and BANNWARTH (E.) Crania Helvetica antiqua. pp. 55. *Leipz.* 1894. fol.
                                 7420. h. 3.

Army : Military History.

FISCH (C.) Das schweizerische Kriegswesen bis
zum Untergang der alten Eidgenossenschaft.
pp. 62. *Aarau,* 1893. 8°.   8829. aa. 21.

MUELINEN (W. F. v.) Das französische Schweizer-Garderegiment am 10. August 1792.
pp. 214. *Luzern,* 1892. 8°.   8828. f. 15.

SCHALLER (H. de) Histoire des Troupes suisses
au service de France sous le règne de Napoleon Ier.
pp. 236. *Lausanne,* 1883. 8°.   8823. o. 12.

MAAG (A.) Geschichte der Schweizertruppen im
Kriege Napoleons I. in Spanien und Portugal,
etc. Biel, 1892, *etc.* 8°.   9079. f. 4.

—— Die Schicksale der Schweizer-Regimenter
in Napoleons I. Feldzug nach Russland 1812.
pp. 315. *Biel,* 1890. 8°.   9080. bbb. 24.

—— Geschichte der Schweizertruppen in französischen Diensten, 1813–15. pp. 568.
Biel, 1894. 8°.   8829. i. 23.

LA RIVE (E. de) Les Formations de Marche du
Corps d'Armée suisse. pp. 46. *Genève,* 1892. 8°.
                                 8824. i. 36.

SWITZERLAND, *Army.* Ordre de bataille der
schweizerischen Armée. 2 pt.
Bern, 1892, 93. 4°.   8830. m. 5.

—— État der Offiziere des Territorial- und Etappendienstes, 1892. pp. 15. *Bern,* 1892. 4°.
                                 8830. l. 27.

WEBER (R.) Zur Wehrfrage. pp. 52. 1893. 8°.
Schweizer-Zeitfragen. Hft. 24.   8074. f.

T., A. Du Landsturm. Lettres d'un soldat.
pp. 31. *Neuchatel,* 1892. 8°. 8830. bbb. 13. (7.)

Constitution and Government.

BONAPARTE (R. N.) *Prince.* Assemblées démocratiques en Suisse. pp. 27. *Paris,* 1890. 4°.
                             8074. aaaa. 15. (1.)

—— Démocratie suisse. pp. 26.
Paris, 1890. 4°.   8074. aaaa. 15. (2.)

DUNANT (A.) La Législation par le peuple en
Suisse. pp. 138. *Genève,* 1894. 8°.
                                 8072. eee. 13.

HIESTAND (P.) Zur Lehre von den Rechtsquellen im schweizerischen Staatsrecht. pp. 87.
Zürich, 1891. 8°.   5510. ec. 1. (2.)

HILTY (C.) Die Bundesverfassungen der schweizerischen Eidgenossenschaft. pp. 469.
Bern, 1891. 8°.   9304. e. 6.

JAMES (E. J.) Federal Constitution of Switzerland. 1890. 8°. Ac. Philadelphia. *University
of Pennsylvania.* Publications. Pol. Economy
Series. No. 8.   Ac. 2692. p.

MARSAUCHE (L.) La Confédération helvétique
d'après sa constitution. pp. 319.
Neuchatel, 1891. 8°.   8052. cc. 16.

P.P. *Berne.* Politisches Jahrbuch der schweizerischen Eidgenossenschaft.
Bern, 1886, *etc.* 8°.   P.P. 3527. fb.

SWITZERLAND. — Constitution, etc.— *continued.*

RASCHER (J. M. v.) Die Bundesverfassung vom Jahre 1874. pp. 214. 1888. 8°. SWITZERLAND. Sammlung schweizerischer Gesetze. Bd. 1.
5511. e.

SALIS (L. R. v.) Schweizerisches Bundesrecht. *Bern,* 1891, *etc.* 8°.   05551. f. 1.

VINCENT (J. M.) State and federal Government in Switzerland. pp. 247. 1891. 8°. Ac. Baltimore. *Johns Hopkins University.* Studies in Historical Science. Extra vol. 9. Ac. 2689.

WYSS (P. F. v.) Abhandlungen zur Geschichte des schweizerischen öffentlichen Rechts. pp. 475. *Zürich,* 1892. 8°.   5551. e. 19.

DEPLOIGE (S.) Le Referendum en Suisse. pp. 190. *Brux.* 1892. 8°.   8072. f. 2.

LA SIZERANNE (R. de) Le Referendum communal. pp. 86. *Paris,* 1893. 8°. 8050. aaa. 10.
See also infra: History: Politics: ELECTIONS.

Emigration.

BOKEMEYER (H.) Das Auswanderungswesen in der Schweiz. pp. 75. *Berl.* 1892. 8°. Pam. 66.

FAURE (C.) Exposé sommaire des voyages et travaux géographiques des Suisses. pp. 47. *Paris,* 1891. 8°.   10025. ee. 7.

STEINACH (A.)   Geschichte und Leben der schweizer Kolonien in den Vereinigten Staaten. pp. 375. *N.Y.* 1889. 8°.   10409. c. 31.

Evangelical and Free Churches.

ADAMINA (J.) Le Réveil religieux dans le canton de Vaud. pp. 44. *Lausanne,* 189:. 8°. Pam. 29.

GLARDON (A.) Les hérétiques dans l'Église Libre. pp. 31. *Lausanne,* 1892. 8°.
3900. bb. 43. (8.)

MARTIN (E.) L'Influence du dogme réformé sur la moralité. pp. 46. *Berne,* 1892. 8°.
4371. ee. 25. (9.)

See also infra: HISTORY, *Ecclesiastical.*

History.

For historical Bibliographies, *see supra: Bibliography.*

BAKER (F. G.) The Model Republic. pp. 550. *Lond.* 1895. 8°.   9304. de. 4.

MAC CRACKEN (W. D.) Rise of the Swiss Republic. pp. 413. *Lond.* 1892. 8°. 9304. de. 2.

Ac. Basle. *Historische Gesellschaft.* Denkschrift zur Erinnerung an den Bund der Eidgenossen vom 1 Aug. 1291. pp. 176. *Basel,* 1891. 8°.
Ac. 6924/5.

OECHSLI (W.) Die Anfänge der schweizerischen Eidgenossenschaft. pp. 391. 319. *Zürich,* 1891. 8°.   9304. e. 5.

ROEHRICH (H.) VIᵉ Centenaire de la Confédération Suisse. pp. 22. *Genève,* 1891. 8°. Pam. 45.

SCHWEIZER (P.) Geschichte der schweizerischen Neutralität. *Frauenfeld,* 1893, *etc.* 8°. 9304. de.

DELBRUECK (H.) Die Perserkriege und die Burgunderkriege. pp. 314. *Berl.* 1887. 8°.
9041. i. 17.

WATTELET (H.) Die Schlacht bei Murten. pp. 84. *Freiburg,* 1894. 8°.   9304. ee. 31.

MAAG (R.) Die Freigrafschaft Burgund und ihre Beziehungen zu der schweizerischen Eidgenossenschaft, 1477–1678. pp. 366. *Zürich,* 1891. 8°.   9305. c. 2.

DUNANT (E.) Les Relations politiques de Genève avec Berne et les Suisses, 1536–1654. pp. 222. *Genève,* 1894, 8°.   9304. f. 16.

GOBAT (A.)   La République de Berne et la France pendant les guerres de religion. pp. 242. *Paris,* 1891. 8°.   9079. h. 15.

SWITZERLAND.—History—*continued.*

RYFE (A.) Une Chronique suisse du XVIᵐᵉ siècle, Circkell der Eidtgnoschaft. pp. 84. *Bâle,* 1892. 8°.   9304. f. 8.

COMBE (E.) Les réfugiés de la Révocation en Suisse. pp. 238. *Lausanne,* 1885. 8°.
4650. ee. 23.

FAZI (H.) Les Suisses et la neutralité de la Savoie. 1703–04. pp. 349. *Genève,* 1895. 8°.
9304. de. 5.

HUCH (R.) Die Neutralität der Eidgenossenschaft während des spanischen Erbfolgekrieges. pp. 285. *Zürich,* 1892. 8°.   9073. e. 18.

PICHARD ( ) Journal sur la Révolution helvétique. pp. 328. *Lausanne,* 1891. 8°.
9304. e. 3.

ERLACH (R. v.) Zur bernischen Kriegsgeschichte, 1798. *Berl.* 1881. 8°.   9304. c. 20.

SCHALLER (J. F. J. P. D. de) Souvenirs d'un officier fribourgeois, 1798–1848. pp. 227. *Fribourg,* 1890. 8°.   010707. g. 23.

GUENTHER (R.) Geschichte des Feldzuges von 1800 in Ober-Deutschland und der Schweiz. pp. 210. *Frauenfeld,* 1893. 8°. 9080. i. 13.

KERN (J. C.) Souvenirs politiques. pp. 382. *Berne,* 1887. 8°.   9305. b. 7.

For the Military History of the Swiss, *see also supra:* Army.

History, *Ecclesiastical.*

EGLI (E.) Kirchengeschichte der Schweiz bis auf Karl den Grossen. pp. 145. *Zürich,* 1893. 8°.   4662. f. 7.

Law.

SWITZERLAND. Sammlung schweizerischer Gesetze. *Bern,* 1888, *etc.* 8°.   5551. e.

ESCHER (C.) Das schweizerischer interkantonale Privatrecht. pp. 287. *Zürich,* 1895. 8°.
05551. k. 2.

FAZY (G.) La centralisation et l'unification du droit en Suisse. 1890. 8°. Ac. Geneva. *Institut National.* Bulletin. Tom. 30. Ac. 610.

KELLER (G.) Der Nachlassvertrag ausser Concurs nach dem schweizerischen Bundesgesetz über Schuldbetreibung und Concurs. pp. 134. *Zürich,* 1891. 8°.   5551. g. 15.

ROGUIN (E.) Conflits des Lois suisses en matière internationale. pp. 920. *Lausanne,* 1891. 8°.
5510. dd. 7.

SCHURTER (E.) Grundzüge des materiellen Beweisrechtes in der Civilprozessgesetzgebung. pp. 438. *Zürich,* 1890. 8°.   5510. dd. 4.
See also LAW, *Commercial: Criminal.*

Politics, *Domestic and Foreign.*

CURTI (T.) Im Bundesratshaus. pp. 108. *Zürich,* 1894. 8°.   8074. c. 16.

DOUGLAS (R. v. B.) *Baron.* Het Conflict tusschen Zwitserland en Duitschland in 1889. pp. 144. *Leiden,* 1891. 8°.   5686. cc. 66.

MAZADE (C. de) L'Europe et les neutralités. pp. 117. *Paris,* 1893. 12°.   8026. bbb. 36.

RASCHER (J. M. v.) Der schweizer Staat und Preussen-Deutschland. pp. 188. *Berl.* 1893. 8°.
8074. bb. 41.

SWITZERLAND. La neutralità della Svizzera. pp. 119. *Roma,* 1892. 8°.   8026. de. 1.

Topography.

BAEDEKER (C.) Die Schweiz. pp. 476. *Leipz.* 1895. 8°.   10108. d. 23.
—— Switzerland. pp. 496. *Leipz.* 1893. 8°.
2352. a.

CONTY (H. A. de) La Suisse circulaire. pp. 356. *Paris,* 1894. 16°.   10196. au. 23.

COOK (T.) Tourist's handbook for Switzerland. pp. 328. *Lond.* 1895. 8°.   10196. aaaa. 35.

SWITZERLAND.—Topography—_cont._

JOANNE (P.) Suisse. pp. 407. _Paris_, 1894. 8°.
　　　　　　　　　　　　　　　　10196. aa. 22.

LUNN (H. S.) Co-operative Swiss tour. pp. 31.
Lond. 1893. 8°. 　　　　　　　　′ Pam. 91.

SWITZERLAND. Führer durch die fränkische
Schweiz. pp. 122. _Erlangen_, 1891. 8°.
　　　　　　　　　　　　　　　　10240. e. 5.

—— Murray's Handbook for Switzerland.
Lond. 1892. 8°. 　　　　　　　　2364. b. 17.

—— Practical Swiss Guide. pp. 199. 1894. 8°.
Practical Guides for tourists. 　　10196. dd.

────────

BURNABY, _afterwards_ MAIN (E. A. F.) My home
in the Alps. pp. 131. _Lond._ 1892. 8°.
　　　　　　　　　　　　　　　　10196. cc. 7.

CHABLOZ (F.) Les sobriquets de communes dans
la Suisse romande. pp. 50. _Gorgier_, 1893. 8°.
　　　　　　　　　　　　　　　　Pam. 91.

DUMAS DAVY DE LA PAILLETERIE (A.) Swiss
Travel. pp. 254. _Lond._ 1890. 8°.
　　　　　　　　　　　　　　　　10196. aaaa. 34.

GUYON (C.) Des Ardennes en Italie. pp. 224.
Paris, 1890. 8°. 　　　　　　　10105. ee. 7.

JACOBSON (J.) Reisebriefe aus Italien und der
Schweiz. pp. 327. _Königsb._ 1893. 8°.
　　　　　　　　　　　　　　　　10107. cc. 13.

MAC CRACKAN (W. D.) Romance Switzerland.
(Teutonic Switzerland.) 2 vol. _Bost._ 1894. 16°.
　　　　　　　　　　　　　　　　10196. aa. 24.

MARSH (H.) Two Seasons in Switzerland.
pp. 261. _Lond._ 1895. 8°. 　　10196. g. 2.

MULLER (A.) À travers l'Oberland bernois.
pp. 355. _Mulhouse_, 1891. 12°. 10196. aaaa. 3.

NAEHER (J.) Die Schlösser, Burgen und Klöster
der romanischen Schweiz, _etc._
Karlsruhe, 1886. 4°. 　　10105 f. 5. (3.)

STEPHEN (L.) The playground of Europe.
pp. 339. _Lond._ 1894. 8°. 　　2302. b. 4.

SYMONDS (J. A.) and (M.) Our life in the Swiss
highlands. pp. 366. _Edinb._ 1892. 8°.
　　　　　　　　　　　　　　　　10196. cc. 9.

See also ALPS.

Trade.

ARAGO (E.) Les conditions du travail en Suisse.
pp. 84. 1890. 8°. FRANCE. _M. des Affaires
étrangères._ Recueil de rapports. 　08276. k.

BUERNER (R.) Zollhandbuch für die Hauptindustrien der Schweiz, _etc._ _Zittau_, 1895, _etc._ 8°.
　　　　　　　　　　　　　　　　08226. i.

BOUROUILL (J. d'A. de) _Baron._ Mededeelingen
omtrent de vermogensbelastingen in de Kantons
van Zwitserland. pp. 55. _Utrecht_, 1892. 8°.
　　　　　　　　　　　　08227. i. 30. (7.)

FREY (E.) Die schweizerische Handelspolitik
der letzten Jahrzehnte. 1892. 8°. Ac. Leipsic.
Verein für Socialpolitik. Schriften. Vol. 49.
　　　　　　　　　　　　　　　　Ac. 2322.

P.P. _Basle._ Annuaire du commerce suisse.
Basel, 1892, _etc._ 8°. 　　　　P.P. 2418.

SIEGMUND (L.) Handbuch für die schweizerischen Handelsregisterführer. pp. 627.
Basel, 1892. 8°. 　　　　　05551. f. 2.

SWORD. _See_ FENCING : WEAPONS.

SYDNEY. P.P. Illustrated Sydney News.
Vol. 27, _etc._ _Sydney_, 1890, _etc._ fol. P.P. 9096. a.

WOOLCOTT (W. C.) Cook's Guide to Sydney.
pp. 135. _Sydney_, 1891. 8°. 　10492. aa. 27.

SYDNEY, _Diocese of._ Ordinances of the Synods
of the Diocese of Sydney. pp. 122.
Sydney, 1880. 8°. 　　　　　5157. aaa. 9.

SYLT. HANSEN (C. P.) Das Nordseebad
Westerland auf Sylt. pp. 234.
Garding, 1891. 8°. 　　　　10256. aa. 38.

SYLT—_continued._

KNUTH (P.) Botanische Wanderungen auf der
Insel Sylt. pp. 116. _Tondern_, 1890. 8°.
　　　　　　　　　　　　　　　　7029. a. 12

SYMBOLISM. _See_ ART, _Christian._

SYMPHORAL. HELBING (H.) and PASS-
MORE (F. W.) Properties and advantages of
Symphoral. pp. 8. _Lond._ 1894. 8°.
　　　　　　　　　　　　7306. df. 22. (9.)

SYNODS. _See_ COUNCILS.

SYPHILIS. _See_ VENEREAL DISEASES.

SYRACUSE, New York. SMITH (E.) History of the Schools of Syracuse. pp. 347.
Syracuse, 1893. 8°. 　　　　8365. dd. 16

SYRACUSE, Sicily. CAVALLARI (F. S.)
Topografia archeologica di Syracusa. 3 pt.
Palermo, 1883, 91. fol. 　　7705. h. 23.

—— Atlante. fol. 　　　　Tab. 1700. d.

ORSI (P.) Necropoli Sicula presso Siracusa.
1894. 4°. Ac. Rome. _Academia de' Lincei._
Monumenti antichi. Vol. 2. 　Ac. 102/15.

AGNELLO ( ) Il Monachismo in Siracusa.
pp. 97. _Siracusa_, 1891. 8°. 　4605. g. 13.

SYRIA. _See_ PALESTINE.

SYRIAN CHURCH. _See_ JACOBITE CHURCH.

**SYRIAN LANGUAGE AND LITERA-
TURE.** BROCKELMANN (C.) Lexicon Syria-
cum. pp. 510. _Berl._ 1895. 8°. 012904. k. 4.

DUVAL (R.) Notes de Lexicographie syriaque et
arabe. 1893. 8°. Journal Asiatic. Sér. 9.
Tom. 2. 　　　　　　　　　2098. d.

—— Traité de Grammaire syriaque. pp. 447.
Paris, 1881. 8°. 　　　　　012904. h. 7.

MACLEAN (A. J.) Grammar of the dialects of
vernacular Syriac. pp. 364. _Camb._ 1895. 8°.
　　　　　　　　　　　　　　　　012904. g. 8.

WRIGHT (W.) Short history of Syriac Literature.
pp. 296. _Lond._ 1894. 8°. 　　2214. e. 1.

ROEDIGER (E.) Chrestomathia Syriaca.
pp. 123. 119. _Halis S._ 1892. 8°. 　753. hh. 3.

CHASE (F. H.) Old Syriac element in the text
of the Codex Bezæ. pp. 160. _Lond._ 1893. 8°.
　　　　　　　　　　　　　　　　3226. e. 33.

—— The Syro-Latin text of the Gospels.
pp. 148. _Lond._ 1895. 8°. 　　3225. ccc. 23.

EPHRAIM, _Saint._ Fragments of the Commentary
of Ephrem Syrus upon the Diatessaron. pp. 101.
Lond. 1895. 8°. 　　　　　753. f. 5.

ANTONY, _Saint._ Probe einer syrischen Version
der Vita St. Antonii. _Syr. & Germ._ pp. 53.
Leipz. 1894. 8°. 　　　　4828. df. 24.

See also SEMITIC LANGUAGES.

SYRJENIC LANGUAGE. WIEDEMANN
(F. J.) Grammatik der syrjänischen Sprache.
pp. 252. _St. Petersburg_, 1884. 8°. 12910. dd. 14.

SYRPHIDAE. _See_ DIPTERA.

SZILAGY-SOMLYO. BAYE (J. de) _Baron._
Le Trésor de Szilagy-Somlyo, Transylvanie.
pp. 17. _Paris_, 1892. 4°. 　　7707. g. 36.

────────

TABASCO. ROVIROSA (J. N.) Nombres geográficos del Estado de Tabasco. pp. 36.
México, 1888. 4°. 　　12903. i. 10. (3.)

See also MEXICO.

TABLES.

General : Mathematical : Scientific.

BLACKIE (W. G.) Arithmetical Tables. pp. 32.
Lond. 1892. 16°. 　　　　　Pam. 38.

TABLES.—General, etc.—*continued.*

CLARKE (J.) Tables for the discovery of mistakes made by reversions and misplacements. *Manch.* 1892. fol. 1804. c. 6.

GAUSS (F. G.) Polygonometrische Tafeln. pp. 194. *Halle*, 1893. 8°. 8548. df. 37.

HENDERSON (H. S.) Tables of equivalents. pp. 21. *Hull*, 1894. 12°. 8548. aa. 34.

HETT (C. L.) Table of the power of Leather Belting and Shafts. *Lond.* 1889. 16°.
8767. aa. 50.

—— Table of falling bodies, in metric measures. *Lond.* 1894. *s. sh.* 8°. 1882. d. 2. (23.)

HOWELL AND Co. Tables of diameters and thicknesses of wrought iron and steel tubes. pp. 32. *Sheffield*, 1891. 4°. 8548. g. 26.

JOHNSTON (F.) Tables for calculating the value of any weight. *Coventry*, 1891. 4°. 8548. de. 17.

JUTA (J. C.) AND Co. Colonial penny Tablebook, *etc.* pp. 64. *Cape Town*, 1892. 8°.
8548. aa. 38. (3.)

LEE (W. R.) Original Tables of calculations: from 1 lb. to 10⅛ lbs. pp. 80. *Manch.* 1894. 8°. 8548. b. 37.

SMITH (F.) Tables, memoranda, and calculated results. pp. 258. *Lond.* 1891. *obl.* 32°.
8548. aa. 27.

SMITH (R. H.) Forty-three Tables for the conversion of measurements in different units. pp. 12. *Lond.* 1895. *obl.* 8°. 1879. b. 3.

SOUTH AFRICAN ARITHMETICAL TABLE BOOK. South African Arithmetical Table book. pp. 40. *Cape Town*, 1890. 16°. 8548. aa. 38. (2.)

TABLES. Mathematical Tables. pp. 78. *Glasg.* 1893. 8°. 8533. de. 27.

WATSON (J.) Addition Tables and ready reckoner. pp. 43. *Bedlington*, 1894. 8°. 8531. dd. 28. (14.)

WOODS (R. C. S.) and DAVIES (S. H.) Office Tables. *Manch.* 1891, *etc.* fol. 1882. d. 2. (74.)

Commercial : Interest.

AMATI (L.) Weights, measures and interest Tables. 2 pt. *Milan*, 1891. 8°. 8548. dd. 43.

ANGLO-AMERICAN STOCK EXCHANGE TABLES. Anglo-American Stock Exchange Tables. *Lond.* 1891. 12°. 8548. c. 48.

HARCOURT ( ) Harcourt's Tables. pp. 179. *Birmingham*, 1895. 8°. 8548. aa. 37.

MATHIESON (F. C.) Russian Tables for calculating Russian four per cent. bonds. pp. 91. *Lond.* 1890. 8°. 8548. de. 28.

NYE (C. H.) Tables showing the Dividend on £1 to £100,000 Stock. pp. 51. *Lond.* 1892. *obl.* 8°. 8548. de. 21.

OWENS (S. H.) Method of solving problems in Annuities. pp. 64. *Richmond, Va.,* 1894. 8°.
8548. bbb. 62.

PEREIRE (E.) Tables de l'intérêt composé des annuités et des rentes viagères. pp. 87. *Paris*, 1882. 4°. 8548. g. 27.

REYNOLDS (E. G.) Tables showing values of American dividends. pp. 19. *Lond.* 1893. 4°.
8548. df. 38.

SHILLING BOOK. Shilling book of interest Tables. pp. 312. 6. *Lond.* 1891. 16°.
8548. aaa. 30.

WILHELM (J.) Comprehensive Tables of compound interest. pp. 109. *Lond.* 1893. *obl.* 8°.
8548. aa. 30.

Engineering. *See* ENGINEERING.

Exchange, *Monetary.*

See supra : Commercial : MONEY.

Nautical. *See* NAVIGATION.

TABLES—*continued.*

Wages.

BEETON (S. O.) 53 hours Wages book. pp. 41. *Lond.* 1890. 16°. 8548. b. 38. (3.)

CARNAFFAN (W.) 48 hours Wages book. *Newcastle*, 1892. 8°. 8548. b. 38. (4.)

GARBUTT (T.) Tables of Wages at 54, 52, 50 and 48 hours per week. pp. 73. *Lond.* 1895. 8°.
8548. c. 53.

MITCHELL (E.) Hourly Wages table for Builders, *etc. Lond.* 1894. *obl.* fol. 1882. d. 2. (106.)

RADCLIFFE (E.) "Radcliffe" 53 hours Wages Table. *Manch.* 1892. 4°. 8548. g. 25.

WARD, LOCK AND Co. Eight hours Wages Book. pp. 48. *Lond.* 1893. 16°. 8548. b. 38. (5.)

TACHYCARDIA. *See* HEART.

TACOMA. TACOMA. The New Northwest and Tacoma. pp. 31. *Tacoma*, 1890. 8°.
10460. e. 37. (3.)

TADEMAIT. *See* SAHARA.

TADOUSSAC. ROY (J. E.) In and around Tadousac. pp. 250. *Levis*, 1891. 8°.
10470. aa. 55.

TAFILET. HARRIS (W. B.) Tafilet. Narrative of a journey of exploration. pp. 386. *Edinb.* 1895. 8°. 010096. ee. 47.

TAGAL RACE AND LANGUAGE.
See PHILIPPINE ISLANDS.

TAHITI & THE SOCIETY ISLANDS.

HORT (D.) Tahiti, the Garden of the Pacific. pp. 352. *Lond.* 1891. 8°. 10491. e. 28.

MELVILLE (H.) Omoo. pp. 365. *Lond.* 1892. 8°. 012706. h. 29.

MONCHOISY ( ) La nouvelle Cythère. pp. 339. *Paris*, 1888. 8°. 10491. aaa. 43.

ROUARD DE CARD (E.) L'annexion de Tahiti et de ses dépendances. pp. 28. *Paris*, 1894. 8°.
Pam. 66.

Ac., *etc.* Sydney. *Australian Museum.* Lord Howe Island. pp. 132. *Sydney*, 1889. 8°
7001. b. 10.

See also PACIFIC OCEAN AND ISLANDS.

TAILLEBOURG. Inventaires du Château de Taillebourg. pp. 51. *La Rochelle*, 1890. 8°.
Pam. 3.

TAILORING. CORNWELL (E.) Columbian Tailor system. pp. 22. 24. *Chicago*, 1892. 4°.
7742. ee. 16.

COX (W.) Angular Shoulder Measure system. pp. 15. *Grimsby*, 1892. 8°. 7743. c. 15.

G. B. & I. *Master Tailors' Association.* National Time Log. pp. 108. *Bolton*, 1893. 8°.
7743. b. 28.

GRIFFITHS (T.) The Eureka Trousers' system. *Halifax*, 1893, 4°. 7743. ee. 19.

HAWKINS (T.) Self-teaching-directions for the A. B. C. Tailor system of Dresscutting. pp. 15. *Lond.* 1894. 8°. 1810. d. 1 (46.)

HERZBERG (G.) Das Schneidergewerbe in München. pp. 135. 1894. 8°. BRENTANO (L). Münchener volkswirtschaftliche Studien. Stück 5. 08276. i.

HOLDING (T. H.) Cutter's Difficulties. pp. 90. *Lond.* 1887. 8°. 7742. b. 16.

—— Cutting for Stout Men. pp. 24. *Lond.* 1892. 8°. 7743. e. 2.

—— Trousers cutting. pp. 67. *Lond,* 1892, 4°.
7742. ee. 14.

KIRKHOPE (G.) Draper's and Tailor's Measurement Book. pp. 132. *Lond.* 1894. 8°.
8548. bbb. 61.

MORENO PÉREZ (G.) Morenómetro. Tratado de corte de vestidos. 2 pt. *Madrid*, 1891. 8°.
7743. bbb. 64.

TAILORING—*continued*.

NEBELING (A.) The Mastership-System. Nouvelle méthode de coupe américaine.
Brux. 1894, *etc.* fol.   7743. i.

P.P. *Sheffield*. Cutter's Gazette of fashion.
Sheffield, 1893, *etc.* 4°.   N.R.

THORNTON (J. P.) Sectional system of gentlemen's garment cutting. pp. 164.
Lond. 1895. 4°.   7743. g. 22.

TOMLIN (J.) Bond Street systems of Cutting.
pp. 77. *Lond.* 1893. 4°.   7743. bbb. 65.

VINCENT (W. D. F.) Cutter's Practical Guide.
6 pt. *Lond.* 1890–95. 4°.   7743. e. 24.
See also COSTUME : DRESS.

TAITA LANGUAGE. *See* AFRICAN LANGUAGES.

TALCAHUANO. FAGALDE (A.) El Puerto de Talcahuano. pp. 180.
Santiago de C. 1895, 8°.   8777. d. 38.

TALMUD. *See* JEWS, *Religion*.

TAMIL LANGUAGE. ANKETELL (C. P.)
English-Tamil Dictionary. pp. 332.
Madras, 1888. 16°.   12907. aa. 66.

LINCOLN (J. H.) English-Tamil Vocabulary.
pp. 87. *Singapore*, 1895. 8°.   12910. aa. 73.

PERCIVAL (P.) Dictionary of English and Tamil.
pp. 492. *Madras*, 1893. 8°.   12907. b. 45.

VISVANĀTHA PILLAI, V. Dictionary, Tamil and English. pp. 735. *Madras*, 1888. 8°.
        12906. dd. 36.

APPĀSĀMI PILLAI. The Translation Guide, English and Tamil. pp. 200. *Madras*, 1890. 8°.
        14172. h. 85.

——— Anglo-Tamil Manual. pp. 244.
Madras, 1893. 8°.   14172. hh. 8.

ARDEN (A. H.) Progressive grammar of common Tamil. pp. 190. *Madras*, 1891. 8°.   12907. c. 37.

——— Companion reader to Arden's Tamil grammar. *Madras*,1893, *etc.* 8°.   12907. c. 38.

FERGUSON (A. M.) "Iñgē Vā !" pp. 156.
Colombo, 1892. 12°.   12907. aaa. 54.

MIṆĀKSHISUNDRAM PILLAI. Student's Guide to Translation [Tamil-English]. pp. 109.
Madras, 1890. 8°.   14172. h. 89.

MUTTUKRISHNAYYA NĀYADU. Anglo-Tamil self-reader. *Madras*, 1892, *etc.* 8°.   14172. h. 83.

PETER (J. S.) Tamil grammar simplified. pp. 68.
Madras, 1892. 16°.   Pam. 49.

POPE (G. U.) First lessons in Tamil. pp. 265.
Oxf. 1891. 8°.   12906. bbb. 31.

——— First Catechism of Tamil Grammar. pp. 39.
Oxf. 1895. 8°.   12907. aaa. 58.

NĀLADIYĀR. The Naladya, with commentary and translation. pp. 290. *Madras*, 1892. 8°.
        14172. b. 45.

——— The Nāladiyār, with translation and notes, by G. U. Pope. pp. 440. *Oxf.* 1893. 8°.
        14172. d. 12.

LAZARUS (J.) Dictionary of Tamil proverbs.
pp. 662. *Madras*, 1894. 8°.   14170. k. 76.

TAMIL PROVERBS. Tamil Proverbs with English equivalents. pp. 12. *Madras*, 1893. 8°.
        14170. k. 58.

ŚIVAŚAŃKARA PANDYA. The Tamil juvenile moral Instructor. pp. 48. 1889. 12°. Hindu Excelsior Series. No. 11.   14003. c.

TAMWORTH. TAMWORTH. *Saint James' College*. Account of S. James' College. pp. 8.
Lond. 1885. 12°.   4707. a. 19.

TANGA. *See* AFRICA, *Colonisation, German*.

TANGANYIKA, Lake. *See* AFRICA, *Central and East*.

TANGIER. REEVES (E.) Homeward Bound after thirty Years. pp. 337. *Lond.* 1892. 8°.
        10024. g. 10.

STODDARD (C. A.) Spanish cities ; with glimpses of Tangier. pp. 228. *Lond.* 1892. 8°.
        10161. de. 26.
See also MOROCCO.

TANIS. *See* EGYPT, *Antiquities*.

TANNIN. TRIMBLE (H.) The Tannins.
Phila. 1892, *etc.* 8°.   07945. h. 35.

TANNING. *See* LEATHER.

TAOISM. *See* CHINA, *Religious*.

TAORMINA. STEFANO (G. di) Guida geologica di Taormina. 1891. 8°. Ac. Rome.
Società Geologica. Bollettino. Vol. 10. Ac. 3104.

TAPESTRY. Ac. London. *South Kensington Museum*. Supplemental descriptive catalogue of Tapestry-woven Specimens. pp. 49.
Lond. 1891. 8°.   Pam. 18.

——— Supplemental descriptive catalogue of Tapestry-woven Egyptian textiles. pp. 57.
Lond. 1891. 8°.   7958. d. 9.

ANDERSON (J. E.) Account of the Tapestry Works, Mortlake. pp. 20. *Richmond*. 1894. 8°.
        07944. g. 8.

BOSTON, *Mass., Museum*. Catalogue of an exhibition of Tapestries. pp. 46. *Bost.* 1893. 8°.
        7807. e. 30. (12.)

CHAMPEAUX (A. de) Les Arts du Tissu. pp. 144.
Paris, 1892. 8°.   7944. h. 33.

FRANCE. *Ministère de l'Instruction*. Inventaires relatifs aux tapisseries des Princes d'Orléans-Valois 1389–1481. pp. 221. *Paris*, 1894. 8°.
        7709. bbb. 41.

GENTILI (P.) Sulla conservazione degli Arazzi.
pp. 36. *Roma*, 1886. 4°.   7943. k. 30. (4.)

GERSPACH (É.) Répertoire des Tapisseries des Gobelins, 1662–1892. pp. 250. *Paris*. 1893. 8°.
        7805. de. 22.

GERSPACH ( ) Les Tapisseries coptes.
Paris, 1890. 4°.   7743. f. 25.

GUIFFREY (J. J.) Les Manufactures parisiennes de Tapisseries au XVIIe siècle. 1892. 8°. Ac.
Paris. *Société de l'Histoire*. Mémoires. Tom. 19.
        Ac. 6883/2.

HAVARD (H.) La Tapisserie. pp. 198.
Paris, 1893. 8°.   7942. f.

MÜNTZ (E.) Rapport de la Commission de la Manufacture des Gobelins. *Paris*, 1890. 8°.
        Pam. 24.

——— Tapisseries, broderies et dentelles. pp. 43.
Paris, 1890. 4°.   7743. g. 17.

PÉRATHON (C.) Essai de catalogue des anciennes Tapisseries d'Aubusson et de Felletin. pp. 124.
Limoges, 1894. 8°.   7742. d. 23.

PERROSSIER (C.) Les Tapisseries de l'Église de Romans. pp. 22. *Valence*, 1891. 8°.
        7808. e. 20. (5.)

RISCHGITZ (É.) Handbook on Tapestry painting with indelible colours. pp. 46.
Lond. 1883. 16°.   7854. aa. 18.

SOIL (E.) Les Tapisseries de Tournai. pp. 460.
1891. 8°. Tournay. *Société historique*. Mémoires. Tom. 22.   Ac. 7600/2.
See also ART, *Decorative :* TEXTILE FABRICS.

Bayeux Tapestry.

FERNANDEZ DURO (C.) La tapiceria de Bayeux.
pp. 22. *Madrid*, 1894. 8°.   Pam. 24.

KING (A. J.) The Bayeux Tapestry. pp. 48.
Belfast, 1881. 8°.   07703. f. 3. (5.)

TAPE-WORMS. *See* PARASITES.

TARANTAISE. RULLIER (J. L.) Le Pays des Centrons. pp 103. *Moutiers*, 1891. 8°.
        09171. f. 35.

TARANTO. Valente (A.) Molle Tarentum.
pp. 129. *Taranto*, 1893. 8°. 10132. c. 6.

TARASCON. Bondurant (É.) Les Coutumes
de Tarascon. 1892. 8°. Ac. Nîmes. *Académie.*
Mémoires. Sér. 7. Tom. 14. Ac. 330/2.

TARAWERA.
See New Zealand : Volcanoes.

TARDINGEN. Debout (H.) Tardingen et
les sépultures sous dalles. pp. 63.
Arras, 1894. 8°. 7705. ee. 33.

TARIFFS. *See* Trade and Finance ; and
under the subheading *Trade* of each country.

TARN, *River.* Solanet ( ) Les Gorges du
Tarn illustrées. pp. 407. *Paris*, 1894. 8°.
10172. h. 4.

TARO, *River.* Bianchedi (C.) Il Taro e le
sue alluvioni. pp. 44. *Parma*, 1892. 8°.
8709. c. 10. (9.)

TAROT. *See* Occult Science.

TARRAGONA. Cuatro Torres (de las)
Baron. El Blasón de Tarragona. pp. 30.
Barcelona, 1891. 8°. 9903. h. 10.

Morera y Llauradó (E.) Tarragona antigua y
moderna. pp. 247. *Tarragona*, 1894. 8°.
10136. h. 15.

TARRANT CRAWFORD. Highton (E.)
The last Resting-Place of a Scottish Queen,
Joan, and a Bishop, R. Poore. pp. 8.
Edinb. 1894. 4°. Pam. 90.

TARTARS. Parker (E. H.) A thousand years
of the Tatars. pp. 372. *Lond.* 1895. 8°.
9055. d. 30.

TASMANIA.

Aborigines.

Etheridge (R.) Contributions to a catalogue of
works on the Tasmanian Aborigines. 1890, *etc.* 4°.
New South Wales. *Geological Survey.* Memoirs.
Palæontology. No. 8, *etc.* 7203. h.

Roth (H. L.) The Aborigines of Tasmania.
pp. 224. *Lond.* 1890. 8°. 10492. f. 32.

History and Topography.

Crozet ( ) Crozet's Voyage to Tasmania,
1771–72. pp. 148. *Lond* 1891. 8°. 10492. e. 15.

White (C.) Convict life in Van Diemen's Land.
pp. 579. *Bathurst*, 1889. 8°. 6057. b. 30.

Nowell (E. C.) History of the relations between
the two Houses of Parliament in Tasmania, *etc.*
pp. 158. *Hobart*, 1890. 8°. 8154. c. 2.

Cabby. Notorious Bushrangers of Tasmania.
pp. 166. *Launceston*, 1891. 8°. 6057. a. 33.

Just (T. C.) Official Handbook of Tasmania.
pp. 144. *Lond.* 1892. 8°. 10492. bb. 40.

Lyde (L. W.) Elementary Geography of Tasmania. pp. 92. *Lond.* 1892. 8°. 10492. aa. 20.

Moosafir. North-West Coast of Tasmania.
pp. 31. *Melbourne*, 1889. 8°. Pam. 87.

Tasmania. The Immigrant's prospects in Tas-
mania. pp. 26. *Lond.* 1883. 8°. Pam. 87.
—— *Ministry of Lands.* Crown lands guide.
pp. 64. *Hobart*, 1891. 8°. Pam. 87.
—— Handbook of Tasmania, 1892, *etc.*
Hobart, 1892, *etc.* 8°. 10492. dd.

Twamley, *afterwards* Meredith (L. A.) Bush
Friends in Tasmania. pp. 76. *Lond.* 1891. fol.
7028. h. 14.

Dio. Maria Island. pp. 48. *Hobart*, 1889. 8°.
Pam. 87.

See also Australia.

TATRA MOUNTAINS.
See Carpathian Mountains.

TATTERSHALL. Pickworth (M. A.) History of Tattershall. pp. 70. *Lincoln*, 1891. 8°.
10352. cc. 43.

TATTOOING. Bailliot (M.) Du Déta-
touage. pp. 41. *Paris*, 1894. 8°.
7306. h. 15. (5.)

Verrier (E.) Du tatouage en Afrique. pp. 30.
Paris, 1895. 8°. 10007. bbb. 27.

TAUNTON, Massachusetts. Taunton,
Mass. Quarter millenial celebration of Taunton.
pp. 426. *Taunton*, 1889. 8°. 10409. d. 24.

TAUNTON, Somerset. Stone (J. M.)
Faithful unto Death. History of the Franciscan
convent at Taunton. pp. 260. *Lond.* 1892. 8°.
4707. cc. 11.

Taunton. Where to buy at Taunton. pp. 54.
Brighton, 1890. 4°. 10368. k. 37.

TAUNUS. Andreae (E. C. A.) Die Geschichte der Jagd im Taunus. pp. 423.
Frankfurt, 1894. 8°. 07905. h. 23.

Sievers (W.) Zur Kenntnis des Taunus. pp. 55.
1891. 8°. Lehmann (R.) Forschungen. Bd. 5.
10235. i. 10.

TAVISTOCK, Abbey. Alford (D. P.) The
Abbots of Tavistock. pp. 364.
Plymouth, 1891. 8°. 4707. aaaa. 25.

TAXATION. *See* Trade and Finance.

**TAXIDERMY : ARRANGEMENT OF
NATURAL HISTORY COLLEC-
TIONS, etc.** Allen (G.) The Taxidermist's
Manual. pp. 64. *N.Y.* 1890. 8°.
07944. ee. 4. (7.)

Gestro (R.) Manuale dell' Imbalsamatore, pre-
paratore tassidermista, *etc.* pp. 148.
Milano, 1892. 8°. 012200. h. 78.

Granger (A.) Manuel du Naturaliste. pp. 326.
Paris, 1894. 8°. 7005. aaa. 24.

Hornaday (W. T.) Taxidermy and zoological
collecting. pp. 362. *Lond.* 1891. 8°.
7206. i. 14.

Murray (J. A.) Syllabus of practical Taxidermy.
pp. 13. *Bombay*, 1891. 8°. 7206. h. 19.

Ward (R.) The Sportsman's handbook. pp. 192.
Lond. 1894. 8°. 7206. e. 18.

TCHAD, Lake. Alis (H) À la Conquête
du Tchad. pp. 296. *Paris*, 1891. 8°.
010096. m. 12.

Béhagle (F. de) Projet de voyage commercial
du Congo à la Méditerranée par le Tchad.
pp. 16. *Paris*, 1895. 8°. Pam. 89.

Brunache (P.) Autour du Tchad. pp. 340.
Paris, 1894. 8°. 8708. cc.

Daglan (P.) La délimitation franco-allemande
dans la région du lac Tchad. pp. 8.
Paris, 1894. 8°. Pam. 67.

Fock (A.) Algérie, Sahara, Tchad. pp. 75.
Paris, 1891. 8°. 8155. ee. 11.

Monteil (P. L.) De Saint-Louis à Tripoli par
le lac Tchad. pp. 462. *Paris*, 1895. 4°.
1786. d. 1.

TEA. Ceylon. Tea Cultivation in Ceylon.
pp. 44. *Colombo*, 1894. 16°. Pam. 1.

Campbell (A.) Dehra Doon Tea Company.
pp. 25. *Pokpuria, Manbhum*, 1894. 8° Pam. 23.

De Rosthorn (A.) On the Tea Cultivation in
Western Ssüch'uan. pp. 40. *Lond.* 1895. 8°.
Pam. 1.

Henderson (J. A.) Account of Tea cultivation
in Ceylon. pp. 38. *Colombo*, 1893. 8°. Pam. 1.

Kandy. Ceylon Tea Fund. Report of the Committee. *Kandy*, 1891, *etc.* 8°. 08227. e.

Money (E.) The Tea Controversy. Indian
versus Chinese Teas. pp. 16. *Lond.* 1884. 8°.
7073. de. 13. (2.)

TEA—*continued.*

OWEN (T. C.) Tea Planting in Ceylon. *Colombo*, 1891. *obl.* 16°. 7078. aa. 17.

PLANTER. Notes on Tea in Darjeeling. pp. 102. *Darjeeling*, 1888. 16°. 7943. a. 60.

STANTON (A. G.) Report on British-grown Tea. pp. 22. *Lond.* 1887. 8°. Pam. 1.

WALSH (J. M.) Tea. Its history and mystery. pp. 265. *Phila.* 1892. 8°. 07077. e. 3. *See also* CAFFEINE.

TEBESSA. BALLU (A.) Monuments antiques de Tébessa, Lambèse, Timgad. pp. 39. *Paris*, 1894. 8°. 07708. f. 44.

SÉRIZIAT (C. V. É.) Études sur Tébessa. 3 pt. *Bône*, 1887. 8°. 010096. m. 7.

TECHNOLOGY.

See EDUCATION, *Technical:* INDUSTRIES.

TEETH : DENTISTRY. BALKWILL (F. H.) Testimony of the Teeth to Man's place in nature. pp. 240. *Lond.* 1893. 8°. 7006. e. 17.

BRIGGS (F. H.) and (H. F.) Advanced Scientific Dentistry. pp. 18. 1893. 8°. 7611. aaaa. 7.

BRYAN (L. C.) Dental Ledger and register. pp. 503. *Lond.* 1892. 4°. 7611. g. 31.

BULKLEY (L. D.) On Dangers arising from Syphilis in the Practice of Dentistry. pp. 16. *N.Y.* 1890. 8°. 07305. h. 9. (3.)

CLIFFORD (H.) Domestic Dentistry and self-aid. pp. 46. *Dublin*, 1891. 8°. 7306. df. 16. (5.)

COLLINS (W. J.) Associated and related ocular and dental Diseases, *etc.* pp. 23. *Lond.* 1891. 8°. Pam. 39.

CUNNINGHAM (G.) Defective personal hygiene as it affects the teeth. pp. 24. *Lond.* 1894. 8°. 7306. e. 25. (5.)

DITCHAM (V.) Our Teeth : care and preservation. pp. 52. *Lond.* 1895. 8°. 7610. aaaa. 1.

ESTABROOK (C. E.) Intelligent care of the Teeth. pp. 21. *Halifax*, 1892. 8°. 07305. f. 17. (3.)

FEUER (N.) Relation between affections of the Teeth and of the eyes. pp. 53. *Lond.* 1894. 8°. Pam. 39.

FORSHAW (C. F.) Hints to parents on the management of their children's Teeth. pp. 12. *Bradford*, 1889. 8°. Pam. 39.

GODON (C. H.) and RONNET (A.) L'Art dentaire aux Etats-Unis en 1893. pp. 138. *Paris*, 1894. 8°. 7610. cc. 4.

GORHAM (J.) Tooth Extraction. pp. 43. *Lond.* 1893. 8°. 7610. a. 3.

HASKELL (L. P.) Student's Manual for the dental Laboratory. pp. 97. *Phila.* 1890. 8°. 7611. d. 8.

HEWITT (F. W.) An inquiry concerning the safety of Chloroform in dental surgery. pp. 32. *Lond.* 1895. 8°. Pam. 39.

HUNTER (C.) Manual of the dental Laboratory. pp. 171. *Lond.* 1892. 8°. 7611. c. 3.

LA GRANGE (B. J.) Manual of Dentistry. pp. 63. *Brussels*, 1895. 8°. 7611. aaaa. 19.

LECHE (W.) Zur Entwicklungsgeschichte des Zahnsystems der Säugethiere. 1895, *etc.* 4°. LEUCKART (R.) Bibliotheca Zoologica. Hft. 17. 7205. f.

METNITZ (J. v.) Lehrbuch der Zahnheilkunde. pp. 375. *Wien*, 1891. 8°. 7610. g. 4.

MILLER (W. D.) Einleitung zum Studium der Bacterio-Pathologie der Zahnpulpa. 1894. 8°. Ac. Berlin. *Odontologische Gesellschaft.* Verhandlungen. Bd. 6. Ac. 3774.

OTTOLENGUI (R.) Methods of filling Teeth. pp. 200. *Phila.* 1892. 8°. 7610. g. 9.

TEETH, etc.—*continued.*

PEDLEY (R. D.) Diseases of children's Teeth. pp. 268. *Lond.* 1895. 8°. 7611. dd. 1.

P.P. *Chicago.* The Dental Tribune. *Chicago*, 1892, *etc.* 8°. P.P. 3259. eb.

—— *London.* Dental patients. *Lond.* 1892, *etc.* 4°. 1677.

QUINBY (H. C.) Notes on dental Practice. pp. 216. *Lond.* 1892. 8°. 7610. g. 6.

RICHARDSON (J.) Practical treatise on mechanical Dentistry. pp. 662. *Lond.* 1893. 8°. 7611. d. 6.

RYMER (J. F.) Note-book for dental Students. pp. 67. *Lond.* 1892. 8°. 7611. aaaa. 4.

SCHEFF (J.) Die Replantation der Zähne. pp. 104. *Wien*, 1890. 8°. 7611. g. 26.

SEWILL (H.) The dental Profession. pp. 36. *Lond.* 1893. 8°. 07305. h. 16. (16.)

SMALE (M. A.) and COLYER (J. F.) Diseases and injuries of the Teeth. pp. 423. *Lond.* 1893. 8°. 7611. cc. 6.

STOCKEN (J.) Dental Materia Medica and therapeutics. pp. 155. *Lond.* 1895. 8°. 7510. df. 29.

TOMES (C. S.) Manual of dental Anatomy. pp. 559. *Lond.* 1894. 8°. 7611. cc. 8.

TOUCHARD (F.) L'Enseignement de l'art dentaire en Angleterre. pp. 67. *Paris*, 1893. 8°. 7610. ee. 39.

TURNER (A.) Manual of dental Education. pp. 72. *Edinb.* 1890. 8°. 7321. aaa. 22. (1.)

UNDERWOOD (A. S.) Aids to dental Histology. pp. 80. *Lond.* 1892. 8°. 7611. c. 2.

—— Notes on Anaesthetics in dental surgery. pp. 166. *Lond.* 1893. 8°. 7442. aa. 16.

WALKHOFF (O.) Die Unregelmaessigkeiten in den Zahnstellungen und ihre Behandlung. pp. 130. *Leipz.* 1891. 8°. 7611. g. 29. *See also* JAW : MOUTH.

TEIGNMOUTH. TEIGNMOUTH GUIDE. Teignmouth guide. pp. 56. *Teignmouth*, 1893. 8°. 10358. g. 44.

TELEGRAPHY.

General.

BAR (L. v.) Das Gesetz über das Telegraphenwesen des Reiches. pp. 35. *Berl.* 1892. 8°. 5604. e. 1. (5.)

BOUSSAC (A.) Construction des lignes électriques aériennes. pp. 313. *Paris*, 1894. 8°. 8757. k. 10.

BUGGE (J. U. F.) Den norske Statstelegrafs Grundlæggelse. pp. 376. *Christiania*, 1890. 8°. 08235. h. 21.

COPENHAGEN. *Store Nordiske Telegraf-Selskab.* 1869–94. Det store Nordiske Telegraf-Selskab. pp. 282. *Kjøbenh.* 1894. 4°. 8757. l. 18.

DAVIES (C. L.) Une explication du Phonopore, se rapportant plus spécialement au Télégraphe. pp. 68. *Londres*, 1891. 4°. 8756. eee. 15.

DEARLOVE (A.) Tables to find the working speed of Cables. pp. 20. *Lond.* 1890. *obl.* 16°. 8548. aa. 22.

HOUSTON (E. J.) Electric Transmission of Intelligence. pp. 330. *N.Y.* 1893. 8°. 8758. b. 8.

ISTRUZIONE. Istruzione sulla telegrafia elettrica. 2 pt. *Roma*, 1891. 8°. 8757. aaa. 58.

JAMES (C. S.) The "Morse" Signaller's Companion. pp. 41. *Nürnberg*, 1894. fol. 8757. m. 6.

JAPAN. *Imperial Telegraphs.* Service regulations applicable to Telegraph Correspondence. pp. 42. *Tokio*, 1885. 8°. 11099. a. 8.

KEASBEY (E. L.) Law of electric wires in streets, *etc.* pp. 190. *Chicago*, 1892. 8°. 6617. aaa. 13.

TELEGRAPHY.—General—_continued._

MUNIER (J.) Le télégraphe imprimeur J. Munier. pp. 72. _Paris_, 1892. 8°. 8755. dd. 32. (6.)

OAKSHOTT (A.) Answers to the technical Telegraphy questions prescribed by the Engineer-in-chief to officers in the P.O. Telegraph Dept. pp. 40. _Bristol_, 1894. 8°. 8757. a. 53.

P.P. _London._ The Telegraph Journal. Vol. 1–4. _Lond._ 1889–93. 8°. P.P. 1607. dd.

POPE (F. L.) Modern practice of the Electric Telegraph. pp. 234. _N.Y._ 1891. 8°. 8757. g. 32.

PREECE (W. H.) and SIVEWRIGHT (_Sir_ J.) Telegraphy. pp. 417. 1895. 8°. GOODEVE (T. M.) Text-books of Science. 2244. a. 19.

THOM (C.) and JONES (W. H.) Telegraphic Connections. pp. 59. _N.Y._ 1892. _obl._ 8°. 8757. a. 40.

THOMAS (H.) Traité de télégraphie électrique. pp. 911. _Paris_, 1894. 8°. 8757. k. 8.

WEBB (H. L.) Guide to the testing of insulated Wires and Cables. pp. 118. _N.Y._ 1891. 8°. 8757. cc. 21.

WEILLER (L.) and VIVAREZ (H.) Traité des lignes et transmissions électriques. pp. 828. _Paris_, 1892. 8°. 8757. h. 18.

CARLSON (V.) Maritime Telegraph System. _Stockholm_, 1890. 4°. 8805. g. 32.

SILVERTOWN. _India Rubber and Telegraph Works Company._ Soundings taken by the Company. 2 pt. _Lond._ 1895. 8°. 8758. d. 3.

SMITH (W.) Rise and extension of Submarine Telegraphy. pp. 390. _Lond._ 1891. 8°. 8756. eee. 17.

TRAVERS (A.) Vocabulaire télégraphique anglais-français et français-anglais. pp. 346. _Paris_, 1894. 8°. 8247. aaa. 41. _See also_ ELECTRICITY, _Applications_: HELIOGRAPH.

History.

MUNRO (J.) Heroes of the Telegraph. pp. 288. _Lond._ 1891. 8°. 4429. ee. 14.

GAUTIER (F.) Centenaire de la Télégraphie. pp. 81. _Paris_, 1893. 8°. 8757. e. 17.

SIME (J.) Sir F. Ronalds and his work in connection with telegraphy in 1816. pp. 12. _Lond._ 1893. 8°. Pam. 7.

COOKE (_Sir_ W. F.) Extracts from the letters of Sir W. F. Cooke, 1836–39, relating to the invention of the Electric Telegraph. pp. 95. _Lond._ 1895. 8°. 8758. ccc. 4.

SIEMENS (W. v.) Personal Recollections of W. von Siemens. pp. 416. _Lond._ 1893. 8°. 010707. ee. 14.

Military Telegraphy. _See_ MILITARY SCIENCE.

Telegraph Codes.

AGER (G.) Social Code, 1885. pp. 224. _Lond._ 1885. 8°. 8756. ccc. 30.

—— Simplex Standard Telegram Code. pp. 824. _Lond._ 1893. 4°. 8756. ccc. 28.

—— A Y Z Telegram Code. pp. 520. _Lond._ 1895. 8°. 8757. dd. 26.

BERNE. _International Telegraph Office._ Official vocabulary for Telegrams in preconcerted language. pp. 856. _Berne_, 1894. 4°. 8757. m. 7.

BLACKBURN (A. H.) and STEVENS (J.) Engineering Telegraph Code for Engineers, Contractors, Manufacturers, _etc._ pp. 740. _Lond._ 1892. 4°. 8756. eee. 20.

BROCKES (J.) Series Book. _Manch._ 1893. fol. 1882. d. 2. (88.)

BUREAU INTERNATIONAL DES ADMINISTRATIONS TÉLÉGRAPHIQUES. Vocabulaire official pour la rédaction des télégrammes en langage convenu. pp. 856. _Berne._ 1894. 4°. 8756. f. 42.

TELEGRAPHY. — Telegraph Codes — _continued._

BURKHARD (A.) Tables and Code. Bradford Yarns, _etc._ _Lond._ 1894. 8°. 8548. b. 34.

CLARE (W. E.) Telegraph Code for Black Sea to Mediterranean Trade. pp. 21. _Lond._ 1894. 4°. 8756. g. 31.

COHEN (G.) "Ironscrap" Telegraph Code. pp. 136. _Lond._ 1891. fol. 8756. eee. 14.

DAVID (M.) Private Telegraph Code. pp. 36. _Penang_, 1891. 8°. 8757. dd. 20.

EWART'S CHAIN MANUFACTURING CO. Cable Code. 1893. pp. 166. _Birmingham_, 1894. 8°. 8756. ccc. 28.

GILBURT (E. B.) Tourists' Telegraphic Code. pp. 45. 1892. 32°. Pam. 48.

GLOVER BROTHERS. Telegraph Code for the use of captains, _etc._ pp. 66. _Lond._ 1891. 8°. 8756. de. 40.

GRIMSDITCH (F. J. D.) European-American Tables, adapted for use in the Cotton Trade. _Liverp._ 1894. 4°. 8756. ere. 30.

HOWARD AND JONES. Improved Telegraphic Code. pp. 160. _Lond._ 1891. _obl._ fol. 8752. bb. 6.

JAPAN. _Imperial Government Telegraphs._ Telegraph Code. (Notification No. 8.) pp. 20. _Tokio_, 1885. 8°. 11099. a. 9.

LOW (E. H.) Pocket Cable Code adapted for American travellers. pp. 214. _N.Y._ 1891. 16°. 8757. a. 29.

MAC NEILL (B.) McNeill's Code. pp. 807. _Lond._ 1893. 8°. 8757. k. 3.

MERCURY-CODE. Mercuur-Code. _Dutch & Eng._ pp. 1327. _Amsterd._ 1891. 4°. 8757. k. 2.

MEYER (H. R.) Atlantic Cotton Code. pp. 548. _Liverp._ 1895. 8°. 8757. i. 27.

—— Anglo - International Code for Bankers, Merchants, _etc._ pp. 392. _Lond._ 1885. 4°. 8757. k. 12.

MOREING (C. A.) and NEAL (T.) New general and Mining Telegraph Code. pp. 676. _Lond._ 1891. 8°. 8756. de. 39.

PELLIGERO (G.) Clave para obtener secreto y economía en toda clase de correspondencia. _Madrid_, 1893. _obl._ 8°. 8756. a. 39.

PENNY (R.) Cipher Code. _Lond._ 1894. 8°. 8756. cc. 40.

PROCTOR (R.) Private Telegraphic Code. pp. 216. _Liverp._ 1891. _obl._ 4°. 8756. eee. 18.

RICHARDSON, FINDLAY & CO. General Code. pp. 644. _Glasg._ 1890. fol. 8755. m. 13.

ROBINSON (T. H.) Insurance and maritime Telegraphic Code. pp. 901. _Lond._ 1892. 8°. 8757. f. 25.

SCOTT (E. B.) "Scott's Code." pp. 23. _Lond._ 1892. 8°. 8757. cc. 26.

SEDGWICK (H. B.) Private Telegraphic Code. pp. 47. _Lond._ 1892. 8°. 8756. de. 45.

SIMSON (E. C.) Code télégraphique. pp. 93. _Anvers_, 1893. 8°. 8757. a. 43.

SPICER (J.) AND SONS. Private Telegraph Code for the continent. 1895. 8°. 8755. dd. 7. (15.)

THAMES AND MERSEY MARINE INSURANCE COMPANY. Private Telegraphic Code for the Company. pp. 173. _Manch._ 1891. fol. 8753. b 2.

THOMAS AND SHORT. The "Shortener" code. pp. 231. _Lond._ 1894. 8°. 8757. a. 49.

TELEPATHY. GURNEY (E.) Telepathie, Eine Erwiderung auf die Kritik des Herrn W. Preyer. pp. 63. _Leipz._ 1887. 8°. 8632. g. 25. (1.)

LAZARE (B.) La Télépathie et le neo spiritualisme. pp. 36. _Paris_, 1893. 8°. Pam. 36.

TELEPATHY—continued.

P.P. *London.* Borderland. Edited by W. T. Stead. *Lond.* 1893, *etc.* 4°. P.P. 636. cl.

—— *Paris.* Annales des Sciences psychiques. *Paris,* 1891, *etc.* 8°. P.P. 597. ge.

PODMORE (F.) Apparitions and Thought-transference. pp. 401. 1894. 8°. Contemporary Science Series. Vol. 26. 8709. i.

See also OCCULT SCIENCE.

TELEPHONE. ALLSOP (F. C.) Telephones: their construction and fitting. pp. 256 *Lond.* 1892. 8°. 8757. aaaa. 50.

BENNETT (A. R.) Municipal Telephony. pp. 34. *Manch.* 1895. 8°. Pam. 79.

—— On the Telephoning of great cities. 2 pt. *Lond.* 1892. 8°. 8757. cc. 25.

—— Telephone systems of Europe. pp. 436. *Lond.* 1895. 8°. 8758. ccc. 5.

—— Report on Telephone systems of Scandinavia. pp. 44. *Lond.* 1892. 8°. Pam. 79.

CARY (G. H.) How to make and use the Telephone. pp. 117. *Lynn, Mass.* 1894. 8°. 8758. bb. 4.

COLDBROOK (W.) Invention of the Telephone predicted in the Book of Revelation. pp. 15. *Lond.* 1891. 8°. 3187. aaa. 6. (5.)

HOUSTON (E. J.) Electric transmission of Intelligence. pp. 330. *N.Y.* 1893. 8°. 8758. b. 8.

HUGHES (N.) Magneto Hand Telephone. pp. 8. *N.Y.* 1894. 8°. 8757. a. 50.

KEENAN (W. J.) and RILEY (J.) The Transmitted Word. pp. 113. *Bost.* 1893. 8°. 8756. aaa. 56.

LANGDON-DAVIES (C.) Explication du Phonophore. *Fr.* and *Eng.* pp. 68. *Lond.* 1891. 4°. 8757. l. 8.

LONDON. *Telephone Company.* Telephone Company's Coupon. 1891. *obl.* 16°. 8756. a. 35.

—— List of Subscribers. 1893, *etc.* 8°. 8754. c.

MONTILLOT (L.) Téléphonie pratique. pp. 502. *Paris,* 1893. 8°. 8757. h. 21.

PASCOLATO (A.) Il Telefono alla Camera dei deputati. pp. 25. *Firenze,* 1890. 8°. 08227. ee. 45. (10.)

PIÉRARD (É.) La Téléphonie. pp. 372. *Liège,* 1894. 8°. 8757. dd. 23.

POOLE (J.) Practical Telephone handbook. pp. 347. *Lond.* 1895. 8°. 8758. b. 11.

PREECE (W. H.) and MAIER (J.) Le Téléphone. pp. 421. *Paris,* 1891. 8°. 8757. i. 15.

—— and STUBBS (A. J.) Manual of Telephony. pp. 508. 1893. 8°. Specialist's Series. 8708. k.

STERNE (S.) Speech in favour of Bill limiting telephone charges. pp. 20. *N.Y.* 1889. 8°. 8227 bbb. 69.

—— The Telephone Bill 1895. pp. 22. *Wash.* 1895. 8°. 8227. d. 68.

See also ELECTRICITY.

TELESCOPE. COOKE (T.) AND SONS. On the adjustment of Telescopic Objectives. pp. 49. *York,* 1891. 8°. 8176. aaa. 37.

GIBSON (F. M.) Amateur Telescopist's handbook. pp. 163. *Lond.* 1894. 8°. 8563. aa. 33.

NELZON (E. M.) Theory of Telescopic Vision. pp. 24. *Lond.* 1893. 8°. 8716. cc. 38.

PICKERING (E. C.) A Large southern Telescope. pp. 3. *Camb., Mass.* 1892. 4°. Pam. 4.

STREHL (C.) Theorie des Fernrohrs auf Grund der Beugung des Lichts. *Leipz.* 1894, *etc.* 8°. 8715. i.

See also ASTRONOMY : OPTICS.

TELL-EL-AMARNA. *See* EGYPT, *Antiquities.*

TELL-EL-AMARNA TABLETS. *See* ASSYRIA, *Inscriptions :* EGYPT, *History.*

TELL-EL-HESY. *See* PALESTINE, *Antiquities.*

TELL-EL-YAHUDIYEH. *See* EGYPT, *Antiquities.*

TELUGU LANGUAGE. ENGLISH-TELUGU VOCABULARY. English-Telugu Vocabulary. pp. 132. *Madras,* 1893. 12°. 12910. cc. 19.

RAJAGOPĀLA SETTI. Telugu, Canarese, and Hindustani vocabulary in Canarese Character. Pt. 3. pp. 62. *Bellary,* 1887. 8°. 760. e. 9.

ŚAṄKARANĀRĀYANA. English-Telugu dictionary. pp. 726. *Madras,* 1894. 8° 12907. bb. 45.

ANGLO-TELUGU READERS. Vade Mecum of all Anglo-Telugu Readers. pp. 100. *Madras,* 1892. 8°. 14174. n. 25.

APPASĀMI PIḶḶAI. Translation guide or exercises, English and Telugu. *Madras,* 1894, *etc.* 8°. 14174. n. 23.

TEMISCONATA, Quebec. GAUVREAU (C. A.) Nos paroisses. 2 tom. *Levis,* 1889–90. 8°. 10470. aa. 45. 46.

TEMPERAMENT. CHADWICK (F. E.) Temperament, disease and health. pp. 85. *N.Y.* 1892. 8°. 7391. de. 6.

STEWART (A.) Our Temperaments. pp. 412. *Lond.* 1892. 8°. 7410. ee. 36.

TEMPERANCE. ABBEY (J.) Temperance in the hay and harvest Field. pp. 12. *Lond.* 1892. 8°. 8435. e. 24. (14.)

AXON (W. E. A.) Claims of the Temperance movement upon the educated classes. pp. 11. *Manch.* 1889. 8°. 8436. e. 1. (4.)

BAKER (J. J.) The Bible and Temperance. pp. 58. *Lond.* 1895. 8°. 8436. f. 13

BECHĀRĀMA CHAṬṬOPĀDHYĀYA. Lectures on Drunkenness. pp. 22. *Sukkur,* 1893. 8°. 4503. aaa. 19.

BLACK (G.) Some physical aspects of Temperance. pp. 23. *Lond.* 1890. 8°. 8436. f. 1. (13.)

BLOXAM (S. U. C.) Temperance Talks with Children. pp. 64. *Lond.* 1894. 8°. 8435. aa. 94.

BOYCE (F. B.) The Drink problem in Australia. pp. 324. *Lond.* 1893. 8°. 8436. bb. 42.

BRANDRETH (H.) Traditional Temperance teaching. pp. 8. *Lond.* 1891. 8°. 8436. f. 1. (17.)

—— Two Papers read at clerical meetings. pp. 16. *Lond.* 1895. 8°. Pam. 85.

BRODRIBB (T.) Manual of Health and Temperance. pp. 168. *Lond.* 1893. 8°. 8436. c. 8.

BURNS (D.) Pen-pictures of some Temperance notables. pp. 160. *Lond.* 1895. 8°. 8436. f. 4.

CAUDERLIER (É.) Petit dialogue dédié aux membres de la Ligue patriotique contre l'Alcoolisme. pp. 20. *Brux.* 1895. 8°. Pam. 85.

CHESHIRE (F. R.) Scientific Temperance handbook. pp. 285. *Lond.* 1891. 8°. 8436. c. 2

COOPER (J. J.) Devil-Sickness and its cure. pp. 8. *Birmingham,* 1894. 8°. 4475. g. 49. (10.)

CULPEN (D.) The Bible and Total Abstinence. pp. 16. *Lond.* 1893. 8°. 8436. f. 3. (8.)

DALHOFF (N.) Skitser fra en Studie-Rejse i specielt Øjemed. pp. 181. *Kjøbenh.* 1892. 8°. 8436. c. 5.

EDWARDS (W. W.) The Bible on the side of Total Abstinence. pp. 56. *Croydon,* 1895. 8°. 8436. e. 2.

ELLISON (H. J.) Sermons and addresses on Temperance subjects. pp. 369. *Lond.* 1895. 8°. 4477. ce. 12.

TEMPERANCE—*continued.*

ENCYCLOPÆDIAS. Cyclopædia of Temperance and prohibition. pp. 671. *N.Y.* 1891. 8°.
8435. f. 15.

ENGLAND. *Church of England Temperance Society.* Annual Report. *Lond.* 1893, *etc.* 8°. 8436. c.

—— Church of England Temperance Tracts. *Lond.* 1891, *etc.* 8°. 8436. c.

—— Hints to the clergy on the formation of a parochial Society. pp. 7. *Lond.* 1891. 8°.
8435. e. 24. (10.)

—— Declaration of Membership. *Lond.* 1890. 8°. 8436. a. 48

—— History and Work of the C.E.T.S. *Lond.* 1894. 8°. Pam. 85.

—— Missionary Efforts of the C.E.T.S. pp. 14. *Lond.* 1895. 8°. Pam. 85.

—— Manual for the formation and guidance of branches. pp. 45. *Lond.* 1890. 16°.
8436. de. 1. (3.)

HIRD (J. D.) Guide to C.E.T.S. Work in the London Diocese. pp. 76. *Lond.* 1890. 8°.
8436. a. 54.

SPAIN (T. D.) Guide to the formation of branches of the C.E.T.S. pp. 132. *Lond.* 1891. 8°.
8436. bb. 38.

WEST (J. R. O.) The C.E.T.S. and Party Politics. pp. 8. *Lond.* 1891. 8°.
8435. e. 24. (3.)

ENVELOPE SERIES. Envelope Series of tracts. *Lond.* 1890. 16°. 8436. a

EVANS (E.) Are you a Teetotaller? pp. 8. *Lond.* 1892. 8°. 8435. e. 24. (18.)

FARQUHARSON (R.) The Case for Moderate Drinking, *etc.* pp. 16. *Edinb.* 1892. 8°.
8435. e. 24. (19.)

FARRAR (F. W.) Reasons for Total Abstinence. pp. 15. *Lond.* 1886. 8°. 8435. a. 108. (12.)

FORSAITH (F.) Woman's share in juvenile Temperance work. pp. 8. *Lond.* 1894. 8°.
8436. f. 3. (17.)

FRENCH (R. V.) Nineteen centuries of drink in England. pp. 398. *Lond.* 1891. 8°. 8436. bb. 39.

G. B. & I. *National Temperance League.* Total Abstainers in the new Parliament. pp. 16. *Lond.* 1886. 8°. Pam. 85.

—— *United Kingdom Alliance.* United Report. *Lond.* 1891, *etc.* 8°. 8436. cc.

—— *Travellers' Total Abstainers' Union.* Report. *York,* 1895. *etc.* 8°. 8435. de.

GUSTAFSON (A.) The Foundation of Death. pp. 566. *Lond.* 1888. 8°. 8435. de. 15.

HOLE (S. R.) The Dean and the Drink. pp. 16. *Lond.* 1892. 8°. 8435. e. 24. (20.)

INDIAN DRINK QUESTION. Indian drink question in Parliament. pp. 28. *Lucknow,* 1890. 8°.
Pam. 85.

JESUS CHRIST. Did our Lord indeed speak sense? pp. 19. *Lond.* 1895. 8°. 4371. bb. 9. (9.)

KIMBALL (A. R.) The Blue Ribbon. What T. E. Murphy has done for the promotion of temperance. pp. 353. *Lond.* 1894. 8°. 8436. c. 16.

KINGSTON (W. B.) Intemperance. Its causes and remedies. pp. 64. *Lond.* 1892. 8°.
Pam. 85.

LEES (F. R.) and BURNS (D.) Temperance Bible-Commentary. pp. 512. *Lond.* 1894. 8°.
8435. e. 23.

LEGH (H. E.) How to make a Temperance Speech. pp. 111. *Westminster,* 1892. 8°.
8436. aaa. 55.

LONDON. *Friends' Temperance Union.* To the Glory of God. Address to Members of the Society of Friends. pp. 8. *Lond.* 1891. 9°.
Pam. 85.

TEMPERANCE—*continued.*

LONDON. *National Temperance League.* The National Temperance Congress. 1889. pp. 224. *Lond.* 1890. 8°. 8436. c. 1,

MAC ROBERT (G.) The Truth about strong Drink. pp. 16. *Lond.* 1893. 12°. 8436. f. 3. (9.)

MANNERS (J.) *Duchess of Rutland.* How Intemperance has been successfully combated. pp. 31. *Lond.* 1893. 8°. 8435. e. 24. (28.)

MANNING (H. E.) *Cardinal.* Temperance speeches of Cardinal Manning. pp. 147. *Lond.* 1894. 8°.
8436. f. 7.

MARTIUS (W.) Handbuch der deutschen Trinker- und Trunksuchtsfrage. pp. 392. *Gotha,* 1891. 8°. 8435. e. 19.

MARTYN (C.) J. B. Gough, the Apostle of cold Water. pp. 336. *Lond.* 1893. 8°. 4985. dd. 31.

MOFFAT (R. S.) "The Times' Drinking Bout." pp. 67. *Lond.* 1892. 8°. 8435. e. 24. (23.)

NEECH (J. T.) Intemperance: what it is, and how to deal with it. pp. 16. *Manch.* 1890. 8°.
8436. f. 1. (11.)

PARKER (J. C.) Mission Work among Licensed Victuallers. pp. 16. *Lond.* 1892. 16°.
8436. de. 1. (4.)

PAULL, afterwards RIPLEY (M. A.) Teetotaler and Traveller. pp. 328. *Lond.* 1893. 8°.
4906. de 20.

PARENT (M.) Le rôle de la femme dans la lutte contre l'Alcoolisme. pp. 46. *Brux.* 1890. 12°.
Pam. 85.

P.P. *Beckenham.* The Abstainers' Advocate. *Beckenham,* 1889, *etc.* 4°. P.P. 1132. ab.

—— *Colombo.* Bydand I.O.G.T. Good Templar. No. 1-4. *Colombo,* 1891. 4°. 1865. a. 15.

—— *London.* The Congregational Abstainer. *Lond.* 1889, *etc.* 8°. P.P. 1139. d.

—— The Medical Pioneer. *Lond.* 1892, *etc.* 8°.
P.P. 2767 and 2020.

—— The Journal, official organ of the British Women's Temperance Association. *Lond.* 1893, *etc.* 4°. 681.

PORTRAIT ENVELOPE SERIES. Portrait Envelope Series of tracts. *Lond.* 1893, *etc.* 16°. 8436. a.

QUESTIONS. Questions of the Day. *Lond.* 1893, *etc.* 8°. 8436. c.

REASONS. Strong Reasons against strong Drink. pp. 173. *Lond.* 1891. 8°. 8436. aaa. 54.

RICHARDSON (A. W.) Lecture on dangers of moderate Drinking. pp. 5. *Sukkur,* 1893. 8°.
8436. f. 3. (11.)

SMITH (J. M.) Nuts to crack for moderate Drinkers. pp. 30. *Lond.* 1890. 8°.
8436. e. 1. (7.)

SPIERS (W.) The Methodist Temperance Manual. pp. 250. *Lond.* 1895. 8°. 8436. f. 9.

STACPOOLE (F.) The health view of Temperance. pp. 15. *Lond.* 1891. 8°. 8436. e. 1. (8.)

TAYLOR (W.) The physiological side of Temperance. pp. 14. *Lond.* 1895. 8°. Pam. 85.

TEMPERANCE SPEAKER. The Temperance Speaker's companion. *Lond.* 1894, *etc.* 8°. 8435. bbb. 46.

THOMPSON (C. J.) The Drink difficulty. pp. 12. *Lond.* 1893. 12°. 8436. f. 3. (12.)

TINLING (J. F. B.) Alcohol in the Sanctuary. pp. 16. *Lond.* 1890. 8°. 8436. f. 1. (15.)

TOLSTOI (L. N.) *Count.* Why do Men Intoxicate themselves. pp. 80. *Lond.* 1892. 8°.
8436. a. 57.

U.S. *National Woman's Christian Temperance Union.* Reports. *Chicago,* 1893, *etc.* 8°. 8435. e.

WAGSTAFF (F.) and BONNER (J.) Twelve Temperance addresses. pp. 27. *Lond.* 1894. 8°.
8436. f. 3. (19.)

TEMPERANCE—*continued.*

WAKELY (C.) Abstinence and hard work. pp. 76. *Lond.* 1894. 8°.   8436. cc. 3.

WHITTAKER (T.) Brighter England and the way to it. pp. 322. *Lond.* 1891. 8°.   8436. c. 3.

WILLARD (F. E.) Address by F. E. Willard, President Woman's Christian Temperance Union. pp. 107. *Atlanta*, 1890. 8°   8435. e. 24. (9.)

—— My Happy Half-Century. Autobiography of an American woman. pp. 392. *Lond.* 1894. 8°.   10883. c. 26.

—— Do Everything : handbook for the White Ribboners. pp. 191. *Lond.* 1895. 8°. 8436. f. 12.

WILSON (G. R.) Drunkenness. pp. 161. *Lond.* 1893. 8°.   08276. e. 49.

WINSKILL (P. T.) The Temperance movement and its workers. *Edinb.* 1890, *etc.* 8°.   8435. f. 17.

WOOLLEY (J. G.) Seed. Six speeches. pp. 149. *N.Y.* 1893. 8°.   8436. c. 10.

WRIGHT (L.) Modern teetotal Heresy at the Lord's Table. pp. 79. *Lond.* 1891. 8°.   8436. f. 1. (20.)

Band of Hope : Temperance Literature for the Young, etc.

BAND OF HOPE MANUAL. The Band of Hope manual. pp. 40. *Lond.* 1894. 8°. 8436. cc. 4.

BAND OF HOPE OUTLINE ADDRESSES. Band of Hope outline addresses. *Lond.* 1892, *etc.* .8°.   8436. c.

CLARKE (H. F.) Blackboard addresses for Bands of Hope. *Lond.* 1892, *etc.* 8°.   8436. c.

—— The Sunday School in relation to the Band of Hope. pp. 8. *Lond.* 1892. 8°.   8436. f. 1. (21.)

—— How to avoid leakage between the Band of Hope and the adult society. pp. 8. *Lond.* 1894. 8°.   8436. f. 3. (14.)

DAVIS (C. A.) The relation of Sunday School teachers to the Band of Hope movement. pp. 4. *Lond.* 1894. 8°.   8436. f. 3. (16.)

FARQUHARSON (D.) Band of Hope service book. pp. 32. *Lond.* 1895. 8°.   8436. f. 6.

GEE (W. M.) The Nation's hope : text book for Band of Hope workers. pp. 146. *Lond.* 1891. 8°.   8436. aaa. 53.

GLASSPOOL (A. J.) The Band of Hope Companion. pp. 112. *Lond.* 1891. 8°. 8436. b. 39.

HIRD (J. D.) Health, Wealth and Temperance instruction for Bands of Hope. pp. 15. *Westminster*, 1890. 8°.   Pam. 78.

JAMES (H. T.) Industrial Bands of Hope. pp. 15. *Lond.* 1892. 8°.   8436. f. 3. (3.)

RIDGE (J. J.) Band of Hope catechism. pp. 16. *Lond.* 1894. 8°.   8436. e. 1. (9.)

WAKELY (C.) Bands of Hope and Sunday Schools. pp. 8. *Lond.* 1894. 8°.   Pam. 85.

———

AXON (W. E. A.) Temperance teaching in education. pp. 8. *Manch.* 1892. 8°.   8435. e. 24. (15.)

BALFOUR (C. L.) Morning Dew-Drops ; or, the juvenile abstainer. pp. 286. *Lond.* 1891. 8°.   8436. b. 40.

ENGLAND. *Church of England Temperance Society.* Young Crusader's union manual. pp. 11. *Lond.* 1895. 32°.   Pam. 85.

—— Juvenile Union. Outline Addresses. *Lond.* 1887, *etc.* 8°.   8436. c.

SANDFORD (E. G.) Temperance at school and the university. pp. 8. *Lond.* 1890. 8°.   8436. f. 1. (12.)

SMITH (F.) Simple lessons for young Abstainers. 8 pt. *Lond.* 1894. 8°.   8435. e. 24. (30.)

TEMPERANCE.—Band of Hope, etc.—*continued.*

TINLING (J. F. B.) For the sake of the Children. pp. 16. *Lond.* 1890. 8°.   8436. f. 1. (6.)

WAKELY (C.) Temperance Manual for the young. pp. 16. *Lond.* 1890. 8°.   8435. e. 24. (8.)

—— Temperance Manual for the Young. Text-book for diagrams. pp. 16. *Lond.* 1894. 8°.   8436. f. 3. (20.)

See also infra : Recitations, *etc.*

Legislation: Local Option.

See LICENSING LAWS.

Recitations : Poems : Tales.

COLLINGS (J. B.) Popular readings for the Lodge Room. pp. 112. *Birmingham*, 1893. 8°.   8436. c. 12.

COURTENAY (C.) For the Good of the House, and other readings. pp. 184. *Lond.* 1895. 8°.   4429. g. 12.

ENGLAND. *Church of England Temperance Society.* Member's Hymnal. pp. 111. *Lond.* 1895. 32°.   3436. de. 6.

—— Young Crusader's Hymn and Song Book. pp. 99. *Lond.* 1894. 16°.   Pam. 30.

KIRTON (J. W.) Young Abstainers' Reciter. pp. 255. *Lond.* 1893. 8°.   8436. aa. 44.

MACRITCHIE, afterwards HAYCRAFT (M. S.) The Springtide Reciter. pp. 103. *Lond.* 1890. 8°.   11653. dd. 48.

MILES (A. H.) The New Temperance Reciter. pp. 200. *Lond.* 1890. 8°.   12273. e.

P.P. *Maidstone.* Wide-Awake Temperance Reciter. *Maidstone*, 1895, *etc.* 8°.   P.P. 1137. i.

RECITATIONS. Recitations and dialogues for Bands of Hope. *Lond.* 1894, *etc.* 8°.   8436. a.

TEMPERANCE RECITER. Illustrated Temperance Reciter. *Lond.* 1894, *etc.* 8°.   8436. c.

TEMPLARS, Order of Knights. GMELIN (J.) Schuld oder Unschuld des Templerordens. pp. 532. *Stuttgart*, 1893. 8°.   04785. m. 4.

NAEF (F.) Recherches sur les opinions religieuses des Templiers. pp. 54. *Nîmes*, 1890. 8°.   4784. cc. 47. (4.)

WHEATER (W.) Temple Newsam : its history and antiquities. pp. 138. *Leeds*, 1889. 4°.   10352. dd. 8.

TEMPLE NEWSAM. WHEATER (W.) Temple Newsam : its history and antiquities. pp. 138. *Leeds*, 1889. 4°.   10352. dd. 8.

TEMNE LANUAGE.
See AFRICAN LANGUAGES.

TENERIFE. *See* CANARY ISLANDS.

TENNESSEE. THRUSTON (G. P.) Antiquities of Tennessee. pp. 369. *Cincinnati*, 1890. 8°.   07708. f. 29.

ALEXANDER (J. E.) Brief history of the Synod of Tennessee, 1817–87. pp. 155. *Phila.* 1890. 8°.   4744. ee. 27.

BARCLAY (W. F.) Manual of Tennessee corporations. pp. 355. *Nashville*, 1892. 8°.   6625. aaa. 9.

TENNESSEE. *Depart. of Agriculture.* Tennessee : its resources. *Nashville*, 1892 *obl.* fol.   1853. a. 18.

TENNI LANGUAGE.
See INDIAN LANGUAGES.

TENNIARDS. LAWS. The Laws of Tenniards, a game. *Tottenham*, 1892. 32°.   7915. de. 13. (4.)

TENNIS AND LAWN TENNIS. HEATHCOTE (J. M.) Tennis—Lawn Tennis. pp. 488. 1894. 8°. Badminton Library.   2264. aa. 11.

TENNIS, etc.—continued.

MARSHALL (J.) Tennis. pp. 104. 1890. 8°.
All England Series.   7908. df.

PUSSELLAWA. *Tennis Club.* Rules. pp. 3.
Colombo, 1893. 32°.   Pam. 83.

BENEKE (L.) Lawn Tennis. Anleitung und
Beschreibung. pp. 29. *Dresd.* 1892. 8°.
       7912. ee. 1. (10.)

HEATHCOTE (C. G.) Lawn Tennis. 1891. 4°.
Badminton Library.   2264. aa. 11.

LAWN TENNIS. Laws, etc. pp. 20.
Manch. 1892. 8°.   Pam. 83.

"LET." Lawn-Tennis. pp. 140. *Paris,* 1894. 8°.
       7912. aa. 36.

LONDON. *Lawn Tennis Association.* Laws of
Lawn Tennis. pp. 19. *Lond.* 1892. 12°.
       Pam. 83.

—— Regole del Lawn Tennis. pp. 33.
Roma, 1893. 12°.   Pam. 83.

MANUAL. Manual of Lawn Tennis. pp. 49.
Lond. 1894. 8°.   7906. ee. 36.

PARIS. *Union des Sociétés de Sports.* Règles du
jeu de lawn tennis. pp. 24. *Paris,* 1891. 16°.
       7915. de. 15. (4.)

See also GAMES.

TENTS. LOWNDES (G. R.) Gipsy Tents, and
how to use them. pp. 111. *Lond.* 1890. 8°.
       7907. de. 41.

TERATOLOGY. *See* MONSTERS ; OBSTETRICS.

TERRACINA. LA BLANCHÈRE (R. de)
Terracine. pp. 218. 1884. 8°. Bibliothèque
des Ecoles françaises d'Athènes et de Rome.
       Ac. 5206/12.

TERRA-COTTA. Ac. Vienna. *Museum
für Kunst und Industrie.* MASNER (C.) Die
Sammlung antiker Vasen und Terracotten.
pp. 104. *Wien,* 1892. 4°.   Ac. 4430/5.

BLANCHET (A.) Étude sur les Figurines en terre
cuite de la Gaule. 1891. 8°. Ac. Paris.
Société des Antiquaires. Mémoires. Sér. 6.
Tom. 1.   Ac. 5331.

CARTAULT (A.) Terres cuites grecques. pp. 97.
Paris, 1890. 4°.   7875. f. 16.

DAVIS (C. T.) Treatise on the manufacture of
Terra-cotta. pp. 628. *Phila.* 1895. 8°.
       07945. m. 25.

FROEHNER (W.) Collection Gréau. Catalogue
des terres cuites grecques. pp. 292.
Paris, 1891. 4°.   K.T.C. 4. b. 1.

LECHAT (H.) Terres cuites de Corcyre. pp. 112.
1891. 8°. Ac. Athens. *École française.*
An. 5.   Ac. 5206/3.

PARIS. *Louvre.* Terres cuites trouvées dans la
Nécropole de Myrina. pp. 348. *Paris,* 1886. 8°.
       7706. e. 23.

POTTIER (E.) Les Statuettes de terre cuite
dans l'antiquité. pp. 314. *Paris,* 1890. 8°.
       7875. a. 36.

TERROR. *See* FEAR.

TERUEL. EIXARCH SANTAPAU (M.) Los
Obispos de Teruel. pp. 312. *Teruel,* 1893. 8°.
       4864. aa. 12.

TESCHEN. BIERMANN (G.) Geschichte des
Herzogthums Teschen. pp. 301.
Teschen, 1894. 8°.   10210. e. 4.

TETANUS. FRANKL-HOCHWART (L. v.) Die
Tetanie. pp. 134. *Berl.* 1891. 8°. 7630. f. 21.

VINSON (E. L.) Contribution à l'étude du
tétanos. pp. 60. *Paris,* 1889. 8°. 7641. i. 17.

TETRAONIDAE. *See* GROUSE.

TEUTOBURGER-WALD. MEYER (E.)
Untersuchungen über die Schlacht im Teutoburger Walde. pp. 232. *Berl.* 1893. 8°.
       9040. f. 24.

TEUTOBURGER-WALD—continued.

STAMFORD (T. v.) Das Schlachtfeld im Teutoburger Walde. pp. 330. *Cassel,* 1892. 8°.
       9041. g. 14.

VELDE (P. v. d.) Het Teutoburger-woud.
pp. 58. *Amersfoort,* 1890. 8°. 10106. de. 6. (2.)

TEUTONIC MYTHOLOGY, etc. GER-
MANIC PHILOLOGY. Lehrbücher der germanischen Philologie. Th. 1. *Berl.* 1891. 8°.
       12962. l. 17.

MEYER (E. H.) Germanische Mythologie.
pp. 354. 1891. 8°. Lehrbücher, *etc.* Vol. 1.
       12962. l. 17.

ROSENKRANZ (C.) Anklänge an die deutsche
Mythologie in unserem Volksleben. pp. 45.
Neuwied, 1892. 8°.   Pam. 41.

SEPP (J. N.) Die Religion der alten Deutschen.
pp. 419. *München,* 1890. 8°. 4506. bb. 28.

WAEGNER (W.) Unsere Vorzeit. 3 pt.
Leipz. 1887–91. 8°.   12411. h. 1.

See also GERMANY, *Antiquities :* GOTHS.

TEUTONIC ORDER. Ac. Konigsberg.
Verein für die Geschichte der Provinz Preussen.
Handelsrechnungen des deutschen Ordens.
pp. 629. *Leipz.* 1887. 8°.   Ac. 7351/3.

TEUTONIC ORDER. Die Statuten des deutschen
Ordens. pp. 354. *Halle,* 1890. 4°. 4785. h. 14.

TEWKESBURY ABBEY. SPENCE (H. D.
M.) Cloister life in the days of Cœur de Lion.
pp. 203. *Lond.* 1892. 4°.   4707. g. 12.

TEXAS. WILLIAMS (A. M.) S. Houston and
the war of Independence in Texas. pp. 405.
Bost. 1893. 8°.   010882. e. 25.

SOWELL (A. J.) Rangers and pioneers of Texas.
pp. 411. *San Antonio,* 1884. 8°. 9605. aaa. 25.

COPE (E. D.) On the zoological position of
Texas. pp. 51. 1880. 8°. Bulletin of the U.S.
National Museum. No. 17.   Ac. 1875/13.

JAQUES (M. J.) Texan Ranch life. pp. 363.
Lond. 1894. 8°.   10411. dd. 40.

RABE (J. E.) Eine Erholungsfahrt nach Texas
und Mexico. pp. 284. *Hamburg,* 1893. 8°.
       10413. h. 37.

RUX. Through the Mill : or Rambles in Texas.
pp. 136. *Lond.* 1892. 8°.   10413. b. 36.

TEXAS. Statistics and information concerning
Texas. pp. 93. *St Louis,* 1893. 8°.
       10412. bb. 37.

TEXTILE FABRICS : WEAVING, etc.
FORRER (R.) Römische und byzantinische
Seiden-Textilien aus dem Gräberfelde von
Achmim-Panopolis. pp. 28. *Strassb.* 1891. 4°.
       K.T.C. 26. b. 9.

—— Die Graeber- und Textilfunde von Achmim.
pp. 27. *Strassb.* 1891. 4°.   7705. h. 22.

Ac. Washington. *Smithsonian Institution.*
HOLMES (W. H.) Textile Fabrics of ancient
Peru. pp. 17. *Wash.* 1889. 8°.   Pam. 3.

ARARAT. Oriental Carpets and rugs.
Lond. 1891. *obl. fol.*   7943. k. 27.

ASHENHURST (T. R.) Practical treatise on weaving and designing of Textile Fabrics. pp. 402.
Huddersfield, 1893. 8°.   7743. bbb. 66.

—— Treatise on Textile calculations. pp. 220.
Huddersfield, 1893. 8°.   07944. ee. 6.

AUSTRIA. *Oesterreichischer Textilarbeitertag.* Protokoll des ersten österreichischen Textilarbei-
tertages. pp. 51. *Reichenberg,* 1890. 8°.
       Pam. 82.

BARKER (A. F.) Analysis and reproduction of
Textile Fabrics. pp. 230. *Manch.* 1894. 8°.
       7743. bb. 62.

THEATRICALS—*continued.*

TOPLIS (S. G.) Charades and Plays. pp. 112.
Lond. 1889. 8°. 11779. c. 10.

WHINYATES (A.) Plays for young actors. 4 pt.
Lond. 1892. 8°. 11779. aa. 20.
See also DRAMA.

THEBES, Boeotia. FABRICIUS (E.) Theben.
pp. 32. *Freiburg,* 1890. fol. 7705. h. 34. (6.)

STERN (E. v.) Geschichte der spartanischen und
thebanischen Hegemonie. pp. 248.
Dorpat, 1884. 8°. 9026. ff. 33.

THEISM. *See* DEITY.

THEOLOGY.

Bibliography.

HURTER (H.) Nomenclator literarius recentioris
Theologiae Catholicae. *Oeniponte,* 1892, *etc.* 8°.
4999. ee. 6.

KOELLING (W.) Die Lehre von der Theo-
pneustie. pp. 470. *Breslau,* 1891. 8°.
4376. gg. 12.

TAVAGNUTTI (M. S.) Katholisch-theologische
Bücherkunde der letzten 50 Jahre.
Wien, 1891, *etc.* 8°. 4999. ee.

General.

ACHELIS (E. C.) Grundriss der theologischen
Wissenschaften. *Freiburg,* 1893, *etc.* 8°.
3622. ee.

BERNHARD (J.) Biblisch-theologische Untersuchungen. *Lübeck,* 1890, *etc.* 8°. 3127. m.

BEYSCHLAG (W.) Neutestamentliche Theologie.
Halle, 1891, *etc.* 8°. 3225. dd. 13.

DALPONTE (J.) Compendium Theologiae Dogmaticae specialis. pp. 815. *Tridenti,* 1890. 8°.
3557. i. 15.

DIDIOT (J.) Cours de Théologie catholique.
pp. 557. *Paris,* 1891. 8°. 4373. k. 11.

EGGER (F.) Enchiridion Theologiae Dogmaticae
generalis. pp. 644. *Brixinae.* 1893. 8°.
3554. gg. 13.

FIGG (E. G.) Analysis of Theology. pp. 556.
Lond. 1891. 8°. 3558. f. 9.

FRANK (F. H. R.) Dogmatische Studien.
pp. 135. *Erlangen,* 1892. 8°. 4376. e. 3.

GREGORY (J. R.) The Theological Student.
Handbook of elementary theology. pp. 301.
1892. 8°. GREGORY (A. E.) Books for Bible
students. 3125. dd.

GRETILLAT (A.) Exposé de Théologie systéma-
tique. 4 tom. *Paris,* 1885–1892. 8°.
3554. gg. 12.

HARRIES (J.) Handbook of Theology. pp. 166.
Lond. 1895. 8°. 4376. ee. 23.

HEBBELYNCK (A.) Theologia dogmatica Dni.
Lambrecht. Index analyticus quem confecit
A. H. pp. 67. *Gandavi,* 1892. 8°. Pam. 77.

HUNTER (S. J.) Outlines of Dogmatic Theology.
1895, *etc.* 8°. Manuals of Catholic Theology.
3622. df.

HURTER (H.) Theologiae Dogmaticae compendium. *Oeniponte,* 1893, *etc.* 8°. 3557. f.

JAMIESON (G.) A revised Theology. pp. 316.
Lond. 1891. 8°. 4372. ee. 29.

KRAUSS (A.) Lehrbuch der praktischen Theologie. 1890, *etc.* 8°. Sammlung theologischer
Lehrbücher. 3554. i.

KROGH-TONNING (K.) Den christelige Dogmatik.
4 Bde. *Christiania,* 1885–94. 8°. 3554. ee.

MONSABRÉ (J. M. L.) Exposition du Dogme
catholique. 18 vol. *Paris,* 1889–91. 8°.
4427. d. 1.

PERCIVAL (H. R.) A Digest of Theology.
pp. 311. *Lond.* 1893. 8°. 3554. ee. 3.

THEOLOGY.—General—*continued.*

PESCH (C.) Praelectiones dogmaticae.
Friburgi, 1894, *etc.* 8°. 3622. c.

PRATT (P. P.) Key to the Science of Theology.
pp. 182. *Liverp.* 1883. 8°. 4182. c. 25.

PUSEY (E. B.) Notes and questions on the
Catholic Faith and Religion. pp. 346.
Lond. 1891. 8°. 3505. df. 52.

ROSMINI SERBATI (A.) Rosminiarum Proposi-
tionum trutina theologica. *Romae,* 1892. 8°.
3900. h. 51.

RUSSELL (H. P.) Doctrine and discipline of
Holy Church. pp. 165. *Lond.* 1893. 8°.
4109. e. 36.

SCHMID (F.) Questiones selectae ex Theologia
dogmatica. pp. 493. *Paderbornae,* 1891. 8°.
4371. ee. 5.

SCOTT (J.) Outlines of Theology. pp. 193.
Colombo, 1891. 12°. 4375. dd. 2.

STRONG (T. B.) Manual of Theology. pp. 424.
Lond. 1892. 8°. 4376. i. 17.

ANGUS (J.) Theology, an inductive and progressive science. pp. 44. 1892. 8°. Present Day
Tracts. No. 68. 4018. aa.

CLIFFORD (J.) The coming Theology. pp. 43.
Lond. 1891. 8°. Pam. 77.

COX (W. L. P.) Scientific study of Theology.
pp. 180. *Lond.* 1893. 8°. 4376. ee. 14.

DRUMMOND (J.) Religion and Theology.
1891. 8°. BARTRAM (R.) Religion and Life.
4372. ee. 10.

G., G. P. Die Königin der Wissenschaften.
pp. 37. *Salzburg,* 1891. 8°. 4371. ee. 7. (4.)

GLAGE (M.) Der Grundfehler der Ritschlschen
Theologie. *Kiel,* 1893. *etc.* 8°. 3910. ee.

KRAUSE (C. C. F.) Zur Religions-philosophie
und speculativen Theologie. pp. 180.
Leipz. 1893. 8°. 4371. ee. 12.

LENOIR (F.) De la Théologie du XIXᵉ siècle.
pp. 102. *Paris,* 1893. 8°. 3900. i. 21.

MEAD C. M.) Some current Notions concerning
Dogmatic Theology. *Hartford,* 1894. 8°.
4371. ee. 29. (7.)

MIELKE (G.) Das System A. Ritschl's dargestellt. pp. 60. *Bonn,* 1894. 8°. 3914. bb. 17.

MICHAUD (E.) La Théologie et le temps présent.
pp. 44. *Berne,* 1893. 8°. 4371. ee. 27. (5.)

OUTLINES. Outlines of Theological Study.
pp. 60. *Camb.* 1890. 8°. 3366. b. 46.

OWEN (J.) Free Learning and free teaching
in Theology. pp. 34. *Lond.* 1891. 8°.
4371. ee. 2. (9.)

P.P. *Edinburgh.* Critical Review of theological literature. *Edinb.* 1890, *etc.* 8°.
P.P. 409. c.

—— *Montauban.* Revue de Théologie.
Montauban, 1891, *etc.* 8°. P.P. 37. caa.

ROBINS (H. E.) Harmony of Ethics with Theology. pp. 100. *N.Y.* 1891. 8°. 4257. aaa. 22.

STEARNS (L. F.) Present Day Theology; popular
discussion. pp. 568. *Lond.* 1893. 8°. 4371. e. 13.
See also CHRISTIANITY : CHURCH HISTORY, *History of Dogma :* CREEDS : ENGLAND, *Church of :*
ROMAN CATHOLIC CHURCH : TRINITY.

Biblical and Theological Dictionaries.

DICTIONARIES. Theologisches Hilfslexikon.
Gotha, 1891, *etc.* 8°. 3560. k.

ENCYCLOPÆDIAS. Calwer Kirchenlexikon. Theologisches Handwörterbuch. pp. 996.
Calw, 1889–93. 8°. 3553. df. 1.

EASTON (M. G.) Illustrated Bible Dictionary.
pp. 724. *Lond.* 1893. 8°. 3125. df. 15.

THEOLOGY, — Biblical Dictionaries, etc.—*continued*.

MACPHERSON (J.) Universal Bible Dictionary. pp. 350. *Lond.* 1892. 8°.   3104. b. 7.

RICE (E. W.) People's Dictionary of the Bible. pp. 228. *Lond.* 1893. 8°.   3125. de. 40.

RIEHM (E. C. A.) Handwörterbuch des biblischen Altertums. 2 Bde. *Bielefeld,* 1893. 8°.   3149. i. 15.

SMITH (*Sir* W.) Dictionary of the Bible. Vol. I. Pt. 1, 2. *Lond.* 1893. 8°.   2000. d.

WESTCOTT (A.) and WATT (J.) Concise Bible Dictionary. pp. 175. *Lond.* 1893. 8°.   3109. cc. 6.

Moral and Ascetic Theology.

BUCCERONI (J.) Institutiones Theologiae moralis. *Romae,* 1892, *etc.* 8°.   3554. g. 8.

CARDINI (E.) Dei supremi principii della Teologia morale. 4 vol. *Quaracchi,* 1891. 8°.   3554. gg. 11.

ERBEL (B.) Theologia moralis per modum Conferentiarum. *Paderbornae,* 1891, *etc.* 8°.   3554. gg. 10.

GURY (J. P.) Compendium Theologiae moralis. 2 tom. *Romae,* 1889. 8°.   4061. dd. 10.

COBRE (J. M.) Notæ addititiæ ad P. Gury. pp. 622. *Hongkong,* 1890. 8°.   4061. dd. 13.

LEHMKUHL (A.) Theologia moralis. 2 vol. *Friburgi,* 1890. 8°.   3557. i. 12.

MOEREN (A. B. v. d.) Introductio in studium Theologiæ moralis. pp. 161. *Gandavi,* 1887. 8°.   3557. i. 11.

SCARAMELLI (G. B.) Direttorio ascetico. 2 vol. *Torino,* 1892. 8°.   3455. i. 11.

SCAVINI (P.) Theologia moralis universa. 3 lib. *Mediolani,* 1890. 8°.   3557. i. 7.

SCHEICHER (J.) Compendium repetitorium theologiae moralis. pp. 376. *Viennae,* 1890. 8°.   3559. aa. 27.

Mystical Theology. *See* MYSTICISM.

Natural Theology. *See* RELIGION.

Pastoral Theology.

BERARDI (A.) Theologia pastoralis. pp. 372. *Faventiae,* 1890. 8°.   4061. dd. 11.

CHADWICK (W. E.) Work of the Church in suburban and residential parishes. pp. 77. *Lond.* 1895. 8°.   4429. a. 107.

ELLERTON (J.) Manual of parochial work. pp. 551. *Lond.* 1892. 8°.   4429. bbb. 6.

GIBSON (E. C. S.) Self-discipline in relation to the life of a Priest. pp. 157. *Lond.* 1894. 8°.   4429. c. 17.

GOTT (J.) *Bp. of Truro.* The Parish Priest of the Town. pp. 294. *Lond.* 1895. 8°.   4430. aaa. 13.

INGRAM (A. F. W.) Work in great cities. pp. 184. *Lond.* 1896. 8°.   4499. b. 26.

KENRICK (C. W. H.) The work of the Ministry. pp. 110. *Lond.* 1893. 8°.   4499. dc. 3.

LEEKE (E. T.) Ourselves, our people, our work. pp. 153. *Lond.* 1891. 8°.   4429. aa. 40.

LIBERMANN (F. M. P.) Das Ideal des Priestertums. pp. 200. 1893. 8°. P.P. *Paderborn.* Der katholische Seelsorger. Ergänzung 1.   P.P. 86. i.

LIDDON (H. P.) Clerical life and work. pp. 377. *Lond.* 1894. 8°.   2210. c. 3.

LIGHTFOOT (J. B.) *Bp. of Durham.* Ordination Addresses and counsels to clergy. pp. 318. *Lond.* 1890. 8°.   4473. cc. 18.

LITTLETON (*Hon.* C. J.) The Office and work of a Priest. pp 164. *Lond.* 1894. 8°.   4499. cc. 30.

THEOLOGY.—Pastoral—*continued*.

MOORHOUSE (J.) *Bp. of Manchester.* Church Work: its means and methods. pp. 231. *Lond.* 1894. 8°.   4499. cc. 29.

MOULE (H. C. G.) Chapters on pastoral life and work. pp. 303. *Lond.* 1892. 8°.   4409. f. 1.

MOUSSARD (L. F.) Le Prêtre et la vie d'étude. pp. 300. *Paris,* 1890. 8°.   4498. ff. 9.

NEWBOLT (W. C. E.) Speculum Sacerdotum, the Divine model of the priestly life. pp. 321. *Lond.* 1894. 8°.   4499. c. 25.

SACERDOCE. The Ancient Fathers on the office and work of the Priesthood. pp. 172. *Lond.* 1891. 8°.   4499. cc. 24.

SIDEBOTHAM (H.) Pastoral visitation of the sick and suffering. 2 pt. *Lond.* 1895. 8°.   4430. aaa. 16.

TIBERGE (L.) Retraite ecclésiastique. pp. 375. *Hongkong,* 1893. 8°.   4427. ee. 1.

WILLCOX (G. B.) The Pastor amidst his flock. pp. 186. *N.Y.* 1890. 8°.   4376. dd. 3.

See also CLERGY : ENGLAND, *Church of* : HOMILETICS.

Scholastic Theology and Philosophy.

APPEL (H.) Die Lehre der Scholastiker von der Synteresis. pp. 60. *Rostock,* 1891. 8°. Pam. 49.

BERTHIER (J. J.) Tabulae systematicae totius Summae Theologicae. *Friburgi,* 1893. 4°   3676. c. 15.

CORNOLDI (G. M.) The physical system of St. Thomas Aquinas. pp. 228. *Lond.* 1893. 8°.   3805. b. 4.

GARDAIR (J.) Corps et Ame. Essais sur la philosophie de S. Thomas. pp. 391. *Paris,* 1892. 8°.   8469. d. 31.

PORTMANN (A.) Das System der theologischen Summe des hl. Thomas von Aquin. pp. 422. *Luzern,* 1894. 8°.   3627. cc. 3.

STOECKL (A.) Doctrine philosophique de S. Thomas d'Aquin. pp. 398. *Paris,* 1890. 12°.   8466. e. 26.

WEISS (C.) S. Thomae Aquinatis De septem donis Spiritus Sancti doctrina proposita. pp. 209. *Viennae,* 1895. 8°.   4227. h. 27.

See also PHILOSOPHY, *History.*

THEOSOPHY AND ESOTERIC BUDDHISM.
ANDERSON (J. A.) Reincarnation. pp. 192. *San Francisco,* 1894. 8°.   8632. f. 32

BANCROFT (H.) Threads of Theosophy. pp. 15. *Lond.* 1891. 8°.   Pam. 41.

BARBERIS (T.) Il Buddismo esoterico. pp. 68. *Milano,* 1890. 8°.   Pam. 41.

BEHRE (C.) Spiritisten, Mystiker und Theosophen. pp. 85. *Leipz.* 1890. 8°. 8632. e. 36. (9.)

BESANT (A.) *Mrs.* Building of the Kosmos. pp. 157. *Lond.* 1894. 8°.   8631. aaa. 58.

—— In the Outer Court. pp. 164 *Lond.* 1895. 8°.   8631. bb. 52.

—— Reinkarnation oder Wiederverkörperungslehre. pp. 182. *Leipz.* 1895.8°. 4503. aaa. 27.

—— Birth and evolution of the Soul. pp. 56. *Lond.* 1895. 8°.   8462. c. 32.

—— The Self and its Sheaths. pp. 86. *Benares,* 1895. 8°.   8631. cc. 46.

—— De theosofische Sfinx. pp. 25. *Amsterd.* 1891. 8°.   Pam. 41.

—— India Past and Present. pp. 93. *Madras,* 1894. 8°.   8022. aa. 4.

—— Dangers of Spiritualism. pp. 15. *Bellary,* 1894. 16°.   Pam. 36.

BESANT (A.) and BURROWS (H.) Petit glossaire de termes théosophiques. pp. 23. *Paris,* 1894. 16°.   8632. b. 45.

THEOSOPHY—*continued.*

BESANT (A.) *Mrs.* Who is Mrs. Besant? Why has she come to India? pp. 44.
Madras, 1894. 8°.   10803. de. 7. (11.)

KĀLĪPRASANNA KĀVYAVIṢĀRADA. Mrs. Besant in India. Her stratagem exposed. pp. 34.
Calcutta, 1894. 8°.   Pam. 46.

MURDOCH (J.) Theosophy exposed: or, Mrs. Besant and her Guru. pp. 113.
Madras, 1893. 8°.   8631. bb. 50.

WYNN (W.) Theosophy. Reply to Mrs. Besant. pp. 32. *Bradford*, 1892. 8°.   Pam. 36.

BLAVATSKY (H. P.) The Theosophical Glossary. pp. 389. *Lond.* 1892. 8°.   8632. h. 10.

—— Glossary of Theosophical terms. pp. 62.
Lond. 1891. 4°.   8632. d. 16.

—— Madame Blavatsky: her tricks and her dupes. pp. 44. *Madras*, 1894. 8°.
    8630. cc. 38. (7.)

CIMINO FOLLIERO DE LUNA (A.) Elena Blavatsky, Annie Besant e la Teosofia moderna. pp. 37.
Roma, 1893. 8°.   8632. g. 25. (9.)

FOOTE (G. W.) The New Cagliostro. Letter to Madame Blavatsky. pp. 16. *Lond.* 1889. 8°.
    8630. ee. 30. (4.)

JUDGE (W. Q.) The Esoteric She. Mme. Blavatsky. pp. 19. *Surat*, 1893. 16°.   Pam. 8.

LILLIE (A.) Madame Blavatsky and her "Theosophy." pp. 228. *Lond.* 1895. 8°. 8631. ce. 35.

SOLOV'EV (V. S.) A modern Priestess of Isis: Madame Blavatsky. pp. 366. *Lond.* 1895. 8°.
    8632. e. 32.

WACHTMEISTER (C.) Reminiscences of H. P. Blavatsky. pp. 162. *Lond.* 1893. 8°.
    8632. c. 42.

—— H. P. Blavatsky and the crisis in the Theosophical Society. pp. 12. *Lond.* 1895. 8°.
    Pam. 36.

BIBLIOTHEK. Theosophische Bibliothek.
Braunschweig, 1893, *etc.* 8°.   8631. aa.

CHRISTIAN IDEA. "Things to Come": essays towards a fuller apprehension of the Christian idea. pp. 248. *Lond.* 1892. 8°. 4372. ee. 26.

CLARKE (R. F.) Theosophy: its teaching and character. pp. 90. *Lond.* 1892. 8°.
    3939. ccc. 12.

CLIFFORD (J.) The new Theosophy and Christian teaching. pp. 19. *Colombo*, 1894. 16°.
    8631. a. 49. (4.)

COULOMB (E. J.) Le secret de l'absolu. pp. 254.
Paris, 1892. 12°.   8632. ccc. 25.

DEANS (J.) Plain talk about Theosophy. pp. 14.
Lond. 1891. 8°.   Pam. 41.

G., A. K. The Yoga of Christ. pp. 116.
Lond. 1894. 8°.   4371. bb. 4.

GARRETT (F. E.) Isis very much Unveiled.
pp. 136. 1895. 8°. Westminster Gazette Library. Vol. 2.   012200. l.

GEIJERSTAM (C. af) Modern Vidskepelse.
pp. 197. *Stockholm*, 1892. 8°. 8631. aaa. 53.

GOERING (H.) Theosophische Schriften.
Braunschweig, 1894, *etc.* 16°.   8631. aa.

HARDEN-HICKEY (J. L.) *Baron.* La Théosophie. pp. 233. *Paris*, 1890. 12°.   8630. bbb. 32.

HARTE (R.) Lay Religion. pp. 178.
Lond. 1894. 8°.   4015. aa. 1.

INNES (J. W. B.) The True Church of Christ.
pp. 130. *Lond.* 1892. 8°.   4371. aaa. 33.

JUDGE (W. Q.) Echoes from the Orient. Outline of Theosophical doctrines. pp. 64.
N.Y. 1893. 8°.   8631. ee. 44.

—— The ocean of Theosophy. pp. 154.
N.Y. 1893. 8°.   8631. ee. 43.

THEOSOPHY—*continued.*

K., B. Why one should join the Theosophical Society. pp. 4. *Lond.* 1890. 8°.   Pam. 36.

KINGSLAND (W.) The esoteric Basis of Christianity. pp. 195. *Lond.* 1895. 8°. 4018. ff. 16.

LEADBEATER (C. W.) The Astral Plane. pp. 94.
Lond. 1895. 8°.   8631. bbb. 39.

MAHĀBHĀRATA. *Bhagavadgītā.* Thoughts on Bagavad Gita. pp. 162.
Kumbhakonam, 1893. 8°.   4503. cc. 30.

MEAD (G. R. S.) The World-mystery. pp. 160.
Lond. 1895. 8°.   4504. b. 8.

—— Notes on Nirvana. pp. 28. *Lond.* 1893. 4°.
    8632. h. 11.

OLCOTT (H. S.) A united Buddhist world.
pp. 5. *Madras*, 1892. 8°.   Pam. 41.

—— Old Diary Leaves. Story of the Theosophical Society. pp. 491. *N.Y.* 1895. 8°.
    8631. eee. 33.

OLD (W. R.) What is Theosophy? pp. 128.
Lond. 1891. 12°.   8632. aaa. 47.

PATAÑJALI. The Yoga Aphorisms of Patanjali.
pp. 65. *N.Y.* 1893. 12°.   8632. aa. 27.

PEMBER (G. H.) Theosophy, Buddhism and the signs of the end. pp. 80. *Lond.* 1891. 8°.
    4503. bb. 30.

P.P. Bombay. *The Theosophist.* Five Years of Theosophy. pp. 385. *Lond.* 1894. 8°. 8632. g. 21.

—— *Colombo.* The Buddhist. English organ of the Southern Church of Buddhism.
Colombo, 1888, *etc.* 8°.   P.P. 636. cn.

—— *Dublin.* The Irish Theosophist.
Dublin, 1892, *etc.* 4°.   P.P. 646 and 2185.

—— *London.* The Vâhan. Vehicle for the interchange of theosophical opinions. Vol. 1, 2.
Lond. 1891–93. 4°.   P.P. 636. cka.

—— Book-notes theosophical, occult, *etc.*
Lond. 1893, *etc.* 8°.   P.P. 6481. k. and 2221.

—— *Santa Cruz, California.* The Buddhist Ray. *Santa Cruz*, 1888, *etc.* 8°.   1066.

PHILANGI DASA. Swedenborg the Buddhist.
pp. 322. *Los Angeles*, 1887. 8°.   3716. f. 5.

RĀMA PRASĀDA. The Science of Breath and Philosophy of the Tatwas. pp. 258.
Lond. 1890. 8°.   759. . 15.

ROSNY (L. L. de) Le Bouddhisme éclectique.
pp. 180. *Paris*, 1894. 12°.   4506. 9.

SALZER (L.) Scientific basis of Theosophy.
pp. 49. *Calcutta*, 1893. 8°.   8632. d. 30.

SATYANĀTHA (S.) Theosophy: an appeal.
pp. 18. *Madras*, 1893. 8°.   Pam. 36.

SINNETT (P.) The purpose of Theosophy. pp. 55.
Bombay, 1887. 8°.   8632. cc. 38.

SLATER (T. W.) Theosophy. Popular explanation. pp. 13. *Lond.* 1891. 8°.   Pam. 41.

SUBBA RĀVA. Collection of Esoteric Writings.
pp. 356. *Bombay*, 1895. 8°.   8632. dd. 12.

THEOSOPHICAL SOCIETY. Transactions of the Blavatsky Lodge of the Theosophical Society.
Pt. 1, 2. *Lond.* 1890, 91. 4°.   8632. f. 33.

—— European section. Constitution and rules.
pp. 19. *Lond.* 1891. 8°.   Pam. 36.

—— European Section. Information for enquirers. pp. 12. *Lond.* 1891. 8°.   Pam. 36.

—— Report of the Galle Convention. pp. 27.
Galle, 1891. 8°.   Pam. 36.

—— Transactions of the London Lodge.
Lond. 1895, *etc.* 8°.   8631. cc.

—— Qué es la theosophia? pp. 22.
Madrid, 1889. 8°.   Pam. 36.

—— *Swedish Section.* Skrifter, *etc.*
Stockholm, 1889, *etc.* 8°   8632. ccc.

THEOSOPHY.—*continued.*

THEOSOPHICAL TRACT SERIES. Theosophical Tract series. *Bombay*, 1890, *etc.* 12° & 16°.
4503. de.

THEOSOPHY. Theosophy. pp. 12.
Lond. 1892. 12°.   Pam. 36.

—— Practische Theosophie. pp. 15.
Amsterdam, 1891. 8°.   Pam. 41.

TUKĀRĀMA TĀTYĀ. Theosophía. pp. 95.
Madrid, 1890. 8°.   Pam. 41.

V., H. A. Wat is de beteckenis der Theosofie.
pp. 8. *Amsterdam*, 1891. 8°.   Pam. 41.

WARD (H. S.) The A B C of Theosophy. pp. 14.
Lond. 1891. 8°.   Pam. 41.

—— Karma and its twin doctrine Re-incarnation.
pp. 14. *Lond.* 1891. 8°.   Pam. 41.

WEATHERLY (L. A.) The Supernatural? pp. 273.
Bristol, 1891. 8°.   8632. ccc. 8.

WELSH (R. E.) The Truth about Theosophy.
pp. 24. *Lond.* 1891. 8°.   Pam. 41.

WEST. Het Westen door Oostersch licht be-schenen. pp. 45. *Amsterdam*, 1891. 8°. Pam. 41.

WRIGHT (C. F.) Outline of the principles of modern Theosophy. pp. 192. *Bost.* 1894. 8°.
8631. bbb. 38.

WYLD (G.) Christo-Theosophy. pp. 264.
Lond. 1895. 8°.   8631. aa. 46.
See also OCCULT SCIENCE.

THERAPEUTICS. ALLEN (H.) Handbook of local Therapeutics. pp. 505.
Lond. 1893. 8°.   7442. g. 26.

BARTHOLOW (R.) Practical treatise of Thera-peutics. pp. 820. *Lond.* 1893. 8°.   07509. i. 1.

BRADBURY (J. B.) Inaugural lecture on Thera-peutics. pp. 35. *Camb.* 1894. 8°.   Pam. 39.

BROUARDEL (P.) Traité de Médecine et de Thérapeutique. *Paris*, 1895, *etc.* 8°. 07305. k.

BRUCE (J. M.) Materia Medica and Therapeutics.
pp. 582. *Lond.* 1891. 8°.   2255. a. 13.

BRUNTON (T. L.) Introduction to modern Thera-peutics. pp. 195. *Lond.* 1892. 8°. 7442. e. 11.

BUM (A.) Therapeutisches Lexicon. pp. 1807.
Wien, 1890, 91. 8°.   7460. ff. 21.

CERNA (D.) Notes on the newer Remedies.
pp. 177. *Phila.* 1893. 8°.   7509. b. 12.

COHEN (S. S.) The Therapeutic Properties of animal extracts. *Phila.* 1893. 8°.   Pam. 39.

FARQUHARSON (R.) A Guide to Therapeutics.
pp. 417. *Lond.* 1891. 8°.   2254. e. 8.

FENWICK (S.) Outlines of medical Treatment.
pp. 502. *Lond.* 1894. 8°.   2254. a. 8.

HARE (H. A.) Text-book of practical Thera-peutics. pp. 632. *Phila.* 1890. 8°. 7460. dd. 1.

—— System of practical Therapeutics. 3 vol.
Edinb. 1892. 8°.   7460. ff. 27.

HUSBAND (H. A.) Student's pocket Prescriber.
pp. 64. *Edinb.* 1888. 32°.   7509. de. 59.

LEONARD (C. H.) and CHRISTY (T.) Dictionary of Therapeutics, *etc.* pp. 387. *Lond.* 1892. 8°.
07509. de. 19.

NAPHEYS (G. H.) Modern Therapeutics medical and surgical. 2 vol. *Phila.* 1892, 93. 8°.
7460. e. 1.

NOTHNAGEL (H.) Specielle Therapie.
Wien, 1894, *etc.* 8°.   7441. d.

NUÑEZ (T.) Tratado de terapeutica. pp. 627.
México, 1893. 8°.   7461. g. 7.

P P. *Edinburgh.* Journal of comparative Therapeutics. *Edinb.* 1888, *etc.* 8°.
P.P. 2856. aa.

—— *London.* The A B C Excerpta therapeu-tica. *Lond.* 1893, *etc.*   P.P. 2487. be.

THERAPEUTICS.—*continued.*

P.P. *London.* The Therapist. Monthly journal.
Lond. 1891, *etc.* 4°.   P.P. 3190. ab. and 2081.

POTTER (S. O. L.) Index of comparative Thera-peutics. pp. 279. *Chicago*, 1882. 8°. 7460. a. 2.

—— Progress of Medicine, measured by the progress of therapeutics, *etc.* pp. 76.
San Francisco, 1888. 8°.   07305. h. 4. (9.)

—— Handbook of Therapeutics. pp. 767.
Phila. 1891. 8°.   07509. e. 14.

ROSENBACH (O.) Grundlagen, Aufgaben und Grenzen der Therapie. pp. 196. *Wien*, 1891. 8°.
7460. ff. 22.

SCHWALBE (J.) Grundriss der speciellen Thera-pie. pp. 763. *Stuttgart*, 1892. 8°.   7442. i. 3.

SEMPLE (C. E. A.) Elements of Therapeutics.
pp. 480. *Lond.* 1892. 8°.   07509. de. 20.

SHOEMAKER (J. V.) Practical treatise on Thera-peutics. pp. 1108. *Phila.* 1895. 8°. 07509. i. 6.

SOULIER (H.) Traité de Thérapeutique.
Paris, 1891, *etc.* 8°.   7442. d.

TROUESSART (É. L.) La Thérapeutique antisep-tique. pp. 280. *Paris*, 1892. 8°. 7482. e. 17.

WHEELER (A.) Student's handbook of Thera-peutics. pp. 396. *Edinb.* 1894. 8°. 7460. aa. 5.

WHITE (W. H.) Materia Medica and Thera-peutics. pp. 614. *Lond.* 1892. 8°. 07509. de. 21.

WHITLA (W.) Dictionary of Treatment; or Therapeutic Index. pp. 948. *Lond.* 1892. 8°.
7320. aa. 3.

—— Elements of Pharmacy and Therapeutics.
pp. 646. *Lond.* 1892. 8°.   2256. a. 25.

WOOD (H. C.) Therapeutics. pp. 1007.
Lond. 1894. 8°.   2246. e. 15.

YEO (I. B.) Manual of Medical Treatment.
2 vol. *Lond.* 1893. 8°.   7442. aaa. 20.
See also HOMOEOPATHY : ELECTRICITY, *Medical* : MATERIA MEDICA : MEDICINE : PHARMACY.

THERMO-DYNAMICS. *See* HEAT.

THETFORD. THETFORD. Thetford. pp. 28.
Thetford, 1894. 8°.   10348. c. 25. (12.)

THEUX. LIMBOURG (P. de) Organisation de la communauté de Theux. 1885. 8°. Ac.
Liége. Institut Archéologique. Bulletin. Tom. 18.
Ac. 5527.

THIAKI. *See* ITHACA.

THIERS, Puy-de-Dôme. JACQUETON (H.)
Études sur la ville de Thiers.
Paris, 1894, *etc.* 8°.   10174. f.

THIRTY YEARS' WAR. KLOPP (O.)
Der dreissigjährige Krieg bis zum Tode Gustav Adolfs 1632. *Paderborn*, 1891, *etc.* 8°. 9080. g.

HAMANN (C.) Bildnisse einiger berühmter Per-sönlichkeiten des dreissigjährigen Krieges auf Münzen und Medaillen. pp. 11. *Hamb.* 1891. 4°.
Pam. 44.

KVACSALA (J.) Irenische Bestrebungen zur Zeit des dreissigjährigen Krieges. pp. 22.
Dorpat, 1894. 8°.   4532. g. 9. (8.)

GEBAUER (J.) Die Publicistik über den böhmis-chen Aufstand von 1618. *Halle*, 1892. 8°.
9327. ccc.

BAUMGARTEN (H.) Gustav Adolf und die deut-schen Protestanten. pp. 19. *Coburg*, 1893. 8°.
10601. d. 33. (7.)

BJÖRLIN (G.) Gustaf Adolf. pp. 401.
Stockholm, 1890. 8°.   10761. ee. 29.

BLUEMEL (E.) Gustav Adolf. pp. 226.
Eisleben, 1894. 8°.   10761. aa. 63.

BURG (J.) Gustav Adolph im Lichte der neueren Geschichtsforschung. pp. 47. *Essen*, 1894. 8°.
Pam. 8.

THIRTY YEARS' WAR—*continued.*

FLETCHER (C. R. L.) Gustavus Adolphus. pp. 316. 1892. 8°. ABBOTT (E.) Heroes of the Nations.   10601. f.

GUTJAHR (E.) Gustav Adolfs Beweggründe zur Teilnahme am deutschen Kriege. pp. 72. *Leipz.* 1894. 8°.   Pam. 28.

LAMPARTER (E.) Gustav Adolf. pp. 652. *Barmen,* 1892. 8°.   10761. cc. 21.

TREITSCHKE (H. v.) Gustav Adolf und Deutschlands Freiheit. pp. 29. *Leipz.* 1895. 8°.   Pam. 28.

WIBLING (C,) Sveriges förhållande till Siebenbürgen 1623-48. pp. 211. *Lund,* 1890. 8°.   9431. bb. 23.

LORENTZEN (T.) Die schwedische Armee im dreissigjährigen Kriege. pp. 216. *Leipz.* 1894. 8°.   9078. g. 19.

KOLLER (J.) Wallenstein. pp. 69. *Wien,* 1892. 8°.   10601. ee. 18. (8.)

LOEWE (V.) Die Organisation der wallensteinschen Heer. pp. 99. *Freiburg,* 1895. 8°.   8824. e. 50.

IRMER (G.) H. G. von Arnim. Lebensbild. pp. 397. *Leipz.* 1894. 8°.   010707. ff. 7.

BAUER (B.) Geschichte Memmingen vom Beginne des dreissigjährigen Krieges. 1891. 8°. Ac. Augsburg. *Hist. Verein.* Zeitschrift. Jahrg. 18.   Ac. 7013/2.

CASATI (A.) Die Correspondenz von A. und G. Casati mit Erzherzog Leopold v. von Oesterreich, 1620-23. pp. 214. 1894. 4°. Ac. Fribourg. *Universität.* Collectanea Friburgensia. Fasc. I.   Ac. 607/2.

REITZENSTEIN (C. v.) Der Feldzug des Jahres 1622 am Oberrhein und in Westfalen. *München,* 1891, *etc.* 8°.   8823. n. 3.

WESKAMP (A.) Das Heer der Liga in Westfalen, 1622-23. pp 371. *Münster,* 1891. 8°.   9079. h. 14.

RUETHNING (G.) Tilly in Oldenburg und Mansfelds Abzug aus Ostfriesland. pp. 24. *Oldenburg,* 1890. 4°.   9004. n. 11. (14.)

LEINUNG (W.) and STUMVOLL (R.) Aus Magdeburgs Sage und Geschichte. pp. 237. *Magdeburg,* 1894. 8°.   10256. c. 16.

NEUBAUER (E.) Wallenstein und die Stadt Magdeburg. pp. 246. *Magdeburg,* 1891. 8°.   9326. dd. 5.

OPITZ (W.) Die Schlacht bei Breitenfeld, 17. Sept. 1631. pp. 116. *Leipz.* 1892. 8°.   9079. h. 19.

DONAUBAUER ( ) Nürnberg in der Mitte des dreissigjährigen Krieges. 1893. 8°. Ac. Nuremberg. *Verein für Geschichte der Stadt.* Mittheilungen. Hft. 10.   Ac. 7134.

STRUCK (W.) Die Schlacht bei Nördlingen, 1634. pp. 106. *Stralsund,* 1893. 8°.   9079. i. 19.

OGIER (F.) Journal du Congrès de Munster. pp. 268. *Paris,* 1893. 8°.   9079. i. 11.

THOMPSON, Norfolk. CRABBE (G.) Materials for a history of the parish of Thompson. pp. 115. *Norwich,* 1892. 4°.   10360. k. 17.

—— Church of St. Martin, Thompson. 1882. obl. fol.   10360. k. 17.

THORAX. *See* VOICE.

THORN, Limburg. THORN, *Abbey of.* De Archieven van het Kapittel der Rijksabdij Thorn. *s' Gravenh.* 1889, *etc.* 8°.   4685. i. 3.

THORN, Prussia. SEMRAU (A.) Gedenkschrift zur hundertjährigen Feier der Vereinigung Thorns mit Preussen, 1793. pp. 91. 1893. 8°. Ac. Thorn. *Copernicus-Verein.* Mittheilungen. Hft. 8.   8752. cc. 5.

THOUARS. CARRÉ DE BUSSEROLLE (J. X.) Les Vendéens à Thouars, 1793. pp. 60. *Montsoreau,* 1890. 8°.   9072. cc. 4. (6.)

POISSON (J. F.) Les Fiefs de la vicomté de Thouars. pp. 235. *Niort,* 1893. 4°.   10171. h. 3.

THOUGHT READING. TARCHANOV (I.) Hypnotisme et lecture des pensées. pp. 163. *Paris,* 1891. 12°.   7410. df. 34.

WILLIS (C.) How to become a Thought-Reader. pp. 19. *Bolton,* 1895. 8°.   Pam. 36.

THREE RIVERS, Quebec. THREE RIVERS, *Diocese of.* Extrait de l'exposé de la question de la division du diocèse. pp. 38. 25. 1885. 8°.   4745. e. 36.

THRIFT. *See* FRIENDLY SOCIETIES.

THROAT. BALCOMB (J. T.) Diagrams of the Mouth, Fauces and Larynx. *Lond.* 1891. 4°.   7616. a. 35.

BROWNE (L.) The Throat. pp. 734. *Lond.* 1893. 8°.   7615. f. 43.

BULKLEY (L. D.) Clinical notes on Chancre of the Tonsil. pp. 10. *N.Y.* 1893. 8°.   7305. f. 6. (4.)

BURNETT (C. H.) System of diseases of the Throat. 2 vol. *Lond.* 1893. 8°.   7615. cc. 14.

COHEN (S. S.) Esophageal Stethoscope: with remarks on intra-thoracic auscultation. pp. 4. *Phila.* 1893. 8°.   Pam. 39.

—— Some of the Throat-Conditions observed in gouty subjects. pp. 12. *Phila.* 1893. 8°.   7306. df. 25. (5.)

D'ORSEY (C.) Correct Voice Use as a preventive to throat disease. pp. 32. *Lond.* 1895. 8°.   07305. f. 19. (7.)

DOWNIE (J. W.) Clinical manual for the study of diseases of the Throat. pp. 268. *Glasg.* 1894. 8°.   7616. aaa. 11.

HALL (F. de H.) Diseases of the Throat. pp. 524. 1894. 8°. Lewis's Practical Series.   7482. a.

HENSMAN (A.) The Thorax. 1893. 8°. MORRIS (H.) Treatise on human Anatomy. 7419. l. 10.

HUTCHINSON (P. S.) Manual of Diseases of the Throat. pp. 127. *Lond.* 1891. 8°. 7616. aaa. 4.

IVINS (H. F.) Diseases of the Throat. pp. 507. *Phila.* 1893. 8°.   7616. i. 8.

KAISER (O.) Die Funktionen der Ganglienzellen des Halsmarkes. pp. 80. *Haag,* 1891. 8°.   7419. l. 8.

KNIGHT (C. H.) Chronic diseases of the Tonsils. 1893. 8°. BURNETT (C. H.) System of diseases of the Ear. Vol. 2.   7613. cc. 14.

MACBRIDE (P.) Diseases of the Throat. pp. 640. 1892. 8°. Pentland's Medical Series. Vol. 3.   7641. ee.

NEWMAN (D.) Malignant disease of the Throat. pp. 213. *Edinb.* 1892. 8°.   7616. f. 7.

THORNER (M.) Soor des Rachens bei einem Erwachsenen als Begleiterscheinung der Influenza. pp. 6. 1892. 8°.   Pam. 39.

—— Rheumatic Throat affections. pp. 8. 1893. 8°.   7305. f. 6. (12.)
See also DIPHTHERIA : LARYNX.

THUN. THUN. Thun and the Lake. pp. 40. 1880. 8°. Illustrated Europe. No. 5.   10108. bb.

THUNDER STORMS. *See* METEOROLOGY.

THURINGIAN FOREST. HOLDER-EGGER (O.) Studien zu thüringischen Geschichtsquellen. 1895, *etc.* 8°. Ac. Germany. *Gesellschaft für ältere deutsche Geschichtskunde.* Neues Archiv. Bd. 20.   Ac. 7003.

THURINGIAN FOREST—*continued.*

Proescholdt (H.) Der thüringer Wald. pp. 51.
1891. 8°. Lehmann (R.) Forschungen, *etc.*
Bd. 5. 10235. i. 10.

Regel (F.) Thüringen. *Jena*, 1892, *etc.* 8°.
10250. g.

Herwig (M.) Idiotismen aus Thüringen. pp. 32.
Eisleben, 1893. 4°. Pam. 47.
See also Germany, *History.*

TIAHUANACO. *See* Peru, *Antiquities.*

TIBET. Ac. Washington. *Smithsonian In-
stitution.* Rockhill (W. W.) Diary of a
Journey through Thibet. pp. 413.
Wash. 1894. 8°. 10075. ff. 24.

Bird, *afterwards* Bishop (I. L.) Among the
Tibetans. pp. 159. *Lond.* 1894. 8°. 4429. g. 5.

Bonvalot (G.) De Paris au Tonkin à travers
le Tibet. pp. 506. *Paris*, 1892. 8°.
10057. e. 5.

—— Across Thibet. 2 vol. *Lond.* 1891. 8°.
010057. ee. 21.

Bower (H.) Diary of a Journey across Thibet.
pp. 309. *Lond.* 1894. 8°. 10058. d. 12.

Forbes (H. F. G.) The Road from Simla to
Shepki in Chinese Thibet. pp. 45.
Calcutta, 1893. 8°. 10058. a. 30.

Gautier (H.) Nouvelle étude sur la Rhubarbe
du Thibet. pp. 19. *La Rochelle*, 1890. 8°.
Pam. 1.

Henry, d'Orléans, *Prince.* Le Père Huc et ses
critiques. pp. 65. *Paris*, 1893. 12°. 10058. de. 8.

Knight (E. F.) Where Three Empires Meet.
pp. 528. *Lond.* 1893. 8°. 010057. e. 22.

Landsdell (H.) Chinese Central Asia. 2 vol.
Lond. 1893. 8°. 10075. f. 16.

Louis (J. A. H.) The Gates of Thibet. pp. 183.
Calcutta, 1894. 8°. 010057. k. 13.

Marston (A. W.) The great closed Land.
pp. 112. *Lond.* 1894. 8°. 4766. ee. 24.

Murray (C. A.) *Earl of Dunmore.* The Pamirs.
2 vol. *Lond.* 1893. 8°. 10076. e. 4.

Pratt (A. E.) To the Snows of Tibet through
China. pp. 268. *Lond.* 1892. 8°. 010057. ee. 29.

Rockhill (W. W.) The land of the Lamas.
pp. 399. *Lond.* 1891. 8°. 010057. l. 5.

Schneider (H. G.) Working and Waiting for
Tibet. pp. 95. *Lond.* 1891. 8°. 4767. c. 27.

Tibet. *Tibetan Pioneer Mission.* Origin of the
Tibetan Pioneer Mission. pp. 20.
Lond. 1894. 4°. Pam. 40.
See also Asia, *Central*: China.

TICINO. Vidari (G.) Frammenti cronis-
torici dell' Agro ticinese. *Pavia*, 1891, *etc.* 8°.
9166. d.

Maulde de Clavière (A. R. de) La conquête
du Canton du Tessin, 1590–03. pp. 47.
Torino, 1890. 8°. 9008. g. 8. (4.)

TIDES. *See* Sea.

TIENTSIN. P.P. *Tientsin.* Peking and
Tientsin Times. *Tientsin*, 1894. *etc.* fol.
P.P. 9990. ff.

TIERRA DEL FUEGO. Diaz (J. V.) Descripcion del Territorio argentino de la Tierra
del Fuego. pp. 80. *Buenos A.* 1891. 8°.
10480. df. 1. (5.)

Stirling (W. H.) *Bp. of the Falkland Islands.*
Account of the Falkland Islands and Tierra del
Fuego. pp. 27. *Buenos A.* 1891. 8°.
4745. aa. 46.

Brinton (D. G.) Further Notes on Fuegian
Languages. 1892. 8°. Pam 47.
See also America, *Central and South* : Pata-
gonia.

TIGER. Littledale (H.) Notes on Wild
Dogs, Tigers, *etc.* pp. 21. *Bombay*, 1892. 8°.
Pam. 42.
See also Carnivora : Sport : Zoology.

TIGRÉ LANGUAGE. Schreiber (J.)
Manuel de la Langue tigraï. 2 pt.
Vienne, 1887–93. 8°. 12910. dd. 33.

Vito (L. de) Grammatica della lingua tigrigna.
pp. 85. *Roma*, 1895. 8°. 012904. h. 25.

TILES. *See* Ceramics.

TILSIT. Lenz (M.) Tilsit. 1893, *etc.* 8°. Ac.
Berlin. *Verein für Geschichte der Mark Brandenburg.* Märkische Forschungen. N.F. Bd.
6, *etc.* Ac. 7325.

Thimm (R.) Quellen und Bearbeitungen der
Geschichte von Tilsit. *Tilsit*, 1893, *etc.* 8°.
10235. dd.

Tilsit. Aus Tilsits Vergangenheit. 4 Tle.
Tilsit, 1888–91. 8°. 10235. aaa. 34.

TIMBER. *See* Forestry.

TIMBUKTU. Barth (H.) Travels and discoveries in North and Central Africa. pp. 548.
1890. 8°. Bettany (G. T.) Minerva Library.
012207. h.

Bonnetain (*Mme.* P.) Une Française au Soudan.
sur la route de Tombouctou. pp. 377.
Paris, 1894. 8°. 10097. cc. 15.

Jaime (G.) De Koulikoro à Timbouctou.
pp. 436. *Paris*, 1892. 8°. 010096. m. 13.

Joffre (J. J. C.) Opérations de la Colonne
Joffre avant et après l'occupation de Tombouc-
tou. pp. 76. *Paris*, 1895. 8°. 9061. ccc. 33.
See also Africa, *West* : Sahara : Soudan.

TIME, Methods of Reckoning, etc. Ac.
Bologna. *Istituto delle Scienze.* Exposé des
raisons appuyant la transaction proposée par
l'Académie de Bologne au sujet du méridien
initial et de l'heure universelle. pp. 54.
Bologne, 1890. 4°. 8563. g. 8.

Ball (*Sir* R. S.) Time and tide. pp. 192.
1895. 8°.. Romance of Science Series. 4421. dc.

Clauder (H. T.) What Time is it? Manual
of instruction in teaching and reckoning time.
pp. 38. *N.Y.* 1894. 8°. Pam. 38.

Fleming (S.) Time-Reckoning for the twentieth
century. *Washington*, 1889. 8°. Pam. 4.

Grotefend (H.) Zeitrechnung des deutschen
Mittelalters und der Neuzeit.
Hannover, 1891, *etc.* 4°. 8562. ff.

Hammer (E.) Zeitbestimmung, Uhr-Kontrole,
ohne Instrumente. pp. 47. *Stuttgart*, 1893. 8°.
Pam. 4.

Johnson (A. C.) Time-altitudes for expediting
the calculation of apparent-time. pp. 44.
Lond. 1894. 8°. 8548. de. 32.

Laporte (E.) L'heure de Greenwich, ou guide
de l'heure universelle. *Brux.* 1892. *s. sh.* fol.
1810. d. 1. (28.)

Menabrea (L. F.) *Count.* Du méridien initial
et de l'heure universelle. pp. 2.
Paris, 1890. 4°. Pam. 4.

Tondini (C.) Une Solution de la question de
l'heure universelle. 6 pt. *Paris*, 1890. fol.
Pam. 4.

—— Les propositions de la France au sujet de
l'heure universelle. pp. 6. *Paris*, 1890. 8°.
Pam. 4.

—— Examen critique du choix du méridien
initial de Jérusalem. pp. 38. *Rouen*, 1890. 4°.
Pam. 4.

—— Deux appareils indiquant automatiquement
l'heure, *etc.* pp. 4. *Paris*, 1892. fol. Pam. 4.

TIME.—Methods of Reckoning, etc. — *continued.*

TONDINI (C.) La double date sur la surface du globe déterminée par le méridien de l'Observatoire de Bologne. pp. 4. *Paris*, 1892. fol. Pam. 4.

TIME AND SPACE. CRANZ (C.) Gemeinverständliches über die sogenannte vierte Dimension. pp. 70. 1890. 8°. VIRCHOW (R.) Sammlung wissenschaftlicher Vorträge. N.F. Ser. 5. 12249. m.

DEICHMANN (C.) Das Problem des Raumes in der griechischen Philosophie. pp. 103. *Leipz.* 1893. 8°. 8460. f. 24.

DOERING (A.) Über Zeit und Raum. pp. 41. 1894. 8°. Ac. Berlin. *Philosophische Gesellschaft.* Philosophische Vorträge. Folge 3. Hft. 1. Ac. 2737/2.

FARGES (A.) L'Idée de continu dans l'Espace et le Temps. pp. 278. *Paris*, 1892. 8°. 8462. g. 9.

GISEVIUS (H.) Kant's Lehre von Raum und Zeit. pp. 38. *Hannover*, 1890. 8°. 8468. k. 26. (3.)

KEYSERLING (A. v.) *Count.* Einige Worte über Raum und Zeit. pp. 31. *Stuttgart*, 1894. 8°. 8461. b. 29. (11.)

KRASSNIG (J.) Die Zeit- und Raumvorstellung. pp. 39. *Nikolsburg*, 1894. 8°. 8468. k. 28. (10.)

JOVACCHINI (A.) La formazione della vitta nello Spazio e nell Tempo. pp. 359. *Lanciano*, 1891. 8°. 7006. e. 9.

NICHOLS (H.) Our notions of Number and Space. pp. 201. *Bost.* 1894. 8°. 8532. bb. 43.

WHITMELL (C. T.) Space and its dimensions. pp. 28. *Cardiff*, 1893. 8°. Pam. 38.

WILLINK (A.) The World of the unseen. pp. 184. *Lond.* 1893. 8°. 4256. de. 5.

TIMGAD. BOESWILLWALD (E.) and CAGNAT (R.) Timgad, une Cité africaine. *Paris*, 1891, *etc.* 4°. 7703. b.

BALLU (A.) Monuments antiques de l'Algérie. pp. 39. *Paris*, 1894. 8°. 07708 f. 44.

TIN. REYER (E.) History of Tin. pp. 12. *Truro*, 1881. 8°. Pam. 27.

WRAY (L.) Tin Mines of Perak. pp. 78. 1894. 8°. Perak Museum Notes. No. 3. 7297. bb.

See also METALS.

TINTERN ABBEY. TAYLOR (J.) An Hour at Tintern Abbey. pp. 8. *Bristol*, 1891. 4°. Pam. 90.

TIPPERAH. SAMBHUCHANDRA MUKHOPĀD-HYĀYA. Travels between Calcutta and Tipperah. pp. 323. *Calcutta*, 1887. 8°. 10058. cc. 29.

TIPPERARY, County. BASSETT (G. H.) The book of County Tipperary. pp. 422. *Dublin*, 1889. 8°. 10390. df. 8.

WHITE (J. D.) Anthologia Tipperariensis. Account of abbeys, churches, castles, *etc.* pp. 143. *Cashel*, 1892. 4°. 10390. g. 18.

TIRCONNELL. *See* DONEGAL.

TIRYNS. *See* GREECE, *Antiquities.*

TITANIUM. LÉVY (L.) Contribution à l'étude du titane. pp. 87. *Paris*, 1891. 4°. 7109. dd. 4.

See also METALS.

TITHES. BRAMWELL (G. W. W.) *Baron Bramwell.* Tithes. Speeches. pp. 23. *Lond.* 1887. 12°. Pam. 92.

CLARKE (H. W.) History of Tithes. pp. 268. *Lond.* 1891. 8°. 4109. e. 22.

DAWSON (J.) Injustice of recent and present Tithes. pp. 24. *Bradford*, 1891. 8°. 4109. aaaa. 21. (6.)

TITHES—*continued.*

FISHER (F. W.) Tithe Rent Charge Legislation. Session 1888. pp. 15. *Doncaster*, 1888. 8°. 6190. cc. 3. (2.)

LESLIE (R. J.) Tract upon Tithes. pp. 32. *Lond.* 1894. 8°. 4109. k. 12. (12.)

PALMER (R.) *Earl of Selbourne.* Ancient facts and fictions concerning Churches and Tithes. pp. 413. *Lond.* 1892, 8°. 2216. b. 2.

SLATER (J. H.) God and our Right. Defence of tithe, *etc.* pp. 134. *Lond.* 1894. 8°. 4109. bb. 28.

SQUIRE (W. H.) and PETERSON (E. W. I.) Tithe Rentcharge Recovery Bill, 1890. pp. 12. *Lond.* 1891. 8°. 5155. b. 7. (4.)

STUDD (E. F.) Law of Tithes and Tithe Rent-Charge. pp. 229. *Lond.* 1891. 12°. 5155. f. 10.

THOMAS (W.) The Anti-Tithe Movement in Wales. pp. 111. *Whitland*, 1891. 8°. 4109. b. 24.

THRING (A. T.) The Tithe Act, 1891. pp. 174. *Lond.* 1891. 8°. 5155. de. 21.

WHALLEY (G. H.) The Tithe Acts. pp. 315. *Lond.* 1891. 8°. 5155. de. 20.

WILLIAMSON (S.) The relations between Church and State and the Tithing system. pp. 14. *Liverp.* 1886. 8°. Pam. 92.

BLACK (W. G.) What are Teinds? pp. 110. *Edinb.* 1893. 8°. 5157. b. 13.

ELLIOT (N.) Teinds and procedure in the Court of Teinds, Scotland. pp. 242. *Edinb.* 1893. 8°. 5157. b. 12.

See also LAW, *Ecclesiastical.*

TIVERTON. SNELL (F. J.) Chronicles of Twyford History of Tiverton. pp 394. *Tiverton*, 1892. 8°. 010358. f. 30.

—— Palmerston's Borough. Electioneering anecdotes, *etc.* pp. 141. *Lond.* 1894. 8°. 8139. c. 14.

TIVOLI. WINNEFELD (H.) Die Villa des Hadrian bei Tivoli. pp. 168. 1895. 4°. Ac. Berlin. *Deutsches archäologisches Institut.* Jahrbuch. Erganzungsheft 3. Ac. 5388.

TOBACCO.

Culture : Preparation : Taxation, etc.

LARBALÉTRIER (A.) Le Tabac. pp. 303. *Paris*, 1891. 12°. 7075. bbb. 3.

LEWINSTEIN (G.) Die Belastung des Tabaks in den europäischen Staaten. pp. 106. *Berl.* 1894. 8°. 08226. g. 16.

EPHEM. The Cigar and Tobacco World Diary. *Lond.* 1894, *etc.* 4°. P.P. 2505. sna.

P.P. London. *Tobacco.* "Tobacco" Year Book and Diary. 1894, *etc.* 4°. & fol. P.P. 2505. sn. & 1882. d. 3. (140.)

COMES (O.) La coltivazione sperimentale dei tabacchi durante la campagna 1893. 1894. 4°. Ac. Naples. *Reale Istituto d'Incoraggiamento alle Scienze.* Atti. Ser. 4. Vol. 7. Ac. 2815.

NOVI (G.) La coltivazione dei tabacchi esteri in Napoli nel 1850. 1890. 8°. Ac. Naples. *Società Pontaniana.* Atti. Vol. 20. Ac. 94/2.

ATIENZA Y SIRVENT (M.) Cultivo del tabaco en España. pp. 64. *Madrid*, 1890. 8°. 7073. e. 4. (3.)

PEREZ DEL TORO (F.) El Tabaco canario y las pesquerías en Africa. pp. 236. *Madrid*, 1881. 8°. 7077. de. 44.

MATOSO (E.) Cultivo del tabaco en Argentina, Paraguay y Uruguay. pp. 94. *Corrientes*, 1893. 8°. Pam. 1.

BORNEO. *British North Borneo Company.* The new Tobacco country. pp. 16. *Lond.* 1892. 8°. Pam. 83.

3 н 2

TOBACCO.—Culture, etc.—continued.

AMSTERDAM. *Internationale Koloniale Tentoonstelling.* De Tabak uit de Nederlandsche kolonien. pp. 41. *Amsterdam.* 1883. 8°.
8155. ee. 18. (7.)

HAARSMA (G. E.) Der Tabaksbau in Deli. pp. 240. *Amsterdam,* 1890. 8°. 7077. i. 6.

SUMATRA. Tabaks-Ondernemingen op de oostkust van Sumatra. pp. 21.
Amsterdam, 1891. *obl.* 4°. 8228. aaaa. 21. (4.)

KARSAI (S.) Das deutsche Tabaksteuer-Gesetz, 1879. pp. 120. *Budapest,* 1892. 8°.
08227. h. 25.

LINCKH (O.) Das Tabakmonopol in Württemberg. pp. 75. *Stuttgart,* 1894. 8°. 8228. i. 76.

Tobacco Smoking.

ARNOLD (*Mrs.* R. A.) A woman on Tobacco. pp. 12. *Manchester,* 1885. 8°. 8425. bbb. 43. (1.)

LAURENT (É.) Le Nicotinisme. pp. 221. *Paris,* 1893. 8°. 7660. de. 12.

LEWINSTEIN (G.) Für und wider den Tabak. pp. 112. *Berl.* 1890. 8°. 8435. bb. 61.

PARIS. *Société contre l'abus du Tabac.* Congrès international contre l'abus du Tabac. pp. 236. *Paris,* 1890. 8°. 8436. aaa. 57.

SEUTIN (E.) and (L.) Étude sur les dangers inhérents à l'abus du tabac. pp. 187. *Brux.* 1890. 8°. 7391. g. 17.

SILBERBERG (L.) Tobacco: its use and abuse. pp. 103. *Lond.* 1893. 8°. 7404. df. 6.

TOBACCO TALK. Tobacco Talk. pp. 95. *Phila.* 1894. 8°. 8436. e. 6.

TOBAGO. EPHEM. Creole Almanack for Tobago. *Port of Spain,* 1890, etc. 8°.
P.P. 2587. ab.

PORT OF SPAIN. *Trinidad and Tobago Exhibition.* Official Catalogue. pp. 73. *Port-of-Spain,* 1891. 8°. 7958. g. 17.
See also ENGLAND, *Colonies :* WEST INDIES.

TOBOGGANING. *See* SKATING.

TOILET. BEAUTY : how to get it and keep it. pp. 32. *Lond.* 1885. 8°. 7306. df. 17. (1.)

DRUETTI (G.) L'Arte dei Cosmetici. pp. 142. *Roma,* 1894. 8°. 7404. aaa. 23.

GARCHES (de) *Marquise.* Les secrets de beauté d'une Parisienne. pp 210. *Paris,* 1894. 12°. 7742. bb. 34.

RIS-PAQUOT (O. E.) Le Livre de la Femme d'intérieur. pp. 440. *Paris,* 1892. 8°. 07945. m. 17.

ROAD. The royal road to Beauty. pp. 87. *Bombay,* 1894. 8°. 7404. df. 11.

RUPPERT (A.) A Book of beauty. *Lond.* 1892. *obl.* 8°. 7743. aaa. 47.
—— Natural beauty. pp. 34. 1892. *obl.* 8°. 7743. aaa. 46.
—— Dermatology. A book of beauty. pp. 32. *Lond.* 1892. 8°. 07305. i. 13. (3.)

SCHELENZ-AHLGREEN (H.) Kosmetik. pp. 37. 1894. 8°. VIRCHOW (R.) Sammlung wissenschaftlicher Vorträge. Hft. 203. 12249. l., etc.

STAFFE ( ), *Baroness.* The Lady's Dressing-room. pp. 366. *Lond.* 1892. 8°. 7743. bb. 58.
See also PERFUMERY : HYGIENE : WOMEN, *Diseases, Hygiene, etc.*

TOLEDO. ARRÚE (F. M.) Historia del Alcázar de Toledo. pp. 190. *Madrid,* 1889. 8°. 10160. f. 6.

IBAÑEZ MARÍN (J.) Recuerdos de Toledo. pp. 219. *Madrid,* 1893. 8°. 10160. bbb. 15.

MORALEDA Y ESTEBAN (J.) Leyendas históricas de Toledo. pp. 56. *Toledo,* 1892. 16°. Pam. 91.
—— Numismática Toledana. pp. 35. *Toledo,* 1893. 8°. Pam. 44.

TOLERATION. CREIGHTON (M.) *Bp. of Peterborough.* Persecution and Tolerance. pp. 140. *Lond.* 1895. 8°. 4455. de. 14.

TOMATO. COLLINS (C.) How to grow Tomatoes. 1888. 8°. Fruit Grower's Library. No. 2. 07028. f.

HARRIMAN (G.) Tomato growing as an industry for women. pp. 55. *Lond.* 1894. 8°. 07077. g. 3.

RAVENSCROFT (B. C.) Tomato culture for amateurs. pp. 126. *Lond.* 1890. 8°. 7073. de. 10.
See also GARDENING.

TONG. GRIFFITHS (G.) History of Tong. pp. 236. *Newport,* 1894. 8°. 010358. f. 54.
—— Guide to Tong Church. pp. 83. *Oswestry,* 1885. 8°. 10352. bb. 43.
—— Tong Church, 1892. pp. 8. *Oswestry,* 1892. 4°. Pam. 90.

TONGA. MONFAT (A.) Les Tonga et le R.P. J. Chevron. pp. 473. *Lyon,* 1893. 8°. 4766. dd. 13.

THOMSON (B.) Diversions of a Prime Minister. pp. 407. *Edinb.* 1894. 8°. 10491. e. 29.

TONGA. The Criminal and Civil Code of Tonga. pp. 139. *Auckland,* 1891. 8°. 6785. b. 13.
See also PACIFIC OCEAN AND ISLANDS.

TONGARIRO. *See* NEW ZEALAND.

TONGUE. JESSETT (F. B.) Cancer of the Tongue. pp. 183. *Lond.* 1892. 8°. 7616. f. 6.

THIÉRY (P.) Ulcération tuberculeuse de la langue guérie par l'iodoforme. 1890. 8°.

VERNEUIL (A. A.) Études sur la tuberculose. Tom. 2. 7561. k. 1.
See also MOUTH.

TONIC SOL FA NOTATION. *See* MUSIC, *General.*

TONKIN. *See* TUNG-KING.

TONNERE. MOREAU (G.) Tonnerre pendant la Révolution. pp. 306. *Tonnerre,* 1890. 8°. 9226. bbb. 18.

TÖNSBERG. TÖNSBERG. Tönsberg. *Tönsberg,* 1893. *obl.* 12°. 10281. a. 1.

TONSILS. *See* THROAT.

TOPEKA. GILES (F. W.) Thirty Years in Topeka. pp. 412. *Topeka,* 1886. 8°. 10413. e. 9.

JACKSON (M. S.) Topeka pen and camera Sketches. pp. 192. *Topeka,* 1890. 8°. 10408. e. 29.

TOPS. PERRY (J.) Spinning Tops. pp. 136. 1890. 8°. Romance of Science Series. 4421. de.

TORONTO. ROBERTSON (J. R.) Landmarks of Toronto. *Toronto,* 1894, *etc.* 8°. 10460. ff. 20.

AC. Toronto. *University of Toronto.* Calendar of the University. *Toronto,* 1889, *etc.* 8°. P.P. 2539. hb.
—— Benefactors of the University of Toronto after the fire of 1890. pp. 58. *Toronto,* 1892. 8°. 8365. aa. 20.

TORPEDOES. DRAKE (F. J.) Automobile Torpedoes. pp. 52. 1893. 8°. Ac. Annapolis. *U.S. Naval Institute.* Papers. Vol. 19. Ac. 4398.

HENNEBERT (E.) Torpilles sèches. pp. 239. 1894. 8°. Encyclopédie des aide-mémoire. 8709. g.

JONES (G. H.) Improved Torpedo Guard for ships of war. pp. 12. *Lond.* 1893. 4°. 8806. g. 25.

See also NAVAL SCIENCE.

TORQUAY. TORQUAY. Where to buy at Torquay. pp. 38. *Brighton,* 1890. 4°. 10368. k. 38.

TORRE DEL GRECO. CASTALDI (G.) and
(F.) Storia di Torre del Greco. pp. 294.
Torre del Greco, 1890. 8°.   10131. h. 11.

TORRES STRAITS. *See* NEW GUINEA.

TORTOISE. SAUZIER (T.) Les Tortues de
terre gigantesques des Mascareignes. pp. 32.
Paris, 1893. 8°.   7204. c. 17. (13.)

VAILLANT (L.) Les Tortues éteintes de l'île
Rodriguez. pp. 37. *Paris,* 1893. 4°. 7203. h. 13.
See also REPTILES.

TORTS, Law of. ADDISON (C. G.) Treatise
on the law of Torts. pp. 893. *Lond.* 1893. 8°.
     2018. e.

FRASER (H.) Compendium of the law of Torts.
pp. 204. *Lond.* 1895. 8°.   6325. de. 42.

GIRIDHĀRI LĀLA. Selection from the law of
Torts. pp. 20. *Allahabad,* 1889. 8°. Pam. 34.

INNES (L. C.) Principles of the law of Torts.
pp. 308. *Lond.* 1891. 8°.   6325. cc. 20.

POLLOCK (*Sir* F.) Law of Torts. pp. 636.
Lond. 1895. 8°.   2230. bb. 6.

RINGWOOD (R.) Outlines of the law of Torts.
pp. 253. *Lond.* 1894. 8°.   6325. df. 23.

UNDERHILL (A.) Summary of the law of Torts.
pp. 388. *Lond.* 1894. 8°.   2230. b. 19.

TOTOWA. TOTOWA. *Dutch Church.* History of the old Dutch Church at Totowa.
pp. 170. *Paterson, N.J.,* 1892. 8°. 9903. f. 15.

TOTTENHAM. TOTTENHAM. History of
Tottenham. pp. 35. *Lond.* 1891. 4°.
     10368. cc. 40.

TOUL. DENIS (A.) Le Club des Jacobins de
Toul. pp. 130. *Paris,* 1895. 8°.   9231. l. 5.

TOULON. LAMBERT (G.) Histoire du siège
de Toulon, 1707. pp. 101. *Toulon,* 1891. 8°.
     9080. bbb. 32.

TOULOUSE. DOUAIS (C.) La Confrérie de
l'Assomption à Saint-Étienne de Toulouse.
pp. 24. *Paris,* 1892. 8°.   4629. ee. 7. (8.)

—— Des fortunes commerciales à Toulouse
d'après deux testaments, XIIIᵉ-XVᵉ siècle.
pp. 27. *Paris,* 1894. 4°.   Pam. 91.

LAHONDÈS (J. de) L'église Saint-Étienne.
pp. 482. *Toulouse,* 1890. 8°.   4629. i. 15.

CLAUDIN (A.) Les enlumineurs, les relieurs et
les imprimeurs de Toulouse aux XVᵉ et XVIᵉ siècles.
pp. 67. *Paris,* 1893. 8°.   011902. m. 21. (12.)

CASTERAS (P. de) La Société toulousaine à la
fin du dix-huitième siècle. pp. 363.
Toulouse, 1891. 8°.   010171. e. 8.

DUBOUL (A.) La fin du Parlement de Toulouse.
pp. 430. *Toulouse,* 1890. 8°.   9231. i. 9.

—— Le Tribunal révolutionnaire de Toulouse,
1794. pp. 168. *Toulouse,* 1894. 8°. 9231. i. 13.

—— L'Armée révolutionnaire de Toulouse.
pp. 265. *Toulouse,* 1891. 8°.   9226. e. 6.

BOUGLON (R. de) Les reclus de Toulouse sous
la Terreur. *Toulouse,* 1893, *etc.* 8°.
     10660. gg. 32.

TOURAINE. BOUSREZ (L.) Les monuments
mégalithiques de la Touraine. pp. 112.
Tours, 1894. 8°.   7708. de. 41.

BRUNG (F.) L'âge de pierre en Touraine.
pp. 64. *Tours,* 1892. 8°.   07708. g. 20.

ESPINAY (G. d') Les réformes de la Coutume de
Touraine au XVIᵉ siècle. pp. 246.
Tours, 1891. 8°.   5406. e. 3.

DUPIN DE SAINT-ANDRÉ (A.) Les Églises réformées disparues en Touraine. pp. 58.
Paris, 1892. 8°.   4629. f. 33.

ARNAULT (V.) Le Clergé de Touraine pendant
la Révolution, 1789-1800. pp. 409.
Tours, 1893. 8°.   4629. d. 11.

TOURAINE—*continued.*

CARRÉ DE BUSSEROLLE (J. X.) La Chouannerie
en Touraine. 1799-1801. pp. 20.
Montsoreau, 1890. 8°.   9072. cc. 4. (5.)

COOK (T. A.) Old Touraine. 2 vol.
Lond. 1893. 8°.   010171. e. 16.

PARAMONDON (G.) Quinze jours en Touraine.
pp. 103. *Paris,* 1894. 12°.   10168. b. 55.

ROBIDA (A.) La vieille France. La Touraine.
Paris, 1892. 8°.   10172. i.
See also TOURS.

TOURC'H. VILLIERS DU TERRAGE ( ) *Viscount.* Notes sur la paroisse de Tourc'h. pp. 18.
Quimper, 1894. 8°.   10106. i. 1. (15.)

TOURNAI. HERBOMEZ (A. d') Histoire des
châtelains de Tournai de la maison de Mortagne. 2 tom. 1895. 8°. Ac. Tournay.
Société historique. Mémoires. Tom. 24, 25.
     Ac. 7600/2.

HOYOIS (J.) Un Coin de l'histoire littéraire belge.
pp. 202. *Gand,* 1893. 8°.   011850. i. 52.

LA GRANGE (A. de) Documents relatifs à quel-
ques anciens monuments de Tournai. 1890. 8°.
Ac. Tournay. *Société historique.* Bulletins.
Tom. 23.   Ac. 7600.

TOURNON. MASSIP (M.) Le Collège de
Tournon en Vivarais. pp. 323. *Paris,* 1890. 8°.
     8356. f. 37.

TOURNUS. Ac. Tournus. *Société des Amis
des Arts.* Histoire de la ville & du canton de
Tournus. pp. 344. *Tournus,* 1892. 8°.
     10171. g. 1.

TOURS. DUCHESNE (L.) Les anciens Catalogues episcopaux de Tours. pp. 102.
Paris, 1890. 8°.   4865. dd. 11.

MOUETTE (A.) Dix ans à Tours sous Louis XI.
pp. 78. *Tours,* 1890. 12°.   10169. c. 15.

RATEL (S.) Les Basiliques de Saint Martin à
Tours. 2 pt. *Brux.* 1886, 90. 8°. 7709. g. 29.

MESNAGE (V.) Les Vitraux de l'Église Saint-
Saturnin de Tours. pp. 46. *Tours,* 1890. 4°.
     7805. eec. 28.

DUMAS (F.) La Généralité de Tours au XVIIIᵉ
siècle. pp. 437. *Paris,* 1894. 8°. 08226. l. 2.
See also TOURAINE.

TOWEDNACK. MATTHEWS (J. H.) History
of the parishes of St. Ives, Towednack and
Zennor. pp. 56. *Lond.* 1892. 4°. 10368. h. 30.

TOWER, of London. *See* LONDON, *Tower.*

**TOWNS: MUNICIPALITIES: VIL-
LAGES.** ARNOLD (T. J.) Law relating to
Municipal Corporations in England and Wales.
pp. 931. *Lond.* 1894. 8°.   6425. de. 23.

BROWN (F. J.) Streets and Slums. pp. 21.
Baltimore, 1891. 8°.   8277. ee. 28. (2.)

CAPITALES. Les Capitales du Monde.
Paris, 1892, *etc.* 4°.   10025. g.

CHAMPERNOWNE (H.) The Boss. Essay upon
the art of governing American cities. pp. 243.
N.Y. 1894. 8°.   8176. de. 2.

CHARTERIS (F. W.) *Earl of Wemyss.* Modern
Municipalism. pp. 23. *Lond.* 1893. 8°.
     8277. ee. 30. (19.)

CHICAGO. How to Govern Chicago. pp. 118.
Chicago, 1895. 8°.   8176. de. 7.

CONKLING (A. R.) City government in the
United States. pp. 227. *N.Y.* 1894. 8°.
     8176. de. 3.

CROFTS (W. C.) Municipal Socialism. pp. 14.
Lond. 1892. 8°.   08276. de. 8. (10.)

DOLMAN (F.) Municipalities at work. pp. 143.
1895. 8°. GIBBINS (H. de B.) Social Questions
of to-day.   08276. e.

TOWNS, etc.—*continued.*

GORRINI (G.) La concessione délla Cittadinanza. pp. 216. *Voghera,* 1890. 8°.   8009. c. 26.

GRAHAM (P. A.) The rural Exodus. Problem of the village and the town. pp. 216 1892. 8°.

GIBBINS H. de B.) Social Questions of to-day.   08276. e.

IZOULET (J.) La Cité moderne et la métaphysique de la sociologie. pp. 691. *Paris,* 1894. 8°.   08277. g. 15.

LIFE. Life in our Villages. By the Special Commissioner of the Daily News. pp. 192. *Lond.* 1891. 8°.   8139. aa. 46.

COOPER (A. N.) Our Villages. Reply to the Daily News Commissioner. pp. 26. *Lond.* 1891. 8°.   08276. f. 20. (16.)

MEYN (E.) Stadterweiterungen in rechtlicher Beziehung. pp. 97. *Berl.* 1893. 8°. 05604. i. 25.

MUIRHEAD (J.) Byelaws and standing orders for Burghs in Scotland. pp. 284. *Glasg.* 1895. 8°.   6583. g. 17.

PARKHURST (C. H.) Our fight with Tammany. pp. 296. *N.Y.* 1895. 8°.   8176. de. 4.

STUEBBEN (J.) Der Städtebau. pp. 561. 1890. 8°. DURM (J.) Handbuch der Architektur. Thl. 4.   7815. bb. 12.

SCRIVENER (S. C.) The de-population of Villages. pp. 16. *Lond.* 1891. 8°.   08276. f. 20. (19.)

SHAW (A.) Municipal government in Great Britain. pp. 385. *Lond.* 1895. 8°. 8139. d. 2.

WHITE (A.) The problems of a Great City. pp. 275. *Lond.* 1895. 8°.   08275. e. 36.

See also BUILDING, *Law* : LOCAL GOVERNMENT : SANITATION.

History of the growth of Municipalities, etc.

BELOW (G. von) Der Ursprung der deutschen Stadtverfassung. pp. 147. *Düsseldorf,* 1892. 8°.   5604. bb. 5.

KEUTGEN (F.) Untersuchungen über den Ursprung der deutschen Stadtverfassung. pp. 236. *Leipz.* 1895. 8°.   5604. e. 4.

NAEHER (J.) Die deutsche Burg, ihre Entstehung und ihr Wesen. pp. 43. *Berl.* 1885. 8°.   7709. bb. 66.

RIETSCHEL (S.) Die civitas auf deutschem Boden bis zum Ausgange der Karolingerzeit. pp. 102. *Leipz.* 1894. 8°.   5206. c. 1.

KUNTZE (J. E.) Die deutschen Stadtgründungen. pp. 79. *Leipz.* 1891. 8°.   8009. c. 27.

HEGEL (C.) Städte der germanischen Völker im Mittelalter. 6 Bde. *Leipz.* 1891. 8°. 8248. g. 13.

GREEN (A. S.) Town Life in the fifteenth century. 2 vol. *Lond.* 1894. 8°.   2258. b. 23.

JEWITT (L.) Corporation Plate and insignia of office of England and Wales. 2 vol. *Lond.* 1895. 4°.   7709. l. 21.

TOXICOLOGY. AUTENRIETH (W.) Kurze Anleitung zur Auffindung der Gifte. pp. 65. *Freiburg,* 1892. 8°.   7305. f. 5. (1.)

BLYTH (A. W.) Poisons : their effects and detection. pp. 724. *Lond.* 1895. 8°. 2255. d. 6.

BROUARDEL (P.) and OGIER (J.) La Laboratoire de toxicologie. pp. 224. *Paris,* 1891. 8°.   7510. dd. 14.

CHAPMAN (H. C.) Manual of Medical Jurisprudence and Toxicology. pp. 237. *Phila.* 1892. 8°.   6095. aaa. 33.

CHARRIN (A.) Les poisons de l'organisme. pp. 188. 1895. 8°. Encyclopédie des aide-mémoire.   8709. a.

G. B. & I. Pharmacy and Poison Laws of the United Kingdom. pp. 220. *Lond.* 1892. 8°.   6095. a. 34.

TOXICOLOGY—*continued.*

GUÉRIN (G.) Traité d'analyse chimique et de recherches toxicologiques. pp. 492. *Paris,* 1893. 8°.   8908. h. 37.

HUGOUNENQ (L.) Traité des poisons. pp. 509. *Paris,* 1891. 8°.   7510. d. 2.

JAKSCH (R. v.) Die Vergiftungen. 2 Hfte. 1894. 8°. NOTHNAGEL (H.) Specielle Pathologie.   7441. d.

KOHUT (A.) Berühmte und berüchtigte Giftmischerinnen. pp. 184. *Berl.* 1893. 8°.   6057. b. 32.

LINSTOW (O. v.) Die Giftthiere und ihre Wirkung auf dem Menschen. pp. 147. *Berl.* 1894. 8°.   7204. c. 18.

LOEW (O.) Ein natürliches System der Gift-Wirkungen. pp. 136. *München,* 1893. 8°.   07509. i. 4.

LUFF (A. P.) Text-book of Forensic Medicine and Toxicology. 2 vol. *Lond.* 1895. 8°.   6095. df. 1.

MANN (J. D.) Forensic Medicine and Toxicology. pp. 639. *Lond.* 1893. 8°. 6095. d. 36.

MURRELL (W.) First aid in Poisoning. *Lond.* 1893. s. sh. fol.   1830. c. 1. (86.)

—— What to do in cases of Poisoning. pp. 276. *Lond.* 1893. 8°.   7509. a. 10.

—— Aids to Forensic Medicine and Toxicology. pp. 114. *Lond.* 1894. 8°. 6095. a. 35.

OLIVER (T.) Lead poisoning. pp. 121. *Edinb.* 1891. 8°.   7620. df. 24.

POLIN (L. H. A. M.) and LABIT (H. J. J. P.) Étude sur les Empoisonnements alimentaires. pp. 226. *Paris,* 1890. 8°.   7560. e. 17.

SANGER (C. R.) Quantitative determination of Arsenic by the Berzelius-Marsh process. pp. 21. 1891. 8°.   Pam. 13.

—— On the formation of volatile compounds of Arsenic from arsenical Wall Papers. pp. 65. 1894. 8°.   Pam. 13.

See also CRIME : MEDICINE, *Legal* : PTOMAINES.

TOYS. CLARÉTIE (L.) Les Jouets. Histoire—fabrication. pp. 324. *Paris,* 1894. 4°.   7944. h. 35.

TRADE, FINANCE, TAXATION, etc.

Finance, *General, Public.*

BASTABLE (C. F.) Public Finance. pp. 716. *Lond.* 1895. 8°.   2020. c.

CARROLL (E.) Principles and practice of Finance. pp. 311. *Lond.* 1895. 8°. 08226. h. 28.

COSSA (E.) I fenomeni della Finanza pubblica. pp. 120. *Milano,* 1892. 8°.   08227. i. 27.

KOERNER (A.) Staatsschuldentilgung und Staatsbankerott. pp. 104. *Wien,* 1893. 8°.   08227. i. 31.

LEROY-BEAULIEU (P. P.) Traité de la science des Finances. 2 tom. *Paris,* 1892, 91. 8°.   08227. g. 37.

MUZII (A.) Trattato sulla stima dei Fondi. pp. 559. *Napoli,* 1891. 8°.   8229. f. 41.

ROSS (E. A.) Sinking Funds. pp. 106. *Baltimore,* 1892. 8°.   08227. i. 9.

SCOTT (W. A.) Repudiation of State Debts. pp. 325. 1893. 8°. ELY (R. T.) Library of Economics. No. 2.   08225. ee.

SEIDLER (G.) Leitfaden der Staatsverrechnung. *Wien,* 1891, *etc.* 8°.   08225. h.

STOURM (R.) Cours de Finances. Le Budget. pp. 655. *Paris,* 1889. 8°.   08227. ee. 19.

WAGNER (A.) Finanzwissenschaft. 3 Thle. *Leipz.* 1883-90. 8°.   08227. g. 22.

WORMS (É.) Doctrine, histoire et réforme financière. pp. 401. *Paris,* 1891. 8°.   08227. h. 20.

TRADE AND FINANCE—*continued.*

See also POLITICAL ECONOMY, and under the sub-heading *Trade and Finance* of each country.

Tariffs. *See infra: Free Trade, etc.*

Taxation, *National and Local.*

ATKINSON (E.) Taxation and work. pp. 296. *N.Y.* 1892. 8°.   08276. f. 64.

COHEN (S. S.) Moral purport of the single Tax. pp. 12. *N.Y.* 1895. 12°.   Pam. 82.

CONIGLIANI (C. A.) Teoria degli effetti delle imposte. pp. 281. *Milano,* 1890. 8°.   8207. g. 41.

COURTRAY (L.) Les Impôts sur le luxe en France et à l'etranger. pp. 196. *Paris,* 1895. 8°.   08226. k. 8.

DAVIDSON (D.) Öfversikt af den i utlandet gällande lagstiftningen angående Inkomstskatt. pp. 210. *Upsala,* 1893. 8°.   8227. h. 42.

DEFOURNY (P. G.) Le Militarisme et les impô s modernes. pp. 24. *Grenoble,* 1890. 8°. Pam. 67.

FRANCE. *M. des Finances.* L'Impôt sur le Revenu et l'Impôt sur les Revenus dans les pays étrangers. pp. 914. *Paris,* 1894, 4°.   8223. d. 52.

HELFERICH (J. A. R.) Teoria dell' imposta. 1889. 8°. Biblioteca dell' economista. Ser. 3. Vol. 14.   8205. l.

MACDONALD (J.) Poverty, Wealth and Taxation. pp. 194. *Lond.* 1891. 8°.   08276. h. 12.

MALLET (B.) Principle of progression in Taxation. 1894. 8°. MACKAY (T.) Policy of free exchange.   08225. k. 5.

PATTEN (S. N.) Principles of rational Taxation. pp. 25. 1890. 8°. Ac. Philadelphia. *University.* Publications. Pol. Economy Series. No. 6.   Ac. 2692. p.

RICARDO (D.) Principles of Political Economy and Taxation. pp. 455. 1891. 8°. Bohn's Economic Library.   2500. i.

SELIGMAN (E. R. A.) Essays in Taxation. pp. 434. *N.Y.* 1895. 8°.   08226. h. 31.

—— On the shifting and incidence of Taxation. pp. 191. 1892. 8°. Ac. Saratoga. *American Economic Association.* Publications. Vol. 7.   Ac. 2388.

SHEARMAN (T. G.) Natural Taxation. pp. 239. *N.Y.* 1895. 8°.   8176. bbb.

BAUMANN (A. A.) Betterment. pp. 110. *Lond.* 1893. 8°   8277. de. 25.

—— Betterment, worsement and recoupment. pp. 116. *Lond.* 1894. 8°.   08275. e. 10.

O'MEARA (J. J.) Municipal Taxation at home and abroad. pp. 310. *Lond.* 1894. 8°.   08225. ee. 12.

ROSEWATER (V.) Special Assessments. Study in municipal finance. pp. 152. 1893. 8°. Ac. New York. *Columbia College.* Studies, *etc.* Vol. 2.   Ac. 2688/2.

See also LAND, *England, Taxation of :* POLITICAL ECONOMY, and under the sub-heading *Trade and Finance* of each country.

For Local Taxation. *See also* LOCAL GOVERNMENT.

Trade, *General.*

BITHELL (R.) A Counting-House dictionary. pp. 326. *Lond.* 1893. 8°.   08227. de. 19.

BORGHT (R. v. d.) Das Verkehrswesen. pp. 468. 1894. 8°. FRANKENSTEIN (K.) Handbuch der Staatswissenschaften. Bd. 7.   8009. k.

BRASILIER (A.) Théorie mathématique des placements et emprunts à long terme. *Paris,* 1891, *etc.* 8°.   08225. l. 1.

TRADE AND FINANCE—*continued.*

CANTILLON (R.) Essai sur le Commerce. pp. 430. *Lond.* 1892. 12°.   08226. f. 6.

CARDENAL MARTÍN (J.) Cálculos mercantiles. Operaciones de banca y bolsa. pp. 199. *Madrid,* 1890. 8°.   8228. aa. 55.

COHN (G.) The science of Finance. pp. 800. *Chicago,* 1895. 8°.   8229. df. 37.

COQUEUGNIOT (E.) L'Avocat des commerçants et des industriels. pp. 578. *Paris,* 1892. 8°.   5405. de. 5.

COUNSELS. Brief counsels concerning Business. pp. 223. *Lond.* 1891. 8°.   4429. ee. 20.

FOWLER (N. C.) Building Business. pp. 518. *Bost.* 1893. 4°.   08227. ee. 34.

FRANÇOIS (G.) Le Commerce. pp. 211. *Paris,* 1894. 8°.   8227. aa. 45.

GAMBARO (R.) Lessons in Commerce. pp. 247. *Lond.* 1895. 8°.   08226. f. 28.

GARLAND (S. C.) How to purchase and succeed in a Business. pp. 8. *Deptford,* 1891. 8°.   08227. ee. 46. (8.)

GIBBINS (H. de B.) Economics of Commerce. pp. 94. 1894. 8°. Methuen's Commercial Series.   08227. de.

GUNN (E. S.) Business Training manual. pp. 146. *Lond.* 1893. 8°.   08225. g. 3.

JACKSON (S.) Primer of Business. pp. 96. 1894. 8°. Methuen's Commercial Series. No. 2.   08227. de.

JEANS (J. S.) Trusts, Pools and Corners as affecting commerce and industry. pp. 190. 1894. 8°. GIBBINS (H. de B.) Social Questions of to-day. Vol. 11.   08276. e.

HAGE (C.) Haandbog i Handelsvidenskab. *Kjøbenh.* 1890, *etc.* 8°.   08227. ee.

JANNET (C.) Le Capital, la Spéculation et la finance au XIXᵉ siècle. pp. 607. *Paris,* 1892. 8°.   8227. h. 38.

LESSONS. One hundred lessons in Business. *Lond.* 1892. 8°.   08227. e. 36.

LÉVY (R. G.) Mélanges financiers. pp. 316. *Paris,* 1894. 8°.   8228. cc. 49.

MAC LEAN (G. N.) How to do Business. pp. 207. *Chicago,* 1890. 8°.   08227. h. 1.

MALLETT (D. T.) When : Business hints. pp. 41. *N.Y.* 1890. 4°.   Pam. 23.

MATAJA (V.) Grossmagazine und Kleinhandel. pp. 105. *Leipz.* 1891. 8°.   08227. ee. 39.

OOSTING (J.) Practisch Handelswoordenboek. *Dutch. Ger. Eng.* and *Fr.* pp. 579. *Gouda,* 1890. 8°.   12902. dd. 25.

PARIS. *Congrès International du Commerce.* Rapports, discussions et résolutions. pp. 637. *Paris,* 1890. 8°.   08227. k. 29.

PEEZ (A.) Zur neuesten Handelspolitik. pp. 347. *Wien,* 1895. 8°.   8226. ff. 35.

PHILLIPS H. (J.) Enciclopedia comercial. pp. 227. *Valparaiso,* 1888. fol.   6785. l. 1.

PHILP (R. K.) Handy-book of Shop-keeping. *Lond.* 1892. 8°.   8228. aaa. 27.

WEICHS-GLON (F. zu) *Baron.* Das finanzielle und soziale Wesen der modernen Verkehrsmittel. pp. 252. *Tübingen,* 1894. 8°.   08235. f. 42.

WHITFIELD (E. E.) School introduction to Commercial Sciences. pp. 304. *Lond.* 1892. 8°.   08227. de. 29.

See also BANKING : BILLS : CAPITAL AND LABOUR : COMPANIES : LAW, *Commercial :* MONOPOLIES : POLITICAL ECONOMY : STOCKS AND SHARES : and under the sub-heading *Trade and Finance* of each country.

TRADE AND FINANCE—continued.
Depressions in Trade, etc.

ARMSDEN (J.) Trade Depressions. pp. 31.
Lond. 1892. 8°.   8228. aaaa. 17. (13.)

CROCKER (U. H.) Over-production and commercial Distress. pp. 37. *Bost.* 1887. 8°.
                                        08227. f. 16.

—— Cause of hard times. pp. 114.
Bost. 1895. 8°.   08275. g. 3.

HAYWARD (M. P.) Protection the only remedy for depression. pp. 31. *Cheltenham,* 1888. 8°.
                                    8228. aaaa. 19. (2.)

HYNDMAN (H. M.) Commercial Crises of the nineteenth century. pp. 174. *Lond.* 1892. 8°.
                                        08276. e. 35.

JUGLAR (C.) History of Panics and their periodical occurrence in the United States. pp. 150.
N.Y. 1893. 8°.   08225. ee. 8.

LAYCOCK (F. U.) Economics and socialism.
pp. 390. *Lond.* 1895. 8°.   08277. g. 8.

O., A. J. The Cause of a Crisis. pp. 19.
Hobart, 1894. 8°.   08226. h. 14. (17.)

RUHKOPF (C.) Rodbertus Theorie von den Handelskrisen. pp. 87. *Leipz.* 1892. 8°.
                                    8277. h. 18. (10.)

SMITH (C. W.) Original theories upon and remedies for Depression in Trade. pp. 74.
Lond. 1893. 8°.   8226. aaa. 51.

—— Commercial Gambling : causes of depression.
pp. 170. *Lond.* 1893. 8°.   08227. de. 32.

U.S. *Bureau of Labour.* Industrial Depressions.
pp. 496. 1886. 8°. First Annual Report of the
Bureau of Labour.   8275. k.

Free Trade and Protection : Tariffs.

Ac. *London. Cobden Club.* LEADAM (I. S.)
What Protection does for the farmer and
labourer. pp. 104. *Lond.* 1893. 8°.   8228. bb.

ACHTUNDVIERZIGER. Freihandel. pp. 40. 1891. 8°.
Schweizer Zeitfragen. No. 21.   8074. f.

BONHAM (J. M.) Industrial Liberty. pp. 414.
N.Y. 1888. 8°.   8275. dd. 19.

BANCROFT (H.) England and free trade versus
the U.S. and protection. pp. 12.
Lond. 1891. 8°.   Pam. 23.

CABALLERO Y ESTEVAN (T. T.) La Protección y
el libre cambio ante la producción nacional.
pp. 287. *Madrid,* 1883. 8°.   8229. aaaa. 16.

CHARLES-ROUX (J.) La Liberté commerciale et
la politique des traités de Commerce. pp. 61.
Paris, 1895. 8°.   Pam. 23.

CRAVEN (J.) Tariffs. pp. 8.
Bradford, 1893. 8°.   08227. de. 40. (12.)

DOMERGUE (J.) La Comédie libre-échangiste.
pp. 286. *Paris,* 1891. 12°.   08227. e. 21.

—— Les Dessous du libre-échange lyonnais.
pp. 69. *Paris,* 1891. 8°.   Pam. 23.

EPHEM. Fair-trade Almanack and Diary.
Lond. 1891, *etc.* 8°.   P.P. 2502. h.

FARQUHAR (A. B.) and (H.) Economic and industrial Delusions. pp. 424. *N.Y.* 1891. 8°.
                                        8227. dd. 30.

GEORGE (H.) Protection or free trade ? pp. 216.
N.Y. 1891. 8°.   8228. aaa. 24.

GLADSTONE (*Right Hon.* W. E.) A Duel. Free
Trade—W. E. Gladstone. Protection—J. G.
Blaine. pp. 54. *N.Y.* 1890. 8°.   08227. g. 17.

H., M. Socialism or protection ? pp. 79.
Lond. 1894. 8°.   08275. e. 19.

HARTE (J. J. I.) Vrijhandel en Bescherming.
pp. 102. *'s-Gravenh.* 1890. 8°.   08227. ee. 16.

HAYWARD (M. P.) Protection the only remedy
for agricultural and other depression. pp. 31.
Cheltenham, 1888. 8°.   8228. aaaa. 19. (2.)

TRADE AND FINANCE.—Free Trade, etc.—continued.

HEWES (F. W.) and MAC KINLEY (W.) What Are
The Facts ? Protection and Reciprocity illustrated. pp. 126. *N.Y.* 1892. 8°.   8226. i. 11.

HUNT (J.) A Home and Work for every man.
[Argument for protection.] pp. 161.
Lond. 1895. 8°.   08275. ee. 28.

LOFFT (R. E.) The Great Experiment : mock
free trade. pp. 15. *Bury St. Edmund's,* 1894. 8°.
                                    08226. h. 14. (16.)

LOMBARD (F.) Le Protectionnisme et la ligue
contre le renchérissement de la vie. pp. 23.
Genève, 1891. 8°.   08227. ee. 46. (10.)

NICHOLSON (J. S.) Tariffs and international commerce. 1892. 8°. Ac. Edinburgh. *Scottish
Geographical Society.* Britannic Confederation.
                                        Ac. 6182/2.

PARETO (V.) Le Protectionnisme en Italie.
pp. 16. *Paris,* 1891. 8°.   Pam. 23.

PATTEN (S. N.) Economic basis of Protection.
pp. 144. *Phila.* 1890. 12°.   08225. ee. 4.

POINSARD (L.) Libre-Échange et Protection.
pp. 631. *Paris,* 1893. 8°.   8226. bbb. 40.

RABBENO (U.) Protezionismo Americano.
pp. 511. *Milano,* 1893. 8°.   08226. g. 4.

S., S. L. The Great Bread Riots ; or, What came
of fair trade. pp. 60. *Lond.* 1885. 16°.
                                    12315. aaa. 49.

SALOMON (L.) Deux années de protectionnisme
en France et en Italie. pp. 58.
Milan, 1890. fol.   8228. l. 6.

SIDES. Both Sides of the Tariff question.
pp. 298. *N.Y.* 1890. 8°.   08227. ee. 35.

TENREIRO (L.) Protección ó libre cambio.
pp. 38. *Madrid,* 1893. 8°.   08226. k. 5. (9.)

TRUMBULL (M. M.) The Free Trade struggle in
England. pp. 288. *Chicago,* 1892. 8°.
                                    08227. de. 30. (1.)

WILLIAMSON (A.) British Industries and foreign
competition. pp. 311. *Lond.* 1894. 8°. 08226. f. 11.

See also GEOGRAPHY, *Commercial :* LAW, *Commercial :* MONOPOLIES : PRICES.

History : International Commerce.

BASTABLE (C. F.) The Commerce of nations.
pp. 216. 1892. 8°. GIBBINS (H. de B.) Social
Questions of to-day.   08276. e.

BONASSIEUX (P.) Les grandes Compagnies de
Commerce. pp. 562. *Paris,* 1892. 8°. 9009. h. 4.

BOURNE (H. R. F.) Famous London Merchants.
pp. 314. *Lond.* 1890. 8°.   10803. aa. 24.

BRENNWALD (A.) Zur Lage des Welthandels.
Berl. 1891, *etc.* 8°.   08229. k.

CUNNINGHAM (W.) Growth of English industry
and commerce. 2 vol. *Camb.* 1890–92. 2020. d.

CHISHOLM (G. G.) The Commerce of the British
Empire. 1892. 8°. Ac. Edinburgh. *Scottish
Geographical Society.* Britannic Confederation.
                                        Ac. 6182/2.

GIBBINS (H. de B.) History of Commerce in
Europe. pp. 233. *Lond.* 1891. 8°. 8226. aaa. 47.

HUBBARD (G. G.) Evolution of Commerce.
pp. 18. 1892. 8°. Ac. Washington. *National
Geographic Society.* National Geographic Magazine. Vol. 4.   Ac. 6192.

HUBER (F. C.) Die geschichtliche Entwickelung
des modernen Verkehrs. pp. 232.
Tübingen, 1893. 8°.   08247. ff. 24.

NOËL (O.) Histoire du Commerce du Monde.
Paris, 1891, *etc.* 8°.   8228. l.

RAVALOVICH (A.) L'Année économique, 1888-
89. pp. 279. *Paris,* 1889. 8°.   08227. ee. 9.

—— Le Marché financier, 1893-94. pp. 475.
Paris, 1894. 8°.   08225. l. 25.

TRADE AND FINANCE. — History, etc.—continued.

SCHMIDT-WEISSENFELS (E.) Geschichte des modernen Reichtums, in biographischen und sachlichen Beispielen. pp. 391. *Berl.* 1893. 8°.
09325. g, 8.

SONNDORFER (R.) Die Technik des Welthandels. pp. 406. *Wien,* 1889. 8°. 08227. h. 16.
See also GEOGRAPHY, *Commercial,* and under the subheading *Trade and Finance* of each country. For Imperial Federation, *see* ENGLAND, *Colonies.*

TRADE MARKS. AMERICA. Patent and Trade-mark laws of America. pp. 48. 1891. 8°. U.S. *Bureau of American Republics.* Bulletin. No. 3. 08225. k. 1.

BEWES (W. A.) Copyright, Trade Marks, *etc.* pp. 351. *Lond.* 1891. 8°. 6376. d. 14.

BRUNSTEIN (J. L.) Studien im österreichischen Markenrecht. pp. 115. *Wien,* 1895. 8°.
5549. d. 17.

CARTMELL (J. A.) Abstract of reported cases relating to Trade Marks, 1876–92. pp. 417. *Lond.* 1893. 8°. 6376. dd. 4.

DAVIS (C T.) Merchants' Marks. pp. 9. *Lond.* 1893. 8°. 07703. g. 3. (14.)

DAY (C. A.) Handbook on British, Colonial and Foreign Trade Marks. pp. 40. *Lond.* 1895. 8°.
6006. a. 40.

DENMARK. Law respecting the protection of Trade-Marks in Denmark. pp. 7. *Copenh.* 1890. 8°. 5725. bb. 19. (3.)

DEWHURST (G.) and (R.) City Police Court Manchester. Crighton, on behalf of G. and R. Dewhurst *v.* Ellinger for infringement of trade mark. pp. 51. *Manch.* 1893. fol. 6496. k. 2.

DONZEL (L.) Commentaire de la convention signée à Paris le 20 mars 1883 pour la protection de la propriété industrielle. pp. 492. *Paris,* 1893. 8°. 6825. ee. 20.

EDMUNDS (L.) The Patents, Designs and Trade Marks Acts, 1883–88. pp. 86. *Lond.* 1895. 8°.
6376. dd. 6.

FULTON (D.) Treatise on Patents and Trade Marks. pp. 488. *Lond.* 1894. 8°. 6376. ee. 6.

G. B. & I. "Made in Germany." Das englische Gesetz der Waarenbezeichnung. *Eng.* and *Ger.* pp. 67. *Hamburg,* 1895. 8°. 6376. o. 29.

HADDAN (R.) Inventor's Adviser and Manufacturer's Handbook to Trade Marks, *etc.* pp. 441. *Lond.* 1894. 8°. 6376. de. 5.

KERLY (D. M.) The Law of Trade Marks. pp. 752. *Lond.* 1894. 8°. 6376. ee. 10.

KLOESSEL (M. H.) "Made in Germany." Das englische Handelsmarken Schutz-Gesetz von 1887. pp. 139. *Leipz.* 1892. 8°. 6405. cc. 22.

NEWTON (A. V.) Patent Law : including the Registration of Trade Marks. pp. 172. *Lond.* 1893. 8°. 6375. aa. 54.

NEW ZEALAND. "The Patents, Designs, and Trade Marks Act, 1889." pp. 428. *Wellington,* 1889. 4°. 6605. ff. 7.

PELLETIER (M.) Brevets d'invention, marques de fabrique, *etc.* pp. 428. 1893. 8°. LECHALAS (M. C.) Encyclopédie des travaux publics.
012216. i.

SAFFORD (F.) Law of Merchandise Marks. pp. 311. *Lond.* 1893. 8°. 6375. bb. 29.
See also PATENTS.

TRAFALGAR, Battle of. MAHAN (A. T.) Influence of Sea Power upon the French Revolution, *etc.* 2 vol. *Lond.* 1892. 8°. 9079. g. 21.

LETUAIRE (H.) Combat de Trafalgar. Rapport fait au Ministre de la Marine par E. Lucas. pp. 27. *Hyères,* 1891. 8°. 9004. m. 9. (7.)

TRAFALGAR, Battle of—continued.

PAROW (W.) Die Seeschlacht bei Trafalgar. pp. 33. *Berl.* 1890. 4°. 9004. n. 10. (8.)

TRAMWAYS. CHAMPION (L.) Monographie de la Compagnie des tramways de Bordeaux. pp. 92. *Bordeaux,* 1892. 8°. Pam. 76.

CLARK (D. K.) Tramways. Their construction and working. pp. 758. *Lond.* 1894. 8°.
2249. f. 3.

CROWTHER (F. J.) Provisional Orders of the Board of Trade in reference to Gas and Water and Tramway Undertakings. pp. 48. *Lond.* 1893. 8°. 6126. aaaa. 18.

DENIZET (F.) Note sur le tramway électrique de Marseille. pp. 64. *Paris,* 1893. 8°.
8757. i. 25.

GADOT (P.) La Traction électrique et la traction animale des tramways. pp. 139. *Paris,* 1891. 8°. 8757. aa. 32.

MARTINEZ (G.) La Trazione elettrica. pp. 317. *Milano,* 1894. 8°. 8757. g. 35.

RECKENZAUN (A.) Electric Traction. pp. 422. *Lond.* 1892. 8°. 8757. cc. 32.

VIAPPIANI (A.) La costruzione e l'esercizio delle Tramvie. pp. 317. *Torino,* 1893. 8°. 8235. f. 50.

TRANSCASPIAN TERRITORY, Russian. *See* KHIVA : MERV.

TRANSCAUCASIA. *See* CAUCASUS.

TRANSFUSION, of Blood. *See* BLOOD.

TRANSPORTATION. BURCHARD (J. L.) Das Recht der Spedition, pp. 536. *Stuttgart,* 1894. 8°. 05604. i. 31.

CARBO (T.) La Lutte entre la navigation et les chemins de fer. pp. 32. *Meaux,* 1895. 8°.
Pam. 76.

CHICAGO. *Columbian Exposition.* Official Catalogue. Pt. VII. Transportation Exhibition. pp. 60. *Chicago,* 1893. 8°. 7958. bb. 29.

COOLEY (C. H.) Theory of Transportation. pp. 148. 1894. 8°. Ac. Saratoga. *American Economic Association.* Publications. Vol. 9.
Ac. 2388.

DREDGE (J.) Record of the Transportation Exhibits of the Columbian Exposition. pp. 779. 1894. 4°. Engineering Series. 8755. m.

KIRKMAN (M. M.) Classical Portfolio of Primitive Carriers. *Chicago,* 1895. obl. fol. 1803. a. 20.

MAC CAIN (C. C.) Compendium of Transportation Theories. pp. 295. *Wash.* 1893. 8°.
08235. f. 43.

See also CARRIAGES : NAVAL SCIENCE : POSTS : RAILWAYS : TRAMWAYS.

TRANSVAAL.

History, Topography, etc.

ALBRACHT (M. J.) La République Sud-Africaine au point de vue de l'immigration européenne. pp. 44. *Brux.* 1890. 8°. Pam. 66.

BALFOUR (A. B.) Twelve hundred miles in a Wagon. pp. 265. *Lond.* 1895. 8°. 010097. g. 8.

BARTLETT (*Sir* E. A.) British, Natives and Boers in the Transvaal. pp. 24. *Lond.* 1894. 8°.
Pam. 66.

BLINK (H.) De Zuid-Afrikaansche Republiek en hare bewoners, *etc.* pp. 125. *Amsterdam,* 1890. 8°. 10097. cc. 19.

CROMB (J.) The Majuba Disaster. pp. 44. *Dundee,* 1891. 8°. Pam. 28.

DISTANT (W. L.) Naturalist in the Transvaal. pp. 277. *Lond.* 1892. 8°. 7002. f. 9.

DUTOIT (S. J.) Afrika : het land der toekomst. pp. 47. *Amsterdam,* 1890. 8°. Pam. 66.

HOFMEYR (S.) Twintig jaren in Zoutpansberg. pp. 322. *Kaapstad,* 1890. 4°. 010096. ee. 15.

TRANSVAAL.—History, etc.—continued.

LONGLAND (H) The Golden Transvaal. pp. 60.
Lond. 1893. 4°.   10096. g. 12.

P.P. Johannesburg. South African Financial
Record. Johannesburg, 1893, etc. fol.
        P.P. 9996. k.

—— The South African Mining Journal and
financial news. Johannesburg, 1893, etc. 4°.
        P.P. 9996. l.

SPIEGEL (E.) Die Südafrikanische Republik und
ihre Gold-produktion. pp. 31. Berl. 1893. 8°.
        07109. e. 23. (11.)

See also AFRICA, South: GOLD AND SILVER:
JOHANNESBURG : MINERALOGY : SWAZILAND.

Law.

SOUTH AFRICAN REPUBLIC. De locale Wetten
der Zuid-Afrikaansche Republiek, 1849–85.
2 vol. Pretoria, 1887, 88. 8°.   06606. g. 8.

—— Codex van de locale Wetten der Zuid-
Afrikaansche Republiek. pp. 721.
Groningen, 1894. 8°.   5685. a. 4.

COSTER (H. J.) De locale Wetten der Zuid-Afr.
Republiek. pp. 1018. Pretoria, 1894. 8°.
        06606. h. 9.

DE WILDE (H. N.) Manual for Everyone.
Attempt at Codification. Eng. & Dutch. 2 pt.
Cape Town, 1894, etc. 8°.   06605. f.

SOUTH AFRICAN REPUBLIC. Laws having special
reference to Gold Fields and mining districts.
pp. 233. Johannesburg, 1892. 8°. 6606. a. 6.

KOTZÉ (J. G.) Reports of cases decided in the
Supreme Court of the South African Republic,
1881–84. Cape Town, 1894, etc. 8°. 06606. h.

TRANSYLVANIA. AC. Hermannstadt.
Verein für siebenbürgische Landeskunde. Ur-
kundenbuch zur Geschichte der Deutschen in
Siebenbürgen. Hermannstadt, 1892, etc. 8°.
        9315. e.

—— Pest. Tudományos Akadémia. Trans-
sylvania et Bellum Boreo-Orientale.
Budapestini, 1890, etc. 8°.   Ac. 825/99.

BALACEANŬ (C.) La Question transylvaine.
pp. 14. Bucarest, 1893. 8°.   Pam. 72.

BROTE (E.) Die rümanische Frage in Siebenbürgen. pp. 432. Berl. 1895. 8°. 8074. h. 4.

FAVA (R.) Ricordi rumeni. Note di un viaggio.
pp. 311. Parma, 1894. 8°.   10215. aa. 25.

FRANK (P. J.) Gegenwart und Zukunft der
siebenbürger Sachsen. pp. 368.
Hermannstadt, 1892. 8°.   08276. h. 26.

GHERGHEL (I.) Zur Geschichte Siebenbürgens.
pp. 47. Wien, 1891. 8°.   9008. g. 12. (7.)

KOHN (S.) Die Sabbatharier in Siebenbürgen.
pp. 296. Budapest, 1894. 8°.   4662. f. 10.

LEMHARDT (J.) Geschichten aus Siebenbürgen.
pp. 120. Wien, 1890. 8°.   10215. ee. 18.

PENELL (E. R.) To Gipsyland. pp. 240.
Lond 1893. 8°.   10007. bb. 16.

TEUTSCH (F.) Die Art der Ansiedelung der
siebenbürger Sachsen. pp. 55. 1895. 8°.

LEHMANN (R.) Forschungen zur deutschen
Landeskunde. Bd. 9.   10235. i. 10.

TRANSYLVANIA. La quistione romena nella
Transilvania. pp. 139. Vienna, 1893. 8°.
        8028. ff. 20.

—— The Roumanian Question in Transylvania.
pp. 151. Vienna, 1892. 8°.   8074. h. 1.

WIBLING (C.) Sveriges förhållande till Siebenbürgen, 1623–48. pp. 211. Lund, 1890. 8°.
        9431. bb. 23.

WLISLOCKI (H. v.) Märchen und Sagen der
Bukowinaer und siebenbürger Armenier.
pp. 188. Hamburg, 1891. 8°. 12430. g. 38.

See also AUSTRIA-HUNGARY.

TRAPANI. BULGARELLA-QUARTANA (A.) La
Cavalcata, processione di personaggi a cavallo
con la quale si chiude il secondo giorno dell'
annue feste Mariane. pp. 17.
Trapani, 1891. 8°.   Pam. 18.

BUTLER (S.) On the Trapanese origin of the
Odyssey. pp. 24. 13. Camb. 1893. 8°.
        11315. d. 30. (7.)

SUGAMELI (P.) Origine trapanese dell' "Odissea"
secondo S. Butler. pp. 66. Trapani, 1892. 8°.
        11315. d. 30. (6.)

TALOTTI (G. B.) Cenni su di alcuni studi geologici nella Provincia di Trapani. pp. 54.
Trapani, 1881. 8°.   7462. e. 2. (9.)

TRAUTENAU, Battle of. See AUSTRIA,
PRUSSIA, History.

TRAVANCORE. SUNDARAM PILLAI. Some
early Sovereigns of Travancore. pp. 74.
Madras, 1894. 8°.   14170. e. 23.

KRISHNA RAU. Revenue handbook. pp. 524.
Madras, 1889. 4°.   08227. g. 27.

TRAVANCORE MEMORIALS. Travancore Memorials
and counter memorials. ff. 17.
Madras, 1891. fol.   Pam. 67.

TREATIES. AITCHISON (Sir C. U.) Collection
of Treaties relating to India and neighbouring
countries. 11 vols. Calcutta, 1892. 8°. 2386. g.

GERMANY. Die wirthschaftlichen Verträge
Deutschlands. Berl. 1892, etc. 8°. 08227. i.

VAST (H.) Les grands Traités du Règne de
Louis XIV. pp. 187. 1893. 8°. Collection de
textes.   09210. de.

WEGMANN (F.) Die Ratifikation von Staatsver-
traegen. pp. 100. Berl. 1892. 8°. 8009. i. 28.

See also LAW, International.

TREES. See FORESTRY.

TRÉGUIER. IVO, Saint. Inauguration du
tombeau de Saint Yves à Tréguier. pp. 176.
Saint-Brieuc, 1890. 12°.   4827. aaa. 1.

LECOQU (T. M.) Le Culte de Saint Yves pen-
dant les XVII° et XVIII° siècles. 1891. 8°. Ac.
Saint Brieuc. Société Archéologique. Mémoires.
Sér. 2. Tom. 4.   Ac. 5294/2.

TRENT AND THE TRENTINO. BREN-
TARI (O.) Guida del Trentino.
Bassano, 1891, etc. 8°.   10215. aa.

—— Stazioni balneari nel Trentino, etc.
pp. 208. Bassana, 1892. 8°.   10215. a. 5.

SCHNELLER (F.) Beiträge zur Geschichte des
Bisthums Trient aus dem spätern Mittelalter.
1894 8°. Ac. Innsbruck. Ferdinandeum.
Beiträge zur Geschichte von Tirol. Htf. 38.
        Ac. 760.

TRENT, Council of. BIANCHI (G.) Il Clero
piacentino dal concilia di Trento. pp. 79.
Piacenza, 1891. 8°.   Pam. 29.

SCHUERMANS (H.) Amyot au Concile de Trente.
pp. 30. Bruxelles, 1891. 8°.   Pam. 29.

VERMEULEN ( ) Die Verlegung des Konzils
von Trient. pp. 74. Regensburg, 1890. 8°.
        4535. c. 10. (4.)

See also CHURCH HISTORY, Reformation.

TREVES. HETTNER (F.) Die römischen
Steindenkmäler des Provinzialmuseums zu
Trier. pp. 294. Trier, 1893. 8°. 7705. c. 38.

MOHR (J.) Die Heiligen der Diözese Trier.
pp. 364. Trier, 1892. 8°.   4829. c. 15.

KNIPSCHAAR (C.) Kurfürst Philipp Christoph
und seine Beziehungen zu Frankreich. pp. 66.
Marburg, 1895. 8°.   9078. g. 20.

JANKE (A.) Die Belagerungen der Stadt Trier,
1683 bis 1675. pp. 108. Trier, 1890. 8°.
        9079. g. 11.

TREVES—*continued.*

BACH (J.) Der heilige Rock zu Trier. pp. 27. 1891. 8°. Frankfurter zeitgemässe Broschüren. N.F. Bd. 12. Hft. 11.   12209. g.

BEISSEL (S.) Nachtrag zur Geschichte des heiligen Rockes. pp. 15. *Trier,* 1891. 8°.   Pam. 10.

BENECKE (H.) Der heilige Rock zu Trier. pp. 56. *Berl.* 1891. 8°.   Pam. 10.

—— Bischof Dr. Korum und die Wunderwirkung des heiligen Rocks zu Trier. pp. 36. *Berl.* 1891. 8°.   Pam. 10.

BEYSCHLAG (W.) Vaterländisch - kirchliche Erinnerungen aus Triér. Pro-memoria zur trierer Rockaustellung von 1891. pp. 31. *Halle,* 1891. 8°.   3911. ee. 51. (6.)

CLARKE (R. F.) Pilgrimage to the Holy Coat of Treves. pp. 141. *Lond.* 1892. 8°. 4806. bbb. 12.

FOERSTER (T.) Der heilige Rock von Trier im Jahre 1844 und 1891. pp. 23. *Halle,* 1891. 8°.   Pam. 10.

GERMANUS. Wallfahrt zum heiligen Rock. pp. 92. *Bonn,* 1891. 8°.   Pam. 10.

GRUNAU (J. E.) Der heilige ungenähte Rock zu Trier. pp. 16. *Neuss,* 1892. 8°. Pam. 10.

HENNING (L.) Der heilige Rock zu Trier im Jahre 1844 und 1891. pp. 24. *Berl.* 1891. 8°.   Pam. 10.

HULLEY (J.) Kurze Geschichte der Wallfahrt zum hl. Rock in Trier. pp. 159. *Trier,* 1891. 8°.   4807. cc. 3.

JASKOWSKI (F.) Der heilige Rock von Trier, gerichtet von seinen eigenen Freunden. pp. 122. *Saarbrücken,* 1891. 8°.   Pam. 10.

—— Verzeichniss der unzähligen Reliquien der Stadt Trier. pp. 24. *Saarbrücken,* 1891. 8°.   Pam. 10.

—— Verlauf und Fiasko des trierer Schauspiels. pp. 84. *Saarbrücken,* 1891. 8°. Pam. 10.

JUNIUS. *Dr.* Der sogenannte "heilige Rock" zu Trier, ein Betrug der Clerisei. pp. 48. *Leipz.* 1892. 8°.   Pam. 10.

KREUTZKAMP (J.) Auf nach Trier! Eine Beschreibung des heiligen Rockes. pp. 40. *Dülmen,* 1891. 16°.   Pam. 10.

KURTZ (H.) Trier und der heilige Rock. pp. 128. *Zürich,* 1892. 8°.   4807. cc. 2.

LINDNER (M.) Der heilige Rock zu Trier und die Wunderheilungen. pp. 34. *Leipz.* 1891. 8°.   Pam. 10.

PLATER (E. A.) The Holy Coat of Treves. pp. 120. *Lond.* 1891. 8°.   4806. c. 2.

SCHNEIDER (J.) Der heilige Rock. pp. 120. *Aachen,* 1891. 16°.   4223. a. 26.

STOECK (A.) Die Wallfahrt nach Trier zum heiligen Rock. *Dülmen,* 1891. 16°. 10235. a. 13.

TREVES. Die Rockfahrt nach Trier unter der Aera Korum. pp. 55. *Trier,* 1891. 8°. Pam. 10.

WILLEMS (C.) Der hl. Rock zu Trier. pp. 186. *Trier,* 1891. 8°.   4808. bb. 17.

—— Der h. Rock zu Trier und seine Gegner. pp. 122. *Trier,* 1892. 8°.   4808. bb. 20.

CHEVALLIER (M. A.) Questions sur une brochure intitulée : La Sainte Robe de Trèves, du Dr. Willems. pp. 25. *Paris,* 1892. 8°. Pam. 10.

TREVISO. SANTALENA (A.) Vecchai gente e vecchie storie. *Padova,* 1891, *etc.* 8°.   9166. ccc. 13.

SIMONSFELD (H.) Eine deutsche Colonie zu Treviso im späteren Mittelalter. 1891. 4°. Ac. Munich. *K. Akademie.* Abhandlungen der hist. Classe. Bd. 19. Abt. 3.   Ac. 713/5.

NINNI (A. P.) *Count.* Materiali per un vocabolario della Lingua rusticana di Treviso. 2 pt. *Venezia,* 1891. 8°.   12942. bbb. 32.

TRIALS. *See* LAW REPORTS.

TRIEST. ROBERT (F.) Studie über den triester Handel sammt Platz-Usancen. pp. 159. *Wien,* 1890. 8°.   08227. g. 16

TOMASIN (P.) Die Volksstämme im Gebiete von Trieste. pp. 107. *Triest,* 1890. 8°.   10215. bb. 24.

BUCHWALD (S. v.) Geschichte des Hafencastells von Triest. pp. 40. *Linz,* 1895. 8°.   10215. de. 20.

TRIGONOMETRY. ASTRAND (J. J.) Hulfstafeln zur Auflösung des Kepler'schen Problems. pp. 110. *Leipz.* 1890, 8°. 8561. h. 39.

CASEY (J.) Treatise on elementary Trigonometry. pp. 187. *Dublin,* 1895. 8°.   8534. a. 22.

CLARKE (A. D.) Plane Trigonometry. pp. 365. *Lond.* 1893. 8°.   8535. cc. 35.

DYER (J. M.) and WHITCOMBE (R. H.) Elementary Trigonometry. pp. 266. *Camb.* 1891. 8°.   8535. b. 38.

ELFRINK (W. F.) Goniometrische en trigonometrische Vraagstukken. pp. 113. *Amsterd.* 1893. 8°.   8534. bbb. 39.

GOODWIN (H. B.) Plane and spherical Trigonometry. pp. 271. *Lond.* 1893. 8°. 8533. d. 24.

GRAF (J. H.) Einleitung in die Theorie der Gammafunktion und der Euler'schen Integrale. pp. 64. *Bern,* 1894. 8°.   8530. ee. 38.

GUYOU (E.) Traité de Trigonométrie rectiligne et sphérique. pp. 261. *Paris,* 1891. 8°.   8533. cc. 41.

HALL (H. S.) and KNIGHT (S. R.) Elementary Trigonometry. pp. 356. *Lond.* 1893. 8°.   8533. e. 37.

HALL (H. S.) Solutions of examples in Hall and Knight's Trigonometry. pp. 242. *Lond.* 1895. 8°.   8533. e. 42.

HOBSON (E. W.) Treatise on plane Trigonometry. pp. 356. *Camb.* 1891. 8°.   8535. d. 3.

HOBSON (E. W.) and JESSOP (C. M.) Elementary treatise on plane Trigonometry. pp. 299. 1892. 8°. Pitt Press Mathematical Series.   8535. aaa.

HOLT (H. F.) Spherical Trigonometry. *Lond.* 1891. obl. 8°.   Pam. 38.

KLINGATSCH (A.) Die graphische Ausgleichung bei der trigonometrischen Punktbestimmung durch Einschneiden. pp. 46. *Wien.* 1894. 8°.   8535. h. 31.

LÁSKA (W.) Lehrbuch der sphärischen Trigonometrie. pp. 187. 1890. 8°. Kleyers Encyklopädie.   8705. g.

LEVETT (R.) and DAVISON (C.) Elements of plane Trigonometry. pp. 520. *Lond.* 1892. 8°.   8534. aa. 41.

LOCK (J. B.) Trigonometry of one Angle. pp. 100. *Lond.* 1891. 8°.   8534. aa. 32.

LONEY (S. L.) Plane Trigonometry. pp. 480. *Camb.* 1893. 8°.   8533. e. 36.

MACFARLANE (A.) Principles of elliptic and hyperbolic Analysis. pp. 47. *Bost.* 1894. 8°.   Pam. 38.

—— Definitions of the trigonometric Functions. pp. 49. *Bost.* 1894. 8°.   8535. gg. 6. (10.)

NEWMAN (F. W.) The higher Trigonometry. pp. 117. *Camb.* 1892. 8°.   8535. d. 11.

NIXON (R. C. J.) Elementary Trigonometry. pp. 380. 1892. 8°. Clarendon Press Series.   2319. b. 2.

ORLANDI (G.) Tacheometria. pp. 361. *Sassari.* 1894. 8°.   8534. d. 39.

PENDLEBURY (C.) Elementary Trigonometry. pp. 336. *Lond.* 1895. 8°.   8533. de. 36.

SAALSCHUETZ (L.) Vorlesungen über die Bernoullischen Zahlen. pp. 207. *Berl.* 1893. 8°.   8535. g. 10.

TRIGONOMETRY—continued.

SPARKS (F.) Longmans' School Trigonometry. pp. 196. *Lond.* 1891. 8°. 8535. aaa. 51.

STUDY (E.) Sphärische Trigonometrie. pp. 147. 1893. 8°. Ac. Leipsic. *Gesellschaft der Wissenschaften.* Abhandlungen. Bd. 33. Ac. 700/4.

SYNOPSIS. Synopsis of Trigonometry. pp. 43. 1891. 8°. Tutorial Series. 12205. c. 14.

TODHUNTER (I.) Plane Trigonometry. pp. 405. *Lond.* 1891. 8°. 2242. aa. 19.

—— Key to Todhunter and Hogg's Plane Trigonometry. pp. 482. *Lond.* 1895. 8°. 2242. aa. 17.

WARD (G. H.) Examination papers in Trigonometry. *Lond.* 1892. 8°. 12205. f.

—— Key to papers in Trigonometry. pp. 127. 1891. 8°. STEDMAN (A. M. M.) School Examination series. 12205. f.

WARREN (I.) Elements of plane Trigonometry. pp. 186. *Lond.* 1890. 8°. 8534. aaa. 45.

—— Examination papers in Trigonometry. pp. 66. *Dublin*, 1890. 8°. Pam. 38.

KEITH (J.) Key to Warren's Elements of plane Trigonometry. pp. 123. *Lond.* 1893. 8°. 8532. aa. 43.

See also MATHEMATICS.

TRINIDAD, South Atlantic. KNIGHT (E. F.) Cruise of the "Alerte." pp. 328. *Lond.* 1890. 8°. 10481. c. 26.

TRINIDAD. West Indies. CLARK (H. J.) Ière, the Land of the humming-bird. pp. 96. *Port of Spain*, 1893. 8°. 10480. d. 28.

EPHEM. Creole Almanack for Trinidad. *Port of Spain*, 1890, *etc.* 8°. P.P. 2587. ab.

HART (F. R.) Chaguaramas scheme of Don Siegert for constructing docks, *etc.* pp. 18. *Trinidad*, 1894. 12°. Pam. 76.

P.P. *Port of Spain.* The Agricultural Record. Official Journal of the Central Agricultural Board of Trinidad, *etc.* *Port-of-Spain*, 1889, *etc.* 8°. P.P. 2324.

PORT OF SPAIN. *Trinidad and Tobago Exhibition.* Catalogue. pp. 73. *Port of Spain*, 1891. 8°. 7958. g. 17.

WILSON (G.) La Brea, *etc.* pp. 11. *San Fernando*, 1891. 12°. Pam. 27.

See also ENGLAND, *Colonies :* WEST INDIES.

TRINITY. CASPARI (C. P.) Der Glaube an die Trinität in der Kirche des ersten Jahrhunderts. pp. 32. *Leipz.* 1894. 8°. 4371. dd. 8. (8.)

DAVIES (R. N.) Doctrine of the Trinity. pp. 234. *Cincinnati*, 1891. 8°. 4376. de. 1.

HATCH afterwards RICHMOND (O. L. V.) Symbol of the Trinity. pp. 16. 1893. 8°. Copley's Broad-Thought Library. No. 4. 8632. ccc.

HOPE (T. H.) Modern doctrine of the Trinity. pp. 27. *Chowbent*, 1894. 8°. 4371. bb. 9. (3.)

MAC KINNEY (S. B. G.) The Revelation of the Trinity. pp. 190. *Lond.* 1891. 8°. 4376. i. 14.

RÉGNON (T. de) Études de Théologie positive sur la Sainte Trinité. 2 pt. *Paris*, 1892. 8°. 4227. h. 24.

WHITON (J. M.) Gloria Patri, or talks about the Trinity. pp. 162. *Lond.* 1892. 8°. 4227. ec. 4.

See also CHRISTIANITY : DEITY : THEOLOGY.

TRINITY COLLEGE, Glenalmond. GLENALMOND. *Trinity College.* Prospectus. pp. 8. 1891. 8°. 8306. de 20. (8.)

TRINITY HOUSE, Corporation of the. BARRETT (C. R. B.) The Trinity House of Deptford Strond. pp. 159. *Lond.* 1893. 4°. 8807. g. 30.

TRIPENTE, Game. ARNOLD (A. B.) Tripente or Threes and Fives. A game. *Winchester*, 1895. 8°. Tab. 11746. b.

TRIPOLI. MORDACQ (C.) Influence italienne à Tunis et dans la Tripolitaine. pp. 11. *Paris*, 1891. 8°. Pam. 67.

MONTEIL (P. L.) De Saint-Louis à Tripoli par le lac Tchad. pp. 462. *Paris*, 1895. 4°. 1786. d. 1.

RADIOT (P.) Tripoli d'Occident et Tunis. pp. 299. *Paris*, 1894 12°. 10097. ccc. 19.

THOMPSON (G. E.) Life in Tripoli. pp. 116. *Liverpool*, 1894. 8°. 010096. e. 63.

TRONDHJEM. DRONTHEIM. *Turistforening.* Guide to Trondhjem. pp. 96. *Trondhjem*, 1890. 8°. 10280. aa. 18.

SCHULZ (C.) Reisehåndbog over Trondhjem. pp. 114. *Trondhjem*, 1893. 8°. 10280. aaa. 42.

V. S. Trondhjems Domkirke. pp. 14. *Christiania*, 1893. 8°. Pam. 24.

TROPICS. *See* DISEASES, *Tropical :* HYGIENE.

TROTTING. FRŒMER (A.) Le Trotting Club de Paris. pp. 56. *Paris*, 1890. 4°. 7905. k. 16.

P.P. *London.* Racing Calendar of the Trotting Union of Great Britain. *Lond.* 1889, *etc.* 12°. P.P. 2489. sg.

SPLAN (J.) Life with the Trotters. pp. 450. *Chicago*, 1889. 8°. 07291. ee. 3.

See also HORSE.

TROUBADOURS. CHABANEAU (C.) Les Biographies des Troubadours. pp. 204. *Toulouse*, 1885. 4°. 10659. h. 26

DIEZ (F. C.) Die Poesie der Troubadours. pp. 314. *Leipz.* 1883. 8°. 011840. k. 77.

ROWBOTHAM (J. F.) The Troubadours and Courts of love. pp. 324. 1895. 8°. Social England series. 9503. ccc.

SACHSE (M.) Ueber das Leben des Troubadours Wilhelm IX., Graf von Poitou. pp. 57. *Leipz.* 1882. 8°. 10601. d. 33. (3.)

See also FRENCH LITERATURE : PROVENÇAL LANGUAGE AND LITERATURE.

TROUT. *See* FISH, *Culture and Angling.*

TROY. Ac. France. *Comité des Amis des Monuments.* NORMAND (C.) La Troie d'Homère. pp. 116. *Paris*, 1892. 4°. 7705. i. 24.

BOETTICHER (E.) Troja im Jahre 1894. pp. 34. *Schwerin i. M.*, 1894. 8°. Pam. 3.

—— "Sendschreiben" [criticising discoveries made at Troy by H. Schliemann]. 5 pt. *Louvain*, 1889–90. 8°. 7705. c. 36.

SCHLIEMANN (H.) Bericht über die Ausgrabungen in Troja im Jahre 1890. pp. 60. *Leipz.* 1891. 8°. 7706. f. 19. (9)

SCHUCHHARDT (C.) Schliemann's Ausgrabungen in Troja. pp. 405. *Leipz.* 1891. 8°. 7706. f. 22.

—— Schliemann's Excavations. pp. 363. *Lond.* 1891. 8°. 2259. d. 11.

WILSON (*Sir* C. W.) Murray's Handbook for Constantinople and the Troad. pp. 166. *Lond.* 1893. 8°. 2364. b. 26.

See also ASIA MINOR : GREECE, *Antiquities.*

TROYES. BABEAU (A.) Les Académies de musique de Troyes au XVII° et au XVIII° siècle. pp. 19. *Troyes*, 1883. 8°. Pam. 24.

TRUCK ACTS. *See* CAPITAL AND LABOUR, *Laws, etc.*

TRUFFLES. *See* FUNGI.

TRURO, Diocese. TRURO. *Diocesan Society.* Members' Manual. pp. 27. *Lond.* 1893. 16°. 4109. a. 34.

TRUSTS AND TRUSTEES. Ellis (A. L.) The Trustee Act, 1893. pp. 156. *Lond.* 1894. 8°.   6355. aaa. 34.

Godefroi (H.) Law relating to Trusts and Trustees. pp. 936. *Lond.* 1891. 8°. 2230. d. 8.

Kerr (W. W.) Treatise on the law and practice as to Receivers. pp. 252. *Lond.* 1891. 8°.   2230. e. 9.

Lewin (T.) Practical treatise on the law of Trusts. pp. 1402. *Lond.* 1891. 8°. 2017. f.

Rudall (A. R.) and Greig (J. W.) The Trustee Act, 1893. pp. 232. *Lond.* 1894. 8°.   6355. aa. 20.

Underhill (A.) Manual of the law relating to private Trusts and Trustees. pp. 694. *Lond.* 1894. 8°.   2230. b. 20.

Wood (F.) Digest of the law of Administrations and Trusteeships. pp. 470. *Lond.* 1894. 8°.   6355. df. 17.

Howden (C. R. A.) Trusts and the Trusts Acts in Scotland. pp. 437. *Edinb.* 1893. 8°.   6583. g. 13.

Menzies (A. J. P.) The law of Scotland affecting Trustees. *Edinb.* 1893, *etc.* 8°. 6583. cc. 2.

Griffith (W.) The Indian Trusts Act. pp. 265. *Madras,* 1888. 8°.   5319. aaa. 33.

Huc (T.) Traité de la cession des Créances. 2 tom. *Paris,* 1891. 8°.   5406. de. 2.

Adamkiewicz ( ) Der Rechtsbegriff der Curatel —die Pflegschaft—in systematischer Darstellung. pp. 232. *Berl.* 1892. 8°.   6005. e. 6.

Barazetti (C.) Die Vormundschaft (la Tutelle), die Pflegschaft (la Curatelle) und die Beistandschaft (le Conseil). pp. 662. *Hannover,* 1894. 8°.   05604. k. 7.

Schroeder (E.) Das Vormundschaftsrecht in Elsass-Lothringen. pp. 464. *Strassburg,* 1892. 8°.   05604. i. 2.

Ferrini (C.) Teoria dei legati e dei fedecommessi secondo il diritto romano. pp. 709. *Milano,* 1889. 8°.   5254. cc. 15.

See also Children, *Laws, etc.*

For Trust Investments, *see* Stocks and Shares.

TRUSTS, Commercial.
See Companies: Monopolies.

TSHI LANGUAGE.
See African Languages.

TSIEN-TANG-KIANG. G. B. & I. *Admiralty. Hydrographic Office.* Further report on the bore of the Tsien-Tang-Kiang. pp. 7. *Lond.* 1893. 8°.   10497. ee. 37.

TSUNG-MING. Havret (H.) L'Île de Tsong-Ming. pp. 59. 1892. 8°. Variétés sinologiques. No. 1.   010057. k

TUBERCULOSIS. *See* Consumption.

TÜBINGEN. Jolly (L.) Die neueste Geschichte der Universität Tübingen. pp. 28. *Tübingen,* 1891. 8°.   8305 ff. 6. (13.)

Schmoller (O.) Geschichte des theologischen Stipendiums in Tübingen. *Stuttgart,* 1893, *etc.* 8°.   4662. f.

Schwabe (L.) Geschichte der archaeologischen Sammlung der Universität. pp. 45. *Tübingen,* 1891. 4°.   7704. i. 11. (6.)

TUCUMAN. Soprano (P. P.) La conquista del antiguo Tucuman. pp. 429. *Buenos A.* 1889. 8°.   9772. c. 1.

TULLE. Clément-Simon (G.) La prise de Tulle par Jean de la Roche, 1426. pp. 42. *Tulle,* 1895. 8°.   Pam. 28.

—— Histoire du Collège de Tulle. pp. 387. *Paris,* 1892. 8°.   8356. h. 16.

TUMBUKA LANGUAGE.
See African Languages.

TUMOURS. Anderson (T. McC.) Cerebral Tumour: history and diagnosis. pp. 12. *Lond.* 1891. 8°.   7306. df. 16. (6.)

Broca (A.) Traitement des tumeurs blanches chez l'enfant. pp. 155. 1893. 8°. Encyclopédie des aide-mémoire.   8709. g.

Burnett (J. C.) Curability of Tumours by medicines. pp. 332. *Lond.* 1893. 8°.   7630. aa. 21.

Lassalle (C.) Des Tumeurs incluses dans les ligaments larges. pp. 110. *Montpellier,* 1891. 8°.   7580. e. 7.

Oustaniol (J. G.) Contribution à l'étude des Tumeurs des méninges rachidiennes. pp. 148. *Paris,* 1892. 8°.   7620. df. 30.

Steven (J. L.) Pathology of mediastinal Tumours. pp. 100. *Lond.* 1892. 8°. 7616. h. 16.

Sutton (J. B.) Tumours innocent and malignant. pp. 511. *Lond.* 1893. 8°. 7630. e. 18.

Thorner (M.) Benign Tumours of the larynx. *Cincinnati,* 1892. 4°.   Pam. 39.

See also Cancer: Hydrocele.

TUNBRIDGE. Tunbridge. Photographs of Tonbridge. *Tonbridge,* 1895. *obl.* 8°.   10360. aa. 39.

Tunbridge School. Register of Tonbridge School. pp. 315. *Lond.* 1893. 8°. 8364. h. 9.

TUNBRIDGE WELLS. Tunbridge Wells. Album of Photographs of Tunbridge Wells. *Tunbridge Wells,* 1895. *obl.* 8°.   10360. aa. 42

TUNG-KING. Badier (A.) and (H.) Au Tonkin. Journal d'un sous-officier pp. 138. *Paris,* 1894. 8°.   9055. d. 28.

Bennassi-Desplantes (F. J.) L'Amiral Courbet et le Tonkin. pp. 191. *Rouen,* 1892. 8°.   9055. df. 26.

Boisset (T.) À travers le Tonkin pendant la guerre. pp. 302. *Paris,* 1892. 12°. 9055. aaa. 28.

Burgès (J.) Notice sur le Tonkin. pp. 162. *Paris,* 1893. 8°.   7686. bb. 12.

Carteron (R.) Souvenirs de la campagne du Tonkin. pp. 360. *Paris,* 1891. 8°. 9055. df. 23.

Courtois (E.) Le Tonkin français. pp. 399. *Paris,* 1891. 8°.   010057. l. 8.

Deguine (É.) Journal de marche d'un Turco au Tonkin, 1885–87. pp. 99. *Abbeville,* 1895. 8°.   9055. aa. 22.

Destelan (P.) Annam et Tonkin. Notes de voyage. pp. 322. *Paris,* 1892. 12°. 9055. aaa. 24.

Devrez (V. H. G.) Les grandes voies commerciales du Tonkin. pp. 53. *Paris,* 1891. 12°.   Pam. 88.

Famin (P. P.) Au Tonkin. pp. 373. *Paris,* 1895. 8°.   9055. ec. 35.

Frey (H.) Pirates et rebelles au Tonkin. pp. 350. *Paris,* 1892. 8°.   9055. aaa. 23.

Gallais (H.) Vade-mecum de l'officier au Tonkin. pp. 218. *Paris,* 1894. 8°. 10057. aa. 19.

Garcin (F.) Au Tonkin. Un an chez les Muongs. pp. 289. *Paris,* 1891. 12°.   10058. cc. 30.

Gioi (M.) Le Tonkin actuel, 1887–90. pp. 303. *Paris,* 1891. 12°.   10058. aa. 36.

—— Deux années de Lutte, 1890–91. pp. 236. *Paris,* 1892. 12°.   9055. aaa. 26.

Girod (L.) Tonkin occidental. pp. 20. *Lons-le-Saunier,* 1891. 8°.   Pam. 40.

Grépon (E.) Neuf ans en Algérie et Tonkin. pp. 186. *Paris,* 1893. 8°.   10026. ccc. 6.

Harmant (J.) La Vérité sur la retraite de Lang-Son. pp. 339. *Paris,* 1892. 8°. 9055. aaa. 25.

TUNG-KING—*continued.*

HENRY, D'ORLÉANS, *Prince.* Une Excursion en Indo-Chine. pp. 94. *Paris,* 1892. 8°.
       10055. aaaa. 37.

—— Around Tonkin. pp. 426. *Lond.* 1894. 8°.
       10055. e. 16.

HOCQUARD (C. É.) Une Campagne au Tonkin. pp. 539. *Paris,* 1892. 8°.   10055. f. 9.

LAUNAY (A.) Mgr. Retord et le Tonkin catholique, 1831–58. pp. 446. *Lyon,* 1893. 8°.
       4766. ff. 30.

LECOMTE (J. F. A.) Lang-Son. Combats, retraite et négociations. pp. 555. *Paris,* 1895. 8° and fol.
       9055. e. 37.

—— La Vie militaire au Tonkin. pp. 350. *Paris,* 1893. 8°.   9055. ee. 15.

MALARET (F.) Le commerce du Tonquin avec la province du Quang-Si. pp. 100. *Marseille,* 1892. 8°.   Pam. 88.

MICHELLE (P. L.) L'Amiral Courbet au Tonkin. pp. 158. *Tours,* 1887. 8°.   9055. ccc. 26.

MILLOT (E.) Le Tonkin : son commerce. pp. 280. *Paris,* 1888. 12°.   010057. e. 7.

ORY (P.) La Commune annamite au Tonkin. pp. 147. *Paris,* 1894. 8°.   010057. f. 30.

PETIT (É.) Le Tong-Kin. pp. 238. *Paris,* 1892. 8°.   9057. c. 7.

PIÉTRALBA (H.) Dix Mois à Hanoï. pp. 69. *Paris,* 1890. 12°.   Pam. 88.

ROUSSET DE POMARET (M. J. A.) L'Expédition du Tonkin. pp. 166. *Paris,* 1894. 8°.
       9055. a. 22.

SARZEAU (J.) Les Français au Tonkin. pp. 473. *Paris,* 1895. 8°.   9055. de. 15.

TUNG-KING. La Piraterie au Tonkin. pp. 52. *Paris,* 1891. 8°.   9004. gg. 24. (12.)

See also ANNAM : FRANCE, *Colonies :* INDO-CHINA.

TUNGUSIAN LANGUAGE. BANG (W.) Uralaltaische Forschungen. pp. 44. 1890. 8°. Einzelbeiträge zur Sprachwissenschaft. Hft. 10.

See also MANCHU LANGUAGE.

TUNICATA. *See* ASCIDIA.

TUNIS.

Antiquities.

FRANCE. *M. de l'Instruction.* Atlas archéologique de la Tunisie. *Paris,* 1893. fol.   144.

HOUDARD (L.) Étude à propos d'Antiquités recueillies en Tunisie. pp. 51. *Paris,* 1891. 8°.
       07703. g. 1. (4.)

HOUDAS (O.) and BASSET (R.) Épigraphie tunisienne. pp. 40. *Alger,* 1882. 4°. 7707. aaa. 49.

See also AFRICA, *North :* CARTHAGE.

Army.

TUNIS. *Army.* Loi sur le recrutement de l'Armée tunisienne. pp. 32. *Tunis,* 1883. 8°.
       8830. c. 43. (7.)

Dialect. *See* ARABIC LANGUAGE.

History : French Occupation of Tunis.

BOUTROUE (A.) L'Algérie et la Tunisie à travers les âges. pp. 62. *Paris,* 1893. 8°. 9061. dd. 11.

CAT (É.) Petite histoire de l'Algérie, Tunisie. 2 tom. *Alger,* 1888, 91. 8°.   9061. de. 33.

GAUTIER (F.) Coup d'œil sur la régence de Tunis depuis son origine. pp. 63. *Paris,* 1891. 8°.
       9007. ff. 6. (7.)

PAVY (A.) Histoire de la Tunisie. pp. 386. *Tours,* 1894. 4°.   9061. f. 16.

CASTAN (A.) La conquête de Tunis en 1535. pp. 64. *Besançon,* 1891. 8°.   9007. ff. 5. (4.)

TUNIS.—History, etc.—*continued.*

PLANTET (E.) Correspondances des Beys de Tunis et des Consuls de France avec la Cour, 1577–1830. *Paris,* 1893, *etc.* 8°.   9061. h.

CHEVILLET (G.) Scènes de la vie militaire en Tunisie. pp. 239. *Paris,* 1893. 8°. 010096. h. 3.

COSSERON DE VILLENOISY (L. P. J. M.) La France à Tunis. pp. 45. *Paris,* 1891. 8°.
       8028. de. 30. (11.)

FAUCON (N.) La Tunisie avant et depuis l'occupation française. 2 tom. *Paris,* 1893. 8°.
       9061. h. 10.

FRANCE. *Chambre des Députés.* Rapport sur le projet de loi relatif à l'organisation des services en Tunisie. pp. 53. *Paris,* 1882. 4°. Pam. 66.

GUEST (M. J.) The Tunisian Question and Bizerta. pp. 30. *Lond.* 1881. 8°. 8027. bbb. 18.

MORDACQ (C.) Influence italienne à Tunis. pp. 11. *Paris,* 1891. 8°.   8028. de. 30. (12.)

TUNIS. Règlement sur la composition des bureaux de l'administration générale. pp. 11. *Tunis,* 1885. 8°.   Pam. 33.

—— Tunisi ed il protettorato. pp. 244. *Roma,* 1891. 8°.   8028. e. 28.

X., P. H. La Politique française en Tunisie. pp. 489. *Paris,* 1891. 8°.   8028. de. 28.

See also infra : Topography : FRANCE, *Colonies.*

Law.

DIANOUS (P. de) Notes de Législation tunisienne. pp. 328. *Paris,* 1894. 12°.   5318. aa. 2.

MONTELS (J.) Les Biens de mainmorte en Tunisie. pp. 59. *Tunis,* 1889. 8°. Pam. 33.

TUNIS. *Laws.* Loi foncière et règlements annexes. pp. 231. *Paris,* 1893. 8°.   05319. k. 5.

Topography.

FRANCE. *Dépôt des Cartes et Plans.* Instructions nautiques sur les côtes de Tunisie. pp. 124. *Paris,* 1890. 8°.   10497. f. 18.

—— Reconnaissance hydrographique des côtes de Tunisie. pp. 277. *Paris,* 1890. 4°.
       10496. dd. 10.

TUNIS. Rapport sur le fonctionnement du Service topographique 1886–93. pp. 136. *Paris,* 1894. 8°.   010096. m. 21.

PIESSE (L.) Algérie et Tunisie. Guide-Joanne. pp. 429. *Paris,* 1893. 8°.   10097. cc. 28.

PLAYFAIR (*Sir* R. L.) Murray's Handbook for Algeria and Tunis. pp. 363. *Lond.* 1895. 8°.
       2364. a. 1.

BARAUDON (A.) Algérie et Tunisie. Récits de voyage. pp. 327. *Paris,* 1893. 12°.
       10097. de. 25.

BOURNAND (F.) Tunisie et Tunisiens. pp. 368. *Paris,* 1894. 8°.   10097. l. 12.

CAGNAT (R.) and SALADIN (H.) Voyage en Tunisie. pp. 419. *Paris,* 1894. 8°. 010097. g. 3.

CASTONNET DES FOSSES (H.) La Tunisie. Conférence. pp. 20. *Lille,* 1892. 8°.   Pam. 89.

CLARETIE (L.) Feuilles de route en Tunisie. pp. 294. *Paris,* 1893. 12°.   10097. de. 24.

ECKARDT (J. T. v.) Von Carthago nach Kairuan. pp. 317. *Berl.* 1894. 12°.   10096. aa. 11.

FITZNER (R.) Die Regentschaft Tunis. pp. 360. *Berl.* 1895. 8°.   12249. ccc. 8.

GRÉPON (E.) Neuf ans en Algérie, Tunisie. pp. 186. *Paris,* 1893. 8°.   10026. ccc. 6.

GUÉRARD (F. A. H.) and BOUTINEAU (É.) La Khroumirie et sa colonisation. pp. 163. *Paris,* 1892. 8°.   10095. g. 7.

LA FORGE (J. de) Tunis port-de-mer. pp. 284. *Paris,* 1894. 12°.   012314. f. 55.

LALLEMAND (C.) La Tunisie. pp. 253. *Paris,* 1892. 4°.   1783. a. 21.

TURKEY.—Politics—*continued.*

GEORGIADÈS (D.) La Turquie actuelle. pp. 377.
Paris, 1892. 8°. 10126. f. 20.

P.P. *Paris.* La Turquie. Organe des intérêts
de l'Empire Ottoman. No. 1–10.
Paris, 1895. 4°. P.P. 9455. aa.

—— La Turquie libre. No. 1–17.
Paris, 1891, 92. 4°. N.R.

WOODS (H. F.) Blackmailing the Sultan. Refutation of the Calumnies in Osman Bey's
pamphlet. pp. 4. *Lond.* 1890. 8°. Pam. 67.

BÉRARD (E.) Rapport sur l'Égypte et la Turquie.
pp. 27. *Lyon*, 1892. 4°. 8028. f. 30.

BÉRARD '(V.) La Turquie et l'Hellénisme contemporain. pp. 352. *Paris*, 1893. 12°.
8028. aaa. 11.

CHANNEBOT (A.) L'Empire ottomane, l'Italie et
la France. pp. 24. *Paris*, 1891. 12°.
8028. f. 32. (4.)

DES GODINS DE SOUHESMES (G.) Comment les
français sont protégés en Turquie. pp. 87.
Fécamp, 1892. 8°. 8028. de. 31. (8.)

GREENE (F. D.) The Armenian Crisis and the
rule of the Turk. pp. 180. *Lond.* 1895. 8°.
8005. bbb. 29.

LEONOV (R.) Documents secrets de la politique
russe en Orient, 1881–90. pp. 237.
Berl. 1893. 8°. 8028. ee. 29.

MOLTKE (H. C. B. v.) *Count.* Gesammelte
Schriften und Denkwürdigkeiten. 7 Bde.
Berl. 1891–92. 8°. 12252. i. 4.

—— Essays, Speeches and Memoirs. 2 vol.
Lond. 1893. 8°. 12354. k. 16.

MONVOISIN (É.) France et Turquie. L'œuvre
du grand Abd-ul-Hamid. pp. 32.
Paris, 1894. 8°. Pam. 67.

ROSENBOURG (B. de) Solution de la question de
l'Alsace-Lorraine par le partage de la Turquie.
pp. 23. *Lausanne*, 1890. 8°. Pam. 67.

See also ARMENIA.

Topography.

AC. London. *Hakluyt Society.* DALLAM (T.)
Early Voyages and Travels in the Levant, 1599–
1679. pp. 305. *Lond.* 1893. 8°. Ac. 6172/69.

JOANNE (P.) De Paris à Constantinople.
pp. 342. *Paris*, 1886. 8°. 10168. aa. 29

BASMAJIAN (K. H.) Social and religious Life in
the Orient. pp. 247. *N.Y.* 1890. 8°.
10126. cc. 12.

BOROTRA (H.) Lettres orientales.
Paris, 1893, *etc.* 8°. 10126. df.

BUEHLER (A.) Von den Vogesen zum Balkan.
2 vol. *Magdeburg*, 1890. 8°. 10105. ee. 5.

CALLAN (H.) From the Clyde to the Jordan.
pp. 312. *Lond.* 1895. 8°. 10026. ccc. 7.

CAHU (T.) Des Batignolles au Bosphore.
pp. 376. *Paris*, 1890. 8°. 10126. cc. 11.

CENTELLI (A.) L'Oriente d'oggi. pp. 278.
Milano, 1892. 8°. 10125. aaa. 20.

DAVIES (D.) Notes of sport in the Levant.
pp. 108. *Malta*, 1893. 8°. 7912. aaa. 14.

DUKAS-THEODASSOS (J.) Im Zeichen des Halb-
monds. pp. 391. *Köln*, 1893. 8°. 10125. b. 3.

L., J. Manuel de géographie de l'Empire Ottoman. pp. 168. *Constantinople*, 1887. 8°.
10126. bb. 16.

LÜTKEN (A.) Fra Adria til Bosporus.
Kjøbenh. 1892, *etc.* 8°. 10126. f. 19.

SCARFOGLIO (E.) In Levante e a traverso i Balkani. pp. 245. *Milano*, 1890. 8°. 10126. aa. 21.

SPRY (W. J. J.) Life on the Bosphorus. 2 pt.
Lond. 1895. 8°. 10125. ff. 12.

WARNER (C. D.) In the Levant. 2 vol.
Bost. 1893. 8°. 10077. bbb. 20.

TURKEY—Trade.

P.P. *Constantinople.* Annuaire oriental du
commerce *Constantinople*, 1889, *etc.* 8°.
P.P. 2459. m.

—— Le Journal de la Chambre de Commerce.
Galata, 1894, *etc.* fol. P.P. 9103. ie.

TURKEY, Bird. CHEVASSU (F.) Nouvel
art d'élever les dindons. pp. 36.
Paris, 1892. 12°. 7004. de. 22. (7.)

COOK (W.) Pheasants, Turkeys and Geese.
pp. 69. *Lond.* 1894. 8°. 7294. bbb. 16.

WILLIS-HARRIS (W.) The Turkey. pp. 90.
Pulboro', 1893. 8°. 7295. bb. 5.

See also ANIMALS, *Domestic :* BIRDS : POULTRY.

TURKISH LANGUAGE AND LI-
TERATURE. HUART (C.) Notice des livres
turcs, arabes et persans imprimés à Constantinople, 1882–88. 2 vol. *Paris*, 1885–89. 8°.
011900. h. 31, 32.

DICTIONARIES. Fin türkisch-arabisches Glossar.
2 pt. *Leiden*, 1894. 8°. 758. g. 44.

JEHLITSCHKA (H.) Türkische Konversations-
Grammatik. pp. 420. *Heidelberg*, 1895. 8°.
12906. de. 12.

MELIOPOULOS (I. P.) Διαλογοι Τουρκοελληνικοι
και Ελληνο-τουρκικοι. pp. 275.
Εν Κωνσταντινουπολει, 1887. 8°. 758. b. 19.

MUELLER (F. A.) Türkische Grammatik. 2 pt.
1889. 8°. PETERMANN (J. H.) Porta linguarum
orientalium. Pars 11. 12904. de.

PEKOTSCH (L.) Übungsbuch zur gründlicheren
Erlernung der osmanisch-türkischen Sprache.
Wien, 1894, *etc.* 8°. 12910. f.

RADLOV (V. V.) Das türkische Sprachmaterial
der im Gebiete von Semirjetschie aufgefundenen
syrischen Grabinschriften. 1890. 4°. Ac. Saint-
Petersburg. *Academia Scientiarum.* Mémoires.
Sér. 7. Tom. 37. Ac. 1125/3.

SIMONIAN (K.) Guide de la traduction du français en turc. pp. 111. *Constantinople*, 1887. 8°.
12906. aa. 45.

YŪSUF (R.) Grammaire de la langue ottomane.
pp. 340. *Constantinople*, 1892. 8°. 12907. aa. 70.

YŪSUF ZIYĀ. Modèle des Correspondances turc-
français. pp. 40. *Constantinople*, 1891. 8°.
758. d.

TURNING. NORTHCOTT (W. H.) Geometric
Turning simplified. pp. 62. *Lond.* 1889. 8°.
7817. f. 18.

See also CARPENTRY.

TURTLE. *See* TORTOISE.

TUSCANY. *See* FLORENCE.

TWYFORD. *See* TIVERTON.

TYNE. ROBINSON (J.) Handbook to the river
Tyne. pp. 93. *Newcastle*, 1894. 8°. 10352. f. 2.

WATSON (A.) Down the Tyne. pp. 70.
Newcastle, 1894. 16°. 10360. aa. 30.

TYNINGHAME. WADDELL (P. H.) An
Old Kirk Chronicle. pp. 166. *Edinb.* 1893. 8°.
4735. eee. 13.

TYPE-WRITING. COLLYNS (E.) The
Typist's Manual. pp. 138. *Manch.* 1895. 8°.
7942. e. 49.

DROUIN (F.) Les Machines à écrire. pp. 60.
Paris, 1890. 8°. 07945. n. 20.

ELLIS (H. H.) How to double your speed.
pp. 20. *Grand Rapids*, 1893. 8°. Pam. 9.

HARRISON (J.) Manual of the Remington
Standard Typewriter. pp. 135.
Lond. 1890. 8°. 7942. a. 54.

HARTLEY (L.) Employment for Girls. pp. 8.
Woolwich, 1894. 8°. Pam. 94.

3 I

TYPOGRAPHY.—History—_continued._

DEGEORGE (L.) L'Imprimerie en Europe aux xv° et xvi° siècles. pp. 137. *Paris,* 1892. 12°.
11899. a. 13.

DUFF (E. G.) Early Printed Books. pp. 219. 1893. 8°. POLLARD (A. W.) Books about Books.   2312. d.

FAULMANN (C.) Die Erfindung der Buchdruckerkunst nach den neuesten Forschungen. pp. 156. *Wien,* 1891. 8°.   11899. ff. 53.

LOCARD (A.) Recherches historiques sur la coquille des imprimeurs. 1893. 8°. Ac. Lyons. *Académie des Sciences.* Mémoires. Sér. 3. Tom. 1.   Ac. 364/5.

PARIS. *Cercle de la Librairie.* Inventaire des marques d'imprimeurs de la collection du Cercle de la Librairie. pp. 355. *Paris,* 1892. 8°.
11899. k. 23.

P.P. *Lausanne.* Les Archives de l'Imprimerie. *Lausanne,* 1889, *etc.* 8°.   P.P. 1626. and 43.

PROCTOR (R. G. C.) Tracts on early Printing. *Lond.* 1895, *etc.* 8°.   011901. g. 32.

REICHHART (G.) Beiträge zur Incunabelnkunde. pp. 464. 1895. 8°. P.P. *Leipsic.* Centralblatt für Bibliothekswesen. Bd. 5.   P.P. 4649. e.

ROBERTS (W.) Printers' Marks. pp. 261. *Lond.* 1893. 8°.   011900. de. 6.

CASTAN (A.) Catalogue des Incunables de la Bibliothèque de Besançon. pp. 815. *Besançon,* 1893. 8°.   011900. h. 21.

MODONA (L.) Degli incunaboli nella biblioteca della Università di Bologna. pp. 15. *Brescia,* 1890. 8°.   11901. d. 26. (4.)

VOULLIÉME (E.) Die Incunabeln der Universitä's-Bibliothek zu Bonn. pp. 262. 1885. 8°. P.P. *Leipsic.* Centralblatt für Bibliothekswesen. Beihefte. No. 13.   P.P. 4649. e.

NENTWIG (H.) Die Wiegendrucke in der Stadtbibliothek zu Braunschweig. pp. 246. *Wolfenbüttel,* 1891. 8°.   011902. m. 14.

PELLECHET (M.) Catalogue des Incunables des Bibliothèques de Lyon. pp. 472. *Lyon,* 1893. 8°.   011901. f. 3.

VINGTRINIER (M. É. A.) Les Incunables de la Ville de Lyon. pp. 39. *Lyon,* 1890, 8°.
11903. aa. 23. (6)

Ac. New York. *Grolier Club.* Description of the Early Printed Books owned by the Grolier Club. pp. 77. *N.Y.* 1895. fol.   Ac. 4714/5.

—— Catalogue of early printed Books presented by D. W. Bruce. *N.Y.* 1894. 8°.
11903. b. 44. (5.)

MARAIS (P.) and DUFRESNE DE SAINT-LÉON (A.) Catalogue des Incunables de la Bibliothèque Mazarine. pp. 807. *Paris,* 1893. 8°.
011901. g. 18.

COPINGER (W. A.) Corrections and additions to the Catalogue of Incunabula in the Mazarine Library. pp. 11. *Manch.* 1893. 8°.
11903. b. 44. (3.)

DAUNOU (P. C. F.) Catalogue des Incunables de la Bibliothèque Sainte-Geneviève. pp. 309. *Paris,* 1892. 8°.   011900. f. 26.

ZELLER (F.) Die Incunabel-Drucke der Fürstenberg'scher Bibliothek zu Pürglitz. pp. 48. *Stuttgart,* 1885. 8°.   Pam. 6.

HOLTROP (H. v.) Catalogue d'une collection de spécimens d'impression du xv. et xvi. siècles. pp. 40, *Paris,* 1892. 8°.   011900. f. 10. (12.) *See also infra: Various Countries:* BIBLIOGRAPHY.

Printing in Various Countries.

Alsace. See infra: Germany.

TYPOGRAPHY—_continued._

America, Spanish.

MEDINA (J. T.) Historia y bibliografía de la Imprenta en la América española. 2 pt. 1892. fol. Ac. La Plata. *Museo.* Anales.
Tab. 1227. a.

—— La Imprenta en Lima. 1584–1810. pp. 118. *Santiago,* 1890. 8°.   11899. bb. 47.

—— La Imprenta en México. 1539–1810. pp. 291. *Sevilla,* 1893. 8°.   11899. aaa. 22.

—— Bibliografía de la Imprenta en Santiago. pp. 179. *Santiago,* 1891. 4°.   11899. k. 20.

Belgium. See infra: Netherlands.

Chili. See supra: America.

England.

CAXTON (W.) Caxton's Advertisement. Photolithograph of the copy preserved in the Bodleian Library. pp. 7. *Lond.* 1892. 8°.   Pam. 6.

Ac. London. *Bibliographical Society.* Handlists of English Printers 1501–56. *Lond.* 1895, *etc.* 4°.   BB.G. b. 27.

ENGLISH PRINTERS. List of early English Printers and Books. pp. 32. *Lond.* 1880. 4°.
11899. i. 46.

DREDGE (J. I.) Devon Booksellers and Printers in the 17th and 18th centuries. ff. 133. *Plymouth,* 1885. 4°.   011900. ee. 28.

EDWARDS (F. A.) Early Hampshire Printers. pp. 24. *Southampton,* 1891. 8°.
011900. ee. 3. (3.)

Ac. Oxford. *Historical Society.* MADAN (F.) The Early Oxford Press, 1468–1640. pp. 365. *Oxf.* 1895. 8°   Ac. 8126/19.

France.

THIERRY-POUX (O.) Premiers monuments de l'Imprimerie en France au xv° siècle. pp. 24. Planches 40. *Paris,* 1890. fol. Tab. 1216. a.

PICHON (J.) and VICAIRE (G.) Documents pour servir à l'histoire des Libraires de Paris 1486–1600. pp. 294. *Paris,* 1895. 8°. 011901. ee. 34.

DUCOURTIEUX (P.) Les Barbou, imprimeurs: Lyon, Limoges, Paris, 1524–1820. pp. 39. *Limoges,* 1894. 8°.   Pam. 6.

OMONT (H.) Essai sur les débuts de la Typographie grecque à Paris, 1507–16. pp. 72. *Paris,* 1892. 8°.   11899. f. 50.

LOUIS XV., *King of France.* L'Imprimerie du Cabinet du Roi aux Tuileries sous Louis xv., 1718–30. pp. 11. 1891. 8°.   011900. f. 7. (4.)

CLAUDIN (A.) Le premier livre imprimé à Agen. pp. 21. *Paris,* 1894. 8°.   11904. l. 16. (16.)

ADVIELLE (V.) B. Dacquin, premier Imprimeur de la Province d'Artois. pp. 15. *Abbeville,* 1893. 8°.   10601. ff. 11. (4.)

CLAUDIN (A.) Les origines de l'Imprimerie à Auch. pp. 32. *Paris,* 1894. 8°.
11904. l. 16. (14.)

DUHAMEL (L.) Les origines l'Imprimerie à Avignon. pp. 15. *Avignon,* 1890. 8°.
011900. ee. 6. (6.)

REQUIN ( ) Origines de l'Imprimerie en France. Avignon, 1444. pp. 15. *Paris,* 1891. 8°.
011900. f. 10. (10.)

PORCHER (R.) Notice sur les Imprimeurs blésois du xvi° au xix° siècle. pp. 292. *Blois,* 1895. 8°.   011900. de. 10.

LHOTE (A.) Histoire de l'Imprimerie à Châlons-sur-Marne. pp. 232. *Châlons-sur-M.* 1894. 4°.
11901. h. 1.

GRIMAUD (H.) Les origines de l'Imprimerie à Chinon. pp. 6. *Tours,* 1891. 8°.
011900. ee. 5. (12.)

TYPOGRAPHY.—France—*continued.*

MAIGNIEN (E.) L'imprimerie et les libraires de Grenoble du xv⁰ au xviiie siècle. pp. 609. *Grenoble*, 1884. 8°.　　11899. e. 38.

CLAUDIN (A.) Les origines de l'Imprimerie à Hesdin-en-Artois, 1512-18. pp. 16. *Paris*, 1891. 8°.　　011900. ee. 16. (14.)

—— Les origines de l'Imprimerie à La Réole, 1517. *Paris*, 1894. 8°.　　11904. l. 16. (15.)

ANGOT (A.) Histoire de l'Imprimerie à Laval, jusqu'en 1789. pp. 48. *Laval*, 1892. 8°.　　11903. aa. 23. (7.)

CLAUDIN (A.) Notes pour servir à l'histoire de l'Imprimerie à Limoges. pp. 29. *Paris*, 1894. 8°.　　11903. f. 34. (7.)

GUIBERT (L.) Les premiers imprimeurs de Limoges. pp. 44. *Limoges*, 1893. 8°.　　11904. l. 16. (9.)

DUCOURTIEUX (P.) Les marques typographiques des imprimeurs de Limoges. pp. 16. *Limoges*, 1890. 8°.　　11903. aa. 22. (5.)

BAUDRIER (H.) Bibliographie lyonnaise. Recherches sur les imprimeurs de Lyon au xvie siècle. *Lyon*, 1895, etc. 8°.　　011901. ee.

VINGTRINIER (M. E. A.) Histoire de l'Imprimerie à Lyon. pp. 440. *Lyon*, 1894. 8°.　　011901. g. 27.

HAUSER (H.) Histoire d'une grève au xvie siècle. Les imprimeurs lyonnais de 1539-42. pp. 24. *Paris*, 1894. 8°.　　11904. l. 16. (19.)

CLOUZOT (H.) Notes pour servir à l'histoire de l'Imprimerie à Niort. 1890. 8°. Ac. Niort. *Société de Statistique*. Mémoires. Sér. 3. Tom. 7.　　Ac. 316.

CLAUDIN (A.) Les antécédents d'H. Poyvre et de J. de Vingles, imprimeurs de Pau. pp. 3. *Auch*, 1893. 8°.　　11904. l. 16. (5.)

—— Les débuts de l'Imprimerie à Poitiers. pp. 20. *Paris*, 1894. 8°.　　Pam. 6.

—— Les origines de l'Imprimerie à Reims. pp. 24. *Paris*, 1891. 8°.　　011900. ee. 3. (2.)

—— Les origines de l'Imprimerie à Saint-Lô. pp. 37. *Paris*, 1894. 8°.　　11903. f. 34. (8.)

—— Les origines de l'Imprimerie à Salins. pp. 24. *Paris*, 1892. 8°.　　Pam. 6.

—— Les origines de l'Imprimerie à Sisteron. pp. 23. *Paris*, 1894. 8°.　　11903. f. 34. (9.)

—— Les enlumineurs et les imprimeurs de Toulouse aux xv⁰ et xvie siècles. pp. 67. *Paris*, 1891. 8°.　　011902. m. 21. (12.)

LA BOURALIÈRE (A. de) L'Imprimerie à Thouars. pp. 7. *Saint-Maixent*, 1892. 8°.　　011900. f. 10. (11.)

MORIN (L.) Histoire des imprimeries de Troyes depuis 1789. 1892. 8°. Ac. Troyes. *Société d'Agriculture*. Mémoires. Tom. 56. Ac. 260.

Germany.

GERMANY. *Reichsdruckerei.* Monumenta Germaniae typographica. *Berl.* 1892, etc. fol.　　1888. d.

DZIATZKO (C.) Was wissen wir von dem Leben J. Guttenbergs? 1895. 8°. 11904. l. 17. (10.)

—— Gutenbergs früheste Druckerpraxis. pp. 136. 1890. 8°. Sammlung bibliothekswissenschaftlicher Arbeiten. No. 4.　　11904. b. 23.

DELISLE (L. V.) Les Bibles de Gutenberg d'après les recherches de K. Dziatzko. pp. 13. *Paris*, 1894. 4°.　　11905. d. 6.

IHME (F. A.) Gutenberg und die Buchdruckerkunst im Elsass. pp. 52. *Strassburg*, 1891. 8°.　　011900. ee. 6. (18.)

ALSATIAN PRINTED BOOKS. Der Initialschmuck in den elsässischen Drucken des xv. und xvi. Jahrhunderts. *Strassburg*, 1894, etc. 8°.　　11906. c.

TYPOGRAPHY.—Germany—*continued.*

BUECHERMARKEN. Die Büchermarken in Elsass. *Strassburg*, 1892, etc. 4°.　　11901. l.

SCHMIDT (C.) Zur Geschichte der ersten Buchdrucker zu Strassburg. pp. 200. *Strassburg*, 1882. 8°.　　11899. g. 11.

ALDRICH (S. J.) The Augsburg Printers of the fifteenth century. pp. 24. *Lond.* 1894. 8°.　　11904. g. 35. (6.)

ROTH (F. W. E.) Die mainzer Buchdruckerfamilie Schöffer während des xvi. Jahrhunderts. pp. 250. 1892. 8°. P.P. *Leipsic.* Centralblatt für Bibliothekswesen. Beihefte. No. 9.　　P.P. 4649. c.

DOMMER (A. v.) Die ältesten Drucke aus Marburg, 1527-66. pp. 32. 182. *Marburg*, 1892. 8°.　　11852. gg. 32.

RUNGE (H.) Geschichte des osnabrücker Buchdrucks. 1892, etc. 8°. Ac. *Osnaburg. Historischer Verein.* Mittheilungen. Bd. 17, etc.　　Ac. 7145.

Ireland.

ANDERSON (J.) Catalogue of early Belfast Printed Books, 1694-1830. pp. 23. *Belfast*, 1894. 4°.　　11900. i. 37.

Italy.

GERMANY. *Reichsdruckerei.* Monumenta Germaniae et Italiae typographica. *Berl.* 1892, etc. fol.　　1888. d.

ITALIAN RENAISSANCE. L'Arte della stampa nel rinascimento italiano. *Venezia*, 1894, etc. 4°.　　011901. k.

FUMAGALLI (G.) La questione di P. Castaldi. *Milano*, 1891. 8°. pp. 127.　　11899. e. 34.

KRISTELLER (P.) Die italienischen Buchdrucker- und Verlegerzeichen bis 1525. pp. 143. 1893. 8°. Die Büchermarken.　　11901. l.

PANSA (G.) La Tipografia in Abruzzo dal sec. xv. al sec. XVIII. pp. 103. *Lanciano*, 1891. 8°.　　011902. m. 16.

GARIBOLDI (C.) Ricerche sull' arte della stampa in Ancona. pp. 31. *Ancona*, 1890. 8°.　　011900. f. 9. (4.)

BROWN (H. R. F.) The Venetian Printing Press. pp. 463. *Lond.* 1891. 4°.　　11899. g. 50.

ITALIAN RENAISSANCE. Early Venetian Printing illustrated. pp. 228. *Venice*, 1895. 4°.　　011901. k. 3.

MASSENA (A. P. V.) *Duke de Rivoli.* Les Missels imprimés à Venise de 1481 à 1600. *Paris*, 1894, etc. 4°.　　K.T.C. 25. b.

MANUTIUS (A. P.) Catalogues des livres imprimés par Alde Manuce à Venise, 1498-1513. pp. 11. 15. *Paris*, 1892. fol. Tab.　　11748. a.

RENOUARD (A. A.) Bibliographical sketch of the Aldine Press at Venice. 3 pt. *Edinb.* 1887. 8°.　　011901. g. 1.

BERNONI (D.) Dei Torresani, Blado e Ragazzoni, celebri Stampatori a Venezia e Roma. pp. 403. *Milano*, 1890. 8°.　　11899. cc. 19.

Mexico. See supra: America.

Netherlands.

OLTHOFF (F.) De Boekdrukkers in Antwerpen. pp. 134. *Antwerpen*, 1891. 4°. 011900. f. 19.

ANTWERP. *Musée Plantin-Moretus.* Catalogue du Musée. pp. 134. *Anvers*, 1887. 8°.　　11900. aa. 25.

FRICK (G.) Die Elzevir'schen Republiken. pp. 35. *Halle*, 1892. 8°.　　9327. ccc.

Philippine Islands.

PARDO DE TAVERA (T. H.) Noticias sobre la imprenta en Filipinas. pp. 48. *Madrid*, 1893. 8°.　　Pam. 6

Peru. See supra: America.

TYPOGRAPHY—*continued.*

Scotland.

Ac. Edinburgh. *Bibliographical Society.* Handlist of Books and Pamphlets printed by J. Watson, 1695–1722. pp. 4. 1890. 8°.   Pam. 6.

Spain.

Fenollar (B.) Primer libro impreso en España. Les Trobes en lahors de la Verge Maria, 1474. *Valencia,* 1894. 8°.   11450. h. 25.

Pérez-Pastor (C.) La Imprenta en Medina del Campo. pp. 526. *Madrid,* 1895. 8°.   11906. c. 6.

Catalina Garcia (J.) Ensayo de una Tipografía complutense. pp. 673. *Madrid,* 1889. 8°.   11899. h. 34.

Hazañas y la Rua (J.) La imprenta en Sevilla. pp. 142. *Sevilla,* 1892. 8°.   011900. ee. 12.

Switzerland.

Heitz (P.) Die zürcher Büchermarken bis zum Anfang des 17. Jahrhunderts. pp. 48. *Zürich,* 1895. fol.   1890. b. 12.

Turkey.

Omont (H.) Documents sur l'imprimerie à Constantinople au XVIII° siècle. pp. 29. *Paris,* 1895. 8°.   Pam. 6.

United States of America.

Ac. Boston. *Massachusetts Historical Society.* List of early American Imprints. pp. 137. *Camb.* 1895. 8°.   Ac. 8400/11.

—— New York. *Grolier Club.* Catalogue of Books printed by W. Bradford and other printers in the middle colonies. pp. 100. *N.Y.* 1893. 12°.   011899. c. 1.

Hildeburn (C. S. R.) Printing in New York in the 17th century. 1892. 8°. Wilson (J. G.) Memorial History of New York. Vol. I.   9603. f. 5.

Seidensticker (O.) First century of German Printing in America, 1728–1830. pp. 253. *Phila.* 1893. 8°.   011900. ee. 33.

TYRE. Jeremias (F.) Tyrus bis zur Zeit Nebukadnezar's. pp. 48. *Leipz.* 1891. 8°.   07703. g. 3. (10.)

TYROL, Ac. Berlin. *Geodätisches Institut.* Helmert (F. R.) Die Schwerkraft im Hochgebirge insbesondere in den tyroler Alpen. pp. 52. *Berl.* 1890. 4°.   Ac. 4301/25.

—— Germany. *Gesellschaft für Anthropologie.* Beiträge zur Anthropologie und Urgeschichte von Tirol. pp. 277. *Innsbruck,* 1894. 8°.   10201. d. 4.

—— Vienna. *Heraldisch-genealogischer Verein Adler.* Hohenbühel (L. v.) Beiträge zur Geschichte des tiroler Adels. pp. 130. *Wien,* 1891. 8°.   9902. g. 22.

Achleitner (A.) Tirol und Vorarlberg. *Leipz.* 1894, *etc.* 4°.   44.

Baedeker (C.) The Eastern Alps. pp. 518. *Leipz.* 1895. 8°.   2352. a. 1.

Grandjean (M.) En Tyrol. Paysages, mœurs. pp. 288. *Lille,* 1893. 8°.   10205. cee. 8.

Maurer (J.) Tiroler Helden. pp. 116. *Münster i. W.,* 1895. 8°.   010707. ff. 15.

Leland (C. G.) Hans Breitmann in Germany. Tyrol. pp. 168. *Lond.* 1895. 8°. 012314. ee. 67.

Priester (C. A.) Kunstgeschichte von Tirol. pp. 410. *Bozen,* 1885. fol.   7808. f. 13.

Rapp (L.) Kulturgeschichtliche Bilder aus Tirol. pp. 126. *Brixen,* 1892. 8°.   10215. bbb. 10.

Rivière (L.) Entre l'Inn et le lac de Constance. pp. 330. *Paris,* 1891. 12°.   10215. aaa. 35.

Schneller (C.) Tirolische Namenforschungen. pp. 373. *Innsbruck,* 1890. 8°.   12962. dd. 25.

TYROL—*continued.*

Schneller (C.) Beiträge zur Ortsnamenkunde Tirols. *Innsbruck,* 1893, *etc.* 8°.   12962. s.

Taponier (A.) Bavière et Tyrol. pp. 364. *Fribourg,* 1892. 8°.   10235. c. 8.

Trautwein (T.) Tirol, Südbaiern und Salzburg. pp. 538. *Augsburg,* 1889. 8°.   10240. aa. 19.

Zehenter (J.) Die Mineralquellen Tirols. pp. 141. 1893. 8°. Ac. Innspruck. *Ferdinandeum. Zeitschrift. Dritte Folge.* Hft. 37.   Ac. 760.

See also Alps, *Eastern :* Austria-Hungary : Vorarlberg.

ÜBERLINGEN. Schaefer (F.) Wirtschafts- und Finanzgeschichte der Reichsstadt Überlingen, 1550–1628. pp. 196. 1893. 8°. Gierke (O.) Untersuchungen zur deutschen Staats- und Rechtsgeschichte. Hft. 44.   6025. e. 9.

UFTON COURT, Berkshire. Sharp (A. M.) History of Ufton Court. pp. 276. *Lond.* 1892. 8°.   010358. l. 36.

UGANDA. Ashel (R. P.) Chronicles of Uganda. pp. 480. *Lond.* 1894. 8°. 9061. ccc. 30.

Bentley (E. L.) Handbook to the Uganda question. pp. 62. *Lond.* 1892. 8°. 8028. e. 30.

Gordon (E. C.) The Revolution in Uganda. pp. 22. *Lond.* 1889. 8°.   Pam. 40.

G. B. & I. *War Office.* Handbook of British East Africa. pp. 176. *Lond.* 1893. 8°.   10097. dd. 26.

Lugard (F. J. D.) British East Africa and Uganda. pp. 67. *Lond.* 1892. 8°. 8028. e. 31.

—— The Rise of our East African Empire. 2 vol. *Edinb.* 1893. 8°.   010096. h. 4.

M., J. L'Ouganda, la mission catholique et les agents de la Compagnie anglaise. pp. 326. *Paris,* 1893. 8°.   4766. ee. 23.

Macdermott (P. L.) British East Africa or Ibea. pp. 382. *Lond.* 1893. 8°. 8154. dd. 15.

Mackay (A. M.) A. Mackay : Missionary hero of Uganda. pp. 144. *Lond.* 1894. 8°.   4955. df. 1.

Moloney (J. A.) With Captain Stairs to Katanga. pp. 280. *Lond.* 1893. 8°.   010096. c. 59.

Portal (*Sir* G. H.) The British Mission to Uganda in 1893. pp. 351. *Lond.* 1894. 8°.   9061. ccc. 22.

Richter (J.) Uganda. Ein Blatt aus der Geschichte der evangelischen Mission, pp. 268. *Gütersloh,* 1893. 8°.   4766. ee. 22.

Ruwenzori. Arcana in the Ruwenzori. pp. 47. *Lond.* 1892. 8°.   7702. bb. 42.

Smith (R. B) Uganda. Letters to "The Times." pp. 16. *Lond.* 1892. 8°.   8028. de. 30. (13.)

Stock (S. G.) The Story of Uganda. pp. 224. *Lond.* 1894. 8°.   4429. eee. 30.

Tucker (A. R.) Bp. of East. Equatorial Africa. African Sketches. *Lond.* 1892. obl. 4°. 10096. i. 4.

Uganda. L'Ouganda et les agissements de la Compagnie anglaise. pp. 176. *Paris,* 1892. 8°.   8029. c. 9.

See also Africa, *Central and East* and *Colonisation, British :* African Languages : England, Colonies.

UITENHAGE. *See* Cape of Good Hope.

ULCERS. Crawford (W. S.) Ulcers and their treatment. pp. 46. *Lond.* 1894. 8°.   7630. a. 14.

ULIA. *See* CAROLINE ISLANDS.

ULM. Ac. Ulm. *Verein für Kunst und Alterthum.* BAZING (H.) and VEESENMEYER (G.) Urkunden zur Geschichte der Pfarrkirche in Ulm. pp. 215. *Ulm,* 1890. 8°. 4662. a. 7.

NUEBLING (E.) Ulm's Handel und Gewerbe im Mittelalter. *Ulm,* 1892, *etc.* 4°. 8225. ff.

ULSTER. MACDONNELL (J.) The Ulster Civil War of 1641 and its consequences. pp. 187. *Dublin,* 1879. 8°. 9509. bbb. 17.

YOUNG (R. M.) Ulster in '98. Episodes and anecdotes. pp. 96. *Belfast,* 1893. 8°. 9509. aaa. 24.

GLADSTONE (*Right Hon.* W. E.) Mr. Gladstone on Ulster. pp. 16. *Lond.* 1892. 8°. 8146. cc. 6. (11.)

JENKINS (R C) Revival of the exploded doctrine of " Passive Obedience " and " Non-Resistance " in its application to Ulster. pp. 9. *Folkestone,* 1892. 8°. 8138. aa. 20. (5.)

LYNN. *afterwards* LINTON (E.) About Ulster. pp. 68. *Lond.* 1892. 8°. 8146. aaa. 43.

CRONE (J. S.) A run round Ulster. pp. 16. *Lond.* 1894. 4°. 10390. h. 17.

MORRISON (L. A.) Among the Scotch-Irish. 2 pt. *Bost.* 1891. 8°. 10106. ccc. 26.

See also IRELAND.

ULUNDA. *See* LUNDA.

UMBALLA. *See* AMBALA.

UMBRIAN LANGUAGE. PLANTA (R. v.) Grammatik der oskisch-umbrischen Dialekte. *Strassb.* 1892, 8°. 12933, i.

UNIONIDAE. *See* MOLLUSCA.

UNION PACIFIC RAILWAY. *See* RAILWAYS.

UNITARIANISM.

Doctrine : Controversy, etc.

BARTRAM (R.) Religion and Life : essays. pp. 311. *Lond.* 1891. 8°. 4372. ee. 10.

BEARD (C.) The Church, the Bible and free thought. pp. 27. *Lond.* 1892. 8°. Pam. 92.

BRITISH AND FOREIGN UNITARIAN ASSOCIATION. Reasonable Religion. pp. 206. *Lond.* 1893. 8°. 4371. df. 29.

CAPLETON (E.) How I became and why I remain a Unitarian. pp. 16. *Lond.* 1894. 8°. Pam. 92.

CHADWICK (J. W.) Old and new Unitarian Belief. pp. 246. *Bost.* 1894. 8°. 4182. c. 32.

CLARKE (J. F.) Why am I a Unitarian ? pp. 20. *Lond.* 1894. 8°. Pam. 92.

—— Christ and Christianity. pp. 16. *Lond.* 1883. 8°. Pam. 92.

—— False Witnesses answered. pp. 12. *Lond.* 1890. 8°. Pam. 92.

DRUMMOND (J.) Hibbert Lectures on Christianity in its most simple form. pp. 331. *Lond.* 1894. 8°. 2212. c. 17.

DRUMMOND (R. B.) Free Thought and Christian Faith. pp. 123. *Edinb.* 1890. 8°. 4018. c. 17.

DOWSON (E. H.) Unitarianism a positive Faith. pp. 11. *Lond.* 1894. 8°. Pam. 92.

FAY (E.) Is Unitarianism false and is orthodoxy true? pp. 14. *Sheffield,* 1881. 8°. Pam. 16.

HARGROVE (C.) Unitarianism : a protest and a creed. pp. 16. *Lond.* 1894. 8°. 4139. bbb. 21. (14.)

HEDGE (F. H.) Reason in Religion. pp. 458. *Lond.* 1894. 8°. 4136. b. 36.

HERFORD (B.) The forward movement in Religious Thought as interpreted by Unitarians. pp. 99. *Lond.* 1892. 8°. 4136. c. 13.

UNITARIANISM. — Doctrine, etc. — continued.

HOPPS (J. P.) The Unitarian Faith : " good to die by." pp. 4. *Lond.* 1894. 8°. Pam. 92.

MAC QUAKER TRUST LECTURES. McQuaker Trust Lectures. *Lond.* 1890, *etc.* 8°. 4182. bbb.

MARTINEAU (J.) The three stages of Unitarian Theology. pp. 20. *Lond.* 1894. 8°. Pam. 92.

SAVAGE (M. J.) Katekismus Unitara. pp. 63. *Winnipeg,* 1891. 8°. 3506. df. 48.

SHARPE (S.) Unitarian Christianity. pp. 8. *Lond.* 1894. 16°. Pam. 92.

—— Unitarianism. pp. 4. *Lond.* 1894. 8°. Pam. 92.

SPIRIT. In Spirit and in Truth. Essays. pp. 163. *Bost.* 1893. 8°. 4371. aaa. 29.

UNITARIAN CHRISTIANITY. Unitarian Christianity. Lectures. pp. 274. *Lond.* 1894. 8°. 4136. aa. 40.

WALTERS (F.) Unitarian Christianity. pp 4. *Lond.* 1894. 32°. Pam. 16.

WARD (M. A.) Unitarians and the future. pp. 72. *Lond.* 1894. 8°. 4139. aaa. 22.

WICKSTEED (C.) Controversial Lectures. pp. 171. *Lond.* 1887. 8°. 4136. b. 15.

WILLIAMS (S. F.) Beliefs and opinions of a Unitarian. pp. 249. *Lond.* 1885. 8°. 4135. df. 20.

WRIGHT (J.) Religious doctrines believed by Unitarians. 7 pt. *Lond.* 1894. 8°. Pam. 92.

—— Orthodox doctrines denied by Unitarians. 7 pt. *Lond.* 1894. 8°. Pam. 92.

History, etc.

ALLEN (J. H.) Historical sketch of the Unitarian movement since the Reformation. pp. 254. *N.Y.* 1894. 8°. 4745. de. 7.

BONET-MAURY (G.) Des origines de Christianisme unitaire chez les Anglais. pp. 300. *Paris,* 1881. 8°. 4715. g. 11.

DYER (A. S.) Sketches of English Nonconformity. pp. 112. *Lond.* 1893. 8°. 4109. aa. 42.

GORDON (A.) Heads of English Unitarian history. pp. 138. *Lond.* 1895. 8°. 4715. aaa. 50

ALLEN (J. H.) and EDDY (R.) History of the Unitarians in the U.S. pp. 506. 1894. 8°. American Church History Series. Vol. 10. 4744. g.

WILBUR (E. M.) History of the first Unitarian church, of Portland, Oregon. pp. 95. *Portland,* 1893. 8°. 4744. dd. 8.

P.P. *Liverpool.* The Liverpool Unitarian annual. *Liverpool,* 1892, *etc.* 8°. P.P. 2483. wb.

UNITAS FRATRUM. *See* BRETHREN, *Moravian.*

UNITED STATES OF AMERICA. [*See note on page* 1.]

Antiquities.

See AMERICA, *Antiquities* : INDIANS.

Army.

BRESLER (A. L.) Die Armee der Vereinigten Staaten. pp. 38. *Leipz.* 1891. 8°. 8823. h. 24.

MERRITT (W.) The Army of the U.S. Armies of to-day. 8829. i. 9.

BOYD (*Mrs.* O. B.) Cavalry Life in tent and field. pp. 376. *N.Y.* 1894. 8°. 012330. g. 59.

KING (C.) Trials of a Staff-Officer. pp. 214. *Phila.* 1891. 8°. 8830. aaa. 43.

BURNHAM (W. P.) Three roads to a commission in the U.S. Army. pp. 160. *N.Y.* 1893. 8°. 8823. b. 18.

Ac. West Point. *Military Academy.* Biographical Register of the Academy. 3 vol. *Bost.* 1891. 8°. 2407. g. 2.

UNITED STATES.—History—continued.

JOHNSTON (A.) A shorter history of the United States. pp. 340. *N.Y.* 1890. 8°.   9602. cc. 7.

LODGE (H. C.) and ROOSEVELT (T.) Hero Tales from American history. pp. 335. *N.Y.* 1895. 8°.   9605. bb. 23.

LORD (J.) Beacon Lights of history. Vol. VII. *Lond.* 1893. 8°.   9080. cc. 12.

MABIE (H. W.) and BRIGHT (M. H.) Memorial story of America. pp. 851. *Phila.* 1892. 8°.   9555. f. 6.

MOIREAU (A.) Histoire des États-Unis. *Paris,* 1892, *etc.* 8°.   9602. h. 11.

NYE (E. W.) History of the United States. pp. 329. *Phila.* 1894. 8°.   9605. c. 15.

P.P. *New York.* American Historical Review. *N.Y.* 1895, *etc.* 8°.   P.P. 3437. baa.

—— *Philadelphia.* American Historical Register. *Phila.* 1894, *etc.* 8°.   P.P. 3437. bb.

PONTOPPIDAN (M.) De Forenede Staters historie. *Kjøbenh.* 1892, *etc.* 8°.   9602. c.

PRESTON (H. W.) Documents illustrative of American history. pp. 320. *N.Y.* 1891. 8°.   9605. c. 6.

SHALER (N. S.) The United States. 2 vol. *Lond.* 1894. 8°.   10413. dd. 1.

SMITH (Goldwin) The United States. pp. 312. *Lond.* 189;. 8°.   9602. cc. 8.

SWINTON (W.) School history of the United States. pp. 383. *N.Y.* 1893. 8°.   9605. c. 13.

THOMAS (A. C.) History of the United States. pp. 410. *Bost.* 1894. 8°.   9604. bbb. 11.

U.S. The American Republic. pp. 206. *Chicago,* 1892. 16l.   1856. a. 7.

ELLIS (E. S.) Indian Wars of the United States. pp. 516. *N.Y.* 1892. 8°.   9605. ff. 6.

See also AMERICA : NEW ENGLAND, and under each State.

Colonial History to the War of Independence.

BETTS (C. W.) American Colonial history illustrated by contemporary Medals. pp. 332. *N.Y.* 1894. 8°.   77.7. e. 37.

FISHER (G. P.) The Colonial Era. pp. 348. *Lond.* 1892. 8°.   9602. aaa. 10.

THWAITES (R. G.) The Colonies, 1492–1750. pp. 301. 1891. 8°. HART (A. B.) Epochs of American history.   9551. aa.

CAMPBELL (D.) The Puritan in Holland, England and America. 2 vol. *Lond.* 1892. 8°.   9602. dd. 1.

GRIFFIS (W. E.) The Influence of the Netherlands in the making of the American Republic. pp. 40. *Bost.* 1891. 8°.   Pam. 28.

WINSLOW (W. C.) The Pilgrim Fathers in Holland. pp. 24. *Lond.* 1891. 8°.   Pam. 29.

DRAKE (S. A.) The making of Virginia and the middle Colonies. 1578–1701. pp. 228. *Lond.* 1894. 8°.   9605. c. 18.

POINDEXTER (C.) Captain J. Smith and his critics. pp. 74. *Richmond,* 1893. 8°.   10883. cc. 12.

WINSOR (J.) The struggle in America between England and France, 1697–1763. pp. 484. *Lond.* 1895. 8°.   9551. f. 12.

PARKMAN (F.) A half-century of Conflict. 2 vol. *Lond.* 1892. 8°.   9602. de. 12.

DRAKE (S. A.) The Taking of Louisburg, 1745. pp. 136. *Bost.* 1891. 8°.   9602. cc. 5.

WASHINGTON (G.) Journal of Colonel Washington, commanding a detachment of Virginia troops, sent across the Alleghany Mountains, in 1754. pp. 273. *Albany,* 1893. 4°.   10882. ff. 43.

UNITED STATES.—History—continued.

SLOANE (W. M.) The French War, *etc.* pp. 409. *Lond.* 1893. 8°.   9555. b. 12.

War of Independence to the Civil War.

FORD (P. L.) Materials for a Bibliography of official publications of Continental Congress, 1774–89. pp. 57. *Brooklyn,* 1888. 8°.   11901. cc. 28.

HUNNEWELL (J. F.) Illustrated Americana of the Revolution. pp. 9. *Charlestown,* 1892. 4°.   Pam. 24.

WOODBURN (J. A.) Causes of the American Revolution. pp. 74. 1892. 8°. Johns Hopkins University Studies. Ser. 10. No. 12. Ac. 2689.

FISKE (J.) The American Revolution. 2 vol. *Lond.* 1891. 8°.   9605. c. 7.

SLOANE (W. M.) The French War and the Revolution. pp. 409. *Lond.* 1893. 8°.   9555. b. 12.

SAFFELL (W. T. R.) Records of the Revolutionary War. pp. 555. *Baltimore,* 1894. 8°.   9605. dd. 17.

TIFFANY (N. M.) From Colony to Commonwealth. pp. 180. *Bost.* 1891. 8°. 9605. aaa. 18.

CHICAGO. *Columbian Exposition.* Catalogue de l'Exposition des souvenirs franco-américains de la guerre de l'Independance. pp. 108. *Paris,* 1893. 4°.   7959. h. 25.

VOSSION (L.) La célébration du centenaire de la Constitution américaine à Philadelphie. pp. 63. *Paris,* 1893. 8°.   9551. c. 13.

KING (T. S.) Organization of liberty on the Western Continent. Oration. pp. 55. *Bost.* 1892. 8°.   Pam. 45.

BAKER (W. S.) Early sketches of G. Washington. pp. 150. *Phila.* 1894. 8°.   10881. ee. 27.

THAYER (W. M.) G. Washington. pp. 422. *Lond.* 1892. 8°.   010882. k. 6.

HENKELS (S. V.) Revolutionary manuscripts and portraits. Washington's Correspondence. pp. 172. *Phila.* 1892. 8°.   011903. h. 22.

WASHINGTON (G.) Spurious Letters attributed to Washington. pp. 166. *Brooklyn,* 1889. 8°.   010920. f. 11.

BAKER (W. S.) Itinerary of General Washington. June 15, 1775 to Dec. 23, 1783. pp. 334. *Phila.* 1892. 8°.   010882. m. 19.

WASHINGTON (G.) History of the Centennial Celebration of the inauguration of G. Washington as first President. pp. 673. *N.Y.* 1892. 4°.   K.T.C. 9. b. 6.

EELKING (M. v.) German allied troops in the North American War of Independence, 1776–83. pp. 360. *Albany,* 1893. 4°. 9615. eee. 11.

STONE (W. L.) Letters of Brunswick and Hessian officers during the American Revolution. pp. 258. *Albany,* 1891. 4°.   9605. d. 7.

WERTHERN (v.) Die hessischen Hülfstruppen in nordamerikanischen Unabhängigkeitskriege, 1776–83. pp. 47. *Cassel,* 1895. 8°.   Pam. 2.

CAMPBELL (R. A.) Our Flag. Evolution of the Stars and Stripes. pp. 128. *Chicago,* 1890. 8°.   9602 cc. 4.

VAN SCHAAK (H C.) Memoirs of the life of H. Van Schaack, with selections from his correspondence. pp. 233. *Chicago,* 1892. 8°.   010882. f. 25.

LEE (W.) Letters of W. Lee, Commercial Agent of the Continental Congress in France and Minister to Vienna and Berlin. 1766–83. 3 vol. *Brooklyn,* 1891. 8°.   10920. i. 29.

HOWE (W.) *Viscount Howe.* Sir W. Howe's Orderly book at Charlestown, Boston and Halifax, 1775–76. pp. 357. *Lond.* 1890. 8°.   9605. ff. 8.

UNITED STATES.—History · continued.

JONES (C.) Orderly Book of the "Maryland Loyalists Regiment," 1778. pp. 111. *Brooklyn*, 1891. 8°. 8823. n. 21.

STILLÉ (C. J.) General A. Wayne and the Pennsylvania line in the Continental Army. pp. 441. *Phila*. 1893. 8°. 9605. dd. 9.

STONE (W. L.) Visits to the Saratoga Battle-grounds. pp. 344. *Albany*, 1895. 4°. 9605. dd. 15.

WALWORTH (E. H.) Battles of Saratoga, 1777. pp. 191. *Albany*, 1891. 4°. 9605. ff. 7.

U.S. Journal of the Federal Convention, May 14, 1787, kept by J. Madison. pp. 805. *Chicago*, 1893. 8°. 9602. h. 12.

SCHOULER (J.) History of the United States. 1783–1861. 5 vol. *N.Y.* 1880–91. 8°. 9605. d. 8.

MACKEE (T. H.) Presidential Inaugurations from Washington 1789 to Cleveland 1893. pp. 166. *Wash*. 1893. 8°. 9605. d. 10.

STANWOOD (E.) History of Presidential Elections. *Bost*. 1888. 8°. 9602. de. 11.

THOMPSON (R. W.) Recollections of sixteen Presidents from Washington to Lincoln. 2 vol. *Indianapolis*, 1894. 8°. 010882. h. 25.

UPTON (H. T.) Our Early Presidents, their wives and children. pp. 395. *Bost* 1890. 8° 010882. m. 13.

WILSON (J. G.) The Presidents of the United States. 1789–1894. pp. 526. *N.Y.* 1894 8°. 10883. dd. 16.

BOUTELL (L. H.) A. Hamilton, the constructive statesman. pp. 66. *Chicago*, 1890. 8°. 10880. bb. 36.

POIRIER (J. R.) La Naissance d'un peuple; les États-Unis dans la seconde moitié du XVIII° siècle. pp. 208. *Paris*, 1892. 8°. 9603. eee. 8

MOORE (J. W.) The American Congress, 1774–1895. pp. 581. *Lond*. 1895. 8°. 9605. dd. 16.

DYER (O.) General A. Jackson. pp. 378. *N.Y.* 1891. 8°. 010882. e. 12.

PARTON (J.) General Jackson. pp. 332. *N.Y.* 1893. 8°. 10883. bb. 24.

WILSON (W.) Division and Reunion, 1829–89. pp. 326. 1893. 8°. HART (A. B.) Epochs of American History. 9551. aa.

DUBOSE (J. W.) Life of W. L. Yancey. History of political parties in the U.S. 1834–64. pp. 752. *Birmingham*, 1892. 8°. 010882. m. 27.

SENEX. The Evolution of Myth in General Grant's History of the plot of President Polk and Secretary Marcy to sacrifice two American armies, 1846–48. pp. 54. *Wash.* 1890. 8°. Pam. 65.

DYER (O.) Great Senators of the United States forty years ago. pp. 316. *N.Y.* 1889. 8°. 10883. aa. 16.

HINTON (R. J.) J. Brown and his men. pp. 752. 1894. 8°. MARTYN (C.) American Reformers. 10883. bbb. 11.

HOPE (A. R.) Heroes in Homespun. Scenes from the Emancipation movement. pp. 380. *Lond.* 1894. 8°. 8155. aaaa. 8.

ROBINSON (C.) The Kansas Conflict. pp. 487. *N.Y.* 1892. 8°. 9604. c. 1.

RHODES (J. F.) History of the United States from the Compromise of 1850. 2 vol. *Lond.* 1893. 8°. 9605. cc. 17.

LINCOLN (A.) Political Debates between A. Lincoln and S.A. Douglas in 1858 in Illinois. pp. 316. *Cleveland*, 1894. 8°. 8156. dd. 3.

KING (H.) Turning on the Light. Survey of President Buchanan's administration from 1860 pp. 419. *Phila.* 1895. 8°. 9605. bbb. 20.

UNITED STATES.—History—*continued.*
　Civil War 1861 to the present time.

TOWNSEND (T. S.) Indications of what may be found in the department of foreign relations of Townsend's Library. pp. 31. 1892. 4°. 11900. h. 17.

BERNARD (G. S.) War talks of Confederate Veterans. pp. 335. *Petersburg*, 1892. 8°. 9605. dd. 10.

CHANAL (F. V. A. de) The American Army in the War of Secession. pp. 245. *Leavenworth*, 1895. 8°. 8828. dd. 33.

GIBSON (J. W.) Chart History of the Civil War, 1861–65. pp. 117. *Chicago*, 1894. 8°. 9605. ff. 12.

HERR (G. W.) Episodes of the Civil War. pp. 461. *San Francisco*, 1890. 8°. 9604. de. 16.

ROPES (J. C.) Story of the Civil War. *N.Y.* 1894, *etc.* 8°. 9605. d. 13.

SCOTT (E. G.) Reconstruction during the Civil War. pp. 432. *Bost.* 1895. 8°. 9605. c. 23.

WILSON (J. G.) and COAN (T. M.) Personal recollections of the War of the Rebellion. pp. 391. *N.Y.* 1891. 8°. 9605. ff. 5.

WILSON (W. B.) A few Acts and actors in the tragedy of the Civil War. pp. 114. *Phila.* 1892. 8°. 9605. c. 11.

WITTENMYER (A.) Under the Guns. A woman's reminiscences of the Civil War. pp. 272. *Bost.* 1895. 8°. 9605. b. 26.

PIATT (D.) Memories of the Men who saved the Union. pp. 302. *N.Y.* 1887. 8°. 10883. c. 21.

U.S. Heroes of the Republic. Lives of Grant, Lee, Lincoln, *etc.* pp. 488. *Lond.* 1892. 8°. 010882. f. 21.

LINCOLN (A.) Complete Works. 2 vol. *N.Y.* 1894. 8°. 12295. eee. 2.

—— Political Speeches and debates of A. Lincoln and S. A. Douglas. pp. 555. *Battle Creek*, 1895. 8°. 8176. e. 23.

—— A. Lincoln's Speeches. pp. 371. *N.Y.* 1895. 8°. 8175. de. 5.

BROOKS (N.) A. Lincoln and the downfall of slavery. pp. 471. 1894. 8°. ABBOTT (E.) Heroes of the Nations. 10601. f.

CHITTENDEN (L. E.) Recollections of President Lincoln and his administration. pp. 470. *N.Y.* 1891. 8°. 9604. de. 17.

COFFIN (C. C.) A. Lincoln. pp. 542. *N.Y.* 1893. 8°. 10883. cc. 10.

FRENCH (C. W.) A. Lincoln. pp. 398. 1891. 8°. MARTYN (C.) American Reformers. 10883. bbb. 6.

GREELEY (H.) Greeley on Lincoln. To which are added Reminiscences of H. Greeley. pp. 271. *N.Y.* 1893. 8°. 10883. b. 31.

HERNDON (W. H.) and WEIK (J. W.) A. Lincoln. 2 vol. *N.Y.* 1892. 8°. 10883. c. 13.

MAC CLURE (A. K.) A. Lincoln and Men of war-times. pp. 462. *Phila.* 1892. 8°. 010882. g. 15.

MORSE (J. T.) A. Lincoln. 2 vol. *Lond.* 1893. 8°. 10883. b. 29.

SCHURZ (C.) A. Lincoln. An Essay. pp. 117. *Lond.* 1891. 8°. 10883. aa. 29.

BUCKINGHAM (S. G.) Life of W. A. Buckingham, the War Governor of Connecticut. pp. 537. *Springfield*, 1894. 8°. 010882. h. 24.

MAHAN (A. T.) Admiral Farragut. pp. 333. 1893. 8°. WILSON (J. G.) Great Commanders. 10883. d.

GRANT (U. S.) Personal Memoirs of U. S. Grant. 2 vol. *N.Y.* 1895. 8°. 010882. g. 19.

LEE (F.) General Lee. pp. 433. 1894. 8°. WILSON (J. G.) Great Commanders. 10883. d.

UNITED STATES.—History—continued.

SWEENEY (T.) Vindication from a Northern standpoint of Gen. R. E. Lee and his fellow-officers who left the U.S. Army and Navy, 1861. pp. 48. *Richmond*, 1890. 8°. 9004. m. 4. (18.)

POLK (W. M.) L. Polk, Bishop and General. 2 vol. *Lond.* 1893. 8°. 10883. c. 18.

SHERMAN (J.) J. Sherman's Recollections of forty years. 2 vol. *Chicago*, 1895. 8°. 010881. f. 3.

SHERMAN (W. T.) Correspondence between General Sherman and Senator Sherman, 1837-91. pp. 398. *Lond.* 1894. 8°. 010920. i. 1.

DAWES (A. L.) C. Sumner. pp. 330. *N.Y.* 1892. 8°. 10883. aa. 36.

BROOKS (N.) Washington in Lincoln's Time. pp. 328. *N.Y.* 1895. 8°. 9605. c. 20.

RIDDLE (A. G.) Reminiscences of men and events in Washington, 1860-65 pp. 380. *Lond.* 1895. 8°. 9605. dd. 20.

PHISTERER (F.) New York in the War of the Rebellion. pp. 532. *Albany*, 1890. 8°. 9605. ff. 4.

DE LEON (T. C.) Four Years in Rebel Capitals. pp. 376. *Mobile*, 1890. 8°. 9615. dd. 2.

JONES (C. C.) Military operations in Georgia during the war. pp. 52. *Augusta*, 1893. 8°. Pam. 28.

DANIEL (L. C.) Confederate Scrap Book. Copied from a book kept by a young girl. pp. 256. *Richmond*, 1893. 8°. 9605. bbb. 19.

U.S. *Army*. Officers of the Army and Navy who served in the Civil War. pp. 177. *Phila.* 1894. 4°. 10880. k. 14.

GOSS (W. L.) Recollections of a Private of the army of the Potomac. pp. 354. *Lond.* 1890. 8°. 9603. ee. 2.

HYDE (T. W.) Following the Greek Cross, memories of the Sixth Army Corps. pp. 269. *Bost.* 1894. 8°. 9605. aaa. 23.

IRWIN (R. B.) History of the Nineteenth Army Corps. pp. 528. *N.Y.* 1892. 8°. 9615. df. 5.

ALLEN (S. P.) Down in Dixie. Life in a cavalry regiment in the war days. pp. 494. *Bost.* 1892. 8°. 9615. dd. 5.

ISHAM (A. B.) Historical sketch of the Seventh Regiment Michigan Cavalry. pp. 118. *N.Y.* 1894. 8°. 8829. bbb. 48.

MORRIS (G.) The History of a Volunteer Regiment. Account of the Sixth Regiment N.Y. Volunteers. pp. 160. *N.Y.* 1891. 8°. 8823. n. 14.

EMILIO (L. F.) History of the Fifty-fourth Regiment of Massachusetts Infantry. pp. 410. *Bost.* 1891. 8°. 9605. cc. 16.

U.S. *Navy Department*. Naval War Records. pp. 31. *Wash.* 1891. 8°. Pam. 43.

SCHARF (J. J.) History of the Confederate States Navy. pp. 824. *Albany*, 1894. 8°. 8806. ddd. 17.

SINCLAIR (A.) Two Years on the Alabama. pp. 344. *Lond.* 1895. 8°. 9605. dd. 18.

WATSON (W.) Adventures of a Blockade Runner. pp. 324. 1892. 8°. Adventure Series. 012207. k.

PINKERTON (A.) History of the passage of A. Lincoln from Harrisburg, Pa., to Washington, D.C., Feb. 1861. pp. 39. 1892. 8°. 8176. bb. 28.

MAGUIRE (T. M.) Campaigns in Virginia 1861-62. pp. 70. *Lond.* 1891. 8°. 9602. h. 9.

ALLAN (W.) The Army of Northern Virginia in 1862. pp. 537. *Bost.* 1892. 8°. 9615. dd. 4.

SMITH (G. W.) Battle of Seven Pines. pp. 202 *N.Y.* 1891. 8°. 9603. cc. 1.

HENDERSON (G. F. R.) Campaign of Fredericksburg, Nov.-Dec. 1862. pp. 145. 1891. 8°. Gale and Polden's Military Series. 8830. aa.

UNITED STATES.—History—continued.

U.S. *Army*. Kinston, Whitehall and Goldsboro expedition, Dec. 1862. pp. 92. *N.Y.* 1890. 8°. 9605. aa. 3½

—— (Maps.] fol. 1851. c. 10. (8.)

JOHNSON (J.) Defense of Charleston Harbor. pp. 276. *Charleston*, 1890. 8°. 9615. ee. 23.

HEROS VON BORCKE (J. H.) and SCHEIBERT (J.) Die grosse Reiterschlacht bei Brandy Station, 9 Juni 1863. pp. 179. *Berl.* 1893. 8°. 9605. dd. 13.

AUGUSTA. *Confederate Survivors' Association*. Defence of Battery Wagner, July 18, 1863. *Augusta*, 1892. 8°. 9555. f. 4. (6.)

HUMPHREYS (A. A.) Virginia Campaign of '64 and '65. pp. 451. *N.Y.* 1890. 8°. 9605. b. 18.

SMITH (W. F.) From Chattanooga to Petersburg under Grant and Butler. pp. 201. *Bost.* 1893. 8°. 9605. c. 14.

COX (J. D.) Atlanta. pp. 274. *N.Y.* 1892. 8°. 9605. b. 19.

TÊTU (D.) De Têtu et les Raiders de Saint-Alban. pp. 187. *Québec*, 1891. 16°. 9605. aa. 4.

BROWN (J. M.) The Mountain campaigns in Georgia. pp. 72. *Buffalo*, 1890. 4°. 9605. f. 11.

JONES (C. C.) Siege and Evacuation of Savannah. pp. 30. *Augusta*, 1890 8°. Pam. 28.

AMERICAN CIVIL WAR. Famous Adventures and Escapes of the Civil War. pp. 338. *N.Y.* 1893. 8°. 9605. c. 12.

ISHAM (A. B.) Prisoners of war and Military Prisons. Personal narratives. pp. 571. *Cincinnati*, 1890. 8°. 9605. d. 6.

BRAUN (H. A.) Andersonville. pp. 164. *Milwaukee*, 1892. 8°. 9605. a. 2.

EGGLESTON (G. C.) American war Ballads and lyrics. 2 vol. *N.Y.* 1891. 16°. 012202. eeee. 9.

FAGAN (W. L.) Southern War Songs. pp. 389. *N.Y.* 1890. 8°. 11686. i. 9.

HARRIS (T. M.) Assassination of Lincoln. History of the great Conspiracy. pp. 419. *Bost.* 1892. 8°. 010882. k. 11.

DE WITT (D. M.) Judicial Murder of M. E. Surratt. pp. 259. *Baltimore*, 1895. 8°. 6615. aa. 10.

COWAN (F.) A. Johnson, President of the U.S. pp. 16. *Greensburgh*, 1894. 8°. 010881. ee. 1. (9.)

CLEVELAND (S. G.) Writings and speeches of G. Cleveland. pp. 571. *N.Y.* 1892. 8°. 8176. aaa. 47.

PARKER (G. F.) Life of G. Cleveland. pp. 333. *N.Y.* 1892. 8°. 10883. aa. 39.

HARRISON (B.) Public Papers and addresses of B. Harrison, 1889-93. pp. 302. *Wash.* 1893. 4°. 8176. g. 2.

—— Speeches of B. Harrison, 1888-92. pp. 580. *N.Y.* 1892. 8°. 8176. bb. 27.

—— Our President. From the Atlantic to the Pacific. 1891. pp. 199. *Kansas City*, 1891. 8°. 8175. a. 5.

—— Through the South and West with the President. 1891. pp. 152. *N.Y.* 1891. 8°. 8176. bbb. 16.

See also supra: Constitution. *Infra*: Politics. For the history of each State, *see* under the State required.

Indians. *See* INDIANS.

Irish in the United States. *See* IRELAND, *Emigration, etc.*

Literature. *See* AMERICAN LITERATURE : ENGLISH LITERATURE : POETRY.

UNITED STATES—continued.

Law.

Ac. Philadelphia. *Historical Society*. Charlemagne Tower collection of American colonial laws. pp. 298. *Phila.* 1890. 4°.   Ac. 8430/8.

KEMPIN (E.) Die Rechtsquellen der Gliedstaaten der Vereinigten Staaten. pp. 78. *Zürich*, 1892. 8°.   Pam. 33.

BARBOUR (O. L.) Treatise on the rights of persons and rights of property. 2 vol. *Rochester, N.Y.* 1890. 8°.   06616. g. 13.

DILLON (J. F.) Laws and Jurisprudence of England and America. pp. 431. *Bost.* 1894. 8°.   06616. f. 20.

MERRILL (J. H.) American and English Encyclopaedia of Law. *Northport*, 1887, *etc.* 8°.   2016. a. and aa.

P.P. *Cambridge, Mass.* Harvard Law Review. *Camb.* 1894, *etc.* 8°.   P.P. 1352. m.

WILLARD (A. R.) Legislative handbook relating to the preparation of Statutes. pp. 281. *Bost.* 1890. 8°.   8176. bbb. 10.

FOSTER (R.) Treatise on pleading and practice in Equity in the Courts of the U.S. pp. 822. *Bost.* 1890. 8°.   06616. df. 12.

GIBSON (H. R.) Treatise on suits in Chancery. pp. 1188. *Knoxville*, 1891. 8°.   06616. g. 20.

CARSON (H. L.) The Supreme Court of the United States. pp. 745. *Phila.* 1891. 4°.   6006. l. 3.

BENTON (J. H.) Influence of the Bar in our State and Federal Government. pp. 63. *Bost.* 1894. 8°.   Pam. 33.

DONOVAN (J. W.) Skill in Trials, *etc.* pp. 173. *Rochester, N.Y.* 1891. 8°.   06616. de. 1.

HEDDE (E.) Du rôle politique du pouvoir-judiciaire dans la Constitution des États-Unis. pp. 102. *Paris*, 1895. 8°.   8177. d. 1.

WILLARD (J. A.) Half a century with Judges and Lawyers. pp. 371. *Bost.* 1895. 8°.   012330. e. 53.

WRIGHT (J. A.) How to get good Judges. pp. 85. *San Francisco*, 1892. 8°.   6616. aa. 1.

See also LAW REPORTS.

Lutheran Church. *See* LUTHERAN CHURCH.
Methodist Churches. *See* METHODISM.

Navy.

BATES (W. W.) American Marine. pp. 479. *Bost.* 1893. 8°.   8806. dd. 20.

MACLAY (E. S.) History of the U.S. Navy. 2 vol. *Lond.* 1894. 8°.   8805. dd. 65.

AMMEN (D.) The old Navy and the New. pp. 553. *Phila.* 1891. 8°.   010882. l. 1.

THOMAS (C. M.) Instructions for Infantry and Artillery, U.S. Navy. 2 pt. 1891. 8°. Ac. Annapolis. *U.S. Naval Institute*. Papers.   Ac. 4398.

SCHROEDER (S.) The U.S.S. Vesuvius. pp. 65. 1894. 8°. Ac. Annapolis. *U.S. Naval Institute*. Papers. Vol. 20.   Ac. 4398.

CHICAGO. *Columbian Exposition*. Catalogue of the exhibit of the U.S. Navy Department. pp. 233. *Chicago*, 1893. 8°.   7958. bb. 20.

See also NAVAL SCIENCE, *Ships of War*. For the Naval History of the Civil War, 1861–65, *see supra*: *History*.

Politics, *Domestic*.

Ac. Brooklyn. *Ethical Association*. Factors in American civilization. pp. 417. *N.Y.* 1893. 8°.   08276. g. 69.

CHAMPERNOWNE (H.) The Boss. Essay upon the art of governing American cities. pp. 243. *N.Y.* 1894. 8°.   8176. de. 2.

UNITED STATES.—Politics—*continued.*

D., J. W. History of the Gerrymander. pp. 11. *Bost.* 1892. 8°.   12901. f. 43. (3.)

FREDERICK (J. M. H.) National party platforms of the U.S. pp. 83. *Akron*, 1892. 8°. Pam. 65.

FULTON (C.) History of the Democratic Party. pp. 608. *N.Y.* 1892. 8°.   8175. g. 7.

GREGORY (C. N.) The corrupt use of money in Politics and laws for its prevention. pp. 25. *Madison*, 1893. 8°.   Pam. 64.

GRONLUND (L.) Our Destiny. Influence of Nationalism on morals and religion. pp. 219. *Bost.* 1891. 8°.   08276. f. 11.

JACOBSON (A.) The Crisis of a Party. pp. 171. *Chicago*, 1892. 8°.   8176. bbb. 21.

JOHNSTON (A.) History of American Politics. pp. 355. *N.Y.* 1890. 8°.   8177. de. 36.

KNOX (T. W.) The Republican Party and its Leaders. pp. 608. *N.Y.* 1892. 8°.   8175. g. 8.

LODGE (H. C.) Historical and political Essays. pp 213. *Bost.* 1892. 8°.   8175. aaa. 4.

MACPHERSON (E.) Hand-book of Politics for 1890. pp. 280. *Wash.* 1890. 8°.   8176. ee. 7.

MOORE (J. W.) The American Congress. pp. 581. *Lond.* 1895. 8°.   9605. dd. 16.

REDDALL (H. F.) The sunny side of Politics: wit and humour, *etc.* pp. 312. *St. Paul*, 1892. 8°.   8176. bbb. 19.

SEYMOUR (H. W.) Government and Co. Limited. pp. 148. *Chicago*, 1895. 8°.   8175. de. 6.

THOMPSON (D. G.) Politics in a Democracy. pp. 176. *Lond.* 1893. 8°.   8005. ccc. 18.

TYLER (L. G.) Parties and patronage in the U.S. pp. 133. *N.Y.* 1891. 8°.   8177. de. 38.

See also supra: *Constitution*: *History*. *Infra*: *Trade and Finance*: MONEY. SOCIALISM: SOCIAL QUESTIONS.

Foreign Politics.

BOURINOT (J. G.) Canada and the United States. 1891. 8°. Papers. Ac. *American Historical Association*. Vol. 5.   Ac. 8504.

DAVIS (J. C. B.) Mr. Fish and the Alabama claims. pp. 158. *Bost.* 1893. 8°.   8175. a. 6.

U.S. U.S. and Venezuelan Claims Commission, 1889–90. Opinions delivered by the Commissioners. pp. 520. *Wash.* 1890. 8°. 8177. ee. 8.

See also BEHRING SEA.

Protestant Episcopal Church.

JACKSON (S. M.) Bibliography of American Church History. 1820–93. 1894. 8°. American Church History Series. Vol. 12.   4744. g.

AMERICAN CHURCH HISTORY SERIES. American Church History Series. *N.Y.* 1893, *etc.* 8°.   4744. g.

COLEMAN (L.) *Bp. of Delaware*. The Church in America. pp. 391. 1895. 8°. DITCHFIELD (P. H.) The National Churches. Vol. 8. 4534. de.

PERRY (W. S) *Bp. of Iowa*. The Ecclesiastical Constitution of the American Church. pp. 291. *N.Y.* 1891. 8°.   4744. ccc. 1.

—— Christ Church, Philadelphia, in the Revolution. pp. 50. *Phila.* 1892. 8°.   Pam. 29.

—— The Church's Centennial Thanksgiving. pp. 10. *Davenport*, 1889. 8°.   Pam. 95.

MOREHOUSE (F. C.) Some American churchmen. pp. 240. *Milwaukee*, 1892. 8°.   4985. dd. 28.

SMITH (C. E.) The old Church in the new land. pp. 279. *N.Y.* 1894. 8°.   4182. b. 42.

KIP (W. I.) *Bp. of California*. Early Days of my Episcopate. pp. 263. *N.Y.* 1892. 8°.   4745. de. 4.

SPENCER (J. A.) Memorabilia of sixty-five years, 1820–86. pp. 250. *N.Y.* 1890. 8°. 4986. g. 29.

UNITED STATES. — Protestant Episcopal Church—*continued.*

BROOKS (P.) *Bp. of Massachusetts.* P. Brooks: the man, the preacher and the author. pp. 215. *Lond.* 1893. 8°.   4986. e. 30.

PERRY (W. S.) *Bp. of Iowa.* A correspondence [concerning Dr. P. Brooks]. 1891. 4°.   1897. c. 8. (98.)

CARROLL (H. K.) Report of statistics of Churches in the U.S. pp. 812. 1894. 8°. Eleventh Census of the U.S.   1882. c. 1.

COLEMAN (L.) *Bp. of Delaware.* Our financial Relations to the Church. pp. 20. 1894. 8°.   4445. f. 9. (15.)

EX-CHURCHWARDEN. Protestant Episcopal layman's handbook. pp. 319. *N.Y.* 1891. 8°.   3940. bbb. 24.

HUNTINGTON (W. R.) Popular misconceptions of the Episcopal Church. pp. 87. *N.Y.* 1891. 8°.   4182. aaa. 32.

MACQUEARY (H.) Ecclesiastical Liberty; defence of H. MacQueary before the Ecclesiastical Court of Ohio, against the charges of heresy. pp. 51. *N.Y.* 1891. 8°.   Pam. 92.

PERRY (W. S.) *Bp. of Iowa.* Relations of the Church and the Country. pp. 31. *Davenport,* 1893. 8°.   Pam. 92.

—— Relations of the Clergy to their vestries and congregation. pp. 27. *Davenport,* 1892. 8°.   5155. b. 7. (5.)

—— The Changes of the Standard Book of Common Prayer of 1892 as compared with the Standard of 1871. pp. 28. *Davenport,* 1893. 8°.   Pam. 75.

RESTARICK (H. B.) Lay Readers, their history, organisation and work. pp. 269. *N.Y.* 1894. 8°.   4499. d. 4.

SHINN (G. W.) Manual of information concerning the Episcopal Church. pp. 182. *N.Y.* 1892. 8°.   4182. a. 39.

STEVENS (C. E.) The Genesis of the American Prayer Book. pp. 169. *N.Y.* 1893. 8°.   3477. df. 1.

TEMPLE (E. L.) The Church in the Prayer Book. pp. 408. *Milwaukee,* 1893. 8°.   3475. de. 20.

U S. *Churches.* On the Dedications of American Churches. pp. 154. *Camb.* 1891. 8°. 4744. g. 14.

See also ENGLAND, *Church of,* and *History, Ecclesiastical :* MISSIONS.

Roman Catholic Church.

See ROMAN CATHOLIC CHURCH.

Social Life. *See infra : Topography.*

Southern States.

BLACKMAR (F. W.) Spanish institutions of the South-West. pp. 353. 1891. 8°. Johns Hopkins University Series. Extra vol. x. Ac. 2689.

GREEN (T. M.) The Spanish Conspiracy. Review of early Spanish movements in the South-West. pp. 406. *Cincinnati,* 1891. 8°.   9603. d. 4.

CURRY (J. L. M.) The Southern States considered in their relations to the Constitution. pp. 248. *N.Y.* 1894. 8°.   8176. bbb. 26.

FALKINER (W. R.) The South and its people. pp. 98. *Richmond,* 1890. 8°.   8176. aaa. 44.

GOODWIN (M. W.) The Colonial Cavalier or southern Life before the revolution. pp. 304. *N.Y.* 1894. 8°.   9555. b. 34.

HERBERT (H. A.) Why the Solid South? Reconstruction and its results. pp. 452. *Baltimore,* 1890. 8°.   8177. de. 32.

LE CONTE (J.) The Race problem in the South. 1892. 8°. Ac. Brooklyn. *Ethical Association.* Evolution series. No. 29.   7006. bbb.

UNITED STATES. — Southern States— —*continued.*

LUMMIS (C. F.) Some strange Corners of our country. pp. 270. *N.Y.* 1892. 8°.   10409. bb. 32.

MALLARD (R. Q.) Plantation life before Emancipation. pp. 237. *Richmond,* 1892. 8°.   8157. b. 15.

MORTON (O. T.) The Southern Empire. pp. 207. *Bost.* 1892. 8°.   012357. h. 13.

OGLESBY (T. K.) The Britannica answered and the South vindicated. A defense of the South pp. 60. *Montgomery,* 1891. 8°.   Pam. 65.

OTKEN (C. H.) The Ills of the South. pp. 277. *N.Y.* 1894. 8°.   8176. bbb. 25.

SOUTH-LAND. Something of Interest to all. The South-Land. pp. 30. *St. Louis,* 1893. 8°.   10411. aa. 51. (4.)

STRAKER (D. A.) The New South investigated. pp. 230. *Detroit,* 1888. 8°.   8176. de. 1.

See also supra : History. *Infra :* Topography : NEGROES : SLAVERY ; and under the name of each of the Southern States.

Sport. *See* SPORT.

Swiss, *in the United States.*
See SWITZERLAND, *Emigration.*

Tariffs. *See infra : Trade and Finance.*

Topography and Social Life.

COLES (J.) Geography of the United States. pp. 4. *Leeds,* 1891. 8°.   10408. de. 18. (5.)

REDWAY (J. W.) Physical Geography of the United States. pp. 26. *N.Y.* 1890. 8°. Pam. 87.

APPLETON (D.) Handbook of American Winter Resorts. pp. 168. *N.Y.* 1894. 8°.   10413. c. 45.

BAEDEKER (C.) Die Vereinigten Staaten, nebst einem Ausflug nach Mexiko. pp. 488. *Leipz.* 1893. 8°.   10108. d. 6.

—— The United States, with an excursion into Mexico. pp. 156. *Leipz.* 1893. 8°.   2352. a.

GANNETT (H.) The mother Maps of the United States. 1892. 8°. Ac. National Geographic Magazine. Vol. 4.   Ac. 6192.

SIEVERS (W.) Amerika : eine allgemeine Landeskunde. pp. 687. *Leipz.* 1894. 8°.   10412. i. 14.

SWEETSER (M. F.) King's Handbook of the United States. pp. 939. *Lond.* 1891. 8°.   10108. ee. 2.

TOWNSEND (M.) Index to the United States. pp. 482. *Bost.* 1890. 8°.   10410. e. 44.

MICHAUX (A.) Portions of the Journal of A. Michaux written during his travels in the U.S. and Canada, 1785–96. pp. 145. 1889. 8°. Ac. Philadelphia. *American Philosophical Society.* Proceedings. Vol. 26. No. 129.   Ac. 1830.

TWINING (T.) Travels in India a hundred years ago : with a visit to the United States. pp. 529. *Lond.* 1893. 8°.   010057. i. 1.

WHARTON (A. H.) Through colonial Doorways. pp. 237. *Phila.* 1893. 8°.   9555. aaa. 29.

AMERICA. Homeward through America. pp. 32. *Chicago,* 1889. 8°.   10411. dd. 41.

AMRITALĀLA RĀYA. Reminiscences, English and American. *Calcutta,* 1888, *etc.* 8°.   10409. aa. 31.

ARNOLD (*Sir* E.) Seas and Lands. pp. 535. *Lond.* 1891. 8°.   010057. ee. 17.

BARBIER (E.) Voyage au Pays des dollars. pp. 344. *Paris,* 1893. 12°.   10412. aaa. 42.

UNITED STATES.—Topography, etc.—
continued.

BELOW (E.) Bilder aus dem Westen. pp. 289.
Leipz. 1894. 8°.   10408. aa. 33.

BERG (G. v.) *Baron.* Reisebriefe aus Nord-
Amerika. pp. 201. *Wien,* 1894. 8°. 10412. b. 22.

BERNARD (M.) Au Pays des dol'ars. pp. 308.
Paris, 1893. 12°.   10410. c. 40.

BOURGET (P. C. J.) Outre-Mer. Notes sur
l'Amérique. 2 tom. *Paris,* 1895. 12°.
                                     10409. aa. 41.

—— Impressions of America. pp. 425.
Lond. 1895. 8°.   10413. c. 46.

CAMACHO ROLDAN (S.) Notas de viaje. Colombia
y Estados Unidos de America. pp. 896.
Bogotá, 1890. 8°.   10409. d. 18.

CLARETIE (L.) Feuilles de routes aux États-
Unis. pp. 293. *Paris,* 1895. 12°. 10410. c. 41.

CRAIB (A.) America and the Americans.
pp. 325. *Paisley,* 1892. 8°.   10409. d. 25.

CROONENBERGHS (C.) Trois ans dans l'Amérique
septentrionale. 2 tom. *Paris,* 1892. 8°.
                                     10412. cc. 28.

CROSS (J. W.) Impressions of Dante and the
New World. pp. 314. *Edinb.* 1893. 8°.
                                     11420. c. 20.

DECKERT (E.) Die neue Welt. Reiseskizzen.
pp. 488. *Berl.* 1892. 8°.   10413. k. 20.

DIERCKS (G.) Kulturbilder aus den Vereinigten Staaten. pp. 378. *Berl.* 1893. 8°.
                                     12249. ccc. 4.

DIONNE (N. E.) États-Unis, Manitoba et
Nord-Ouest. pp. 184. *Québec,* 1882. 8°.
                                     10409. a. 20.

ERZYBOWSKI (P.) Land und Leute in Amerika.
pp. 290. *Berl.* 1894. 8°.   10410. cc. 18.

FERGUSON (J.) From Ceylon to England by way
of China and the United States. pp. 111.
Colombo, 1891. 4°.   10026. k. 13.

FITZ-PATRICK (T.) A Transatlantic Holiday.
pp. 210. *Lond.* 1891. 8°.   10409. c. 35.

FLOWER (B. O.) Civilization's Inferno : studies in
the social cellar. pp. 237. *Bost.* 1893. 8°.
                                     8277. de. 57.

GAULLIEUR (H.) Études américaines. pp. 299.
Paris, 1891. 12°.   10409. aa. 30.

GIRIODI (C.) Una Signorina italiana in America.
pp. 159. *Torino,* 1893. 8°.   10412. c. 33.

GORDON (H. P.) The Land of the almighty
dollar. pp. 215. *Lond.* 1892. 8°. 10408. c. 34.

GUEST (*Lady* T.) A round trip in North
America. pp. 270. *Lond.* 1895. 8°.
                                     10408. dd. 15.

HADLAND (S.) Education and life in the United
States. pp. 68. *Lond.* 1895. 8°. 10408. aa. 32.

HESSE-WARTEGG (E. v.) Curiosa aus der neuen
Welt. pp. 327. *Leipz.* 1893. 8°. 10408. b. 42.

HIGGINSON (T. W.) The new World and the
new Book. pp. 239. *Bost.* 1892. 8°.
                                     012357. h. 11.

HOLE (S. R.) A little Tour in America. pp. 381.
Lond. 1895. 8°.   10408. dd. 16.

HOME (R.) Columbian Sketches. pp. 370.
Dubl. 1895. 8°.   10408. bbb. 33.

HUGHES (T.) Vacation Rambles. pp. 405.
Lond. 1895. 8°.   010026. h. 1.

JANNET (C.) Die Vereinigten Staaten in der
Gegenwart. pp. 704. *Freiburg,* 1893. 8°.
                                     10412. dd. 20.

JOUSSELIN (S.) Yankees fin de siècle. pp. 333.
Paris, 1892. 12°.   10412. aaa. 39.

KIERULF (M.) Erindringer fra en Rejse til
Amerika in Sommeren 1893. pp. 88.
Odense, 1894. 8°.   10412. c. 37.

UNITED STATES.—Topography, etc.—
continued.

KNORTZ (C.) Kulturhistorisches aus dem Dollar-
Lande. pp. 171. *Basel,* 1892. 8°. 10408. ee. 24.

LINDAU (P.) Altes und Neues aus der neuen
Welt. *Berl.* 1893, *etc.* 8°.   10413. g.

LOVETT (R.) United States Pictures. pp. 223.
Lond. 1891. 8°.   10411. i. 22.

LUMMIS (C. F.) Some strange Corners of our
Country. pp. 270. *N.Y.* 1892. 8°.
                                     10409. bb. 32.

—— Tramp across the Continent. pp. 270.
Lond. 1893. 8°.   10412. bb. 35.

MARMIER (X.) Les États-Unis et le Canada.
pp. 236. *Tours,* 1886. 8°.   10408. i. 14.

NIELSEN (A.) En Sommer i Amerika. pp. 200.
Odense, 1891. 8°.   10408. bbb. 30.

NORDENSKIÖLD (G.) Från fjärran Västern.
pp. 115. *Stockholm,* 1892. 8°.   10412. aa. 20.

O'RELL (M.) A Frenchman in America.
pp. 336. *Bristol,* 1891. 8°.   10409. aaa. 49.

PAASCHE (H.) Kultur- und Reis. skizzen aus
Nord- und Mittel-Amerika. pp. 553.
Magdeburg, 1894. 8°.   10408. dd. 13.

PANTOJA (D. de) Los Estados Unidos y la
América del Sur. pp. 374. *Buenos A.* 1893. 8°.
                                     12354. de. 4.

PORTEOUS (A.) Scamper through some Cities of
America. pp. 116. *Glasg.* 1890. 8°.
                                     10413. aaa. 15.

ROBERTS (C.) Adrift in America. pp. 254.
Lond. 1891. 8°.   10409. d. 23.

ROSSI (A.) Un Italiano in America. pp. 324.
Milano, 1892. 8°.   10408. de. 12.

—— Nel Paese dei dollari. pp. 207.
Milano, 1893. 8°.   10412. b. 39.

ROUSIERS (P. de) La Vie américaine. pp. 698.
Paris, 1892. 8°.   10410. f. 38.

—— American Life. pp. 437. *Paris,* 1892. 8°.
                                     12350. i. 26.

S., J. F. Trip across the Atlantic. pp. 123.
Southampton, 1893. 8°.   10412. aaa. 40.

SAN CARLOS DE PÉDROSO (de) *Marchioness.*
Les Américains chez eux. pp. 362.
Paris, 1890. 12°.   12355. cc. 31.

SANCHEZ SOMOANO (J.) Costumbres Yankees.
pp. 208. *México,* 1894. 8°.   10409. a. 21.

SAUVIN (G.) Autour de Chicago. pp. 263.
Paris, 1893. 12°.   10412. aaa. 41.

SHALER (N. S.) The United States. A study
of the American Commonwealth. 2 vol.
Lond. 1894. 8°.   10413. dd. 1.

—— Nature and man in America. pp. 290.
Lond. 1892. 8°.   7001. b. 9.

SMITH (N.) A tour through the Land of the
West. pp. 90. *Lond.* 1894. 8°.   10410. bb 31.

SMITH (W.) A Yorkshireman's trip to the United
States. pp. 317. *Lond.* 1892. 8°. 10409. d. 21.

SPICE (R. P.) Wanderings of the Hermit of
Westminster between New York and San Francisco. pp. 84. *Lond.* 1882. 8°.   10412. ee. 30.

STANLEY (H. M.) My early Travels and Adventures in America. 2 vol. *Lond.* 1895. 8°.
                                     10027. ee. 4.

U.S. Drei Monate in Amerika. pp. 87.
Berl. 1891. 8°.   Pam. 86.

—— Aux États-Unis et dans Ontario. pp. 64.5.
Montréal, 1892. 8°.   Pam. 86.

UZANNE (O.) Vingt jours dans le Nouveau
Monde. pp. 214. *Paris,* 1893. *obl.* 8°.
                                     10413. e. 4.

VARIGNY (C. de) La Femme aux États-Unis.
pp. 322. *Paris,* 1893. 12°.   8415. de. 27.

UNITED STATES.—Topography, etc.—continued.

VARIGNY (H. de)   En Amérique. Souvenirs de voyage. pp. 300. *Paris*, 1895. 8°. 10410. bbb. 30.

VILLENEUVE (A.) Les États-Unis et l'émigration. pp. 53. *Marseille*, 1891. 8°.   Pam. 86.

WHITNEY (J. D.) The United States : facts and figures. pp. 472. *Bost.* 1889. 8°.   10408. dd. 14.

WORLD. The English-speaking World. Photographs. pp. 192. *Lond.* 1895. 4°. 1797. aa. 29. *See also supra: Southern States. Infra : Western States*, and under the name of each State.

Trade and Finance.
National Finance, Taxation and Tariffs.

BEER (G. L.) Commercial policy of England toward the American Colonies. pp. 167. 1893. 8°. Ac. New York. *Columbia College.* Studies in History, *etc.* Vol. 3.   Ac. 2688/2.

SUMNER (W. G.) The Financier (R. Morris) and the finances of the Revolution. 2 vol. *N.Y.* 1891. 8°.   08227. h. 15.

COPPING PLEHN (C.) Das Kreditwesen der Staaten und Städte der nordamerikanischen Union. pp. 93. 1891. 4°. ELSTER (L.) Staatswissenschaftliche Studien. Bd. 4. Hft. 1.   8207. h.

BURKE (W. E.) Federal Finances. pp. 263. *Chicago*, 1891. 8°.   08227. de. 11.

UPTON (J. K.) Report on wealth, debt and taxation at the Eleventh Census, 1890. 1892, *etc.* 4°. U.S. *Census*. Eleventh Census.   1882. c. 7.

BROOKS (F. A.) Objections to our National Currency System. pp. 56. *Bost.* 1893. 8°.   Pam. 23.

EVANS (G. G.) Illustrated history of the United States Mint. pp. 179. *Phila.* 1892. 8°.   7757. c. 38.

HARVEY (W. H.) Coin's Financial School. pp. 149. *Chicago*, 1894. 8°. 08226. g. 20. (1.)

—— Coin's Financial School up to date. pp. 205. *Chicago*, 1895. 8°. 08226. g. 20. (2.)

GORDON (A. C.) Congressional Currency. pp. 234. *N.Y.* 1895. 8°.   8176. bbb.

KINLEY (D.) History, organization and influence of the Independent Treasury of the U.S. pp. 329. *N.Y.* 1893. 8°.   08227. de. 34.

HOWE (F. C.) Federal Revenues and the Income Tax. *Phila.* 1894. 8°.   08226. k. 4. (11.)

BAUMANN (A. A.) Betterment; the law of special assessment for benefits in America. pp. 110. *Lond.* 1893. 8°.   8277. de. 25.

HALL (B.) Who pays your Taxes? pp. 239. *N.Y.* 1892. 8°.   08225. ee. 5.

HILL (D. B.) The Income-Tax Law. pp. 90. *N.Y.* 1895. 8°.   8228. aa. 65.

SCOTT (S. M.) The Sub-Treasury Plan. pp. 97. *Topeka*, 1891. 8°.   08227. i. 30. (6.)

SCOTT (W. A.) Repudiation of State Debts. pp. 237. *N.Y.* 1893. 8°.   08226. f. 3.

CUSHING (J. P.) Development of the commercial policies of the United States. pp. 59. *Leipz.* 1891. 8°.   08226. k. 4. (8.)

GOSS (J. D.) History of Tariff administration in the United States. pp. 89. 1891. 8°. Ac. New York. *Columbia College.* Studies in History, *etc.* Vol. 1.   Ac. 2688/2.

HILL (W.) The first stages of the Tariff Policy of the United States. pp. 162. 1893. 8°. Ac. Saratoga. *American Economic Association.* Publications. Vol. 8.   Ac. 2388.

RABBENO (U.) The American commercial policy. pp. 414. *Lond.* 1895. 8°.   08226. h. 7.

UNITED STATES.—Trade, etc.—cont.

SMITH (R. M.) and SELIGMAN (E. R. A.) Commercial policy of the U.S. 1860-90. pp. 74. 1892. 8°. Ac. Leipsic. *Verein für Socialpolitik.* Schriften. Vol. 49.   Ac. 2322.

ADAMS (G. H.) Handbook of the Tariff on Imports in the United States. pp. 321. *N.Y.* 1890. 8°.   08225. l. 9.

ANDREW (J. F.) The Tariff. Speech. pp. 8. *Wash.* 1890. 8°.   Pam. 23.

ATKINSON (E.) Taxation and work. Treatises on the tariff, *etc.* pp. 296. *N.Y.* 1892. 8°.   08276. f. 64.

BEATTY (J.) McKinleyism, as it appears to a non-partisan. pp. 156. *Wash.* 1894. 8°.   08226. f. 16.

CHAMBERLAIN (N. H.) What's the Matter? or, our tariff and its taxes. pp. 268. *Bost.* 1890. 8°.   8228. aaa 21.

HEWES (F. W.) and MACKINLEY (W.) What Are the Facts? Protection and reciprocity illustrated. pp. 126. *N.Y.* 1892. 8°.   8226. i. 11.

KNORTZ (C.) Der amerikanische Schutzzoll. pp. 60. *Zürich*, 1892. 8°.   08227. g. 47. (8.)

PHILPOTT (H. J.) Tariff chats. pp. 38. *N.Y.* 1888. 8°.   08226. g. 8.

SCHOENHOF (J.) The destructive influence of the Tariff upon manufacture and commerce. pp. 88. *N.Y.* 1888. 8°.   08226. g. 7.

SIDES. Both Sides of the Tariff question. [pp. 298. *N.Y.* 1890. 8°.   08227. ee. 35.

U.S. *Statutes.* Public Act, commonly known as "The Wilson Bill," No. 4864. pp. 68. *Lond.* 1894. 8°.   08227. g. 52.

Trade.

GREAT BRITAIN. *Privy Council.* Report of a Committee on the trade of Great Britain with the United States. Jan. 1791. pp. 79. *Wash.* 1888. 8°.   08229. f. 44.

ARGENTINE REPUBLIC. *Ministerio de relaciones exteriores.* Reciprocidad comercial. Negociaciones entre Estados Unidos y la República Argentina. pp. 57. *Buenos Aires*, 1892. 8°.   Pam. 65.

CHAMBRUN (A. de) Les Conditions du travail aux États-Unis. pp. 111. 1891. 8°. FRANCE. *M. des Affaires Étrangères.* Recueil de rapports.   08276. k.

COOK (W. W.) Corporation Problem. pp. 262. *Lond.* 1891. 8°.   08227. de. 1.

CURTIS (W. E.) Trade between the United States and Spanish America. pp. 342. *Wash.* 1889. 8°.   08227. ee. 6.

JUGLAR (C.) History of Panics and their occurrence in the United States. pp. 150. *N.Y.* 1893. 8°.   08225. ee. 8.

LECLERC (M.) Choses d'Amérique : les crises économique et religieuse, 1890. pp. 282. *Paris*, 1891. 12°.   8176. bbb. 12.

MACCORMICK (R. S.) Future trade relations between Great Britain and the United States. pp. 48. *Lond.* 1892. 8°.   Pam. 23.

SAVAGE (T.) Manual of intercourse between the United States and Spanish America, 1890-91. pp. 629. *San Francisco*, 1890. 8°. 08227. c. 22.

SCHUYLER (E.) American Diplomacy and the furtherance of Commerce. pp. 469. *Lond.* 1886. 8°.   8175. aaa. 5.

SHALER (N. S.) The United States. Study of the American Commonwealth. 2 vol. *Lond.* 1894. 8°.   10413. dd. 1.

TEELE (A. L.) Money-making in America. pp. 64. *Lond.* 1892. 16°.   8228. a. 50.

UNITED STATES.—Trade, etc.—*cont.*

U.S. *Bureau of American Republics.* Handbook of the American Republics. pp. 288. *Wash.* 1891. 8°.   08225. k. 1.

WRIGHT (C. D.) The industrial evolution of the United States. pp. 362. *Meadville,* 1895. 8°.   08277. ff. 16.

See also infra: Western States: CAPITAL AND LABOUR : MINERALOGY AND MINES : MONOPOLIES AND TRUSTS : TRADE.

Western States.

BANDELIER (A. F.) Hemenway South-western Archæological Expedition. pp. 206. 1890. 8°. Ac. Boston. *Archæological Institute.* Papers. American series. v.   Ac. 5790/8.

WINSOR (J.) Geographical Discovery in the interior of North America. 1537–1700. pp. 379. *Lond.* 1894. 8°.   9551. f. 11.

ROOSEVELT (T.) The winning of the West. 2 vol. *N.Y.* 1889. 8°.   9602. h. 8.

GIST (C.) C. Gist's Journals. pp. 296. *Pittsburgh,* 1893. 8°.   010882. m. 26.

PARKMAN (F.) The Oregon Trail. pp. 411. *Lond.* 1892. 8°.   10410. d. 39.

BLANCHARD (R.) Discovery and conquests of the North-West. pp. 768. *Wheaton,* 1891. 8°.   9605. e. 11.

LEWIS (M.) History of the expedition under the command of Lewis and Clark. 4 vol. *Lond.* 1893. 8°.   10412. i. 11.

DAVIS (R. H) The West from a Car-window. pp. 242. *N.Y.* 1892. 8°.   10410. b. 32.

EDWORDS (C. E.) Camp-fires of a Naturalist. Story of fourteen expeditions after North American mammals. pp. 304. *Lond.* 1893. 8°.   7001. aa. 27.

FINCK (H. T.) The Pacific Coast scenic tour. pp. 309. *Lond.* 1891. 8°.   10413. g. 18.

JACKSON (L.) The Industrial West. pp. 16. *Chicago,* 1890. 8°.   Pam. 23.

KELLER (C.) Als " Greenhorn " im Westen von Nord Amerika. pp. 208. *Hamburg,* 1893. 8°.   10413. aaa. 18.

LUMMIS (C. F.) Some strange corners of our Country. pp. 270. *N.Y.* 189?. 8°. 10409. d. 28.

MAJORS (A.) Seventy years on the Frontier. pp. 325. *Chicago,* 1893. 8°.   10413. bbb. 32.

RALPH (J.) Our Great West. pp. 477. *N.Y.* 1893. 8°.   10413. g. 23.

STEVENSON (R. L.) Across the Plains. pp. 317. *Lond.* 1892. 8°.   012357. f. 51.

WHEELER (O. D.) 6000 Miles through Wonderland. pp. 106. *Chicago,* 1893. 8°.   10412. dd. 22.

See also supra: Topography; and under the name of each of the Western States.

UNIVERSALISM. ALLEN (J. H.) and EDDY (R.) History of the Unitarians and Universalists in the U.S. pp. 506. 1894. 8°. American Church History series. Vol. 10.   4744. g.

CHICAGO. *Columbian Exposition. World's Congress Auxiliary.* Columbian Congress of the Universalist Church. pp. 361. *Bost.* 1894. 8°.   4182. c. 31.

DODGE (J. S.) The Purpose of God. pp. 257. *Bost.* 1894. 8°.   4371. bb. 11.

HANSON (J. W.) Pocket Cyclopædia. Explanations of religious terms as understood by Universalists. pp. 89. *Bost.* 1892. 8°. 4257. e. 15.

RUGG (H. W.) Our word and work for Missions. pp. 254. *Bost.* 1894. 8°.   4767. f. 7.

See also ESCHATOLOGY.

UNTERWALDEN, Canton. SOWERBY (J.) Forest Cantons of Switzerland. pp. 288. *Lond.* 1892. 8°.   10196. cc. 11.

UPMINSTER. WILSON (T. L.) History and topography of Upminster. pp. 208. *Romford,* 1880. 8°.   10358. dd. 29.

UPPINGHAM SCHOOL. UPPINGHAM SCHOOL. Uppingham School Roll, 1824–94. pp. 350. *Lond.* 1894. 8°.   8364. de. 37.

UPSALA. FRÖLÉN (H.) Upsala Domkyrka efter restaureringen. pp 59. *Upsala,* 1893. 8°.   Pam. 24.

MODIN (E.) and SÖDERBERG (E. N.) Matrikel öfver |i Upsala studevande Norrländningar, 1595–1889. pp. 350. *Stockholm,* 1889. 8°.   *8357. f. 9.*

UPTON, Norfolk. HILL (P. O.) History of Upton, Norfolk. pp. 163. *Norwich,* 1891. 8°.   010358. g. 15.

URBINO. CELLI (L.) Storia della sollevazione di Urbino contro il Duca Guidobaldo, 1572–74. pp. 304. *Torino,* 1892. 8°.   9166. ee. 12.

SANTI (G.) Federigo di Montefeltro, duca di Urbino. Cronaca. pp. 230. *Stuttgart,* 1893. 8°.   11422. h. 11.

URDU LANGUAGE. *See* HINDUSTANI.

URETHRA. *See* GENITO-URINARY ORGANS.

URI, Canton. SOWERBY (J.) Forest Cantons of Switzerland. pp. 288. *Lond.* 1892. 8°.   10196. cc. 11.

URIC ACID. HAIG (A.) Uric Acid as a factor in the causation of Disease. pp. 400. *Lond.* 1894. 8°.   7630. e. 19.

ROBERTS (*Sir* W.) On the chemistry and therapeutics of Uric Acid. pp. 136. *Lond.* 1892. 8°.   7630. bbb. 16.

See also GOUT.

URINARY ORGANS. *See* GENITO-URINARY ORGANS.

URQUHART AND GLENMORISTON. MACKAY (W.) Urquhart and Glenmoriston. pp. 594. *Inverness,* 1893. 8°.   010370. f. 31.

URSULINES. DUVAL (T.) *Bp. of Soissons.* Les Ursulines du Hâvre. pp. 226. *Rouen,* 1890. 8°.   4629. i. 8.

See also RELIGIOUS ORDERS.

URUGUAY.

See also AMERICA, *Central and South.*

History.

ARAÚJO (O.) Efemérides Uruguayas.· pp. 267. *Montevideo,* 1894. 8°.   9772. aa. 22.

ARREGUINE (V.) Historia del Uruguay. pp. 416. *Montevideo,* 1892. 8°.   9772. bb. 6.

BERRA (F. A.) Bosquejo histórico de la República del Uruguay. pp. 464. *Montevideo,* 1881. 8°.   9772. bbb. 8.

MAESO (C. M.) Glorias uruguayas. pp. 135. *Montevideo,* 1892. 8°.   9772. c. 10.

MARIA (I. de) Elementos de historia de la República del Uruguay. pp. 69. *Montevideo,* 1891. 8°.   Pam. 28.

——— Páginas his·óricas de la República del Uruguay. pp. 124. *Montevideo,* 1892. 8°.   9772. e. 10.

MASCARÓ (P.) Revista del archivo general administrativo. *Montevideo,* 1885, *etc.* 8°.   9772. g. 4.

ORIENTAL. Aclaraciones históricas. pp. 133. *Montevideo,* 1884. 8°.   9772. de. 8.

BAUZÁ (F.) Historia de la Dominacion española en el Uruguay. 3 tom. *Montevideo,* 1880–82. 8°.   9772. e. 9.

URUGUAY.—History—*continued.*

MAESO (J.) Los primeros patriotas Orientales de 1811. pp. 248. *Montevideo,* 1888. 8°.
        9772. e. 11.

ARÓZTEGUY (A.) La revolucion oriental de 1870. 2 tom. *Buenos A.* 1889. 8°.   9772. f. 17.

PALOMEQUE (A.) La dinastia Santos-Vidal. pp. 130. *Buenos A* 1886. 8°.   9772. d. 2.

MELIAN LAFINUR (G.) Los partidos de la Republica del Uruguay. pp. 635.
Buenos A. 1893. 8°.   9772. de. 10.

Law.

GOYENA (P. V.) Diccionario de la legislación rural de la República. pp. 305.
Montevideo, 1887. 8°.   6784. aaa. 13.

Topography.

MAESO (C. M.) El Oriental. Descripción general de la República. pp. 206.
Montevideo, 1884. 8°.   10481. ee. 34.

RIGUERA MONTERO (M.) Bosquejo geografico de las Re, úblicas Argentina y Oriental. pp. 127. *Montevideo,* 1882. 8°.   10481. c. 33.

Trade and Finance.

MADRID. *Exposición Histórico-americana.* Catálogo de los objetos que presenta la República del Uruguay. pp. 13. *Madrid,* 1892. 8°.
       5959. f. 34.

ORDOÑANA (D.) Pensamientos rurales sobre necesidades sociales de la Republica. 2 tom.
Montevideo, 1892. 8°.   8277. de. 49.

PENA (C. M. de) and ROUSTAN (H.) The Republic of Uruguay at the Columbian Exhibition. pp. 54. *Montevideo,* 1893. 8°.   Pam. 86.

See also AGRICULTURE : MINERALOGY.

USHAW COLLEGE. LAING (R. C.) Ushaw College : a centenary memorial. pp. 254.
Newcastle-on-Tyne, 1895. 4°.   8365. ff. 37.

USTILAGINEAE. *See* FUNGI.

USURY. BLISSARD (W.) The Ethic of Usury and Interest. pp. 194. *Lond.* 1892. 8°.
       08276. e. 45.

CARO (L.) Der Wucher. pp. 311.
Leipz. 1893. 8°.   8277. cc. 50.

See also MONEY-LENDING : POLITICAL ECONOMY : SOCIALISM : TRADE, *etc.*

UTAH. *See* MORMONISM.

UTERUS. *See* WOMEN, *Diseases, etc.*

UTRECHT. MULLER (S.) Catalogus van het Archief. 3 Afdeel. *Utrecht,* 1893. 8°.
       011901. g. 23.

WELSCH (A. G.) Oud-Utrecht. pp. 234.
Utrecht, 1893. 8°.   010271. h. 1.

Ecclesiastical History : Jansenist Church.

BEEK (J. A. v.) Lijst van boeken uitgegeven in de Oud-Katholieke Kerk, 1700–51. pp. 113.
Rotterdam, 1893. 8°.   4999. f. 7.

—— Lijst van boeken uitgegeven in de Oud-Katholieke Kerk, 1751–1842. pp. 24.
Rotterdam, 1892. 8°.   011902. m. 21. (8.)

—— Lijst van boeken uitgegeven in de Oud-Katholieke Kerk sedert 1842. pp. 11.
Rotterdam, 1892. 8°.   Pam. 6.

MULLER (S.) Bijdragen voor een Oorkondenboek van het Sticht Utrecht. pp. 69.
's Gravenh. 1890. 8°.   4685. h. 7.

BROM (G.) Bullarium Trajectense.
Haga-Comitis, 1891, *etc.* 8°.   5035. aa.

DU PAC DE BELLEGARDE (G.) Coup d'œil sur l'ancienne Église catholique de Hollande.
pp. 59. *Le Haye,* 1890. 8°.   4535. bb. 17. (3.)

UTRECHT.—Ecclesiastical History, etc. —*continued.*

HULLER (J. de) Bijdrage tot de geschiedenis van het Utrechtsche Schisma. pp. 160.
's Gravenh. 1892. 8°.   4685. i. 4.

UTRECHT, *Province of.* Neerlandia Catholica, sive Provinciæ Ultrajectensis historia.
pp. 584. 68. *Utrecht,* 1888. fol.   Tab. 442. a.

Treaty of.

WEBER (O.) Der Friede von Utrecht, 1710–13. pp. 485. *Gotha,* 1891. 8°.   9077. ccc. 10.

See also EUROPE, *History.*

UVA. *See* CEYLON.

UVEA LANGUAGE. C., A., *le P.* Dictionnaire Latin-Uvea. 1886. 12°. Œuvre de Saint-Jérôme. No. 2.   12902. aa.

UZÈS. SAINT-VENANT (J. de) Tumulus néolithiques près d'Uzès. pp. 24. *Nimes,* 1894. 8°.
       Pam. 3.

VACCINATION. *See* SMALL POX.

VACHA. GRAU (P.) Chronik der Stadt Vacha. pp. 82. *Weimar,* 1891. 8°.
       10105. ee. 10. (8.)

VADSTENA. SELLIN (E.) Vadstena, Omberg och Alvastra. pp. 110. *Vadstena,* 1890. 8°.
       10280. aaa. 35.

VALAIS, Canton. REBER (B.) Excursions archéologiques dans le Valais. 1892. 8°.. Ac. Geneva. *Institut National.* Bulletin. Tom. 31.
       Ac. 610.

See also ALPS : SWITZERLAND : ZERMATT.

VALBENOITE, Monastery. TESTENOIRE-LAFAYETTE (C. P.) Histoire de l'Abbaye de Valbenoite. pp. 218. 1893. 8°. Ac. Montbrison. *Société de la Diana.* Recueil de mémoires. Tom. 10.   Ac. 6880.

VALENCE. ROCHAS (A.) Journal d'un Bourgeois, de Valence, 1789–99. 2 vol.
Grenoble, 1891, 92. 8°.   9226. k. 22.

VALENCIA, Spain. CASAÑ Y ALEGRE (J.) Colección de documentos del Archivo del Reino de Valencia. *Valencia,* 1894, *etc.* 8°.
       9180. dd.

CHABÁS LLORENS (R.) Los Mozarabes valencianos. pp. 35. *Madrid,* 1891. 8°.   4534. c. 30. (5.)

VALENCIA, Venezuela. FIGUEREDO HERRERA (F.) Topografia médica de Valencia. pp. 50. *Valencia,* 1891. 4°.   Pam. 39.

VALENCIENNES. CAPPLIEZ ( ) Histoire des métiers de Valenciennes et de leurs saints patrons. pp. 380. *Valenciennes,* 1893. 8°.
       8248. h. 5.

MARIAGE (E.) Les Fortifications de Valenciennes. pp. 238. *Valenciennes,* 1891–95. 8°.
       8825. c. 14.

VALLOUISE. SÉRANON (J. de) Une vallée des Alpes pendant la Révolution. La Vallouise. pp. 150. *Aix,* 1891. 8°.   10169. aaa. 2.

VALPARAISO. G. B. & I. *War Office.* The Capture of Valparaiso in 1891. pp. 56.
Lond. 1892. 8°.   9772. ccc. 13.

VAL SESIA. TONETTI (P.) Bibliografia valesiana. *Varallo,* 1893, *etc.* 8°.   12226. bb.

See also ALAGNA : VARALLO.

VALUATIONS. CURTIS (C. E.) Valuation of Property. pp. 88. *Lond.* 1891. 8°.
       08227. g. 32.

FLETCHER (B.) Valuations and compensations. pp. 165. *Lond.* 1893. 8°.   6325. de. 35.

VALUATIONS—*continued.*

WHEELER (J.) The Appraiser and Valuer's pocket assistant. pp. 337. *Lond.* 1893. 16°.
8548. aa. 32.

VALUE. *See* PRICES.

VANADIUM. KLECKI (V. v.) Analytische Chemie des Vanadins. pp. 55.
Hamburg. 1894. 8°. Pam. 13.
See also METALS.

VANDALS. HODGKIN (T.) Italy and her Invaders. Vol. 2, 3. *Oxf.* 1892. 8°. 2068. c.

VANNES, City and Diocese. LE MENÉ (J. M.) Histoire des paroisses du diocèse de Vannes. *Vannes,* 1891, *etc.* 8°. 4629. ee.

—— Église cathédrale de Vannes. 1882. 8°.
Ac. Caen. *Société pour la Conservation des Monuments.* Séances générales. Session 48.
Ac. 5296/2.

VARALLO. BUTLER (S.) Ex Voto. Studio sulle opere d'arte del S. Monte di Varallo e di Crea. pp. 316. *Novara,* 1894. 8°. 7875. a. 42.

FASSÓ (G.) Via ferrata Novara-Varallo. *Borgosesia,* 1888. *obl. fol.* 1787. c. 33.
See also VAL SESIA.

VARENNES. *See* FRANCE, *History, Revolution.*

VARESE. BORRI (L.) Giudizi dei giornali sui Documenti varesini. pp. 34.
Varese, 1892. 8°. 9008. l. 2. (5.)

VARESE. Il Codice degli Statuti varesini del 1347. pp. 93. *Varese,* 1893. 8°. 5357. e. 4.

CAMBIASI (P.) Teatro di Varese. pp. 51.
Milano, 1891. 8°. Pam. 50.

VARIOCOLENE. *See* BLOOD.

VARNISHES. CLARK (R. I.) Few notes on Varnishes. pp. 69. *Lond.* 1891. 8°.
7943. h. 30.

HALPHEN (G. H.) Couleurs et vernis. pp. 380.
Paris, 1895. 8°. 7857. aa. 59.

STANDAGE (H. C.) Practical polish and varnish-maker. pp. 260. *Lond.* 1892. 8°. 07945. e. 86.

VASA. VASA. Separatormejerierna i Wasa län. pp. 25. *Nikolaistad,* 1887. 8°. Pam. 82.

VASCULAR SYSTEM. *See* BLOOD.

VASES. Ac. Geneva. *Institut National.* Vases antiques des collections de la Ville de Genève. pp. 33. *Paris,* 1892. 4°. 7703. b. 28.

—— London. *British Museum.* Catalogue of Greek and Etruscan Vases. *Lond.* 1893. 4°.
7706. f. 28.

—— Designs from Greek Vases in the British Museum. pp. 31. *Lond.* 1894. fol.
K.T.C. 2. a. 10.

—— Vienna. *Osterreichisches Museum.* MASNER (C.) Die Sammlung antiker Vasen und Terracotten. pp. 104. *Wien,* 1892. 4°. Ac. 4430/5.

BENNDORF (O.) Wiener Vorlegeblätter für archaeologische Übungen, 1888(-1891).
Wien, 1889, *etc.* fol. I704. c.

BOSTON. *Museum of Fine Arts.* Catalogue of Greek, Etruscan and Roman Vases. pp. 249.
Bost. 1893. 8°. 7706. cc. 14.

FROEHNER (W.) Collection J. Gréau. Catalogue des terres cuites grecques. pp. 292.
Paris, 1891. 4°. K.T.C. 4. b. 1.

FURTWAENGLER (A.) Führer durch die Vasen-Sammlung K. Ludwigs I. zu München. pp. 52.
Leipz. 1895. 8°. 07807. ee. 4. (6.)

GARDNER (P.) Catalogue of Greek Vases in the Ashmolean Museum. pp. 43. *Oxf.* 1893. 4°.
7704. l. 28.

VASES—*continued.*

HARRISON (J. E.) and MacCOLL (D. S.) Greek Vase Paintings. Selection of examples. pp. 32.
Lond. 1894. fol. K.T.C. 13. b. 6.

HARTWIG (P.) Die griechischen Meisterschalen der Blüthezeit. pp. 701. *Stuttgart,* 1893. 4°.
557. e.

—— Tafeln. 1893. fol. 558. h.

KLEIN (W.) Die griechischen Vasen mit Lieblingsinschriften. pp. 98. 1890. fol. Ac.
Vienna. *Akademie der Wissenschaften.* Denkschriften. Phil.-historische Classe. Bd. 39.
Ac. 810/12.

KRETSCHMER (P.) Die griechischen Vaseninschriften. pp. 251. *Gütersloh,* 1894. 8°.
07708. g. 30.

ORSI (P.) Necropoli sicula con Vasi e Bronzi Micenei. 1894. 4°. Ac. Roma. *Academia de Lincei.* Monumenti antichi. Vol. 2.
Ac. 102/15.

REINACH (S.) Peintures de vases antiques recueillies par Millin, 1808, et Millingen, 1813.
1891. 8°. Bibliothèque des monuments figurés.
Vol. 2. 7705. f. 33.

SITTL (C.) Die Phineusschale und ähnliche Vasen. pp. 23. *Würzburg,* 1892. 4°. 7705. f. 49.
See also ART, *Ancient :* CERAMICS.

VATICAN COUNCILS. VATICAN COUNCIL. Constitutiones dogmaticae Oecumenici Concilii Vaticani. pp. 243. *Friburgi,* 1892. 8°.
5016, bb. 2.

DOELLINGER (J. J. I. v.) Declarations and letters on the Vatican Decrees 1869-87. pp. 178.
Edinb. 1891. 8°. 2210. c. 1.

—— Lettres et Déclarations au sujet des décrets du Vatican. pp. 288. *Paris,* 1893. 12°.
3914. b. 4.

JENKINS (R. C.) The Vatican Constitution "Pastor Æternus," has it altered the relations between the Church of Rome and other Churches.
pp. 8. *Folkestone,* 1890. 8°. 3940. bb. 31. (5.)

MONSABRÉ (J. M. L.) Conférences de Notre Dame. Concile et Jubilé. pp. 264.
Paris, 1890. 8°. 4427. d. 2.

VACANT (J. M. A.) Études sur les constitutions du Concile du Vatican. 2 tom. *Paris,* 1895. 8°.
5015. cc. 4.

See also ROMAN CATHOLIC CHURCH, *Doctrines, and Papacy.*

VAUCLUSE, Department. APOLLINAIRE, *de Valence.* Études franciscaines sur la Révolution dans le Vaucluse. pp. 84.
Avignon, 1895. 8°. 4629. f. 34.

DUHAMEL (L.) Documents sur la Révolution dans Vaucluse, 1793-1800. 2 pt.
Paris, 1894, 95. 8°. 9231. g. 11.
See also AVIGNON : COMTAT-VENAISSIN.

VAUD, Canton. ADAMINA (J.) Le Réveil religieux dans le canton de Vaud. pp. 44.
Lausanne, 1893. 8°. 4535. cc. 2. (6.)

SECRÉTAN (C.) Paysages vaudois. pp. 93.
Lausanne, 1895. 8°. 10196. b. 9.

DUPERTUIS (F.) Recueil des locutions vicieuses dans le Canton de Vaud. pp. 69.
Lausanne, 1892. 8°. 12954. bb. 31.

VEDAS. *See* HINDUISM.

VEGA, Ship. *See* ARCTIC REGIONS.

VEGETABLES. *See* BOTANY, *Economic :* GARDENING.

VEGLIA. VASSILICH (G.) Statuto della città di Veglia. 1885, *etc.* 8°. Ac. Parenzo. *Società Istriana.* Atti. Vol. 1, 2. Ac. 5230.

VEINS. *See* BLOOD.

VELAY. Ac. Le Puy en Velay. *Société d'Agriculture.* VINOLS DE MONTFLEURY (de) Baron. Vocabulaires patois vellavien-français et français-vellavien. pp. 207. *Le Puy,* 1891. 8°.
                                    12950. f. 34.
See also HAUTE-LOIRE : LANGUEDOC.

VELLETRI. PASQUALI (G.) Le due battaglie di Velletri, 1744–1849. 2 pt. *Velletri,* 1891. 8°.   9166. f. 9.

VEMEGERICHT. LINDNER (T.) Der angebliche Ursprung der Vemegerichte aus der Inquisition. pp. 31. *Paderborn,* 1890. 8°.
                                    9004. m. 6. (12.)

VENAISSIN, Comtat. *See* COMTAT-VENAISSIN.

VENDÉE, Department. CHASSIN (C. L.) La préparation de la Guerre de Vendée, 1789–93. 3 tom. *Paris,* 1892. 8°.   9231. l. 1.

ROUILLÉ (A.) Assignats. Guerre de Vendée. pp. 80. *La Roche,* 1891. 4°.   7757. g. 8.

CHASSIN (C. L.) La Vendée patriote, 1793–1800. *Paris,* 1893, *etc.* 8°.   9231. k.

DU VERGIER DE LAROCHEJAQUELEIN (H.) *Count.* H. de La Rochejaquelein et la guerre de la Vendée. pp. 345. *Paris,* 1890. 8°.
                                    010662. h. 2.

GUINEY (L. I.) "Monsieur Henri." A footnote to French History. pp. 139. *N.Y.* 1892. 8°.
                                    10661. aa. 28.

PORT (C.) La Légende de Cathelineau. pp. 350. *Paris,* 1893. 8°.   010662. h. 36.

GAZEAU (A. C.) *Countess de La Bouëre.* Souvenirs. La guerre de La Vendée, 1793–96. pp. 363. *Paris,* 1890. 8°.   9231. g. 13.

JULLIEN (M. A.) Une Mission en Vendée, 1793. pp. 347. *Paris,* 1893. 12°.   9226. bbb. 29.

VALLETTE (R.) La Commission militaire de Fontenay et ses victimes. pp. 22. *Fontenay-le-Comte,* 1894. 8°.   9004. l. 36. (5.)

BITTON (A.) Documents pour servir à l'histoire de l'instruction en Vendée pendant la Révolution. 1890. 8°. Ac. Napoléon. *Société d'Émulation.* Annuaire. Sér. 3. Vol. 10.   Ac. 395.

IMBERT DE SAINT AMAND (A. L.) *Baron.* La Duchesse de Berry en Vendée. pp. 586. *Paris,* 1893. 8°.   10659. i. 11.

LA ROCHEBROCHARD (L. de) L. de la Rochejaquelein en Vendée 1832–33. pp. 49. *Saint Maixent,* 1891. 8°.   010661. m. 47.

VALLETTE (R.) Les Mobiles de la Vendée au siège de Paris, 1870–71. pp. 27. *Vannes,* 1888. 8°.   9007. g. 22. (1.)
See also FRANCE, *History, Revolution :* POITOU.

VENDÔME. Ac. Vendôme. *Société Archéologique.* Cartulaire de l'Abbaye Cardinale de la Trinité de Vendôme. *Paris,* 1893, *etc.* 8°.
                                    4630. dd.

MARTELLIÈRE (P.) Glossaire du vendômois. pp. 366. *Orléans,* 1893. 8°.   12953. f. 26.

VENDSYSSEL. GAARDBOE (A. P.) Fortidsminder fra Vendsyssel. pp. 400. *Aarhus,* 1893. 8°.   10281. bbb. 12.

VENEREAL DISEASES. Ac. *Congrès de Dermatologie.* Comptes rendus. *Paris, etc.,* 1890, *etc.* 8°.   Ac. 3699. c.

ALTHAUS (J.) Treatment of Syphilis of the nervous system. pp. 35. *Lond.* 1890. 8°.
                                    7640. cc. 5.

BLANC (L.) De l'Action des eaux d'Aix-les-Bains, Marlioz et Challes dans le traitement de la syphilis. pp. 56. *Paris,* 1887. 8°.
                                    7462. e. 10. (18.)

BULKLEY (L. D.) Clinical notes on Chancre of the tonsil. pp. 10.   7305. f. 6. (4.)

VENEREAL DISEASES—*continued.*
BULKLEY (L. D.) On the dangers from Syphilis in the Practice of dentistry. pp. 16. *N.Y.* 1890. 8°.
                                    07305. h. 9. (3.)

BURET (F.) La Syphilis aujourd'hui et chez les anciens. pp. 256. *Paris,* 1890. 8°.
                                    7641. aaa. 27.
—— Syphilis in ancient and pre-historic times. pp. 226. *Phila.* 1891. 8°.   K.T.C. 10. b. 1.

COMMENGE (J. R. V. O.) Recherches sur les maladies vénériennes à Paris dans leurs rapports avec la prostitution. pp. 51. *Paris,* 1890. 8°.
                                    Pam. 39.

COOPER (A.) Syphilis. pp. 489. *Lond.* 1895. 8°.
                                    7641. f. 31.

DISSE (J.) and TAGUCHI (K.) Das Contagium der Syphilis. pp. 87. 1887. 4°. Ac. Yedo. *Imperial University.* Mitteilungen aus der medicinischen Facultät. Bd. 1.   Ac. 2697/4.

FRISCH (F.) Ueber Gonorrhoea rectalis. pp. 31. 1891. 8°. Ac. Wurzburg. *Physikalisch-medicinische Gesellschaft.* Verhandlungen. N.F. Bd. 25.   Ac. 3763/3.

GOWERS (W. R.) Syphilis and the nervous system. pp. 131. *Lond.* 1892. 8°. 7641. bb. 27.

KOPP (C.) Lehrbuch der venerischen Erkrankungen. pp. 569. 1889. 8°. Wreden's Sammlung. Bd. 14.   7321. h.

LAMY (H.) La syphilis des centres nerveux. pp. 203. 1894. 8°. Encyclopédie des aide-mémoire.   8709. g.

MILNES (A.) Theory and practice of Vaccino-Syphilis. pp. 24. *Lond.* 1891. 8°.
                                    07305. f. 20. (7.)

MOUNIER (G. J. D.) Onderzoek naar de beteekenis van de statistiek der venerische ziekten bij de landmacht in der Nederlanden. pp. 130. *'s Gravenh.* 1889. 8°.   7641. i. 18.

PROKSCH (J. K.) Die Geschichte der venerischen Krankheiten. *Bonn,* 1895, *etc.* 8°.   7641. dd.

ROBINSON (T.) Illustrations of diseases of the Skin and Syphilis. *Lond.* 1890, *etc.* fol.   1749.

SCHETTINI (V. V.) Della Sifilide. pp. 130. *Trani,* 1889. 8°.   7640. h. 22.

SCHWIMMER (E.) Die Grundlinien der heutigen Syphilistherapie. pp. 119. 1888. 8°. P.P. *Hamburg.* Monatshefte für Dermatologie. Bd 7.
                                    P.P. 3015. e.

STOKES (F. W.) Venereal diseases in both sexes. pp. 56. *Lond.* 1892. 8°.   7306. df. 20. (9.)

UNNA (P. G.) Neurosyphilide und Neuroleppride. 1890. 8°. P.P. *Hamburg.* Monatshefte für Dermatologie. Bd. 9.   P.P. 3015. e.

WEBER (F. P.) Syphilis and lardaceous disease. pp. 6. *Lond.* 1895. 8°.   Pam. 39.

ZIEMSSEN (O.) Treatment of constitutional Syphilis. pp. 70. *Lond.* 1893. 8°. 7641. b. 32.
See also GENITO-URINARY ORGANS.

VENEZUELA. *See also* AMERICA, *South.*
                Antiquities : History.
MARCANO (G.) Ethnographie précolombienne de Venezuela. 2 pt. 1889, 90, 8°. Ac. Paris. *Société d'Anthropologie.* Mémoires. Sér. 2. Tom. 4.   Ac. 6227/2.

Ac. Carácas. *Academia de la Historia.* Memorias. *Carácas,* 1889, *etc.* 8°.   Ac. 8590/2.
—— Documentos para los anales de Venezuela. *Carácas,* 1889, *etc.* 8°.   Ac. 8590.

ESTELLER (A.) Catecismo de historia de Venezuela. pp. 128. *Carácas,* 1891. 8°.
                                    9771. bb. 23.

HEREDIA Y MIESES (J. F.) Memorias sobre las revoluciones de Venezuela. pp. 304. *Paris,* 1893. 8°.   9771. cc. 13.
                                    3 K

VENEZUELA.—Antiquities, etc.—_cont._

OLAVARRÍA (D. A.) Estudios histórico-políticos, 1810-89. pp. 286. _Valencia_, 1894. 8°.
8042. c. 10.

RODRÍGUEZ (T.) Tradiciones populares. Colección de crónicas y leyendas. pp. 340.
Carácas, 1885. 8°. 12430. i. 46.

ROJAS (A.) Historia patria. Orígenes venezolanos. _Carácas_, 1891, _etc._ 8°. 9772. ee. 18.

—— Leyendas historicas de Venezuela.
Carácas, 1890, _etc._ 8°. 9772. ee. 19.

PADULA (A.) Au Vénézuéla. Le général J. Crespo, _etc._ pp. 46. _Rome_, 1893. 8°.
10601. d. 31. (14.)

SOUBLETTE (C.) General C. Soublette. pp. 64. 1889. fol. 10880. i. 9.

PÉPPER (E.) El Areópago revolucionario de Venezuela, ó los industriales políticos. 2 pt. 1888. 8°. Pam. 65.

—— Apuntes para la historia contemporanea de Venezuela. pp. 93. _Curaçao_, 1895. 8°.
9772. d. 17.

OLAVARRÍA (D. A.) Estudios en refutación de "El manifiesto liberal de 1893." pp. 147.
Valencia, 1893. 8°. 8042. c. 9.

Immigration.

VILLEGAS PULIDO (G. T.) Los Extranjeros, su admision, su expulsion. pp. 168.
Carácas, 1891. 8°. 06955. df. 7.

Law. _See_ LAW, _Commercial._

Politics, _Foreign._

VENEZUELA. M. de _Relaciones Exteriores._ Correspondence between the Venezuelan Government and H.B.M.'s Government, about the frontier. 3 pt. _Carácas_, 1887. fol.
8179. i. 20.

—— Latest Correspondence on the limits of Guiana. pp. 66. _Carácas_, 1687. fol.
8179. i. 19.

SEIJAS (R. F.) Limites británicos de Guayana. pp. 661. _Carácas_, 1888. 4°. 8179. k. 3.

GUZMÁN BLANCO (A.) Límites Guayaneses. La epístola del Presidente. pp. 8. _Paris_, 1890. 8°.
Pam. 65.

—— Una palabra más sobre límites guayaneses. pp. 8. _Paris_, 1890. 8°. Pam. 65.

—— Límites guayaneses entre Venezuela y la Gran Bretaña. pp. 11. _Paris_, 1890. 8°.
Pam. 65

—— Limites de Venezuela. Apéndice de documentos que definen los límites entre Venezuela y Colombia al oeste del Orinoco. pp. 51.
Paris, 1891. 8°. 8180. aa. 23.

ROJAS (J. M.) Las Fronteras de Venezuela. pp. 65. _Paris_, 1891. 8°. 8180. dd. 10.

VILLAFAÑE (J. G.) Juicio sobre el Laudo en la cuestion, Límites entre Venezuela y Colombia. pp. 32. _Táriba_, 1891. 8°. Pam. 65.

COLOMBIA. Laudo arbitral en que se fija el límite entre Columbia y Venezuela. pp. 10.
Bogota, 1892. fol. Pam. 65.

U.S. U.S. and Venezuela Claims Commission. 1889-90. Opinions delivered by the Commissioners. pp. 520. _Wash._ 1890. 8°.
8177. ee. 8.

Topography.

ERBACH (E. zu) Wandertage im Strom- und Küstengebiet des Orinoko. pp. 460.
Leipz. 1892. 8°. 10481. e. 33.

LANDAETA ROSALES (M.) Gran recopilacion geográfica de Venezuela. 2 tom.
Carácas, 1889. obl. fol. 1851. a. 9.

VENEZUELA.—Topography—_cont._

LAVERDE AMAYA (I.) Un viajè à Venezuela. p. 406. _Bogotá_, 1889. 8°. 10480. aa. 14.

LEVEL (A.) Nomenclator de Venezuela. 2 tom. _Carácas_, 1883. 8°. 10480. h. 22.

VENEZUELA. Tercer censo de la República. 1891. 4 tom. _Carácas_, 1891. fol. 8223. d. 49.

MACPHERSON (T. A.) Vocabulario del estado Carabobo. 2 pt. _Valencia_, 1890, 91. 4°.
10480. h. 19.

—— Diccionario del estado Miranda. pp. 556. _Carácas_, 1891. 8°. 10480. h. 21.

Trade, etc.

ORSI DE MOMBELLO (G.) Venezuela y sus riquezas. pp. 107. _Carácas_, 1890. 8°.
10481. bbb. 45.

P.P. _Caracas._ Boletin de la riqueza pública de Venezuela. _Carácas_, 1891, _etc._ 4°. 9.

VENEZUELA. Ministerio de Hacienda. Exposicion que dirige al Congreso el Ministro de Hacienda en 1895. 2 tom. _Carácas_, 1895. 4°. 8179. i. 18.

VENICE.

Art. _See infra_: Topography: PAINTING.

History.

BROWN (H. R. F.) Venice: historical sketch of the Republic. pp. 434. _Lond._ 1893. 8°.
9166. f. 11.

LAWLEY, _afterwards_ WIEL (A. J.) Venice. pp. 478. 1894. 8°. Story of the Nations.
9004. ccc. 14.

LENTZ (E. A. L.) Das Verhältnis Venedigs zu Byzanz. _Berl._ 1891, _etc._ 8°. 9165. c.

M. L'Armeno-Veneto. Compendio delle relazioni degli Armeni coi Veneziani.
Venezia, 1893, _etc._ 8°. 9055. g.

MAS LATRIE (J. M. J. L. de) _Count._ De l'empoisonnement politique dans la république de Venise. 1895. 8°. Ac. Paris. _Académie des Inscriptions._ Mémoires. Tom. 34. 2099. f.

MOLMENTI (P. G.) Venezia e le repubbliche marinare. 1890. 8°. Gli albori della vita italiana. Vol. i. 9166. ccc. 11.

—— Studi e Ricerche di storia e d' arte. pp. 350. _Torino_, 1892. 8°. 12354. i. 9.

MUSATTI (E.) Storia della Promissione ducale. pp. 218. _Padova_, 1888. 8°. 9150. g. 2.

VOLPI (E.) Storie intime di Venezia. pp. 330. _Venezia_, 1893. 8°. 9166. cc. 14.

MONTICOLO (G.) Cronache veneziane antichissime. 1890, _etc._ 8°. Fonti per la storia d' Italia. No. 9, _etc._ Ac. 6543.

HAIN (A. G. E.) Der Doge von Venedig, 1032-1172. pp. 133. _Königsberg_, 1883. 8°. 9166. cc. 13.

WIEL (A.) Two Doges of Venice. pp. 142. _Lond._ 1891. 8°. 10629. d. 14.

ROBERTSON (A.) Fra Paoli Sarpi, the Greatest of the Venetians. pp. 196. _Lond._ 1894. 8°.
4864. bbb. 45.

BOLOGNINI (G.) Le Relazioni tra Firenze e Venezia nell' ultimo ventennio del secolo XVI. pp. 109. 1895. 8°. P.P. _Venice._ Archivio veneto. Tom. 9. P.P. 3556. v.

RAULICH (I.) La Congiura spagnola contro Venezia. pp. 86. _Venezia_, 1893. 8°. 9072. c. 22.

MOSCHETTI (A.) Venezia e la elezione di Clemente XIII. pp. 37. 1890. 4°. Ac. Venice. _Deputazione di Storia Patria._ Monumenti. Ser. 4. Vol. 11. Ac. 6580/2.

DALMEDICO (A.) La Massoneria e la repubblica di Venezia. pp. 28. 1891. 8°. Pam. 25.

MUSATTI (E.) Due parole sui Veneziani della decadenza. pp. 123. _Padova_, 1893. 8°.
9167. f. 4.

VENICE.—History—continued.

LEHNERT (J. v.) Geschichte der österreichisch-venetianischen Kriegs-Marine, 1797–1802. pp. 464. 1891. 8°. AUSTRIA. *Navy. Geschichte der Kriegs-Marine.* Thl. 2.   8807. i. 5.

MARCHESI (V.) Settant' anni di storia di Venezia, 1798–1866. pp. 239. *Torino*, 1892. 8°.
                                                9167. g. 1.

GENOVA DI REVEL ( ) La cessione del Veneto. pp. 183. *Milano*, 1890. 8°.   9150. g. 1.

MONTICOLO (G.) L' Ufficio della Giustizia vecchia a Venezia sino al 1330. pp. 172. 1892. 4°. Ac. Venice. *Deputazione di Storia Patria. Monumenti storici.* Ser. 4. Vol. 12.
                                                Ac. 6580/2.

STELLA (A.) Il Servizio di cassa nell' antica Repubblica Veneta. pp. 388. *Venezia*, 1889. 8°.
                                                08225. l. 8.

LEVI (C. A.) Navi Venete, da codici, marmi e dipinti. pp. 285. *Venezia*, 1892. 8°. 8806. k. 24.
See also ITALY, *History* : VERONA.

Topography.

BLANCO (B.) Venecia : impresiones de viage. pp. 38. *Cochabamba*, 1892. 8°.   Pam. 91.

BOITO (C.) Basilica of S. Mark in Venice. 3 pt. *Venice*, 1888, 89. 4°.   7806. de. 13.

BROWN (H. R. F.) Life on the Lagoons. pp. 297. *Lond.* 1894. 8°.   10136. bb. 1.

CLEMENT (C. E.) The Queen of the Adriatic. pp. 380. *Lond.* 1894. 8°.   10132. bb. 28.

COOK (T.) Handbook to Venice. pp 81. *Lond.* 1893. 8°.   10130. aa. 6.

HOWELLS (W. D.) Venetian Life. 2 vol. *Lond.* 1891. 8°.   K.T.C. 7. a. 1.

JAMES (H.) The Grand Canal. 1892. 8° *Great Streets of the World.*   10026. k. 16.

JOANNE (P.) Venise. pp. 88. *Paris*, 1895. 8°.
                                                10136. aaa. 24.

MIARI (F.) *Count.* Venetia anticha. pp. 35. *Venezia*, 1890. 4°.   10131. h. 10.

MUSATTI (E.) La Donna in Venezia. pp. 270. *Padova*, 1891. 8°.   10631. f. 45.

PAOLETTI (P.) L' Architettura e la scultura del rinascimento in Venezia. 2 pt. *Venezia*, 1893. fol.   1733. d. 21.

PERL (H.) Venezia. pp. 248. *Wien*, 1895. 4°.
                                                K.T.C. 40. b. 3.
—— Venezia. Adapted from the German. pp 248. *Lond.* 1894. 8°.   10135. i. 9.

PIDGEON (D.) Venice. pp 152. *Lond.* 1895. 8°.
                                                10136. aaa. 22.

PRATESI (M.) Di Paese in paese. pp. 516. *Milano*, 1892. 8°.   10130. df. 2.

SACCARDO (P.) I restauri della Basilica di San Marco nell' ultimo decennio. pp. 63. *Venezia*, 1890 fol.   7814. f. 15.

SYMONDS (M.) Days spent on a Doge's Farm. pp. 254. *Lond.* 1893. 8°.   10132. f. 16.

VENICE. Calli e canali in Venezia. *Venezia*, 1890, *etc.* fol.   K.T.C. 4. a. 4.

VOLPI (E.) Lapidi murate in Venezia nel secolo XIX. pp. 108. *Venezia*, 1890. 8°.
                                                10629. h. 26.

See also EXHIBITIONS: ITALY.

Typography. *See* TYPOGRAPHY.

VENTILATION. BILLINGS (J. S.) Ventilation and heating. pp. 500. *N.Y.* 1893. 8°.
                                                8777. h. 23.

BOYLE (R.) Ventilation. pp. 54. *Lond.* 1893. 16°.   8777. de. 1.

BUCHAN (W. P.) Ventilation. pp. 226. *Lond.* 1891. 8°.   8777. aaa. 22.

VENTILATION—continued.

CORFIELD (D. H.) Dwelling houses. pp. 125. *Lond.* 1894. 8°.   8777. aaa. 37.

DALY (T.) New plan of Window Ventilation. pp. 22. *Lond.* 1895. 8°.   Pam. 79.

DANGER. A Danger to the public health. *Lond.* 1894, *etc.* 16°.   8777. a.

JACOB (E. H.) Notes on the Ventilation and Warming of houses, churches, schools, *etc.* pp. 124. 1894. 8°. *Manuals of Health.* 7404. a.

KEITH (J.) Houses of Parliament. Report on the ventilation. pp. 18. *Lond.* 1894. 8°.
                                                Pam. 79.

OLDROYD (E.) Brief essay on mechanical Ventilation. pp. 19. *Leeds*, 1894. 8°.
                                                8708. b. 23. (10.)

REEVES (R. H.) Reports and investigations on sewer ventilation. pp. 16. *Lond.* 1894. 8°.
                                                Pam. 79.

SHAW (W. N.) Warming and Ventilation. 1892. 8°. STEVENSON (T.) and MURPHY (S. F.) Treatise on hygiene.   7391. g. 18.

WILLETT (J. R.) Heating and Ventilation of residences. pp. 34. *Chicago*, 1893. 8°.
                                                8777. bbb. 28. (10.)

See also AIR : HYGIENE, *etc.*

VENTRILOQUISM. CALLAHAN (G. W.) Easy method of Ventriloquism. pp. 23. *N.Y.* 1890. 8°.   7913. ccc. 28.

GANTHONY (R.) Practical Ventriloquism. pp. 155. *Lond.* 1893. 8°.   7913. c. 53.

MACCABE (F.) Voice Production, *etc.* pp. 113. *Wolverhampton*, 1893. 8°.   11805. ccc. 29.

VENUS, Planet. Ac. Sydney. *Government Observatory.* Observation of the Transit of Venus, 9 Dec. 1874. pp. 43. *Sydney*, 1892. 4°.   8562. ff. 33.
See also SUN AND SOLAR SYSTEM.

VERCELLI. FISSORE (G.) Le glorie dalla chiesa di Vercelli. pp. 16. *Alba*, 1889. 8°.
                                                Pam. 29.

VERDUN-SUR-MEUSE. LABANDE (H.) Verdun. Inventaire des Archives communales. 1891. 4°. Collection des Inventaires sommaires.
                                                1815. b, *etc.*

POUZET (P.) La Succession de Charlemagne et le Traité de Verdun. pp. 92. 1890. 8°. Ac. Lyons. *Faculté des Lettres.* Bibliothèque. Tom. 7.   Ac. 8922/2.

GABRIEL (C. N.) Verdun au XIe siècle. pp. 519. *Verdun*, 1891. 8°.   010171. g. 9.

PETITOT–BELLAVÈNE ( ) Verdun aux XVIIe et XVIIIe siècles, 1573–1789. 1891. 8°. Ac. Verdun. *Société Philomathique.* Mémoires. Tom. 12.
                                                Ac. 580.

DONY (P.) Monographie des Sceaux de Verdun. 2 pt. *Verdun*, 1880–90. 4°.   7757. e. 15.

LABANDE (L. H.) La Charité à Verdun. pp. 98. *Verdun*, 1894. 4°.   8282. h. 20.

VERDUN-SUR-SAÔNE-ET-DOUBS. JEANDET (J. P. A.) Fragments des annales de la ville de Verdun-sur-Saône-et-Doubs. pp. 470. *Dijon*, 1893. 8°.   010171. f. 44.

VERMAND. PILLOY (J.) Les cimetières de Vermand du quatrième siècle. 1891. 8°. Ac. Saint-Quentin. *Société des Sciences.* Mémoires. Sér. 4. Tom. 9.   Ac. 530.

VERMES. BEDDARD (F. E.) Monograph of the order of Oligochaeta. pp. 769. *Oxf.* 1895. 4°.
                                                7297. i. 15.

FRIEDLAENDER (B.) Über die markhaltigen Nervenfasern der Anneliden. 1889. 8°. Ac. Naples. *Zoologische Station. Mittheilungen, etc.* Bd. 9.   Ac. 3552/2.

                                                3 K 2

VERMES—*continued.*

MALAQUIN (A.) Recherches sur les Syllidiens. pp. 477. *Lille*, 1893. 8°.   7299. g. 25.

PINTNER (T.) Vermes. pp. 66. 1893. 8°. Ac. Naples. *Zoologische Station.* Jahresbericht, 1892.   Ac. 3552./3.

See also HIRUDINEA : MEMERTEA : MYGOSTOMIDAE : PARASITES : POLYZOA : TURBELLARIA.

VERMIFORM APPENDIX. *See* INTESTINES.

VERMONT. CONANT (E.) Geography, history and government of Vermont. pp. 288. *Rutland*, 1890. 8°.   9065. c. 8.

HAZEN (H. A.) New Hampshire and Vermont : historical study. pp. 15. *Concord*, 1894. 8°.   9551. k. 8. (12.)

SPEAR (V. I.) Vermont : scenery and industries. pp. 64. *Montpellier*, 1893. *obl.* 8°. 10413. e. 5.

WOOD (F. A.) History of taxation in Vermont. pp. 128. 1894. 8°. Ac. New York. *Columbia College.* Studies in History. Vol. 4. Ac. 2688/2.

Ac. Burlington. *University of Vermont.* Centennial Addresses. 2 pt. *Burlington*, 1892. 8°.   8366. de. 36.

See also NEW ENGLAND.

VERONA. CIPOLLA (C.) Di alcune opinioni intorno alla storia dei XIII. Comuni veronesi. pp. 88. *Venezia*, 1887. 4°.   10131. h. 13.

—— Note di Storia veronese. 1892. 8°. P.P. *Venice.* Nuovo Archivio veneto. Tom. 4.   P.P. 3556. v.

LENEL (W.) Studien zur Geschichte Veronas im dreizehnten Jahrhundert. pp. 86. *Strassb.* 1893. 8°.   9167. e. 3.

MILANI (L. A.) Le recenti scoperte di antichità in Verona. pp. 30. *Verona*, 1891. fol. Pam. 3.

RUSKIN (J.) Verona : and other lectures. pp. 168. *Orpington*, 1894. 8°. K.T.C. 27. b. 1.

See also VENICE.

VERS. JOSSE (H.) Notice sur la commune de Vers. pp. 186. 1891. 8°. Ac. Amiens. *Société d'Archéologie.* Mémoires. Sér. 4. Tom. 1.   Ac. 5343.

VERSAILLES. BALDUS (É.) Palais de Versailles. Motifs de décorations. ff. 100. *Paris*, 1891. fol.   1733. a. 7.

GATIN (L. A.) Ville de Versailles. Fêtes du centenaire de 1789. pp. 164. *Versailles*, 1891. 8°.   8051. e. 41.

GILLE (P. H.) Une promenade à Versailles. ff. 49. *Versailles*, 1892. *obl.* fol. 1787. aa. 7.

VERSAILLES. *Musée National.* Guide illustré du Musée National. pp. 72. *Versailles*, 1893. 12°.   7807. e. 32.

VERTEBRATA. *See* Zoology, and under each Order, Family, Genus or Species.

VERZY. QUEUTELOT (E.) Saint Basle et le monastère de Verzy. pp. 349. *Reims*, 1892. 8°.   4629. aaa. 29.

VESOUL. LONGIN (É.) Les armoiries de la ville de Vesoul. pp. 28. *Vesoul*, 1890. 8°.   9906. b. 9. (12.)

VESPA CRABRO. *See* HYMENOPTERA.

VESTERBOTTEN. REGNÉR (P. B.) Kriget och tillståndet i Vesterbotten 1809. pp. 67. *Stockholm*, 1891. 8°.   Pam. 28.

VETERINARY MEDICINE AND SURGERY.

General.

Ac. London. *Royal College of Veterinary Surgeons.* Register of Veterinary Surgeons. *Lond.* 1884, *etc.* 8°.   Ac. 3880.

VETERINARY MEDICINE.—General —*continued.*

BAYER (J.) Bildliche Darstellung des gesunden und kranken Auges unserer Hausthiere. *Wien*, 1891, *etc.* 8°.   07293. m. 6.

BOUCHER (H.) Hygiène des animaux domestiques. pp. 504. *Paris*, 1894. 12°.   7291. aa. 31.

COPENHAGEN. *K. Veterinær- og Landbohøjskoles Laboratorium.* Otte og tyvende Beretning fra den Laboratorium. pp. 118. *Kjøbenh.* 1893. 4°.   8223. dd. 20.

COX (W. G. R. A.) Stock-keeper and Agriculturists' text-book on diseases of domesticated animals. pp. 201. *Newcastle*, 1893. 8°.   07293. i. 20.

FLEMING (G.) Text-book of veterinary Obstetrics. pp. 758. *Lond.* 1895. 8°.   07291. h. 1.

G. B. & I. *Board of Agriculture.* Handbook of the laws and regulations relating to contagious diseases among Animals. 2 pt. *Lond.* 1890. 8°.   6425. de. 19.

MILAN. *Scuola di Medicina Veterinaria.* La cerimonia del primo centenario della Scuola. pp. 82. *Milano*, 1891. 8°.   7291. d. 10.

MILLER (W. B. E.) Diseases of live stock. pp. 523. *Lond.* 1893. 8°.   07293. k. 6.

NEUMANN (L. G.) Traité des maladies parasitaires des animaux domestiques. pp. 767. *Paris*, 1892. 8°.   07293. m. 10.

—— Treatise on the parasites and parasitic diseases of Domesticated Animals. pp. 800. *Lond.* 1892. 8°.   07293 m. 7.

SIGNOL (J.) Aide-mémoire du Vétérinaire. pp. 648. *Paris*, 1894. 12°.   7291. aa. 27.

THOMPSON (H.) Elementary lectures on Veterinary Science. pp. 273. *Whitehaven*, 1895. 8°.   07291. h. 2.

See also ANIMALS, *Domestic.*

Anatomy and Physiology.

CADEAC (C.) Pathologie et Anatomie des animaux domestiques. pp. 478. *Paris*, 1893. 12°.   7421. aaa. 28.

CHAUVEAU (A. P.) Comparative anatomy of the domesticated Animals. pp. 1084. *Lond.* 1891. 8°.   2254. f. 2.

KITT (T.) Lehrbuch der pathologisch-anatomischen Diagnostik für Thierärzte. *Stuttgart*, 1894, *etc.* 8°.   7293. l.

SMITH (F.) Manual of veterinary Physiology. pp. 573. *Lond.* 1895. 8°.   7295. ee. 4.

STRANGEWAYS (T.) Veterinary Anatomy. pp. 601. *Edinb.* 1892. 8°.   07293. i. 8.

Homœopathy.

GOODAY (H.) Text-book of veterinary homœopathic Practice. pp. 192. *Lond.* 1880. 8°.   7293. aaa. 25.

MOORE (J.) Outlines of veterinary Homœopathy. pp. 301. *Lond.* 1889. 8°.   7293. aaa. 24.

Surgery.

HOFFMANN (L.) Tierärzliche Chirurgie. 2 Bde. *Stuttgart*, 1892. 8°.   07293. m. 9.

MOELLER (H.) Lehrbuch der speciellen Chirurgie für Thierärzte. pp. 872. *Stuttgart*, 1891. 8°.   07293. m. 8.

—— Operative veterinary Surgery. pp. 733. *Edinb.* 1895. 8°.   07293. m. 17.

Therapeutics and Pharmacy.

BEASLEY (H.) Druggist's general Receipt Book. pp. 538. *Lond.* 1895. 8°.   7509. aa. 13.

DUN (F.) Veterinary Medicines. pp. 776. *Edinb.* 1892. 8°.   7291. i. 16.

HOARE (E. W.) Manual of veterinary Therapeutics and Pharmacology. pp. 560. *Lond.* 1895. 8°.   7293. b. 44.

VETERINARY MEDICINE. — Therapeutics, etc.—continued.

TUSON (R. V.) Pharmacopœia for practitioners of veterinary medicine. pp. 370.
Lond. 1895. 8°.   07293. g. 20.

VETERINARY COUNTER PRACTICE. Veterinary Counter Practice. pp. 268. Lond. 1891. 8°.
       7293. i. 7.

Tuberculosis.

BEHREND (H.) Cattle Tuberculosis and tuberculous meat. pp. 112. Lond. 1893. 8°.
       07293. g. 5.

BRUSAFERRO (S.) La tubercolosi negli animali domestici. 1890. 8°. Ac. Turin. Società Agraria. Annali. Vol. 33.   Ac. 3386/2.

NOCARD (E.) Les tuberculoses animales. pp. 208. 1894. 8°. Encyclopédie des aide-mémoire.   8709. g.

SHUMWAY (H. L.) Handbook of Tuberculosis among cattle. Lond. 1895. 8°.   7291. a. 3.

Diseases and Hygiene of Various Animals.

Cattle and Sheep.

ARLOING (S.) Le Charbon symptomatique du Bœuf. pp. 281. Paris, 1887. 8°. 7291. ccc. 3.

FIELD (W.) Inoculation as a preventive to pleuro-pneumonia. pp. 87. Manch. 1892. 8°.
       Pam. 39.

GRESSWELL (J. B.) and (A.) The Bovine prescriber. pp. 102. Lond. 1894. 8°. 7294. df. 8.

KNOWLSON (J. C.) The Yorkshire Cattle Doctor and farrier. pp. 272. Lond. 1891. 8°.
       7293. i. 9.

SCHMALTZ (R.) Topographische Anatomie der Körperhöhlen des Rindes. Berl. 1890, etc. 4°.
       7294. h. 4.

STANTON (A. J.) Foot-and-Mouth Disease. pp. 16. Lond. 1892. 8°.   Pam. 42.

ARMATAGE (G.) The Sheep Doctor. pp. 608. Lond. 1895. 8°.   7294. dd. 2.

BROWN (G. T.) Contagious Foot-rot in sheep. pp. 16. Lond. 1892. 8°.   7293. i. 12. (10.)
See also supra: Tuberculosis: CATTLE: SHEEP.

Dog.

DALZIEL (H.) The Diseases of Dogs. pp. 118. Lond. 1893. 8°.   7293. bbb. 37.

MUELLER (G.) Die Krankheiten des Hundes und ihre Behandlung. pp. 434. Berl. 1892. 8°.
       07293. k. 3.

See also DOG: HYDROPHOBIA.

Horse.

DALZIEL (H.) Diseases of Horses. pp. 102. Lond. 1891. 8°.   07293. i. 2.

CHAMPETIER (P.) Les maladies du jeune Cheval. pp. 348. Paris, 1892. 8°.   7293. f. 11.

COX (J. R.) Horses in accident and disease. Edinb. 1892. 8°.   07293. i. 14.

G. B. & I. Army. Veterinary Department. Regulations for Army Veterinary services. pp. 86. Lond. 1894. 8°.   8831. aaa. 48.

HAYES (M. H.) Veterinary notes for horse owners. pp. 618. Lond. 1891. 8°. 7293. c. 32.

LECLAINCHE (E.) Précis de Pathologie vétérinaire. pp. 475. Paris, 1891. 12°. 7293. b. 36.

MAYHEW (E.) Illustrated Horse Doctor. pp. 572. Lond. 1891. 8°.   07293. i. 1.

SCHWARZ (A.) The Horse: its external and internal organisation. pp. 24.
Lond. 1894. obl. 8°.   7294. df. 10.

DUPONT (M.) L'âge du Cheval et des principaux animaux domestiques. pp. 187.
Paris, 1893. 8°.   07293. g. 14.

VETERINARY MEDICINE.—Diseases of the Horse—continued.

SCHWAB (C.) Practical pocket guide to ascertain from the teeth the age of the Horse.
Lond. 1893. 8°.   7293. a. 6.

ROBERGE (D.) The Foot of the Horse. pp. 269. N.Y, 1894. 8°.   07293. k. 13.

CADIOT (P. J.) Roaring in Horses. pp. 78. Lond. 1892. 8°.   7293. bbb. 34.

HUNTING (W.) Glanders: how it arises and spreads, etc. pp. 82. Lond. 1887. 8°.
       7295. b. 7.

See also HORSE.

Pig.

G. B. & I. Board of Agriculture. Swine-Fever order of 1893. pp. 13. Lond. 1893. fol.
       Pam. 42.

BOWHILL (T.) Identity of English with American Swine plague. pp. 34. Edinb. 1891. 8°.
       7293. i. 12. (9.)

See also PIG.

VETULONIA. DOTTO DE' DAULI (C.) Vetulonia. Nuovi errori, mistificazioni e menzogne. pp. 190. Pitigliano, 1894. 8°.
       10132. f. 19.

FALCHI (I.) Vetulonia e la sua necropoli antichissima. pp. 323. Firenze, 1891. 4°.
       7705. g. 43.

—— Le reviste del P. de Cara sul libro "Vetulonia e la sua necropoli." pp. 8.
Firenze, 1892. 8°.   07703. h. 1. (8.)

—— Replica alle osservazioni del P. de Cara sul libro "Vetulonia e la sua necropoli." pp. 12.
Firenze, 1892. 8°.   07703. h. 1. (7.)

VEXIN. ACHENBACH-WAHL (G.) Histoire du Vexin. pp. 131. Magny, 1894. 8°. 010171. i. 1.
See also EURE: OISE: SEINE ET OISE.

VIBORG. CHRISTIANSEN (J. D.) Viborg Omegns Fugle. pp. 52. Viborg, 1890. 8°.
       Pam. 42.

VIBRATION (Medical Process).

LIEDBECK (C. H.) Description of the Vibrator and directions for use. pp. 64.
Stockholm, 1891. 8°.   7461. bb. 15.

VICHY. BONNARD (C.) Vichy-Ambulance, son rôle pendant la prochaine guerre. pp. 106. Vichy, 1890. 8°.   8823. c. 52.

CORNILLON (J.) Clinique thermale de Vichy. pp. 246. Cusset, 1891. 8°.   7462. ee. 41.

DÉCORET (G.) Une page sur Vichy. Vichy, 1895, etc. 4°.   10172. g.

MALLAT (A.) Vichy à travers les siècles. Vichy, 1890, etc. 8°.   010171. h. 39.

VICHY. Vichy et ses environs. Guide Joanne. pp. 64. Paris, 1894. 8°.   10169. de. 29.

—— Notice sur les eaux de Vichy. pp. 83. Paris, 1889. 16°.   7462. de. 11. (6.)

VICTORIA, Australia. DYER (E. J.) Victoria and its resources. pp. 88.
Ballarat, 1893. fol.   1854. a. 4.

FITZ GIBBON (E. G.) Party Government and suggestions for better. 2 pt.
Melbourne, 1893; 94. 8°.   Pam. 66.

GOODMAN (G.) The Church in Victoria, during the Episcopate of C. Perry, first Bishop.
pp. 476. Lond. 1892. 8°.   4744. g. 13.

HAYTER (H. H.) Handbook to the Colony of Victoria. pp. 56. Melbourne, 1891. 8°. Pam. 87.

HIRSCH (M.) Protection in Victoria. pp. 29. Melbourne, 1891. 8°.   8282. e. 43. (12.)

JENKS (E.) The Government of Victoria. pp. 403. Lond. 1891. 8°.   8154. ee. 26.

VICTORIA, Australia—continued.

MYERS (F.) and CHAMBERS (T.) Victorian Tourist's Railway Guide. pp. 159. *Melbourne*, 1892. 8°. 10492. c. 35.

SPAWN (A. F.) New homes in the Irrigation Colonies of Victoria. pp. 60. *Lond.* 1891. 8°. 10492. bb. 42.

SUTHERLAND (A.) Geography of Victoria. pp. 122. *Lond.* 1893. 8°. 10492. aa. 26.

VICTORIA. The Victorian Statutes. *Melbourne*, 1890, etc. 8°. 06606. gg.

—— Cities and towns of Victoria. 2 pt. *Ballarat*, 1893. obl. 8°. 10491. de. 20.

—— Victoria and its Metropolis. 2 vol. *Melbourne*, 1888. 4°. 10491. h. 11.

See also AUSTRALIA : MINERALOGY.

VICTORIA, Hong Kong. *See* HONG KONG.

VICTORIA CROSS. MURDOCK (J. E.) " For Valour": the " V. C." Record of brave deeds. pp. 292. *Lond.* 1895. 8°. 8829. bb. 32.

MUNDELL (F.) Stories of the Victoria Cross. pp. 160. *Lond.* 1895. 8°. 8829. aa. 24.

PARRY (D. H.) Britain's Roll of Glory; the Victoria Cross. pp. 368. *Lond.* 1895. 8°. 8829. bb. 34.

RICHARDS (W.) Heroes of To-day : recent winners of the V.C. pp. 230. *Lond.* 1892. 8°. 10803. e. 5.

TOOMEY (T. E.) Heroes of the Victoria Cross. pp. 259. *Lond.* 1895. 8°. 10803. bb. 33.

See also ENGLAND, *Army* : *Navy*.

VIENNA. AMLAUFT (F.) Namenbuch der Stadt Wien. pp. 205. *Wien*, 1895. 8°. 10215. cc. 6.

GUGLIA (E.) Geschichte der Stadt Wien. pp. 306. *Prag*, 1892. 8°. 10215. ee. 22.

LEISS (G. J.) Ursache der 1. Belagerung Wiens durch die Türken, 1529. pp. 30. *Wien*, 1893. 8°. 9004. bbb. 16. (6.)

FERRON (J. F.) Neu-Wien. *Wien*, 1892, etc. 8°. 10215. c.

GREFE (C.) Beiträge zur Geschichte der Israeliten in Wien. *Wien*, 1891, etc. 8°. 1852. a. 9.

JAQUES (H.) Fünf Reden über Österreich und Wien. pp. 69. *Leipz.* 1891. 8°. 10107. ff. 27. (8.)

KELLER (O.) Das Haus Habsburg als Pflegestätte der Tonkunst. pp. 22. *Wien*, 1890. 8°. 7896. c. 43. (7.)

KOBATSCH (R.) Die Armenpflege in Wien. pp. 92. *Wien*, 1893. 8°. 8276. ce. 65.

LAMBER, afterwards LA MESSINE, afterwards ADAM (J.) Vienne. 1892. 4°. Les Capitales du Monde. No. 8. 10025. g.

VIENNA. Gross Wien. pp. 16. *Wien*, 1891. 8°. 10210. ff. 3.

ZETSCHE (E.) Aus den Umgebungen Wiens. pp. 132. *Stuttgart*, 1894. 8°. 10210. ff. 4.

ZSCHOKKE (H.) Geschichte des Metropolitan-Capitels zum heiligen Stephan in Wien. pp. 428. *Wien*, 1895. 8°. 4685. d. 39.

BACCIOCCO (F. A.) Der wiener Dialect. pp. 62. *Wien*, 1890. 8°. 12901. d. 32. (6.)

See also EXHIBITIONS.

Diocese.

KOPALLIK (J.) Regesten zu Geschichte der Erzdiöcese Wien. *Wien*, 1890. etc. 4°. 4695. h.

University.

AC. Vienna. *Universitas*. Übersicht der akademischen Behörden, 1892/93. pp. 64. *Wien*, 1892. 8°. 8357. cc. 48.

—— Die feierliche Inauguration des Rectors 1892/3. *Wien*, 1892, etc. 8°. Ac. 803/5.

VIENNA.—University—continued.

HIMMELBAUR (I.) Führer an der Universität zu Wien. pp. 84. *Wien*, 1894. 8°. 8357. a. 4.

VIENNE, Department of Isère. BAZIN (H.) Vienne et Lyon gallo-romains. pp. 407. *Paris*, 1891. 8°. 7708. cc. 53.

FOURNIER (P.) Les Royaume d'Arles et de Vienne 1138-1378. pp. 554. *Paris*, 1891. 8°. 9225. k. 25.

VIÉVY-LE-RAYÉ. SAINT-VENANT (J. de) Anciennes forteresses à Viévy-le-Rayé. pp. 53. *Vendôme*, 1889. 8°. 07703. i. 1. (5.)

VIGAN. TEISSIER (F.) Inventaire des Archives du Vigan antérieures à 1790. 1890. 4°. Collection des Inventaires. 1814-15. b., etc.

VILLAGES.

See LOCAL GOVERNMENT : TOWNS.

VILLEMEUX. CHRÉTIEN (D.) Notice historique sur la commune de Villemeux. pp. 50. *Chartres*, 1895. 8°. Pam. 91.

VILLENEUVE DE BERG. GIGORD (R. de) La Noblesse de Villeneuve de Berg en 1789. pp. 777. *Lyon*, 1894. 8°. 9906. h. 3.

VILLENEUVE-LOUBET. PANISSE-PASSIS (P. M. H. de) *Marquis*. Villeneuve-Loubet et ses seigneurs. pp. 198. *Paris*, 1892. 4°. 10173. g. 9.

VILLENEUVE-SAINT-GEORGES.

BONNIN (P.) Ablon-sur-Seine et Villeneuve-St.-Georges pendant la Fronde. pp. 112. *Paris*, 1892. 8°. 10169. cc. 15.

VILLEQUIERS. LAUGARDIÈRE (M. de) Histoire du pays de Villequiers. pp. 433. *Bourges*, 1892. 8°. 010171. g. 8.

VILLIERS-LE-BEL. BERTAUTS-COUTURE (L.) Histoire de Villiers-le-Bel pendant la Révolution. pp. 141. *Paris*, 1891. 8°. 9226. k. 13.

VINE : WINE. AMICIS (E. de) Il Vino. pp. 93. *Milano*, 1890. 8°. 8436. bb. 37.

BONAPARTE (L. L.) *Prince*. Words connected with the Vine in Latin and Neo-Latin dialects. pp. 61. 1883. 8°. Ac. Cambridge. *Philological Society*. Transactions. Vol. 2. Ac. 9905/2.

CAMBON (V.) Le Vin et l'art de la vinification. pp. 324. *Paris*, 1892. 12°. 7076. aa. 2.

COSTE-FLORET (P.) Procédés modernes de vinification. pp. 456. *Montpellier*, 1894. 8°. 7078. e. 11.

—— Vinification des vins blancs. pp. 341. *Montpellier*, 1895. 8°. 07077. h. 1.

DUJARDIN (J.) L'Essai commercial des vins. pp. 368. *Paris*, 1892. 8°. 7075. a. 5.

FITZJAMES (M. A. M. de) *Duchess*. La pratique de Viticulture. pp. 380. *Paris*, 1894. 12°. 7078. e. 10.

HELD (P.) Weinbau. Anleitung zur rationellen Traubenzucht. pp. 181. 1894. 8°. Thaer-Bibliothek. Bd. 87. 7078. aaa.

LE SOURD (P.) Traité des vins, cidres, etc. pp. 617. *Paris*, 1890. 8°. 07076. m. 7.

LISSONE (S.) La fabbricazione e conservazione del Vino. pp. 100. *Torino*, 1891. 8°. 7942. h. 31. (6.)

MAGNIER DE LA SOURCE (L.) Analyse des Vins. pp. 196. 1892. 8°. Encyclopédie des aide-mémoire. 8709. g.

MALEPEYRE (F.) Nouveau manuel de la fabrication des Vins de fruits. pp. 352. 1892. 18°. Encyclopédie Roret. 12208. b.

MAUMENÉ (E. J.) Comment s'obtient le bon Vin. pp. 238. *Paris*, 1894. 8°. 07944. g. 3.

VIOLIN—*continued.*

BEAZLEY (J. C.) Aids to the Violinist. pp. 10.
Ryde, 1892. 4°.　　　　　7808. bbb. 31. (4.)

CAFFARELLI (F. di) Gli strumenti ad arco e la
musica de camera. pp. 235. *Milano,* 1894. 8°.
012200. i. 13.

COURVOISIER (C.) The Technics of Violin-playing. pp. 61. *Lond.* 1895. 8°.　　　7899. aaa. 16.

HENRY (J. H.) and BARBER (E. M.) The Violin.
Facts for students preparing for the examinations
of the college of Violinists. pp. 8.
Derby, 1893. obl. 16°.　　　　　　Pam. 24.

LATARCHE (A.) The Violin Student's manual.
pp. 16. *Lond.* 1892. 8°.　　　7808. de. 2. (5.)

—— The Violin positions. pp. 4.
Lond. 1891. 8°.　　　　　　9897. aa. 70.

P.P. *London.* Strings, the Fiddler's Magazine.
Lond. 1894, *etc.* 8°.　　　　　　2094.

—— The Violin Times. A monthly journal.
Lond. 1893, *etc.* 4°. P.P. 1946. gb. and 2193.

RAIKES (A. H.) Violin Chat for beginners.
pp. 96. *Lond.* 1891. 8°.　　　7896. de. 30.

SCHROEDER (C.) Catechism of Violin playing.
pp. 135. *Lond.* 1895. 8°.　　　7899. b. 16.

SECRETS. The Secrets of Violin-Playing. pp. 76.
Edinb. 1894. 8°.　　　　　7898. aa. 58.

VIOLIN. The Violin: how to master it. pp. 106.
Edinb. 1894. 8°.　　　　　7898. aa. 59.

WOOD (R.) Tone and expression in Violin playing. pp. 34. *Sheffield,* 1894. 8°.
7899. aaa. 11. (11.)

See also MUSIC: MUSICAL INSTRUMENTS. For
biographies of Violinists, *see* BIOGRAPHY, *Musical.*

VIOLONCELLO. SCHROEDER (C.) Catechism of Violoncello Playing. pp. 118.
Lond. 1894. 8°.　　　　　7898. cc. 28.

WASIELEWSKI (J. W. v.) Das Violoncell und
seine Geschichte. pp. 245. *Leipz.* 1889. 8°.
7897. g. 58.

—— The Violoncello and its history. pp. 225.
Lond. 1894. 8°.　　　　　7897. g. 61.

See also MUSICAL INSTRUMENTS: VIOLIN.

VIRE, Calvados. GASTÉ (A.) Petite Anthologie viroise. pp. 130. *Caen,* 1891. 8°.
11483. d. 15.

VIRGINIA.

History.

Ac. Richmond. *Virginia Historical Society.*
Virginia Magazine of history and biography.
Richmond, 1893, *etc.* 8°.　　　Ac. 8546/6.

WILLIAMSBURG. *William and Mary College.*
Quarterly Historical papers.
Williamsb. 1892, *etc.* 8°.　　　　08365. k.

SMITH (M. V.) Virginia, 1492–1892. pp. 459.
Wash. 1893. 8°.　　　　　9605. ff. 9.

DRAKE (S. A.) The Making of Virginia, 1578–
1701. pp. 228. *Lond.* 1894. 8°.　9605. c. 18.

HARRIOT (T.) Narrative of the first English
Plantation of Virginia. *Lond.* 1893. 4°.
9551. f. 5.

NEILL (E. D.) Virginian Governors under the
London Company. pp. 35. 1889. 8°. Ac.
Saint Paul. *Macalester College.* Contributions.
Department of History. No. 4. Ac. 2692. s.

BROWN (A.) New views of early Virginia History, 1606–1619. pp. 18. *Liberty,* 1886. 4°.
9004. l. 35. (4.)

NEILL (E. D.) Earliest contest in America on
charter-rights in Virginia Legislature. 1890. 8°.
Ac. Saint Paul. *Macalester College.* Contributions. Department of History. No. 5.
Ac. 2692. s.

BROCK (R. A.) The colonial Virginian. pp. 22.
Richmond, 1891. 8°.　　　　9555. f. 4. (2.)

VIRGINIA.—History—*continued.*

WASHINGTON (G.) Journal of my Journey over
the Mountains while surveying for Lord Fairfax
in the northern neck of Virginia. pp. 144.
Albany, 1892. 4°.　　　　　10882. e. 29.

MAGUIRE (T. M.) The Campaigns in Virginia
1861–62. pp. 70. *Lond.* 1891. 8°. 9602. h. 9.

Topography.

BRUCE (T.) Southwest Virginia and Shenandoah
Valley. pp. 259. *Richmond,* 1891. 8°.
10408. d. 23.

BURWELL (L. M.) A Girl's life in Virginia
before the war. pp. 209. *N.Y.* 1895. 8°.
10881. de. 18.

SHALER (N. S.) Account of the fresh-water
Morasses, with a description of the Dismal
Swamp district of Virginia. 1890. 4°. U.S.
Geological Survey. Annual Report. No. 10.
1828. aa.

VIRGINIA. Virginia: its climate, soil, productions. pp. 36. *Baltimore,* 1893. 8°. Pam. 86.

WHITEHEAD (T.) Virginia: a handbook.
pp. 341. *Richmond,* 1893. 8°. 10412. cc. 33.
See also UNITED STATES OF AMERICA, *History,*
and Southern States.

VIRGINIA, West. *See* WEST VIRGINIA.

VIRIEU. LAGIER (A.) La Révolution dans
les Terres-froides. pp. 147. *Valence,* 1892. 8°.
9226. l. 22.

VIS MAJOR. EXNER (A.) Der Begriff der
höheren Gewalt im römischen und heutigen
Verkehrsrecht. pp. 86. *Wien,* 1888. 8°.
6005. e. 12.

GERTH (G.) Der Begriff der Vis Major in
römischen und Reichsrecht. pp. 213.
Berl. 1890, 8°.　　　　　5206. ee. 14.

VISTULA, River. Ac. Berlin. *Geodätisches*
Institut. SEIBT (W.) Präcisions-Nivellement
der Weichsel. pp. 74. *Berl.* 1891. 4°.
Ac. 4301/27.

VITERBO. CESARIS (L. de) Le acque
minerali di Viterbo. pp. 51. *Viterbo,* 1888. 8°.
7462. e. 1. (7.)

PINZI (C.) Gli Ospizi medioevali e l' Ospedal-
Grande di Viterbo. pp. 430. *Viterbo,* 1893. 8°.
7688. g. 12.

VIVARAIS. MAZON (A.) Essai sur le
Vivarais pendant la guerre de Cent Ans.
pp. 314. *Tournon,* 1889. 8°.　　9210. ccc. 5.

—— Quelques notes sur l'origine des églises
du Vivarais. *Privas,* 1891, *etc.* 8°. 4629. de.

VASCHALDE (H.) Les Inondations du Vivarais.
pp. 126. *Aubenas,* 1890. 8°.　　8755. dd. 39.

VISSAC (R. de) Chronique vivaroise. pp. 85.
Paris, 1895. 8°.　　　　　9231. l. 9.

VOGÜÉ (E. M. de) *Viscount.* Notes sur le Bas-
Vivarais. pp. 105. *Paris,* 1893. 8°.
10172. bb. 1.

See also ARDÈCHE, *Department:* LANGUEDOC:
VILLENEUVE DE BERG.

VIVIERS, Diocese. ROCHE (A.) Armorial
des Évêques de Viviers. 2 tom. *Lyon,* 1894. 8°.
4864. ee. 1.

VIVISECTION. AMERICA, *North. Humane*
Association. Report on Vivisection. pp. 60.
Chicago, 1895. 8°.　　　　　8425. aaa. 38.

BOSC (E.) De la Vivisection. pp. 161.
Paris, 1894. 8°.　　　　　8425. b. 65.

BRYAN (B.) Anti-Vivisection. pp. 268.
Lond. 1895. 8°.　　　　　8425. b. 64.

EYSINGA (S. F. W. R. v.) Vivisectie en hooger
Onderwijs. pp. 56. *'s Gravenh.* 1893. 8°.
8409. l. 24. (9.)

HARVEY (R.) The Pasteur Institute and Vivisection. pp. 24. *Calcutta,* 1895. 8°. Pam. 85.

VIVISECTION—*continued.*

HARTMANN (C. R. E. v.) The Sexes compared, *etc.* pp. 164. *Lond.* 1895. 8°. 8415. df. 31.

LEFFINGWELL (A.) A Dangerous Ideal. pp. 7. *Providence,* 1895. 8°. Pam. 85.

—— Vivisection. pp. 95. *N.Y.* 1889. 8°.
 8425. aaa. 31.

LONDON. *Society for the Protection of Animals from Vivisection.* The Vivisection Controversy. 22 pt. *Lond.* 1890. 8°. 8425. e. 67.

METZGER (D.) La vivisection. pp. 235. *Paris,* 1891. 8°. 8425. f. 17.

MORRIS (F. O.) The cowardly Cruelty of the experimenters on living animals. pp. 12. *Lond.* 1892. 8°. 8425. c. 69. (5.)

—— Defence of our dumb companions against the cowardly cruelty of experimenters. pp. 20. *Lond.* 1890. 8°. 8425. c. 69. (7.)

OUIDA, *pseud.* The new Priesthood. pp. 77. *Lond.* 1893. 16°. 8425. aaa. 34.

REID (H. J.) "That the Reader may judge." pp. 35. *Lond.* 1893. 16°. 8410. a. 45. (5.)

—— Administration of the cruelty to Animals Act, 1876. pp. 15. *Lond.* 1893. 8°.
 8425. c. 69. (8.)

—— Experimental Physiology. pp. 12. *Lond.* 1892. 8°. 8425. b. 62. (9.)

RHODES (G. M.) The circles of the hell of the Innocent. pp. 163. *Lond.* 1892. 8°.
 8425. bbb. 40.

RUBENS (M.) Anti-Vivisection exposed. *Bombay,* 1894, *etc.* 8°. 8425. bbb.

THOMSON (W.) Bacon and Shakespeare on Vivisection. pp. 39. *Melbourne,* 1881. 8°.
 11764. f. 6. (5.)

WALKER (A. de N.) The Bishop of Peterborough on Vivisection. pp. 22. *Norwich,* 1882. 8°.
 8425. c. 69. (2.)

VOGHERA. CAVAGNA SANGIULIANI (A.) L'Agro vogherese.
Casorate Primo, 1890, *etc.* 8°. 10132. h. 9.

LODI (F.) Sommario della storio di Voghera. pp. 304. *Voghera,* 1891. 8°. 10136. g. 24.

SALVI (P. G.) Sulla pubblica Biblioteca della città di Voghera. pp. 16. *Voghera,* 1891. 8°.
 Pam. 6.

VOICE: SINGING.
General.

VOGEL (E.) Biblioteca della musica vocale italiana stampata dal 1500 al 1700. 2 Bde. *Berlino,* 1892. 8°. 7897. dd. 7.

BACH (A. B.) The principles of Singing. pp. 305. *Edinb.* 1894. 8°. 7897. m. 7.

BEHNKE (*Mrs.* E.) and PEARCE (C. W.) Voice-training primer. pp. 76. *Lond.* 1893. 8°.
 7898. bbb. 37.

BERNHARDT (J. W.) Vox Humana; voice production and development. pp. 73. 28. *Lond.* 1892. 4°. 7897. l. 27.

—— A Singing Lesson. pp. 20. *Lond.* 1895. 8°.
 7808. cc. 8. (6.)

BLACKMAN (D. A.) The Psycho Vowel method of Voice culture. pp. 103. *Chicago,* 1895. 8°.
 7898. cc. 23.

BLUMNER (M.) Geschichte der Sing-Akademie zu Berlin. pp. 256. *Berl.* 1891. 8°. 8357. k. 7.

BOURMAN-HART (M. H.) Practical Hints on singing. pp. 14. *Lond.* 1893. 8°.
 7899. dd. 1. (9.)

CASTEX (A.) Hygiène de la voix parlée et chantée. pp. 219. 1894. 8°. Encyclopédie des aide-mémoire. 8709. g.

CROKER (N.) Handbook for Singers. pp. 141. *Lond.* 1895. 8°. 7899. b. 17.

VOICE.—General—*continued.*

D'ORSEY (C.) Address on the cultivation of the speaking Voice. pp. 16. *Lond.* 1894. 8°.
 7899. aaa. 11. (8.)

—— Correct Voice use as a preventive to throat disease. pp. 32. *Lond.* 1895. 8°.
 07305. f. 19. (7.)

DUNN (S.) The art of Singing. pp. 117. *Lond.* 1892. 16°. 7898. bb. 39.

FELL (H.) Voice Production. pp. 12. *Lond.* 1893. 8°. 7898. aa. 51. (8.)

GOLDSCHMIDT (H.) Die italienische Gesangs-methode des xvii. Jahrhunderts. pp. 137. *Breslau,* 1890. 8°. 7896. dd. 10.

GRIFFITHS (W. H.) The human Voice, its cultivation and preservation. pp. 100. *Lond.* 1892. 8°. 011824. de. 40.

HELMORE (F.) The pocket Voice gymnasium. pp. 8. *Lond.* 1893. 24°. Pam. 24.

KELLY (T.) First principles of Voice Production. pp. 16. *Lond.* 1893. 8°. 7898. m. 6. (11.)

LABANCHI (A. G.) Gli eunuchi e le scuole di canto del secolo xviii. pp. 35. *Napoli,* 1893. 8°. 7898. m. 15. (4.)

LEVIEN (J. J. M.) Voice Production and vowel enunciation. pp. 16. *Lond.* 1895. 8°. Pam. 24.

LUNN (C.) Philosophy of Voice. pp. 127. *Lond.* 1895. 8°. 7899. aaa. 17.

MACCABE (F.) Voice Production, arts of speaking, singing and ventriloquism. pp. 113. *Wolverhampton,* 1893. 8°. 11805. ccc. 29.

MAUREL (V.) Un Problème d'art. pp. 314. *Paris,* 1893. 12°. 7898. aa. 54.

MILES (R.) Chart of the whole art of Singing. *Deptford,* 1892. 8°. 1865. c. 1. (4.)

PALMER (E. D.) Manual of Voice-training. pp. 46. *Lond.* 1894. 8°. 7899. aaa. 11. (1.)

P.P. *London.* Song and Speech. A monthly journal. *Lond.* 1891, *etc.* 4°.
 P.P. 1945. hdd. and 2166.

PILTAN (A.) The Human Voice; its mechanism. pp. 107. *Lond.* 1895. 4°. 7895. g. 22.

ROGERS (C. K.) Philosophy of Singing. pp. 218. *Lond.* 1893. 8°. 7898. cc. 19.

ROKITANSKY (V.) Über Sänger und Singen. pp. 191. *Wien,* 1891. 8°. 7898. c. 38.

SANDLANDS (J. P.) New art of Healing; relation between the principles of voice production and health. pp. 136. *Lond.* 1892. 8°. 7616. aaa. 8.

SANDRAS (A.) La Voix modifiée par les inhalations. pp. 107. *Paris,* 1894. 12°. 7898. cc. 27.

SUTRO (E.) The basic law of Vocal Utterance. pp. 124. *Lond.* 1894. 8°. 7616. f. 14.

TAYLOR (J.) How to Teach Sight-singing. pp. 244. *Lond.* 1890. 4°. 7895. dd. 1.

—— The New Code sight-singing book for Divisions I. to iv. pp. 143. *Lond.* 1890. 4°.
 7895 dd. 2.

—— Original sight-singing exercises for Code Divisions I. and II. pp. 16. *Lond.* 1890. 4°,
 7895. dd. 5.

—— Original sight-singing exercises for Code Divisions III. and IV. pp. 19. *Lond.* 1890. 4°.
 7895. dd. 6.

—— School Songs with sight-singing exercises. pp. 95. *Lond.* 1890. 8°. 7895. dd. 4.

TAYLOR (S.) System of sight-singing from the established musical notation. pp. 132. *Lond.* 1890. 8°. 7895. ee. 25.

THORP (G. E.) and NICHOLL (W.) Text-book on the natural use of the Voice. pp. 136. *Lond.* 1895. 8°. 7899. aaa. 26.

VOICE.—General—_continued._

VERNHAM (J. E.) Fifty Three-part Studies
within the compass of an octave. pp. 56.
1895. 8°. Novello, Ewer & Co.'s Music Primers.
7895. ff.

VOICE GYMNASTICS. Voice Gymnastics.
Bethersden, 1891. 16°. 1865. c. 1. (16.)

WARMAN (E. B.) The Voice. How to train it.
pp. 168. _Bost._ 1890. 8°. 7898. k. 34.

See also ELOCUTION: LARYNX: MUSIC: VEN-
TRILOQUISM.

Chanting and Church Choir Singing.
See MUSIC, _Ecclesiastical._

Defects and Diseases of Speech.

BEHNKE (_Mrs._ E.) Causes of Voice-failure.
pp. 15. _Lond._ 1894. 8°. 07305. f. 17. (12.)

FERRAND (　　) Le Langage, la parole et les
aphasies. pp. 229. _Paris,_ 1894. 8°. 7616. a. 49.

FREUND (S.) Zur Auffassung der Aphasien.
pp. 107. _Leipz._ 1891. 8°. 7630. f. 19.

MILLS (C. K.) Aphasia, and other affections of
the speech in their medico-legal relations.
pp. 81. _Phila._ 1891. 8°. 07305. h. 18. (5.)

TREITEL (L.) Grundriss der Sprachstörungen.
pp. 100. _Berl._ 1894. 8°. 7616. i. 13.

—— Über Aphasie im Kindesalter. pp. 26.
1893. 8°. VOLKMANN (R. v.) Sammlung
klinischer Vorträge. Nr. 64. 7441. g.

WYLLIE (J.) The disorders of Speech. pp. 495.
Edinb. 1894. 8°. 7616. i. 12.

ABBOTTS (W.) Impediments of Speech. pp. 60.
Lond. 1884. 8°. 7616. a. 51.

BEHNKE (E.) Stammering; its nature and treatment. pp. 31. _Lond._ 1893. 16°. 7616. de. 1.

CHERVIN (A.) La Méthode-Chervin ¦pour corriger le bégaiement. pp. 48. _Paris,_ 1893. 8°.
7306. e. 23. (8.)

DENHARDT (R.) Das Stottern. pp. 298.
Leipz. 1890. 8°. 7615. f. 31.

ERNST (R.) Das Stottern und seine Heilung.
pp. 279. _Berl._ 1892. 8°. 7616. i. 6.

FOSTER (J. E.) Defects in Speech. pp. 22.
Lond. 1895. 8°. Pam. 39.

MASON (N. H.) Practical guide and introduction
to the natural system for the Cure of Stammering. pp. 26. _Lond._ 1886. 8°. 7306. e. 26. (2.)

POTTER (S. O. L.) Speech and its defects.
pp. 117. _Phila._ 1882. 8°. 7616. e. 10.

WYSS (A.) Le Bégayement. pp. 91.
Genève, 1895. 8°. 7630. ff. 31.

VOIRONS. GONTHIER (J. F.) Les Voirons
autrefois et aujourd'hui. pp. 78.
Annecy, 1893. 12°. 10170. b. 4.

**VOLAPÜK AND OTHER INTERNA-
TIONAL LANGUAGES.**
General.

BOLTZ (A.) Hellenisch, die internationale Gelehrtensprache der Zukunft. pp. 328.
Leipz. 1890. 8°. 12923. eee. 21.

HEINTZELER (E.) Die wissenschaftlich notwen-
digen Grundlagen für eine brauchbare Weltsprache. _Meran,_ 1895. 8°. Pam. 47

LETELLIER (C. L. A.) Théorie du language
international et des progrès scientifiques.
pp. 53. _Caen,_ 1892. 8°. 12903. dd. 33. (10.)

LIPTAY (A.) Eine Gemeinsprache der Kultur-
völker. pp. 272. _Leipz._ 1891. 8°. 12902. cc. 47.

SCHUCHARDT (H. E. M.) "Weltsprache und
Weltsprachen." pp. 53. _Strassb._ 1894. 8°.
12902. e. 47.

VAD (W.) Altes und Neues über Weltsprache.
pp. 48. _Döbeln,_ 1891. 8°. 12901. d. 36. (3.)

VOLAPÜK, etc.—_continued._
Volapük,

BLANCHARD (B.) Plägasbuk velapükik. pp. 44.
Überlingen, 1891. 8°. 12901. aa. 58. (4.)

DICTIONARIES. Vödabuk volapükik-tälänik e
tälänik-volapükik. 2 pt. _Milano,_ 1890. 8°.
12902. a. 30.

HEINE (N.) Der kaufmännische Volapükist.
pp. 192. 8°. _Berl._ 1891. 8°. 12902. dd. 33.

HEYLIGERS (A.) Volledige handleiding tot het
aanleeren der wereldtal Volapük. pp. 100.
Haarlem, 1891. 8°. 12901. de. 13. (8.)

LOTT (J.) Ist Volapük die beste Lösung des
Weltsprache-Problems? _Wien,_ 1888. 8°.
12901. d. 40.

P.P. _Milan._ Nunal Nulik. Il Nuovo Messag-
giero. _Milano,_ 1890, _etc._ fol. 713.

—— _Paris._ Yelabuk pedipedelas, _etc._
Paris, 1887, _etc._ 8°. 12902. ccc.

—— _Sydney._ The Cosmopolitan. Quarterly
gazette for furthering Volapük
Sydney, 1891, _etc._ 4°. 458.

POILLEVEY (P.) Volapük français. pp. 22.
Autun, 1890. 8°. 12902. g. 32. (7.)

POST (A. A.) Comprehensive Volapük grammar.
pp. 62. _Mattapan,_ 1890. 8°. 12901. ccc. 16. (6.)

RUBINO DE BARAZIA (H.) Nouvelle grammaire
du Volapük. pp. 69. _La Rochelle,_ 1890. 12°.
12901. ccc. 18 (4.)

SCHLEYER (J. M.) Hauptgedanken meiner Vor-
träge über die von mir ersonnene Allsprache
Volapük. pp. 23. _Konstanz,_ 1885. 8°.
Pam. 47.

—— Grammatikàlisches Léxicon. pp. 16.
Konstanz, 1893. 12°. 12901. de. 14. (3.)

—— Büds saulik balsena bals. pp. 16.
Konstanz, 1893. 12°. 12901. de. 16. (6.)

—— Notizen über die sog. 'Normàlgrámmatik'
der Pseudoakademie volapüka. pp. 16.
Constance, 1893. 12°. 12901. de. 16. (5.)

Other Systems of Universal Language.

AC. Nuremberg. _Nürnberger Weltsprache-Verein._
La lingvo internacia. pp. 32.
Nürnberg, 1889. 8°. Pam. 47.

DORMOY (É.) Le Balta. pp. 194.
Tours, 1892. 12°. 12902. b. 47.

LIPTAY (A.) Langue catholique. pp. 282.
Paris, 1892. 8°. 12902. d. 30.

—— La Lengua católica. pp. 248.
Paris, 1890. 8°. 12902. dd. 23.

STEMPFL (J.) Communia, oder internationale
Verkehrs-Sprache. pp. 76. _Kempten,_ 1893. 12°.
12902. aaa. 39.

FIEWEGER (　　) Unterrichtsbrief für das Selbst-
Studium der Verkehrssprache Dil.
Breslau, 1893, _etc._ 8°. 12991. ddd.

GUEL (　　) Internationale Verkehrssprache Dil.
Breslau, 1892. 8°. 12902. a.

MARIGNONI (D.) Esperanto, ossia la più pratica
delle lingue internazionali. pp. 75.
Crema, 1890. 8°. 12901. ccc. 13. (6.)

MEIER (L.) La Linguo internacia Esperanto.
pp. 68. _München,_ 1891. 8°. 12903. c. 51. (8.)

NIELSEN (C.) Lærebog til det internationale
Esperantosprog. pp. 71. _Flensborg,_ 1890. 8°.
12901. c. 45. (4.)

P.P. _Nuremberg._ La Esperantisto.
Nürnberg, 1889, _etc._ fol. 605

BERNHARD (S.) Welt-Italienisch Franca, Uni-
versalsprache. pp. 73. _Wien,_ 1891. 8°.
12901. ccc. 17. (4.)

GUARDIOLA (J.) Kosmal Idioma. pp. 96.
Paris, 1893. 8°. 12902. ccc. 34.

VOLAPÜK, etc.—Other Systems.—*cont.*

LOTT (J.) Un lingua internazional. Grammatika et vokabular pro angleses, germanes, romanes et pro kultivates de tut mond. pp. 298. *Leipz.* 1890. 8°. 12902. a. 27.

MILL (F.) Anti Volapük oder die Mezzofanti-Sprache. pp. 52. *Neuwied,* 1893. 8°.
12902. de. 1. (9.)

BRAAKMAN (J.) Gramatico del Mundolinco pro li de Hollando factore. pp. 19. *Noordwijk,* 1894. 8°. Pam 47.

BEERMANN (E.) *Oberlehrer zu Nordhausen.* Novilatiin. pp. 60. *Leipz.* 1895. 8°. Pam. 47.

STEINER (P.) Summary of the universal Language Pasilingua. pp. 36. *Darmstadt,* 1889. Pam. 47.

LEHMANN ( ) Pasilingua contra Volapük. pp. 15. *Neuwied,* 1887. 8°. Pam. 47.

BAUER (G.) Spelin-Wörterbuch, Vodobuk Spelinir. *Agram,* 1892. 8°. 12903. e. 26. (12.)

HEINTZELER (E.) Universala. Weltsprache auf Grund der romanischen Sprachen. pp. 76. *Stuttgart,* 1893. 8°. 12903. e. 29. (4.)

VOLCANOES. DANA (J. D.) Characteristics of Volcanoes. pp. 399. *Lond.* 1890. 8°.
07109. k. 17.

GOOCH (A. E.) On the Causes of volcanic Action. pp. 20. *Lond.* 1890. 8°. Pam. 27.

HULL (E.) Volcanoes: past and present. pp. 270. 1892. 8°. ELLIS (H. H.) Contemporary Science Series. 8709. i.

LOBLEY (J. L.) On the Causes of volcanic Action. pp. 12. 1888. 8°. Pam. 27.

LONGRAIRE (L. de) Séismes et Volcans. 1894. 8°. Ac. Paris. *Société des Ingénieurs.* Mémoires. Sér. 5. Ann. 47. Ac. 4305.

HUPFER (P.) Die Regionen am Ätna. 1895. 8°. Ac. Leipsic. *Verein für Erdkunde.* Wissenschaftliche Veröffentlichungen. Bd. 2.
Ac. 6056/2.

SILVESTRI (A.) L' Eruzione dell' Etna del 1886. pp. 36. 1893. 4°. Ac. Catania. *Accademia Gioenia.* Atti. Anno 70. Ac. 2805.

JOHNSTRUP (J. F.) Om de vulkanske Udbrud i den nordøstlige Del af Island. 1890. 8°. Ac. Copenhagen. *Naturhistoriske Forening.* Festskrift. Ac. 2969.

THORODDSEN (T.) Vulkaner i det nordöstlige Island. pp. 71. 1888. 8°. Ac. Stockholm. *K. Svenska Vetenskaps Academien.* Bihang till Handlingar. Bd. 14. Ac. 1070/7.

SANDICK (R. A. v.) In het Rijk van Vulcaan. De uitbarsting van Krakatau. pp. 195. *Zutphen,* 1890 8°. 07109. h. 14.

WHARTON (J.) Dust from the Krakatoa Eruption of 1883. pp. 3. *Phila.* 1894. 8°. Pam. 27.

IDDINGS (J. P.) On a group of volcanic rocks from the Tewan Mountains, New Mexico. pp. 34. 1890. 8°. U.S. *Geological Survey.* Bulletin. No. 66. 7109. cc.

DILLER (J. S.) A late volcanic Eruption in Northern California. pp. 33. 1891. 8°. U.S. *Geological Survey.* Bulletin. No. 79. 1829. a. 7.

THOMAS (A. P. W.) Report on the eruption of Tarawera and Rotomahana, N.Z. pp. 74. *Wellington,* 1888. 8°. 07109. h. 16.

VOLUNTEERS. *See* ENGLAND, *Army.*

VORARLBERG. PRIESTER (C. A.) Kunstgeschichte von Vorarlberg. pp. 410. *Bozen,* 1885. fol. 7808. f. 13.

VORARLBERG—*continued.*

RAPP (L.) Topographisch-historische Beschreibung des Generalvikariates Vorarlberg. *Brixen,* 1892, *etc.* 8°. 10215. cc. 5.

SANDER (H.) Vorarlberg. Land und Leute. pp. 210. *Innsbruck,* 1891. 8°. 11528. bbb. 60.

—— Vorarlberg zur Zeit des deutschen Bauernkriegs. 1893. 8°. Ac. Vienna. *Universitas.* Mittheilungen des Instituts für oesterreichische Geschichtsforschung. Ergänzungsband 4. Ac. 803.

WINDER (E.) Die vorarlberger Dialectdichtung. pp. 172. *Innsbruck,* 1890. 8°. 011824. i. 6.
See also TYROL.

VOSGES, Mountains and Department.

CONTY (H. A. de) Les Vosges en poche. pp. 284. *Paris,* 1894. 12°. 10171. aa. 27.

EHRENBURG (F.) In die Vogesen! pp. 146. *Zürich,* 1890. 4°. 10256. i. 4.

FOURNIER (A.) Topographie ancienne du département des Vosges. 1894. 8°. Ac. Epinal. *Société d'Émulation.* Annales. Ann. 70.
Ac. 585.

FRAIPONT (G.) Les Vosges. pp. 426. *Paris,* 1895. 4°. 10172. i. 15.

JOUVE (L.) Biographie générale des Vosges. pp. 80. *Paris,* 1890. 12°. Pam. 8.

PARISOT (V.) and HOUOT ( ) Vosges. pp. 80. *Paris,* 1893. 8°. 10172. aaa. 4.

THOULET (J.) Contribution à l'étude des lacs des Vosges. 1894. 8°. Ac. Paris. *Société de Géographie.* Bulletin. Sér. 7. Tom. 15. Ac. 6035.

WOLFF (H. W.) The Country of the Vosges. pp. 368. *Lond.* 1891. 8°. 10231. e. 7.

—— Watering-Places of the Vosges. pp. 155. *Lond.* 1891. 8°. 10169. e. 2.
See also ÉPINAL.

VOYAGES AND TRAVELS.

Bibliography.

Ac. London. *Royal Geographical Society.* Catalogue of the Library. pp. 833. *Lond.* 1895. 8°.
BB.I. c. 22.

General.

ADVENTURE. Adventure and Adventurers, tales of daring. pp. 288. *Lond.* 1895. 8°.
012330. g. 62.

BOLTON (S. K.) Famous voyagers and explorers. pp. 509. *Lond.* 1893. 8°. 10024. ccc. 5.

CAT (É.) Découvertes et explorations du XVI° au XIX° siècle. pp. 279. *Paris,* 1892. 8°.
10026. k. 15.

DRONSART (M.) Les grandes Voyageuses. pp. 436. *Paris,* 1894. 8°. 10025. g. 1.

FRITH (H.) The romance of Navigation. pp. 312. *Lond.* 1893. 8°. 10024. ccc. 4.

GREELY (A. W.) Explorers and travellers. pp. 373. 1894. 8°. Men of Achievement.
10601. df.

OBERLAENDER (R.) and THOMAS (L.) Opdagelsernes Bog. *Kjøbenh.* 1890, *etc.* 8°. 10025. cc.

Q. The Story of the Sea. *Lond.* 1895, *etc.* 8°.
8807. g.

Fourteenth to Eighteenth Centuries.

HAKLUYT (R.) Principal Navigations of the English Nation. 16 vol. *Edinb.* 1884-90. 8°.
10027. dd. 4.

GROSER (H. G.) Out with the old Voyagers. pp. 276. *Lond.* 1895. 8°. 010026. f. 1.

MANDEVILLE (*Sir* J.) The marvellous Adventures of Sir J. Maundevile. pp. 414. *Lond.* 1895. 8°. 10025. cc. 31.

BEAZLEY (C. R.) Prince Henry the Navigator. pp. 336. 1895. 8°. ABBOTT (E.) Heroes of the Nations, XVI. 10601. f.

VOYAGES.—14th to 18th Centuries — *continued.*

PEREIRA (F.) O Centenario do Infante D. Henrique. Livro commemorativo. pp. 373. *Porto*, 1894. 8°. 10632. g. 12.

WAUWERMANS (H. E.) Henri le Navigateur et l'Académie portugaise de Sagres. pp. 173. *Brux.* 1890. 8°. 10002. f. 10.

BETTENCOURT (E. A. de) Descobrimentos dos portuguezes nos seculos XV. e XVI. pp. 420. *Lisboa*, 1881–82. 4°. 1850. a. 6.

OLIVEIRA MARTINS (J. P.) Les Explorations des Portugais antérieures à la découverte de l'Amérique. pp. 33. *Paris*, 1893. 8°. 10026. k. 17.

BUSIRI-VICI (A.) I tre celebri Navigatori italiani del secolo decimosesto. pp. 68. *Roma*, 1892. fol. 10630. i. 9.

GUILLEMARD (F. H. H.) Life of F. Magellan and first circumnavigation of the Globe. pp. 353. 1891. 8°. KELTIE (J. S.) World's great Explorers. 10024. cc.

POPE (J.) J. Cartier, his life and voyages. pp. 168. *Ottawa*, 1890. 8°. 010661. e. 54.

VESPUCCI (A.) The Voyage from Lisbon to India 1505–6. pp. 55. *Lond.* 1894. 4°. 10058. ccc. 5.

MENDES PINTO (F.) Voyages of F. Mendez Pinto. pp. 464. 1891. 8°. Adventure Series. 012207. k.

Ac. London. *Hakluyt Society.* SARMIENTO DE GAMBOA (P.) Narratives of the voyage of P. Sarmiento de Gamboa to the Straits of Magellan. pp. 401. *Lond.* 1895. 8°. Ac. 6172/72.

COOK (J.) Cook's Voyages. 1892. 8°. GLAZE-BROOK (M. G.) English Classics for Schools. 12204. aaa.

—— Cook's Journal during his first voyage round the world. pp. 400. *Lond.* 1893. 8°. 10025. ee. 8.

For early Voyages to America, *see* AMERICA, *Discovery and early Voyages.*

Nineteenth Century.

Ac. London. *Royal Geographical Society of London.* Review of British Geographical Work, 1789–1889. pp. 257. *Lond.* 1893. 8°. BB.I. a. 11.

ARMAND (P.) Voyages classés par parties du monde. 1892. 8°. Ac. Marseilles. *Société de Géographie.* Bulletin. Tom. 16. Ac. 6031.

FAURE (C.) Exposé des Voyages des Suisses dans le XIXᵉ siècle. pp. 47. *Paris*, 1891. 8°. 10025. ee. 7.

MEISSAS (G.) Les grands Voyageurs de notre siècle. pp. 797. *Paris*, 1889. 4°. 10025. f. 7.

MONTEFIORE (A.) Leaders into unknown Lands. pp. 320. *Lond.* 1891. 8°. 10024. c. 27.

ARNOLD (*Sir* E.) Wandering Words. pp. 372. *Lond.* 1894. 8°. 012357. k. 21.

ATCHISON (C. C.) A Winter Cruise in summer seas. pp. 369. *Lond.* 1891. 8°. 10026. i. 17.

AUBERTIN (J. J.) Wanderings and Wonderings. pp. 448. *Lond.* 1892. 8°. 10025. dc. 2.

BESSLER (C.) Meine Reise um die Erde. pp. 295. *Langensalza*, 1892. 8°. 10026. i. 19.

BISLAND (E.) A flying trip around the world. pp. 203. *Lond.* 1891. 8°. 10025. aa. 7.

BRASSEY (T.) *Baron Brassey.* Voyages and travels of Lord Brassey, 1862–94. 2 vol. *Lond.* 1895. 8°. 10024. ccc. 7.

BREWSTER (F. C.) From Independence Hall around the world. pp. 214. *Lond.* 1895. 8°. 10028. e. 12.

BROOKS (P.) *Bp. of Massachusetts.* Letters of Travel. pp. 386. *Lond.* 1893. 8°. 10027. d. 4.

VOYAGES.—19th Century—*continued.*

BUCKLEY (J. M.) Travels in three Continents. pp. 614. *N.Y.* 1895. 8°. 10025. eee. 2.

CHAPIN (J. H.) From Japan to Granada. pp. 325. *N.Y.* 1889. 8°. 10027. d. 2.

DEWAR (J. C.) Voyage of the "Nyanza," schooner yacht. pp. 466. *Edinb.* 1892. 8°. 10026. i. 1.

DEWAR (T. R.) A Ramble round the globe. pp. 316. *Lond.* 1894. 8°. 10025. cc. 28.

DUCKWORTH (J.) A Trip round the world. pp. 166. *Rochdale*, 1890. 8°. 10024. cc. 10.

DUNN (S. H.) The World's Highway. pp. 376. *Lond.* 1894. 8°. 10028. f. 21.

EVANS (A. C.) Cruise of H.M.S. "Calliope" in China, Australian and East African waters. pp. 156. *Portsmouth*, 1890. 8°. 10024. cc. 9.

FRISTEDT (C.) På Forskningsfärd. pp. 256. *Stockholm*, 1891. 8°. 10007. c. 41.

FYFE (G.) The Cruise of the "St. George," R.Y.S. pp. 233. *Wellington*, 1893. 8°. 10024. e. 27.

GERMANY. *Hydrographisches Bureau.* Die Forschungsreise S.M.S. "Gazelle" in den Jahren 1874 bis 1876. 4 Thle. *Berl.* 1889. fol. 1826. b. 12.

GLIMPSES. Glimpses of Life. A Lady's Search for work. pp. 201. *Lond.* 1894. 8°. 4747. d. 17.

GÓMEZ (J. A.) 1889. Impresiones de Viaje de un Chileno. pp. 296. *Valparaiso*, 1893. 8°. 10025. e. 6.

GORDON (E. A.) "Clear Round!" or, Seeds of story from other countries. pp. 442. *Lond.* 1893. 8°. 10024. aa. 26.

HACKS (C.) La Mer. À bord du Courrier de Chine. pp. 285. *Paris*, 1891. 12°. 10498. aa. 16.

HAMILTON (W) A Transatlantic Voyage. pp. 129. *Lond.* 1890. 8°. 10498. aa. 15.

HENSEN (V.) Ergebnisse der in dem Atlantischen Ocean ausgeführten Plankton-Expedition der Humboldt-Stiftung. *Kiel*, 1892, *etc.* 4°. 1826. b.

HILL (C.) A Trip round the World. pp. 115. *Lond.* 1890. 8°. 10025. cc. 24.

HIRSCHBERG (J.) Um die Erde. pp. 531. *Leipz.* 1894. 8°. 10027. g. 8.

JAGAT-JĪT SINGH, *Raja of Kapurthala.* My Travels in Europe and America. pp. 203. *Lond.* 1895. 4°. 10026. l. 16.

JOEST (W.) Welt-Fahrten. 3 Bde. *Berl.* 1895. 8°. 010026. i. 1.

KNIGHT (E. F.) The Cruise of the "Alerte." pp. 328. *Lond.* 1890. 8°. 10481. c. 26.

LAING (C. C.) The Log of the "Speranza," 100-ton yawl. pp. 112. *Lond.* 1889, 8°. 10105. dd. 6.

LANCKOROŃSKE (C.) *Count.* Rund um die Erde. pp. 513. *Stuttgart*, 189. 8°. 10026. i. 16.

LEVER (W. H.) Following the Flag. pp. 132. *Lond.* 1893. 8°. 10028. e. 30.

MOSELEY (H. N.) Notes by a Naturalist. pp. 540. *Lond.* 1892. 8°. 2352. e. 2.

MURDOCH (W. G. B.) From Edinburgh to the Antarctic. pp. 364. *Lond.* 1894. 8°. 10460. f. 29.

ODYSSEY. The Modern Odyssey. pp. 454. *Lond.* 1891. 8°. 10024. ccc. 1.

QUESNEL (É.) Souvenirs de voyage. pp. 301. *Rouen*, 1892. 8°. 10026. i. 18.

RAUM (G. E.) A Tour around the world. pp. 430. *N.Y.* 1895. 8°. 10024. b. 30.

ROBERTS (M.) Land-travel and sea-faring. pp. 259. *Lond.* 1891. 8°. 10491. ee. 25.

VOYAGES.—19th Century—*continued.*

ROBOTTOM (A.) Travels in search of new Trade Products. pp. 224. *Lond.* 1893. 8°.
10026. c. 6.

ROISSARD DE BELLET (E.) *Baron.* Journal de bord. pp. 280. *Paris,* 1881. 8°. 10498. c. 21.

ROPER (C.) Zigzag Travels. 3 vol.
Lond. 1895. 8°. 10025. de. 8.

ROUGET (P.) Voyage autour de la terre.
pp. 414. *Paris,* 1895. 12°. 10024. ccc. 8.

SAYCE (G. C.) Twelve Times round the world, *etc.* pp. 203. *Bristol,* 1892. 8°. 10026. c. 3.

SCOTT (C. W.) Pictures of the world. pp. 285.
Lond. 1894. 8°. 10024. aa. 28.

SEIGNEURIE (A.) Le Tour du monde d'un Épicier. pp. 478. *Paris,* 1889. 8°. 10025. de. 1.

SINCLAIR (T.) Travel Sketch. pp. 271.
Lond. 1891. 8°. 10025. cc. 22.

SLOCUM (J.) Voyage of the "Liberdade." pp. 158.
Bost. 1894. 8°. 10481. bb. 49.

STEPHENS (A. G.) Queenslander's Travel notes. pp. 197. *Sydney,* 1894. 8°. 10026. aaa. 11.

THOMPSON (F. D.) In the Track of the Sun.
pp. 226. *Lond.* 1893. 4°. 10028. g. 13.

TINSEAU (L. de) Du Hâvre à Marseille par l'Amérique et le Japon. pp. 331.
Paris, 1891. 12°. 10024. a. 9.

TISSANDIER (A.) Voyage autour du monde.
pp. 298. *Paris,* 1892. 4°. 10057. g. 6.

URE (J.) A Tour round the world. 2 pt.
Glasg. 1885. 8°. 10024. cc. 17.

WILDE (O. A. K.) Fra Sø og Land. pp. 327.
Københ. 1891. 8°. 10026. b. 10.

WORLD. Round the World. 12 pt.
Lond. 1895. *obl.* fol. 1787. aa. 31.

General Guides, etc. for Travellers.

Ac. London. *Royal Geographical Society.* Hints to Travellers. pp. 500. *Lond.* 1893. 8°.
2352. a. 28.

EUROPE. Useful notes for Travellers in Europe.
pp. 61. *N.Y.* 1891. 16°. Pam. 91.

HIGGINS (F. C.) America abroad. Handbook. 1892, *etc.* 8°. BUREAU. American Press Bureau handbooks. 10024. a.

INTERNATIONAL ALBUM GUIDE. International Album-Guide, illustrated. *Lond.* 1890, *etc.* 4°.
10105. h. 6.

LONDON. *Association for the promotion of Travel.* Glimpses abroad. pp. 53.
Lond. 1893. 8°. 10106. ccc. 31.

For Travels in each continent or country, *see* under the name required.

VULCANITE. *See* INDIA RUBBER.

VULCI. Ac. Rome. *École française.* Fouilles dans la Nécropole de Vulci. pp. 576.
Paris, 1891. fol. Ac. 5233/4.

WAGAP LANGUAGE.
See NEW CALEDONIA.

WAGES. *See* CAPITAL AND LABOUR: READY RECKONERS: TABLES.

WAKEFIELD. PEACOCK (M. H.) History of the Grammar School. pp. 255.
Wakefield, 1892. 8°. 8364. e. 43.

WALDENSES. ALBERT (A.) Les Vaudois de la Vallonise. pp. 97. *Grenoble,* 1891. 8°.
Pam. 29.

CHEVALIER (J.) Mémoire sur les hérésies en Dauphiné avant le xvie siècle; documents inédits sur les Vaudois. pp. 164.
Valence, 1890. 4°. 4629. i. 13.

WALDENSES—*continued.*

COMBA (E.) Storia de' Valdesi. pp. 427.
Torino, 1893. 8°. 4606. aa. 16.

MUGNIER (F) Souvenir de la traversée des Alpes par les Vaudois, 1689. pp. 31.
Chambéry. 1890. 8°. 4629. bbb. 17. (4.)

MEILLE (W.) Le Réveil de 1825 dans les vallées vaudoises du Piémont. pp. 105. *Turin,* 1893. 8°.
4605. aaa. 24.

COCORDA (O.) La Vérité sur le Réveil dissident ; à propos de l'opuscule de W. Meille. pp. 110.
Pignerol, 1894. 8°. 3900. ccc. 6.

WALDENSES. Sunto delle feste del bicentenario del Rimpatrio dei Valdesi e resoconoto del Sinodo del 1889. pp. 72. 125. *Torre Pellice,* 1889. 8°.
4606. e. 14.

——— Rapporto del consiglio di Chiesa all' Assemblea Generale, 1890, pp. 8.
Firenze, 1890. 8°. 3900. g. 12. (6.)

——— Relazione del consiglio della Scuola di Teologia al Sinode, 1890. No. 13.
Firenze, 1890. 8°. 3900. i. 18. (4.)

WALES. For works relating to the United Kingdom, *see* ENGLAND.

Antiquities, History, etc.

DE COSTA (B. F.) Pre-Columbian voyages of the Welsh to America. pp. 12. *Albany,* 1891. 8°.
Pam. 28.

OWEN (R.) The Kymry ; origin, history, *etc.*
pp. 296. *Carmarthen,* 1892. 8°. 10007. i. 6.

SEEBOHM (F.) The Tribal System in Wales.
pp. 238. 111. *Lond.* 1895. 8°. 8276. ee. 66.

STOKES (G. T.) Island Monasteries of Wales, *etc.* 1891. 8°. 4705. e. 34. (2.)

EDWARDS (O. M) Hanes Cymru i ysgolion, *etc.*
Caernarfon, 1895, *etc.* 8°. 9508. aa. 3.

P.P. *Cardiff.* Cymru Fu : notes and queries relating to Wales and the border counties. Vol. 1 Vol. 2, pt. 1. *Cardiff,* 1888, 90. 8°.
PP. 6195. f.

——— *Wrexham.* Wales. A national magazine.
Wrexham, 1894, *etc.* 8°. P.P. 6194. g.

SOUTHALL (J. E.) Wales and her Language, from a historical standpoint. pp. 396.
Newport, 1892. 8°. 2274. c. 24.

TREVELYAN (M.) The Land of Arthur. pp. 436.
Lond. 1895. 8°. 9508. aaa. 2.

WALES. The story of Wales. pp. 223. 1895. 8°. Arnold's School series. 012200. gg.

PAGET (C.) *Lady.* The Northmen in Wales.
pp. 16. *Camb.* 1891. 8°. 7702. de. 10. (5.)

NEVINS (J. B.) Pictures of Wales during the Tudor period. pp. 89. *Liverp.* 1893. 8°.
9510. f. 12.

WILLIAMS (W. R.) Parliamentary history of Wales, 1541–1895. pp. 209. *Brecknock,* 1895. 4°.
9508. dd. 2.

BREESE (C. E.) Welsh Nationality. pp. 58.
Carnarvon, 1895. 8°. 8139. aaa. 50.

HOWELL (D.) Welsh Nationality. An address.
pp. 16. *Liverp.* 1892. 8°. Pam. 68.

P.P. *Aberystwyth.* Young Wales.
Aberystwyth, 1895, *etc.* 8°. P.P. 6194. i. and 437.

Coal Mines. *See* COAL.

Ecclesiastical History: Church of England and Nonconformists.

NEWELL (E. J.) History of the Welsh Church to the dissolution of the monasteries. pp. 435.
Lond. 1895. 8°. 4705. e. 6.

NYE (G. H. F.) Story of the Church in Wales.
pp. 78. *Lond.* 1893. 8°. 4109. c. 27.

ARMYTAGE (N. G.) The Church in Wales. Sermon. pp. 12. *Lond.* 1893. 8°. Pam. 92.

WALES.—Ecclesiastical History, etc.— *continued.*

BALFOUR (*Right Hon.* A. J.) The Church in Wales. Speech. pp. 12. 1892. 8°. ENGLAND. *Church Defence Institution.* Church Defence Handy Volume. 4109. c. 21.

BENSON (E. W.) *Archbp. of Canterbury.* The Church in Wales. Speech. pp. 8. *Lond.* 1891. 8°. Pam. 92.

—— To the Diocese of Canterbury on the Welsh Disestablishment Bill. *Canterbury,* 1894. fol. 1889. d. 3. (312.)

BEVAN (W. L.) Essays on the past and present of the Church in Wales. 2 pt. *Hay,* 1881. 8°. 4109. d. 2.

—— The church revival in Wales. pp. 24. 1891. 8°. ENGLAND. *Church Defence Institution.* Church Defence Handy Volume. 4109. c. 21.

—— The Church in the South Wales coal-field. pp. 14. *Lond.* 1894. 8°. Pam. 92.

BREESE (C. E.) Welsh religious equality : arguments in favour of Disestablishment. pp. 29. *Portmadoc,* 1892. 8°. Pam. 92.

CUTTS (E. L.) The case of the Welsh Church. pp. 24. *Lond.* 1893. 8°. 4429. c. 21. (6.)

EDWARDS (A. G.) *Bp. of St. Asaph.* The truth about the Church in Wales. pp. 20. *Lond.* 1889. 8°. 4109. c. 16. (6.)

—— Handbook on Welsh Church defence. pp. 81. *Lond.* 1895. 8°. 4109. aaaa. 18.

G. B. & I. *Commons, House of.* The Church in Wales. Report of debate on Mr. S. Smith's resolution. Feb. 23, 1892. pp. 92. *Lond.* 1892. 8°. Pam. 92.

JONES (D.) The Welsh Church and Welsh nationality. pp. 117. *Lond.* 1893. 8°. 4109. aaa. 58.

LLOYD (D. L.) *Bp. of Bangor.* The Church in Wales and the Welsh people. 1895. 8°.

TEMPLE (F.) *Bp. of London.* Lectures on Disendowment, etc. 4430. aaa. 11.

MORGAN (J.) Four biographical sketches. With a chapter on " The Church in Wales." pp. 206. *Lond.* 1892. 8°. 4903. c. 96.

NEVINS (J. B.) What the Welsh Nation owes to the Welsh Church. pp. 36. *Liverpool,* 1894. 8°. 4109. k. 12. (13)

OWEN (J.) The Church revival in Wales. pp. 12. 1891. 8°. ENGLAND, *Church Defence Institution.* Church Defence Handy Volume. 4109. c. 21.

PROTHERO (R. E.) The Anti-tithe agitation in Wales. pp. 34. *Lond.* 1889. 8°. 4109. c. 16. (8.)

SCRIBE. The Welsh Pulpit : notes and opinions. pp 156. *Lond.* 1894. 8°. 4136. b. 37.

SLATER (J. H.) The Established Church in Wales. pp. 113. *Lond.* 1893. 8°. 4109. bb. 25.

THOMAS (W.) The Anti-tithe movement in Wales. pp. 111. *Whitland,* 1891. 8°. 4109. b. 24.

THOMAS (W. C.) The Church in Wales. pp. 16. *Birmingham,* 1893. 8°. 4109. aaaa. 21. (11.)

WALES. The Truth told ; what the Church and Nonconformity are in Wales to-day. pp. 20. *Lond.* 1894. 8°. 4109. k. 12. (14.)

Eisteddfod Association.

WALES. *National Eisteddfod Association.* Cofnodion a chyfansoddiadau buddugol. Transactions of the Eisteddfod. *Liverpool,* 1887, *etc.* 8°. 11595. i.

—— Eisteddfod, 1888. Official list of subjects, prizes, *etc.* pp. 16. *Wrexham,* 1887. 8°. Pam. 18.

WALES.—Eisteddfod Association—*cont.*

WALES. Eisteddfod, 1891. Rhaglen Swyddogol. Official programme. pp. 64. *Swansea,* 1891. 8°. 011824. h. 24.

STUART (J. P. C.) *Marquess of Bute.* National Eisteddfod. Address by the Marquess of Bute, 1892. pp. 21. *Llanelwy,* 1892. 4°. Pam. 15.

Language and Literature.
See WELSH LANGUAGE.

Local Government. *See* LOCAL GOVERNMENT.

Topography.

BADDELEY (M. J. B.) and WARD (C. S.) North Wales. 2 pt. 1895. 8°. Thorough Guide Series. No. 8, 9. 10347. aaa.

BAEDEKER (C.) Great Britain. pp. 547. *Leipsic,* 1894. 8°. 2352. a.

BEVAN (G. P.) Geography of England and Wales. pp. 248. *Lond.* 1893. 8°. 10347. c. 35.

BLACK (A.) and (C.) Guide to South-Wales. pp. 204. *Edinb.* 1889. 8°. 10369. aaa. 45.

G. B. & I. Round the coast. Photographs. *Lond.* 1895, *etc. obl.* fol. 1558.

HALL (M.) Notes on the Geography of the British Isles. pp. 110. *Dublin,* 1895. 8°. 10348. b. 27.

HARPER (C. G.) The Marches of Wales. pp. 368. *Lond.* 1894. 8°. 010358. h. 22.

HARTLEY (C. A.) Coaching guide to North Wales. pp. 43. *Llandudno,* 1894. 8°. 10348. c. 26. (6.)

KILNER (E. A.) Four Welsh counties. pp. 266. *Lond.* 1891. 8°. 10369. cc. 44.

LOVETT (R.) Welsh Pictures with pen and pencil. pp. 192. *Lond.* 1892. 8°. 10369. l. 13.

MAHÉ DE LA BOURDONNAIS (A.) *Count.* Voyage dans le Pays de Galles. pp. 248. *Paris,* 1894. 8°. 10368. f. 42.

ROBERTS (A.) Gossiping guide to Wales. pp. 318. *Lond.* 1895. 8. 2366. b. 4.

ROSS (M.) and SOMERVILLE (E. Œ.) Beggars on Horseback. Riding tour in N. Wales. pp. 186. *Edinb.* 1895. 8°. 10369. ccc. 34.

STATHAM (H. H.) Cathedrals of England and Wales. pp. 79. *Lond.* 1894. fol K.T.C. 16. a. 2.

TREVELYAN (M.) Glimpses of Welsh life and character. pp. 406. *Lond.* 1894. 8°. 012330. g. 51.

TURNER (G. W.) Picturesque Wales. pp. 110. *Lond.* 1891. 8°. 10369. bbb. 42.

WALES. Where to stay and what to see in Wales. pp. 32. *Lond.* 1893. 8°. 10347. d. 7. (11).

WHERE. Where shall we go? Guide to Watering-places of England, *etc.* pp. 348. *Lond.* 1892. 8°. 10347. c. 33.

WORRALL (J.) Tourists' guide for N. Wales. pp. 40. *Oldham,* 1890. 4°. 10369. l. 8.
See also ENGLAND.

WALGRAVE. WICKS (W. A.) History of the Baptist Church, Walgrave. pp. 78. *Northampton,* 1892. 8°. 4715. cc. 17.

WALLOONS. GITTÉE (A.) and LEMOINE (J.) Contes populaires du Pays wallon. pp. 176. *Gand,* 1891. 8°. 12430. h. 44.

LAPAILLE (R.) Flamands et Wallons à l'école primaire. pp. 70. *Liège,* 1894. 8°. Pam. 17.

LEURIDAN (T.) Le clergé de la Flandre-Wallonne pendant la Révolution. 1890. 8°. Ac. *Roubaix. Société d'Émulation.* Mémoires. Sér. 2. Tom. 5. Ac. 520.

MONSEUR (E.) Le Folklore wallon. pp. 144. *Brux.* 1892. 12°. 12431. cc. 23.

WALLOONS—*continued.*

WILMOTTE (M.) Le Wallon. Histoire et littérature. pp. 159. *Brux.* 1893. 8°. 10271. bb. 24.

ZÉLIQZON (L.) Aus der Wallonie. pp. 28. *Metz,* 1893. 4°. 12902. h. 19. (4.)

DEFRECHEUX (C.) Anthologie des Poètes wallons. *Liège,* 1889, *etc.* 8°. 11498. i.

DEFRECHEUX (J. N. J.) Vocabulaire de noms wallons d'animaux. pp. 200. *Liège,* 1890. 8°. 12953. cc. 13.

TROMPE-LA-MORT. Écrin de Poésies wallonnes. pp. 31. *Couillet,* 1890. 8°. Pam. 59.

BOURLIER (E.) Souvenir du troisième centenaire de l'église wallonne de La Haye. pp. 105. *La Haye,* 1891. 8°. 4685. g. 15.

LACHERET (E.) La Liturgie wallonne. pp. 132. *La Haye,* 1890. 4°. 3478. g. 14.

P.P. *Leyden.* Le Refuge. Journal des Églises wallonnes des Pays Bas. *Leyde,* 1893, *etc.* fol. 672.

WALMER. GIRAUD (E. F.) Guide to Deal and Walmer. pp. 64. *Deal,* 1891. 8°. Pam. 90.

WALSALL. MATTHEW, *Saint, Church of, at Walsall.* Transcript of the first Register Book, 1570-1649. pp. 300. *Walsall,* 1890. 8°. 9905. dd. 22.

WAR, Laws of.
See LAW, *International* and *Military.*

WAR, Science of. *See* MILITARY SCIENCE.

WAR AND PEACE. ARAGON (J. de) Estudio sobre la guerra. *Bilbao,* 1889, *etc.* 8°. 8425. c. 68.

ARNOLDSON (K. P.) Pax Mundi; account of the progress of the movement for peace. pp. 168. *Lond.* 1892. 8°. 8425. bbb. 39.

BARNIER (L. A.) Compulsory service. *Wisbeach,* 1890. 8°. 8425. c. 70. (9.)

BERNARDOT (F.) La Paix et le désarmement. pp. 31. *Guise,* 1891. 8°. 8425. g. 23. (4.)

BILLARD (E.) Léon XIII. et le Désarmement. pp. 63. *Paris,* 1894. 8°. Pam. 67.

CARLSEN (W.) War as it is. pp. 105. *Lond.* 1892. 8°. 8425. b. 60.

CHERNUSHENKO (D. N.) Union de la Paix universelle. *Paris,* 1890. 4°. 1890. b. 3. (50.)

CORTIMIGLIA PISANI (G.) Les funestes effets de la Guerre. pp. 56. *Florence,* 1893. 8°. 8425. g. 23. (7.)

DEFOURNY (P. G.) Le Pape et la Paix. pp. 15. *Nevers,* 1889. 8°. 4825. c. 70. (8.)

—— La Conférence de Berlin et le militarisme. *Paris,* 1890. 4°. Pam. 67.

—— Le Militarisme et les impôts modernes. pp. 24. *Grenoble,* 1890. 8°. Pam. 67.

GIZYCKI (H. v.) Der Krieg. Ethische Betrachtungen. pp. 20. *Berl.* 1893. 8°. 8425. g. 23. (8.)

HAMON (A. F.) Psychologie du militaire professionnel. pp. 216. *Brux.* 1894. 8°. 8823. aaa. 51.

HARMENING (E.) Peace the Right of nations. pp. 59. *Breslau,* 1891. 8°. 8425. g. 23. (5.)

JAEHNS (M.) Ueber Krieg, Frieden und Kultur. pp 432. *Berl.* 1893. 8°. 12249. ccc. 1.

JANES (L. G.) War and progress. 1893. 8°. Ac. Brooklyn. *Ethical Association.* Evolution Series. No. 38. 7006. bbb.

KOTTIÉ (J. N. v.) Die Gefahren des Krieges und die Bedingungen des Friedens. pp. 62. *Graz,* 1890. 8°. 8026. i. 5. (6.)

KRIEG. Krieg, Friede und Erziehung. pp. 132. *Leipz.* 1891. 8°. 8425. f. 18.

WAR AND PEACE—*continued.*

LA GRASSERIE (R. de) Des moyens pour parvenir à la suppression de la Guerre. pp. 100. *Paris,* 1894. 8°. 8425. g. 25.

MARTIGNONI (G.) Il Militarismo e le sue funeste conseguenze. pp. 103. *Lugano,* 1894. 8°. 8823. g. 33.

MAZZOLENI (A.) L'Italia nel movimento per la Pace. pp. 73. *Milano,* 1891. 8°. Pam. 67.

MONTEITH (R.) Discours sur l'effusion du sang des hommes, *etc.* pp. 168. *Paris,* 1886. 8°. 8425. f. 14.

—— Discourse on the shedding of blood, *etc.* *Lond.* 1885. 8°. 8425. bb. 43.

NOVICOU (J.) La Guerre et ses prétendus bienfaits. pp. 198. *Paris,* 1894. 8°. 8425. de. 3.

PEACE CONGRESS. Proceedings of the Universal Peace Congress, 1890. pp. 249. *Lond.* 1891. 8°. 8425. i. 30.

—— Troisième Congrès de la paix. 1891. pp. 219. *Rome,* 1892. 8°. Ac. 2297.

CAPPER (S. J.) Il Congresso per la pace. 1891. Notes. pp. 15. *Rome,* 1891. 8°. 8408. h. 34. (3.)

RAMBUSCH (E. J. C.) Folkevæbning og Militarisme. pp. 88. *Kjøbenh.* 1891. 8°. 8831. l. 10. (14.)

RETORTILLO Y TORNOS (A.) Apuntes para un estudio sobre la guerra y la paz armada. pp. 174. *Madrid,* 1891. 8°. 8425. bb. 62.

RICHARD (H.) Defensive War. pp. 12. *Lond.* 1890. 8°. 8425. b. 62. (4.)

SPIRIT. The spirit of Militarism. *Wisbech,* 1890. *s. sh.* 8°. 1865. c. 3. (2.)

STATESMAN. Eternal Peace. Views of a Statesman. pp. 40. *San Francisco.* 1891. 8°. 8026. aaa. 14. (4.)

STELLA (S.) La Pace perpetua e l' esercito. pp. 42. *Torino,* 1891. 8°. 8026. ee. 24. (14.)

WILSON (J. J.) Construction and destruction; or, the devilry of War. pp. 14. *Birmingham,* 1891. 8°. 8425. c. 70. (10.)

WISBEACH. *Local Peace Association.* Peace and disarmament. 3 pt. *Lond.* 1895. 8°. Pam. 85.
See also EUROPE, *Politics.*

WARE. DAWES (C. E.) Records of Ware. pp. 79. *Hertford,* 1891. 8°. 10350. aa. 42.

WARD (B.) History of St. Edmund's College. pp. 344. *Lond.* 1893. 8°. 8364. f. 20.

WAR GAME. *See* KRIEGSPIEL.

WARNHAM. ANDRÉ (J. L.) and RICE (R. G.) Warnham in Sussex. pp. 67. *Lewis,* 1883. 8°. Pam. 90.

WARRINGTON. RYLANDS (W. H.) Booksellers and stationers in Warrington, 1639-57. 1888. 8°. Ac. Liverpool. *Historic Society.* Proceedings. Vol. 37. Ac. 8100.

WARWICK. RIVINGTON (T.) Warwick Castle, its history. pp. 55. *Warwick,* 1892. 8°. 10348. bbbb. 14. (6.)

WHITLEY (T. W.) Guide and history of the Town and Castle of Warwick. pp. 16. *Coventry,* 1892. 8°. 10348. c. 15. (4.)

WARWICKSHIRE. ANDREWS (W.) Bygone Warwickshire. pp. 284. *Hull,* 1893. 8°. 010358. i. 11.

BADGER (E. W.) Monumental brasses of Warwickshire. pp. 66. *Birmingham,* 1895. 8°. 7709. bb. 85.

BEVAN (G. P.) Tourist's guide to Warwickshire. pp. 121. *Lond.* 1894. 8°. 10352. aa. 67.

BURGESS (J. T.) Historic Warwickshire. pp. 304. *Birmingham,* 1892, 93. 8°. 10352. dd. 14.

WARWICKSHIRE—continued.

HANNETT (J.) The Forest of Arden. pp. 230.
Birmingham, 1894. 4°.   10352. k. 1.

MORLEY (G.) Sketches of leafy Warwickshire.
pp. 157. *Derby*, 1895. 4°.   10352. dd. 15.

TURNER (C. J. R.) Shakespeare's Land.
pp. 416. *Leamington*, 1893. 8°. K.T.C. 8. a. 9.

WALFORD (E. A.) Making of the Dassett and
Edge Hills. 1895. 8°.   07108. ee. 1. (11.)

WILLIAMS (J. L.) Home and haunts of Shakespeare. 5 sections. *Lond.* 1892. fol.
               K.T.C. 2. a. 7.

WASHING, CALDER (F. L.) Teacher's
manual of Laundry work. pp. 83.
Lond. 1894. 8°.   7942. aaa. 54.

LAUNDRY MANAGEMENT. Laundry management.
pp. 187. *Lond.* 1893. 8°.   07944. e. 16.

LAUNDRY WRINKLES. Laundry wrinkles for
house and factory. pp. 77. *Lond.* 1893. 8°.
            07945. m. 22.

LORD (E.) Theory and practice of Laundry
work. pp. 62. *Lond.* 1894. 8°.   07944. ee. 9.

MACNAUGHTON (M.) Laundry Work. pp. 30.
Liverp. 1895. 8°.   Pam. 94.

P.P. *London.* National Laundry record.
Lond. 1891, *etc.* 4°.   N.R.

RIS-PAQUOT (O. E.) La Vêtement. pp. 122.
Paris, 1893. 8°.   7743. bb. 60.

SMITH (L. E.) Home Washing. pp. 106.
Lond. 1890. 8°.   07945. e. 44.

RUSHTON (M.) Hints on Laundry work. pp. 30.
Lond. 1893. 8°.   Pam. 94.

WASHING. Washing, Cleaning and removing
stains. pp. 104. *Lond.* 1893. 8°. 7942. de. 21.

WASHINGTON, City. THATCHER (E.)
Founding of Washington City. pp. 256.
Washington, 1891. 8°.   10412. dd. 19.

WEBB (W. B.) and WOOLDRIDGE (J.) Centennial
history of the city of Washington. pp. 770.
Dayton, Ohio, 1892. 8°   10412. i. 12.

WASHINGTON, Mount. *See* WHITE
MOUNTAINS.

WASHINGTON, State.

EVANS (E.) and MEANY (E. S.) The State of
Washington. pp. 224. *Tacoma*, 1893. 8°.
            10412. c. 35.

HESTWOOD (J. O.) The Evergreen State
souvenir. pp. 72. *Chicago*, 1893. 8°. 10412. c. 23.

TACOMA. The New North-west. pp. 31.
Tacoma, 1890. 8°.   16460. e. 37. (3.)

VICTOR (F. A.) Atlantis arisen; talks about
Washington. pp. 412. *Phila.* 1891. 8°.
            10413. g. 19.

WASPS. JANET (C.) Études sur les guêpes,
etc. pp. 26. *Limoges*, 1895. 8°.   Pam. 42.

—— Sur les nids de la Vespa crabro. pp. 4.
Paris, 1894. 4°.   Pam. 42.

—— Sur la Vespa crabro. Conservation de la
chaleur dans le nid. pp. 3. *Paris*, 1895. 4°.
            Pam. 42.

WASTE, Law of. BEWES (W. A.) The Law
of Waste. pp. 450. *Lond.* 1894. 8°. 6325. ee. 1.

WASUNGEN. REICHARDT (E.) Die was-
unger Mundart. 1895, *etc.* 8°. Ac. Meiningen.
Verein für meiningische Geschichte. Schriften.
Hft. 17.   Ac. 7114.

WATCHES AND CLOCKS. BILFINGER
(G.) Die mittelalterlichen Horen und die
modernen Stunden. pp. 279.
Stuttgart, 1892. 8°.   8561. cc. 36.

BOHMEYER (C.) Anleitung zur Aufstellung
elektrischer Uhren. pp. 94.
Hanau, 1892 8°.   8757. f. 29.

WATCHES AND CLOCKS—continued.

BRITTEN (F. J.) Former Clock and Watch-
makers. pp. 397. *Lond.* 1894. 8°. 07944. f. 9.

—— Watch and Clockmakers' handbook.
pp. 443. *Lond.* 1892. 8°.   8767. c. 37.

CASPARI (É.) Les Chronomètres de marine.
pp. 203.   1894. 8°.   Encyclopédie des aide-
mémoire.   8709. g.

DRACH (C. A. v.) Die Globusuhr Wilhelms IV.
von Hessen. pp. 24. *Marburg*, 1894. 4°.
            8560. i. 25.

FAVARGER (A.) L'Électricité et ses applications
à la chronométrie. pp. 198. *Genève*, 1892. 8°.
            8757. dd. 21.

FRITTS (C. E.) Watch Adjuster's manual.
pp. 364. *Lond.* 1894. 8°.   8768. c. 33.

GARUFFA (E.) Orologeria moderna. pp. 302.
Milano, 1894. 8°.   012200. i. 1.

GELCICH (E.) Die Uhrmacherkunst und die
Behandlung der Präcisionsuhren. pp. 640.
Wien, 1892. 8°.   8768. l. 18.

—— and DIETZSCHOLD (C.) Die Tabellen der
Uhrmacherkunst. pp. 231. *Wien*, 1892. 8°.
            8548. e. 30.

HAVARD (H.) L'Horlogerie. pp. 182.
Paris, 1893. 8°.   7942. f.

KENDAL (J. F.) History of Watches and other
time-keepers. pp. 247. *Lond.* 1892. 8°.
            8767. f. 19.

KUEHL (W. H.) Führer durch die gesammte
Uhrmacher-Litteratur. pp. 30.
Berl. 1892. 8°.   011900. f. 8. (16.)

MAYETTE (J.) De la Mesure du temps et du
réglage des montres. 1890. 8°. Ac. Lyons.
Société d'Agriculture. Annales. Sér. 6. Tom. 2.
            Ac. 362/3.

SANDOZ (C.) Origine et développement de l'industrie horlogère à Besançon. pp. 67.
Besançon, 1893. 8°.   Pam. 94.

SAUNIER (C.) Watchmaker's handbook. pp. 498.
Lond. 1891. 8°.   2266. ua. 16.

TOBLER (A.) L'Horlogerie électrique. pp. 152.
Paris, 1891. 8°.   8757. b. 13.

TRIPPLIN (J.) Watch and Clock making in
1889. pp. 142. *Lond.* 1890. 8°. 8768. bbb. 35.

WATER.

General: Analysis: Purification, etc.

KIRCHNER (O.) Die mikroskopische Pflanzen-
und Thierwelt des Süsswassers.
Braunschweig, 1891, *etc.* 4°.   7054. g. 15.

FITZGERALD (D.) The temperature of Lakes, *etc.*
1895. 8°.   8757. d. 41.

REGNARD (P.) Recherches sur les conditions
physiques de la vie dans les eaux. pp. 500.
Paris, 1891. 8°.   7290. f. 23.

ZACHARIAS (O.) Die Tier- und Pflanzenwelt des
Süsswassers. *Leipz.* 1891, *etc.* 8°. 7054. f. 23.

AIKMAN (C. M.) Air and Water. pp. 128.
1895. 12°. Manuals of Health.   7404. a.

ATKINS (W. G.) Modern system of Water
Purification. pp. 181. *Lond.* 1894. 8°.
            8777. b. 51.

BLAIR (J. A.) Organic analysis of potable
Waters. pp. 120. *Lond.* 1891. 8°. 8777. aaa. 24.

COLET (H.) Water Softening and purification.
pp. 168. *Lond.* 1895. 8°.   8777. aaa. 42.

DELHOTEL (E.) Traité de l'épuration des eaux.
pp. 441. *Paris*, 1893. 8°.   8777. g. 5.

DEVONSHIRE (E.) Water purification by means
of iron in Anderson's purifier. pp. 70.
Lond. 1888. 8°.   8777. b. 43.

FRANKLAND (P. F.) and (G. C.) Micro-organisms
in Water. pp. 532. *Lond.* 1894. 8°. 8777. g. 10.

WATER.—General, etc.—*continued*.

GUICHARD (P.) L'Eau dans l'industrie. pp. 417. *Paris*, 1894. 12°.   8777. aaa. 40.

JURISCH (C. W.) Die Verunreinigung der Gewässer. pp. 117. *Berl.* 1890. 8°.   8777. h. 19.

NORMANDY (A.) Treble Distillation. pp. 21. *Lond.* 1893. 8°.   07945. h. 38.

—— Quadruple Distillation. pp. 21. *Lond.* 1893. 8°.   07945. h. 37.

ROUX (G.) Précis d'Analyse microbiologique des eaux. pp. 404. *Paris*, 1892. 8°. 8777. aaa. 27.

SAUNDERS (W. S.) Report on analysis of Water from the artesian well in Stoney Lane, Houndsditch. pp. 12. *Lond.* 1891. 8°.   8777. bbb. 24. (4.)

SYSTEM. Modern system of Water purification. pp. 64. *Lond.* 1891. 8°.   8777. bbb. 24. (5.)

See also infra: Water Supply.

Engineering.

See infra: Water Supply: CANALS: ENGINEERING: HYDRAULICS.

Law of Waters and Water Supply.

PRAŽÁK (G.) Wasserrechtliche Competenzfragen erörtert auf Grund des österreichischen Rechtes. pp. 119. *Prag*, 1892. 8°.   5549. dd. 8.

PICARD (A.) Traité des eaux. Droit, *etc.* 4 tom. *Paris*, 1890. 8°.   5403. g. 7.

Water Supply: Waterworks.

BURTON (W. K.) Water supply of towns and construction of Waterworks. pp. 304. *Lond.* 1894. 8°.   8777. i. 7.

CROWTHER (F. J.) Provisional orders of the Board of Trade in reference to Water-undertakings. pp. 48. *Lond.* 1893. 8°.   6426. aaaa. 18.

GREENWELL (A.) and CURRY (W. T.) Rural Water supply. pp. 210. *Lond.* 1895. 8°.   8777. aaa. 41.

KENT (W. G.) The Water-Meter. pp. 122. *Lond.* 1892. 8°.   8777. bbb. 25.

SLAGG (C.) Water Engineering. pp. 309. *Lond.* 1895. 8°.   8776. aaaa. 25.

SMEATON (J.) Plumbing, Water supply, *etc.* pp. 236. *Lond.* 1893. 8°.   8777. b. 46.

TAYLOR (E. B.) and (G. M.) Water Pipe discharge diagrams. pp. 6. *Lond.* 1891. *obl.* 4°.   1802. a. 13.

TURNER (J. H. T.) and BRIGHTMORE (A. W.) Principles of Waterworks Engineering. pp. 429. *Lond.* 1893. 8°.   8777. g. 6.

WALKER (J.) Handbook on domestic hot-water fitting. pp. 32. *Liverp.* 1893. 8°. 8777. aaa. 34.

BARCLAY (T.) Future Water supply of Birmingham. pp. 48. *Birmingham*, 1892. 8°.   8776. a. 68.

FITZGERALD (D.) Description of Boston waterworks. pp. 42. *Bost.* 1895. 8°.   8776. ee. 44.

HALLETT (W. H.) The Brighton Waterworks. pp. 8. 1890. 8°.   8777. bbb. 24. (2.)

JACKSON (D. W.) Discussion on the Water supply of Chicago. pp. 138. *Chicago*, 1892. 8°.   8777. g. 11.

LABUGAMA. Trip to Labugama, source of the Colombo water supply. pp. 86. *Colombo*, 1891. 12°.   Pam. 88.

BEATSON (W. B.) Water supply of Eastbourne. pp. 12. *Eastbourne*, 1895. 8°.   Pam. 79.

MEYER (F. A.) Das Wasserwerk Hamburg's. pp. 36. *Hamb.* 1894. fol.   8776. h. 33.

ELWORTHY (T.) Hastings Water supply. pp. 8. *St. Leonards*, 1894. 8°.   Pam. 79.

WATER.—Water Supply—*continued*.

CRIPPS (H. L.) Position of the London Water Companies. pp. 134, 151. *Lond.* 1892. 8°.   6425. cc. 18.

ENGLAND AND WALES. *Local Government Board,* Metropolitan Water supply. Monthly Report on the condition of the Water. *Lond.* 1893, *etc.* fol.   8776. g.

KENT (W. G.) and (H. H.) The Water waste of London. pp. 21. *Lond.* 1892. 8°.   8777. bbb. 29. (3.)

LOBLEY (J. L.) Supply of Water to London. pp. 32. *Lond.* 1892. 8°.   Pam. 79.

LONDON. *County Council.* Water Supply enquiry. Engineer's reports. pp. 26. *Lond.* 1890. 8°.   N.R.

—— Water Supply enquiry. Preliminary report on the possibility of obtaining supply of water within the Thames basin. *Lond.* 1891. 8°.   8777. bbb. 24. (3.)

MONCKTON (C.) Pure Spring Water supply for London. pp. 10. *Lond.* 1890. 4°.   Pam. 79.

RICHARDS (H. C.) and PAYNE (W. H. C.) Metropolitan Water supply. pp. 122. *Lond.* 1891. 8°.   8777. b. 37.

WEBSTER (G.) Pure Spring Water supply for London. pp. 18. *Lond.* 1892. 4°. 8706. f. 23. (6.)

SPRINGTHORPE (J. W.) Contamination of our Water supply (Melbourne). *Melbourne*, 1893. 8°.   Pam. 79.

See also supra: Analysis: Law of Waters: HYDRAULICS.

Waterways. *See* CANALS: RIVERS.

WATERBURY. ANDERSON (J.) The Churches of Mattatuck. pp. 279. *New Haven*, 1892. 8°.   4745. aaa. 39.

WATERFORD, City and County. EGAN (P. M.) History and directory of Waterford. 2 pt. *Kilkenny*, 1893. 8°.   10390. bb. 45.

WATERING PLACES: HEALTH RESORTS, etc. A., J. D. Curiosities in Cures, experiences of a lady in search of health. pp. 68. *Lond.* 1895. 8°.   7462. bb. 49.

Ac. London. *Royal Med. and Chirurgical Society.* Climate and Baths of Great Britain. *Lond.* 1895, *etc.* 8°.   7462. g.

APPLETON (D.) Handbook of American Winter resorts. pp. 168. *N.Y.* 1894. 8°. 10413. c. 45.

BRADSHAW (B.) Dictionary of Mineral Waters. pp. 438. *Lond.* 1895. 8°.   7462. a. 21.

BURDETT (H. C.) Helps in Sickness and to health. pp. 484. *Lond.* 1894. 8°. 7404. cc. 23.

CUTTER (C.) Guide to the Hot Springs of Arkansas. pp. 66. *St. Louis*, 1893. 8°. Pam. 86.

DARAPSKY (L.) Las Aguas minerales de Chile. pp. 193. *Valparaiso*, 1890. 8°.   7461. i. 2.

DUTT (A. C.) Health notes for the Seaside. pp. 61. *Whitby*, 1895. 16°.   Pam. 39.

DUTTON (T.) Sea-sickness. Voyaging for health. Health resorts. pp. 125. *Lond.* 1892. 8°.   7620. de. 20.

EGASSE (E.) and GUYENOT ( ) Eaux minérales de France et de l'Algérie. pp. 564. *Paris*, 1892. 8°.   7462. ee. 42.

G. B. & I. Inland Watering places. pp. 29. 211. *Lond.* 1891. 8°.   7470. aaa. 2.

—— Guide to Summer resorts. pp. 96. *Lond.* 1893. 8°.   10348 d. 20. (6.)

JACQUOT (E.) and WILLM (E.) Les Eaux minérales de la France. pp. 602. *Paris*, 1894. 8°.   7462. h. 1.

LAVIELLE (C.) Les stations de boues minérales d'Europe. pp. 127. *Paris*, 1892. 8°.   7470. e. 3.

3 L

WATERING PLACES—continued.

LAVIELLE (C.) Les Eaux chlorurées-sodiques d'Europe et d'Algérie. pp. 239. *Paris*, 1894. 8°.
7462. bb. 40.

LINN (T.) Health resorts of Europe. pp. 332. *Lond.* 1894. 8°.   7462. bb. 37.

—— Where to send patients for Water Cures, *etc.* pp. 44. *Lond.* 1894. 8°.   7462. bb. 36.

MONCRIEFF (A. R. H.) Where shall we go? Guide to Watering-places of England, Scotland, Ireland and Wales. pp. 348. *Lond.* 1892. 8°.
10347. c. 33.

—— Where to go Abroad. pp. 466. *Lond.* 1893. 8°.   10108. b. 12.

MUELLER (F. C.) Balneotherapie. pp. 452. *Leipz.* 1890. 8°.   7462. aa. 36.

PAUL (C.) Rapport sur le service médical des Eaux minérales. pp. 52. 1891. 4°. Ac. Paris. *Académie de Médecine.* Mémoires. Tom. 36. Fasc. 2.   Ac. 3725.

P.P. *London.* ABC Holiday Guide. *Lond.* 1892, *etc.* 8°.   P.P. 2497. fa.

—— The sunny corners of Homeland. *Lond.* 1893. 4°.   N.R.

SCHWEITZER (P.) Report on the Mineral Waters of Missouri. pp. 256. 1892. 8°. MISSOURI. *Geological Survey.* Reports. Vol. 3. 07109. l.

SEASIDE WATERING PLACES. Seaside Watering places. pp. 510. *Lond.* 1895. 8°.
10348. bb. 18.

VITRAS (A.) Medical Guide to Mineral Waters of France. pp. 352. *Lond.* 1892. 8°.
7462. aaa. 44.

WINTER RESORTS GUIDE. "Winter Resorts" guides. *Lond.* 1892, *etc.* 8°.   10025. aa.

ZEHENTER (J.) Die Mineralquellen Tirols. pp. 141. 1893. 8°. Ac. Innspruck. *Ferdinandeum.* Zeitschrift. Dritte Folge. Hft. 37.
Ac. 760.

See also AIX-LES-BAINS : ALPS, *Medical Works :* ANDABRE : BOHEMIA : BOURNEMOUTH : BUXTON : CALDIERO : CANARY ISLANDS : CANNES : CARLSBAD : CLIMATOLOGY : ENGADINE : HEUSTRICH : HYDROPATHY : MADEIRA : PAU : RIVIERA : SALZBRUNN : SWITZERLAND : TYROL : VICHY : WESTON-SUPER-MARE, *etc., etc.*

WATERLOO, Battle of. BERTEZÈNE (A.)

Waterloo. pp. 20. *Paris*, 1892. 8°.
9007. ff. 4. (11.)

DE PEYSTER (J. W.) Waterloo; campaign and battle. pp. 32. *N.Y.* 1893. 8°.
9078. gg. 22. (5.)

—— The Prussians in the campaign of Waterloo. pp. 21. *Lancaster, Pa.* 1894. 8°.   Pam. 28.

HORSBURGH (E. L. S.) Waterloo. pp. 312. *Lond.* 1895. 8°.   9080. bbb. 41.

HOUSSAYE (H.) 1815. pp. 636. *Paris*, 1893. 8°.   9226. b. 28.

HUELSEN (C.) Die Alliaschlacht. pp. 33. *Rom*, 1890. 8°.   9008. i. 18. (3.)

MORRIS (W. O'C.) Great Commanders and the campaign of 1815. pp. 364. *Lond.* 1891. 8°.
10604. g. 13.

NAVEZ (L.) Waterloo. pp. 54. *Bruz.* 1894. 8°.
9079. i. 24.

NETHERLANDS. Précis de la Campagne de 1815 dans les Pays-Bas. pp. 304. *Bruz.* 1887. 8°.
9080. ee. 8.

ROBERTS (F. S.) *Baron Roberts.* The Rise of Wellington. pp. 198. 1895. 8°. Pall Mall Magazine Library. Vol. 2.   012208. f.

ROPES (J. C.) Campaign of Waterloo. pp. 401. *Lond.* 1893. 8°.   9079. f. 3.

—— Atlas. 1893. 4°.   14000. h. 13.

WATERLOO.—Battle of—continued.

SIBORNE (H. T.) Waterloo Letters. pp. 415. *Lond.* 1891. 8°.   9079. bb. 36.

SIBORNE (W.) The Waterloo Campaign. pp. 832. 1894. 8°. ARBER (E.) War Library.
8832. bb. 1.

TOMKINSON (W.) Diary of a Cavalry Officer in the Waterloo campaigns. pp. 358. *Lond.* 1894. 8°.   9080. dd. 19.

VILLEMAIN (A. F.) Souvenirs des Cent Jours. pp. 188. *Lond.* 1892. 8°.   9226. aa. 12.

WOLSELEY (G. J.) *Viscount Wolseley.* Decline and fall of Napoleon. pp. 203. 1895. 8°. Pall Mall Magazine Library.   012208. f.
See also under the History of ENGLAND, EUROPE, and FRANCE.

WATER-MARKS. *See* PAPER.

WATFORD. WATFORD. Watford in 1891. pp. 62. *Brighton*, 1891. 4°.   10368. k. 39.

WATTLES. NEW SOUTH WALES. *Department of Public Instruction.* Wattles and wattlebarks. pp. 79. *Sydney*, 1891. 8°.   07076. k. 3.

WAX-WORKS. LE BRETON (G.) Essai sur la Sculpture en cire. pp. 61. *Rouen*, 1894. 8°.
7875. c. 20.

WAY, Rights of. *See* HIGHWAYS.

WEAPONS AND ARMOUR. Ac. Dresden. *Historisches Museum.* Katalog des Saales der mittelalterlichen Waffen. pp. 25. *Dresden*, 1893. 8°.   Pam. 3.

BOEHEIM (W.) Album Gegenstände aus der Waffensammlung des Kaiserhauses. pp. 28. *Wien*, 1894. 4°.   7705. i. 22.

BRETT (E. J.) Pictorial and descriptive Record of Arms and Armour. pp. 120. 8. *Lond.* 1894. 4°.   K.T.C. 24. b. 7.

CAMPBELL (*Lord* A.) Notes on Swords from Culloden. pp. 24. *Lond.* 1894. 8°.
8829. bbb. 47.

DEMMIN (A.) Die Kriegswaffen. pp. 1110. *Gera-Untermhaus*, 1891. 8°.   07708. g. 11.

—— Ergänzungsband für die vier Auflagen der Kriegswaffen. pp. 235. *Wiesbaden*, 1893. 8°.
7708. c. 41.

EGERTON (W.) Handbook of Indian Arms. pp. 162. *Lond.* 1880. 8°.   8824. i. 37.

FORRER (R.) Die Waffensammlung des Herrn Zschille. 2 vol. *Berl.* 1893. fol.   7701. k. 1.

HENDLEY (T. H.) Damascening on steel or iron, as practised in India. *Lond.* 1892. fol.
K.T.C. 9. h. 11.

MAINDRON (G. R. M.) Les Armes. pp. 343. *Paris*, 1890. 8°.   2261. c.

PARIS. *Musée d'Artillerie.* Catalogue des collections. *Paris*, 1889, *etc.* 8°.   8823. ddd. 1.
See also GUNNERY.

WEATHER AND WEATHER FORECASTS. *See* METEOROLOGY.

WEAVING. *See* TEXTILE FABRICS.

WEERT. GOOFERS (L.) Chroniek der stad Weert, 1784 tot 1802. 1888. 8°. Ac. Maestricht. *Société d'Archéologie.* Publications. N.S. Tom. 5.   Ac. 5500.

WEIGHTS AND MEASURES. SOUTZO (M. S.) Recherches sur les origines de quelques poids antiques. pp. 49. *Paris*, 1895. 8°.
07708. f. 45.

PERNICE (E.) Griechische Gewichte. pp. 215. *Berl.* 1894. 8°.   07708. i. 1.

MAUSS (C.) Le Rectangle de Khorsabad, at la théorie des mesures antiques. pp. 22. *Paris*, 1895. 8°.   Pam. 3.

WERDEN AN DER RUHR. JACOBS (P.) Geschichte der Pfarreien im Gebiete des Stiftes Werden. *Düsseldorf*, 1893, etc. 8°.   4662. f.

WERNIGERODE. Ac. Halle. *Historische Commission.* Urkundenbuch der Stadt Wernigerode bis 1460. pp. 604. 1891. 8°. Ac. *Saxony.* Geschichtsquellen. Vol. 25. Ac. 7161.

CUBE (M. v.) Die geschichtliche Entwickelung der stolbergischen Forsten zu Wernigerode. pp. 220. *Berl.* 1893. 8°.   7077. dd. 1.

WESLEYAN METHODISM. *See* METHODISM.

WESSOBRUNN. HAGER (G.) Die Bauthätigkeit im Kloster Wessobrunn. 1894. 8°. Ac. Munich. *Historischer Verein.* Oberbayerisches Archiv. Bd. 48.   Ac. 7121/2.

WESTERWALD. WESTERWALD. Führer durch den Westerwald. pp. 277. *Wiesbaden*, 1891. 8°.   10256. a. 17.

WEST GRINSTEAD. TRENQUALÉON (M. de) West-Grinstead et les Caryll. 2 vol. *Paris*, 1893. 8°.   4707. ee. 19.

WEST INDIES. BRONKHURST (H. V. P.) Geography of the West India Islands. pp. 140. *Demerara*, 1890. 8°.   10470. aa. 40.

BALLOU (M. M.) Equatorial America. pp. 371. *Bost.* 1892. 8°.   10480. bbb. 38.

CARIBBEE LEEWARD ISLANDS. Leeward Islands Magistrates acts. pp. 314. *Lond.* 1892. 8°.   06606. f. 12.

CASTONNET DES FOSSES (H.) Les petites Antilles françaises. pp. 43. *Angers*, 1890. 8°.   10480. df. 9. (4.)

EXQUEMELIN (A. O.) The Buccaneers of America. pp. 508. *Lond.* 1893. 8°.   9555. f. 8.

G. B. & I. *Hydrographic Office.* West India Pilot. *Lond.* 1893, etc. 8°.   10496. i. 23.

HEARN (L.) Midsummer trip to the West Indies. *Trinidad*, 1891. 8°.   Pam. 86.

INGHAM (E. G.) *Bp. of Sierra Leone.* The African in the West Indies. pp. 5. *Lond.* 1895. 8°.   Pam. 66.

LUCAS (C. P.) Historical Geography of the British Colonies. Vol. II. *Oxf.* 1894. 8°.   10004. dd. 2.

LE HIRBEC (D.) Voyages aux Antilles, 1642–44. pp. 92. *Laval*, 1890. 8°.   10028. g. 12.

LONDON. *British and West Indian Alliance.* Proceedings. *Lond.* 1893, etc. 8°.   8154. d.

OBER (F. A.) In the Wake of Columbus. pp. 515. *Bost.* 1893. 8°.   10480. dd. 30.

P.P. *Bridgetown*, Barbadoes. West Indian civil rights guardian. *Barbados*, 1891, etc. 8°.   P.P. 3699.

PHILLPOTTS (E.) In Sugar-cane Land. *Lond.* 1894. 8°.   10480. bb. 34.

PROVANCHER (L.) Une Excursion aux climats tropicaux. pp. 359. *Québec*, 1890. 8°.   10480. ee. 34.

STODDARD (C. A.) Cruising among the Caribbees. pp. 198. *Lond.* 1895. 8°.   10480. c. 33.

STUART (H. W. V.) Adventures amidst the equatorial forests and rivers of South America; also in the West Indies. pp. 268. *Lond.* 1891. 8°.   10481. i. 23.

See also ANTIGUA : BAHAMAS : BARBADOES : CAYMAN ISLANDS : CUBA : GRENADA : GUADELOUPE : HAYTI : JAMAICA : MARTINIQUE : MONTSERRAT : PUERTO RICO : SAINT VINCENT ; TRINIDAD.

WESTMEATH, County. WOODS (J.) Sketches of the County Westmeath. 2 vol. *Dublin*, 189 . 8°.   10390. e. 23.

WESTMINSTER AND WESTMINSTER ABBEY. *See* LONDON, *Churches and Parishes.*

WESTMINSTER SCHOOL. BARKER (G. F. R.) Memoir of Richard Busby. pp. 164. *Lond.* 1895. 4°.   4905. f. 24.

—— and STENNING (A. H.) Westminster School Register, 1764–1883. pp. 276. *Lond.* 1892. 8°.   8365. f. 39.

BUTLER (W. J.) Westminster School. A sermon. pp. 20. *Lond.* 1891. 8°.   4473. cc. 23. (11.)

WESTMORLAND. Ac. Cumberland. *Antiquarian Society.* JACKSON (W.) Papers and pedigrees relating to Cumberland and Westmorland. 2 vol. *Lond.* 1892. 8°.   9914. f. 13.

—— TAYLOR (M. W.) Manorial halls of Westmorland. pp. 382. *Kendal*, 1892. 8°.   Ac. 5630/9.

—— Series of Wills from the registers of the Bishops of Carlisle, 1358–86. *Kendal*, 1893. 8°.   Ac. 5630/10.

CUMBERLAND. Pedigrees recorded at the Herald's Visitations of Westmorland 1615 and 1616. pp. 172. *Carlisle*, 1891. 8°.   9914. cc. 1.

ELLWOOD (T.) Landnama Book of Iceland as it illustrates the dialect and antiquities of Westmorland. pp. 69. *Kendal*, 1894. 8°.   10280. e. 16.

FERGUSON (R. S.) History of Westmorland. pp. 312. 1894. 8°. Popular County Histories.   2368. e.

P.P. *Kendal.* Westmorland Note-book. Vol. 1. *Kendal*, 1888. 8°.   P.P. 6083. ag. (1.)

—— Westmorland Natural history record. Vol. 1. *Kendal*, 1888. 8°.   P.P. 6083. ag. (2.)

See also ENGLAND, *Lake District.*

WESTON-SUPER-MARE. WESTON-SUPER-MARE, illustrated. pp. 47. *Weston-s.-M.* 1891. 4°.   010358. l. 31.

—— Weston-super-Mare pictorial. pp. 26. *Bristol*, 1892. 8°.   Pam. 90.

—— Weston-super-Mare photographed. *Weston-s.-M.* 1895. 8°.   10358. a. 53.

WESTON-UNDER-LIZARD. GRIFFITHS (G.) Weston-under-Lizard. pp. 12. *Newport*, 1889. 8°.   10352. e. 15. (7.)

WESTPHALIA. KLEINSCHMIDT (A.) Geschichte des Königreichs Westfalen. pp. 678. 1893. 8°. HEEREN (A. H. L.) and UKERT (F. A.) Geschichte der europäischen Staaten. Lief. 54.   2378. e. 8.

KNIEKE (A.) Die Einwanderung in den westfälischen Städten bis 1400. pp. 176. *Münster*, 1893. 8°.   9365. c. 2.

LUDORFF (A.) Die Kunstdenkmäler von Westfalen. *Münster*, 1893, etc. 4°.   7808. g.

PHILIPPI (F.) Zur Verfassungsgeschichte der westfälischen Bischofstädte. pp. 102. *Osnabrück*, 1894. 8°.   9327. dd. 12. (5.)

TIBUS (A.) Beiträge zur Namenkunde westfälischer Orte. pp. 124. *Münster*. 1890. 8°.   10256. cc. 13.

WESTPHALIA. Aus Westfalens Vergangenheit. pp. 128. *Münster*, 1893. 8°.   10255. f. 31.

WEST PRUSSIA. LISSAUER (A.) Alterthümer der Bronzezeit in Westpreussen. 1891, etc. 4°. PRUSSIA, *West.* *Provinzial-Kommission.* Abhandlungen. Hft. 2, etc.   7706. i.

PRUSSIA, *West.* Westpreussische Heimat. *Danzig.* 1891, etc. 8°.   10256. d.

—— Die Kunstdenkmäler der Provinz Westpreussen. *Danzig*, 1884, etc. 4°.   7808. f.

WEST PRUSSIA—*continued.*

PRUSSIA, *West. Provinzial-Kommission.* Abhandlungen zur Landeskunde der Provinz Westpreussen. *Graudenz*, 1890, *etc.* 4°.   7706. i.

VALLENTIN ( ) Westpreussen seit den ersten Jahrzehnten dieses Jahrhunderts. pp. 225. 1892. 8°. NEUMANN (F. J.) Beiträge zur Geschichte der Bevölkerung, *etc.* Bd. 4.
           8223. cc.

See also DANZIG.

WEST VIRGINIA. SUMMERS (G. W.) The Mountain State: natural resources of West Virginia. pp. 259.
Charleston, W. Va. 1893. 8°.   40412. c. 36.

VIRGINIA, *West.* Code of West Virginia. pp. 1303. *Charleston*, 1891. 8°.   06616. g. 1.

WETTINGEN, Abbey. LEHMANN (H.) Führer durch die Cisterzienserabtei Wettingen. pp. 88. *Aarau*, 1894. 8°.   10196. bb. 11.

WEVELGHEM. COULON (A. M.) Histoire de Wevelghem. pp, 378. *Bruges*, 1890. 8°.
           010271. f. 12.

WEY, River. SCOTCHER (R.) Origin of the River Wey Navigation. pp. 27. *Guildford*, 1895. 8°.   8768. cc. 38.

WEYMOUTH. MOORE (G. W.) Visitors-Handbook. pp. 55. *Lond.* 1891. 16°. Pam. 90.

MUDGE (R. C.) Coast Gems. pp. 23. *Weymouth*, 1895. 8°.   Pam. 90.

WHALE. BARRON (W.) Old Whaling days. pp. 211. *Hull*, 1895. 8°.   10460. df. 7.

PAZ GRAELLS (M. de la) Las Ballenas en las costas de España. pp. 115. 1889. 8°. Ac. Madrid. *R. Academia de Ciencias.* Memorias. Tom. 13.   Ac. 2825.

RIOS RIAL (C.) La Ballena Euskara. pp. 102. *San Sebastian*, 1890. 4°.   7290. g. 10.

WHARFEDALE. BOGG (E.) A Thousand miles in Wharfedale. pp. 268. *Leeds*, 1892. 8°.
           10352. dd. 4.

WHARFEDALE. Wharfedale Album of views. *Lond.* 1888. *obl.* 8°.   10360. a. 24.

WHERSTEAD. ZINCKE (F. B.) Wherstead; materials for its history. pp. 410.
Lond. 1893. 8°.   010358. g. 28.

WHIST. BROWNLEE (W. M.) Arrowsmith's Whist ledger. *Bristol*, 1893. 24°. 7913. a. 63.

CAVENDISH. Laws and principles of Whist. pp. 306. *Lond.* 1895. 8°.   7913. df. 16.

—— Laws and principles of Whist. American edition. pp. 318. *N.Y.* 1895. 8°.   7912. b. 2.

—— Whist Developments. American leads and the unblocking game. pp. 181. *Lond.* 1891. 8°.   7913. ccc. 27.

—— American Leads simplified. pp. 15. *Lond.* 1894. 8°.   Pam. 83.

COURTNEY (W. P.) English Whist and whist-players. pp. 400. *Lond.* 1894. 8°. 7913. c. 26.

DEANE (W. M.) Letters on Whist. pp. 98. *Lond.* 1894. 16°.   7915. de. 11.

DRAYSON (A. W.) Art of practical Whist. pp. 314. *Lond.* 1892. 8°.   7913. ccc. 33.

—— Whist. 1891. 8°. HOFFMANN (L.) The Cyclopædia of Games.   2264. b. 20.

FOSTER (R. F.) Pocket guide to Whist. pp. 35. *Lond.* 1892. 16°.   7915. de. 14. (5.)

—— Whist Manual, with American leads. pp. 214. *N.Y.* 1894. 8°.   7913. ccc. 42.

FOSTER ( ) American Leads, and how to learn them. pp. 34. *N.Y.* 1894. 8°. 7913. ccc. 41.

WHIST—*continued.*

FOSTER ( ) Whist Tactics. pp. 141. *Lond.* 1895. 8°.   7912. aaa. 21.

HAMILTON (C. D. P.) Modern scientific Whist. pp. 599. *N.Y.* 1894. 8°.   7913. e. 29.

MAC GUCKIN (W. G.) Whist Nuggets. pp. 320. *N.Y.* 1895. 8°.   012202. eeee. 15.

P., G. W. Whist in diagrams. pp. 290. *Bost.* 1891. 8°.   7913. ee. 28.

P.P. *Milwaukee.* Whist. *Milwaukee*, 1891, *etc.* 4°.   P.P. 1826.

POLE (W.) Philosophy of Whist. pp. 248. *Lond.* 1892. 8°.   7915. aaa. 63.

—— Evolution of Whist. pp. 269. *Lond.* 1895. 8°.   7913. cc. 39.

PORTLAND. The Whist Table. pp. 472. *Lond.* 1895. 8°.   7913. ee. 37.

S., C. S. Concise Whist. Principles of whist as modified by American leads. pp. 71. *Salem*, 1890. 16°.   7915. aaa. 60.

SMITH (*Sir* W. C.) Encyclopedia of Whist. pp. 72. *Lond.* 1893. 8°.   7913. de. 14.

TRUMPS. Modern Whist. pp. 72. *N.Y.* 1892. 8°.   7913. df. 9.

CAVENDISH. Musical Whist with Living Cards. pp. 42. *Lond.* 1892. 4°.   Pam. 83.

DUPLICATE WHIST. Duplicate Whist rules. pp. 36. *Kalamazoo*. 1891. 12°.   Pam. 83.

FOSTER (R. F.) Duplicate Whist. pp. 245. *N.Y.* 1894. 8°.   7913. ccc. 40.

MITCHELL (J. T.) Duplicate Whist. pp. 110. *Chicago*, 1891. 8°.   7913. cc. 34.

CRAWLEY (R.) Solo Whist. pp. 30. *Lond.* 1889. 16°.   7915. de. 17. (3.)

GREEN (R. F.) Solo Whist. pp. 64. 1894. 8°. Club Series.   7908. ee.

ROSE (E.) Solo. pp. 131. *Bristol*, 1891. 16°.   7915. aa. 56.

WILKS (A. S.) Solo Whist. 1895. 8°. PORTLAND. The Whist Table. 7913. ee. 37.

See also CARDS : GAMES.

WHITBY. ATKINSON (J. C.) Memorials of old Whitby. pp. 332. *Lond.* 1894. 8°.
         010358. e. 30.

HORNE AND SON. Guide to Whitby. pp. 136. *Whitby*, 1895. 8°.   10358. aaa. 59.

WHITCHURCH, Oxfordshire. SLATTER (J.) Notes on the history of Whitchurch. pp. 150. *Lond.* 1895. 8°.   010358. f. 61.

WHITCHURCH, Shropshire. EVANS (G. E.) Whitchurch of long ago. pp. 29. *Oswestry*, 1893. 8°.   10351. cc. 63.

WHITEKIRK, Haddingtonshire. WADDELL (P. H.) An old Kirk Chronicle. pp. 166. *Edinb.* 1893. 8°.   4735. eee. 13.

WHITE MOUNTAINS, New Hampshire. PRIME (W. C.) Among the Northern Hills. pp. 209. *N.Y.* 1895. 8°. 012356. f. 45.

WALDRON (H. D.) The Crown of New England. *Bost.* 1893. *obl.* 8°.   10413. a. 20.

WARD (J. H.) The White Mountains. pp. 258. *N.Y.* 1890. 8°.   10413. b. 35.

WHITE'S CLUB. *See* CLUBS.

WHITKIRK, Yorkshire. PLATT (G. M.) and MORKILL (J. W.) Records of the parish of Whitkirk. pp. 238. *Leeds*, 1892. 8°.
        10360. k. 18.

WHITTINGHAM, Northumberland. DIXON (D. D.) Whittingham Vale. pp. 347. *Newcastle*, 1895. 8°.   010358. f. 58.

WIESBADEN. NIPPOLD (F.) Der Jesuiten-streit in Wiesbaden. pp. 80.
Halle, 1891. 8°.   Pam. 25.

WIGAN. F., H. T. Wigan County Council chamber. pp. 36. *Wigan*, 1890. 8°.
      010358. l. 27.

WIGHT, Isle of. BLACK (A.) and (C.) Guide to the Isle of Wight. Edited by A. R. H. Moncrieff. pp. 122. *Lond.* 1895. 8°. 10347. bb. 41.

CHARPENTIER (W. H.) Illustrated Guide to Southsea, Isle of Wight, *etc.* pp. 143.
Portsmouth, 1892. 8°.   10358. cc. 55.

CHURCH (A. J.) The Laureate's Country.
pp. 111. *Lond.* 1891. fol.   Tab. 440. b.

COLE (H. D.) Heraldic bearings of families of the Isle of Wight. *Lond.* 1891, *etc.* 4°. 9902. i. 7.

CORNISH (C. J.) The Isle of Wight. pp. 79. 1895. fol. P.P. *London.* The Portfolio. Monographs. No. 19.   P.P. 1931. pcd.

COWPER (F.) Sailing Tours. Pt. II. Isle of Wight. *Lond.* 1892, *etc.* 8°.   10360. e.

ISLAND SCENERY. Island Scenery. pp. 144.
Lond. 1893. 8°.   10368. e. 32.

MUNDAY (S. D.) The Isle of Wight. pp. 77.
Lond. 1894. obl. 8°.   10360. a. 20.

SHORE (T. W.) History of Hampshire and the Isle of Wight. pp. 286. 1892. 8°. Popular County Histories.   2368. e.

STONE (P. G.) Architectural antiquities of the Isle of Wight. 4 pt. *Lond.* 1891. fol.
      7816. d. 3.

WARD (C. S.) The Isle of Wight. pp. 86. 1895. 8°. Thorough Guide Series. No. 17.
      10347. aaa.

See also HAMPSHIRE : SOLENT.

WIGTON, Cumberland. WILSON (J.) Monumental Inscriptions of Wigton. pp. 158.
Wigton, 1892. 8°.   9914. h. 21.

WIJK. WIJK BIJ DUURSTEDE. Inventaris der Charters van de Stad Wijk. pp. 48.
Wijk, 1891. 8°.   10105. ee. 12. (7.)

WILDON. JOHERL (I. H.) Wildon, einst und jetzt. pp. 159. *Graz*, 1891. 8°. 10240. bb. 19.

WILL. GIRARDEAU (J. L.) The Will in its theological relations. pp. 497.
Columbia, 1891. 8°.   8470. ccc. 18.

HAMERLING (R.) Die Atomistik des Willens.
2 Bde. *Hamb.* 1891. 8°.   8467. e. 34.

HILLER (H. C.) Against Dogma and Free-will and for Weismannism. pp. 300.
Lond. 1893. 8°.   7006. bb. 33.

JOYAU (E.) La liberté morale de l'homme et la théorie de la grâce. 1889. 8°. Ac. Havre-de-Grâce. *Société d'Études.* Recueil, 1889. Ac. 2612.

KURT (N.) Willensfreiheit ? pp. 136.
Leipz. 1890. 8°.   8463. de. 45.

MAUDSLEY (H.) Physical basis of Will. pp. 30. 1880. 8°. LONDON. *Sunday Lecture Society.* Selection IV.}   4018. c.

MAYER (J. V.) Von der Freiheit. pp. 120.
Freiburg, 1891. 8°.   8006. cc. 7.

PAYOT (J.) L'Éducation de la volonté. pp. 276.
Paris. 1894. 8°.   8470. e. 13.

SALA (E.) Tomismo e Molinismo. pp. 31.
Parma, 1891. 8°.   Pam. 77.

TRAEGER (L.) Wille, Determinismus, Strafe.
pp. 272. *Berl.* 1895. 8°.   6005. ee. 30.

WERNICK (F. G. F.) Leibniz' Lehre von der Freiheit des menschlichen Willens. pp. 59.
Würzburg, 1890. 8°.   Pam. 49.

See also PERSONALITY : PSYCHOLOGY.

WILLIAMSBURG, William and Mary College. WILLIAMSBURG. *College of William and Mary.* Catalogue. *Richmond*, 1894. 8°.
      8365. dd. 18.

—— William and Mary College Quarterly Historical Papers. *Williamsburg*, 1892, *etc.* 8°.
      08365. k.

WILLIAMS COLLEGE, Mass. Ac. Williamstown. *Williams College.* Catalogue of Officers and Students, 1889–90. pp. 51.
Williamstown, 1889. 8°.   8365. c. 72.

WILLS. *See* SUCCESSION.

WILTSHIRE. HOLGATE (C. W.) A proposed Bibliography of Wilts. pp. 21.
Devizes, 1892. 8°.   011902. m. 20. (16.)

ELYARD (S. J.) Some Old Wiltshire homes.
pp. 88. *Lond.* 1894. fol.   10348. l. 9.

NIGHTINGALE (J. E.) Church plate of the County of Wilts. pp. 256. *Salisbury*, 1891. 8°.
      3478. g. 15.

P.P. *London.* Wiltshire Notes and Queries.
Lond. 1893, *etc.* 8°.   P.P. 6049. m.

WEBB (E. D.) History of the Hundred of Ramsbury. *Salisbury*, 1890, *etc.* fol. 10352. m. 6.

Ac. Devizes. *Wiltshire Archæological Society.* Catalogue of collection of Wiltshire Trade Tokens. pp. 22. *Devizes*, 1893. 8°.   Pam. 44.

—— London. *English Dialect Society.* DARTNELL (G. E.) and GODDARD (E. H.) Glossary of words used in Wiltshire. pp. 235.
Lond. 1893. 8°.   Ac. 9934/33.

WIMBLEDON. WIMBLEDON. Views of Wimbledon. *Wimbledon*, 1892. obl. 8°.
      10352. e. 7.

WIMBORNE. SCORE (G. F.) Guide to Wimborne Minster. pp. 64. *Lond.* 1893. 8°.
      10358. cc. 56.

WINCHCOMBE. WINCHCOMBE, *Monastery.* Landboc sive registrum monasterii de Winchelcumba. *Exoniæ*, 1892, *etc.* 8°.   4705. f.

WINCHELSEA. INDERWICK (F. A.) Story of King Edward and New Winchelsea. pp. 219.
Lond. 1892. 8°.   10360. ee. 34.

WINCHESTER.

City and Cathedral.

Ac. Hampshire. *Record Society.* Liber Vitæ; Register of New Minster and Hyde Abbey, Winchester. pp. 335. *Lond.* 1892. 8°.
      Ac. 8123/5.

—— Compotus Rolls of the obedientiaries of St. Swithun's Priory, Winchester. pp. 540.
Lond. 1892. 8°.   Ac. 8123/7.

BENHAM (W.) Winchester Cathedral. 1893. 8°.
FARRAR (F. W.) Our English Minsters.
      07816. ee. 2.

BRAMSTON (A. R.) and LEROY (A. C.) A City of memories. pp. 100. *Winchester*, 1893. 8°.
      10358. d. 47.

KITCHIN (G. W.) Winchester. pp. 227. 1891. 8°.
FREEMAN (E. A.) and HUNT (W.) Historic Towns.   2368. a.

—— Great Screen of Winchester Cathedral.
pp. 40. *Winchester*, 1891. 8°.   7875. de. 28.

SAVAGE (W.) Guide to Winchester. pp. 103.
Winchester, 1884. 8°.   10360. e. 23.

WARD, LOCK AND Co. Handbook to Winchester Cathedral. *Lond.* 1890. 8°.   010358. l. 13.

WINCHESTER. Guide to Winchester. pp. 138.
Lond. 1893. 8°.   10351. aaa. 60.

WINCHESTER CATHEDRAL. Story of Winchester Cathedral. pp. 20. *Winchester*, 1893. 8°.
      4705. b. 46. (9.)

WINCHESTER—continued.

College.

MOBERLY (G. H.) Life of William of Wykeham. pp. 365. *Winchester*, 1893. 8°. 4902. g. 27.

KIRBY (T. F.) Annals of Winchester College. pp. 551. *Lond.* 1892. 8°. 8364. f. 18.

MANSFIELD (R. B.) School-life at Winchester College. pp. 243. *Lond.* 1893. 8°. 8364. b. 71.

TUCKWELL (W.) Winchester fifty years ago. pp. 171. *Lond.* 1893. 8°. 8365. b. 56.

WINCHESTER COLLEGE. Winchester College, 1393–1893. pp. 187. *Lond.* 1893. 4°. 8364. i. 5.

—— Inscriptiones Wiccamicae. pp. 89. *Oxf.* 1885. 8°. 8364. aaa. 48.

—— Winchester Commoners, 1800–35. pp. 43. *Salisbury*, 1893. 8°. 8365. dd. 17. (20.)

—— Winchester Commoners. 1836–90. pp. 304. *Salisbury*, 1891. 8°. 8364. e. 41.

Diocese.

P.P. *Winchester.* Winchester Diocesan chronicle. *Winchester*, 1893, *etc.* 8°. P.P. 344. f. and 1996.
For the Life of William of Wykeham. See *supra : Winchester College.*

WIND. See METEOROLOGY.

WINDHAM, New Hampshire. WINDHAM. History of the celebration of the 150th anniversary of the incorporation of the settlement. pp. 124. *Windham*, 1892. 8°. 10410. e. 47.

WINDSOR CASTLE. COLLMANN (L.) Windsor Castle. pp. 86. *Windsor*, 1894. 8°. 10350. bb. 47.

WINSCOMBE. COMPTON (T.) A Mendip Valley. pp. 288. *Lond.* 1892. 8°. 10350. de. 23.

WIPPERFÜRTH. KORTH (L.) Wipperfürth. 1891. 8°. Ac. Cologne. *Historischer Verein.* Annalen. Hft. 51. Ac. 7335.

WIRE. SMITH (J. B.) Treatise upon Wire. pp. 347. *Lond.* 1891. 8°. 07945. g. 1.

WISCONSIN. TURNER (F. J.) The Indian trade in Wisconsin. pp. 75. 1891. 8°. Johns Hopkins University Studies in History, *etc.* Ser. 9. No. 11–12. Ac. 2689.

WISMAR. CRULL (F.) and TECHEN (F.) Die Grabsteine der wismarschen Kirchen. 1889–91. 8°. Ac. Schewerin. *Verein für mecklenburgische Geschichte.* Jahrbücher. Jahrg. 54, 55, 56. Ac. 7165.

LUNDIN (C. F.) Wismars pansättande till Meklenburg-Schwerin. pp. 87. *Upsala*, 1892. 8°. 10256. d. 2.

WIT AND HUMOUR. BACKHAUS (W. E.) Das Wesen des Humors. pp. 208. *Leipz.* 1894. 8°. 011824. h. 15.

FENN (G. M.) World of Wit and Humour. *Lond.* 1895, *etc.* 8°. 12315. k.

JESTS. English, Scottish, American and Irish Jests. 4 vol. 1886–95. 16°. Nuggets for Travellers. 12314. a. 48.

LARCHEY (L.) L'Esprit de tout le monde. pp. 358. *Paris*, 1892. 8°. 12314. cc. 46.

MORRIS (C.) Half-hours with humorous Authors. 2 vol. 1890. 8°. Cavendish Library. 12295. ee.

WITS. With the Wits, *etc.* 14 pt. *Lond.* 1892. 8°. 12315. k. 11.

BARR (J.) Humour of America. pp. 462. *Lond.* 1893. 8°. 012314. g.

LEE (E.) Humour of France. pp. 463. *Lond.* 1893. 8°. 012314. g.

WIT AND HUMOUR—continued.

MUELLER CASENOV (H.) Humour of Germany. pp. 437. *Lond.* 1892. 8°. 012314. g.

WERNER (A.) Humour of Holland. pp. 398.. *Lond.* 1893. 8°. 012314. g.

O'DONOGHUE (D. J.) Humour of Ireland. pp. 434. *Lond.* 1894. 8°. 012314. g.

WERNER (A.) Humour of Italy. pp. 345. *Lond.* 1892. 8°. 012314. g.

RASI (L.) I Comici Italiani. *Firenze*, 1894, *etc.* 8°. 10629. h.

MEHRJĪBHĀĪ NAUSHĪRVĀNJĪ KŪKĀ. Wit and Humour of the Persians. pp. 255. *Bombay*, 1894. 8°. 757. e. 43.

VOYNICH (E. L.) Humour of Russia. pp. 349. *Lond.* 1895. 8°. 012314. g.

FORD (R.) Thistledown. Book of Scotch humour. pp. 402. *Paisley*, 1895. 8°. 012314. g. 13.

TAYLOR (S. M.) Humour of Spain. pp. 362. *Lond.* 1894. 8°. 012314. g.
See also POETRY: QUOTATIONS: RECITATIONS: SATIRE.

WITCHCRAFT. AMMANN (H.) Die innsbrucker Hexenprocess von 1485. pp. 87. 1890. 8°. Ac. Innsbruck. *Ferdinandeum.* Zeitschrift. Folge 3. Hft. 34. Ac. 760.

DELACROIX (F.) Les Procès de Sorcellerie au XVIII° siècle. pp. 328. *Paris*, 1894. 12°. 8632. dd. 9.

DIESENBACH (J.) Besessenheit, Zauberei und Hexenfabeln. 1893, 8°. Frankfurter zeitgemässe Brochüren. N.F. Bd. 14. 12209. g.

FAIRFAX (E.) Dæmonologia : a discourse on witchcraft. pp. 189. *Harrogate*, 1882. 8°. 8632. d. 15.

FINCH (A. E.) Witchcraft. pp. 34. 1887. 8°. London. *Sunday Lecture Society.* Selection 5. 4018. c.

FOURNIER (A.) Une épidémie de Sorcellerie en Lorraine aux XVI° et XVII° siècles. pp. 34. *Nancy*, 1891. 8°. 8632. g. 25. (7.)

HENNE-AM-RHYN (O.) Der Teufels- und Hexenglaube. pp. 159. *Leipz.* 1892. 8°. 8630. ee. 25.

INNES (J. W. B.) Scottish Witchcraft trials. pp. 49. 1891. 16°. London. *Sette of Odd Volumes.* Opuscula. No. 25. 012202. ff.

KIRK (R.) Secret Commonwealth of elves, fauns and fairies. pp. 92. 1893. 8°. *Bibliothèque de Carabas.* Vol. 8. 12204. hh.

KOLDEWEY (F.) Der Exorcismus im Herzogtum Braunschweig. pp. 50. *Wolfenbüttel*, 1893. 8°. 8632. g. 25. (10.)

LADAME (P.) Les Mandragores à Genève au XVIme et XVIIme siècles. 1892.8°. Ac. Geneva. Soc. d'histoire. Mémoires. N.S. Tom. 3. Ac. 6941.

LAENGIN (G.) Religion und Hexenprozess. pp. 385. *Leipz.* 1895. 8°. 8603. g. 41.

NEVINS (W. S.) Witchcraft in Salem Village, 1692. pp. 273. *Salam*, 1892. 8°. 8632. d. 22.

PROEHLE (H.) Brockensagen. pp. 70. *Harzburg*, 1888. 8°. 12430. a. 37.

SNELL (O.) Hexenprozesse und Geistesstörung. pp. 130. *München*, 1891. 8°. 8632. f. 25.
See also DEMONOLOGY: EXORCISM.

WITTENBERG. KOESTLIN (J.) Friedrich der Weise und die Schlosskirche zu Wittenberg. pp. 110. *Wittenberg*, 1892. 4°. 4662. d. 16.

STIER (G.) Denkwürdigkeiten Wittenbergs in geschichtlicher Anordnung. pp. 32. *Dessau*, 1894. 8°. 3913. d. 50. (10.)

WITTE (L.) Die Erneuerung der Schlosskirche zu Wittenberg. pp. 93. *Wittenberg*, 1893. 4°. 4651. f. 25. (2.)

WITTENBERG—*continued.*

WITTENBERG. Urkunde über die Einweihung der erneuerten Schlosskirche zu Wittenberg. *Wittenberg*, 1893. 4°. 4661. f 25. (1.)

University.

Ac. Wittenberg. *Academia.* Album Academiae Vitebergensis, 1502–1602. *Halis*, 1894, *etc.* 4°. 8355. f.

—— Wittenberger Ordiniertenbuch, 1537–60. pp. 141. *Leipz.* 1894. 8°. 8357. i. 4.

WITTINGEN. KAYHAUSEN (C.) Aus Wittingens Vergangenheit. pp. 65. *Gifhorn*, 1893. 8°. 10106. ff. 7. (5.)

WITWATERSRAND.

See AFRICA, *South :* GOLD AND SILVER : TRANSVAAL.

WOBURN SANDS. CAMERON (A. C. G.) Excursion to Woburn Sands. 1892. 8°. 07109. e. 20. (9.)

WOLDENBERG. NIESSEN (P. v.) Geschichte der Stadt Woldenberg. pp. 511. *Stettin*, 1893. 8°. 10255. f. 28.

WOLF. GRUAU (L.) Nouvelle invention de chasse pour prendre et oster les loups de la France. pp. 142. 1888. 8°. JULLIEN (E.) and LACROIX (P.) Cabinet de Vénerie. 7908. e.

MIVART (St. G.) Dogs, Wolves, *etc.* pp. 216. *Lond.* 1890. 4°. 7206. dd. 7.

WOLGAST. HEBERLEIN (B.) Beiträge zur Geschichte der Burg Wolgast. *Wolgast*, 1891, *etc.* 8°. 10215. dd.

WOLVERHAMPTON. B, E. Remnants of old Wolverhampton. Pt. 1–12. *Wolverhampton*, 1880–86. fol. 1784. a. 4.

JONES (W. H.) History of the Congregational Churches of Wolverhampton. pp. 178. *Lond.* 1894. 8°. 4715. bb. 31.

WOMEN, Diseases, Hygiene, etc. Ac. Germany. *Gesellschaft für Gynäkologie.* Festschrift zur Feier des Jubiläums der Gesellschaft für Gynäkologie. pp. 419. *Wien*, 1894. 8°. Ac. 3783.

—— London. *University College Museum.* Catalogue of specimens illustrating the pathology of Gynæcology. pp. 72. *Lond.* 1891. 8°. 07581. e. 8.

AUVARD (A.) Gynécologie. pp. 175. 1892. 8°. Encyclopédie des aide-mémoire. 8709. g.

BREWIS (N. T.) Outlines of gynæcological Diagnosis. pp. 68. *Edinb.* 1894. 8°. 7581. aaa. 27.

BRIVOIS (L.) Manuel d'Électrothérapie gynécologique. pp. 400. *Paris*, 1890. 18°. 07581. de. 14.

BUSHONG (C. H.) Modern Gynecology. pp. 380. *Lond.* 1894. 8°. 7581. b. 31.

CUTTER (E.) Contributions to Gynecology. *N.Y.* 1887, *etc.* 8°. 07581. df. 17.

DUEHRSSEN (A.) Manual of gynæcological Practice. pp. 241. *Lond.* 1895. 8°. 07581. f. 8.

FEHLING (H. v.) Lehrbuch der Frauenkrankheiten. pp. 540. *Stuttgart*, 1893. 8°. 7580. d. 3.

GALABIN (A. L.) Diseases of Women. pp. 516. *Lond.* 1893. 8°. 2256. a. 9.

GARRIGUES (H. J.) Text-book of Diseases of Women. pp. 690. *Phila.* 1894. 8°. 07581. e. 25.

GOLDSPIEGEL-SOSNOWSKA ( ) Traitement des Maladies des femmes par la méthode de Thure Brandt. pp. 24. *Paris*, 1894. 8°. 7305. f. 16. (15.)

GRECHEN (M.) Gynäkologische Studien. pp. 317. *Berl.* 1891. 8°. 7581. f. 18.

GUBB (A. S.) Aids to Gynæcology. pp. 116. *Lond.* 1893. 8°. 7581. a. 10.

WOMEN.—**Diseases, etc.**—*continued.*

HANDBOOK. Students' handbook of Gynecology. pp. 178. *Edinb.* 1893. 8°. 7581. aaa. 26.

HEADLEY (W. B.) Evolution of the Diseases of Women. pp. 375. *Lond.* 1894. 8°. 07581. e. 2°.

HEITZMANN (J.) Compendium der Gynäkologie. pp. 452. *Wien*, 1891. 8°. 07581. e. 10.

HELLIER (J. B.) Notes on gynæcological Nursing. pp. 80. *Lond.* 1891. 8°. 07581. de. 26.

JONES (H. M.) Manual of Diseases of Women. pp. 766. *Lond.* 1894. 8°. 07581. de. 40.

KESWICK (J. B.) Sexual Physiology. pp. 140. *Carlisle*, 1891. 8°. 7641. aa. 38.

KUESTNER (O.) Berichte aus der Universitäts-Frauenklinik zu Dorpat. pp. 912. *Wiesbaden*, 1894. 8°. 7580. ee. 28.

LEWERS (A. H. N.) Textbook of the Diseases of Women. pp. 439. 1893. 8°. Lewis's Practical Series. 7482. a.

MADDEN (T. M.) Clinical Gynaecology. pp. 562. *Phila.* 1893. 8°. 07581. e. 21.

MARTIN (A.) Handbuch der Krankheiten der weiblichen Adnexorgane. *Leipz.* 1895, *etc.* 8°. 07581. i.

MEADOWS (A.) Inaugural address to the British Gynæcological Society. pp. 24. *Lond.* 1885. 8°. Pam. 39.

NAPIER (A. D. L.) Thermometer in Gynæcology. pp. 30. *Lond.* 1890. 8°. 07305. e. 21. (15,)

OLIVER (J.) Manual of the Diseases peculiar to Women. pp. 211. *Lond.* 1893. 8°. 07581. de. 33.

PHILLIPS (J.) Outlines of the Diseases of Women. pp. 273. *Lond.* 1893. 8°. 07581. de. 30.

POZZI (S.) Traité de Gynécologie. pp. 1182. *Paris*, 1892. 8°. 7581. d. 13.

Ac. London. *New Sydenham Society.* POZZI (S.) Treatise on Gynæcology. *Lond.* 1892, *etc.* 8°. Ac. 3838/56.

RABAGLIATI (A.) On Symptoms which simulate disease of the Pelvic Organs in women. pp. 77. *Lond.* 1895. 8°. 07581. df. 23.

REYNOLDS (J. J.) Notes on Diseases of Women. pp. 176. *Lond.* 1894. 8°. 7581. bbb. 39.

ROBB (H.) Aseptic Surgical technique : with especial reference to gynæcological operations. pp. 264. *Phila.* 1894. 8°. 07482. e. 16.

SKENE (A. J. C.) Treatise on the Diseases of Women. pp. 968. *Lond.* 1892. 8°. 7580. dd. 7.

SNOW (H. L.) Proclivity of Women to cancerous diseases. pp. 58. *Lond.* 1891. 8°. 7581. e. 14.

SORANUS II., *of Ephesus.* Die Gynäkologie des Soranus. pp. 173. 1894. 8°. HUBER (J. C.) Bibliothek medicinischer Klassiker. Bd. 1. 07305. e.

STRATZ (C. H.) Gynäcologische Anatomie. pp. 41. *Berl.* 1892. 4°. 7580. g. 19.

STUDII. Studii di Ginecologia. pp. 385. *Milano*, 1890. 8°. 7580. g. 16.

TAIT (R. L.) Diseases of Women and abdominal surgery. *Leicester*, 1889, *etc.* 8°. 2255. e. 16.

THOMAS (T. G.) Treatise on the Diseases of Women. pp. 826. *Lond.* 1891. 8°. 2256. f. 12.

WEBSTER (J. C.) Researches in female Pelvic Anatomy. pp. 129. *Edinb.* 1892. 4°. 7580. g. 20.

WINCKEL (F. v.) Die Universitäts-Frauenklinik in München, 1884–90. pp. 677. *Leipz.* 1892. 8°. 07581. df. 21.

WOOD (J. C.) Text-book of Gynecology. pp. 858. *Phila.* 1894. 8°. 07581. e. 29.

ZWEIFEL (P.) Vorlesungen über klinische Gynäkologie. pp. 440. *Berl.* 1892. 8°. 7581. f. 19.

WOMEN.—Diseases, etc.—continued.

AUVARD (A.) Menstruation et fécondation. pp. 195. 1892. 8°. Encyclopédie des aide-mémoire.
8709. g.

CHAMPNEYS (F. H.) On painful Menstruation. pp. 88. Lond. 1891. 8°. 07581. e. 5.

SMITH (A. L.) Disorders of Menstruation. 1894. 8°. BIGELOW (H. R.) International System of electro-therapeutics. 2024. e.

STEINHAUS (J.) Menstruation und Ovulation. pp. 122. Leipz. 1890. 8°. 07581. e. 6.

WEBSTER (J. C.) Puberty and the change of life. pp. 56. Edinb. 1892. 8°.
7306. df. 20. (10.)

CUTTER (E.) Galvanism of Uterine Fibroids. Phila. 1890. 8°. 07305. e. 27. (8.)

FEHLING (H. v.) Über Uterusruptur. pp. 16. 1892. 8°. VOLKMANN (R. v.) Sammlung klinischer Vorträge. Nr. 54. 7441. g.

GOELET (A. H.) Treatment of diseases of the Uterine Appendages by electricity. 1894. 8°. BIGELOW (H. R.) International System of Electro Therapeutics. 2024. e.

HERZFELD (C. A.) Klinischer Bericht über tausend Bauchhöhlen-Operationen. pp. 224. Leipz. 1895. 4°. 07581. i. 5.

JESSETT (F. B.) Lectures on cancer of the Uterus. pp. 80. Lond. 1894. 8°. 07581. df. 22.

VINAVER ( ) Étude sur le curettage de l'Utérus et l'opération de Schröder. pp. 72. Paris, 1890. 8°. 07581. e. 3.

CUTTER (E.) A Porcelain Stem Pessary. pp. 8. N.Y. 1884. 8°. 07305. l. 6. (1.)

—— Contras and pros of the Cutter Stem Pessary. pp. 9. N.Y. 1888. 8°.
07305. k. 6. (1.)

KHOLMOGOROV (S. S.) Die vaginale Totalexstirpation des Uterus. 1894. 8°. VOLKMANN (R. v.) Sammlung klinischer Vorträge. Nr. 108.
7441. g.

NORDAU (M. S.) De la Castration de la femme. pp. 62. Paris, 1882. 8°. 07305. e. 24. (7.)

WELLS (Sir T. S.) Modern abdominal surgery. With appendix on castration of women. pp. 51. Lond. 1891. 8°. Pam. 39.

CONZETTE (G.) Contribution à l'étude des Ovaires à petits kystes. pp. 84. Paris, 1890. 8°. Pam. 39.

LARNAUDIE (T.) Contribution à l'étude des tumeurs solides de l'Ovaire. pp. 155. Montpellier, 1891. 8°. 07581. i. 2.

SUTTON (J. B.) Surgical diseases of the Ovaries and Fallopian Tubes. pp. 500. Lond. 1891. 8°. 07581. de. 22.

TAIT (R. L.) Second series of fifty cases of Ovariotomy. pp. 8. Birmingham, 1880. 8°. 7306. c. 24. (7.)

WACQUEZ (A.) Les tumeurs végétantes de l'Ovaire. pp. 126. Paris, 1890. 8°.
07581. df. 11.

WINTERNITZ (E.) Die chronische Oophoritis. pp. 125. Tübingen, 1893. 8°. 7581. d. 14.

FREUND (W. A.) Eine neue Operation zur Schliessung gewisser Harnfisteln beim Weibe. 1895. 8°. VOLKMANN (R. v.) Sammlung klinischer Vorträge. N.F. Nr. 118. 7441. g.

See also ABDOMEN: BREAST: GENITO-URINARY ORGANS: OBSTETRICS: STERILITY.

Hygiene, etc.

ALLBUTT (H. A.) The Wife's Handbook. pp. 59. Lond. 1894. 8°. 7641. e. 5. (6.)

ALLINSON (T. R.) A Book for married Women. pp. 64. Lond. 1894. 8°. Pam. 39.

WOMEN.—Hygiene, etc.—continued.

DAVIS (E. P.) and KEATING (J. M.) Mother and Child. pp. 472. Phila. 1893. 8°. 07581. e. 15.

GALBRAITH (A. M.) Hygiene and Physical culture for Women. pp. 294. Lond. 1895. 8°.
7404. aaaa. 3.

HAWKINS-AMBLER (G. A.) Health gossips for Women. pp. 130. Liverp. 1893. 8°.
7581. bb. 16.

KER (A. J. S.) Motherhood. pp. 128. Manch. 1891. 8°. 07581. de. 23.

KESWICK (J. B.) Woman; her physical culture. 3 vol. Lond. 1895. 8°. 07581. f. 7.

MARIE CHRISTINE. Boudoir gossip on Health and Appearance. pp. 25. Lond. 1892. 16°.
07305. i. 12. (3.)

NAPHEYS (G. H.) Physical life of Women. pp. 320. Lond. 1895. 8°. 07581. de. 44.

NORVILLE (de) Countess. Les coulisses de la Beauté. pp. 233. Paris, 1894. 8°. 7404. ee. 1.

PANTON (J. E.) Within Four Walls. Handbook for invalids. pp. 277. Lond. 1893. 8°.
7688. aaa. 46.

RYLEY (J. B.) Words of advice to young Wives. pp. 45. Lond. 1895. 8°. 07581. f. 10.

SCHARLIEB (M.) Woman's words to Women on the care of their health in England and India. pp. 240. Lond. 1895. 8°. 8415. de. 45.

SPECIALIST. Beauty and hygiene for Women. pp. 188. Lond. 1893. 8°. 7581. bbb. 38.

SPERRY (L. B.) Confidential talks with young Women. pp. 164. Edinb. 1894. 8°. 7641. aa. 36.

STABLES (W. G.) Wife's guide to Health and Happiness. pp. 241. Lond. 1894. 8°.
07581. de. 36.

—— Girl's own book of Health and Beauty. pp. 254. Lond. 1891. 8°. 07581. de. 25.

WALKER (A.) Beauty in Woman, analysed and classified. pp. 339. Glasg. 1892. 8°.
7858. gg. 10.

WALKER (J. H.) Handbook for Mothers. pp. 200. Lond. 1893. 8°. 07581. de. 32.

WESTLAND (A.) The Wife and Mother. pp. 282. Lond. 1895. 8°. 07581. f. 9.

See also HYGIENE: TOILET.

Social, Legal, Political Works.
General.

ACOSTA DE SAMPER AGUDELO (S.) La Mujer en la sociedad moderna. pp. 429. Paris, 1895. 8°.
8416. ff. 10.

ADAMS (O. F.) The Presumption of Sex. pp. 149. Bost. 1892. 8°. 8416. d. 35.

AUGSPURG (A.) Die ethische Seite der Frauenfrage. pp. 35. Minden, 1894. 8°. Pam. 37.

BANI (G. V.) La Donna nella società moderna. pp. 29. Firenze, 1893. 8°. Pam. 37.

BEBEL (A.) Die Frau und der Sozialismus. pp. 382. Stuttgart, 1891. 8°. 08276. f. 16.

BENDER (H.) Frauenwünsche und Frauenbestrebungen. pp. 55. 1891. 8°. Deutsche Zeit- und Streit-Fragen. Hft. 91. 12290. f.

BLACK (W. H.) Womanhood. pp. 110. Nashville, 1890. 8°. 8416. d. 34.

BOELTE (A.) Neues Frauen-Brevier. pp. 262. Leipz. 1893. 16°. 8415. de. 30.

CAHOON (H. H.) What one Woman thinks. pp. 269. Lond. 1894. 8°. 012357. e. 87.

CHADWICK (J. W.) Social and political status of Women. 1893. 8°. Ac. Brooklyn. Brooklyn Ethical Association. Evolution Series. No. 41.
7006. bbb.

CHAVARD (F.) Le Célibat, le prêtre et la femme. pp. 521. Paris, 1894. 8°. 8416. f. 49.

WOMEN.—General—*continued.*

CHICAGO. *Columbian Exposition.* World's Congress of representative Women. 2 vols. *Chicago*, 1894. 8°. 8415. h. 36.

—— Catalogue. Part XIV. Woman's Building. pp. 141. *Chicago*, 1893. 8°. 7958. bb. 25.

COBBE (F. P.) Duties of Women. pp. 193. *Lond.* 1894. 8°. 8416. ccc. 48.

CREPAZ (A.) Die Gefahren der Frauen-Emancipation. pp. 55. *Leipz.* 1892. 8°. 8416. f. 53.

—— The Emancipation of Women. pp. 130. *Lond.* 1893. 8°. 08276. e. 47.

DAHL (N. A.) Mand og Kvinde. pp. 205. *Kristiania*, 1893. 8°. 8146. cc. 46.

DERAISMES (M.) Ève dans l'humanité. pp. 223. *Paris*, 1891. 8°. 8416. h. 12.

DUCKWORTH (*Sir* D.) Women : their place in the twentieth century. pp. 30. *Glasg.* 1894. 8°. Pam. 37.

ELLIS (H. H.) Man and Woman. pp. 409. 1894. 8°. Contemporary Science Series. 9709. i.

FARRAR (F. W.) Woman's Work in the home. pp. 109. *Lond.* 1895. 8°. 8416. ff. 11.

FITZMAURICE (M. O.) Woman a help meet for Man. pp. 26. *Lond.* 1894. 8°. 8416. df. 21.

FERNALD (J. C.) The new Womanhood. pp. 369. *Bost.* 1891. 8°. 8416. e. 30.

FRANK (L.) Essai sur la condition politique de la Femme. pp. 598. *Paris*, 1892. 8°. 8415. ee. 35.

—— Le grand catéchisme de la Femme. pp. 123. *Paris*, 1894. 12°. 8416. df. 23.

GAMBLE (E. B.) The evolution of Woman. pp. 356. *N.Y.* 1894. 8°. 8416. e. 36.

GIANNI (S.) La Donna. pp. 46. *Petralia*, 1888. 8°. Pam. 37.

GNAUCK-KUEHNE (E.) Die soziale Lage der Frau. pp. 34. *Berl.* 1895. 8°. Pam. 37.

GONETTA (G.) La Donna e l' emancipazione. pp. 162. *Milano*, 1893. 8°. 8415. de. 37.

GREVILLE (B. V.) *Baroness Greville.* The Gentlewoman in society. pp. 271. 1892. 8°. ADAMS (W. H. D.) Victoria Library. 012208. f.

GUÉROULT (G.) Du rôle de la Femme dans notre rénovation sociale. pp. 61. *Caen*, 1891. 8°. Pam. 37.

HAAG (E.) Die wahre Emanzipation der Frau. pp. 61. *Berl.* 1895. 8°. 8415. ee. 49.

HARPER (C. G.) Revolted Woman. pp. 140. *Lond.* 1894. 8°. 8415. h. 35.

HEINZEN (C.) The rights of Women and the sexual relations. pp. 173. *Bost.* 1891. 8°. 7390. e. 2.

HERBERT (L.) Women's Responsibilities. pp. 14. *Lond.* 1891. 8°. Pam. 37.

KELLEN (T.) Weibliches Sklaventum in neuerer Zeit. pp. 96. *Neuwied*, 1894. 8°. 8285. cc. 46.

KRETSCHMAN, afterwards GIŻYCKI (L. v.) Die Stellung der Frau in der Gegenwart. pp. 24. *Berl.* 1895. 8°. Pam. 37.

—— Die Bürgerpflicht der Frau. pp. 24. *Berl.* 1895. 8°. Pam. 37.

LE ROW (C. B.) Economic position of Woman. 1893. 8°. Ac. Brooklyn. *Ethical Association.* Evolution Series. No. 42. 7006. bbb.

MAC DONALD (A.) Abnormal Woman. pp. 189. *Wash.* 1895. 8°. 8416. ff. 8.

MANTEGAZZA (P.) Fisiologia della Donna. 2 vol. *Milano*, 1893. 8°. 8416. ff. 7.

MERCIER (H.) Verbonden Schakels. pp. 253. *Haarlem*, 1891. 8°. 8416. dd. 46.

MITCHELL (C. P.) Enlargement of the sphere of Women. pp. 24. *Lond.* 1892. 8°. Pam. 37.

WOMEN.—General—*continued.*

MOHR (L. A.) La Mujer y la política. pp. 186. *Buenos Aires*, 1890. 8°. 8415. de. 20.

MORGENSTERN (L.) Die Stellung der Frau im Leben. pp. 52. 1891. 8°. WOLFF (E.) Deutsche Schriften. Reihe 1. Hft. 6. 12250. l.

NAVILLE (E.) La condition sociale des Femmes. pp. 166. *Lausanne*, 1891. 8°. 8416. de. 26.

NESTORI (H.) Die chinesische Mauer. Ein Beitrag zur Frauenfrage. pp. 170. *Wolfenbüttel*, 1895. 8°. 8415. ee. 47.

ORSINI (A.) La Donna nella società humana. pp. 207. *Orvieto*, 1890. 8°. 8415. dd. 35.

OSTROGORSKI (M.) The rights of Women. pp. 232. *Lond*, 1893. 8°. 08276. e. 59.

PASSER (A. v. d.) Eva aus dem Mittelstand. pp. 59. *Leipz.* 1894. 8°. Pam. 37.

PEDERZANI - WEBER (J.) Die moderne Kultur und die Frauen. pp 48. *Leipz.* 1890. 8°. Pam. 37.

PHILIPPI (A.) Die Frauenfrage. pp. 70. *Bielefeld*, 1894. 8°. 8415. de. 47.

PLATT (W.) Women, Love and life. pp. 200. *Lond.* 1895. 8°. 8415. ccc. 42.

POMBERY (É. de) Quintessences féminines. pp. 340. *Paris*, 1893. 8°. 8416. de. 39.

REED (J.) Woman's Place and work. pp. 27. *Bost.* 1893. 8°. Pam. 37.

ROSS (W. S.) Janet Smith. Essay on Woman. pp. 220. *Lond.* 1894. 8°. 8415. df. 26.

SALAMAN (M. C.) Woman—through a man's eyeglass. pp. 237. *Lond.* 1892. 8°. 8416. e. 28.

SCHREIBER (C.) Eva. Naturalistische Studien einer Idealistin. pp. 155. *Dresden*, 1893. 8°. 8415. d. 50.

SHAME. Transplanted Shame. Symposium on the evils of modern conventionality. pp. 115. *N.Y.* 1892. 8°. 8416. df. 10.

SIMMS (J.) Past, present and future of Women. pp. 40. *San Francisco*, 1889. 8°. Pam. 37.

SIMON (J. F.) and (G.) La Femme du vingtième siècle. pp. 410. *Paris*, 1892. 8°. 8416. dd. 45.

SIMON (M. P. E.) À la femme. pp. 39. *Paris*, 1891. 16°. 8415. de. 19.

SULLIVAN (*Sir* E. R.) Woman, the predominant partner. pp. 115. *Lond.* 1894. 8°. 8415. df. 28.

SUNDT (K.) Kvinden i det private og offentlige Liv. pp. 142. *Laurvik*, 1890. 8°. 8416. de. 17.

WALKER (E. A.) Womanhood. pp. 126. *Lond.* 1891. 8°. 8416. de. 16.

WARD (H. O.) Social Ethics and society duties. pp. 310. *Bost.* 1892. 8°. 8411. ee. 2.

WOLLSTONECRAFT, afterwards GODWIN (M.) Vindication of the rights of Woman. pp. 282. 1892. 8°. The Scott Library. 012208. ee.

WOODHULL afterwards MARTIN (V. C. W.) The human Body the temple of God. pp. 617. *Lond.* 1890. 8°. 8415. ee. 36.

WYTZES ( ) Zur Frauenfrage. 1893. 8°. WEBER ( ) Sammlung theologischer Reden. Ser. 4. Lief. 4. 4224. ff. 25.

LEWES (L.) Shakespeares Frauengestalten. pp. 409. *Stuttgart*, 1893. 8°. 11766. c. 46.

BOCCARDI (A.) La Donna nell' opera di H. Ibsen. pp. 51. *Milano*, 1893. 8°. Pam. 15.

GILLILAND (M. S.) Ibsen's Women. pp. 32. *Lond.* 1894. 4°. Pam. 15.

CHARLES (E.) Ecce Ancilla Domini. Studies on the Christian ideal of womanhood. pp. 173. *Lond.* 1894. 8°. 4429. c. 51.

WOMEN.—General—_continued._

CHRISTIAN VIRGIN. The Christian Virgin in her family and in the world. pp. 368.
Lond. 1890. 8°.   4402. c. 6.

DEMANTE (H.) Le Femme forte et l'état religieux. pp. 266. _Paris,_ 1890. 12°.   3900. bb. 34.

LITRÁN (C.) La mujer en el Christianismo. pp. 91. _Barcelona,_ 1892. 8°.   8416. de. 53.

MARTIN (M. B.) The Master's words to Women. pp. 128. _Lond._ 1891. 8°.   4224. aaa. 43.

MASON (E.) Womanhood in the God-Man. pp. 324. _Lond._ 1891. 8°.   4224. bbb. 19.

SKINNER (C.) The Master's messages to Women. pp. 110. _Lond._ 1895. 8°.   4371. de. 15.

VERDIER (C.) Le bréviaire des Dames. pp. 140. _· Paris,_ 1890. 12°.   4400. cc. 3.

VIVES (J. L.) Livre de l'institution de la Femme chrestienne. pp. 392. _Havre,_ 1891. 8°.
                                            8416. de. 22.

WORDS. Words to Mothers. pp. 94.
Lond. 1893. 8°.   4399. aa. 46.

ASHMORE (R.) Side talks with Girls. pp. 252.
Lond. 1895. 8°.   8415. ff. 7.

AVIS (W.) A Catholic Girl in the world.
pp. 114. _Lond._ 1894. 8°.   8415. de. 36.

BLACKBURNE (G. M. I.) A Girl's difficulties.
pp. 95. _Lond._ 1895. 16°.   4399. bb. 7.

CAPP (W. M.) The Daughter. pp. 144.
Phila. 1891. 8°.   8416. dd. 32.

CHESTER (E.) Chats with Girls on self-culture.
pp. 213. _N.Y._ 1891. 8°.   8416. df. 11.

—— Girls and Women. pp. 248.
Lond. 1891. 8°.   8416. de. 12.

DODGE (G. H.) Thoughts of busy Girls.
pp. 137. _Lond._ 1893. 12°.   8416. de. 35.

FARNINGHAM (M.) Girlhood. pp. 231.
Lond. 1895. 8°.   8415. de. 48.

GIRLS. Shall Girls propose? pp. 141.
Lond. 1893. 12°.   8416. de. 34.

MAIDEN. The Maiden's Birthday Book.
pp. 252. _Lond._ 1892. 32°.   3128. eee. 40.

MILLER (J. R.) Girls. Faults and ideals.
pp. 28. _Lond._ 1895. 8°.   8415. de. 46.

SOULSBY (L. H. M.) Home Rule, or, daughters of to-day. pp. 34. _Oxf._ 1894. 16°. Pam. 37.

—— Stray thoughts for Girls. pp. 186.
Lond. 1895. 8°.   4399. a. 58.

TALKS. Talks to Girls by one of themselves.
pp. 160. _Lond._ 1891. 8°.   4429. aa. 17.

TEE (E.) This everyday Life. pp. 254.
Lond. 1894. 8°.   8415. de. 34.

See also MARRIAGE : SOCIAL QUESTIONS.

Biography. _See_ BIOGRAPHY, _Female._

Criminal Women, etc.

FERRIANI (L.) Madri snaturate. pp. 248.
Milano, 1893. 8°.   6057. bb. 37.

LOMBROSO (C.) and FERRERO (G.) The Female Offender. pp. 313. 1895. 8°. The Criminology Series. Vol. 1.   6057. aaaa.

ROGER-MILÈS (L.) Nos Femmes et nos enfants. Choses sanglantes et criminalité. pp. 358.
Paris, 1893. 12°.   8415. de. 28.

MEM., _pseud._ Farm life for Reformatory Girls.
pp. 8. _Melbourne,_ 1890. 8°.   Pam. 82.

NAECKE (P.) Verbrechen und Wahnsinn beim Weibe. pp. 257. _Wien,_ 1894. 8°. 7660. g. 29.
See also CRIME : PRISONS.

Education. _See_ EDUCATION, _Female._

WOMEN—_continued._

Female Suffrage.

BALFOUR (_Right Hon._ A. J.) Speech in support of the Parliamentary Franchise Extension to Women bill. pp. 7. _Westminster,_ 1892. 8°. Pam. 37.

DIALOGUE. Dialogue between a member of a Women's Liberal Association and a "Liberal" M.P. pp. 8. _Lond._ 1893. 8°.   Pam. 68.

FAWCETT (M. G.) Reply to the letter of Mr. S. Smith, M.P., on Woman's Suffrage. pp. 11.
Westminster, 1892. 8°.   8415. g. 63. (6.)

GLADSTONE (_Right Hon._ W. E.) Female Suffrage. pp. 8. _Lond._ 1892. 8°. 8139. bb. 47. (10.)

G. B. & I. _Commons, House of._ Appeal and warning to the members of the House of Commons. pp. 2. _Lond._ 1893. 8°. 8415. g. 63. (9.)

GREY (_Sir_ G.) Speech at th emeeting of the Committee of the National Society for Women's Suffrage. pp. 3. _Westminster,_ 1894. 8°.
                                    8415. g. 63. (15.)

HAMMERSMITH. _Women's Liberal Association._ Report. _Lond._ 1893, _etc._ 8°.   8138. aa.

JACOBI (M. P.) "Common Sense" applied to Woman's Suffrage. pp. 236. _N.Y._ 1894. 8°.
                                    3415. ee. 40.

LAWYER. The Woman-Suffrage movement in the U.S. pp. 153. _Bost._ 1895. 8°.   8410. i. 2.

LEVY (J. H.) The enfranchisement of Women.
pp. 7. _Lond._ 1892. 12°.   Pam. 37.

MAC ILQUHAM ( ) The enfranchisement of Women. pp. 18. _Lond._ 1894. 8°.   Pam. 37.

MILLER (F. F.) Programme of the Women's Franchise League. pp. 16. _Lond._ 1890. 8°. Pam. 37.

ROLLIT (_Sir_ A. K.) Speech in moving the Extension of the Parliamentary Franchise to Women bill. pp. 16. _Westminster,_ 1892. 8°.
                                    8415. g. 63. (8.)

STOPES (C. C.) British Freewomen. pp. 196.
Lond. 1894. 8°.   08276. e. 66.

WOMEN. Women's Suffrage.
Lond. 1889. _s. sh._ 8°.   1889. d. 3. (120.)
See also supra: General.

History : Women in various Countries.

MASON (O. T.) Women's Share in primitive culture. pp. 295. 1894. 8°. STARR (F.) Anthropological Series.

HENNE-AM-RHYN (O.) Die Frau in der Kulturgeschichte. pp. 369. _Berl._ 1892. 8°. 12249. cc. 2.

BERNHOEFT (F.) Frauenleben in der Vorzeit.
pp. 78. _Wismar,_ 1893. 8°.   8416. d. 38.

KRAUSE (H. L.) Die Amazonensage. pp. 104.
Berl. 1893. 8°.   9026. e. 21.

PARIS (P.) Quatenus Feminæ res publicas in Asia Minore, Romanis imperantibus, attigerint. pp. 142. _Parisiis,_ 1891. 8°.   9026. ff. 30.

GAGE (M. J.) Woman, Church and State : historical account of woman through the Christian ages. pp. 554. _Chicago,_ 1893. 8°. 8416. e. 35.

HELSINGFORS. _Unionen, Kvinnosaksförbund i Finland._ Kvinnan och Kvinnoarbetet i Finland. pp. 76. _Helsingfors,_ 1893. 8°.   8410. f. 51.

GAHIER (J.) La Journée d'une dame de qualité au XVII° siècle. pp. 23. _Nantes,_ 1894. 8°. Pam. 3.

FRANCE. _Société nouvelle des Femmes._ La Société nouvelle des Femmes de France. pp. 13.
Paris, 1894. 16°.   08275. e. 30. (7.)

TURQUAN (J.) Les Femmes de France pendant l'invasion. pp. 445. _Paris,_ 1893. 8°. 9080. e. 3.

UZANNE (O.) La Femme à Paris. Nos contemporaines. pp. 328. _Paris,_ 1894. 4°.
                                    K.T.C. 28. b. 1.

BUSCHAN (G.) Leben der deutschen Frau in der Urzeit. pp. 31. 1893. 8°. Sammlung wissenschaftlicher Vorträge. N.F. Hft. 186. 12249. m.

WOMEN.—History, etc.—*continued*.

OELSNER (E.) Die Leistungen der deutschen Frau in den letzten vierhundert Jahren. *Guhrau*, 1894, *etc.* 8°.   8415. df.

STREITBERG (G. v.) *Countess.* Die deutschen Frauen und der Bismarckkultus. pp. 44. *Leipz.* 1895. 8°.   Pam. 72.

SAVI-LOPEZ (M.) La Donna italiana del trecento. pp. 35. *Napoli*, 1891. 8°.   Pam. 37.

MUSATTI (E.) La Donna in Venezia. pp. 270. *Padova*, 1891. 8°.   10631. f. 45.

COSTA (A. da) A Mulher em Portugal. pp. 470. *Lisboa*, 1892. 8°.   8415. ee. 37.

U.S. Women of colonial and revolutionary times in America. *Lond.* 1895, *etc.* 8°.   10883. bbb.

VARIGNY (C. de.) La Femme aux États-Unis. pp. 322. *Paris*, 1893. 12°.   8415. de. 27.

———

KOETSVELD (C. E. v.) De Vrouw in den Bijbel. pp. 340. *Amsterdam*, 1891. 8°.   3127. m. 16.

REMY (N.) The Jewish Woman. pp. 263. *Cincinnati*, 1895. 8°.   8415. df. 34.

DĀRĀB PESHOTAN SANJĀNĀ. Position of Zoroastrian Women in remote antiquity. pp. 85. *Bombay*, 1892. 8°.   8416. d. 37.

BRANDT (M. v.) Sittenbilder aus China. Mädchen und Frauen. pp. 87. *Stuttgart*, 1895. 8°.   010057. f. 35.

AMĪR 'ALĪ, *Maulawi.* Women in Islam. pp. 41. *Lahore*, 1893. 8°.   Pam. 41.

BILLINGTON (M. F.) Woman in India. pp. 342. *Lond.* 1895. 8°.   8416. g. 32.

BLACKWOOD (H. G.) *Marchioness of Dufferin and Ava.* Record of work of the National Association for supplying female medical aid to the Women of India. pp. 102. *Calcutta*, 1888. 8°.   7688. a. 31.

CALCUTTA. *National Association for supplying Female Medical Aid.* The Countess of Dufferin's Fund. Report. pp. 132. *Calcutta*, 1887. 8°.   7688. g. 7.

DHĪRENDRANĀTHA PĀLA. The Hindu wife. pp. 49. *Calcutta*, 1888. 12°.   8416. de. 6.

ENSOR (G.) "Help these Women." Plea for the Church of England Zenana Missionary Society. pp. 15. *Lond.* 1864. 16°.   Pam. 40.

INDIA. The Women of India. pp. 150. *Madras*, 1888. 8°.   8415. e. 52.

MALIK-KHĀNAM. Thirty years in the Harem. pp. 200. *Calcutta*, 1888. 8°.   10606. aaa. 23.

LAHORE. *Punjab Purity Association.* Opinions on the Nautch question. pp. 40. *Lahore*, 1894. 8°.   Pam. 85.

NAUTCH WOMEN. Nautch Women : an appeal to English ladies. pp. 7. *Madras*, 1895. 8°.   8425. bbb. 43. (15.)

BACON (A. M.) A Japanese interior. pp. 287. *Bost.* 1893. 8°.   10058. de. 7.

MOSSELL (N. F.) Work of the Afro-American woman. pp. 178. *Phila.* 1894. 8°. 8415. de. 44.

See also supra : General. *Infra :* Laws, Professions, Societies : BIOGRAPHY, *Female :* MARRIAGE, and under the subheading *Social Life* of each country.

Laws relating to Women.

BILCESCŬ (S.) De la condition légale de la Mère. pp. 505. *Paris*, 1890. 8°.   5403. g. 9.

BRIDEL (L.) Le Mouvement féministe et le droit des femmes. pp. 30. *Genève*, 1893. 8°. Pam. 37.

——— Le Droit de la Femme mariée sur le produit de son travail. pp. 33. *Genève*, 1893. 8°.   5510. cc. 1. (5.)

——— Le droit des Femmes et le mariage. pp. 167. *Paris*, 1893. 12°.   8416. df. 19.

WOMEN.—Laws relating to—*continued*.

BRUNO (T.) La condizione giuridica della Donna nella legislazione italiana. pp. 199. *Firenze*, 1894. 8°.   5359. a. 5.

KEMPIN (E.) Die Stellung der Frau nach den zur Zeit in Deutschland gültigen Gesetzes-Bestimmungen. pp. 118. *Leipz.* 1892. 8°.   8416. de. 58.

OPET (O.) Die erbrechtliche Stellung der Weiber in der Zeit der Volksrechte. pp. 86. 1888. 8°. GIERKE (O.) Untersuchungen zur deutschen Staatsgeschichte. No. 25.   6025. e. 9.

PROELSS (S.) and RASCHK (M.) Die Frau im bürgerlichen Gesetzbuch. pp. 58. *Berl.* 1895. 8°.   8415. g. 61.

See also supra : General. *Infra :* Professions, *etc. :* MARRIAGE, *Law of.*

Professions and Employments of Women.

BATESON (M.) Professional Women upon their professions. pp. 133. *Lond.* 1895. 8°.   8415. ee. 43.

BELGIUM. Éléments d'enquête sur le rôle de la Femme dans l'industrie et les sciences en Belgique. pp. 426. *Brux.* 1893. 8°. 8416. h. 14.

BLACKBURN (H.) Handbook for Women engaged in social and political work. pp. 116. *Bristol*, 1895. 8°.   8416. df. 27.

BRISTOL. *Ladies' Association for the Care of Girls.* Women workers. Papers. 2 pt. *Bristol*, 1893. 8°.   8416. g. 39.

BULLEY (A. A.) and WHITLEY (M.) Women's work. pp. 172. 1894. 8°. GIBBINS (H. de B.) Social Questions of to-day. No. 13. 08276. e.

BURDETT-COUTTS (A. G.) *Baroness Burdett-Coutts.* British Commission, Chicago Exhibition, 1893. Woman's mission. A series of papers. pp. 485. *Lond.* 1893. 8°.   4192. g. 3.

CHAUVIN (J.) Étude sur les professions accessibles aux Femmes. pp. 296. *Paris*, 1892. 8°.   8416. g. 40.

DAHMS (G.) Der Existenzkampf der Frau im modernen Leben. *Berl.* 1895, *etc.* 8°. 8416. g.

DAVIDSON (*Mrs.* H. C.) What our Daughters can do for themselves. pp. 303. *Lond.* 1894. 8°.   8416. df. 16.

DONVILLE (F. de) Les Professions des femmes. pp. 388. *Paris*, 1895. 12°.   8416. ff. 9.

FRANK (L.) La Femme dans les emplois publics. pp. 150. *Brux.* 1893. 8°.   8416. g. 41.

GAUSSERON (B. H.) Que faire de nos Filles ? pp. 332. *Paris*, 1891. 8°.   8415. df. 25.

GLIMPSES. A Lady's search for work about the world. pp. 201. *Lond.* 1894. 8°. 4767. d. 17.

GRAFFENRIED (C. de) Needs of self-supporting Women. pp. 10. 1890. 8°. Johns Hopkins University Studies Notes, 1890. No. 1.   Ac. 2689.

HARTLEY (L.) Employment for Girls. pp. 8. *Woolwich*, 1894. 8°.   Pam. 94.

HARTT (I. W.) How to Make Money, although a woman. pp. 142. *N.Y.* 1895. 8°. 8416. df. 25.

HONE (A. M.) Woman's enterprise and genius. pp. 324. *Lond.* 1893. 8°.   8416. e. 31.

KARSLAND (V.) Women and their work. pp. 166. *Lond.* 1891. 8°.   8416. dd. 43.

LADIES. Ladies at Work. Papers on paid employments for ladies. pp. 143. *Lond.* 1893. 8°.   8415. h. 34.

LINCK (J.) Det qvinliga arbetet. Statistisk-ekonomisk afhandling. pp. 136. *Stockholm*, 1884. 8°.   8415. ee. 45.

MERCIER (A.) Work and how to do it. pp. 178. *Lond.* 1891. 8°.   8415. de. 16.

WOMEN.—Professions, etc.—_continued._

PAQUET-MILLE (A.) Nouveau guide des jeunes filles dans le choix d'une profession. pp. 358.
| _Paris_, 1891. 12°.   8416. dd. 39.

REBIÈRE (A.) Les Femmes dans la science. pp. 85. _Paris_, 1894. 8°.   8415. g. 60.

SIGNOREL (J.) La Femme-avocat. pp. 53. _Toulouse_, 1894. 8°.   6005. h. 26. (12.)

U.S. _Patent Office._ Women Inventors to whom Patents have been granted. pp. 44. _Wash._ 1888. 4°.   8228. k. 30.

WATSON (J.) Our Boys and Girls and what to do with them. pp. 173. _Lond._ 1892. 8°.   08227. de. 36.

———

CADBY (P.) Should Women preach? pp. 79. _Lond._ 1892. 8°.   8416. df. 7.

CHARTERIS (A. H.) Christo in Pauperibus : Organisation of women's work in the Church of Scotland. pp. 30. _Edinb._ 1890. 8°.   4175. de. 35. (4.)

HALLOWES (F. S.) Place and service of Women in our churches. pp. 48. _Lond._ 1891. 8°.   8416. de. 18.

MOULE (H. C. G.) Public ministry of Women. pp. 24. _Lond._ 1892. 24°.   Pam. 37.

———

ALQ (L. d') Anthologie féminine. pp. 412. _Paris_, 1893. 8°.   12238. aa. 21.

BLACK (H. C.) Notable Women authors of the day. pp. 312. _Glasg._ 1893. 8°.   10856. f. 7.

FILOGYNO (E.) Las Mujeres y las academias. pp. 50. _Madrid_, 1891. 8°.   8416. c. 44.

HAMILTON (C. J.) Women writers. _Lond._ 1892, etc. 8°.   10601. ee.

LHOMME (F.) Les Femmes écrivains. Œuvres choisies. pp. 546. _Paris_, 1892. 8°.   12237. k. 2.

VACHON (M.) La Femme dans l'art. pp. 616. _Paris_, 1893. 4°.   7808. g. 14.

———

ADAMS (H. B.) Work among working-women in Baltimore. pp. 12. 1889. 8°. John Hopkins University Studies. Notes, 1889. No. 6.   Ac. 2689.

CAMPBELL (H.) Women Wage-earners. pp. 313. _Bost._ 1893. 8°.   8415. df. 30.

DELCROIX (A.) Loi du 13 Décembre 1886 concernant le travail des femmes. pp. 39. _Gand_, 1891. 8°.   Pam. 82.

LONDON. _Liberty and Property Defence League._ Women and Factory Legislation. Debate in the House of Lords. pp. 7. _Lond._ 1891. 8°.   8277. h. 19. (9.)

MORGENSTERN (L.) Frauenarbeit in Deutschland. 2 Bde. _Berl._ 1893. 8°.   8416. g. 43.

MUN (A. de) _Count._ Le Travail des Femmes. pp. 23. _Paris_, 1891. 8°.   Pam. 37.

P.P. _Offenbach._ Die Staatsbürgerin. Organ für die Interessen der Arbeiterinnen. No. 1–24. | _Offenbach_, 1886. fol.   P.P. 9530. a.

SALLARÉS Y PLA (J.) El Trabajo de las Mujeres. pp. 211. _Sabadell_, 1892. 8°.   08276. i. 15.

U.S. _Bureau of Labour._ Working Women in large cities. pp. 631. 1889. 8°. Report, etc. Report IV.   8275. k.

_See also supra: _General. _Infra: _Societies, etc. BIOGRAPHY, _Female : _LAW AND MEDICINE, _Professions of : _MISSIONS, _Foreign._

Societies : Trade Unions, etc,

HOLYOAKE (E. A.) Capacity of Women for trade organisation. pp. 7. _Lond._ 1894. 8°.   Pam. 82.

WOMEN.—Societies, etc.—_continued._

LONDON. _Women's Trades Union League._ Women's Union journal. _Lond._ 1883–90. 4°.   P.P. 1103. baa.

—— Annual Report. _Lond._ 1891, etc. 8°.   8416. f.

—— Quarterly Report and review. _Lond._ 1891, etc. 8°. P.P. 1103. bab. and. 845.

—— _Women's Co-operative Self-Help Society._ Programme of the Society. pp. 57. _Lond._ 1895. 12°.   Pam. 23.

PATTISON (E. F. S.) afterwards DILKE (E. F. S.) _Lady._ Trades Unionism among women. pp. 12. _Lond._ 1893. 8°.   Pam. 37.

—— Benefit Societies and trades unions for women. pp. 7. _Lond._ 1893. 8°.   Pam. 37.

ROUGIER (P.) Les Femmes dans les Sociétés de secours mutuels. pp. 59. 1893. 8°. Ac. Lyons. _Académie des Sciences._ Mémoires. Sciences et Lettres. Sér. 3. Tom. 2. Ac. 364/5.

STOCKHOLM. Svenska Qvinnoföreningen. Svenska Qvinnoföreningen. pp. 107. _Stockholm_, 1890. 8°.   8416. g. 37.

OTTO, afterwards PETERS (L.) Das erste Vierteljahrhundert des allgemeinen deutschen Frauen-Vereins. pp. 103. _Leipz._ 1890. 8°   8416. f. 52.

See also GIRLS' FRIENDLY SOCIETY.

WONGROWITZ. HOCKENBECK (H.) Die Stadt Wongrowitz. 1893. 8°. Ac. Posen. _Historische Gesellschaft._ Zeitschrift. Jahrg. 8. Ac. 7365.

WOOD: WOODWORK AND WOOD-CARVING. ADAMS (H.) Joints in Woodwork. pp. 30. _Lond._ 1883. 8°.   Pam. 24.

—— Timber Piling in foundations and other works. pp. 24. _Lond._ 1892. 8°. 8768. l. 15. (9.)

BALE (M. P.) Woodworking Machinery. pp. 434. _Lond._ 1894. 8°.   8767. cc. 34.

SIMMONDS (T. C.) Woodwork, carpentry and joinery. pp. 70. _Lond._ 1892. 8°. 7828. aa. 26.

STEVENSON (W.) Wood : its use as a constructive material. pp. 240. _Lond._ 1894. 8°.   07028. k. 19.

SUTHERLAND (W.) and (W. G.) Art of Graining and imitating woods. 2 pt. _Manch._ 1892. fol.   1811. b. 21.

See also CARPENTRY : FORESTRY : FURNITURE.

Woodcarving.

BARTER (S.) Manual Instruction. Woodwork. pp. 343. _Lond._ 1892. 8°.   7817. f. 26.

CADDY (W. H.) Practical Woodcarving. _Brighton_, 1892. obl. 8°.   7817. g. 26.

—— Working drawings for Woodcarving. _Brighton_, 1892. obl. 4°.   7817. e. 17.

DEGERDON (W. E.) Grammar of Woodwork. _Lond._ 1893. 4°.   7943. k. 31.

DENNING (D.) Fretwork and marquetry. pp. 158. _Lond._ 1895. 8°.   7817. bb. 6.

GIBSON (J. S.) The Wood-carver. _Edinb._ 1886. fol.   1807. c. 6.

—— Quarterly supplement to the Wood-carver. _Edinb._ 1892, etc. fol.   1545.

GOSS (W. F. M.) Bench-work in Wood. pp. 161. _Bost._ 1890. 8°.   7817. bb. 3.

HARTSHORNE (A.) English effigies in Wood. 1894. fol. CHURCH (A. H.) Some minor Arts.   K.T.C. 24. b. 3.

HASLUCK (P. N.) Woodworker's handy-book of Manual Instruction. pp. 144. _Lond._ 1894. 8°.   7817. b. 2.

JAY (H.) Exercises for technical instruction in Wood-working. 3 pt. _Lond._ 1891. obl. 16°.   7820. a. 23.

WOOD.—Woodcarving—*continued.*

LAWLEY (T. S.) Lessons in Woodwork drawing. pp. 48. *Lond.* 1895. 4°.   7857. f. 58.

LESSONS. Lessons in Woodwork. pp. 44. *Lond.* 1893. fol.   7820. i. 12.

MARTINEAU (G.) Village class for Woodcarving. pp. 106. *Lond.* 1891. 8°.   7808. a. 36.

NELSON (W.) Woodwork course for Boys. *Lond.* 1893. 8°.   7820. g. 18.

OLDERSHAW (S. B.) and COLLIS (A. E.) Graduated exercises in Woodwork. *Manch.* 1894. *obl.* fol.   7817. e. 25.

PEARSON (J. C.) Manual instruction. "Woodwork." pp. 11. *Lond.* 1893. *obl.* fol. 1810. a. 30.

P.P. *London.* The Carver's designer. *Lond.* 1891, *etc.* 4°.   N.R.

ROWE (E.) Hints on Chip-carving. pp. 67. *S. Kensington,* 1892. 8°.   7808. aa. 44. (8.)

—— Notes for Lecture on "Simple Woodcarvings." pp. 16. *Lond.* 1892. 8°. 7807. e. 30. (8.)

SAINT JOHN (G.) Manual instruction. Woodwork. pp. 82. *Lond.* 1891. 8°. 7820. aaa. 34.

SCHAUERMANN (F. L.) Wood-carving in practice and theory. pp. 90. *Lond.* 1891. 8°.   7875. aaa. 32.

SCHERER (C.) Technik und Geschichte der Intarsia. pp. 164. *Leipz.* 1891. 8°.   7858. f. 9.

SIMMONDS (T. C.) Wood-carving. pp. 91. *Lond.* 1892. 8°.   7820. aa. 27.

THOMPSON (T.) Evans's Class Book of Woodwork. pp. 48. *Lond.* 1895. *obl.* 8°. 7817. aa. 1.

WILLIAMS (J.) Elementary Wood-carving. *Lond.* 1893, *etc.* fol.   7805. g.

WOOD (G.) Manual Instruction in Woodwork. pp. 104. *Leeds,* 1892. 8°.   7942. dd. 7.

WOOD-CARVING. Wood-carving for Amateurs. pp. 80. *Lond.* 1894. 8°.   7875. aa. 53.

See also ART, *Decorative.*

WOODBRIDGE. REDSTONE (V. B.) Bygone Woodbridge. pp. 103. *Woodbridge,* 1893. 8°.   010358. e. 26.

WOOL. COUPUT (G.) Les Laines de l'Algérie à l'Exposition de 1889. pp. 101. *Alger,* 1889. 8°.   Pam. 23.

DELMART (A.) Die Echtfärberei der losen Wolle in ihrem ganzen Umfange. 3 Bde. *Reichenberg,* 1887–91. 12°.   07944. k. 3.

LEFÈVRE (É.) Les Droits d'entrée sur la laine. pp. 69. *Roubaix,* 1890. 8°. 08227. e. 16. (11.)

NEW SOUTH WALES. *Commissioners for the Exposition, Chicago.* Sheep and Wool in New South Wales. pp. 23. *Sydney,* 1893. 8°.   7958. g. 34.

—— New South Wales Wool exhibits. pp. 19. *Sydney,* 1893. 8°.   7958. g. 29.

PIERRARD (P.) French Parities and ready reckoner for purchasing wool in London. *Lond.* 1891. *s. sh.* fol.   1882. d. 2. (66.)

U.S. *Association of Wool Manufacturers.* The Wool book. Statistical manual. pp. 122. *Bost.* 1892. 8°.   7291. a. 2.

VICKERMAN (C.) Woollen Spinning. pp. 352. *Lond.* 1894. 8°.   07944. e. 22.

See also SHEEP : TEXTILE FABRICS.

WOOLWICH. VINCENT (W. T.) Records of the Woolwich district. 2 vol. *Woolwich,* 1880–90. 8°.   010358. l. 33.

Ac. Woolwich. *Royal Military Academy.* Records, 1741–1892. *Woolwich,* 1895. 4°.   8365. h. 31.

—— Regulations respecting admission. pp. 8. *Lond.* 1893. 8°.   8830. aaa. 58.

WORCESTER.

City.

MARSH (F. T.) Annals of the Hospital of S. Wulstan. pp. 140. *Worcester,* 1890. 8°.   4705. g. 23.

WORCESTER. Where to buy at Worcester. pp. 64. *Brighton,* 1891. 4°.   10368. k. 42.

County and Diocese.

Ac. Worcester. *Historical Society.* Inquisitiones post mortem for the County from 1242. *Oxf.* 1894, *etc.* 8°.   Ac. 8166/5.

—— HABINGTON (T.) Survey of Worcestershire. *Oxf.* 1893, *etc.* 8°..   Ac. 8166/2.

—— Index to Nash's Collections. *Oxf.* 1894, *etc.* 4°.   Ac. 8166/6.

SCOTT (C. W.) Among the Apple Orchards. pp. 138. *Lond.* 1895. 8°.   10350. aaa. 53.

WORCESTER. Murray's Handbook for Worcestershire, pp. 16. 168. *Lond.* 1894. 8°. 2364. a. 17.

Ac. London. *English Dialect Society.* SALISBURY (J.) Glossary of words used in S.E. Worcestershire. pp. 92. *Lond.* 1894. 8°.   Ac. 9934/35.

—— Worcester. *Historical Society.* Register of the Diocese of Worcester during the vacancy of the See. *Oxf.* 1893, *etc.* 8°.   Ac. 8166/4.

P.P. *Birmingham.* Worcester Diocesan Magazine. *Birmingham,* 1893, *etc.* 8°.   P.P. 344. d.

WORCESTER, Massachusetts. BLAKE (F. E.) Incidents of the settlements of Worcester. pp. 33. *Worcester,* 1884. 8°.   Pam. 86.

RICE (F. P.) Dictionary of Worcester, Massachusetts. pp. 135. *Worcester,* 1893. 8°.   10413. e. 10.

WORCESTER. Worcester : its past and present. pp. 242. *Worcester,* 1888. 4°.   10411. i. 23.

WORKSHOPS. *See* FACTORIES.

WORMS. *See* VERMES.

WORMS, City of. KANNENGIESSER (P.) Der Reichstag zu Worms vom Jahre 1545. pp. 131. *Strassb.* 1891. 8°.   4650. dd. 10.

WORMS. Die Hafen- und Uferbauten zu Worms. 1890–93. pp. 100. *Worms,* 1893. 4°.   10230. i. 1.

WÖRTH, Battle of. *See* GERMAN-FRENCH WAR.

WORTHENBURY. PULESTON (*Sir* T. H.G.) Story of a quiet Country Parish. pp. 195. *Lond.* 1895. 8°.   10352. g. 17.

WORTHING. WORTHING. New album of Worthing views. 1891. 4°.   10352. cc. 44.

WOTIAK LANGUAGE. WIEDEMANN (F. J.) Syrjänischdeutsches Wörterbuch, *etc.* pp. 692. *St. Petersburg,* 1880. 8°. 12910. dd. 15.

WOUNDS. CHEYNE (W. W.) Treatment of Wounds. pp. 197. *Edinb.* 1894. 8°.   7481. aaa. 36.

HACKER (V. R. v.) Introduction to the antiseptic Treatment of Wounds. pp. 66. *Lond.* 1891. 8°.   07482. e. 7.

TILLMANNS (H.) Über das Wesen und die Erfolge der modernen Wundbehandlungsmethoden. 1891. 8°. VOLKMANN (R. v.) Sammlung klinischer Vorträge. N.F. Nr. 27.   7441. g.

HARRIS (J. D.) Scab healing. pp. 28. *Lond.* 1893. 8°ᵒ   07305. h. 16. (14.)

See also SURGERY.

WRESTLING. ARMSTRONG (W.) Wrestling. pp. 304. 1893. 8°. Badminton Library.   2264. aa. 5.

INOUYE (J.) Wrestlers and wrestling in Japan. pp. 18. *Tokyo,* 1895. fol.   7912. k. 1.

WRESTLING—continued.

ROBINSON (J.) and GILPIN (S.) North Country sports and pastimes. Wrestling and Wrestlers. pp. 251. *Lond.* 1893. 8°. 7912. aa. 26.

VILLE (L.) La Lutte française. pp. 108. *Paris*, 1891. 8°. 7912. a. 15.

—— La Lutte et les lutteurs. pp. 132. *Paris*, 1891. 8°. 7908. dd. 11. *See also* SPORT.

WREXHAM. PALMER (A. N.) History of the town of Wrexham. pp. 293. *Wrexham*, 1893. 8°. 10369. f. 10.

—— History of the older Nonconformity of Wrexham. pp. 167. *Wrexham*, 1888. 8°. 4715. df. 4.

WRITS. *See* ENGLAND, *Law, Legal Forms.*

WÜRTEMBERG. *See also* GERMANY.

Bibliography.

AC. Stuttgard. *K. statistisch-topographisches Bureau.* HEYD (W. v.) Bibliographie der württembergischen Geschichte. *Stuttgart*, 1895, *etc.* 8°. 011899. l.

ECK (H.) Verzeichniss der Literatur von Württemberg, *etc.* 2 pt. 1890. 8°. AC. Heidelberg. *Geologische Landesanstalt. Mitteilungen.* Bd. 1. AC. 3141.

Antiquities.

STUTTGARD. *K. Staats-Sammlung vaterländischer Kunst - Denkmale.* Katalog der Staats-Sammlung. *Stuttgart*, 1883, *etc.* 8°. 7709. bb. 50.

MILLER (C.) Die römischen Kastelle in Württemberg. pp. 48. *Stuttgart*, 1892. 8°. 07703. h. 1. (10.)

Army. *See* GERMANY.

Emigration.

HUBER (F. C.) Auswanderung im Königreich Württemberg. 1892. 8°. PHILIPPOVICH (E. v.) *Auswanderung, etc.* No. 52. AC. 2322.

History.

DIETER (E.) Württembergs Geschichte. pp. 163. *Schorndorf*, 1892. 8°. 9366. aaa. 7.

SCHAEFER (D.) Württembergische Geschichtsquellen. *Stuttgart*, 1894, *etc.* 8°. 9385. g.

WURTEMBERG. Illustrierte Geschichte von Württemburg. *Stuttgart*, 1893, *etc.* 4°. 9340. i.

BOSSERT (G.) Das Interim in Württemberg. pp. 204. 1895. 8°. AC. Halle. *Verein für Reformationsgeschichte.* Schriften. Nr. 46, 47. AC. 2027.

WURTEMBERG. *Kommission für Landesgeschichte.* Geschichte des Feldzuges 1814 gegen Frankreich. pp. 481. *Stuttgart*, 1893. 8°. 9080. dd. 21.

CHARLES, *King of Wurtemberg.* Karl I. 1823-91. pp. 32. *Stuttgart*, 1891. 8°. 10601. aa. 35. (1.)

History, *Ecclesiastical.*

WURTEMBERG. Württembergische Kirchengeschichte. pp. 756. *Calw*, 1893. 8°. 4662. f. 5.

MOSAPP (H.) Die württembergischen Religions-Reversalien. pp. 113. *Tübingen*, 1894. 8°. 4662. e. 21.

CLAUS (W.) Württembergische Väter. 2 Bde. *Stuttgart*, 1887, 88. 8°. 4888. a. *See also* EVANGELICAL CHURCH.

Law.

FLEISCHHAUER (C.) Die württembergische Gesetzgebung. *Stuttgart*, 1892, *etc.* 8°. 05604. h. 27.

Topography.

See BLACK FOREST : GERMANY.

WÜRZBURG. OEGG (J. A.) Entwicklungsgeschichte der Stadt Würzburg. pp. 480. *Würzburg*, 1880. 8°. 10230. ee. 11.

WÜRZBURG—continued.

THUENA (L. v.) Die würzburger Hilfstruppen im Dienste Österreichs 1756-63. pp. 257. *Würzburg*, 1893. 8°. 8829. i. 13.

WURZBURG. Würzburg, seine Einrichtungen für Gesundheitspflege. pp. 378. *Wiesbaden*, 1892. 8°. 10261. h. 19.

WYE, River. BEVAN (G. P.) Tourist's guide to the Wye. pp. 113. *Lond.* 1892. 8°. 10352. a. 64.

XYLOPHAGA. *See* COLEOPTERA.

YACHTING : BOATING. AMERICAN YACHTS. American Yachts and yachting. pp. 159. *Lond.* 1887. 8°. 8807. i. 18.

BIDDLE (T. E.) Amateur Sailing in open and half-decked boats. pp. 64. *Lond.* 1886. 8°. 8807. c. 39.

COWPER (F.) Sailing Tours. Yachtsman's guide to cruising waters of the English Coast. *Lond.* 1892, *etc.* 8°. 10360. e.

CUTHELL (T. G.) Sailing guide to the Solent and Poole harbour. With hints on working a small yacht. pp. 100. *Lond.* 1893. 8°. 10498. aa. 18.

DARYL (P.) Le Yacht : histoire de la navigation maritime de plaisance. pp. 366. *Paris*, 1890. 4°. 8805. ff. 29.

EPHEM. Yacht Racing in the Solent. *Southampton*, 1892, *etc.* 16°. P.P. 2489. hac.

—— Thames Yachting Almanack. *Lond.* 1893, *etc.* 16°. P.P. 2489. bab.

FATIO (G.) Le Yachting sur le Lac Leman. pp. 202. *Genève*, 1894. 8°. 8806. b. 51.

FOLIN (L. de) *Marquis.* Bateaux et Navires, progrès de la construction navale. pp. 328. *Paris*, 1892. 8°. 8807. dd. 33.

GABE (J.) Sketches of Yachting life. pp. 105. *Lond.* 1893. 8°. 012330. f. 53.

HAYWARD (J. D.) Canoeing with sail and paddle. pp. 152. 1893. 8°. All England Series. 7908. df.

KEMP (D.) Manual of Yacht and Boat sailing. pp. 732. *Lond.* 1895. 8°. 2249. i. 1.

—— Yacht Architecture. pp. 528. *Lond.* 1891. 8°. 8805. ff. 28.

KENEALY (A. J.) Yacht Races for the America's Cup, 1851-93. pp. 180. 1894. 8°. Outing Library. No. 1. 07905. l.

"KINGDON" MACHINERY. Description of the "Kingdon" Machinery, its advantages for steam launches, *etc.* pp. 90. *Lond.* 1891. 8°. 8807. cc. 34.

KUNHARDT (C. P.) Steam Yachts and Launches. pp. 267. *N.Y.* 1891. 8°. 8806. dd. 18.

LESLIE (R. C.) The Sea-Boat, how to build, rig and sail her. pp. 172. *Lond.* 1892. 8°. 8807. dd. 36.

LONDON. *Yacht Racing Association.* Report of the Council on the Racing Rule. pp. 58. *Lond.* 1892. 4°. 8806. g. 23.

MACDONELL (A. A.) Camping out. pp. 153. 1892. 8°. All England Series. 7908. df.

MACMULLEN (R. T.) Down Channel. pp. 418. *Lond.* 1893. 8°. 10368. ccc. 39.

MOTT (H. A.) Yachts and yachtsmen of America. *N.Y.* 1894, *etc.* 4°. 8807. l. 25.

O'NEILL (W.) Yacht Master's racing record. pp. 163. *Lond.* 1895. 8°. 8806. b. 50.

YACHTING—*continued.*

PARIS. *Union des Yachts.* Union des Yachts français. pp. 257. *Paris,* 1894. 8°.
                                8806. a. 63.

PRESTON (R. A. B.) Yachting under Statute. Maritime law applicable to pleasure yachts. pp. 68. *Lond.* 1884. 8°.   6835. bb. 12.

ROSSER (W. H.) Yachtman's handy-book for Sea use. pp. 112. *Lond.* 1892. 8°. 8807. b. 59.

SULLIVAN (*Sir* E.) *Bart.* Yachting. 2 vol. 1895. 8°. Badminton Library.   2264. aa. 15.

WHITE (D.) By Ocean, Firth and Channel; amateur cruising. pp. 148. *Lond.* 1894. 8°.
                                10498. aa. 21.

WINN (W.) Boating Man's vade-mecum. pp. 336. *Lond.* 1892. 8°.   8807. dd. 35.

WOGAN (T. de) *Baron.* Voyages du canot en papier le "Qui-Vive." pp. 352. *Paris,* 1887. 8°.   10107. cc. 9.

—— Épitomé de Yachting. pp. 96. *Paris,* 1893, *etc.* 8°.   8807. dd. 38.

For Yachting Voyages, *see* VOYAGES AND TRAVELS. For Life-boats, *see* SHIPWRECKS.

YALE COLLEGE. Ac. New Haven, *Connecticut. Yale College.* Catalogue of Officers and Graduates 1701–1892. pp. 192. *New Haven,* 1892. 8°.   8366. de. 34.

—— Catalogue of Yale University, 1893–94, *etc. New Haven,* 1893, *etc.* 8°.   P.P. 2521. p.

—— Catalogue of the portraits, busts, *etc.,* belonging to Yale University. pp. 130. *New Haven,* 1892. 8°.   7857. e. 46.

—— Bibliographies of the present Officers of Yale University. pp. 160. *New Haven,* 1893. 8°.   011900. h. 14.

HADLEY (A. T.) Yale University. 1895. 4°. Four American Universities.   8364. i. 9.

YAMACHICHE, Quebec. CARON (N.) Histoire de la paroisse d'Yamachiche. pp. 300. *Trois-Rivières,* 1892. 8°.   4685. e. 36.

YANGTSE-KIANG, River. BENKO (J. v.) *Baron.* Die Reise S.M. Schiffes "Zrinyi" nach Ost-Asien, Yang-tse-kiang, *etc.* pp. 439. *Wien,* 1894. 8°.   010057. l. 15.

GOEBEL (M.) Compte-rendu d'un voyage sur le Yang-tzé-kiang. pp. 102. *Brux.* 1891. 8°.
                                   Pam. 88.

PARKER (E. H.) Up the Yang-tse. pp. 308. *Hongkong,* 1891. 8°.   010057. e. 5.

YAP. *See* CAROLINE ISLANDS.

YARMOUTH. FLOOD (J.) Popular guide to Yarmouth, *etc.* pp. 48. *Lowestoft,* 1895. 16°.
                                   Pam. 90.

LUBERTA. Summer sojourn on the East Coast. pp. 255. *Lowestoft,* 1892. 8°.   10360. e. 26.

STEWARD (C. J.) Notes on the climate and weather during the summer months at Gt. Yarmouth. pp. 11. *Great Yarmouth,* 1890. 8°.
                                   Pam. 79.

YARMOUTH. The Rows of Great Yarmouth. pp. 32. *Yarmouth,* 1893. 8°. 10347. cc. 26. (7.)

YARNTON. Ac. Oxford. *Historical Society.* STAPLETON (M. H. A.) Three Oxfordshire Parishes. pp. 400. *Oxf.* 1893. 8°. Ac. 8126/15.

YARROW, Peebleshire. BORLAND (R.) Yarrow: its poets and poetry. pp. 239. *Dalbeattie,* 1890. 8°.   011840. l. 36.

YELLOW FEVER. *See* FEVERS.

YELLOW RIVER. FIJNJE VAN SALVERDA (J. G. W.) Memorandum relative to the improvement of the Hwang-ho. pp. 103. *The Hague,* 1891. 8°.   8777. i. 4.

YELLOWSTONE NATIONAL PARK. SYNGE (G. M) Ride through Wonderland. pp. 166. *Lond.* 1892. 8°.   10409. aa. 35.

WILEY (W. H.) and (S. K.) The Yosemite and the Yellowstone. pp. 230. *Lond.* 1893. 4°.
                                10410. g. 21.

YEMEN. 'UMĀRAH IBN 'ALĪ, *al-Hakami.* Yaman, its early mediæval history. pp. 358. 152 *Lond.* 1892. 8°.   14555. a. 21.

HARRIS (W. B.) Journey through the Yemen. pp. 385. *Lond.* 1893. 8°.   10076. eee. 25.

See also ARABIA : SABAEANS.

YENISEI. THOMSEN (V.) Déchiffrement des inscriptions de l'Orkhon et de l'Jénisséï. pp. 15. *Copenhague,* 1894. 8°. 07703. h. 1. (19.)

YEOMANRY. *See* ENGLAND, *Army* : IRELAND, *Army in.*

YEOVIL. YEOVIL. Where to buy at Yeovil. pp. 40. *Brighton,* 1891. 4°.   10368. k. 43.

YEZIDIS. *See* KURDISTAN.

YEZO. *See* AINOS : JAPAN.

YIDDISH DIALECT. JACOBS (J.) and LANDAU (H.) Yiddish-English manual. pp. 187. *Lond.* 1893. 8°.   012904. e. 2.

YONNE, Department. MOISET (C.) Les corporations dans les pays qui forment le département de l'Yonne. 1891. 8°. Ac. Auxerre. *Société des Sciences historiques.* Bulletin. Vol. 44.   Ac. 2860.

MONCEAUX (H.) La Révolution dans le département de l'Yonne, 1788–1800. pp. 734. *Paris,* 1890. 8°.   011902. f. 43.

YONNE. Procès-verbaux de l'administration départementale de 1790 à 1800. *Auxerre,* 1889, *etc.* 8°.   9225. dd.

BELIN (L.) État du radicalisme dans l'Yonne. pp. 141. *Vitry-le-F.* 1893. 8°.   8052. b. 2.

See also CHAMPAGNE : GATINAIS.

YORK, City. BENSON (G.) Handbook to the Cathedral Church of St. Peter, York. pp. 133. *York,* 1893. 8°.   10360. aa. 29.

DAVIES (R.) Historie of the King's Mannour House at York. pp. 23. *York,* 1893. 8°.
                                010358. l. 41.

CAINE (C.) Martial annals of the City of York. pp. 287. *Lond.* 1893. 8°.   10360. h. 27.

RAINE (J.) York. pp. 223. 1893. 8°. FREEMAN (E. A.) and HUNT (W.) Historic Towns.
                                 2368. a.

ROBINSON (E.) The York Blue Coat School. pp. 14. *York,* 1887. 8°.   8366. cc. 39. (10.)

SAMPSON (J.) Handbook for the City of York. pp. 122. *York,* 1893. 8°.   10352. f. 1.

YORKSHIRE.

Bibliography.

BRADFORD. *Free Libraries.* Catalogue of books and pamphlets relating to Yorkshire. pp. 89. *Bradford,* 1892. 4°.   11901. g. 38.

History, Antiquities, etc.

Ac. Durham. *Surtees Society.* Publications. Vol. 85. English Miscellanies illustrating the history and language of the northern Counties. pp. 100. *Durham,* 1890. 8°.   Ac. 8045/65.

—— Publications. Vol. 91, *etc.* Certificates of Commissioners appointed to survey the chantries, guilds, hospitals, *etc. Durham,* 1894, *etc.* 8°.   Ac. 8045/70.

Ac. Huddersfield. *Yorkshire Archæological Association.* Annual Report. 1890, *etc.* 8°.
                                 Ac. 5652/9.

YORKSHIRE.—History, etc.—continued.

ADDY (S. O.) The Hall of Waltheof: early condition and settlement of Hallamshire. pp. 295. *Lond.* 1893. 4°.   7709. g. 33.

ANDREWS (W.) Bygone Yorkshire. pp. 267. *Hull,* 1892. 8°.   010358. i. 7.

LEFROY (W. C.) Ruined Abbeys of Yorkshire. pp. 296. *Lond.* 1891. 8°.   10358. ccc. 39.

P.P. *Bradford.* Yorkshire County Magazine. *Bingley,* 1891, *etc.* 8°.   P.P. 6081. bad.

ROSS (F.) Legendary Yorkshire. pp. 246. *Hull,* 1892, 8°.   010358. i. 8.

—— Yorkshire Family Romance. pp. 254. *Hull,* 1891. 8°.   9903. c. 18.

YORK, *County of.* Yorkshire Inquisitions of the reigns of Henry III. and Edward I. 1892, *etc.* 8°. Ac. *Huddersfield. Yorkshire Archæological Association.* Record Series. Vol. 12, *etc.*   Ac. 5652/8.

BAILDON (W. P.) Yorkshire Star Chambers Proceedings. *Huddersfield,* 1893, *etc.* 9510. f. 13.

GRAINAGE (W.) Battles and battle-fields of Yorkshire. pp. 184. *Ripon,* 1895. 8°.   09504. h. 2.

LAMPLOUGH (E.) Yorkshire Battles. pp. 232. *Hull,* 1891. 8°.   09504. f. 5.

LEADMAN (A. D. H.) Prœlia Eboracensia. Battles fought in Yorkshire. pp. 192. *Lond.* 1891. 8°.   9510. g. 2.

COLLINS (F.) Index of Wills in the York Registry, 1514–53. pp. 246. 1891. 8°. Ac. *Huddersfield. Yorkshire Archæological Association.* Record Series. Vol. 11.   Ac. 5652/8.

GIBBONS (A.) Index of Wills in the York Registry, 1554–68. pp. 212. 1893. 8°. Ac. *Huddersfield. Yorkshire Archæological Association.* Record Series. Vol. 14.   Ac. 5652/8.

BLOOM (J. H.) Heraldry in the Churches of the West Riding. 6 pt. *Harnsworth,* 1892–95. 8°.   9904. e. 6.

DICKINSON (I. W.) Yorkshire Life and character sixty years ago. pp. 243. *Hull,* 1894. 8°.   010358. f. 47.

PRESS (C. A. M.) Yorkshire Leaders. *Leeds,* 1892, *etc.* 4°.   10804. g. 2.

Topography.

Ac. *Malton. Field Naturalists' Society.* North and East Yorkshire Science Notes. *Malton,* 1895, *etc.* 8°.   Ac. 3027. c. and 414.

BEVAN (G. P.) Tourist's guide to the West Riding. pp. 128. *Lond.* 1894. 8°. 10352. a. 72.

BLACKMAN (R. D.) Deacon's Map of Yorkshire. pp. 56. *Lond.* 1893. 8°.   S. 178. (40.)

BAKER (J. G.) North Yorkshire. 1888, *etc.* 8°. Ac. *Huddersfield. Yorkshire Naturalists' Union.* Transactions. Pt. 11–13, 15, 17, *etc.* Ac. 3016/2.

BUCKLE (A.) Yorkshire Etchings. *Leeds,* 1885. fol.   1875. b. 16.

BEVAN (G. P.) Tourist's guide to the East and North Ridings. pp. 142. *Lond.* 1891. 8°.   10352. a. 57.

COTTERELL (C.) Summer holidays in N.E. England. pp. 143. *Lond.* 1895. 8°. 010358. e. 32.

LEYLAND (J.) The Yorkshire Coast and the Cleveland Hills. pp. 334. *Lond.* 1892. 8°.   010358. h. 9.

RADFORD (G.) Yorkshire by the Sea. pp. 192. *Leeds,* 1891. 4°.   10368. l. 2.

ROWELL (H.) Cycling mileage guide and Diary. Yorkshire, *etc.* pp. 48. *Lond.* 1891. 16°.   7906. a. 69.

SPEIGHT (H.) Craven and North-West Yorkshire Highlands. pp. 470. *Lond.* 1892. 8°.   010358. g. 31.

YORKSHIRE.—Topography—continued.

T., J. Yorkshire fishing and shooting. pp. 40. *Lond.* 1894. 8°.   07905. h. 22.

THOMPSON (W.) Sedbergh, Garsdale and Dent. Peeps at some picturesque Yorkshire Dales. pp. 280. *Leeds,* 1892. 8°.   10360. k. 12.

W., W. Handbook for Tourists in Yorkshire. 2 vol. *Leeds,* 1891. 4°.   010358. l. 29.

YORK. The Yorkshire Coast Line. pp. 56. *York,* 1894. 8°.   Pam. 90.

—— Yorkshire Health Resorts. pp. 56. *Scarborough,* 1891. *obl. fol.*   1789. a. 28.

See also NIDDERDALE : WHARFEDALE.

Dialect and Literature.

Ac. *London. English Dialect Society.* WRIGHT (J.) Grammar of the dialect of Windhill in the West Riding. pp. 255. *Lond.* 1892. 8°.   Ac. 9934/32.

MORRIS (M. C. F.) Yorkshire Folk-talk. pp. 408. *Lond.* 1892. 8°.   12981. ccc. 1.

HOLROYD (A.) Collection of Yorkshire Ballads. pp. 318. *Lond.* 1892. 8°.   11603. bbb. 36.

FORSHAW (C. F.) Yorkshire Poets past and present. 4 vol. *Bradford,* 1888–91. 8°.   11602. ee. 38.

—— Yorkshire Sonneteers. *Bradford,* 1889, *etc.* 4°.   11652. ff. 53.

STUART (J. A. E.) Literary Shrines of Yorkshire. pp. 206. *Lond.* 1892. 8°. 010358. g. 24.

YORUBA COUNTRY.
See AFRICA, *West :* AFRICAN LANGUAGES.

YOSEMITE VALLEY. BUNNELL (L. H.) Discovery of the Yosemite. pp. 349. *N.Y.* 1892. 8°.   9602. de. 14.

WILEY (W. H.) The Yosemite, *etc.* pp. 230. *Lond.* 1893. 4°.   10410. g. 21.

See also CALIFORNIA : UNITED STATES OF AMERICA, *Topography.*

YPRES. B., H. K. Het Klooster der Engelsche Damen te Yper. pp. 83. *Yper,* 1888. 8°.   4783. bbb. 31. (3.)

YUCATAN. *See* MEXICO.

YUNNAN. HOSKIÆR (O. V. v.) Les routes commerciales du Yunnan. pp. 32. *Paris,* 1883. 8°.   Pam. 88.

PICHON (L.) Un voyage au Yunnan. pp. 286. *Paris,* 1893. 12°.   10057. aa. 14.

ZAMBEZI, River: ZAMBESIA. FERREIRA (J. J.) Recordações da expedição da Zambezia, 1869. pp. 111. *Elvas,* 1884. 8°.   010096. ee. 35.

G. B. & I. *Admiralty. Hydrographic Office.* Information on the Navigation of the river Zambesi. pp. 31. *Lond.* 1890. 8°. 10496. b. 73.

MATHERS (E. P.) Zambesia, England's El Dorado. pp. 480. *Lond.* 1891. 8°.   010096. ee. 21.

RANKIN (D. J.) The Zambesi Basin and Nyassaland. pp. 277. *Edinb.* 1893. 8°.   010096. c. 64.

See also AFRICA, *Central : Colonisation, English and Portuguese : South :* MASHONALAND : NYASSALAND.

ZAMORA, Spain. FERNÁNDEZ DURO (C.) Coleccion de noticias referentes á la Provincia de Zamora. pp. 579. *Madrid,* 1891. 8°.   11899. h. 45.

ZANZIBAR. G. B. & I. *War Office.* Handbook of British East Africa, including Zanzibar. pp. 176. *Lond.* 1893. 8°.   10097. dd. 26.

3 M

ZANZIBAR—*continued.*

WALLER (H.) Heligoland for Zanzibar. pp. 51. *Lond.* 1893. 8°.   Pam. 81.

WESTPHAL (G.) Sansibar und das deutsche Ost-Afrika. pp. 94. *Weimar,* 1886. 12°.
Pam. 89.

ZANZIBAR. Decree for the abolition of Slavery and the slave trade. *Arab., Eng.,* and *Swahili.* *Zanzibar,* 1890. fol.   14003. c. 3. (19.)

See also AFRICA, *Central and East : Colonisation, English.*

ZAPOTECO LANGUAGE. *See* INDIAN LANGUAGES, *South and Central America.*

ZARA, Austria. NANI (A.) Notizie storiche di Zara. pp. 190. *Zara,* 1883. 8°.
10136. bbb. 25.

ZEBRA. TEGETMEIER (W. B.) and SUTHERLAND (C. L.) Horses, Asses, Zebras, *etc.* pp. 166. *Lond.* 1895. 8°.   07293. i. 27.

ZELL. DEHNING (H.) Die Geschichte der Stadt Celle. pp. 280. *Celle,* 1891. 8°.
10256. c. 8.

ZEND-AVESTA AND ZOROASTRIAN RELIGION. ZAND-AVASTĀ. The Zend-Avesta. Translated by J. Darmesteter. 1895, *etc.* 8°. MUELLER (F. M.) Sacred Books of the East. Vol. 4, *etc.*   2003. a.

JACKSON (A. V. W.) An Avesta Grammar in comparison with Sanskrit. *Stuttgart,* 1892, *etc.* 8°.
12907. dd. 32.

—— Avesta Reader. *Stuttgart,* 1893, *etc.* 8°.
12906. df. 40.

—— The Avestan Alphabet and its transcription. pp. 36. *Stuttgart,* 1890. 8°.
12901. d. 37. (6.)

KĀVASJĪ EDALJĪ KĀNGĀ. Grammar of the Avesta Language. pp. 312. *Bombay,* 1891. 8°.
12907. c. 32.

MONACO (A.) Orientalia. I geni siderali nel Zend-Avesta. pp. 189. *Roma,* 1891. 8°.
4506. bb. 30.

BRODBECK (A.) Zoroaster. pp. 346. *Leipz.* 1893. 8°.   4506. ee. 1.

CASARTELLI (L. C.) Philosophy of the Mazdayasnian Religion under the Sassanids. pp. 234. *Bombay,* 1889. 8°.   4503. c. 2.

DĀRĀB PESHOTAN SANJĀNĀ. Position of Zoroastrian Women in remote antiquity. pp. 85. *Bombay,* 1892. 8°.   8416. d. 37.

SHEHRIYARJĪ DĀDĀBHĀI BHARUCHA, *Ervad.* Sketch of the Zoroastrian Religion and Customs. pp. 41. *Bombay,* 1893. 8°. 4504. bb. 8.
See also PARSIS.

ZENNOR. MATTHEWS (J. H.) History of the parish of Zennor, *etc.* pp. 56. *Lond.* 1892. 4°.
10368. h. 30.

ZERMATT. YUNG (É.) Zermatt et la vallée de la Viège. pp. 102. *Genève,* 1894. 4°.
K.T.C. 26. b. 6.
See also ALPS : SWITZERLAND.

ZHOB VALLEY. MAC FALL (A. W. C.) With the Zhob Field Force, 1890. pp. 232. *Lond.* 1895. 8°.   9057. aaa. 38.

ZINC. BURTON (W. M.) Atomic weight of Zinc. pp. 33. *Baltimore,* 1889. 8°   Pam. 13.
See also METALS.

ZÖBLITZ. ZABEL (H.) Chronik von Zöblitz. pp. 272. *Annaberg,* 1890. 8°.   10255 f. 20.

ZOOLOGY.

Bibliography.

Ac. London. *Zoological Society.* Catalogue of the Library. pp. 515. *Lond.* 1887. 8°.
BB.E. c. 17.

ZOOLOGY.—**Bibliography**—*continued.*

GRAFF (L. v.) Bibliothek des Professors der Zoologie. pp. 337. *Graz,* 1891. 8°.
011902. m. 15.

General and Miscellaneous.

Ac. *Congrès International de Zoologie.* Compterendu des séances. *Paris,* 1889, *etc.* 8°. Ac. 3553.

—— Dresden. *Königliches Zoologisches Museum.* Abhandlungen und Berichte des Museums. Herausgegeben von Dr. A. B. Meyer. *Berl.* 1887, *etc.* 4°.   Ac. 3562.

—— Geneva. *Musée d'Histoire Naturelle.* Revue suisse de Zoologie. *Genève,* 1893, *etc.* 8°.
Ac. 2870. b.

—— London. *University College.* Elementary course of practical Zoology. ff. 20. *Lond.* 1893. 4°.   7207. k. 9.

—— Manchester. *Manchester Museum.* Museum Handbooks. *Manch.* 1891, *etc.* 8°. Ac. 2672/6.

Ac. Montpellier. *Université.* Travaux originaux du Laboratoire zoologique. *Montpellier,* 1885, *etc.* 8°.   Ac. 379/2.

—— Philadelphia. *University of Pennsylvania.* Contributions from the Zoological Laboratory. *Phila.* 1893, *etc.* 8°.   Ac. 2692. p./4.

BEDDARD (F. E.) Text-book of Zoo-geography. pp. 246. 1895. 8°. SHIPLEY (A. E.) Cambridge Natural Science Manuals. Biological Series.   8709. h.

BOAS (J. E. V.) Lærebog i Dyrerigets Naturhistorie. pp. 224. *Kjøbenh.* 1892. 8°.
7002. f. 13.

BOS (H.) Het Leven der Dieren. *Zwolle,* 1893, *etc.* 8°.   7205. dd.

BOS (J. R.) and (H.) Leerboek der dierkunde. pp. 345. *Groningen,* 1893. 8°.   7205. c. 1.

BOS (J. R.) Zoologie für Landwirte. pp. 182. 1892. 8°. Thaer-Bibliothek. Bd. 78. 7078. d.

—— Agricultural Zoology. pp. 256. *Lond.* 1894. 8°.   7204. a. 30.

BOULGER (G. S.) Physiological unity of Plants and Animals. pp. 16. 1881. 8°. LONDON. *Sunday Lecture Society.* Selection 4. 4018. c.

CORNEVIN (A. M. C. I.) Traité de zootechnie générale. pp. 1088. *Paris,* 1891. 8°.
07293. m. 2.

DUNCAN (P. M.) Cassell's Natural History. 6 vol. *Lond.* 1890, 96. 8°.   7205. e.

FORBES (H. O.) Handbook to the Primates. 2 vol. 1894. 8°. SHARPE (R. B.) Allen's Naturalist's Library.   7001. eee.

GÉRARDIN (L.) Traité élémentaire d'Histoire Naturelle. Zoologie. pp. 468. *Paris,* 1893. 8°.
7204. aaa. 25.

GORDON (W. J.) Popular Natural History. pp. 256. *Lond.* 1894. 8°.   4429. eee. 22.

HARMER (S. F.) and SHIPLEY (A. E.) Cambridge Natural History. *Lond.* 1895, *etc.* 8°. 7001. ee.

HERTWIG (R.) Lehrbuch der Zoologie. *Jena,* 1891, *etc.* 8°.   7296. dd. 9.

JOHNSTONE (A.) Zoology Notes for Students of Medicine. 3 pt. *Edinb.* 1894. 8°. 7204. a. 29.

LINDSAY (B.) Introduction to the study of Zoology. pp. 356. *Lond.* 1895. 8°. 7206. e. 21.

LINSTOW (O. v.) Die Giftthiere und ihre Wirkung auf dem Menschen. pp. 147. *Berl.* 1894. 8°.   7204. c. 18.

LOEB (J.) Untersuchungen zur physiologischen Morphologie der Thiere. *Würzburg,* 1891, *etc.* 8°.   7205. e. 13.

LYDEKKER (R.) The Royal Natural History. 6 vol. *Lond.* 1893–96. 8°.   7206. m. 5.

—— Phases of Animal Life. pp. 248. *Lond.* 1892. 8°.   7204. a. 23.

ZOOLOGY.—General, etc.—*continued.*

MACALISTER (A.) Zoology of the vertebrate animals. pp. 134. 1894. 8°. FORSTER (G. C.) and MAGNUS (*Sir* P.) London Science Classbooks. Elementary series. 8709. a.

MARSHALL (A. M.) Biological Lectures and addresses. pp. 363. *Lond.* 1894. 8°. 7006. b. 49.

—— and HURST (C. H.) Junior course of practical Zoology. pp. 486. *Lond.* 1895. 8°. 7204. a. 34.

MARSHALL (W.) Zoologische Vorträge. *Leipz.* 1889, *etc.* 8°. 7204. bb. 33.

MIVART (S. G.) Types of Animal life. pp. 374. *Lond.* 1893. 8°. 7204. aa. 35.

MORGAN (C. L.) Animal Life and Intelligence. pp. 512. *Lond.* 1890–91. 8°. 7206. i. 12.

NEWTON (A.) Zoology. pp. 128. 1891. 8°. Manuals of Elementary Science. 8708. e.

NICHOLSON (H. A.) Text-book of Zoology. pp. 567. *Edinb.* 1894. 8°. 7204. aaa. 26.

P.P. *London.* Novitates Zoologicae. Journal of Zoology. *Lond.* 1894, *etc.* 8°. P.P. 2038. b.

—— *San Francisco.* Zoe. Biological journal. *San Francisco,* 1890, *etc.* 8°. P.P. 1985.

PERRIER (E.) Traité de Zoologie. pp. 864. *Paris,* 1893. 8°. 7206. d. 5.

ROME. *Società per gli Studi Zoologici.* Bollettino. *Roma,* 1892, *etc.* 8°. Ac. 3551. b.

SAHLERTZ (L.) Vejledning ved den første Undervisning i Naturhistorie. pp. 245. *Kjøbenh.* 1889. 8°. 7204. b. 1.

SCHERREN (H.) Popular history of Animals. pp. 376. *Lond.* 1895. 8°. 7204. df. 1.

SHARPE (R. B.) Allen's Naturalist's Library. Edited by R. B. Sharpe. *Lond.* 1894, *etc.* 8°. 7001. eee.

SIMROTH (H.) Die Entstehung der Landtiere. pp. 492. *Leipz.* 1891. 8°. 7205. cc. 1.

THOMSON (J. A.) Outlines of Zoology. pp. 820. 1895. 8°. Pentland's Student's Manuals. 7383. d.

—— Study of Animal Life. pp. 375. 1892. 8°. KNIGHT (W.) University Extension Manuals. 12204. f.

BUMPUS (H. C.) Laboratory course in invertebrate Zoölogy. pp. 135. *Providence,* 1892. 8°. 7298. aaa. 20.

SHIPLEY (A. E.) Zoology of the Invertebrata. pp. 458. *Lond.* 1893. 8°. 7299. f. 17.

See also BIOLOGY: EMBRYOLOGY: NATURAL HISTORY: PALAEONTOLOGY: SPORT, and for each Order, Family, Genus or Species under the name required.

Miscellaneous.

ADDOSIO (C. d') Bestie delinquenti. pp. 15. 364. *Napoli,* 1892. 8°. 7709. aa. 31.

ANIMAL FRIENDS. Our Animal Friends. *Lond.* 1893. 4°. 7206. l. 6.

BENSON (M.) Subject to Vanity. pp. 144. *Lond.* 1895. 8°. 7206. e. 20.

BOOK. Favourite book of Beasts, Birds and Fishes. pp. 126. *Lond.* 1895. 8°. 7204. a. 32.

BOWDICH, afterwards LEE (S.) Anecdotes of Animals. pp. 312. *Lond.* 1891. 8°. 7020. a. 22.

BRIGHTWEN (E.) Wild Nature won by Kindness. pp. 230. *Lond.* 1893. 8°. 7285. de. 28.

—— More about Wild Nature. pp. 261. *Lond.* 1892. 8°. 7004. a. 6.

—— Inmates of my house and garden. pp. 277. *Lond.* 1895. 8°. 7005. bb. 17.

BUGGE (M.) Pattedyr. Skildringer samlede af M. Bugge. pp. 355. *Kristiania,* 1892. 8°. 7206. cc. 8.

ZOOLOGY.—General, etc.—*continued.*

CARRINGTON (E.) Workers without wage. pp. 184. *Lond.* 1893. 8°. 7005. bb. 16.

—— and BELL (E.) Animal Life readers. *Lond.* 1895, *etc.* 8°. 7206. aa.

COULTAS (H.) Animals and their young. pp. 112. *Lond.* 1891. 8°. 7206. f. 7.

COUTEAUX (A.) Chez les Bêtes. pp. 292. *Paris,* 1892. 12°. 7908. eee. 17.

CUÉNOT (L.) Les Moyens de Défense dans la série animale. pp. 183. 1892. 8°. Encyclopédie des aide-mémoire. 8709. g.

—— L'influence du milieu sur les Animaux. pp. 176. 1894. 8°. Encyclopédie des aide-mémoire. 8709. g.

DRION (A.) *Baron.* Les petits Animaux de rapine. pp. 388. *Tournai,* 1890. 8°. 7208. aa. 11.

FEATHERS. Feathers and Fur. 4 pt. *Lond.* 1892. 4°. 7205. f. 5.

FOREST. In Forest and Field. pp. 98. *Lond.* 1892. 4°. 7206. m. 3.

FOREST TITHES. Forest Tithes, and other studies from nature. pp. 208. *Lond.* 1893. 8°. 7001. b. 11.

FUR COATS. Fur Coats and feather frocks. *Lond.* 1892. 4°. 12806. l. 64.

GIROD (P.) Les Sociétés chez les animaux. pp. 342. *Paris,* 1891. 8°. 7206. e. 8.

HARRY, *Uncle.* Holiday Hours in animal land. pp. 72. *Lond.* 1895. 8°. 012803. f. 74.

HOUSSAY (F.) Industries of animals. pp. 258. 1893. 8°. ELLIS (H. H.) Contemporary Science series. 8709. i.

HUNTERS. Hunters and hunted. pp. 64. *Lond.* 1892. 4°. 7206. m. 4.

JOHNSTON (W.) and (A. K.) Coloured sheets of Natural History. *Edinb.* 1892, *etc.* fol. Tab. 11747. a. (26.)

KOHLHOFER (M.) Die Natur des thierischen Leben und Lebensprinzips. pp. 405. *Kempten,* 1894. 8°. 7003. aa. 12.

L., H. M. Unnatural Natural History notes. pp. 139. *Lond.* 1884. 8°. 7002. f. 14.

LACROIX-DANLIARD ( ) Le Poil des Animaux et les fourrures. pp. 419. *Paris,* 1892. 12°. 7206. b. 21.

LESLIE (G. D.) Letters to Marco. pp. 259. *Lond.* 1893. 8°. 7002. e. 10.

MILES (A. H.) Natural History in Anecdote. pp. 384. *Lond.* 1895. 8°. 7207. cc. 5.

MORGAN (C. L.) Animal Sketches. pp. 312. *Lond.* 1893. 8°. 7001. aa. 28.

NATURAL HISTORY BOOK. Natural History Book for children. pp. 95. *Lond.* 1891. 4°. 7206. k. 22.

PEMBER (G. H.) Animals, their past and future. pp. 66. *Lond.* 1895. 8°. 8425. a. 68.

ROBINSON (P.) Some Country Sights and Sounds. pp. 322. *Lond.* 1893. 8°. 012357. i. 40.

STABLES (W. G.) Our Humble Friends and fellow mortals. 3 pt. *Lond.* 1892. 8°. 7206. e. 11.

TURNER (C.) Zoology and Things. pp. 45. *Sydney,* 1880. 8°. 12314. e. 52.

WINTELER (J.) Naturlaute und Sprache. pp. 37. *Aarau,* 1892. 4°. 12902. i. 6. (5.)

WOODLAND. Woodland, Moor and Stream. pp. 224. *Lond.* 1889. 8°. 7204. aa. 33.

See also NATURAL HISTORY: SPORT.

Anatomy. *See* ANATOMY.

Classification and Nomenclature.

BLANCHARD (R.) De la Nomenclature des êtres organisés. 1889. 8°. Ac. *Congrès de Zoologie.* Compte-rendu des séances. Ac. 3553.

ZOOLOGY.—Classification, etc.—cont.

BRANFORD (V. V.) Handbook of Animal Classification. ff. 21. *Edinb.* 1890. 8°. 7002. e. 11. (8.)

MONET DE LAMARCK (J. B. P. A. de) Sur l'état actuel de la classification des animaux. *Paris*, 1892. 12°. 7006. aaa. 17.

Collection and Preservation of Zoological Objects.

See NATURAL HISTORY, *Museums:* TAXIDERMY.

Domestic Animals. *See* ANIMALS, *Domestic*, and under each Genus or Species.

Extinct Animals. *See* PALAEONTOLOGY.

Folk Lore of Animals.

See BESTIARIES: FOLK LORE.

Instinct and Mental Development.

See INSTINCT.

Taxidermy. *See* TAXIDERMY.

Zoological Gardens: Museums, etc.

See NATURAL HISTORY, *Museums, etc.*

Local Fauna.

See also BIRDS: FISH: INSECTS: LEPIDOPTERA, etc.

Africa.

BOTTEGO (V.) Esplorazione del Giuba. Resultati zoologici. pp. 558. 1895. 8°. Ac. Genoa. *Museo di Storia Naturale.* Annali. Vol. 35.
Ac. 2809.

NOACK (T.) Beiträge zur Kenntnis der Säugetier-Fauna von Ostafrika. 1891. 8°. P.P. *Hamburg.* Jahrbuch der hamburgischen Wissenschaftliche Anstalten. Jahrg. IX.
P.P. 1766. f.

RODLER (A.) and WEITHOFER (K. A.) Die Wiederkäuer der Fauna von Maragha. 1890. fol. Ac. Vienna. *K. Akad. der Wissenschaften.* Denkschriften. Math. - naturwissenschaftliche Classe. Bd. 57. Ac. 810/13.

DISTANT (W. L.) Naturalist in the Transvaal. pp. 277. *Lond.* 1892. 8°. 7002. f. 9.

America.

U.S. *Dept. of Agriculture.* North American Fauna. *Wash.* 1889, *etc.* 8°. 7053. e. 13.

EDWORDS (C. E.) Camp-Fires of a Naturalist. pp. 304. *N.Y.* 1893. 8°. 07905. f. 14.

COPE (E. D.) On the zoological Position of Texas. pp. 51. 1880. 8°. Ac. Washington. *Smithsonian Institution.* Bulletin of the U.S. National Museum. No. 17. Ac. 1875/13.

ARANZADI Y UNAMUNO (T. de) Fauna americana. pp. 49. *Madrid*, 1892. 8°. 7004. df. 21. (9.)

BATES (H. W.) The Naturalist on the Amazons. pp. 389. *Lond.* 1892. 8°. 2374. f. 1.

LATASTE (F.) Études sur la Faune chilienne. 1892, *etc.* 4°. Ac. Santiago. *Société scientifique.* Actes. Tom. 1, *etc.* Ac. 3092.

HUDSON (W. H.) The Naturalist in La Plata. pp. 388. *Lond.* 1892. 8°. 7002. f. 8.

Asia.

PALESTINE. *Exploration Fund.* Account of the Fauna and Flora of Sinai, Petra and Wâdy 'Arabah. pp. 255. *Lond.* 1891. 4°. 2057. e.

EHA. A Naturalist on the Prowl : or, In the Jungle. pp. 257. *Lond.* 1894. 8°. 7204. a. 33.

KIPLING (J. L.) Beast and man in India. pp. 401. *Lond.* 1891. 8°. 7002. f. 6.

WEBER (M.) Zoologische Ergebnisse einer Reise in niederländisch Ost-Indien. *Leiden*, 1890, *etc.* 8°. 7205. f. 4.

ZOOLOGY.—Local Fauna—continued.

MOELLENDORFF (O. F. v.) Materialien zur Fauna der Philippinen. Die Insel Leyte. 1893. 8°. Ac. Frankfort on the Main. *Senckenbergische Naturforschende Gesellschaft.* Bericht, 1893.
Ac. 2878/3.

Australia.

Ac. Sydney. *Australian Museum.* Records. *Sydney*, 1890, *etc.* 8°. Ac. 1973.

Europe.

DUBOIS (A. J. C.) Les Animaux nuisibles de la Belgique. pp. 203. *Brux.* 1893. 8°.
7206. e. 16.

FALSAN (A.) Les Alpes françaises. La flore et la faune. pp. 356. *Paris*, 1893. 8°.
7001. aa. 29.

LACROIX-DANLIARD ( ) Nos Animaux des bois et de la plaine. pp. 171. *Paris*, 1890. 4°.
7208. h. 30.

MARTIN (R.) and ROLLINAT (R.) Vertèbres Sauvages de l'Indre. pp. 455. *Paris*, 1894. 8°.
7206. d. 7.

BLASIUS (W.) Die faunistische Litteratur Braunschweigs und der Nachbargebiete. pp. 239. *Braunschweig*, 1891. 8°. 011902. h. 15.

FICKEL (J.) Die Litteratur über die Tierwelt des Königreichs Sachsen. pp. 44. *Dresd.* 1893. 4°. 11906. c. 4. (3.)

MACPHERSON (H. A.) Vertebrate Fauna of Lakeland. pp. 552. *Edinb.* 1892. 8°. 7208. g. 26.

WITCHELL (C. A.) and STRUGNELL (W. B.) Fauna and Flora of Gloucestershire. pp. 301. *Stroud*, 1892. 8°. 7003. e. 3.

EMERSON (P. H.) Birds Beasts and Fishes of the Norfolk Broadland. pp. 396. *Lond.* 1895. 8°.
7205. cc. 2.

SINEL (J.) and HORNELL (J.) Zoology of the Channel Islands. 1893. 8°. ANSTED (D. T.) The Channel Islands. 2368. e. 1.

P.P. *Edinburgh.* Annals of Scottish Natural History. *Edinb.* 1892, *etc.* 8°. P.P. 1890. c.

EVANS (W.) Mammalian Fauna of the Edinburgh District. ff. 123. *Edinb.* 1892. 8°.
7206. k. 25.

BROWN (J. A. H.) and BUCKLEY (T. E.) Vertebrate Fauna of Argyll and the Inner Hebrides. pp. 262. *Edinb.* 1892. 8°. 7208. d. 7.

—— Vertebrate Fauna of the Outer Hebrides. pp. 279. *Edinb.* 1888. 8°. 7206. i. 10.

LUMSDEN (J.) Guide to the Natural History of Loch Lomond. pp. 103. *Glasg.* 1895. 8°.
7208. cc. 1.

BROWN (J. A. H.) and BUCKLEY (T. E.) Fauna of the Moray Basin. 2 vol. *Edinb.* 1895. 8°.
7208. d. 8.

—— Vertebrate Fauna of the Orkney Islands. pp. 314. *Edinb.* 1891. 8°. 7206. d. 6.

CHAPMAN (A.) Wild Spain. pp. 472. *Lond.* 1893. 8°. 7908. f. 25.

SIMROTH (H.) Die Nacktschnecken der portugiesisch-azorischen Fauna. pp. 224. 1891. 4°. Ac. Germany. *Academia Naturæ Curiosorum.* Nova acta. Bd. 56. Ac, 2871.

Marine Fauna.

DOLLO (L.) La Vie au sein des Mers. pp. 304. *Paris*, 1891. 8°. 7290. a. 18.

FOLIN (L. de) *Marquis.* Pêches et chasses zoologiques. pp. 332. *Paris*, 1893. 8°. 7206. e. 15.

GOGORZA Y GONZÁLEZ (J.) Influencia del agua dulce en los animales marinos. pp. 54. *Madrid*, 1891. 8°. 7002. f. 16. (3.)

HAECKEL (E. H. P. A.) Plankton-Studien. pp. 105. *Jena*, 1890. 8°. 7002. gg. 14.

ZOOLOGY.—Marine Fauna.—*continued*.

HICKSON (S. J.) Fauna of the Deep Sea. pp. 169. 1894. 8°. LUBBOCK (*Sir J.*) Modern Science. Vol. 6.   8709. f..

INDIA. *Royal Indian Marine.* Illustrations of the Zoology of H.M. India Surveying Steamer "Investigator." *Calcutta*, 1892, *etc.* 4°. 7290. k.

LA BLANCHÈRE (P. R. M. H. de) Sous les Eaux. pp. 299. *Paris*, 1886. 8°.   12805. m. 32.

MOSELEY (H. N.) Animal life on the Ocean surface. pp. 21. 1886. 8°. LONDON. *Sunday Lecture Society.* Selection 4.   4018. c.

P.P. *Saint Helier.* Journal of Marine Zoology. *St. Helier*, 1893, *etc.* 8°.   P.P. 2035. b.

REGNARD (P.) Recherches sur les conditions physiques de la vie dans les eaux. pp. 500. *Paris*, 1891. 8°.   7290. f. 23.

SEQUEIRA (E.) Á beira mar. pp. 182. *Porto*, 1889. *obl.* 8°.   K.T.C. 22. a. 1.

TAYLOR (J. E.) Half-Hours at the sea-side. pp. 266. *Lond.* 1890. 8°.   7001. aa. 20.

See also AQUARIUM : CRUSTACEA : FISH : MOLLUSCA : PALAEONTOLOGY, *etc.*

ZUIDERZEE. MANSHOLT (D. R.) De Ontwerp-Plannen der Zuiderzee-Commissie. pp. 59. *Groningen*, 1893. 8°.   Pam. 79.

ZULULAND. MARTINEAU (J.) Liife of Sir B. Frere. 2 vol. *Lond.* 1895. 8°. 10816. cc. 27.

G. B. & I. *War Office.* Narrative of the Field operations connected with the Zulu War of 1879. pp. 174. *Lond.* 1881. 8°.   9061. dd. 5.

LONDON. *MacKenzie Memorial Mission to Zululand.* Report. *Derby*, 1889, *etc.* 8°. 4767. ccc.

TYLER (J.) Forty years among the Zulus. pp. 300. *Bost.* 1891. 8°.   4765. df. 25.

See also AFRICA, *South* : AFRICAN LANGUAGES : MISSIONS.

ZURICH. AC. Zurich. *Allgemeine Geschichtforschende Gessellschaft.* Turicensia. Beiträge zur zürcherischen Geschichte. pp. 243. *Zürich*, 1891. 8°.   9304. e. 4.

—— *Stiftung von Schnyder von Wartensee.* Sigelabbildungen zum Urkundenbuch der Stadt Zürich. *Zürich*, 1891, *etc.* 8°.   523.

WIRZ (C.) Etat des zürcher Ministeriums von der Reformation bis zur Gegenwart, *etc.* pp. 240. *Zürich*, 1890. 8°.   4662. g. 2.

VETTER (T.) J. Hooper Bischof von Gloucester und seine Beziehungen zu Zurich. *Zürich*, 1891. 8°.   4804. d. 1. (8.)

FAZY (H.) L'alliance de 1584 entre Berne, Zurich et Genève. pp. 127. *Genève*, 1891. 8°.   9305. b. 12.

VETTER (T.) Zürich als Vermittlerin englischer Literatur im 18. Jahrhundert. pp. 26. *Zürich*, 1891. 8°.   011824. h. 30. (17.)

HADORN (A.) Die politischen und sozialen Zustände im Kanton Zürich gegen Ende des 18. Jahrhunderts. pp. 95. *Bern*, 1891. 8°.   9305. b. 11.

HEITZ (P.) Die zürcher Büchermarken. pp. 48. *Zürich*, 1895. fol.   1890. b. 12.

REBSTEIN (J.) Mittheilungen über die Neuvermessung der Stadt Zürich. pp. 58. *Zürich*, 1892. 8°.   8535. d. 19.

SCHUBERT-FEDER (C.) Das Leben der Studentinnen in Zürich. pp. 29. *Berl.* 1893. 8°.   8304. bb. 6. (10.)

ZUTPHEN. BIENTJES (J. A.) and GIMBERG (J.) Geïllustreede Gids voor Zutphen. *Zutphen*, 1889. 8°.   10271. aaa. 20.

ZWOLLE. ELBERTS (W. A.) Historische wandelingen in Zwolle. pp. 295. *Zwolle*, 1890. 8°.   10271. bb. 21.